Looking for ways to integrate the Web into your curriculum?

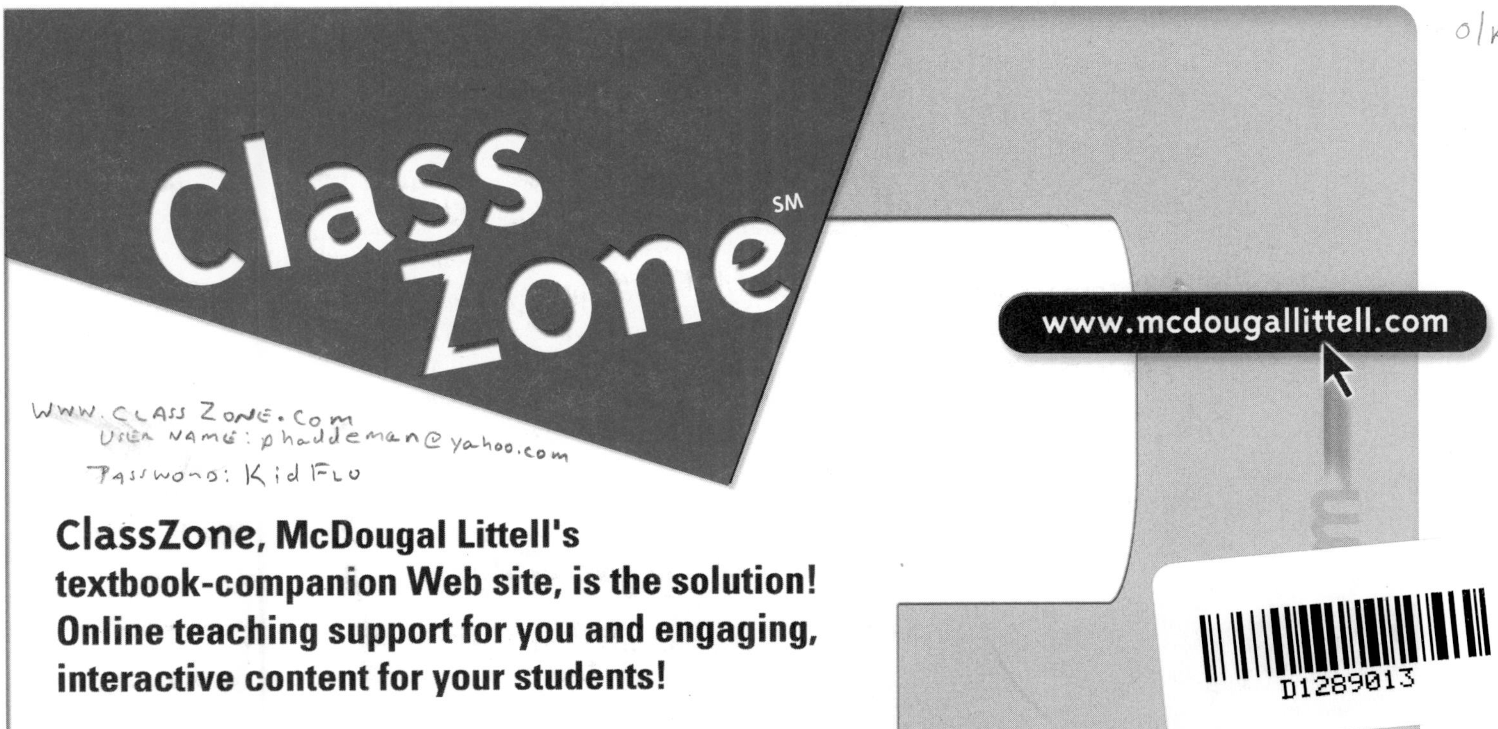

ClassZone, McDougal Littell's textbook-companion Web site, is the solution! Online teaching support for you and engaging, interactive content for your students!

ClassZone is your online guide to ***McDougal Littell Geometry***.

- **Student Help** provides online homework support with Extra Examples, Problem Solving help, and more.
- **Career Links** and **Application Links** extend real-life connections.
- **Data Updates** keep information current.
- **Teacher Center** provides lesson planning support and teaching ideas.

Log on to ClassZone at
www.mcdougallittell.com

With the purchase of ***McDougal Littell Geometry***, you have immediate access to ClassZone.

Teacher Access Code

MCD2CBKAGB6C9

Use this code to create your own user name and password. Then, access both teacher only and student resources.

Student Access Code

MCDIB5VTK7EHW

Give this code to your class. Each student creates a unique user name and password to access resources for students.

McDougal Littell

GEOMETRY

CALIFORNIA TEACHER'S EDITION

Larson Boswell Stiff

McDougal Littell
A HOUGHTON MIFFLIN COMPANY
Evanston, Illinois • Boston • Dallas

ISBN: 0-618-07726-X 123456789–DWO–04 03 02 01

Internet Web Site: http://www.mcdougallittell.com

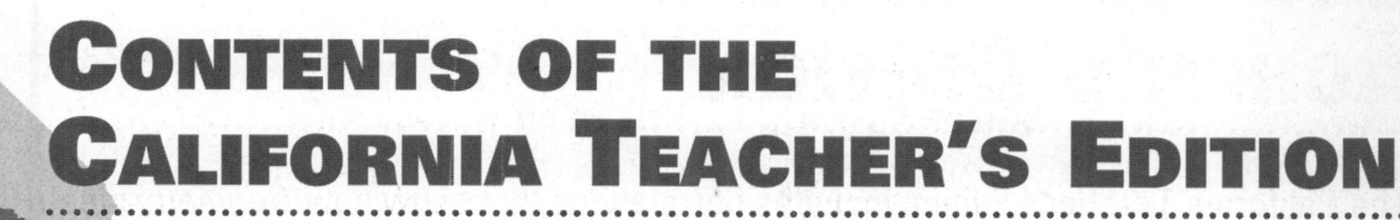

Contents of the California Teacher's Edition

USING THE CALIFORNIA TEACHER'S EDITION

The California Teacher's Edition includes correlations that show how *Geometry* meets the California Standards and the objectives for the Stanford Achievement Test (SAT9). The full correlations appear at the front of the California Teacher's Edition, and lesson and chapter correlations appear at point of use throughout.

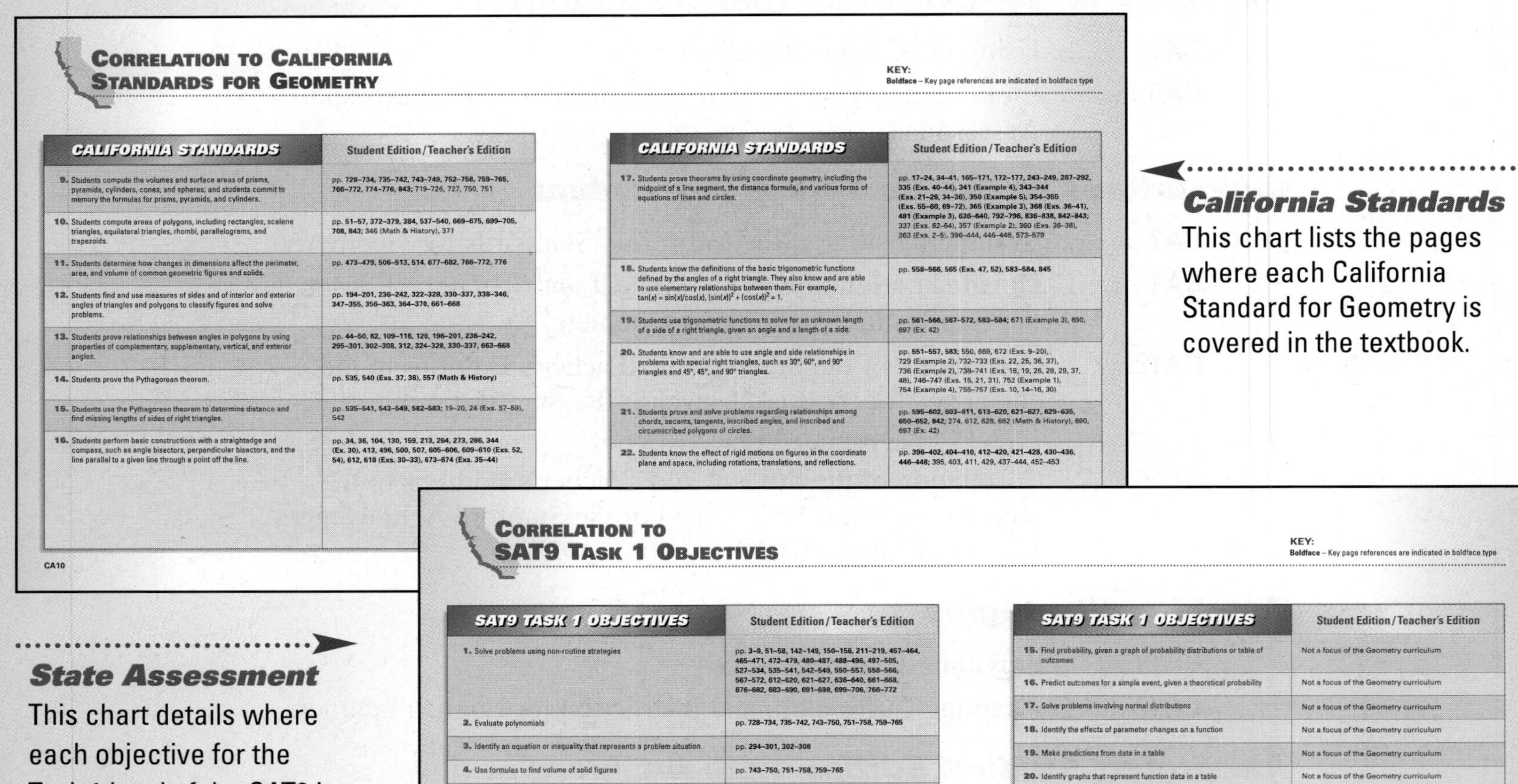

CORRELATION TO CALIFORNIA STANDARDS FOR GEOMETRY

KEY:
Boldface – Key page references are indicated in boldface type

CALIFORNIA STANDARDS	Student Edition/Teacher's Edition
9. Students compute the volumes and surface areas of prisms, pyramids, cylinders, cones, and spheres; and students commit to memory the formulas for prisms, pyramids, and cylinders.	pp. **728–734, 735–742, 743–749, 752–758, 759–765, 766–772, 774–776, 843;** 719–726, 727, 750, 751
10. Students compute areas of polygons, including rectangles, scalene triangles, equilateral triangles, rhombi, parallelograms, and trapezoids.	pp. **51–57, 372–379, 384, 537–540, 669–675, 699–705, 708, 843;** 346 (Math & History), 371
11. Students determine how changes in dimensions affect the perimeter, area, and volume of common geometric figures and solids.	pp. **473–479, 506–513, 514, 677–682, 766–772, 776**
12. Students find and use measures of sides and of interior and exterior angles of triangles and polygons to classify figures and solve problems.	pp. **194–201, 236–242, 322–328, 330–337, 338–346, 347–355, 356–363, 364–370, 661–668**
13. Students prove relationships between angles in polygons by using properties of complementary, supplementary, vertical, and exterior angles.	pp. **44–50, 62, 109–116, 120, 196–201, 236–242, 295–301, 302–308, 312, 324–328, 330–337, 663–668**
14. Students prove the Pythagorean theorem.	pp. **535, 540 (Exs. 37, 38), 557 (Math & History)**
15. Students use the Pythagorean theorem to determine distance and find missing lengths of sides of right triangles.	pp. **535–541, 543–549, 582–583;** 19–20, 24 (Exs. 57–59), 542
16. Students perform basic constructions with a straightedge and compass, such as angle bisectors, perpendicular bisectors, and the line parallel to a given line through a point off the line.	pp. **34, 36, 104, 130, 159, 213, 264, 273, 286, 344 (Ex. 30), 413, 496, 500, 507, 605–606, 609–610 (Exs. 52, 54), 612, 618 (Exs. 30–33), 673–674 (Exs. 35–44)**
17. Students prove theorems by using coordinate geometry, including the midpoint of a line segment, the distance formula, and various forms of equations of lines and circles.	pp. **17–24, 34–41, 165–171, 172–177, 243–249, 287–292, 335 (Exs. 40–44), 341 (Example 4), 343–344 (Exs. 21–26, 34–36), 350 (Example 5), 354–355 (Exs. 55–60, 69–72), 365 (Example 3), 368 (Exs. 36–41), 481 (Example 3), 636–640, 792–796, 836–838, 842–843;** 337 (Exs. 62–64), 357 (Example 2), 360 (Exs. 36–38), 363 (Exs. 2–5), 396–444, 446–448, 573–579
18. Students know the definitions of the basic trigonometric functions defined by the angles of a right triangle. They also know and are able to use elementary relationships between them. For example, $\tan(x) = \sin(x)/\cos(x)$, $(\sin(x))^2 + (\cos(x))^2 = 1$.	pp. **558–566, 565 (Exs. 47, 52), 583–584, 845**
19. Students use trigonometric functions to solve for an unknown length of a side of a right triangle, given an angle and a length of a side.	pp. **561–566, 567–572, 583–584;** 671 (Example 3), 690, 697 (Ex. 42)
20. Students know and are able to use angle and side relationships in problems with special right triangles, such as 30°, 60°, and 90° triangles and 45°, 45°, and 90° triangles.	pp. **551–557, 583;** 550, 669, 672 (Exs. 9–20),. 729 (Example 2), 732–733 (Exs. 22, 25, 36, 37), 736 (Example 2), 738–741 (Exs. 18, 19, 26, 28, 29, 37, 48), 746–747 (Exs. 15, 21, 31), 752 (Example 1), 754 (Example 4), 755–757 (Exs. 10, 14–16, 30)
21. Students prove and solve problems regarding relationships among chords, secants, tangents, inscribed angles, and inscribed and circumscribed polygons of circles.	pp. **595–602, 603–611, 613–620, 621–627, 629–635, 650–652, 842;** 274, 612, 628, 682 (Math & History), 690, 697 (Ex. 42)
22. Students know the effect of rigid motions on figures in the coordinate plane and space, including rotations, translations, and reflections.	pp. **396–402, 404–410, 412–420, 421–428, 430–436, 446–448;** 395, 403, 411, 429, 437–444, 452–453

CA10

CORRELATION TO SAT9 TASK 1 OBJECTIVES

KEY:
Boldface – Key page references are indicated in boldface type

SAT9 TASK 1 OBJECTIVES	Student Edition/Teacher's Edition
1. Solve problems using non-routine strategies	pp. **3–9, 51–58, 142–149, 150–156, 211–219, 457–464, 465–471, 472–479, 480–487, 488–496, 497–505, 527–534, 535–541, 542–549, 550–557, 558–566, 567–572, 612–620, 621–627, 636–640, 661–668, 676–682, 683–690, 691–698, 699–706, 766–772**
2. Evaluate polynomials	pp. **728–734, 735–742, 743–750, 751–758, 759–765**
3. Identify an equation or inequality that represents a problem situation	pp. **294–301, 302–308**
4. Use formulas to find volume of solid figures	pp. **743–750, 751–758, 759–765**
5. Solve equations with radicals	pp. **535–541, 542–549**
6. Solve inequalities	pp. **294–301**
7. Solve linear equations	pp. **96–101, 102–107, 108–116**
8. Make a prediction from a statistical sample	Not a focus of the Geometry curriculum
9. Determine a correlation, given a set of data	Not a focus of the Geometry curriculum
10. Draw inferences from tables and graphs	Not a focus of the Geometry curriculum
11. Identify the effect on the mean, median, or range of a set of data	Not a focus of the Geometry curriculum
12. Identify the mean, median, mode, or range of a set of data	Not a focus of the Geometry curriculum
13. Predict outcomes of a compound event, given a theoretical probability	Not a focus of the Geometry curriculum
14. Estimate probability, given experimental data or a graph	pp. **699–706**
15. Find probability, given a graph of probability distributions or table of outcomes	Not a focus of the Geometry curriculum
16. Predict outcomes for a simple event, given a theoretical probability	Not a focus of the Geometry curriculum
17. Solve problems involving normal distributions	Not a focus of the Geometry curriculum
18. Identify the effects of parameter changes on a function	Not a focus of the Geometry curriculum
19. Make predictions from data in a table	Not a focus of the Geometry curriculum
20. Identify graphs that represent function data in a table	Not a focus of the Geometry curriculum
21. Identify the equation of a function, given a table of values	Not a focus of the Geometry curriculum
22. Find measures of corresponding parts of similar figures	pp. **202–210, 211–219, 220–228, 229–235, 236–242, 472–479, 480–487, 488–496, 497–505, 527–534**
23. Find the area of a closed figure within a closed figure	pp. **371–380, 669–675, 676–682, 691–698, 699-706**
24. Deduce the measure of an angle in a polygon from given assumptions	pp. **26–32, 108–116, 211–219, 220–228, 229–235, 236–242, 294–301, 302–308, 321–328, 661–668**
25. Identify geometric models that represent problem situations	pp. **272–277, 558–566, 573–580, 699–706**
26. Deduce the length of a side of a polygon from given assumptions	pp. **17–25, 96–101, 102–107, 202–210, 211–219, 220–228, 229–235, 236–242, 294–301, 302–308, 628–635**
27. Find the area of the rectangle or triangle, given the coordinates of the vertices	pp. **51–58**
28. Find the circumference of a circle, given the endpoints of a diameter or radius	pp. **51–58, 683–689**

CA12 CA13

California Standards

This chart lists the pages where each California Standard for Geometry is covered in the textbook.

State Assessment

This chart details where each objective for the Task 1 level of the SAT9 is covered in the textbook. A chart for the Task 2 level is also provided.

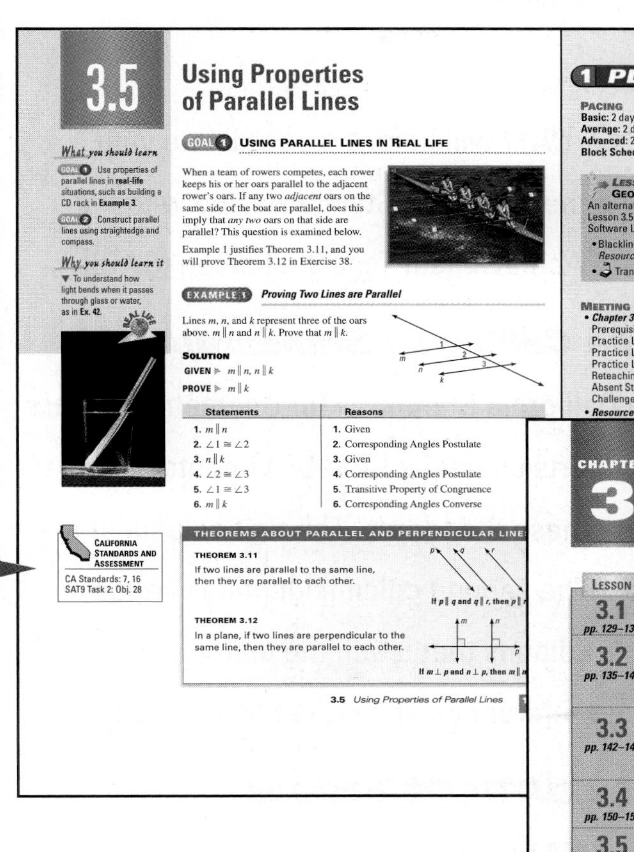

3.5 Using Properties of Parallel Lines

What you should learn

GOAL 1 Use properties of parallel lines in **real-life** situations, such as building a CD rack in **Example 3**.

GOAL 2 Construct parallel lines using straightedge and compass.

Why you should learn it

▼ To understand how light bends when it passes through glass or water, as in **Ex. 42**.

REAL LIFE

CALIFORNIA STANDARDS AND ASSESSMENT

CA Standards: 7, 16
SAT9 Task 2: Obj. 28

GOAL 1 Using Parallel Lines in Real Life

When a team of rowers competes, each rower keeps his or her oars parallel to the adjacent rower's oars. If any two *adjacent* oars on the same side of the boat are parallel, does this imply that *any two* oars on that side are parallel? This question is examined below.

Example 1 justifies Theorem 3.11, and you will prove Theorem 3.12 in Exercise 38.

EXAMPLE 1 ***Proving Two Lines are Parallel***

Lines m, n, and k represent three of the oars above. $m \parallel n$ and $n \parallel k$. Prove that $m \parallel k$.

SOLUTION

GIVEN ▸ $m \parallel n$, $n \parallel k$

PROVE ▸ $m \parallel k$

Statements	Reasons
1. $m \parallel n$	1. Given
2. $\angle 1 \cong \angle 2$	2. Corresponding Angles Postulate
3. $n \parallel k$	3. Given
4. $\angle 2 \cong \angle 3$	4. Corresponding Angles Postulate
5. $\angle 1 \cong \angle 3$	5. Transitive Property of Congruence
6. $m \parallel k$	6. Corresponding Angles Converse

THEOREMS ABOUT PARALLEL AND PERPENDICULAR LINE

THEOREM 3.11

If two lines are parallel to the same line, then they are parallel to each other.

If $p \parallel q$ and $q \parallel r$, then $p \parallel$

THEOREM 3.12

In a plane, if two lines are perpendicular to the same line, then they are parallel to each other.

If $m \perp p$ and $n \perp p$, then $m \parallel$

3.5 *Using Properties of Parallel Lines*

1 PLAN

PACING
Basic: 2 days
Average: 2 days
Advanced: 2 days
Block Schedule: 1 block

LESSON OPENER
GEOMETRY SOFTWARE
An alternative way to approach Lesson 3.5 is to use the Geometry Software Lesson Opener:
- Blackline Master (*Chapter 3 Resource Book*, p. 69)
- Transparency (p. 18)

MEETING INDIVIDUAL NEEDS
- ***Chapter 3 Resource Book***
  Prerequisite Skills Review (p. 5)
  Practice Level A (p. 70)
  Practice Level B (p. 71)
  Practice Level C (p. 72)
  Reteaching with Practice (p. 73)
  Absent Student Catch-Up (p. 75)
  Challenge (p. 78)
- ***Resources in Spanish***

Curriculum Overview

This column provides an overview of how the chapter addresses the California Standards.

Lesson Content

The lesson content is correlated to the California Standards and to the objectives for the SAT9.

CHAPTER 3

Planning the Chapter

Perpendicular and Parallel Lines

Lesson	GOALS	NCTM	ITED	SAT9 (Task 1)	Terra-Nova	Local
3.1 *pp. 129–134*	GOAL 1 Identify relationships between lines. GOAL 2 Identify angles formed by transversals.	3	MIGE	28	14	7, 16
3.2 *pp. 135–141*	CONCEPT ACTIVITY: 3.2 *Investigate forming a flow proof.* GOAL 1 Write different types of proofs. GOAL 2 Prove results about perpendicular lines.	3, 7, 8	MIGE	28	14, 17, 18	2, 4
3.3 *pp. 142–149*	TECHNOLOGY ACTIVITY: 3.3 *Explore the properties of parallel lines using geometry software.* GOAL 1 Prove and use results about parallel lines and transversals. GOAL 2 Use properties of parallel lines to solve real-life problems.	3, 6, 7, 8, 9, 10	MIGE, RQGE	1, 28	14, 17, 18	4, 7
3.4 *pp. 150–156*	GOAL 1 Prove that two lines are parallel. GOAL 2 Use properties of parallel lines to solve real-life problems.	3, 6, 7, 8, 9, 10	MIGE, RQGE	1, 28	14, 17, 18	4, 7
3.5 *pp. 157–164*	GOAL 1 Use properties of parallel lines in real-life situations. GOAL 2 Construct parallel lines using straightedge and compass.	3, 9, 10	MIGE	28	14	7, 16
3.6 *pp. 165–171*	GOAL 1 Find slopes of lines and use slope to identify parallel lines in a coordinate plane. GOAL 2 Write equations of parallel lines in a coordinate plane.	1, 2, 3, 4, 8, 9, 10	MCWN, MIGE	28	11, 13, 14, 16, 18, 48, 49, 51	17
3.7 *pp. 172–178*	GOAL 1 Use slope to identify perpendicular lines in a coordinate plane. GOAL 2 Write equations of perpendicular lines.	1, 2, 3, 4, 8, 9, 10	MCWN, MIGE	28	11, 13, 14, 16, 18, 48, 49, 51, 52	17

126A

Additional California Teaching Resources

Look on the Internet at **www.mcdougallittell.com** for more planning, teaching, and student resources.

Assessment Overview

This column provides an overview of how the chapter addresses the objectives for the Task 2 level of the SAT9.

California Curriculum and Assessment

The material on pages CA7–CA17 will help you coordinate your teaching of *Geometry* with the California Standards and with the objectives for the Stanford Achievement Test, 9th Edition (SAT9).

➤ *Correlations to the California Standards*

A complete listing of the California Standards for Geometry appears on pages CA7–CA8. The charts on pages CA9–CA11 contain a correlation of *Geometry* to these Standards. The first column of the charts lists the Standards. The second column identifies pages in the Student and Teacher's Editions that teach the material included in the Standards. Key page references appear in boldface type.

➤ *Correlations to the SAT9 Objectives*

The charts on pages CA12–CA14 contain a correlation of *Geometry* to the objectives for the Task 1 level of the SAT9. The first column of the charts lists and assigns numbers to the content objectives. The second column identifies pages in the Student and Teacher's Editions that teach the material included in the content objectives. Key page references appear in boldface type. A correlation of *Geometry* to the objectives for the Task 2 level of the SAT9 appears on pages CA15–CA17.

California Standards for Geometry

1. Students demonstrate understanding by identifying and giving examples of undefined terms, axioms, theorems, and inductive and deductive reasoning.
2. Students write geometric proofs, including proofs by contradiction.
3. Students construct and judge the validity of a logical argument and give counterexamples to disprove a statement.
4. Students prove basic theorems involving congruence and similarity.
5. Students prove that triangles are congruent or similar, and they are able to use the concept of corresponding parts of congruent triangles.
6. Students know and are able to use the triangle inequality theorem.
7. Students prove and use theorems involving the properties of parallel lines cut by a transversal, the properties of quadrilaterals, and the properties of circles.
8. Students know, derive, and solve problems involving the perimeter, circumference, area, volume, lateral area, and surface area of common geometric figures.
9. Students compute the volumes and surface areas of prisms, pyramids, cylinders, cones, and spheres; and students commit to memory the formulas for prisms, pyramids, and cylinders.
10. Students compute areas of polygons, including rectangles, scalene triangles, equilateral triangles, rhombi, parallelograms, and trapezoids.
11. Students determine how changes in dimensions affect the perimeter, area, and volume of common geometric figures and solids.
12. Students find and use measures of sides and of interior and exterior angles of triangles and polygons to classify figures and solve problems.
13. Students prove relationships between angles in polygons by using properties of complementary, supplementary, vertical, and exterior angles.
14. Students prove the Pythagorean theorem.
15. Students use the Pythagorean theorem to determine distance and find missing lengths of sides of right triangles.
16. Students perform basic constructions with a straightedge and compass, such as angle bisectors, perpendicular bisectors, and the line parallel to a given line through a point off the line.
17. Students prove theorems by using coordinate geometry, including the midpoint of a line segment, the distance formula, and various forms of equations of lines and circles.

18. Students know the definitions of the basic trigonometric functions defined by the angles of a right triangle. They also know and are able to use elementary relationships between them. For example, $\tan(x) = \frac{\sin(x)}{\cos(x)}$, $(\sin(x))^2 + (\cos(x))^2 = 1$.

19. Students use trigonometric functions to solve for an unknown length of a side of a right triangle, given an angle and a length of a side.

20. Students know and are able to use angle and side relationships in problems with special right triangles, such as 30°, 60°, and 90° triangles and 45°, 45°, and 90° triangles.

21. Students prove and solve problems regarding relationships among chords, secants, tangents, inscribed angles, and inscribed and circumscribed polygons of circles.

22. Students know the effect of rigid motions on figures in the coordinate plane and space, including rotations, translations, and reflections.

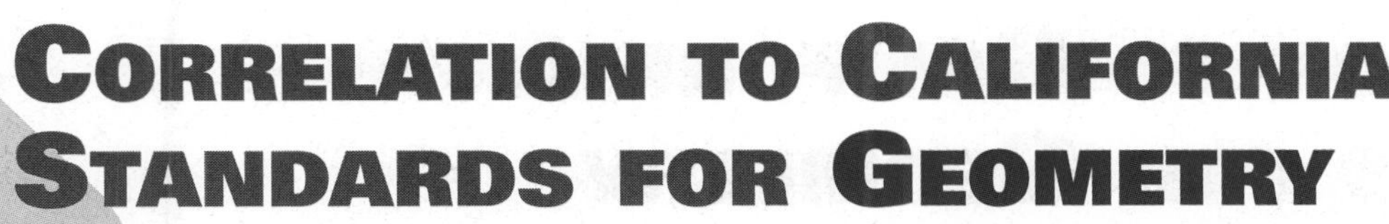

CORRELATION TO CALIFORNIA STANDARDS FOR GEOMETRY

CALIFORNIA STANDARDS	Student Edition / Teacher's Edition
1. Students demonstrate understanding by identifying and giving examples of undefined terms, axioms, theorems, and inductive and deductive reasoning.	pp. **3–9, 10–16, 17–18, 71–78, 79–85, 87–95, 827–832;** 86
2. Students write geometric proofs, including proofs by contradiction.	pp. **102–107, 109–116, 136–141, 212–219, 220–227, 229–235, 243–250, 302–307, 312 (Exs. 24, 25), 355 (Ex. 83)**
3. Students construct and judge the validity of a logical argument and give counterexamples to disprove a statement.	pp. **3–9, 71–78, 79–85, 87–95;** 82 (Ex. 2), 86, 104 (Ex. 2), 138 (Ex. 10), 162 (Ex. 32), 216 (Ex. 2), 360 (Ex. 34), 562 (Ex. 2)
4. Students prove basic theorems involving congruence and similarity.	pp. **102–107, 109–116, 136–141, 143–149, 150–156, 202–209, 330–337, 338–346, 347–355, 356–363, 603–611, 613–620, 629–635, 677–681**
5. Students prove that triangles are congruent or similar, and they are able to use the concept of corresponding parts of congruent triangles.	pp. **202–210, 212–219, 220–227, 229–235, 236–242, 243–250, 480–487, 488–496, 527–534;** 211, 228, 330–337, 338–345
6. Students know and are able to use the triangle inequality theorem.	pp. **297–301, 302–308, 312;** 294, 300 (Ex. 34)
7. Students prove and use theorems involving the properties of parallel lines cut by a transversal, the properties of quadrilaterals, and the properties of circles.	pp. **129–134, 143–149, 150–156, 157–164, 322–328, 330–337, 338–346, 347–355, 356–363, 364–370, 372–380, 498–505, 595–602, 603–611, 613–620, 621–627, 629–635;** 612, 628
8. Students know, derive, and solve problems involving the perimeter, circumference, area, volume, lateral area, and surface area of common geometric figures.	pp. **51–57, 372–379, 384, 537–540, 669–675, 677–682, 683–689, 691–698, 699–705, 708, 728–734, 735–742, 743–749, 752–758, 759–765, 766–772, 774–776, 843;** 346 (Math & History), 371, 690, 706, 719–726, 727, 750, 751

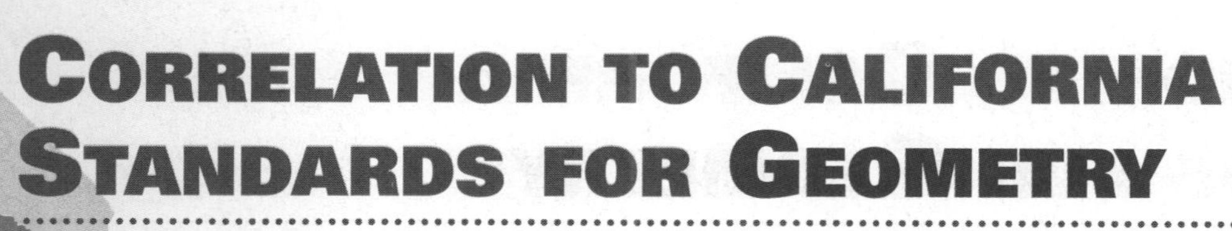

Correlation to California Standards for Geometry

CALIFORNIA STANDARDS	Student Edition / Teacher's Edition
9. Students compute the volumes and surface areas of prisms, pyramids, cylinders, cones, and spheres; and students commit to memory the formulas for prisms, pyramids, and cylinders.	pp. **728–734, 735–742, 743–749, 752–758, 759–765, 766–772, 774–776, 843**; 719–726, 727, 750, 751
10. Students compute areas of polygons, including rectangles, scalene triangles, equilateral triangles, rhombi, parallelograms, and trapezoids.	pp. **51–57, 372–379, 384, 537–540, 669–675, 699–705, 708, 843**; 346 (Math & History), 371
11. Students determine how changes in dimensions affect the perimeter, area, and volume of common geometric figures and solids.	pp. **473–479, 506–513, 514, 677–682, 766–772, 776**
12. Students find and use measures of sides and of interior and exterior angles of triangles and polygons to classify figures and solve problems.	pp. **194–201, 236–242, 322–328, 330–337, 338–346, 347–355, 356–363, 364–370, 661–668**
13. Students prove relationships between angles in polygons by using properties of complementary, supplementary, vertical, and exterior angles.	pp. **44–50, 62, 109–116, 120, 196–201, 236–242, 295–301, 302–308, 312, 324–328, 330–337, 663–668**
14. Students prove the Pythagorean theorem.	pp. **535, 540 (Exs. 37, 38), 557 (Math & History)**
15. Students use the Pythagorean theorem to determine distance and find missing lengths of sides of right triangles.	pp. **535–541, 543–549, 582–583;** 19–20, 24 (Exs. 57–59), 542
16. Students perform basic constructions with a straightedge and compass, such as angle bisectors, perpendicular bisectors, and the line parallel to a given line through a point off the line.	pp. **34, 36, 104, 130, 159, 213, 264, 273, 286, 344 (Ex. 30), 413, 496, 500, 507, 605–606, 609–610 (Exs. 52, 54), 612, 618 (Exs. 30–33), 673–674 (Exs. 35–44)**

KEY:
Boldface – Key page references are indicated in boldface type

CALIFORNIA STANDARDS	Student Edition / Teacher's Edition
17. Students prove theorems by using coordinate geometry, including the midpoint of a line segment, the distance formula, and various forms of equations of lines and circles.	pp. **17–24, 34–41, 165–171, 172–177, 243–249, 287–292, 335 (Exs. 40–44), 341 (Example 4), 343–344 (Exs. 21–26, 34–36), 350 (Example 5), 354–355 (Exs. 55–60, 69–72), 365 (Example 3), 368 (Exs. 36–41), 481 (Example 3), 636–640, 792–796, 836–838, 842–843;** 337 (Exs. 62–64), 357 (Example 2), 360 (Exs. 36–38), 363 (Exs. 2–5), 396–444, 446–448, 573–579
18. Students know the definitions of the basic trigonometric functions defined by the angles of a right triangle. They also know and are able to use elementary relationships between them. For example, $\tan(x) = \sin(x)/\cos(x)$, $(\sin(x))^2 + (\cos(x))^2 = 1$.	pp. **558–566, 565 (Exs. 47, 52), 583–584, 845**
19. Students use trigonometric functions to solve for an unknown length of a side of a right triangle, given an angle and a length of a side.	pp. **561–566, 567–572, 583–584;** 671 (Example 3), 690, 697 (Ex. 42)
20. Students know and are able to use angle and side relationships in problems with special right triangles, such as 30°, 60°, and 90° triangles and 45°, 45°, and 90° triangles.	pp. **551–557, 583;** 550, 669, 672 (Exs. 9–20), 729 (Example 2), 732–733 (Exs. 22, 25, 36, 37), 736 (Example 2), 738–741 (Exs. 18, 19, 26, 28, 29, 37, 48), 746–747 (Exs. 15, 21, 31), 752 (Example 1), 754 (Example 4), 755–757 (Exs. 10, 14–16, 30)
21. Students prove and solve problems regarding relationships among chords, secants, tangents, inscribed angles, and inscribed and circumscribed polygons of circles.	pp. **595–602, 603–611, 613–620, 621–627, 629–635, 650–652, 842;** 274, 612, 628, 682 (Math & History), 690, 697 (Ex. 42)
22. Students know the effect of rigid motions on figures in the coordinate plane and space, including rotations, translations, and reflections.	pp. **396–402, 404–410, 412–420, 421–428, 430–436, 446–448;** 395, 403, 411, 429, 437–444, 452–453

Correlation to SAT9 Task 1 Objectives

SAT9 TASK 1 OBJECTIVES	Student Edition / Teacher's Edition
1. Solve problems using non-routine strategies	pp. **3–9, 51–58, 142–149, 150–156, 211–219, 457–464, 465–471, 472–479, 480–487, 488–496, 497–505, 527–534, 535–541, 542–549, 550–557, 558–566, 567–572, 612–620, 621–627, 636–640, 661–668, 676–682, 683–690, 691–698, 699–706, 766–772**
2. Evaluate polynomials	pp. **728–734, 735–742, 743–750, 751–758, 759–765**
3. Identify an equation or inequality that represents a problem situation	pp. **294–301, 302–308**
4. Use formulas to find volume of solid figures	pp. **743–750, 751–758, 759–765**
5. Solve equations with radicals	pp. **535–541, 542–549**
6. Solve inequalities	pp. **294–301**
7. Solve linear equations	pp. **96–101, 102–107, 108–116**
8. Make a prediction from a statistical sample	Not a focus of the Geometry curriculum
9. Determine a correlation, given a set of data	Not a focus of the Geometry curriculum
10. Draw inferences from tables and graphs	Not a focus of the Geometry curriculum
11. Identify the effect on the mean, median, or range of a set of data	Not a focus of the Geometry curriculum
12. Identify the mean, median, mode, or range of a set of data	Not a focus of the Geometry curriculum
13. Predict outcomes of a compound event, given a theoretical probability	Not a focus of the Geometry curriculum
14. Estimate probability, given experimental data or a graph	pp. **699–706**

KEY:
Boldface – Key page references are indicated in boldface type

SAT9 TASK 1 OBJECTIVES	Student Edition / Teacher's Edition
15. Find probability, given a graph of probability distributions or table of outcomes	Not a focus of the Geometry curriculum
16. Predict outcomes for a simple event, given a theoretical probability	Not a focus of the Geometry curriculum
17. Solve problems involving normal distributions	Not a focus of the Geometry curriculum
18. Identify the effects of parameter changes on a function	Not a focus of the Geometry curriculum
19. Make predictions from data in a table	Not a focus of the Geometry curriculum
20. Identify graphs that represent function data in a table	Not a focus of the Geometry curriculum
21. Identify the equation of a function, given a table of values	Not a focus of the Geometry curriculum
22. Find measures of corresponding parts of similar figures	pp. **202–210, 211–219, 220–228, 229–235, 236–242, 472–479, 480–487, 488–496, 497–505, 527–534**
23. Find the area of a closed figure within a closed figure	pp. **371–380, 669–675, 676–682, 691–698, 699-706**
24. Deduce the measure of an angle in a polygon from given assumptions	pp. **26–32, 108–116, 211–219, 220–228, 229–235, 236–242, 294–301, 302–308, 321–328, 661–668**
25. Identify geometric models that represent problem situations	pp. **272–277, 558–566, 573–580, 699–706**
26. Deduce the length of a side of a polygon from given assumptions	pp. **17–25, 96–101, 102–107, 202–210, 211–219, 220–228, 229–235, 236–242, 294–301, 302–308, 628–635**
27. Find the area of the rectangle or triangle, given the coordinates of the vertices	pp. **51–58**
28. Find the circumference of a circle, given the endpoints of a diameter or radius	pp. **51–58, 683–689**

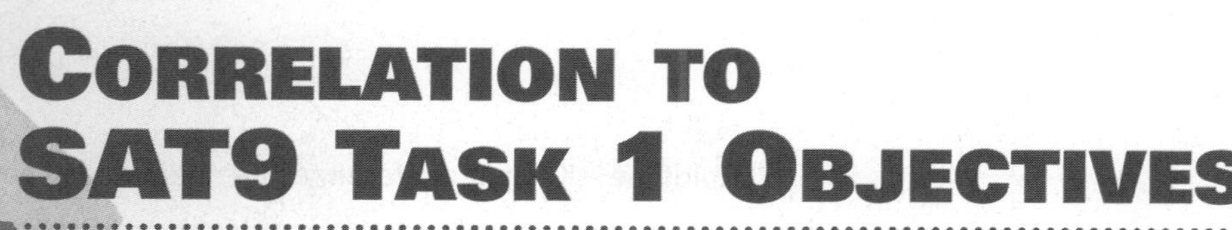

Correlation to SAT9 Task 1 Objectives

SAT9 TASK 1 OBJECTIVES	Student Edition / Teacher's Edition
29. Find the dimensions of the polygon, given the coordinates of a polygon	pp. **51–58**
30. Find the midpoint of a segment, given its coordinates	pp. **34–42, 338–346**
31. Identify the coordinates of transformation, given the endpoints of a segment	pp. **395–402, 403–410, 411–420, 421–428, 429–436, 437–444, 506–514**
32. Given two sides of a right triangle and a trigonometry table, find the measure of a missing angle	pp. **567–572**
33. Read and interpret the graph of a trigonometric function	Not a focus of the Geometry curriculum
34. Solve problems involving enumeration	Not a focus of the Geometry curriculum
35. Solve problems involving sequences with recurrence relations	Not a focus of the Geometry curriculum
36. Identify the results of an algorithm	Not a focus of the Geometry curriculum
37. Estimate the area under a curve	p. **706**
38. Solve problems involving infinite sequences	Not a focus of the Geometry curriculum
39. Determine the maximum or minimum points of a graph	Not a focus of the Geometry curriculum

Correlation to SAT9 Task 2 Objectives

SAT9 TASK 2 OBJECTIVES	Student Edition / Teacher's Edition
1. Solve problems using non-routine strategies	pp. **3–9, 51–58, 142–149, 150–156, 211–219, 457–464, 465–471, 472–479, 480–487, 488–496, 497–505, 527–534, 535–541, 542–549, 550–557, 558–566, 567–572, 612–620, 621–627, 636–640, 661–668, 676–682, 683–690, 691–698, 699–706, 766–772**
2. Identify an equation or inequality that represents a problem situation	pp. **294–301, 302–308**
3. Solve inequalities	pp. **294–301**
4. Solve linear equations	pp. **96–101, 102–107, 108–116**
5. Use formulas to find the volume of solid figures	pp. **743–750, 751–758, 759–765**
6. Evaluate polynomials	pp. **728–734, 735–742, 743–750, 751–758, 759–765**
7. Solve equations with radicals	pp. **535–541, 542–549**
8. Identify the equation for the line of regression for a scattergram	Not a focus of the Geometry curriculum
9. Make a prediction from a statistical sample	Not a focus of the Geometry curriculum
10. Determine a correlation, given a set of data	Not a focus of the Geometry curriculum
11. Draw inferences from tables and graphs	Not a focus of the Geometry curriculum
12. Identify the effect on mean, median, or mode when data is changed	Not a focus of the Geometry curriculum
13. Identify the mean, median, mode, or range of a set of data	Not a focus of the Geometry curriculum
14. Predict outcomes for a compound event, given a theoretical probability	Not a focus of the Geometry curriculum

Correlation to SAT9 Task 2 Objectives

SAT9 TASK 2 OBJECTIVES	Student Edition / Teacher's Edition
15. Estimate probability, given experimental data or a graph	pp. **699–706**
16. Find probability, given a graph of probability distributions or table of outcomes	Not a focus of the Geometry curriculum
17. Predict outcomes for a simple event, given a theoretical probability	Not a focus of the Geometry curriculum
18. Solve problems involving normal distributions	Not a focus of the Geometry curriculum
19. Make predictions from data in a table	Not a focus of the Geometry curriculum
20. Identify graphs that represent function data in a table	Not a focus of the Geometry curriculum
21. Identify equations that represent graphs	Not a focus of the Geometry curriculum
22. Identify the effects of parameter changes on a function	Not a focus of the Geometry curriculum
23. Identify the equation of a function, given a table of values	Not a focus of the Geometry curriculum
24. Find measures of corresponding parts of similar figures	pp. **202–210, 211–219, 220–228, 229–235, 236–242, 472–479, 480–487, 488–496, 497–505, 527–534**
25. Use the Pythagorean Theorem to find the length of an unknown side of a triangle	pp. **535–541, 542–549, 550–557, 567–572**
26. Deduce the length of a side of a polygon from given assumptions	pp. **17–25, 96–101, 102–107, 202–210, 211–219, 220–228, 229–235, 236–242, 294–301, 302–308, 628–635**
27. Deduce the measure of an angle in a polygon from given assumptions	pp. **26–32, 108–116, 211–219, 220–228, 229–235, 236–242, 294–301, 302–308, 321–328, 661–668**
28. Determine the relation between lines and transversals	pp. **129–134, 135–141, 142–149, 150–156, 157–164, 165–171, 172–178**

KEY:

Boldface – Key page references are indicated in boldface type

SAT9 TASK 2 OBJECTIVES	Student Edition / Teacher's Edition
29. Find the area of a closed figure within a closed figure	pp. **371–380, 669–675, 676–682, 691–698, 699–706**
30. Find the area of the rectangle or triangle, given the coordinates of its vertices	pp. **51–58**
31. Find the circumference of a circle, given the endpoints of a diameter or radius	pp. **51–58, 683–689**
32. Find the dimensions of a polygon, given the coordinates of the polygon	pp. **51–58**
33. Find the midpoint, given the coordinates of its segment	pp. **34–42, 338–346**
34. Identify the coordinates of transformation, given the endpoints of a segment	pp. **395–402, 403–410, 411–420, 421–428, 429–436, 437–444, 506–514**
35. Given one side of a right triangle, an angle measure, and the graph of a trigonometric function, find the length of another side	pp. **558–566**
36. Given two sides of a right triangle and the graph of a trigonometric function, find the measure of a missing angle	pp. **567–572**
37. Read and interpret the graph of a trigonometric function	Not a focus of the Geometry curriculum
38. Solve problems involving enumeration	Not a focus of the Geometry curriculum
39. Solve problems involving sequences with recurrence relations	Not a focus of the Geometry curriculum
40. Solve problems involving infinite sequences	Not a focus of the Geometry curriculum
41. Estimate the area under a curve	p. **706**
42. Solve problems involving infinite sequences	Not a focus of the Geometry curriculum
43. Determine the maximum or minimum points of a graph	Not a focus of the Geometry curriculum

Providing Universal Access

by Catherine Barkett

Introduction

In most classrooms, students present a variety of achievement levels, skills, and needs. The goal for all students is the same: We want them to develop sufficient computational, procedural, and problem solving skills to provide a solid foundation for further study in mathematics. However, all students do not arrive at these competencies at the same time or in the same way. In this article we suggest research-based strategies teachers can use to modify curriculum and instruction for special needs students. The basic instructional plan in *Geometry* is designed for students who are achieving at near grade level; but just prior to each chapter we include specific suggestions for students who are achieving above and below grade level, and for students who are not fluent in English (see also the article titled "Adapting Curriculum and Instruction for English Learners").

With careful planning, teachers can help all students reach a level of mathematical competence needed to continue their education in mathematics.

Teachers may find it helpful to view students as members of four basic groups. (English learners can be found in all four groups.) Teachers do not need to place students in these groups; the categories are suggested so teachers can plan ahead to meet different needs of students. Note the use of the term *strategic learners* to emphasize the kind of instruction needed by students achieving below grade level. This term is not synonymous with special education. It may include some special education pupils but includes many more students whose low achievement levels are the result of inadequate prior schooling or attendance, high mobility rates, or a host of other reasons that have nothing to do with their abilities or disabilities. The term *strategic learner* was selected because it is a positive term that emphasizes what needs to happen in order for these students to be successful and implies what we believe: students achieving below grade level *can* be successful in mathematics given carefully designed instruction.

Setting the Right Tone

There are three key strategies recommended for teachers as they adapt any program to students' needs:

- Use frequent assessment as a way to determine what each student does or does not know, and use that assessment as the basis for planning.
- Plan modifications of curriculum and instruction ahead of time so that you are ready to differentiate as the need arises.
- Use a variety of grouping strategies to facilitate learning. A combination of whole class instruction and temporary groupings of students, with groups organized around students' needs, will facilitate management of the variety of achievement levels and learning needs in the classroom.

Assessment, planning, and flexible grouping are essential to ensuring that your students have the optimal chance for success. In addition to these three key strategies, general guidelines for establishing a classroom designed to meet students' needs are:

1. Establish an atmosphere where students feel comfortable asking questions and are rewarded for asking about things they don't understand.
2. Maintain the same goals for all students. Allow additional time and practice for students who need it, and provide challenging alternatives for those who are ready to move more quickly.
3. Clearly identify the skill, concept, or standards you are working on and measure progress towards those ends.
4. Have students show their work. It is much easier for teachers to understand where a student gets confused if they have evidence of the student's thought process.
5. Try small modifications in curriculum and instruction before more drastic ones.
6. Don't persist with a strategy that is not working. Try something else.
7. Encourage effort and persistence, and celebrate successes with your students.

Varying Curriculum and Instruction

1. **TIME** Most students whose achievement is below grade level will need more time. Students who are not fluent in English will need more time. The contents of this book might be offered over a two-year period, or two periods a day. Perhaps the day can be extended through study hall, regular homework assignments, tutoring, or Saturday, summer, or "off track" catch-up sessions. Advanced students might "test out" of portions of the

Four Basic Student Groups

Advanced Group	Grade Level Group	Strategic Group	Intensive Needs Group
Advanced students have already completed some of the grade-level material. They make rapid progress and become bored with repetition. They may or may not have been formally identified as gifted or talented in the area of mathematics. **Suggested Plan** 1. Assess what these students already know. 2. Allow these students to "test out" of chapters or assignments. 3. Substitute challenge assignments for easier ones. 4. Modify instruction so that it is more complex or more in-depth.	Students achieving at grade level may have minor, occasional difficulties, but they can be assisted to maintain their progress with extra practice, individual, or group assistance on an ad hoc basis. **Suggested Plan** 1. Assess what these students already know. 2. Progress through *Geometry* at the recommended pace and sequence. 3. On an ad hoc basis, review or provide additional practice as needed.	Strategic learners are not achieving at expected grade level but can, with a carefully designed program that provides targeted assistance. Systematic differentiation such as preteaching, reteaching, and additional instructional time should be planned for these students, as suggested in each chapter. **Suggested Plan** 1. Assess what these students already know. 2. Provide additional scaffolding and vary instruction as suggested in this book. 3. Focus on the key concepts and present material systematically. 4. Vary the kinds of instruction so that students have several opportunities to understand. 5. Provide additional practice homework.	Intesive needs students are those whose performance is two or more standard deviations below the mean on standardized measures. These students will probably already be eligible for special education services. This is a very small percentage of the general population. **Suggested Plan** 1. Assess what these students already know. 2. Determine if these students have an IEP. 3. Refer students for special education testing or child study team discussion: enlist the help of specialists. 4. Carefully consider each student's most appropriate placement in mathematics. 5. Use the specific suggestions for strategic learners.

(Adapted from the Mathematics Framework for California Public Schools, K-12, California Department of Education, 1999.)

book and complete the material in half a year, or they may compact two courses into one.

2. **PRESENTATION** Instructing in a variety of ways and taking a single concept and explaining it verbally and visually with concrete and abstract examples provide students multiple opportunities for understanding. Factoring, for example, is a key concept for success in algebra. It can be introduced and practiced in a variety of ways: with tree diagrams, with repeated division by hand and on a calculator, and with oral problems or games that require students to factor mentally. If students don't understand factoring when presented one way, they can be retaught using a different approach.

3. **TASK PARAMETERS** Multi-step problems can be especially difficult for students. These types of problems are just combinations of simpler problems and can be broken down into those simpler steps, with additional help and practice at each step. Confusing elements can be minimized and extraneous material can be eliminated. For advanced students, simpler problems can be replaced by more challenging ones.

4. **METHODS OF ASSESSMENT** Students learning English may be able to demonstrate on paper what they cannot yet verbalize. Students with physical challenges may be unable to draw a graph but may be able to select the right graph from a series of options or verbally describe the graph so that someone else can draw it. Allow students to demonstrate their knowledge in a variety of ways while helping all students to master the skills and knowledge necessary to exhibit their understanding in standard ways.

Geometry is organized so that much of the differentiation for special needs students is built into the design of the program. Note that simpler concepts are introduced before more complex ones. Ample practice is provided. Challenge exercises are included throughout the pupil text. The program provides students with models for conceptual understanding of the mathematical reasoning behind each key concept. Mathematical reasoning is stressed throughout each chapter. Vocabulary words, examples, and Guided Practice exercises are standard features of each chapter. Each lesson includes Mixed Review exercises so

Students need to be taught strategies for organizing their work and keeping track of where they are.

that students recall and use skills and understandings from previous chapters. These features were designed to help you meet the needs of the students in your class.

Strategies:

FOR STUDENTS WHO HAVE TROUBLE PAYING ATTENTION

Some students in your classroom may be formally identified as having Attention Deficit Hyperactivity Disorder (ADHD) or Attention Deficit Disorder (ADD). Others may exhibit the same learning challenges but may not be formally identified. Whether formally identified or not, students who have trouble paying attention generally share the following characteristics:

- Trouble paying attention is not just occasional. It occurs most or all of the time, across content areas, and is inappropriate for the age of the child.
- Forgetfulness, memory problems, losing things, disorganization
- Restlessness, fidgeting
- Socially inappropriate behavior such as excessive talking, interrupting others, and difficulty waiting their turn

These students may be very bright and capable in mathematics but have a hard time staying focused for long periods of time. They need to be taught strategies for organizing their work and keeping track of where they are. In general, students with attention problems need to be helped to develop coping strategies. The teacher should approach the student in a problem solving mode: "Let's find ways to help you concentrate and organize your work," rather than using one of the following strategies in a punitive way.

1. **Present the work in smaller chunks, over smaller time periods,** and then gradually increase expectations. If students have trouble completing long tests, for example, break the material into smaller quizzes and increase the length of the quizzes as the year progresses.
2. **Use cumulative review and practice.** Have students periodically review what they learned in previous chapters and provide additional practice if they have forgotten.
3. **Make it more obvious what the student should focus on.** For example, use the test generator to put only four problems on each page; use a large font; or use an index card or piece of cardboard with a hole cut out of the middle to place on the page so that the student can focus on one problem at a time. A pencil, finger, highlighter, or sticky paper can also be used by the student to keep track of which problem he or she is working on.
4. **Have students race against the clock.** For some students, racing against the clock to see how many problems can be completed accurately within a five-minute time period is more motivating than doing the same number of problems at their leisure. The time period can be extended gradually.
5. **Help students develop simple strategies for bringing work to and from class.** A two-pocket folder, where homework goes home in the left pocket and comes back in the right, is a simple way to keep track of assignments.
6. **Allow movement and schedule breaks.**
7. **Minimize distractions by seating students that are easily distracted near the teacher** and away from hallway noise. Tables with several students at a table are more distracting than rows of desks. When students are to work quietly, offer headphones to block out noise. Headphones can be set to play quiet music, "white noise," or can be used just as earplugs to help block out noise.
8. **Graphic organizers** such as Venn diagrams, tree diagrams, lists, outlines, tables, and charts can all provide structures for organizing and remembering information. Mental images, choral responses, or even hand signals can help students remember. Highlighters can be used to make sure that decimal points are lined up. Graph paper is excellent for keeping homework problems neat, even when a graph is not required.
9. **Keep instructions simple and clear, especially at the beginning of the year.** Establish routines (*e.g.*, the week's homework is always due on Thursday; assignments are written in a specific place on the board; the last ten minutes of class is used to make sure everyone understands what homework is expected and how to do it). Students who know the routine find it easier to work independently.

FOR STUDENTS WHO HAVE TROUBLE UNDERSTANDING THE CONCEPTS

Success in mathematics, as in music, sports, or other areas, comes for most students only with hard work and persistent effort. Concepts may seem difficult at first, but with repeated teaching and practice virtually all students can master the mathematics they need to graduate from high school, access a variety of jobs, and lay the foundation for further study in mathematics or a related field.

Several strategies can help students make steady progress in mathematics. These include:

1. Focus on key mathematical concepts.
2. Review key concepts and skills from earlier lessons, chapters, or years.
3. Preteach key concepts and vocabulary.
4. Anticipate problem areas.
5. Provide scaffolding (guided practice) for students who need extra help.
6. Think out loud to show hidden steps.
7. Provide a sample problem to which students can return when they get stuck.
8. Break problems into simpler components.
9. Explicitly teach students a variety of problem solving strategies and help them select one that fits the situation.
10. Present concepts in a variety of ways: visually, verbally, concretely, abstractly, etc.
11. Encourage students to draw a picture or use a visual aid such as a number line, graph, or diagram.
12. Provide sufficient practice.

Finally, good teachers are perpetual students themselves. They are always looking for ways to deepen their understanding of mathematics and for good ways to explain and teach mathematics to others.

FOR ADVANCED STUDENTS

Occasionally students can demonstrate mastery of all the mathematics expected to be learned in a given grade level. Repeating previously learned material for a year is deadly to these students. It can make them dislike mathematics. For these students, moving them up a grade level for math is a simple and cost-effective solution.

Most advanced students, however, are advanced in some areas but not in others. They tend to learn quickly and need more instructional material, as well as more difficult material. The pupil edition, teacher's edition, Web site, and ancillaries to this program provide challenge exercises that can be used when students have demonstrated competence in a particular area. These challenge exercises should be substituted for the easier exercises in a homework assignment or lesson. When they have the time and interest, all students should be encouraged to work the challenge exercises.

General strategies for differentiating the curriculum for advanced learners include:

1. **Vary the pacing.** Allow advanced students some flexibility in how they progress through the course. Students who can demonstrate mastery of the objectives for a given lesson or chapter can be working on challenge exercises. Advanced students may become fascinated with a particular aspect of mathematics and want to spend *more* time on it.
2. **Differentiate in terms of depth.** Encourage advanced students to delve more in-depth into mathematics. Looking at the details and the patterns; studying the language of the discipline; and looking at trends, themes, properties, theorems, proofs, and unanswered questions can enrich the curriculum for advanced students.
3. **Differentiate in terms of complexity.** Advanced students may be ready to connect ideas across disciplines in ways characteristic of older students or adults. Encourage them to investigate relationships between mathematics and art, history, science, and music, and to look at the development of mathematics over time.

USING GROUPING TO BENEFIT ALL STUDENTS

Grouping advanced learners together for investigations of challenge problems can provide you with time to work more closely with a group of students who need help in a particular area. Alternatively, while students who need more help are working on additional reinforcement activities or practice, you can work with a group of advanced students on a challenge project. Groups can be organized and revised daily, weekly, or by lesson according to how proficient students are with the concepts and skills targeted for that day, week, or lesson. At times you may have only one student who is ready for a challenge problem; at other times the whole class may be ready. Flexible grouping is the key to ensuring that students do not become "tracked." Asking advanced students to report to the whole class on their progress on challenge problems can provide the opportunity for the whole class to engage in more abstract and theoretical thinking.

Adapting Curriculum and Instruction for English Learners

by Olga Bautista and Catherine Barkett

Introduction

English learners come to the classroom with all the variety of English speakers in regard to mathematics achievement. They may be at, behind, or ahead of grade expectations in mathematics. They may be gifted or eligible for special education services. They may have been born in the United States, or they may have arrived in this country very recently. They may speak one or more languages, and they may be literate in one or more languages other than English. They have in common one characteristic: They are all learning English.

With careful planning, teachers can maximize success for English learners in the mathematics classroom. Assessing each student's competencies in mathematics and English will form a basis for program planning.

Getting to know your students

Before school starts, check the cumulative folder on each student in your class to determine which ones are learning English. See if there is recent testing. Two types of testing are most useful: mathematics achievement and reading achievement levels. Use the chart on the following page as a guide to understanding student assessment data.

General Suggestions for Mathematics Teachers of English Learners

1. Allocate additional time for mathematics. Many students will be translating from English to their primary language and back again. The meaning of many words will not be immediately clear. When you ask questions, allow extra time for students to respond. Reading mathematics textbooks and understanding what is asked for in a word problem will take more time.
2. Use students' background knowledge. Some English learners will have developed substantial background in mathematics; others will have very little. Find out what students know and then build on that knowledge.
3. Reduce the amount and sophistication of the English language used. This may be done by reordering the lessons in each chapter to begin with key vocabulary, followed by problems with a minimum of written English, followed by at least one word problem each day. Monitor and simplify the speech you use. Speak more slowly, avoid idioms and slang, be precise and concise, and use short sentences and simple vocabulary. Using hand gestures and pictures as well as words aids communication.
4. Limit the number of concepts introduced per day. Keeping the focus of each day simple will aid students in understanding the point of the lesson. Focus on key concepts, and use mathematics instructional time well. See the pacing suggestions preceding each chapter of the *Geometry* Teacher's Edition.
5. Use a variety of different methods for getting a point across. Presenting concepts verbally and visually, with concrete examples and in abstract mathematical symbols, and using pictures, graphs, diagrams, and charts will enhance the chance that students will understand at least one of the presentations. As you introduce a new word, rule, or theorem, write it down.
6. Provide opportunities for English learners to interact with their English-speaking peers. Students who are learning a language need to hear native speakers using the language, and they need opportunities to use their new mathematics vocabulary in their speech and in their writing.
7. Provide opportunities for English learners to discuss their understandings with each other, confirm the homework assignments, or ask questions of each other in whatever language they may have in common.
8. Allow English learners to demonstrate what they know in a variety of ways. When students first learn a language, they are usually shy about speaking. They generally understand spoken language before they can reproduce it. Students who have recently arrived from another country with good prior schooling may be able to read in English but not speak it. Allow students to

English Learners

	LOW MATHEMATICS ACHIEVEMENT	HIGH MATHEMATICS ACHIEVEMENT
LOW READING ACHIEVEMENT	**Who is this student?** • Student may be new to the class, school, or country. • Student may have had inadequate schooling. • Student may have moved often. • Student may be unmotivated or have test anxiety. • Low reading achievement may be depressing mathematics scores. • Student may have gaps and holes in knowledge. • Student may need special education assistance. **What to do?** • Examine cumulative folder for other testing, notes, etc. • Delay any testing for a week or two. Help student feel comfortable in the class during that period of time. • Administer mathematics achievement test and reading test, preferably in an individual setting. • Plan to assess this student at weekly intervals and closely monitor classroom work to determine if progress is being made. • Look at the English Learners suggestions in each chapter.	**Who is this student?** • Student has had good prior mathematics instruction. • Mathematics is an area where this student can excel. • Math achievement level may actually be higher than scores indicate. (Inability to read affects mathematics achievement as well.) • Word problems will be especially difficult. **What to do?** • Mathematics instruction should proceed at normal or near normal pace. • Student should be involved in a systematic English language development program and intensive reading program outside of mathematics class. • Spend part of each class period on mathematics vocabulary study. • Provide a bilingual dictionary and grade-level mathematics text in the home language for home use. • Look at the English Learners suggestions in each chapter for those that are most useful.
HIGH READING ACHIEVEMENT	**Who is this student?** • Student may have been designated as an English learner because oral fluency is not at grade level. • Student may be able to use reading ability to improve math scores. • Student may not test well in mathematics. • Most students can make rapid progress in mathematics; a few may have learning difficulties that require the help of a specialist. **What to do?** • Assess mathematics achievement in a variety of ways. • Concentrate on developing oral fluency. • Focus on vocabulary specific to mathematics.	**Who is this student?** • May be a student who is ready for re-designation as a fluent English speaker. • May need extra study in academic vocabulary, *i.e.*, the specialized vocabulary of mathematics. • Given systematic instruction, this student should be able to achieve at or above grade level. **What to do?** • Scan all of the suggestions for English Learners in each chapter and progress through the ones the student needs as quickly as possible. • Monitor carefully to make sure this student continues to progress at a reasonable pace.

point, nod, gesture, draw a picture, or work math problems without words as they learn English.

9. Extend mathematics instructional time through homework, an extra class period, summer school, or tutoring. Many of the language-related suggestions for English learners in this series can be carried out by the language arts teacher.
10. Keep on hand picture dictionaries, foreign language dictionaries, and drawing materials.

Specific Suggestions

Prior to each chapter you will find suggestions to help you modify curriculum and instruction so that the content is accessible to English learners. Many of the suggestions are well suited for discussion in a language arts class, English as a second language class, or in a tutorial. In these sections we will provide you with suggestions and activities designed to (1) teach the vocabulary commonly used in mathematics; (2) explain mathematical concepts in a variety of ways; and (3) dissect the structure of word problems. Much of the vocabulary study in this book may be review for your students, and in that case, you should feel free to work as quickly as possible through the activities. For those students who need more systematic study, progressing through the activities as indicated will ensure that students have refreshed their understanding of basic terms prior to statewide testing that generally occurs toward the end of each school year. We recommend that if you have English learners in your classroom, you skim all the chapter suggestions for English learners so that you may use them as you need them.

McDougal Littell

GEOMETRY

TEACHER'S EDITION

Ron Larson
Laurie Boswell
Lee Stiff

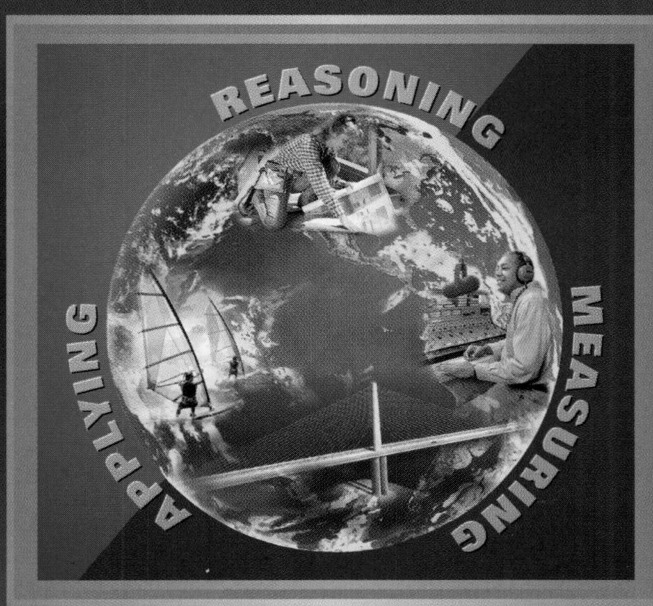

McDougal Littell
A HOUGHTON MIFFLIN COMPANY
Evanston, Illinois • Boston • Dallas

CONTENTS

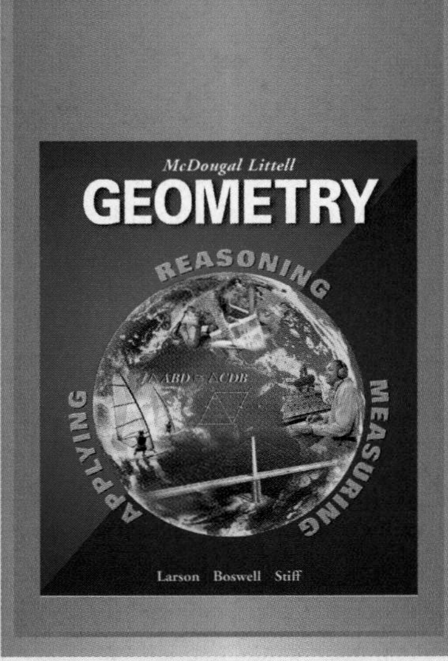

About the Cover

Geometry brings math to life with many real-life applications. The cover illustrates some of the applications used in this book. Examples of mathematics in sports, engineering, and carpentry are shown on pages 127, 152, 191, and 234. Circling the globe are three key aspects of Geometry—*measuring, reasoning,* and *applying* geometrical ideas. As you explore the applications presented in the book, try to make your own connections between mathematics and the world around you!

ISBN: 0-395-97889-0 23456789–DWO–04 03 02 01 00

Internet Web Site: http://www.mcdougallittell.com

About the Authors

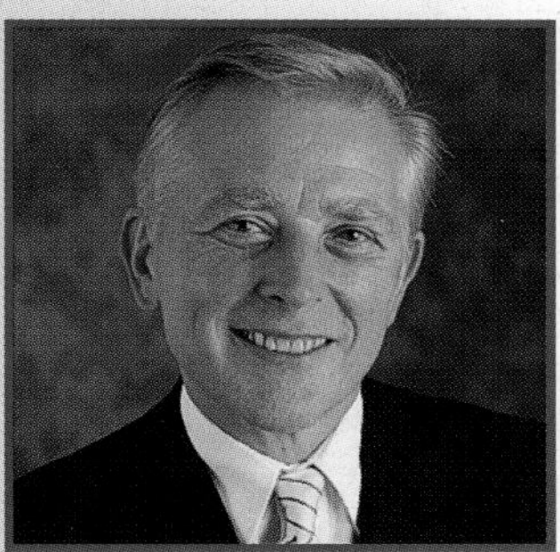

Ron Larson is a professor of mathematics at Penn State University at Erie. He is the author of a broad range of mathematics textbooks for middle school, high school, and college students. He is one of the pioneers in the use of multimedia and the Internet to enhance the learning of mathematics. Dr. Larson is a member of the National Council of Teachers of Mathematics and is a frequent speaker at NCTM and other national and regional mathematics meetings.

Laurie Boswell is a mathematics teacher at Profile Junior-Senior High School in Bethlehem, New Hampshire. She is active in NCTM and local mathematics organizations. A recipient of the 1986 Presidential Award for Excellence in Mathematics Teaching, she is also the 1992 Tandy Technology Scholar and the 1991 recipient of the Richard Balomenos Mathematics Education Service Award presented by the New Hampshire Association of Teachers of Mathematics.

Lee Stiff is a professor of mathematics education in the College of Education and Psychology of North Carolina State University at Raleigh and has taught mathematics at the high school and middle school levels. He served on the NCTM Board of Directors and was elected President of NCTM for the years 2000–2002. He is the 1992 recipient of the W. W. Rankin Award for Excellence in Mathematics Education presented by the North Carolina Council of Teachers of Mathematics.

REVIEWERS

Jose Anaya
Mathematics Teacher
Juarez High School
Chicago, IL

Pamela W. Coffield
Mathematics Teacher
Brookstone School
Columbus, GA

Tom Griffith
Mathematics Teacher
Scripps Ranch High School
San Diego, CA

Judy Hicks
Mathematics Teacher
Ralston Valley High School
Arvada, CO

Viola Okoro
Mathematics Teacher
Laguna Creek High School
Elk Grove, CA

Carol Sander
Mathematics Resource Teacher
Rockville High School
Rockville, MD

CALIFORNIA TEACHER PANEL

Marianne Clarke
Mathematics Teacher
Westminster High School
Westminster, CA

Janet Eichsteadt
Mathematics Teacher
Woodbridge High School
Irvine, CA

Tom Griffith
Mathematics Teacher
Scripps Ranch High School
San Diego, CA

Jerry Hickman
Mathematics Teacher
El Camino Real Senior High School
Woodland Hills, CA

Roger Hitchcock
Mathematics Teacher
The Clovis Center
Clovis, CA

Jerry Lewin
Mathematics Department Chair
Alhambra High School
Alhambra, CA

Viola Okoro
Mathematics Teacher
Laguna Creek High School
Elk Grove, CA

Patricia Schubert
Mathematics Teacher
Capistrano Valley High School
Mission Viejo, CA

Gary Smith
Mathematics Teacher
Mira Costa High School
Manhattan Beach, CA

Jeff Speranza
Mathematics Department Chair
Westmoor High School
Daly City, CA

PENNSYLVANIA TEACHER PANEL

Bill Garrett
Mathematics Department Chair
Norristown High School
Norristown, PA

Adrienne Kapisak
Mathematics Teacher
Gateway High School
Monroeville, PA

Patricia Klagholz
Mathematics Department Chair
Lamberton School
Philadelphia, PA

Ed Lorinchak
Mathematics Teacher
Pittsburgh School for the Performing Arts
Pittsburgh, PA

Kathryn Nalevanko
Mathematics Teacher
Scranton High School
Scranton, PA

Ben Preddy
Mathematics Teacher
Haverford High School
Havertown, PA

Cerise Sawyer
Mathematics Teacher
Cumberland Valley High School
Mechanicsburg, PA

Don Stark
Mathematics Teacher
Baldwin High School
Pittsburgh, PA

Brenda Williams
Mathematics Teacher
Abington Heights High School
Clarks Summit, PA

STUDENT REVIEW PANEL

Racquel Allen
Watertown High School
Massachusetts

Kristin Biedinger
Gateway Senior High School
Pennsylvania

Brett Brown
El Camino Real High School
California

James Bruce DeMark
Lakota West High School
Ohio

Anthony Espinoza
Thomas A. Edison High School
Texas

Jessica Langton
Danbury High School
Connecticut

Molly McClure
William Henry Harrison High School
Indiana

Kevin W. Mechtley
Topeka High School
Kansas

Andy Nichols
Brandon High School
Mississippi

Annie Phare
Ferndale High School
Washington

Andrew J. Polsky
Parkway North High School
Missouri

Malavika Prabhu
Riverside High School
South Carolina

Lauren Reed
Naperville North High School
Illinois

Kelly Riordan
Cherry Creek High School
Colorado

Cecilia Serna
South Forsyth High School
Georgia

B. J. Singletary
Clinch County High School
Georgia

Jaclyn Stancu
Lower Moreland High School
Pennsylvania

Dustin Stuflick
Montgomery High School
California

Julie Testerman
Memorial High School
New Hampshire

Angel Nicole Todd
Harrison High School
Michigan

Van Tran
Montgomery Blair High School
Maryland

Steven L. White
Mandarin High School
Florida

CHAPTER 1

Basics of Geometry

APPLICATION HIGHLIGHTS

Airport Runways *1, 32*
Bacteria Growth *8*
Two-Point Perspective *15*
Long-Distance Rates *23*
Playing Darts *31*
Kite Design *37*
Strike Zone *40*
Paper Airplanes *41*
Bridges *49*
Millennium Dome *56*

MATH & HISTORY

Geometric Constructions *25*

INTERNET CONNECTIONS

www.mcdougallittell.com

Application Links
1, 25, 49, 56

Student Help
7, 12, 22, 28, 39, 40, 41, 45, 56

Career Links
8, 30

Extra Challenge
9, 16, 24, 32, 41

ASSESSMENT

Skill Review, *2*
Quizzes, *25, 42, 58*
Test Preparation Questions, *9, 16, 24, 31, 41, 50, 57*
Chapter Summary, Review, and Test, *59*
Chapter Standardized Test, *64*
Project, Chapter 1, *66*

CHAPTER 2

Reasoning and Proof

APPLICATION HIGHLIGHTS

Robotics *69, 93*
Advertising *77*
Research Buggy *77*
Winds at Sea *84*
Zoology *90*
Fitness *97*
Auto Racing *98*
Wind-Chill Factor *99*
Pay Raises *100*
Optical Illusion *106*
Wall Trim *115*

MATH & HISTORY

Recreational Logic Puzzles *95*

INTERNET CONNECTIONS

www.mcdougallittell.com

Application Links *69, 84, 95*

Student Help *72, 76, 88, 93, 97, 114*

Career Links *77, 90, 106*

Extra Challenge *78, 85, 94, 101, 107*

ASSESSMENT

Skill Review, *70*
Quizzes, *95, 116*
Test Preparation Questions, *78, 85, 94, 101, 107, 115*
Chapter Summary, Review, and Test, *117*
Chapter Standardized Test, *122*
Algebra Review, *124*

CHAPTER 3

Perpendicular and Parallel Lines

APPLICATION HIGHLIGHTS

MATH & HISTORY

INTERNET CONNECTIONS

www.mcdougallittell.com

ASSESSMENT

CHAPTER 4

Congruent Triangles

APPLICATION HIGHLIGHTS

MATH & HISTORY

INTERNET CONNECTIONS

www.mcdougallittell.com

ASSESSMENT

CHAPTER 5

Properties of Triangles

APPLICATION HIGHLIGHTS

MATH & HISTORY

INTERNET CONNECTIONS

www.mcdougallittell.com

ASSESSMENT

CHAPTER
6

Quadrilaterals

APPLICATION HIGHLIGHTS

Scissors Lift *319, 336*
Traffic Signs *326*
Plant Shapes *327*
Furniture Design *333*
Hinged Box *339*
Changing Gears *343*
Carpentry *350*
Layer Cake *361*
Gem Cutting *369*
Energy Conservation *377*

MATH & HISTORY

History of Finding Area *346*

INTERNET CONNECTIONS

www.mcdougallittell.com
Application Links
319, 346, 377
Student Help
335, 341, 344, 349, 357, 369
Career Links
333, 361, 369
Extra Challenge
328, 337, 345, 355, 362, 379

ASSESSMENT

CHAPTER 7

Transformations

APPLICATION HIGHLIGHTS

Architecture *393, 435*
Construction *398*
Machine Embroidery *401*
Kaleidoscopes *406*
Logo Design *415*
Wheel Hubs *418*
Pentominoes *432*
Stenciling *435*
Pet Collars *441*
Celtic Knots *443*

MATH & HISTORY

History of Decorative Patterns *420*

INTERNET CONNECTIONS

www.mcdougallittell.com

Application Links
393, 406, 418, 420

Student Help
400, 408, 414, 424, 426, 434, 443

Career Links
409, 415, 435

Extra Challenge
402, 410, 419, 428, 436

ASSESSMENT

Skill Review, *394*
Quizzes, *420, 444*
Test Preparation Questions, *402, 410, 419, 428, 436, 443*
Chapter Summary, Review, and Test, *445*
Chapter Standardized Test, *450*
Project, Chapters 6 and 7, *452*

CHAPTER 8

Similarity

APPLICATION HIGHLIGHTS

MATH & HISTORY

INTERNET CONNECTIONS

www.mcdougallittell.com

ASSESSMENT

CHAPTER 9

Right Triangles and Trigonometry

CHAPTER 10

Circles

CHAPTER 11

Area of Polygons and Circles

APPLICATION HIGHLIGHTS

MATH & HISTORY

INTERNET CONNECTIONS

www.mcdougallittell.com

ASSESSMENT

CHAPTER 12

Surface Area and Volume

APPLICATION HIGHLIGHTS

Spherical Buildings *717, 764*
Soccer Ball *722*
Wax Cylinder Records *733*
Pyramids *740*
Candles *748*
Nautical Prism *754*
Automatic Pet Feeder *756*
Baseball *760*
Ball Bearings *761*
Model Car *770*

MATH & HISTORY

History of Containers *742*

INTERNET CONNECTIONS

www.mcdougallittell.com

Application Links *717, 722, 742, 763*

Student Help *725, 730, 739, 747, 756, 760, 764*

Career Links *725, 757, 768*

Extra Challenge *726, 734, 741, 749, 765, 771*

ASSESSMENT

Student Resources

Who Uses Mathematics in Real Life?

Here are some careers that use the mathematics you will study in Geometry.

FOCUS ON CAREERS

REAL LIFE

EMTs *p. 609*
Some Emergency Medical Technicians (EMTs) train specifically for wilderness emergencies. These EMTs must be able to improvise with materials they have on hand.

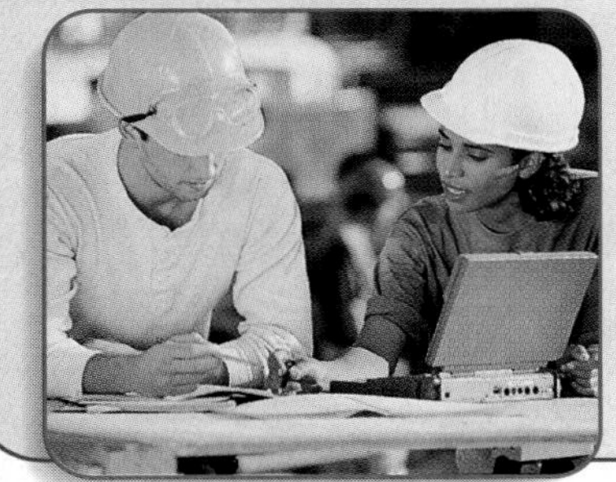

CIVIL ENGINEERING *p. 170*
Civil engineers design and supervise the construction of roads, buildings, tunnels, bridges, and water supply systems.

ADVERTISING COPYWRITER *p. 77*
Advertising copywriters write the advertisements you see and hear every day. These ads appear in many forms including Internet home pages.

LOGO DESIGNERS *p. 415*
Logo designers create symbols that represent the name of a company or organization. The logos appear on packaging, letterheads, and Web sites.

GEOSCIENTISTS *p. 644*
Geoscientists do a variety of things, including locating earthquakes, searching for oil, studying fossils, and mapping the ocean floor.

STUDENT HELP

YOUR BUILT-IN LEARNING SUPPORT

Your textbook contains many special elements to help you learn. It provides several study helps that may be new to you. For example, every chapter begins with a Study Guide.

Chapter Preview The Study Guide starts with a short description of what you will be learning.

Key Vocabulary This list highlights important new terms that will be introduced in the chapter as well as reviewing terms that you already know.

Skill Review These exercises review key skills that you'll apply in the chapter. They will help you identify any topics that you need to review.

Study Strategy The study strategies suggest ideas to help you better understand the math you are learning as well as help you prepare for tests.

CHAPTER 3

Study Guide

PREVIEW

What's the chapter about?

Chapter 3 is about **lines** and **angles**. In Chapter 3, you'll learn

- properties of parallel and perpendicular lines.
- six ways to prove that lines are parallel.
- how to write an equation of a line with given characteristics.

KEY VOCABULARY

▶ Review
- linear pair, p. 44
- vertical angles, p. 44
- perpendicular lines, p. 79

▶ New
- parallel lines, p. 129
- skew lines, p. 129
- parallel planes, p. 129
- transversal, p. 131
- alternate interior angles, p. 131
- alternate exterior angles, p. 131
- consecutive interior angles, p. 131
- flow proof, p. 136

PREPARE

Are you ready for the chapter?

SKILL REVIEW Do these exercises to review key skills that you'll apply in this chapter. See the given **reference page** if there is something you don't understand.

USING ALGEBRA Solve each equation. (Skills Review, p. 789 and 790)

1. $47 + x = 180$ **2.** $135 = 3x - 6$ **3.** $m = \frac{5-7}{2-(-6)}$

4. $\frac{1}{2} = -5\left(\frac{7}{2}\right) + b$ **5.** $5x + 9 = 6x - 11$ **6.** $2(x - 1) + 15 = 90$

Use the diagram. Write the reason that supports the statement. (Review pp. 44–46)

7. $m\angle 1 = 90°$

8. $\angle 2 \cong \angle 4$

9. $\angle 2$ and $\angle 3$ are supplementary.

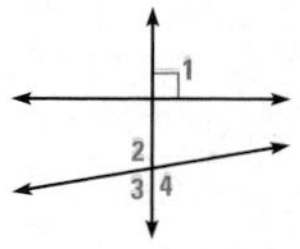

Write the reason that supports the statement. (Review pp. 96–98)

10. If $m\angle A = 30°$ and $m\angle B = 30°$, then $\angle A \cong \angle B$.

11. If $x + 4 = 9$, then $x = 5$.

12. $3(x + 5) = 3x + 15$

STUDY STRATEGY

Here's a study strategy!

Write Sample Questions

Write at least six questions about topics in the chapter. Focus on the concepts that you found difficult. Include both short-answer questions and more involved ones. Then answer your questions.

128 Chapter 3

Also, in every lesson you will find a variety of Student Help notes.

STUDENT HELP

In the Book

Study Tip The study tips will help you avoid common errors.

Skills Review Here you can find where to review skills you've studied in earlier math classes.

Look Back Here are references to material in earlier lessons that may help you understand the lesson.

Extra Practice Your book contains more exercises to practice the skills you are learning.

Homework Help Here you can find suggestions about which Examples may help you solve Exercises.

On the Internet

Homework Help: These are places where you can find additional examples on the Web site, and additional suggestions for solving an exercise.

Keystroke Help These provide the exact keystroke sequences for many different kinds of calculators.

Software Help These provide the instructions for geometry software applications.

STUDENT HELP

Study Tip
When you prove a theorem, the hypotheses of the theorem becomes the GIVEN, and the conclusion is what you must PROVE.

EXAMPLE 1 ***Proving the Alternate Interior Angles Theorem***

Prove the Alternate Interior Angles Theorem.

SOLUTION

GIVEN ▶ $p \parallel q$

PROVE ▶ $\angle 1 \cong \angle 2$

Statements	Reasons
1. $p \parallel q$	**1.** Given
2. $\angle 1 \cong \angle 3$	**2.** Corresponding Angles Postulate
3. $\angle 3 \cong \angle 2$	**3.** Vertical Angles Theorem
4. $\angle 1 \cong \angle 2$	**4.** Transitive Property of Congruence

EXAMPLE 2 ***Using Properties of Parallel Lines***

Given that $m\angle 5 = 65°$, find each measure. Tell which postulate or theorem you use.

a. $m\angle 6$ **b.** $m\angle 7$

c. $m\angle 8$ **d.** $m\angle 9$

SOLUTION

a. $m\angle 6 = m\angle 5 = 65°$ — Vertical Angles Theorem

b. $m\angle 7 = 180° - m\angle 5 = 115°$ — Linear Pair Postulate

c. $m\angle 8 = m\angle 5 = 65°$ — Corresponding Angles Postulate

d. $m\angle 9 = m\angle 7 = 115°$ — Alternate Exterior Angles Theorem

GUIDED PRACTICE

Vocabulary Check ✓
Concept Check ✓
Skill Check ✓

1. Define *slope of a line.*

2. The slope of line m is $-\frac{1}{5}$. What is the slope of a line perpendicular to m?

3. In the coordinate plane shown at the right, is $\overleftrightarrow{AC}$ perpendicular to $\overleftrightarrow{BD}$? Explain.

4. Decide whether the lines with the equations $y = 2x - 1$ and $y = -2x + 1$ are perpendicular.

5. Decide whether the lines with the equations $5y - x = 15$ and $y + 5x = 2$ are perpendicular.

6. The line ℓ_1 has the equation $y = 3x$. The line ℓ_2 is perpendicular to ℓ_1 and passes through the point $P(0, 0)$. Write an equation of ℓ_2.

PRACTICE AND APPLICATIONS

STUDENT HELP

Extra Practice
to help you master skills is on p. 808.

SLOPES OF PERPENDICULAR LINES **The slopes of two lines are given. Are the lines perpendicular?**

7. $m_1 = 2, m_2 = -\frac{1}{2}$ **8.** $m_1 = \frac{2}{3}, m_2 = \frac{3}{2}$ **9.** $m_1 = \frac{1}{4}, m_2 = -4$

10. $m_1 = \frac{5}{7}, m_2 = -\frac{7}{5}$ **11.** $m_1 = -\frac{1}{2}, m_2 = -\frac{1}{2}$ **12.** $m_1 = -1, m_2 = 1$

SLOPES OF PERPENDICULAR LINES **Lines j and n are perpendicular. The slope of line j is given. What is the slope of line n? Check your answer.**

13. 2 **14.** 5 **15.** -3 **16.** -7

17. $\frac{2}{3}$ **18.** $\frac{1}{5}$ **19.** $-\frac{1}{3}$ **20.** $-\frac{4}{3}$

IDENTIFYING PERPENDICULAR LINES **Find the slope of $\overleftrightarrow{AC}$ and $\overleftrightarrow{BD}$. Decide whether $\overleftrightarrow{AC}$ is perpendicular to $\overleftrightarrow{BD}$.**

21.

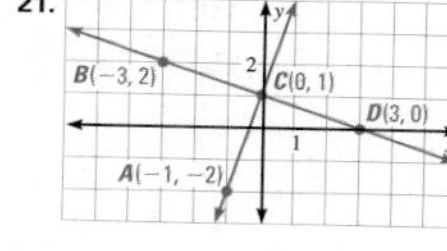

22.

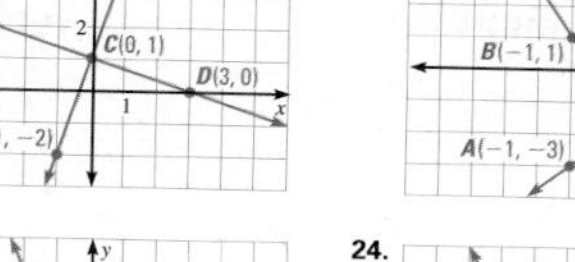

23.

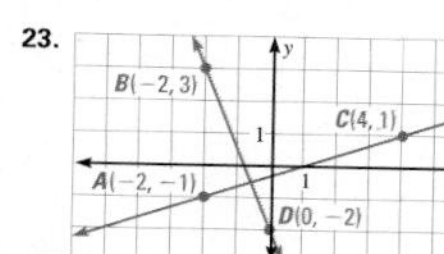

24.

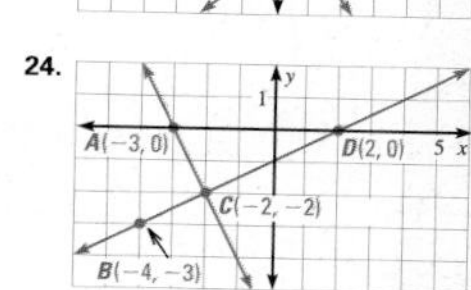

STUDENT HELP

HOMEWORK HELP
Example 1: Exs. 7–20
Example 2: Exs. 21–24, 33–37
Example 3: Exs. 25–28, 47–50
Example 4: Exs. 29–32
Example 5: Exs. 38–41
Example 6: Exs. 42–46

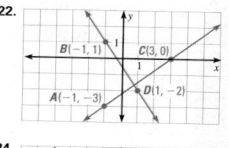

Plot a course to success with McDougal Littell Geometry!

How... can I make geometry understandable to all my students?

Where... can my students go for help with their homework?

What... resources are available to help me succeed as a teacher?

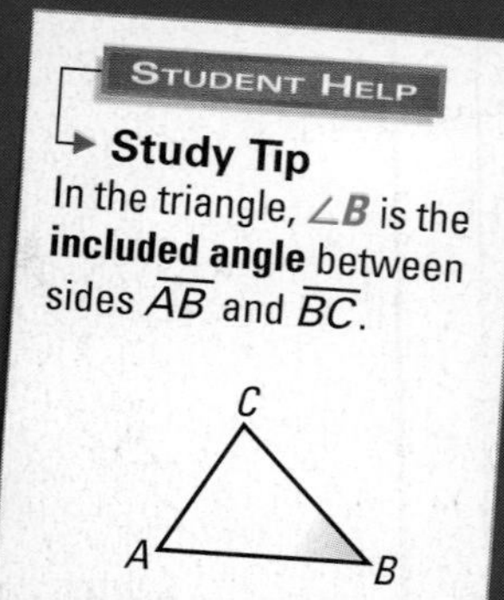

STUDENT HELP
Study Tip
In the triangle, ∠B is the included angle between sides $\overline{AB}$ and $\overline{BC}$.
C
A
B

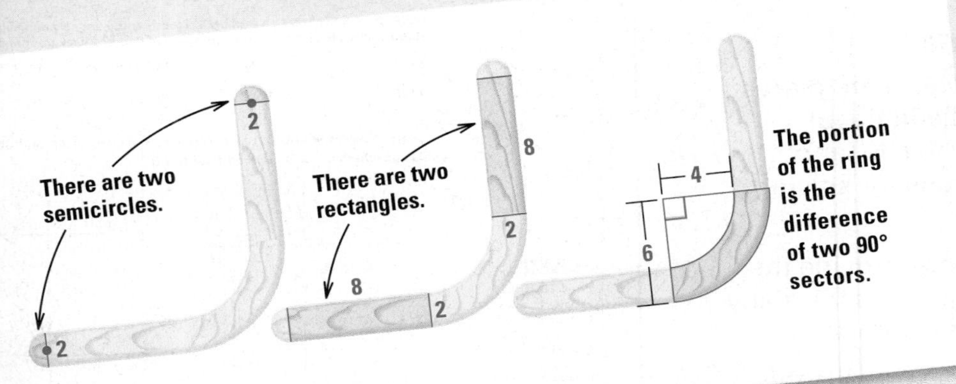

FIND THE ANSWERS you're looking for in McDougal Littell Geometry!

HOW?

Important concepts are made understandable to all students through instructional diagrams and graphics, interactive activities, and numerous examples throughout the text.

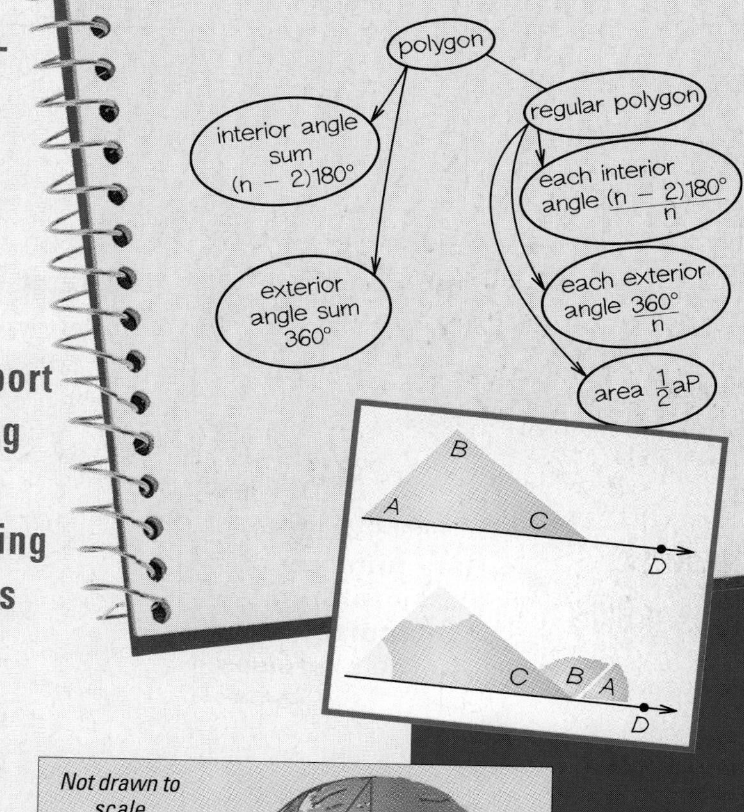

WHERE?

Students receive support when they are learning on their own through Student Help notes throughout the book, including homework exercises correlated to the examples and Homework Help on the Internet.

WHAT?

A variety of resources help you adapt the program to your teaching styles and to the needs of your students.

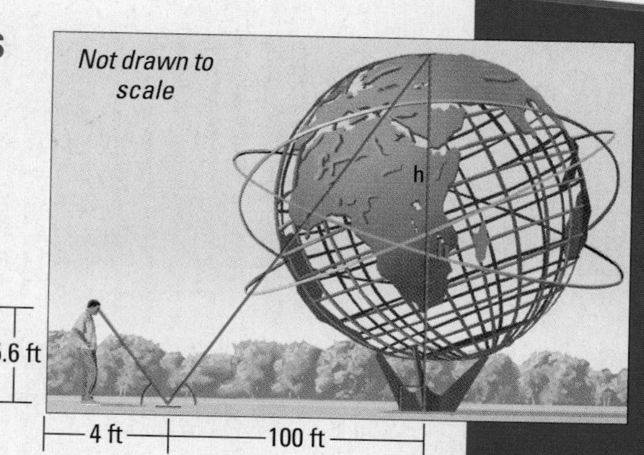

How... can I make geometry understandable to all my students?

McDougal Littell Geometry provides clear, visual explanations that every student can follow.

CONCEPT SUMMARY BOXES present ideas clearly and concisely to help students master key concepts.

EXAMPLES are numerous, easy to follow, and correspond to the exercises.

GOAL 2 **PROOF WITH SPECIAL QUADRILATERALS**

When you want to prove that a quadrilateral has a specific shape, you can use either the definition of the shape as in Example 2, *or* you can use a theorem.

STUDENT HELP

Look Back
For help with proving a quadrilateral is a parallelogram, see pp. 338–341.

CONCEPT SUMMARY **PROVING QUADRILATERALS ARE RHOMBUSES**

You have learned three ways to prove that a quadrilateral is a rhombus.

1. You can use the definition and show that the quadrilateral is a *parallelogram* that has four congruent sides. It is easier, however, to use the Rhombus Corollary and simply show that all four sides of the quadrilateral are congruent.
2. Show that the quadrilateral is a parallelogram *and* that the diagonals are perpendicular. (*Theorem 6.11*)
3. Show that the quadrilateral is a parallelogram *and* that each diagonal bisects a pair of opposite angles. (*Theorem 6.12*)

EXAMPLE 3 ***Proving a Quadrilateral is a Rhombus***

Show that *KLMN* is a rhombus.

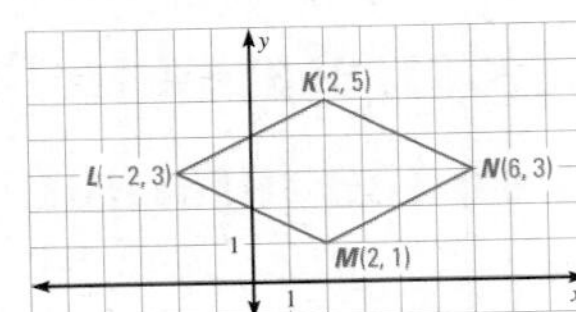

SOLUTION You can use any of the three ways described in the concept summary above. For instance, you could show that opposite sides have the same slope and that the diagonals are perpendicular. Another way, shown below, is to prove that all four sides have the same length.

$LM = \sqrt{[2 - (-2)]^2 + (1 - 3)^2} = \sqrt{4^2 + (-2)^2} = \sqrt{20}$

$NK = \sqrt{(2 - 6)^2 + (5 - 3)^2} = \sqrt{(-4)^2 + 2^2} = \sqrt{20}$

$MN = \sqrt{(6 - 2)^2 + (3 - 1)^2} = \sqrt{4^2 + 2^2} = \sqrt{20}$

$KL = \sqrt{(-2 - 2)^2 + (3 - 5)^2} = \sqrt{(-4)^2 + (-2)^2} = \sqrt{20}$

▶ So, because $LM = NK = MN = KL$, *KLMN* is a rhombus.

STUDY GUIDES

in every chapter will help students review key prerequisites and prepare for the chapter.

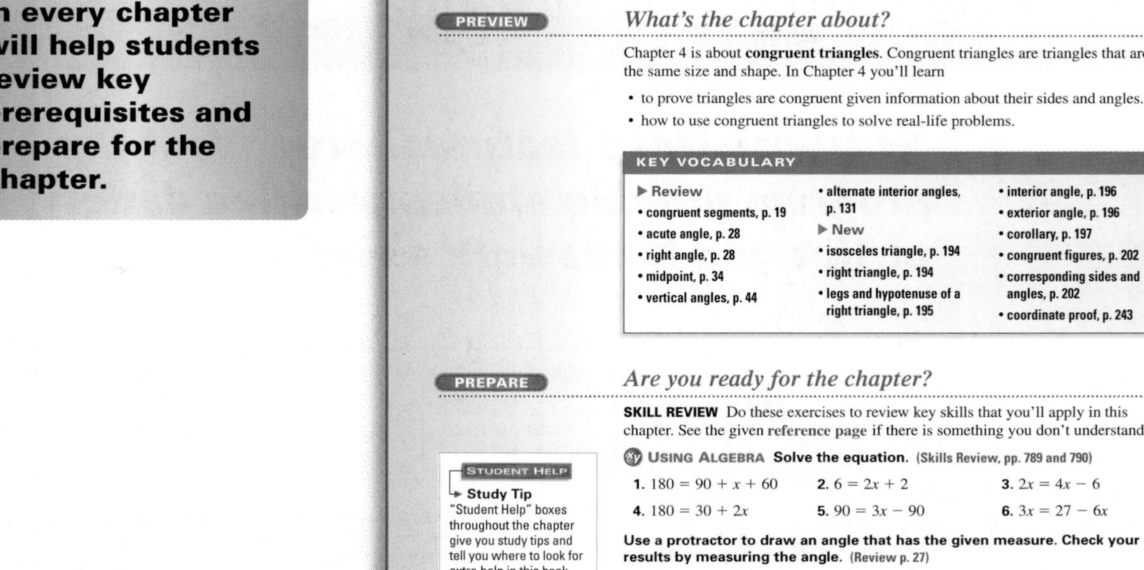

CHAPTER 4

Study Guide

PREVIEW

What's the chapter about?

Chapter 4 is about **congruent triangles**. Congruent triangles are triangles that are the same size and shape. In Chapter 4 you'll learn

- to prove triangles are congruent given information about their sides and angles.
- how to use congruent triangles to solve real-life problems.

KEY VOCABULARY

▶ Review
- congruent segments, p. 19
- acute angle, p. 28
- right angle, p. 28
- midpoint, p. 34
- vertical angles, p. 44
- alternate interior angles, p. 131

▶ New
- isosceles triangle, p. 194
- right triangle, p. 194
- legs and hypotenuse of a right triangle, p. 195
- interior angle, p. 196
- exterior angle, p. 196
- corollary, p. 197
- congruent figures, p. 202
- corresponding sides and angles, p. 202
- coordinate proof, p. 243

PREPARE

Are you ready for the chapter?

SKILL REVIEW Do these exercises to review key skills that you'll apply in this chapter. See the given reference page if there is something you don't understand.

STUDENT HELP

Study Tip
"Student Help" boxes throughout the chapter give you study tips and tell you where to look for extra help in this book and on the Internet.

USING ALGEBRA Solve the equation. (Skills Review, pp. 789 and 790)

1. $180 = 90 + x + 60$
2. $6 = 2x + 2$
3. $2x = 4x - 6$
4. $180 = 30 + 2x$
5. $90 = 3x - 90$
6. $3x = 27 - 6x$

Use a protractor to draw an angle that has the given measure. Check your results by measuring the angle. (Review p. 27)

7. 30°
8. 135°
9. 72°

Use the diagram at the right. Write the theorem that supports each statement. (Review pp. 112 and 143)

10. $\angle 1 \cong \angle 2$
11. $\angle 3 \cong \angle 4$
12. $\angle 1 \cong \angle 5$

STUDY STRATEGY

Here's a study strategy!

Remembering Theorems

In this chapter you will learn many theorems that you will use throughout the rest of the book.

- *Keep a list of theorems in your math notebook.*
- *Make up a helpful name for each theorem, or draw a sketch to help you recognize it.*

192 Chapter 4

3 APPLY

ASSIGNMENT GUIDE

BASIC
Day 1: pp. 216–219 Exs. 6–21
Day 2: pp. 217–219 Exs. 22–28, 32–37, 39–46

AVERAGE
Day 1: pp. 216–219 Exs. 6–21
Day 2: pp. 217–219 Exs. 22–28, 32–37, 39–46

ADVANCED
Day 1: pp. 216–219 Exs. 6–21
Day 2: pp. 217–219 Exs. 22–28, 30–46

BLOCK SCHEDULE
pp. 216–219 Exs. 6–21 (with 4.2)
pp. 216–219 Exs. 22–28, 30–37, 39–46 (with 4.4)

EXERCISE LEVELS
Level A: *Easier* 6–17
Level B: *More Difficult* 18–37
Level C: *Most Difficult* 38

HOMEWORK CHECK
To quickly check student understanding of key concepts, go over the following exercises: Exs. 8, 16, 18, 20, 26, 28, 32, 34. See also the Daily Homework Quiz:
- Blackline Master (*Chapter 4 Resource Book*, p. 55)
- Transparency (p. 28)

216

GUIDED PRACTICE

Vocabulary Check ✓ 1. Sketch a triangle and label its vertices. N… angle between the sides. See margin.

Concept Check ✓ 2. **ERROR ANALYSIS** Henry believes he c… diagram and the SAS Congruence Postu… congruent. Explain Henry's mistake.

2. The congruent angles are not the angles included between the congruent sides.

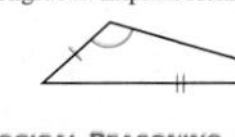

Skill Check ✓ **LOGICAL REASONING** Decide wheth… prove that the triangles are congruent. If… which congruence postulate you would u…

3. $\triangle ABC, \triangle DEC$
4. $\triangle FGH, \triangle J$…

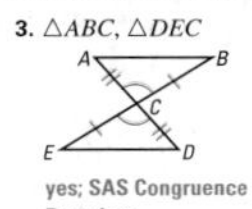

yes; SAS Congruence Postulate

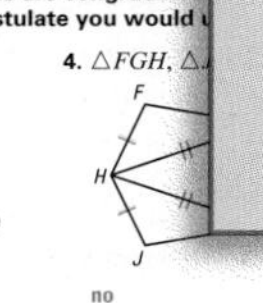

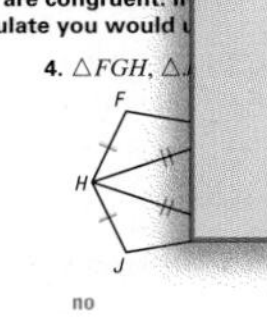

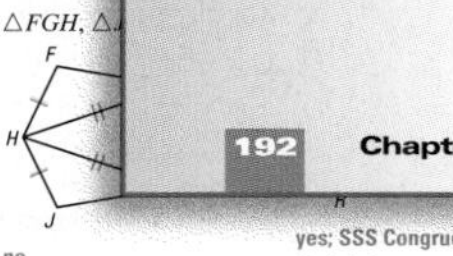

no

yes; SSS Congruence Postulate

PRACTICE AND APPLICATIONS

STUDENT HELP
Extra Practice to help you master skills is on p. 809.

NAMING SIDES AND INCLUDED ANGLES Use the diagram. Name the included angle between the pair of sides given.

6. $\overline{JK}$ and $\overline{KL}$ $\angle JKL$
7. $\overline{PK}$ and $\overline{LK}$ $\angle LKP$
8. $\overline{LP}$ and $\overline{LK}$ $\angle KLP$
9. $\overline{JL}$ and $\overline{JK}$ $\angle KJL$
10. $\overline{KL}$ and $\overline{JL}$ $\angle JLK$
11. $\overline{KP}$ and $\overline{PL}$ $\angle KPL$

12. no
13. yes; SAS Congruence Postulate
14. yes; SSS Congruence Postulate
15. yes; SAS Congruence Postulate
16. no
17. yes; SSS Congruence Postulate

LOGICAL REASONING Decide whether enough information is given to prove that the triangles are congruent. If there is enough information, state the congruence postulate you would use. 12–17. See margin.

12. $\triangle UVT, \triangle WVT$
13. $\triangle LMN, \triangle TNM$
14. $\triangle YZW, \triangle YXW$

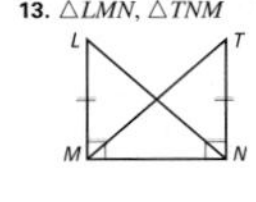

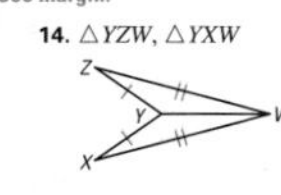

15. $\triangle ACB, \triangle ECD$
16. $\triangle RST, \triangle WVU$
17. $\triangle GJH, \triangle HLK$

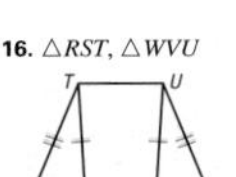

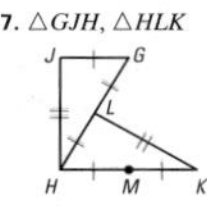

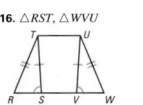

STUDENT HELP
HOMEWORK HELP
Example 1: Exs. 18, 20–28
Example 2: Exs. 19–28
Example 3: Exs. 12–17
Example 4: Exs. 20–28
Example 5: Exs. 30, 31
Example 6: Exs. 33–35

216 Chapter 4 Congruent Triangles

PRACTICE SETS

- **include exercises of three difficulty levels — Levels A, B, and C — which are labeled in the Teacher's Edition.**
- **Also available: Practice Worksheets (Levels A, B, and C)**

CHALLENGE PROBLEMS

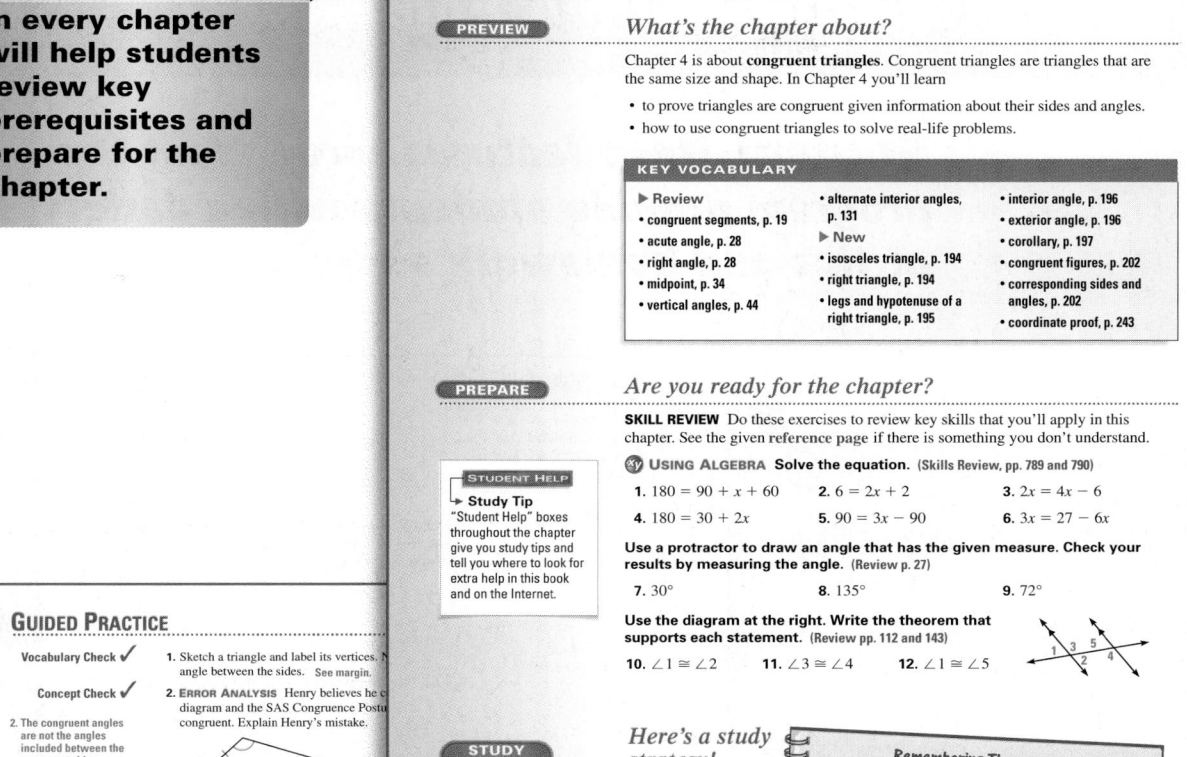

(not pictured) are included in every practice set, with extra challenge online at www.mcdougallittell.com

WHERE... can my students go for help with their homework?

Student Help features throughout the program provide students with a variety of tips and homework support.

HOMEWORK HELP

provides online suggestions for solving exercises.

SOFTWARE HELP

(not pictured) guides students in the use of geometry software in a way that is tailored to a particular activity or exercise.

EXTRA EXAMPLES

show where students can find additional support on the Internet at www.mcdougallittell.com

---

STUDENT HELP
HOMEWORK HELP Visit our Web site www.mcdougallittell.com for help with Exs. 31–33.

FINDING ANGLE MEASURES Find the measure of the numbered angles.

31. 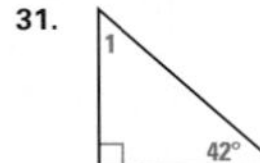

32. 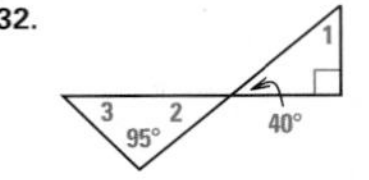

33. 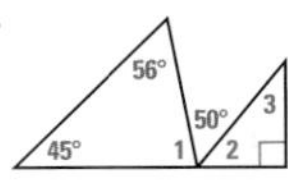

USING ALGEBRA The variable expressions represent the angle measures of a triangle. Find the measure of each angle. Then classify the triangle by its angles.

34. $m\angle A = x°$
$m\angle B = 2x°$
$m\angle C = (2x + 15)°$

35. $m\angle R = x°$
$m\angle S = 7x°$
$m\angle T = x°$

36. $m\angle W = (x - 15)°$
$m\angle Y = (2x - 165)°$
$m\angle Z = 90°$

EXTERIOR ANGLES Find the measure of the exterior angle shown.

37. (2x − 8)° x° 31°

38. 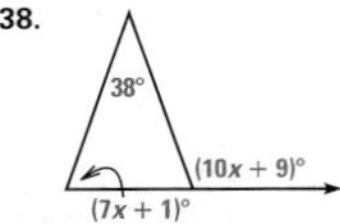

39. 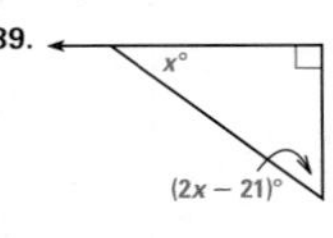

40.  **TECHNOLOGY** Use geometry software to demonstrate the Triangle Sum Theorem or the Exterior Angle Theorem. Describe your procedure.

EXAMPLE 2 *Using Equilateral and Isosceles Triangles*

a. Find the value of x.

b. Find the value of y.

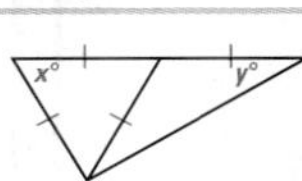

SOLUTION

a. Notice that x represents the measure of an angle of an equilateral triangle. From the corollary above, this triangle is also equiangular.

$3x° = 180°$ Apply the Triangle Sum Theorem.

$x = 60$ Solve for x.

STUDENT HELP
HOMEWORK HELP Visit our Web site www.mcdougallittell.com for extra examples.

b. Notice that y represents the measure of a base angle of an isosceles triangle. From the Base Angles Theorem, the other base angle has the same measure. The vertex angle forms a linear pair with a 60° angle, so its measure is 120°.

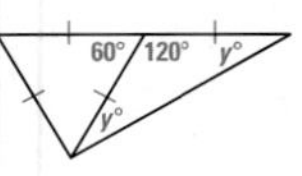

$120° + 2y° = 180°$ Apply the Triangle Sum Theorem.

$y = 30$ Solve for y.

Skills Review

guides students to review skills they've studied in earlier math classes to help them succeed with current concepts.

EXAMPLE 3 *Finding an Angle Measure*

You can apply the Exterior Angle Theorem to find the measure of the exterior angle shown. First write and solve an equation to find the value of x:

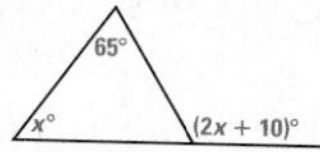

$x° + 65° = (2x + 10)°$ **Apply the Exterior Angles Theorem.**

$55 = x$ **Solve for x.**

▶ So, the measure of the exterior angle is $(2 \cdot 55 + 10)°$, or $120°$.

STUDENT HELP
Skills Review
For help with solving equations, see p. 790.

A **corollary to a theorem** is a statement that can be proved easily using the theorem. The corollary below follows from the Triangle Sum Theorem.

COROLLARY

COROLLARY TO THE TRIANGLE SUM THEOREM

The acute angles of a right triangle are complementary.

$m\angle A + m\angle B = 90°$

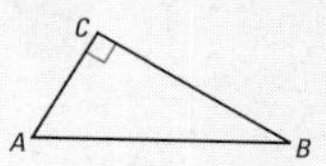

Look Back

contains references to material in earlier lessons that may help students understand the lesson.

EXAMPLE 4 *Using Ratios*

The ratios of the side lengths of $\triangle DEF$ to the corresponding side lengths of $\triangle ABC$ are 2 : 1. Find the unknown lengths.

SOLUTION

- DE is twice AB and $DE = 8$, so $AB = \frac{1}{2}(8) = 4$.
- Using the Pythagorean Theorem, you can determine that $BC = 5$.
- DF is twice AC and $AC = 3$, so $DF = 2(3) = 6$.
- EF is twice BC and $BC = 5$, so $EF = 2(5) = 10$.

STUDENT HELP
Look Back
For help with the Pythagorean Theorem, see p. 20.

458 **Chapter 8** *Similarity*

Extra Practice

is provided in the book for every section, in addition to the large number of exercises found with each lesson.

Numerous Examples

in every lesson are correlated to the exerrcises and support students with their homework.

PRACTICE AND APPLICATIONS

STUDENT HELP
Extra Practice
to help you master skills is on p. 814.

RECTANGLE **For any rectangle $ABCD$, decide whether the statement is *always*, *sometimes*, or *never* true. Draw a sketch and explain your answer.**

12. $\angle A \cong \angle B$ **13.** $\overline{AB} \cong \overline{BC}$

14. $\overline{AC} \cong \overline{BD}$ **15.** $\overline{AC} \perp \overline{BD}$

PROPERTIES **List each quadrilateral for which the statement is true.**

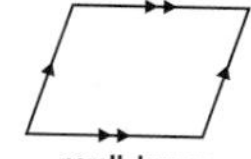
parallelogram

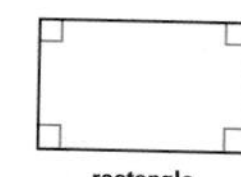
rectangle

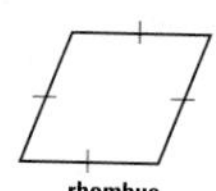
rhombus

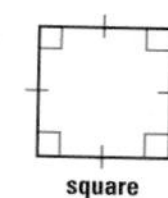
square

16. It is equiangular. **17.** It is equiangular and equilateral.

18. The diagonals are perpendicular. **19.** Opposite sides are congruent.

20. The diagonals bisect each other. **21.** The diagonals bisect opposite angles.

PROPERTIES **Sketch the quadrilateral and list everything you know about it.**

22. parallelogram $FGHI$ **23.** rhombus $PQRS$ **24.** square $ABCD$

STUDENT HELP
HOMEWORK HELP
Example 1: Exs. 12–15, 27–32
Example 2: Exs. 27–32, 51
Example 3: Exs. 33–43
Example 4: Exs. 44–52
Example 5: Exs. 55–60
Example 6: Exs. 61, 62

6.4 *Rhombuses, Rectangles, and Squares* 351

WHERE... can I find algebra review and projects or activities?

Algebra Review, Projects, and Activities occur throughout the body of the Geometry textbook.

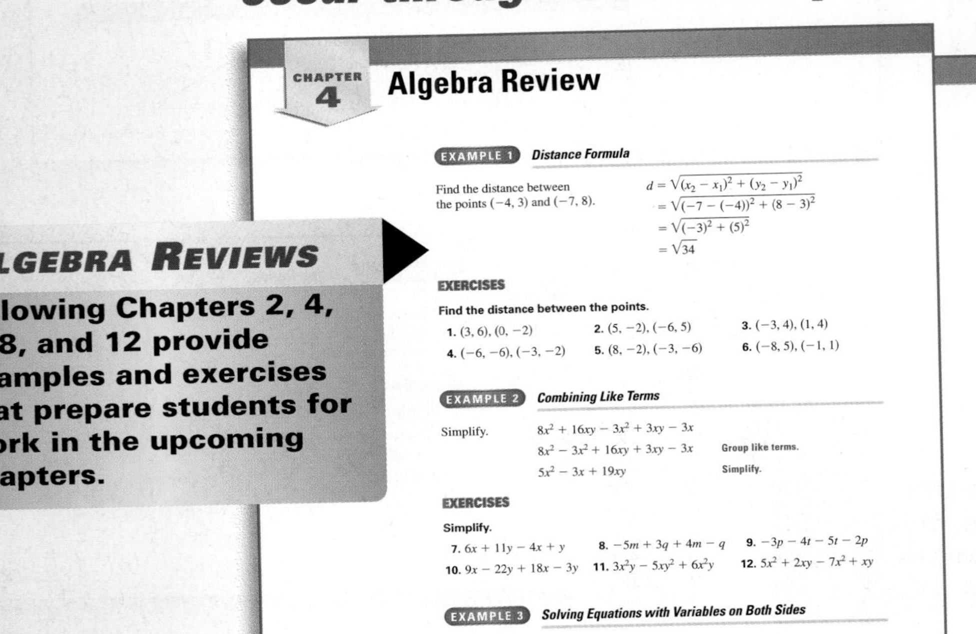

CHAPTER 4

Algebra Review

EXAMPLE 1 *Distance Formula*

Find the distance between the points $(-4, 3)$ and $(-7, 8)$.

$$d = \sqrt{(x_2 - x_1)^2 + (y_2 - y_1)^2}$$
$$= \sqrt{(-7 - (-4))^2 + (8 - 3)^2}$$
$$= \sqrt{(-3)^2 + (5)^2}$$
$$= \sqrt{34}$$

EXERCISES

Find the distance between the points.

1. $(3, 6), (0, -2)$ **2.** $(5, -2), (-6, 5)$ **3.** $(-3, 4), (1, 4)$

4. $(-6, -6), (-3, -2)$ **5.** $(8, -2), (-3, -6)$ **6.** $(-8, 5), (-1, 1)$

EXAMPLE 2 *Combining Like Terms*

Simplify. $8x^2 + 16xy - 3x^2 + 3xy - 3x$

$8x^2 - 3x^2 + 16xy + 3xy - 3x$ **Group like terms.**

$5x^2 - 3x + 19xy$ **Simplify.**

EXERCISES

Simplify.

7. $6x + 11y - 4x + y$ **8.** $-5m + 3q + 4m - q$ **9.** $-3p - 4t - 5t - 2p$

10. $9x - 22y + 18x - 3y$ **11.** $3x^2y - 5xy^2 + 6x^2y$ **12.** $5x^2 + 2xy - 7x^2 + xy$

EXAMPLE 3 *Solving Equations with Variables on Both Sides*

Solve. $6a - 12 = 5a + 9$

$a - 12 = 9$ **Subtract 5a from each side.**

$a = 21$ **Add 12 to each side.**

EXERCISES

Solve the equation.

13. $3x + 5 = 2x + 11$ **14.** $-14 + 3a = 10 - a$ **15.** $8m + 1 = 7m - 9$

16. $y - 18 = 6y + 7$ **17.** $2s + 1 = 7s + 1$ **18.** $3a - 12 = -6a - 12$

19. $-2t + 10 = -t$ **20.** $11q - 6 = 3q + 8q$ **21.** $-7x + 7 = 2x - 11$

258 Chapter 4

ALGEBRA REVIEWS

following Chapters 2, 4, 6, 8, and 12 provide examples and exercises that prepare students for work in the upcoming chapters.

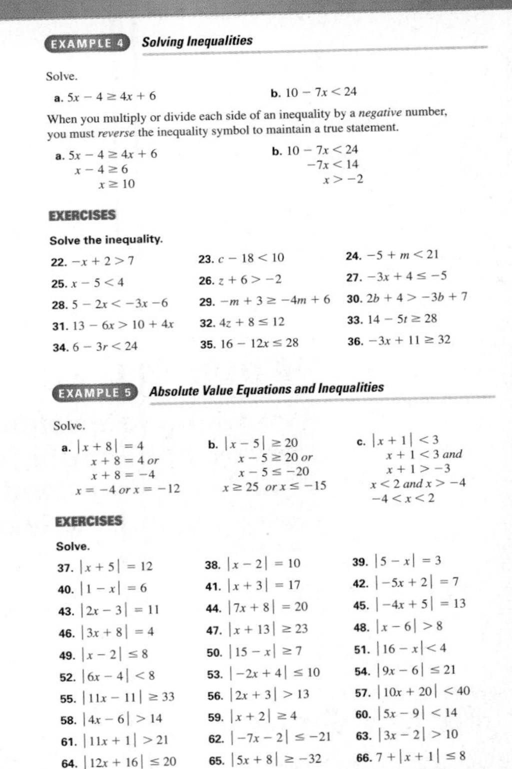

EXAMPLE 4 *Solving Inequalities*

Solve.

a. $5x - 4 \geq 4x + 6$ **b.** $10 - 7x < 24$

When you multiply or divide each side of an inequality by a *negative* number, you must *reverse* the inequality symbol to maintain a true statement.

a. $5x - 4 \geq 4x + 6$
$x - 4 \geq 6$
$x \geq 10$

b. $10 - 7x < 24$
$-7x < 14$
$x > -2$

EXERCISES

Solve the inequality.

22. $-x + 2 > 7$ **23.** $c - 18 < 10$ **24.** $-5 + m < 21$

25. $x - 5 < 4$ **26.** $z + 6 > -2$ **27.** $-3x + 4 \leq -5$

28. $5 - 2x < -3x - 6$ **29.** $-m + 3 \geq -4m + 6$ **30.** $2b + 4 > -3b + 7$

31. $13 - 6x > 10 + 4x$ **32.** $4z + 8 \leq 12$ **33.** $14 - 5t \geq 28$

34. $6 - 3r < 24$ **35.** $16 - 12x \leq 28$ **36.** $-3x + 11 \geq 32$

EXAMPLE 5 *Absolute Value Equations and Inequalities*

Solve.

a. $|x + 8| = 4$
$x + 8 = 4$ *or*
$x + 8 = -4$
$x = -4$ *or* $x = -12$

b. $|x - 5| \geq 20$
$x - 5 \geq 20$ *or*
$x - 5 \leq -20$
$x \geq 25$ *or* $x \leq -15$

c. $|x + 1| < 3$
$x + 1 < 3$ *and*
$x + 1 > -3$
$x < 2$ *and* $x > -4$
$-4 < x < 2$

EXERCISES

Solve.

37. $|x + 5| = 12$ **38.** $|x - 2| = 10$ **39.** $|5 - x| = 3$

40. $|1 - x| = 6$ **41.** $|x + 3| = 17$ **42.** $|-5x + 2| = 7$

43. $|2x - 3| = 11$ **44.** $|7x + 8| = 20$ **45.** $|-4x + 5| = 13$

46. $|3x + 8| = 4$ **47.** $|x + 13| \geq 23$ **48.** $|x - 6| > 8$

49. $|x - 2| \leq 8$ **50.** $|15 - x| \geq 7$ **51.** $|16 - x| < 4$

52. $|6x - 4| < 8$ **53.** $|-2x + 4| \leq 10$ **54.** $|9x - 6| \leq 21$

55. $|11x - 11| \geq 33$ **56.** $|2x + 3| > 13$ **57.** $|10x + 20| < 40$

58. $|4x - 6| > 14$ **59.** $|x + 2| \geq 4$ **60.** $|5x - 9| < 14$

61. $|11x + 1| > 21$ **62.** $|-7x - 2| \leq -21$ **63.** $|3x - 2| > 10$

64. $|12x + 16| \leq 20$ **65.** $|5x + 8| \geq -32$ **66.** $7 + |x + 1| \leq 8$

Algebra Review 259

EXAMPLE 4 *Using Properties of Parallel Lines*

Use properties of parallel lines to find the value of x.

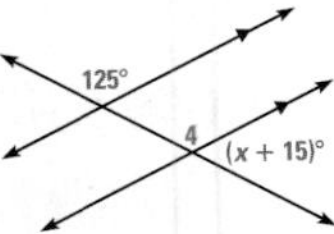

SOLUTION

$m\angle 4 = 125°$ **Corresponding Angles Postulate**

$m\angle 4 + (x + 15)° = 180°$ **Linear Pair Postulate**

$125° + (x + 15)° = 180°$ **Substitute.**

$x = 40$ **Subtract.**

ALGEBRA EXAMPLES

that review algebra skills are integrated throughout the textbook.

PROJECTS

every third chapter provide opportunities for students to study geometric concepts in greater depth.

PROJECT for Chapters 4 and 5

Balancing Shapes

OBJECTIVE Explore the balancing points of triangles and other shapes.

Materials: cardboard, straightedge, scissors, hole punch, string, paper clip, pencil with eraser

HOW TO FIND A BALANCING POINT

1. Draw a large triangle on cardboard and cut it out. Punch holes in the triangle near the vertices.

2. Tie a weight to a string and attach the string to a paper clip. Hang your triangle from the paper clip. Mark the vertical line the string makes on the triangle.

3. Repeat Step 2 with the other holes in the triangle. The three lines should intersect near the same point. Balance the triangle by placing this point on a pencil eraser.

INVESTIGATION

1. Are the lines you drew in **Steps 2 and 3** *perpendicular bisectors, angle bisectors, medians,* or *altitudes* of the triangle? medians
2. Is the balancing point of the triangle the *orthocenter, incenter, circumcenter,* or *centroid*? centroid
3. Choose one of the following special shapes: *square, rectangle, parallelogram,* or *rhombus*.

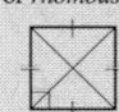
square

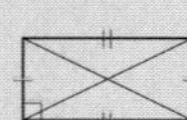
rectangle

parallelogram

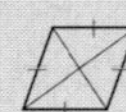
rhombus

Draw and cut out a large example of the shape you have chosen. Follow the steps above to find its balancing point. Check students' points.

4. Make a conjecture about the location of the balancing point in relation to the *diagonals* of the shape. The balancing point is at the intersection of the diagonals.
5. Test your conjecture. Then explain how you tested your conjecture and describe the results of the test. Check students' work.

PRESENT YOUR RESULTS

Write a report to present your results.

- Include your answers to Investigation Exercises 1–5 on the previous page.
- Include your cut-out shapes or sketches of them. Mark the balancing point of each shape.
- Describe the conjectures that you made and your reasons for believing them to be true.
- What advice would you give to someone else who is going to do this project?
- Which geometric facts did this project help you to understand better?

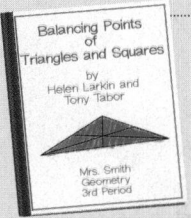

Balancing Points of Triangles and Squares
by Helen Larkin and Tony Tabor
Mrs. Smith Geometry 3rd Period

You may wish to display your cut-out shapes on a poster or as a mobile. Here are some hints for creating a mobile.

- Punch a small hole at the balancing point of each shape.
- Tie a knot in a string and thread the string through the hole until the string stops at the knot.
- You can hang all of your shapes from one string, or you can hang them from several strings tied to a stick.

EXTENSION

Do you think your conjecture about balancing points of certain four-sided shapes is true for *all* four-sided shapes? Cut out and test more shapes to find out. In your report, describe your investigation and the results.
No, the balancing point of a four-sided shape is not always at the intersection of its diagonals.

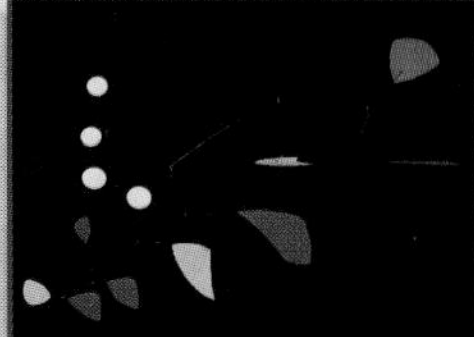

This mobile includes horizontal red and yellow plates that hang from their balancing points.

ACTIVITY 4.3 Developing Concepts

Group Activity for use with Lesson 4.3

Investigating Congruent Triangles

QUESTION How much information do you need to know to tell whether two triangles are congruent?

GROUP ACTIVITY
Work with a partner.

MATERIALS
- 3 pencils
- protractor
- ruler

EXPLORING THE CONCEPT: SSS
Steps 1–3. Check drawings.

1. On a piece of paper, place three pencils of different lengths so they make a triangle.
2. Mark each vertex of your triangle by pressing the pencil points to the paper.
3. Remove the pencils and draw the sides of your triangle.
4. Have your partner repeat **Steps 1–3** using the same three pencils. Try to make a triangle that is *not* congruent to the one you drew.

Step 4. It is not possible to do so.

EXPLORING THE CONCEPT: SAS
Steps 5–7. Check drawings.

5. On a piece of paper, place two pencils so their erasers are at the center of a protractor. Arrange them to form a 45° angle.
6. Mark two vertices of a triangle by pressing the pencil points to the paper. Mark the center of the protractor as the third vertex.
7. Remove the pencils and protractor and draw the sides of your triangle.
8. Have your partner repeat **Steps 5–7** using the same two pencils. Try to make a triangle that has a 45° angle but is *not* congruent to the one you drew. It is not possible to do so.

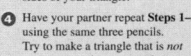

DRAWING CONCLUSIONS

1. What do you notice about the triangles you made with three pencils? What do you notice about the triangles you made with two pencils and a 45° angle between them?
2. CRITICAL THINKING If you know that two sides of a triangle are congruent to two sides of another triangle, what other information do you need to tell whether the triangles are congruent?

1. All triangles made with three pencils appear to be congruent; All triangles made with two pencils and a 45° angle appear to be congruent.
2. the length of the third side or the measure of the angle between the sides whose lengths are known

IN-CLASS ACTIVITIES

allow students to use mathematical reasoning to explore geometric concepts.

WHAT... resources are available to help me succeed as a teacher?

The McDougal Littell resources are conveniently organized and include a variety of materials to help you adapt the program to your teaching style and to the specific needs of your students!

TEACHER'S RESOURCE PACKAGE

- Chapter Resource Books (one for each chapter, organized by lesson)
- Basic Skills Workbook: Diagnosis and Remediation (TE)
- Practice Workbook with Examples (TE)
- Standardized Test Practice Workbook (TE)
- Warm-Up Transparencies and Daily Homework Quiz
- Worked-Out Solution Key

Finally! Resources organized the way you teach... one lesson at a time!

McDougal Littell's Chapter Resource Books ***allow you to easily carry the resources you have for a chapter in one manageable book. The materials are organized by lesson so that you can see everything you have available for a specific section.***

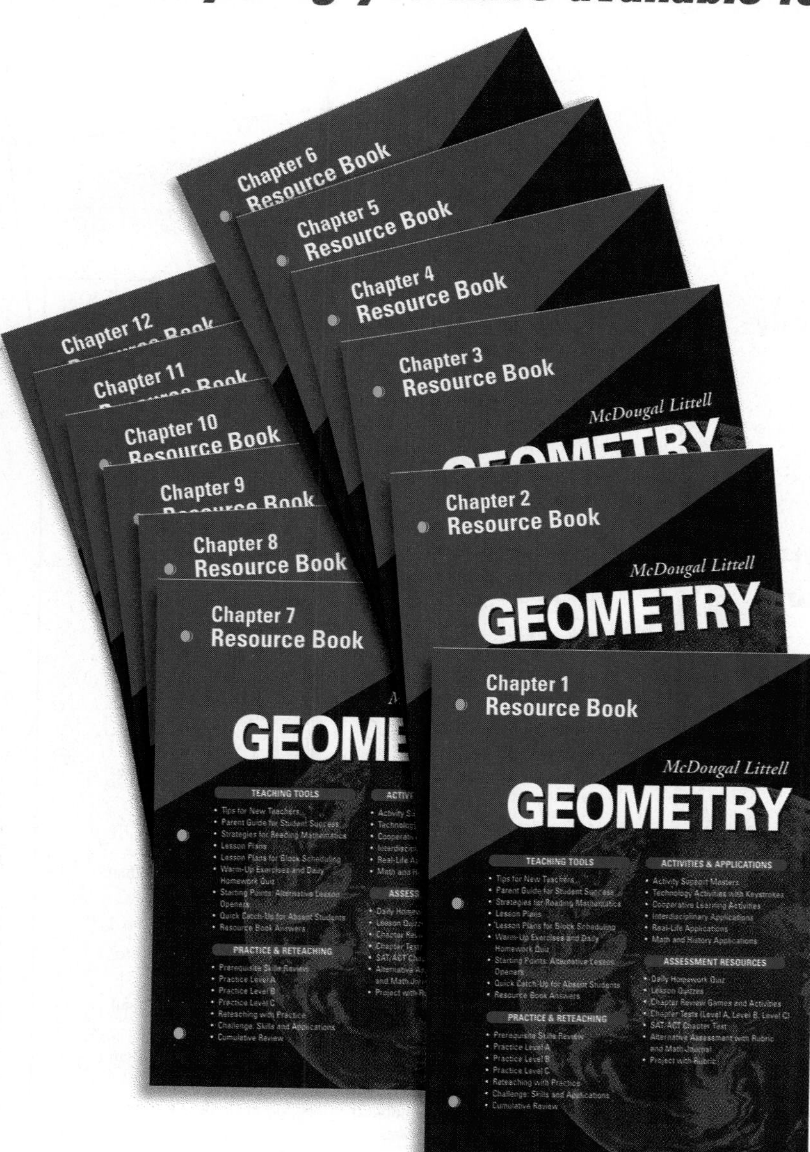

CHAPTER RESOURCE BOOKS INCLUDE:

- Tips for New Teachers
- Parent Guide for Student Success
- Prerequisite Skills Review
- Strategies for Reading Mathematics
- Lesson Plans
- Lesson Plans for Block Scheduling
- Activity Support Masters
- Technology Activities with Keystrokes
- Practice (Levels A, B, and C)
- Reteaching with Practice
- Quick Catch-Up for Absent Students
- Cooperative Learning Activities
- Interdisciplinary Applications
- Real-Life Applications: When Will I Ever Use This?
- Math and History Applications
- Quizzes
- Chapter Review Games and Activities
- Chapter Tests (Levels A, B, and C)
- SAT/ACT Chapter Test
- Alternative Assessment with Rubric and Math Journal
- Project with Rubric
- Cumulative Review
- Resource Book Answers

WHAT... materials are available for me to use while I teach?

A number of transparency packages give you many easy-to-use options for reviewing homework, starting class, and teaching a lesson.

Answer Transparencies for Checking Homework

Warm-Up Transparencies and Daily Homework Quiz

- Warm-Up Exercises
- Daily Homework Quizzes

Extra Example Transparencies with Standardized Test Practice

- Extra Examples
- Checkpoint Exercises
- Standardized Test Practice Questions

Starting Points: Alternative Lesson Opener Transparency Package

There are many ways to introduce a lesson — and we provide alternative ideas for teachers on ready-to-use transparencies.

- Application Lesson Openers
- Technology Lesson Openers
- Activity Lesson Openers
- Visual Approach Lesson Openers

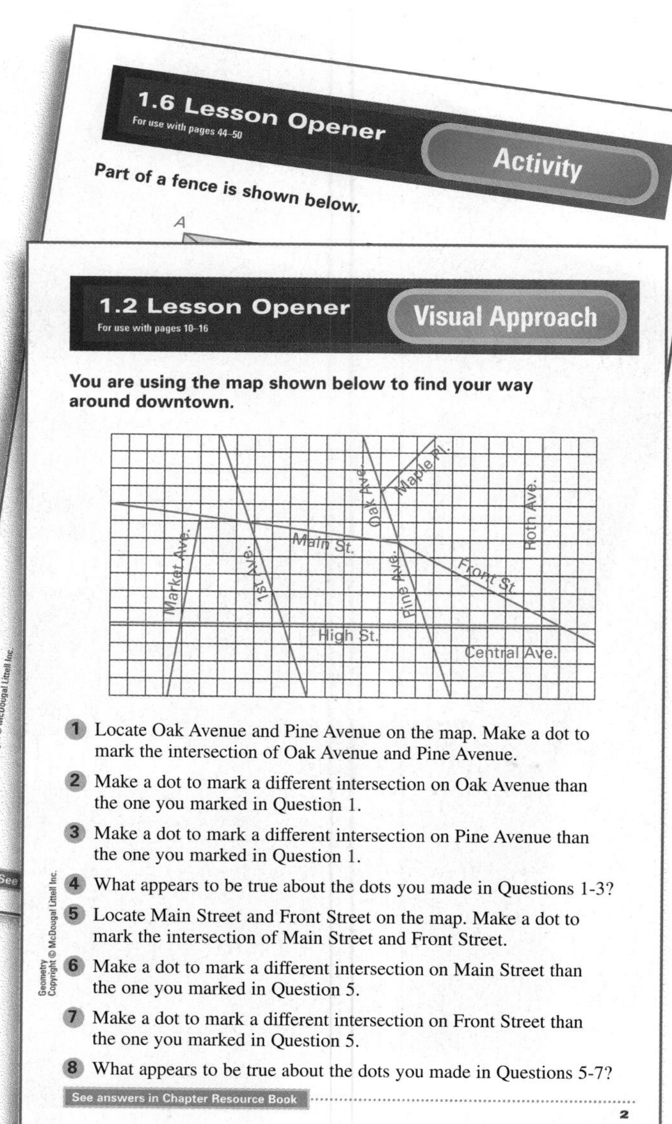
1.6 Lesson Opener
For use with pages 44–50
Activity
Part of a fence is shown below.

1.2 Lesson Opener
For use with pages 10–16
Visual Approach

You are using the map shown below to find your way around downtown.

1. Locate Oak Avenue and Pine Avenue on the map. Make a dot to mark the intersection of Oak Avenue and Pine Avenue.
2. Make a dot to mark a different intersection on Oak Avenue than the one you marked in Question 1.
3. Make a dot to mark a different intersection on Pine Avenue than the one you marked in Question 1.
4. What appears to be true about the dots you made in Questions 1-3?
5. Locate Main Street and Front Street on the map. Make a dot to mark the intersection of Main Street and Front Street.
6. Make a dot to mark a different intersection on Main Street than the one you marked in Question 5.
7. Make a dot to mark a different intersection on Front Street than the one you marked in Question 5.
8. What appears to be true about the dots you made in Questions 5-7?

See answers in Chapter Resource Book

2

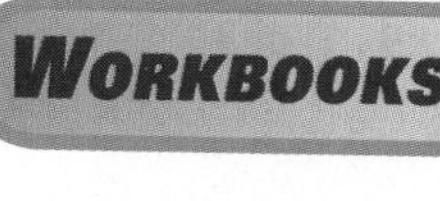

Workbooks

- **Basic Skills Workbook: Diagnosis and Remediation**
- **Practice Workbook with Examples**
- **Standardized Test Practice Workbook**

Spanish Resources

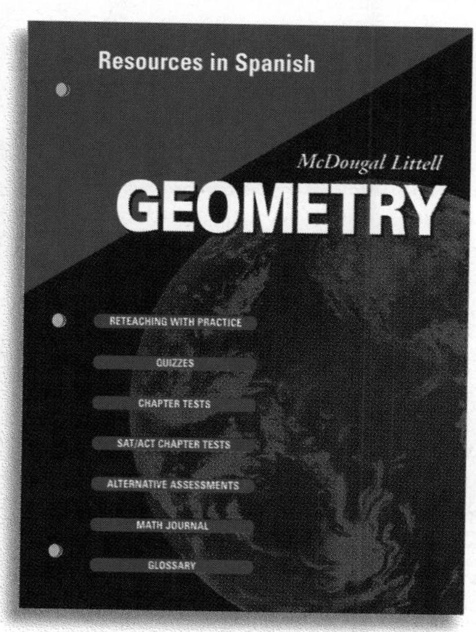

Resources in Spanish Include:

- **Reteaching with Practice**
- **Quizzes**
- **Chapter Tests**
- **SAT/ACT Chapter Tests**
- **Alternative Assessments with Rubrics**
- **Math Journal**
- **Glossary**

can I incorporate technology into my classroom?

McDougal Littell technology resources help you and your students meaningfully use technology to enhance lessons and build understanding.

Technology for PLANNING AND TEACHING

Online Lesson Planner

- Create customized lesson plans.
- Adjust to schedule changes.
- Adapt the program to local and state objectives.

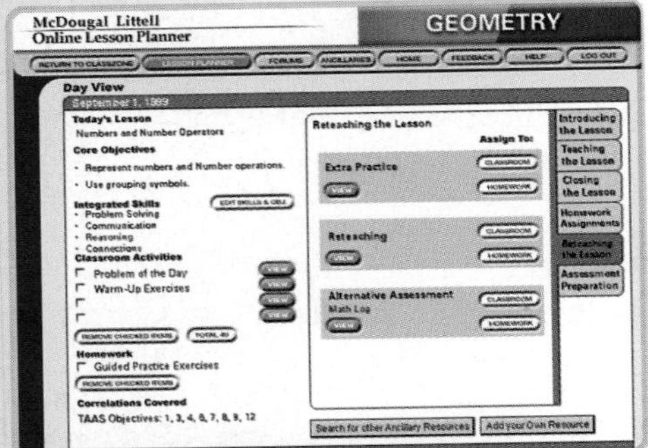

Electronic Teacher Tools

This handy tool provides all your teaching resources on one CD-ROM.

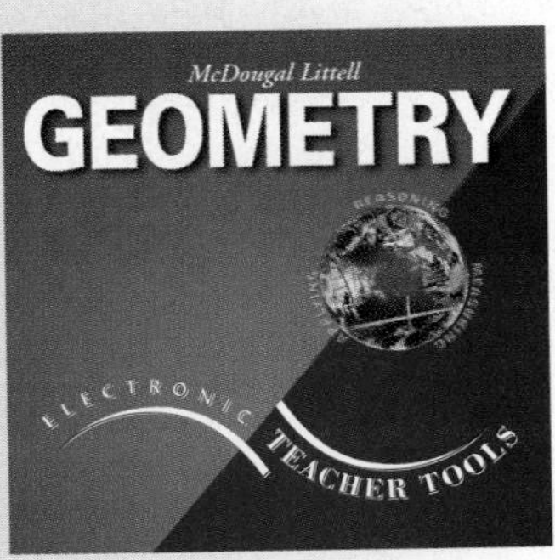

Electronic Lesson Presentations

The Electronic Lesson Presentations help you introduce concepts through colorful diagrams and animated instructional techniques.

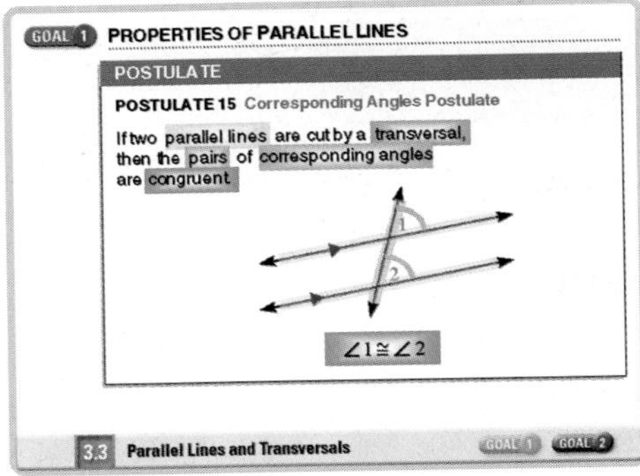

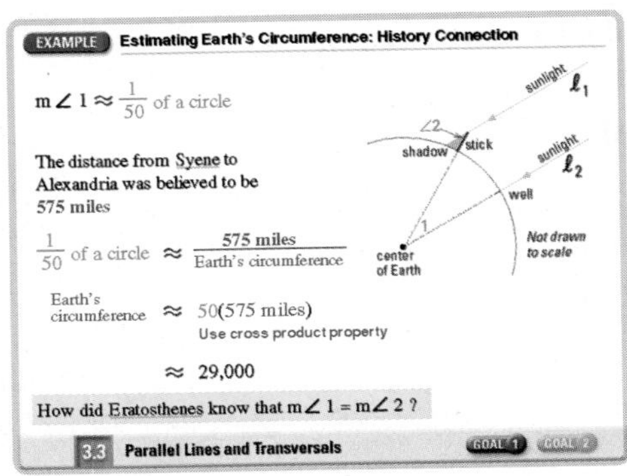

Technology for STUDENT SUPPORT

Personal Student Tutor

This tutorial program is correlated to the McDougal Littell series. It provides:

- animated examples
- student hints
- exercises that are automatically graded
- student progress reports

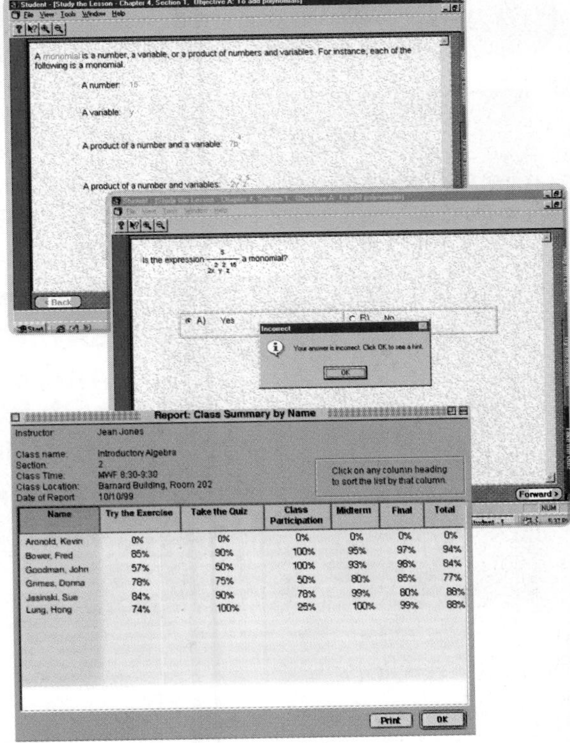

Name	Try the Exercise	Take the Quiz	Class Participation	Midterm	Final	Total
Aronold, Kevin	0%	0%	0%	0%	0%	0%
Bower, Fred	85%	90%	100%	95%	97%	94%
Goodman, John	57%	50%	100%	93%	96%	84%
Grimes, Donna	78%	75%	50%	80%	85%	77%
Jasinski, Sue	84%	90%	78%	99%	80%	88%
Lung, Hong	74%	100%	25%	100%	99%	88%

ClassZone

ClassZone is the companion Web site to McDougal Littell Geometry that includes Student Help, career links, data updates, and more. To access ClassZone, go to www.mcdougallittell.com.

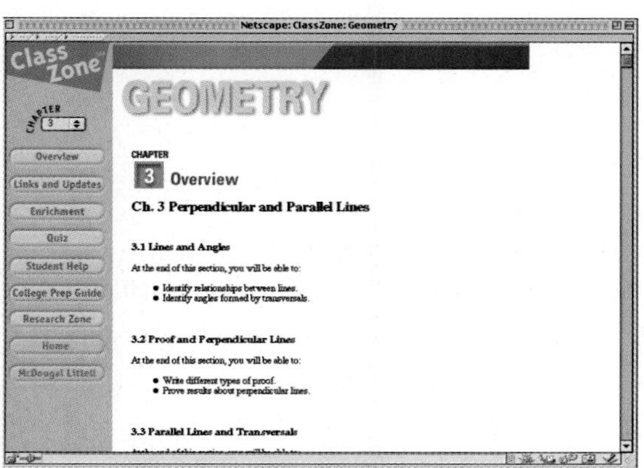

Technology for Review and Assessment

Time-Saving Test and Practice Generator

- Develop tests and practice sheets.
- Instantly create answer keys.

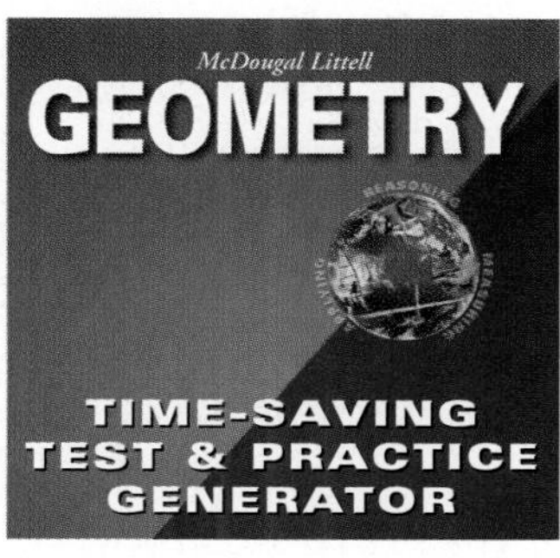

Geometry in Motion Video

The Geometry in Motion Video brings geometry to life through animations that help students visualize and undertand geometric concepts. Now you can quickly and easily help students see geometric concepts develop.

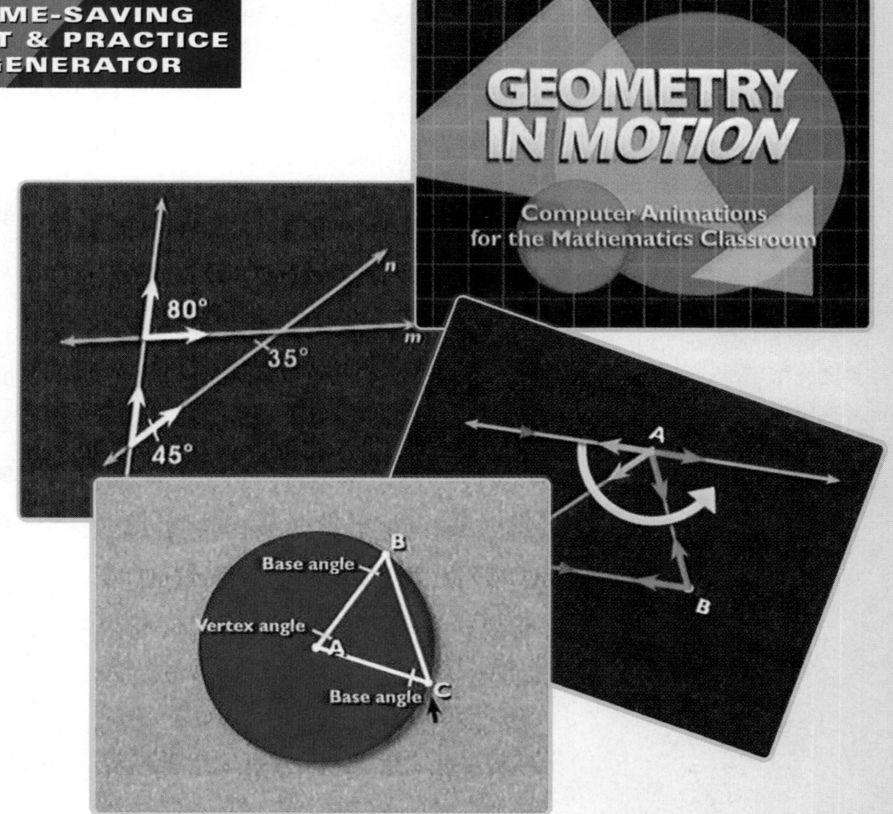

Pacing the Course

Course Pacing Chart

The Pacing Chart below shows the number of days allotted for each chapter. The Regular Schedule requires 160 days. The Block Schedule requires 80 days. These time frames include days for review and assessment: 2 days per chapter for the Regular Schedule and 1 day per chapter for the Block Schedule. Semester and trimester divisions are indicated by red and blue rules, respectively. Recommended pacing for Geometry over two years is also provided.

Chapter	1	2	3	4	5 (Trimester)	6	7 (Semester; End of year one)	8	9 (Trimester)	10	11	12
Regular Schedule	13	12	12	15	13	15	13	14	13	14	13	13
Block Schedule	6.5	6	6	7.5	6.5	7.5	6.5	7	6.5	7	6.5	6.5
Two-Year Pacing	26	24	24	30	26	30	26	28	26	28	26	26

Assignments are provided with each lesson for a basic course, an average course, an advanced course, and a block-scheduled course. Each of the four courses covers all twelve chapters.

Basic Course

The basic course is intended for students who enter with below-average mathematical and problem-solving skills. Assignments include:

- substantial work with the skills and concepts presented in the lesson
- straightforward applications of these skills and concepts
- test preparation and mixed review exercises

Average Course

The average course is intended for students who enter with typical mathematical and problem-solving skills. Assignments include:

- substantial work with the skills and concepts presented in the lesson
- application of these skills and concepts
- test preparation and mixed review exercises

Advanced Course

The advanced course is intended for students who enter with above-average mathematical and problem-solving skills. Assignments include:

- substantial work with the skills and concepts presented in the lesson
- more complex applications and challenge exercises
- test preparation and mixed review exercises

Block-Scheduled Course

The block-scheduled course is intended for schools that use a block schedule. The exercises assigned are comparable to the exercises for the average course.

Two-Year Pacing

The two-year pacing allows more time for pre-course review using the prerequisite skills material. The schedule also provides more opportunities to use activities or reteaching and practice materials.

Pacing each Chapter

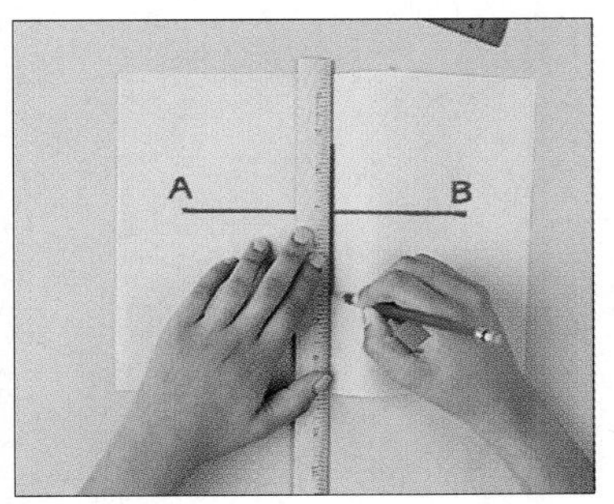

The Pacing Chart for each chapter is located on the interleaved pages preceding the chapter. Part of the Pacing Chart for Chapter 3 is shown here. The regular schedule chart provides pacing for the basic, average, and advanced courses. The block schedule chart provides pacing for the block-scheduled course.

Regular Schedule

Day 8

3.6

Starting Options
- Homework Check
- Warm-Up or Daily Quiz

Teaching Options
- Motivating the Lesson
- Les. Opener (Application)
- Examples 1–8
- Closure Question
- Guided Practice Exs.

Apply/Homework
- See Assignment Guide.
- See the CRB: Practice, Reteach, Apply, Extend

Assessment Options
- Checkpoint Exercises
- Daily Quiz (3.6)
- Stand. Test Practice

Each day provides a number of options for the lesson, including starting, teaching, applying, and assessing.

The Chapter Resource Book includes a number of follow-up options for the lesson. These options include three levels of practice, reteaching examples with practice, inter-disciplinary and real-life applications, and challenge exercises.

A black dot indicates that the option can be found in the Student Edition, a green dot in the Chapter Resource Book, and a red dot in the Teacher's Edition.

Block Schedule

Day 4

3.6 & 3.7

Day 5 Start Options
- Homework Check
- Warm-Up (Les. 3.6) or Daily Quiz (Les. 3.5)

Teaching 3.6 Options
- Motivating the Lesson
- Les. Opener (Appl.)
- Examples 1–6
- Closure Question
- Guided Practice Exs.

Beginning 3.7 Options
- Warm-Up (Les. 3.7)
- Les. Opener (Activity)
- Technology Activity
- Examples 1–6
- Guided Pract. Exs.

Apply/Homework
- See Assignment Guide.
- See the CRB: Practice, Reteach, Apply, Extend

Assessment Options
- Checkpoint Exercises
- Daily Quiz (Les. 3.6)
- Stand. Test Practice (3.6)

Assignment Guide

An Assignment Guide for each lesson is provided at point-of-use at the beginning of the exercise set.

Assignments are provided for basic, average, advanced, and block-scheduled courses.

Assignment Guide

Basic
Day 1: pp. 216–219 Exs. 6–21
Day 2: pp. 217–219 Exs. 22–28, 32–37, 39–46

Average
Day 1: pp. 216–219 Exs. 6–21
Day 2: pp. 217–219 Exs. 22–28, 32–37, 39–46

Advanced
Day 1: pp. 216–219 Exs. 6–21
Day 2: pp. 217–219 Exs. 22–28, 30–46

Block Schedule
pp. 216–219 Exs. 6–21 (with 4.2)
pp. 216–219 Exs. 22–28, 30–37, 39–46 (with 4.4)

PROOF STRAND

Geometry offers students many opportunities to explore geometric situations, develop conjectures, and prove their conjectures using a variety of methods. Following the recommendations of the National Council of Teachers of Mathematics *Curriculum and Evaluation Standards for School Mathematics*, the textbook encourages students to use an axiomatic system and to communicate their geometric reasoning using standard two-column proofs as well as paragraph proofs, flow proofs, and coordinate proofs.

INDUCTIVE REASONING SETS THE STAGE

Beginning in Lesson 1.1, students look for patterns and make predictions about geometric problem situations. In these sections, students learn that generalizations based on specific cases are called *conjectures*, and that they are the outcome of inductive reasoning. Students see that a single *counterexample* is enough to disprove a conjecture, but that no number of examples is enough to prove one.

- Lesson 1.1 **Patterns and Inductive Reasoning** (pp. 3–5)

ACTIVITIES LEAD TO CONJECTURES

In every chapter, two or three lessons feature Activities in which students gather information to help them make conjectures. (See the table of contents on pp. vi–xvii.) Here are a few examples:

- Lesson 1.5 **Folding Bisectors** (p. 33)
- Lesson 4.3 **Investigating Congruent Triangles** (p. 211)
- Lesson 5.5 **Side Lengths and Angle Measures** (p. 294)

Concept Activities use a variety of methods to introduce geometric concepts, including logic (pp. 86, 135, 321), manipulations (pp. 33, 108, 193, 371, 727, 751), and models (pp. 211, 263, 395, 403, 429, 472, 550, 612, 676).

Technology Activities encourage the student to explore concepts using geometry software (pp. 43, 142, 228, 286, 294, 329, 411, 497, 514, 542, 628, 641, 690, 706, 750).

Proof Strand

Deductive reasoning proves conjectures

In Chapter 1, students are introduced to *definitions*, *postulates*, *axioms*, and *theorems*. These are further developed in Chapter 2 with an introduction to proofs. Also in Chapter 2, students begin to study conditional statements, including symbolic notation and the laws of logic.

- Lesson 2.1 **Conditional Statements** (pp. 71–74)
- Lesson 2.2 **Definitions and Biconditional Statements** (pp. 79–81)
- Lesson 2.3 **Deductive Reasoning** (pp. 87–90)
- Lesson 2.4 **Reasoning with Properties from Algebra** (pp. 96–98)
- Lesson 2.5 **Proving Statements about Segments** (pp. 102–103)

Deductive reasoning, logic, and proof are used throughout the rest of the textbook. To help students develop proofs, many exercises are included in which students must complete a proof that is partially presented.

Communication through various kinds of proof

Students are encouraged to make convincing arguments in paragraph, flow proof, indirect, coordinate, and two-column formats, as well as through algebraic methods. These strategies are described in the following sections, and then used throughout:

- Lesson 2.5 **two-column proof** (pp. 102–103)
- Lesson 2.5 **paragraph proof** (pp. 102–103)
- Lesson 3.2 **flow proof** (pp. 135, 136–138)
- Lesson 4.7 **coordinate proof** (pp. 243–246)
- Lesson 5.6 **indirect proof** (pp. 302–304)

Students are also asked to prepare Plans for Proof, describing how they would prove a given statement. Plans for proof are provided throughout as a learning aid in selected examples and exercises.

Non-Euclidean geometries

Although the textbook primarily focuses on the axiomatic system of Euclidean geometry, the Chapter 11 Project, pp. 714–715, explores spherical geometry. Students see that different assumptions can be used to frame different mathematical systems.

References

The Student Resources in the back of the textbook provide these additional proof-related references for students:

Postulates and Theorems (pp. 827–832) are listed in order of appearance, and include page numbers referring to where the postulates and theorems are first introduced and explained.

Additional Proofs (pp. 833–840) are supplied for a few theorems not proved in the text or exercises.

Proof Strand

Developing proof

Plan for proof

Plan for proof cont'd

Two-column proof

PROOF STRAND

TWO-COLUMN PROOF *cont'd*

335 (Ex. 39)
336 (Exs. 55–58)
339 (Example 1)
362 (Ex. 46)
504 (Ex. 31)
535 (Theorem 9.4)
548 (Ex. 41)
565 (Ex. 47)
626 (Ex. 40)

PARAGRAPH PROOF

102 (Theorem 2.1)
136 (Theorem 2.6)
139 (Ex. 17)
151 (Example 2)
212 (Example 1)
214 (Example 3)
217 (Exs. 23, 24)
220 (Theorem 4.5)
229 (Example 1)
237 (Example 1)
238 (Example 3)
266 (Example 2)
296 (Theorem 5.10)
332 (Example 4)
334 (Ex. 38)
349 (Example 4)
362 (Ex. 47)
366 (Example 5)
405 (Example 2)
408 (Exs. 33–35)
413 (Example 1)
417 (Exs. 20, 21)
421 (Theorem 7.4)
488 (Example 1)
494 (Exs. 30, 31)
504 (Exs. 32, 33)
556 (Exs. 35, 36)
618 (Ex. 35)
629 (Theorem 10.15)
634 (Exs. 31, 32)
666 (Exs. 43–46)
669 (Example 1)

FLOW PROOF

135 (Activity)
136–138
139 (Ex. 18)
140 (Exs. 20–23)
158 (Example 3)
162 (Ex. 38)
340 (Example 3)
598 (Example 6)

COORDINATE PROOF

243–246
248 (Exs. 26, 27)
249 (Ex. 34)
288 (Example 3)
335 (Exs. 40–44)
350 (Example 5)
836 (Theorem 5.7)
838 (Theorem 5.8)

INDIRECT PROOF

302–304
306 (Exs. 24, 25)
307 (Exs. 26, 27)
601 (Exs. 50–52)
840 (Theorem 10.11)

STUDENT CHOICE

140 (Ex. 24)
148 (Exs. 28, 29)
155 (Exs. 34, 35)
208 (Ex. 38)
218 (Exs. 25–28)
224 (Exs. 19–22)
233 (Exs. 11–13)
234 (Exs. 17, 18)
240 (Exs. 26–28, 31)
241 (Exs. 33, 34, 39)
269 (27–30)
284 (Ex. 35)
344 (Exs. 32, 33)
353 (Exs. 45, 46, 51, 52)
362 (Ex. 53)
369 (Exs. 49, 50)
470 (Exs. 36, 37)
478 (Ex. 45)
485 (Ex. 48)
486 (Ex. 49)
533 (Exs. 34–36)
547 (Exs. 34–36)
548 (Exs. 42, 43)
610 (Exs. 59–62)
619 (Exs. 38, 40)
680 (Ex. 22)

Construction Strand

Informal constructions

Informal constructions develop an intuitive understanding of geometric concepts. Here are some early examples:

- Lesson 1.2 **modeling intersections** (p. 12)
- Lesson 1.5 **folding bisectors** (p. 33)

Traditional constructions with straightedge and compass

The standard tools of straightedge and compass are used in traditional constructions shown or suggested in the following lessons.

- Lesson 1.5 **segment bisector and midpoint** (p. 34)
- Lesson 1.5 **angle bisector** (p. 36)
- Lesson 2.5 **copy a segment** (p. 104)
- Lesson 3.1 **perpendicular to a line** (p. 130)
- Lesson 3.5 **copying an angle** (p. 159)
- Lesson 3.5 **parallel lines** (p. 159)
- Lesson 4.3 **copying a triangle** (p. 213)
- Lesson 5.1 **perpendicular through a point on a line, perpendicular bisector** (p. 264)
- Lesson 5.2 **circumcircle of a triangle** (p. 273)
- Lesson 5.3 **angle bisectors of a triangle**, **medians of a triangle** (p. 286)
- Lesson 6.2 **parallelogram** (p. 329)
- Lesson 7.3 **rotating a figure** (p. 413)
- Lesson 8.5 **golden rectangle** (p. 496)
- Lesson 8.6 **dividing a segment into equal parts** (p. 500)
- Lesson 8.7 **drawing a dilation** (p. 507)
- Lesson 10.2 **center of a circle** (pp. 605–606; 609–610, Exs. 52, 54)
- Lesson 10.3 **inscribed angle** (p. 612)
- Lesson 10.3 **tangent to a circle from a point on the circle, tangent to a circle from a point not on the circle** (p. 618, Exs. 30–33)
- Lesson 11.2 **regular polygons** (pp. 673–674, Exs. 35–44)

Dynamic constructions with geometry software

Dynamic geometry software, such as the Geometry Inventor component of the McDougal Littell *Mathpack: Software for Exploring and Applying Mathematics*, offers teachers and students a chance to explore a variety of geometric concepts.

- Lesson 1.6 **Angles and Intersecting Lines** (p. 43)
- Lesson 3.3 **Parallel Lines and Angles** (p. 142)
- Lesson 4.4 **Triangles and Congruence** (p. 228)
- Lesson 5.3 **Concurrent Lines** (p. 286)
- Lesson 5.5 **Side Lengths and Angle Measures** (p. 294)
- Lesson 6.2 **Parallelograms** (p. 329)
- Lesson 7.3 **Double Reflections** (p. 411)
- Lesson 8.6 **Proportional Segments** (p. 497)
- Lesson 8.7 **Dilations** (p. 514)
- Lesson 9.3 **Sides and Angles of Triangles** (p. 542)
- Lesson 10.5 **Segment Lengths in Circles** (p. 628)
- Lesson 10.7 **Points Equidistant from a Point and a Line** (p. 641)

References

The Construction entry in the Index (pp. 862–863) includes a list of constructions arranged alphabetically.

PLANNING FOR OTHER COURSES:

What other books come in the McDougal Littell series?

The same solid approach and features that are found in McDougal Littell Geometry to help you and your students succeed are also found in the Algebra 1 and Algebra 2 books.

McDougal Littell ALGEBRA 1

1 **Connections to Algebra**
2 **Properties of Real Numbers**
3 **Solving Linear Equations**
4 **Graphing Linear Equations and Functions**
5 **Writing Linear Functions**
6 **Solving and Graphing Linear Inequalities**
7 **Systems of Linear Equations and Inequalities**
8 **Exponents and Exponential Functions**
9 **Quadratic Equations and Functions**
10 **Polynomials and Factoring**
11 **Rational Equations and Functions**
12 **Radicals and Connections to Geometry**

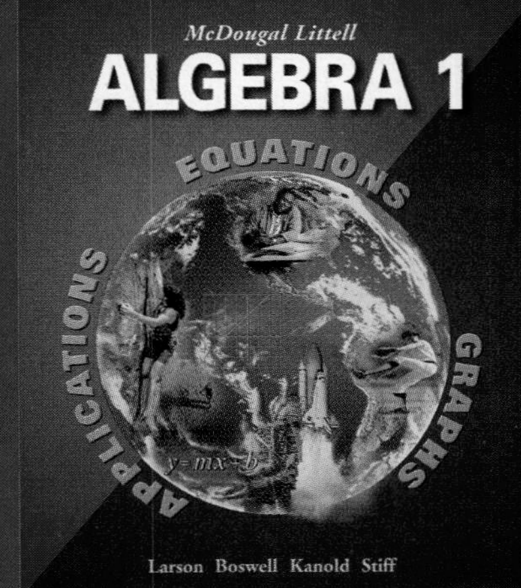

McDougal Littell ALGEBRA 2

1 **Equations and Inequalities**
2 **Linear Equations and Functions**
3 **Systems of Linear Equations and Inequalities**
4 **Matrices and Determinants**
5 **Quadratic Functions**
6 **Polynomials and Polynomial Functions**
7 **Powers, Roots, and Radicals**
8 **Exponential and Logarithmic Functions**
9 **Rational Equations and Functions**
10 **Quadratic Relations and Conic Sections**
11 **Sequences and Series**
12 **Probability and Statistics**
13 **Trigonometric Ratios and Functions**
14 **Trigonometric Graphs, Identities, and Equations**

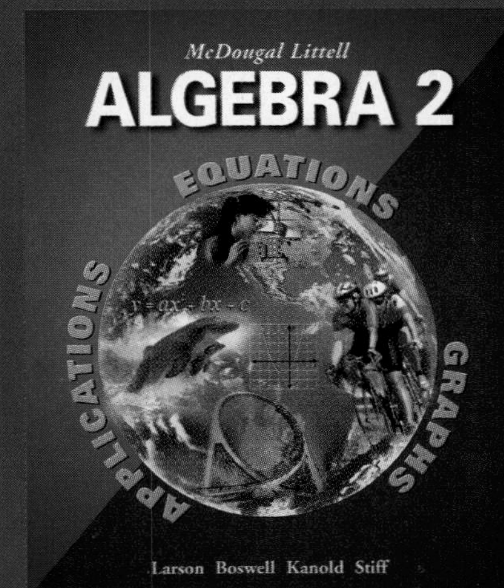

McDougal Littell

GEOMETRY

STUDENT EDITION

CHAPTER 1

PLANNING THE CHAPTER

Basics of Geometry

Lesson	GOALS	NCTM	ITED	SAT9 (TASK 1)	Terra-Nova	Local
1.1 *pp. 3–9*	GOAL 1 Find and describe patterns. GOAL 2 Use inductive reasoning to make real-life conjectures.	1, 2, 3, 6, 7, 8, 9	MCWN, MIGE, RQWN, RQGE	1	11, 14, 16, 17, 18, 51, 52	1, 3
1.2 *pp. 10–16*	GOAL 1 Understand and use the basic undefined terms and defined terms of geometry. GOAL 2 Sketch the intersections of lines and planes.	3, 8, 10	MIGE, RQGE		14, 18	1
1.3 *pp. 17–25*	GOAL 1 Use segment postulates. GOAL 2 Use the Distance Formula to measure distances.	1, 2, 3, 4, 9	MCWN, MIM, MIGE, RQWN, RQGE	26	11, 13, 14, 16, 49, 51	1, 15, 17
1.4 *pp. 26–32*	GOAL 1 Use angle postulates. GOAL 2 Classify angles as acute, right, obtuse, or straight.	1, 3, 4, 7	MCWN, MIM, MIGE, RQGE	27	13, 14	4, 12
1.5 *pp. 33–42*	CONCEPT ACTIVITY: 1.5 *Investigate segment bisectors and angle bisectors by paper folding.* GOAL 1 Bisect a segment. GOAL 2 Bisect an angle.	3	MIGE, RQGE	33	14	16, 17
1.6 *pp. 43–50*	TECHNOLOGY ACTIVITY: 1.6 *Construct intersecting lines and measure the angles formed by the lines using geometry software.* GOAL 1 Identify vertical angles and linear pairs. GOAL 2 Identify complementary and supplementary angles.	1, 3, 4	MCWN, MIM, MIGE, RQWN, RQGE		11, 13, 14, 49	13
1.7 *pp. 51–58*	GOAL 1 Find the perimeter and area of common plane figures. GOAL 2 Use a general problem-solving plan.	1, 2, 3, 4, 6	MCE, SAPE, MCWN, MIM, MIGE, RQWN, RQGE	1, 30, 31, 32	10, 11, 13, 14, 16, 17, 48, 49, 51, 52	8, 10

RESOURCES

Chapter Resource Booklets

Chapter Support

Tips for New Teachers	p. 1
Parent Guide for Student Success	p. 3
Prerequisite Skills Review	p. 5
Strategies for Reading Mathematics	p. 7

Lesson Support

Lesson Support	1.1	1.2	1.3	1.4	1.5	1.6	1.7
Lesson Plans (regular and block)	p. 9	p. 22	p. 34	p. 49	p. 61	p. 78	p. 92
Warm-Up Exercises and Daily Quiz	p. 11	p. 24	p. 36	p. 51	p. 63	p. 80	p. 94
Activity Support Masters							
Lesson Openers	p. 12	p. 25	p. 37	p. 52	p. 64	p. 81	p. 95
Technology Activities & Keystrokes					p. 65	p. 82	p. 96
Practice (3 levels)	p. 14	p. 26	p. 38	p. 53	p. 69	p. 84	p. 100
Reteaching with Practice	p. 17	p. 29	p. 41	p. 56	p. 72	p. 87	p. 103
Quick Catch-Up for Absent Students	p. 19	p. 31	p. 43	p. 58	p. 74	p. 89	p. 105
Cooperative Learning Activities			p. 44				p. 106
Interdisciplinary Applications		p. 32		p. 59		p. 90	
Real-Life Applications	p. 20		p. 45		p. 75		p. 107
Math & History Applications			p. 46				
Challenge: Skills and Applications	p. 21	p. 33	p. 47	p. 60	p. 76	p. 91	p. 108

Review and Assessment

Quizzes	pp. 48, 77
Chapter Review Games and Activities	p. 109
Chapter Test (3 levels)	pp. 110–115
SAT/ACT Chapter Test	p. 116
Alternative Assessment with Math Journal	p. 117
Project with Rubric	p. 119
Cumulative Review	p. 121
Resource Book Answers	p. A1

Transparencies

	1.1	1.2	1.3	1.4	1.5	1.6	1.7
Warm-Up Exercises and Daily Quiz	p. 2	p. 3	p. 4	p. 5	p. 6	p. 7	p. 8
Alternative Lesson Opener Transparencies	p. 1	p. 2	p. 3	p. 4	p. 5	p. 6	p. 7
Examples/Standardized Test Practice	✓	✓	✓	✓	✓	✓	✓
Answer Transparencies	✓	✓	✓	✓	✓	✓	✓

Technology

- Electronic Teaching Tools
- Online Lesson Planner
- Internet Support
- Personal Student Tutor
- Test and Practice Generator
- Geometry in Motion video
- Electronic Lesson Presentations (Lesson 1.2)

Additional Resources

- Basic Skills Workbook: Diagnosis and Remediation
- Worked-Out Solution Key
- Resources in Spanish
- Standardized Test Practice Workbook
- Practice Workbook with Examples

Correlations to the California Curriculum

Correlations to California Standards
See Teacher's Edition pp. CA9–CA11

Correlations to SAT9
Task 1: See Teacher's Edition pp. CA12–CA14
Task 2: See Teacher's Edition pp. CA15–CA17

CHAPTER 1

PACING THE CHAPTER

Resource Key
- Student Edition
- Chapter 1 Resource Book
- Teacher's Edition

REGULAR SCHEDULE

Day 1

1.1

STARTING OPTIONS
- Prereq. Skills Review
- Strategies for Reading
- Warm-Up

TEACHING OPTIONS
- Les. Opener (Technology)
- Examples 1–6
- Closure Question
- Guided Practice Exs.

APPLY/HOMEWORK
- See Assignment Guide.
- See the CRB: Practice, Reteach, Apply, Extend

ASSESSMENT OPTIONS
- Checkpoint Exercises
- Daily Quiz (1.1)
- Stand. Test Practice

Day 2

1.2

STARTING OPTIONS
- Homework Check
- Warm-Up or Daily Quiz

TEACHING OPTIONS
- Motivating the Lesson
- Les. Opener (Visual)
- Examples 1–4
- Closure Question
- Guided Practice Exs.

APPLY/HOMEWORK
- See Assignment Guide.
- See the CRB: Practice, Reteach, Apply, Extend

ASSESSMENT OPTIONS
- Checkpoint Exercises
- Daily Quiz (1.2)
- Stand. Test Practice

Day 3

1.3

STARTING OPTIONS
- Homework Check
- Warm-Up or Daily Quiz

TEACHING OPTIONS
- Motivating the Lesson
- Les. Opener (Activity)
- Examples 1–3
- Guided Practice Exs.

APPLY/HOMEWORK
- See Assignment Guide.
- See the CRB: Practice, Reteach, Apply, Extend

ASSESSMENT OPTIONS
- Checkpoint Exercises, pp. 18–19

Day 4

1.3 *(cont.)*

STARTING OPTIONS
- Homework Check

TEACHING OPTIONS
- Example 4
- Closure Question

APPLY/HOMEWORK
- See Assignment Guide.
- See the CRB: Practice, Reteach, Apply, Extend

ASSESSMENT OPTIONS
- Checkpoint Exercises, p. 20
- Daily Quiz (1.3)
- Stand. Test Practice
- Quiz (1.1–1.3)

Day 5

1.4

STARTING OPTIONS
- Homework Check
- Warm-Up or Daily Quiz

TEACHING OPTIONS
- Motivating the Lesson
- Les. Opener (Activity)
- Technology Activity
- Examples 1–4
- Closure Question
- Guided Practice Exs.

APPLY/HOMEWORK
- See Assignment Guide.
- See the CRB: Practice, Reteach, Apply, Extend

ASSESSMENT OPTIONS
- Checkpoint Exercises
- Daily Quiz (1.4)
- Stand. Test Practice

Day 6

1.5

STARTING OPTIONS
- Homework Check
- Warm-Up or Daily Quiz

TEACHING OPTIONS
- Motivating the Lesson
- Concept Activity
- Les. Opener (Application)
- Technology Activity
- Examples 1–4
- Guided Practice Exs.

APPLY/HOMEWORK
- See Assignment Guide.
- See the CRB: Practice, Reteach, Apply, Extend

ASSESSMENT OPTIONS
- Checkpoint Exercises, pp. 35–37

Day 9

1.6 *(cont.)*

STARTING OPTIONS
- Homework Check

TEACHING OPTIONS
- Examples 4–6
- Technology Activity
- Closure Question
- Guided Practice Exs. 1, 3, 7

APPLY/HOMEWORK
- See Assignment Guide.
- See the CRB: Practice, Reteach, Apply, Extend

ASSESSMENT OPTIONS
- Checkpoint Exercises, p. 46
- Daily Quiz (1.6)
- Stand. Test Practice

Day 10

1.7

STARTING OPTIONS
- Homework Check
- Warm-Up or Daily Quiz

TEACHING OPTIONS
- Motivating the Lesson
- Les. Opener (Activity)
- Technology Activity
- Examples 1–3
- Guided Practice Exs. 1–5

APPLY/HOMEWORK
- See Assignment Guide.
- See the CRB: Practice, Reteach, Apply, Extend

ASSESSMENT OPTIONS
- Checkpoint Exercises, p. 52

Day 11

1.7 *(cont.)*

STARTING OPTIONS
- Homework Check

TEACHING OPTIONS
- Examples 4–6
- Closure Question
- Guided Practice Exs. 6–8

APPLY/HOMEWORK
- See Assignment Guide.
- See the CRB: Practice, Reteach, Apply, Extend

ASSESSMENT OPTIONS
- Checkpoint Exercises, pp. 53–54
- Daily Quiz (1.7)
- Stand. Test Practice
- Quiz (1.6–1.7)

Day 12

Review

DAY 12 START OPTIONS
- Homework Check

REVIEWING OPTIONS
- Chapter 1 Summary
- Chapter 1 Review
- Chapter Review Games and Activities

APPLY/HOMEWORK
- Chapter 1 Test (practice)
- Ch. Standardized Test (practice)

Day 13

Assess

DAY 13 START OPTIONS
- Homework Check

ASSESSMENT OPTIONS
- Chapter 1 Test
- SAT/ACT Ch. 1 Test
- Alternative Assessment

APPLY/HOMEWORK
- Skill Review, p. 70

Day 7

1.5 (cont.)

Starting Options
- Homework Check

Teaching Options
- Example 5
- Closure Question

Apply/Homework
- See Assignment Guide.
- See the CRB: Practice, Reteach, Apply, Extend

Assessment Options
- Checkpoint Exercises, p. 37
- Daily Quiz (1.5)
- Stand. Test Practice
- Quiz (1.4–1.5)

Day 8

1.6

Starting Options
- Homework Check
- Warm-Up or Daily Quiz

Teaching Options
- Les. Opener (Activity)
- Examples 1–3
- Guided Practice Exs. 2, 4–6

Apply/Homework
- See Assignment Guide.
- See the CRB: Practice, Reteach, Apply, Extend

Assessment Options
- Checkpoint Exercises, p. 45

BLOCK SCHEDULE

Day 1

1.1 & 1.2

Day 1 Start Options
- Prereq. Skills Review
- Strategies for Reading
- Warm-Up (Les. 1.1)

Teaching 1.1 Options
- Les. Opener (Tech.)
- Examples 1–6
- Closure Question
- Guided Practice Exs.

Teaching 1.2 Options
- Warm-Up (Les. 1.2)
- Motivating the Lesson
- Les. Opener (Visual)
- Examples 1–4
- Closure Question
- Guided Practice Exs.

Apply/Homework
- See Assignment Guide.
- See the CRB: Practice, Reteach, Apply, Extend

Assessment Options
- Checkpoint Exercises
- Daily Quiz (Les. 1.1, 1.2)
- Stand. Test Practice

Day 2

1.3

Day 2 Start Options
- Homework Check
- Warm-Up (Les. 1.3) or Daily Quiz (Les. 1.2)

Teaching 1.3 Options
- Motivating the Lesson
- Les. Opener (Activity)
- Examples 1–4
- Closure Question
- Guided Practice Exs.

Apply/Homework
- See Assignment Guide.
- See the CRB: Practice, Reteach, Apply, Extend

Assessment Options
- Checkpoint Exercises
- Daily Quiz (Les. 1.3)
- Stand. Test Practice
- Quiz (1.1–1.3)

Day 3

1.4 & 1.5

Day 3 Start Options
- Homework Check
- W-Up 1.4 or D. Quiz 1.3

Teaching 1.4 Options
- Motivating the Lesson
- Les. Opener (Activity)
- Technology Activity
- Examples 1–4
- Closure Question
- Guided Practice Exs.

Beginning 1.5 Options
- Warm-Up (Les. 1.5)
- Motivating the Lesson
- Concept Activity
- Les. Opener (Appl.)
- Technology Activity
- Examples 1–4
- Guided Practice Exs.

Apply/Homework
- See Assignment Guide.
- See the CRB: Practice, Reteach, Apply, Extend

Assessment Options
- Checkpoint Exercises
- Daily Quiz (Les. 1.4)
- Stand. Test Prac. (1.4)

Day 4

1.5 & 1.6

Day 4 Start Options
- Homework Check
- Daily Quiz (Les. 1.4)

Finishing 1.5 Options
- Example 5
- Closure Question

Beginning 1.6 Options
- Warm-Up (Les. 1.6)
- Les. Opener (Activity)
- Examples 1–3
- Guided Practice Exs. 2, 4–6

Apply/Homework
- See Assignment Guide.
- See the CRB: Practice, Reteach, Apply, Extend

Assessment Options
- Checkpoint Exercises
- Daily Quiz (Les. 1.5)
- Stand. Test Prac. (1.5)
- Quiz (1.4–1.5)

Day 5

1.6 & 1.7

Day 5 Start Options
- Homework Check
- Daily Quiz (Les. 1.5)

Finishing 1.6 Options
- Examples 4–6
- Technology Activity
- Closure Question
- Guided Practice Exs. 1, 3, 7

Beginning 1.7 Options
- Warm-Up (Les. 1.7)
- Motivating the Lesson
- Les. Opener (Activity)
- Technology Activity
- Examples 1–3
- Guided Prac. Exs. 1–5

Apply/Homework
- See Assignment Guide.
- See the CRB: Practice, Reteach, Apply, Extend

Assessment Options
- Checkpoint Exercises
- Daily Quiz (Les. 1.6)
- Stand. Test Prac. (1.6)

Day 6

1.7 & Review

Day 6 Start Options
- Homework Check
- Daily Quiz (Les. 1.6)

Finishing 1.7 Options
- Examples 4–6
- Closure Question
- Guided Prac. Exs. 6–8

Reviewing Options
- Chapter 1 Summary
- Chapter 1 Review
- Chapter Review Games and Activities

Apply/Homework
- See Assignment Guide.
- See the CRB: Practice, Reteach, Apply, Extend
- Chapter 1 Test (prac.)
- Ch. Standardized Test (practice)

Assessment Options
- Checkpoint Exercises
- Daily Quiz (Les. 1.7)
- Stand. Test Practice
- Quiz (1.6–1.7)

Day 7

Assess & 2.1

(Day 7 = Ch. 2 Day 1)

Assessment Options
- Chapter 1 Test
- SAT/ACT Ch. 1 Test
- Alternative Assessment

Ch. 2 Start Options
- Skills Review, p. 70
- Prereq. Skills Review
- Strategies for Reading

Teaching 2.1 Options
- Warm-Up (Les. 2.1)
- Les. Opener (Visual)
- Examples 1–7
- Closure Question
- Guided Practice Exs.

Apply/Homework
- See Assignment Guide.
- See the CRB: Practice, Reteach, Apply, Extend

Assessment Options
- Checkpoint Exercises
- Daily Quiz (Les. 2.1)
- Stand. Test Practice

CHAPTER 1

MEETING INDIVIDUAL NEEDS

BEFORE THE CHAPTER

The *Chapter 1 Resource Book* has the following materials to distribute and use before the chapter:

- **Parent Guide for Student Success**
- **Prerequisite Skills Review (pictured below)**
- **Strategies for Reading Mathematics**

PREREQUISITE SKILLS *Pages 5–6*

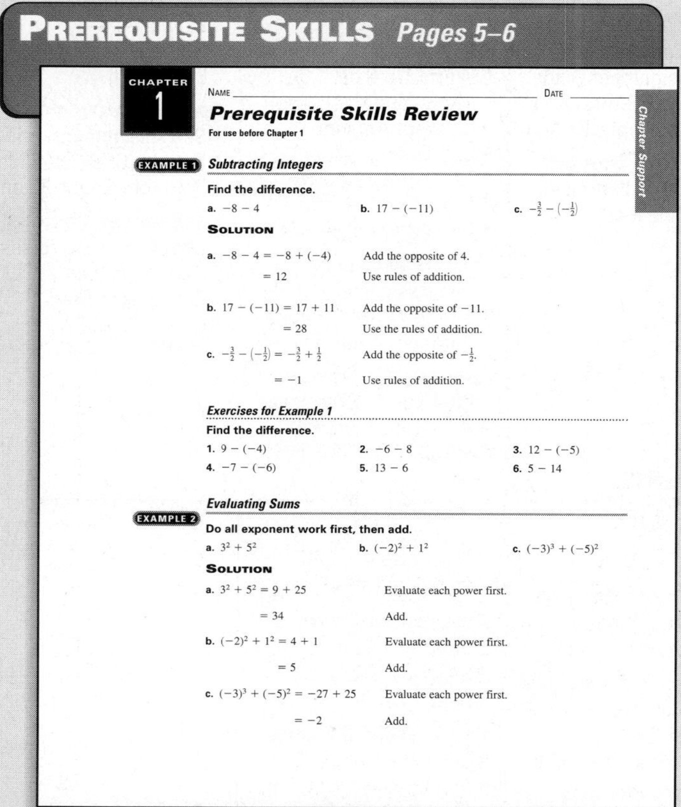

CHAPTER 1

NAME ______ DATE ______

Prerequisite Skills Review

For use before Chapter 1

Chapter Support

EXAMPLE 1 *Subtracting Integers*

Find the difference.

a. $-8 - 4$ b. $17 - (-11)$ c. $-\frac{3}{2} - (-\frac{1}{2})$

SOLUTION

a. $-8 - 4 = -8 + (-4)$ Add the opposite of 4.

$= 12$ Use rules of addition.

b. $17 - (-11) = 17 + 11$ Add the opposite of -11.

$= 28$ Use the rules of addition.

c. $-\frac{3}{2} - (-\frac{1}{2}) = -\frac{3}{2} + \frac{1}{2}$ Add the opposite of $-\frac{1}{2}$.

$= -1$ Use rules of addition.

Exercises for Example 1

Find the difference.

1. $9 - (-4)$ 2. $-6 - 8$ 3. $12 - (-5)$
4. $-7 - (-6)$ 5. $13 - 6$ 6. $5 - 14$

EXAMPLE 2 *Evaluating Sums*

Do all exponent work first, then add.

a. $3^2 + 5^2$ b. $(-2)^2 + 1^2$ c. $(-3)^3 + (-5)^2$

SOLUTION

a. $3^2 + 5^2 = 9 + 25$ Evaluate each power first.

$= 34$ Add.

b. $(-2)^2 + 1^2 = 4 + 1$ Evaluate each power first.

$= 5$ Add.

c. $(-3)^3 + (-5)^2 = -27 + 25$ Evaluate each power first.

$= -2$ Add.

PREREQUISITE SKILLS REVIEW These two pages support the Study Guide on page 2. They help students prepare for Chapter 1 by providing worked-out examples and practice for the following skills needed in the chapter:

- **Subtract integers.**
- **Evaluate sums.**
- **Evaluate radical expressions.**

TECHNOLOGY RESOURCE

Students can use the Personal Student Tutor to find additional reteaching and practice for skills from the Skills Review Handbook that are used in Chapter 1.

DURING EACH LESSON

The *Chapter 1 Resource Book* has the following alternatives for introducing the lesson:

- **Lesson Openers (pictured below)**
- **Technology Activities with Keystrokes**

LESSON OPENER *Page 37*

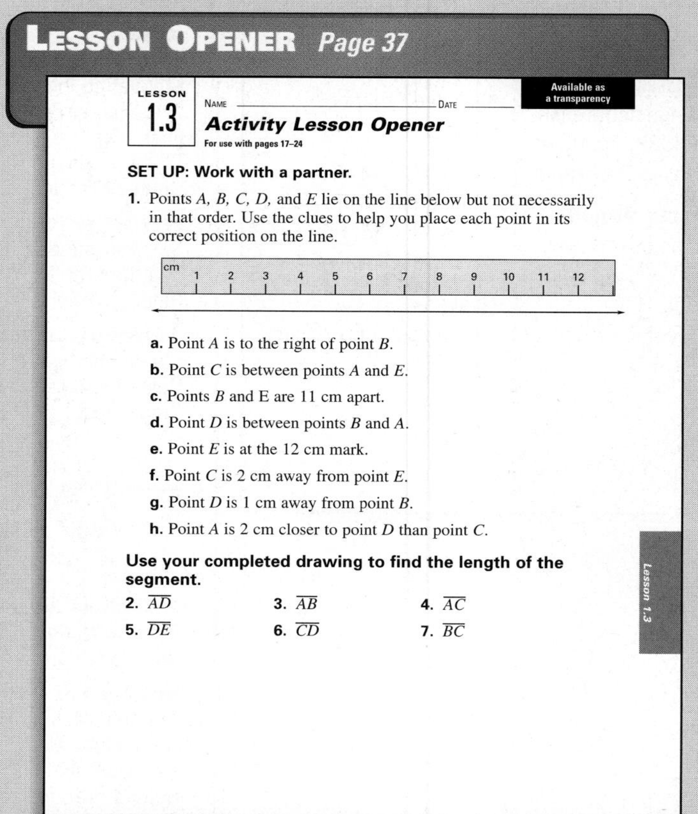

LESSON 1.3

Available as a transparency

NAME ______ DATE ______

Activity Lesson Opener

For use with pages 17–24

SET UP: Work with a partner.

1. Points *A, B, C, D,* and *E* lie on the line below but not necessarily in that order. Use the clues to help you place each point in its correct position on the line.

a. Point *A* is to the right of point *B*.
b. Point *C* is between points *A* and *E*.
c. Points *B* and E are 11 cm apart.
d. Point *D* is between points *B* and *A*.
e. Point *E* is at the 12 cm mark.
f. Point *C* is 2 cm away from point *E*.
g. Point *D* is 1 cm away from point *B*.
h. Point *A* is 2 cm closer to point *D* than point *C*.

Use your completed drawing to find the length of the segment.

2. $\overline{AD}$ 3. $\overline{AB}$ 4. $\overline{AC}$
5. $\overline{DE}$ 6. $\overline{CD}$ 7. $\overline{BC}$

Lesson 1.3

ACTIVITY LESSON OPENER This Lesson Opener provides an alternative way to start Lesson 1.3 in the form of an activity. In this activity, students work with a partner to place points on a line as they learn about measuring line segments.

FOLLOWING EACH LESSON

The *Chapter 1 Resource Book* has a variety of materials to follow-up each lesson. They include the following:

- **Practice (3 levels)**
- **Reteaching with Practice**
- **Quick Catch-Up for Absent Students (pictured below)**
- **Interdisciplinary Applications**
- **Real-Life Applications**

QUICK CATCH-UP *Page 19*

LESSON 1.1

NAME ______ DATE ______

Quick Catch-Up for Absent Students

For use with pages 3–9

Lesson 1.1

The items checked below were covered in class on (date missed) ______

Lesson 1.1: Patterns and Inductive Reasoning

____ **Goal 1:** Find and describe patterns. (p. 3)

Material Covered:

____ Example 1: Describing a Visual Pattern

____ Example 2: Describing a Number Pattern

____ **Goal 2:** Use inductive reasoning to make real-life conjectures. (pp. 4–5)

Material Covered:

____ Example 3: Making a Conjecture

____ Example 4: Finding a Counterexample

____ Example 5: Examining an Unproven Conjecture

____ Example 6: Using Inductive Reasoning in Real Life

Vocabulary:

conjecture, p. 4 — inductive reasoning, p. 4

counterexample, p. 4

____ Other (specify) ______

Homework and Additional Learning Support

____ Textbook (specify) pp. 6–9

____ *Reteaching with Practice* worksheet (specify exercises) ______

____ *Personal Student Tutor* for Lesson 1.1

QUICK CATCH-UP FOR ABSENT STUDENTS You can use this form to let students know what they have missed when they've been absent from class. It allows you to quickly check off which Examples and other elements of Lesson 1.1 were covered on a given day and provides space for filling in the homework assignment.

TECHNOLOGY RESOURCE

Students who have missed class can find extra examples for Lessons 1.2, 1.4, and 1.6 on the Internet at www.mcdougallittell.com.

ASSESSING THE CHAPTER

The *Chapter 1 Resource Book* has the following review and assessment materials:

- **Quizzes**
- **Chapter Review Games and Activities (pictured below)**
- **Chapter Test (3 levels)**
  SAT/ACT Chapter Test
- **Alternative Assessment with Rubric and Math Journal**
- **Project with Rubric**
- **Cumulative Review**

CHAPTER REVIEW GAMES *Page 109*

CHAPTER 1

NAME ______ DATE ______

Chapter Review Games and Activities

For use after Chapter 1

What do you get if you divide the circumference of a jack o' lantern by its diameter?

The first letters of the answers to the following questions will spell out the answer to this riddle.

1. What is the name of an object with no dimension that is represented by a small dot?
2. What kind of a statement is a conjecture?
3. What is the point called that divides a line segment into two congruent segments?
4. What is the name of an object that extends in two dimensions and is represented by a shape that looks like a tabletop?
5. What is the name of a recreational toy that has a frame that bisects at least two of the angles it supports?
6. When two lines have a point in common, we say that they ______.
7. Three or more points that do not all lie on the same line are described as being ______.
8. What is the name of the theorem on which the distance formula is based?
9. The point A is the ______ point of the ray $\overrightarrow{AB}$.

Review and Assess

CHAPTER REVIEW GAMES AND ACTIVITIES On this worksheet, students answer questions to solve a riddle as a motivating means of reviewing the material in Chapter 1.

CHAPTER OVERVIEW

CHAPTER GOALS

Chapter 1 introduces students to many of the basic ideas and terms in geometry. The chapter begins with a study of patterns and inductive reasoning. The basic undefined terms and defined terms of geometry are then introduced. The Segment Addition Postulate, Ruler Postulate, and Distance Formula are used to find the distance between two points. Angle postulates are used to find the measures of angles. Angles are classified as acute, right, obtuse, or straight. Vertical angles, linear pairs, complementary angles and supplementary angles are identified. Students learn to sketch the intersections of lines and planes as well as use a straight edge and compass to construct segment and angle bisectors. The Midpoint Formula is used to find the coordinates of the midpoint of a segment. Finally a general problem-solving plan is introduced and used to solve problems involving perimeter, area, and circumference.

APPLICATION NOTE

Students may not have seen angles greater than 180° before. Point out that bearings are measured around a circle so that they can have measures between 0° and 360°. Students will gain more experience with angles measuring greater than 180° when they study circles in Chapter 10. Point out also that, in addition to an angle measure, each bearing has a direction. If the angle measure is positive, the bearing is measured from the North in a clockwise direction.

Additional information about airport runways is available at **www.mcdougallittell.com.**

BASICS OF GEOMETRY

▶ *How are airport runways named?*

CHAPTER 1

APPLICATION: Runways

Air traffic controllers and pilots need a way to refer to runways that is consistent among different airports.

Runways are named based on the angles they form with due north, measured in a clockwise direction. These angles are called *bearings*.

The bearing of a runway is divided by 10 to find the runway number.

Approach	Bearing	Runway
from west to east	90°	9
from north to south	180°	18
from east to west	270°	27
from south to north	360°	36

Think & Discuss

1. Why is it important to use a consistent runway naming scheme?
See below.
2. The bearing of the unlabeled runway in the diagram is 50°. What are the missing runway numbers?
5 and 23

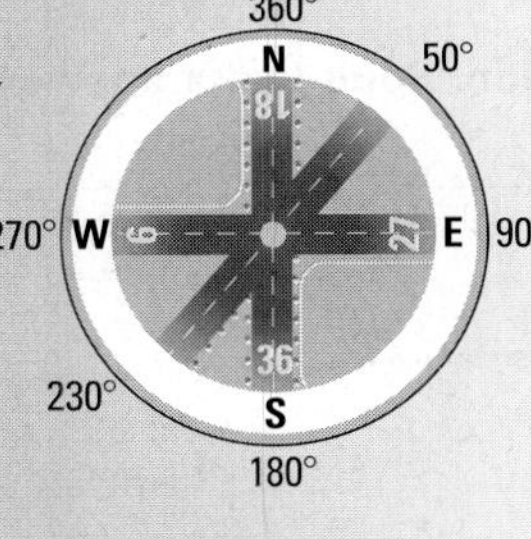

Learn More About It

You will learn more about angles of intersecting runways in Exercises 55–60 on p. 32.

APPLICATION LINK Visit www.mcdougallittell.com for more information about airport runways.

Sample answer: to avoid confusion among pilots and air traffic controllers and, so, to avoid collisions

PROJECTS

A project covering Chapter 1 appears on pages 60–61 of the Student Edition. An additional project for Chapter 1 is available in the *Chapter 1 Resource Book*, pp. 119–120.

TECHNOLOGY

Software

- *Electronic Teaching Tools*
- *Online Lesson Planner*
- *Personal Student Tutor*
- *Test and Practice Generator*
- *Electronic Lesson Presentations (Lesson 1.2)*

Video

- *Geometry in Motion*

Internet Connections
www.mcdougallittell.com

- **Application Links**
1, 25, 41, 49, 56
- **Student Help**
7, 12, 22, 28, 39, 40, 43, 45, 56
- **Career Links**
8, 30
- **Extra Challenge**
9, 16, 24, 32, 41

PREPARE

DIAGNOSTIC TOOLS

The **Skill Review** exercises can help you diagnose whether students have the following skills needed in Chapter 1:

- Subtract integers.
- Add squares of integers.
- Evaluate radical expressions.

The following resources are available for students who need additional help with these skills:

- Prerequisite Skills Review (*Chapter 1 Resource Book,* p. 5; *Warm-Up Transparencies,* p. 1)
- *Personal Student Tutor*

ADDITIONAL RESOURCES

The following resources are provided to help you prepare for the upcoming chapter and customize review materials:

- ***Chapter 1 Resource Book***
  Tips for New Teachers (p. 1)
  Parent Guide (p. 3)
  Lesson Plans (every lesson)
  Lesson Plans for Block Scheduling (every lesson)
- ***Electronic Teaching Tools***
- ***Online Lesson Planner***
- ***Test and Practice Generator***

ENGLISH LEARNERS

You may want to have English learners begin keeping a geometry glossary to describe in their own words the many terms, properties, and rules they will encounter in this course. Encourage them to use the glossary as a reference guide, consulting it as necessary to recall the meanings of terms previously introduced.

CHAPTER 1

Study Guide

PREVIEW

What's the chapter about?

Chapter 1 is about the **basic elements of geometry**. In Chapter 1, you'll learn

- how to measure segments and angles.
- how to divide a segment or angle into two equal parts.
- relationships among special pairs of angles.

KEY VOCABULARY

▶ **New**

- **conjecture, p. 4**
- **point, line, plane, p. 10**
- **segment, ray, p. 11**
- **postulate, p. 17**
- **length of a segment, p. 17**
- **congruent segments, p. 19**
- **congruent angles, p. 26**
- **measure of an angle, p. 27**
- **acute angle, p. 28**
- **right angle, p. 28**
- **obtuse angle, p. 28**
- **straight angle, p. 28**
- **segment bisector, p. 34**
- **angle bisector, p. 36**
- **vertical angles, p. 44**
- **complementary angles, p. 46**
- **supplementary angles, p. 46**

PREPARE

Are you ready for the chapter?

SKILL REVIEW Do these exercises to review key skills that you'll apply in this chapter. See the given **reference page** if there is something you don't understand.

Subtract the integers. **(Skills Review, p. 785)**

1. $17 - 9$ 8 **2.** $9 - 17$ −8 **3.** $5 - (-3)$ 8 **4.** $3 - (-5)$ 8

5. $-7 - 2$ −9 **6.** $-7 - (-2)$ −5 **7.** $-6 - (-5)$ −1 **8.** $-5 - (-6)$ 1

Evaluate the sum. **(Skills Review, p. 786)**

9. $2^2 + 4^2$ 20 **10.** $5^2 + (-2)^2$ 29 **11.** $(-1)^2 + 1^2$ 2 **12.** $(-5)^2 + 0^2$ 25

Evaluate the radical expression. Round your answer to two decimal places. **(Skills Review, p. 799)**

13. $\sqrt{36 + 4}$ 6.32 **14.** $\sqrt{1 + 49}$ 7.07 **15.** $\sqrt{225 + 100}$ 18.03 **16.** $\sqrt{9 + 9}$ 4.24

STUDENT HELP

Study Tip
"Student Help" boxes throughout the chapter give you study tips and tell you where to look for extra help in this book and on the Internet.

STUDY STRATEGY

Here's a study strategy!

Learning Vocabulary

Important words in this book are in bold type and are highlighted in yellow.

- Keep a section in your notebook for writing down definitions of new words.
- Draw and label sketches near your definitions, if this helps you.
- Use your vocabulary pages to review for quizzes and tests.

Patterns and Inductive Reasoning

What you should learn

GOAL 1 Find and describe patterns.

GOAL 2 Use inductive reasoning to make **real-life** conjectures, as in **Ex. 42**.

Why you should learn it

▼ To make predictions based on observations, such as predicting full moons in **Example 6**.

CALIFORNIA STANDARDS AND ASSESSMENT

CA Standards: 1, 3
SAT9 Task 1: Obj. 1
SAT9 Task 2: Obj. 1

GOAL 1 FINDING AND DESCRIBING PATTERNS

Geometry, like much of mathematics and science, developed when people began recognizing and describing patterns. In this course, you will study many amazing patterns that were discovered by people throughout history and all around the world. You will also learn to recognize and describe patterns of your own. Sometimes, patterns allow you to make accurate predictions.

EXAMPLE 1 *Describing a Visual Pattern*

Sketch the next figure in the pattern.

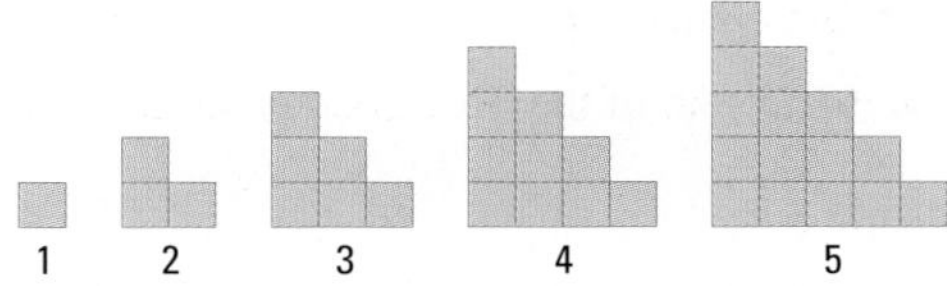

SOLUTION

Each figure in the pattern looks like the previous figure with another row of squares added to the bottom. Each figure looks like a stairway.

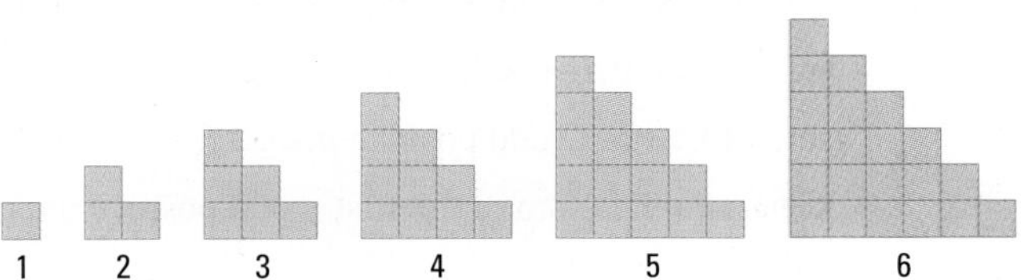

▶ The sixth figure in the pattern has six squares in the bottom row.

EXAMPLE 2 *Describing a Number Pattern*

Describe a pattern in the sequence of numbers. Predict the next number.

a. 1, 4, 16, 64, . . .   **b.** $-5, -2, 4, 13, \ldots$

SOLUTION

a. Each number is four times the previous number. The next number is 256.

b. You add 3 to get the second number, then add 6 to get the third number, then add 9 to get the fourth number. To find the fifth number, add the next multiple of 3, which is 12.

▶ So, the next number is 13 + 12, or 25.

1 PLAN

PACING

Basic: 1 day
Average: 1 day
Advanced: 1 day
Block Schedule: 0.5 block with 1.2

LESSON OPENER
CALCULATOR

An alternative way to approach Lesson 1.1 is to use the Calculator Lesson Opener:

- Blackline Master (*Chapter 1 Resource Book*, p. 12)
- Transparency (p. 1)

MEETING INDIVIDUAL NEEDS

- ***Chapter 1 Resource Book***
  Prerequisite Skills Review (p. 5)
  Practice Level A (p. 14)
  Practice Level B (p. 15)
  Practice Level C (p. 16)
  Reteaching with Practice (p. 17)
  Absent Student Catch-Up (p. 19)
  Challenge (p. 21)
- ***Resources in Spanish***
-  ***Personal Student Tutor***

NEW-TEACHER SUPPORT

See the Tips for New Teachers on pp. 1–2 of the *Chapter 1 Resource Book* for additional notes about Lesson 1.1.

WARM-UP EXERCISES

Transparency Available

Evaluate each expression for the indicated value of x.

1. x^2, for $x = 0.5, 1, -1$ 0.25, 1, 1
2. $(x+1)(x-1)$, for $x = 1, 2, 3$ 0, 3, 8
3. $\frac{(x+1)}{2}$, for $x = 1, 2, 3$ $1, \frac{3}{2}, 2$
4. $\sqrt{x}$, for $x = \frac{1}{4}, 4, 9$ $\frac{1}{2}, 2, 3$

2 TEACH

EXTRA EXAMPLE 1
Sketch the next figure.

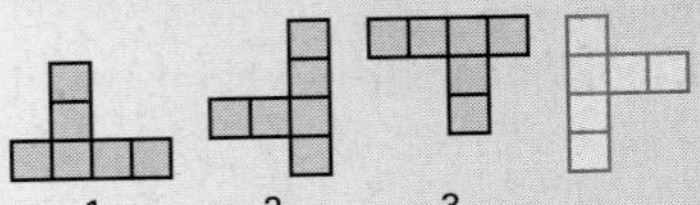

EXTRA EXAMPLE 2
Predict the next number.
a. 17, 15, 12, 8, . . . 3.
b. 48, 16, $\frac{16}{3}$, $\frac{16}{9}$, . . . $\frac{16}{27}$.

EXTRA EXAMPLE 3
Complete: The product of any two consecutive positive integers is ____. $n(n + 1)$

EXTRA EXAMPLE 4
Show the conjecture is false by finding a counterexample: The difference of two positive numbers is always positive.
Sample answer: 3 − 9 = −6

CHECKPOINT EXERCISES
For use after Examples 1–4:
Use the pattern.

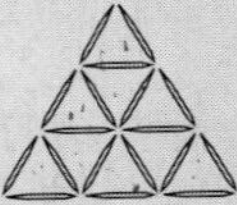

1. Sketch the next figure.

2. Write the first four terms of a sequence of numbers that gives the number of toothpicks used to form each figure. Predict the next number. 3, 9, 18, 30

3. The number of toothpicks needed to make the nth figure is $3 + 3n$. Show that this conjecture is false by finding a counterexample. *Sample answer:* when $n = 1$, you need 3 toothpicks, not 6 toothpicks.

GOAL 2 USING INDUCTIVE REASONING

Much of the reasoning in geometry consists of three stages.

1. **Look for a Pattern** Look at several examples. Use diagrams and tables to help discover a pattern.
2. **Make a Conjecture** Use the examples to make a general *conjecture*. A **conjecture** is an unproven statement that is based on observations. Discuss the conjecture with others. Modify the conjecture, if necessary.
3. **Verify the Conjecture** Use logical reasoning to verify that the conjecture is true in all cases. (You will do this in Chapter 2 and throughout this book.)

Looking for patterns and making conjectures is part of a process called **inductive reasoning**.

EXAMPLE 3 *Making a Conjecture*

Complete the conjecture.

Conjecture: The sum of the first n odd positive integers is __?__.

SOLUTION

List some specific examples and look for a pattern.

Examples:

first odd positive integer:	$1 = 1^2$
sum of first **two** odd positive integers:	$1 + 3 = 4 = 2^2$
sum of first **three** odd positive integers:	$1 + 3 + 5 = 9 = 3^2$
sum of first **four** odd positive integers:	$1 + 3 + 5 + 7 = 16 = 4^2$

Conjecture: The sum of the first n odd positive integers is n^2.

To prove that a conjecture is true, you need to prove it is true in *all* cases. To prove that a conjecture is false, you need to provide a single *counterexample*. A **counterexample** is an example that shows a conjecture is false.

EXAMPLE 4 *Finding a Counterexample*

Show the conjecture is false by finding a counterexample.

Conjecture: For all real numbers x, the expression x^2 is greater than or equal to x.

SOLUTION

The conjecture is false. Here is a counterexample: $(0.5)^2 = 0.25$, and 0.25 is *not* greater than or equal to 0.5. In fact, any number between 0 and 1 is a counterexample.

Not every conjecture is known to be true or false. Conjectures that are not known to be true or false are called *unproven* or *undecided.*

EXAMPLE 5 *Examining an Unproven Conjecture*

In the early 1700s a Prussian mathematician named Goldbach noticed that many even numbers greater than 2 can be written as the sum of two primes.

Specific Cases:

$4 = 2 + 2$	$10 = 3 + 7$	$16 = 3 + 13$
$6 = 3 + 3$	$12 = 5 + 7$	$18 = 5 + 13$
$8 = 3 + 5$	$14 = 3 + 11$	$20 = 3 + 17$

Conjecture: Every even number greater than 2 can be written as the sum of two primes.

This is called *Goldbach's Conjecture.* No one has ever proved that this conjecture is true or found a counterexample to show that it is false. As of the writing of this book, it is unknown whether this conjecture is true or false. It is known, however, that all even numbers up to 4×10^{14} confirm Goldbach's Conjecture.

EXAMPLE 6 *Using Inductive Reasoning in Real Life*

MOON CYCLES A full moon occurs when the moon is on the opposite side of Earth from the sun. During a full moon, the moon appears as a complete circle.

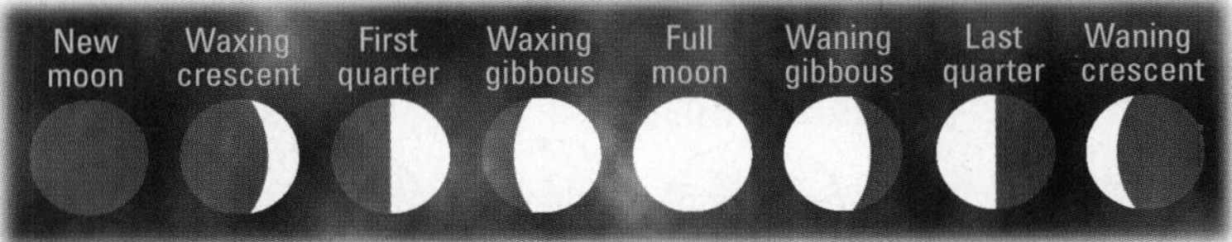

Use inductive reasoning and the information below to make a conjecture about how often a full moon occurs.

Specific Cases: In 2005, the first six full moons occur on January 25, February 24, March 25, April 24, May 23, and June 22.

SOLUTION

Conjecture: A full moon occurs every 29 or 30 days.

This conjecture is true. The moon revolves around Earth once approximately every 29.5 days.

....

Inductive reasoning is important to the study of mathematics: you look for a pattern in specific cases and then you write a conjecture that you think describes the general case. Remember, though, that just because something is true for several specific cases does not *prove* that it is true in general.

FOCUS ON APPLICATIONS

REAL LIFE **CALENDARS** The earliest calendars were based on lunar or seasonal patterns. The ancient Egyptians were the first to introduce a calendar based on the solar year.

EXTRA EXAMPLE 5

Show that Goldbach's conjecture is true for $n = 44$.
Sample answer: $44 = 13 + 31$

EXTRA EXAMPLE 6

An observer notices that during the evening commute, buses arrive at a particular bus stop at the same times each day. Use inductive reasoning and the information below to make a conjecture about how often a bus comes to this stop during rush hour.

Buses stop every day at 5:15 P.M., 5:38 P.M., 6:01 P.M., and 6:24 P.M. **A bus comes to the stop every 23 minutes during the evening commute.**

CHECKPOINT EXERCISES

For use after Example 5:

1. Show that Goldbach's conjecture is true for $n = 42$.
Sample answer: $42 = 19 + 23$

For use after Example 6:

2. Four adults attended a movie for $28. Three adults attended the same movie for $21 and 6 adults attended the movie for $42. Use inductive reasoning to make a conjecture about the price of each adult movie ticket.
Each adult ticket costs $7.

FOCUS ON VOCABULARY

What is a counterexample?
A counterexample is an example that shows that a conjecture is false.

CLOSURE QUESTION

Describe the process of inductive reasoning. **Several examples are examined to find a pattern.**

DAILY PUZZLER

To get the next number in a sequence, you multiply the previous number by 2 and subtract 1. If the fourth number is 17, what is the first number in the sequence? **3**

3 APPLY

Assignment Guide

Basic
Day 1: pp. 6–9 Exs. 12–26 even, 27, 28–46 even, 47, 48, 52–70 even

Average
Day 1: pp. 6–9 Exs. 12–26 even, 27, 28–46 even, 47, 48, 52–70 even

Advanced
Day 1: pp. 6–9 Exs. 12–26 even, 27, 28–46 even, 47–51, 52–70 even

Block Schedule with 1.2
pp. 6–9 Exs. 12–26 even, 27, 28–46 even, 47, 48, 52–70 even

Exercise Levels

Level A: ***Easier***
12–21, 23, 29–31

Level B: ***More Difficult***
22, 24–28, 32–40, 42–48

Level C: ***Most Difficult***
41, 49–51

✓ Homework Check

To quickly check student understanding of key concepts, go over the following exercises: Exs. 14, 18, 28, 38, 42, 46. See also the Daily Homework Quiz:

- Blackline Master (*Chapter 1 Resource Book,* p. 24)
- Transparency (p. 3)

3, 4, 12–15. See Additional Answers beginning on page AA1.

Guided Practice

Vocabulary Check ✓
Concept Check ✓
Skill Check ✓

1. Explain what a *conjecture* is. an unproven statement that is based on observation

2. How can you prove that a conjecture is false? by providing a counterexample

Sketch the next figure in the pattern. 3, 4. See margin.

3.

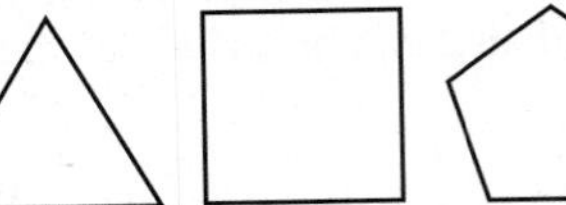

4.

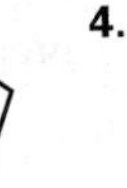

Describe a pattern in the sequence of numbers. Predict the next number. 5–10. See margin.

5. 2, 6, 18, 54, . . .

6. 0, 1, 4, 9, . . .

7. 256, 64, 16, 4, . . .

8. 3, 0, −3, 0, 3, 0, . . .

9. 7.0, 7.5, 8.0, 8.5, . . .

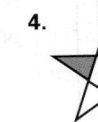

10. 13, 7, 1, −5, . . .

5. Each number is 3 times the previous number; 162.
6. Numbers are consecutive perfect squares; 16.
7. Each number is $\frac{1}{4}$ the previous number; 1.
8. The odd-numbered terms in the sequence alternate between 3 and −3, while each even-numbered term is 0; −3.
9. Each number is 0.5 greater than the previous number; 9.0.
10. Each number is 6 less than the previous number; −11.

11. Complete the conjecture based on the pattern you observe.

$3 + 4 + 5 = 4 \cdot 3$ $\quad$ $6 + 7 + 8 = 7 \cdot 3$ $\quad$ $9 + 10 + 11 = 10 \cdot 3$

$4 + 5 + 6 = 5 \cdot 3$ $\quad$ $7 + 8 + 9 = 8 \cdot 3$ $\quad$ $10 + 11 + 12 = 11 \cdot 3$

$5 + 6 + 7 = 6 \cdot 3$ $\quad$ $8 + 9 + 10 = 9 \cdot 3$ $\quad$ $11 + 12 + 13 = 12 \cdot 3$

Conjecture: The sum of any three consecutive integers is ___?___. 3 times the middle integer

Practice and Applications

Student Help
Extra Practice to help you master skills is on p. 803.

Sketching Visual Patterns **Sketch the next figure in the pattern.** 12–15. See margin.

12.

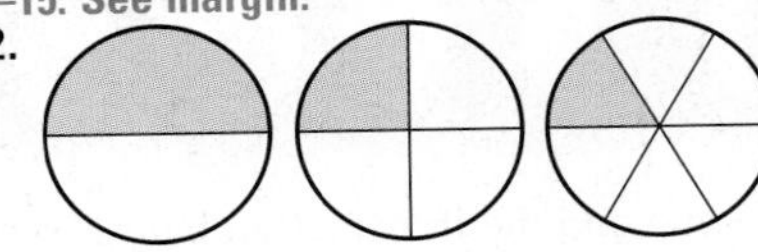

13.

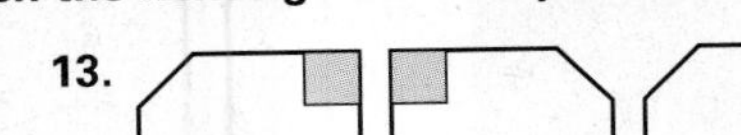

14.

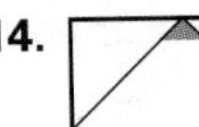
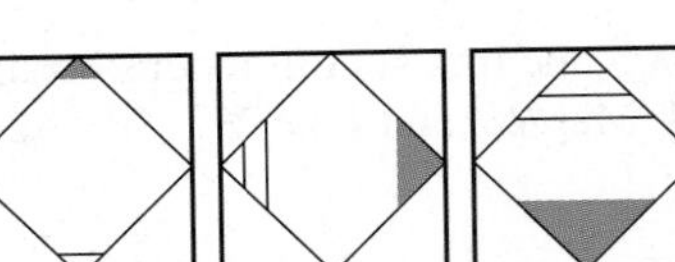

15.

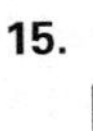
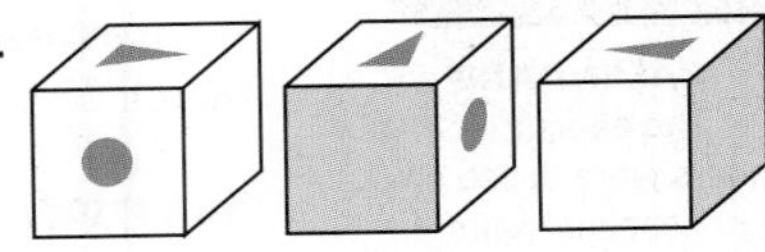

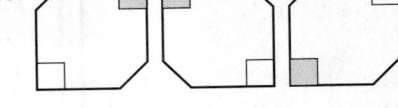

Student Help
Homework Help
Example 1: Exs. 12–15, 24, 25
Example 2: Exs. 16–23, 26–28
Example 3: Exs. 29–33
Example 4: Exs. 34–39
Example 5: Exs. 40, 41
Example 6: Exs. 42, 43

Describing Number Patterns **Describe a pattern in the sequence of numbers. Predict the next number.** 16–23. See margin.

16. 1, 4, 7, 10, . . .

17. 10, 5, 2.5, 1.25, . . .

18. 1, 11, 121, 1331, . . .

19. 5, 0, −5, −10, . . .

20. 7, 9, 13, 19, 27, . . .

21. 1, 3, 6, 10, 15, . . .

22. 256, 16, 4, 2, . . .

23. 1.1, 1.01, 1.001, 1.0001, . . .

VISUALIZING PATTERNS **The first three objects in a pattern are shown. How many blocks are in the next object?**

24. 16 blocks

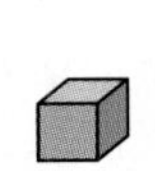
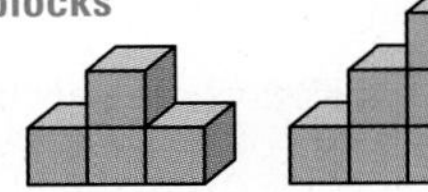

25. 28 blocks

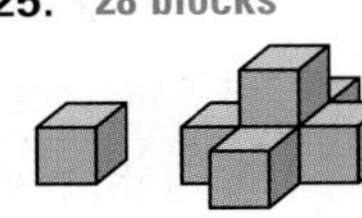
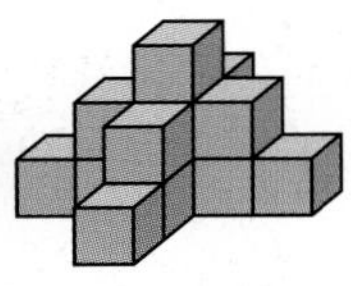

MAKING PREDICTIONS **In Exercises 26–28, use the pattern from Example 1 shown below. Each square is 1 unit × 1 unit.** 26–28. See margin.

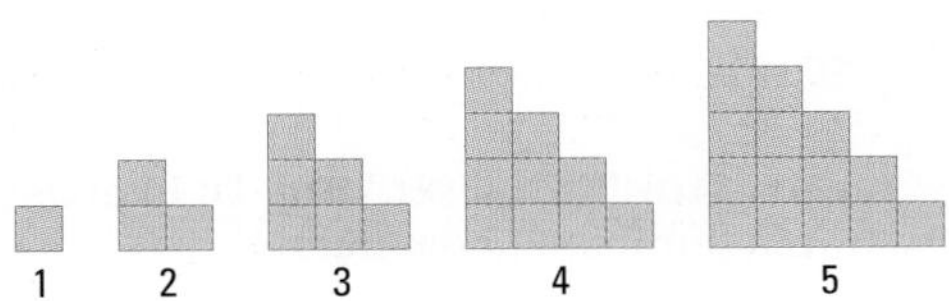

1 2 3 4 5

26. Find the distance around each figure. Organize your results in a table. See margin.

27. Use your table to describe a pattern in the distances.
The distance is 4 times the figure number.

28. Predict the distance around the twentieth figure in this pattern.
80 units

MAKING CONJECTURES **Complete the conjecture based on the pattern you observe in the specific cases.**

29. Conjecture: The sum of any two odd numbers is ___?___. even

$1 + 1 = 2$	$7 + 11 = 18$
$1 + 3 = 4$	$13 + 19 = 32$
$3 + 5 = 8$	$201 + 305 = 506$

30. Conjecture: The product of any two odd numbers is ___?___. odd

$1 \times 1 = 1$	$7 \times 11 = 77$
$1 \times 3 = 3$	$13 \times 19 = 247$
$3 \times 5 = 15$	$201 \times 305 = 61{,}305$

31. Conjecture: The product of a number $(n - 1)$ and the number $(n + 1)$ is always equal to ___?___. $n^2 - 1$

$3 \cdot 5 = 4^2 - 1$	$6 \cdot 8 = 7^2 - 1$
$4 \cdot 6 = 5^2 - 1$	$7 \cdot 9 = 8^2 - 1$
$5 \cdot 7 = 6^2 - 1$	$8 \cdot 10 = 9^2 - 1$

CALCULATOR **Use a calculator to explore the pattern. Write a conjecture based on what you observe.** 32, 33. See margin.

32. $101 \times 34 =$ ___?___
$101 \times 25 =$ ___?___
$101 \times 97 =$ ___?___
$101 \times 49 =$ ___?___

33. $11 \times 11 =$ ___?___
$111 \times 111 =$ ___?___
$1111 \times 1111 =$ ___?___
$11{,}111 \times 11{,}111 =$ ___?___

STUDENT HELP

INTERNET HOMEWORK HELP
Visit our Web site www.mcdougallittell.com for help with Exs. 29–31.

32. 3434; 2525; 9797; 4949; the product of 101 and a two-digit number is the four-digit number formed by writing the two digits in order twice.

33. 121; 12,321; 1,234,321; 123,454,321; the square of the n-digit number consisting of all 1's is the number obtained by writing the digits from 1 to n in increasing order, then the digits from $n - 1$ to 1 in decreasing order. This pattern does not continue forever.

! COMMON ERROR

EXERCISES 5–10 AND 16–23
Students may assume that an increasing sequence has a pattern involving adding a constant amount to the previous number. Point out that the sequence may be based on multiplication rather than addition, or if addition is used, the increase may not be constant. Students should make a conjecture about the pattern and then test it with all the numbers in the sequence.

STUDENT HELP NOTES

Homework Help Students can find help for Exs. 29–31 at **www.mcdougallittell.com.** The information can be printed out for students who don't have access to the Internet.

GRAPHING CALCULATOR NOTE

EXERCISES 32 AND 33
A graphing calculator is used to help students focus on the pattern rather than the computation in these exercises. A standard calculator or pencil and paper calculations could be used if necessary.

16. Each number is 3 more than the previous number; 13.
17. Each number is half the previous number; 0.625
18. Each number is 11 times the previous number; 14,641.
19. Each number is 5 less than the previous number; –15.
20. Numbers after the first are found by adding consecutive multiples of 2; 37.
21. Numbers after the first are found by adding consecutive whole numbers; 21.
22. Each number is the square root of the previous number; $\sqrt{2}$.
23. Numbers after the first are found by adding a zero after the decimal point of the previous number; 1.00001.

26.

Figure number	1	2	3	4	5
Distance (units)	4	8	12	16	20

MATHEMATICAL REASONING

EXERCISE 40 After students complete this exercise, remind them that although they know that Goldbach's conjecture is true for even numbers from 20 to 40, they do not know that the conjecture itself is true. Point out that it would be impossible to prove the conjecture true for every single case. Instead, conjectures such as these must be proven by using logical reasoning with a general case.

CAREER NOTE

EXERCISE 43 Additional information about laboratory technologists is available at **www.mcdougallittell.com.**

43.
```
 F F F F F
 | | | | |
F-C-C-C-C-C-F
 | | | | |
 F F F F F
```
C_5F_{12}

```
 F F F F F F
 | | | | | |
F-C-C-C-C-C-C-F
 | | | | | |
 F F F F F F
```
C_6F_{14}

44. The y-coordinate is half the opposite of the x-coordinate; $-1\frac{1}{2}$.

45. The y-coordinate is $\frac{1}{2}$ more than the opposite of the x-coordinate; $-2\frac{1}{2}$.

46. The y-coordinate is 1 less than half the x-coordinate; $\frac{1}{2}$.

ADDITIONAL PRACTICE AND RETEACHING

For Lesson 1.1:

- Practice Levels A, B, and C (*Chapter 1 Resource Book,* p. 14)
- Reteaching with Practice (*Chapter 1 Resource Book,* p. 17)
- See Lesson 1.1 of the *Personal Student Tutor*

For more Mixed Review:

- Search the *Test and Practice Generator* for key words or specific lessons.

35–39. *Sample answers are given.*

35. $2 + (-5) = -3$, which is not greater than 2.

36. $2 \cdot 17 = 34$ but 17 is not even.

37. $(-4)(-5) = 20$

38. $\sqrt{\frac{1}{4}} = \frac{1}{2}$ and $\frac{1}{2} > \frac{1}{4}$.

39. Let $m = -1$; $\left(\frac{-1+1}{-1}\right) = 0$.

40. *Sample answers:* $20 = 3 + 17$; $22 = 5 + 17$; $24 = 5 + 19$; $26 = 7 + 19$; $28 = 11 + 17$; $30 = 13 + 17$; $32 = 13 + 19$; $34 = 17 + 17$; $36 = 17 + 19$; $38 = 19 + 19$; $40 = 17 + 23$

41. *Sample answer*: 3

FOCUS ON CAREERS

LABORATORY TECHNOLOGIST

Laboratory technologists study microscopic cells, such as bacteria. The time it takes for a population of bacteria to double (the *doubling period*) may be as short as 20 min.

CAREER LINK
www.mcdougallittell.com

FINDING COUNTEREXAMPLES **Show the conjecture is false by finding a counterexample.**

34. All prime numbers are odd. 2 is prime, but it is not odd.

35. The sum of two numbers is always greater than the larger number.

36. If the product of two numbers is even, then the two numbers must be even.

37. If the product of two numbers is positive, then the two numbers must both be positive.

38. The square root of a number x is always less than x.

39. If m is a nonzero integer, then $\frac{m+1}{m}$ is always greater than 1.

GOLDBACH'S CONJECTURE **In Exercises 40 and 41, use the list of the first prime numbers given below.**

$$\{2, 3, 5, 7, 11, 13, 17, 19, 23, 29, 31, 37, \ldots\}$$

40. Show that Goldbach's Conjecture (see page 5) is true for the even numbers from 20 to 40 by writing each even number as a sum of two primes.

41. Show that the following conjecture is not true by finding a counterexample.

Conjecture: All *odd* numbers can be expressed as the sum of two primes.

42. **BACTERIA GROWTH** Suppose you are studying bacteria in biology class. The table shows the number of bacteria after n doubling periods. 768 billion bacteria

n (periods)	0	1	2	3	4	5
Billions of bacteria	3	6	12	24	48	96

Your teacher asks you to predict the number of bacteria after 8 doubling periods. What would your prediction be?

43. SCIENCE CONNECTION Diagrams and formulas for four molecular compounds are shown. Draw a diagram and write the formula for the next two compounds in the pattern. See margin.

```
  F        F F         F F F         F F F F
  |        | |         | | |         | | | |
F-C-F    F-C-C-F     F-C-C-C-F     F-C-C-C-C-F
  |        | |         | | |         | | | |
  F        F F         F F F         F F F F
```
CF_4 C_2F_6 C_3F_8 C_4F_{10}

USING ALGEBRA **Find a pattern in the coordinates of the points. Then use the pattern to find the y-coordinate of the point (3, ?).** 44–46. See margin.

44.

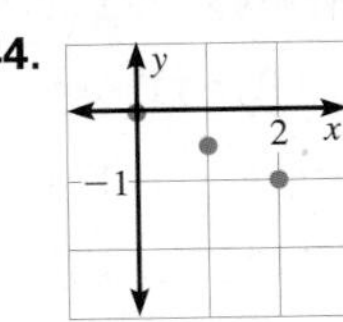

45.

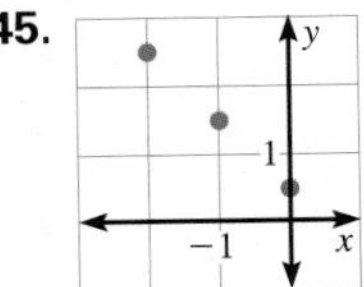

46.

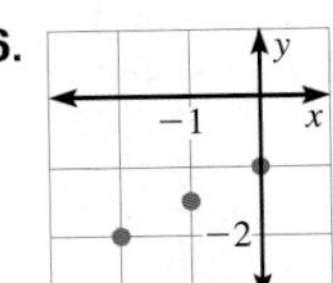

Test Preparation

47. MULTIPLE CHOICE Which number is next in the sequence? E

45, 90, 135, 180, . . .

(A) 205 (B) 210 (C) 215 (D) 220 (E) 225

48. MULTIPLE CHOICE What is the next figure in the pattern? D

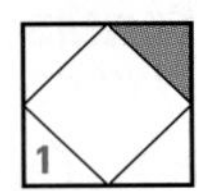

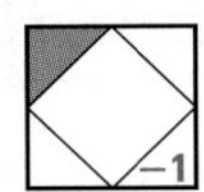

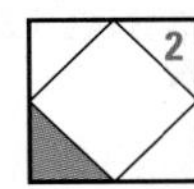

(A) 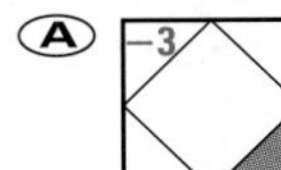

(B) 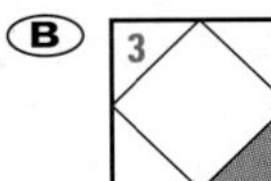

(C) 

(D) 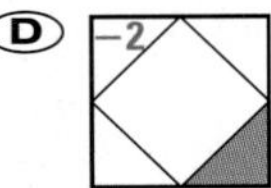

(E) 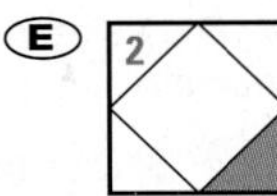

★ Challenge

DIVIDING A CIRCLE In Exercises 49–51, use the information about regions in a circle formed by connecting points on the circle.

If you draw points on a circle and then connect every pair of points, the circle is divided into a number of regions, as shown.

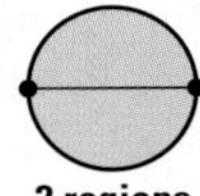
2 regions

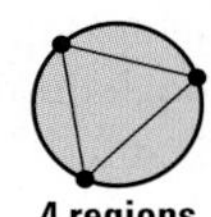
4 regions

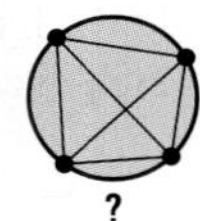
?

49. Copy and complete the table for the case of 4 and 5 points. 8; 16

Number of points on circle	2	3	4	5	6
Maximum number of regions	2	4	?	?	?

50. Make a conjecture about the relationship between the number of points on the circle and number of regions in the circle. See margin.

51. Test your conjecture for the case of 6 points. What do you notice? See margin.

50. *Sample answer:* Since the number of regions doubles each time, the number of regions for 6 points is 32. (This sample conjecture is not true.)

51. The actual maximum number of regions is 31. The conjecture suggested by the cases of 2, 3, 4, and 5 points is not true.

EXTRA CHALLENGE
www.mcdougallittell.com

MIXED REVIEW

PLOTTING POINTS Plot in a coordinate plane. (Skills Review, p. 792, for 1.2)
52–59. See margin.

52. (5, 2) **53.** (3, −8) **54.** (−4, −6) **55.** (1, −10)

56. (−2, 7) **57.** (−3, 8) **58.** (4, −1) **59.** (−2, −6)

EVALUATING EXPRESSIONS Evaluate the expression. (Skills Review, p. 786)

60. 3^2 9 **61.** 5^2 25 **62.** $(-4)^2$ 16 **63.** -7^2 −49

64. $3^2 + 4^2$ 25 **65.** $5^2 + 12^2$ 169 **66.** $(-2)^2 + 2^2$ 8 **67.** $(-10)^2 + (-5)^2$ 125

FINDING A PATTERN Write the next number in the sequence. (Review 1.1)

68. 1, 5, 25, 125, . . . 625 **69.** 4.4, 40.4, 400.4, 4000.4, . . . 40,000.4

70. 3, 7, 11, 15, . . . 19 **71.** −1, +1, −2, +2, −3, . . . +3

4 ASSESS

DAILY HOMEWORK QUIZ

Transparency Available

Describe a pattern in the sequence of numbers. Predict the next number.

1. 11, 23, 47, 95, . . . double each number and add 1; 191

2. 3, −11, −53, −179, . . . triple each number and subtract 20; −557

Show the conjecture is false by finding a counterexample.

3. No two prime numbers are consecutive. 2 and 3 are both prime and are consecutive.

4. Division by an integer is always defined. Zero is an integer but division by zero is not defined.

EXTRA CHALLENGE NOTE

Challenge problems for Lesson 1.1 are available in **blackline** format in the *Chapter 1 Resource Book,* p. 21 and at **www.mcdougallittell.com.**

ADDITIONAL TEST PREPARATION

1. WRITING Use inductive reasoning to complete the following conjecture. The product of an odd number and an even number is ________. Explain your work. even; Check explanations.

2. OPEN ENDED Think of a visual pattern. Draw the first three figures in the pattern and describe how to find the next figure. Check work.

52–59.

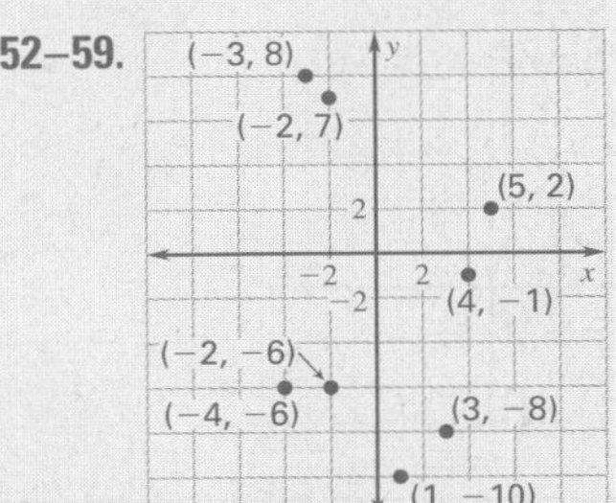

1 PLAN

PACING
Basic: 1 day
Average: 1 day
Advanced: 1 day
Block Schedule: 0.5 block with 1.1

LESSON OPENER
VISUAL APPROACH
An alternative way to approach Lesson 1.2 is to use the Visual Approach Lesson Opener:

- Blackline Master (*Chapter 1 Resource Book*, p. 25)
- Transparency (p. 2)

MEETING INDIVIDUAL NEEDS

- ***Chapter 1 Resource Book***
  Prerequisite Skills Review (p. 5)
  Practice Level A (p. 26)
  Practice Level B (p. 27)
  Practice Level C (p. 28)
  Reteaching with Practice (p. 29)
  Absent Student Catch-Up (p. 31)
  Challenge (p. 33)
- ***Resources in Spanish***
-  ***Personal Student Tutor***

NEW-TEACHER SUPPORT
See the Tips for New Teachers on pp. 1–2 of the *Chapter 1 Resource Book* for additional notes about Lesson 1.2.

WARM-UP EXERCISES

Transparency Available

Give the coordinates of each point graphed below.

1. Point A (−2, 1)
2. Point B (4, 0)
3. Point C (3, −2)
4. Point D (−1, −3)

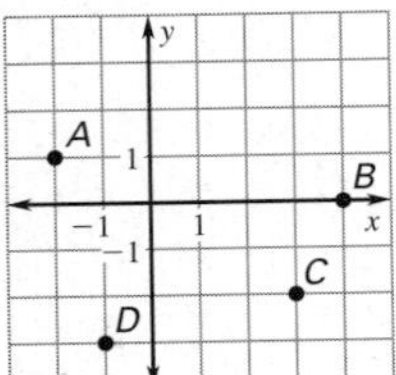

1.2 Points, Lines, and Planes

What you should learn

GOAL 1 Understand and use the basic undefined terms and defined terms of geometry.

GOAL 2 Sketch the intersections of lines and planes.

Why you should learn it

▼ To name and draw the basic elements of geometry, including lines that intersect, as in the perspective drawing in **Exs. 68–72**. REAL LIFE

GOAL 1 USING UNDEFINED TERMS AND DEFINITIONS

A **definition** uses known words to describe a new word. In geometry, some words, such as *point*, *line*, and *plane*, are **undefined terms**. Although these words are not formally defined, it is important to have general agreement about what each word means.

A **point** has no dimension. It is usually represented by a small dot.

A **line** extends in one dimension. It is usually represented by a straight line with two arrowheads to indicate that the line extends without end in two directions. In this book, lines are always straight lines.

A **plane** extends in two dimensions. It is usually represented by a shape that looks like a tabletop or wall. You must imagine that the plane extends without end, even though the drawing of a plane appears to have edges.

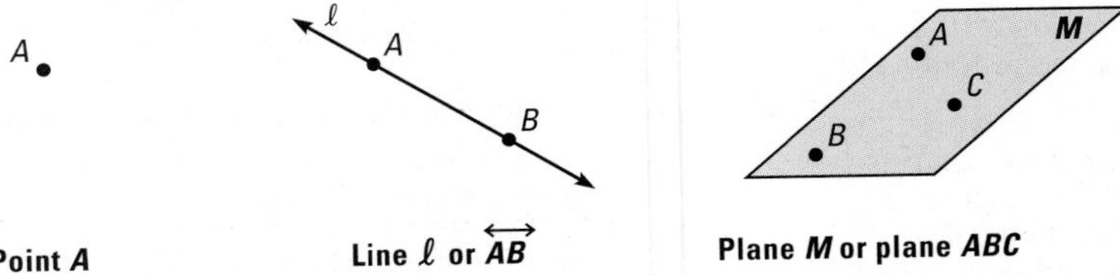

Point A **Line ℓ or $\overleftrightarrow{AB}$** **Plane M or plane ABC**

A few basic concepts in geometry must also be commonly understood without being defined. One such concept is the idea that a point *lies on* a line or a plane.

Collinear points are points that lie on the same line.

Coplanar points are points that lie on the same plane.

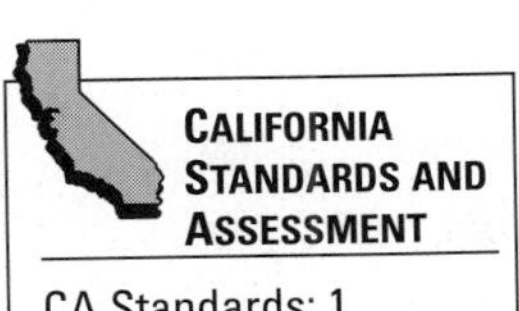

CALIFORNIA STANDARDS AND ASSESSMENT
CA Standards: 1

EXAMPLE 1 *Naming Collinear and Coplanar Points*

a. Name three points that are collinear.

b. Name four points that are coplanar.

c. Name three points that are not collinear.

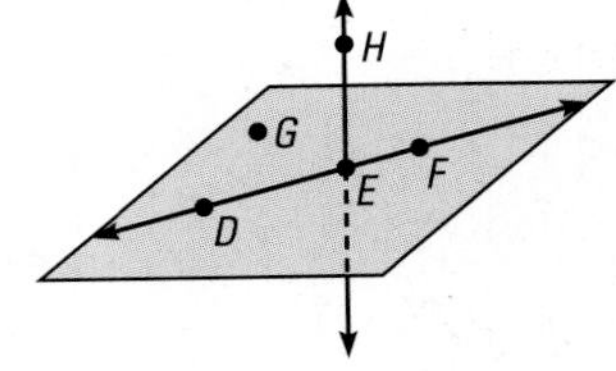

SOLUTION

a. Points D, E, and F lie on the same line, so they are collinear.

b. Points D, E, F, and G lie on the same plane, so they are coplanar. Also, D, E, F, and H are coplanar, although the plane containing them is not drawn.

c. There are many correct answers. For instance, points H, E, and G do not lie on the same line.

Another undefined concept in geometry is the idea that a point on a line *is between* two other points on the line. You can use this idea to define other important terms in geometry.

Consider the **line** AB (symbolized by $\overleftrightarrow{AB}$). The **line segment** or **segment** AB (symbolized by $\overline{AB}$) consists of the **endpoints** A and B, and all points on $\overleftrightarrow{AB}$ that are between A and B.

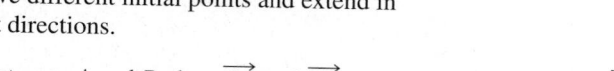

line
A B

segment
A B

The **ray** AB (symbolized by $\overrightarrow{AB}$) consists of the **initial point** A and all points on $\overleftrightarrow{AB}$ that lie on the same side of A as point B.

ray
A B

Note that $\overleftrightarrow{AB}$ is the same as $\overleftrightarrow{BA}$, and $\overline{AB}$ is the same as $\overline{BA}$. However, $\overrightarrow{AB}$ and $\overrightarrow{BA}$ are *not* the same. They have different initial points and extend in different directions.

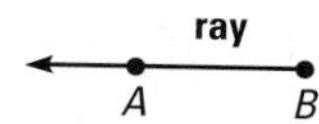

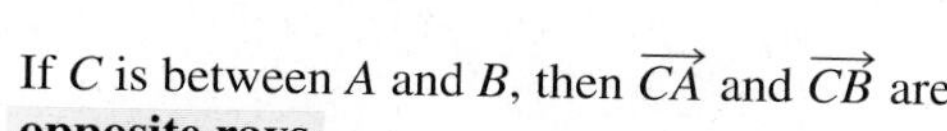

If C is between A and B, then $\overrightarrow{CA}$ and $\overrightarrow{CB}$ are **opposite rays**.

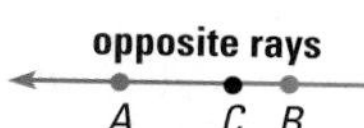

Like points, segments and rays are collinear if they lie on the same line. So, any two opposite rays are collinear. Segments, rays, and lines are coplanar if they lie on the same plane.

EXAMPLE 2 Drawing Lines, Segments, and Rays

Draw three noncollinear points, J, K, and L. Then draw $\overleftrightarrow{JK}$, $\overline{KL}$ and $\overline{LJ}$.

SOLUTION

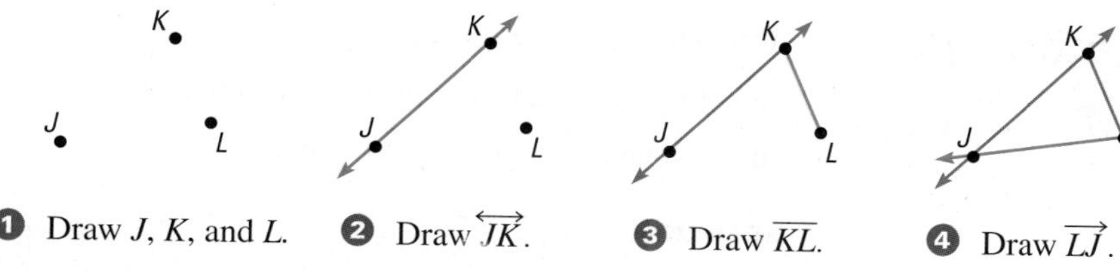

❶ Draw J, K, and L. ❷ Draw $\overleftrightarrow{JK}$. ❸ Draw $\overline{KL}$. ❹ Draw $\overline{LJ}$.

EXAMPLE 3 Drawing Opposite Rays

Draw two lines. Label points on the lines and name two pairs of opposite rays.

SOLUTION

M Q X P N

Points M, N, and X are collinear and X is between M and N. So, $\overrightarrow{XM}$ and $\overrightarrow{XN}$ are opposite rays.

Points P, Q, and X are collinear and X is between P and Q. So, $\overrightarrow{XP}$ and $\overrightarrow{XQ}$ are opposite rays.

2 TEACH

MOTIVATING THE LESSON

Ask students to imagine that they are teaching someone to use a computer. What special vocabulary words would you want this person to learn? Why would it be important for them to understand the meaning of these words? Explain that geometry also has some special vocabulary words. Understanding the meaning of these terms is a goal of this lesson.

EXTRA EXAMPLE 1

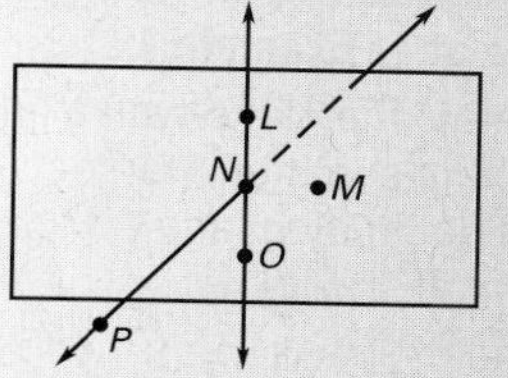

a. Name four points that are coplanar. *L, M, N, and O*

b. Name four points that are not coplanar. *Sample answer: L, M, N, and P*

c. Name three points that are collinear. *L, N, and O*

EXTRA EXAMPLE 2

Draw three collinear points A, B, and C. Draw point D which is not collinear with A, B, and C. Draw $\overleftrightarrow{AB}$ and $\overrightarrow{BD}$.

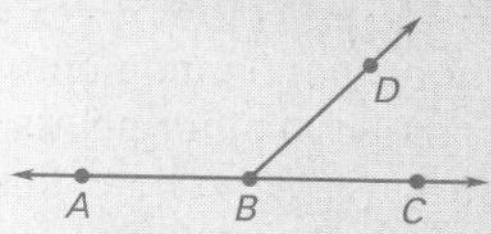

EXTRA EXAMPLE 3

Name two pairs of opposite rays in the figure.

Sample answer: $\overrightarrow{GF}$ *and* $\overrightarrow{GH}$

CHECKPOINT EXERCISES

For use after Examples 1–3:

1. Draw and label four points so that three of them are collinear but all four of them are not collinear. Draw and name one segment and a pair of opposite rays. *Check work.*

EXTRA EXAMPLE 4

Sketch the figure described.

a. a line and a plane that do not intersect *Sample answer:*

b. two planes that do not intersect and a line that intersects each plane in one point

Sample answer:

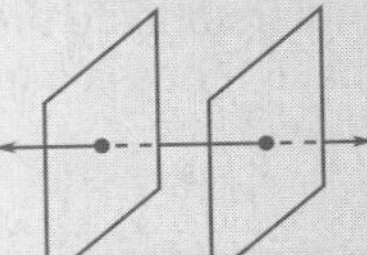

CHECKPOINT EXERCISES

For use after Example 4:

1. Sketch one plane with a line in the plane that intersects a line not in the plane.

Sample answer:

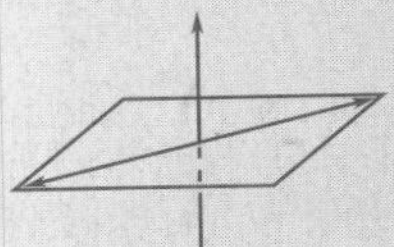

FOCUS ON VOCABULARY

Give the three undefined terms from geometry and a brief description of each. **A point has no dimension. A line extends in one dimension. A plane extends in two dimensions.**

CLOSURE QUESTION

One pair of rays connecting one point to each of two other points are opposite rays. What does this tell you about the points? **They are collinear.**

DAILY PUZZLER

Draw three different planes that intersect in one point.

Sample answer:

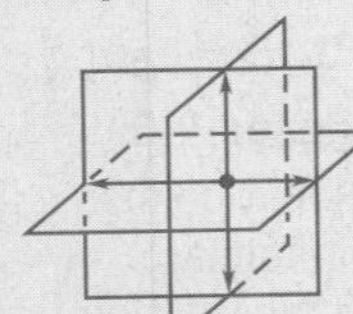

GOAL 2 SKETCHING INTERSECTIONS OF LINES AND PLANES

Two or more geometric figures **intersect** if they have one or more points in common. The **intersection** of the figures is the set of points the figures have in common.

ACTIVITY Developing Concepts

Modeling Intersections

Use two index cards. Label them as shown and cut slots halfway along each card.

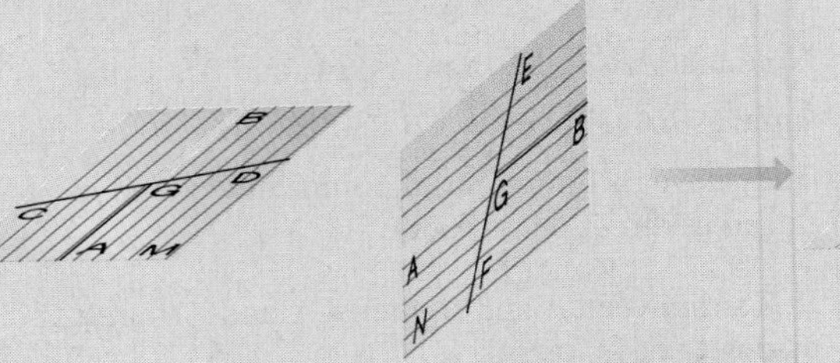

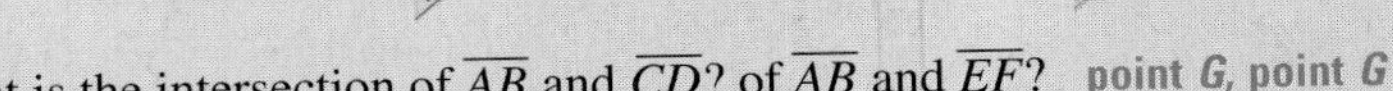

1. What is the intersection of $\overline{AB}$ and $\overline{CD}$? of $\overline{AB}$ and $\overline{EF}$? **point *G*, point *G***

2. Slide the cards together. What is the intersection of $\overline{CD}$ and $\overline{EF}$? **point *G***

3. What is the intersection of planes M and N? $\overleftrightarrow{AB}$

4. Are $\overleftrightarrow{CD}$ and $\overleftrightarrow{EF}$ coplanar? Explain.
Yes; *Sample answer:* They are in plane *CEG*.

STUDENT HELP

HOMEWORK HELP Visit our Web site www.mcdougallittell.com for extra examples.

EXAMPLE 4 *Sketching Intersections*

Sketch the figure described.

a. a line that intersects a plane in one point

b. two planes that intersect in a line

SOLUTION

a.

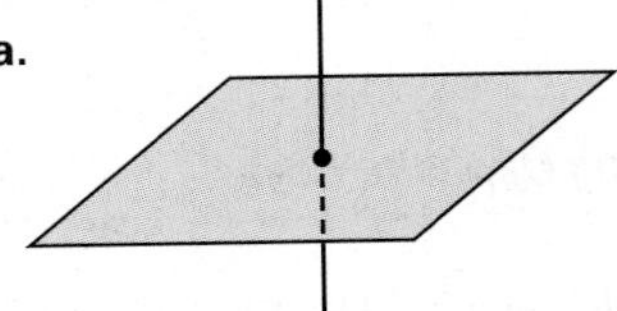

Draw a plane and a line.

Emphasize the point where they meet.

Dashes indicate where the line is hidden by the plane.

b.

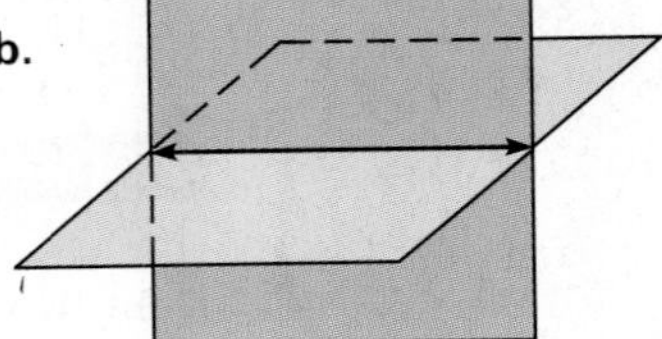

Draw two planes.

Emphasize the line where they meet.

Dashes indicate where one plane is hidden by the other plane.

GUIDED PRACTICE

Vocabulary Check ✓

Concept Check ✓

1. Describe what each of these symbols means: $\overline{PQ}$, $\overrightarrow{PQ}$, $\overleftrightarrow{PQ}$, $\overrightarrow{QP}$. See margin.

2. Sketch a line that contains point R between points S and T. Which of the following are true?

A. $\overrightarrow{SR}$ is the same as $\overrightarrow{ST}$.

B. $\overleftrightarrow{SR}$ is the same as $\overleftrightarrow{RT}$.

C. $\overrightarrow{RS}$ is the same as $\overrightarrow{TS}$.

D. $\overrightarrow{RS}$ and $\overrightarrow{RT}$ are opposite rays.

E. $\overline{ST}$ is the same as $\overline{TS}$.

F. $\overrightarrow{ST}$ is the same as $\overrightarrow{TS}$.

1. line segment PQ, ray PQ, line PQ, ray QP.

2. A, B, D, and E are true.

Skill Check ✓

Decide whether the statement is *true* or *false*.

3. Points A, B, and C are collinear. false
4. Points A, B, and C are coplanar. true
5. Point F lies on $\overleftrightarrow{DE}$. false
6. $\overleftrightarrow{DE}$ lies on plane DEF. true
7. $\overleftrightarrow{BD}$ and $\overleftrightarrow{DE}$ intersect. true
8. $\overleftrightarrow{BD}$ is the intersection of plane ABC and plane DEF. false

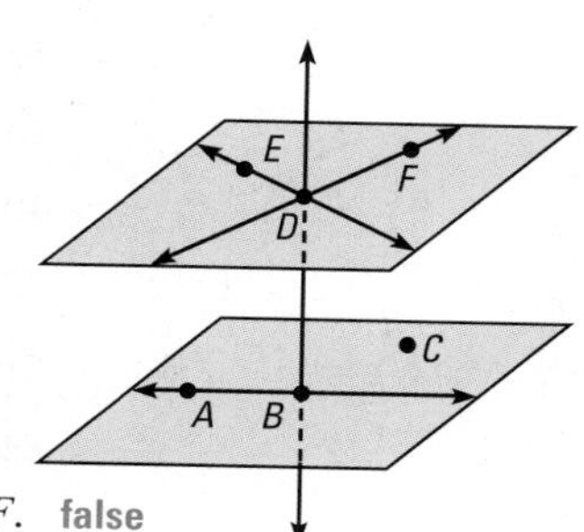

PRACTICE AND APPLICATIONS

STUDENT HELP

Extra Practice
to help you master skills is on p. 803.

EVALUATING STATEMENTS **Decide whether the statement is *true* or *false*.**

9. Point A lies on line ℓ. false
10. A, B, and C are collinear. false
11. Point B lies on line ℓ. true
12. A, B, and C are coplanar. true
13. Point C lies on line m. true
14. D, E, and B are collinear. true
15. Point D lies on line m. false
16. D, E, and B are coplanar. true

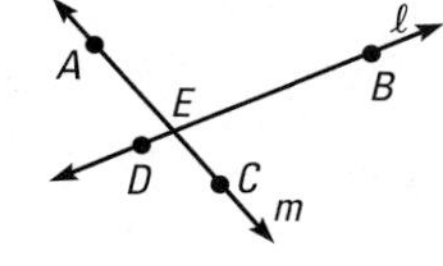

NAMING COLLINEAR POINTS **Name a point that is collinear with the given points.**

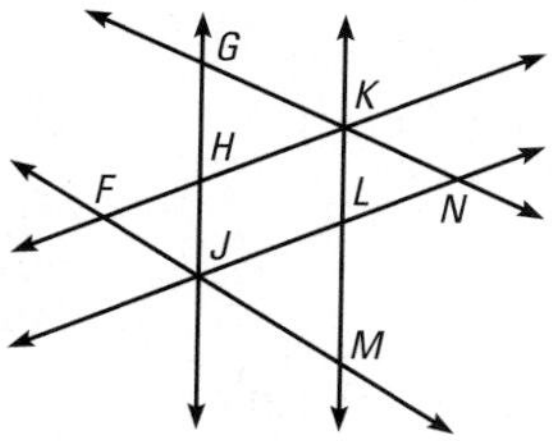

17. F and H K
18. G and K N
19. K and L M
20. M and J F
21. J and N L
22. K and H F
23. H and G J
24. J and F M

NAMING NONCOLLINEAR POINTS **Name three points in the diagram that are not collinear.** 25–27. See margin.

25.

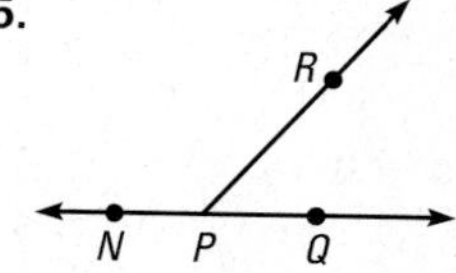

26.

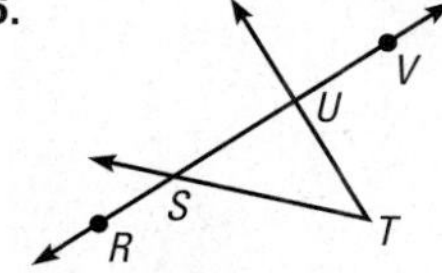

27.

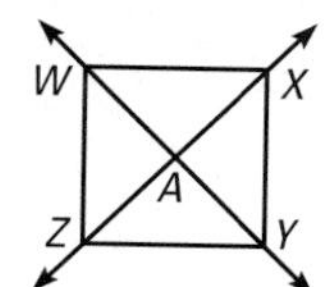

25. N, P, and R; N, Q, and R; P, Q, and R

26. R, S, and T; R, U, and T; R, V, and T; S, U, and T; S, V, and T; U, V, and T

27. A, W, and X; A, W, and Z; A, X, and Y; A, Y, and Z; W, X, and Y; W, X, and Z; W, Y, and Z; X, Y, and Z

STUDENT HELP

HOMEWORK HELP
Example 1: Exs. 9–43
Example 2: Exs. 44–49
Example 3: Exs. 50, 51
Example 4: Exs. 52–67

3 APPLY

ASSIGNMENT GUIDE

BASIC
Day 1: pp. 13–16 Exs. 9, 12, 15, . . ., 42, 44–51, 56–66 even, 73–75, 80, 85, 90, 95

AVERAGE
Day 1: pp. 13–16 Exs. 9, 12, 15, . . ., 42, 44–51, 56–66 even, 68–75, 80, 85, 90, 95

ADVANCED
Day 1: pp. 13–16 Exs. 9, 12, 15, . . ., 42, 44–51, 56–66 even, 68–76, 80, 85, 90, 95

BLOCK SCHEDULE WITH 1.1
pp. 13–16 Exs. 9, 12, 15, . . ., 42, 44–51, 56–66 even, 68–75, 80, 85, 90, 95

EXERCISE LEVELS

Level A: *Easier*
9–33, 52–57, 61–63, 66, 67

Level B: *More Difficult*
34–51, 58–60, 64, 65, 68, 69, 73–75

Level C: *Most Difficult*
70–72, 76

✓ HOMEWORK CHECK

To quickly check student understanding of key concepts, go over the following exercises: Exs. 12, 24, 27, 30, 42, 48, 58, 64. See also the Daily Homework Quiz:

- Blackline Master (*Chapter 1 Resource Book*, p. 36)
- Transparency (p. 4)

TEACHING TIPS

EXERCISES 36–43 You may want to ask students to draw three points that are not coplanar. This should lead them to realize that any group of three points is always coplanar. Thus, a fourth point is always needed to have a set of points that are not coplanar.

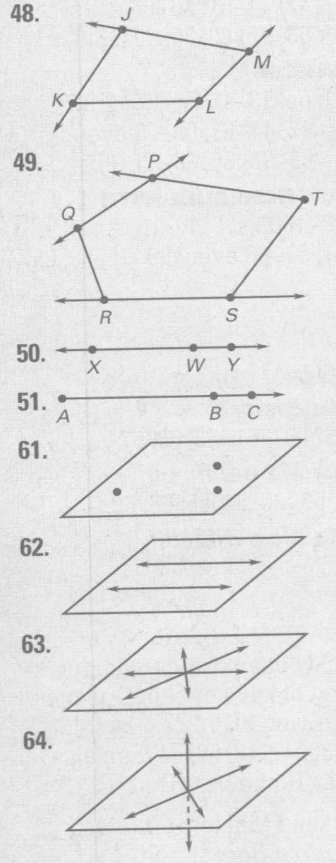

NAMING COPLANAR POINTS **Name a point that is coplanar with the given points.**

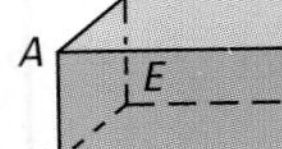

28. A, B, and C *D*

29. D, C, and F *G*

30. G, A, and D *H*

31. E, F, and G *H*

32. A, B, and H *E*

33. B, C, and F *E*

34. A, B, and F *G*

35. B, C, and G *H*

NAMING NONCOPLANAR POINTS **Name all the points that are not coplanar with the given points.**

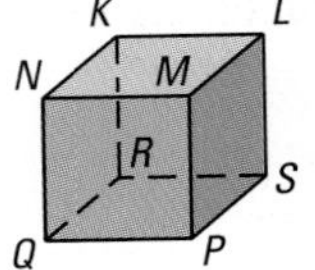

36. N, K, and L *P, Q, R, and S*

37. S, P, and M *K, N, Q, and R*

38. P, Q, and N *K, L, R, and S*

39. R, S, and L *M, N, P, and Q*

40. P, Q, and R *K, L, M, and N*

41. R, K, and N *L, M, P, and S*

42. P, S, and K *L, M, Q, and R*

43. Q, K, and L *M, N, R, and S*

COMPLETING DEFINITIONS **Complete the sentence.**

44. $\overline{AB}$ consists of the endpoints A and B and all the points on the line $\overleftrightarrow{AB}$ that lie __?__. *between A and B*

45. $\overrightarrow{CD}$ consists of the initial point C and all points on the line $\overleftrightarrow{CD}$ that lie __?__. *on the same side of C as point D*

46. Two rays or segments are collinear if they __?__. *lie on the same line*

47. $\overrightarrow{CA}$ and $\overrightarrow{CB}$ are opposite rays if __?__. *A, B, and C are collinear and C is between A and B.*

SKETCHING FIGURES **Sketch the lines, segments, and rays.** *48-51. Sample figures are given. See margin.*

48. Draw four points J, K, L, and M, no three of which are collinear. Then sketch $\overrightarrow{JK}$, $\overline{KL}$, $\overleftrightarrow{LM}$, and $\overrightarrow{MJ}$.

49. Draw five points P, Q, R, S, and T, no three of which are collinear. Then sketch $\overrightarrow{PQ}$, $\overleftrightarrow{RS}$, $\overline{QR}$, $\overline{ST}$, and $\overrightarrow{TP}$.

50. Draw two points, X and Y. Then sketch $\overleftrightarrow{XY}$. Add a point W between X and Y so that $\overrightarrow{WX}$ and $\overrightarrow{WY}$ are opposite rays.

51. Draw two points, A and B. Then sketch $\overrightarrow{AB}$. Add a point C on the ray so that B is between A and C.

EVERYDAY INTERSECTIONS **What kind of geometric intersection does the photograph suggest?**

52. intersecting lines

53. the intersection of a line and a plane

54. intersecting planes

52.

53.

54.

58. $\overleftrightarrow{DC}$
59. $\overleftrightarrow{DH}$
60. $\overleftrightarrow{AD}$

COMPLETING SENTENCES Fill in each blank with the appropriate response based on the points labeled in the photograph.

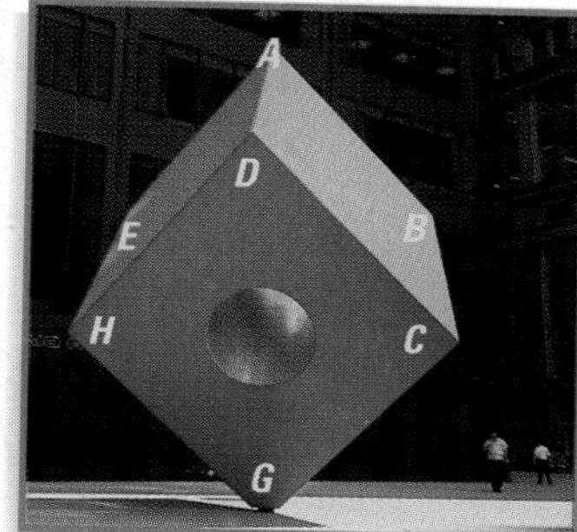

Red Cube, by sculptor Isamu Noguchi

55. $\overleftrightarrow{AB}$ and $\overleftrightarrow{BC}$ intersect at ___?___. B
56. $\overleftrightarrow{AD}$ and $\overleftrightarrow{AE}$ intersect at ___?___. A
57. $\overleftrightarrow{HG}$ and $\overleftrightarrow{DH}$ intersect at ___?___. H
58. Plane ABC and plane DCG intersect at ___?___.
59. Plane GHD and plane DHE intersect at ___?___.
60. Plane EAD and plane BCD intersect at ___?___.

SKETCHING FIGURES Sketch the figure described.
61–67. Sample figures are given. See margin.

61. Three points that are coplanar but not collinear.
62. Two lines that lie in a plane but do not intersect.
63. Three lines that intersect in a point and all lie in the same plane.
64. Three lines that intersect in a point but do not all lie in the same plane.
65. Two lines that intersect and another line that does not intersect either one.
66. Two planes that do not intersect.
67. Three planes that intersect in a line.

TWO-POINT PERSPECTIVE In Exercises 68–72, use the information and diagram below.

In *perspective drawing*, lines that do not intersect in real life are represented in a drawing by lines that appear to intersect at a point far away on the horizon. This point is called a *vanishing point*.

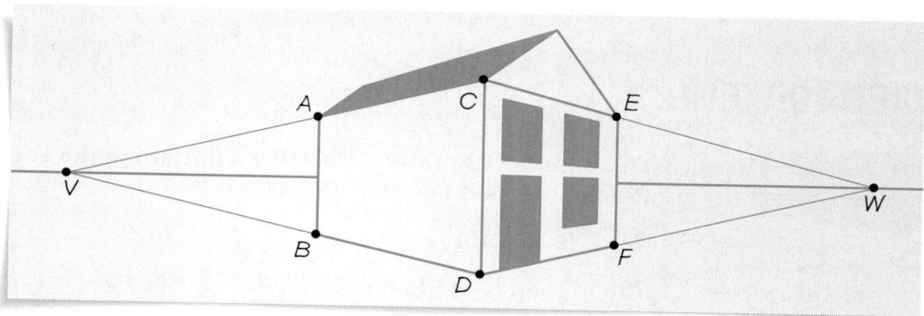

The diagram shows a drawing of a house with two vanishing points. You can use the vanishing points to draw the hidden parts of the house. 70–72. See margin.

68. Name two lines that intersect at vanishing point V. $\overleftrightarrow{AC}$, $\overleftrightarrow{BD}$
69. Name two lines that intersect at vanishing point W. $\overleftrightarrow{CE}$, $\overleftrightarrow{DF}$
70. Trace the diagram. Draw $\overleftrightarrow{EV}$ and $\overleftrightarrow{AW}$. Label their intersection as G.
71. Draw $\overleftrightarrow{FV}$ and $\overleftrightarrow{BW}$. Label their intersection as H.
72. Draw the hidden edges of the house: $\overline{AG}$, $\overline{EG}$, $\overline{BH}$, $\overline{FH}$, and $\overline{GH}$.

70–72.

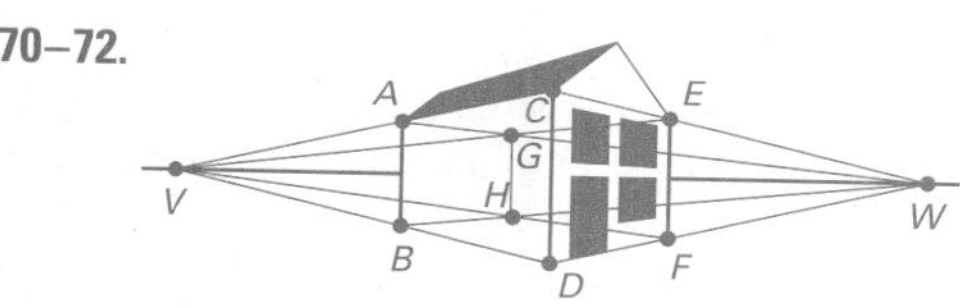

! COMMON ERROR

EXERCISES 61–67 Students may have difficulty picturing the three dimensional objects described in these exercises. It may be helpful for students to make a model for each problem similar to the one in the Activity on page 11. Index cards could be used to represent planes while toothpicks or straws represent lines.

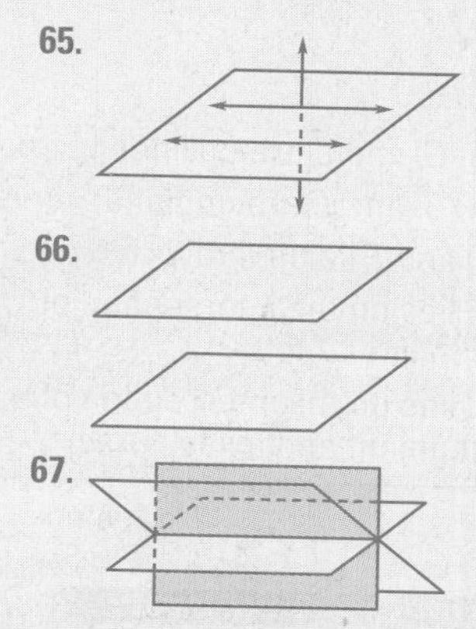

70–72. See answer below.

ADDITIONAL PRACTICE AND RETEACHING

For Lesson 1.2:

- Practice Levels A, B, and C (*Chapter 1 Resource Book*, p. 26)
- Reteaching with Practice (*Chapter 1 Resource Book*, p. 29)
- See Lesson 1.2 of the *Personal Student Tutor*

For more Mixed Review:

- Search the *Test and Practice Generator* for key words or specific lessons.

4 ASSESS

DAILY HOMEWORK QUIZ

Transparency Available

Decide whether the statement is *true* or *false.*

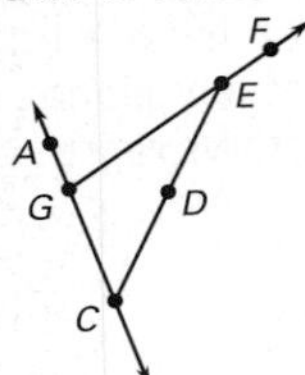

1. *A, G,* and *C* are collinear. true
2. *A, G,* and *D* are coplanar. true
3. *D* and *E* lie on a ray. false
4. *G* lies on the intersection of two lines. false
5. *C* lies on the intersection of a segment and a line. true

EXTRA CHALLENGE NOTE

Challenge problems for Lesson 1.2 are available in **blackline** format in the *Chapter 1 Resource Book,* p. 33 and at **www.mcdougallittell.com.**

ADDITIONAL TEST PREPARATION

1. **OPEN ENDED** Draw a figure that contains at least one segment, one ray, one line, and one plane. Label the points in the figure and name the segment, ray, line and plane. Check figures.
2. **WRITING** Think of the walls of a cube-shaped classroom. Explain how you can use the walls to investigate the possible intersections of two or three planes. See answer below.

76. Each time a line is added to a figure with *n* lines, *n* points of intersection are added.

Number of lines	2	3	4	5	6
Number of intersection points	1	3	6	10	15

Test Preparation

73. **MULTIPLE CHOICE** Which statement(s) are true about the two lines shown in the drawing to the right? C

 I. The lines intersect in one point.

 II. The lines do not intersect.

 III. The lines are coplanar.

 (A) I only (B) I and II only (C) I and III only

 (D) II and III only (E) I, II, and III

74. **MULTIPLE CHOICE** What is the intersection of $\overrightarrow{PQ}$ and $\overrightarrow{QP}$? B

 (A) $\overleftrightarrow{PQ}$ (B) $\overline{PQ}$ (C) P and Q (D) P only (E) Q only

75. **MULTIPLE CHOICE** Points K, L, M, and N are not coplanar. What is the intersection of plane KLM and plane KLN? D

 (A) K and L (B) M and N (C) $\overline{KL}$ (D) $\overleftrightarrow{KL}$

 (E) The planes do not intersect.

★ Challenge

76. **INTERSECTING LINES** In each diagram below, every line intersects all the other lines, but only two lines pass through each intersection point.

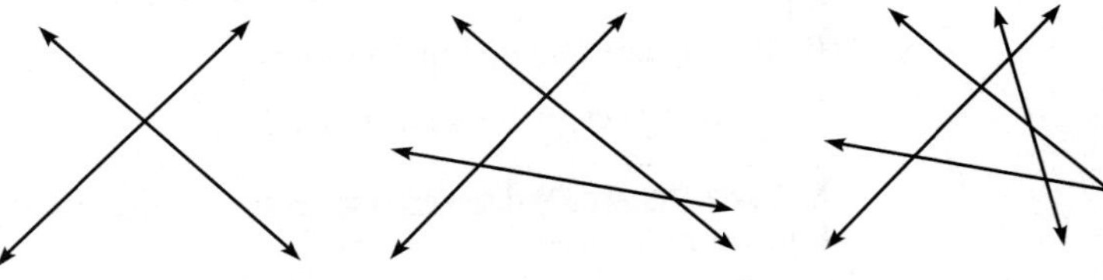

Can you draw 5 lines that intersect in this way? 6 lines? Is there a pattern to the number of intersection points? See margin.

EXTRA CHALLENGE
www.mcdougallittell.com

MIXED REVIEW

DESCRIBING PATTERNS **Describe a pattern in the sequence of numbers. Predict the next number.** (Review 1.1)

77. 1, 6, 36, 216, . . .
78. 2, −2, 2, −2, 2, . . .
79. 8.1, 88.11, 888.111, 8888.1111, . . .
80. 0, 3, 9, 18, 30, . . .

77. Each number is 6 times the previous number; 1296.
78. The numbers alternate between 2 and −2; −2.
79. Numbers after the first are found by adding an 8 immediately before the decimal point of the previous number and a 1 immediately after the decimal point; 88,888.11111
80. Numbers after the first are found by adding consecutive multiples of 3; 45.

OPERATIONS WITH INTEGERS **Simplify the expression.** (Skills Review, p.785)

81. $0 - 2$ −2
82. $3 - 9$ −6
83. $9 - (-4)$ 13
84. $-5 - (-2)$ −3
85. $5 - 0$ 5
86. $4 - 7$ −3
87. $3 - (-8)$ 11
88. $-7 - (-5)$ −2

RADICAL EXPRESSIONS **Simplify the expression. Round your answer to two decimal places.** (Skills Review, p. 799, for 1.3)

89. $\sqrt{21 + 100}$ 11
90. $\sqrt{40 + 60}$ 10
91. $\sqrt{25 + 144}$ 13
92. $\sqrt{9 + 16}$ 5
93. $\sqrt{5^2 + 7^2}$ 8.60
94. $\sqrt{3^2 + (-2)^2}$ 3.61
95. $\sqrt{(-3)^2 + 3^2}$ 4.24
96. $\sqrt{(-5)^2 + 10^2}$ 11.18

Additional Test Preparation *Sample answer:*

2. The floor and ceiling are an example of two planes that do not intersect. Two adjacent walls of the classroom are an example of two planes that intersect in a line. The adjacent walls and the floor are an example of three planes that intersect in a point.

1.3 Segments and Their Measures

What you should learn

GOAL 1 Use segment postulates.

GOAL 2 Use the Distance Formula to measure distances, as applied in **Exs. 45–54**.

Why you should learn it

▼ To solve **real-life** problems, such as finding distances along a diagonal city street in **Example 4**.

GOAL 1 Using Segment Postulates

In geometry, rules that are accepted without proof are called **postulates** or **axioms**. Rules that are proved are called *theorems*. In this lesson, you will study two postulates about the lengths of segments.

POSTULATE

POSTULATE 1 ***Ruler Postulate***

The points on a line can be matched one to one with the real numbers. The real number that corresponds to a point is the **coordinate** of the point.

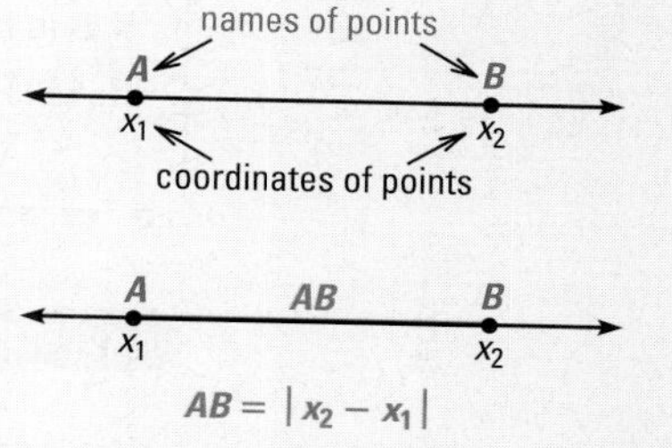

The **distance** between points A and B, written as AB, is the absolute value of the difference between the coordinates of A and B.

AB is also called the **length** of $\overline{AB}$.

EXAMPLE 1 *Finding the Distance Between Two Points*

Measure the length of the segment to the nearest millimeter.

SOLUTION

Use a metric ruler. Align one mark of the ruler with A. Then estimate the coordinate of B. For example, if you align A with 3, B appears to align with 5.5.

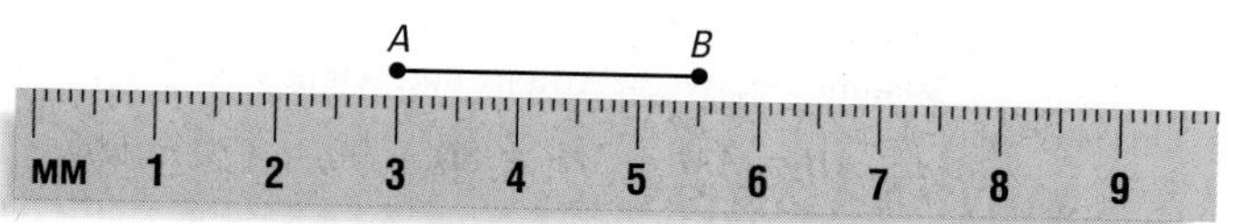

$$AB = |5.5 - 3| = |2.5| = 2.5$$

▶ The distance between A and B is about 2.5 cm.

It doesn't matter how you place the ruler. For example, if the ruler in Example 1 is placed so that A is aligned with 4, then B aligns with 6.5. The difference in the coordinates is the same.

CALIFORNIA STANDARDS AND ASSESSMENT

CA Standards: 1, 15, 17
SAT9 Task 1: Obj. 26
SAT9 Task 2: Obj. 26

1 PLAN

PACING
Basic: 2 days
Average: 2 days
Advanced: 2 days
Block Schedule: 1 block

LESSON OPENER ACTIVITY

An alternative way to approach Lesson 1.3 is to use the Activity Lesson Opener:

- Blackline Master (*Chapter 1 Resource Book*, p. 37)
- Transparency (p. 3)

MEETING INDIVIDUAL NEEDS

- ***Chapter 1 Resource Book***
  Prerequisite Skills Review (p. 5)
  Practice Level A (p. 38)
  Practice Level B (p. 39)
  Practice Level C (p. 40)
  Reteaching with Practice (p. 41)
  Absent Student Catch-Up (p. 43)
  Challenge (p. 47)
- ***Resources in Spanish***
- ***Personal Student Tutor***

NEW-TEACHER SUPPORT

See the Tips for New Teachers on pp. 1–2 of the *Chapter 1 Resource Book* for additional notes about Lesson 1.3.

WARM-UP EXERCISES

Evaluate each expression.

1. $|4 - 7|$ 3

2. $|4.3 - 1.2|$ 3.1

3. $\sqrt{4^2 + 3^2}$ 5

4. $\sqrt{(-2)^2 + 3^2}$ $\sqrt{13}$

2 TEACH

MOTIVATING THE LESSON
Ask three students to arrange themselves so that one student is between the other two. Have students try to define the term *between* using geometric terms. They will probably realize that the three points must be collinear. Explain that they will also need to know something about the lengths of the segments joining the points to give a complete mathematical definition of *between*. Finding segment lengths is a focus of Lesson 1.3.

EXTRA EXAMPLE 1
Measure the length of the segment to the nearest millimeter. about 37 mm

EXTRA EXAMPLE 2
Two friends leave their homes and walk in a straight line toward the other's home. When they meet, one has walked 425 yards and the other has walked 267 yards. How far apart are their homes? 692 yd

CHECKPOINT EXERCISES

For use after Example 1:

1. Measure the length of the segment to the nearest millimeter. about 13 mm

G H

For use after Example 2:

2. A car with a trailer has a total length of 27 feet. If the trailer has a total length of 13 feet, how long is the car? 14 ft

MATHEMATICAL REASONING
Point out to students the difference between the two statements in the Segment Addition Postulate. They should realize that the hypothesis and conclusion are reversed. These two statements could be put together into a single biconditional statement. Biconditional statements are introduced in Chapter 2.

When three points lie on a line, you can say that one of them is **between** the other two. This concept applies to collinear points only. For instance, in the figures below, point B is between points A and C, but point E is not between points D and F.

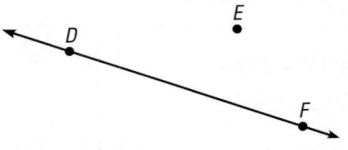

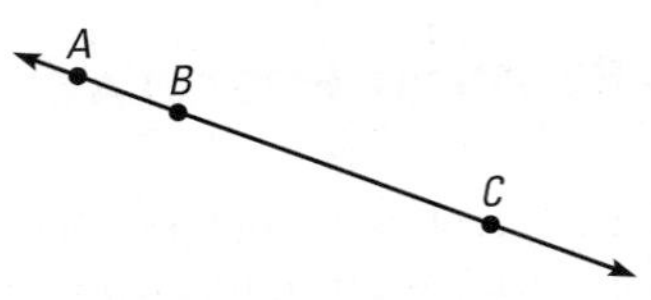

Point *B* is between points *A* and *C*.

D E F

Point *E* is not between points *D* and *F*.

POSTULATE

POSTULATE 2 ***Segment Addition Postulate***

If B is between A and C, then $AB + BC = AC$.

If $AB + BC = AC$, then B is between A and C.

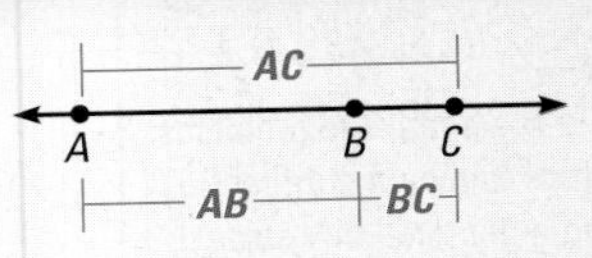

EXAMPLE 2 *Finding Distances on a Map*

MAP READING Use the map to find the distances between the three cities that lie on a line.

SOLUTION

Using the scale on the map, you can estimate that the distance between Athens and Macon is

$$AM = 80 \text{ miles.}$$

The distance between Macon and Albany is

$$MB = 90 \text{ miles.}$$

Knowing that Athens, Macon, and Albany lie on the same line, you can use the Segment Addition Postulate to conclude that the distance between Athens and Albany is

$$AB = AM + MB = 80 + 90 = 170 \text{ miles.}$$

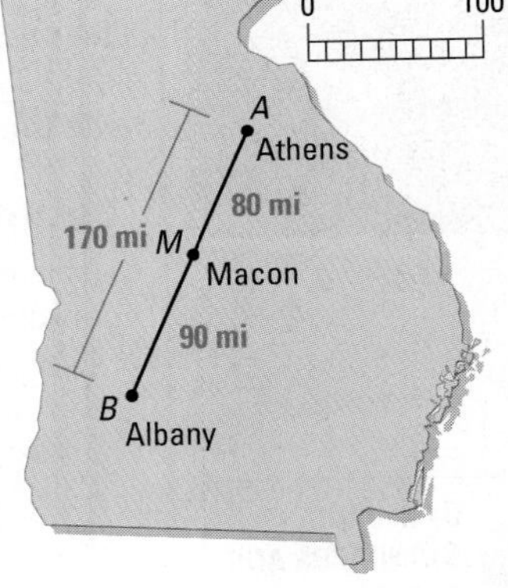

....

The Segment Addition Postulate can be generalized to three or more segments, as long as the segments lie on a line. If P, Q, R, and S lie on a line as shown, then

$$PS = PQ + QR + RS.$$

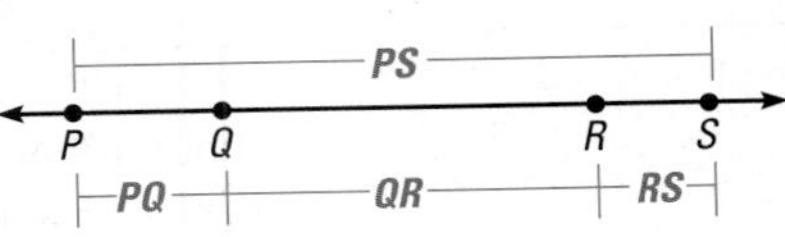

GOAL 2 USING THE DISTANCE FORMULA

STUDENT HELP

Study Tip
The small numbers in x_1 and x_2 are called *subscripts*. You read them as "x sub 1" and "x sub 2."

The **Distance Formula** is a formula for computing the distance between two points in a *coordinate* plane.

THE DISTANCE FORMULA

If $A(x_1, y_1)$ and $B(x_2, y_2)$ are points in a coordinate plane, then the distance between A and B is

$$AB = \sqrt{(x_2 - x_1)^2 + (y_2 - y_1)^2}.$$

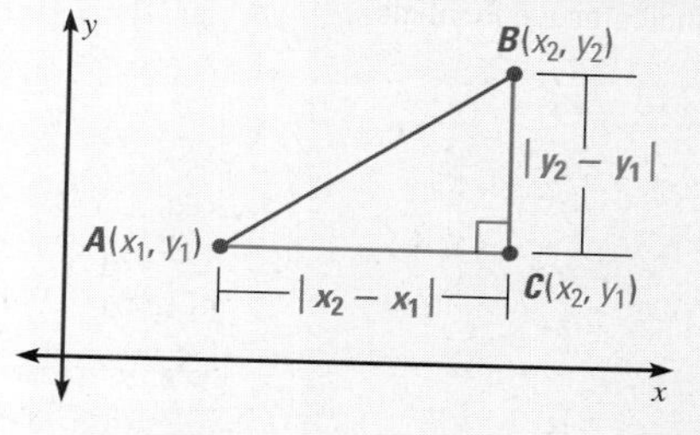

EXAMPLE 3 *Using the Distance Formula*

Find the lengths of the segments. Tell whether any of the segments have the same length.

SOLUTION

Use the Distance Formula.

$$AB = \sqrt{[(-4) - (-1)]^2 + (3 - 1)^2}$$
$$= \sqrt{(-3)^2 + 2^2} = \sqrt{9 + 4} = \sqrt{13}$$

$$AC = \sqrt{[3 - (-1)]^2 + (2 - 1)^2}$$
$$= \sqrt{4^2 + 1^2} = \sqrt{16 + 1} = \sqrt{17}$$

$$AD = \sqrt{[2 - (-1)]^2 + (-1 - 1)^2}$$
$$= \sqrt{3^2 + (-2)^2} = \sqrt{9 + 4} = \sqrt{13}$$

▶ So, $\overline{AB}$ and $\overline{AD}$ have the same length, but $\overline{AC}$ has a different length.

Segments that have the same length are called **congruent segments**. For instance, in Example 3, $\overline{AB}$ and $\overline{AD}$ are congruent because each has a length of $\sqrt{13}$. There is a special symbol, $\cong$, for indicating *congruence*.

LENGTHS ARE EQUAL.	SEGMENTS ARE CONGRUENT.
$AB = AD$	$\overline{AB} \cong \overline{AD}$
"is equal to"	"is congruent to"

EXTRA EXAMPLE 3

Find the lengths of the segments. Tell whether any of the segments have the same length.

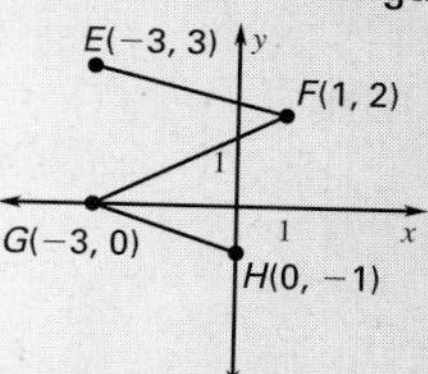

$EF = \sqrt{17}$, $FG = 2\sqrt{5}$, $GH = \sqrt{10}$; None of these segments have the same length.

CHECKPOINT EXERCISES

For use after Example 3:

1. Find the distance between each pair of points.

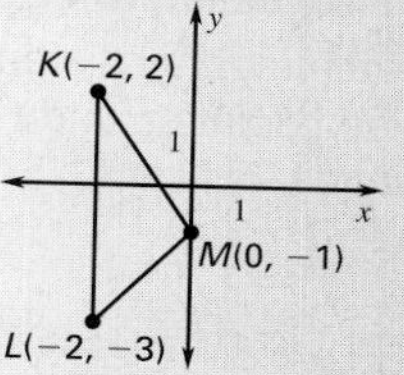

$KM = \sqrt{13}$, $KL = 5$, $LM = 2\sqrt{2}$

MULTIPLE REPRESENTATIONS

A diagram such as the one in the box at the top of page 19 can help students understand the distance formula. The geometric representation provides a context for the variables in the algebraic formula.

EXTRA EXAMPLE 4

On the map, the city blocks are 410 feet apart east-west and 370 feet apart north-south.

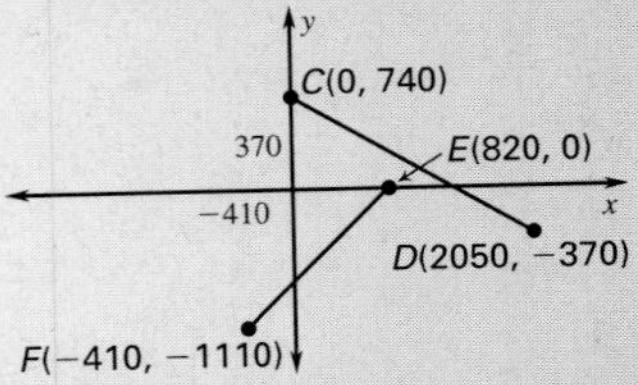

a. Find the walking distance between C and D. **3160 ft**

b. What would the distance be if a diagonal street existed between the two points? **about 2331 ft**

CHECKPOINT EXERCISES

For use after Example 4:

1. Find the diagonal distance between points E and F on the map above. **about 1657 ft**

FOCUS ON VOCABULARY

What is an axiom? **An axiom (or postulate) is a rule in geometry that is accepted without proof.**

CLOSURE QUESTION

Describe how to use the Ruler Postulate and the Distance Formula. **The Ruler Postulate is used to measure the distance between two points on a line. The Distance Formula is used to find the distance between two points in the plane.**

DAILY PUZZLER

A, B, C, and D are collinear points. Find BC if $AC = 2x + 4$, $BC = x$, $BD = 3x + 1$, and $AD = 17$. **3**

ENGLISH LEARNERS

EXAMPLE 4 Explain that *walking* distance means "how far it is to walk between two places." Note that it can be difficult for a non-native speaker to sense whether an *-ing* form preceding a noun has the function of a transitive verb (for example, running laps) or an adjective (for example, running shoes).

The Distance Formula is based on the *Pythagorean Theorem,* which you will see again when you work with right triangles in Chapter 9.

STUDENT HELP

Study Tip
The red mark at one corner of each triangle indicates a right angle.

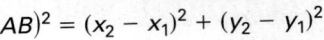

CONCEPT SUMMARY — DISTANCE FORMULA AND PYTHAGOREAN THEOREM

DISTANCE FORMULA

$$(AB)^2 = (x_2 - x_1)^2 + (y_2 - y_1)^2$$

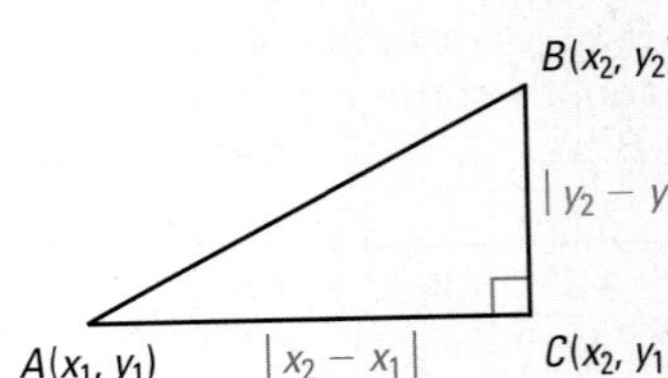

PYTHAGOREAN THEOREM

$$c^2 = a^2 + b^2$$

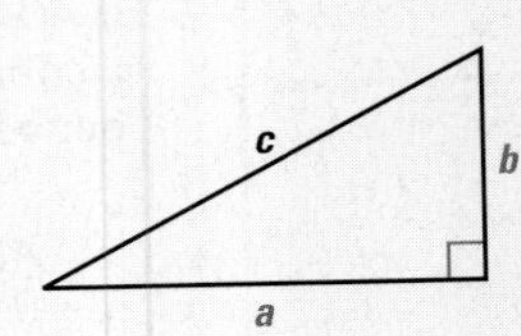

EXAMPLE 4 *Finding Distances on a City Map*

MAP READING On the map, the city blocks are 340 feet apart east-west and 480 feet apart north-south.

a. Find the walking distance between A and B.

b. What would the distance be if a diagonal street existed between the two points?

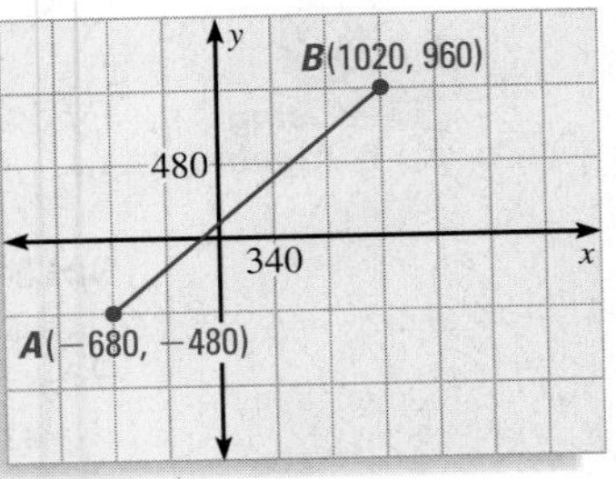

SOLUTION

a. To walk from A to B, you would have to walk five blocks east and three blocks north.

$$5 \text{ blocks} \cdot 340 \frac{\text{feet}}{\text{block}} = 1700 \text{ feet}$$

$$3 \text{ blocks} \cdot 480 \frac{\text{feet}}{\text{block}} = 1440 \text{ feet}$$

▶ So, the walking distance is **1700 + 1440**, which is a total of **3140** feet.

b. To find the diagonal distance between A and B, use the Distance Formula.

$$AB = \sqrt{[1020 - (-680)]^2 + [960 - (-480)]^2}$$

$$= \sqrt{1700^2 + 1440^2}$$

$$= \sqrt{4{,}963{,}600} \approx \mathbf{2228} \text{ feet}$$

▶ So, the diagonal distance would be about 2228 feet, which is 912 feet less than the walking distance.

STUDENT HELP

Study Tip
If you use a calculator to compute distances, use the parenthesis keys to group what needs to be squared.

2. ***Sample answer:*** P Q R

If Q is between P and R, then $PQ + QR = PR$.
If $PQ + QR = PR$, then Q is between P and R.

GUIDED PRACTICE

Vocabulary Check ✓

1. What is a *postulate*? a rule accepted without proof

Concept Check ✓

2. Draw a sketch of three collinear points. Label them. Then write the Segment Addition Postulate for the points. See margin.

3. Use the diagram. How can you determine BD if you know BC and CD? if you know AB and AD?

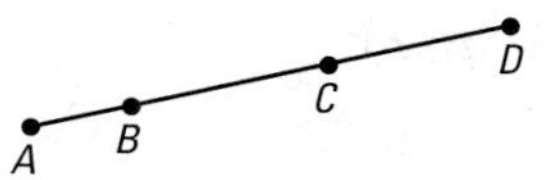

$BD = BC + CD$; $AB + BD = AD$, so $BD = AD - AB$.

Skill Check ✓

Find the distance between the two points.

4. $C(0, 0)$, $D(5, 2)$ $\sqrt{29}$
5. $G(3, 0)$, $H(8, 10)$ $5\sqrt{5}$
6. $M(1, -3)$, $N(3, 5)$ $2\sqrt{17}$
7. $P(-8, -6)$, $Q(-3, 0)$ $\sqrt{61}$
8. $S(7, 3)$, $T(1, -5)$ 10
9. $V(-2, -6)$, $W(1, -2)$ 5

Use the Distance Formula to decide whether $\overline{JK} \cong \overline{KL}$.

10. $J(3, -5)$, $K(-1, 2)$, $L(-5, -5)$ — $\overline{JK} \cong \overline{KL}$; $JK = KL = \sqrt{65}$
11. $J(0, -8)$, $K(4, 3)$, $L(-2, -7)$ — $\overline{JK}$ and $\overline{KL}$ are not congruent; $JK = \sqrt{137}$, $KL = 2\sqrt{34}$.
12. $J(10, 2)$, $K(7, -3)$, $L(4, -8)$ — $\overline{JK} \cong \overline{KL}$; $JK = KL = \sqrt{34}$

PRACTICE AND APPLICATIONS

STUDENT HELP

Extra Practice to help you master skills is on p. 803.

MEASUREMENT Measure the length of the segment to the nearest millimeter.

13. 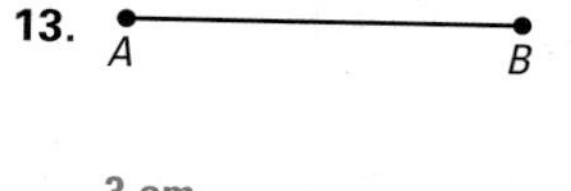

3 cm

14. 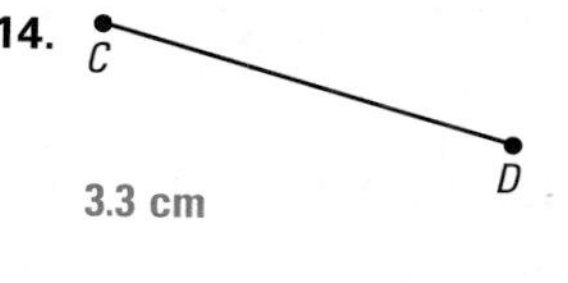

3.3 cm

15. 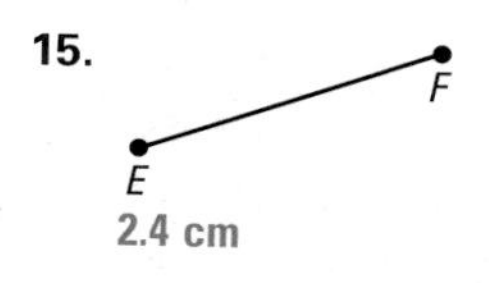

2.4 cm

16. 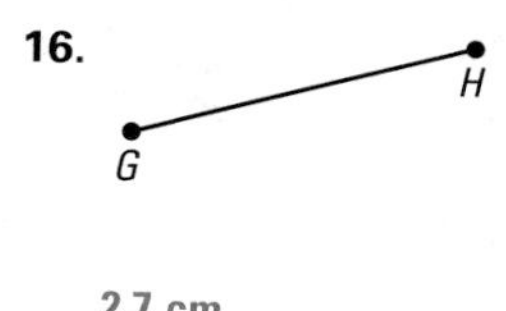

2.7 cm

17. 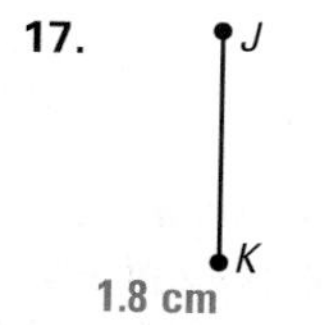

1.8 cm

18. 

3.4 cm

BETWEENNESS Draw a sketch of the three collinear points. Then write the Segment Addition Postulate for the points. 19–22. See margin.

19. E is between D and F.
20. H is between G and J.
21. M is between N and P.
22. R is between Q and S.

LOGICAL REASONING In the diagram of the collinear points, $PT = 20$, $QS = 6$, and $PQ = QR = RS$. Find each length.

P Q R S T

23. QR 3
24. RS 3
25. PQ 3
26. ST 11
27. RP 6
28. RT 14
29. SP 9
30. QT 17

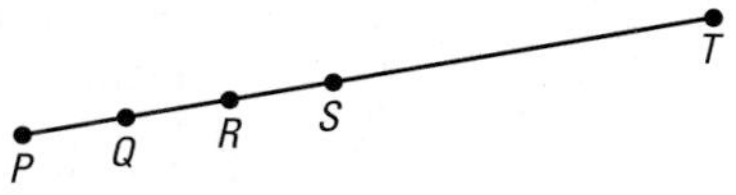

STUDENT HELP

HOMEWORK HELP
Example 1: Exs. 13–18
Example 2: Exs. 19–33
Example 3: Exs. 34–43
Example 4: Exs. 44–54

3 APPLY

ASSIGNMENT GUIDE

BASIC
Day 1: pp. 21–22 Exs. 14–42 even
Day 2: pp. 22–24 Exs. 44–49, 55, 56, 60–71, Quiz 1 Exs. 1–7

AVERAGE
Day 1: pp. 21–22 Exs. 14–42 even
Day 2: pp. 22–24 Exs. 44–49, 53–56, 60–71, Quiz 1 Exs. 1–7

ADVANCED
Day 1: pp. 21–22 Exs. 14–42 even
Day 2: pp. 22–24 Exs. 44–49, 53–71, Quiz 1 Exs. 1–7

BLOCK SCHEDULE
pp. 21–24 Exs. 14–42 even, 44–49, 53–56, 60–71, Quiz 1 Exs. 1–7

EXERCISE LEVELS

Level A: *Easier*
13–22
Level B: *More Difficult*
23–51, 53–56
Level C: *Most Difficult*
52, 57–59

✓ HOMEWORK CHECK

To quickly check student understanding of key concepts, go over the following exercises: Exs. 16, 20, 28, 32, 34, 38, 40, 46, 48. See also the Daily Homework Quiz:

- Blackline Master (*Chapter 1 Resource Book*, p. 51)
- Transparency (p. 5)

19–22. See Additional Answers beginning on page AA1.

STUDENT HELP NOTES

Homework Help Students can find help for Exs. 34–36 at **www.mcdougallittell.com.** The information can be printed out for students who don't have access to the Internet.

COMMON ERROR
EXERCISES 34–43
Computational errors are common in these problems. Caution students to be especially careful when some of the coordinates are negative.

44.
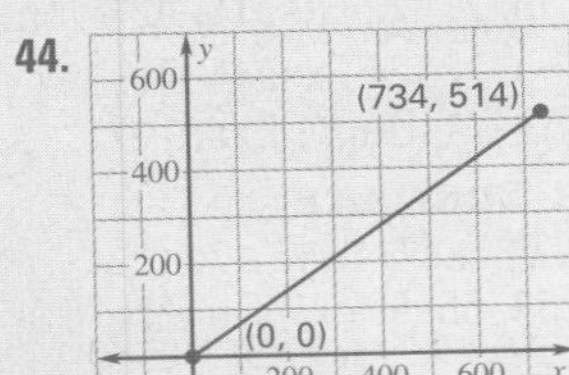

31. 4; 20, 3, 23

32. 13; 100, 43, 143

33. 1; $2\frac{1}{2}$, $4\frac{1}{2}$, 7

STUDENT HELP

Visit our Web site www.mcdougallittell.com for help with Exs. 34–36.

34. $AB = 5\sqrt{5}$, $BC = 5$, $AC = \sqrt{130}$

35. $DE = \sqrt{85}$, $EF = 6\sqrt{2}$, $DF = 5$

36. $GH = 5\sqrt{2}$, $HJ = \sqrt{37}$, $GJ = \sqrt{61}$

37. $AC = 3\sqrt{5}$, $BC = 3\sqrt{5}$, $CD = 2\sqrt{10}$; $\overline{AC}$ and $\overline{BC}$ have the same length.

38. $GE = 5$, $GF = 5$, $GH = \sqrt{26}$; $\overline{GE}$ and $\overline{GF}$ have the same length.

39. $LN = 3\sqrt{13}$, $MN = \sqrt{109}$, $PN = 3\sqrt{10}$; no two segments have the same length.

40. $\overline{PQ} \cong \overline{QR}$; $PQ = QR = \sqrt{13}$

41. $\overline{PQ} \cong \overline{QR}$; $PQ = QR = \sqrt{170}$

42. $\overline{PQ}$ and $\overline{QR}$ are not congruent; $PQ = 2\sqrt{41}$, $QR = \sqrt{173}$.

43. $\overline{PQ} \cong \overline{QR}$; $PQ = QR = 2\sqrt{85}$

USING ALGEBRA Suppose M is between L and N. Use the Segment Addition Postulate to solve for the variable. Then find the lengths of $\overline{LM}$, $\overline{MN}$, and $\overline{LN}$.

31. $LM = 3x + 8$
$MN = 2x - 5$
$LN = 23$

32. $LM = 7y + 9$
$MN = 3y + 4$
$LN = 143$

33. $LM = \frac{1}{2}z + 2$
$MN = 3z + \frac{3}{2}$
$LN = 5z + 2$

DISTANCE FORMULA Find the distance between each pair of points.

34.
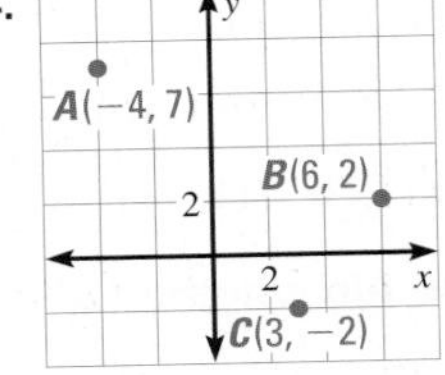

35.
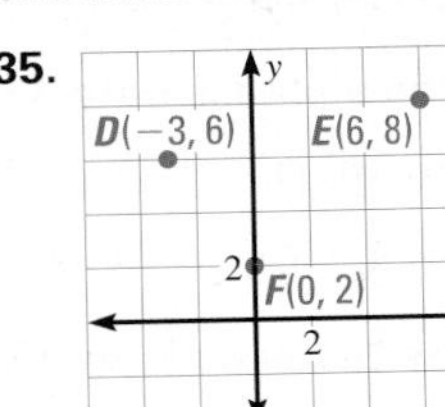

36.
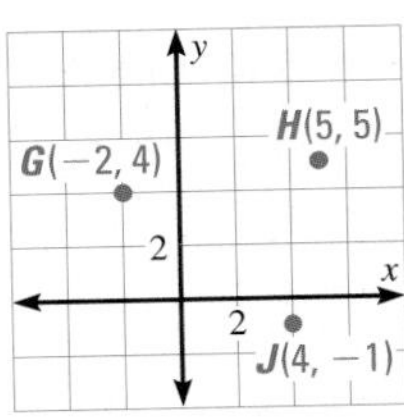

DISTANCE FORMULA Find the lengths of the segments. Tell whether any of the segments have the same length.

37.
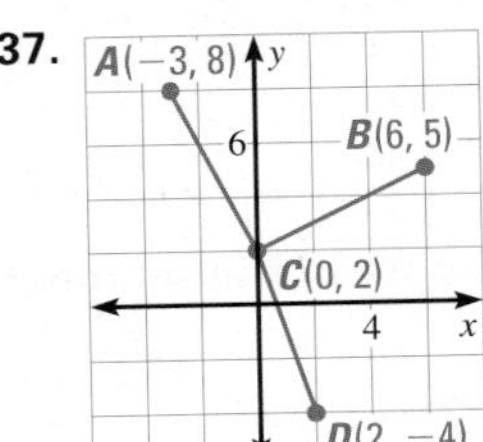

38.
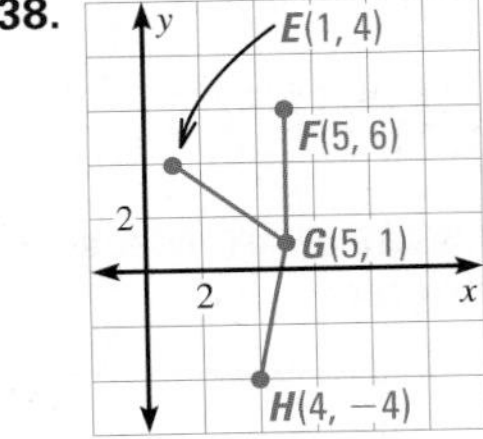

39.
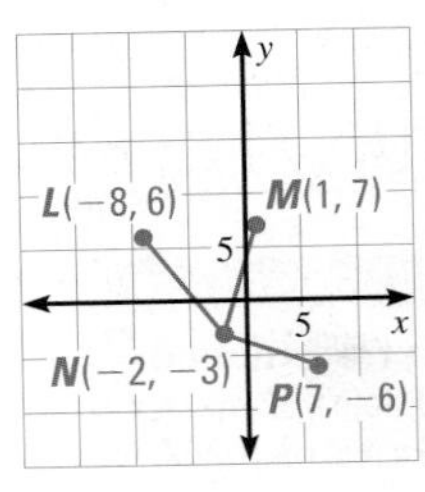

CONGRUENCE Use the Distance Formula to decide whether $\overline{PQ} \cong \overline{QR}$.

40. $P(4, -4)$
$Q(1, -6)$
$R(-1, -3)$

41. $P(-1, -6)$
$Q(-8, 5)$
$R(3, -2)$

42. $P(5, 1)$
$Q(-5, -7)$
$R(-3, 6)$

43. $P(-2, 0)$
$Q(10, -14)$
$R(-4, -2)$

CAMBRIA INCLINE In Exercises 44 and 45, use the information about the incline railway given below.

In the days before automobiles were available, railways called "inclines" brought people up and down hills in many cities. In Johnstown, Pennsylvania, the Cambria Incline was reputedly the steepest in the world when it was completed in 1893. It rises about 514 feet vertically as it moves 734 feet horizontally.

44. On graph paper, draw a coordinate plane and mark the axes using a scale that allows you to plot (0, 0) and (734, 514). Plot the points and connect them with a segment to represent the incline track. See margin.

45. Use the Distance Formula to estimate the length of the track. about 896 ft

Workers constructing the Cambria Incline

DRIVING DISTANCES In Exercises 46 and 47, use the map of cities in Louisiana shown below. Coordinates on the map are given in miles.

The coordinates of Alexandria, Kinder, Eunice, Opelousas, Ville Platte, and Bunkie are $A(26, 56)$, $K(0, 0)$, $E(26, 1)$, $O(46, 5)$, $V(36, 12)$, and $B(40, 32)$.

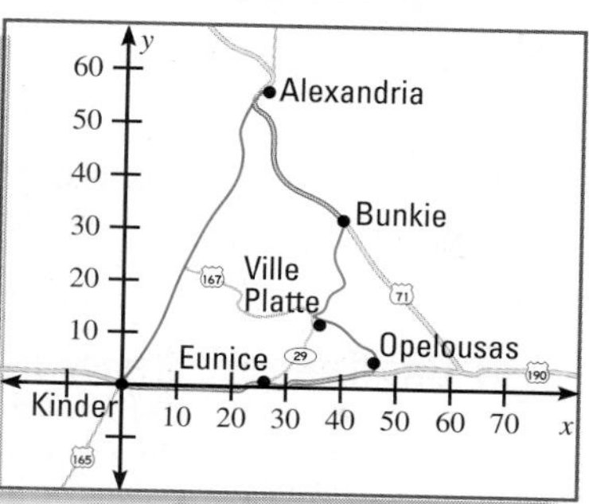

46. What is the shortest flying distance between Eunice and Alexandria?
55 mi

47. Using only roads shown on the map, what is the approximate shortest driving distance between Eunice and Alexandria?
Sample answer: about 63 mi

LONG-DISTANCE RATES In Exercises 48–52, find the distance between the two cities using the information given in the table, which is from a coordinate system used for calculating long-distance telephone rates.
48–51. Answers rounded to the nearest whole unit.

Buffalo, NY	(5075, 2326)	Omaha, NE	(6687, 4595)
Chicago, IL	(5986, 3426)	Providence, RI	(4550, 1219)
Dallas, TX	(8436, 4034)	San Diego, CA	(9468, 7629)
Miami, FL	(8351, 527)	Seattle, WA	(6336, 8896)

48. Buffalo and Dallas
3770 units

49. Chicago and Seattle
5481 units

50. Miami and Omaha
4395 units

51. Providence and San Diego
8079 units

52. The long-distance coordinate system is measured in units of $\sqrt{0.1}$ mile. Convert the distances you found in Exs. 48–51 to miles.

52. Buffalo and Dallas: 1192 mi; Chicago and Seattle: 1733 mi; Miami and Omaha: 1390 mi; Providence and San Diego: 2555 mi

CAMPUS PATHWAYS In Exercises 53 and 54, use the campus map below. Sidewalks around the edge of a campus quadrangle connect the buildings. Students sometimes take shortcuts by walking across the grass along the pathways shown. The coordinate system shown is measured in yards.

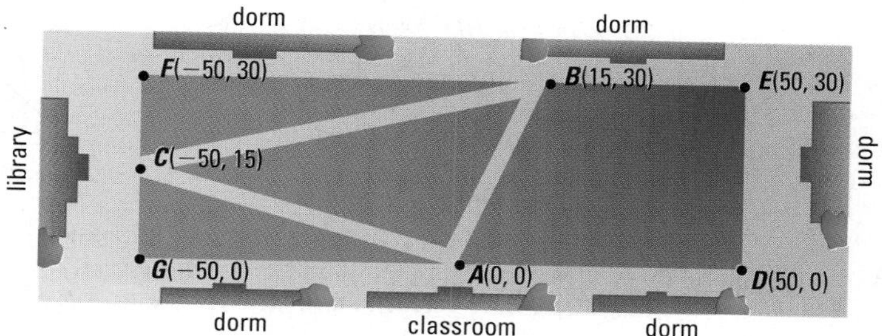

53. Find the distances from A to B, from B to C, and from C to A if you have to walk around the quadrangle along the sidewalks.
115 yards, 80 yards, 65 yards

54. Find the distances from A to B, from B to C, and from C to A if you are able to walk across the grass along the pathways.
$15\sqrt{5} \approx 33.5$ yards, $5\sqrt{178} \approx 66.7$ yards, $5\sqrt{109} \approx 52.2$ yards

ADDITIONAL PRACTICE AND RETEACHING

For Lesson 1.3:

- Practice Levels A, B, and C (*Chapter 1 Resource Book*, p. 38)
- Reteaching with Practice (*Chapter 1 Resource Book*, p. 41)
- See Lesson 1.3 of the *Personal Student Tutor*

For more Mixed Review:

- Search the *Test and Practice Generator* for key words or specific lessons.

4 ASSESS

Daily Homework Quiz

Transparency Available

Points A, D, F, and X are on a segment in this order. $AD = 15$, $AF = 22$, and $AX = 30$. Find each length.

1. DF 7 **2.** FX 8

Use the Distance Formula to decide whether $PQ = QR$.

3. $P(2, 4)$, $Q(4, 10)$, $R(0, 6)$ no

4. $P(-1, -2)$, $Q(2, 0)$, $R(4, 3)$ yes

Extra Challenge Note

Challenge problems for Lesson 1.3 are available in **blackline** format in the *Chapter 1 Resource Book,* p. 47 and at **www.mcdougallittell.com.**

Additional Test Preparation

1. Open Ended Describe a real-life situation in which you would use the Ruler Postulate and a real-life situation in which you would use the Distance Formula. Explain why the method would be appropriate for each example. Check work.

2. Writing Explain the difference between the terms *equal* and *congruent.* Numbers such as the lengths of two segments are equal if they have the same value. Segments are congruent if they have the same length.

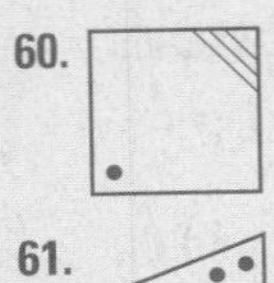

Test Preparation

55. Multiple Choice Points K and L are on $\overline{AB}$. If $AK > BL$, then which statement must be true? C

(A) $AK < KB$ (B) $AL < LB$ (C) $AL > BK$

(D) $KL < LB$ (E) $AL + BK > AB$

56. Multiple Choice Suppose point M lies on $\overline{CD}$, $CM = 2 \cdot MD$, and $CD = 18$. What is the length of MD? B

(A) 3 (B) 6 (C) 9 (D) 12 (E) 36

★ Challenge

Three-Dimensional Distance **In Exercises 57–59, use the following information to find the distance between the pair of points.**

In a three-dimensional coordinate system, the distance between two points (x_1, y_1, z_1) and (x_2, y_2, z_2) is

$$\sqrt{(x_2 - x_1)^2 + (y_2 - y_1)^2 + (z_2 - z_1)^2}.$$

Extra Challenge

www.mcdougallittell.com

57. $P(0, 20, -32)$ $Q(2, -10, -20)$ $2\sqrt{262}$

58. $A(-8, 15, -4)$ $B(10, 1, -6)$ $2\sqrt{131}$

59. $F(4, -42, 60)$ $G(-7, -11, 38)$ $3\sqrt{174}$

Mixed Review

Sketching Visual Patterns **Sketch the next figure in the pattern.** **(Review 1.1)** 60, 61. See margin.

60.

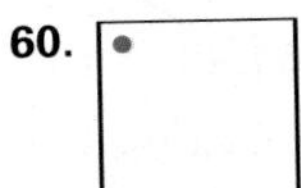

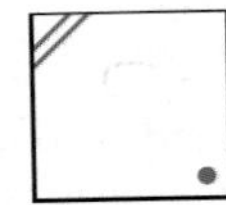

61.

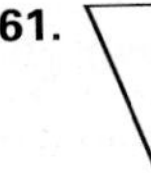

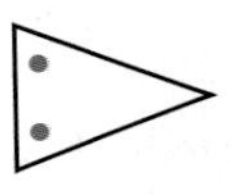

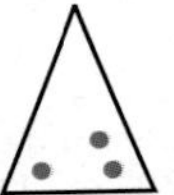

Evaluating Statements **Determine if the statement is *true* or *false*.** **(Review 1.2)**

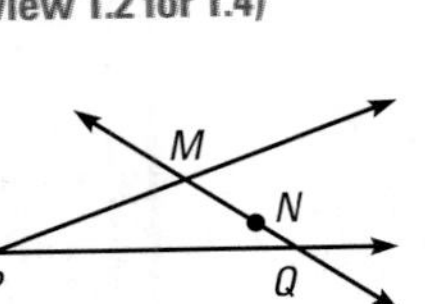

62. E lies on $\overrightarrow{BD}$. true

63. E lies on $\overrightarrow{BD}$. false

64. A, B, and D are collinear. false

65. $\overrightarrow{BD}$ and $\overrightarrow{BE}$ are opposite rays. true

66. B lies in plane ADC. true

67. The intersection of $\overleftrightarrow{DE}$ and $\overleftrightarrow{AC}$ is B. true

Naming Rays **Name the ray described.** **(Review 1.2 for 1.4)**

M, N, P, Q

68. Name a ray that contains M.

69. Name a ray that has N as an endpoint.

70. Name two rays that intersect at P.

71. Name a pair of opposite rays.

68. $\overrightarrow{PM}$, $\overrightarrow{NM}$, $\overrightarrow{QM}$, $\overrightarrow{MN}$, $\overrightarrow{MQ}$

69. $\overrightarrow{NM}$, $\overrightarrow{NQ}$

70. $\overrightarrow{PM}$ and $\overrightarrow{PQ}$

71. $\overrightarrow{NM}$, $\overrightarrow{NQ}$

Quiz 1

Self-Test for Lessons 1.1–1.3

Write the next number in the sequence. (Lesson 1.1)

1. 10, 9.5, 9, 8.5, . . . 8
2. 0, 2, −2, 4, −4, . . . 6

Sketch the figure described. (Lesson 1.2) 3–6. See margin.

3. Two segments that do not intersect.
4. Two lines that do not intersect, and a third line that intersects each of them.
5. Two lines that intersect a plane at the same point.
6. Three planes that do not intersect.
7. **MINIATURE GOLF** At a miniature golf course, a water hazard blocks the direct shot from the tee at $T(0, 0)$ to the cup at $C(-1, 7)$. If you hit the ball so it bounces off an angled wall at $B(3, 4)$, it will go into the cup. The coordinate system is measured in feet. Draw a diagram of the situation. Find TB and BC. (Lesson 1.3) See margin.

Math & History

Geometric Constructions

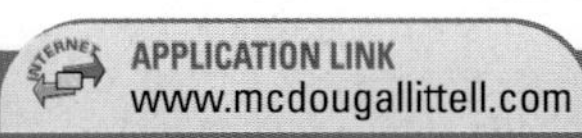

THEN

MORE THAN 2000 YEARS AGO, the Greek mathematician Euclid published a 13 volume work called *The Elements*. In his systematic approach, figures are *constructed* using only a *compass* and a *straightedge* (a ruler without measuring marks).

NOW

TODAY, geometry software may be used to construct geometric figures. Programs allow you to perform constructions as if you have only a compass and straightedge. They also let you make measurements of lengths, angles, and areas. 1–3. See margin.

1. Draw two points and use a *straightedge* to construct the line that passes through them.
2. With the points as centers, use a *compass* to draw two circles of different sizes so that the circles intersect in two points. Mark the two points of intersection and construct the line through them.
3. Connect the four points you constructed. What are the properties of the shape formed?

An early printed edition of *The Elements*

Euclid develops The Elements.

c. 300 B.C.

Gauss proves constructing a shape with 17 congruent sides and 17 congruent angles is possible.

1796

Geometry software duplicates the tools for construction on screen.

1990s

ADDITIONAL RESOURCES

An alternative Quiz for Lessons 1.1–1.3 is available in the *Chapter 1 Resource Book,* p. 48.

A **blackline** master with additional Math & History exercises is available in the *Chapter 1 Resource Book,* p. 46.

3. 

4.

5. 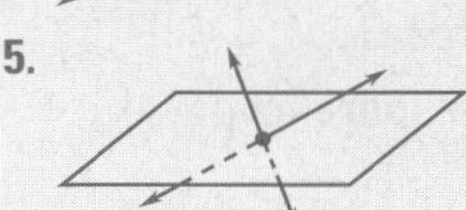

6. 

7. 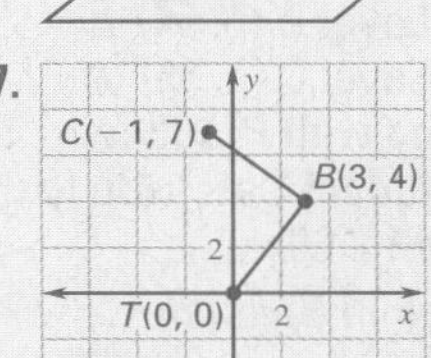

$TB = 5$ ft, $BC = 5$ ft

1–2. 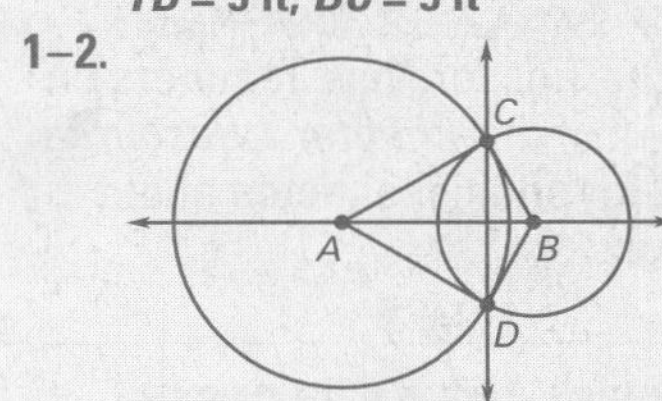

3. $ADBC$ is a four-sided shape with $AD = AC$ and $BD = BC$. It appears that $\overleftrightarrow{AB}$ and $\overleftrightarrow{CD}$ intersect to form right angles.

1 PLAN

PACING
Basic: 1 day
Average: 1 day
Advanced: 1 day
Block Schedule: 0.5 block with 1.5

LESSON OPENER ACTIVITY
An alternative way to approach Lesson 1.4 is to use the Activity Lesson Opener:
- Blackline Master (*Chapter 1 Resource Book,* p. 52)
- Transparency (p. 4)

MEETING INDIVIDUAL NEEDS
- ***Chapter 1 Resource Book***
  Prerequisite Skills Review (p. 5)
  Practice Level A (p. 53)
  Practice Level B (p. 54)
  Practice Level C (p. 55)
  Reteaching with Practice (p. 56)
  Absent Student Catch-Up (p. 58)
  Challenge (p. 60)
- ***Resources in Spanish***
- ***Personal Student Tutor***

NEW-TEACHER SUPPORT
See the Tips for New Teachers on pp. 1–2 of the *Chapter 1 Resource Book* for additional notes about Lesson 1.4.

WARM-UP EXERCISES
Transparency Available
Fill in the blanks.
1. The endpoint of $\overrightarrow{RQ}$ is ________. *R*
2. Line segments with equal measures are ________. congruent
3. A rule of geometry that is accepted without proof is a ________. postulate or axiom
4. A pair of opposite rays form a ________. line

1.4 Angles and Their Measures

What you should learn

GOAL 1 Use angle postulates.

GOAL 2 Classify angles as acute, right, obtuse, or straight.

Why you should learn it

▼ To solve **real-life** problems about angles, such as the field of vision of a horse wearing blinkers in **Example 2**.

CALIFORNIA STANDARDS AND ASSESSMENT
CA Standards: 4, 12
SAT9 Task 1: Obj. 24
SAT9 Task 2: Obj. 27

GOAL 1 USING ANGLE POSTULATES

An **angle** consists of two different rays that have the same initial point. The rays are the **sides** of the angle. The initial point is the **vertex** of the angle.

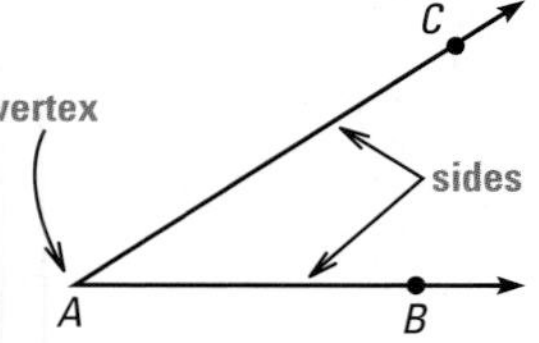

The angle that has sides $\overrightarrow{AB}$ and $\overrightarrow{AC}$ is denoted by $\angle BAC$, $\angle CAB$, or $\angle A$. The point A is the vertex of the angle.

EXAMPLE 1 *Naming Angles*

Name the angles in the figure.

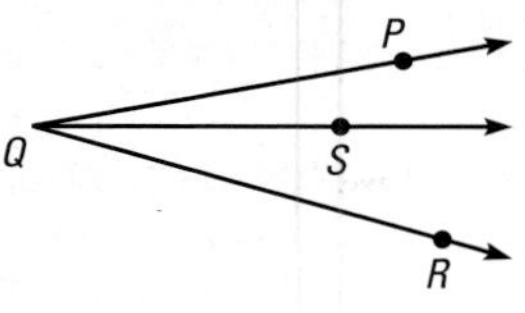

SOLUTION

There are three different angles.

- $\angle PQS$ or $\angle SQP$
- $\angle SQR$ or $\angle RQS$
- $\angle PQR$ or $\angle RQP$

You should not name any of these angles as $\angle Q$ because all three angles have Q as their vertex. The name $\angle Q$ would not distinguish one angle from the others.

. . . .

The *measure* of $\angle A$ is denoted by $m\angle A$. The measure of an angle can be approximated with a protractor, using units called *degrees* (°). For instance, $\angle BAC$ has a measure of 50°, which can be written as

$$m\angle BAC = 50°.$$

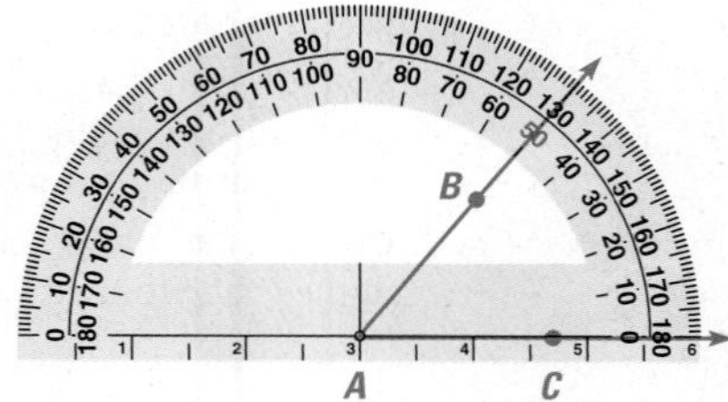

Angles that have the same measure are called **congruent angles**. For instance, $\angle BAC$ and $\angle DEF$ each have a measure of 50°, so they are congruent.

D
50°
E
F

MEASURES ARE EQUAL.	ANGLES ARE CONGRUENT.
$m\angle BAC = m\angle DEF$	$\angle BAC \cong \angle DEF$
"is equal to"	"is congruent to"

POSTULATE

POSTULATE 3 *Protractor Postulate*

Consider a point A on one side of $\overleftrightarrow{OB}$. The rays of the form $\overrightarrow{OA}$ can be matched one to one with the real numbers from 0 to 180.

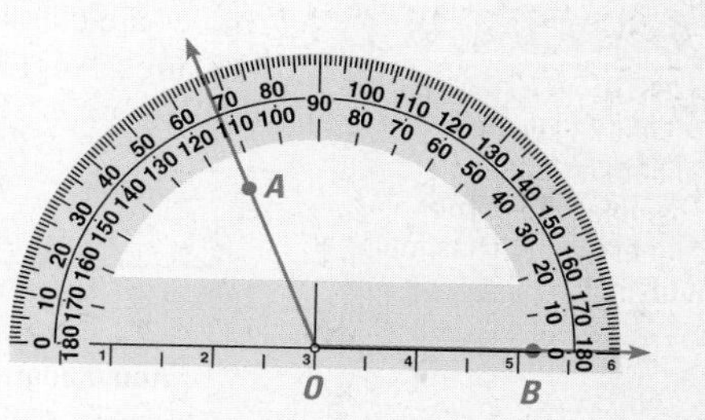

The **measure** of $\angle AOB$ is equal to the absolute value of the difference between the real numbers for $\overrightarrow{OA}$ and $\overrightarrow{OB}$.

A point is in the **interior** of an angle if it is between points that lie on each side of the angle.

A point is in the **exterior** of an angle if it is not on the angle or in its interior.

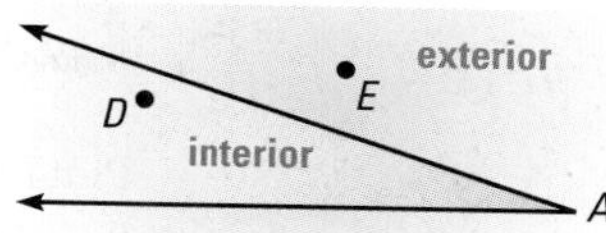

POSTULATE

POSTULATE 4 *Angle Addition Postulate*

If P is in the interior of $\angle RST$, then

$m\angle RSP + m\angle PST = m\angle RST.$

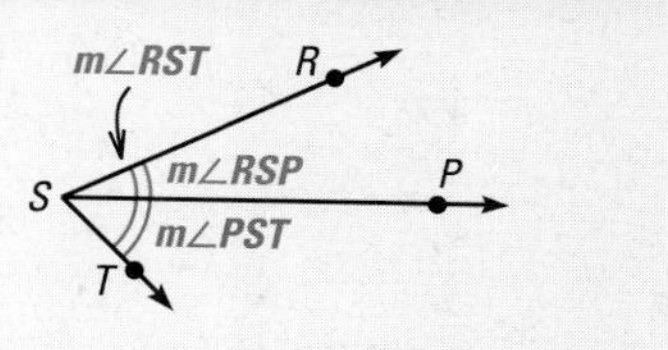

EXAMPLE 2 *Calculating Angle Measures*

VISION Each eye of a horse wearing blinkers has an angle of vision that measures 100°. The angle of vision that is seen by both eyes measures 60°.

Find the angle of vision seen by the left eye alone.

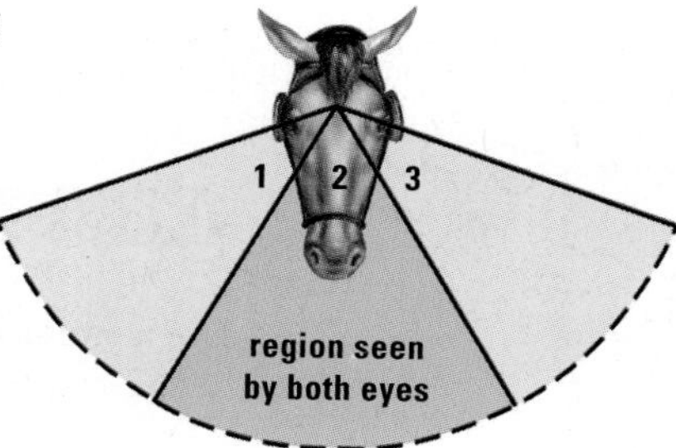

SOLUTION

You can use the Angle Addition Postulate.

$m\angle 2 + m\angle 3 = 100°$	**Total vision for left eye is 100°.**
$m\angle 3 = 100° - m\angle 2$	**Subtract $m\angle 2$ from each side.**
$m\angle 3 = 100° - 60°$	**Substitute 60° for $m\angle 2$.**
$m\angle 3 = 40°$	**Subtract.**

▶ So, the vision for the left eye alone measures 40°.

STUDENT HELP

Study Tip
As shown in Example 2, it is sometimes easier to label angles with numbers instead of letters.

2 TEACH

MOTIVATING THE LESSON
Ask students to define the term angle as it is used in everyday language. Explain that in mathematics, it is important to have a precise definition that all mathematicians can agree on. In today's lesson, students will learn the mathematical definition of angle as well as ways to measure and classify angles.

EXTRA EXAMPLE 1
Name the angles in the figure.

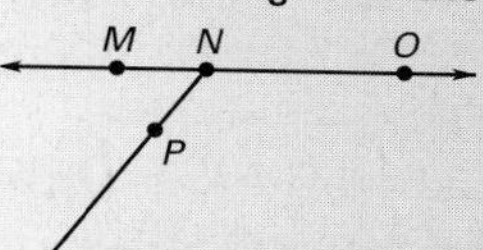

$\angle MNP$ or $\angle PNM$, $\angle PNO$ or $\angle ONP$, $\angle ONM$ or $\angle MNO$

EXTRA EXAMPLE 2
The backyard of a house is illuminated by a light fixture that has two bulbs. Each bulb illuminates an angle of 120°. If the angle illuminated only by the right bulb is 35°, what is the angle illuminated by both bulbs? 85°

CHECKPOINT EXERCISES
For use after Example 1:

1. Name the angles in the figure.

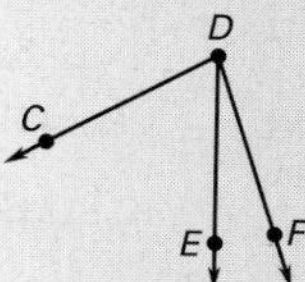

$\angle CDE$ or $\angle EDC$, $\angle EDF$ or $\angle FDE$, $\angle CDF$ or $\angle FDC$

2. In the figure above, $m\angle CDE = 62°$ and $m\angle EDF = 18°$. Find the measure of $\angle CDF$. 80°

EXTRA EXAMPLE 3

Plot the points $A(-3, -1)$, $B(-1, 1)$, $C(2, 4)$, $D(2, 1)$, and $E(2, -2)$. Then measure and classify the following angles as acute, right, obtuse, or straight.

a. $\angle DBE$ 45°; acute
b. $\angle EBC$ 90°; right
c. $\angle ABC$ 180°; straight
d. $\angle ABD$ 135°; obtuse

EXTRA EXAMPLE 4

Use a protractor to draw two adjacent angles $\angle LMN$ and $\angle NMO$ so that $\angle LMN$ is acute and $\angle LMO$ is straight.

Sample answer:

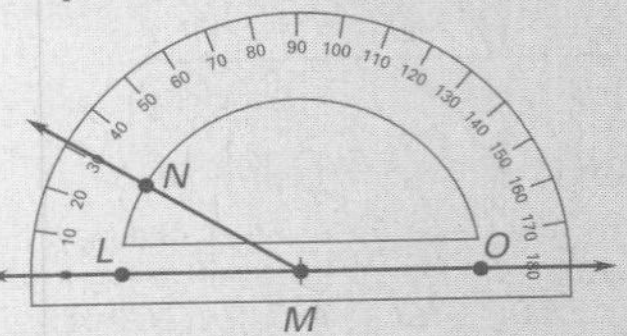

CHECKPOINT EXERCISES

For use after Examples 3 and 4:

1. Draw 5 points A, B, C, D, and E so that all four statements are true.
$\angle AEC$ and $\angle BEC$ are adjacent.
$\angle AEB$ is obtuse.
D is in the exterior of $\angle AEB$.
$\angle DEC$ is a right angle.
Sample answer:

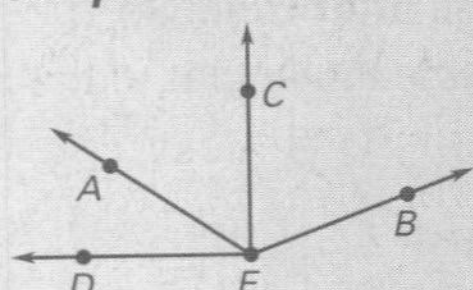

FOCUS ON VOCABULARY

What is the interior of an angle?
See answer below.

CLOSURE QUESTION

Describe how angles are classified.
See answer below.

DAILY PUZZLER

$\angle JKL$ is a straight angle and $m\angle JKM = 115°$. H is in the interior of $\angle JKM$ and $m\angle HKL = 130°$. What is $m\angle HKM$? 65°

CLASSIFYING ANGLES

STUDENT HELP

Study Tip
The mark used to indicate a right angle resembles the corner of a square, which has four right angles.

Angles are classified as **acute**, **right**, **obtuse**, and **straight**, according to their measures. Angles have measures greater than 0° and less than or equal to 180°.

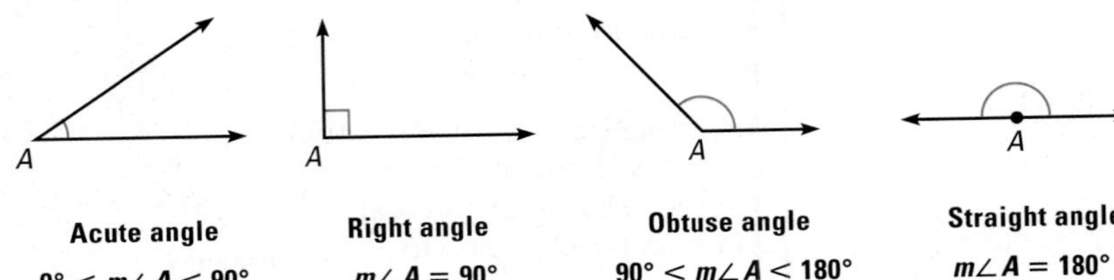

EXAMPLE 3 *Classifying Angles in a Coordinate Plane*

Plot the points $L(-4, 2)$, $M(-1, -1)$, $N(2, 2)$, $Q(4, -1)$, and $P(2, -4)$. Then measure and classify the following angles as acute, right, obtuse, or straight.

a. $\angle LMN$ **b.** $\angle LMP$ **c.** $\angle NMQ$ **d.** $\angle LMQ$

SOLUTION

Begin by plotting the points. Then use a protractor to measure each angle.

MEASURE	CLASSIFICATION
a. $m\angle LMN = 90°$	right angle
b. $m\angle LMP = 180°$	straight angle
c. $m\angle NMQ = 45°$	acute angle
d. $m\angle LMQ = 135°$	obtuse angle

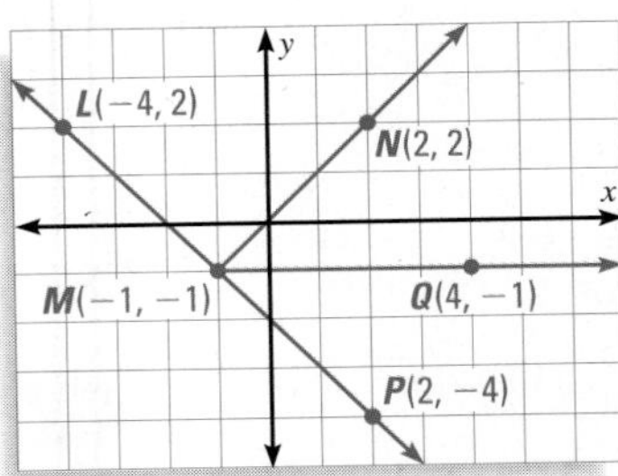

Two angles are **adjacent angles** if they share a common vertex and side, but have no common interior points.

EXAMPLE 4 *Drawing Adjacent Angles*

Use a protractor to draw two adjacent acute angles $\angle RSP$ and $\angle PST$ so that $\angle RST$ is (**a**) acute and (**b**) obtuse.

SOLUTION

a.

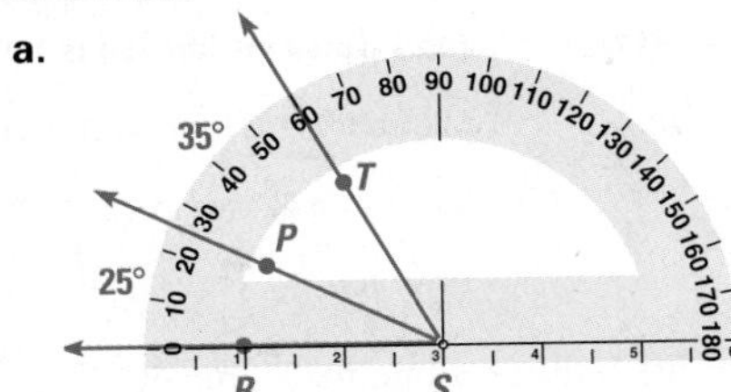

b.

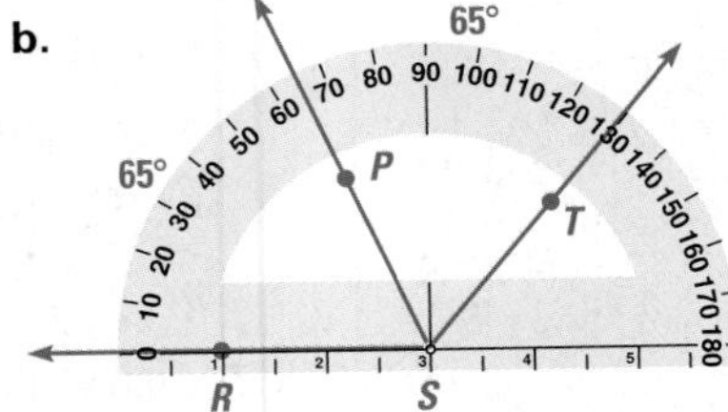

STUDENT HELP

INTERNET HOMEWORK HELP
Visit our Web site www.mcdougallittell.com for extra examples.

Focus on Vocabulary *Sample answer:*
All the points that lie between points on each side of the angle.

Closure Question *Sample answer:*
Angles are classified according to their measure. Those measuring less than 90° are acute. Those measuring 90° are right. Those measuring between 90° and 180° are obtuse, and those measuring 180° are straight angles.

GUIDED PRACTICE

Vocabulary Check ✓

Match the angle with its classification.

A. acute **B.** obtuse **C.** right **D.** straight

1. C

2. D

3. B

4. A

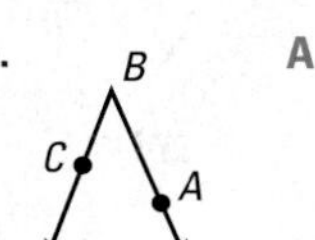

Concept Check ✓

Use the diagram at the right to answer the questions. Explain your answers.

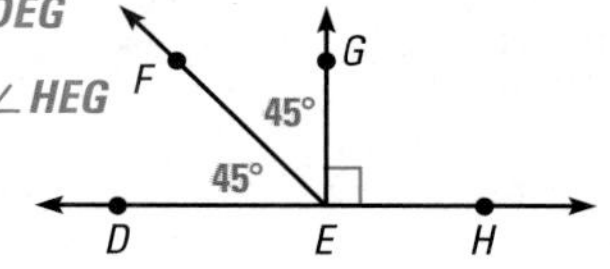

5. Is $\angle DEF \cong \angle FEG$? yes; $m\angle DEF = m\angle DEG$

6. Is $\angle DEG \cong \angle HEG$? yes; $m\angle DEG = m\angle HEG$

7. Are $\angle DEF$ and $\angle FEH$ adjacent?

8. Are $\angle GED$ and $\angle DEF$ adjacent?
No; they have common interior points.

7. Yes; they share a common vertex and side, but have no common interior points.

Skill Check ✓

Name the vertex and sides of the angle. Then estimate its measure.

9.

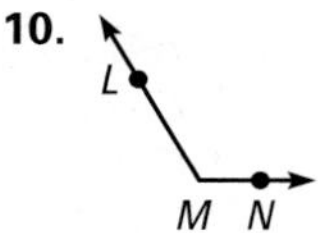

10.

11.

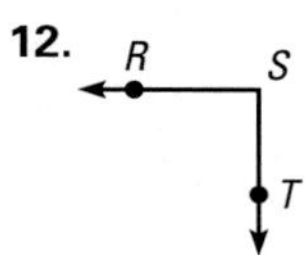

12.

9. E, $\overrightarrow{ED}$, $\overrightarrow{EF}$; about 35°

10. M, $\overrightarrow{ML}$, $\overrightarrow{MN}$; about 120°

11. J, $\overrightarrow{JH}$, $\overrightarrow{JK}$; about 75°

12. S, $\overrightarrow{SR}$, $\overrightarrow{ST}$; about 90°

Classify the angle as *acute, obtuse, right,* or *straight.*

13. $m\angle A = 180°$ straight

14. $m\angle B = 90°$ right

15. $m\angle C = 100°$ obtuse

16. $m\angle D = 45°$ acute

PRACTICE AND APPLICATIONS

STUDENT HELP

Extra Practice to help you master skills is on pp. 803 and 804.

NAMING PARTS **Name the vertex and sides of the angle.**

17.

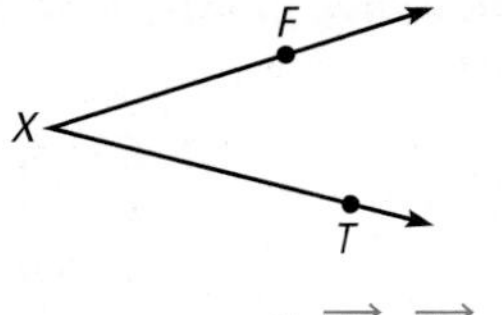

X, $\overrightarrow{XF}$, $\overrightarrow{XT}$

18.

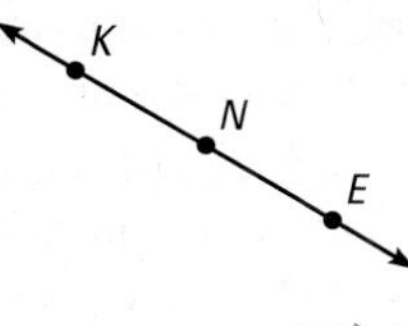

N, $\overrightarrow{NK}$, $\overrightarrow{NE}$

19.

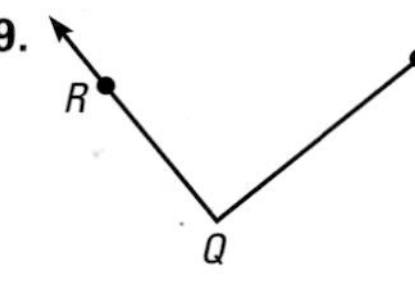

Q, $\overrightarrow{QR}$, $\overrightarrow{QS}$

STUDENT HELP

HOMEWORK HELP
Example 1: Exs. 17–22
Example 2: Exs. 23–34
Example 3: Exs. 35–43
Example 4: Exs. 38, 39

NAMING ANGLES **Write two names for the angle.**

20.

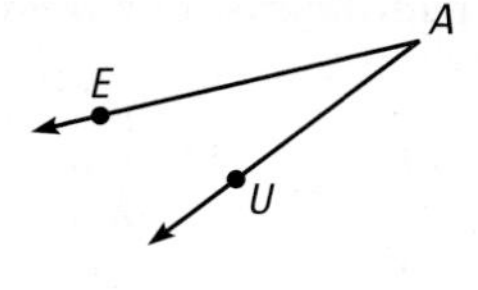

$\angle A$, $\angle EAU$, $\angle UAE$

21.

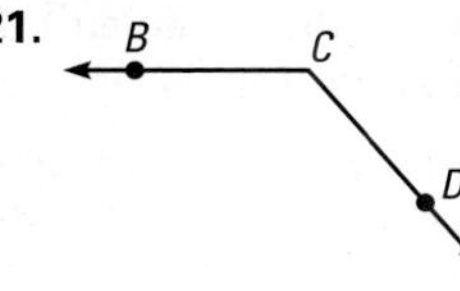

$\angle C$, $\angle BCD$, $\angle DCB$

22.

$\angle T$, $\angle PTS$, $\angle STP$

3 APPLY

ASSIGNMENT GUIDE

BASIC
Day 1: pp. 29–32 Exs. 17–25, 26–48 even, 51, 62–78 even

AVERAGE
Day 1: pp. 29–32 Exs. 17–25, 26–48 even, 51, 62–78 even

ADVANCED
Day 1: pp. 29–32 Exs. 17–25, 26–48 even, 51, 55–60, 62–78 even

BLOCK SCHEDULE WITH 1.5
pp. 29–32 Exs. 17–25, 26–48 even, 51, 62–78 even

EXERCISE LEVELS

Level A: *Easier*
17–28, 35–37

Level B: *More Difficult*
29–34, 38–54

Level C: *Most Difficult*
55–60

✓ HOMEWORK CHECK

To quickly check student understanding of key concepts, go over the following exercises: Exs. 18, 20, 24, 28, 32, 38, 40, 46. See also the Daily Homework Quiz:

- Blackline Master (*Chapter 1 Resource Book,* p. 63)
- Transparency (p. 6)

! COMMON ERROR

EXERCISES 20–22 Stress to students that when naming angles, the letter at the vertex must be the middle letter in the angle name.

CAREER NOTE

EXERCISE 23–25
Additional information about surveyors is available at **www.mcdougallittell.com.**

MATHEMATICAL REASONING

EXERCISES 29–34, 38 AND 39 Students may need to use trial-and-error to complete the drawings in these exercises. They should begin with a drawing that uses only one or two of the pieces of information. They can then change or redraw the figure to accommodate each of the remaining pieces of information. After this procedure students should check that each condition is met in the final drawing.

29. ; 50°

38.

39.

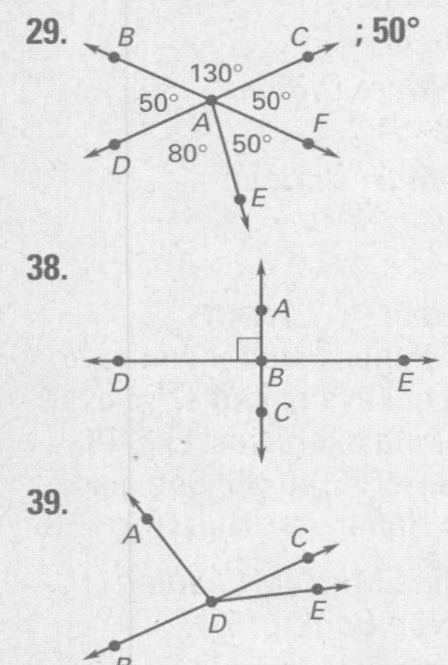

FOCUS ON CAREERS

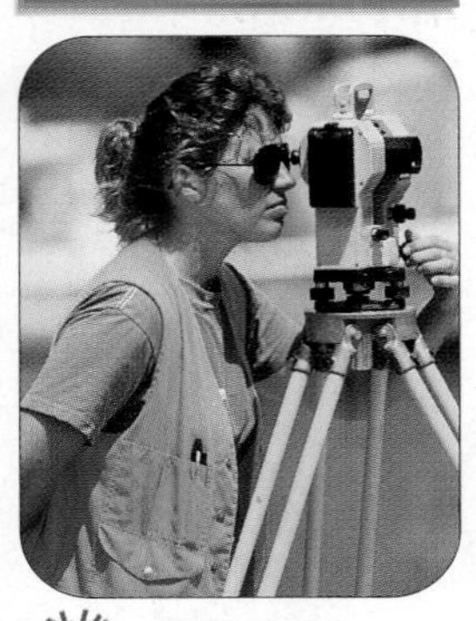

SURVEYOR
Surveyors use a tool called a theodolite, which can measure angles to the nearest 1/3600 of a degree.

CAREER LINK
www.mcdougallittell.com

MEASURING ANGLES **Copy the angle, extend its sides, and use a protractor to measure it to the nearest degree.**

23.

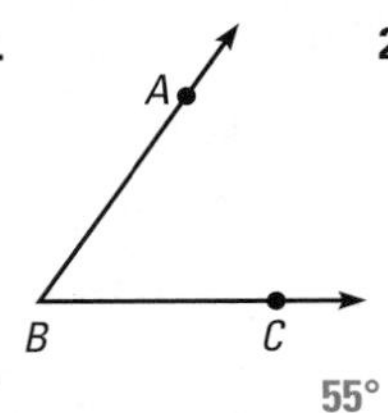

55°

24. Y Z X

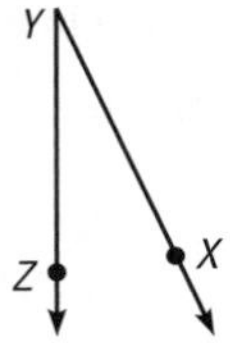

25°

25.

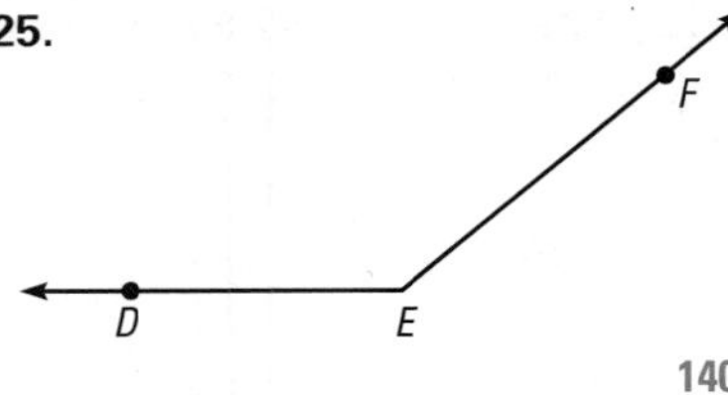

140°

ANGLE ADDITION **Use the Angle Addition Postulate to find the measure of the unknown angle.**

26. $m\angle ABC = \underline{\ ?\ }$

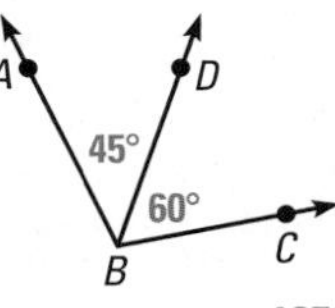

105°

27. $m\angle DEF = \underline{\ ?\ }$

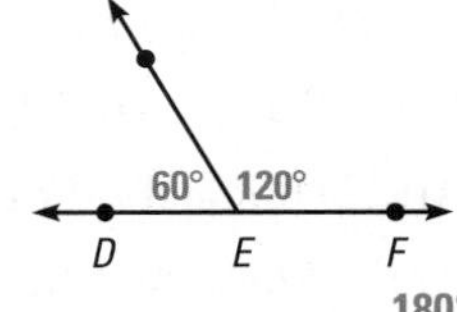

180°

28. $m\angle PQR = \underline{\ ?\ }$

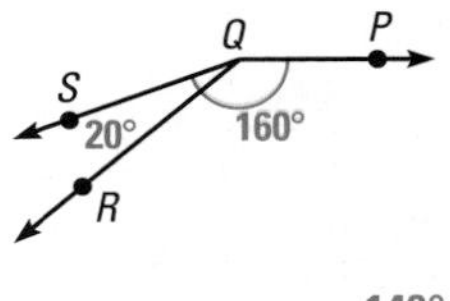

140°

LOGICAL REASONING **Draw a sketch that uses all of the following information.** See margin.

D is in the interior of $\angle BAE$.	$m\angle BAC = 130°$
E is in the interior of $\angle DAF$.	$m\angle EAC = 100°$
F is in the interior of $\angle EAC$.	$m\angle BAD = m\angle EAF = m\angle FAC$

29. Find $m\angle FAC$. 50°

30. Find $m\angle BAD$. 50°

31. Find $m\angle FAB$. 180°

32. Find $m\angle DAE$. 80°

33. Find $m\angle FAD$. 130°

34. Find $m\angle BAE$. 130°

CLASSIFYING ANGLES **State whether the angle appears to be *acute, right, obtuse,* or *straight*. Then estimate its measure.**

35.

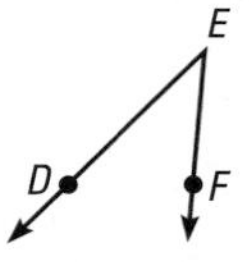

acute; about 40°

36.

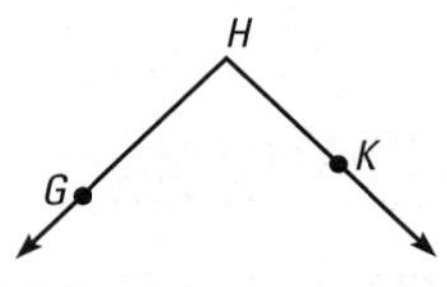

right; about 90°

37.

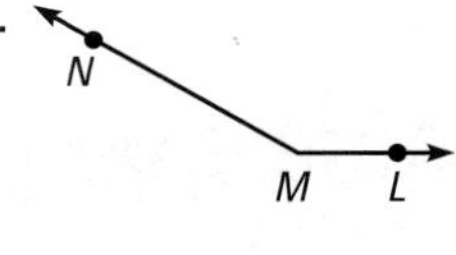

obtuse; about 150°

LOGICAL REASONING **Draw five points, *A, B, C, D,* and *E* so that all three statements are true.** 38, 39. See margin.

38. $\angle DBE$ is a straight angle.
$\angle DBA$ is a right angle.
$\angle ABC$ is a straight angle.

39. C is in the interior of $\angle ADE$.
$m\angle ADC + m\angle CDE = 120°$.
$\angle CDB$ is a straight angle.

USING ALGEBRA **In a coordinate plane, plot the points and sketch $\angle ABC$. Classify the angle. Write the coordinates of a point that lies in the interior of the angle and the coordinates of a point that lies in the exterior of the angle.** 40–43. See margin.

40. $A(3, -2)$
$B(5, -1)$
$C(4, -4)$

41. $A(5, -1)$
$B(3, -2)$
$C(4, -4)$

42. $A(5, -1)$
$B(3, -2)$
$C(0, -1)$

43. $A(-3, 1)$
$B(-2, 2)$
$C(-1, 4)$

GEOGRAPHY **For each city on the polar map, estimate the measure of $\angle BOA$, where B is on the Prime Meridian (0° longitude), O is the North Pole, and A is the city.** Estimates may vary.

44. Clyde River, Canada
about 70°

45. Fairbanks, Alaska
about 150°

46. Angmagssalik, Greenland
about 40°

47. Old Crow, Canada
about 140°

48. Reykjavik, Iceland
about 20°

49. Tuktoyaktuk, Canada
about 135°

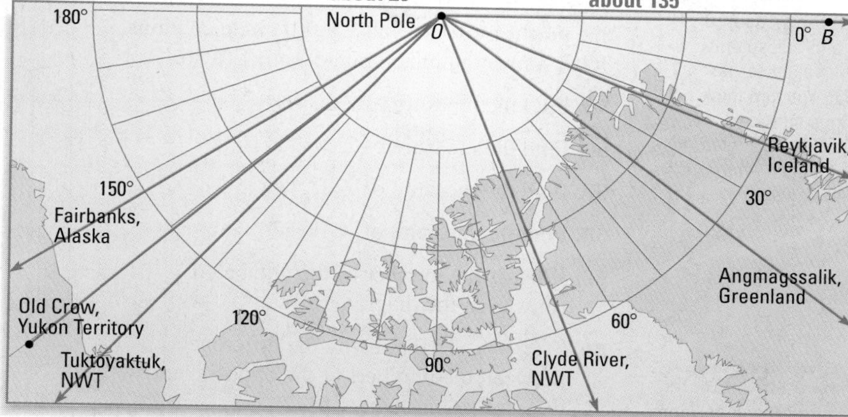

PLAYING DARTS **In Exercises 50–53, use the following information to find the score for the indicated dart toss landing at point A.**

A dartboard is 18 inches across. It is divided into twenty wedges of equal size. The score of a toss is indicated by numbers around the board. The score is doubled if a dart lands in the *double ring* and tripled if it lands in the *triple ring*. Only the top half of the dart board is shown.

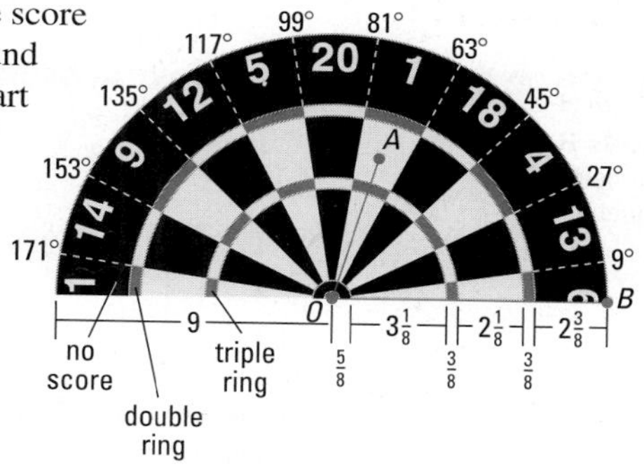

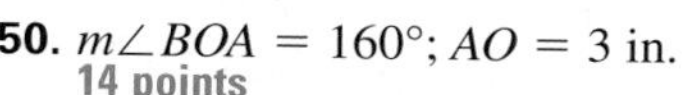

50. $m\angle BOA = 160°$; $AO = 3$ in.
14 points

51. $m\angle BOA = 35°$; $AO = 4$ in.
12 points

52. $m\angle BOA = 60°$; $AO = 5$ in.
18 points

53. $m\angle BOA = 90°$; $AO = 6.5$ in.
40 points

Test Preparation

54. MULTI-STEP PROBLEM Use a piece of paper folded in half three times and labeled as shown.

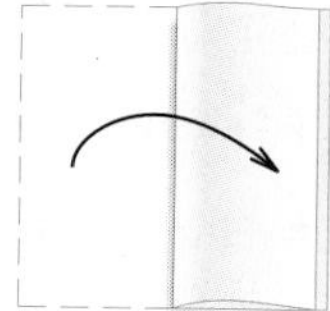
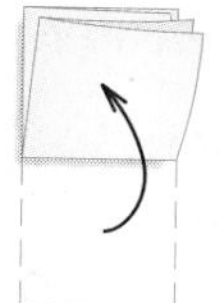
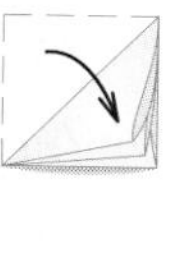
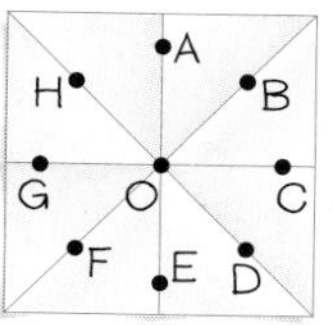

a. Name eight congruent acute angles.
$\angle GOH$, $\angle HOA$, $\angle AOB$, $\angle BOC$, $\angle COD$, $\angle DOE$, $\angle EOF$, $\angle FOG$

b. Name eight right angles.
$\angle GOA$, $\angle HOB$, $\angle AOC$, $\angle BOD$, $\angle COE$, $\angle DOF$, $\angle EOG$, $\angle FOH$

c. Name eight congruent obtuse angles.
$\angle GOB$, $\angle HOC$, $\angle AOD$, $\angle BOE$, $\angle COF$, $\angle DOG$, $\angle EOH$, $\angle FOA$

d. Name two adjacent angles that combine to form a straight angle.
Sample answers: $\angle FOA$ and $\angle AOB$, $\angle GOA$ and $\angle AOC$

40–43. Coordinates of sample points are given.

40.

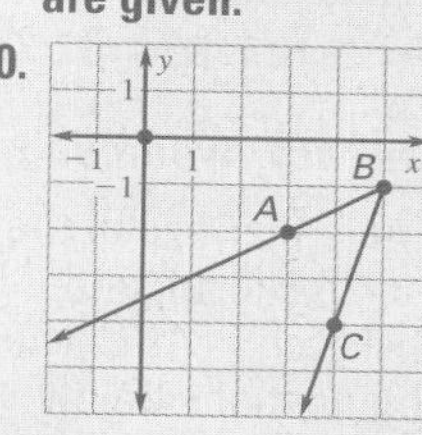

acute; (3, −3), (0, 0)

41.

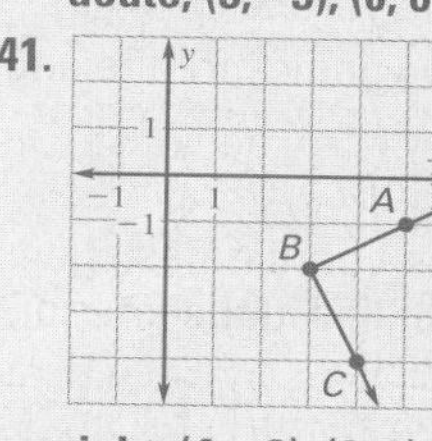

right; (4, −3), (0, 0)

42.

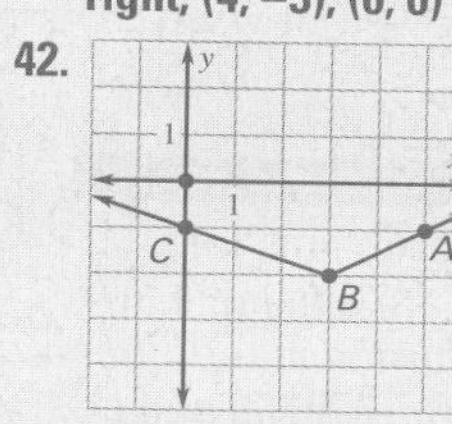

obtuse; (0, 0), (0, −3)

43.

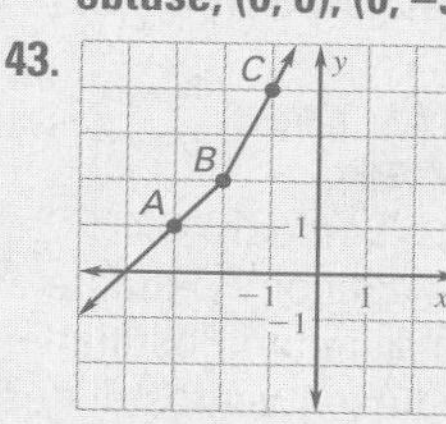

obtuse; (−3, 3), (0, 0)

ADDITIONAL PRACTICE AND RETEACHING

For Lesson 1.4:

- Practice Levels A, B, and C (*Chapter 1 Resource Book,* p. 53)
- Reteaching with Practice (*Chapter 1 Resource Book,* p. 56)
- See Lesson 1.4 of the *Personal Student Tutor*

For more Mixed Review:

- Search the *Test and Practice Generator* for key words or specific lessons.

4 ASSESS

DAILY HOMEWORK QUIZ

Transparency Available

In a coordinate plane, plot the points $A(-6, 2)$, $B(0, 0)$, and $C(1, 3)$ and sketch $\angle ABC$. Then answer the questions below.

1. Name the vertex. *B*
2. Write two names for the angle. *two of $\angle ABC$, $\angle CBA$, $\angle B$*
3. Find $m\angle ABC$. 90°
4. Write the coordinates of a point that lies in the interior of the angle. *Sample answer:* (0, 2)

EXTRA CHALLENGE NOTE

Challenge problems for Lesson 1.4 are available in **blackline** format in the *Chapter 1 Resource Book,* p. 60 and at **www.mcdougallittell.com**.

ADDITIONAL TEST PREPARATION

1. **WRITING** Compare the Segment Addition Postulate and the Angle Addition Postulate. How are these two postulates similar? How are they different? *Sample answer:* Both of these postulates state that the measure of the whole is equal to the sum of the measures of the parts. In the case of the Segment Addition Postulate, the whole and parts are segments and in the case of the Angle Addition Postulate the whole and parts are angles.

★ **Challenge**

STUDENT HELP

HOMEWORK HELP
Bearings are measured around a circle, so they can have values larger than 180°. You can think of bearings between 180° and 360° as angles that are "bigger" than a straight angle.

EXTRA CHALLENGE
www.mcdougallittell.com

AIRPORT RUNWAYS In Exercises 55–60, use the diagram of Ronald Reagan Washington National Airport and the information about runway numbering on page 1.

An airport runway is named by dividing its *bearing* (the angle measured clockwise from due north) by 10. Because a full circle contains 360°, runway numbers range from 1 to 36.

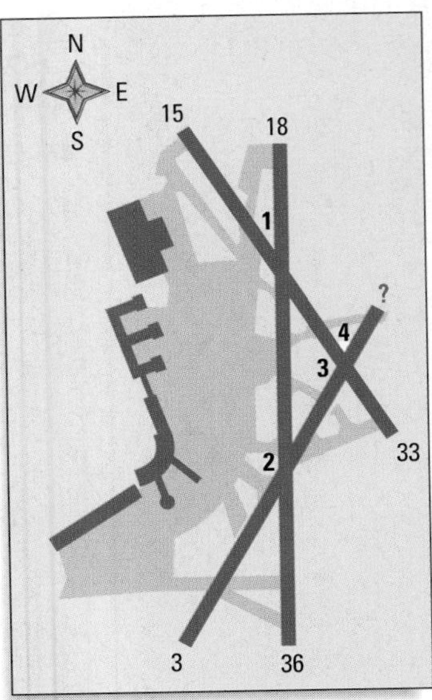

55. Find the measure of $\angle 1$. 30°
56. Find the measure of $\angle 2$. 150°
57. Find the measure of $\angle 3$. 120°
58. Find the measure of $\angle 4$. 60°
59. What is the number of the unlabeled runway in the diagram? 21
60. *Writing* Explain why the difference between the numbers at the opposite ends of a runway is always 18.
If the bearing of one end of a runway is $x°$, the bearing of the other is $180° + x°$ and the difference between the bearings is 180°. Then the difference between the runway numbers is $\frac{180}{10}$, or 18.

MIXED REVIEW

STUDENT HELP

Skills Review
For help solving equations, see p.790.

USING ALGEBRA Solve for *x*. (Skills Review, p. 790, for 1.5)

61. $\frac{x+3}{2} = 3$ 3
62. $\frac{5+x}{2} = 5$ 5
63. $\frac{x+4}{2} = -4$ −12
64. $\frac{-8+x}{2} = 12$ 32
65. $\frac{x+7}{2} = -10$ −27
66. $\frac{-9+x}{2} = -7$ −5
67. $\frac{x+(-1)}{2} = 7$ 15
68. $\frac{8+x}{2} = -1$ −10
69. $\frac{x+(-3)}{2} = -4$ −5

EVALUATING STATEMENTS Decide whether the statement is *true* or *false*. (Review 1.2)

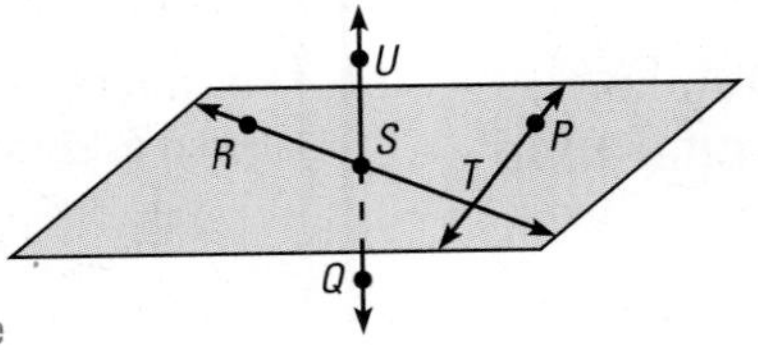

70. *U, S,* and *Q* are collinear. true
71. *T, Q, S,* and *P* are coplanar. false
72. $\overleftrightarrow{UQ}$ and $\overleftrightarrow{PT}$ intersect. false
73. $\overrightarrow{SR}$ and $\overrightarrow{TS}$ are opposite rays. false

DISTANCE FORMULA Find the distance between the two points. (Review 1.3 for 1.5)

74. $A(3, 10)$, $B(-2, -2)$ 13
75. $C(0, 8)$, $D(-8, 3)$ $\sqrt{89}$
76. $E(-3, 11)$, $F(4, 4)$ $7\sqrt{2}$
77. $G(10, -2)$, $H(0, 9)$ $\sqrt{221}$
78. $J(5, 7)$, $K(7, 5)$ $2\sqrt{2}$
79. $L(0, -3)$, $M(-3, 0)$ $3\sqrt{2}$

ACTIVITY 1.5

Developing Concepts

Folding Bisectors

GROUP ACTIVITY
Work with a partner.

MATERIALS
- rulers
- paper
- protractor
- pencils

QUESTION **How can you divide a segment or an angle into two equal parts?**

You can fold a piece of paper so that one half of a segment or angle lies exactly on the other half.

EXPLORING THE CONCEPT: SEGMENT BISECTOR

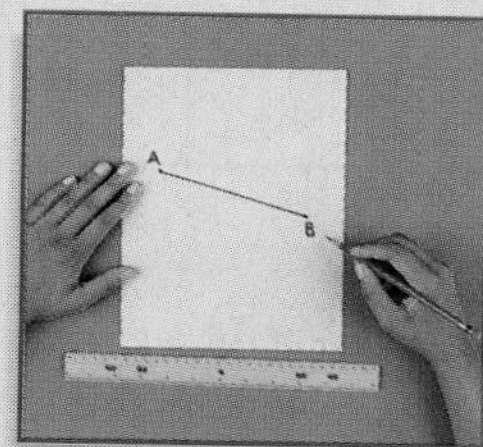

1. On a piece of paper, draw $\overline{AB}$.

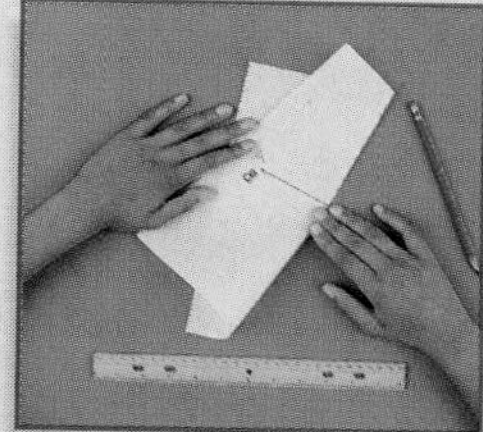

2. Fold the paper so that B is on top of A.

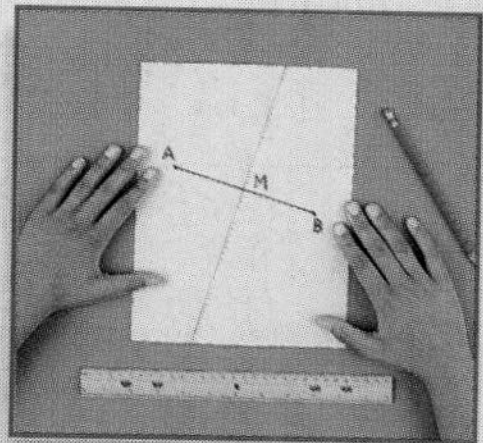

3. Label the point where the fold intersects $\overline{AB}$ as point M.

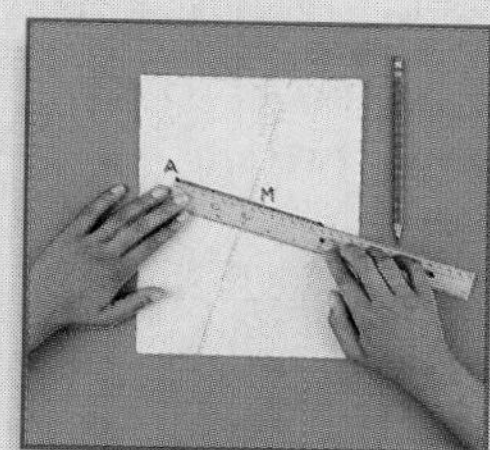

4. Use a ruler to measure $\overline{AM}$ and $\overline{MB}$.
$\overline{AM}$ and $\overline{MB}$ are congruent.

EXPLORING THE CONCEPT: ANGLE BISECTOR

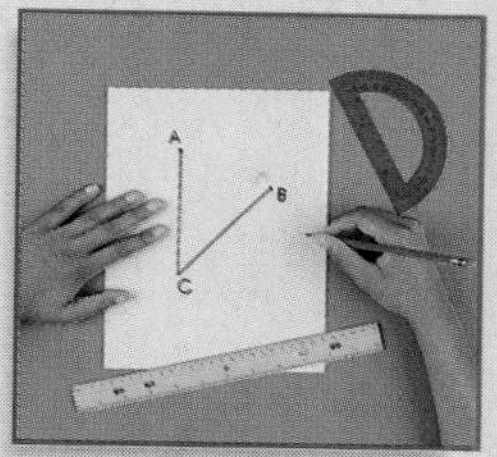

5. On a piece of paper, draw $\angle ACB$.

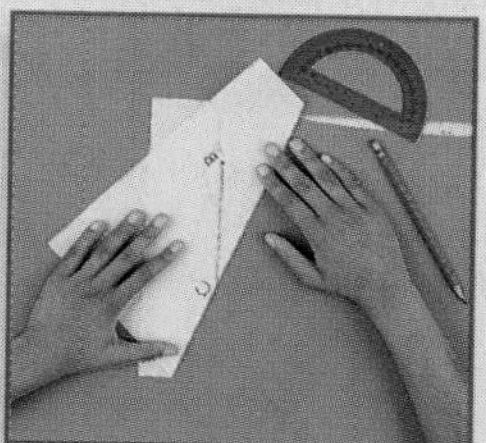

6. Fold the paper so $\overrightarrow{CB}$ is on top of $\overrightarrow{CA}$.

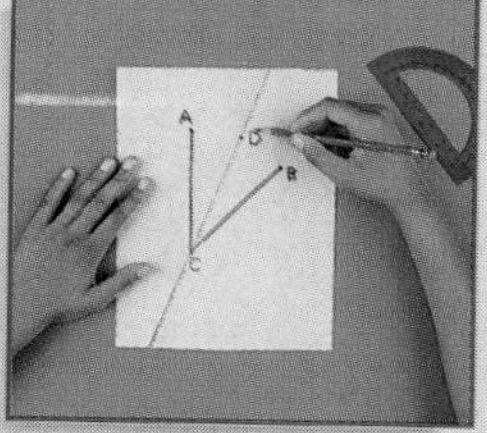

7. Draw any point on the fold and label the point D.

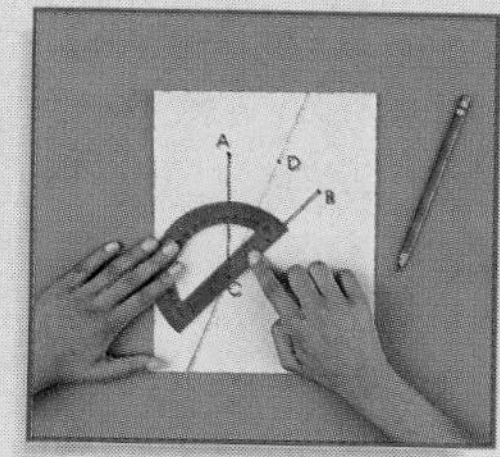

8. Use a protractor to measure $\angle ACD$ and $\angle BCD$.
$\angle ACD$ and $\angle BCD$ are congruent.

DRAWING CONCLUSIONS

1. What do you notice about the segments you measured in Step 4? They have the same length.
2. What do you notice about the angles you measured in Step 8? They have the same measure.

EXTENSION

CRITICAL THINKING Is it possible to fold congruent angles from a straight angle if you are given the vertex of the angle? Explain. Yes; proceed as in Steps 5–8. ($\overrightarrow{CB}$ and $\overrightarrow{CA}$ are opposite rays.)

1 Planning the Activity

PURPOSE
In this activity, students use paper folding to explore segment bisectors and angle bisectors.

MATERIALS
- ruler and protractor
- paper and pencil

PACING
- Exploring the Concept — 10 min
- Drawing Conclusions — 10 min

LINK TO LESSON
When discussing the definitions of midpoint and segment bisector on page 34, ask students which parts of the folded paper correspond to the midpoint and the segment bisector. Similarly, relate the definition of angle bisector on page 36 to the fold line.

2 Managing the Activity

COOPERATIVE LEARNING
Each student in the group should draw a segment and angle and complete the steps of the exploration. Group members can then discuss their results and answer the questions together.

CLASSROOM MANAGEMENT
Thin paper should be used so that students can see the segments or rays through it when folding.

3 Closing the Activity

KEY DISCOVERY
You can divide a segment or an angle into two equal parts.

ACTIVITY ASSESSMENT
You take an angle that measures 105° and follow Steps 5–8. What will be the measures of the angles formed by each side of the original angle with the fold line? 52.5°

1 PLAN

PACING
Basic: 2 days
Average: 2 days
Advanced: 2 days
Block Schedule: 0.5 block with 1.4
0.5 block with 1.6

LESSON OPENER APPLICATION
An alternative way to approach Lesson 1.5 is to use the Application Lesson Opener:
- Blackline Master (*Chapter 1 Resource Book*, p. 64)
- Transparency (p. 5)

MEETING INDIVIDUAL NEEDS
- ***Chapter 1 Resource Book***
  Prerequisite Skills Review (p. 5)
  Practice Level A (p. 69)
  Practice Level B (p. 70)
  Practice Level C (p. 71)
  Reteaching with Practice (p. 72)
  Absent Student Catch-Up (p. 74)
  Challenge (p. 76)
- ***Resources in Spanish***
- ***Personal Student Tutor***

NEW-TEACHER SUPPORT
See the Tips for New Teachers on pp. 1–2 of the *Chapter 1 Resource Book* for additional notes about Lesson 1.5.

WARM-UP EXERCISES

Transparency Available

Solve each equation.

1. $\frac{x+1}{2} = 3$ 5
2. $\frac{y-3}{-1} = 4$ −1
3. $x + 30 = 2x - 20$ 50
4. $3y + 15 = 5y - 20$ 17.5

1.5 Segment and Angle Bisectors

What you should learn

GOAL 1 Bisect a segment.

GOAL 2 Bisect an angle, as applied in **Exs. 50–55**.

Why you should learn it

▼ To solve **real-life** problems, such as finding the angle measures of a kite in **Example 4**.

CALIFORNIA STANDARDS AND ASSESSMENT
CA Standards: 16, 17
SAT9 Task 1: Obj. 30
SAT9 Task 2: Obj. 33

GOAL 1 BISECTING A SEGMENT

The **midpoint** of a segment is the point that divides, or **bisects**, the segment into two congruent segments. In this book, matching red *congruence marks* identify congruent segments in diagrams.

A **segment bisector** is a segment, ray, line, or plane that intersects a segment at its midpoint.

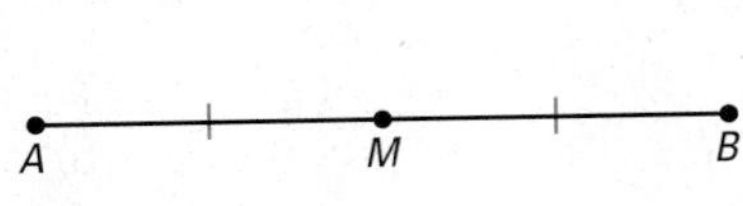

M is the midpoint of $\overline{AB}$ if *M* is on $\overline{AB}$ and $AM = MB$.

$\overleftrightarrow{CD}$ is a bisector of $\overline{AB}$.

You can use a **compass** and a **straightedge** (a ruler without marks) to **construct** a segment bisector and midpoint of $\overline{AB}$. A **construction** is a geometric drawing that uses a limited set of tools, usually a compass and a straightedge.

ACTIVITY Construction: Segment Bisector and Midpoint

Use the following steps to construct a bisector of $\overline{AB}$ and find the midpoint *M* of $\overline{AB}$. Check drawings.

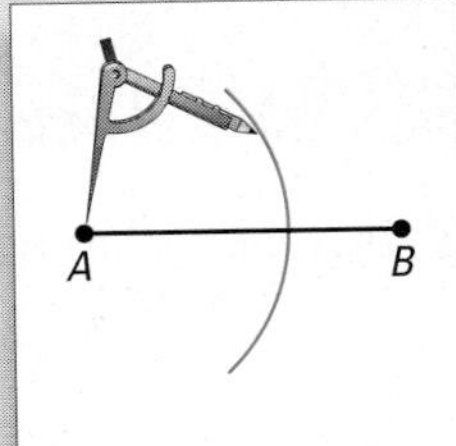

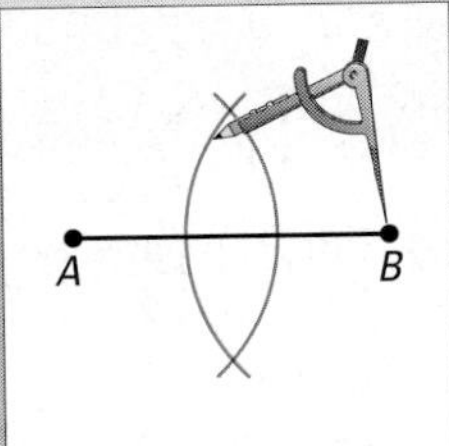

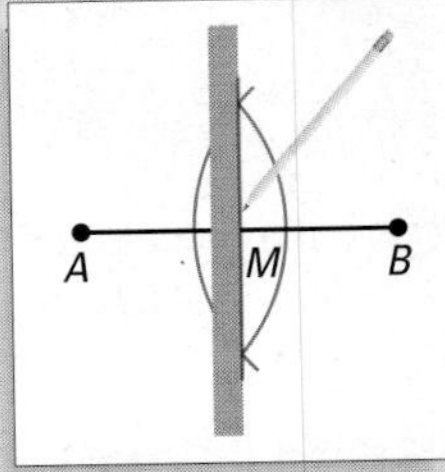

1. Place the compass point at *A*. Use a compass setting greater than half the length of $\overline{AB}$. Draw an arc.
2. Keep the same compass setting. Place the compass point at *B*. Draw an arc. It should intersect the other arc in two places.
3. Use a straightedge to draw a segment through the points of intersection. This segment bisects $\overline{AB}$ at *M*, the midpoint of $\overline{AB}$.

If you know the coordinates of the endpoints of a segment, you can calculate the coordinates of the midpoint. You simply take the mean, or average, of the x-coordinates and of the y-coordinates. This method is summarized as the **Midpoint Formula**.

THE MIDPOINT FORMULA

If $A(x_1, y_1)$ and $B(x_2, y_2)$ are points in a coordinate plane, then the midpoint of $\overline{AB}$ has coordinates

$$\left(\frac{x_1 + x_2}{2}, \frac{y_1 + y_2}{2}\right).$$

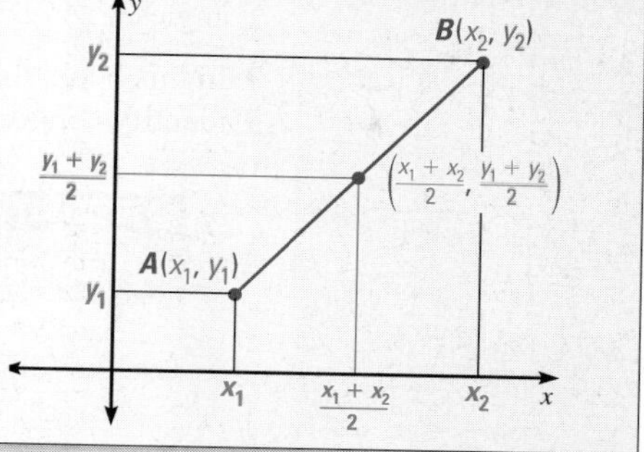

EXAMPLE 1 ***Finding the Coordinates of the Midpoint of a Segment***

Find the coordinates of the midpoint of $\overline{AB}$ with endpoints $A(-2, 3)$ and $B(5, -2)$.

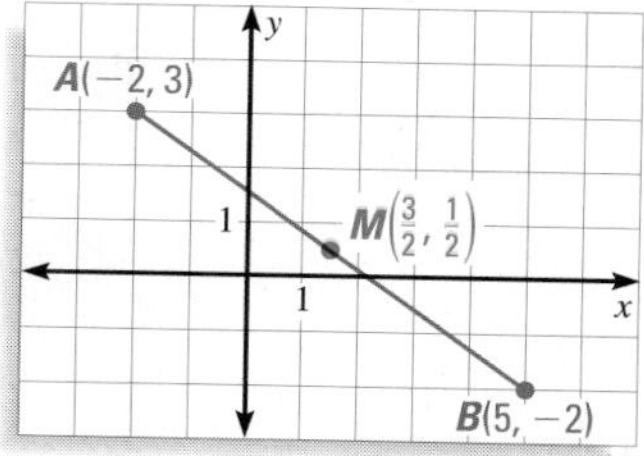

SOLUTION

Use the Midpoint Formula as follows.

$$M = \left(\frac{-2 + 5}{2}, \frac{3 + (-2)}{2}\right)$$

$$= \left(\frac{3}{2}, \frac{1}{2}\right)$$

EXAMPLE 2 ***Finding the Coordinates of an Endpoint of a Segment***

The midpoint of $\overline{RP}$ is $M(2, 4)$. One endpoint is $R(-1, 7)$. Find the coordinates of the other endpoint.

SOLUTION

Let (x, y) be the coordinates of P. Use the Midpoint Formula to write equations involving x and y.

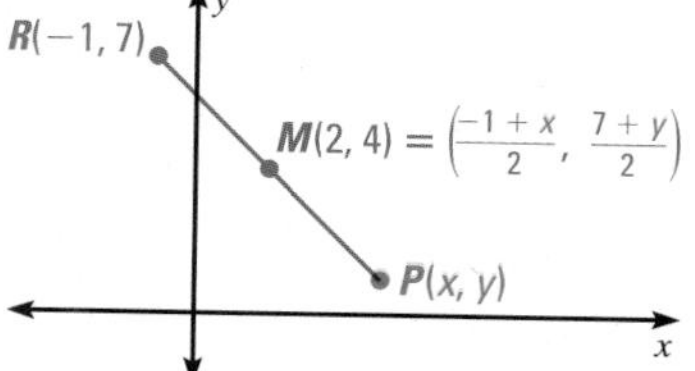

$$\frac{-1 + x}{2} = 2 \qquad \frac{7 + y}{2} = 4$$

$$-1 + x = 4 \qquad 7 + y = 8$$

$$x = 5 \qquad y = 1$$

▶ So, the other endpoint of the segment is $P(5, 1)$.

STUDENT HELP

Study Tip
Sketching the points in a coordinate plane helps you check your work. You should sketch a drawing of a problem even if the directions don't ask for a sketch.

2 TEACH

MOTIVATING THE LESSON
Ask students how to find the point that divides a segment in two equal pieces or the ray that divides an angle in two equal angles. They should recall the paper folding method from Activity 1.5. Point out that there are several other methods that may be more appropriate depending on the context of the problem. Tell students that the focus of Lesson 1.5 is to explore several of these methods.

ACTIVITY NOTE
In this activity students construct a segment bisector using a compass and straight edge. Each student should have practice making this construction. Note that the bisector constructed is the perpendicular bisector though it is not necessary that a bisector be perpendicular in general.

EXTRA EXAMPLE 1
Find the midpoint of $\overline{DE}$ with endpoints $D(3, 5)$ and $E(-4, 0)$.
$M = \left(-\frac{1}{2}, \frac{5}{2}\right)$

EXTRA EXAMPLE 2
The midpoint of $\overline{XY}$ is $M(3, -4)$. One endpoint is $Y(-3, -1)$. Find the coordinates of the other endpoint. $X(9, -7)$

CHECKPOINT EXERCISES

For use after Example 1:

1. Find the midpoint of $\overline{PQ}$ with endpoints $P(0, -7)$ and $Q(-2, -1)$. $M(-1, -4)$

For use after Example 2:

2. The midpoint of $\overline{JK}$ is $M\left(0, \frac{1}{2}\right)$. One endpoint is $J(2, -2)$. Find the coordinates of the other endpoint. $K(-2, 3)$

ACTIVITY NOTE

In this activity students construct an angle bisector using a compass and straight edge. Each student should have practice making this construction.

GOAL 2 BISECTING AN ANGLE

An **angle bisector** is a ray that divides an angle into two adjacent angles that are congruent. In the diagram at the right, the ray $\overrightarrow{CD}$ bisects $\angle ABC$ because it divides the angle into two congruent angles, $\angle ACD$ and $\angle BCD$.

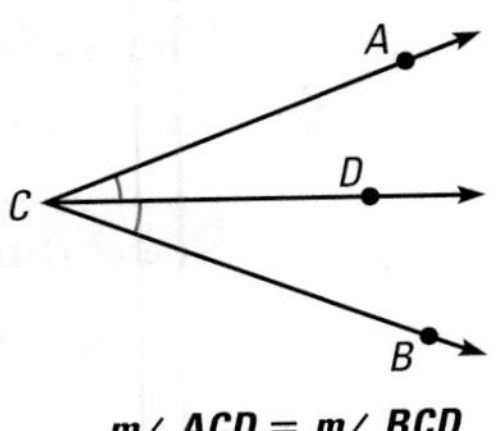

$m\angle ACD = m\angle BCD$

In this book, matching *congruence arcs* identify congruent angles in diagrams.

ACTIVITY

Construction

Angle Bisector

Use the following steps to construct an angle bisector of $\angle C$. **Check drawings.**

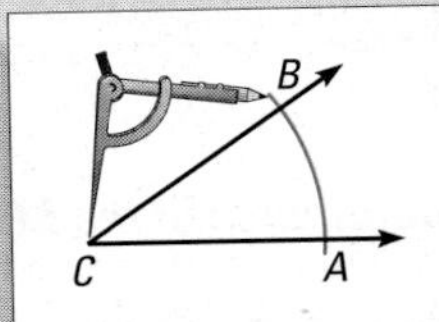

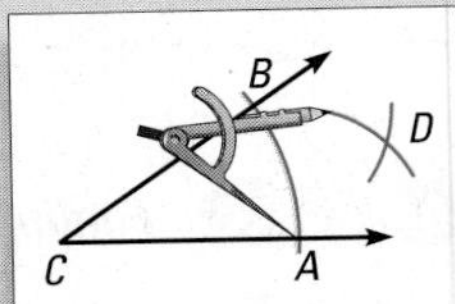

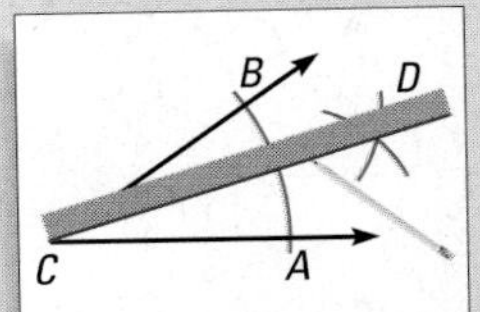

1. Place the compass point at *C*. Draw an arc that intersects both sides of the angle. Label the intersections *A* and *B*.
2. Place the compass point at *A*. Draw an arc. Then place the compass point at *B*. Using the same compass setting, draw another arc.
3. Label the intersection *D*. Use a straightedge to draw a ray through *C* and *D*. This is the angle bisector.

After you have constructed an angle bisector, you should check that it divides the original angle into two congruent angles. One way to do this is to use a protractor to check that the angles have the same measure.

Another way is to fold the piece of paper along the angle bisector. When you hold the paper up to a light, you should be able to see that the sides of the two angles line up, which implies that the angles are congruent.

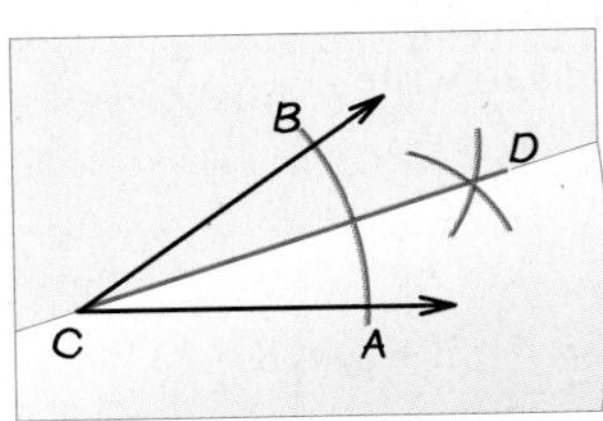

Fold on $\overrightarrow{CD}$.

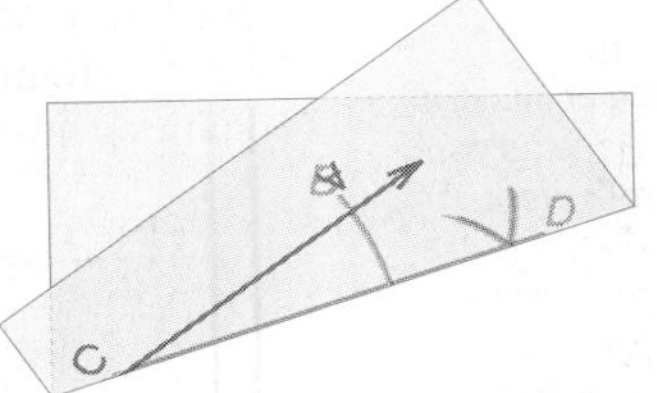

The sides of angles $\angle BCD$ and $\angle ACD$ line up.

EXAMPLE 3 Dividing an Angle Measure in Half

The ray $\overrightarrow{FH}$ bisects the angle $\angle EFG$. Given that $m\angle EFG = 120°$, what are the measures of $\angle EFH$ and $\angle HFG$?

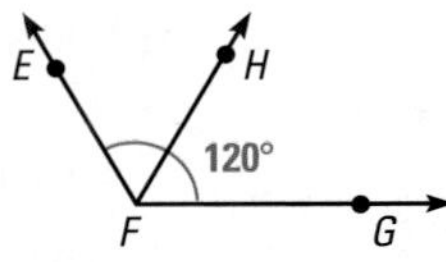

SOLUTION

An angle bisector divides an angle into two congruent angles, each of which has half the measure of the original angle. So,

$$m\angle EFH = m\angle HFG = \frac{120°}{2} = 60°.$$

EXAMPLE 4 Doubling an Angle Measure

KITE DESIGN In the kite, two angles are bisected.

$\angle EKI$ is bisected by $\overrightarrow{KT}$.

$\angle ITE$ is bisected by $\overrightarrow{TK}$.

Find the measures of the two angles.

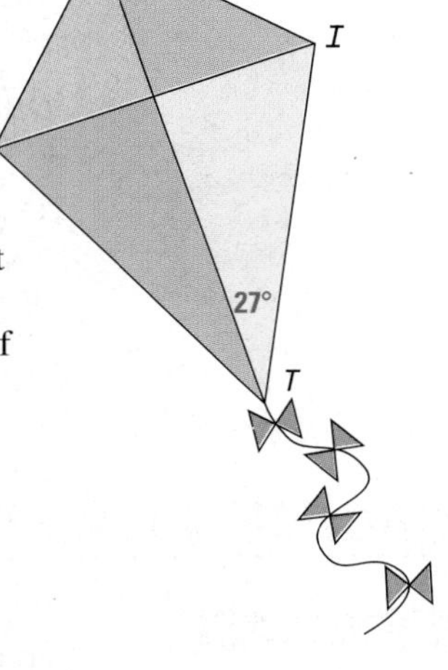

SOLUTION

You are given the measure of one of the two congruent angles that make up the larger angle. You can find the measure of the larger angle by doubling the measure of the smaller angle.

$$m\angle EKI = 2m\angle TKI = 2(45°) = 90°$$

$$m\angle ITE = 2m\angle KTI = 2(27°) = 54°$$

EXAMPLE 5 Finding the Measure of an Angle

In the diagram, $\overrightarrow{RQ}$ bisects $\angle PRS$. The measures of the two congruent angles are $(x + 40)°$ and $(3x - 20)°$. Solve for x.

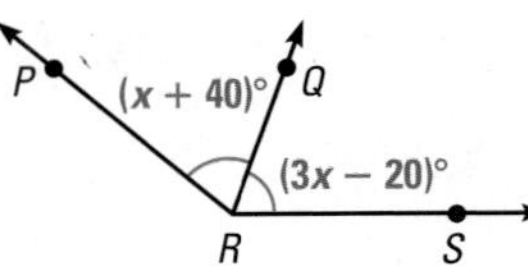

SOLUTION

$m\angle PRQ = m\angle QRS$	**Congruent angles have equal measures.**
$(x + 40)° = (3x - 20)°$	**Substitute given measures.**
$x + 60 = 3x$	**Add 20° to each side.**
$60 = 2x$	**Subtract x from each side.**
$30 = x$	**Divide each side by 2.**

▶ So, $x = 30$. You can check by substituting to see that each of the congruent angles has a measure of 70°.

FOCUS ON PEOPLE

JOSÉ SAÍNZ, a San Diego kite designer, uses colorful patterns in his kites. The struts of his kites often bisect the angles they support.

Using Algebra

EXTRA EXAMPLE 3

$\overrightarrow{JK}$ bisects $\angle HJL$. Given that $m\angle HJL = 42°$, what are the measures of $\angle HJK$ and $\angle KJL$? **21° and 21°**

EXTRA EXAMPLE 4

A cellular phone tower bisects the angle formed by the two wires that support it. Find the measure of the angle formed by the two wires. **94°**

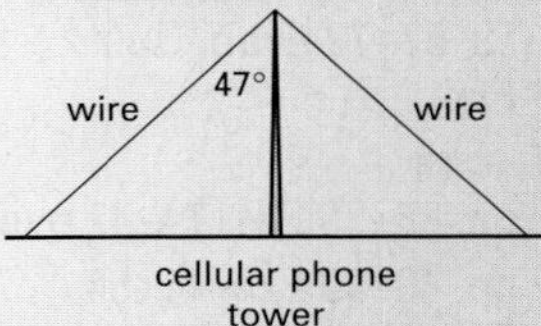

EXTRA EXAMPLE 5

In the diagram $\overrightarrow{MO}$ bisects $\angle LMN$. The measures of the two congruent angles are $(3x - 20)°$ and $(x + 10)°$. Solve for x. **15**

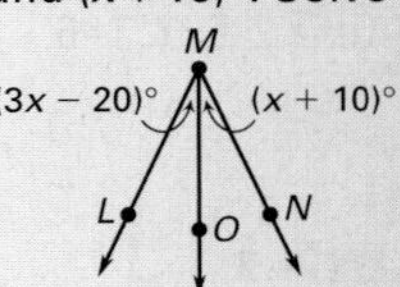

CHECKPOINT EXERCISES

For use after Examples 3–5:

1. In the diagram $\overrightarrow{BD}$ bisects $\angle ABC$. Find x and use it to find $m\angle ABD$, $m\angle DBC$, and $m\angle ABC$. **15; 80°, 80°, 160°**

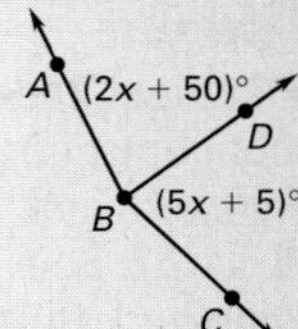

FOCUS ON VOCABULARY

What is the midpoint of a segment? **See answer below.**

CLOSURE QUESTION

What methods can you use to bisect a segment? **See below.**

DAILY PUZZLER

The midpoint of vertical segment $\overline{RS}$ is $(-2, 5)$. Find a and b if $R(-2, a)$, $S(-2, b)$ and $RS = 6$. **$a = 2$, $b = 8$ or $a = 8$, $b = 2$**

Focus on Vocabulary ***Sample answer:*** **The midpoint of a segment is the point that divides the segment into two congruent segments.**

Closure Question ***Sample answer:*** **You can do a compass and straightedge construction, you can use paper folding, or you can use the midpoint formula.**

3 APPLY

ASSIGNMENT GUIDE

BASIC
Day 1: pp. 38–39 Exs. 14–42 even
Day 2: pp. 40–42 Exs. 44–54, 58, 62–72 even, Quiz 2 Exs. 1–6

AVERAGE
Day 1: pp. 38–39 Exs. 14–42 even
Day 2: pp. 40–42 Exs. 44–54, 56, 58, 62–72 even, Quiz 2 Exs. 1–6

ADVANCED
Day 1: pp. 38–39 Exs. 14–42 even
Day 2: pp. 40–42 Exs. 44–54, 56–60, 62–72 even, Quiz 2 Exs. 1–6

BLOCK SCHEDULE
pp. 38–39 Exs. 14–42 even (with 1.4)
pp. 40–42 Exs. 44–54, 56, 58, 62–72 even, Quiz 2 Exs. 1–6 (with 1.6)

EXERCISE LEVELS

Level A: ***Easier***
14–24, 31–42, 52–54

Level B: ***More Difficult***
25–30, 43–51, 56

Level C: ***Most Difficult***
55, 57–60

✔ HOMEWORK CHECK

To quickly check student understanding of key concepts, go over the following exercises: Exs. 18, 24, 26, 38, 44, 52. See also the Daily Homework Quiz:

- Blackline Master (*Chapter 1 Resource Book*, p. 80)
- Transparency (p. 7)

GUIDED PRACTICE

Vocabulary Check ✓

Concept Check ✓

2. matching congruence marks; matching congruence arcs

Skill Check ✓

3. The midpoint of the segment has coordinates $\left(\frac{x}{2}, \frac{y}{2}\right)$.

1. What kind of geometric figure is an *angle bisector*? a ray

2. How do you indicate congruent segments in a diagram? How do you indicate congruent angles in a diagram?

3. What is the simplified form of the Midpoint Formula if one of the endpoints of a segment is (0, 0) and the other is (x, y)?

Find the coordinates of the midpoint of a segment with the given endpoints.

4. $A(5, 4), B(-3, 2)$ (1, 3) **5.** $A(-1, -9), B(11, -5)$ (5, −7) **6.** $A(6, -4), B(1, 8)$ $\left(3\frac{1}{2}, 2\right)$

Find the coordinates of the other endpoint of a segment with the given endpoint and midpoint *M*.

7. $C(3, 0)$ (3, 8)
$M(3, 4)$

8. $D(5, 2)$ (9, 10)
$M(7, 6)$

9. $E(-4, 2)$ (−2, −6)
$M(-3, -2)$

10. Suppose $m\angle JKL$ is 90°. If the ray $\overrightarrow{KM}$ bisects $\angle JKL$, what are the measures of $\angle JKM$ and $\angle LKM$? 45°

$\overrightarrow{QS}$ is the angle bisector of $\angle PQR$. Find the two angle measures not given in the diagram.

11.

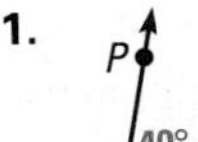

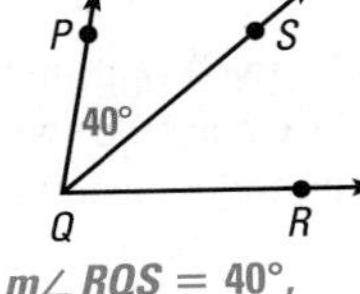

$m\angle RQS = 40°$, $m\angle PQR = 80°$

12.

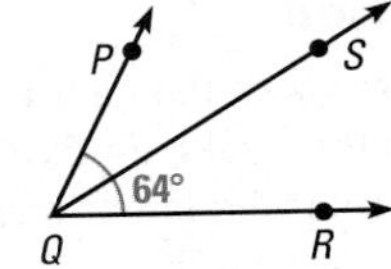

$m\angle PQS = m\angle RQS = 32°$

13.

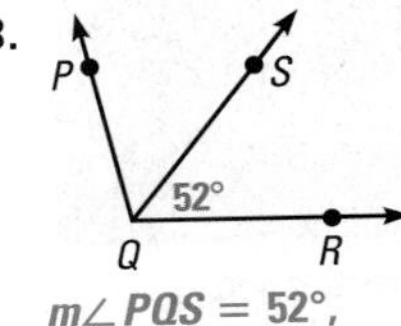

$m\angle PQS = 52°$, $m\angle PQR = 104°$

PRACTICE AND APPLICATIONS

STUDENT HELP
Extra Practice to help you master skills is on p. 804.

CONSTRUCTION **Use a ruler to measure and redraw the line segment on a piece of paper. Then use construction tools to construct a segment bisector.** 14–16. Check drawings.

14. A ———— B

15.

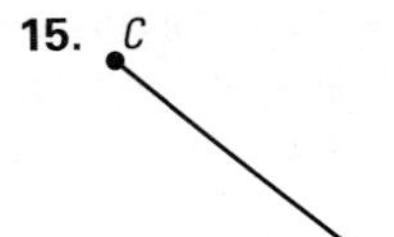

16.

STUDENT HELP
HOMEWORK HELP
Example 1: Exs. 17–24
Example 2: Exs. 25–30
Example 3: Exs. 37–42
Example 4: Exs. 37–42
Example 5: Exs. 44–49

FINDING THE MIDPOINT **Find the coordinates of the midpoint of a segment with the given endpoints.**

17. $A(0, 0)$ (−4, 3)
$B(-8, 6)$

18. $J(-1, 7)$ (1, 2)
$K(3, -3)$

19. $C(10, 8)$ $\left(4, 6\frac{1}{2}\right)$
$D(-2, 5)$

20. $P(-12, -9)$
$Q(2, 10)$ $\left(-5, \frac{1}{2}\right)$

21. $S(0, -8)$ (−3, 3)
$T(-6, 14)$

22. $E(4, 4)$ (4, −7)
$F(4, -18)$

23. $V(-1.5, 8)$
$W(0.25, -1)$
(−0.625, 3.5)

24. $G(-5.5, -6.1)$
$H(-0.5, 9.1)$
(−3, 1.5)

USING ALGEBRA **Find the coordinates of the other endpoint of a segment with the given endpoint and midpoint M.**

25. $R(2, 6)$ (−4, −4)
$M(-1, 1)$

26. $T(-8, -1)$ (8, 7)
$M(0, 3)$

27. $W(3, -12)$ (1, 10)
$M(2, -1)$

28. $Q(-5, 9)$ (−11, −13)
$M(-8, -2)$

29. $A(6, 7)$ (14, −21)
$M(10, -7)$

30. $D(-3.5, -6)$ (6.5, 15)
$M(1.5, 4.5)$

RECOGNIZING CONGRUENCE **Use the marks on the diagram to name the congruent segments and congruent angles.**

33. $\overline{XW}$ and $\overline{XY}$, $\angle ZXW$ and $\angle ZXY$

31.

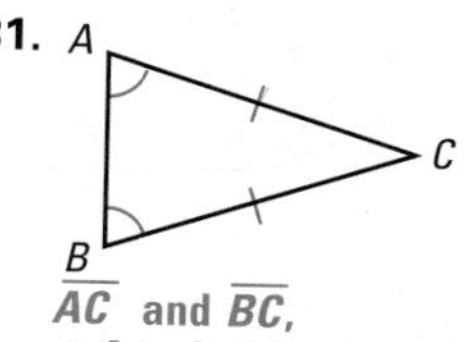

$\overline{AC}$ and $\overline{BC}$, $\angle A$ and $\angle B$

32. D E F G

$\overline{GF}$ and $\overline{GD}$, $\angle DGE$ and $\angle FGE$

33. Z W X Y

CONSTRUCTION **Use a protractor to measure and redraw the angle on a piece of paper. Then use construction tools to find the angle bisector.**

34–36. Check drawings.

34.

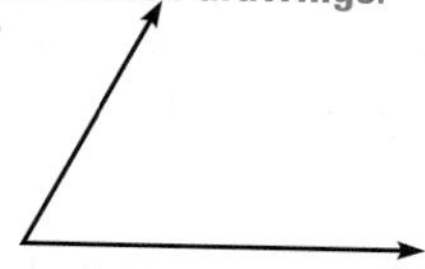

35.

36.

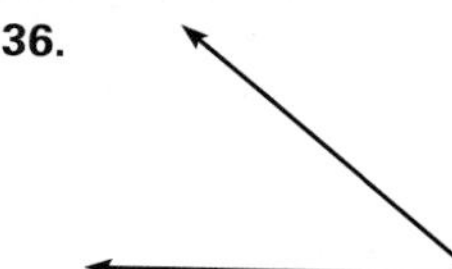

ANALYZING ANGLE BISECTORS $\overrightarrow{QS}$ **is the angle bisector of** $\angle PQR$**. Find the two angle measures not given in the diagram.**

37.

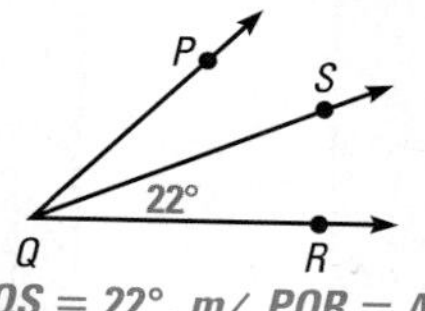

$m\angle PQS = 22°$, $m\angle PQR = 44°$

38. P S 91° Q R

$m\angle PQS = m\angle RQS = 45.5°$

39.

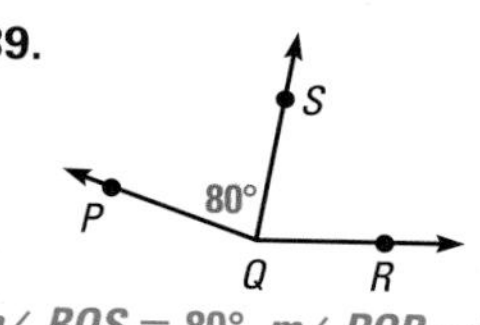

$m\angle RQS = 80°$, $m\angle PQR = 160°$

40.

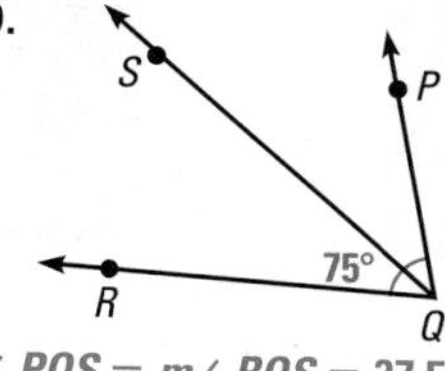

$m\angle PQS = m\angle RQS = 37.5°$

41. Q 45° P R S

$m\angle RQS = 45°$, $m\angle PQR = 90°$

42.

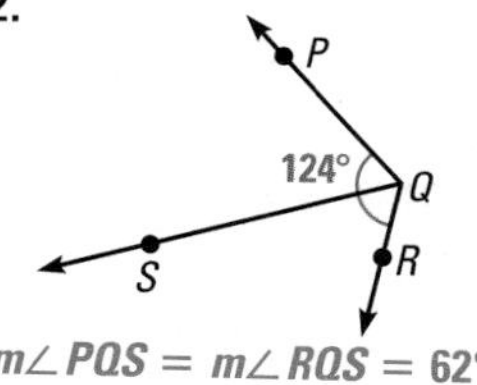

$m\angle PQS = m\angle RQS = 62°$

43. **TECHNOLOGY** Use geometry software to draw a triangle. Construct the angle bisector of one angle. Then find the midpoint of the opposite side of the triangle. Change your triangle and observe what happens.

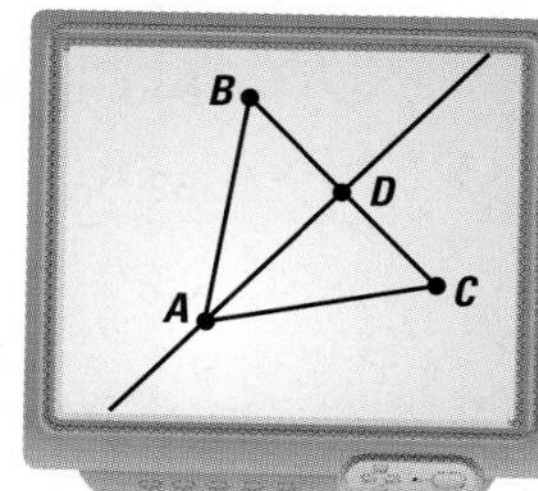

Does the angle bisector *always* pass through the midpoint of the opposite side? Does it *ever* pass through the midpoint?
No; yes; the angle bisector of an angle of a triangle passes through the midpoint of the opposite side if the two sides of the triangle contained in the angle are congruent.

STUDENT HELP

INTERNET SOFTWARE HELP
Visit our Web site www.mcdougallittell.com to see instructions for several software applications.

! COMMON ERROR

EXERCISES 17–24 Students may subtract coordinates when finding a midpoint rather than adding. To help students avoid this error have them think of the coordinates of the midpoint as the *average* of the corresponding coordinates of the endpoints. Also, students should graph the endpoints and midpoints to check their work.

STUDENT HELP NOTES

Software Help Instructions for several software packages are available in blackline format in the *Chapter 1 Resource Book,* p. 68 and at **www.mcdougallittell.com.**

STUDENT HELP NOTES

Homework Help Students can find help for Exs. 44–49 at **www.mcdougallittell.com.** The information can be printed out for students who don't have access to the Internet.

56. Construction tools: Let A and B be the endpoints of the segment. Construct the bisector $\overline{AB}$ and label the midpoint of $\overline{AB}$ M. Then construct the bisectors of $\overline{AM}$ and $\overline{MB}$. Midpoint Formula: Assign coordinates to A and B and use the Midpoint Formula to find the coordinates of M, the midpoint of $\overline{AB}$. Then use the Midpoint Formula again to find the coordinates of the midpoints of $\overline{AM}$ and $\overline{MB}$.

58c. If the three sides of a triangle are different lengths, none of the angle bisectors pass through the midpoint of the opposite side. If the triangle has two congruent sides, the bisector of the angle that contains them would pass through the midpoint of the opposite side and if the triangle has three congruent sides, all three angle bisectors would pass through the midpoints of the opposite sides.

ADDITIONAL PRACTICE AND RETEACHING

For Lesson 1.5:

- Practice Levels A, B, and C (*Chapter 1 Resource Book*, p. 69)
- Reteaching with Practice (*Chapter 1 Resource Book*, p. 72)
- See Lesson 1.5 of the *Personal Student Tutor*

For more Mixed Review:

- Search the *Test and Practice Generator* for key words or specific lessons.

STUDENT HELP

HOMEWORK HELP Visit our Web site www.mcdougallittell.com for help with Ex. 44–49.

USING ALGEBRA $\overrightarrow{BD}$ **bisects** $\angle ABC$. **Find the value of** x.

44. $(x + 15)°$, $(4x - 45)°$ — 20

45.

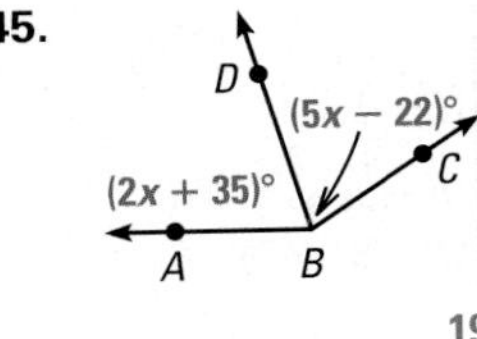

19

46.

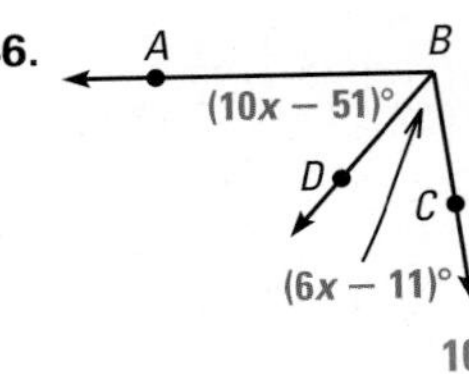

10

47. $(2x + 7)°$, $(4x - 9)°$ — 8

48.

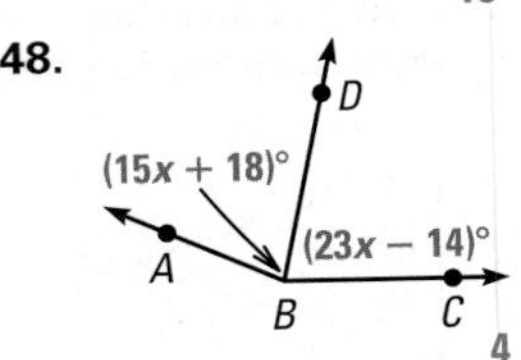

4

49.

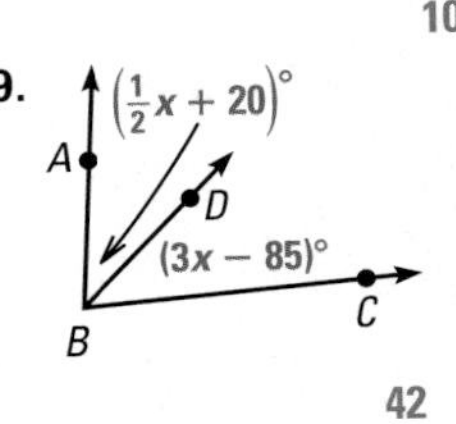

42

STRIKE ZONE In Exercises 50 and 51, use the information below. For each player, find the coordinate of T, a point on the top of the strike zone. In baseball, the "strike zone" is the region a baseball needs to pass through in order for an umpire to declare it a strike if it is not hit. The *top of the strike zone* is a horizontal plane passing through the midpoint between the top of the hitter's shoulders and the top of the uniform pants when the player is in a batting stance.

▶ Source: Major League Baseball

50.

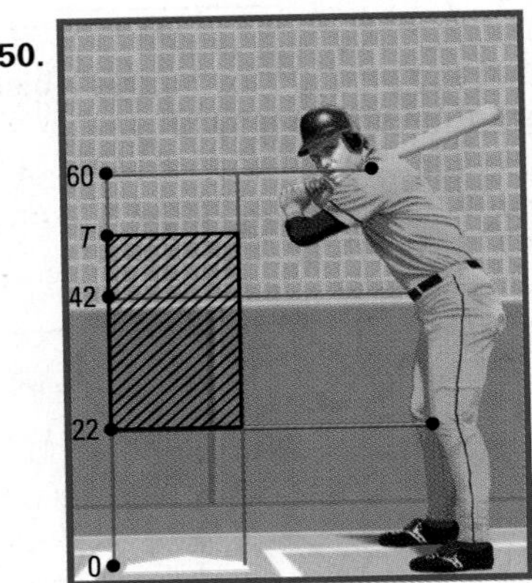

51

51.

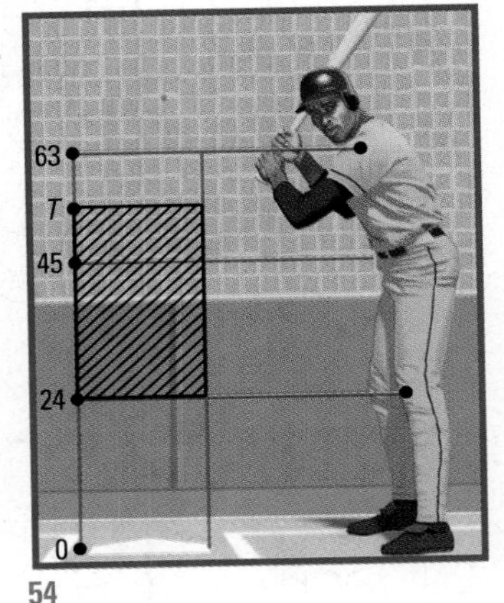

54

AIR HOCKEY When an air hockey puck is hit into the sideboards, it bounces off so that $\angle 1$ and $\angle 2$ are congruent. Find $m\angle 1$, $m\angle 2$, $m\angle 3$, and $m\angle 4$.

52. 106° — 53°, 53°, 37°, 37°

53.

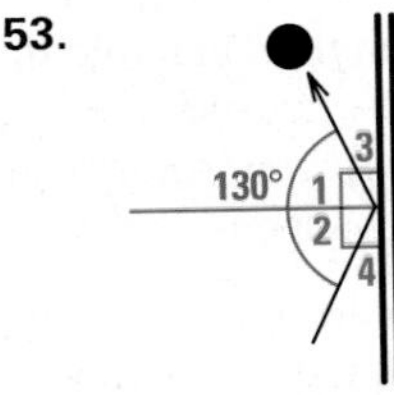

65°, 65°, 25°, 25°

54.

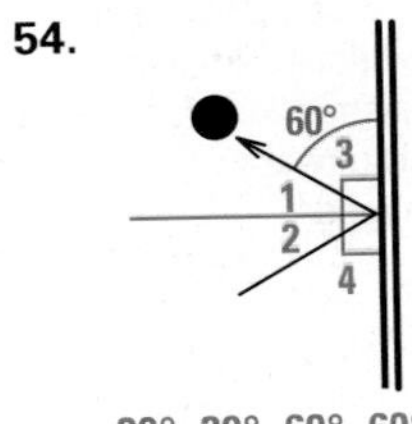

30°, 30°, 60°, 60°

55. **PAPER AIRPLANES** The diagram represents an unfolded piece of paper used to make a paper airplane. The segments represent where the paper was folded to make the airplane.

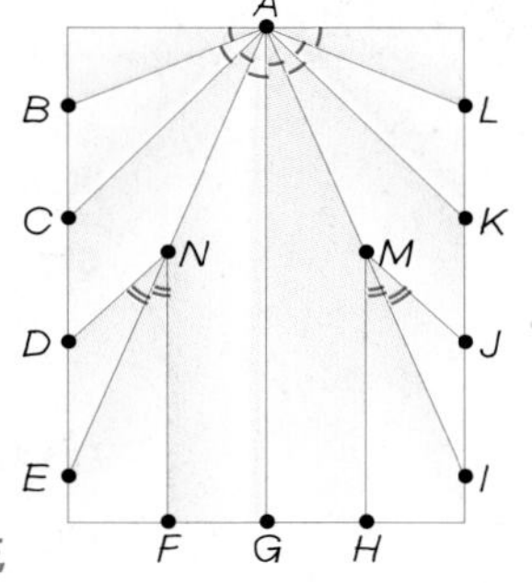

Using the diagram, name as many pairs of congruent segments and as many congruent angles as you can. **Sample answers:** $\overline{AB}$ **and** $\overline{AL}$, $\overline{AC}$ **and** $\overline{AK}$, $\overline{AN}$ **and** $\overline{AM}$, $\overline{AE}$ **and** $\overline{AI}$, $\overline{NE}$ **and** $\overline{MI}$, $\overline{ND}$ **and** $\overline{MJ}$, $\angle BAC$, $\angle CAN$, $\angle NAG$, $\angle GAM$, $\angle MAK$, **and** $\angle KAL$; $\angle DNE$, $\angle ENF$, $\angle HMI$, **and** $\angle JMI$.

56. *Writing* Explain, in your own words, how you would divide a line segment into four congruent segments using a compass and straightedge. Then explain how you could do it using the Midpoint Formula. **See margin.**

57. **MIDPOINT FORMULA REVISITED** Another version of the Midpoint Formula, for $A(x_1, y_1)$ and $B(x_2, y_2)$, is

$$M\left[x_1 + \frac{1}{2}(x_2 - x_1), y_1 + \frac{1}{2}(y_2 - y_1)\right].$$

Redo Exercises 17–24 using this version of the Midpoint Formula. Do you get the same answers as before? Use algebra to explain why the formula above is equivalent to the one in the lesson. **See margin.**

Test Preparation

58. **MULTI-STEP PROBLEM** Sketch a triangle with three sides of different lengths.

a. Using construction tools, find the midpoints of all three sides and the angle bisectors of all three angles of your triangle. **Check drawings.**

b. Determine whether or not the angle bisectors pass through the midpoints. **no**

c. *Writing* Write a brief paragraph explaining your results. Determine if your results would be different if you used a different kind of triangle. **See margin.**

★ Challenge

INFINITE SERIES A football team practices running back and forth on the field in a special way. First they run from one end of the 100 yd field to the other. Then they turn around and run half the previous distance. Then they turn around again and run half the previous distance, and so on.

59. Suppose the athletes continue the running drill with smaller and smaller distances. What is the coordinate of the point that they approach? **66.6 yards**

60. What is the total distance that the athletes cover? **200 yards**

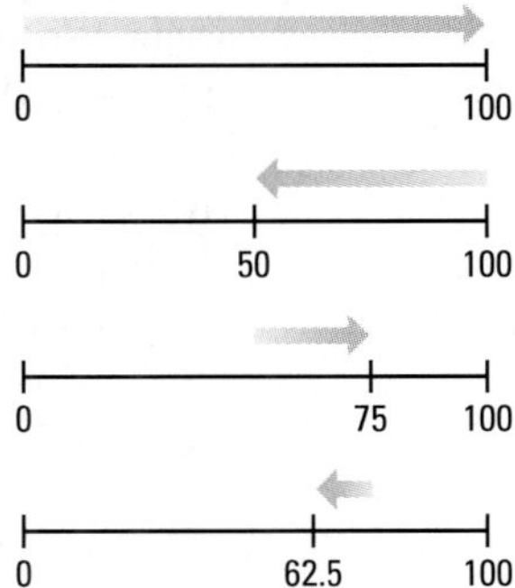

57. Yes; $x_1 + \frac{1}{2}(x_2 - x_1) = x_1 + \frac{1}{2}x_2 - \frac{1}{2}x_1 = \frac{1}{2}x_1 + \frac{1}{2}x_2 = \frac{x_1 + x_2}{2}$. Similarly, $y_1 + \frac{1}{2}(y_2 - y_1) = \frac{y_1 + y_2}{2}$.

EXTRA CHALLENGE
www.mcdougallittell.com

4 ASSESS

DAILY HOMEWORK QUIZ

Transparency Available

Find the coordinates of the midpoint of a segment with the given endpoints.

1. $A(-4, 6)$, $B(-2, 12)$ **(−3, 9)**
2. $C(0, 5)$, $D(-4, -5)$ **(−2, 0)**

Find the coordinates of the other endpoint of a segment with the given endpoint and midpoint M.

3. $L(-1, 9)$, $M(3, 7)$ **(7, 5)**

$\overrightarrow{BD}$ bisects $\angle ABC$. Find the value of x.

4. **7**

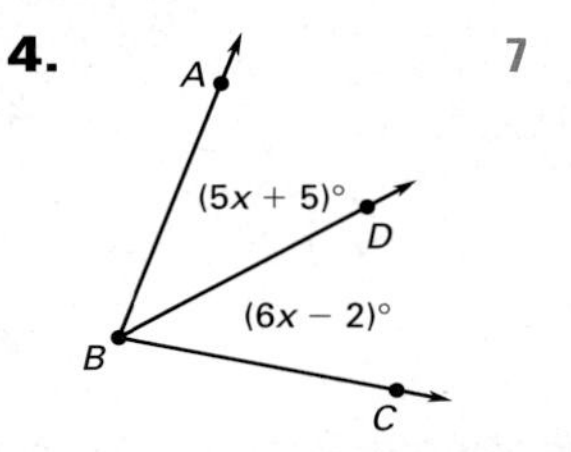

EXTRA CHALLENGE NOTE
Challenge problems for Lesson 1.5 are available in **blackline** format in the *Chapter 1 Resource Book*, p. 76 and at **www.mcdougallittell.com.**

ADDITIONAL TEST PREPARATION

1. **OPEN ENDED** Draw any angle $\angle ABC$. Use a compass and straightedge to bisect the angle. Describe each step as you proceed through the construction. **Check constructions and descriptions.**

ADDITIONAL RESOURCES

An alternative Quiz for Lessons 1.4–1.5 is available in the *Chapter 1 Resource Book,* p. 77.

61.  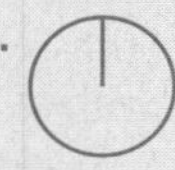

62.

2–5. Coordinates of sample points are given.

2. 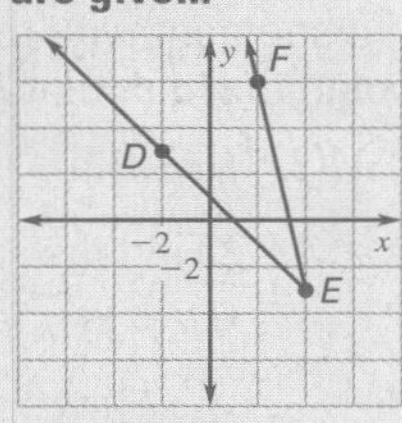

acute; (2, 2), (0, 0)

3. 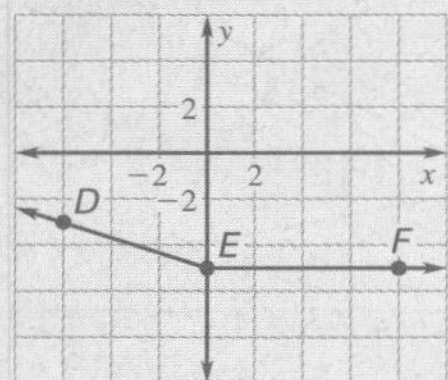

obtuse; (0, 0), (4, −6)

4. 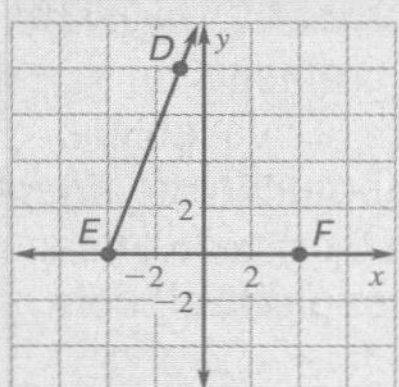

acute; (0, 2), (0, −2)

5. 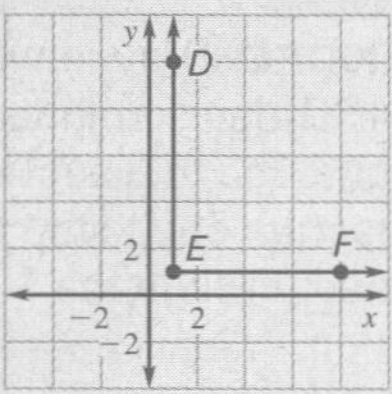

right; (2, 2), (0, 0)

MIXED REVIEW

SKETCHING VISUAL PATTERNS **Sketch the next figure in the pattern.** (Review 1.1) 61, 62. See margin.

61. 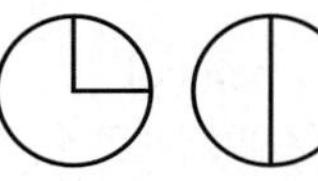

62. 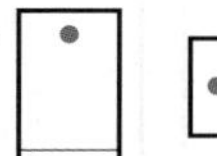 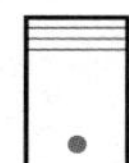

DISTANCE FORMULA **Find the distance between the two points.** (Review 1.3)

63. $A(3, 12), B(-5, -1)$ **64.** $C(-6, 9), D(-2, -7)$ **65.** $E(8, -8), F(2, 14)$

66. $G(3, -8), H(0, -2)$ **67.** $J(-4, -5), K(5, -1)$ **68.** $L(-10, 1), M(-4, 9)$

63. $\sqrt{233}$
64. $4\sqrt{17}$
65. $2\sqrt{130}$
66. $3\sqrt{5}$
67. $\sqrt{97}$
68. 10

MEASURING ANGLES **Use a protractor to find the measure of the angle.** (Review 1.4 for 1.6)

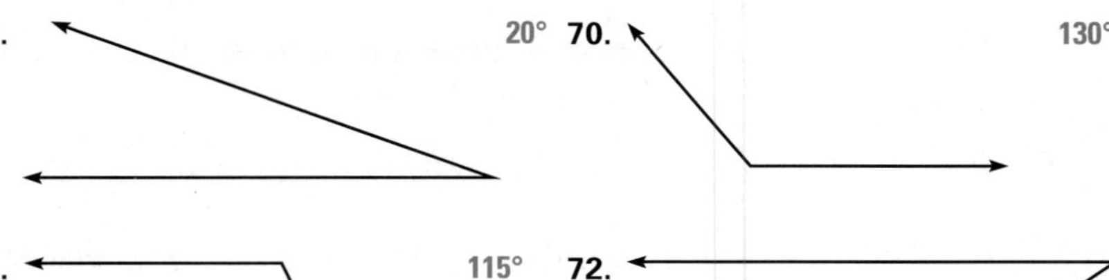

QUIZ 2

Self-Test for Lessons 1.4 and 1.5

1. State the Angle Addition Postulate for the three angles shown at the right. (Lesson 1.4)

If *Q* is in the interior of $\angle PSR$, then $m\angle PSQ + m\angle QSR = m\angle PSR$.

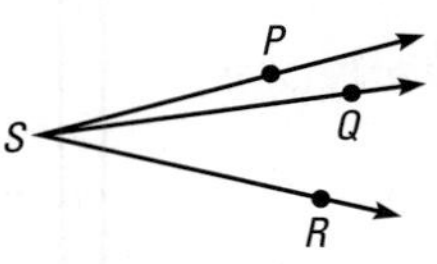

In a coordinate plane, plot the points and sketch $\angle DEF$. Classify the angle. Write the coordinates of a point that lies in the interior of the angle and the coordinates of a point that lies in the exterior of the angle. (Lesson 1.4) 2–5. See margin for graphs. Coordinates of sample points are given.

2. $D(-2, 3)$	**3.** $D(-6, -3)$	**4.** $D(-1, 8)$	**5.** $D(1, 10)$
$E(4, -3)$	$E(0, -5)$	$E(-4, 0)$	$E(1, 1)$
$F(2, 6)$	$F(8, -5)$	$F(4, 0)$	$F(8, 1)$
acute; (2, 2), (0, 0)	obtuse; (0, 0), (4, −6)	acute; (0, 2), (0, −2)	right; (2, 2), (0, 0)

6. In the diagram, $\overrightarrow{KM}$ is the angle bisector of $\angle JKL$. Find $m\angle MKL$ and $m\angle JKL$. (Lesson 1.5) 21°, 42°

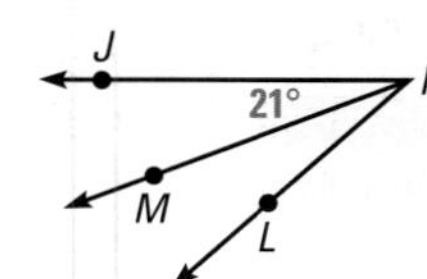

ACTIVITY 1.6

Using Technology

Angles and Intersecting Lines

You can use geometry software to construct intersecting lines and measure the angles formed by the lines.

STUDENT HELP

SOFTWARE HELP

Visit our Web site www.mcdougallittell.com to see instructions for several software applications.

▶ CONSTRUCT Construct intersecting lines.

1. Draw a line. Label two points A and B on the line.
2. Draw a second line that intersects the first line. Label two points C and D on the line.
3. Select the two lines and construct their point of intersection. Label the point E.

▶ INVESTIGATE

1–3. $m\angle AEC = m\angle BED$ and $m\angle AED = m\angle BEC$ and the sum of the measures of any two adjacent angles in the figure is 180°.

1. Measure the four angles formed by the intersecting lines: $\angle AEC$, $\angle AED$, $\angle BEC$, and $\angle BED$. When measuring angles, select the points *in order,* with the vertex as the second point. Record the measures.

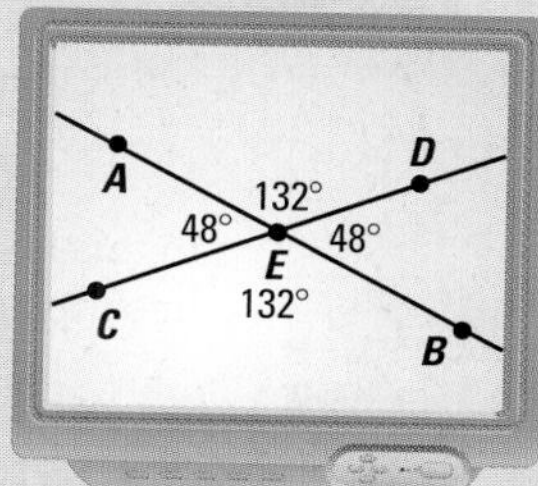

2. Move the lines into different positions by dragging the points. Record the measures of the four angles again.

▶ MAKE A CONJECTURE

3. What do you notice about the angle measures?

▶ INVESTIGATE

You can use geometry software to perform calculations with measures.

4–6. The sum of the measures of any two adjacent angles in the figure is 180°.

4. Select all four angle measures you have made. Calculate the sum of the measures of any two adjacent angles.

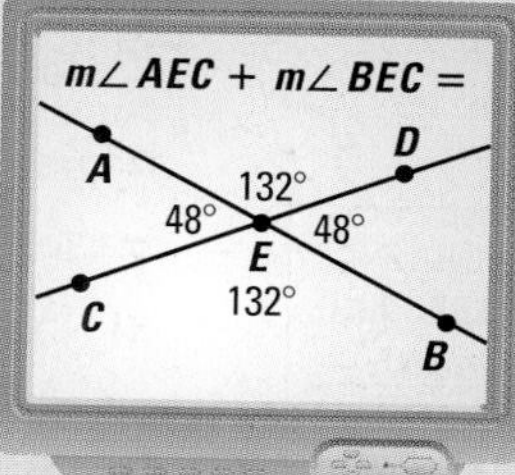

5. Move the lines into different positions by dragging the points. Then find the sum of the two angle measures again.

▶ MAKE A CONJECTURE

6. What do you notice about the sum of the measures of adjacent angles formed by intersecting lines?

1 Planning the Activity

PURPOSE
To investigate the angles formed by intersecting lines using graphing software on a computer.

MATERIALS
- computer with geometry software
- Software Help (*Chapter 1 Resource Book,* p. 82)

PACING
- Exploring the Concept — 10 min
- Drawing Conclusions — 15 min

▶ *LINK TO LESSON*
Refer back to this activity when discussing vertical angles and linear pairs on p. 44.

2 Managing the Activity

COOPERATIVE LEARNING
This activity can be done with pairs or small groups of students, but each student should have a turn using the software. The group can discuss the conjectures together.

ALTERNATIVE APPROACH
This activity can be done as a demonstration using a computer with an overhead display. If graphing software is not available, students can complete this activity using a ruler and protractor. If this approach is used there will be some differences in angle measures due to measurement inaccuracy.

3 Closing the Activity

★ *KEY DISCOVERY*
Two intersecting lines form two pairs of congruent angles. Of these angles, those that are adjacent have measures whose sum is 180°.

ACTIVITY ASSESSMENT
JOURNAL Write and illustrate a paragraph explaining the relationships between the angles formed by two intersecting lines.
Check paragraphs.

1 PLAN

PACING
Basic: 2 days
Average: 2 days
Advanced: 2 days
Block Schedule: 0.5 block with 1.5
0.5 block with 1.7

LESSON OPENER ACTIVITY
An alternative way to approach Lesson 1.6 is to use the Activity Lesson Opener:
- Blackline Master (*Chapter 1 Resource Book*, p. 81)
- Transparency (p. 6)

MEETING INDIVIDUAL NEEDS
- ***Chapter 1 Resource Book***
  Prerequisite Skills Review (p. 5)
  Practice Level A (p. 84)
  Practice Level B (p. 85)
  Practice Level C (p. 86)
  Reteaching with Practice (p. 87)
  Absent Student Catch-Up (p. 89)
  Challenge (p. 91)
- ***Resources in Spanish***
-  ***Personal Student Tutor***

NEW-TEACHER SUPPORT
See the Tips for New Teachers on pp. 1–2 of the *Chapter 1 Resource Book* for additional notes about Lesson 1.6.

WARM-UP EXERCISES
Transparency Available
Name an example of each type of angle from the figure below.
Sample answers are given.

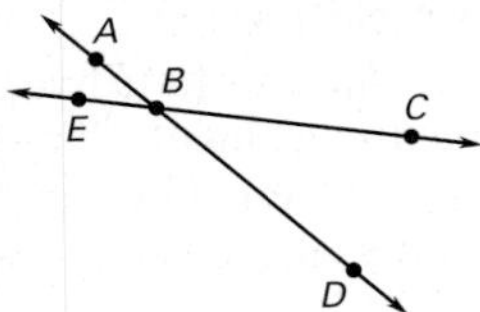

1. obtuse ∠*ABC*
2. acute ∠*ABE*
3. straight ∠*ABD*
4. a pair of adjacent angles ∠*ABC* and ∠*CBD*

1.6 Angle Pair Relationships

What you should learn

GOAL 1 Identify vertical angles and linear pairs.

GOAL 2 Identify complementary and supplementary angles.

Why you should learn it

▼ To solve **real-life** problems, such as finding the measures of angles formed by the cables of a bridge in **Ex. 53**.

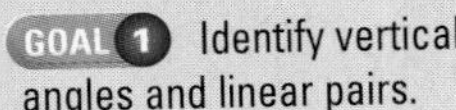

CALIFORNIA STANDARDS AND ASSESSMENT
CA Standards: 13

GOAL 1 VERTICAL ANGLES AND LINEAR PAIRS

In Lesson 1.4, you learned that two angles are *adjacent* if they share a common vertex and side but have no common interior points. In this lesson, you will study other relationships between pairs of angles.

Two angles are **vertical angles** if their sides form two pairs of opposite rays. Two adjacent angles are a **linear pair** if their noncommon sides are opposite rays.

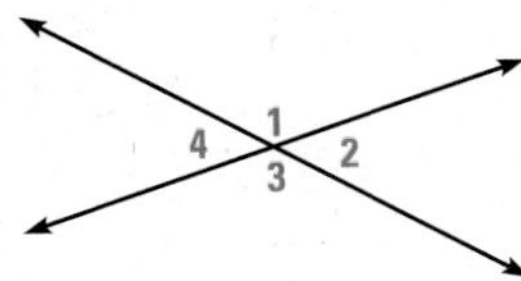

∠1 and ∠3 are vertical angles.
∠2 and ∠4 are vertical angles.

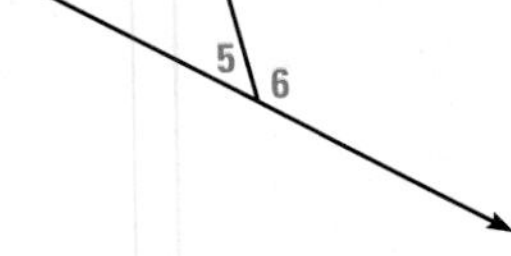

∠5 and ∠6 are a linear pair.

In this book, you can assume from a diagram that two adjacent angles form a linear pair if the noncommon sides appear to lie on the same line.

EXAMPLE 1 *Identifying Vertical Angles and Linear Pairs*

a. Are ∠2 and ∠3 a linear pair?

b. Are ∠3 and ∠4 a linear pair?

c. Are ∠1 and ∠3 vertical angles?

d. Are ∠2 and ∠4 vertical angles?

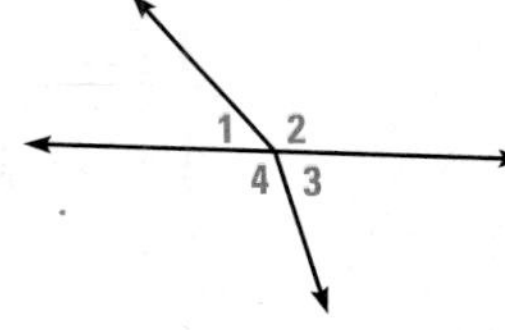

SOLUTION

a. No. The angles are adjacent but their noncommon sides are not opposite rays.

b. Yes. The angles are adjacent and their noncommon sides are opposite rays.

c. No. The sides of the angles do not form two pairs of opposite rays.

d. No. The sides of the angles do not form two pairs of opposite rays.

In Activity 1.6 on page 43, you may have discovered two results:

- *Vertical angles are congruent.*
- *The sum of the measures of angles that form a linear pair is 180°.*

Both of these results will be stated formally in Chapter 2.

Logical Reasoning

EXAMPLE 2 Finding Angle Measures

In the stair railing shown at the right, $\angle 6$ has a measure of 130°. Find the measures of the other three angles.

SOLUTION

$\angle 6$ and $\angle 7$ are a linear pair. So, the sum of their measures is 180°.

$$m\angle 6 + m\angle 7 = 180^\circ$$

$$130^\circ + m\angle 7 = 180^\circ$$

$$m\angle 7 = 50^\circ$$

$\angle 6$ and $\angle 5$ are also a linear pair. So, it follows that $m\angle 5 = 50^\circ$.

$\angle 6$ and $\angle 8$ are vertical angles. So, they are congruent and have the same measure.

$$m\angle 8 = m\angle 6 = 130^\circ$$

Using Algebra

EXAMPLE 3 Finding Angle Measures

Solve for x and y. Then find the angle measures.

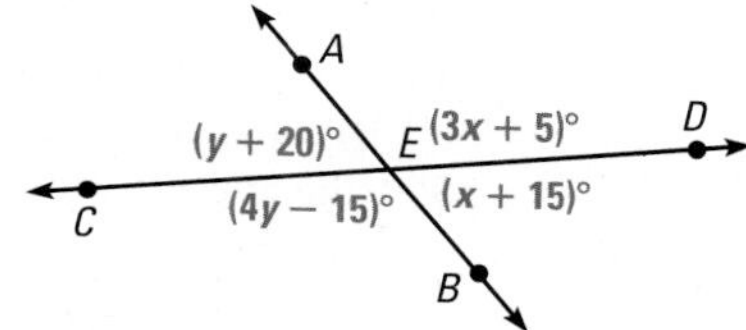

SOLUTION

Use the fact that the sum of the measures of angles that form a linear pair is 180°.

$$m\angle AED + m\angle DEB = 180^\circ$$

$$(3x + 5)^\circ + (x + 15)^\circ = 180^\circ$$

$$4x + 20 = 180$$

$$4x = 160$$

$$x = 40$$

$$m\angle AEC + m\angle CEB = 180^\circ$$

$$(y + 20)^\circ + (4y - 15)^\circ = 180^\circ$$

$$5y + 5 = 180$$

$$5y = 175$$

$$y = 35$$

Use substitution to find the angle measures.

$$m\angle AED = (3x + 5)^\circ = (3 \cdot 40 + 5)^\circ = 125^\circ$$

$$m\angle DEB = (x + 15)^\circ = (40 + 15)^\circ = 55^\circ$$

$$m\angle AEC = (y + 20)^\circ = (35 + 20)^\circ = 55^\circ$$

$$m\angle CEB = (4y - 15)^\circ = (4 \cdot 35 - 15)^\circ = 125^\circ$$

▶ So, the angle measures are 125°, 55°, 55°, and 125°. Because the vertical angles are congruent, the result is reasonable.

STUDENT HELP

HOMEWORK HELP
Visit our Web site www.mcdougallittell.com for extra examples.

2 TEACH

EXTRA EXAMPLE 1

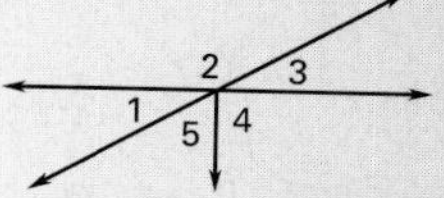

a. Are $\angle 1$ and $\angle 2$ a linear pair? yes

b. Are $\angle 4$ and $\angle 5$ a linear pair? no

c. Are $\angle 5$ and $\angle 3$ vertical angles? no

d. Are $\angle 1$ and $\angle 3$ vertical angles? yes

EXTRA EXAMPLE 2

In one town, Main Street and Columbus Avenue intersect to form an angle of 36°. Find the measures of the other three angles. **144°, 36°, 144°**

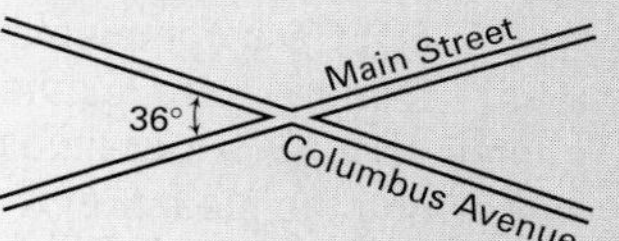

EXTRA EXAMPLE 3

Solve for x and y. Then find the angle measures. $x = 15$, $y = 30$; $m\angle LPM = m\angle OPN = 75^\circ$, $m\angle MPN = m\angle LPO = 105^\circ$

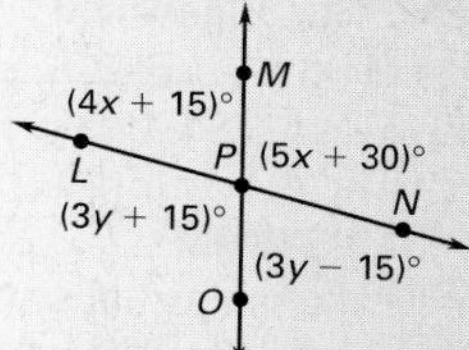

CHECKPOINT EXERCISES

For use after Example 1:

1. Name one pair of vertical angles and one pair of angles that form a linear pair. *Sample answer:* $\angle IHJ$ and $\angle GHK$, $\angle IHJ$ and $\angle JHK$

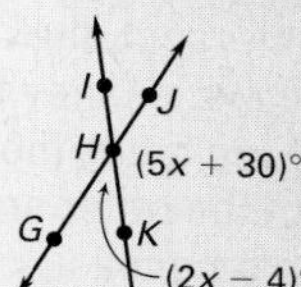

For use after Examples 2 and 3:

2. What is the measure of $\angle GHI$ in the figure above? **140°**

EXTRA EXAMPLE 4

State whether the two angles are complementary, supplementary, or neither. **neither**

EXTRA EXAMPLE 5

a. Given that $\angle G$ is a supplement of $\angle H$ and $m\angle G$ is 82°, find $m\angle H$. **98°**

b. Given that $\angle U$ is a complement of $\angle V$, and $m\angle U$ is 73°, find $m\angle V$. **17°**

EXTRA EXAMPLE 6

$\angle T$ and $\angle S$ are supplementary. The measure of $\angle T$ is half the measure of $\angle S$. Find $m\angle S$. **120°**

CHECKPOINT EXERCISES

For use after Examples 4–6:

1. $\angle D$ and $\angle E$ are complements and $\angle D$ and $\angle F$ are supplements. If $m\angle E$ is four times $m\angle D$, find the measure of each of the three angles. **$m\angle D = 18°$, $m\angle E = 72°$, $m\angle F = 162°$**

FOCUS ON VOCABULARY

Fill in the blank. The angles in a linear pair are always __________. **supplementary**

CLOSURE QUESTION

Describe the relationships between the four angles formed by two intersecting lines. **The angles across from each other are vertical angles. Each pair of vertical angles are congruent. The adjacent angles formed by the lines are linear pairs. The angles in a linear pair are supplementary.**

DAILY PUZZLER

When two lines intersect, the measure of one of the angles they form is 20° less than three times the measure of one of the other angles formed. What are the measures of all four angles formed by the lines? **50°, 50°, 130°, 130°**

STUDENT HELP

Study Tip
In mathematics, the word *complement* is related to the phrase *to complete*. When you draw the complement of an angle, you are "completing" a right angle. (The word *compliment* is different. It means something said in praise.)

GOAL 2 COMPLEMENTARY AND SUPPLEMENTARY ANGLES

Two angles are **complementary angles** if the sum of their measures is 90°. Each angle is the **complement** of the other. Complementary angles can be adjacent or nonadjacent.

Two angles are **supplementary angles** if the sum of their measures is 180°. Each angle is the **supplement** of the other. Supplementary angles can be adjacent or nonadjacent.

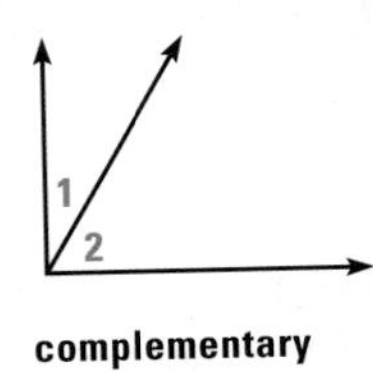

complementary adjacent

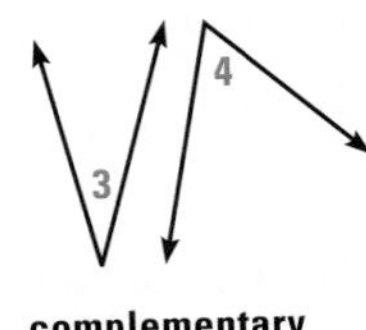

complementary nonadjacent

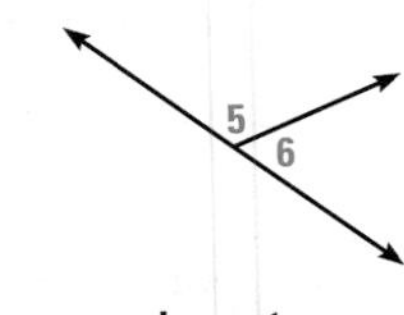

supplementary adjacent

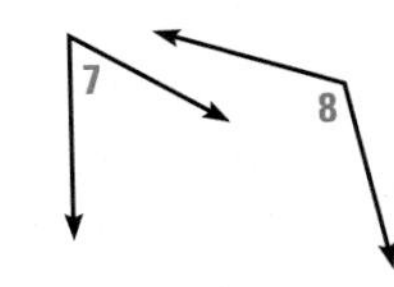

supplementary nonadjacent

EXAMPLE 4 *Identifying Angles*

State whether the two angles are complementary, supplementary, or neither.

SOLUTION

The angle showing 4:00 has a measure of 120° and the angle showing 10:00 has a measure of 60°. Because the sum of these two measures is 180°, the angles are supplementary.

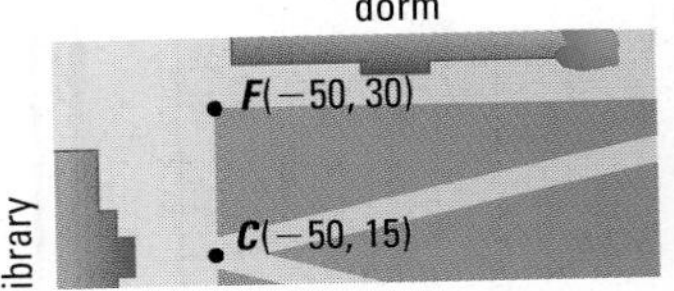

EXAMPLE 5 *Finding Measures of Complements and Supplements*

a. Given that $\angle A$ is a complement of $\angle C$ and $m\angle A = 47°$, find $m\angle C$.

b. Given that $\angle P$ is a supplement of $\angle R$ and $m\angle R = 36°$, find $m\angle P$.

SOLUTION

a. $m\angle C = 90° - m\angle A = 90° - 47° = 43°$

b. $m\angle P = 180° - m\angle R = 180° - 36° = 144°$

EXAMPLE 6 *Finding the Measure of a Complement*

xy Using Algebra

$\angle W$ and $\angle Z$ are complementary. The measure of $\angle Z$ is five times the measure of $\angle W$. Find $m\angle W$.

SOLUTION

Because the angles are complementary, $m\angle W + m\angle Z = 90°$. But $m\angle Z = 5(m\angle W)$, so $m\angle W + 5(m\angle W) = 90°$. Because $6(m\angle W) = 90°$, you know that $m\angle W = 15°$.

GUIDED PRACTICE

Vocabulary Check ✓

1–3. See margin.

1. Explain the difference between *complementary angles* and *supplementary angles.*

Concept Check ✓

2. Sketch examples of acute vertical angles and obtuse vertical angles.

3. Sketch examples of adjacent congruent complementary angles and adjacent congruent supplementary angles.

Skill Check ✓

FINDING ANGLE MEASURES **Find the measure of ∠1.**

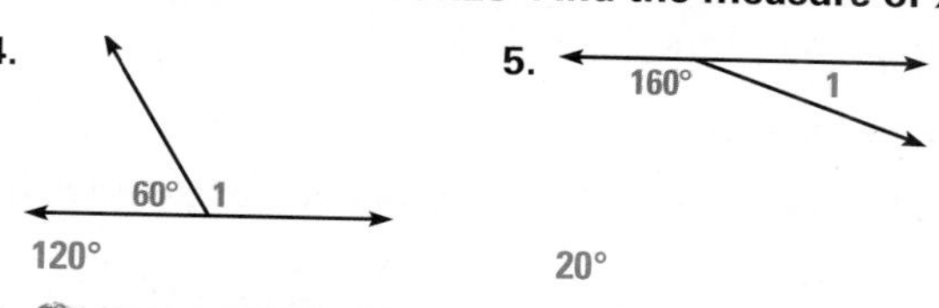

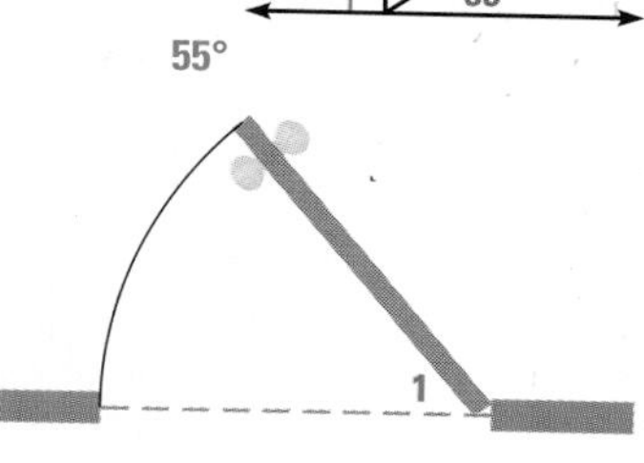

7. **OPENING A DOOR** The figure shows a doorway viewed from above. If you open the door so that the measure of ∠1 is 50°, how many more degrees would you have to open the door so that the angle between the wall and the door is 90°? 40°

1. The sum of the measures of two complementary angles is 90°. The sum of the measures of two supplementary angles is 180°.

2. Any sketch of two pairs of intersecting lines that are not perpendicular will include a pair of acute vertical angles and a pair of obtuse vertical angles.

PRACTICE AND APPLICATIONS

STUDENT HELP

Extra Practice to help you master skills is on p. 804.

IDENTIFYING ANGLE PAIRS **Use the figure at the right.**

8. Are ∠5 and ∠6 a linear pair? no
9. Are ∠5 and ∠9 a linear pair? yes
10. Are ∠5 and ∠8 a linear pair? no
11. Are ∠5 and ∠8 vertical angles? yes
12. Are ∠5 and ∠7 vertical angles? no
13. Are ∠9 and ∠6 vertical angles? no

EVALUATING STATEMENTS **Decide whether the statement is *always, sometimes,* or *never* true.**

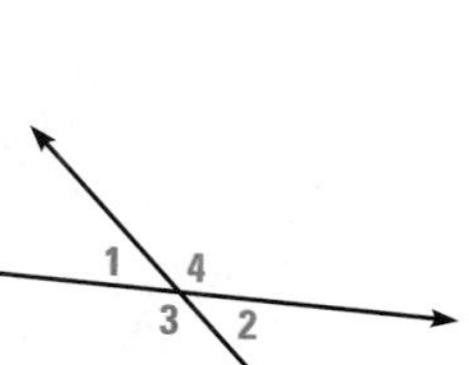

14. If $m\angle 1 = 40°$, then $m\angle 2 = 140°$. never
15. If $m\angle 4 = 130°$, then $m\angle 2 = 50°$. always
16. ∠1 and ∠4 are congruent. sometimes
17. $m\angle 2 + m\angle 3 = m\angle 1 + m\angle 4$ always
18. $\angle 2 \cong \angle 1$ always
19. $m\angle 2 = 90° - m\angle 3$ never

STUDENT HELP

HOMEWORK HELP
Example 1: Exs. 8–13
Example 2: Exs. 14–27
Example 3: Exs. 28–36
Example 4: Exs. 37–40
Example 5: Exs. 41, 42
Example 6: Exs. 43, 44

3 APPLY

ASSIGNMENT GUIDE

BASIC
Day 1: pp. 47–48 Exs. 8–36
Day 2: pp. 48–50 Exs. 37–52, 57, 58, 62, 63, 65, 66–74 even

AVERAGE
Day 1: pp. 47–48 Exs. 8–36
Day 2: pp. 48–50 Exs. 37–54, 57, 58, 62, 63, 65, 66–74 even

ADVANCED
Day 1: pp. 47–48 Exs. 8–36
Day 2: pp. 48–50 Exs. 37–59, 62, 63, 65, 66–74 even

BLOCK SCHEDULE
pp. 47–48 Exs. 8–36 (with 1.5)
pp. 48–50 Exs. 37–54, 57, 58, 62, 63, 65, 66–74 even (with 1.7)

EXERCISE LEVELS

Level A: *Easier*
8–13, 20–27, 37–42

Level B: *More Difficult*
14–19, 28–36, 43–54, 57, 58

Level C: *Most Difficult*
55, 56, 59

HOMEWORK CHECK

To quickly check student understanding of key concepts, go over the following exercises: Exs. 10, 12, 22, 28, 32, 42, 46, 50. See also the Daily Homework Quiz:

- Blackline Master (*Chapter 1 Resource Book,* p. 94)
- Transparency (p. 8)

3.

! COMMON ERROR
EXERCISES 28–36
Computational or algebraic errors are common in these problems. Have students check their answers by finding the measures of the angles. They can then verify that the measures are consistent with the drawings.

FINDING ANGLE MEASURES **Use the figure at the right.**

20. If $m\angle 6 = 72°$, then $m\angle 7 =$ __?__. 108°

21. If $m\angle 8 = 80°$, then $m\angle 6 =$ __?__. 80°

22. If $m\angle 9 = 110°$, then $m\angle 8 =$ __?__. 70°

23. If $m\angle 9 = 123°$, then $m\angle 7 =$ __?__. 123°

24. If $m\angle 7 = 142°$, then $m\angle 8 =$ __?__. 38°

25. If $m\angle 6 = 13°$, then $m\angle 9 =$ __?__. 167°

26. If $m\angle 9 = 170°$, then $m\angle 6 =$ __?__. 10°

27. If $m\angle 8 = 26°$, then $m\angle 7 =$ __?__. 154°

9 6
8 7

 **USING ALGEBRA** **Find the value(s) of the variable(s).**

28.
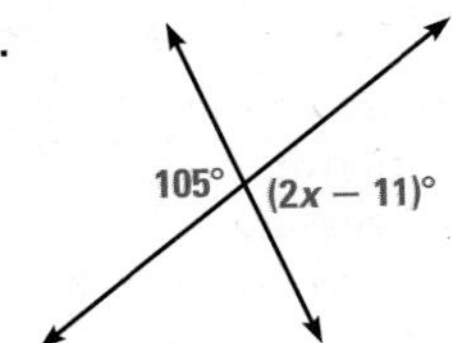

58

29.
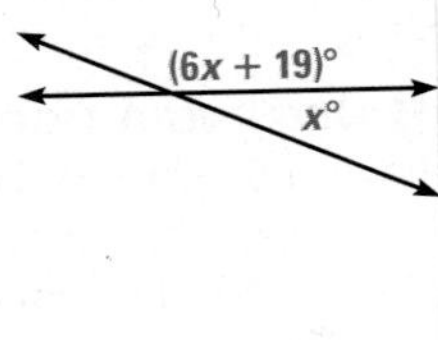

23

30.
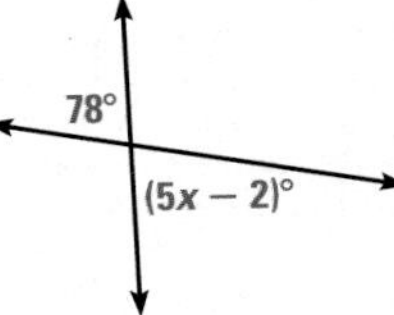

16

31.
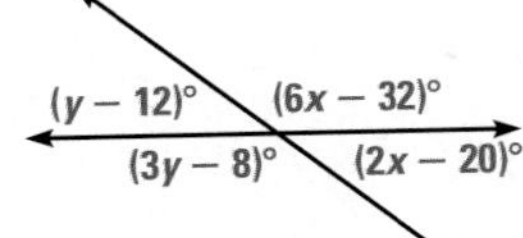

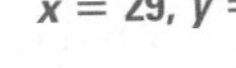
x = 29, y = 50

32.
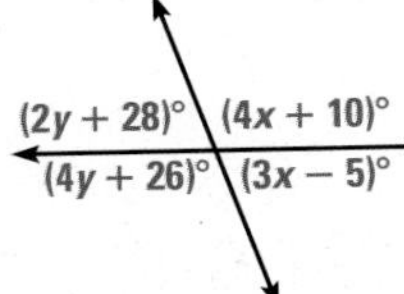

x = 25, y = 21

33.
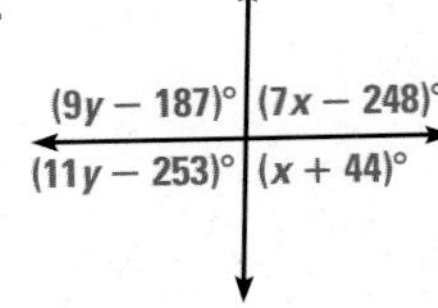

x = 48, y = 31

34.
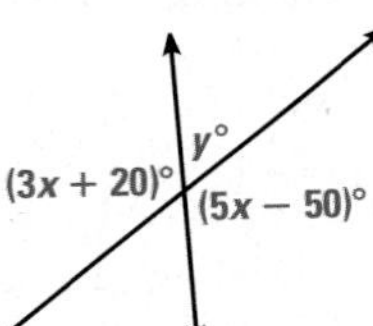

x = 35, y = 55

35.
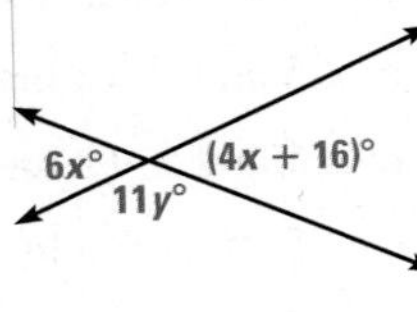

x = 8, y = 12

36.
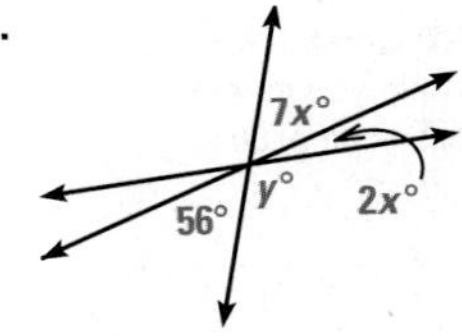

x = 8, y = 108

IDENTIFYING ANGLES **State whether the two angles shown are *complementary, supplementary,* or *neither*.**

37.

supplementary

38.

neither

39.

complementary

40.

neither

41. FINDING COMPLEMENTS In the table, assume that $\angle 1$ and $\angle 2$ are complementary. Copy and complete the table. See margin.

$m\angle 1$	2°	10°	25°	33°	40°	49°	55°	62°	76°	86°
$m\angle 2$	?	?	?	?	?	?	?	?	?	?

42. FINDING SUPPLEMENTS In the table, assume that $\angle 1$ and $\angle 2$ are supplementary. Copy and complete the table. See margin.

$m\angle 1$	4°	16°	48°	72°	90°	99°	120°	152°	169°	178°
$m\angle 2$	?	?	?	?	?	?	?	?	?	?

43. USING ALGEBRA $\angle A$ and $\angle B$ are complementary. The measure of $\angle B$ is three times the measure of $\angle A$. Find $m\angle A$ and $m\angle B$. $m\angle A = 22.5°$; $m\angle B = 67.5°$

44. USING ALGEBRA $\angle C$ and $\angle D$ are supplementary. The measure of $\angle D$ is eight times the measure of $\angle C$. Find $m\angle C$ and $m\angle D$. $m\angle C = 20°$; $m\angle D = 160°$

FINDING ANGLES $\angle A$ **and** $\angle B$ **are complementary. Find** $m\angle A$ **and** $m\angle B$**.**

45. $m\angle A = 5x + 8$; $m\angle B = x + 4$ — $m\angle A = 73°$; $m\angle B = 17°$

46. $m\angle A = 3x - 7$; $m\angle B = 11x - 1$ — $m\angle A = 14°$; $m\angle B = 76°$

47. $m\angle A = 8x - 7$; $m\angle B = x - 11$ — $m\angle A = 89°$; $m\angle B = 1°$

48. $m\angle A = \frac{3}{4}x - 13$; $m\angle B = 3x - 17$ — $m\angle A = 11°$; $m\angle B = 79°$

FINDING ANGLES $\angle A$ **and** $\angle B$ **are supplementary. Find** $m\angle A$ **and** $m\angle B$**.**

49. $m\angle A = 3x$; $m\angle B = x + 8$ — $m\angle A = 129°$; $m\angle B = 51°$

50. $m\angle A = 6x - 1$; $m\angle B = 5x - 17$ — $m\angle A = 107°$; $m\angle B = 73°$

51. $m\angle A = 12x + 1$; $m\angle B = x + 10$ — $m\angle A = 157°$; $m\angle B = 23°$

52. $m\angle A = \frac{3}{8}x + 50$; $m\angle B = x + 31$ — $m\angle A = 77°$; $m\angle B = 103°$

53. BRIDGES The Alamillo Bridge in Seville, Spain, was designed by Santiago Calatrava. In the bridge, $m\angle 1 = 58°$ and $m\angle 2 = 24°$. Find the supplements of both $\angle 1$ and $\angle 2$. 122°, 156°

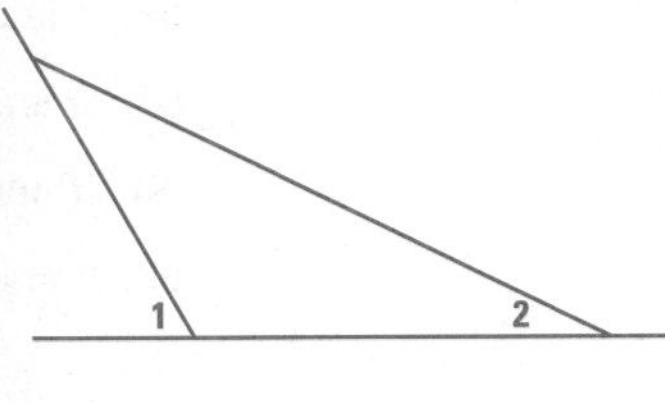

54. BASEBALL The foul lines of a baseball field intersect at home plate to form a right angle. Suppose you hit a baseball whose path forms an angle of 34° with the third base foul line. What is the angle between the first base foul line and the path of the baseball? 56°

FOCUS ON PEOPLE

SANTIAGO CALATRAVA, a Spanish born architect, has developed designs for bridges, train stations, stadiums, and art museums.

APPLICATION LINK
www.mcdougallittell.com

APPLICATION NOTE
EXERCISE 53
Additional information about Santiago Calatrava is available at **www.mcdougallittell.com.**

41. 88°; 80°; 65°; 57°; 50°; 41°; 35°; 28°; 14°; 4°

42. 176°; 164°; 132°; 108°; 90°; 81°; 60°; 28°; 11°; 2°

ADDITIONAL PRACTICE AND RETEACHING

For Lesson 1.6:
- Practice Levels A, B, and C (*Chapter 1 Resource Book,* p. 84)
- Reteaching with Practice (*Chapter 1 Resource Book,* p. 87)
- See Lesson 1.6 of the *Personal Student Tutor*

For more Mixed Review:
- Search the *Test and Practice Generator* for key words or specific lessons.

4 ASSESS

DAILY HOMEWORK QUIZ

Transparency Available

Use the figure to answer the questions.

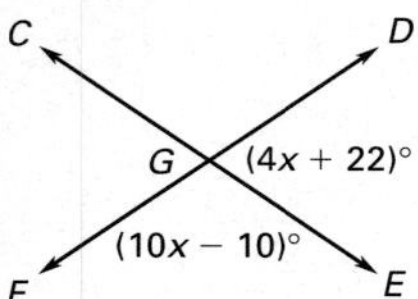

1. Are angles $\angle CGF$ and $\angle FGE$ vertical angles? no
2. Are angles $\angle CGF$ and $\angle FGE$ a linear pair? yes
3. If $m\angle CGD = 120°$, find $m\angle CGF$. 60°
4. Find the value of x. 12

$\angle A$ and $\angle B$ are complementary. Find $m\angle A$ and $m\angle B$.

5. $m\angle A = 7x + 1$, $m\angle B = 4x + 1$ $m\angle A = 57°$; $m\angle B = 33°$

EXTRA CHALLENGE NOTE

Challenge problems for Lesson 1.6 are available in **blackline** format in the *Chapter 1 Resource Book*, p. 91 and at **www.mcdougallittell.com.**

ADDITIONAL TEST PREPARATION

1. **OPEN ENDED** Draw a figure that includes vertical angles, linear pairs, complementary angles, and supplementary angles. Write and answer 5 true-false questions about your figure. Check work.

55. **PLANTING TREES** To support a young tree, you attach wires from the trunk to the ground. The obtuse angle the wire makes with the ground is supplementary to the acute angle the wire makes, and it is three times as large. Find the measures of the angles. 135°, 45°

56. *Writing* Give an example of an angle that *does not* have a complement. In general, what is true about an angle that has a complement? Sample answer: 100°; an angle that has a complement has a measure less than 90°.

Test Preparation

57. **MULTIPLE CHOICE** In the diagram shown at the right, what are the values of x and y? E

    (A) $x = 74, y = 106$
    (B) $x = 16, y = 88$
    (C) $x = 74, y = 16$
    (D) $x = 18, y = 118$
    (E) $x = 18, y = 94$

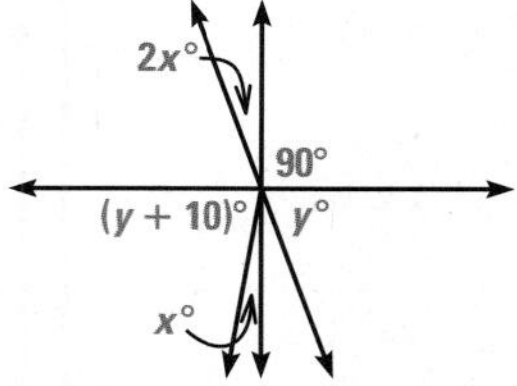

58. **MULTIPLE CHOICE** $\angle F$ and $\angle G$ are supplementary. The measure of $\angle G$ is six and one half times the measure of $\angle F$. What is $m\angle F$? B

    (A) 20° (B) 24° (C) 24.5° (D) 26.5° (E) 156°

★ Challenge

59. **USING ALGEBRA** Find the values of x and y in the diagram shown at the right. $x = 10$, $y = 70$

2x°
90°
(y + 10)°
y°
x°

MIXED REVIEW

SOLVING EQUATIONS **Solve the equation.** (Skills Review, p. 802, for 1.7)

60. $3x = 96$ 32
61. $\frac{1}{2} \cdot 5 \cdot h = 20$ 8
62. $\frac{1}{2} \cdot b \cdot 6 = 15$ 5
63. $s^2 = 200$ $-10\sqrt{2}, 10\sqrt{2}$
64. $2 \cdot 3.14 \cdot r = 40$ $\frac{20}{3.14} \approx 6.4$
65. $3.14 \cdot r^2 = 314$ $-10, 10$

FINDING COLLINEAR POINTS **Use the diagram to find a third point that is collinear with the given points.** (Review 1.2)

66. A and J E, D
67. D and F C
68. H and E B, C
69. B and G A

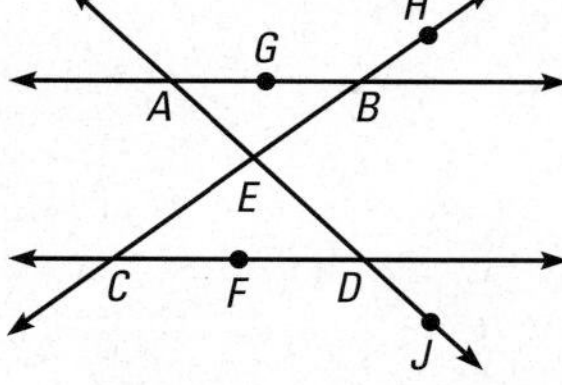

FINDING THE MIDPOINT **Find the coordinates of the midpoint of a segment with the given endpoints.** (Review 1.5)

70. $A(0, 0), B(-6, -4)$ $(-3, -2)$
71. $F(2, 5), G(-10, 7)$ $(-4, 6)$
72. $K(8, -6), L(-2, -2)$ $(3, -4)$
73. $M(-14, -9), N(0, 11)$ $(-7, 1)$
74. $P(-1.5, 4), Q(5, -9)$ $(1.75, -2.5)$
75. $S(-2.4, 5), T(7.6, 9)$ $(2.6, 7)$

1.7 Introduction to Perimeter, Circumference, and Area

What you should learn

GOAL 1 Find the perimeter and area of common plane figures.

GOAL 2 Use a general problem-solving plan.

Why you should learn it

▼ To solve **real-life** problems about perimeter and area, such as finding the number of bags of seed you need for a field in **Example 4**.

California Standards and Assessment

CA Standards: 8, 10
SAT9 Task 1: Objs. 1, 27, 28, 29
SAT9 Task 2: Objs. 1, 30, 31, 32

GOAL 1 Reviewing Perimeter, Circumference, and Area

In this lesson, you will review some common formulas for perimeter, circumference, and area. You will learn more about area in Chapters 6, 11, and 12.

PERIMETER, CIRCUMFERENCE, AND AREA FORMULAS

Formulas for the perimeter P, area A, and circumference C of some common plane figures are given below.

SQUARE
side length s

$P = 4s$

$A = s^2$

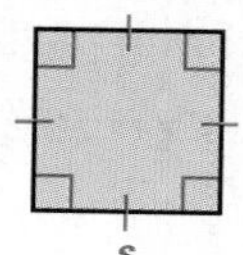

RECTANGLE
length ℓ and width w

$P = 2\ell + 2w$

$A = \ell w$

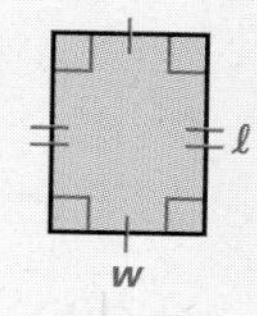

TRIANGLE
side lengths a, b, and c, base b, and height h

$P = a + b + c$

$A = \frac{1}{2}bh$

CIRCLE
radius r

$C = 2\pi r$

$A = \pi r^2$

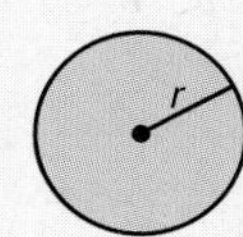

Pi (π) is the ratio of the circle's circumference to its diameter.

The measurements of perimeter and circumference use units such as centimeters, meters, kilometers, inches, feet, yards, and miles. The measurements of area use units such as square centimeters (cm^2), square meters (m^2), and so on.

EXAMPLE 1 *Finding the Perimeter and Area of a Rectangle*

Find the perimeter and area of a rectangle of length 12 inches and width 5 inches.

Solution

Begin by drawing a diagram and labeling the length and width. Then, use the formulas for perimeter and area of a rectangle.

$P = 2\ell + 2w$
$= 2(12) + 2(5)$
$= 34$

$A = \ell w$
$= (12)(5)$
$= 60$

▶ So, the perimeter is 34 inches and the area is 60 square inches.

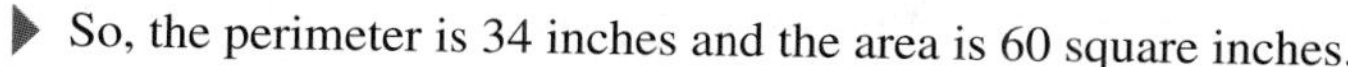

1 PLAN

Pacing
Basic: 2 days
Average: 2 days
Advanced: 2 days
Block Schedule: 0.5 block with 1.6; 0.5 block with Ch. Rev.

Lesson Opener Activity
An alternative way to approach Lesson 1.7 is to use the Activity Lesson Opener:

- Blackline Master (*Chapter 1 Resource Book*, p. 95)
- Transparency (p. 7)

Meeting Individual Needs

- ***Chapter 1 Resource Book***
  Prerequisite Skills Review (p. 5)
  Practice Level A (p. 100)
  Practice Level B (p. 101)
  Practice Level C (p. 102)
  Reteaching with Practice (p. 103)
  Absent Student Catch-Up (p. 105)
  Challenge (p. 108)
- ***Resources in Spanish***
- ***Personal Student Tutor***

New-Teacher Support
See the Tips for New Teachers on pp. 1–2 of the *Chapter 1 Resource Book* for additional notes about Lesson 1.7.

Warm-Up Exercises

Transparency Available

Find the distance between each pair of points in the coordinate plane.

1. (3, 1) and (3, –5) 6
2. (–2, 0) and (4, 2) $2\sqrt{10}$
3. (–1, –5) and (3, –5) 4
4. (6, –4) and (4, –2) $2\sqrt{2}$

2 TEACH

MOTIVATING THE LESSON
Ask students to imagine they are moving into a new room. They want to decorate the room with a carpet and a wallpaper border that will go around the top of the wall. They know the dimensions of the room. How will they determine the number of feet of border needed and the number of square feet of carpeting needed? Today's lesson will focus on finding the perimeter and area of common geometric figures.

EXTRA EXAMPLE 1
Find the perimeter and area of a rectangle of length 4.5 m and width 0.5 m. 10 m, 2.25 m^2

EXTRA EXAMPLE 2
A road sign consists of a pole with a circular sign on top. The top of the circle is 10 feet high and the bottom of the circle is 8 feet high. Find the diameter, radius, circumference, and area of the circle. Use 3.14 as an approximation for π. 2 ft, 1 ft, about 6.3 ft, about 3.1 ft^2

EXTRA EXAMPLE 3
Find the area and perimeter of the triangle defined by $H(-2, 2)$, $J(3, -1)$, and $K(-2, -4)$.
15 square units, $6 + 2\sqrt{34}$ units

CHECKPOINT EXERCISES

For use after Examples 1 and 2:

1. A circular compact disc fits exactly in a square box with sides 12 centimeters long. Find the diameter, radius, circumference, and area of the compact disc, and the perimeter and area of the box. Use 3.14 as an approximation for π.
12 cm, 6 cm, about 37.7 cm, about 113 cm^2, 48 cm, 144 cm

For use after Example 3:

2. Find the area and perimeter of the triangle defined by $T(-2, 6)$, $U(4, 6)$, and $V(4, -2)$.
24 square units, 24 units

STUDENT HELP
Study Tip
Some approximations for $\pi = 3.141592654\ldots$ are 3.14 and $\frac{22}{7}$.

EXAMPLE 2 *Finding the Area and Circumference of a Circle*

Find the diameter, radius, circumference, and area of the circle shown at the right. Use 3.14 as an approximation for π.

SOLUTION

From the diagram, you can see that the diameter of the circle is

$$d = 13 - 5 = 8 \text{ cm.}$$

The radius is one half the diameter.

$$r = \frac{1}{2}(8) = 4 \text{ cm}$$

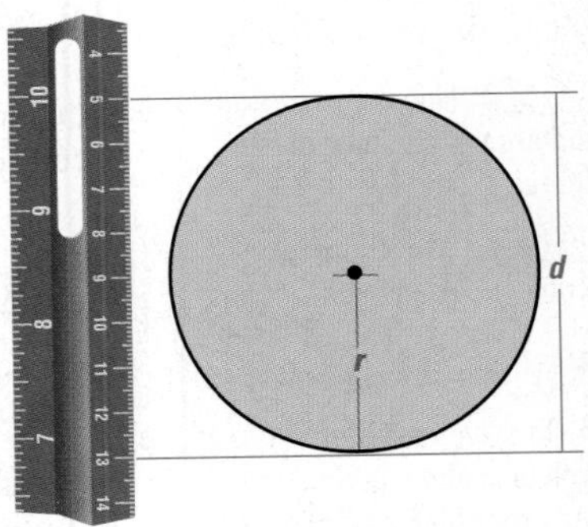

Using the formulas for circumference and area, you have

$$C = 2\pi r \approx 2(3.14)(4) \approx 25.1 \text{ cm}$$

$$A = \pi r^2 \approx 3.14(4^2) \approx 50.2 \text{ cm}^2.$$

EXAMPLE 3 *Finding Measurements of a Triangle in a Coordinate Plane*

Find the area and perimeter of the triangle defined by $D(1, 3)$, $E(8, 3)$, and $F(4, 7)$.

SOLUTION

Plot the points in a coordinate plane. Draw the height from F to side $\overline{DE}$. Label the point where the height meets $\overline{DE}$ as G. Point G has coordinates (4, 3).

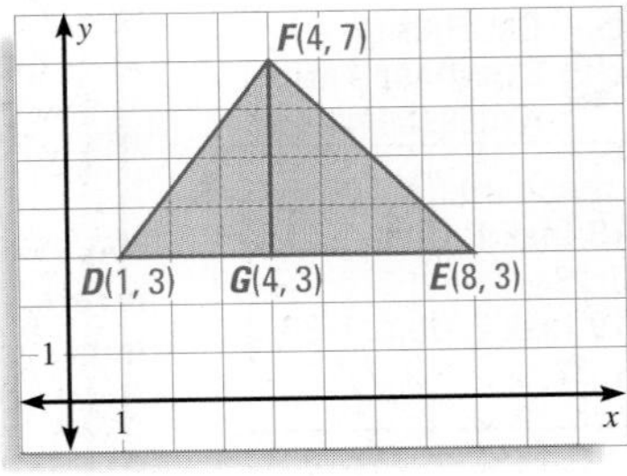

base: $DE = 8 - 1 = 7$

height: $FG = 7 - 3 = 4$

$$A = \frac{1}{2}(\text{base})(\text{height})$$

$$= \frac{1}{2}(7)(4)$$

$$= 14 \text{ square units}$$

To find the perimeter, use the Distance Formula.

$$EF = \sqrt{(4-8)^2 + (7-3)^2} = \sqrt{(-4)^2 + 4^2} = \sqrt{32} = 4\sqrt{2} \text{ units}$$

$$DF = \sqrt{(4-1)^2 + (7-3)^2} = \sqrt{3^2 + 4^2} = \sqrt{25} = 5 \text{ units}$$

▶ So, the perimeter is $DE + EF + DF = (7 + 4\sqrt{2} + 5)$, or $12 + 4\sqrt{2}$, units.

STUDENT HELP
Skills Review
For help with simplifying radicals, see page 799.

GOAL 2 USING A PROBLEM-SOLVING PLAN

A problem-solving plan can help you organize solutions to geometry problems.

A PROBLEM-SOLVING PLAN

1. Ask yourself what you need to solve the problem. Write a **verbal model** or **draw a sketch** that will help you find what you need to know.
2. **Label known and unknown facts** on or near your sketch.
3. Use labels and facts to **choose related definitions, theorems, formulas**, or other results you may need.
4. **Reason logically** to link the facts, using a proof or other written argument.
5. Write a **conclusion** that answers the original problem. **Check** that your reasoning is correct.

EXAMPLE 4 *Using the Area of a Rectangle*

REAL LIFE **SOCCER FIELD** You have a part-time job at a school. You need to buy enough grass seed to cover the school's soccer field. The field is 50 yards wide and 100 yards long. The instructions on the seed bags say that one bag will cover 5000 square feet. How many bags do you need?

SOLUTION

Begin by rewriting the dimensions of the field in feet. Multiplying each of the dimensions by 3, you find that the field is 150 feet wide and 300 feet long.

PROBLEM SOLVING STRATEGY

VERBAL MODEL [Area of field] = [Bags of seed] · [Coverage per bag]

LABELS

Area of field = **150 · 300** (square feet)

Bags of seed = $\boldsymbol{n}$ (bags)

Coverage per bag = **5000** (square feet per bag)

REASONING

$150 \cdot 300 = n \cdot 5000$ Write model for area of field.

$\frac{150 \cdot 300}{5000} = n$ Divide each side by 5000.

$9 = n$ Simplify.

▶ You need 9 bags of seed.

✓**UNIT ANALYSIS** You can use *unit analysis* to verify the units of measure.

$$\text{ft}^2 = \text{bags} \cdot \frac{\text{ft}^2}{\text{bag}}$$

EXTRA EXAMPLE 4

A maintenance worker needs to fertilize a 9-hole golf course. The entire golf course covers a rectangular area that is approximately 1800 feet by 2700 feet. Each bag of fertilizer covers 20,000 square feet. How many bags will the worker need?
243 bags

CHECKPOINT EXERCISES

For use after Example 4:

1. A painter is painting one side of a wooden fence along a highway. The fence is 926 feet long and 12 feet tall. The directions on each 5 gallon paint can say that each can will cover 2000 square feet. How many cans of paint will be needed to paint the fence?
6 cans

EXTRA EXAMPLE 5

You are designing a mat for a picture. The picture is 8 inches wide and 10 inches tall. The mat is to be 2 inches wide. What is the area of the mat? 88 in.^{2}

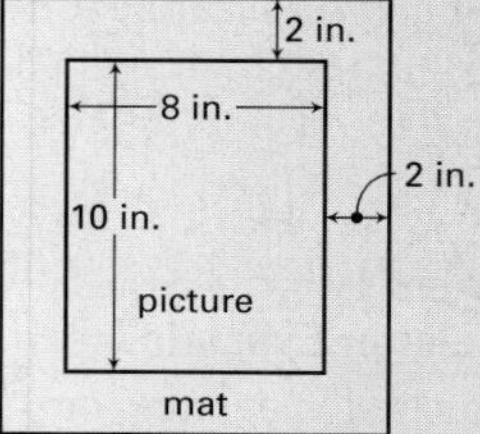

EXTRA EXAMPLE 6

You are making a triangular window. The height of the window is 18 inches and the area should be 297 inches. What should the base of the window be? 33 in.

CHECKPOINT EXERCISES

For use after Examples 5 and 6:

1. You are designing a quilt that is made of rectangles sewn together. Each rectangle follows the pattern below. Each of the small triangles has a base of 3 centimeters and an area of 9 square centimeters.

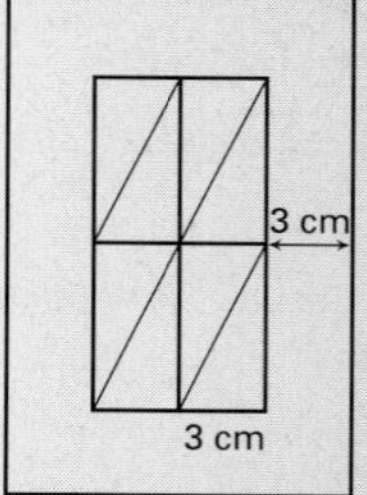

a. What is the height of each of the small triangles? 6 cm

b. What is the area of the border if its width is 3 cm? 144 cm^2

FOCUS ON VOCABULARY

What is the difference between the area and perimeter of a figure? See answer at right.

CLOSURE QUESTION

Explain how to find the circumference and area of a circle if you know its diameter. See right.

EXAMPLE 5 *Using the Area of a Square*

SWIMMING POOL You are planning a deck along two sides of a pool. The pool measures 18 feet by 12 feet. The deck is to be 8 feet wide. What is the area of the deck?

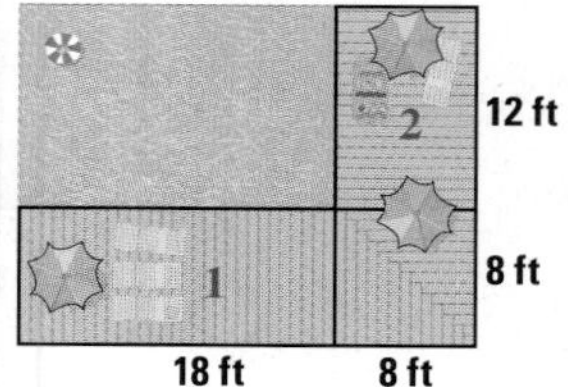

SOLUTION

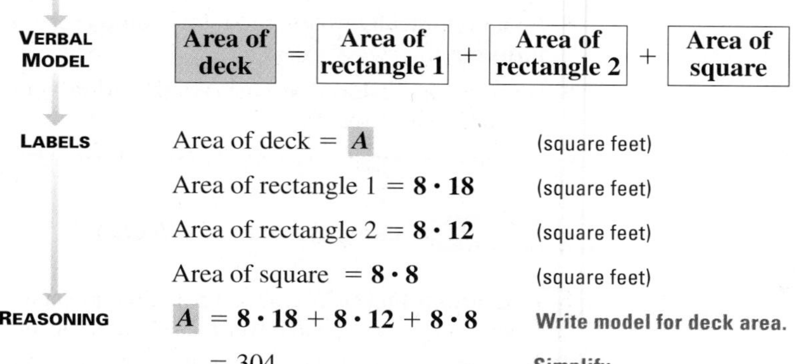

PROBLEM SOLVING STRATEGY

DRAW A SKETCH From your diagram, you can see that the area of the deck can be represented as the sum of the areas of two rectangles and a square.

VERBAL MODEL

Area of deck	=	Area of rectangle 1	+	Area of rectangle 2	+	Area of square

LABELS

Area of deck $= A$ (square feet)

Area of rectangle 1 $= \mathbf{8 \cdot 18}$ (square feet)

Area of rectangle 2 $= \mathbf{8 \cdot 12}$ (square feet)

Area of square $= \mathbf{8 \cdot 8}$ (square feet)

REASONING

$A = \mathbf{8 \cdot 18 + 8 \cdot 12 + 8 \cdot 8}$ **Write model for deck area.**

$= 304$ **Simplify.**

▶ The area of the deck is 304 square feet.

EXAMPLE 6 *Using the Area of a Triangle*

FLAG DESIGN You are making a triangular flag with a base of 24 inches and an area of 360 square inches. How long should it be?

24 in.

$A = 360$ in.^{2}

SOLUTION

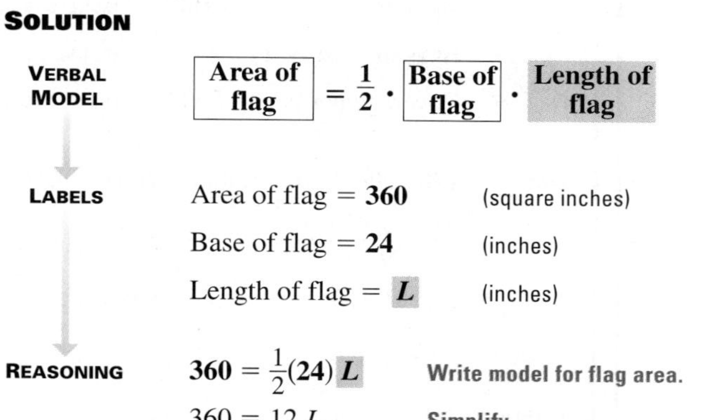

PROBLEM SOLVING STRATEGY

VERBAL MODEL

Area of flag	=	$\frac{1}{2}$	·	Base of flag	·	Length of flag

LABELS

Area of flag $= \mathbf{360}$ (square inches)

Base of flag $= \mathbf{24}$ (inches)

Length of flag $= L$ (inches)

REASONING

$\mathbf{360} = \frac{1}{2}(\mathbf{24})\,L$ **Write model for flag area.**

$360 = 12\,L$ **Simplify.**

$30 = L$ **Divide each side by 12.**

▶ The flag should be 30 inches long.

Focus on Vocabulary *Sample answer:* The area of a figure is the measure of the space inside the figure. The perimeter is the measure of the distance around the figure.

Closure Question *Sample answer:* Divide the diameter by 2 to find the radius. Multiply the radius by 2π to find the circumference. Square the radius and multiply it by π to find the area.

GUIDED PRACTICE

Vocabulary Check ✓
Concept Check ✓
Skill Check ✓

1. The perimeter of a circle is called its __?__. circumference

2. Explain how to find the perimeter of a rectangle. See margin.

In Exercises 3–5, find the area of the figure. (Where necessary, use $\pi \approx 3.14$.)

3. 8, 9
36 square units

4. 13, 7
91 square units

5. 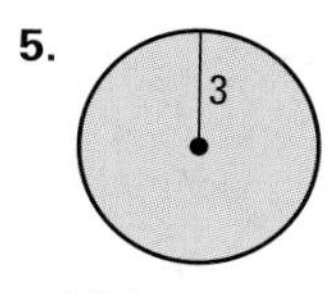

28.3 square units

6. The perimeter of a square is 12 meters. What is the length of a side of the square? 3 m

7. The radius of a circle is 4 inches. What is the circumference of the circle? (Use $\pi \approx 3.14$.) 25.1 in.^{2}

8. **FENCING** You are putting a fence around a rectangular garden with length 15 feet and width 8 feet. What is the length of the fence that you will need? 46 ft

PRACTICE AND APPLICATIONS

STUDENT HELP
Extra Practice to help you master skills is on p. 804.

FINDING PERIMETER, CIRCUMFERENCE, AND AREA Find the perimeter (or circumference) and area of the figure. (Where necessary, use $\pi \approx 3.14$.)

9. 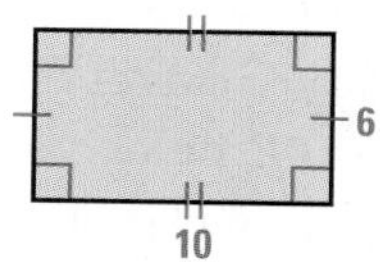

32 units; 60 square units

10. 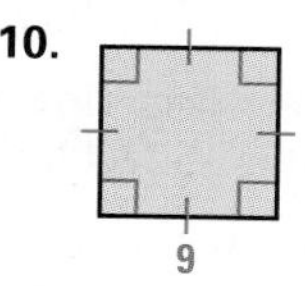

36 units; 81 square units

11. 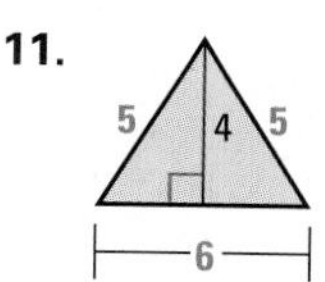

16 units; 12 square units

12. 

44 units; 153.9 square units

13. 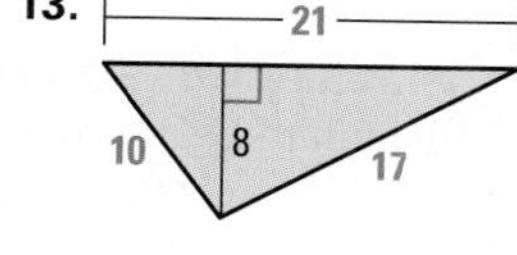

48 units; 84 square units

14. 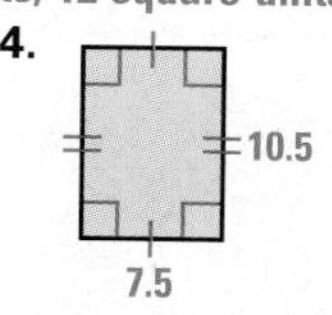

36 units; 78.75 square units

15. 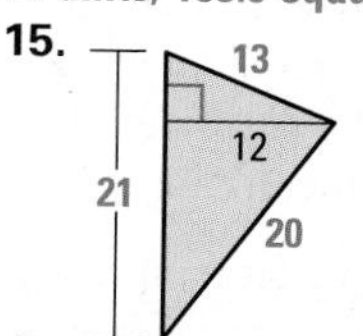

54 units; 126 square units

16. 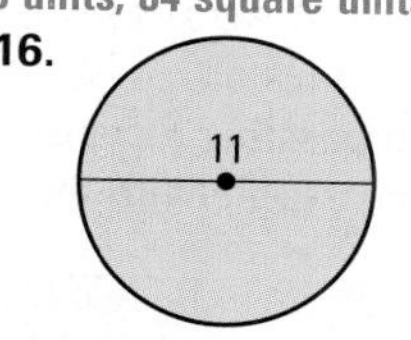

34.5 units; 95 square units

17. 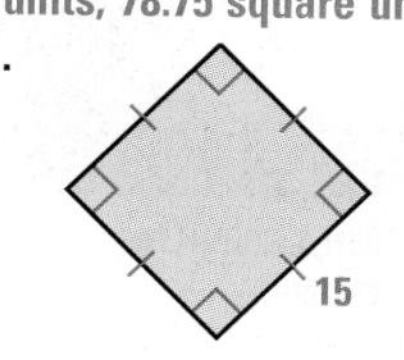

60 units; 225 square units

18. 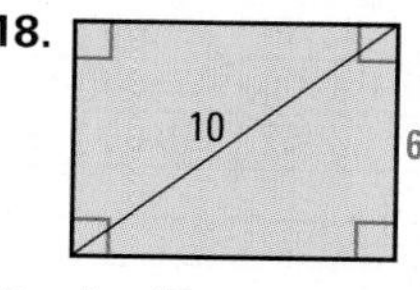

28 units; 48 square units

19. 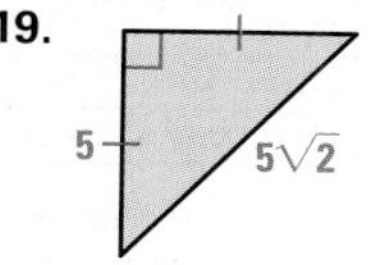

$10 + 5\sqrt{2}$ units; 12.5 square units

20. 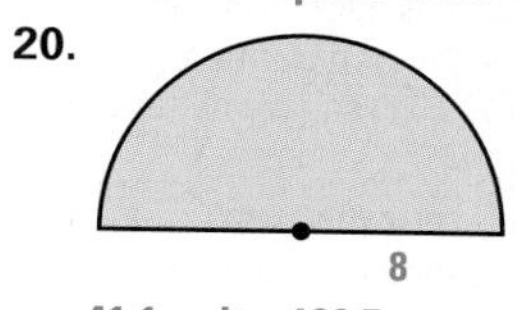

41.1 units; 100.5 square units

STUDENT HELP
HOMEWORK HELP
Example 1: Exs. 9–26
Example 2: Exs. 9–26
Example 3: Exs. 27–33
Example 4: Exs. 34–40
Example 5: Exs. 34–40
Example 6: Exs. 41–48

3 APPLY

ASSIGNMENT GUIDE

BASIC
Day 1: pp. 55–56 Exs. 9–33
Day 2: pp. 56–58 Exs. 34–36, 41–49, 51, 52–62 even, Quiz 3 Exs. 1–10

AVERAGE
Day 1: pp. 55–56 Exs. 9–33
Day 2: pp. 56–58 Exs. 34–36, 38–49, 51, 52–62 even, Quiz 3 Exs. 1–10

ADVANCED
Day 1: pp. 55–56 Exs. 9–33
Day 2: pp. 56–58 Exs. 34–36, 38–51, 52–62 even, Quiz 3 Exs. 1–10

BLOCK SCHEDULE
pp. 55–56 Exs. 9–33 (with 1.6)
pp. 56–58 Exs. 34–36, 38–49, 51, 52–62 even, Quiz 3 Exs. 1–10 (with Ch. Rev.)

EXERCISE LEVELS
Level A: *Easier*
9–29, 34
Level B: *More Difficult*
30–33, 35–48
Level C: *Most Difficult*
49, 50

HOMEWORK CHECK
To quickly check student understanding of key concepts, go over the following exercises: Exs. 11, 12, 18, 25, 30, 36, 42, 47. See also the Daily Homework Quiz:

- Blackline Master (*Chapter 2 Resource Book*, p. 11)
- Transparency (p. 10)

2. Add the lengths of the four sides; multiply the length by two and the width by two and then add the products; or add the length and width and multiply the result by 2.

STUDENT HELP NOTES

Homework Help Students can find help for Exs. 21–26 at **www.mcdougallittell.com.** The information can be printed out for students who don't have access to the Internet.

APPLICATION NOTE

EXERCISE 36 Additional information about the Millennium Dome is available at **www.mcdougallittell.com.**

ENGLISH LEARNERS

EXERCISE 49 Keep in mind that language contained in word problems is often specialized, and can be difficult for English learners. You might use a world globe and a length of string to illustrate what must be determined in this multi-step problem.

30.

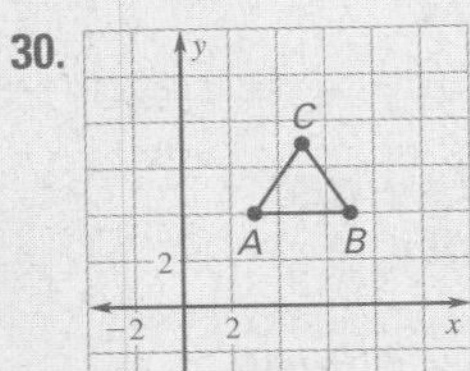

6 square units

31.

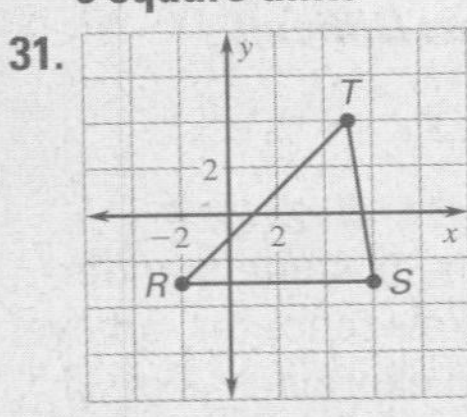

28 square units

ADDITIONAL PRACTICE AND RETEACHING

For Lesson 1.7:

- Practice Levels A, B, and C (*Chapter 1 Resource Book*, p. 100)
- Reteaching with Practice (*Chapter 1 Resource Book*, p. 103)
- See Lesson 1.7 of the *Personal Student Tutor*

For more Mixed Review:

- Search the *Test and Practice Generator* for key words or specific lessons.

STUDENT HELP

HOMEWORK HELP Visit our Web site www.mcdougallittell.com for help with problem solving in Exs. 21–26.

FINDING AREA **Find the area of the figure described.**

21. Triangle with height 6 cm and base 5 cm **15 cm^2**

22. Rectangle with length 12 yd and width 9 yd **108 yd^2**

23. Square with side length 8 ft **64 ft^2**

24. Circle with radius 10 m (Use $\pi \approx 3.14$.) **314 m^2**

25. Square with perimeter 24 m **36 m^2**

26. Circle with diameter 100 ft (Use $\pi \approx 3.14$.) **7850 ft^2**

FINDING AREA **Find the area of the figure.**

27.

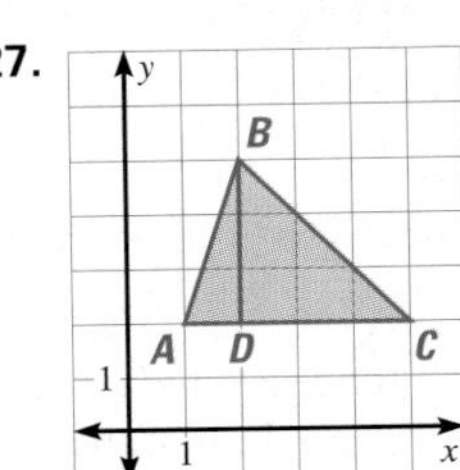

6 square units

28.

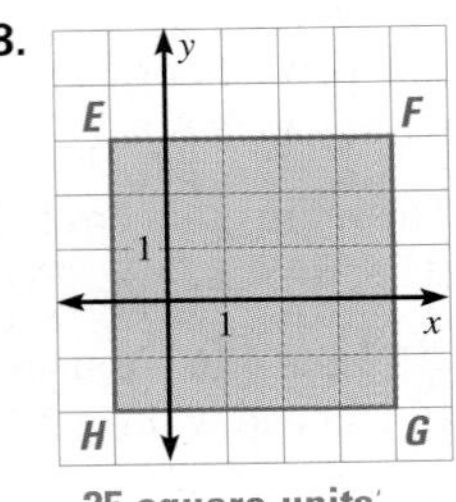

25 square units

29.

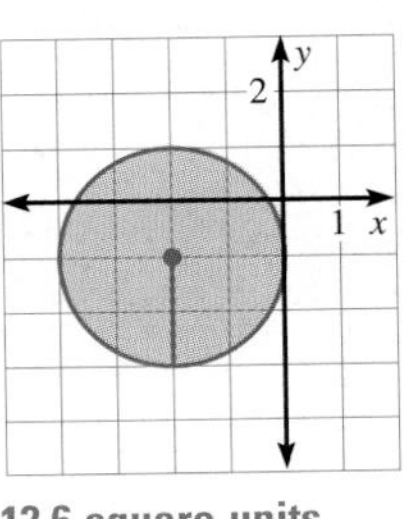

12.6 square units

FINDING AREA **Draw the figure in a coordinate plane and find its area.**
30–33. See margin for graphs.

30. Triangle defined by $A(3, 4)$, $B(7, 4)$, and $C(5, 7)$ **6 square units**

31. Triangle defined by $R(-2, -3)$, $S(6, -3)$, and $T(5, 4)$ **28 square units**

32. Rectangle defined by $L(-2, -4)$, $M(-2, 1)$, $N(7, 1)$, and $P(7, -4)$ **45 square units**

33. Square defined by $W(5, 0)$, $X(0, 5)$, $Y(-5, 0)$, and $Z(0, -5)$ **50 square units**

34. **CARPETING** How many square yards of carpet are needed to carpet a room that is 15 feet by 25 feet? **$41\frac{2}{3}$ yd^2**

35. **WINDOWS** A rectangular pane of glass measuring 12 inches by 18 inches is surrounded by a wooden frame that is 2 inches wide. What is the area of the window, including the frame? **352 in.^{2}**

36. **MILLENNIUM DOME** The largest fabric dome in the world, the Millennium Dome covers a circular plot of land with a diameter of 320 meters. What is the circumference of the covered land? What is its area? (Use $\pi \approx 3.14$.) **about 1004.8 m; about 80,384 m^2**

37. **SPREADSHEET** Use a spreadsheet to show many different possible values of length and width for a rectangle with an area of 100 m^2. For each possible rectangle, calculate the perimeter. What are the dimensions of the rectangle with the smallest perimeter? **10 m by 10 m**

FOCUS ON APPLICATIONS

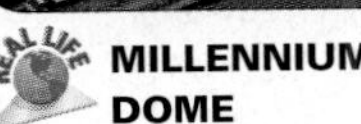

MILLENNIUM DOME

Built for the year 2000, this dome in Greenwich, England, is over 50 m tall and is covered by more than 100,000 square meters of fabric.

APPLICATION LINK www.mcdougallittell.com

Perimeter of Rectangle

	A	B	C	D	E	F	G	H
1	Length	1.00	2.00	3.00	4.00	5.00	6.00	...
2	Width	100.00	50.00	33.33	25.00	20.00	16.67	...
3	Area	100.00	100.00	100.00	100.00	100.00	100.00	...
4	Perimeter	202.00	104.00	72.67	58.00	50.00	45.33	...
5								

32–33. See Additional Answers beginning on page AA1.

FOCUS ON APPLICATIONS

REAL LIFE **CRANBERRIES** Cranberries were once called "bounceberries" because they bounce when they are ripe.

38. **CRANBERRY HARVEST** To harvest cranberries, the field is flooded so that the berries float. The berries are gathered with an inflatable boom. What area of cranberries can be gathered into a circular region with a radius of 5.5 meters? (Use $\pi \approx 3.14$.) about 95 m^2

39. **BICYCLES** How many times does a bicycle tire that has a radius of 21 inches rotate when it travels 420 inches? (Use $\pi \approx 3.14$.) about 3 times

40. **FLYING DISC** A plastic flying disc is circular and has a circular hole in the middle. If the diameter of the outer edge of the ring is 13 inches and the diameter of the inner edge of the ring is 10 inches, what is the area of plastic in the ring? (Use $\pi \approx 3.14$.) about 54.2 $in.^2$

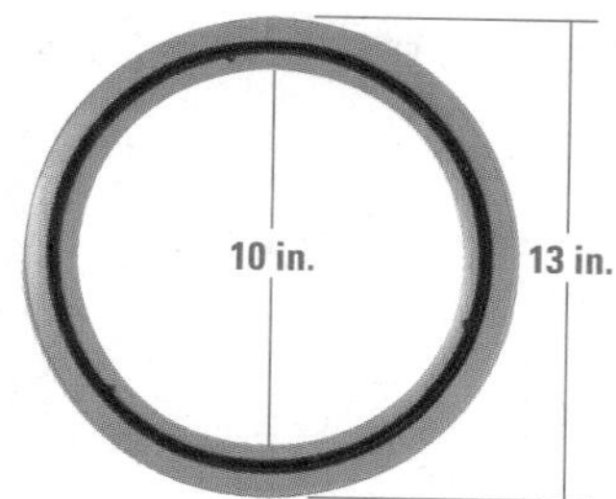

LOGICAL REASONING **Use the given measurements to find the unknown measurement. (Where necessary, use $\pi \approx 3.14$.)**

41. A rectangle has an area of 36 $in.^2$ and a length of 9 in. Find its perimeter. 26 in.

42. A square has an area of 10,000 m^2. Find its perimeter. 400 m

43. A triangle has an area of 48 ft^2 and a base of 16 ft. Find its height. 6 ft

44. A triangle has an area of 52 yd^2 and a height of 13 yd. Find its base. 8 yd

45. A circle has an area of 200π cm^2. Find its radius. $10\sqrt{2} \approx 14.1$ cm

46. A circle has an area of 1 m^2. Find its diameter. about 1.1 m

47. A circle has a circumference of 100 yd. Find its area. about 796.2 yd^2

48. A right triangle has sides of length 4.5 cm, 6 cm, and 7.5 cm. Find its area. 13.5 cm^2

Test Preparation

49. **MULTI-STEP PROBLEM** **Use the following information.**
Earth has a radius of about 3960 miles at the equator. Because there are 5280 feet in one mile, the radius of Earth is about 20,908,800 feet.

a. Suppose you could wrap a cable around Earth to form a circle that is snug against the ground. Find the length of the cable in feet by finding the circumference of Earth. (Assume that Earth is perfectly round. Use $\pi \approx 3.14$.) 131,307,264 ft

b. Suppose you add 6 feet to the cable length in part (a). Use this length as the circumference of a new circle. Find the radius of the larger circle. about 20,908,801 ft

c. Use your results from parts (a) and (b) to find how high off of the ground the longer cable would be if it was evenly spaced around Earth. about 1 ft

d. Would the answer to part (c) be different on a planet with a different radius? Explain. See margin.

50. **DOUBLING A RECTANGLE'S SIDES** The length and width of a rectangle are doubled. How do the perimeter and area of the new rectangle compare with the perimeter and area of the original rectangle? Illustrate your answer. See margin.

4 ASSESS

DAILY HOMEWORK QUIZ

Transparency Available

Find the perimeter (or circumference) and area of each figure. Use $\pi = 3.14$.

1. a circle with radius 4 units
25.1 units; 50.2 square units
2. a rectangle with length 8 units and width 2 units
20 units; 16 square units
3. 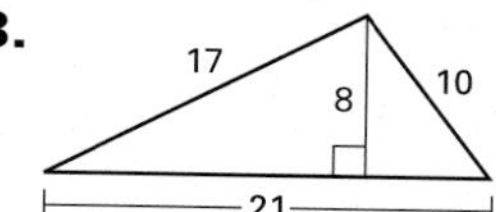

48 units; 84 square units

Find each unknown measurement.

4. the area of a square with perimeter 20 units
25 square units
5. the circumference of a circle with area 452.2 m^2 75.4 m

EXTRA CHALLENGE NOTE

Challenge problems for Lesson 1.7 are available in **blackline** format in the *Chapter 1 Resource Book,* p. 108 and at **www.mcdougallittell.com.**

ADDITIONAL TEST PREPARATION

1. **OPEN ENDED** Write a real-life problem that involves finding the area of a triangle. Show how to use the problem-solving plan to solve the problem. Check work.
2. **WRITING** Write a journal entry explaining how to find the areas, and perimeters or circumferences of common figures. Use examples to illustrate your work. Check work.

49d, 50. See next page.

49d. No; let r and C be the radius and circumference of the planet and r' and C' be the radius and circumference of the cable circle. $C = 2\pi r$ and $C' = 2\pi r' = 2\pi r + 6$. So $2\pi r' = 2\pi r + 6$. Therefore $r' - r = \frac{6}{2\pi} \approx 1$.

50. The perimeter is doubled and the area is multiplied by 4; for example, suppose the dimensions of a rectangle that is 3 in. by 5 in. are doubled. The perimeter of the original rectangle is 16 in. and the area is 15 in.^{2}. The perimeter of the enlarged rectangle is 32 in. and the area is 60 in.^{2}.

51.

52. *Sample answer:*

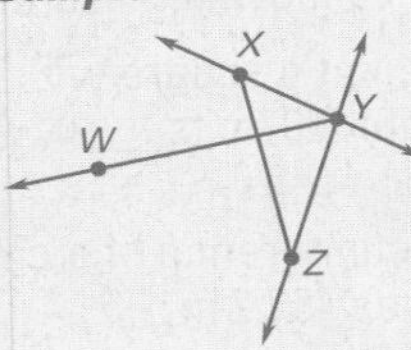

MIXED REVIEW

SKETCHING FIGURES **Sketch the points, lines, segments, and rays.** (Review 1.2 for 2.1) 51, 52. See margin.

51. Draw opposite rays using the points A, B, and C, with B as the initial point for both rays.

52. Draw four noncollinear points, W, X, Y, and Z, no three of which are collinear. Then sketch $\overleftrightarrow{XY}$, $\overrightarrow{YW}$, $\overline{XZ}$ and $\overleftrightarrow{ZY}$.

USING ALGEBRA **Plot the points in a coordinate plane and sketch $\angle DEF$. Classify the angle. Write the coordinates of one point in the interior of the angle and one point in the exterior of the angle.** (Review 1.4)

53–56. See margin.

53. $D(2, -2)$, $E(4, -3)$, $F(6, -2)$

54. $D(0, 0)$, $E(-3, 0)$, $F(0, -2)$

55. $D(0, 1)$, $E(2, 3)$, $F(4, 1)$

56. $D(-3, -2)$, $E(3, -4)$, $F(1, 3)$

FINDING THE MIDPOINT **Find the coordinates of the midpoint of a segment with the given endpoints.** (Review 1.5)

57. $A(0, 0)$, $B(5, 3)$ $\left(2\frac{1}{2}, 1\frac{1}{2}\right)$

58. $C(2, -3)$, $D(4, 4)$ $\left(3, \frac{1}{2}\right)$

59. $E(-3, 4)$, $F(-2, -1)$ $\left(-2\frac{1}{2}, 1\frac{1}{2}\right)$

60. $G(-2, 0)$, $H(-7, -6)$ $\left(-4\frac{1}{2}, -3\right)$

61. $J(0, 5)$, $K(14, 1)$ (7, 3)

62. $M(-44, 9)$, $N(6, -7)$ (−19, 1)

QUIZ 3

Self-Test for Lessons 1.6 and 1.7

In Exercises 1–4, find the measure of the angle. (Lesson 1.6)

1. Complement of $\angle A$; $m\angle A = 41°$ 49°

2. Supplement of $\angle B$; $m\angle B = 127°$ 53°

3. Supplement of $\angle C$; $m\angle C = 22°$ 158°

4. Complement of $\angle D$; $m\angle D = 35°$ 55°

5. $\angle A$ and $\angle B$ are complementary. The measure of $\angle A$ is five times the measure of $\angle B$. Find $m\angle A$ and $m\angle B$. (Lesson 1.6) 15°, 75°

In Exercises 6–9, use the given information to find the unknown measurement. (Lesson 1.7)

6. Find the area and circumference of a circle with a radius of 18 meters. (Use $\pi \approx 3.14$.) 1017.4 m^2, 113.0 m

7. Find the area of a triangle with a base of 13 inches and a height of 11 inches. 71.5 in.^{2}

8. Find the area and perimeter of a rectangle with a length of 10 centimeters and a width of 4.6 centimeters. 46 cm^2, 29.2 cm

9. Find the area of a triangle defined by $P(-3, 4)$, $Q(7, 4)$, and $R(-1, 12)$. 40 square units

10. **WALLPAPER** You are buying rolls of wallpaper to paper the walls of a rectangular room. The room measures 12 feet by 24 feet and the walls are 8 feet high. A roll of wallpaper contains 28 ft^2. About how many rolls of wallpaper will you need? (Lesson 1.7) at least 21 rolls

CHAPTER 1 Chapter Summary

WHAT did you learn?	*WHY did you learn it?*
Find and describe patterns. **(1.1)**	Use a pattern to predict a figure or number in a sequence. **(p. 3)**
Use inductive reasoning. **(1.1)**	Make and verify conjectures such as a conjecture about the frequency of full moons. **(p. 5)**
Use defined and undefined terms. **(1.2)**	Understand the basic elements of geometry.
Sketch intersections of lines and planes. **(1.2)**	Visualize the basic elements of geometry and the ways they can intersect.
Use segment postulates and the Distance Formula. **(1.3)**	Solve real-life problems, such as finding the distance between two points on a map. **(p. 20)**
Use angle postulates and classify angles. **(1.4)**	Solve problems in geometry and in real life, such as finding the measure of the angle of vision for a horse wearing blinkers. **(p. 27)**
Bisect a segment and bisect an angle. **(1.5)**	Solve problems in geometry and in real life, such as finding an angle measure of a kite. **(p. 37)**
Identify vertical angles, linear pairs, complementary angles, and supplementary angles. **(1.6)**	Find the angle measures of geometric figures and real-life structures, such as intersecting metal supports of a stair railing. **(p. 45)**
Find the perimeter, circumference, and area of common plane figures. **(1.7)**	To solve problems related to measurement, such as finding the area of a deck for a pool. **(p. 54)**
Use a general problem-solving plan. **(1.7)**	To solve problems related to mathematics and real life, such as finding the number of bags of grass seed you need for a soccer field. **(p. 53)**

How does Chapter 1 fit into the BIGGER PICTURE of geometry?

In this chapter, you learned a basic reasoning skill—inductive reasoning. You also learned many fundamental terms—*point*, *line*, *plane*, *segment*, and *angle*, to name a few. Added to this were four basic postulates. These building blocks will be used throughout the remainder of this book to develop new terms, postulates, and theorems to explain the geometry of the world around you.

STUDY STRATEGY

How did you use your vocabulary pages?

The definitions of vocabulary terms you made, using the **Study Strategy** on page 2, may resemble this one.

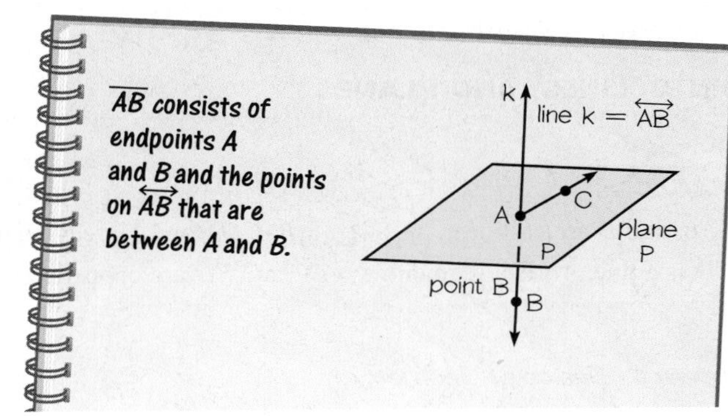

53–56. Coordinates of sample points are given.

53.

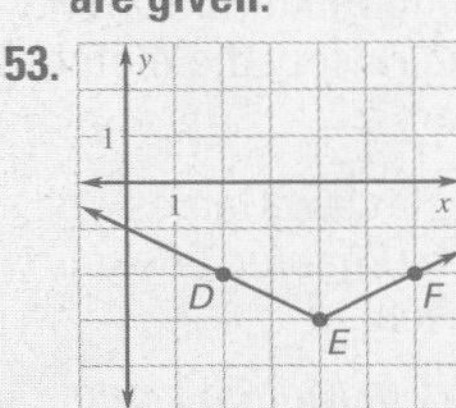

obtuse; (0, 0), (0, –2)

54.

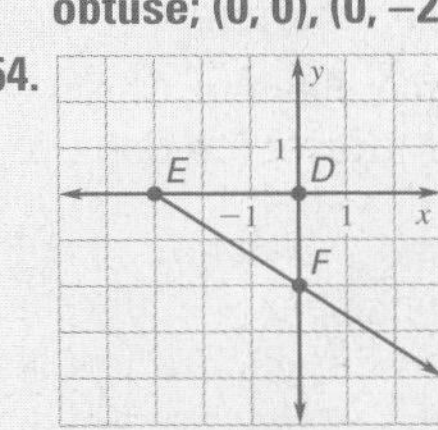

acute; (1, –1), (0, 1)

55.

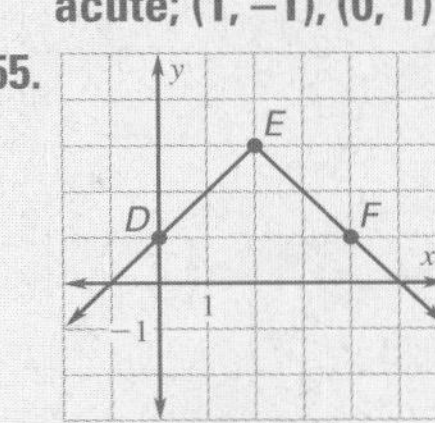

right; (0, 0), (0, 2)

56.

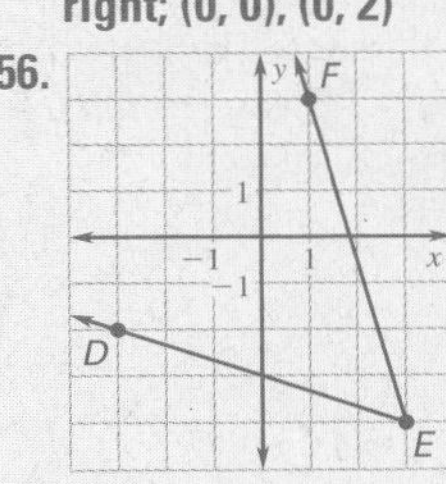

acute; (0, 0), (3, 0)

ADDITIONAL RESOURCES

The following resources are available to help review the material in this chapter.

- Chapter Review Games and Activities (*Chapter 1 Resource Book,* p. 109)
- *Geometry in Motion video*
- *Personal Student Tutor*
- Cumulative Review, Chs. 1–3 (*Chapter 1 Resource Book,* p. 121)

1. Each number is 7 more than the previous number.
2. Numbers after the first are found by adding consecutive powers of 2.
3. Each number is 3 times the previous number.
4. 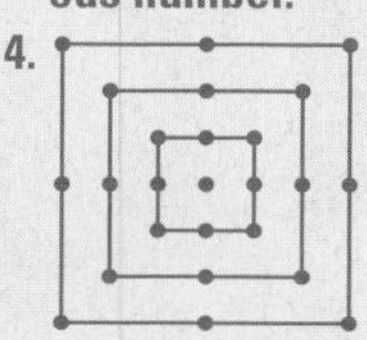
5. If 1 is added to the product of four consecutive positive integers, n through $n + 3$, the sum is equal to the square of $[n(n + 3) + 1]$.

CHAPTER 1

Chapter Review

VOCABULARY

1.1 PATTERNS AND INDUCTIVE REASONING

Examples on pp. 3–5

EXAMPLE Make a conjecture based on the results shown.

Conjecture: Given a 3-digit number, form a 6-digit number by repeating the digits. Divide the number by 7, then 11, then 13. The result is the original number.

$456{,}456 \div 7 \div 11 \div 13 = 456$
$562{,}562 \div 7 \div 11 \div 13 = 562$
$109{,}109 \div 7 \div 11 \div 13 = 109$

In Exercises 1–3, describe a pattern in the sequence of numbers. 1–5. See margin.

1. 5, 12, 19, 26, 33, . . .
2. 0, 2, 6, 14, 30, . . .
3. 4, 12, 36, 108, 324, . . .
4. Sketch the next figure in the pattern.

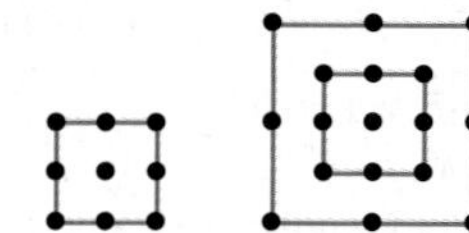

5. Make a conjecture based on the results.

$4 \cdot 5 \cdot 6 \cdot 7 + 1 = 29 \cdot 29$
$5 \cdot 6 \cdot 7 \cdot 8 + 1 = 41 \cdot 41$
$6 \cdot 7 \cdot 8 \cdot 9 + 1 = 55 \cdot 55$

6. Show the conjecture is false by finding a counterexample:
Conjecture: *The cube of a number is always greater than the number.*

Sample answer: $(-2)^3 = -8$ and $-8 < -2$

1.2 POINTS, LINES, AND PLANES

Examples on pp. 10–12

EXAMPLE

C, E, and *D* are collinear. $\overleftrightarrow{CD}$ is a line. $\overline{AB}$ is a segment.

A, B, C, D, and *E* are coplanar. $\overrightarrow{EC}$ and $\overrightarrow{ED}$ are opposite rays.

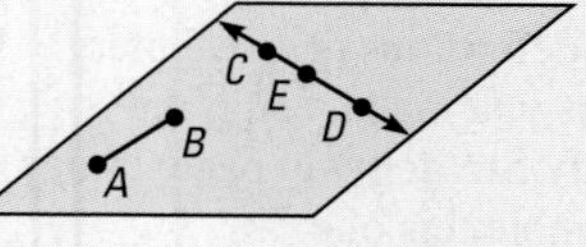

7–9. See margin.

7. Draw five coplanar points, A, B, C, D, and E so that $\overrightarrow{BA}$ and $\overrightarrow{BC}$ are opposite rays, and $\overline{DE}$ intersects $\overleftrightarrow{AC}$ at B.

8. Sketch three planes that do not intersect.

9. Sketch two lines that are not coplanar and do not intersect.

1.3 SEGMENTS AND THEIR MEASURES

Examples on pp. 17–20

EXAMPLE B is between A and C, so $AB + BC = AC$.
Use the Distance Formula to find AB and BC.

$$AB = \sqrt{[-3-(-5)]^2 + (1-2)^2} = \sqrt{2^2 + (-1)^2} = \sqrt{5}$$

$$BC = \sqrt{[3-(-3)]^2 + (-2-1)^2} = \sqrt{6^2 + (-3)^2} = \sqrt{45}$$

Because $AB \neq BC$, $\overline{AB}$ and $\overline{BC}$ are *not* congruent segments.

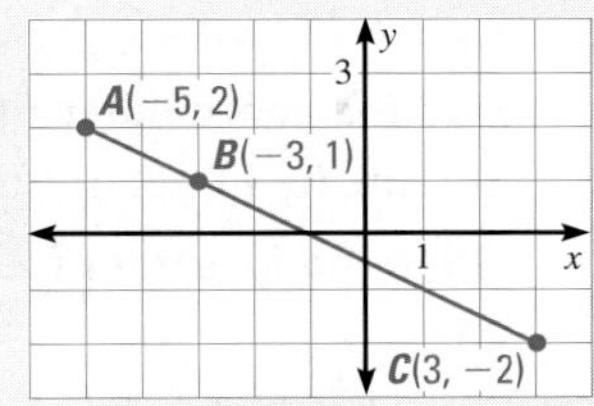

10. Q is between P and S. R is between Q and S. S is between Q and T. $PT = 30$, $QS = 16$, and $PQ = QR = RS$. Find PQ, ST, and RP. $PQ = 8$, $ST = 6$, $RP = 16$

Use the Distance Formula to decide whether $\overline{PQ} \cong \overline{QR}$.

11. $P(-4, 3)$, $Q(-2, 1)$, $R(0, -1)$
$\overline{PQ} \cong \overline{QR}$; $PQ = QR = 2\sqrt{2}$

12. $P(-3, 5)$, $Q(1, 3)$, $R(4, 1)$
See margin.

13. $P(-2, -2)$, $Q(0, 1)$, $R(1, 4)$
See margin.

1.4 ANGLES AND THEIR MEASURES

Examples on pp. 26–28

EXAMPLE

$m\angle ACD + m\angle DCB = m\angle ACB$

$\angle ACD$ is an acute angle: $m\angle ACD < 90°$.

$\angle DCB$ is a right angle: $m\angle DCB = 90°$.

$\angle ACB$ is an obtuse angle: $m\angle ACB > 90°$.

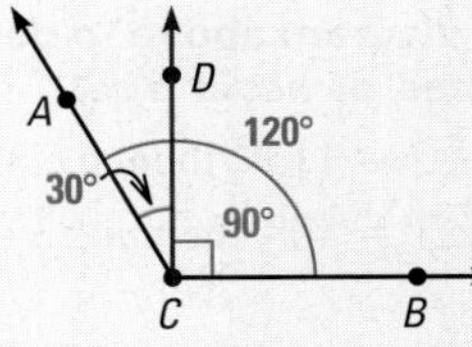

Classify the angle as *acute, right, obtuse,* or *straight*. Sketch the angle. Then use a protractor to check your results. 14–16. See margin for graphs.

14. $m\angle KLM = 180°$ straight

15. $m\angle A = 150°$ obtuse

16. $m\angle Y = 45°$ acute

Use the Angle Addition Postulate to find the measure of the unknown angle.

17. $m\angle DEF$ 105°

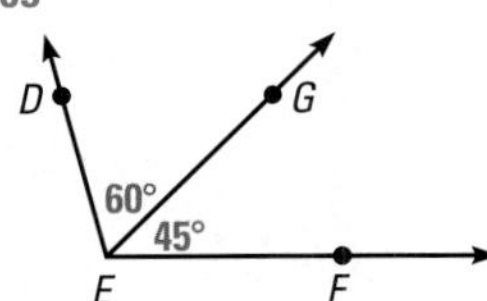

18. $m\angle HJL$ 50°

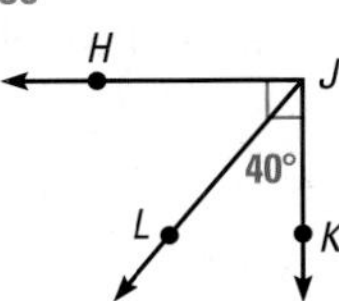

19. $m\angle QNM$ 70°

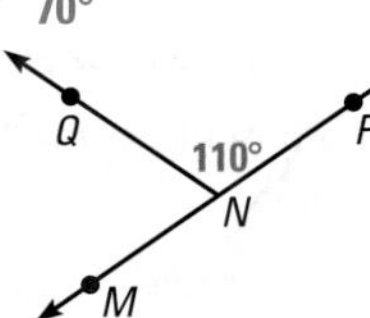

7.

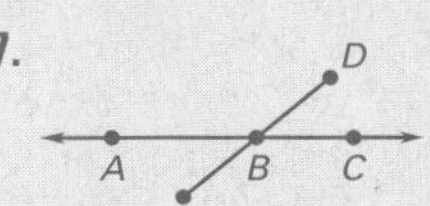

8.

9.

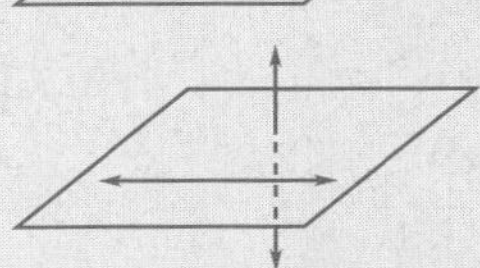

12. $\overline{PQ}$ and $\overline{QR}$ are not congruent; $PQ = 2\sqrt{5}$, $QR = \sqrt{13}$.

13. $\overline{PQ}$ and $\overline{QR}$ are not congruent; $PQ = \sqrt{13}$, $QR = \sqrt{10}$.

14. straight

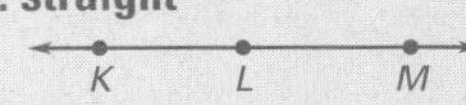

15. obtuse

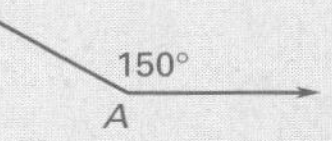

16. acute

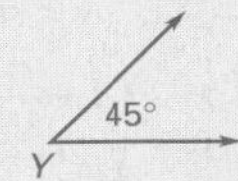

1.5 SEGMENT AND ANGLE BISECTORS

Examples on pp. 35–37

EXAMPLE If $\overleftrightarrow{CD}$ is a bisector of $\overline{AB}$, then $\overleftrightarrow{CD}$ intersects $\overline{AB}$ at its midpoint M: $M = \left(\frac{-2+0}{2}, \frac{0+2}{2}\right) = (-1, 1)$.

$\overrightarrow{ME}$ bisects $\angle BMD$, so $m\angle BME = m\angle EMD = 45°$.

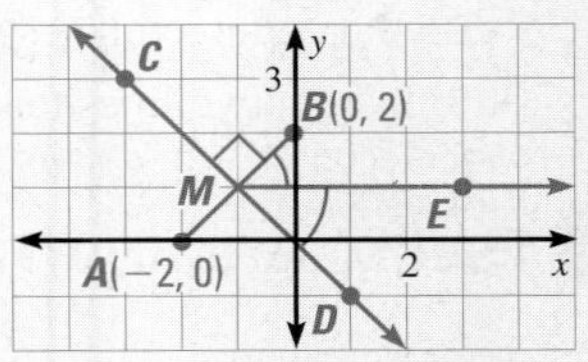

Find the coordinates of the midpoint of a segment with the given endpoints.

20. $A(0, 0)$, $B(-8, 6)$ $(-4, 3)$ **21.** $J(-1, 7)$, $K(3, -3)$ $(1, 2)$ **22.** $P(-12, -9)$, $Q(2, 10)$ $\left(-5, \frac{1}{2}\right)$

$\overrightarrow{QS}$ **is the bisector of** $\angle PQR$. **Find any angle measures not given in the diagram.**

23.

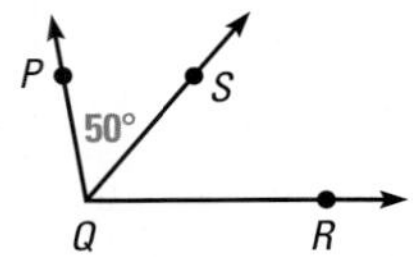

$m\angle SQR = 50°$; $m\angle PQR = 100°$

24.

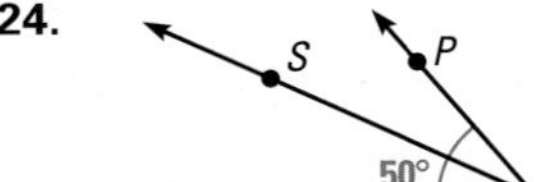

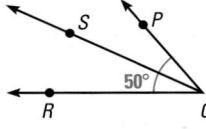

$m\angle PQS = m\angle SQR = 25°$

25.

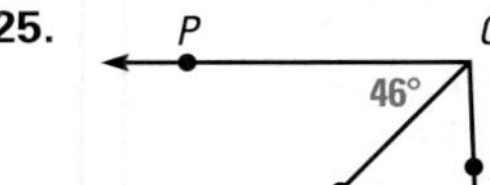

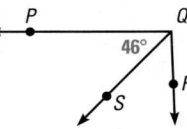

$m\angle RQS = 46°$; $m\angle PQR = 92°$

1.6 ANGLE PAIR RELATIONSHIPS

Examples on pp. 44–46

EXAMPLE $\angle 1$ and $\angle 3$ are vertical angles.
$\angle 1$ and $\angle 2$ are a linear pair and are supplementary angles.
$\angle 3$ and $\angle 4$ are complementary angles.

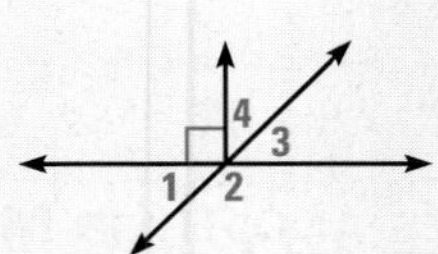

Use the diagram above to decide whether the statement is *always*, *sometimes*, or *never* true.

26. If $m\angle 2 = 115°$, then $m\angle 3 = 65°$. always **27.** $\angle 3$ and $\angle 4$ are congruent. sometimes

28. If $m\angle 1 = 40°$, then $m\angle 3 = 50°$. never **29.** $\angle 1$ and $\angle 4$ are complements. sometimes

1.7 INTRODUCTION TO PERIMETER, CIRCUMFERENCE, AND AREA

Examples on pp. 51–54

EXAMPLES A circle has diameter 24 ft.
Its circumference is $C = 2\pi r \approx 2(3.14)(12) = 75.36$ feet.
Its area is $A = \pi r^2 \approx 3.14(12^2) = 452.16$ square feet.

Find the perimeter (or circumference) and area of the figure described.

30. Rectangle with length 10 cm and width 4.5 cm 29 cm, 45 cm^2

31. Circle with radius 9 in. (Use $\pi \approx 3.14$.) 56.52 in., 254.34 in.^{2}

32. Triangle defined by $A(-6, 0)$, $B(2, 0)$, and $C(-2, -3)$ 18 units, 12 square units

33. A square garden has sides of length 14 ft. What is its perimeter? 56 ft

CHAPTER 1

Chapter Test

Use the diagram to name the figures.

1. Three collinear points **Q, T, and N, or N, X, and U**
2. Four noncoplanar points *Sample answer: S, L, M, and P.*
3. Two opposite rays **See margin.**
4. Two intersecting lines **See margin.**
5. The intersection of plane *LMN* and plane *QLS* $\overleftrightarrow{QL}$

Find the length of the segment.

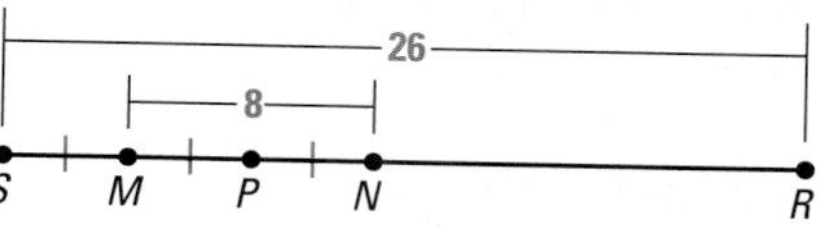

6. $\overline{MP}$ 4
7. $\overline{SM}$ 4
8. $\overline{NR}$ 14
9. $\overline{MR}$ 22

Find the measure of the angle.

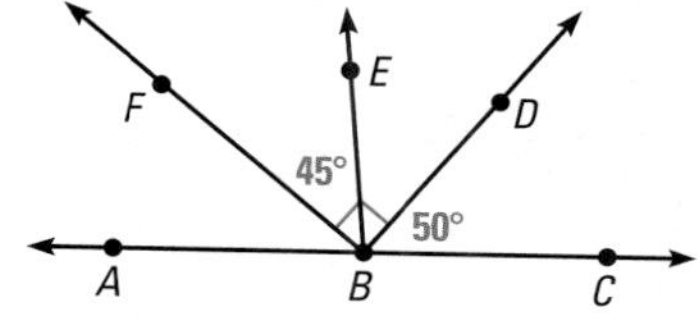

10. $\angle DBE$ 45°
11. $\angle FBC$ 140°
12. $\angle ABF$ 40°
13. $\angle DBA$ 130°

14. Refer to the diagram for Exercises 10–13. Name an obtuse angle, an acute angle, a right angle, and two complementary angles. **See margin.**
15. Q is between P and R. $PQ = 2w - 3$, $QR = 4 + w$, and $PR = 34$. Find the value of w. Then find the lengths of $\overline{PQ}$ and $\overline{QR}$. **11; 19; 15**
16. $\overline{RT}$ has endpoints $R(-3, 8)$ and $T(3, 6)$. Find the coordinates of the midpoint, S, of $\overline{RT}$. Then use the Distance Formula to verify that $RS = ST$. **See margin.**
17. Use the diagram. If $m\angle 3 = 68°$, find the measures of $\angle 5$ and $\angle 4$. **68°, 112°**
18. Suppose $m\angle PQR = 130°$. If $\overrightarrow{QT}$ bisects $\angle PQR$, what is the measure of $\angle PQT$? **65°**

The first five figures in a pattern are shown. Each square in the grid is 1 unit × 1 unit.

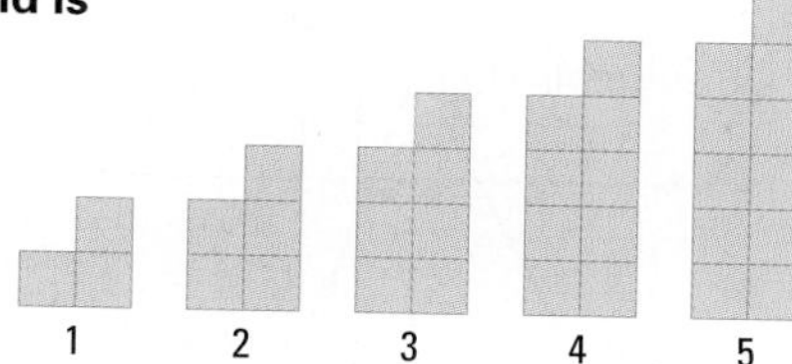

19. Make a table that shows the distance around each figure at each stage. **See margin.**
20. Describe the pattern of the distances and use it to predict the distance around the figure at stage 20.
The distance is 6 more than twice the figure number; 46 units

A center pivot irrigation system uses a fixed water supply to water a circular region of a field. The radius of the watering system is 560 feet long. (Use $\pi \approx 3.14$.)

21. If some workers walked around the circumference of the watered region, how far would they have to walk? Round to the nearest foot. **3517 ft**
22. Find the area of the region watered. Round to the nearest square foot. **984,704 ft²**

ADDITIONAL RESOURCES

- ***Chapter 1 Resource Book***
  Chapter Test (3 levels) (p. 110)
  SAT/ACT Chapter Test (p. 116)
  Alternative Assessment (p. 117)
- ***Test and Practice Generator***

3. $\overrightarrow{TQ}$ and $\overrightarrow{TN}$ or $\overrightarrow{XN}$ and $\overrightarrow{XU}$
4. *Sample answer:* $\overleftrightarrow{SL}$ and $\overleftrightarrow{LM}$
14. *Sample answers:* $\angle ABD$, $\angle ABF$, $\angle FBD$; $\angle FBE$ and $\angle EBD$
16. (0, 7);
$RS = \sqrt{(-3-0)^2 + (8-7)^2} = \sqrt{10}$;
$ST = \sqrt{(0-3)^2 + (7-6)^2} = \sqrt{10}$

19.

Figure number	1	2	3	4	5
Distance (units)	8	10	12	14	16

ADDITIONAL RESOURCES

- ***Chapter 1 Resource Book***
  Chapter Test (3 levels) (p. 110)
  SAT/ACT Chapter Test (p. 116)
  Alternative Assessment (p. 117)
- ***Test and Practice Generator***

CHAPTER 1

Chapter Standardized Test

TEST-TAKING STRATEGY Work as quickly as you can through the easier sections, but avoid making careless errors on easy questions.

1. **MULTIPLE CHOICE** What is the next number in the sequence? C

   4488; 44,088; 440,088; 4,400,088; . . .

   Ⓐ 400,008 Ⓑ 40,000,088
   Ⓒ 44,000,088 Ⓓ 440,000,088
   Ⓔ 44,000,008

2. **MULTIPLE CHOICE** Which of the following statements is *false*? E

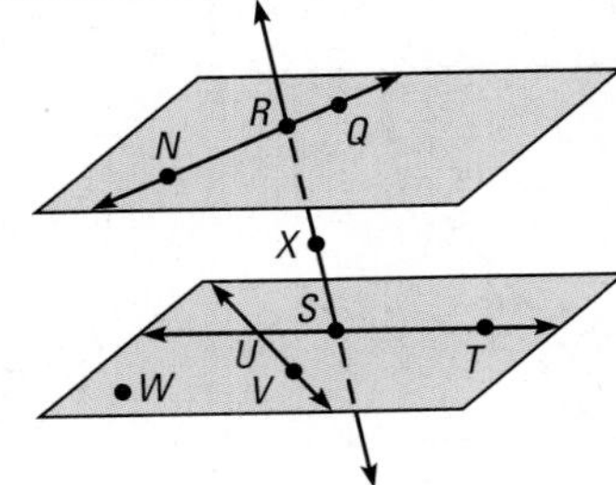

   Ⓐ S, T, V, and W are coplanar.
   Ⓑ X, T, S, and U are coplanar.
   Ⓒ Q, N, and R are collinear.
   Ⓓ S, R, and X are collinear.
   Ⓔ $\overrightarrow{TS}$ and $\overrightarrow{TU}$ are opposite rays.

3. **MULTIPLE CHOICE** Which of the line segments shown in the coordinate plane are congruent? E

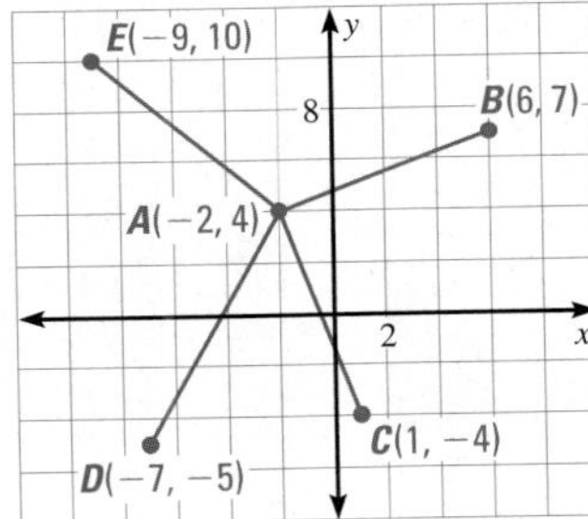

   Ⓐ $\overline{AC}$ and $\overline{AE}$ Ⓑ $\overline{AB}$ and $\overline{AE}$
   Ⓒ $\overline{AD}$ and $\overline{AC}$ Ⓓ $\overline{AD}$ and $\overline{AB}$
   Ⓔ $\overline{AB}$ and $\overline{AC}$

4. **MULTIPLE CHOICE** B is between A and C, D is between B and C, and C is between B and E. $AE = 28$, $BC = 10$, and $AB = DB = DC$. What is the length of $\overline{CE}$? D

   Ⓐ 5 Ⓑ 10 Ⓒ 12
   Ⓓ 13 Ⓔ 15

5. **MULTIPLE CHOICE** If $\angle 4$ and $\angle 5$ are complementary and $m\angle 4 = 19°$, find $m\angle 5$. B

   Ⓐ 19° Ⓑ 71° Ⓒ 109°
   Ⓓ 161° Ⓔ cannot be determined

6. **MULTIPLE CHOICE** $\angle 1$ and $\angle 2$ in the diagram are ___?___. A

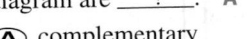

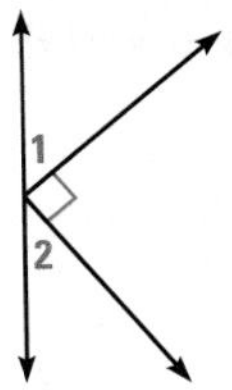

   Ⓐ complementary
   Ⓑ supplementary
   Ⓒ congruent
   Ⓓ vertical angles
   Ⓔ a linear pair

7. **MULTIPLE CHOICE** The midpoint of $\overline{BC}$ is $M(-10, -16)$. One endpoint is $B(-1, 8)$. What are the coordinates of C? C

   Ⓐ $(-21, -40)$ Ⓑ $(-20, -40)$
   Ⓒ $(-19, -40)$ Ⓓ $(-21, -24)$
   Ⓔ $(8, 32)$

8. **MULTIPLE CHOICE** If $\overrightarrow{QS}$ bisects $\angle PQR$, find the measure of $\angle PQR$. E

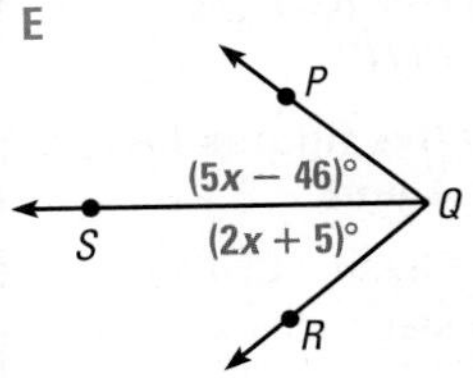

   Ⓐ 17°
   Ⓑ 56°
   Ⓒ 21°
   Ⓓ 39°
   Ⓔ 78°

9. **MULTIPLE CHOICE** Two angles are complementary and one angle has a measure that is 9 times the measure of the other angle. What is the angle measure of the larger angle? C

   Ⓐ 9°
   Ⓑ 18°
   Ⓒ 81°
   Ⓓ 90°
   Ⓔ 162°

10. QUANTITATIVE COMPARISON Consider the areas of the two triangles that are described below. C

COLUMN A	COLUMN B
The area of a triangle defined by $A(-6, 7)$, $B(-6, -1)$, and $C(-3, 2)$	The area of a triangle defined by $D(0, 4)$, $E(6, 4)$, and $F(6, 0)$

Choose the statement that is true.

Ⓐ The quantity in column A is greater.

Ⓑ The quantity in column B is greater.

Ⓒ The two quantities are equal.

Ⓓ The relationship cannot be determined from the information given.

MULTI-STEP PROBLEM In Exercises 11–14, use the figure at the right.

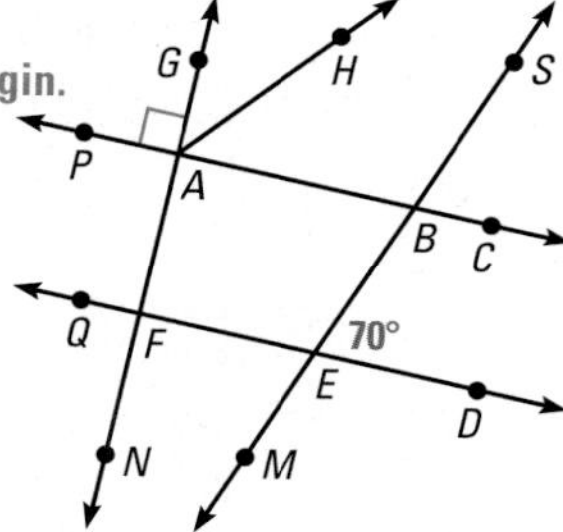

11. Name an angle that is (a) acute, (b) obtuse, (c) straight, and (d) right. See margin.

12. Classify each pair of angles as *complementary*, *supplementary*, or *vertical angles*.

a. $\angle ABS$ and $\angle SBC$ supplementary

b. $\angle BAH$ and $\angle GAH$ complementary

c. $\angle BEF$ and $\angle FEM$ supplementary

d. $\angle ABS$ and $\angle EBC$ vertical angles

13. If $\overrightarrow{AH}$ bisects $\angle GAB$, find the measures of $\angle GAH$ and $\angle BAH$. 45°, 45°

14. If $m\angle QFN = x°$, express the measures of $\angle QFA$, $\angle AFE$, and $\angle EFN$ in terms of x. $(180 - x)°$, $x°$, $(180 - x)°$

MULTI-STEP PROBLEM Consider some rectangles with a perimeter of 24 inches.

15. Copy and complete the table below.

Width (in.)	Perimeter (in.)	Length (in.)	Area (in.²)
1	? 24	? 11	? 11
2	? 24	? 10	? 20
3	? 24	? 9	? 27
4	? 24	? 8	? 32
5	? 24	? 7	? 35
6	? 24	? 6	? 36
7	? 24	? 5	? 35

16. Which rectangle in the table has the greatest area? the square (the 6 in. by 6 in. rectangle)

17. Look at the entries in the table. Describe a pattern in the widths and lengths. Use the pattern to predict the length of a rectangle with a width of 3.5 inches. For each rectangle, the sum of the length and width is 12; 8.5 in.

18. Make a conjecture about the dimensions of a rectangle with greatest area if the perimeter of the rectangle is known. Describe a way to test your conjecture. See margin.

11. *Sample answers:* (a) $\angle GAH$, (b) $\angle FEB$, (c) $\angle PAB$, (d) $\angle PAG$

18. *Sample answer:* Of all rectangles with given perimeter P, the rectangle with largest area is the square with sides of length $\frac{P}{4}$. To show this for any given value of P, let x be the width of a rectangle with perimeter P. Then its length is $\frac{1}{2}P - x$, and its area is $x\left(\frac{1}{2}P - x\right)$. Use a graphing calculator to graph $y = x\left(\frac{1}{2}P - x\right)$ and find the x-coordinate that corresponds to the maximum value of y.

PROJECT OVERVIEW

PROJECT GOALS

- Measure distances and circumferences in taxicab geometry.
- Find distances using the distance formula.
- Compare distances in taxicab geometry and Euclidean Geometry.

MANAGING THE PROJECT

CLASSROOM MANAGEMENT

The Chapter 1 Project may be completed by students working alone or with a partner. If students work with a partner, they should work on Questions 1–9 together. Partners can work on different parts of the report, but they should discuss each part before hand and edit each other's work before a final draft is made.

ALTERNATIVE APPROACH

This project can be done as a classroom demonstration using an overhead projector. Have students each work at their desks using graph paper to work through the various steps of the investigation as you discuss them as a class.

CONCLUDING THE PROJECT

Display and discuss students' posters in class. You might invite students from other classrooms to visit the exhibit and have the class prepare a short presentation to explain the exhibit to the visitors.

Present Your Results

A distance in taxicab geometry is greater than or equal to the corresponding Euclidean distance. A circle is associated with a location and a distance in both Euclidean and taxicab geometry, but the circles have different shapes and circumferences in the two geometries. Their diameters, however, are the same: twice the given distance.

PROJECT *for Chapter 1*

Taxicab Geometry

OBJECTIVE **Compare distances in taxicab geometry to distances in Euclidean geometry.**

Materials: ruler, graph paper, colored pencils, poster paper

In *taxicab geometry*, distances are measured along paths that are made of horizontal and vertical segments. Diagonal paths are not allowed. This simulates the movement of taxicabs in a city, which can travel only on streets, never through buildings.

FINDING TAXICAB DISTANCES

Follow these steps to learn more about distance in taxicab geometry.

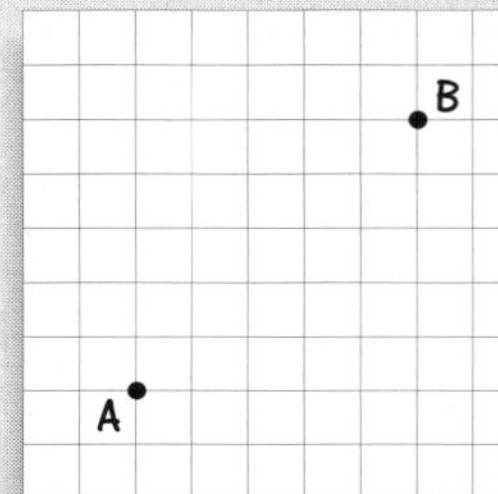

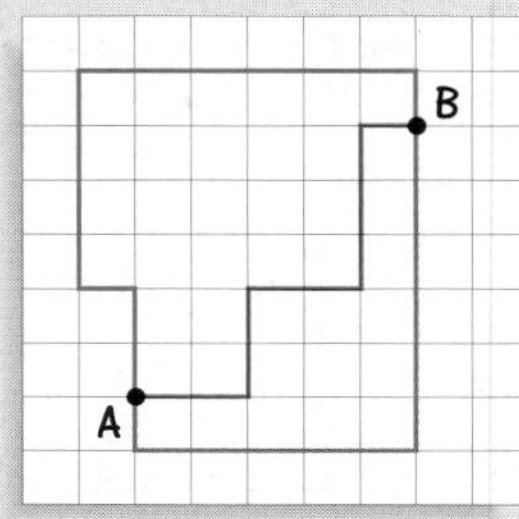

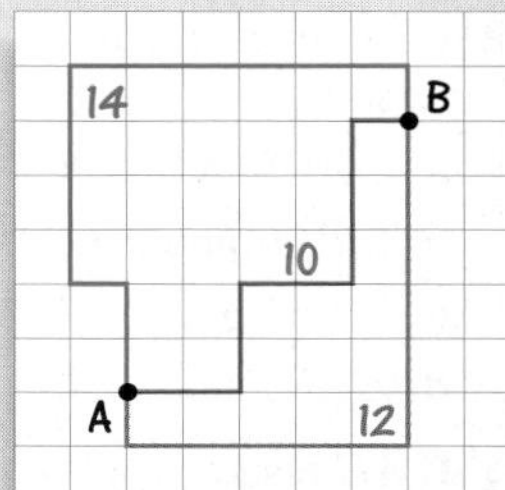

1. Copy points A and B on a piece of graph paper.
2. Trace paths from A to B using the grid lines. You may move horizontally and vertically but not diagonally.
3. Calculate the distances covered by your paths.

INVESTIGATION

Repeat Steps 2 and 3 above several times, then answer the exercises.

1. Compare your paths and those of your classmates. Are the distances always the same? What is the length of the shortest possible path from A to B? **No; 10**
2. The length of the shortest path from A to B is called the *taxicab distance* from A to B. Can you find other paths from A to B that have the same distance? **Yes; for example, from *A* go to the right until you are under *B*, then go up until you reach *B*.**
3. Use the Distance Formula to find the Euclidean distance from A to B. Which is greater, the taxicab distance from A to B or the Euclidean distance? **$5\sqrt{2} \approx 7.07$; the taxicab distance is greater.**
4. On another piece of graph paper, plot a new pair of points. Find the taxicab distance and Euclidean distance for the points. Repeat this for several pairs of points. Write a general statement that compares taxicab distance and Euclidean distance. **Graphs will vary. Check graphs. A taxicab distance is greater than or equal to the corresponding Euclidean distance.**
5. Write a general formula for the taxicab distance from $A(x_1, y_1)$ to $B(x_2, y_2)$. **Taxicab distance $= |x_2 - x_1| + |y_2 - y_1|$**

TAXICAB CIRCLES

Suppose you are in a city with a square grid and want to find all the places you can reach if you walk 4 blocks along the streets. This forms a figure in taxicab geometry in the same way that a circle is formed in Euclidean geometry.

INVESTIGATION

6. On a piece of graph paper, plot a point $O(0, 0)$. Plot all the points that have a taxicab distance of 4 units from point O. How are the points arranged?
The points lie on a square with horizontal and vertical diagonals.

7. To find the circumference of your taxicab circle, imagine that you are walking a shortest taxicab path that passes through all the points you drew in Investigation Exercise 6. Draw one such path. What is its total length? (Remember that all distances in taxicab geometry are horizontal or vertical.)
Check taxicab paths; 32.

8. To find the diameter of your taxicab circle, draw a shortest taxicab path that joins two points on the circumference and also passes through the center O. What is its length?
Check taxicab paths; 8

9. In Euclidean geometry, the constant π is defined as the ratio of a circle's circumference to its diameter. If π is defined in the same way in taxicab geometry, does it have a constant value? If so, what is the value?
Yes; the true value of π in taxicab geometry is 4.

PRESENT YOUR RESULTS

Gather your work and present it as a poster.

- Include your answers to the Investigation Exercises.
- Include your calculations and drawings you used to find the value of π in taxicab geometry.
- Summarize how taxicab geometry and Euclidean geometry are different. **See margin.**

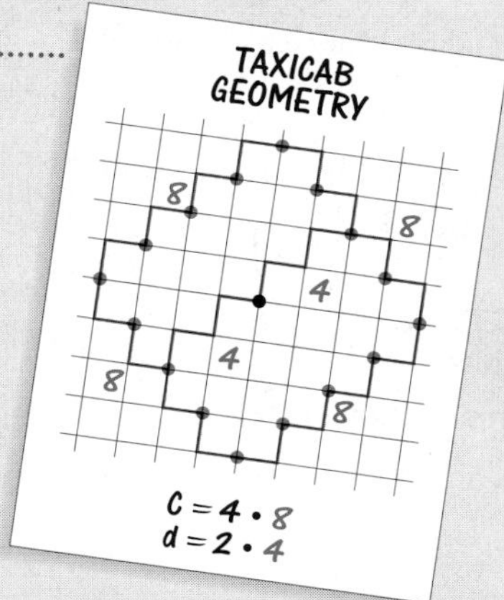

EXTENSIONS

In Euclidean geometry, the points that lie between two points A and B form a segment. In taxicab geometry, what kind of region do the points that lie *between* two points A and B form? (*Hint:* A point C lies *between* A and B in taxicab geometry if this equation is true for the taxicab distances: $AC + CB = AB$.) **See margin.**

In Euclidean geometry, the midpoint of $\overline{AB}$ *bisects* the segment into two parts. All the points in one part are closer to A than to B, and all the points in the other part are closer to B than to A. Is there a set of points that *bisects* the set of points between A and B in taxicab geometry? What does it look like? **See margin.**

GRADING THE PROJECT RUBRIC FOR CHAPTER PROJECT

4 Students' answers to the Investigation Exercises are correct and complete. The graphs are clear and well-labeled. The written report demonstrates an understanding of the project and the mathematics involved.

3 Students' answers to the Investigation Exercises are included but may be lacking in some details. Some of the graphs are incorrect or are poorly labeled. The calculation of π may be incorrect or may not be fully supported. The written report contains all the required elements but may not explain each part well.

2 The Investigation Exercise answers or the graphs contain serious errors or are incomplete. Not all of the questions are answered in the report.

1 The answers to the Investigation Exercises show that students do not have an understanding of the method presented. The graphs are missing or are incorrectly marked. The report is incomplete or not understandable. The project should be returned with a new deadline for completion. The students should speak with the teacher as soon as possible so that they understand the purpose and format of the project.

Extensions

The answers below assume that A and B do not lie on a horizontal or vertical line.

The points that lie *between* two points A and B form a rectangle with A and B at two corners. All the grid points on the perimeter of the rectangle (except A and B) and all the grid points inside the rectangle lie *between* A and B in taxicab geometry.

Yes; the set of points lies on a line that is tilted 45° from horizontal. The line divides the rectangular region of points between A and B into two regions. All the points in one region are closer to A than to B. All the points in the other region are closer to B than to A.

CHAPTER 2

PLANNING THE CHAPTER

Reasoning and Proof

GOALS

Lesson	Goals	NCTM	ITED	SAT9 (TASK 1)	Terra-Nova	Local
2.1 *pp. 71–78*	GOAL 1 Recognize and analyze a conditional statement. GOAL 2 Write postulates about points, lines, and planes using conditional statements.	3, 7, 8, 10	MIGE		14, 17, 18	1, 3
2.2 *pp. 79–85*	GOAL 1 Recognize and use definitions. GOAL 2 Recognize and use biconditional statements.	3, 7, 8, 10	MIGE		14, 17, 18	1, 3
2.3 *pp. 86–95*	CONCEPT ACTIVITY: 2.3 *Investigate how to use deductive reasoning to solve a logic puzzle.* GOAL 1 Use symbolic notation to represent logical statements. GOAL 2 Form conclusions by applying the laws of logic to true statements.	2, 3, 7, 8, 9, 10	MIGE		14, 16, 17, 18	1, 3
2.4 *pp. 96–101*	GOAL 1 Use properties from algebra. GOAL 2 Use properties of length and measure to justify segment and angle relationships.	2, 4, 7, 8, 9, 10	MIM, MIGE	4, 26	13, 14, 16, 17, 18, 51, 52	3
2.5 *pp. 102–107*	GOAL 1 Justify statements about congruent segments. GOAL 2 Write reasons for steps in a proof.	3, 4, 7, 8	MIM, MIGE	4, 26	13, 14, 17, 18	2, 4, 16
2.6 *pp. 108–116*	CONCEPT ACTIVITY: 2.6 *Investigate complementary angles.* GOAL 1 Use angle congruence properties. GOAL 2 Prove properties about special pairs of angles.	1, 3, 4, 7	MIM, MIGE	4, 27	11, 13, 14, 17, 49	2, 4, 13

RESOURCES

CHAPTER RESOURCE BOOKLETS

CHAPTER SUPPORT

Tips for New Teachers	p. 1	Prerequisite Skills Review	p. 5
Parent Guide for Student Success	p. 3	Strategies for Reading Mathematics	p. 7

LESSON SUPPORT

LESSON SUPPORT	2.1	2.2	2.3	2.4	2.5	2.6
Lesson Plans (regular and block)	p. 9	p. 22	p. 38	p. 53	p. 66	p. 82
Warm-Up Exercises and Daily Quiz	p. 11	p. 24	p. 40	p. 55	p. 68	p. 84
Activity Support Masters			p. 41			
Lesson Openers	p. 12	p. 25	p. 42	p. 56	p. 69	p. 85
Technology Activities & Keystrokes	p. 13	p. 26			p. 70	p. 86
Practice (3 levels)	p. 14	p. 30	p. 43	p. 57	p. 73	p. 89
Reteaching with Practice	p. 17	p. 33	p. 46	p. 60	p. 76	p. 92
Quick Catch-Up for Absent Students	p. 19	p. 35	p. 48	p. 62	p. 78	p. 94
Cooperative Learning Activities				p. 63	p. 79	
Interdisciplinary Applications	p. 20		p. 49		p. 80	
Real-Life Applications		p. 36		p. 64		p. 95
Math & History Applications			p. 50			
Challenge: Skills and Applications	p. 21	p. 37	p. 51	p. 65	p. 81	p. 96

REVIEW AND ASSESSMENT

Quizzes	pp. 52, 97	Alternative Assessment with Math Journal	p. 106
Chapter Review Games and Activities	p. 98	Project with Rubric	p. 108
Chapter Test (3 levels)	pp. 99–104	Cumulative Review	p. 110
SAT/ACT Chapter Test	p. 105	Resource Book Answers	p. A1

TRANSPARENCIES

	2.1	2.2	2.3	2.4	2.5	2.6
Warm-Up Exercises and Daily Quiz	p. 10	p. 11	p. 12	p. 13	p. 14	p. 15
Alternative Lesson Opener Transparencies	p. 8	p. 9	p. 10	p. 11	p. 12	p. 13
Examples/Standardized Test Practice	✓	✓	✓	✓	✓	✓
Answer Transparencies	✓	✓	✓	✓	✓	✓

TECHNOLOGY

- Electronic Teaching Tools
- Online Lesson Planner
- Internet Support
- Personal Student Tutor
- Test and Practice Generator
- Geometry in Motion video
- Electronic Lesson Presentations (Lesson 2.6)

ADDITIONAL RESOURCES

- Basic Skills Workbook: Diagnosis and Remediation
- Worked-Out Solution Key
- Resources in Spanish
- Standardized Test Practice Workbook
- Practice Workbook with Examples

CORRELATIONS TO THE CALIFORNIA CURRICULUM

Correlations to California Standards
See Teacher's Edition pp. CA9–CA11

Correlations to SAT9
Task 1: See Teacher's Edition pp. CA12–CA14
Task 2: See Teacher's Edition pp. CA15–CA17

CHAPTER 2

PACING THE CHAPTER

Resource Key
- STUDENT EDITION
- CHAPTER 2 RESOURCE BOOK
- TEACHER'S EDITION

REGULAR SCHEDULE

Day 1

2.1

STARTING OPTIONS
- Prereq. Skills Review
- Strategies for Reading
- Homework Check
- Warm-Up or Daily Quiz

TEACHING OPTIONS
- Les. Opener (Visual)
- Examples 1–7
- Closure Question
- Guided Practice Exs.

APPLY/HOMEWORK
- See Assignment Guide.
- See the CRB: Practice, Reteach, Apply, Extend

ASSESSMENT OPTIONS
- Checkpoint Exercises
- Daily Quiz (2.1)
- Stand. Test Practice

Day 2

2.2

STARTING OPTIONS
- Homework Check
- Warm-Up or Daily Quiz

TEACHING OPTIONS
- Motivating the Lesson
- Les. Opener (Technology)
- Technology Activity
- Examples 1–3
- Guided Practice Exs. 1–8

APPLY/HOMEWORK
- See Assignment Guide.
- See the CRB: Practice, Reteach, Apply, Extend

ASSESSMENT OPTIONS
- Checkpoint Exercises, p. 80

Day 3

2.2 *(cont.)*

STARTING OPTIONS
- Homework Check

TEACHING OPTIONS
- Examples 4–5
- Closure Question
- Guided Practice Exs. 9–12

APPLY/HOMEWORK
- See Assignment Guide.
- See the CRB: Practice, Reteach, Apply, Extend

ASSESSMENT OPTIONS
- Checkpoint Exercises, p. 81
- Daily Quiz (2.2)
- Stand. Test Practice

Day 4

2.3

STARTING OPTIONS
- Homework Check
- Warm-Up or Daily Quiz

TEACHING OPTIONS
- Motivating the Lesson
- Concept Act. & Wksht.
- Les. Opener (Application)
- Examples 1–6
- Guided Practice Exs.

APPLY/HOMEWORK
- See Assignment Guide.
- See the CRB: Practice, Reteach, Apply, Extend

ASSESSMENT OPTIONS
- Checkpoint Exercises

Day 5

2.3 *(cont.)*

STARTING OPTIONS
- Homework Check

TEACHING OPTIONS
- Examples 1–6
- Closure Question

APPLY/HOMEWORK
- See Assignment Guide.
- See the CRB: Practice, Reteach, Apply, Extend

ASSESSMENT OPTIONS
- Checkpoint Exercises
- Daily Quiz (2.3)
- Stand. Test Practice
- Quiz (2.1–2.3)

Day 6

2.4

STARTING OPTIONS
- Homework Check
- Warm-Up or Daily Quiz

TEACHING OPTIONS
- Les. Opener (Activity)
- Examples 1–5
- Closure Question
- Guided Practice Exs.

APPLY/HOMEWORK
- See Assignment Guide.
- See the CRB: Practice, Reteach, Apply, Extend

ASSESSMENT OPTIONS
- Checkpoint Exercises
- Daily Quiz (2.4)
- Stand. Test Practice

Day 9

2.6

STARTING OPTIONS
- Homework Check
- Warm-Up or Daily Quiz

TEACHING OPTIONS
- Concept Activity
- Les. Opener (Activity)
- Examples 1–5
- Guided Practice Exs. 1, 3, 4, 6, 8

APPLY/HOMEWORK
- See Assignment Guide.
- See the CRB: Practice, Reteach, Apply, Extend

ASSESSMENT OPTIONS
- Checkpoint Exercises, pp. 110–112

Day 10

2.6 *(cont.)*

STARTING OPTIONS
- Homework Check

TEACHING OPTIONS
- Example 6
- Closure Question
- Guided Practice Exs. 2, 5, 7, 9

APPLY/HOMEWORK
- See Assignment Guide.
- See the CRB: Practice, Reteach, Apply, Extend

ASSESSMENT OPTIONS
- Checkpoint Exercises, p. 112
- Daily Quiz (2.6)
- Stand. Test Practice
- Quiz (2.4–2.6)

Day 11

Review

DAY 11 START OPTIONS
- Homework Check

REVIEWING OPTIONS
- Chapter 2 Summary
- Chapter 2 Review
- Chapter Review Games and Activities

APPLY/HOMEWORK
- Chapter 2 Test (practice)
- Ch. Standardized Test (practice)

Day 12

Assess

DAY 12 START OPTIONS
- Homework Check

ASSESSMENT OPTIONS
- Chapter 2 Test
- SAT/ACT Ch. 2 Test
- Alternative Assessment

APPLY/HOMEWORK
- Skill Review, p. 128

Day 7

2.5

Starting Options
- Homework Check
- Warm-Up or Daily Quiz

Teaching Options
- Motivating the Lesson
- Les. Opener (Application)
- Technology Activity
- Examples 1–3
- Guided Practice Exs.

Apply/Homework
- See Assignment Guide.
- See the CRB: Practice, Reteach, Apply, Extend

Assessment Options
- Checkpoint Exercises

Day 8

2.5 *(cont.)*

Starting Options
- Homework Check

Teaching Options
- Examples 1–3
- Closure Question

Apply/Homework
- See Assignment Guide.
- See the CRB: Practice, Reteach, Apply, Extend

Assessment Options
- Checkpoint Exercises
- Daily Quiz (2.5)
- Stand. Test Practice

BLOCK SCHEDULE

Day 1

Assess & 2.1

(Day 1 = Ch. 1 Day 7)

Assessment Options
- Chapter 1 Test
- SAT/ACT Ch. 1 Test
- Alternative Assessment

Ch. 2 Start Options
- Skills Review, p. 70
- Prereq. Skills Review
- Strategies for Reading

Teaching 2.1 Options
- Warm-Up (Les. 2.1)
- Les. Opener (Visual)
- Examples 1–7
- Closure Question
- Guided Practice Exs.

Apply/Homework
- See Assignment Guide.
- See the CRB: Practice, Reteach, Apply, Extend

Assessment Options
- Checkpoint Exercises
- Daily Quiz (Les. 2.1)
- Stand. Test Practice

Day 2

2.2

Day 2 Start Options
- Homework Check
- Warm-Up or Daily Quiz

Teaching 2.2 Options
- Motivating the Lesson
- Les. Opener (Tech.)
- Technology Activity
- Examples 1–5
- Closure Question
- Guided Practice Exs.

Apply/Homework
- See Assignment Guide.
- See the CRB: Practice, Reteach, Apply, Extend

Assessment Options
- Checkpoint Exercises
- Daily Quiz (Les. 2.2)
- Stand. Test Practice

Day 3

2.3

Day 3 Start Options
- Homework Check
- Warm-Up or Daily Quiz

Teaching 2.3 Options
- Motivating the Lesson
- Concept Act. & Wksht.
- Les. Opener (Appl.)
- Examples 1–6
- Closure Question
- Guided Practice Exs.

Apply/Homework
- See Assignment Guide.
- See the CRB: Practice, Reteach, Apply, Extend

Assessment Options
- Checkpoint Exercises
- Daily Quiz (Les. 2.3)
- Stand. Test Practice
- Quiz (2.1–2.3)

Day 4

2.4 & 2.5

Day 4 Start Options
- Homework Check
- Warm-Up (Les. 2.4) or Daily Quiz (Les. 2.3)

Teaching 2.4 Options
- Les. Opener (Activity)
- Examples 1–5
- Closure Question
- Guided Practice Exs.

Beginning 2.5 Options
- Warm-Up (Les. 2.5)
- Motivating the Lesson
- Les. Opener (Appl.)
- Technology Activity
- Examples 1–3
- Guided Practice Exs.

Apply/Homework
- See Assignment Guide.
- See the CRB: Practice, Reteach, Apply, Extend

Assessment Options
- Checkpoint Exercises
- Daily Quiz (Les. 2.4)
- Stand. Test Prac. (2.4)

Day 5

2.5 & 2.6

Day 5 Start Options
- Homework Check
- Daily Quiz (Les. 2.4)

Finishing 2.5 Options
- Examples 1–3
- Closure Question

Beginning 2.6 Options
- Warm-Up (Les. 2.6)
- Concept Activity
- Les. Opener (Activity)
- Examples 1–5
- Guided Practice Exs. 1, 3, 4, 6, 8

Apply/Homework
- See Assignment Guide.
- See the CRB: Practice, Reteach, Apply, Extend

Assessment Options
- Checkpoint Exercises
- Daily Quiz (Les. 2.5)
- Stand. Test Prac. (2.5)

Day 6

2.6 & Review

Day 6 Start Options
- Homework Check
- Daily Quiz (Les. 2.5)

Finishing 2.6 Options
- Example 6
- Closure Question
- Guided Practice Exs. 2, 5, 7, 9

Reviewing Options
- Chapter 2 Summary
- Chapter 2 Review
- Chapter Review Games and Activities

Apply/Homework
- See Assignment Guide.
- See the CRB: Practice, Reteach, Apply, Extend
- Chapter 2 Test (prac.)
- Ch. Standardized Test (practice)

Assessment Options
- Checkpoint Exercises
- Daily Quiz (Les. 2.6)
- Stand. Test Practice
- Quiz (2.4–2.6)

Day 7

Assess & 3.1

(Day 7 = Ch. 3 Day 1)

Assessment Options
- Chapter 2 Test
- SAT/ACT Ch. 2 Test
- Alternative Assessment

Ch. 3 Start Options
- Skills Review, p. 128
- Prereq. Skills Review
- Strategies for Reading

Teaching 3.1 Options
- Warm-Up (Les. 3.1)
- Les. Opener (Appl.)
- Examples 1–2
- Closure Question
- Guided Practice Exs.

Apply/Homework
- See Assignment Guide.
- See the CRB: Practice, Reteach, Apply, Extend

Assessment Options
- Checkpoint Exercises
- Daily Quiz (Les. 3.1)
- Stand. Test Practice

MEETING INDIVIDUAL NEEDS

BEFORE THE CHAPTER

The *Chapter 2 Resource Book* has the following materials to distribute and use before the chapter:

- **Parent Guide for Student Success**
- **Prerequisite Skills Review**
- **Strategies for Reading Mathematics (pictured below)**

STRATEGIES FOR READING *Pages 7–8*

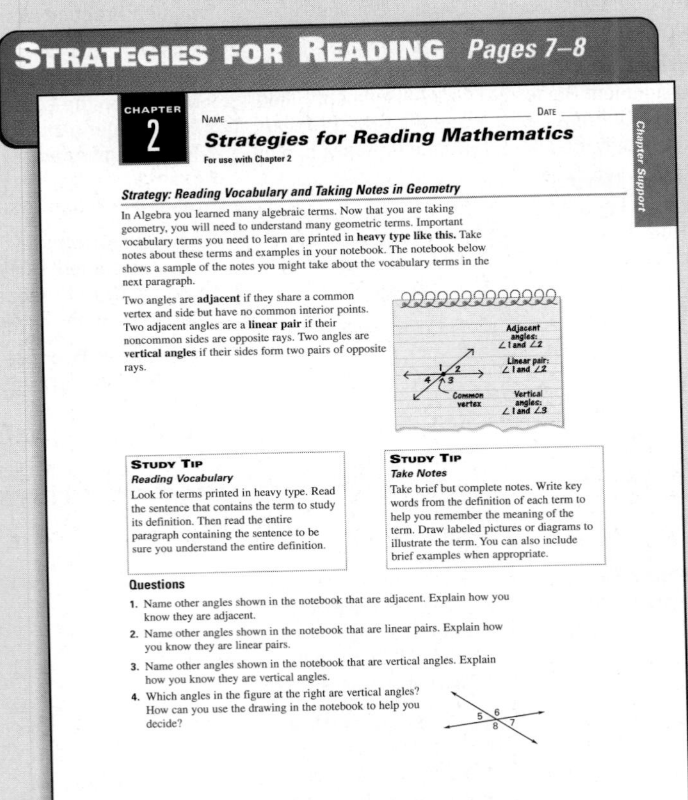

CHAPTER 2

NAME ______________________ DATE ________

Strategies for Reading Mathematics

For use with Chapter 2

Chapter Support

Strategy: Reading Vocabulary and Taking Notes in Geometry

In Algebra you learned many algebraic terms. Now that you are taking geometry, you will need to understand many geometric terms. Important vocabulary terms you need to learn are printed in **heavy type like this.** Take notes about these terms and examples in your notebook. The notebook below shows a sample of the notes you might take about the vocabulary terms in the next paragraph.

Two angles are **adjacent** if they share a common vertex and side but have no common interior points. Two adjacent angles are a **linear pair** if their noncommon sides are opposite rays. Two angles are **vertical angles** if their sides form two pairs of opposite rays.

STUDY TIP
Reading Vocabulary
Look for terms printed in heavy type. Read the sentence that contains the term to study its definition. Then read the entire paragraph containing the sentence to be sure you understand the entire definition.

STUDY TIP
Take Notes
Take brief but complete notes. Write key words from the definition of each term to help you remember the meaning of the term. Draw labeled pictures or diagrams to illustrate the term. You can also include brief examples when appropriate.

Questions

1. Name other angles shown in the notebook that are adjacent. Explain how you know they are adjacent.
2. Name other angles shown in the notebook that are linear pairs. Explain how you know they are linear pairs.
3. Name other angles shown in the notebook that are vertical angles. Explain how you know they are vertical angles.
4. Which angles in the figure at the right are vertical angles? How can you use the drawing in the notebook to help you decide?

STRATEGIES FOR READING MATHEMATICS These two pages give students tips about reading vocabulary and taking notes as they prepare for Chapter 2 and provide a visual glossary of key vocabulary words in the chapter, such as converse and contrapositive.

DURING EACH LESSON

The *Chapter 2 Resource Book* has the following alternatives for introducing the lesson:

- **Lesson Openers (pictured below)**
- **Technology Activities with Keystrokes**

LESSON OPENER *Page 12*

LESSON 2.1

NAME ______________________ DATE ________

Available as a transparency

Visual Approach Lesson Opener

For use with pages 71–78

Lesson 2.1

Use the map at the right to determine whether the statement is *true* or *false*. Explain why your answer is correct.

1. If you are in Massachusetts, then you are in New England.
2. If you are in New England, then you are in Massachusetts.
3. If you are in Hartford, then you are in Connecticut.
4. If you are in Connecticut, then you are in Hartford.

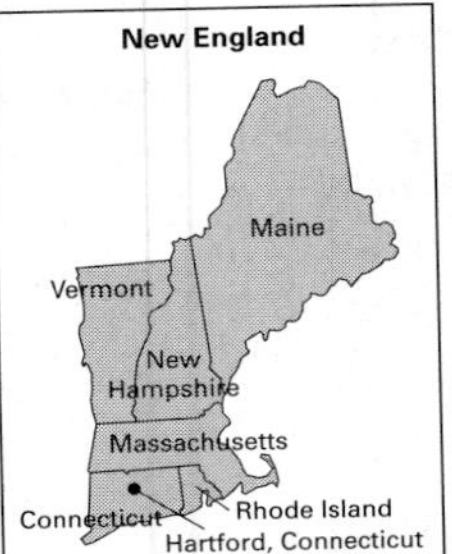

Use the Venn diagram at the right to determine whether the statement is *true* or *false*. Explain why your answer is correct.

Animals

Dogs

Beagles

5. If an animal is a beagle, then it is a dog.
6. If an animal is a dog, then it is a beagle.
7. All animals are dogs.
8. All dogs are animals.
9. Draw a Venn diagram to show that all robins are birds, but not all birds are robins. Explain why your Venn diagram clearly shows this is true.

VISUAL APPROACH LESSON OPENER This Lesson Opener uses visuals as an alternative way to start Lesson 2.1. Students look at Venn diagrams as an introduction to conditional statements.

TECHNOLOGY RESOURCE

The Geometry in Motion video can be used to give dynamic presentations of selected material in Chapter 2.

FOLLOWING EACH LESSON

The *Chapter 2 Resource Book* has a variety of materials to follow-up each lesson. They include the following:

- **Practice (3 levels)**
- **Reteaching with Practice**
- **Quick Catch-Up for Absent Students**
- **Interdisciplinary Applications (pictured below)**
- **Real-Life Applications**

APPLICATION *Page 49*

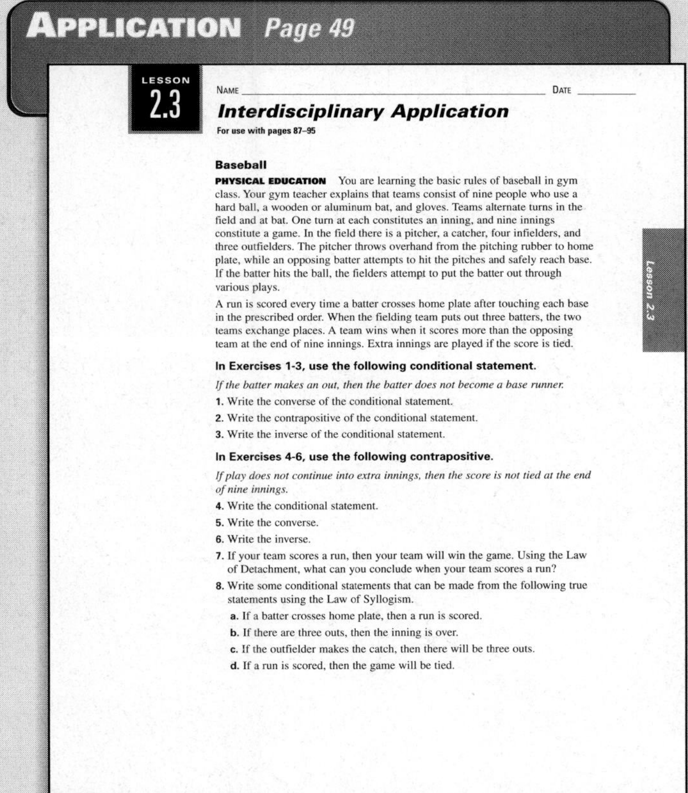

LESSON 2.3

NAME ______ DATE ______

Interdisciplinary Application

For use with pages 87–95

Baseball

PHYSICAL EDUCATION You are learning the basic rules of baseball in gym class. Your gym teacher explains that teams consist of nine people who use a hard ball, a wooden or aluminum bat, and gloves. Teams alternate turns in the field and at bat. One turn at each constitutes an inning, and nine innings constitute a game. In the field there is a pitcher, a catcher, four infielders, and three outfielders. The pitcher throws overhand from the pitching rubber to home plate, while an opposing batter attempts to hit the pitches and safely reach base. If the batter hits the ball, the fielders attempt to put the batter out through various plays.

A run is scored every time a batter crosses home plate after touching each base in the prescribed order. When the fielding team puts out three batters, the two teams exchange places. A team wins when it scores more than the opposing team at the end of nine innings. Extra innings are played if the score is tied.

In Exercises 1-3, use the following conditional statement.

If the batter makes an out, then the batter does not become a base runner.

1. Write the converse of the conditional statement.
2. Write the contrapositive of the conditional statement.
3. Write the inverse of the conditional statement.

In Exercises 4-6, use the following contrapositive.

If play does not continue into extra innings, then the score is not tied at the end of nine innings.

4. Write the conditional statement.
5. Write the converse.
6. Write the inverse.
7. If your team scores a run, then your team will win the game. Using the Law of Detachment, what can you conclude when your team scores a run?
8. Write some conditional statements that can be made from the following true statements using the Law of Syllogism.
   a. If a batter crosses home plate, then a run is scored.
   b. If there are three outs, then the inning is over.
   c. If the outfielder makes the catch, then there will be three outs.
   d. If a run is scored, then the game will be tied.

Lesson 2.3

INTERDISCIPLINARY APPLICATION This application makes a connection between baseball and laws of logic, the topic of Lesson 2.3.

ASSESSING THE CHAPTER

The *Chapter 2 Resource Book* has the following review and assessment materials:

- **Quizzes**
- **Chapter Review Games and Activities**
- **Chapter Test (3 levels) (pictured below)**
- **SAT/ACT Chapter Test**
- **Alternative Assessment with Rubric and Math Journal**
- **Project with Rubric**
- **Cumulative Review**

CHAPTER TEST *Pages 101–102*

2

NAME ______ DATE ______

Chapter Test B

For use after Chapter 2

Write the inverse, converse, and contrapositive of the conditional statement.

1. If the sky is clear, then we can see the stars at night.
   Inverse: ______
   Converse: ______
   Contrapositive: ______
2. If I ride on the Ferris wheel, then I am not afraid of heights.
   Inverse: ______
   Converse: ______
   Contrapositive: ______
3. If the point is on the line, then it is in the plane.
   Inverse: ______
   Converse: ______
   Contrapositive: ______

Determine whether the biconditional statement about the diagram is *true* or *false*.

1 2 3

4. $\angle 1$ and $\angle 2$ are supplementary if and only if they form a linear pair.
5. $\angle 3$ and $\angle 2$ are equal if and only if $\angle 1$ and $\angle 3$ are equal.

Using *p* and *q* below, write the symbolic statement in words.

p: Points X, Y, and Z are noncollinear.

q: Points X, Y, and Z are coplanar.

6. $p \to q$ 7. $\sim q$ 8. $\sim p$
9. $q \to p$ 10. $\sim p \to \sim q$ 11. $\sim q \to \sim p$

Answers

1. see left
2. see left
3. see left
4. ______
5. ______
6. ______
7. ______
8. ______
9. ______
10. ______
11. ______

Review and Assess

CHAPTER TEST There are three versions of this two-page Chapter Test, one each for basic (A), average (B), and advanced (C) students. Level B involves more advanced work with conditional statements than Level A but does not have as much difficult work with writing proofs as Level C.

TECHNOLOGY RESOURCE

Teachers can use the Time-Saving Test and Practice Generator to create customized review and assessment materials for Chapter 2.

CHAPTER OVERVIEW

Chapter Goals

The goals of this chapter include recognizing, analyzing, and writing conditional statements as well as writing postulates using conditional statements. Students recognize and use definitions and biconditional statements. They use symbolic notation to represent logical statements and use laws of logic to draw conclusions from arguments. Students use properties from algebra and geometry to measure and justify segment and angle relationships and congruence. Students also prove statements about segments and angles using congruence.

Application Note

Robots are used in situations that would be dangerous or inaccessible to humans, such as locating land mines, monitoring radiation, winding through crevices, or mapping the ocean floor. Though they cannot think, they can be programmed to react differently to different conditions.

Additional information about robots is available at **www.mcdougallittell.com.**

REASONING AND PROOF

▶ *How do robots use reasoning?*

CHAPTER 2

APPLICATION: Robotics

Dante II is a robot that investigates live volcanoes. It processes data collected from sensors to choose a path to follow.

Think & Discuss

1, 2. See margin.

1. Dante II has to travel 700 feet to reach the bottom of a crater. Dante II has an average stride of 45 inches. The robot concludes that it will take about 187 steps to reach the bottom. Explain the reasoning Dante II used to reach this conclusion.
2. Instruct Dante II how to calculate the amount of steps needed to reach the bottom of any crater. Start your instructions with "If the distance to the bottom of the crater is x feet and your stride is y inches, then ___?___."

Learn More About It

You will explore reasoning in robots in Exercise 49 on p. 93.

APPLICATION LINK Visit www.mcdougallittell.com for more information about reasoning and robots.

PROJECTS

A project covering Chapters 2–3 appears on pages 188–189 of the Student Edition. An additional project for Chapter 2 is available in the *Chapter 2 Resource Book,* p. 108.

TECHNOLOGY

Software

- *Electronic Teaching Tools*
- *Online Lesson Planner*
- *Personal Student Tutor*
- *Test and Practice Generator*
- *Electronic Lesson Presentations (Lesson 2.6)*

Video

- *Geometry in Motion*

Internet Connections
www.mcdougallittell.com

- **Application Links**
  69, 84, 95
- **Student Help**
  72, 76, 88, 93, 97, 114
- **Career Links**
  77, 90, 106
- **Extra Challenge**
  78, 85, 94, 101, 107

1. 700 ft is 8400 in., $\frac{8400}{45} \approx 187$

2. If your distance to the bottom of the crater is x ft, and your stride is y in., use $s = \frac{12x}{y}$.

PREPARE

Diagnostic Tools

The **Skill Review** exercises can help you diagnose whether students have the following skills needed in Chapter 2:

- Name points that are coplanar.
- Find the measure of a given angle.

The following resources are available for students who need additional help with these skills:

- Prerequisite Skills Review (*Chapter 2 Resource Book,* p. 5; *Warm-Up Transparencies,* p. 9)
- *Personal Student Tutor*

Additional Resources

The following resources are provided to help you prepare for the upcoming chapter and customize review materials:

- ***Chapter 2 Resource Book***
  Tips for New Teachers (p. 1)
  Parent Guide (p. 3)
  Lesson Plans (every lesson)
  Lesson Plans for Block Scheduling (every lesson)
- ***Electronic Teaching Tools***
- ***Online Lesson Planner***
- ***Test and Practice Generator***

CHAPTER 2

Study Guide

PREVIEW

What's the chapter about?

Chapter 2 is about **reasoning** and developing **proof**. Reasoning and proof are important tools used in geometry. In Chapter 2, you'll learn how to

- write a two-column proof and a paragraph proof.
- prove segment and angle relationships.

KEY VOCABULARY

▶ **Review**
- **conjecture, p. 4**
- **inductive reasoning, p. 4**
- **counterexample, p. 4**
- **definition, p. 10**
- **postulates, p. 17**
- **vertical angles, p. 44**
- **linear pair, p. 44**

▶ **New**
- **if-then form, p. 71**
- **converse, p. 72**
- **inverse, p. 72**
- **contrapositive, p. 72**
- **biconditional statement, p. 80**
- **theorem, p. 102**
- **two-column proof, p. 102**
- **paragraph proof, p. 102**

PREPARE

Are you ready for the chapter?

SKILL REVIEW Do these exercises to review skills that you'll apply in this chapter. See the given **reference page** if there is something you don't understand.

STUDENT HELP

Study Tip
"Student Help" boxes throughout the chapter give you study tips and tell you where to look for extra help in this book and on the Internet.

Use the diagram below to name the point. **(Review Example 1, p. 10)**

1. A fourth point coplanar with points A, B, and C
D

2. A fourth point coplanar with points A, E, and F
B

3. A fourth point coplanar with points B, C, and G
F

4. A fourth point coplanar with points D, C, and F
E

Find the measure of the angle, given that $m\angle 7 = 38°$. **(Review Example 2, p. 45)**

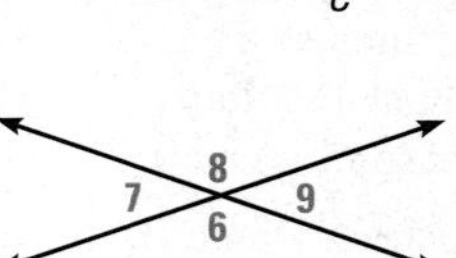

5. $m\angle 6$
142°

6. $m\angle 8$
142°

7. $m\angle 9$
38°

STUDY STRATEGY

Here's a study strategy!

Previewing Lessons

Preview each lesson of the chapter. Knowing what you are about to learn can help you make the mental connections to what you already know. When previewing a lesson, look for the following:

- terms defined in a previous lesson
- properties that have been introduced in a previous lesson

2.1 Conditional Statements

What you should learn

GOAL 1 Recognize and analyze a conditional statement.

GOAL 2 Write postulates about points, lines, and planes using conditional statements.

Why you should learn it

▼ Point, line, and plane postulates help you analyze **real-life** objects, such as the research buggy below and in **Ex. 54**.

REAL LIFE

Coastal Research Amphibious Buggy

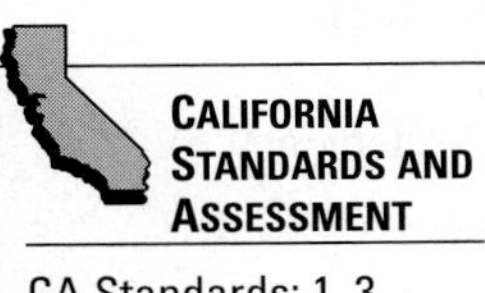

CALIFORNIA STANDARDS AND ASSESSMENT

CA Standards: 1, 3

GOAL 1 RECOGNIZING CONDITIONAL STATEMENTS

In this lesson you will study a type of logical statement called a conditional statement. A **conditional statement** has two parts, a *hypothesis* and a *conclusion*. When the statement is written in **if-then form**, the "if" part contains the **hypothesis** and the "then" part contains the **conclusion**. Here is an example:

If it is noon in Georgia, then it is 9 A.M. in California.

(Hypothesis: it is noon in Georgia; Conclusion: it is 9 A.M. in California)

EXAMPLE 1 *Rewriting in If-Then Form*

Rewrite the conditional statement in *if-then form.*

a. Two points are collinear if they lie on the same line.

b. All sharks have a boneless skeleton.

c. A number divisible by 9 is also divisible by 3.

SOLUTION

a. If two points lie on the same line, then they are collinear.

b. If a fish is a shark, then it has a boneless skeleton.

c. If a number is divisible by 9, then it is divisible by 3.

Conditional statements can be either true or false. To show that a conditional statement is true, you must present an argument that the conclusion follows for *all* cases that fulfill the hypothesis. To show that a conditional statement is false, describe a single counterexample that shows the statement is not always true.

EXAMPLE 2 *Writing a Counterexample*

Write a counterexample to show that the following conditional statement is false.

$$\text{If } x^2 = 16, \text{ then } x = 4.$$

SOLUTION

As a counterexample, let $x = -4$. The hypothesis is true, because $(-4)^2 = 16$. However, the conclusion is false. This implies that the given conditional statement is false.

1 PLAN

PACING
Basic: 1 day
Average: 1 day
Advanced: 1 day
Block Schedule: 0.5 block with Ch. 1 Assess.

LESSON OPENER
VISUAL APPROACH
An alternative way to approach Lesson 2.1 is to use the Visual Approach Lesson Opener:
- Blackline Master (*Chapter 2 Resource Book*, p. 12)
- Transparency (p. 8)

MEETING INDIVIDUAL NEEDS
- ***Chapter 2 Resource Book***
  Prerequisite Skills Review (p. 5)
  Practice Level A (p. 14)
  Practice Level B (p. 15)
  Practice Level C (p. 16)
  Reteaching with Practice (p. 17)
  Absent Student Catch-Up (p. 19)
  Challenge (p. 21)
- ***Resources in Spanish***
-  ***Personal Student Tutor***

NEW-TEACHER SUPPORT
See the Tips for New Teachers on pp. 1–2 of the *Chapter 2 Resource Book* for additional notes about Lesson 2.1.

WARM-UP EXERCISES

Transparency Available

Use the diagram to name the point(s).

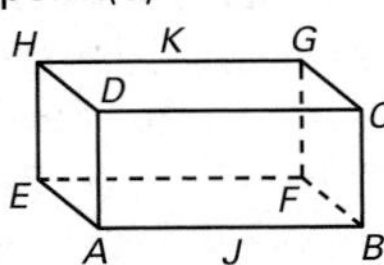

1. a point collinear with *G* and *H* *K*

2. a point coplanar with *D*, *C*, and *G* *K* or *H*

3. a point coplanar with *H*, *G*, and *E* *F* or *K*

4. a point coplanar with *A*, *D*, *E* *H*

2 TEACH

EXTRA EXAMPLE 1
Rewrite in *if-then form.*
All mammals breathe oxygen.
If an animal is a mammal, then it breathes oxygen.

EXTRA EXAMPLE 2
Write a counterexample.
If a number is odd, then it is divisible by 3. ***Sample answer:*** **7 is odd and 7 is not divisible by 3.**

EXTRA EXAMPLES 3–4
Write the (**a**) inverse, (**b**) converse, and (**c**) contrapositive of the statement. If the amount of available food increases, the deer population increases.

a. **If the amount of available food does not increase, the deer population does not increase.**
b. **If the deer population increases, the amount of available food increases.**
c. **If the deer population does not increase, the amount of available food does not increase.**

CHECKPOINT EXERCISES

For use after Example 1:

1. Rewrite in *if-then form.*
All monkeys have tails.
If an animal is a monkey, then it has a tail.

For use after Example 2:

2. Write a counterexample.
If a number is divisible by 2, then it is divisible by 4.
Sample answer: **14 is divisible by 2 but not divisible by 4.**

For use after Examples 3 and 4:

3. Write the (**a**) inverse, (**b**) converse, and (**c**) contrapositive of the statement. If an animal is a fish, then it can swim.

a. **If an animal is not a fish, then it cannot swim.**
b. **If an animal can swim, then it is a fish.**
c. **If an animal cannot swim, then it is not a fish.**

The **converse** of a conditional statement is formed by switching the hypothesis and conclusion. Here is an example.

Statement: If you see lightning, then you hear thunder.

Converse: If you hear thunder, then you see lightning.

STUDENT HELP

HOMEWORK HELP Visit our Web site www.mcdougallittell.com for extra examples.

EXAMPLE 3 *Writing the Converse of a Conditional Statement*

Write the converse of the following conditional statement.

Statement: If two segments are congruent, then they have the same length.

SOLUTION

Converse: If two segments have the same length, then they are congruent.

....

A statement can be altered by **negation**, that is, by writing the negative of the statement. Here are some examples.

STATEMENT	NEGATION
$m\angle A = 30°$	$m\angle A \neq 30°$
$\angle A$ is acute.	$\angle A$ is not acute.

When you negate the hypothesis and conclusion of a conditional statement, you form the **inverse**. When you negate the hypothesis and conclusion of the converse of a conditional statement, you form the **contrapositive**.

Original	If $m\angle A = 30°$, then $\angle A$ is acute.	Both true (with Contrapositive)
Inverse	If $m\angle A \neq 30°$, then $\angle A$ is not acute.	Both false (with Converse)
Converse	If $\angle A$ is acute, then $m\angle A = 30°$.	Both false (with Inverse)
Contrapositive	If $\angle A$ is not acute, then $m\angle A \neq 30°$.	Both true (with Original)

When two statements are both true or both false, they are called **equivalent statements**. A conditional statement is equivalent to its contrapositive. Similarly, the inverse and converse of any conditional statement are equivalent. This is shown in the table above.

FOCUS ON APPLICATIONS

CROCUS There are some exceptions to the statement in Example 4. For instance, crocuses can bloom when snow is on the ground.

EXAMPLE 4 *Writing an Inverse, Converse, and Contrapositive*

Write the (**a**) inverse, (**b**) converse, and (**c**) contrapositive of the statement.

If there is snow on the ground, then flowers are not in bloom.

SOLUTION

a. Inverse: If there is no snow on the ground, then flowers are in bloom.

b. Converse: If flowers are not in bloom, then there is snow on the ground.

c. Contrapositive: If flowers are in bloom, then there is no snow on the ground.

GOAL 2 USING POINT, LINE, AND PLANE POSTULATES

In Chapter 1, you studied four postulates.

Ruler Postulate	(Lesson 1.3, page 17)
Segment Addition Postulate	(Lesson 1.3, page 18)
Protractor Postulate	(Lesson 1.4, page 27)
Angle Addition Postulate	(Lesson 1.4, page 27)

Remember that postulates are assumed to be true—they form the foundation on which other statements (called *theorems*) are built.

STUDENT HELP

Study Tip
There is a list of all the postulates in this course at the end of the book beginning on page 827.

POINT, LINE, AND PLANE POSTULATES

POSTULATE 5 Through any two points there exists exactly one line.

POSTULATE 6 A line contains at least two points.

POSTULATE 7 If two lines intersect, then their intersection is exactly one point.

POSTULATE 8 Through any three noncollinear points there exists exactly one plane.

POSTULATE 9 A plane contains at least three noncollinear points.

POSTULATE 10 If two points lie in a plane, then the line containing them lies in the plane.

POSTULATE 11 If two planes intersect, then their intersection is a line.

Logical Reasoning

EXAMPLE 5 *Identifying Postulates*

Use the diagram at the right to give examples of Postulates 5 through 11.

SOLUTION

a. Postulate 5: There is exactly one line (line n) that passes through the points A and B.

b. Postulate 6: Line n contains at least two points. For instance, line n contains the points A and B.

c. Postulate 7: Lines m and n intersect at point A.

d. Postulate 8: Plane P passes through the noncollinear points A, B, and C.

e. Postulate 9: Plane P contains at least three noncollinear points, A, B, and C.

f. Postulate 10: Points A and B lie in plane P. So, line n, which contains points A and B, also lies in plane P.

g. Postulate 11: Planes P and Q intersect. So, they intersect in a line, labeled in the diagram as line m.

EXTRA EXAMPLE 5

Give examples of Postulates 5 through 11.

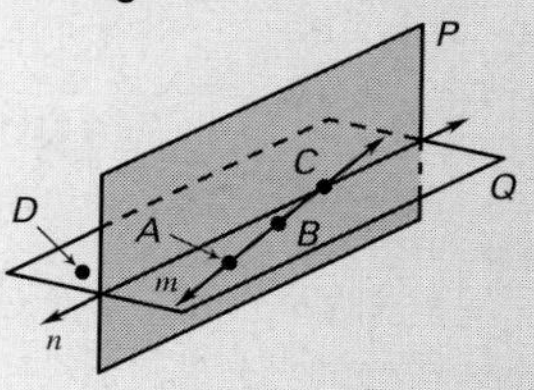

a. P 5: There is exactly one line (m) through A and B.
b. P 6: m contains at least two points (A and B).
c. P 7: m and n intersect at C.
d. P 8: Q passes through A, B, and D.
e. P 9: Q contains at least A, B, and D.
f. P 10: A and B lie in Q. So m, which contains A and B, also lies in Q.
g. P 11: P and Q intersect in line n.

CHECKPOINT EXERCISES

For use after Example 5:

1. Give examples of Postulates 5 through 11.

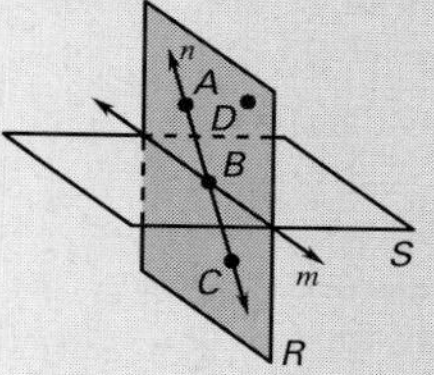

a. P 5: There is exactly one line (n) through A and C.
b. P 6: n contains at least two points (A and B).
c. P 7: m and n intersect at B.
d. P 8: R passes through A, C, and D.
e. P 9: R contains at least A, C, and D.
f. P 10: A and B lie in R. So n, which contains A and B, also lies in R.
g. P 11: R and S intersect in line m.

EXTRA EXAMPLE 6

Write the inverse, converse, and contrapositive of Postulate 6. **Inverse: If a figure is not a line, then it does not contain at least two points. Converse: If a figure contains at least two points, then it is a line. Contrapositive: If a figure does not contain at least two points, then it is not a line.**

EXTRA EXAMPLE 7

Decide whether the statement is *true* or *false.* If it is false, give a counterexample.
Three points are always contained in a line. **false**

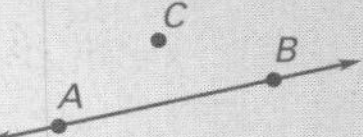

CHECKPOINT EXERCISES

For use after Example 6:

1. Write the inverse, converse, and contrapositive of Postulate 8. **Inverse: If three noncollinear points are not distinct, then it is not true that there is exactly one plane that passes through them. Converse: If exactly one plane passes through three noncollinear points, then the three points are distinct. Contrapositive: If it is not true that exactly one plane passes through three noncollinear points, then the three points are not distinct.**

For use after Example 7:

2. Decide whether the statement is *true* or *false.* If it is false, give a counterexample. A line can contain more than two points. **true**

CLOSURE QUESTION

Write the (**a**) inverse, (**b**) converse, and (**c**) contrapositive of the statement: If an animal is a dog, then it is a mammal **(a) If an animal is not a dog, then it is not a mammal; (b) If an animal is a mammal, then it is a dog; (c) If an animal is not a mammal, then it is not a dog.**

EXAMPLE 6 *Rewriting a Postulate*

a. Rewrite Postulate 5 in if-then form.

b. Write the inverse, converse, and contrapositive of Postulate 5.

SOLUTION

a. Postulate 5 can be rewritten in if-then form as follows:

If two points are distinct, then there is exactly one line that passes through them.

b. Inverse: If two points are not distinct, then it is not true that there is exactly one line that passes through them.

Converse: If exactly one line passes through two points, then the two points are distinct.

Contrapositive: If it is not true that exactly one line passes through two points, then the two points are not distinct.

EXAMPLE 7 *Using Postulates and Counterexamples*

Logical Reasoning

Decide whether the statement is *true* or *false*. If it is false, give a counterexample.

a. A line can be in more than one plane.

b. Four noncollinear points are always coplanar.

c. Two nonintersecting lines can be noncoplanar.

SOLUTION

a. In the diagram at the right, line k is in plane S and line k is in plane T.

So, it is *true* that a line can be in more than one plane.

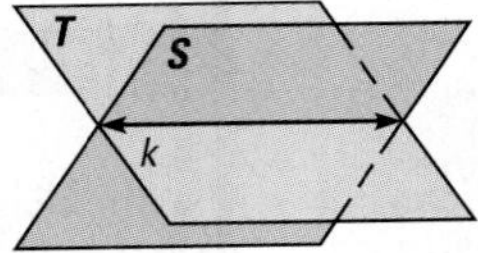

b. Consider the points A, B, C, and D at the right. The points A, B, and C lie in a plane, but there is no plane that contains all four points.

So, as shown in the counterexample at the right, it is *false* that four noncollinear points are always coplanar.

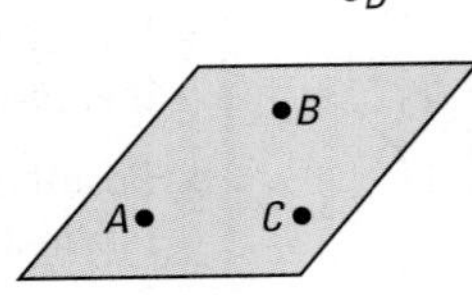

c. In the diagram at the right, line m and line n are nonintersecting and are also noncoplanar.

So, it is *true* that two nonintersecting lines can be noncoplanar.

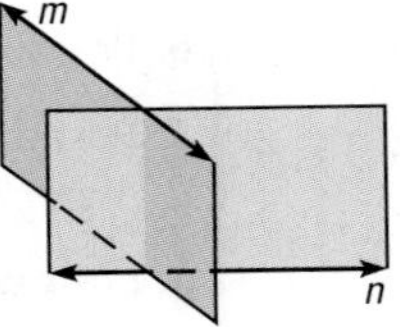

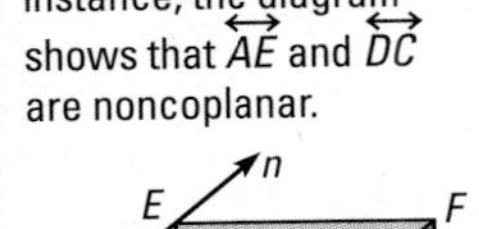

STUDENT HELP

Study Tip

A box can be used to help visualize points and lines in space. For instance, the diagram shows that $\overleftrightarrow{AE}$ and $\overleftrightarrow{DC}$ are noncoplanar.

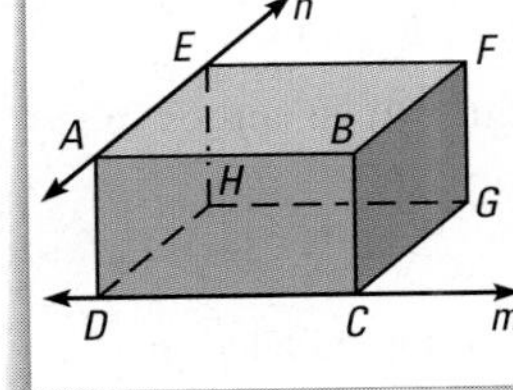

GUIDED PRACTICE

Vocabulary Check ✓

1. The ___?___ of a conditional statement is found by switching the hypothesis and conclusion. converse

Concept Check ✓

2. State the postulate described in each diagram.
a. Postulate 7: If two lines intersect, then their intersection is exactly one point.

a.

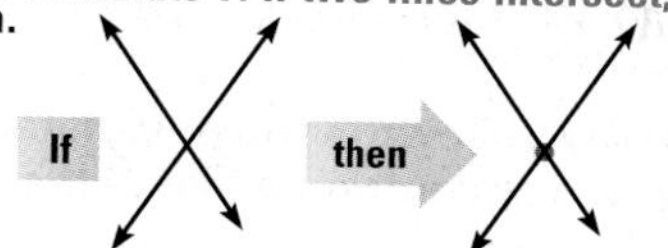

b.

If then

b. Postulate 10: If two points lie in a plane, then the line containing them lies in the plane.

Skill Check ✓

3. Write the hypothesis and conclusion of the statement, "If the dew point equals the air temperature, then it will rain."
hypothesis: the dew point equals the air temperature; conclusion: it will rain

In Exercises 4 and 5, write the statement in if-then form.

4. When threatened, the African ball python protects itself by coiling into a ball with its head in the middle. If the African ball python is threatened, then it protects itself by coiling into a ball with its head in the middle.
5. The measure of a right angle is 90°.
If an angle is a right angle, then its measure is 90°.
6. Write the inverse, converse, and contrapositive of the conditional statement, "If a cactus is of the *cereus* variety, then its flowers open at night."

6. inverse: If a cactus is not of the *cereus* variety, then its flowers do not open at night; converse: If a cactus' flowers open at night, then it is of the *cereus* variety; contrapositive: If a cactus' flowers do not open at night, then it is not of the *cereus* variety.

Decide whether the statement is *true* or *false*. Make a sketch to help you decide.

7. Through three noncollinear points there exists exactly one line. false
8. If a line and a plane intersect, and the line does not lie in the plane, then their intersection is a point. true

PRACTICE AND APPLICATIONS

STUDENT HELP

Extra Practice to help you master skills is on p. 805.

REWRITING STATEMENTS Rewrite the conditional statement in if-then form.

9. An object weighs one ton if it weighs 2000 pounds.
If an object weighs 2000 pounds, then it weighs one ton.
10. An object weighs 16 ounces if it weighs one pound.
If an object weighs one pound, then it weighs 16 ounces.
11. Three points are collinear if they lie on the same line.
If three points lie on the same line, then the points are collinear.
12. Blue trunkfish live in the waters of a coral reef.
If a fish is a blue trunkfish, then it lives in the waters of a coral reef.
13. Hagfish live in salt water.
If a fish is a hagfish, then it lives in salt water.

STUDENT HELP

HOMEWORK HELP

Example 1: Exs. 9–13
Example 2: Exs. 14–17
Example 3: Exs. 18–21
Example 4: Exs. 46–52
Example 5: Exs. 25–34
Example 6: Exs. 22–24
Example 7: Exs. 35–38

ANALYZING STATEMENTS Decide whether the statement is *true* or *false*. If false, provide a counterexample.

14. A point may lie in more than one plane. true
15. If x^4 equals 81, then x must equal 3. False. Let $x = -3$. The hypothesis is true because $(-3)^4 = 81$. However, the conclusion is false, so the conditional statement is false.
16. If it is snowing, then the temperature is below freezing. true
17. If four points are collinear, then they are coplanar. true

3 APPLY

ASSIGNMENT GUIDE

BASIC
Day 1: pp. 75–78 Exs. 10–50 even, 55, 56, 64, 68, 74

AVERAGE
Day 1: pp. 75–78 Exs. 10–50 even, 51, 55, 56, 64, 68, 74

ADVANCED
Day 1: pp. 75–78 Exs. 10–50 even, 51, 54–60, 64, 68, 74

BLOCK SCHEDULE (WITH CH. 1 ASSESS.)
pp. 75–78 Exs. 10–50 even, 51, 55, 56, 64, 68, 74

EXERCISE LEVELS

Level A: ***Easier***
9–11, 18–21, 35–38

Level B: ***More Difficult***
12–17, 22–34, 39–53, 55, 56

Level C: ***Most Difficult***
54, 57–60

✓ HOMEWORK CHECK

To quickly check student understanding of key concepts, go over the following exercises: Exs. 12, 15, 18, 22, 32, 43, 48. See also the Daily Homework Quiz:

- Blackline Master (*Chapter 2 Resource Book*, p. 24)
- Transparency (p. 11)

! COMMON ERROR

EXERCISES 22–24 Students tend to confuse the inverse, converse, and contrapositive. Refer students to the definitions, chart, and Example 4 on page 72.

STUDENT HELP NOTES

Homework Help Students can find help for Exs. 29–34 at **www.mcdougallittell.com.** The information can be printed out for students who don't have access to the Internet.

22. If-then form: If a line exists, then it contains at least two points; inverse: If a line does not exist, then it is not true that it contains at least two points; converse: If a line contains at least two points, then the line exists; contrapositive: If it is not true that a line contains at least two points, then the line does not exist.

23. If-then form: If three noncollinear points are distinct, then there is exactly one plane that they lie in; inverse: If three noncollinear points are not distinct, then it is not true that there is exactly one plane that they lie in; converse: If exactly one plane contains three noncollinear points, then the three points are distinct; contrapositive: If it is not true that there is exactly one plane that contains three noncollinear points, then the three points are not distinct.

24. If-then form: If a plane exists, then it contains at least three noncollinear points; inverse: If a plane does not exist, then it is not true that it contains at least three noncollinear points; converse: If a plane contains at least three noncollinear points, then the plane exists; contrapositive: If it is not true that a plane contains at least three noncollinear points, then the plane does not exist.

WRITING CONVERSES **Write the converse of the statement.**

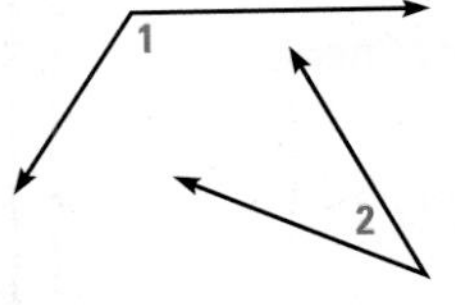

18. If $\angle 1$ measures 123°, then $\angle 1$ is obtuse.
If $\angle 1$ is obtuse, then $\angle 1$ measures 123°.
19. If $\angle 2$ measures 38°, then $\angle 2$ is acute.
If $\angle 2$ is acute, then $\angle 2$ measures 38°.
20. I will go to the mall if it is not raining.
If I go to the mall, then it is not raining.
21. I will go to the movies if it is raining.
If I go to the movies, then it is raining.

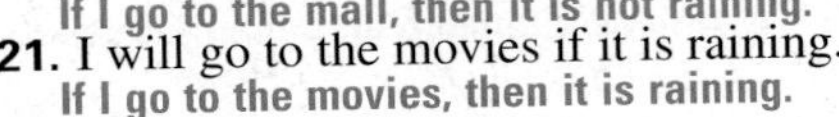

REWRITING POSTULATES **Rewrite the postulate in if-then form. Then write the inverse, converse, and contrapositive of the conditional statement.**

22. A line contains at least two points. See margin.
23. Through any three noncollinear points there exists exactly one plane. See margin.
24. A plane contains at least three noncollinear points. See margin.

ILLUSTRATING POSTULATES **Fill in the blank. Then draw a sketch that helps illustrate your answer.**

25. If two lines intersect, then their intersection is __?__ point(s). one
26. Through any __?__ points there exists exactly one line. two
27. If two points lie in a plane, then the __?__ containing them lies in the plane. line
28. If two planes intersect, then their intersection is __?__. a line

STUDENT HELP

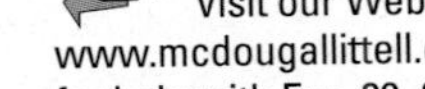

HOMEWORK HELP Visit our Web site www.mcdougallittell.com for help with Exs. 29–34.

LINKING POSTULATES **Use the diagram to state the postulate(s) that verifies the truth of the statement.**

29. The points U and T lie on line ℓ.
Postulate 5: Through any two points there exists exactly one line.
30. Line ℓ contains points U and T.
Postulate 6: A line contains at least two points.
31. The points W, S, and T lie in plane A.
See margin.
32. The points S and T lie in plane A. Therefore, line m lies in plane A.
See margin.
33. The planes A and B intersect in line ℓ.
See margin.
34. Lines m and ℓ intersect at point T.
Postulate 7: If two lines intersect, then their intersection is exactly one point.

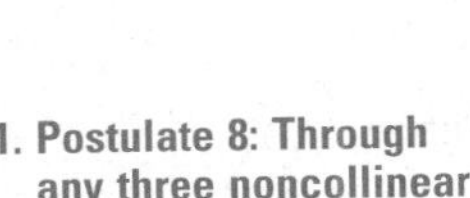

31. Postulate 8: Through any three noncollinear points there exists exactly one plane.

32. Postulate 10: If two points lie in a plane, then the line containing them lies in the plane.

33. Postulate 11: If two planes intersect, then their intersection is a line.

USING POSTULATES **In Exercises 35–38, state the postulate that shows that the statement is false.**

35. A line contains only one point.
Postulate 6: A line contains at least two points.
36. Two planes intersect in exactly one point.
Postulate 11: If two planes intersect, then their intersection is a line.
37. Three points, A, B, and C, are noncollinear, and two planes, M and N, each contain points A, B, and C. Postulate 8: Through any three noncollinear points there exists exactly one plane.
38. Two points, P and Q, are collinear and two different lines, $\overleftrightarrow{RS}$ and $\overleftrightarrow{XY}$, each pass through points P and Q. Postulate 5: Through any two points there exists exactly one line.
39. *Writing* Give an example of a true conditional statement with a true converse. *Sample answer:* If you received an A or B in all of your classes, then you made the honor roll.

42. Yes. Take point A and any two points on line k and you can form a plane through those three points that contains all of line k.

43. Yes. The plane that runs from the front of the room to the back of the room through points A and B, contains both points and a point on the front wall.

44. inverse: If $x \neq y$, then $5x \neq 5y$; converse: If $5x = 5y$, then $x = y$; contrapositive: If $5x \neq 5y$, then $x \neq y$.

45. inverse: If $x \neq 4$, then $6x - 6 \neq x + 14$; converse: If $6x - 6 = x + 14$, then $x = 4$; contrapositive: If $6x - 6 \neq x + 14$, then $x \neq 4$.

POINTS AND LINES IN SPACE Think of the intersection of the ceiling and the front wall of your classroom as line *k*. Think of the center of the floor as point *A* and the center of the ceiling as point *B*.

40. Is there more than one line that contains both points A and B? No. Through any two points there exists exactly one line.

41. Is there more than one plane that contains both points A and B? Yes. Points A and B could lie on the line intersecting two planes.

42. Is there a plane that contains line k and point A?

43. Is there a plane that contains points A, B, and a point on the front wall?

USING ALGEBRA Find the inverse, converse, and contrapositive of the statement.

44. If $x = y$, then $5x = 5y$.

45. $6x - 6 = x + 14$ if $x = 4$.

QUOTES OF WISDOM Rewrite the statement in if-then form. Then (a) determine the hypothesis and conclusion, and (b) find the inverse of the conditional statement. 46–49. See margin.

46. "If you tell the truth, you don't have to remember anything." — Mark Twain

47. "One can never consent to creep when one feels the impulse to soar." — Helen Keller

48. "Freedom is not worth having if it does not include the freedom to make mistakes." — Mahatma Ghandi

49. "Early to bed and early to rise, makes a man healthy, wealthy, and wise." — Benjamin Franklin

ADVERTISING In Exercises 50–52, use the following advertising slogan: "You want a great selection of used cars? Come and see Bargain Bob's Used Cars!" 50–52. See margin.

50. Write the slogan in if-then form. What are the hypothesis and conclusion of the conditional statement?

51. Write the inverse, converse, and contrapositive of the conditional statement.

52. *Writing* Find a real-life advertisement or slogan similar to the one given. Then repeat Exercises 50 and 51 using the advertisement or slogan.

53. TECHNOLOGY Use geometry software to draw a segment with endpoints A and C. Draw a third point B not on $\overline{AC}$. Measure $\overline{AB}$, $\overline{BC}$, and $\overline{AC}$. Move B closer to $\overline{AC}$ and observe the measures of $\overline{AB}$, $\overline{BC}$, and $\overline{AC}$. See margin.

54. RESEARCH BUGGY The diagram at the right shows the 35 foot tall Coastal Research Amphibious Buggy, also known as CRAB. This vehicle moves along the ocean floor collecting data that are used to make an accurate map of the ocean floor. Using the postulates you have learned, make a conjecture about why the CRAB was built with three legs instead of four. See margin.

FOCUS ON CAREERS

ADVERTISING COPYWRITER
Advertising copywriters write the advertisements you see and hear everyday. These ads appear in many forms including Internet home pages.

CAREER LINK
www.mcdougallittell.com

TEACHING TIPS
EXERCISES 40–43 Students may have difficulty visualizing points on the planes formed by the intersection of the ceiling with the wall. Ask them to sketch the planes and label points on each plane to help with these exercises.

! COMMON ERROR
EXERCISE 48 Students may believe that the first part of a statement is the hypothesis when the word "if" is not present. Students should note that some conditional statements reverse the order of a statement.

ENGLISH LEARNERS
EXERCISES 46–49 Consider mixing English learners with students fluent in English in small groups to complete these exercises. Encourage students to discuss the sense of each quote before reformulating them as if–then statements.

CAREER NOTE
EXERCISES 50–52 Additional information about advertising copywriters is available at **www.mcdougallittell.com.**

46–54. See Additional Answers beginning on page AA1.

ADDITIONAL PRACTICE AND RETEACHING

For Lesson 2.1:

- Practice Levels A, B, and C (*Chapter 2 Resource Book,* p. 14)
- Reteaching with Practice (*Chapter 2 Resource Book,* p. 17)
- See Lesson 2.1 of the *Personal Student Tutor*

For more Mixed Review:

- Search the *Test and Practice Generator* for key words or specific lessons.

4 ASSESS

DAILY HOMEWORK QUIZ

Transparency Available

Using the true conditional statement, "Constrictors such as pythons are not poisonous," write each of the following.

1. Rewrite the statement in if-then form. **If a snake is a constrictor, then it is not poisonous.**
2. Write the converse of the if-then statement. **If a snake is not poisonous, then it is a constrictor.**
3. Write the contrapositive of the if-then statement. **If a snake is poisonous, then it is not a constrictor.**
4. Write the hypothesis and conclusion of the if-then statement. **hypothesis: a snake is a constrictor; conclusion: it is not poisonous**

EXTRA CHALLENGE NOTE

Challenge problems for Lesson 2.1 are available in **blackline** format in the *Chapter 2 Resource Book,* p. 21 and at **www.mcdougallittell.com.**

ADDITIONAL TEST PREPARATION

1. **OPEN ENDED** Give an example of a conditional statement about lines. Then give the inverse, converse, and contrapositive. ***Sample answer:*** **If a figure is a line, then it contains at least two points. Inverse: If a figure isn't a line, then it doesn't contain at least two points. Converse: If a figure contains at least two points, then it is a line. Contrapositive: If a figure doesn't contain at least two points, then it isn't a line.**

Test Preparation

55. **MULTIPLE CHOICE** Use the conditional statement "If the measure of an angle is 44°, then the angle is acute" to decide which of the following are true. **D**

I. The statement is true.
II. The converse of the statement is true.
III. The contrapositive of the statement is true.

Ⓐ I only Ⓑ II only Ⓒ I and II Ⓓ I and III Ⓔ I, II, and III

56. **MULTIPLE CHOICE** Which one of the following statements is *not* true? **D**

Ⓐ If $x = 2$, then $x^2 = 4$.

Ⓑ If $x = -2$, then $x^2 = 4$.

Ⓒ If $x^3 = -8$, then $x = -2$.

Ⓓ If $x^2 = 4$, then $x = 2$.

Ⓔ If $x = -2$, then $x^3 = -8$.

★ Challenge

MAKING A CONJECTURE Sketch a line k and a point P not on line k. Make a conjecture about how many planes can be drawn through line k and point P, and then answer the following questions.

57. Which postulate allows you to state that there are two points, R and S, on line k? **Postulate 6: A line contains at least two points.**

58. Which postulate allows you to conclude that exactly one plane X can be drawn to contain points P, R, and S? **Postulate 8: Through any three noncollinear points there exists exactly one plane.**

59. Which postulate guarantees that line k is contained in plane X? **Postulate 10: If two points lie in a plane, then the line containing them lies in the plane.**

60. Was your conjecture correct? **Answers will vary.**

EXTRA CHALLENGE
www.mcdougallittell.com

MIXED REVIEW

DRAWING ANGLES Plot the points in a coordinate plane. Then classify ∠*ABC*. (Review 1.4 for 2.2)

61. $A(0, 7)$, $B(2, 2)$, $C(6, -1)$ **obtuse**

62. $A(-1, 0)$, $B(-6, 4)$, $C(-6, -1)$ **acute**

63. $A(1, 3)$, $B(1, -5)$, $C(-5, -5)$ **right angle**

64. $A(-3, -1)$, $B(2, 5)$, $C(3, -2)$ **acute**

FINDING THE MIDPOINT Find the coordinates of the midpoint of the segment joining the two points. (Review 1.5)

65. $A(-2, 8)$, $B(4, -12)$ **(1, −2)**

66. $A(8, 8)$, $B(-6, 1)$ **(1, 4.5)**

67. $A(-7, -4)$, $B(4, 7)$ **(−1.5, 1.5)**

68. $A(0, -9)$, $B(-8, 5)$ **(−4, −2)**

69. $A(1, 4)$, $B(11, -6)$ **(6, −1)**

70. $A(-10, -10)$, $B(2, 12)$ **(−4, 1)**

FINDING PERIMETER AND AREA Find the area and perimeter (or circumference) of the figure described. (Use $\pi \approx 3.14$ when necessary.) (Review 1.7 for 2.2)

71. circle, radius = 6 m **113.04 m²; 37.68 m**

72. square, side = 11 cm **121 cm²; 44 cm**

73. square, side = 38.75 mm **1501.5625 mm²; 155 mm**

74. circle, diameter = 23 ft **415.265 ft²; 72.22 ft**

2.2 Definitions and Biconditional Statements

What you should learn

GOAL 1 Recognize and use definitions.

GOAL 2 Recognize and use biconditional statements.

Why you should learn it

▼ You can use biconditional statements to help analyze geographic relations, such as whether three cities in Florida lie on the same line, as in **Ex. 50**.

REAL LIFE

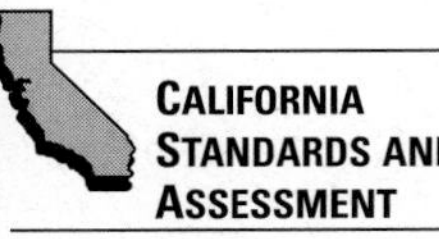

CALIFORNIA STANDARDS AND ASSESSMENT

CA Standards: 1, 3

GOAL 1 RECOGNIZING AND USING DEFINITIONS

In Lesson 1.2 you learned that a *definition* uses known words to describe a new word. Here are two examples.

Two lines are called **perpendicular lines** if they intersect to form a right angle. A **line perpendicular to a plane** is a line that intersects the plane in a point and is perpendicular to every line in the plane that intersects it. The symbol ⊥ is read as "is perpendicular to."

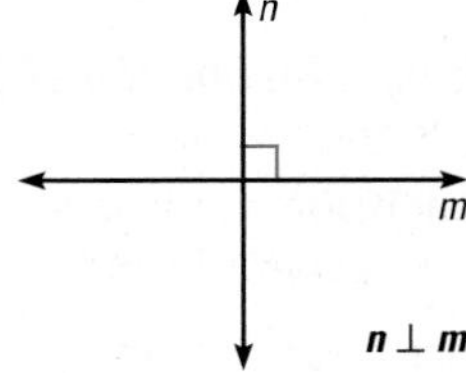

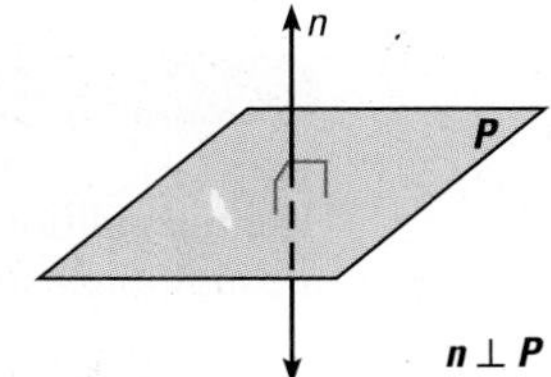

All definitions can be interpreted "forward" and "backward." For instance, the definition of perpendicular lines means (1) if two lines are perpendicular, then they intersect to form a right angle, *and* (2) if two lines intersect to form a right angle, then they are perpendicular.

EXAMPLE 1 *Using Definitions*

Decide whether each statement about the diagram is true. Explain your answer using the definitions you have learned.

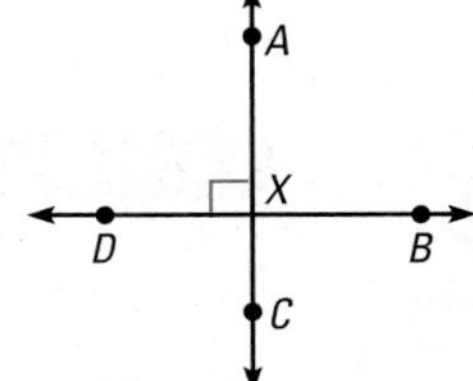

a. Points D, X, and B are collinear.

b. $\overleftrightarrow{AC}$ is perpendicular to $\overleftrightarrow{DB}$.

c. $\angle AXB$ is adjacent to $\angle CXD$.

SOLUTION

a. This statement is true. Two or more points are *collinear* if they lie on the same line. The points D, X, and B all lie on line $\overleftrightarrow{DB}$ so they are collinear.

b. This statement is true. The right angle symbol in the diagram indicates that the lines $\overleftrightarrow{AC}$ and $\overleftrightarrow{DB}$ intersect to form a right angle. So, the lines are perpendicular.

c. This statement is false. By definition, adjacent angles must share a common side. Because $\angle AXB$ and $\angle CXD$ do not share a common side, they are not adjacent.

1 PLAN

PACING

Basic: 2 days
Average: 2 days
Advanced: 2 days
Block Schedule: 1 block

LESSON OPENER
GEOMETRY SOFTWARE

An alternative way to approach Lesson 2.2 is to use the Geometry Software Lesson Opener:

- Blackline Master (*Chapter 2 Resource Book,* p. 25)
- Transparency (p. 9)

MEETING INDIVIDUAL NEEDS

- ***Chapter 2 Resource Book***
  Prerequisite Skills Review (p. 5)
  Practice Level A (p. 30)
  Practice Level B (p. 31)
  Practice Level C (p. 32)
  Reteaching with Practice (p. 33)
  Absent Student Catch-Up (p. 35)
  Challenge (p. 37)
- ***Resources in Spanish***
- 

NEW-TEACHER SUPPORT

See the Tips for New Teachers on pp. 1–2 of the *Chapter 2 Resource Book* for additional notes about Lesson 2.2.

WARM-UP EXERCISES

Transparency Available

Write the converse of each statement.

1. If M is the midpoint of $\overline{AB}$, then $AM = MB$. **If $AM = MB$, then M is the midpoint of $\overline{AB}$.**
2. If $AB + BC = AC$, then points A, B, and C are collinear. **If points A, B, and C are collinear, then $AB + BC = AC$.**
3. If $|x| = 6$, then $x = 6$ or -6. **If $x = 6$ or -6, then $|x| = 6$.**
4. You score a goal if the ball crosses the goal line. **If you score a goal, then the ball crosses the goal line.**

2 TEACH

MOTIVATING THE LESSON

Tell students that assuming that the converse of "if he committed a crime, then he was at the scene of the crime" is true may be a mistake in a court of law. If the converse of a true statement is also true, however, the conditional and its converse can be combined to form a *true biconditional.* Biconditional statements are the focus of this lesson.

EXTRA EXAMPLE 1

Decide whether each statement about the diagram is true. Explain your answer using the definitions you have learned.

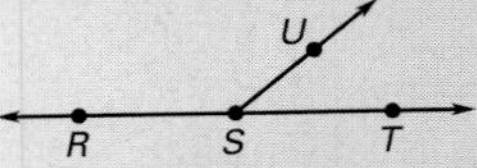

a. Points R, S, and T are collinear. true; points are collinear if they lie on the same line

b. $\overrightarrow{SU}$ is perpendicular to $\overleftrightarrow{RT}$ false; $\angle RSU$ is not a right angle

EXTRA EXAMPLE 2

Rewrite the biconditional statement as a conditional statement and its converse. Two lines intersect if and only if their intersection is exactly one point. Conditional: If two lines intersect, then they intersect in exactly one point. Converse: If two lines contain exactly one point, then the two lines intersect.

EXTRA EXAMPLE 3

Consider the following statement: $x^2 < 49$ if and only if $x < 7$.

a. Is this a biconditional statement? yes

b. Is the statement true? no

CHECKPOINT EXERCISES

For use after Examples 1–3:

1. Consider the following statement: $x^2 = 4x$ if and only if $x = 4$.

a. Is this a biconditional statement? yes

b. Is the statement true? no

STUDENT HELP

Study Tip

When a conditional statement contains the word "if," the hypothesis does not always follow the "if." This is shown in the "only-if" statement at the right.

GOAL 2 USING BICONDITIONAL STATEMENTS

Conditional statements are not always written in if-then form. Another common form of a conditional statement is *only-if* form. Here is an example.

It is Saturday, only if **I am working at the restaurant.**

Hypothesis — Conclusion

You can rewrite this conditional statement in if-then form as follows:

If **it is Saturday**, then **I am working at the restaurant**.

A **biconditional statement** is a statement that contains the phrase "if and only if." Writing a biconditional statement is equivalent to writing a conditional statement *and* its converse.

EXAMPLE 2 *Rewriting a Biconditional Statement*

The biconditional statement below can be rewritten as a conditional statement and its converse.

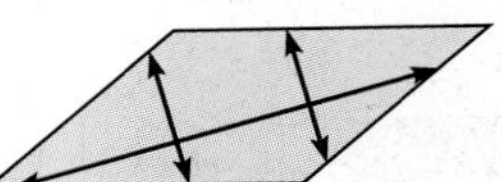

Three lines are coplanar if and only if they lie in the same plane.

Conditional statement: If three lines are coplanar, then they lie in the same plane.

Converse: If three lines lie in the same plane, then they are coplanar.

A biconditional statement can be either true or false. To be true, *both* the conditional statement and its converse must be true. This means that a true biconditional statement is true both "forward" and "backward." All definitions can be written as true biconditional statements.

EXAMPLE 3 *Analyzing a Biconditional Statement*

Using Algebra

Consider the following statement: $x = 3$ if and only if $x^2 = 9$.

a. Is this a biconditional statement?

b. Is the statement true?

SOLUTION

a. The statement is biconditional because it contains "if and only if."

b. The statement can be rewritten as the following statement and its converse.

Conditional statement: If $x = 3$, then $x^2 = 9$.

Converse: If $x^2 = 9$, then $x = 3$.

▶ The first of these statements is true, but the second is false. So, the biconditional statement is false.

EXAMPLE 4 *Writing a Biconditional Statement*

Each of the following statements is true. Write the converse of each statement and decide whether the converse is *true* or *false*. If the converse is true, combine it with the original statement to form a true biconditional statement. If the converse is false, state a counterexample.

a. If two points lie in a plane, then the line containing them lies in the plane.

b. If a number ends in 0, then the number is divisible by 5.

SOLUTION

a. Converse: If a line containing two points lies in a plane, then the points lie in the plane.

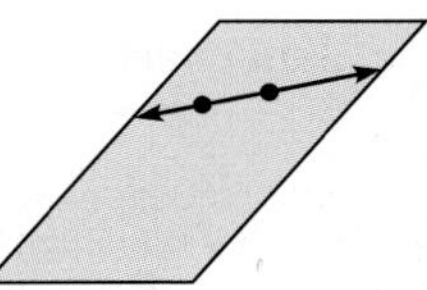

The converse is true, as shown in the diagram. So, it can be combined with the original statement to form the true biconditional statement written below.

Biconditional statement: Two points lie in a plane if and only if the line containing them lies in the plane.

b. Converse: If a number is divisible by 5, then the number ends in 0.

The converse is false. As a counterexample, consider the number 15. It is divisible by 5, but it does not end in 0, as shown at the right.

$10 \div 5 = 2$
▶ $15 \div 5 = 3$
$20 \div 5 = 4$

Knowing how to use true biconditional statements is an important tool for reasoning in geometry. For instance, if you can write a true biconditional statement, then you can use the conditional statement or the converse to justify an argument.

EXAMPLE 5 *Writing a Postulate as a Biconditional*

The second part of the Segment Addition Postulate is the converse of the first part. Combine the statements to form a true biconditional statement.

SOLUTION

The first part of the Segment Addition Postulate can be written as follows:

If B lies between points A and C, then $AB + BC = AC$.

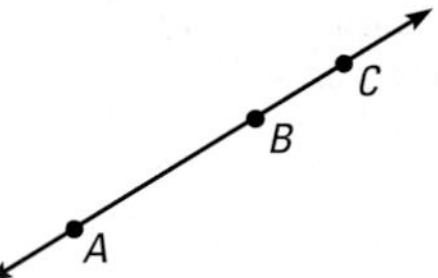

The converse of this is as follows:

If $AB + BC = AC$, then B lies between A and C.

Combining these statements produces the following true biconditional statement:

Point B lies between points A and C if and only if $AB + BC = AC$.

STUDENT HELP

Study Tip
Unlike definitions, not all postulates can be written as true biconditional statements.

EXTRA EXAMPLE 4

The following statement is true. Write the converse and decide whether it is *true* or *false*. If the converse is true, combine it with the original to form a biconditional.
If $x^2 = 4$, then $x = 2$ or -2.
Converse: If $x = 2$ or -2, then $x^2 = 4$; true; Biconditional: $x^2 = 4$ if and only if $x = 2$ or -2.

EXTRA EXAMPLE 5

The converse of the Angle Addition Postulate is true. Write the converse and combine it with the postulate to form a true biconditional statement.
Converse: If $m\angle RSP + m\angle PST = m\angle RST$, then P is in the interior of $\angle RST$. Biconditional: P is in the interior of $\angle RST$ if and only if $m\angle RSP + m\angle PST = m\angle RST$.

CHECKPOINT EXERCISES

For use after Examples 4 and 5:

1. The following statement is true. Write the converse and decide whether it is *true* or *false*. If the converse is true, combine it with the original to form a biconditional.
If two planes intersect, then they contain the same line.
Converse: If two planes contain the same line, then they intersect; true; Biconditional: Two planes intersect if and only if they contain the same line.

CLOSURE QUESTION

Rewrite the biconditional statement as a conditional statement and its converse. Two angles are complementary if and only if their sum is 90°. **If two angles are complementary, then their sum is 90°. Converse: If the sum of two angles is 90°, then they are complementary.**

3 APPLY

ASSIGNMENT GUIDE

BASIC
Day 1: pp. 82–83 Exs. 13–31
Day 2: pp. 83–85 Exs. 32–44, 46, 50–55, 60–68

AVERAGE
Day 1: pp. 82–83 Exs. 13–31
Day 2: pp. 83–85 Exs. 32–44, 46, 50–55, 60–68

ADVANCED
Day 1: pp. 82–83 Exs. 13–31
Day 2: pp. 83–85 Exs. 32–44, 46, 50–58, 60–68

BLOCK SCHEDULE
pp. 82–85 Exs. 13–44, 46, 50–55, 60–68

EXERCISE LEVELS

Level A: *Easier*
13–23

Level B: *More Difficult*
24–44, 46, 50–55

Level C: *Most Difficult*
45, 47–49, 56–58

✔ HOMEWORK CHECK

To quickly check student understanding of key concepts, go over the following exercises: Exs. 20, 24, 30, 36, 40, 50, 52. See also the Daily Homework Quiz:

- Blackline Master (*Chapter 2 Resource Book,* p. 40)
- Transparency (p. 12)

GUIDED PRACTICE

Vocabulary Check ✓

Concept Check ✓

1. Describe in your own words what a *true biconditional statement* is. **See margin.**

2. **ERROR ANALYSIS** What is wrong with Jared's argument below?

> ~~The statements "I eat cereal only if it is morning" and "If I eat cereal, then it is morning" are not equivalent.~~

The statements are equivalent. If the first statement used the phrase "if and only if," rather than "only if," then they would not be equivalent.

1. *Sample answer:* **A true biconditional statement is one that is true when read both forwards and backwards.**

Skill Check ✓

Tell whether the statement is a biconditional.

3. I will work after school only if I have the time. **No. For a statement to be a biconditional statement it must contain the phrase "if and only if."**
4. An angle is called a right angle if and only if it measures 90°. **Yes.**
5. Two segments are congruent if and only if they have the same length. **Yes.**

Rewrite the biconditional statement as a conditional statement and its converse. **6–8. See margin.**

6. The ceiling fan runs if and only if the light switch is on.
7. You scored a touchdown if and only if the football crossed the goal line.
8. The expression $3x + 4$ is equal to 10 if and only if x is 2.

6. **conditional statement: If the ceiling fan runs, then the light switch is on; converse: If the light switch is on, then the ceiling fan runs.**
7. **conditional statement: If you scored a touchdown, then the football crossed the goal line; converse: If the football crossed the goal line, then you scored a touchdown.**
8. **conditional statement: If the expression $3x + 4$ is equal to 10, then x is 2; converse: If x is 2, then the expression $3x + 4$ is equal to 10.**

WINDOWS **Decide whether the statement about the window shown is true. Explain your answer using the definitions you have learned.**

9. The points D, E, and F are collinear. **False. The points do not lie on the same line.**
10. $m\angle CBA = 90°$ **False. $\angle CBA$ is a straight angle, so its measure is 180°.**
11. $\angle DBA$ and $\angle EBC$ are not complementary. **True. $\angle DBA$ and $\angle EBC$ each are supplementary to right angle $\angle DBC$, so each measures 90°.**
12. $\overline{DE} \perp \overline{AC}$

12. **True. $\overline{DE}$ and $\overline{AC}$ intersect at a right angle.**

PRACTICE AND APPLICATIONS

STUDENT HELP

Extra Practice to help you master skills is on p. 805.

PERPENDICULAR LINES **Use the diagram to determine whether the statement is *true* or *false*.**

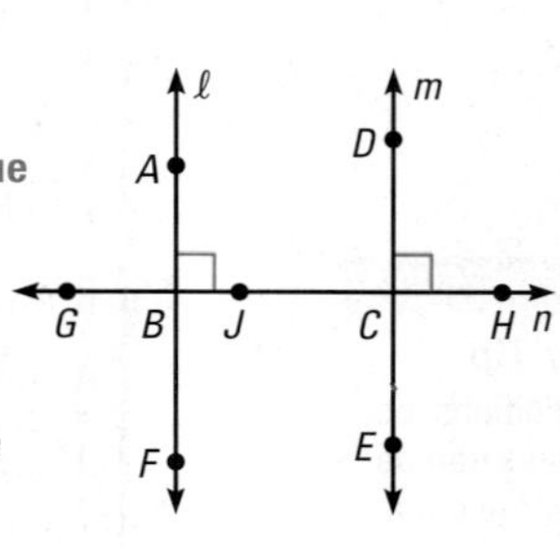

13. Points A, F, and G are collinear. **false**
14. $\angle DCJ$ and $\angle DCH$ are supplementary. **true**
15. $\overline{DC}$ is perpendicular to line ℓ. **false**
16. $\overline{FB}$ is perpendicular to line n. **true**
17. $\angle FBJ$ and $\angle JBA$ are complementary. **false**
18. Line m bisects $\angle JCH$. **true**
19. $\angle ABJ$ and $\angle DCH$ are supplementary. **true**

STUDENT HELP

HOMEWORK HELP
Example 1: Exs. 13–19
Example 2: Exs. 20–23
Example 3: Exs. 28–31
Example 4: Exs. 32–37
Example 5: Exs. 44–46

BICONDITIONAL STATEMENTS Rewrite the biconditional statement as a conditional statement and its converse. 20–23. See margin.

20. Two angles are congruent if and only if they have the same measure.

21. A ray bisects an angle if and only if it divides the angle into two congruent angles.

22. Two lines are perpendicular if and only if they intersect to form right angles.

23. A point is a midpoint of a segment if and only if it divides the segment into two congruent segments.

FINDING COUNTEREXAMPLES Give a counterexample that demonstrates that the converse of the statement is false.

24. If an angle measures 94°, then it is obtuse.
A 100° angle is obtuse, but does not measure 94°.

25. If two angles measure 42° and 48°, then they are complementary.

26. If Terry lives in Tampa, then she lives in Florida.
Terry could live in Orlando, Florida, not in Tampa, Florida.

27. If a polygon is a square, then it has four sides.
A rectangle with width 2 cm and length 3 cm has four sides, but is not a square.

25. Two angles measuring 30° and 60° are complementary, but they do not measure 42° and 48°.

ANALYZING BICONDITIONAL STATEMENTS Determine whether the biconditional statement about the diagram is *true* or *false*. If false, provide a counterexample.

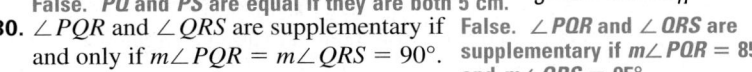

28. $\overline{SR}$ is perpendicular to $\overline{QR}$ if and only if $\angle SRQ$ measures 90°. true

29. PQ and PS are equal if and only if PQ and PS are both 8 centimeters.
False. PQ and PS are equal if they are both 5 cm.

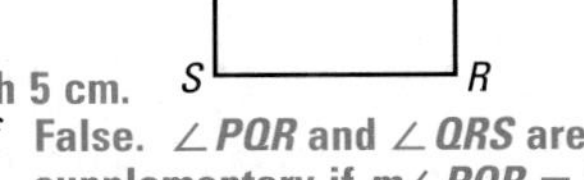

30. $\angle PQR$ and $\angle QRS$ are supplementary if and only if $m\angle PQR = m\angle QRS = 90°$. False. $\angle PQR$ and $\angle QRS$ are supplementary if $m\angle PQR = 85°$ and $m\angle QRS = 95°$.

31. $\angle PSR$ measures 90° if and only if $\angle PSR$ is a right angle. true

REWRITING STATEMENTS Rewrite the true statement in if-then form and write the converse. If the converse is true, combine it with the if-then statement to form a true biconditional statement. If the converse is false, provide a counterexample. 32–37. See margin.

32. Adjacent angles share a common side.

33. Two circles have the same circumference if they have the same diameter.

34. The perimeter of a triangle is the sum of the lengths of its sides.

35. All leopards have spots.

36. Panthers live in the forest.

37. A leopard is a snow leopard if the leopard has pale gray fur.

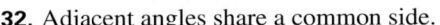

FOCUS ON APPLICATIONS

REAL LIFE

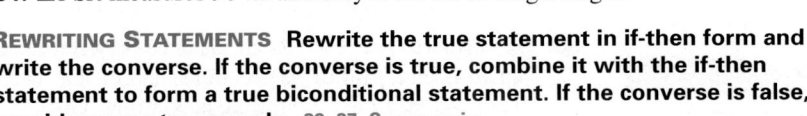

SNOW LEOPARDS The pale coat of the snow leopard, as mentioned in Ex. 37, allows the animal to blend in with the snow 3960 meters (13,000 feet) high in the mountains of Central Asia.

USING ALGEBRA Determine whether the statement can be combined with its converse to form a true biconditional.

38. If $3u + 2 = u + 12$, then $u = 5$.
Yes. $3u + 2 = u + 12$ if and only if $u = 5$.

39. If $v = 1$, then $9v - 4v = 2v + 3v$.
No. v can be any number if $9v - 4v = 2v + 3v$.

40. If $w^2 - 10 = w + 2$, then $w = 4$.

41. If $x^3 - 27 = 0$, then $x = 3$.
Yes. $x^3 - 27 = 0$ if and only if $x = 3$.

42. If $y = -3$, then $y^2 = 9$.
No. If $y = 3$, then $(3)^2 = 9$.

43. If $z = 3$, then $7 + 18z = 5z + 7 + 13z$.
No. z can be any number if $7 + 18z = 5z + 7 + 13z$.

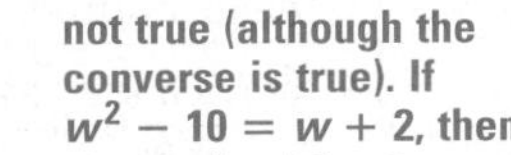

40. No. The statement is not true (although the converse is true). If $w^2 - 10 = w + 2$, then w equals *either* 4 or −3.

MATHEMATICAL REASONING

EXERCISES 20–23 Another way to rewrite a biconditional is using the notation *p only if q* for the conditional and *q only if p* for the converse. You may wish to ask students to write the conditional statement and its converse in Exs. 20–23 using this notation.

TEACHING TIPS

EXERCISES 35–37 Students may have difficulty writing statements when they know the content is false. Help students by having them write simple wrong statements, such as "Dogs are blue." Then guide them through writing false statements and labeling them false.

20. conditional statement: If two angles are congruent, then they have the same measure; converse: If two angles have the same measure, then they are congruent.
21. conditional statement: If a ray bisects an angle, then it divides the angle into two congruent angles; converse: If a ray divides an angle into two congruent angles, then the ray bisects the angle.
22. conditional statement: If two lines are perpendicular, then they intersect to form right angles; converse: If two lines intersect to form right angles, then the two lines are perpendicular.
23. conditional statement: If a point is a midpoint of a segment, then it divides the segment into two congruent segments; converse: If a point divides a segment into two congruent segments, then the point is the midpoint of the segment.
32–37. See Additional Answers beginning on page AA1.

APPLICATION NOTE

EXERCISES 51–53 The Beaufort Wind Scale was officially adopted in 1838 to help coastal observers report winds at sea. This scale categorizes wind force as breezes, gales, storms, or hurricanes.

Additional information about winds at sea is available at **www.mcdougallittell.com.**

49. The statements from Exercises 47 and 48 can both be written as true biconditionals. The sides of the square are doubled if and only if the area is quadrupled, and the sides of a square are doubled if and only if the perimeter is doubled, are both true.

52. False. Winds of 41–47 knots are classified as strong gale on the Beaufort scale.

46. See Additional Answers beginning on page AA1.

ADDITIONAL PRACTICE AND RETEACHING

For Lesson 2.2:

- Practice Levels A, B, and C (*Chapter 2 Resource Book,* p. 30)
- Reteaching with Practice (*Chapter 2 Resource Book,* p. 33)
- See Lesson 2.2 of the *Personal Student Tutor*

For more Mixed Review:

- Search the *Test and Practice Generator* for key words or specific lessons.

44. converse: If $m\angle ABC + m\angle CBD = m\angle ABD$, then C is in the interior of $\angle ABD$; true; C is in the interior of $\angle ABD$ if and only if $m\angle ABC + m\angle CBD = m\angle ABD$.

45. *Sample answer:* You received an A or B in all of your classes if and only if you made the honor roll.

44. REWRITING A POSTULATE Write the converse of the Angle Addition Postulate and decide whether the converse is *true* or *false*. If true, write the postulate as a true biconditional. If false, provide a counterexample.

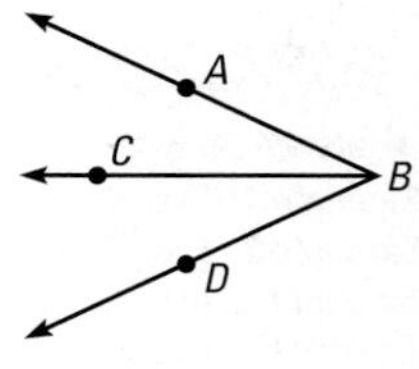

Angle Addition Postulate: If C is in the interior of $\angle ABD$, then $m\angle ABC + m\angle CBD = m\angle ABD$.

45. *Writing* Give an example of a true biconditional statement.

46. MUSICAL GROUPS The table shows four different groups, along with the number of instrumentalists in each group. Write your own definitions of the musical groups and verify that they are true biconditional statements by writing each definition "forward" and "backward." The first one is started for you. See margin.

Sample: A musical group is a *piano trio* if and only if it contains exactly one pianist, one violinist, and one cellist.

Musical group	Pianist	Violinist	Cellist	Violist
Piano trio	1	1	1	—
String quartet	—	2	1	1
String quintet	—	2	1	2
Piano quintet	1	2	1	1

TECHNOLOGY In Exercises 47–49, use geometry software to complete the statement.

47. If the sides of a square are doubled, then the area is ___?___. quadrupled

48. If the sides of a square are doubled, then the perimeter is ___?___. doubled

49. Decide whether the statements in Exercises 47 and 48 can be written as true biconditionals. If not, provide a counterexample. See margin.

50. AIR DISTANCES The air distance between Jacksonville, Florida, and Merritt Island, Florida, is 148 miles and the air distance between Merritt Island and Fort Pierce, Florida, is 70 miles. Given that the air distance between Jacksonville and Fort Pierce is 218 miles, does Merritt Island fall on the line connecting Jacksonville and Fort Pierce? Yes.

FOCUS ON APPLICATIONS

WINDS AT SEA Along with wind speed, sailors need to know the direction of the wind. Flags, also known as telltales, help sailors determine wind direction.

APPLICATION LINK www.mcdougallittell.com

WINDS AT SEA Use the portion of the Beaufort wind scale table shown to determine whether the biconditional statement is *true* or *false*. If false, provide a counterexample.

51. A storm is a hurricane if and only if the winds of the storm measure 64 knots or greater. True.

52. Winds at sea are classified as a strong gale if and only if the winds measure 34–40 knots. See margin.

53. Winds are classified as 10 on the Beaufort scale if and only if the winds measure 41–55 knots.

False. Winds are classified as 9 on the Beaufort scale if the winds measure 41–47 knots.

Beaufort Wind Scale for Open Sea

Number	Knots	Description
8	34–40	gale winds
9	41–47	strong gale
10	48–55	storm
11	56–63	violent storm
12	64+	hurricane

Test Preparation

54. **MULTIPLE CHOICE** Which one of the following statements cannot be written as a true biconditional statement? D

(A) Any angle that measures between 90° and 180° is obtuse.

(B) $2x - 5 = x + 1$ only if $x = 6$.

(C) Any angle that measures between 0° and 90° is acute.

(D) If two angles measure 110° and 70°, then they are supplementary.

(E) If the sum of the measures of two angles equals 180°, then they are supplementary.

55. **MULTIPLE CHOICE** Which of the following statements about the conditional statement "If two lines intersect to form a right angle, then they are perpendicular" is true? B

I. The converse is true.
II. The statement can be written as a true biconditional.
III. The statement is false.

(A) I only (B) I and II only (C) II and III only
(D) III only (E) I, II, and III

★ Challenge

WRITING STATEMENTS In Exercises 56 and 57, determine (a) whether the contrapositive of the true statement is *true* or *false* and (b) whether the true statement can be written as a true biconditional. 56, 57. See margin.

56. If I am in Des Moines, then I am in the capital of Iowa.

57. If two angles measure 10° and 80°, then they are complementary.

58. **LOGICAL REASONING** You are given that the contrapositive of a statement is true. Will that help you determine whether the statement can be written as a true biconditional? Explain. (*Hint:* Use your results from Exercises 56 and 57.)
Sample answer: No. The contrapositive of a true conditional statement will always be true, but for a biconditional statement to be true, the original conditional statement and the converse need to be true.

EXTRA CHALLENGE
www.mcdougallittell.com

MIXED REVIEW

STUDYING ANGLES Find the measures of a complement and a supplement of the angle. (Review 1.6 for 2.3)

59. 87° 3°; 93° 60. 73° 17°; 107° 61. 14° 76°; 166° 62. 29° 61°; 151°

FINDING PERIMETER AND AREA Find the area and perimeter, or circumference of the figure described. (Use $\pi \approx 3.14$ when necessary.) (Review 1.7 for 2.3)

63. rectangle: $w = 3$ ft, $l = 12$ ft
36 ft^2; 30 ft

64. rectangle: $w = 7$ cm, $l = 10$ cm
70 cm^2; 34 cm

65. circle: $r = 8$ in.
200.96 in.^{2}; 50.24 in.

66. square: $s = 6$ m
36 m^2; 24 m

CONDITIONAL STATEMENTS Write the converse of the statement. (Review 2.1 for 2.3)

67. If the sides of a rectangle are all congruent, then the rectangle is a square.
If a rectangle is a square, then the sides of the rectangle are all congruent.

68. If $8x + 1 = 3x + 16$, then $x = 3$.
If $x = 3$, then $8x + 1 = 3x + 16$.

4 ASSESS

DAILY HOMEWORK QUIZ

Transparency Available

Rewrite the biconditional statement as a conditional statement and its converse.

1. We will go to the beach if and only if it is sunny. If we go to the beach, then it is sunny; If it is sunny, then we will go to the beach.

Give a counterexample that demonstrates that the converse of the statement is false.

2. If a polygon has four equal sides, then it is a square. A rhombus has four equal sides but is not a square.
3. If a vehicle has wheels, then it is a car. A bicycle has wheels but is not a car.

Determine whether the statement can be combined with its converse to form a true biconditional.

4. If $2x > 8$, then $x = 5$. No; x can be any number greater than 4.

EXTRA CHALLENGE NOTE

Challenge problems for Lesson 2.2 are available in **blackline** format in the *Chapter 2 Resource Book*, p. 37 and at **www.mcdougallittell.com.**

ADDITIONAL TEST PREPARATION

1. **WRITING** Describe how to write a conditional and its converse from the biconditional statement: Two lines are perpendicular if and only if they intersect in a right angle.
Determine the *if-then* sequence for the conditional, or "if two lines are perpendicular, then they intersect in a right angle." Then find the converse, or "if two lines intersect in a right angle, then they are perpendicular."

56–57. See Additional Answers beginning on page AA1.

1 Planning the Activity

PURPOSE
To use deductive reasoning to solve a puzzle.

MATERIALS
- grid paper
- Activity Support Master (*Chapter 2 Resource Book,* p. 41)

PACING
- Exploring the Concept — 10 min
- Drawing Conclusions — 1–3: 10 min, 4: 30+ min

LINK TO LESSON
Using a grid to represent pieces of a puzzle is a good problem solving strategy. When students use symbols to represent statements in Example 1 of Lesson 2.3, ask them to apply the critical thinking skills they learned in this activity.

2 Managing the Activity

CLASSROOM MANAGEMENT
If students have difficulty shading the boxes in the grid, ask them first to represent the clues in if-then form. This should make them more understandable.

ALTERNATIVE APPROACH
To save time, do this activity as a demonstration. Show the grid on an overhead and ask students to help you shade the boxes.

3 Closing the Activity

★ ***KEY DISCOVERY***
Eliminating possibilities as well as other deductive reasoning strategies can be used to solve puzzles.

ACTIVITY ASSESSMENT
JOURNAL Describe how to solve a logic puzzle from given clues. **See sample answer at right.**

ACTIVITY 2.3
Developing Concepts

Logic Puzzle

GROUP ACTIVITY
Work with a partner.

MATERIALS
- grid paper
- pencils

▶ QUESTION How can deductive reasoning be used to solve a logic puzzle?

▶ EXPLORING THE CONCEPT

Using the clues below, determine the favorite hobbies and hometowns of five students: Maynard, Tamara, Dave, Marie, and Brad. They live in Hart's Location, Grand Rapids, Stockton, Ravenna, and Springdale. Their favorite hobbies are playing basketball, reading, playing computer games, playing the guitar, and in-line skating.

To keep track of the information given in the clues, record it in a grid like the one shown. For each clue, shade the appropriate boxes in the grid. The unshaded boxes show the solution of the puzzle.

CLUES
1. Brad lives in Grand Rapids.
2. Marie does not live in Hart's Location.
3. If Maynard lives in Ravenna, then his favorite hobby is playing the guitar.
4. Tamara's favorite hobby is playing basketball.
5. The favorite hobby of the person who lives in Grand Rapids is in-line skating.
6. Tamara, Dave, and Marie do not live in Ravenna.
7. The person whose favorite hobby is reading does not live in Stockton or Hart's Location.
8. Neither Marie nor Dave lives in Stockton.

	basketball	reading	computers	guitar	in-line skating	Hart's Location	Grand Rapids	Stockton	Ravenna	Springdale
Maynard							■			
Tamara							■			
Dave							■			
Marie							■			
Brad						■		■	■	■
Hart's Location										
Grand Rapids										
Stockton										
Ravenna										
Springdale										

Brad lives in Grand Rapids, so he doesn't live elsewhere, and none of the others live in Grand Rapids.

▶ DRAWING CONCLUSIONS

1. Write Clue 2 as a conditional statement in if-then form. Then write the contrapositive of the statement. Explain why the contrapositive of this statement is a helpful clue.

1. if-then form: If Marie exists, then she does not live in Hart's Location; contrapositive: If Marie lives in Hart's Location, then Marie does not exist; *Sample answer:* The contrapositive is a helpful clue because it is clear that Marie exists, therefore she cannot live in Hart's Location.

2. Using Clue 3, what additional information do you need to conclude that Maynard's favorite hobby is playing the guitar? **Maynard lives in Ravenna.**

3. Explain how you can use Clue 1 and Clue 5 to conclude that Brad's favorite hobby is in-line skating. **See margin.**

4. **CRITICAL THINKING** Make up a logic puzzle similar to the one shown above. Be sure that the clues you give make the puzzle solvable. Then trade puzzles with your partner and solve each other's puzzles. **Check puzzles.**

3. From we kn the fa hobby perso in Gra Rapid line s From we kn Brad Grand There Brad's hobby line s

Activity Assessment *Sample answer:*
Draw a grid representing the possibilities. Keep track of the information in the clues by shading the grid in the boxes that represents information that eliminates possibilities. The remaining (non-shaded) areas of the grid represent possible solutions to the puzzle.

2.3 Deductive Reasoning

What *you should learn*

GOAL 1 Use symbolic notation to represent logical statements.

GOAL 2 Form conclusions by applying the laws of logic to true statements, such as statements about a trip to Alabama in **Example 6**.

Why *you should learn it*

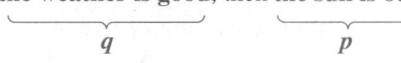

▼ The laws of logic help you with classification. For instance, the Law of Syllogism is used to determine true statements about birds in **Example 5**.

REAL LIFE

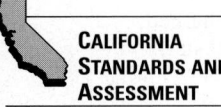

CALIFORNIA STANDARDS AND ASSESSMENT

CA Standards: 1, 3

GOAL 1 USING SYMBOLIC NOTATION

In Lesson 2.1 you learned that a conditional statement has a hypothesis and a conclusion. Conditional statements can be written using symbolic notation, where p represents the hypothesis, q represents the conclusion, and $\rightarrow$ is read as "implies." Here are some examples.

If $\underbrace{\text{the sun is out}}_{p}$, then $\underbrace{\text{the weather is good}}_{q}$.

This conditional statement can be written symbolically as follows:

If p, then q or $p \rightarrow q$.

To form the converse of an "If p, then q" statement, simply switch p and q.

If $\underbrace{\text{the weather is good}}_{q}$, then $\underbrace{\text{the sun is out}}_{p}$.

The converse can be written symbolically as follows:

If q, then p or $q \rightarrow p$.

A biconditional statement can be written using symbolic notation as follows:

If p, then q and if q, then p or $p \leftrightarrow q$.

Most often a biconditional statement is written in this form:

p if and only if q.

EXAMPLE 1 *Using Symbolic Notation*

Let p be "the value of x is -5" and let q be "the absolute value of x is 5."

a. Write $p \rightarrow q$ in words.

b. Write $q \rightarrow p$ in words.

c. Decide whether the biconditional statement $p \leftrightarrow q$ is true.

SOLUTION

a. If the value of x is -5, then the absolute value of x is 5.

b. If the absolute value of x is 5, then the value of x is -5.

c. The conditional statement in part (a) is true, but its converse in part (b) is false. So, the biconditional statement $p \leftrightarrow q$ is false.

1 PLAN

PACING

Basic: 2 days
Average: 2 days
Advanced: 2 days
Block Schedule: 1 block

LESSON OPENER ACTIVITY

An alternative way to approach Lesson 2.3 is to use the Activity Lesson Opener:

- Blackline Master (*Chapter 2 Resource Book,* p. 42)
- Transparency (p. 10)

MEETING INDIVIDUAL NEEDS

- ***Chapter 2 Resource Book***
  Prerequisite Skills Review (p. 5)
  Practice Level A (p. 43)
  Practice Level B (p. 44)
  Practice Level C (p. 45)
  Reteaching with Practice (p. 46)
  Absent Student Catch-Up (p. 48)
  Challenge (p. 51)
- ***Resources in Spanish***
- ***Personal Student Tutor***

NEW-TEACHER SUPPORT

See the Tips for New Teachers on pp. 1–2 of the *Chapter 2 Resource Book* for additional notes about Lesson 2.3.

WARM-UP EXERCISES

Transparency Available

Write the contrapositive of each statement.

1. If it thunders, the golf tournament is canceled. **If the golf tournament is not canceled, it does not thunder.**

2. If $x(x-1)=0$, then $x=0$ or 1. **If x does not equal 0 or 1, then $x(x-1) \neq 0$.**

3. If $m\angle A = 45°$, then $\angle A$ is congruent to $\angle B$. **If $\angle A$ is not congruent to $\angle B$, then $m\angle A \neq 45°$.**

2 TEACH

MOTIVATING THE LESSON
Ask students what they can conclude from the 19th century Lewis Carroll passage: "Dictionaries are useful. Useful books are valuable. Dictionaries are valuable." Point out that the conclusion is valid not because it is easy to understand, but because it follows a certain law, the Law of Syllogism, a topic in this lesson.

EXTRA EXAMPLE 1
Let p be "the value of x is –4" and q be "the square of x is 16."
a. Write $p \to q$ in words.
If the value of x is –4, then the square of x is 16.
b. Write $q \to p$ in words. If the square of x is 16, then the value of x is –4.
c. Decide whether the biconditional statement $p \leftrightarrow q$ is true.
no

EXTRA EXAMPLE 2
Let p be "today is Monday" and q be "there is school."
a. Write the contrapositive of $p \to q$. $\sim q \to \sim p$, If there is no school, then today is not Monday.
b. Write the inverse of $p \to q$.
$\sim p \to \sim q$, If today is not Monday, then there is no school.

CHECKPOINT EXERCISES
For use after Examples 1 and 2:
1. Let p be "a number is divisible by 3" and q be "a number is divisible by 6."
a. Write $p \to q$ in words.
If a number is divisible by 3, then it is divisible by 6.
b. Write $q \to p$ in words.
If a number is divisible by 6, then it is divisible by 3.
c. Decide whether the biconditional statement $p \leftrightarrow q$ is true. no
d. Write the contrapositive of $p \to q$. See right.
e. Write the inverse of $p \to q$. See right.

STUDENT HELP
Study Tip
The negation of a negative statement is a positive statement. This is shown at the right with the statement, "∠3 is not acute."

To write the inverse and contrapositive in symbolic notation, you need to be able to write the negation of a statement symbolically. The symbol for negation (~) is written before the letter. Here are some examples.

STATEMENT	SYMBOL	NEGATION	SYMBOL
∠3 measures 90°.	p	∠3 does not measure 90°.	$\sim p$
∠3 is not acute.	q	∠3 is acute.	$\sim q$

The inverse and contrapositive of $p \to q$ are as follows:

Inverse: $\sim p \to \sim q$

If ∠3 does not measure 90°, then ∠3 is acute.

Contrapositive: $\sim q \to \sim p$

If ∠3 is acute, then ∠3 does not measure 90°.

Notice that the inverse is false, but the contrapositive is true.

EXAMPLE 2 Writing an Inverse and a Contrapositive

STUDENT HELP

HOMEWORK HELP
Visit our Web site www.mcdougallittell.com for extra examples.

Let p be "it is raining" and let q be "the soccer game is canceled."

a. Write the contrapositive of $p \to q$.

b. Write the inverse of $p \to q$.

SOLUTION

a. Contrapositive: $\sim q \to \sim p$

If the soccer game is not canceled, then it is not raining.

b. Inverse: $\sim p \to \sim q$

If it is not raining, then the soccer game is not canceled.

Recall from Lesson 2.1 that a conditional statement is equivalent to its contrapositive and that the converse and inverse are equivalent.

Equivalent Statements
Conditional Statement $p \to q$ If the car will start, then the battery is charged.
Contrapositive $\sim q \to \sim p$ If the battery is not charged, then the car will not start.

Equivalent Statements
Converse $q \to p$ If the battery is charged, then the car will start.
Inverse $\sim p \to \sim q$ If the car will not start, then the battery is not charged.

In the table above the conditional statement and its contrapositive are true. The converse and inverse are false. (Just because a car won't start does not imply that its battery is dead.)

Checkpoint Exercises *Sample answer:*
d. If a number is not divisible by 6, then it is not divisible by 3.
e. If a number is not divisible by 3, then it is not divisible by 6.

GOAL 2 USING THE LAWS OF LOGIC

Deductive reasoning uses facts, definitions, and accepted properties in a logical order to write a **logical argument**. This differs from *inductive reasoning*, in which previous examples and patterns are used to form a conjecture.

EXAMPLE 3 *Using Inductive and Deductive Reasoning*

The following examples show how inductive and deductive reasoning differ.

a. Andrea knows that Robin is a sophomore and Todd is a junior. All the other juniors that Andrea knows are older than Robin. Therefore, Andrea reasons *inductively* that Todd is older than Robin based on past observations.

b. Andrea knows that Todd is older than Chan. She also knows that Chan is older than Robin. Andrea reasons *deductively* that Todd is older than Robin based on accepted statements.

There are two *laws of deductive reasoning*. The first is the **Law of Detachment**, shown below. The **Law of Syllogism** follows on the next page.

LAW OF DETACHMENT

If $p \rightarrow q$ is a true conditional statement and p is true, then q is true.

EXAMPLE 4 *Using the Law of Detachment*

State whether the argument is valid.

a. Jamal knows that if he misses the practice the day before a game, then he will not be a starting player in the game. Jamal misses practice on Tuesday so he concludes that he will not be able to start in the game on Wednesday.

b. If two angles form a linear pair, then they are supplementary; $\angle A$ and $\angle B$ are supplementary. So, $\angle A$ and $\angle B$ form a linear pair.

SOLUTION

a. This logical argument is a valid use of the Law of Detachment. It is given that both a statement $(p \rightarrow q)$ and its hypothesis (p) are true. So, it is valid for Jamal to conclude that the conclusion (q) is true.

b. This logical argument is not a valid use of the Law of Detachment. Given that a statement $(p \rightarrow q)$ and its conclusion (q) are true does not mean the hypothesis (p) is true. The argument implies that all supplementary angles form a linear pair.

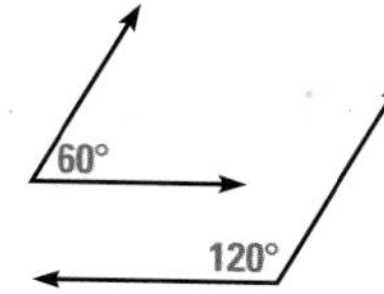

The diagram shows that this is not a valid conclusion.

EXTRA EXAMPLE 3

Is the reasoning inductive or deductive?

a. Josh knows that Brand X computers cost less than Brand Y computers. All other brands that Josh knows of cost less than Brand X. Josh reasons that Brand Y costs more than all other brands. **inductive**

b. Josh knows that Brand X computers cost less than Brand Y computers. He also knows that Brand Y computers cost less than Brand Z. Josh reasons that Brand X costs less than Brand Z. **deductive**

EXTRA EXAMPLE 4

State whether the argument is valid.

a. Michael knows that if he does not do his chores in the morning, he will not be allowed to play video games later the same day. Michael does not play video games on Friday afternoon. So Michael did not do his chores on Friday morning. **not valid**

b. If two angles are vertical, then they are congruent. $\angle ABC$ and $\angle DBE$ are vertical. So $\angle ABC$ and $\angle DBE$ are congruent. **valid**

CHECKPOINT EXERCISES

For use after Examples 3 and 4:

1. State whether the argument is valid.

a. Sarah knows that all sophomores take driver education in her school. Hank takes driver education. So Hank is a sophomore. **not valid**

b. If $m\angle ABC < 90°$, then $\angle ABC$ is an acute angle. $m\angle ABC = 42°$. So $\angle ABC$ is an acute angle. **valid**

EXTRA EXAMPLE 5

Write some conditional statements that can be made from the following true statements using the Law of Syllogism.

1. If a fish swims at 68 mi/h, then it swims at 110 km/h.
2. If a fish can swim at 110 km/h, then it is a sailfish.
3. If a fish is the largest species of fish, then it is a great white shark.
4. If a fish weighs over 2000 lb, then it is the largest species of fish.
5. If a fish is the fastest species of fish, then it can reach speeds of 68 mi/h.

1. If a fish swims at 68 mi/h, then it is a sailfish. (1 and 2)
2. If a fish is the fastest species of fish, then it is a sailfish. (1, 2, and 5)
3. If a fish weighs over 2000 lb, then it is a great white shark. (3 and 4)

EXTRA EXAMPLE 6

Casey goes to a music store. Given the following true statements, can you conclude that Casey buys a CD? If Casey goes to a music store, she shops for a CD. If Casey shops for a CD, then Casey will buy a CD. yes

CHECKPOINT EXERCISES

For use after Examples 5 and 6:

1. Write a conditional statement that can be made from the following true statements using the Law of Syllogism. If a plant is the largest plant on Earth, then the plant is a Sierra Redwood tree. If a plant is a Sierra Redwood tree, then the plant can weigh 1,800,000 kg. **If a plant is the largest plant on Earth, then the plant can weigh 1,800,000 kg.**

CLOSURE QUESTION

What statement is necessary to apply the Law of Detachment to the statement: If today is Saturday, then tomorrow is Sunday. **Today is Saturday.** Give the valid conclusion. **Tomorrow is Sunday.**

FOCUS ON CAREERS

ZOOLOGY

Zoologists use facts about a bird's appearance to classify it. Ornithology is the branch of zoology that studies birds.

CAREER LINK
www.mcdougallittell.com

LAW OF SYLLOGISM

If $p \rightarrow q$ and $q \rightarrow r$ are true conditional statements, then $p \rightarrow r$ is true.

EXAMPLE 5 *Using the Law of Syllogism*

ZOOLOGY Write some conditional statements that can be made from the following true statements using the Law of Syllogism.

1. If a bird is the fastest bird on land, then it is the largest of all birds.
2. If a bird is the largest of all birds, then it is an ostrich.
3. If a bird is a bee hummingbird, then it is the smallest of all birds.
4. If a bird is the largest of all birds, then it is flightless.
5. If a bird is the smallest bird, then it has a nest the size of a walnut half-shell.

SOLUTION

Here are the conditional statements that use the Law of Syllogism.

a. If a bird is the fastest bird on land, then it is an ostrich. (Use 1 and 2.)

b. If a bird is a bee hummingbird, then it has a nest the size of a walnut half-shell. (Use 3 and 5.)

c. If a bird is the fastest bird on land, then it is flightless. (Use 1 and 4.)

EXAMPLE 6 *Using the Laws of Deductive Reasoning*

Over the summer, Mike visited Alabama. Given the following true statements, can you conclude that Mike visited the Civil Rights Memorial?

If Mike visits Alabama, then he will spend a day in Montgomery.

If Mike spends a day in Montgomery, then he will visit the Civil Rights Memorial.

Civil Rights Memorial in Montgomery, Alabama

SOLUTION

Let p, q, and r represent the following.

p: Mike visits Alabama.

q: Mike spends a day in Montgomery.

r: Mike visits the Civil Rights Memorial.

Because $p \rightarrow q$ is true and $q \rightarrow r$ is true, you can apply the Law of Syllogism to conclude that $p \rightarrow r$ is true.

If Mike visits Alabama, then he will visit the Civil Rights Memorial.

▶ You are told that Mike visited Alabama, which means p is true. Using the Law of Detachment, you can conclude that he visited the Civil Rights Memorial.

GUIDED PRACTICE

Vocabulary Check ✓

1. If the statements $p \rightarrow q$ and $q \rightarrow r$ are true, then the statement $p \rightarrow r$ is true by the Law of ___?___. If the statement $p \rightarrow q$ is true and p is true, then q is true by the Law of ___?___. **Syllogism; Detachment**

Concept Check ✓

2. State whether the following argument uses inductive or deductive reasoning: "If it is Friday, then Kendra's family has pizza for dinner. Today is Friday, therefore, Kendra's family will have pizza for dinner." **deductive reasoning**

Skill Check ✓

3. Given the notation for a conditional statement is $p \rightarrow q$, what statement is represented by $q \rightarrow p$? **converse**
4. A conditional statement is defined in symbolic notation as $p \rightarrow q$. Use symbolic notation to write the inverse of $p \rightarrow q$. $\sim p \rightarrow \sim q$
5. Write the contrapositive of the following statement: "If you don't enjoy scary movies, then you wouldn't have liked this one." **If you like this movie, then you enjoy scary movies.**
6. If a ray bisects a right angle, then the congruent angles formed are complementary. In the diagram, $\angle ABC$ is a right angle. Are $\angle ABD$ and $\angle CBD$ complementary? Explain your reasoning. **See margin.**

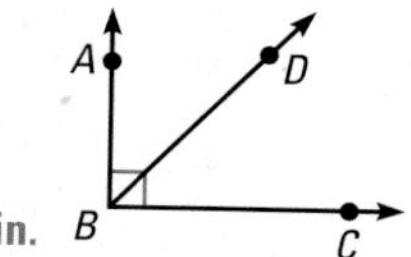

7. If $f \rightarrow g$ and $g \rightarrow h$ are true statements, and f is true, does it follow that h is true? Explain. **See margin.**

6. Yes. Ray BD bisects $\angle ABC$ and forms the angles $\angle ABD$ and $\angle CBD$. Therefore $\angle ABD$ and $\angle CBD$ are complementary.

7. Yes. If f is true, then by the Law of Detachment, g is true. If g is true, then by the Law of Detachment, h is true. Therefore if f is true, then h is true.

PRACTICE AND APPLICATIONS

STUDENT HELP

Extra Practice to help you master skills is on p. 805.

WRITING STATEMENTS **Using p and q below, write the symbolic statement in words.** **8–13. See margin.**

p: Points X, Y, and Z are collinear.

q: Points X, Y, and Z lie on the same line.

8. $q \rightarrow p$
9. $\sim q$
10. $\sim p$
11. $\sim p \rightarrow \sim q$
12. $p \leftrightarrow q$
13. $\sim q \rightarrow \sim p$

WRITING INVERSE AND CONTRAPOSITIVE **Given that the statement is of the form $p \rightarrow q$, write p and q. Then write the inverse and the contrapositive of $p \rightarrow q$ both symbolically and in words.** **14–20. See margin.**

14. If Jed gets a C on the exam, then he will get an A for the quarter.
15. If Alberto finds a summer job, then he will buy a car.
16. If the fuse has blown, then the light will not go on.
17. If the car is running, then the key is in the ignition.
18. If you dial 911, then there is an emergency.
19. If Gina walks to the store, then she will buy a newspaper.
20. If it is not raining, then Petra will ride her bike to school.

STUDENT HELP

HOMEWORK HELP
Example 1: Exs. 8–13
Example 2: Exs. 14–20
Example 3: Exs. 21, 22
Example 4: Exs. 23–25
Example 5: Exs. 30–48
Example 6: Exs. 30–48

3 APPLY

ASSIGNMENT GUIDE

BASIC
Day 1: pp. 91–93 Exs. 8–42 even, 45–48
Day 2: pp. 91–95 Exs. 9–41 odd, 51, 56–62 even, Quiz 1 Exs. 1–5

AVERAGE
Day 1: pp. 91–93 Exs. 8–42 even, 45–48
Day 2: pp. 91–95 Exs. 9–41 odd, 49–51, 56–62 even, Quiz 1 Exs. 1–5

ADVANCED
Day 1: pp. 91–93 Exs. 8–42 even, 45–48
Day 2: pp. 91–95 Exs. 9–41 odd, 44, 49–55, 56–62 even, Quiz 1 Exs. 1–5

BLOCK SCHEDULE
pp. 91–95 Exs. 8–42, 45–51, 56–62 even, Quiz 1 Exs. 1–5

EXERCISE LEVELS

Level A: ***Easier***
8–13, 26–35
Level B: ***More Difficult***
14–25, 36–43, 45–51
Level C: ***Most Difficult***
44, 52–55

HOMEWORK CHECK

To quickly check student understanding of key concepts, go over the following exercises: Exs. 10, 16, 22, 24, 30, 34, 38, 46. See also the Daily Homework Quiz:

- Blackline Master (*Chapter 2 Resource Book,* p. 55)
- Transparency (p. 13)

COMMON ERROR

EXERCISES 8–13 Watch for students who confuse the symbol ≈ meaning approximately with the symbol ~. Stress that ~ represents a negation in symbolic logic.

8–20. See Additional Answers beginning on page AA1.

MATHEMATICAL REASONING
EXERCISE 31 If the Law of Syllogism applies to an argument, then the argument is valid. The actual statement may not always be true. Ask students how this applies to the answer for Ex. 31. **If the stereo is on, the volume isn't always necessarily loud. The statement is assumed to be true, however, and this makes the argument valid.**

ENGLISH LEARNERS
EXERCISES 33–35 English learners may be less familiar than English proficient students with the meanings of helping verbs—*must, may, might, can, could, should*—as well as the relative meanings of adverbs used to express frequency—*often, frequently, sometimes, occasionally, seldom.*

26. It can be concluded that $y = 3$. Since the hypothesis is true, $3 > 2 \times 3 - 10$, the conclusion is true, $x = y$.
27. It can be concluded that $y \leq 3$. Since the hypothesis is true, $2 \times 3 + 3 < 4 \times 3 < 5 \times 3$, the conclusion is true, $y \leq x$.
28. It can be concluded that $y = 18$. Since the hypothesis is true, $4 \times 3 \geq 12$, the conclusion is true, $y = 6x$.
29. No conclusions can be made because the hypothesis is not true for the given value of x.

21. inductive reasoning; Inductive reasoning depends on previous examples and patterns to form a conjecture. Dana came to her conslusion based on previous examples.
22. deductive reasoning; Deductive reasoning is based on logic and order. If Marcus is a 16–18-year-old with a license in Nevada, then Marcus must have taken the required driver education.
23. valid; p: the sum of the measures of $\angle A$ and $\angle C$ is 90°.
q: $\angle A$ and $\angle C$ are complementary.
$p \rightarrow q$ is true and p is true, so q is true.
24. not valid; $\angle A$ and $\angle C$ are complementary, but they are not adjacent.
25. valid; It can be concluded that $\angle B$ is acute, since the measure of $\angle B$ is between the measures of $\angle A$ and $\angle C$.

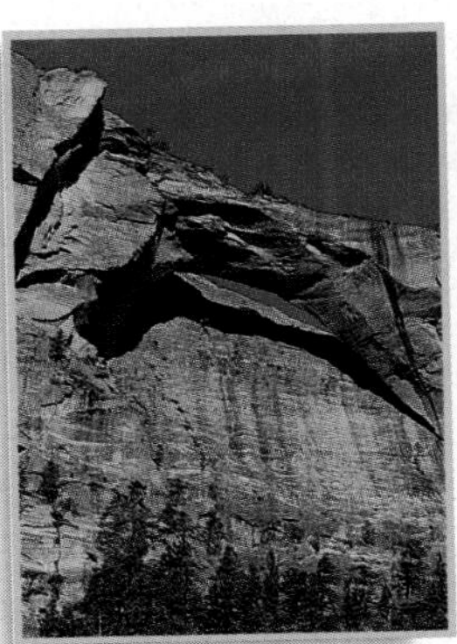
The Kolob Arch mentioned in Ex. 34, spans 310 feet.

LOGICAL REASONING **Decide whether *inductive* or *deductive* reasoning is used to reach the conclusion. Explain your reasoning.**

21. For the past three Wednesdays the cafeteria has served macaroni and cheese for lunch. Dana concludes that the cafeteria will serve macaroni and cheese for lunch this Wednesday.

22. If you live in Nevada and are between the ages of 16 and 18, then you must take driver's education to get your license. Marcus lives in Nevada, is 16 years old, and has his driver's license. Therefore, Marcus took driver's education.

USING THE LAW OF DETACHMENT **State whether the argument is valid. Explain your reasoning.** **23–25. See margin.**

23. If the sum of the measures of two angles is 90°, then the two angles are complementary. Because $m\angle A + m\angle C = 90°$, $\angle A$ and $\angle C$ are complementary.

24. If two adjacent angles form a right angle, then the two angles are complementary. Because $\angle A$ and $\angle C$ are complementary, $\angle A$ and $\angle C$ are adjacent.

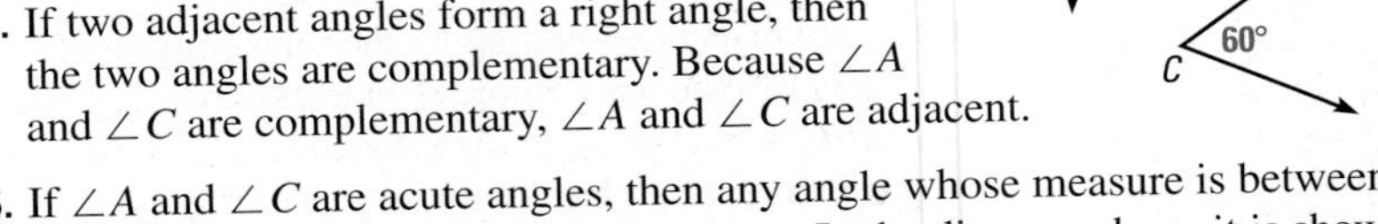

25. If $\angle A$ and $\angle C$ are acute angles, then any angle whose measure is between the measures of $\angle A$ and $\angle C$ is also acute. In the diagram above it is shown that $m\angle A \leq m\angle B \leq m\angle C$, so $\angle B$ must be acute.

USING ALGEBRA **State whether any conclusions can be made using the true statement, given that $x = 3$.** **26–29. See margin.**

26. If $x > 2x - 10$, then $x = y$.

27. If $2x + 3 < 4x < 5x$, then $y \leq x$.

28. If $4x \geq 12$, then $y = 6x$.

29. If $x + 3 = 10$, then $y = x$.

MAKING CONCLUSIONS **Use the Law of Syllogism to write the statement that follows from the pair of true statements.**

30. If the sun is shining, then it is a beautiful day.
If it is a beautiful day, then we will have a picnic.
If the sun is shining, then we will have a picnic.

31. If the stereo is on, then the volume is loud.
If the volume is loud, then the neighbors will complain.
If the stereo is on, then the neighbors will complain.

32. If Ginger goes to the movies, then Marta will go to the movies.
If Yumi goes to the movies, then Ginger will go to the movies.
If Yumi goes to the movies, then Marta will go to the movies.

USING DEDUCTIVE REASONING **Select the word that makes the concluding statement true.**

33. The Oak Terrace apartment building does not allow dogs. Serena lives at Oak Terrace. So, Serena (must, may, may not) keep a dog. **may not**

34. The Kolob Arch is the world's widest natural arch. The world's widest arch is in Zion National Park. So, the Kolob Arch (is, may be, is not) in Zion. **is**

35. Zion National Park is in Utah. Jeremy spent a week in Utah. So, Jeremy (must have, may have, never) visited Zion National Park. **may have**

37. $\angle 1$ and $\angle 2$ are supplementary angles, therefore their measures add up to 180°.

38. $\angle 1$ and $\angle 4$ are congruent angles, therefore their measures are equal.

39. $\angle 4$ and $\angle 3$ are vertical angles, therefore their measures are equal.

40. $\angle 3$ and $\angle 5$ are congruent angles, therefore their measures are equal.

41. $\angle 5$ and $\angle 6$ are supplementary angles, therefore their measures add up to 180°.

STUDENT HELP

HOMEWORK HELP Visit our Web site www.mcdougallittell.com for help with problem solving in Exs. 45–48.

45. True. The mall is open, therefore Angela and Diego went shopping, and therefore Diego bought a pretzel.

46. True. The mall is open, therefore Angela and Diego went shopping.

47. False. The mall is open, therefore Angela and Diego went shopping, and therefore Angela bought a pizza. We cannot conclude that she also bought a pretzel.

48. False. The mall is open, therefore Angela and Diego went shopping, and therefore Diego bought a pretzel and Angela bought a pizza. We cannot conclude whether or not Diego had some of Angela's pizza.

USING THE LAWS OF LOGIC In Exercises 36–42, use the diagram to give a reason for each true statement. In the diagram, $m\angle 2 = 115°$, $\angle 1 \cong \angle 4$, $\angle 3 \cong \angle 5$.

36. p_1: $m\angle 2 = 115°$ given

37. $p_1 \rightarrow p_2$: If $m\angle 2 = 115°$, then $m\angle 1 = 65°$.

38. $p_2 \rightarrow p_3$: If $m\angle 1 = 65°$, then $m\angle 4 = 65°$.

39. $p_3 \rightarrow p_4$: If $m\angle 4 = 65°$, then $m\angle 3 = 65°$.

40. $p_4 \rightarrow p_5$: If $m\angle 3 = 65°$, then $m\angle 5 = 65°$.

41. $p_5 \rightarrow p_6$: If $m\angle 5 = 65°$, then $m\angle 6 = 115°$.

42. $p_1 \rightarrow p_6$: If $m\angle 2 = 115°$, then $m\angle 6 = 115°$. See margin.

43. *Writing* Describe a time in your life when you use deductive reasoning. See margin.

44. **CRITICAL THINKING** Describe an instance where inductive reasoning can lead to an incorrect conclusion. See margin.

LOGICAL REASONING In Exercises 45–48, use the true statements to determine whether the conclusion is *true* or *false*. Explain your reasoning.

- If Diego goes shopping, then he will buy a pretzel.
- If the mall is open, then Angela and Diego will go shopping.
- If Angela goes shopping, then she will buy a pizza.
- The mall is open.

45. Diego bought a pretzel.

46. Angela and Diego went shopping.

47. Angela bought a pretzel.

48. Diego had some of Angela's pizza.

49. **ROBOTICS** Because robots can withstand higher temperatures than humans, a fire-fighting robot is under development. Write the following statements about the robot in order. Then use the Law of Syllogism to complete the statement, "If there is a fire, then _?_." D, B, A, E, C; the robot extinguishes the fire.

A. If the robot sets off a fire alarm, then it concludes there is a fire.

B. If the robot senses high levels of smoke and heat, then it sets off a fire alarm.

C. If the robot locates the fire, then the robot extinguishes the fire.

D. If there is a fire, then the robot senses high levels of smoke and heat.

E. If the robot concludes there is a fire, then it locates the fire.

50. **DOGS** Use the true statements to form other conditional statements.

A. If a dog is a gazehound, then it hunts by sight.

B. If a hound bays (makes long barks while hunting), then it is a scent hound.

C. If a dog is a foxhound, then it does not hunt primarily by sight.

D. If a dog is a coonhound, then it bays when it hunts.

E. If a dog is a greyhound, then it is a gazehound.

Sample answers: If a dog is a greyhound, then it hunts by sight; If a dog is a coonhound, then it is a scent hound.

! COMMON ERROR

EXERCISES 43–44 Some students may confuse inductive and deductive reasoning. These exercises should help clarify whether students have the definitions correct.

STUDENT HELP NOTES

Homework Help Students can find help for Exs. 45–48 at **www.mcdougallittell.com.** The information can be printed out for students who don't have access to the Internet.

42. $p_1 \rightarrow p_3$ by the Law of Syllogism, from Exs. 36–38; then $p_1 \rightarrow p_4$ (with Ex. 39), then $p_1 \rightarrow p_5$ (with Ex. 40), then $p_1 \rightarrow p_6$ (with Ex. 41) by applying the Law of Syllogism each time.

43. *Sample answer:* When I am deciding whether I am late for school. If I am late for school if I arrive after 8:00 A.M., and I get to school at 8:05 A.M., then I can deduce that I am late for school.

44. *Sample answer:* The train always runs once an hour during the week when you go to school. Assuming that the schedule is the same on Sunday may be incorrect.

ADDITIONAL PRACTICE AND RETEACHING

For Lesson 2.3:

- Practice Levels A, B, and C (*Chapter 2 Resource Book,* p. 43)
- Reteaching with Practice (*Chapter 2 Resource Book,* p. 46)
- See Lesson 2.3 of the *Personal Student Tutor*

For more Mixed Review:

- Search the *Test and Practice Generator* for key words or specific lessons.

4 ASSESS

DAILY HOMEWORK QUIZ

Transparency Available

Using p and q below, write each statement as directed.

p: This animal has stripes.

q: This animal is a tiger.

1. $\sim p$ **This animal has no stripes.**
2. Write the inverse of $p \to q$ in symbols and words. **$\sim p \to \sim q$; if this animal does not have stripes, then it is not a tiger.**
3. Write the contrapositive of $p \to q$ in symbols and words. **$\sim q \to \sim p$; if this animal is not a tiger, then it does not have stripes.**

Use the Law of Syllogism to write the statement that follows from the pair of true statements.

4. If it is Friday, then tomorrow is Saturday. If it is Saturday, we will swim. **If it is Friday, then tomorrow we will swim.**

EXTRA CHALLENGE NOTE

Challenge problems for Lesson 2.3 are available in **blackline** format in the *Chapter 2 Resource Book,* p. 51 and at **www.mcdougallittell.com.**

ADDITIONAL TEST PREPARATION

1. **OPEN ENDED** Give an example of a logical argument about rain that uses the Law of Detachment and the Law of Syllogism. ***Sample answer:*** **If it is raining outside, then the sun isn't shining. If the sun isn't shining, then it is chilly. So, if it is raining outside, then it is chilly. It is raining. Conclusion: it is chilly.**

Test Preparation 

51. a. If Jana wins the contest, then Jana gets two free tickets to the concert.

b. $q \to p$; If Jana gets two free tickets to the concert, then Jana won the contest.

c. $\sim q \to \sim p$; If Jana does not get two free tickets to the concert, then Jana did not win the contest.

d. converse

★ Challenge

e. To conclude that Jana gets two free tickets to the concert, it is necessary to know whether p, Jana wins the contest, is true.

f. *Sample answer:* If Jana gets two free tickets to the concert, then she will bring Greg to the concert.

EXTRA CHALLENGE

www.mcdougallittell.com

51. **MULTI-STEP PROBLEM** Let p be "Jana wins the contest" and q be "Jana gets two free tickets to the concert."
   a. Write $p \to q$ in words.
   b. Write the converse of $p \to q$, both in words and symbols.
   c. Write the contrapositive of $p \to q$, both in words and symbols.
   d. Suppose Jana gets two free tickets to the concert but does not win the contest. Is this a counterexample to the converse or to the contrapositive?
   e. What do you need to know about the conditional statement from part (a) so the Law of Detachment can be used to conclude that Jana gets two free tickets to the concert?
   f. *Writing* Use the statement in part (a) to write a second statement that uses the Law of Syllogism to reach a valid conclusion.

CONTRAPOSITIVES **Use the true statements to answer the questions.**

- If a creature is a fly, then it has six legs.
- If a creature has six legs, then it is an insect.

52. Use symbolic notation to describe the statements. **$p \to q$; $q \to r$**
53. Use the statements and the Law of Syllogism to write a conditional statement, both in words and symbols. **$p \to r$; If a creature is a fly, then it is an insect.**
54. Write the contrapositive of each statement, both in words and symbols.
55. Using the contrapositives and the Law of Syllogism, write a conditional statement. Is the statement true? Does the Law of Syllogism work for contrapositives?

54. **$\sim q \to \sim p$: If a creature does not have six legs, then it is not a fly; $\sim r \to \sim q$: If a creature is not an insect, then it does not have six legs.**

55. **If a creature is not an insect, then it is not a fly; The statement is true; The Law of Syllogism works for contrapositives.**

MIXED REVIEW

NAMING POINTS **Use the diagram to name a point.** (Review 1.2)

56. A third point collinear with A and C **K**
57. A fourth point coplanar with A, C, and E ***Sample answer: F***
58. A point coplanar with A and B, but not coplanar with A, B, and C ***Sample answer: G***
59. A point coplanar with A and C, but not coplanar with E and F ***Sample answer: B***

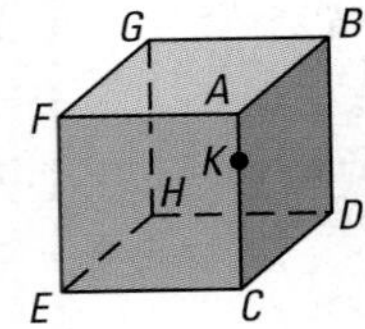

FINDING ANGLE MEASURES **Find $m\angle ABD$ given that $\angle ABC$ and $\angle CBD$ are adjacent angles.** (Review 1.4 for 2.4)

60. $m\angle ABC = 20°$, $m\angle CBD = 10°$ **30°**
61. $m\angle CBD = 13°$, $m\angle ABC = 28°$ **41°**
62. $m\angle ABC = 3y + 1$, $m\angle CBD = 12 - y$ **$2y + 13$**
63. $m\angle CBD = 11 + 2f - g$, $m\angle ABC = 5g - 4 + f$ **$3f + 4g + 7$**

QUIZ 1

1. See margin.
2. if-then form: If a time period is a century, then it is a period of 100 years; converse: If a time period is 100 years, then it is a century; both the statement and its converse are true so they can be combined to form a biconditional statement: A time period is a century if and only if it is a period of 100 years.
3. See margin.
4. Yes; John backs the car out, therefore he drives into the fence.

Write the true statement in if-then form and write its converse. Determine whether the statement and its converse can be combined to form a true biconditional statement. (Lesson 2.1 and Lesson 2.2)

1. If today is June 4, then tomorrow is June 5.
2. A century is a period of 100 years.
3. Two circles are congruent if they have the same diameter.

LOGICAL REASONING **Use the true statements to answer the questions.** (Lesson 2.3)

- If John drives into the fence, then John's father will be angry.
- If John backs the car out, then John will drive into the fence.
- John backs the car out.

4. Does John drive into the fence?
5. Is John's father angry?

5. Yes; John backs the car out, therefore he drives into the fence, and therefore his father is angry

MATH & History

History of Recreational Logic Puzzles

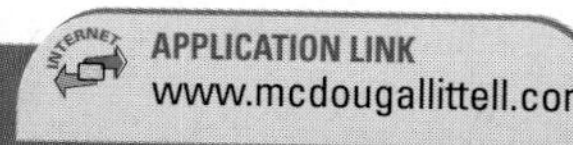

THEN

IN THE 1600S, puzzles involving "formal" logic first became popular in Europe. However, logic has been a part of games such as mancala and chess for thousands of years.

NOW

TODAY, logic games and puzzles are a popular pastime throughout the world. Lewis Carroll, author of *Alice in Wonderland*, was also a mathematician who wrote books on logic. The following problem is based on notes he wrote in his diary in the 1890s.

A says B lies; B says C lies; C says A and B lie.
Who is telling the truth? Who is lying?

Complete the exercises to solve the problem.

See margin.

1. If A is telling the truth, then B is lying. What can you conclude about C's statement?
2. Assume A is telling the truth. Explain how this leads to a contradiction.
3. Who is telling the truth? Who is lying? How do you know? (*Hint*: For C to be lying, only one other person (A or B) must be telling the truth.)

c. 1400 BC — Game of mancala is played in Thebes, Egypt.

c. 600 — First recorded chess game

1865 — Lewis Carroll writes *Alice in Wonderland.*

1997 — Computer beats World Chess Champion.

ADDITIONAL RESOURCES

An alternative Quiz for Lessons 2.1–2.3 is available in the *Chapter 2 Resource Book,* p. 52.

A **blackline** master with additional Math & History exercises is available in the *Chapter 2 Resource Book,* p. 50.

1. The statement is already in if-then form; converse: If tomorrow is June 5, then today is June 4. Both the statement and its converse are true, so they can be combined to form a biconditional statement: Today is June 4 if and only if tomorrow is June 5.
3. If-then form: If two circles have the same diameter, then they are congruent; converse: If two circles are congruent, then they have the same diameter; Both the statement and its converse are true, so they can be combined to form a biconditional statement: Two circles are congruent if and only if they have the same diameter.

Math & History

1. If A is telling the truth, then B is lying. Therefore, B's statement that C is lying is itself a lie, so C must be telling the truth.
2. Begin by assuming that A is telling the truth. Then B must be lying. If B is lying, then C must be telling the truth. But C says that A and B are both lying, which contradicts the original assumption that A is telling the truth. So the original assumption is false and A is lying.
3. From Exercise 2, you know that A is lying. So B must be telling the truth. C says that both A and B are lying, but C's statement cannot be true because B is telling the truth. So B is telling the truth and A and C are both lying.

1 PLAN

PACING
Basic: 1 day
Average: 1 day
Advanced: 1 day
Block Schedule: 0.5 block with 2.5

LESSON OPENER ACTIVITY

An alternative way to approach Lesson 2.4 is to use the Activity Lesson Opener:

- Blackline Master (*Chapter 2 Resource Book,* p. 56)
- Transparency (p. 11)

MEETING INDIVIDUAL NEEDS

- ***Chapter 2 Resource Book***
  Prerequisite Skills Review (p. 5)
  Practice Level A (p. 57)
  Practice Level B (p. 58)
  Practice Level C (p. 59)
  Reteaching with Practice (p. 60)
  Absent Student Catch-Up (p. 62)
  Challenge (p. 65)
- ***Resources in Spanish***
- ***Personal Student Tutor***

NEW-TEACHER SUPPORT

See the Tips for New Teachers on pp. 1–2 of the *Chapter 2 Resource Book* for additional notes about Lesson 2.4.

WARM-UP EXERCISES

Transparency Available

Solve each equation.

1. $3x = 27$ 9
2. $x + 6 = -17$ -23
3. $x - 9 = 18$ 27
4. $\frac{2}{3}x = 6$ 9
5. $-x = 4$ -4

2.4 Reasoning with Properties from Algebra

What you should learn

GOAL 1 Use properties from algebra.

GOAL 2 Use properties of length and measure to justify segment and angle relationships, such as the angles at the turns of a racetrack, as in **Example 5** and **Ex. 28**.

Why you should learn it

▼ Using algebraic properties helps you when rewriting a formula, such as the formula for an athlete's target heart rate in **Example 3**.

REAL LIFE

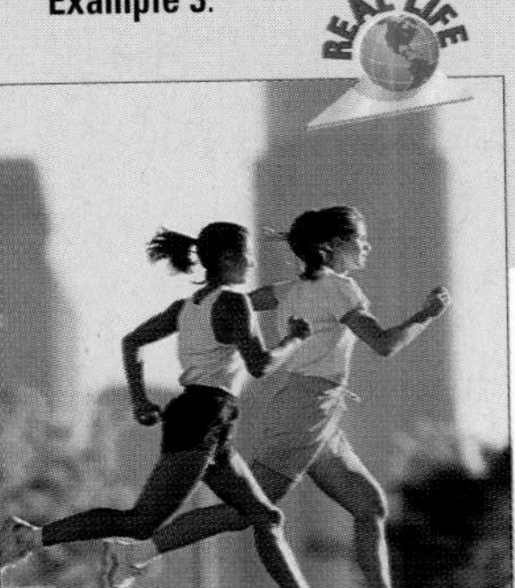

GOAL 1 USING PROPERTIES FROM ALGEBRA

Many properties from algebra concern the equality of real numbers. Several of these are summarized in the following list.

ALGEBRAIC PROPERTIES OF EQUALITY

Let a, b, and c be real numbers.

ADDITION PROPERTY	If $a = b$, then $a + c = b + c$.
SUBTRACTION PROPERTY	If $a = b$, then $a - c = b - c$.
MULTIPLICATION PROPERTY	If $a = b$, then $ac = bc$.
DIVISION PROPERTY	If $a = b$ and $c \neq 0$, then $a \div c = b \div c$.
REFLEXIVE PROPERTY	For any real number a, $a = a$.
SYMMETRIC PROPERTY	If $a = b$, then $b = a$.
TRANSITIVE PROPERTY	If $a = b$ and $b = c$, then $a = c$.
SUBSTITUTION PROPERTY	If $a = b$, then a can be substituted for b in any equation or expression.

Properties of equality along with other properties from algebra, such as the *distributive property,*

$$a(b + c) = ab + ac$$

can be used to solve equations. For instance, you can use the subtraction property of equality to solve the equation $x + 3 = 7$. By subtracting 3 from each side of the equation, you obtain $x = 4$.

EXAMPLE 1 ***Writing Reasons***

Solve $5x - 18 = 3x + 2$ and write a reason for each step.

Using Algebra

SOLUTION

$5x - 18 = 3x + 2$	**Given**
$2x - 18 = 2$	**Subtraction property of equality**
$2x = 20$	**Addition property of equality**
$x = 10$	**Division property of equality**

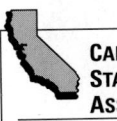

CALIFORNIA STANDARDS AND ASSESSMENT

CA Standards: 3
SAT9 Task 1: Objs. 7, 26
SAT9 Task 2: Objs. 4, 26

EXAMPLE 2 Writing Reasons

STUDENT HELP

INTERNET HOMEWORK HELP Visit our Web site www.mcdougallittell.com for extra examples.

Solve $55z - 3(9z + 12) = -64$ and write a reason for each step.

SOLUTION

$55z - 3(9z + 12) = -64$	Given
$55z - 27z - 36 = -64$	Distributive property
$28z - 36 = -64$	Simplify.
$28z = -28$	Addition property of equality
$z = -1$	Division property of equality

EXAMPLE 3 Using Properties in Real Life

REAL LIFE **FITNESS** Before exercising, you should find your target heart rate. This is the rate at which you achieve an effective workout while not placing too much strain on your heart. Your target heart rate r (in beats per minute) can be determined from your age a (in years) using the equation $a = 220 - \frac{10}{7}r$.

a. Solve the formula for r and write a reason for each step.

b. Use the result to find the target heart rate for a 16 year old.

c. Find the target heart rate for the following ages: 20, 30, 40, 50, and 60. What happens to the target heart rate as a person gets older?

SOLUTION

a.

$a = 220 - \frac{10}{7}r$	Given
$a + \frac{10}{7}r = 220$	Addition property of equality
$\frac{10}{7}r = 220 - a$	Subtraction property of equality
$r = \frac{7}{10}(220 - a)$	Multiplication property of equality

b. Using $a = 16$, the target heart rate is:

$r = \frac{7}{10}(220 - a)$	Given
$r = \frac{7}{10}(220 - 16)$	Substitute 16 for a.
$r = 142.8$	Simplify.

▶ The target heart rate for a 16 year old is about 143 beats per minute.

c. From the table, the target heart rate appears to decrease as a person ages.

Age	20	30	40	50	60
Rate	140	133	126	119	112

2 TEACH

EXTRA EXAMPLES 1–2

Solve $3x + 12 = 8x - 18$ and write a reason for each step.

Statements (Reasons)

$3x + 12 = 8x - 18$ (Given)

$12 = 5x - 18$ (Subt. prop. of =)

$30 = 5x$ (Addition prop. of equality)

$6 = x$ (Division prop. of equality)

EXTRA EXAMPLE 3

A child's dose c for a medicine with an adult dose of 500 mg can be found by using the child's age a in years in the formula $a = \frac{24}{500}c - 1$.

a. Solve the formula for c and write a reason for each step.

Statements (Reasons)

$a = \frac{24}{500}c - 1$ (Given)

$a + 1 = \frac{24}{500}c$ (Add. prop. of =)

$\frac{500}{24}(a + 1) = c$ (Mult. prop. of =)

b. Use the result to find the child's dosage for an 8-year-old. 187.5 mg

CHECKPOINT EXERCISES

For use after Examples 1–3:

1. The formula to convert Fahrenheit to Celsius is $C = \frac{5}{9}(F - 32)$.

a. Solve the formula for F and write the reason for each step.

Statements (Reasons)

$C = \frac{5}{9}(F - 32)$ (Given)

$\frac{9}{5}C = F - 32$ (× prop. of =)

$\frac{9}{5}C + 32 = F$ (+ prop. of =)

b. Use the result to find the Fahrenheit temperature at 24° C. 75.2° F

EXTRA EXAMPLE 4

$AC = BD$. Verify that $AB = CD$.

A B C D

Statements (Reasons)

$AC = BD$ (Given)
$BC = BC$ (Refl. prop. of =)
$AC - BC = BD - BC$ (– prop. of =)
$AB + BC = AC$; $BC + CD = BD$ (Segment Addition Post.)
$AB = AC - BC$; $CD = BD - BC$ (Subtraction prop. of equality)
$AB = CD$ (Subs. prop. of =)

EXTRA EXAMPLE 5

A baseball diamond is shown below.

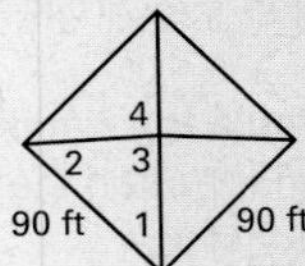

The pitcher's mound is at ∠3. Use the information to find $m\angle 4$:
$m\angle 1 + m\angle 2 + m\angle 3 = 180°$
$m\angle 1 + m\angle 2 = 93°$
$m\angle 3 + m\angle 4 = 180°$

Statements (Reasons)

$m\angle 1 + m\angle 2 + m\angle 3 = 180°$ (Given)
$m\angle 1 + m\angle 2 = 93°$ (Given)
$93° + m\angle 3 = 180°$ (Subs. prop. of =)
$m\angle 3 = 87°$ (– prop. of =)
$m\angle 3 + m\angle 4 = 180°$ (Given)
$87° + m\angle 4 = 180°$ (Subs. prop. of =)
$m\angle 4 = 93°$ (– prop. of =)

CHECKPOINT EXERCISES

For use after Examples 4 and 5:

1. $m\angle ABC = m\angle DBE$. Show that $m\angle ABD = m\angle CBE$.

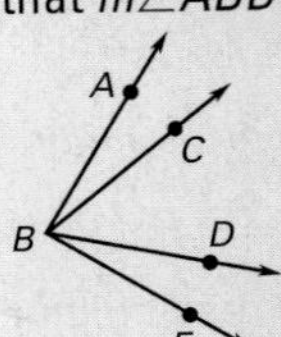

See answer below.

CLOSURE QUESTION

If $AB = CD$, and $CD = EF$, write a valid statement about AB and EF and give a reason. $AB = EF$; Transitive prop. of equality.

GOAL 2 USING PROPERTIES OF LENGTH AND MEASURE

The algebraic properties of equality can be used in geometry.

CONCEPT SUMMARY PROPERTIES OF EQUALITY

	SEGMENT LENGTH	ANGLE MEASURE
REFLEXIVE	For any segment AB, $AB = AB$.	For any angle A, $m\angle A = m\angle A$.
SYMMETRIC	If $AB = CD$, then $CD = AB$.	If $m\angle A = m\angle B$, then $m\angle B = m\angle A$.
TRANSITIVE	If $AB = CD$ and $CD = EF$, then $AB = EF$.	If $m\angle A = m\angle B$ and $m\angle B = m\angle C$, then $m\angle A = m\angle C$.

EXAMPLE 4 Using Properties of Length

Logical Reasoning

In the diagram, $AB = CD$. The argument below shows that $AC = BD$.

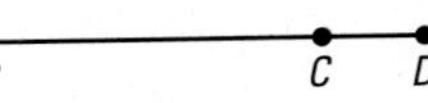

$AB = CD$	Given
$AB + BC = BC + CD$	Addition property of equality
$AC = AB + BC$	Segment Addition Postulate
$BD = BC + CD$	Segment Addition Postulate
$AC = BD$	Substitution property of equality

EXAMPLE 5 Using Properties of Measure

AUTO RACING The Talladega Superspeedway racetrack in Alabama has four banked turns, which are described in the diagram at the left. Use the given information about the maximum banking angle of the four turns to find $m\angle 4$.

$m\angle 1 + m\angle 2 = 66°$
$m\angle 1 + m\angle 2 + m\angle 3 = 99°$
$m\angle 3 = m\angle 1$
$m\angle 1 = m\angle 4$

FOCUS ON APPLICATIONS

AUTO RACING

banking angle

REAL LIFE **AUTO RACING** Banked turns help the cars travel around the track at high speeds. The angles provide an inward force that helps keep the cars from flying off the track.

SOLUTION

$m\angle 1 + m\angle 2 = 66°$	Given
$m\angle 1 + m\angle 2 + m\angle 3 = 99°$	Given
$66° + m\angle 3 = 99°$	Substitution property of equality
$m\angle 3 = 33°$	Subtraction property of equality
$m\angle 3 = m\angle 1$, $m\angle 1 = m\angle 4$	Given
$m\angle 3 = m\angle 4$	Transitive property of equality
$m\angle 4 = 33°$	Substitution property of equality

Checkpoint Exercises *Sample answer:*

1. Statements (Reasons)

$m\angle ABC = m\angle DBE$ (Given)
$m\angle ABC + m\angle CBD = m\angle DBE + m\angle CBD$ (+ prop. of =)
$m\angle ABD = m\angle ABC + m\angle CBD$ (Angle Addition Post.)
$m\angle CBE = m\angle DBE + m\angle CBD$ (Angle Addition Post.)
$m\angle ABD = m\angle CBE$ (Subs. prop. of =)

GUIDED PRACTICE

Vocabulary Check ✓ 1. Name the property that makes the following statement true:
"If $m\angle 3 = m\angle 5$, then $m\angle 5 = m\angle 3$."
Symmetric property of angle measure

Concept Check ✓ **Use the diagram at the right.**

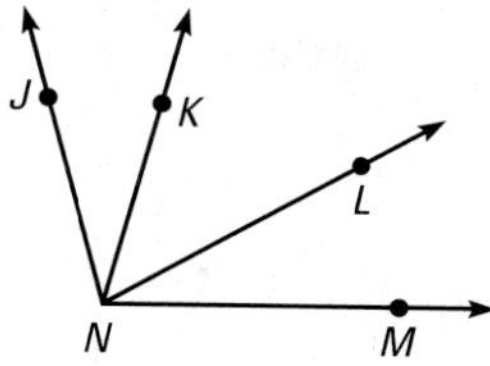

2. Explain how the addition property of equality supports this statement: "If $m\angle JNK = m\angle LNM$, then $m\angle JNL = m\angle KNM$." **See margin.**

3. Explain how the subtraction property of equality supports this statement: "If $m\angle JNL = m\angle KNM$, then $m\angle JNK = m\angle LNM$." **See margin.**

Skill Check ✓ **In Exercises 4–8, match the conditional statement with the property of equality.**

4. If $JK = PQ$ and $PQ = ST$, then $JK = ST$. **C**
5. If $m\angle S = 30°$, then $5° + m\angle S = 35°$. **A**
6. If $ST = 2$ and $SU = ST + 3$, then $SU = 5$. **B**
7. If $m\angle K = 45°$, then $3(m\angle K) = 135°$. **E**
8. If $m\angle P = m\angle Q$, then $m\angle Q = m\angle P$. **D**

A. Addition property
B. Substitution property
C. Transitive property
D. Symmetric property
E. Multiplication property

9. **WIND-CHILL FACTOR** If the wind is blowing at 20 miles per hour, you can find the wind-chill temperature W (in degrees Fahrenheit) by using the equation $W = 1.42T - 38.5$, where T is the actual temperature (in degrees Fahrenheit). Solve this equation for T and write a reason for each step. What is the actual temperature if the wind chill temperature is $-24.3°$F and the wind is blowing at 20 miles per hour? **See margin.**

PRACTICE AND APPLICATIONS

STUDENT HELP
Extra Practice to help you master skills is on p. 806.

COMPLETING STATEMENTS **In Exercises 10–14, use the property to complete the statement.**

10. Symmetric property of equality: If $m\angle A = m\angle B$, then ___?___. **$m\angle B = m\angle A$**
11. Transitive property of equality: If $BC = CD$ and $CD = EF$, then ___?___. **$BC = EF$**
12. Substitution property of equality: If $LK + JM = 12$ and $LK = 2$, then ___?___. **$JM = 10$**
13. Subtraction property of equality: If $PQ + ST = RS + ST$, then ___?___. **$PQ = RS$**
14. Division property of equality: If $3(m\angle A) = 90°$, then $m\angle A =$ ___?___. **30°**
15. Copy and complete the argument below, giving a reason for each step.

$2(3x + 1) = 5x + 14$	**Given**
$6x + 2 = 5x + 14$	___?___ **Distributive property;**
$x + 2 = 14$	___?___ **Subtraction property of equality;**
$x = 12$	___?___ **Subtraction property of equality.**

STUDENT HELP
HOMEWORK HELP
Example 1: Exs. 10–23
Example 2: Exs. 15–23
Example 3: Exs. 29–31
Example 4: Exs. 24–27
Example 5: Ex. 28

3 APPLY

ASSIGNMENT GUIDE

BASIC
Day 1: pp. 99–101 Exs. 10–15, 16–26 even, 32, 36–50 even

AVERAGE
Day 1: pp. 99–101 Exs. 10–15, 16–28 even, 32, 36–50 even

ADVANCED
Day 1: pp. 99–101 Exs. 10–15, 16–26 even, 28–34, 36–50 even

BLOCK SCHEDULE WITH 2.5
pp. 99–101 Exs. 10–15, 16–28 even, 32, 36–50 even

EXERCISE LEVELS
Level A: ***Easier***
10–14
Level B: ***More Difficult***
15–28, 32
Level C: ***Most Difficult***
29–31, 33, 34

✓ HOMEWORK CHECK
To quickly check student understanding of key concepts, go over the following exercises: Exs. 10, 12, 14, 18, 22, 26. See also the Daily Homework Quiz:
- Blackline Master (*Chapter 2 Resource Book*, p. 68)
- Transparency (p. 14)

2–3, 9. See Additional Answers beginning on page AA1.

! COMMON ERROR

EXERCISES 16–23 Watch for students who skip steps in their proofs. Suggest that students imagine they are explaining the proof to someone who knows very little about algebra, and so they have to show every step to help the person understand.

16. $p - 1 = 6$ (Given)
    $p = 7$ (Addition prop. of equality)
17. $q + 9 = 13$ (Given)
    $q = 4$ (Subtraction prop. of equality)
18. $2r - 7 = 9$ (Given)
    $2r = 16$ (Addition prop. of equality)
    $r = 8$ (Division prop. of equality)
19. $7s + 20 = 4s - 13$ (Given)
    $3s + 20 = -13$ (Subtraction prop. of equality)
    $3s = -33$ (Subtraction prop. of equality)
    $s = -11$ (Division prop. of equality)
20. $3(2t + 9) = 30$ (Given)
    $6t + 27 = 30$ (Distributive prop.)
    $6t = 3$ (Subtraction prop. of equality)
    $t = \frac{1}{2}$ (Division prop. of equality)

21–23, 26–29, 31.
See Additional Answers beginning on page AA1.

ADDITIONAL PRACTICE AND RETEACHING

For Lesson 2.4:

- Practice Levels A, B, and C (*Chapter 2 Resource Book,* p. 57)
- Reteaching with Practice (*Chapter 2 Resource Book,* p. 60)
- See Lesson 2.4 of the *Personal Student Tutor*

For more Mixed Review:

- Search the *Test and Practice Generator* for key words or specific lessons.

SOLVING EQUATIONS In Exercises 16–23, solve the equation and state a reason for each step. 16–23. See margin.

16. $p - 1 = 6$

17. $q + 9 = 13$

18. $2r - 7 = 9$

19. $7s + 20 = 4s - 13$

20. $3(2t + 9) = 30$

21. $-2(-w + 3) = 15$

22. $26u + 4(12u - 5) = 128$

23. $3(4v - 1) - 8v = 17$

24. **LOGICAL REASONING** In the diagram, $m\angle RPQ = m\angle RPS$. Verify each step in the argument that shows $m\angle SPQ = 2(m\angle RPQ)$.

$m\angle RPQ = m\angle RPS$ Given

$m\angle SPQ = m\angle RPQ + m\angle RPS$
Angle Addition Post.

$m\angle SPQ = m\angle RPQ + m\angle RPQ$
Substitution prop. of equality

$m\angle SPQ = 2(m\angle RPQ)$
Distributive prop.

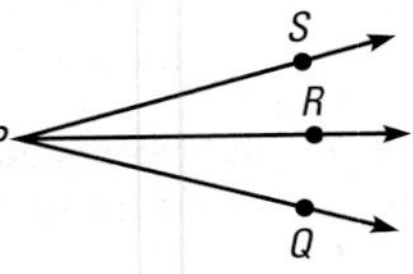

25. **LOGICAL REASONING** In the diagram, $m\angle ABF = m\angle BCG$ and $m\angle ABF = 90°$. Verify each step in the argument that shows $\overleftrightarrow{GK} \perp \overleftrightarrow{AD}$.

$m\angle ABF = 90°$ Given

$m\angle ABF = m\angle BCG$ Given

$m\angle BCG = 90°$
Transitive property of equality

$\angle BCG$ is a right angle.
Definition of right angles

$\overleftrightarrow{GK} \perp \overleftrightarrow{AD}$
Definition of perpendicular lines

F G B C A D J K

DEVELOPING ARGUMENTS In Exercises 26 and 27, give an argument for the statement, including a reason for each step. 26, 27. See margin.

26. If $\angle 1$ and $\angle 2$ are right angles, then they are supplementary.

27. If B lies between A and C and $AB = 3$ and $BC = 8$, then $AC = 11$.

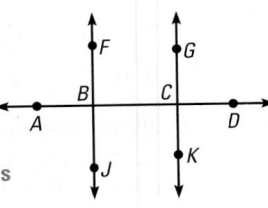

28. **AUTO RACING** Some facts about the maximum banking angles of Daytona International Speedway at corners 1, 2, 3, and 4 are at the right. Find $m\angle 3$. Explain your steps. (Banked corners are described on page 98.) See margin.

$m\angle 1 + m\angle 3 + m\angle 4 = 93°$

$m\angle 2 + m\angle 4 = 62°$

$m\angle 2 = m\angle 3$

$m\angle 1 = m\angle 2$

FOCUS ON PEOPLE

BILL ELLIOTT holds the qualifying record at Daytona International Speedway with a speed of 210.364 miles per hour.

PAY RAISES In Exercises 29–31, suppose you receive a raise at work. You can calculate your percent increase by using the pay raise formula $c(r + 1) = n$, where c is your current wage (in dollars per hour), r is your percent increase (as a decimal), and n is your new wage (in dollars per hour). 29, 31. See margin.

29. Solve the formula for r and write a reason for each step.

30. Use the result from Exercise 29 to find your percent increase if your current wage is \$10.00 and your new wage will be \$10.80. 0.08 or 8%

31. Suppose Donald gets a 6% pay raise and his new wage is \$12.72. Find Donald's old wage. Explain the steps you used to find your answer.

Test Preparation

32. **MULTI-STEP PROBLEM** State a reason that makes the statement true.

a. If $4(x - 5 + 2x) = 0.5(12x - 16)$, then $4x - 20 + 8x = 6x - 8$. Distributive property

b. If $4x - 20 + 8x = 6x - 8$, then $12x - 20 = 6x - 8$. Simplify

c. If $12x - 20 = 6x - 8$, then $6x - 20 = -8$. Subtraction property of equality

d. If $6x - 20 = -8$, then $6x = 12$. Addition property of equality

e. If $6x = 12$, then $x = 2$. Division property of equality

f. *Writing* Use parts (a) through (e) to provide an argument for "If $4(x - 5 + 2x) = 0.5(12x - 16)$, then $x = 2$." See margin.

★ Challenge

DETERMINING PROPERTIES Decide whether the relationship is *reflexive*, *symmetric*, or *transitive*. When the relationship does not have any of these properties, give a counterexample.

33. **Set:** students in a geometry class
Relationship: "earned the same grade as"
Example: Jim earned the same grade as Mario. Symmetric

34. **Set:** letters of the alphabet
Relationship: "comes after"
Example: H comes after G. Transitive

EXTRA CHALLENGE
www.mcdougallittell.com

MIXED REVIEW

32f. *Sample answer:* Given that $4(x - 5 + 2x) = 0.5(12x - 16)$, the equation can be solved using the distributive property, simplifying, and using the subtraction, addition, and division properties of equality to show that $x = 2$.

USING THE DISTANCE FORMULA Find the distance between the two points. Round your result to two decimal places. (Review 1.3 for 2.5)

35. $A(4, 5), B(-3, -2)$ 9.90
36. $E(-7, 6), F(2, 0)$ 10.82
37. $J(1, 1), K(-1, 11)$ 10.20
38. $P(8, -4), Q(1, -4)$ 7
39. $S(9, -1), T(2, -6)$ 8.60
40. $V(7, 10), W(1, 5)$ 7.81

DETERMINING ENDPOINTS In Exercises 41–44, you are given an endpoint and the midpoint of a line segment. Find the coordinates of the other endpoint. Each midpoint is denoted by *M*(*x*, *y*). (Review 1.5 for 2.5)

41. $B(5, 7)$, $M(-1, 0)$ (−7, −7)
42. $C(-4, -5)$, $M(3, -6)$ (10, −7)
43. $F(0, 9)$, $M(6, -2)$ (12, −13)
44. $Q(-1, 14)$, $M(2, 7)$ (5, 0)

45. Given that $m\angle A = 48°$, what are the measures of a complement and a supplement of $\angle A$? (Review 1.6) 42°; 132°

ANALYZING STATEMENTS Use the diagram shown at the right to determine whether the statement is *true* or *false*. (Review 2.2)

46. Points G, L, and J are collinear. false
47. $\overline{BC} \perp \overline{FG}$ false
48. $\angle ECB \cong \angle ACD$ true
49. $\angle JHL$ and $\angle JHF$ are complementary. false
50. $\overleftrightarrow{AK} \perp \overleftrightarrow{BD}$ true

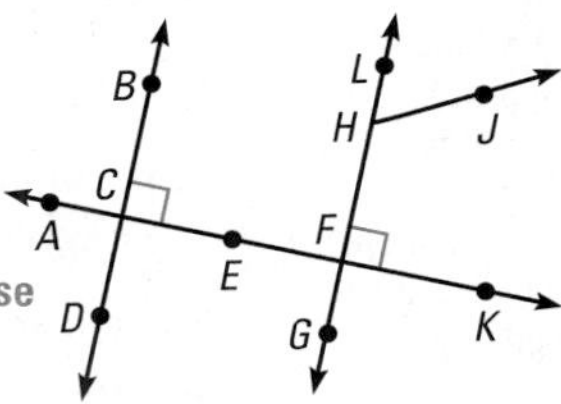

4 ASSESS

DAILY HOMEWORK QUIZ

Transparency Available

Use the property to complete each statement.

1. Multiplication property of equality: If $x = y$, then $ax =$ _____ ay
2. Symmetric property of equality: If $FG = HJ$, then _____ $HJ = FG$
3. Transitive property of equality: If $BC = KL$, and $KL = YZ$, then _____ $BC = YZ$

Solve the equation and state a reason for each step.

4. $3m - 2 = m + 8$
Statements (Reasons)
$3m - 2 = m + 8$ (Given)
$2m - 2 = 8$ (Subtraction property of equality)
$2m = 10$ (Addition property of equality)
$m = 5$ (Division property of equality)

EXTRA CHALLENGE NOTE
Challenge problems for Lesson 2.4 are available in **blackline** format in the *Chapter 2 Resource Book*, p. 65 and at **www.mcdougallittell.com.**

ADDITIONAL TEST PREPARATION

1. **OPEN ENDED** Give a geometric example of the addition property of equality. *Sample answer:*

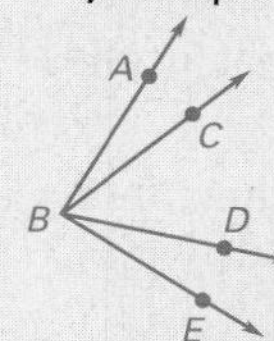

If $m\angle ABC = m\angle DBE$, then $m\angle ABC + m\angle CBD = m\angle DBE + m\angle CBD$.

1 PLAN

PACING
Basic: 2 days
Average: 2 days
Advanced: 2 days
Block Schedule: 0.5 block with 2.4
0.5 block with 2.6

LESSON OPENER
APPLICATION
An alternative way to approach Lesson 2.5 is to use the Application Lesson Opener:

- Blackline Master (*Chapter 2 Resource Book*, p. 69)
- Transparency (p. 12)

MEETING INDIVIDUAL NEEDS

- ***Chapter 2 Resource Book***
  Prerequisite Skills Review (p. 5)
  Practice Level A (p. 73)
  Practice Level B (p. 74)
  Practice Level C (p. 75)
  Reteaching with Practice (p. 76)
  Absent Student Catch-Up (p. 78)
  Challenge (p. 81)
- ***Resources in Spanish***
- 

NEW-TEACHER SUPPORT
See the Tips for New Teachers on pp. 1–2 of the *Chapter 2 Resource Book* for additional notes about Lesson 2.5.

WARM-UP EXERCISES
Transparency Available
Give the property that justifies each statement.

1. If $m\angle 1 = m\angle 2$, then $m\angle 2 = m\angle 1$. **Symmetric prop. of equality**
2. $m\angle 2 = m\angle 2$ **Reflexive prop. of equality**
3. If $EF = GH$ and $GH = IJ$ then $EF = IJ$. **Transitive prop. of equality**
4. If $EF = 8$ and $EF = GH$, then $GH = 8$. **Substitution prop. of equality**

2.5 Proving Statements about Segments

***What** you should learn*

GOAL 1 Justify statements about congruent segments.

GOAL 2 Write reasons for steps in a proof.

***Why** you should learn it*

▼ Properties of congruence allow you to justify segment relationships in **real life**, such as the segments in the trestle bridge shown and in **Exs. 3–5**.

GOAL 1 PROPERTIES OF CONGRUENT SEGMENTS

A true statement that follows as a result of other true statements is called a **theorem**. All theorems must be proved. You can prove a theorem using a *two-column proof.* A **two-column proof** has numbered statements and reasons that show the logical order of an argument.

THEOREM

THEOREM 2.1 ***Properties of Segment Congruence***

Segment congruence is reflexive, symmetric, and transitive. Here are some examples:

REFLEXIVE For any segment AB, $\overline{AB} \cong \overline{AB}$.

SYMMETRIC If $\overline{AB} \cong \overline{CD}$, then $\overline{CD} \cong \overline{AB}$.

TRANSITIVE If $\overline{AB} \cong \overline{CD}$, and $\overline{CD} \cong \overline{EF}$, then $\overline{AB} \cong \overline{EF}$.

EXAMPLE 1 *Symmetric Property of Segment Congruence*

You can prove the Symmetric Property of Segment Congruence as follows.

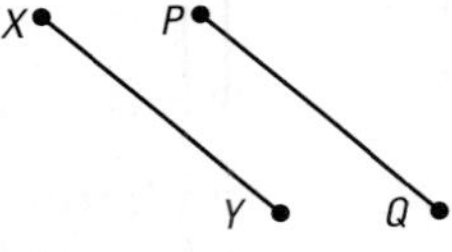

GIVEN ▶ $\overline{PQ} \cong \overline{XY}$

PROVE ▶ $\overline{XY} \cong \overline{PQ}$

Statements	Reasons
1. $\overline{PQ} \cong \overline{XY}$	1. Given
2. $PQ = XY$	2. Definition of congruent segments
3. $XY = PQ$	3. Symmetric property of equality
4. $\overline{XY} \cong \overline{PQ}$	4. Definition of congruent segments

STUDENT HELP
Study Tip
When writing a reason for a step in a proof, you must use one of the following: given information, a definition, a property, a postulate, or a previously proven theorem.

You are asked to complete proofs for the Reflexive and Transitive Properties of Segment Congruence in Exercises 6 and 7.

....

A proof can be written in paragraph form, called **paragraph proof**. Here is a paragraph proof for the Symmetric Property of Segment Congruence.

Paragraph Proof You are given that $\overline{PQ} \cong \overline{XY}$. By the definition of congruent segments, $PQ = XY$. By the symmetric property of equality, $XY = PQ$. Therefore, by the definition of congruent segments, it follows that $\overline{XY} \cong \overline{PQ}$.

CALIFORNIA STANDARDS AND ASSESSMENT

CA Standards: 2, 4, 16
SAT9 Task 1: Objs. 7, 26
SAT9 Task 2: Objs. 4, 26

GOAL 2 USING CONGRUENCE OF SEGMENTS

EXAMPLE 2 *Using Congruence*

Use the diagram and the given information to complete the missing steps and reasons in the proof.

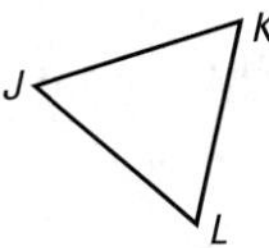

GIVEN ▶ $LK = 5$, $JK = 5$, $\overline{JK} \cong \overline{JL}$

PROVE ▶ $\overline{LK} \cong \overline{JL}$

Statements	Reasons
1. **a.**	1. Given
2. **b.**	2. Given
3. $LK = JK$	3. Transitive property of equality
4. $\overline{LK} \cong \overline{JK}$	4. **c.**
5. $\overline{JK} \cong \overline{JL}$	5. Given
6. **d.**	6. Transitive Property of Congruence

SOLUTION

a. $LK = 5$ **b.** $JK = 5$ **c.** Definition of congruent segments **d.** $\overline{LK} \cong \overline{JL}$

EXAMPLE 3 *Using Segment Relationships*

In the diagram, Q is the midpoint of $\overline{PR}$.

Show that PQ and QR are each equal to $\frac{1}{2}PR$.

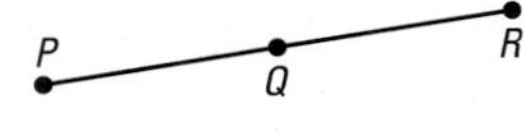

SOLUTION

Decide what you know and what you need to prove. Then write the proof.

GIVEN ▶ Q is the midpoint of $\overline{PR}$.

PROVE ▶ $PQ = \frac{1}{2}PR$ and $QR = \frac{1}{2}PR$.

Statements	Reasons
1. Q is the midpoint of $\overline{PR}$.	1. Given
2. $PQ = QR$	2. Definition of midpoint
3. $PQ + QR = PR$	3. Segment Addition Postulate
4. $PQ + PQ = PR$	4. Substitution property of equality
5. $2 \cdot PQ = PR$	5. Distributive property
6. $PQ = \frac{1}{2}PR$	6. Division property of equality
7. $QR = \frac{1}{2}PR$	7. Substitution property of equality

STUDENT HELP

Study Tip
The distributive property can be used to simplify a sum, as in Step 5 of the proof. You can think of $PQ + PQ$ as follows: $1(PQ) + 1(PQ) = (1 + 1)(PQ) = 2 \cdot PQ$.

2 TEACH

MOTIVATING THE LESSON

Ask students if they have ever tried to measure a room by pacing it off with their feet. How does this give them an approximate room measure? The logical sequence of steps they use to justify the measurement is an application of using segment congruence to prove a statement.

EXTRA EXAMPLE 1

Given: $EF = GH$

Prove: $\overline{EG} \cong \overline{FH}$

Statements (Reasons)

1. $EF = GH$ (Given)
2. $EF + FG = GH + FG$ (+ prop. of =)
3. $EG = EF + FG$, $FH = GH + FG$ (Segment Addition Post.)
4. $EG = FH$ (Subs. prop. of =)
5. $\overline{EG} \cong \overline{FH}$ (Def. of ≅ seg.)

EXTRA EXAMPLE 2

Complete the proof.

Given: $\overline{RT} \cong \overline{WY}$, $ST = WX$

Prove: $\overline{RS} \cong \overline{XY}$

Statements (Reasons)

1. ________ (Given) $\overline{RT} \cong \overline{WY}$
2. $RT = WY$ ________ (Def. of congruent segments)
3. $RT = RS + ST$; $WY = WX + XY$ (Segment Addition Post.)
4. $RS + ST = WX + XY$ (Substitution prop. of equality)
5. $ST = WX$ ________ (Given)
6. $RS = XY$ (– prop. of =)
7. ________ (Def. of congruent segments) $\overline{RS} \cong \overline{XY}$

Extra Example 3 and Checkpoint Exercises on next page.

EXTRA EXAMPLE 3

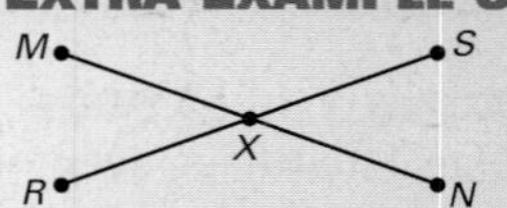

Given: X is the midpoint of $\overline{MN}$, and $MX = RX$.
Prove: $XN = RX$

Statements (Reasons)

1. X is the midpoint of $\overline{MN}$. (Given)
2. $XN = MX$ (Def. of midpoint)
3. $MX = RX$ (Given)
4. $XN = RX$ (Transitive prop. of equality)

CHECKPOINT EXERCISES

For use after Examples 1–3:

1.

Given: $RS = XY$, $ST = WX$
Prove: $RT = WY$

Statements (Reasons)

1. $RS = XY$, $ST = WX$ (Given)
2. $RS + ST = XY + WX$ (Addition prop. of equality)
3. $RT = RS + ST$ (Segment Addition Post.)
4. $WY = XY + WX$ (Segment Addition Post.)
5. $RT = WY$ (Substitution prop. of equality)

CLOSURE QUESTION

In the diagram, if $\overline{AB} \cong \overline{BC}$ and $\overline{BC} \cong \overline{CD}$, find BC. 11

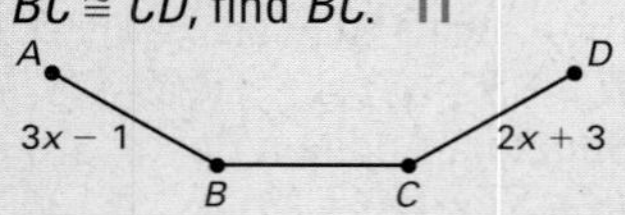

ACTIVITY Construction

Copy a Segment

Use the following steps to construct a segment that is congruent to $\overline{AB}$.

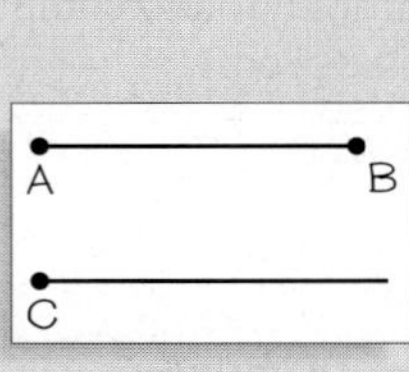
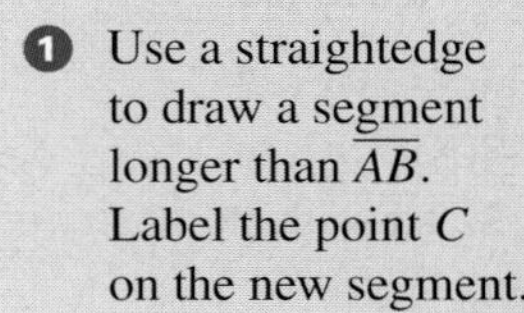

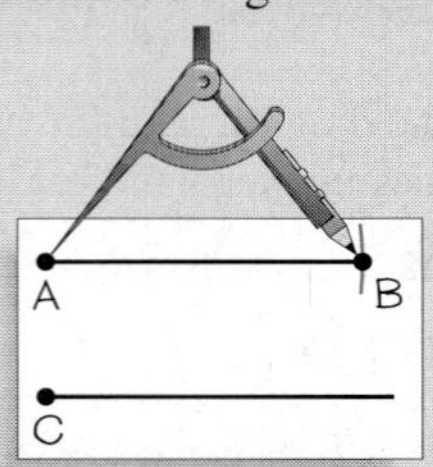

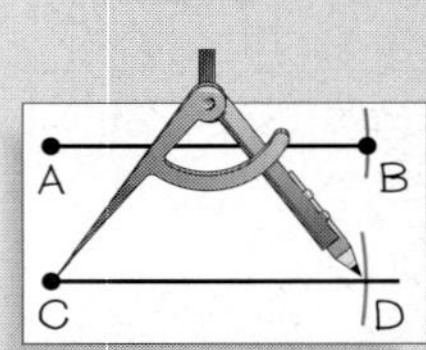

❶ Use a straightedge to draw a segment longer than $\overline{AB}$. Label the point C on the new segment.

❷ Set your compass at the length of $\overline{AB}$.

❸ Place the compass point at C and mark a second point, D, on the new segment. $\overline{CD}$ is congruent to $\overline{AB}$.

You will practice copying a segment in Exercises 12–15. It is an important construction because copying a segment is used in many constructions throughout this course.

GUIDED PRACTICE

Vocabulary Check ✓

1. An example of the Symmetric Property of Segment Congruence is "If $\overline{AB} \cong$ __?__, then $\overline{CD} \cong$ __?__." $\overline{CD}$; $\overline{AB}$

Concept Check ✓

2. **ERROR ANALYSIS** In the diagram below, $\overline{CB} \cong \overline{SR}$ and $\overline{CB} \cong \overline{QR}$. Explain what is wrong with Michael's argument.

Because $\overline{CB} \cong \overline{SR}$ and $\overline{CB} \cong \overline{QR}$, then $\overline{CB} \cong \overline{AC}$ by the Transitive Property of Segment Congruence.

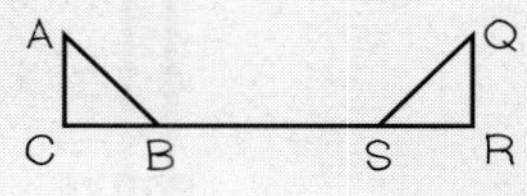

2. Using the Transitive Property of Segment Congruence, we can only assume that $\overline{SR} \cong \overline{QR}$.

Skill Check ✓

BRIDGES **The diagram below shows a portion of a trestle bridge, where $\overline{BF} \perp \overline{CD}$ and D is the midpoint of $\overline{BF}$.**

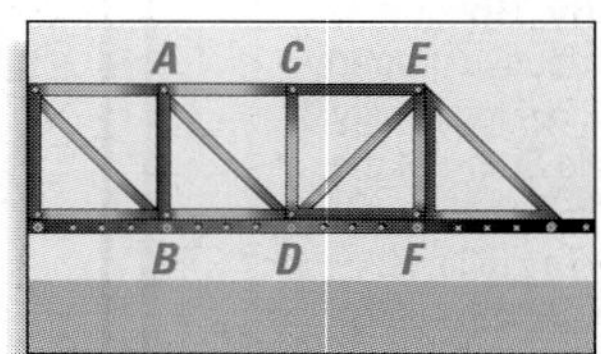

3. Give a reason why $\overline{BD}$ and $\overline{FD}$ are congruent.
4. Are $\angle CDE$ and $\angle FDE$ complementary? Explain. See margin.
5. If $\overline{CE}$ and $\overline{BD}$ are congruent, explain why $\overline{CE}$ and $\overline{FD}$ are congruent.

3. By the definition of midpoint, Point D is halfway between B and F. Therefore $\overline{BD} \cong \overline{FD}$.

5. By the Transitive Property of Segment Congruence, if $\overline{CE} \cong \overline{BD}$ and $\overline{BD} \cong \overline{FD}$, then $\overline{CE} \cong \overline{FD}$.

Practice and Applications

Student Help

Extra Practice to help you master skills is on p. 806.

Proving Theorem 2.1 Copy and complete the proof for two of the cases of the Properties of Segment Congruence Theorem.

6. Reflexive Property of Segment Congruence

GIVEN ▶ EF is a line segment

PROVE ▶ $\overline{EF} \cong \overline{EF}$

Statements	Reasons
1. $EF = EF$	**1.** ? Reflexive property of equality
2. ? $\overline{EF} \cong \overline{EF}$	**2.** Definition of congruent segments

7. Transitive Property of Segment Congruence

GIVEN ▶ $\overline{AB} \cong \overline{JK}$, $\overline{JK} \cong \overline{ST}$

PROVE ▶ $\overline{AB} \cong \overline{ST}$

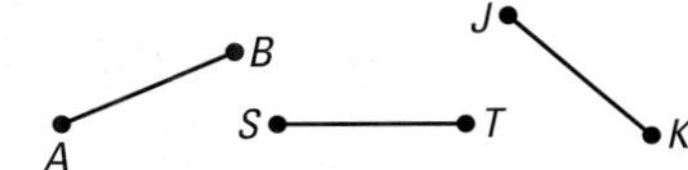

Statements	Reasons
1. $\overline{AB} \cong \overline{JK}$, $\overline{JK} \cong \overline{ST}$	**1.** ? Given
2. $AB = JK$, $JK = ST$	**2.** ? Definition of congruent segments
3. $AB = ST$	**3.** ? Transitive property of equality
4. $\overline{AB} \cong \overline{ST}$	**4.** ? Definition of congruent segments

Using Algebra Solve for the variable using the given information. Explain your steps. 8–11. See margin.

8. GIVEN ▶ $\overline{AB} \cong \overline{BC}$, $\overline{CD} \cong \overline{BC}$

A 2x + 1 B C 4x − 11 D

9. GIVEN ▶ $PR = 46$

P 2x + 5 Q 6x − 15 R

10. GIVEN ▶ $\overline{ST} \cong \overline{SR}$, $\overline{QR} \cong \overline{SR}$

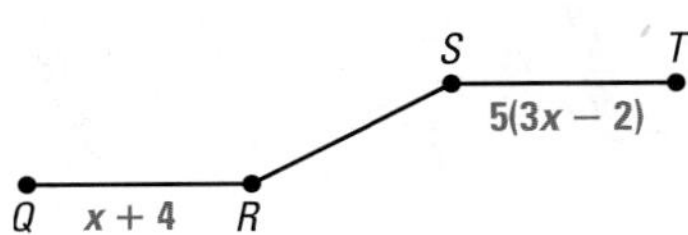

11. GIVEN ▶ $\overline{XY} \cong \overline{WX}$, $\overline{YZ} \cong \overline{WX}$

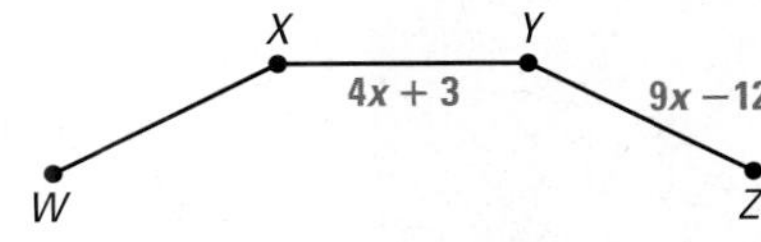

Construction In Exercises 12–15, use the segments, along with a straightedge and compass, to construct a segment with the given length. 12–15. Check students' work.

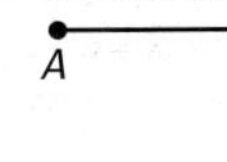

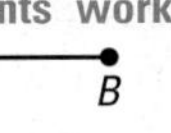

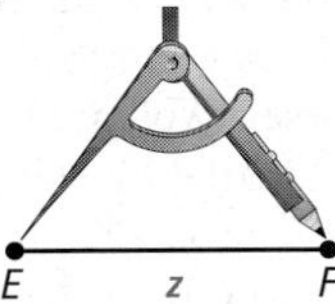

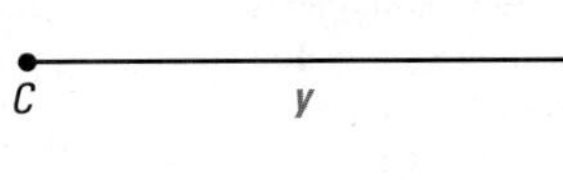

12. $x + y$ **13.** $y - z$ **14.** $3x - z$ **15.** $z + y - 2x$

Student Help

Homework Help
Example 1: Exs. 6, 7
Example 2: Exs. 16–18
Example 3: Exs. 16–18

3 Apply

Assignment Guide

Basic
Day 1: p. 105 Exs. 6–11
Day 2: pp. 105–107 Exs. 12–18, 21, 22, 28–40 even

Average
Day 1: p. 105 Exs. 6–11
Day 2: pp. 105–107 Exs. 12–18, 21, 22, 28–40 even

Advanced
Day 1: p. 105 Exs. 6–11
Day 2: pp. 105–107 Exs. 12–18, 21–27, 28–40 even

Block Schedule
p. 105 Exs. 6–11 (with 2.4)
pp. 105–107 Exs. 12–18, 21, 22, 28–40 even (with 2.6)

Exercise Levels

Level A: *Easier*
6, 7, 12

Level B: *More Difficult*
8–11, 13–16, 19, 21, 22

Level C: *Most Difficult*
17, 18, 20, 23–27

Homework Check

To quickly check student understanding of key concepts, go over the following exercises: Exs. 6, 8, 10, 14, 16, 18. See also the Daily Homework Quiz:

- Blackline Master (*Chapter 2 Resource Book,* p. 84)
- Transparency (p. 15)

4, 8–11. See Additional Answers beginning on page AA1.

Teaching Tips

Exercise 19 This is an example of the construction to copy a segment. You may want to give students the tactile experience of cutting strips of paper of the same size by using strip 1 as a guide for cutting strip 2, strip 2 for cutting strip 3, and so on to 10. Ask: Is the last strip of paper the same length as the first? Discuss how errors in measurement occur.

Career Note

Exercise 19 Additional information about carpentry is available at **www.mcdougallittell.com.**

17. $XY = 8$, $XZ = 8$ (Given)
$XY = XZ$ (Transitive prop. of equality)
$\overline{XY} \cong \overline{XZ}$ (Definition of congruent segments)
$\overline{XY} \cong \overline{ZY}$ (Given)
$\overline{XZ} \cong \overline{ZY}$ (Transitive Prop. of Segment Cong.)
18. $\overline{NK} \cong \overline{NL}$, $NK = 13$ (Given)
$NK = NL$ (Definition of congruent segments)
$NL = 13$ (Substitution prop. of equality)
20. See Additional Answers beginning on page AA1.

Additional Practice and Reteaching

For Lesson 2.5:

- Practice Levels A, B, and C (*Chapter 2 Resource Book*, p. 73)
- Reteaching with Practice (*Chapter 2 Resource Book*, p. 76)
- See Lesson 2.5 of the *Personal Student Tutor*

For more Mixed Review:

- Search the *Test and Practice Generator* for key words or specific lessons.

16. Given; Transitive Property of Segment Congruence; Definition of congruent segments; Addition property of equality; Segment Addition Postulate; Substitution property of equality; Definition of congruent segments

16. DEVELOPING PROOF Write a complete proof by rearranging the reasons listed on the pieces of paper.

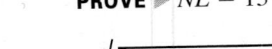

GIVEN ▶ $\overline{UV} \cong \overline{XY}$, $\overline{VW} \cong \overline{WX}$, $\overline{WX} \cong \overline{YZ}$

PROVE ▶ $\overline{UW} \cong \overline{XZ}$

Statements	Reasons
1. $\overline{UV} \cong \overline{XY}$, $\overline{VW} \cong \overline{WX}$, $\overline{WX} \cong \overline{YZ}$	Transitive Property of Segment Congruence
2. $\overline{VW} \cong \overline{YZ}$	Addition property of equality
3. $UV = XY$, $VW = YZ$	Definition of congruent segments
4. $UV + VW = XY + YZ$	Given
5. $UV + VW = UW$, $XY + YZ = XZ$	Segment Addition Postulate
6. $UW = XZ$	Definition of congruent segments
7. $\overline{UW} \cong \overline{XZ}$	Substitution property of equality

TWO-COLUMN PROOF **Write a two-column proof.** 17, 18. See margin.

17. GIVEN ▶ $XY = 8$, $XZ = 8$, $\overline{XY} \cong \overline{ZY}$

PROVE ▶ $\overline{XZ} \cong \overline{ZY}$

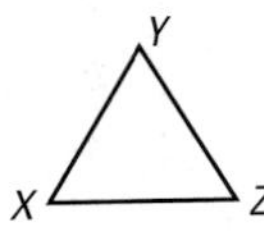

18. GIVEN ▶ $\overline{NK} \cong \overline{NL}$, $NK = 13$

PROVE ▶ $NL = 13$

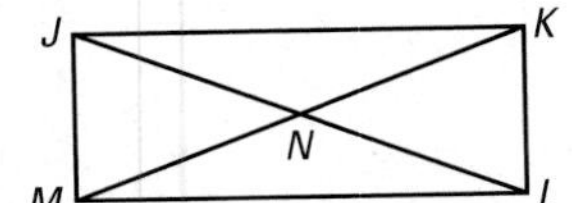

19. CARPENTRY You need to cut ten wood planks that are the same size. You measure and cut the first plank. You cut the second piece, using the first plank as a guide, as in the diagram below. The first plank is put aside and the second plank is used to cut a third plank. You follow this pattern for the rest of the planks. Is the last plank the same length as the first plank? Explain. Yes, by the Transitive Property of Segment Congruence.

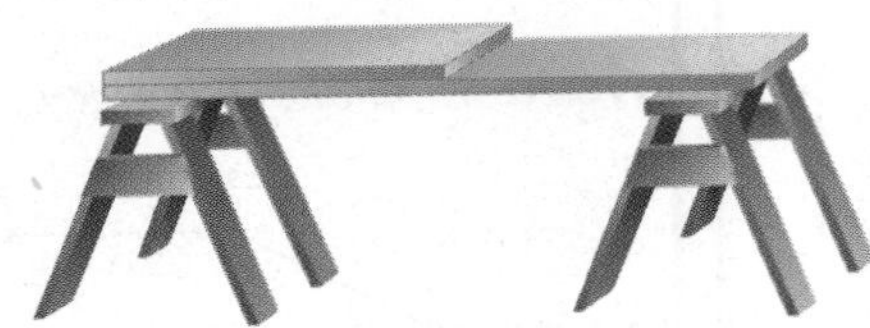

Focus on Careers

CARPENTRY For many projects, carpenters need boards that are all the same length. For instance, equally-sized boards in the house frame above insure stability.

CAREER LINK
www.mcdougallittell.com

20. OPTICAL ILLUSION To create the illusion, a special grid was used. In the grid, corresponding row heights are the same measure. For instance, $\overline{UV}$ and $\overline{ZY}$ are congruent. You decide to make this design yourself. You draw the grid, but you need to make sure that the row heights are the same. You measure $\overline{UV}$, $\overline{UW}$, $\overline{ZY}$, and $\overline{ZX}$. You find that $\overline{UV} \cong \overline{ZY}$ and $\overline{UW} \cong \overline{ZX}$. Write an argument that allows you to conclude that $\overline{VW} \cong \overline{YX}$. See margin.

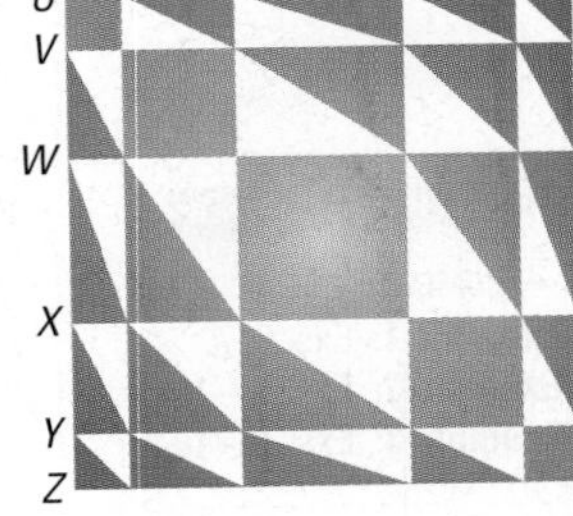

Test Preparation

21. **MULTIPLE CHOICE** In $QRST$, $\overline{QT} \cong \overline{TS}$ and $\overline{RS} \cong \overline{TS}$. What is x? B

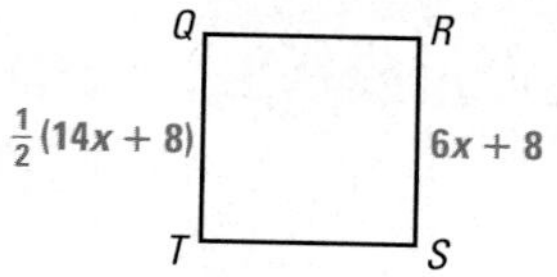

Ⓐ 1 Ⓑ 4 Ⓒ 12

Ⓓ 16 Ⓔ 32

22. **MULTIPLE CHOICE** In the figure shown below, $\overline{WX} \cong \overline{YZ}$. What is the length of $\overline{XZ}$? E

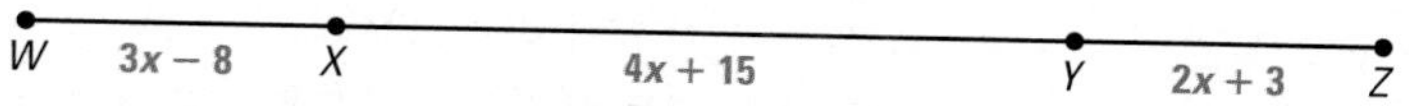

Ⓐ 25 Ⓑ 34 Ⓒ 59 Ⓓ 60 Ⓔ 84

★ Challenge

REPRESENTING SEGMENT LENGTHS In Exercises 23–26, suppose point T is the midpoint of $\overline{RS}$ and point W is the midpoint of $\overline{RT}$. If $\overline{XY} \cong \overline{RT}$ and $\overline{TS}$ has a length of z, write the length of the segment in terms of z.

23. $\overline{RT}$ $RT = z$

24. $\overline{XY}$ $XY = z$

25. $\overline{RW}$ $RW = \frac{1}{2}z$

26. $\overline{WT}$ $WT = \frac{1}{2}z$

27. **CRITICAL THINKING** Suppose M is the midpoint of $\overline{AB}$, P is the midpoint of $\overline{AM}$, and Q is the midpoint of $\overline{PM}$. If a and b are the coordinates of points A and B on a number line, find the coordinates of P and Q in terms of a and b. $P = a + \frac{1}{4}(b - a)$; $Q = a + \frac{3}{8}(b - a)$

EXTRA CHALLENGE

www.mcdougallittell.com

MIXED REVIEW

FINDING COUNTEREXAMPLES Find a counterexample that shows the statement is false. (Review 1.1)

28. For every number n, $2^n > n + 1$.
Sample answer: If $n = 0$, then $2^n = 1$ and $n + 1 = 1$, so $2^n = n + 1$ and $2^n \not> n + 1$.

29. The sum of an even number and an odd number is always even.
Sample answer: $2 + 3 = 5$

30. If a number is divisible by 5, then it is divisible by 10.
Sample answer: 25 is divisible by 5, but not 10.

FINDING ANGLE MEASURES In Exercises 31–34, use the diagram to find the angle measure. (Review 1.6 for 2.6)

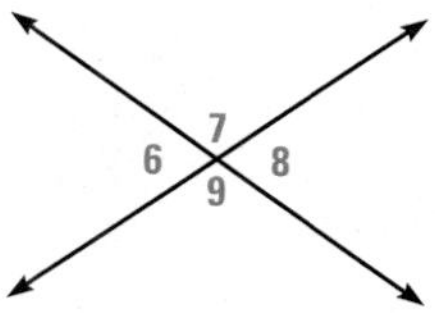

31. If $m\angle 6 = 64°$, then $m\angle 7 =$ __?__. 116°

32. If $m\angle 8 = 70°$, then $m\angle 6 =$ __?__. 70°

33. If $m\angle 9 = 115°$, then $m\angle 8 =$ __?__. 65°

34. If $m\angle 7 = 108°$, then $m\angle 8 =$ __?__. 72°

35. Write the contrapositive of the conditional statement, "If Matthew wins this wrestling match, then he will win first place." (Review 2.1) See margin.

36. Is the converse of a true conditional statement always true? Explain. (Review 2.1) See margin.

USING SYMBOLIC NOTATION Let p be "the car is in the garage" and let q be "Mark is home." Write the statement in words and symbols. (Review 2.3)
37–40. See margin.

37. The conditional statement $p \rightarrow q$

38. The converse of $p \rightarrow q$

39. The inverse of $p \rightarrow q$

40. The contrapositive of $p \rightarrow q$

35. If Matthew does not win first place, then Matthew did not win the wrestling match.

36. No. Consider the true conditional statement "If $x = 5$, then $x^2 = 25$." The statement is true when read forwards. However, reading it backwards, or reading the converse, "If $x^2 = 25$, then $x = 5$" is false. x is not necessarily 5 just because $x^2 = 25$. x could also equal -5.

37. $p \rightarrow q$; If the car is in the garage, then Mark is home.

38. $q \rightarrow p$; If Mark is home, then the car is in the garage.

39. $\sim p \rightarrow \sim q$; If the car is not in the garage, then Mark is not home.

40. $\sim q \rightarrow \sim p$; If Mark is not home, then the car is not in the garage.

4 ASSESS

DAILY HOMEWORK QUIZ

Transparency Available

Solve for the variable using the given information. Explain your steps.

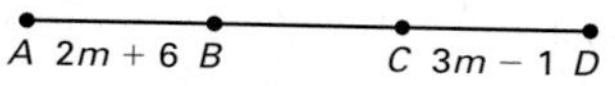

1. Given $\overline{AB} \cong \overline{BC}$, $\overline{CD} \cong \overline{BC}$
Statements (Reasons)
$\overline{AB} \cong \overline{BC}$, $\overline{CD} \cong \overline{BC}$ (Given)
$\overline{AB} \cong \overline{CD}$ (Transitive Prop. of Segment Cong.)
$AB = CD$ (Definition of congruent segments)
$2m + 6 = 3m - 1$ (Substitution prop. of equality)
$-m + 6 = -1$ (Subtraction prop. of equality)
$-m = -7$ (Subtraction prop. of equality)
$m = 7$ (Division prop. of equality)

Using the segments for Exercises 12–15 on p. 105, along with a straightedge and compass, construct a segment with the given length.

2. $x + y - z$
Check students' work.

EXTRA CHALLENGE NOTE

Challenge problems for Lesson 2.5 are available in **blackline** format in the *Chapter 2 Resource Book*, p. 81 and at **www.mcdougallittell.com.**

ADDITIONAL TEST PREPARATION

1. **WRITING** Describe a two-column proof.
A two-column proof is a sequence of numbered statements and reasons that show the logical order of an argument given to prove something. You use given information to prove something.

1 Planning the Activity

PURPOSE
To investigate complements of the same angle.

MATERIALS
- paper
- pencil

PACING
- Exploring the Concept — 5 min
- Drawing Conclusions — 10 min

LINK TO LESSON
This activity is a demonstration of Theorem 2.5 on page 111.

2 Managing the Activity

CLASSROOM MANAGEMENT
To help students better visualize $\angle 2$ and $\angle 3$, have them mark the crease with a pencil.

ALTERNATIVE APPROACH
Do this activity as a demonstration. To use the overhead projector, have rectangular sheets of transparency acetate available along with a pen to mark the angles.

3 Closing the Activity

KEY DISCOVERY
Complements of the same angle are congruent.

ACTIVITY ASSESSMENT
$\angle 2$ and $\angle 3$ are complementary, $m\angle 1 = 14°$, and $m\angle 2 = 76°$. Explain how to show $\angle 1 \cong \angle 3$.
Since $\angle 2$ and $\angle 3$ are complementary, their sum is 90°. Since the sum of $\angle 1$ and $\angle 2$ is 90°, they are also complementary. Since $\angle 1$ and $\angle 3$ are complements of the same angle, they are congruent.

1. See Additional Answers beginning on page AA1.

ACTIVITY 2.6
Developing Concepts

Investigating Complementary Angles

GROUP ACTIVITY
Work with a partner.

MATERIALS
- paper
- pencils

▶ **QUESTION** **If you know that two angles are complementary to the same angle, can you state that the angles are congruent?**

▶ **EXPLORING THE CONCEPT**

1. Fold a piece of paper in half to make a crease perpendicular to the bottom edge of the paper.

2. Open the piece of paper. Place a corner of a second piece of paper at the vertex of the right angles formed by the crease.

3. Trace the outline of the corner. Label the four angles formed by the lines and the crease.

STUDENT HELP
Look Back
For help with complementary and supplementary angles, see page 46.

▶ **DRAWING CONCLUSIONS**

1. Explain how you know the following: **1a–c. See margin.**
   a. $\angle 1$ and $\angle 2$ are complementary.
   b. $\angle 3$ and $\angle 4$ are complementary.
   c. $\angle 2$ and $\angle 3$ are complementary.
2. If $m\angle 1 + m\angle 2 = 90°$ and $m\angle 2 + m\angle 3 = 90°$, does $m\angle 1 = m\angle 3$? If $m\angle 3 + m\angle 4 = 90°$ and $m\angle 2 + m\angle 3 = 90°$, does $m\angle 2 = m\angle 4$? Explain your reasoning.
3. Repeat the steps above but change the position of the traced corner. Does $m\angle 1 = m\angle 3$? Does $m\angle 2 = m\angle 4$? Explain. **Yes; same reasoning as 2.**

2. Yes, $m\angle 1 = 90 - m\angle 2$ and $m\angle 3 = 90 - m\angle 2$, so by substitution, $m\angle 1 = m\angle 3$, so $\angle 1 \cong \angle 3$. $m\angle 4 = 90 - m\angle 3$ and $m\angle 2 = 90 - m\angle 3$, so by substitution, $m\angle 2 = m\angle 4$, so $\angle 2 \cong \angle 4$.

▶ **MAKE A CONJECTURE**

4. Use your results to make a conjecture about two angles that are complementary to the same angle. **Two angles that are complementary to the same angle are congruent.**

EXTENSION

If you know that two angles are *supplementary* to the same angle, can you state that the angles are congruent? If so, provide an argument. If not, provide a counterexample. **Yes. If $m\angle 1 = 180 - m\angle 2$ and $m\angle 3 = 180 - m\angle 2$, by substitution, $m\angle 1 = m\angle 3$, so $\angle 1 \cong \angle 3$.**

2.6 Proving Statements about Angles

What you should learn

GOAL 1 Use angle congruence properties.

GOAL 2 Prove properties about special pairs of angles.

Why you should learn it

▼ Properties of special pairs of angles help you determine angles in wood-working projects, such as the corners in the piece of furniture below and in the picture frame in **Ex. 30**.

CALIFORNIA STANDARDS AND ASSESSMENT

CA Standards: 2, 4, 13
SAT9 Task 1: Objs. 7, 24
SAT9 Task 2: Objs. 4, 27

GOAL 1 CONGRUENCE OF ANGLES

In Lesson 2.5, you proved segment relationships. In this lesson, you will prove statements about angles.

THEOREM

THEOREM 2.2 ***Properties of Angle Congruence***

Angle congruence is reflexive, symmetric, and transitive.

Here are some examples.

REFLEXIVE	For any angle A, $\angle A \cong \angle A$.
SYMMETRIC	If $\angle A \cong \angle B$, then $\angle B \cong \angle A$.
TRANSITIVE	If $\angle A \cong \angle B$ and $\angle B \cong \angle C$, then $\angle A \cong \angle C$.

The Transitive Property of Angle Congruence is proven in Example 1. The Reflexive and Symmetric Properties are left for you to prove in Exercises 10 and 11.

EXAMPLE 1 *Transitive Property of Angle Congruence*

Prove the Transitive Property of Congruence for angles.

SOLUTION

To prove the Transitive Property of Congruence for angles, begin by drawing three congruent angles. Label the vertices as A, B, and C.

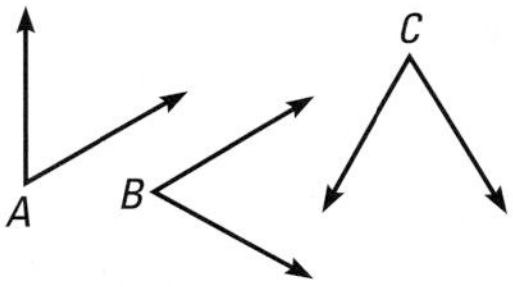

GIVEN ▶ $\angle A \cong \angle B$,
$\angle B \cong \angle C$

PROVE ▶ $\angle A \cong \angle C$

Statements	Reasons
1. $\angle A \cong \angle B$, $\angle B \cong \angle C$	**1.** Given
2. $m\angle A = m\angle B$	**2.** Definition of congruent angles
3. $m\angle B = m\angle C$	**3.** Definition of congruent angles
4. $m\angle A = m\angle C$	**4.** Transitive property of equality
5. $\angle A \cong \angle C$	**5.** Definition of congruent angles

1 PLAN

PACING
Basic: 2 days
Average: 2 days
Advanced: 2 days
Block Schedule: 0.5 block with 2.5
0.5 block with Ch Rev.

***LESSON OPENER* ACTIVITY**

An alternative way to approach Lesson 2.6 is to use the Activity Lesson Opener:

- Blackline Master (*Chapter 2 Resource Book*, p. 85)
- Transparency (p. 13)

MEETING INDIVIDUAL NEEDS

- ***Chapter 2 Resource Book***
  Prerequisite Skills Review (p. 5)
  Practice Level A (p. 89)
  Practice Level B (p. 90)
  Practice Level C (p. 91)
  Reteaching with Practice (p. 92)
  Absent Student Catch-Up (p. 94)
  Challenge (p. 96)
- ***Resources in Spanish***
-  ***Personal Student Tutor***

NEW-TEACHER SUPPORT

See the Tips for New Teachers on pp. 1–2 of the *Chapter 2 Resource Book* for additional notes about Lesson 2.6.

WARM-UP EXERCISES

Transparency Available

Find the measure of each angle.

1. a right angle 90°
2. the complement of 42° 48°
3. the supplement of 42° 138°
4. two congruent angles that are complementary 45°, 45°
5. two congruent angles that are supplementary 90°, 90°

2 TEACH

EXTRA EXAMPLE 1

Given: $\angle 1 \cong \angle 2$, $\angle 3 \cong \angle 4$, $\angle 2 \cong \angle 3$

Prove: $\angle 1 \cong \angle 4$

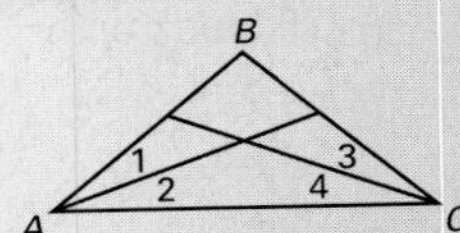

Statements (Reasons)

1. $\angle 1 \cong \angle 2$, $\angle 2 \cong \angle 3$ (Given)
2. $\angle 1 \cong \angle 3$ (Trans. Prop. of $\cong$)
3. $\angle 3 \cong \angle 4$ (Given)
4. $\angle 1 \cong \angle 4$ (Trans. Prop. of $\cong$)

EXTRA EXAMPLE 2

Given: $m\angle 1 = 63°$, $\angle 1 \cong \angle 3$, $\angle 3 \cong \angle 4$

Prove: $m\angle 4 = 63°$

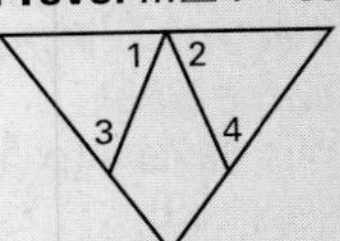

Statements (Reasons)

1. $m\angle 1 = 63°$, $\angle 1 \cong \angle 3$, $\angle 3 \cong \angle 4$ (Given)
2. $\angle 1 \cong \angle 4$ (Trans. Prop. of $\cong$)
3. $m\angle 1 = m\angle 4$ (Def. of $\cong$ ∠s)
4. $m\angle 4 = 63°$ (Subs. prop. of =)

EXTRA EXAMPLE 3

Given: $\angle DAB$, $\angle ABC$ are right angles, $\angle ABC \cong \angle BCD$

Prove: $\angle DAB \cong \angle BCD$

Statements (Reasons)

1. $\angle DAB$, $\angle ABC$ are right angles (Given)
2. $\angle DAB \cong \angle ABC$ (Right ∠s are $\cong$.)
3. $\angle ABC \cong \angle BCD$ (Given)
4. $\angle DAB \cong \angle BCD$ (Trans. Prop. of $\cong$)

Checkpoint Exercises for Examples 1–3 on next page.

EXAMPLE 2 *Using the Transitive Property*

This two-column proof uses the Transitive Property.

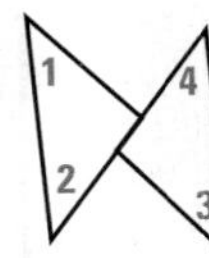

GIVEN ▶ $m\angle 3 = 40°$, $\angle 1 \cong \angle 2$, $\angle 2 \cong \angle 3$

PROVE ▶ $m\angle 1 = 40°$

Statements	Reasons
1. $m\angle 3 = 40°$, $\angle 1 \cong \angle 2$, $\angle 2 \cong \angle 3$	**1.** Given
2. $\angle 1 \cong \angle 3$	**2.** Transitive Property of Congruence
3. $m\angle 1 = m\angle 3$	**3.** Definition of congruent angles
4. $m\angle 1 = 40°$	**4.** Substitution property of equality

THEOREM

THEOREM 2.3 ***Right Angle Congruence Theorem***

All right angles are congruent.

Proof

EXAMPLE 3 *Proving Theorem 2.3*

You can prove Theorem 2.3 as shown.

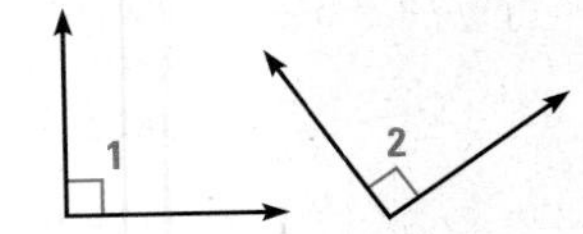

GIVEN ▶ $\angle 1$ and $\angle 2$ are right angles

PROVE ▶ $\angle 1 \cong \angle 2$

Statements	Reasons
1. $\angle 1$ and $\angle 2$ are right angles	**1.** Given
2. $m\angle 1 = 90°$, $m\angle 2 = 90°$	**2.** Definition of right angle
3. $m\angle 1 = m\angle 2$	**3.** Transitive property of equality
4. $\angle 1 \cong \angle 2$	**4.** Definition of congruent angles

ACTIVITY Using Technology

Investigating Supplementary Angles

Use geometry software to draw and label two intersecting lines.

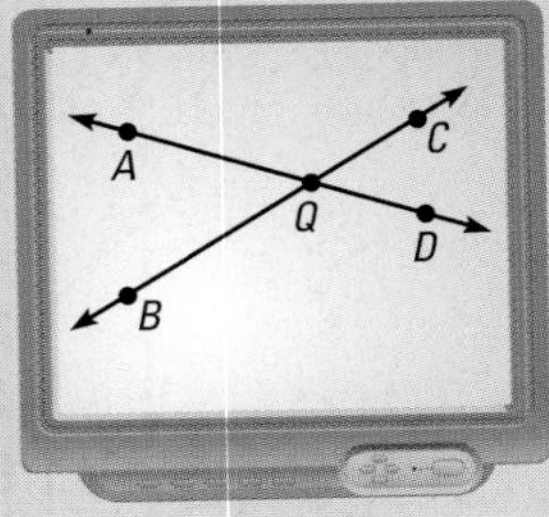

1. What do you notice about the measures of $\angle AQB$ and $\angle AQC$? $\angle AQC$ and $\angle CQD$? $\angle AQB$ and $\angle CQD$? **supplementary; supplementary; equal**
2. Rotate $\overleftrightarrow{BC}$ to a different position. Do the angles retain the same relationship? **yes**
3. Make a conjecture about two angles supplementary to the same angle. **They are congruent.**

GOAL 2 PROPERTIES OF SPECIAL PAIRS OF ANGLES

THEOREMS

THEOREM 2.4 ***Congruent Supplements Theorem***

If two angles are supplementary to the same angle (or to congruent angles) then they are congruent.

If $m\angle 1 + m\angle 2 = 180°$ and $m\angle 2 + m\angle 3 = 180°$, then $\angle 1 \cong \angle 3$.

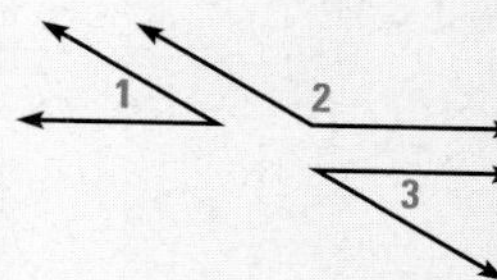

THEOREM 2.5 ***Congruent Complements Theorem***

If two angles are complementary to the same angle (or to congruent angles) then the two angles are congruent.

If $m\angle 4 + m\angle 5 = 90°$ and $m\angle 5 + m\angle 6 = 90°$, then $\angle 4 \cong \angle 6$.

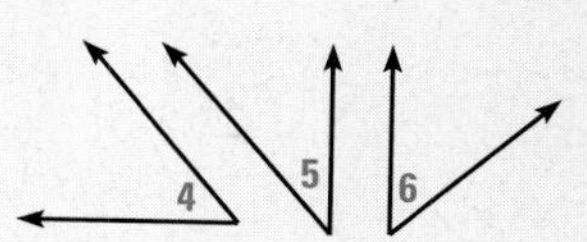

Proof

EXAMPLE 4 *Proving Theorem 2.4*

GIVEN ▶ $\angle 1$ and $\angle 2$ are supplements, $\angle 3$ and $\angle 4$ are supplements, $\angle 1 \cong \angle 4$

PROVE ▶ $\angle 2 \cong \angle 3$

Statements	Reasons
1. $\angle 1$ and $\angle 2$ are supplements, $\angle 3$ and $\angle 4$ are supplements, $\angle 1 \cong \angle 4$	**1.** Given
2. $m\angle 1 + m\angle 2 = 180°$ $m\angle 3 + m\angle 4 = 180°$	**2.** Definition of supplementary angles
3. $m\angle 1 + m\angle 2 = m\angle 3 + m\angle 4$	**3.** Transitive property of equality
4. $m\angle 1 = m\angle 4$	**4.** Definition of congruent angles
5. $m\angle 1 + m\angle 2 = m\angle 3 + m\angle 1$	**5.** Substitution property of equality
6. $m\angle 2 = m\angle 3$	**6.** Subtraction property of equality
7. $\angle 2 \cong \angle 3$	**7.** Definition of congruent angles

POSTULATE

POSTULATE 12 ***Linear Pair Postulate***

If two angles form a linear pair, then they are supplementary.

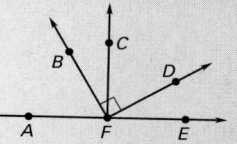

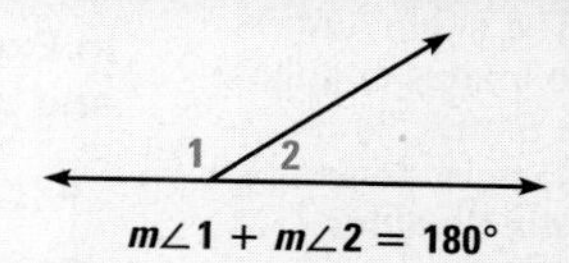

CHECKPOINT EXERCISES

For use after Examples 1–3:

1.

Given: $\angle AFC$, $\angle BFD$, are right angles, $\angle BFD \cong \angle CFE$
Prove: $\angle AFC \cong \angle CFE$

Statements (Reasons)

1. $\angle AFC$, $\angle BFD$ are right angles (Given)
2. $\angle AFC \cong \angle BFD$ (Right ∠s are ≅.)
3. $\angle BFD \cong \angle CFE$ (Given)
4. $\angle AFC \cong \angle CFE$ (Trans. Prop. of ≅)

EXTRA EXAMPLE 4

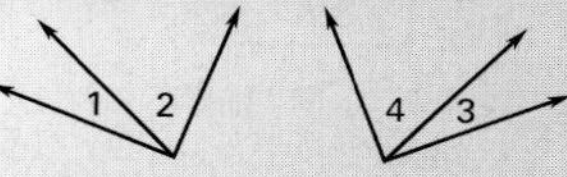

Given: $m\angle 1 = 24°$, $m\angle 3 = 24°$, $\angle 1 = \angle 2$ are complementary, $\angle 3 = \angle 4$ are complementary
Prove: $\angle 2 \cong \angle 4$

Statements (Reasons)

1. $m\angle 1 = 24°$, $m\angle 3 = 24°$, $\angle 1$ and $\angle 2$ are complementary, $\angle 3$ and $\angle 4$ are complementary (Given)
2. $m\angle 1 = m\angle 3$ (Transitive prop. of equality)
3. $\angle 1 \cong \angle 3$ (Def. of congruent ∠s)
4. $\angle 2 \cong \angle 4$ (≅ Complements Thm.)

CHECKPOINT EXERCISES

For use after Example 4:

1. In a diagram, $\angle 1$ and $\angle 2$ are supplementary and $\angle 2$ and $\angle 3$ are supplementary. Explain how to show that $\angle 1 \cong \angle 3$. **Using the definition of supplementary angles, $m\angle 1 + m\angle 2 = 180°$ and $m\angle 2 + m\angle 3 = 180°$. So $m\angle 1 + m\angle 2 = m\angle 2 + m\angle 3$ by the transitive property of equality. So $m\angle 1 = m\angle 3$ by the subtraction property of equality. Therefore $\angle 1 \cong \angle 3$ by the definition of congruent angles.**

Extra Example 5

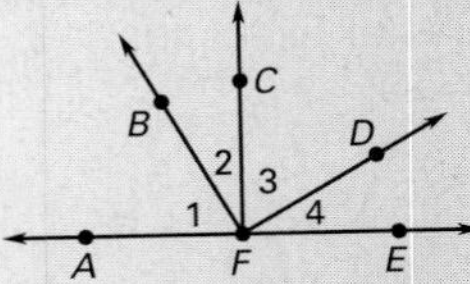

In the diagram $m\angle 1 = 60°$ and $\angle BFD$ is right. Explain how to show $m\angle 4 = 30°$. **Using the substitution property, you know that $m\angle 1 + m\angle BFD = 150°$. $m\angle 1 + m\angle BFD = m\angle AFD$ by the Angle Addition Post. The diagram shows that $m\angle AFD + m\angle 4 = 180°$. Substitute 150° for $m\angle AFD$ to show $m\angle 4 = 30°$.**

Extra Example 6

Given: $\angle 1$ and $\angle 2$ are a linear pair, $\angle 2$ and $\angle 3$ are a linear pair
Prove: $\angle 1 \cong \angle 3$

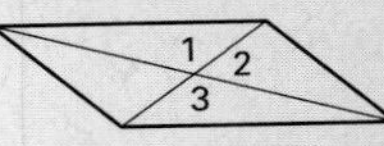

Statements (Reasons)

1. **$\angle 1$ and $\angle 2$ are a linear pair, $\angle 2$ and $\angle 3$ are a linear pair (Given)**
2. **$\angle 1$ and $\angle 2$ are supplementary, $\angle 2$ and $\angle 3$ are supplementary (Linear Pair Post.)**
3. **$\angle 1 \cong \angle 3$ (Cong. Supplements Thm.)**

Checkpoint Exercises

For use after Examples 5–6:

1. Find the measures of the angles in the diagram given $\angle 1$ and $\angle 2$ are complementary and $\angle 1 \cong \angle 3 \cong \angle 4$.

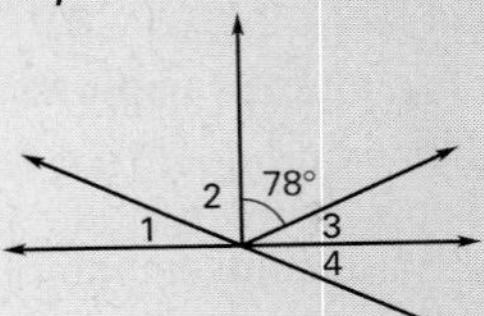

$m\angle 2 = 78°$, $m\angle 1 = m\angle 3 = m\angle 4 = 12°$

Closure Question

Draw an example diagram to show $\angle 1$ and $\angle 3$ are linear pairs with $\angle 2$. Tell two ways you can prove $\angle 1 \cong \angle 3$. **See answer at right.**

EXAMPLE 5 *Using Linear Pairs*

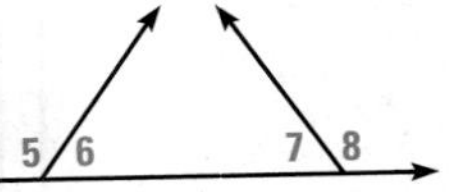

In the diagram, $m\angle 8 = m\angle 5$ and $m\angle 5 = 125°$. Explain how to show $m\angle 7 = 55°$.

SOLUTION

Using the transitive property of equality, $m\angle 8 = 125°$. The diagram shows $m\angle 7 + m\angle 8 = 180°$. Substitute 125° for $m\angle 8$ to show $m\angle 7 = 55°$.

THEOREM

THEOREM 2.6 ***Vertical Angles Theorem***

Vertical angles are congruent.

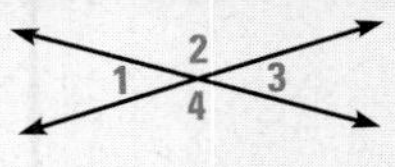

$\angle 1 \cong \angle 3$, $\angle 2 \cong \angle 4$

STUDENT HELP

Study Tip
Remember that previously proven theorems can be used as reasons in a proof, as in **Step 3** of the proof at the right.

EXAMPLE 6 *Proving Theorem 2.6*

GIVEN ▶ $\angle 5$ and $\angle 6$ are a linear pair, $\angle 6$ and $\angle 7$ are a linear pair

PROVE ▶ $\angle 5 \cong \angle 7$

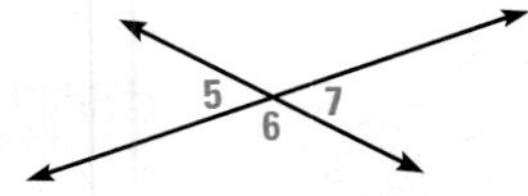

Statements	Reasons
1. $\angle 5$ and $\angle 6$ are a linear pair, $\angle 6$ and $\angle 7$ are a linear pair	1. Given
2. $\angle 5$ and $\angle 6$ are supplementary, $\angle 6$ and $\angle 7$ are supplementary	2. Linear Pair Postulate
3. $\angle 5 \cong \angle 7$	3. Congruent Supplements Theorem

GUIDED PRACTICE

Vocabulary Check ✓

1. "If $\angle CDE \cong$ __?__ and $\angle QRS \cong \angle XYZ$, then $\angle CDE \cong \angle XYZ$," is an example of the __?__ Property of Angle Congruence. **$\angle QRS$; Transitive**

Concept Check ✓

2. To close the blades of the scissors, you close the handles. Will the angle formed by the blades be the same as the angle formed by the handles? Explain. **See margin.**

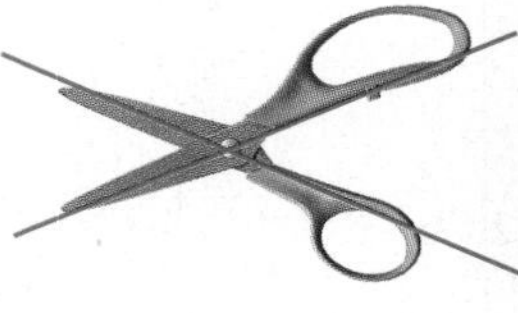

Skill Check ✓

3. By the Transitive Property of Congruence, if $\angle A \cong \angle B$ and $\angle B \cong \angle C$, then __?__ $\cong \angle C$. **$\angle A$**

2. Yes. The angle formed by the blades and the angle formed by the handles are an example of vertical angles, which are congruent.

In Exercises 4–9, $\angle 1$ and $\angle 3$ are a linear pair, $\angle 1$ and $\angle 4$ are a linear pair, and $\angle 1$ and $\angle 2$ are vertical angles. Is the statement true?

4. $\angle 1 \cong \angle 3$ **no**
5. $\angle 1 \cong \angle 2$ **yes**
6. $\angle 1 \cong \angle 4$ **no**
7. $\angle 3 \cong \angle 2$ **no**
8. $\angle 3 \cong \angle 4$ **yes**
9. $m\angle 2 + m\angle 3 = 180°$ **yes**

Closure Question *Sample answer:*

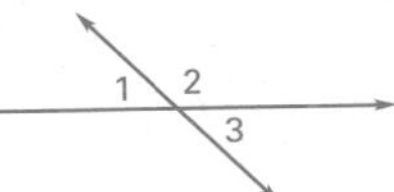

$\angle 1 \cong \angle 3$ either by the Vertical Angles Thm. or by the $\cong$ Supplements Thm.

PRACTICE AND APPLICATIONS

STUDENT HELP

Extra Practice to help you master skills is on p. 806.

10. **PROVING THEOREM 2.2** Copy and complete the proof of the Symmetric Property of Congruence for angles.

GIVEN ▶ $\angle A \cong \angle B$

PROVE ▶ $\angle B \cong \angle A$

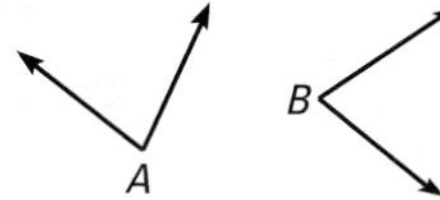

Statements	Reasons
1. $\angle A \cong \angle B$	1. ___?___ Given
2. ___?___ $m\angle A = m\angle B$	2. Definition of congruent angles
3. $m\angle B = m\angle A$	3. ___?___ Symmetric property of equality
4. $\angle B \cong \angle A$	4. ___?___ Definition of congruent angles

11. **PROVING THEOREM 2.2** Write a two-column proof for the Reflexive Property of Congruence for angles. See margin.

FINDING ANGLES In Exercises 12–17, complete the statement given that $m\angle EHC = m\angle DHB = m\angle AHB = 90°$

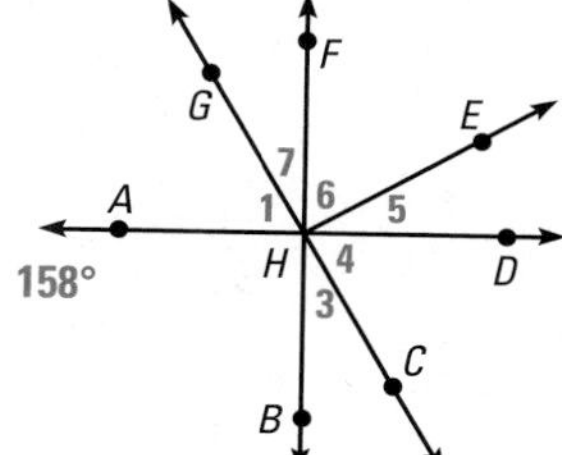

12. If $m\angle 7 = 28°$, then $m\angle 3 =$ ___?___. 28°

13. If $m\angle EHB = 121°$, then $m\angle 7 =$ ___?___. 31°

14. If $m\angle 3 = 34°$, then $m\angle 5 =$ ___?___. 34°

15. If $m\angle GHB = 158°$, then $m\angle FHC =$ ___?___. 158°

16. If $m\angle 7 = 31°$, then $m\angle 6 =$ ___?___. 59°

17. If $m\angle GHD = 119°$, then $m\angle 4 =$ ___?___. 61°

18. **PROVING THEOREM 2.5** Copy and complete the proof of the Congruent Complements Theorem.

GIVEN ▶ $\angle 1$ and $\angle 2$ are complements, $\angle 3$ and $\angle 4$ are complements, $\angle 2 \cong \angle 4$

PROVE ▶ $\angle 1 \cong \angle 3$

Statements	Reasons
1. $\angle 1$ and $\angle 2$ are complements, $\angle 3$ and $\angle 4$ are complements, $\angle 2 \cong \angle 4$	1. ___?___ Given
2. ___?___, ___?___ $m\angle 1 + m\angle 2 = 90°$, $m\angle 3 + m\angle 4 = 90°$	2. Def. of complementary angles
3. $m\angle 1 + m\angle 2 = m\angle 3 + m\angle 4$	3. Transitive property of equality
4. $m\angle 2 = m\angle 4$	4. ___?___ Definition of congruent angles
5. $m\angle 1 + m\angle 2 = m\angle 3 + m\angle 2$	5. ___?___ Substitution property of equality
6. $m\angle 1 = m\angle 3$	6. ___?___ Subtraction property of equality
7. ___?___ $\angle 1 \cong \angle 3$	7. Definition of congruent angles

STUDENT HELP

HOMEWORK HELP
Example 1: Exs. 10, 11
Example 2: Exs. 12–17
Example 3: Exs. 12–17
Example 4: Exs. 19–22
Example 5: Exs. 23–28
Example 6: Exs. 23–28

3 APPLY

ASSIGNMENT GUIDE

BASIC
Day 1: p. 113 Exs. 10–22, 29, 30
Day 2: pp. 114–115 Exs. 23–28, 33–36, 38–45, Quiz 2 Exs. 1–9

AVERAGE
Day 1: p. 113 Exs. 10–22, 29, 30
Day 2: pp. 114–115 Exs. 23–28, 33–36, 38–45, Quiz 2 Exs. 1–9

ADVANCED
Day 1: p. 113 Exs. 10–22, 29, 30
Day 2: pp. 114–115 Exs. 23–28, 33–45, Quiz 2 Exs. 1–9

BLOCK SCHEDULE
p. 113 Exs. 10–22, 29, 30 (with 2.5)
pp. 114–115 Exs. 23–28, 33–36, 38–45, Quiz 2 Exs. 1–9 (with Ch. Rev.)

EXERCISE LEVELS
Level A: *Easier* 10–18
Level B: *More Difficult* 19–30, 32–36
Level C: *Most Difficult* 31, 37

HOMEWORK CHECK
To quickly check student understanding of key concepts, go over the following exercises: Exs. 10, 16, 18, 20, 24, 26, 28. See also the Daily Homework Quiz:

- Blackline Master (*Chapter 3 Resource Book,* p. 11)
- Transparency (p. 17)

11. A is an angle (Given)
$m\angle A = m\angle A$ (Reflexive prop. of equality)
$\angle A \cong \angle A$ (Definition of congruent angles)

! COMMON ERROR

EXERCISES 20–22 Students often confuse supplementary and complementary. One way to avoid this confusion is to remind students that "*c* comes before *s* and 90 comes before 180." Also, you can have students think up mnemonics they can use to help them remember which word is which.

STUDENT HELP NOTES

Homework Help Students can find help for Exs. 23–26 at **www.mcdougallittell.com.** The information can be printed out for students who don't have access to the Internet.

23. $m\angle 3 = 120°$, $\angle 1 \cong \angle 4$, $\angle 3 \cong \angle 4$ (Given)
$\angle 1 \cong \angle 3$ (Transitive Prop. of Angle Cong.)
$m\angle 1 = m\angle 3$ (Definition of congruent angles)
$m\angle 1 = 120°$ (Substitution prop. of equality)

24. $\angle 3$ and $\angle 2$ are complementary (Given)
$m\angle 1 + m\angle 2 = 90°$ (Given)
$m\angle 3 + m\angle 2 = 90°$ (Definition of complementary angles)
$m\angle 1 + m\angle 2 = m\angle 3 + m\angle 2$ (Transitive prop. of equality)
$m\angle 1 = m\angle 3$ (Subtraction prop. of equality)
$\angle 1 \cong \angle 3$ (Definition of congruent angles)

25. $\angle QVW$ and $\angle RWV$ are supplementary (Given)
$\angle QVW$ and $\angle QVP$ are a linear pair (Defintion of linear pair)
$\angle QVP$ and $\angle QVW$ are supplementary (Linear Pair Post.)
$\angle QVP \cong \angle RWV$ (Congruent Supplements Theorem)

FINDING CONGRUENT ANGLES **Make a sketch using the given information. Then, state all of the pairs of congruent angles.**

19. $\angle 1$ and $\angle 2$ are a linear pair. $\angle 2$ and $\angle 3$ are a linear pair. $\angle 3$ and $\angle 4$ are a linear pair. $\angle 1 \cong \angle 3$, $\angle 2 \cong \angle 4$

20. $\angle XYZ$ and $\angle VYW$ are vertical angles. $\angle XYZ$ and $\angle ZYW$ are supplementary. $\angle VYW$ and $\angle XYV$ are supplementary. $\angle XYZ \cong \angle VYW$, $\angle XYV \cong \angle ZYW$

21. $\angle 1$ and $\angle 3$ are complementary. $\angle 4$ and $\angle 2$ are complementary. $\angle 1$ and $\angle 2$ are vertical angles. $\angle 1 \cong \angle 2$, $\angle 3 \cong \angle 4$

22. $\angle ABC$ and $\angle CBD$ are adjacent, complementary angles. $\angle CBD$ and $\angle DBF$ are adjacent, complementary angles. $\angle ABC \cong \angle DBF$, $\angle ABD \cong \angle CBF$

STUDENT HELP

INTERNET HOMEWORK HELP
Visit our Web site www.mcdougallittell.com for help with Exs. 23–26.

WRITING PROOFS **Write a two-column proof.** 23–26. See margin.

23. GIVEN ▶ $m\angle 3 = 120°$, $\angle 1 \cong \angle 4$, $\angle 3 \cong \angle 4$

PROVE ▶ $m\angle 1 = 120°$

Plan for Proof First show that $\angle 1 \cong \angle 3$. Then use transitivity to show that $m\angle 1 = 120°$.

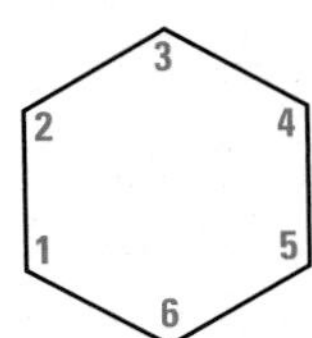

24. GIVEN ▶ $\angle 3$ and $\angle 2$ are complementary, $m\angle 1 + m\angle 2 = 90°$

PROVE ▶ $\angle 3 \cong \angle 1$

Plan for Proof First show that $\angle 1$ and $\angle 2$ are complementary. Then show that $\angle 3 \cong \angle 1$.

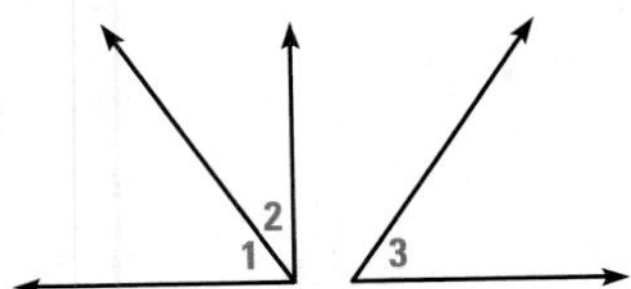

25. GIVEN ▶ $\angle QVW$ and $\angle RWV$ are supplementary

PROVE ▶ $\angle QVP \cong \angle RWV$

Plan for Proof First show that $\angle QVP$ and $\angle QVW$ are supplementary. Then show that $\angle QVP \cong \angle RWV$.

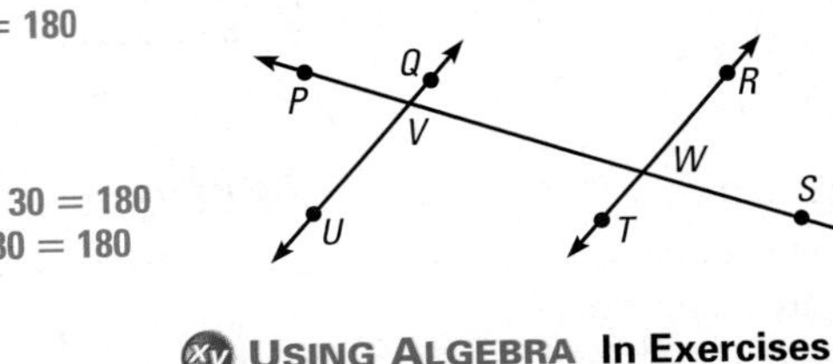

26. GIVEN ▶ $\angle 5 \cong \angle 6$

PROVE ▶ $\angle 4 \cong \angle 7$

Plan for Proof First show that $\angle 4 \cong \angle 5$ and $\angle 6 \cong \angle 7$. Then use transitivity to show that $\angle 4 \cong \angle 7$.

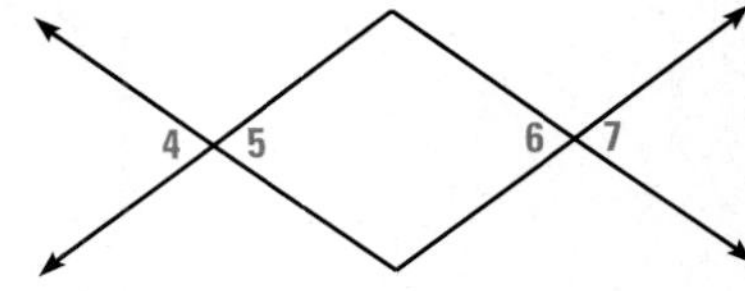

27. $4w + 10 + 13w = 180$
$17w + 10 = 180$
$17w = 170$
$w = 10$
$2(x + 25) + 2x - 30 = 180$
$2x + 50 + 2x - 30 = 180$
$4x + 20 = 180$
$4x = 160$
$x = 40$

28. $4y - 35 = 3y$
$y - 35 = 0$
$y = 35$
$3(6z + 7) = 10z + 45$
$18z + 21 = 10z + 45$
$8z = 24$
$z = 3$

USING ALGEBRA **In Exercises 27 and 28, solve for each variable. Explain your reasoning.** 27, 28. See margin.

27.

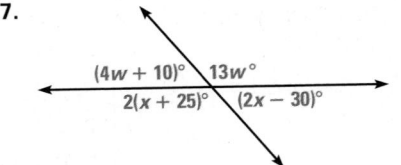

$(4w + 10)°$ $13w°$ $2(x + 25)°$ $(2x - 30)°$

28.

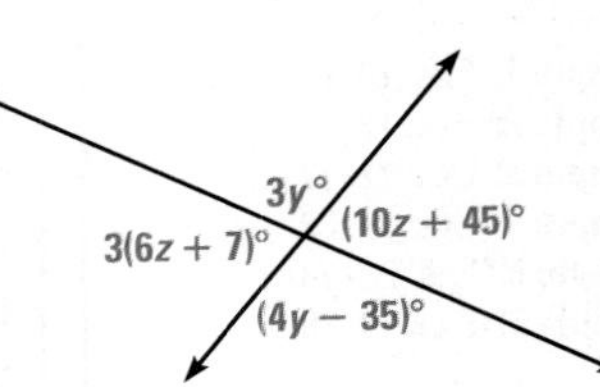

FOCUS ON APPLICATIONS

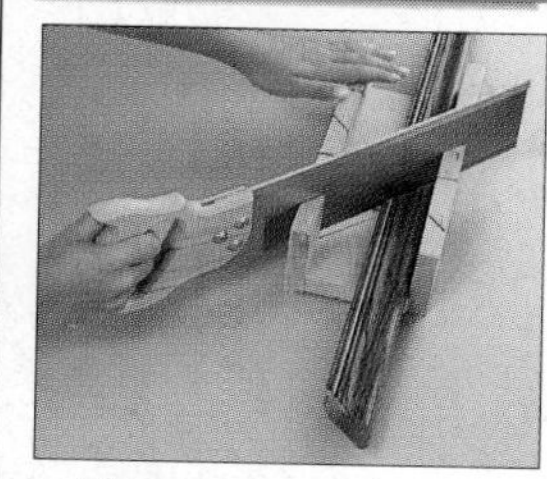

REAL LIFE **MITER BOX** This box has slotted sides to guide a saw when making angled cuts.

29. **WALL TRIM** A chair rail is a type of wall trim that is placed about three feet above the floor to protect the walls. Part of the chair rail below has been replaced because it was damaged. The edges of the replacement piece were angled for a better fit. In the diagram, $\angle 1$ and $\angle 2$ are supplementary, $\angle 3$ and $\angle 4$ are supplementary, and $\angle 2$ and $\angle 3$ each have measures of 50°. Is $\angle 1 \cong \angle 4$? Explain.

Yes. $\angle 2 \cong \angle 3$ and $\angle 1$ and $\angle 4$ are supplementary to congruent angles. $\angle 1 \cong \angle 4$ by the Congruent Supplements Theorem.

30. **PICTURE FRAMES** Suppose you are making a picture frame, as shown at the right. The corners are all right angles, and $m\angle 1 = m\angle 2 = 52°$. Is $\angle 4 \cong \angle 3$? Explain why or why not.

30. Yes. $m\angle 4 = 90° - 52° = 38°$. $m\angle 3 = 90° - 52° = 38°$. $\angle 4 \cong \angle 3$ by the definition of congruent angles

31. *Writing* Describe some instances of mitered, or angled, corners in the real world.

31. *Sample answers:* the walls of a room, a shoebox, a window frame, CD case

32. **TECHNOLOGY** Use geometry software to draw two overlapping right angles with a common vertex. Observe the measures of the three angles as one right angle is rotated about the other. What theorem does this illustrate?
Congruent Complements Theorem

Test Preparation

QUANTITATIVE COMPARISON **Choose the statement that is true about the diagram. In the diagram, $\angle 9$ is a right angle and $m\angle 3 = 42°$.**

Ⓐ The quantity in column A is greater.

Ⓑ The quantity in column B is greater.

Ⓒ The two quantities are equal.

Ⓓ The relationship can't be determined from the given information.

	Column A	Column B	
33.	$m\angle 3 + m\angle 4$	$m\angle 1 + m\angle 2$	C
34.	$m\angle 3 + m\angle 6$	$m\angle 7 + m\angle 8$	B
35.	$m\angle 5$	$3(m\angle 3)$	A
36.	$m\angle 7 + m\angle 8$	$m\angle 9$	C

★ Challenge

37. **PROOF** Write a two-column proof.

GIVEN ▶ $m\angle ZYQ = 45°$, $m\angle ZQP = 45°$

PROVE ▶ $\angle ZQR \cong \angle XYQ$

See margin.

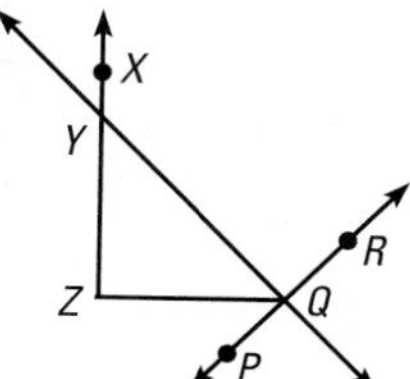

APPLICATION NOTE

EXERCISE 29 A chair rail is so named because it keeps a chair from hitting a wall. Miter boxes and coping saws are carpentry tools used to cut wood so that it can fit together around a corner as well as along a straight line.

26. $\angle 4$ and $\angle 5$ are vertical angles (Given)
$\angle 6$ and $\angle 7$ are vertical angles (Given)
$\angle 4 \cong \angle 5$, $\angle 6 \cong \angle 7$ (Vertical Angles Theorem)
$\angle 5 \cong \angle 6$ (Given)
$\angle 4 \cong \angle 7$ (Transitive Prop. of Angle Cong.)

37. See Additional Answers beginning on page AA1.

ADDITIONAL PRACTICE AND RETEACHING

For Lesson 2.6:

- Practice Levels A, B, and C (*Chapter 2 Resource Book*, p. 89)
- Reteaching with Practice (*Chapter 2 Resource Book*, p. 92)
- See Lesson 2.6 of the *Personal Student Tutor*

For more Mixed Review:

- Search the *Test and Practice Generator* for key words or specific lessons.

4 ASSESS

DAILY HOMEWORK QUIZ

Transparency Available

Make a sketch using the given information. Then state all the pairs of congruent angles.

1. $\angle 1$ and $\angle 2$ are vertical angles. $\angle 3$ and $\angle 4$ are vertical and supplementary angles. Check students' sketches; $\angle 1 \cong \angle 2 \cong \angle 3 \cong \angle 4$

Solve for each variable. Explain your reasoning.

2.

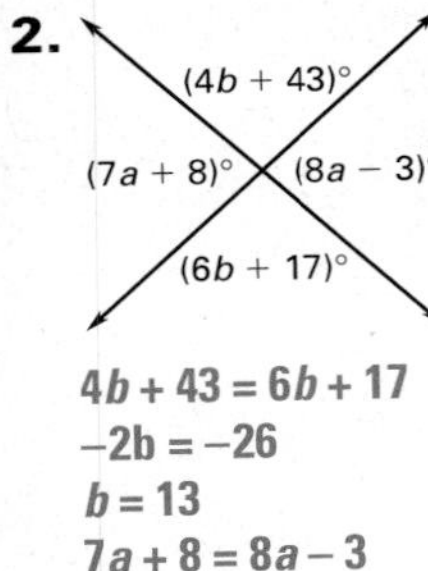

$4b + 43 = 6b + 17$
$-2b = -26$
$b = 13$
$7a + 8 = 8a - 3$
$-a = -11$
$a = 11$

EXTRA CHALLENGE NOTE

Challenge problems for Lesson 2.6 are available in **blackline** format in the *Chapter 2 Resource Book*, p. 96 and at **www.mcdougallittell.com.**

ADDITIONAL TEST PREPARATION

2. **WRITING** What does it mean for angle congruence to be symmetric? *Sample answer:* If you are given that $\angle A \cong \angle B$, then you can state that $\angle B \cong \angle A$.

1. $x - 3 = 7$ (Given)
 $x = 10$ (Addition prop. of equality)
2. $x + 8 = 27$ (Given)
 $x = 19$ (Subtraction prop. of equality)
3. $2x - 5 = 13$ (Given)
 $2x = 18$ (Addition prop. of equality)
 $x = 9$ (Division prop. of equality)

MIXED REVIEW

FINDING ANGLE MEASURES **In Exercises 38–40, the measure of $\angle 1$ and the relationship of $\angle 1$ to $\angle 2$ is given. Find $m\angle 2$.** (Review 1.6 for 3.1)

38. $m\angle 1 = 62°$, complementary to $\angle 2$ 28°

39. $m\angle 1 = 8°$, supplementary to $\angle 2$ 172°

40. $m\angle 1 = 47°$, complementary to $\angle 2$ 43°

41. **PERPENDICULAR LINES** The definition of perpendicular lines states that if two lines are perpendicular, then they intersect to form a right angle. Is the converse true? Explain. (Review 2.2 for 3.1)

41. All definitions are true biconditionals. So the conditionals "If two lines are perpendicular, then they intersect to form a right angle" and "If two lines intersect to form a right angle, then the two lines are perpendicular" are both true.

USING ALGEBRA **Use the diagram and the given information to solve for the variable.** (Review 2.5)

42. $\overline{AD} \cong \overline{EF}$, $\overline{EF} \cong \overline{CF}$ $w = 3$

43. $\overline{AB} \cong \overline{EF}$, $\overline{EF} \cong \overline{BC}$ $x = \frac{1}{2}$

44. $\overline{DE} \cong \overline{EF}$, $\overline{EF} \cong \overline{JK}$ $y = 2$

45. $\overline{JM} \cong \overline{ML}$, $\overline{ML} \cong \overline{KL}$ $z = \frac{1}{3}$

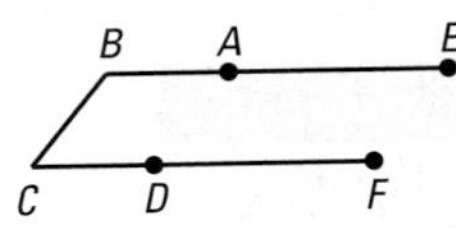

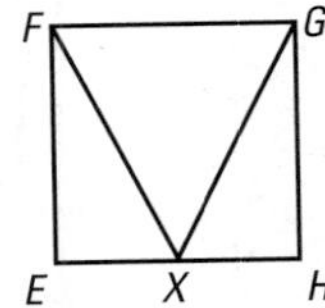

QUIZ 2

Self-Test for Lessons 2.4–2.6

Solve the equation and state a reason for each step. (Lesson 2.4) 1–6. See margin.

1. $x - 3 = 7$
2. $x + 8 = 27$
3. $2x - 5 = 13$
4. $2x + 20 = 4x - 12$
5. $3(3x - 7) = 6$
6. $-2(-2x + 4) = 16$

PROOF **In Exercises 7 and 8 write a two column proof.** (Lesson 2.5)

7. **GIVEN** ▶ $\overline{BA} \cong \overline{BC}$, $\overline{BC} \cong \overline{CD}$, $\overline{AE} \cong \overline{DF}$
 PROVE ▶ $\overline{BE} \cong \overline{CF}$ 7, 8. See margin.

B A E
C D F

8. **GIVEN** ▶ $\overline{EH} \cong \overline{GH}$, $\overline{FG} \cong \overline{GH}$
 PROVE ▶ $\overline{FG} \cong \overline{EH}$

F G
E X H

9. **ASTRONOMY** While looking through a telescope one night, you begin looking due east. You rotate the telescope straight upward until you spot a comet. The telescope forms a 142° angle with due east, as shown. What is the angle of inclination of the telescope from due west? (Lesson 2.6) 38°

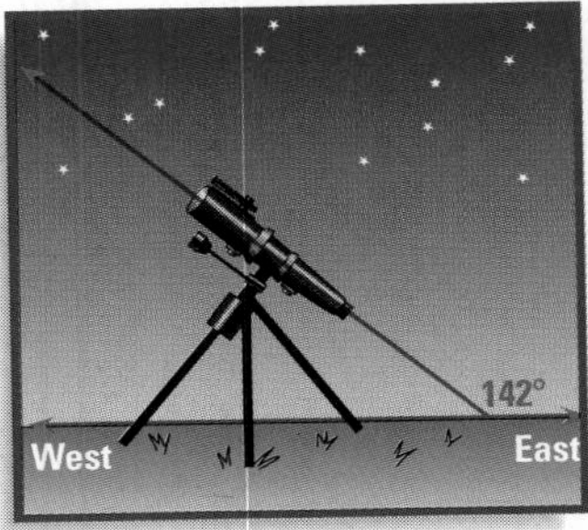

CHAPTER 2

Chapter Summary

WHAT did you learn?	*WHY did you learn it?*
Recognize and analyze conditional statements, and write their inverses, converses, and contrapositives. **(2.1)**	Use postulates about points, lines, and planes to analyze real-life objects, such as a research buggy. **(p. 77)**
Recognize and use definitions and biconditional statements. **(2.2)**	Rewrite postulates in a form suitable for solving a particular problem, such as analyzing geographic relations. **(p. 84)**
Use symbolic notation to represent logical statements. **(2.3)**	Decide whether a logical statement is valid. **(p. 89)**
Use the laws of logic to write a logical argument. **(2.3)**	Write true statements about birds using a list of facts about birds. **(p. 90)**
Use properties from algebra. **(2.4)**	Use properties from algebra to solve equations, such as an athlete's target heart rate. **(p. 97)**
Use properties of length and measure. **(2.4)**	Find the measure of the angle of a banked turn at the Talladega Superspeedway. **(p. 98)**
Use the properties of segment congruence to prove statements about segments. **(2.5)**	Prove statements about segments in real life, such as the segments in a trestle bridge. **(p. 104)**
Use the properties of angle congruence to prove properties about special pairs of angles. **(2.6)**	Decide which angles are congruent when constructing a picture frame. **(p. 115)**

How does it fit into the BIGGER PICTURE of geometry?

In this chapter, you were introduced to the formal side of geometry. You learned that the structure of geometry consists of undefined terms, defined terms, postulates, and theorems. You were also introduced to the need for proofs, and the form of a proof. In later chapters, you will study other ways to write proofs. The goal of writing a proof will remain the same—to convince a person about the truth of a statement.

STUDY STRATEGY

How was previewing each lesson helpful?

Some of the notes you made while previewing a lesson, following the **Study Strategy** on page 70, may resemble these.

Previewing Lesson 2.1

- Counterexamples were used in Lesson 1.1 to show that a statement was not always true. Lesson 2.1 seems to use counterexamples for the same reason.
- Postulate was defined in Chapter 1, and four postulates were presented. Lesson 2.1 presents seven more postulates.

4. $2x + 20 = 4x - 12$ (Given)
$-2x + 20 = -12$ (Subtraction prop. of equality)
$-2x = -32$ (Subtraction prop. of equality)
$x = 16$ (Division prop. of equality)
5. $3(3x - 7) = 6$ (Given)
$9x - 21 = 6$ (Distributive prop.)
$9x = 27$ (Addition prop. of equality)
$x = 3$ (Division prop. of equality)
6. $-2(-2x + 4) = 16$ (Given)
$4x - 8 = 16$ (Distributive prop.)
$4x = 24$ (Addition prop. of equality)
$x = 6$ (Division prop. of equality)
7. $\overline{BA} \cong \overline{BC}$, $\overline{BC} \cong \overline{CD}$ (Given)
$\overline{BA} \cong \overline{CD}$ (Transitive Prop. of Segment Cong.)
$\overline{AE} \cong \overline{DF}$ (Given)
$BA + AE = BE$ (Segment Addition Post.)
$BA = CD$ (Definition of congruent segments)
$AE = DF$ (Definition of congruent segments)
$CD + DF = BE$ (Substitution prop. of equality)
$CD + DF = CF$ (Segment Addition Post.)
$BE = CF$ (Transitive prop. of equality)
$\overline{BE} \cong \overline{CF}$ (Definition of congruent segments)
8. $\overline{EH} \cong \overline{GH}$, $\overline{FG} \cong \overline{GH}$ (Given)
$\overline{EH} \cong \overline{FG}$ (Transitive Prop. of Segment Cong.)

ADDITIONAL RESOURCES

The following resources are available to help review the material in this chapter.

- Chapter Review Games and Activities (*Chapter 2 Resource Book,* p. 98)
- *Geometry in Motion video*
- *Personal Student Tutor*
- Cumulative Review, Chs. 1–2 (*Chapter 2 Resource Book,* p. 110)

1. If-then form: If there is a teacher's meeting, then we are dismissed early; hypothesis: there is a teacher's meeting; conclusion: we are dismissed early; inverse: If there is not a teacher's meeting, then we are not dismissed early; converse: If we are dismissed early, then there is a teacher's meeting; contrapositive: If we are not dismissed early, then there is not a teacher's meeting.
2. If-then form: If it is Wednesday night, then I prepare dinner; hypothesis: it is Wednesday night; conclusion: I prepare dinner; inverse: If it is not Wednesday night, then I do not prepare dinner; converse: If I prepare dinner, then it is Wednesday night; contrapositive: If I do not prepare dinner, then it is not Wednesday night.
7. If the measure of $\angle A$ is 90°, then $\angle A$ is a right angle.
8. If the measure of $\angle A$ is not 90°, then $\angle A$ is not a right angle.
9. $\angle A$ is not a right angle.
10. If $\angle A$ is not a right angle, then the measure of $\angle A$ is not 90°.

CHAPTER 2

Chapter Review

VOCABULARY

- conditional statement, p. 71
- if-then form, p. 71
- hypothesis, p. 71
- conclusion, p. 71
- converse, p. 72
- negation, p. 72
- inverse, p. 72
- contrapositive, p. 72
- equivalent statement, p. 72
- perpendicular lines, p. 79
- line perpendicular to a plane, p. 79
- biconditional statement, p. 80
- logical argument, p. 89
- Law of Detachment, p. 89
- Law of Syllogism, p. 90
- theorem, p. 102
- two-column proof, p. 102
- paragraph proof, p. 102

2.1 CONDITIONAL STATEMENTS

Examples on pp. 71–74

EXAMPLES

If-then form	If a person is 2 meters tall, then he or she is 6.56 feet tall.
Inverse	If a person is not 2 meters tall, then he or she is not 6.56 feet tall.
Converse	If a person is 6.56 feet tall, then he or she is 2 meters tall.
Contrapositive	If a person is not 6.56 feet tall, then he or she is not 2 meters tall.

Write the statement in if-then form. Determine the hypothesis and conclusion, and write the inverse, converse, and contrapositive. 1, 2. See margin.

1. We are dismissed early if there is a teacher's meeting.
2. I prepare dinner on Wednesday nights.

Fill in the blank. Then draw a sketch that illustrates your answer.

3. Through any three noncollinear points there exists __?__ plane. exactly one
4. A line contains at least __?__ points. two

2.2 DEFINITIONS AND BICONDITIONAL STATEMENTS

Examples on pp. 79–81

EXAMPLE The statement "If a number ends in 0, then the number is divisible by 10," and its converse "If a number is divisible by 10, then the number ends in 0," are both true. This means that the statement can be written as the true biconditional statement, "A number is divisible by 10 if and only if it ends in 0."

Can the statement be written as a true biconditional statement?

5. If $x = 5$, then $x^2 = 25$.
No. If $x^2 = 25$ does not necessarily mean that $x = 5$. x could also $= -5$.
6. A rectangle is a square if it has four congruent sides.
Yes. If a figure is a square, then it is a rectangle with four congruent sides.

2.3 DEDUCTIVE REASONING

Examples on pp. 87–90

EXAMPLES Using symbolic notation, let p be "it is summer" and let q be "school is closed."

Statement	$p \rightarrow q$	If it is summer, then school is closed.
Inverse	$\sim p \rightarrow \sim q$	If it is not summer, then school is not closed.
Converse	$q \rightarrow p$	If the school is closed, then it is summer.
Contrapositive	$\sim q \rightarrow \sim p$	If school is not closed, then it is not summer.

Write the symbolic statement in words using p and q given below.
7–10. See margin.

p: $\angle A$ is a right angle. q: The measure of $\angle A$ is 90°.

7. $q \rightarrow p$ **8.** $\sim q \rightarrow \sim p$ **9.** $\sim p$ **10.** $\sim p \rightarrow \sim q$

Use the Law of Syllogism to write the statement that follows from the pair of true statements.

11. If there is a nice breeze, then the mast is up.

If the mast is up, then we will sail to Dunkirk.
If there is a nice breeze, then we will sail to Dunkirk.

12. If Chess Club meets today, then it is Thursday.

If it is Thursday, then the garbage needs to be taken out.
If the Chess Club meets today, then the garbage needs to be taken out.

2.4 REASONING WITH PROPERTIES FROM ALGEBRA

Examples on pp. 96–98

EXAMPLE In the diagram, $m\angle 1 + m\angle 2 = 132°$ and $m\angle 2 = 105°$. The argument shows that $m\angle 1 = 27°$.

$m\angle 1 + m\angle 2 = 132°$	Given
$m\angle 2 = 105°$	Given
$m\angle 1 + 105° = 132°$	Substitution property of equality
$m\angle 1 = 27°$	Subtraction property of equality

Match the statement with the property.

13. If $m\angle S = 45°$, then $m\angle S + 45° = 90°$. C

14. If $UV = VW$, then $VW = UV$. A

15. If $AE = EG$ and $EG = JK$, then $AE = JK$. D

16. If $m\angle K = 9°$, then $3(m\angle K) = 27°$. B

A. Symmetric property of equality

B. Multiplication property of equality

C. Addition property of equality

D. Transitive property of equality

Solve the equation and state a reason for each step. 17–19. See margin.

17. $5(3y + 2) = 25$ **18.** $8t - 4 = 5t + 8$ **19.** $23 + 11d - 2c = 12 - 2c$

17. $5(3y + 2) = 25$ (Given)
$15y + 10 = 25$ (Distributive prop.)
$15y = 15$ (Subtraction prop. of equality)
$y = 1$ (Division prop. of equality)

18. $8t - 4 = 5t + 8$ (Given)
$3t - 4 = 8$ (Subtraction prop. of equality)
$3t = 12$ (Addition prop. of equality)
$t = 4$ (Division prop. of equality)

19. $23 + 11d - 2c = 12 - 2c$ (Given)
$23 + 11d = 12$ (Addition prop. of equality)
$11d = -11$ (Subtraction prop. of equality)
$d = -1$ (Division prop. of equality)

20. $\overline{AE} \cong \overline{BD}$, $\overline{CD} \cong \overline{CE}$ (Given)
$AE = BD$, $CD = CE$ (Definition of congruent segments)
$AE = AC + CE$ (Segment Addition Post.)
$BD = AC + CD$ (Substitution prop. of equality)
$AC = BD - CD$ (Subtraction prop. of equality)
$BD = BC + CD$ (Segment Addition Post.)
$BC = BD - CD$ (Subtraction prop. of equality)
$AC = BC$ (Transitive prop. of equality)
$\overline{AC} \cong \overline{BC}$ (Definition of congruent segments)

21. $\angle 1$ and $\angle 2$ are complementary (Given)
$\angle 3$ and $\angle 4$ are complementary (Given)
$\angle 1 \cong \angle 3$ (Given)
$\angle 2 \cong \angle 4$ (Congruent Complements Theorem)

2.5 PROVING STATEMENTS ABOUT SEGMENTS

Examples on pp. 102–104

EXAMPLE A proof that shows $AC = 2 \cdot BC$ is shown below.

GIVEN ▶ $AB = BC$

PROVE ▶ $AC = 2 \cdot BC$

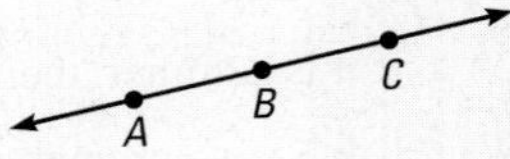

Statements	Reasons
1. $AB = BC$	**1.** Given
2. $AC = AB + BC$	**2.** Segment Addition Postulate
3. $AC = BC + BC$	**3.** Substitution property of equality
4. $AC = 2 \cdot BC$	**4.** Distributive property

20. Write a two-column proof. **See margin.**

GIVEN ▶ $\overline{AE} \cong \overline{BD}$, $\overline{CD} \cong \overline{CE}$

PROVE ▶ $\overline{AC} \cong \overline{BC}$

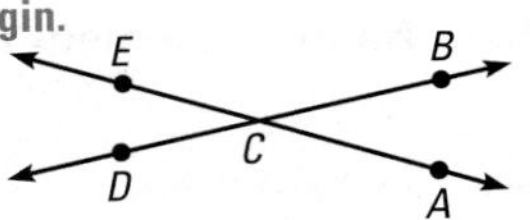

2.6 PROVING STATEMENTS ABOUT ANGLES

Examples on pp. 109–112

EXAMPLE A proof that shows $\angle 2 \cong \angle 3$ is shown below.

GIVEN ▶ $\angle 1$ and $\angle 2$ form a linear pair,
$\angle 3$ and $\angle 4$ form a linear pair,
$\angle 1 \cong \angle 4$

PROVE ▶ $\angle 2 \cong \angle 3$

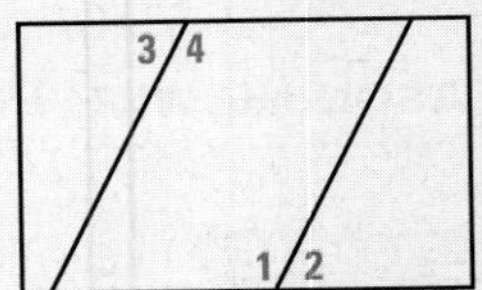

Statements	Reasons
1. $\angle 1$ and $\angle 2$ form a linear pair, $\angle 3$ and $\angle 4$ form a linear pair, $\angle 1 \cong \angle 4$	**1.** Given
2. $\angle 1$ and $\angle 2$ are supplementary, $\angle 3$ and $\angle 4$ are supplementary	**2.** Linear Pair Postulate
3. $\angle 2 \cong \angle 3$	**3.** Congruent Supplements Theorem

21. Write a two-column proof using the given information. **See margin.**

GIVEN ▶ $\angle 1$ and $\angle 2$ are complementary,
$\angle 3$ and $\angle 4$ are complementary,
$\angle 1 \cong \angle 3$

PROVE ▶ $\angle 2 \cong \angle 4$

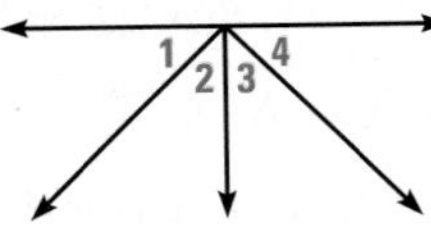

CHAPTER 2

Chapter Test

State the postulate that shows that the statement is false.

1. Plane R contains only two points A and B. **Postulate 9: A plane contains at least three noncollinear points.**
2. Plane M and plane N are two distinct planes that intersect at exactly two distinct points. **Postulate 11: If two planes intersect, then their intersection is a line.**
3. Any three noncollinear points define at least three distinct planes. **Postulate 8: Through any three noncollinear points there exists exactly one plane.**
4. Points A and B are two distinct points in plane Q. Line $\overleftrightarrow{AB}$ does not intersect plane Q. **Postulate 10: If two points lie in a plane, then the line containing them lies in the plane.**

Find a counterexample that demonstrates that the converse of the statement is false.

5. If an angle measures 34°, then the angle is acute. **A 60° angle is acute, but it does not measure 34°.**
6. If the lengths of two segments are each 17 feet, then the segments are congruent. **Two segments of lengths 10 feet each are congruent, but their lengths do not measure 17 feet.**
7. If two angles measure 32° and 148°, then they are supplementary. **Two angles of measure 130° and 50° are supplementary, but their measures do not equal 32° and 148°.**
8. If you chose number 13, then you chose a prime number. **You can chose the prime number 7, which is not equal to 13.**

State what conclusions can be made if $x = 5$ and the given statement is true.

9. If $x > x - 2$, then $y = 14x$. **$y = 70$**
10. If $-x < 2x < 11$, then $x = y - 12$. **$y = 17$**
11. If $|x| > -x$, then $y = -x$. **$y = -5$**
12. If $y = 4x$, then $z = 2x + y$. **$z = 30$**

In Exercises 13–16, name the property used to make the conclusion.

13. If $13 = x$, then $x = 13$. **Symmetric property of equality**
14. If $x = 3$, then $5x = 15$. **Multiplication property of equality**
15. If $x = y$ and $y = 4$, then $x = 4$. **Transitive property of equality**
16. If $x + 3 = 17$, then $x = 14$. **Subtraction property of equality**

17. **PROOF** Write a two-column proof.

GIVEN ▶ $\overline{AX} \cong \overline{DX}$, $\overline{XB} \cong \overline{XC}$

PROVE ▶ $\overline{AC} \cong \overline{BD}$

See margin.

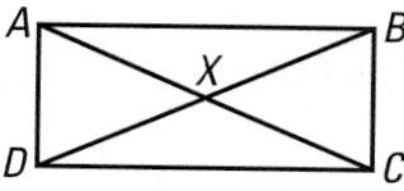

18. **PLUMBING** A plumber is replacing a small section of a leaky pipe. To find the length of new pipe that he will need, he first measures the leaky section of the old pipe with a steel tape measure, and then uses this measure to find the same length of new pipe. What property of segment congruence does this process illustrate? Use the wording of the property to explain how it is illustrated. **See margin.**

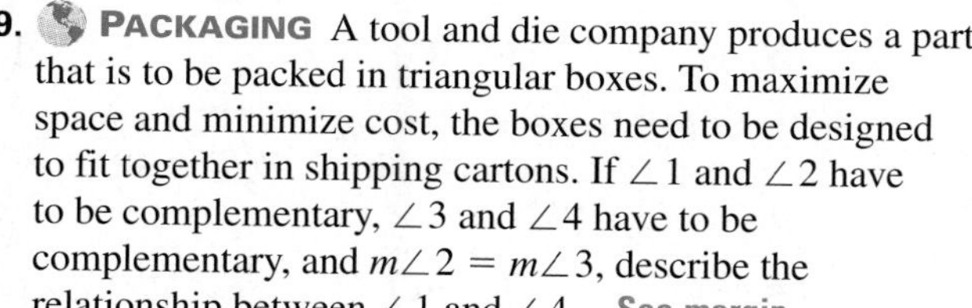

19. **PACKAGING** A tool and die company produces a part that is to be packed in triangular boxes. To maximize space and minimize cost, the boxes need to be designed to fit together in shipping cartons. If $\angle 1$ and $\angle 2$ have to be complementary, $\angle 3$ and $\angle 4$ have to be complementary, and $m\angle 2 = m\angle 3$, describe the relationship between $\angle 1$ and $\angle 4$. **See margin.**

ADDITIONAL RESOURCES

- ***Chapter 2 Resource Book***
  Chapter Test (3 levels) (p. 99)
  SAT/ACT Chapter Test (p. 105)
  Alternative Assessment (p. 106)
- ***Test and Practice Generator***

17. $\overline{AX} \cong \overline{DX}$, $\overline{XB} \cong \overline{XC}$ (Given)
$AX = DX$, $XB = XC$ (Definition of congruent segments)
$AC = AX + XC$ (Segment Addition Post.)
$DB = DX + XB$ (Segment Addition Post.)
$AC = DX + XB$ (Substitution prop. of equality)
$DB = AC$ (Transitive prop. of equality)
$\overline{DB} \cong \overline{AC}$ (Definition of congruent segments)

18. The process illustrates the Transitive Property of Segment Congruence which states, if $\overline{AB} \cong \overline{CD}$ and $\overline{CD} \cong \overline{EF}$, then $\overline{AB} \cong \overline{EF}$. The length of leaky pipe represents the length of $\overline{AB}$, the length measured on the steel tape measure represents the length of $\overline{CD}$, and the length of new pipe represents the length of $\overline{EF}$.

19. If $\angle 1$ and $\angle 2$ are complementary, and $\angle 3$ and $\angle 4$ are complementary, and $m\angle 2 = m\angle 3$, then $\angle 1 \cong \angle 4$. The Congruent Complements Theorem states that if two angles are complementary to the same angle or to congruent angles, then the two angles are congruent. $\angle 1$ and $\angle 4$ are complementary to congruent angles, $\angle 2$ and $\angle 3$, so $\angle 1$ and $\angle 4$ are congruent.

ADDITIONAL RESOURCES

- ***Chapter 2 Resource Book***
  Chapter Test (3 levels) (p. 99)
  SAT/ACT Chapter Test (p. 105)
  Alternative Assessment (p. 106)
- ***Test and Practice Generator***

CHAPTER 2

Chapter Standardized Test

TEST-TAKING STRATEGY Make sure that you are familiar with the directions before taking a standardized test. This way, you do not need to worry about the directions during the test.

1. **MULTIPLE CHOICE** What is the contrapositive of "If it is Tuesday, then Marie has soccer practice?" C

   (A) If it is not Tuesday, then Marie does not have soccer practice.

   (B) If Marie has soccer practice, then it is Tuesday.

   (C) If Marie does not have soccer practice, then it is not Tuesday.

   (D) Marie has soccer practice if and only if it is Tuesday.

   (E) None of the above.

2. **MULTIPLE CHOICE** Which statement about the diagram is *not* true? A

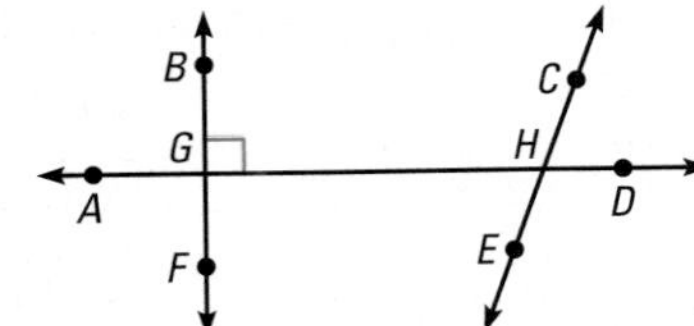

   (A) $\angle GHE$ is adjacent to $\angle CHD$.

   (B) $\overline{BF}$ is perpendicular to $\overline{AH}$.

   (C) $\angle BGH$ and $\angle BGA$ are supplementary.

   (D) $\angle GHC \cong \angle EHD$

   (E) $m\angle BGH = 90°$

3. **QUANTITATIVE COMPARISON** Two quantities are described below. C

Column A	Column B
The number of lines that can be drawn through two points.	The number of planes that can be drawn through three noncollinear points.

   Choose the statement that is true.

   (A) The quantity in column A is greater.

   (B) The quantity in column B is greater.

   (C) The two quantities are equal.

   (D) The relationship cannot be determined from the given information.

4. **MULTIPLE CHOICE** "If $m\angle A = 75°$, then $10° + m\angle A = 85°$" is an example of the B

   (A) Substitution property of equality.

   (B) Addition property of equality.

   (C) Symmetric property of equality.

   (D) Subtraction property of equality.

   (E) Distributive property.

5. **MULTIPLE CHOICE** In the diagram, $\overline{AB} \cong \overline{CD}$. Find the length of $\overline{CA}$. E

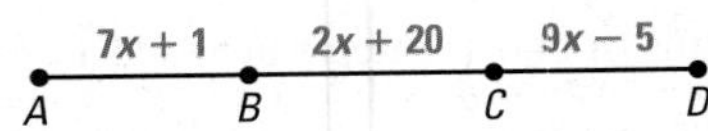

   (A) 22 (B) 26 (C) 39
   (D) 44 (E) 48

6. **MULTIPLE CHOICE** Let p be "there is lightning" and let q be "we cannot go hiking." What is the converse of $p \to q$? C

   (A) If there is lightning, then we cannot go hiking.

   (B) If we can go hiking, then there is no lightning.

   (C) If we cannot go hiking, then there is lightning.

   (D) If there is no lightning, then we can go hiking.

   (E) None of the above.

7. **MULTIPLE CHOICE** In $WXYZ$, $\overline{WZ} \cong \overline{YZ}$ and $\overline{YX} \cong \overline{YZ}$. What is the value of x? C

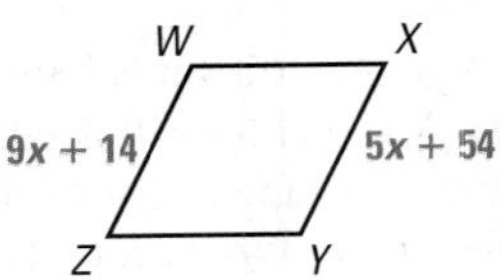

   (A) 4 (B) 9 (C) 10
   (D) 12 (E) 16

8. **MULTIPLE CHOICE** Two angles $\angle PQR$ and $\angle RQS$ form a linear pair. If $m\angle PQR = 48°$, what is $m\angle RQS$? D

   (A) 42° (B) 48° (C) 90°
   (D) 132° (E) 180°

9. MULTIPLE CHOICE Two angles, $\angle 7$ and $\angle 8$, are both complementary to $\angle 9$. If $m\angle 7 = 61°$, what is $m\angle 8$? B

Ⓐ 29° Ⓑ 61° Ⓒ 90° Ⓓ 119° Ⓔ 180°

10. MULTIPLE CHOICE In the diagram below, $\angle 1 \cong \angle 2$. Which of the following is *not* true? E

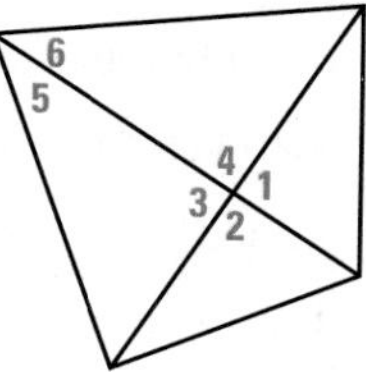

Ⓐ $\angle 1 \cong \angle 4$

Ⓑ $m\angle 1 + m\angle 2 = 180°$

Ⓒ $\angle 1 \cong \angle 3$

Ⓓ $\angle 2$ and $\angle 4$ are supplementary.

Ⓔ $m\angle 6 = m\angle 4$

MULTI-STEP PROBLEM In Exercises 11–13, use the diagram. In the diagram, $\overleftrightarrow{BF} \perp \overleftrightarrow{HD}$ and $\overleftrightarrow{GC} \perp \overleftrightarrow{AE}$.

11. Complete each statement.

a. If $m\angle 3 = 31°$, then $m\angle 5 = \underline{\ ?\ }$. 31°

b. If $m\angle 5 = 29°$, then $m\angle 4 = \underline{\ ?\ }$. 61°

c. If $m\angle CAF = 122°$, then $m\angle GAB = \underline{\ ?\ }$. 122°

d. If $m\angle 7 = 35°$, then $m\angle 3 = \underline{\ ?\ }$. 35°

12. Write a two-column proof that shows $\angle BAH \cong \angle CAE$. See margin.

13. Write a paragraph proof that shows $\angle 6 \cong \angle 2$. See margin.

MULTI-STEP PROBLEM In Exercises 14–17, use the following information.

The International Space Station (ISS) is a NASA project which will involve about 45 launch missions. The space station is scheduled for completion in early 2004. The diagram shows a portion of the space station. In the diagram, $\overline{AE} \perp \overline{XC}$ and X is the midpoint of $\overline{AE}$.

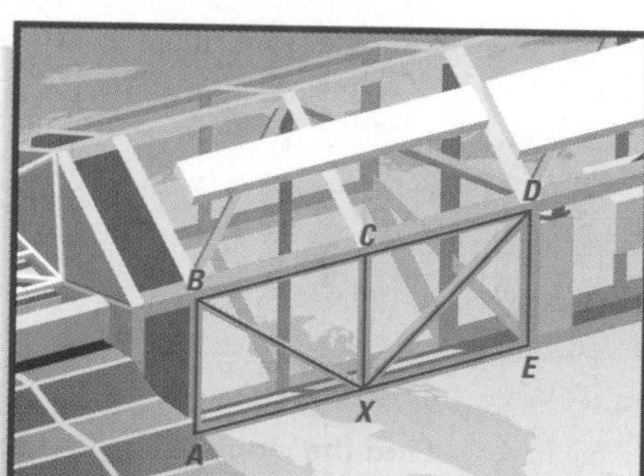
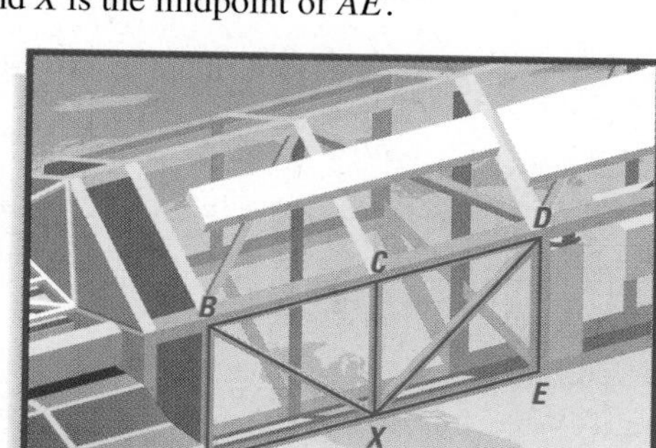

14. Are $\angle DXC$ and $\angle DXE$ complementary or supplementary? Complementary.

15. Determine whether there is enough information to prove each of the following. If so, write a plan for the proof.

a. $\overline{XE} \cong \overline{XC}$ No.

b. $\angle AXC \cong \angle EXC$ Yes; show that both are 90° angles and are thus congruent.

c. $\overline{EX} \cong \overline{AX}$ Yes; show that each segment has length $\frac{1}{2}AE$.

16. Tell whether the statement is *true* or *false*.

a. $m\angle BXD + m\angle BXE = m\angle EXA$ False.

b. $m\angle AXD + m\angle DXE = m\angle EXA$ True.

c. $m\angle AXD + m\angle DXB = m\angle EXA$ False.

17. Write a two-column proof to show that $\angle BXA$ and $\angle CXB$ are complementary. See margin.

12. $\overleftrightarrow{BF} \perp \overleftrightarrow{HD}$ (Given)
$m\angle BAH = 90°$, $m\angle BAD = 90°$ (Definition of perpendicular lines)
$\overleftrightarrow{GC} \perp \overleftrightarrow{AE}$ (Given)
$m\angle GAE = 90°$, $m\angle CAE = 90°$ (Definition of perpendicular lines)
$m\angle BAH = m\angle CAE$ (Transitive prop. of equality)
$\angle BAH \cong \angle CAE$ (Definition of congruent angles)

13. You are given that $\angle 6$ and $\angle 2$ are vertical angles. By the Vertical Angles Theorem, vertical angles are congruent. Therefore $\angle 6 \cong \angle 2$.

17. $\overline{AE} \perp \overline{XC}$ (Given)
$\angle CXA$ is a right $\angle$ (Def. of perpendicular)
$m\angle CXA = 90°$ (Def. of a right $\angle$)
$m\angle BXA + m\angle CXB = m\angle CXA$ (Angle Addition Post.)
$m\angle BXA + m\angle CXB = 90°$ (Substitution Prop. of Equality)
$\angle BXA$ and $\angle CXB$ are complementary (Def. of complementary $\angle$s)

EXTRA EXAMPLE 1
Decide whether (–4, 7) is a solution of the equation $y = -\frac{3}{2}x + 4$. no

EXTRA EXAMPLE 2
Find the slope of a line passing through (–5, 2) and (0, –3). –1

CHECKPOINT EXERCISES

For use after Example 1:

1. Decide whether (0, 2) is a solution of the equation $3x - y = -2$. yes

For use after Example 2:

2. Find the slope of a line passing through (–3, 2) and (9, –7). $-\frac{3}{4}$

CHAPTER 2

Algebra Review

EXAMPLE 1 Determining Whether a Point is on a Line

Decide whether $(3, -2)$ is a solution of the equation $y = 2x - 8$.

$-2 = 2(3) - 8$ **Substitute 3 for *x* and −2 for *y*.**

$-2 = -2$ **Simplify.**

The statement is true, so $(3, -2)$ is a solution of the equation $y = 2x - 8$.

STUDENT HELP

Look Back
For help with the properties of equality, see p. 96.

EXERCISES

Decide whether the given ordered pair is a solution of the equation.

1. $y = 6x + 4$; $(-2, 8)$ no
2. $y = -10x - 2$; $(1, -12)$ yes
3. $y = -\frac{1}{4}x - 18$; $(-4, -17)$ yes
4. $y = \frac{3}{2}x + 10$; $(4, 12)$ no
5. $y = \frac{5}{9}x + 34$; $(-9, 27)$ no
6. $y = \frac{2}{3}x - 6$; $(9, 0)$ yes
7. $y = \frac{4}{5}x - 2$; $(10, -3)$ no
8. $y = \frac{1}{2}x + 7$; $(4, 7)$ no
9. $2x - 3y = 10$; $(3, 4)$ no
10. $9x - y = -4$; $(-1, -5)$ yes
11. $y - 6 = \frac{3}{4}x$; $(8, 12)$ yes
12. $y + 5 = \frac{5}{3}x$; $(9, 10)$ yes

EXAMPLE 2 Calculating Slope

Find the slope of a line passing through $(3, -9)$ and $(2, -1)$.

$m = \frac{y_2 - y_1}{x_2 - x_1}$ **Formula for slope**

$m = \frac{-1 - (-9)}{2 - 3} = \frac{-1 + 9}{-1}$ **Substitute values and simplify.**

$m = \frac{8}{-1} = -8$ **Slope is −8.**

EXERCISES

Find the slope of the line that contains the points.

13. $(4, 1), (3, 6)$ -5
14. $(-8, 0), (5, -2)$ $-\frac{2}{13}$
15. $(5, 6), (9, 8)$ $\frac{1}{2}$
16. $(0, -4), (7, -3)$ $\frac{1}{7}$
17. $(-1, 7), (-3, 18)$ $-\frac{11}{2}$
18. $(-6, -4), (1, 10)$ 2
19. $(4, -10), (-2, 2)$ -2
20. $(11, 1), (-11, 1)$ 0
21. $(14, -5), (5, 8)$ $-\frac{13}{9}$
22. $(-7, 5), (-1, -1)$ -1
23. $(-12, 8), (-3, -6)$ $-\frac{14}{9}$
24. $(-9, 13), (2, -10)$ $-\frac{23}{11}$
25. $(12, 3), (0, -4)$ $\frac{7}{12}$
26. $(9, -8), (-7, 10)$ $-\frac{9}{8}$
27. $(2, -5), (6, -6)$ $-\frac{1}{4}$

EXAMPLE 3 Finding the Equation of a Line

Find an equation of the line that passes through the point (3, 4) and has a y-intercept of 5.

$y = mx + b$	Write the slope-intercept form.
$4 = 3m + 5$	Substitute 5 for b, 3 for x, and 4 for y.
$-1 = 3m$	Subtract 5 from each side.
$-\frac{1}{3} = m$	Divide each side by 3.

The slope is $m = -\frac{1}{3}$. The equation of the line is $y = -\frac{1}{3}x + 5$.

EXERCISES

Write the equation of the line that passes through the given point and has the given y-intercept. See margin.

28. $(2, 1); b = 5$ **29.** $(-5, 3); b = -12$ **30.** $(-3, 10); b = 8$

31. $(7, 0); b = 13$ **32.** $(-3, -3); b = -2$ **33.** $(-1, 4); b = -8$

34. $(-11, 8); b = -14$ **35.** $(4, -6); b = -2$ **36.** $(5, -8); b = 7$

37. $(-2, -1); b = -5$ **38.** $(2, 3); b = 2$ **39.** $(3, 0.5); b = 1.5$

EXAMPLE 4 Finding the Equation of a Line

Write an equation of the line that passes through the points (4, 8) and (3, 1).

Find the slope of the line.

$m = \frac{1-8}{3-4}$	Substitute values.
$m = \frac{-7}{-1} = 7$	Simplify.
$1 = 7(3) + b$	Substitute values into $y = mx + b$.
$1 = 21 + b$	Multiply.
$-20 = b$	Solve for b.

The equation of the line is $y = 7x - 20$.

EXERCISES

Write an equation of the line that passes through the given points. See margin.

40. $(6, -3), (1, 2)$ **41.** $(-7, 9), (-5, 3)$ **42.** $(5, -1), (4, -5)$

43. $(-2, 4), (3, -6)$ **44.** $(-3, -7), (0, 8)$ **45.** $(1, 2), (-1, -4)$

46. $(6, -2), (0, 4)$ **47.** $(-4, 3), (-3, -3)$ **48.** $(-3, 2), (-5, -2)$

49. $(10, -9), (14, -1)$ **50.** $(-1, -2), (5, 0)$ **51.** $(-6, 4), (6, -1)$

28. $y = -2x + 5$
29. $y = -3x - 12$
30. $y = -\frac{2}{3}x + 8$
31. $y = -\frac{13}{7}x + 13$
32. $y = \frac{1}{3}x - 2$
33. $y = -12x - 8$
34. $y = -2x - 14$
35. $y = -x - 2$
36. $y = -3x + 7$
37. $y = -2x - 5$
38. $y = \frac{1}{2}x + 2$
39. $y = -\frac{1}{3}x + 1.5$
40. $y = -x + 3$
41. $y = -3x - 12$
42. $y = 4x - 21$
43. $y = -2x$
44. $y = 5x + 8$
45. $y = 3x - 1$
46. $y = -x + 4$
47. $y = -6x - 21$
48. $y = 2x + 8$
49. $y = 2x - 29$
50. $y = \frac{1}{3}x - \frac{5}{3}$
51. $y = -\frac{5}{12}x + \frac{3}{2}$

EXTRA EXAMPLE 3
Find an equation of the line that passes through (2, –5) with y-intercept –3. $y = -x - 3$

EXTRA EXAMPLE 4
Write an equation of the line that passes through the points (–3, 8) and (5, 2). $y = -\frac{3}{4}x + \frac{23}{4}$

CHECKPOINT EXERCISES

For use after Examples 1 and 2:

1. Find an equation of the line that passes through (–6, 1) with y-intercept 3. $y = \frac{1}{3}x + 3$

For use after Extra Example 4:

2. Write an equation of the line that passes through the points (2, 2) and (5, –13). $y = -5x + 12$

CHAPTER 3

PLANNING THE CHAPTER

Perpendicular and Parallel Lines

GOALS

Lesson	Goals	NCTM	ITED	SAT9 (TASK 1)	Terra-Nova	Local
3.1 *pp. 129–134*	GOAL 1 Identify relationships between lines. GOAL 2 Identify angles formed by transversals.	3	MIGE	28	14	7, 16
3.2 *pp. 135–141*	CONCEPT ACTIVITY: 3.2 *Investigate forming a flow proof.* GOAL 1 Write different types of proofs. GOAL 2 Prove results about perpendicular lines.	3, 7, 8	MIGE	28	14, 17, 18	2, 4
3.3 *pp. 142–149*	TECHNOLOGY ACTIVITY: 3.3 *Explore the properties of parallel lines using geometry software.* GOAL 1 Prove and use results about parallel lines and transversals. GOAL 2 Use properties of parallel lines to solve real-life problems.	3, 6, 7, 8, 9, 10	MIGE, RQGE	1, 28	14, 17, 18	4, 7
3.4 *pp. 150–156*	GOAL 1 Prove that two lines are parallel. GOAL 2 Use properties of parallel lines to solve real-life problems.	3, 6, 7, 8, 9, 10	MIGE, RQGE	1, 28	14, 17, 18	4, 7
3.5 *pp. 157–164*	GOAL 1 Use properties of parallel lines in real-life situations. GOAL 2 Construct parallel lines using straightedge and compass.	3, 9, 10	MIGE	28	14	7, 16
3.6 *pp. 165–171*	GOAL 1 Find slopes of lines and use slope to identify parallel lines in a coordinate plane. GOAL 2 Write equations of parallel lines in a coordinate plane.	1, 2, 3, 4, 8, 9, 10	MCWN, MIGE	28	11, 13, 14, 16, 18, 48, 49, 51	17
3.7 *pp. 172–178*	GOAL 1 Use slope to identify perpendicular lines in a coordinate plane. GOAL 2 Write equations of perpendicular lines.	1, 2, 3, 4, 8, 9, 10	MCWN, MIGE	28	11, 13, 14, 16, 18, 48, 49, 51, 52	17

RESOURCES

Chapter Resource Booklets

Chapter Support

Tips for New Teachers	p. 1	Prerequisite Skills Review	p. 5
Parent Guide for Student Success	p. 3	Strategies for Reading Mathematics	p. 7

Lesson Support

Lesson Support	3.1	3.2	3.3	3.4	3.5	3.6	3.7
Lesson Plans (regular and block)	p. 9	p. 21	p. 34	p. 49	p. 66	p. 80	p. 93
Warm-Up Exercises and Daily Quiz	p. 11	p. 23	p. 36	p. 51	p. 68	p. 82	p. 95
Activity Support Masters		p. 24					
Lesson Openers	p. 12	p. 25	p. 37	p. 52	p. 69	p. 83	p. 96
Technology Activities & Keystrokes			p. 38	p. 53		p. 84	p. 97
Practice (3 levels)	p. 13	p. 26	p. 40	p. 57	p. 70	p. 85	p. 100
Reteaching with Practice	p. 16	p. 29	p. 43	p. 60	p. 73	p. 88	p. 103
Quick Catch-Up for Absent Students	p. 18	p. 31	p. 45	p. 62	p. 75	p. 90	p. 105
Cooperative Learning Activities				p. 63			p. 106
Interdisciplinary Applications	p. 19		p. 46		p. 76		p. 107
Real-Life Applications		p. 32		p. 64		p. 91	
Math & History Applications					p. 77		
Challenge: Skills and Applications	p. 20	p. 33	p. 47	p. 65	p. 78	p. 92	p. 108

Review and Assessment

Quizzes	pp. 48, 79	Alternative Assessment with Math Journal	p. 117
Chapter Review Games and Activities	p. 109	Project with Rubric	p. 119
Chapter Test (3 levels)	pp. 110–115	Cumulative Review	p. 121
SAT/ACT Chapter Test	p. 116	Resource Book Answers	p. A1

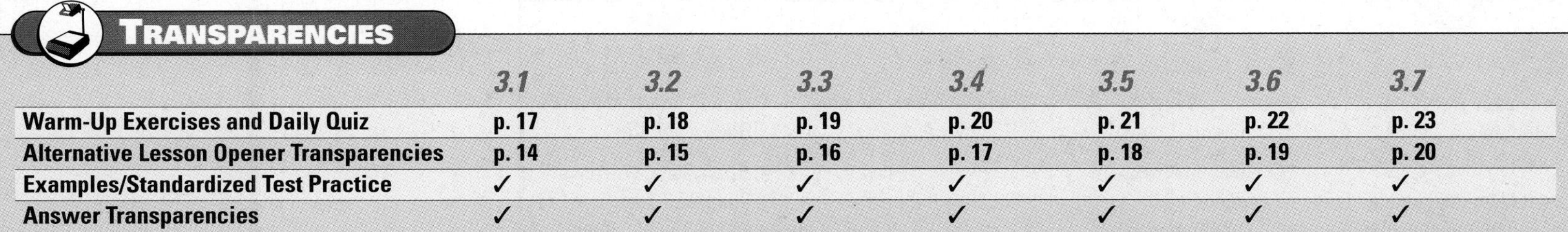

Transparencies

Transparencies	3.1	3.2	3.3	3.4	3.5	3.6	3.7
Warm-Up Exercises and Daily Quiz	p. 17	p. 18	p. 19	p. 20	p. 21	p. 22	p. 23
Alternative Lesson Opener Transparencies	p. 14	p. 15	p. 16	p. 17	p. 18	p. 19	p. 20
Examples/Standardized Test Practice	✓	✓	✓	✓	✓	✓	✓
Answer Transparencies	✓	✓	✓	✓	✓	✓	✓

Technology

- Electronic Teaching Tools
- Online Lesson Planner
- Internet Support
- Personal Student Tutor
- Test and Practice Generator
- Geometry in Motion video
- Electronic Lesson Presentations (Lesson 3.3)

Additional Resources

- Basic Skills Workbook: Diagnosis and Remediation
- Worked-Out Solution Key
- Resources in Spanish
- Standardized Test Practice Workbook
- Practice Workbook with Examples

Correlations to the California Curriculum

Correlations to California Standards
See Teacher's Edition pp. CA9–CA11

Correlations to SAT9
Task 1: See Teacher's Edition pp. CA12–CA14
Task 2: See Teacher's Edition pp. CA15–CA17

CHAPTER 3

PACING THE CHAPTER

Resource Key
- STUDENT EDITION
- CHAPTER 3 RESOURCE BOOK
- TEACHER'S EDITION

REGULAR SCHEDULE

Day 1

3.1

STARTING OPTIONS
- Prereq. Skills Review
- Strategies for Reading
- Homework Check
- Warm-Up or Daily Quiz

TEACHING OPTIONS
- Les. Opener (Application)
- Examples 1–2
- Closure Question
- Guided Practice Exs.

APPLY/HOMEWORK
- See Assignment Guide.
- See the CRB: Practice, Reteach, Apply, Extend

ASSESSMENT OPTIONS
- Checkpoint Exercises
- Daily Quiz (3.1)
- Stand. Test Practice

Day 2

3.2

STARTING OPTIONS
- Homework Check
- Warm-Up or Daily Quiz

TEACHING OPTIONS
- Concept Act. & Wksht.
- Les. Opener (Technology)
- Examples 1–2
- Closure Question
- Guided Practice Exs.

APPLY/HOMEWORK
- See Assignment Guide.
- See the CRB: Practice, Reteach, Apply, Extend

ASSESSMENT OPTIONS
- Checkpoint Exercises
- Daily Quiz (3.2)
- Stand. Test Practice

Day 3

3.3

STARTING OPTIONS
- Homework Check
- Warm-Up or Daily Quiz

TEACHING OPTIONS
- Motivating the Lesson
- Les. Opener (Application)
- Examples 1–5
- Guided Practice Exs.

APPLY/HOMEWORK
- See Assignment Guide.
- See the CRB: Practice, Reteach, Apply, Extend

ASSESSMENT OPTIONS
- Checkpoint Exercises

Day 4

3.3 *(cont.)*

STARTING OPTIONS
- Homework Check

TEACHING OPTIONS
- Examples 1–5
- Technology Activity
- Closure Question

APPLY/HOMEWORK
- See Assignment Guide.
- See the CRB: Practice, Reteach, Apply, Extend

ASSESSMENT OPTIONS
- Checkpoint Exercises
- Daily Quiz (3.3)
- Stand. Test Practice
- Quiz (3.1–3.3)

Day 5

3.4

STARTING OPTIONS
- Homework Check
- Warm-Up or Daily Quiz

TEACHING OPTIONS
- Les. Opener (Visual)
- Technology Activity
- Examples 1–5
- Closure Question
- Guided Practice Exs.

APPLY/HOMEWORK
- See Assignment Guide.
- See the CRB: Practice, Reteach, Apply, Extend

ASSESSMENT OPTIONS
- Checkpoint Exercises
- Daily Quiz (3.4)
- Stand. Test Practice

Day 6

3.5

STARTING OPTIONS
- Homework Check
- Warm-Up or Daily Quiz

TEACHING OPTIONS
- Les. Opener (Technology)
- Examples 1–3
- Guided Practice Exs.

APPLY/HOMEWORK
- See Assignment Guide.
- See the CRB: Practice, Reteach, Apply, Extend

ASSESSMENT OPTIONS
- Checkpoint Exercises

Day 9

3.7

STARTING OPTIONS
- Homework Check
- Warm-Up or Daily Quiz

TEACHING OPTIONS
- Les. Opener (Activity)
- Technology Activity
- Examples 1–6
- Guided Practice Exs.

APPLY/HOMEWORK
- See Assignment Guide.
- See the CRB: Practice, Reteach, Apply, Extend

ASSESSMENT OPTIONS
- Checkpoint Exercises

Day 10

3.7 *(cont.)*

STARTING OPTIONS
- Homework Check

TEACHING OPTIONS
- Examples 1–6
- Closure Question

APPLY/HOMEWORK
- See Assignment Guide.
- See the CRB: Practice, Reteach, Apply, Extend

ASSESSMENT OPTIONS
- Checkpoint Exercises
- Daily Quiz (3.7)
- Stand. Test Practice
- Quiz (3.6–3.7)

Day 11

Review

DAY 11 START OPTIONS
- Homework Check

REVIEWING OPTIONS
- Chapter 3 Summary
- Chapter 3 Review
- Chapter Review Games and Activities

APPLY/HOMEWORK
- Chapter 3 Test (practice)
- Ch. Standardized Test (practice)

Day 12

Assess

DAY 12 START OPTIONS
- Homework Check

ASSESSMENT OPTIONS
- Chapter 3 Test
- SAT/ACT Ch. 3 Test
- Alternative Assessment

APPLY/HOMEWORK
- Skill Review, p. 192

Day 7

3.5 *(cont.)*

Starting Options
- Homework Check

Teaching Options
- Examples 1–3
- Closure Question

Apply/Homework
- See Assignment Guide.
- See the CRB: Practice, Reteach, Apply, Extend

Assessment Options
- Checkpoint Exercises
- Daily Quiz (3.5)
- Stand. Test Practice
- Quiz (3.4–3.5)

Day 8

3.6

Starting Options
- Homework Check
- Warm-Up or Daily Quiz

Teaching Options
- Motivating the Lesson
- Les. Opener (Application)
- Examples 1–6
- Closure Question
- Guided Practice Exs.

Apply/Homework
- See Assignment Guide.
- See the CRB: Practice, Reteach, Apply, Extend

Assessment Options
- Checkpoint Exercises
- Daily Quiz (3.6)
- Stand. Test Practice

BLOCK SCHEDULE

Day 1

Assess & 3.1

(Day 1 = Ch. 2 Day 7)

Assessment Options
- Chapter 2 Test
- SAT/ACT Ch. 2 Test
- Alternative Assessment

Ch. 3 Start Options
- Skills Review, p. 128
- Prereq. Skills Review
- Strategies for Reading

Teaching 3.1 Options
- Warm-Up (Les. 3.1)
- Les. Opener (Appl.)
- Examples 1–2
- Closure Question
- Guided Practice Exs.

Apply/Homework
- See Assignment Guide.
- See the CRB: Practice, Reteach, Apply, Extend

Assessment Options
- Checkpoint Exercises
- Daily Quiz (Les. 3.1)
- Stand. Test Practice

Day 2

3.2 & 3.3

Day 2 Start Options
- Homework Check
- Warm-Up (Les. 3.2) or Daily Quiz (Les. 3.1)

Teaching 3.2 Options
- Concept Act. & Wksht.
- Les. Opener (Tech.)
- Examples 1–2
- Closure Question
- Guided Practice Exs.

Beginning 3.3 Options
- Warm-Up (Les. 3.3)
- Motivating the Lesson
- Les. Opener (Appl.)
- Examples 1–5
- Guided Practice Exs.

Apply/Homework
- See Assignment Guide.
- See the CRB: Practice, Reteach, Apply, Extend

Assessment Options
- Checkpoint Exercises
- Daily Quiz (Les. 3.2)
- Stand. Test Prac. (3.2)

Day 3

3.3 & 3.4

Day 3 Start Options
- Homework Check
- Daily Quiz (Les. 3.2)

Finishing 3.3 Options
- Examples 1–5
- Technology Activity
- Closure Question

Teaching 3.4 Options
- Warm-Up (Les. 3.4)
- Les. Opener (Visual)
- Technology Activity
- Examples 1–5
- Closure Question
- Guided Practice Exs.

Apply/Homework
- See Assignment Guide.
- See the CRB: Practice, Reteach, Apply, Extend

Assessment Options
- Checkpoint Exercises
- Daily Quiz (Les. 3.3, 3.4)
- Stand. Test Practice
- Quiz (3.1–3.3)

Day 4

3.5

Day 4 Start Options
- Homework Check
- Warm-Up or Daily Quiz

Teaching 3.5 Options
- Les. Opener (Tech.)
- Examples 1–3
- Closure Question
- Guided Practice Exs.

Apply/Homework
- See Assignment Guide.
- See the CRB: Practice, Reteach, Apply, Extend

Assessment Options
- Checkpoint Exercises
- Daily Quiz (Les. 3.5)
- Stand. Test Practice
- Quiz (3.4–3.5)

Day 5

3.6 & 3.7

Day 5 Start Options
- Homework Check
- Warm-Up (Les. 3.6) or Daily Quiz (Les. 3.5)

Teaching 3.6 Options
- Motivating the Lesson
- Les. Opener (Appl.)
- Examples 1–6
- Closure Question
- Guided Practice Exs.

Beginning 3.7 Options
- Warm-Up (Les. 3.7)
- Les. Opener (Activity)
- Technology Activity
- Examples 1–6
- Guided Practice Exs.

Apply/Homework
- See Assignment Guide.
- See the CRB: Practice, Reteach, Apply, Extend

Assessment Options
- Checkpoint Exercises
- Daily Quiz (Les. 3.6)
- Stand. Test Prac. (3.6)

Day 6

3.7 & Review

Day 6 Start Options
- Homework Check
- Daily Quiz (Les. 3.6)

Finishing 3.7 Options
- Examples 1–6
- Closure Question

Reviewing Options
- Chapter 3 Summary
- Chapter 3 Review
- Chapter Review Games and Activities

Apply/Homework
- See Assignment Guide.
- See the CRB: Practice, Reteach, Apply, Extend
- Chapter 3 Test (practice)
- Ch. Standardized Test (practice)

Assessment Options
- Checkpoint Exercises
- Daily Quiz (Les. 3.7)
- Stand. Test Practice
- Quiz (3.6–3.7)

Day 7

Assess & 4.1

(Day 7 = Ch. 4 Day 1)

Assessment Options
- Chapter 3 Test
- SAT/ACT Ch. 3 Test
- Alternative Assessment

Ch. 4 Start Options
- Skills Review, p. 192
- Prereq. Skills Review
- Strategies for Reading

Beginning 4.1 Options
- Warm-Up (Les. 4.1)
- Concept Act. & Wksht.
- Les. Opener (Activity)
- Examples 1–4
- Guided Practice Exs.

Apply/Homework
- See Assignment Guide.
- See the CRB: Practice, Reteach, Apply, Extend

Assessment Options
- Checkpoint Exercises

CHAPTER 3

MEETING INDIVIDUAL NEEDS

BEFORE THE CHAPTER

The *Chapter 3 Resource Book* has the following materials to distribute and use before the chapter:

- **Parent Guide for Student Success (pictured below)**
- **Prerequisite Skills Review**
- **Strategies for Reading Mathematics**

PARENT GUIDE *Pages 3–4*

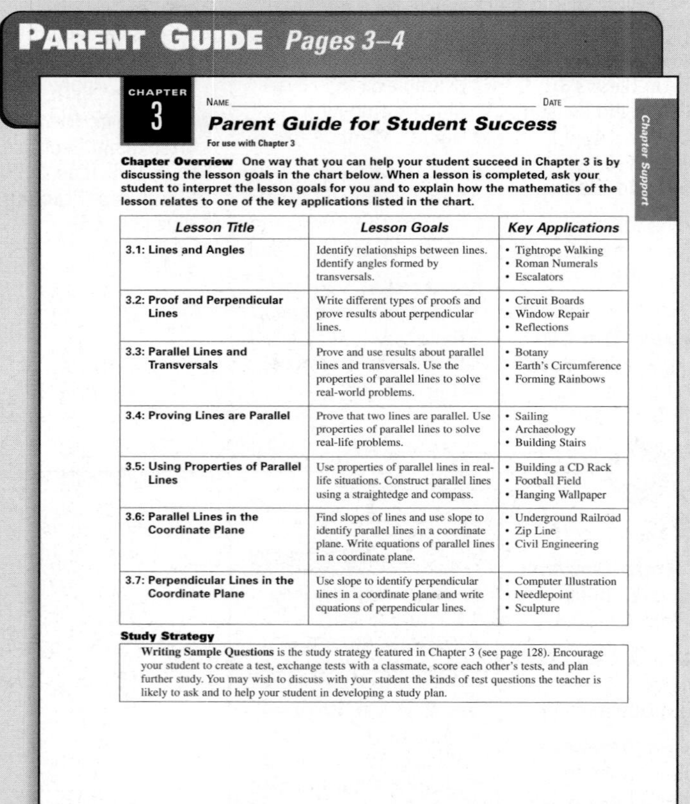

CHAPTER 3

NAME ______ DATE ______

Parent Guide for Student Success

For use with Chapter 3

Chapter Support

Chapter Overview One way that you can help your student succeed in Chapter 3 is by discussing the lesson goals in the chart below. When a lesson is completed, ask your student to interpret the lesson goals for you and to explain how the mathematics of the lesson relates to one of the key applications listed in the chart.

Lesson Title	Lesson Goals	Key Applications
3.1: Lines and Angles	Identify relationships between lines. Identify angles formed by transversals.	• Tightrope Walking • Roman Numerals • Escalators
3.2: Proof and Perpendicular Lines	Write different types of proofs and prove results about perpendicular lines.	• Circuit Boards • Window Repair • Reflections
3.3: Parallel Lines and Transversals	Prove and use results about parallel lines and transversals. Use the properties of parallel lines to solve real-world problems.	• Botany • Earth's Circumference • Forming Rainbows
3.4: Proving Lines are Parallel	Prove that two lines are parallel. Use properties of parallel lines to solve real-life problems.	• Sailing • Archaeology • Building Stairs
3.5: Using Properties of Parallel Lines	Use properties of parallel lines in real-life situations. Construct parallel lines using a straightedge and compass.	• Building a CD Rack • Football Field • Hanging Wallpaper
3.6: Parallel Lines in the Coordinate Plane	Find slopes of lines and use slope to identify parallel lines in a coordinate plane. Write equations of parallel lines in a coordinate plane.	• Underground Railroad • Zip Line • Civil Engineering
3.7: Perpendicular Lines in the Coordinate Plane	Use slope to identify perpendicular lines in a coordinate plane and write equations of perpendicular lines.	• Computer Illustration • Needlepoint • Sculpture

Study Strategy

Writing Sample Questions is the study strategy featured in Chapter 3 (see page 128). Encourage your student to create a test, exchange tests with a classmate, score each other's tests, and plan further study. You may wish to discuss with your student the kinds of test questions the teacher is likely to ask and to help your student in developing a study plan.

PARENT GUIDE FOR STUDENT SUCCESS The first page summarizes the content of Chapter 3. Parents are encouraged to have their students explain how the material relates to key applications in the chapter, such as hanging wallpaper. The second page (not shown) provides exercises and an activity that parents can do with their students. In the activity, parents and students draw a floor plan of their house and analyze the angles formed.

DURING EACH LESSON

The *Chapter 3 Resource Book* has the following alternatives for introducing the lesson:

- **Lesson Openers**
- **Technology Activities with Keystrokes (pictured below)**

TECHNOLOGY ACTIVITY *Page 97*

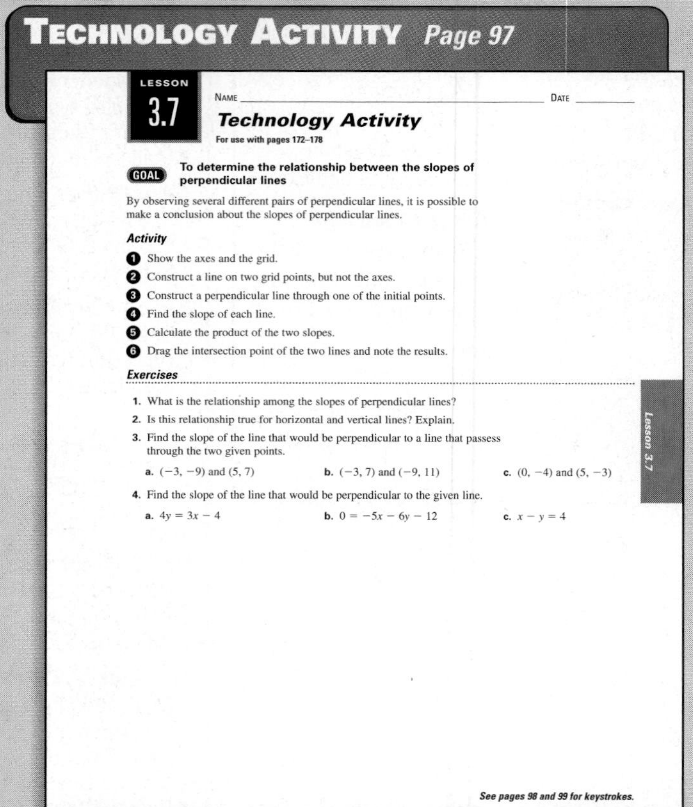

LESSON 3.7

NAME ______ DATE ______

Technology Activity

For use with pages 172–178

GOAL **To determine the relationship between the slopes of perpendicular lines**

By observing several different pairs of perpendicular lines, it is possible to make a conclusion about the slopes of perpendicular lines.

Activity

1. Show the axes and the grid.
2. Construct a line on two grid points, but not the axes.
3. Construct a perpendicular line through one of the initial points.
4. Find the slope of each line.
5. Calculate the product of the two slopes.
6. Drag the intersection point of the two lines and note the results.

Exercises

Lesson 3.7

1. What is the relationship among the slopes of perpendicular lines?
2. Is this relationship true for horizontal and vertical lines? Explain.
3. Find the slope of the line that would be perpendicular to a line that passess through the two given points.

   a. $(-3, -9)$ and $(5, 7)$ **b.** $(-3, 7)$ and $(-9, 11)$ **c.** $(0, -4)$ and $(5, -3)$
4. Find the slope of the line that would be perpendicular to the given line.

   a. $4y = 3x - 4$ **b.** $0 = -5x - 6y - 12$ **c.** $x - y = 4$

See pages 98 and 99 for keystrokes.

TECHNOLOGY ACTIVITY This activity uses a graphing calculator to develop an understanding of slopes of perpendicular lines, one of the concepts covered in Lesson 3.7. Keystrokes for this activity are provided on a separate sheet.

TECHNOLOGY RESOURCE

The Geometry in Motion video can be used to give dynamic presentations of selected material in Chapter 3.

Following Each Lesson

The *Chapter 3 Resource Book* has a variety of materials to follow-up each lesson. They include the following:

- **Practice (3 levels) (pictured below)**
- **Reteaching with Practice**
- **Quick Catch-Up for Absent Students**
- **Interdisciplinary Applications**
- **Real-Life Applications**

Practice *Page 41*

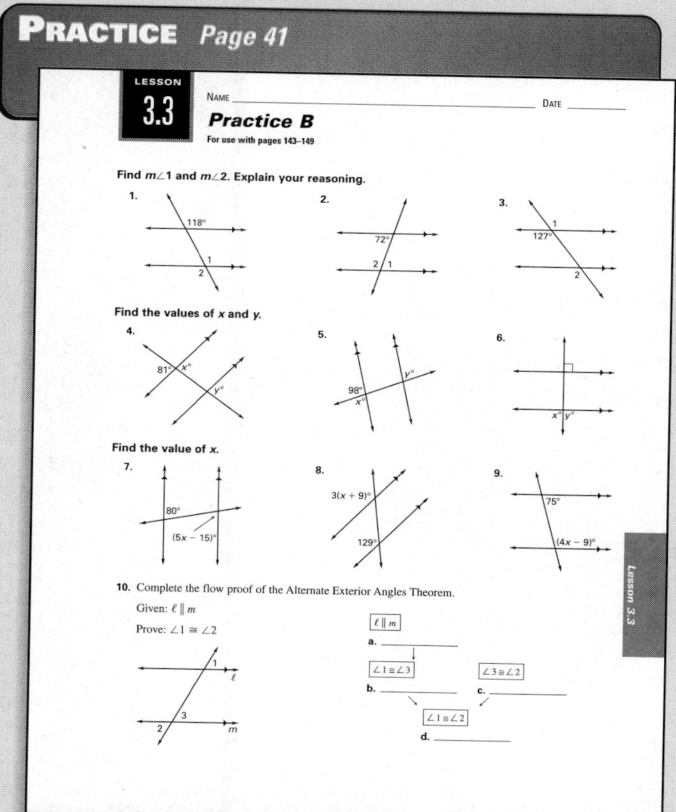

LESSON 3.3

NAME ______________________ DATE ________

Practice B

For use with pages 143–149

Find $m\angle 1$ and $m\angle 2$. Explain your reasoning.

1.
2.
3.

Find the values of x and y.

4.
5.
6.

Find the value of x.

7.
8.
9.

10. Complete the flow proof of the Alternate Exterior Angles Theorem.

Given: $\ell \parallel m$

Prove: $\angle 1 \cong \angle 2$

$\ell \parallel m$

a. ____________

$\angle 1 \cong \angle 3$

b. ____________

$\angle 3 \cong \angle 2$

c. ____________

$\angle 1 \cong \angle 2$

d. ____________

Practice Each lesson has three levels of practice: basic (A), average (B), and advanced (C). This Practice B involves more work with proofs than Practice A but does not have as much work with finding the measures of angles as Practice C.

Technology Resource

Teachers can use the Time-Saving Test and Practice Generator to create additional practice worksheets for Lesson 3.3 and for the other lessons in Chapter 3.

Assessing the Chapter

The *Chapter 3 Resource Book* has the following review and assessment materials:

- **Quizzes**
- **Chapter Review Games and Activities**
- **Chapter Test (3 levels)**
- **SAT/ACT Chapter Test**
- **Alternative Assessment and Math Journal (pictured below)**
- **Project with Rubric**
- **Cumulative Review**

Alternative Assessment *Pages 117–118*

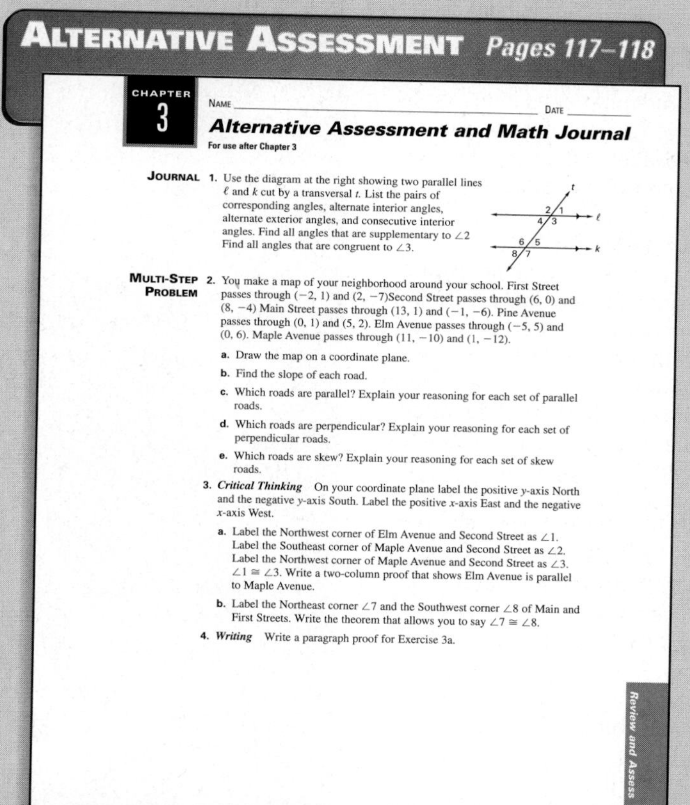

CHAPTER 3

NAME ______________________ DATE ________

Alternative Assessment and Math Journal

For use after Chapter 3

Journal 1. Use the diagram at the right showing two parallel lines ℓ and k cut by a transversal t. List the pairs of corresponding angles, alternate interior angles, alternate exterior angles, and consecutive interior angles. Find all angles that are supplementary to $\angle 2$ Find all angles that are congruent to $\angle 3$.

Multi-Step Problem 2. You make a map of your neighborhood around your school. First Street passes through (−2, 1) and (2, −7)Second Street passes through (6, 0) and (8, −4) Main Street passes through (13, 1) and (−1, −6). Pine Avenue passes through (0, 1) and (5, 2). Elm Avenue passes through (−5, 5) and (0, 6). Maple Avenue passes through (11, −10) and (1, −12).

a. Draw the map on a coordinate plane.

b. Find the slope of each road.

c. Which roads are parallel? Explain your reasoning for each set of parallel roads.

d. Which roads are perpendicular? Explain your reasoning for each set of perpendicular roads.

e. Which roads are skew? Explain your reasoning for each set of skew roads.

3. ***Critical Thinking*** On your coordinate plane label the positive y-axis North and the negative y-axis South. Label the positive x-axis East and the negative x-axis West.

a. Label the Northwest corner of Elm Avenue and Second Street as $\angle 1$. Label the Southeast corner of Maple Avenue and Second Street as $\angle 2$. Label the Northwest corner of Maple Avenue and Second Street as $\angle 3$. $\angle 1 \cong \angle 3$. Write a two-column proof that shows Elm Avenue is parallel to Maple Avenue.

b. Label the Northeast corner $\angle 7$ and the Southwest corner $\angle 8$ of Main and First Streets. Write the theorem that allows you to say $\angle 7 \cong \angle 8$.

4. ***Writing*** Write a paragraph proof for Exercise 3a.

Alternative Assessment with Rubric and Math Journal The journal exercise asks students to demonstrate their understanding of parallel lines in writing. The Multi-Step Problem has students pull together a variety of concepts from Chapter 3 to solve a problem about determining parallel and perpendicular lines. Answers and a scoring rubric are provided on a separate sheet.

CHAPTER OVERVIEW

CHAPTER GOALS

Students will investigate the relationships between lines and angles on a plane and in space. They will study the angles formed when two lines are cut by a transversal. They will learn how to write flow proofs and use these proofs along with two-column and paragraph proofs to prove theorems about perpendicular and parallel lines. Students will apply properties of parallel lines to solve real-life problems. They will also use a straightedge and a compass to construct parallel lines. Students will find the slopes of lines and use slope to identify parallel and perpendicular lines in a coordinate plane. They will write equations of parallel and perpendicular lines in a coordinate plane.

APPLICATION NOTE

If a sailboat's destination is upwind of its position, it must sail a series of zigzag courses that are 45° to the direction of the wind. The courses alternate between left of the direction of the wind to right of the direction of the wind. This sailing maneuver is called tacking. When a boat is ready to change its direction of tack, it can be turned into the direction of the wind, which will cause its sails to flap and the boat to lose speed. The boat's inertia then carries it into the opposite tack. If the boat's inertia is not great enough to complete the turn, the boat will stop with its sail pointing ineffectively into the wind.

Additional information about sailing is available at **www.mcdougallittell.com.**

PERPENDICULAR AND PARALLEL LINES

▶ *Will the boats' paths ever cross?*

CHAPTER

3

APPLICATION: Sailing

When you float in an inner tube on a windy day, you get blown in the direction of the wind. Sailboats are designed to sail against the wind.

Most sailboats can sail at an angle of 45° to the direction from which the wind is blowing, as shown below. If a sailboat heads directly into the wind, the sail flaps and is useless.

You'll learn how to analyze lines such as the paths of sailboats in Chapter 3.

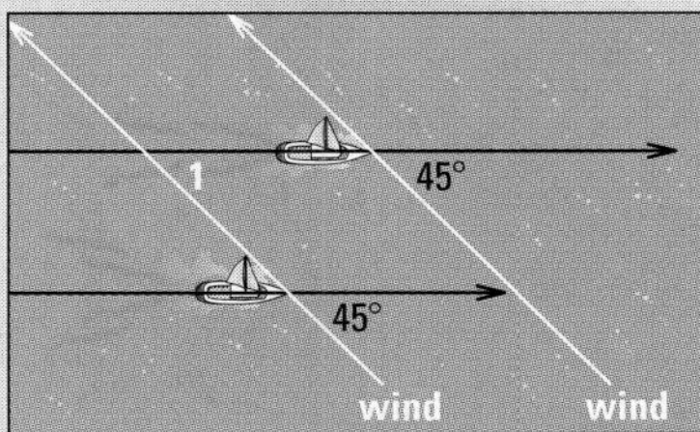

Think & Discuss

1. What do you think the measure of $\angle 1$ is? Use a protractor to check your answer. **45°**
2. If the boats always sail at a 45° angle to the wind, and the wind doesn't change direction, do you think the boats' paths will ever cross? **No.**

Learn More About It

You will learn more about the paths of sailboats in Example 4 on p. 152.

APPLICATION LINK Visit www.mcdougallittell.com for more information about sailing.

PROJECTS

A project covering Chapters 2 and 3 appears on pages 188–189 of the Student Edition. An additional project for Chapter 3 is available in the *Chapter 3 Resource Book,* p. 119.

TECHNOLOGY

Software

- *Electronic Teaching Tools*
- *Online Lesson Planner*
- *Personal Student Tutor*
- *Test and Practice Generator*
- *Electronic Lesson Presentations (Lesson 3.3)*

Video

- *Geometry in Motion*

Internet Connections
www.mcdougallittell.com

- **Application Links** 127, 130, 145, 154, 163, 164
- **Student Help** 131, 140, 142, 145, 147, 152, 155, 161, 167, 176
- **Career Links** 144, 170, 174
- **Extra Challenge** 134, 141, 148, 156, 177

PREPARE

DIAGNOSTIC TOOLS

The **Skill Review** exercises can help you diagnose whether students have the following skills needed in Chapter 3:

- Solve linear equations in one variable.
- Identify algebraic and geometric definitions, postulates, or theorems that support a conclusion.

The following resources are available for students who need additional help with these skills:

- Prerequisite Skills Review (*Chapter 3 Resource Book,* p. 5; *Warm-Up Transparencies,* p. 16)
- Reteaching with Practice (Chapter Resource Books for Lessons 1.6 and 2.4)
- *Personal Student Tutor*

ADDITIONAL RESOURCES

The following resources are provided to help you prepare for the upcoming chapter and customize review materials:

- ***Chapter 3 Resource Book***
  Tips for New Teachers (p. 1)
  Parent Guide (p. 3)
  Lesson Plans (every lesson)
  Lesson Plans for Block Scheduling (every lesson)
- ***Electronic Teaching Tools***
- ***Online Lesson Planner***
- ***Test and Practice Generator***

CHAPTER 3

Study Guide

PREVIEW

What's the chapter about?

Chapter 3 is about **lines** and **angles**. In Chapter 3, you'll learn

- properties of parallel and perpendicular lines.
- six ways to prove that lines are parallel.
- how to write an equation of a line with given characteristics.

KEY VOCABULARY

▶ **Review**
- linear pair, p. 44
- vertical angles, p. 44
- perpendicular lines, p. 79

▶ **New**
- parallel lines, p. 129
- skew lines, p. 129
- parallel planes, p. 129
- transversal, p. 131
- alternate interior angles, p. 131
- alternate exterior angles, p. 131
- consecutive interior angles, p. 131
- flow proof, p. 136

PREPARE

Are you ready for the chapter?

SKILL REVIEW Do these exercises to review key skills that you'll apply in this chapter. See the given **reference page** if there is something you don't understand.

USING ALGEBRA Solve each equation. (Skills Review, p. 789 and 790)

1. $47 + x = 180$ 133

2. $135 = 3x - 6$ 47

3. $m = \dfrac{5-7}{2-(-6)}$ $-\frac{1}{4}$

4. $\frac{1}{2} = -5\left(\frac{7}{2}\right) + b$ 18

5. $5x + 9 = 6x - 11$ 20

6. $2(x - 1) + 15 = 90$ $\frac{77}{2}$

Use the diagram. Write the reason that supports the statement. (Review pp. 44–46)

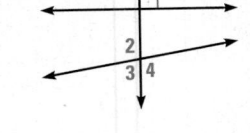

7. $m\angle 1 = 90°$
Definition of a right angle

8. $\angle 2 \cong \angle 4$
Vertical angles are congruent.

9. $\angle 2$ and $\angle 3$ are supplementary.
$\angle 2$ and $\angle 3$ form a linear pair.

Write the reason that supports the statement. (Review pp. 96–98)

10. If $m\angle A = 30°$ and $m\angle B = 30°$, then $\angle A \cong \angle B$.
Definition of congruent angles

11. If $x + 4 = 9$, then $x = 5$.
Subtraction property of equality

12. $3(x + 5) = 3x + 15$
Distributive property

STUDY STRATEGY

Here's a study strategy!

Write Sample Questions

Write at least six questions about topics in the chapter. Focus on the concepts that you found difficult. Include both short-answer questions and more involved ones. Then answer your questions.

3.1 Lines and Angles

What you should learn

GOAL 1 Identify relationships between lines.

GOAL 2 Identify angles formed by transversals.

Why you should learn it

▼ To describe and understand **real-life** objects, such as the escalator in **Exs. 32–36**.

REAL LIFE

GOAL 1 RELATIONSHIPS BETWEEN LINES

Two lines are **parallel lines** if they are coplanar and do not intersect. Lines that do not intersect and are not coplanar are called **skew lines.** Similarly, two planes that do not intersect are called **parallel planes.**

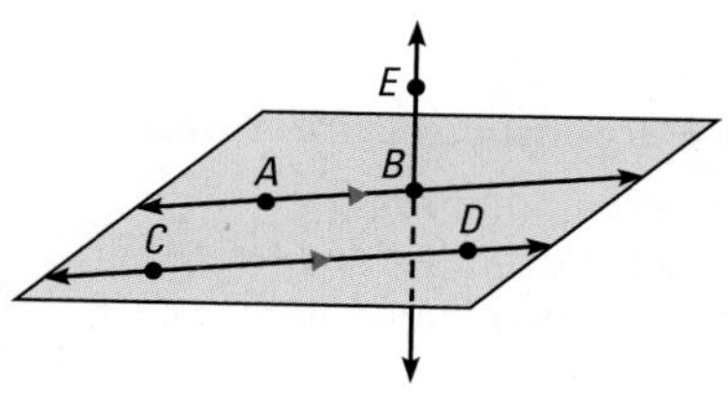

$\overleftrightarrow{AB}$ and $\overleftrightarrow{CD}$ are parallel lines.
$\overleftrightarrow{CD}$ and $\overleftrightarrow{BE}$ are skew lines.

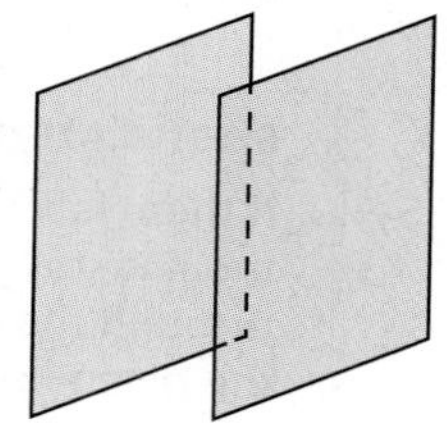

Planes *U* and *W* are parallel planes.

To write "$\overleftrightarrow{AB}$ is parallel to $\overleftrightarrow{CD}$," you write $\overleftrightarrow{AB} \parallel \overleftrightarrow{CD}$. Triangles like those on $\overleftrightarrow{AB}$ and $\overleftrightarrow{CD}$ are used on diagrams to indicate that lines are parallel. Segments and rays are parallel if they lie on parallel lines. For example, $\overline{AB} \parallel \overline{CD}$.

EXAMPLE 1 *Identifying Relationships in Space*

Think of each segment in the diagram as part of a line. Which of the lines appear to fit the description?

a. parallel to $\overleftrightarrow{AB}$ and contains *D*

b. perpendicular to $\overleftrightarrow{AB}$ and contains *D*

c. skew to $\overleftrightarrow{AB}$ and contains *D*

d. Name the plane(s) that contain *D* and appear to be parallel to plane *ABE*.

SOLUTION

a. $\overleftrightarrow{CD}$, $\overleftrightarrow{GH}$, and $\overleftrightarrow{EF}$ are all parallel to $\overleftrightarrow{AB}$, but only $\overleftrightarrow{CD}$ passes through *D* and is parallel to $\overleftrightarrow{AB}$.

b. $\overleftrightarrow{BC}$, $\overleftrightarrow{AD}$, $\overleftrightarrow{AE}$, and $\overleftrightarrow{BF}$ are all perpendicular to $\overleftrightarrow{AB}$, but only $\overleftrightarrow{AD}$ passes through *D* and is perpendicular to $\overleftrightarrow{AB}$.

c. $\overleftrightarrow{DG}$, $\overleftrightarrow{DH}$, and $\overleftrightarrow{DE}$ all pass through *D* and are skew to $\overleftrightarrow{AB}$.

d. Only plane *DCH* contains *D* and is parallel to plane *ABE*.

CALIFORNIA STANDARDS AND ASSESSMENT

CA Standards: 7, 16
SAT9 Task 2: Obj. 28

STUDENT HELP

Look Back
For help identifying perpendicular lines, see p. 79.

1 PLAN

PACING
Basic: 1 day
Average: 1 day
Advanced: 1 day
Block Schedule: 0.5 block with Ch. 2 Assess.

LESSON OPENER APPLICATION

An alternative way to approach Lesson 3.1 is to use the Application Lesson Opener:

- Blackline Master (*Chapter 3 Resource Book,* p. 12)
- Transparency (p. 14)

MEETING INDIVIDUAL NEEDS

- ***Chapter 3 Resource Book***
  Prerequisite Skills Review (p. 5)
  Practice Level A (p. 13)
  Practice Level B (p. 14)
  Practice Level C (p. 15)
  Reteaching with Practice (p. 16)
  Absent Student Catch-Up (p. 18)
  Challenge (p. 20)
- ***Resources in Spanish***
- ***Personal Student Tutor***

NEW-TEACHER SUPPORT

See the Tips for New Teachers on pp. 1–2 of the *Chapter 3 Resource Book* for additional notes about Lesson 3.1.

WARM-UP EXERCISES

Transparency Available

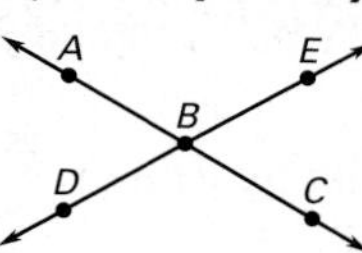

1. Name a line that contains *C*. $\overleftrightarrow{AC}$

2. Name a ray with endpoint *B* that contains *A*. $\overrightarrow{BA}$

3. Name an acute angle with vertex *B* that contains *C*. $\angle EBC$

4. Name a segment with endpoint *B* that contains *C*. $\overline{BC}$

2 TEACH

EXTRA EXAMPLE 1

Think of each segment in the diagram as part of a line. Which of the lines appear to fit the description?

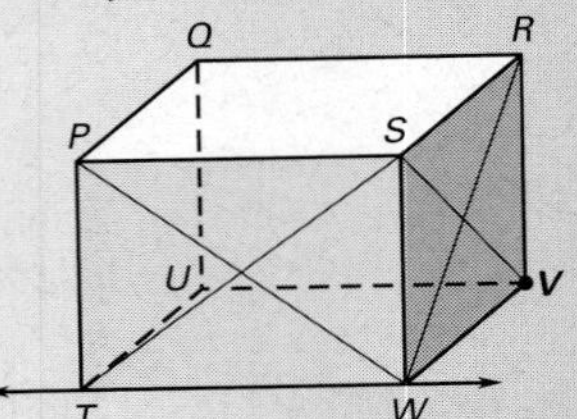

a. parallel to $\overleftrightarrow{TW}$ and contains V $\overleftrightarrow{UV}$

b. perpendicular to $\overleftrightarrow{TW}$ and contains V $\overleftrightarrow{VW}$

c. skew to $\overleftrightarrow{TW}$ and contains V $\overleftrightarrow{RV}$, $\overleftrightarrow{SV}$

d. Name the plane(s) that contain V and appear to be parallel to plane TPQ. **plane RVW**

CHECKPOINT EXERCISES

For use after Example 1:

Think of each segment in the diagram as part of a line. Which of the lines appear to fit the description?

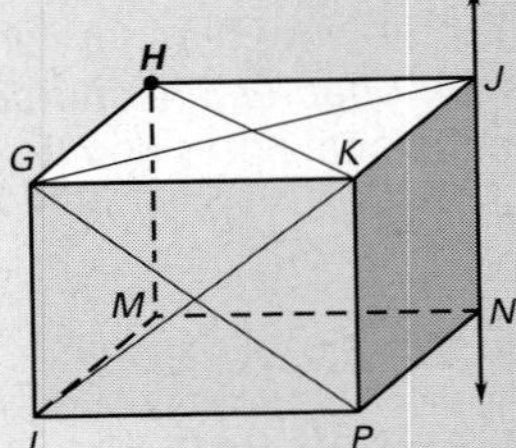

1. parallel to $\overleftrightarrow{JN}$ and contains H $\overleftrightarrow{HM}$

2. perpendicular to $\overleftrightarrow{JN}$ and contains H $\overleftrightarrow{JH}$

3. skew to $\overleftrightarrow{JN}$ and contains H $\overleftrightarrow{GH}$, $\overleftrightarrow{HK}$

4. Name the plane(s) that contain H and appear to be parallel to plane LMN. **plane GHJ**

Notice in Example 1 that, although there are many lines through D that are skew to $\overleftrightarrow{AB}$, there is only one line through D that is parallel to $\overleftrightarrow{AB}$ and there is only one line through D that is perpendicular to $\overleftrightarrow{AB}$.

STUDENT HELP

APPLICATION LINK Visit our Web site www.mcdougallittell.com for more information about the parallel postulate.

PARALLEL AND PERPENDICULAR POSTULATES

POSTULATE 13 ***Parallel Postulate***

If there is a line and a point not on the line, then there is exactly one line through the point parallel to the given line.

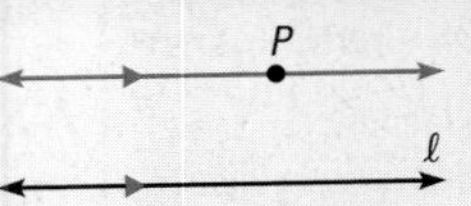

There is exactly one line through P parallel to ℓ.

POSTULATE 14 ***Perpendicular Postulate***

If there is a line and a point not on the line, then there is exactly one line through the point perpendicular to the given line.

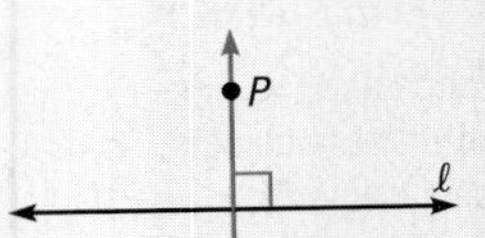

There is exactly one line through P perpendicular to ℓ.

You can use a compass and a straightedge to construct the line that passes through a given point and is perpendicular to a given line. In Lesson 6.6, you will learn why this construction works.

You will learn how to construct a parallel line in Lesson 3.5.

ACTIVITY

Construction

A Perpendicular to a Line

Use the following steps to construct a line that passes through a given point P and is perpendicular to a given line ℓ.

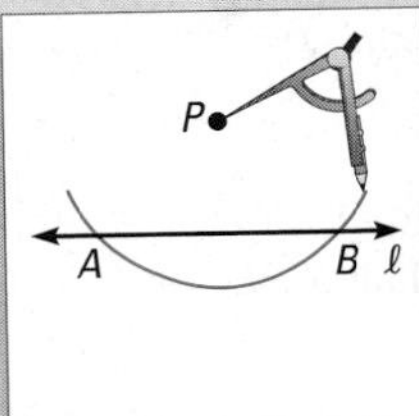

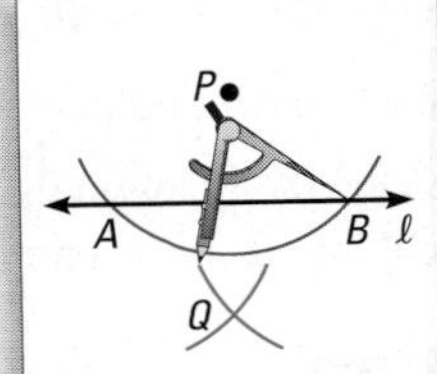

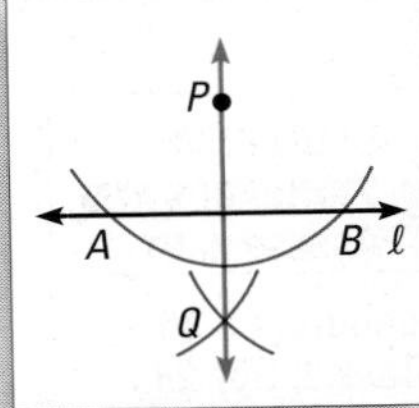

1 Place the compass point at P and draw an arc that intersects line ℓ twice. Label the intersections A and B.

2 Draw an arc with center A. Using the same radius, draw an arc with center B. Label the intersection of the arcs Q.

3 Use a straightedge to draw $\overleftrightarrow{PQ}$. $\overleftrightarrow{PQ} \perp \ell$.

GOAL 2 IDENTIFYING ANGLES FORMED BY TRANSVERSALS

A **transversal** is a line that intersects two or more coplanar lines at different points. For instance, in the diagrams below, line t is a transversal. The angles formed by two lines and a transversal are given special names.

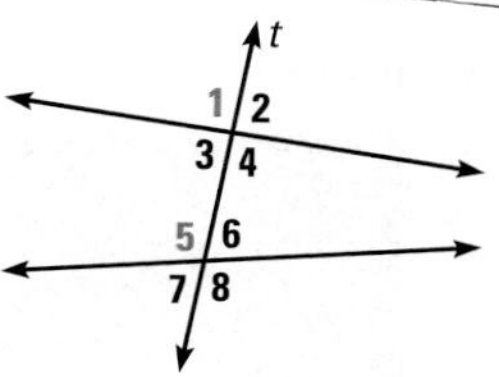

Two angles are **corresponding angles** if they occupy corresponding positions. For example, angles 1 and 5 are corresponding angles.

Two angles are **alternate exterior angles** if they lie outside the two lines on opposite sides of the transversal. Angles 1 and 8 are alternate exterior angles.

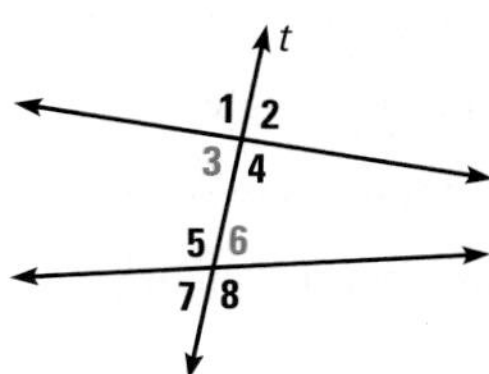

Two angles are **alternate interior angles** if they lie between the two lines on opposite sides of the transversal. Angles 3 and 6 are alternate interior angles.

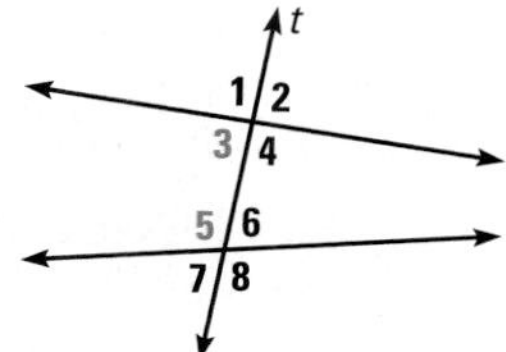

Two angles are **consecutive interior angles** if they lie between the two lines on the same side of the transversal. Angles 3 and 5 are consecutive interior angles.

Consecutive interior angles are sometimes called **same side interior angles**.

EXAMPLE 2 *Identifying Angle Relationships*

STUDENT HELP

INTERNET HOMEWORK HELP
Visit our Web site www.mcdougallittell.com for extra examples.

List all pairs of angles that fit the description.

a. corresponding **b.** alternate exterior

c. alternate interior **d.** consecutive interior

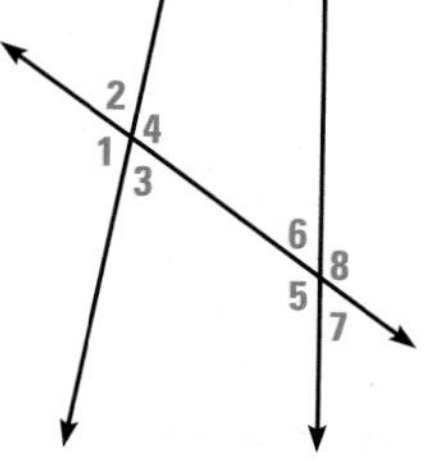

SOLUTION

a. ∠1 and ∠5
∠2 and ∠6
∠3 and ∠7
∠4 and ∠8

b. ∠1 and ∠8
∠2 and ∠7

c. ∠3 and ∠6
∠4 and ∠5

d. ∠3 and ∠5
∠4 and ∠6

EXTRA EXAMPLE 2

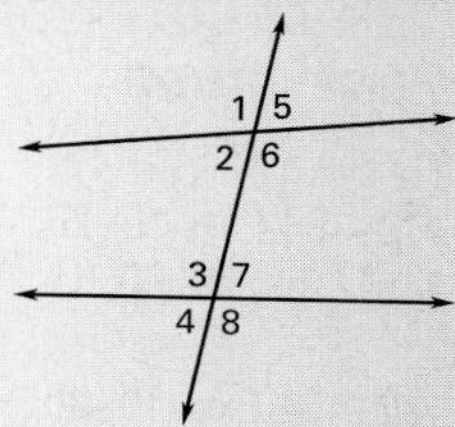

List all pairs of angles that fit the description.

a. corresponding
∠1 and ∠3; ∠2 and ∠4; ∠5 and ∠7; ∠6 and ∠8

b. alternate exterior
∠1 and ∠8; ∠4 and ∠5

c. alternate interior
∠2 and ∠7; ∠3 and ∠6

d. consecutive interior
∠2 and ∠3; ∠6 and ∠7

CHECKPOINT EXERCISES

For use after Example 2:

List all pairs of angles that fit the description.

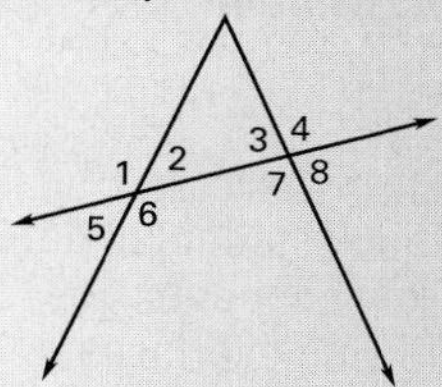

1. corresponding
∠1 and ∠3; ∠2 and ∠4; ∠5 and ∠7; ∠6 and ∠8

2. alternate exterior
∠1 and ∠8; ∠4 and ∠5

3. alternate interior
∠2 and ∠7; ∠3 and ∠6

4. consecutive interior
∠6 and ∠7; ∠2 and ∠3

FOCUS ON VOCABULARY

How do alternate exterior angles differ from alternate interior angles? **Alternate exterior angles lie outside two lines that are intersected by a transversal. Alternate interior angles lie between two lines that are intersected by a transversal.**

CLOSURE QUESTION

If two lines are cut by a transversal how many pairs of corresponding angles are formed? **four**

3 APPLY

ASSIGNMENT GUIDE

BASIC
Day 1: pp. 132–134 Exs. 10–26, 37–42, 47, 50, 54, 60, 61

AVERAGE
Day 1: pp. 132–134 Exs. 10–26, 37–42, 47, 50, 54, 60, 61

ADVANCED
Day 1: pp. 132–134 Exs. 10–26, 37–47, 50, 54, 60, 61

BLOCK SCHEDULE (WITH CH. 2 ASSESS.)
pp. 132–134 Exs. 10–26, 37–42, 47, 50, 54, 60, 61

EXERCISE LEVELS
Level A: *Easier*
10–19
Level B: *More Difficult*
20–42
Level C: *Most Difficult*
43–46

✔ **HOMEWORK CHECK**
To quickly check student understanding of key concepts, go over the following exercises: Exs. 12, 14, 18, 22, 28, 36, 40. See also the Daily Homework Quiz:
- Blackline Master (*Chapter 3 Resource Book,* p. 23)
- Transparency (p. 18)

1. *Sample Answer:*

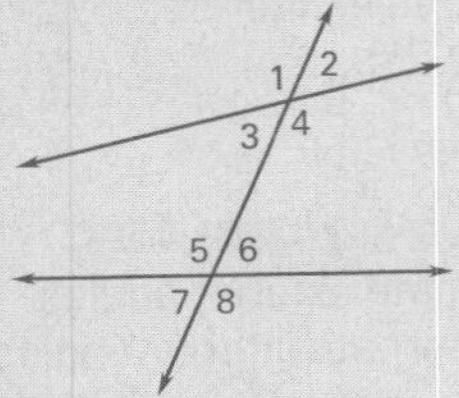

GUIDED PRACTICE

Vocabulary Check ✔
Concept Check ✔
Skill Check ✔

1. Draw two lines and a transversal. Identify a pair of alternate interior angles.
Sample answer: See margin. ∠3 and ∠6 or ∠4 and ∠5

2. How are skew lines and parallel lines alike? How are they different?
See margin.

2. *Sample answer:* Skew lines and parallel lines are alike in that they do not intersect. They are different in that parallel lines are coplanar and skew lines are not coplanar.

Match the photo with the corresponding description of the chopsticks.

A. skew **B.** parallel **C.** intersecting

3. B

4. C

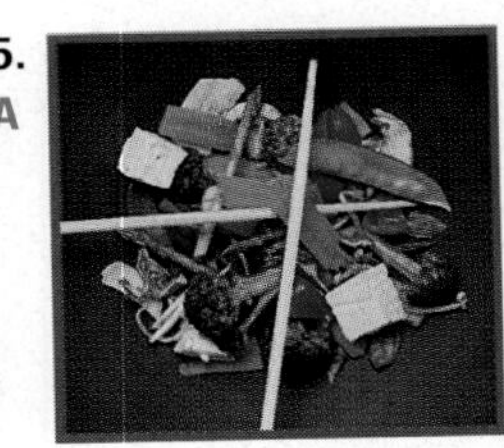

5. A

In Exercises 6–9, use the diagram at the right.

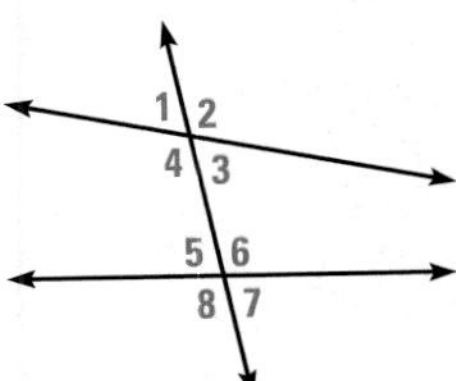

6. Name a pair of corresponding angles.
∠1 and ∠5, ∠4 and ∠8, ∠2 and ∠6, or ∠3 and ∠7
7. Name a pair of alternate interior angles.
∠3 and ∠5, or ∠4 and ∠6
8. Name a pair of alternate exterior angles.
∠1 and ∠7, or ∠2 and ∠8
9. Name a pair of consecutive interior angles.
∠3 and ∠6, or ∠4 and ∠5

PRACTICE AND APPLICATIONS

STUDENT HELP
Extra Practice to help you master skills is on p. 807.

LINE RELATIONSHIPS **Think of each segment in the diagram as part of a line. Fill in the blank with *parallel, skew,* or *perpendicular*.**

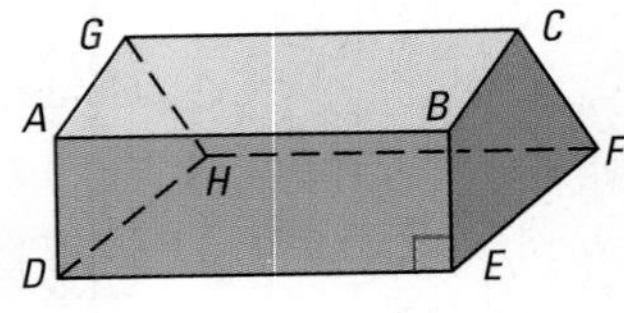

10. $\overleftrightarrow{DE}$, $\overleftrightarrow{AB}$, and $\overleftrightarrow{GC}$ are __?__. parallel
11. $\overleftrightarrow{DE}$ and $\overleftrightarrow{BE}$ are __?__. perpendicular
12. $\overleftrightarrow{BE}$ and $\overleftrightarrow{GC}$ are __?__. skew
13. Plane GAD and plane CBE are __?__. parallel

IDENTIFYING RELATIONSHIPS **Think of each segment in the diagram as part of a line. There may be more than one right answer.**

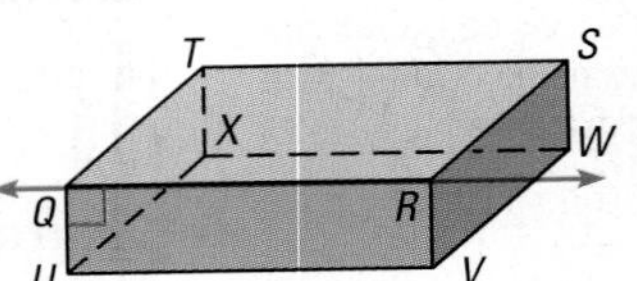

14. Name a line parallel to $\overleftrightarrow{QR}$. $\overleftrightarrow{UV}$, $\overleftrightarrow{TS}$, or $\overleftrightarrow{XW}$
15. Name a line perpendicular to $\overleftrightarrow{QR}$.
16. Name a line skew to $\overleftrightarrow{QR}$.
17. Name a plane parallel to plane QRS. UVW

15. $\overleftrightarrow{QU}$, $\overleftrightarrow{QT}$, $\overleftrightarrow{RV}$, or $\overleftrightarrow{RS}$
16. $\overleftrightarrow{TX}$, $\overleftrightarrow{SW}$, $\overleftrightarrow{UX}$, or $\overleftrightarrow{VW}$

STUDENT HELP
HOMEWORK HELP
Example 1: Exs. 10–20, 27–36
Example 2: Exs. 21–26

APPLYING POSTULATES **How many lines can be drawn that fit the description?**

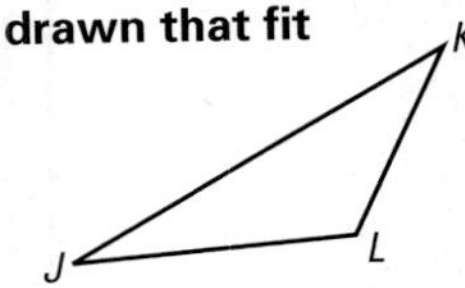

18. through L parallel to $\overleftrightarrow{JK}$ 1
19. through L perpendicular to $\overleftrightarrow{JK}$ 1

FOCUS ON PEOPLE

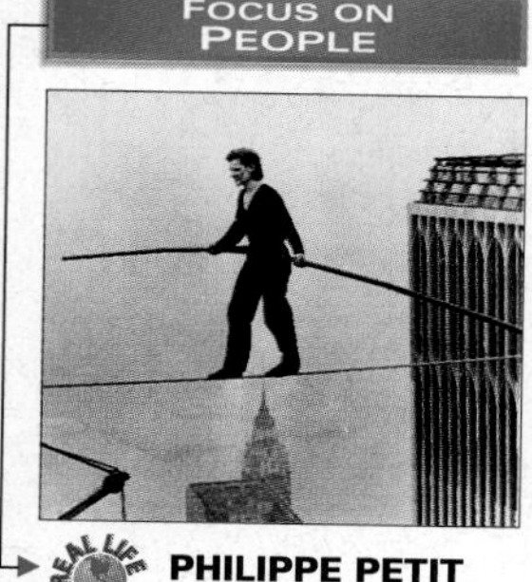

PHILIPPE PETIT walked more than 2000 feet up an inclined cable to the Eiffel Tower. The photo above is from a performance in New York City.

20. **TIGHTROPE WALKING** Philippe Petit sometimes uses a long pole to help him balance on the tightrope. Are the rope and the pole at the left *intersecting*, *perpendicular*, *parallel*, or *skew*? skew

ANGLE RELATIONSHIPS **Complete the statement with *corresponding*, *alternate interior*, *alternate exterior*, or *consecutive interior*.**

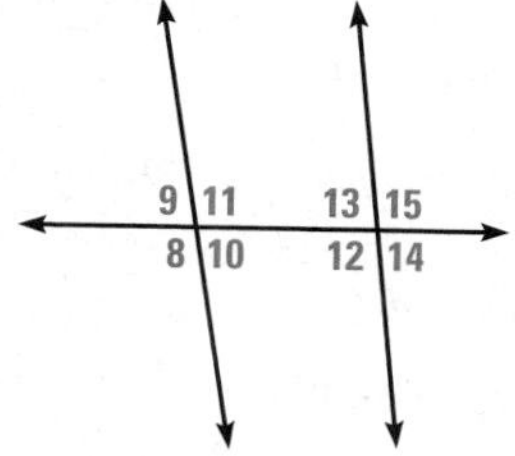

21. $\angle 8$ and $\angle 12$ are __?__ angles. corresponding
22. $\angle 9$ and $\angle 14$ are __?__ angles. alternate exterior
23. $\angle 10$ and $\angle 12$ are __?__ angles. consecutive interior
24. $\angle 11$ and $\angle 12$ are __?__ angles. alternate interior
25. $\angle 8$ and $\angle 15$ are __?__ angles. alternate exterior
26. $\angle 10$ and $\angle 14$ are __?__ angles. corresponding

ROMAN NUMERALS **Write the Roman numeral that consists of the indicated segments. Then write the base ten value of the Roman numeral. For example, the base ten value of XII is 10 + 1 + 1 = 12.**

Roman numeral	I	V	X	L	M
Base ten value	1	5	10	50	1000

27. Three parallel segments III; 3
28. Two non-congruent perpendicular segments L; 50
29. Two congruent segments that intersect to form only one angle V; 5
30. Two intersecting segments that form vertical angles X; 10
31. Four segments, two of which are parallel M; 1000

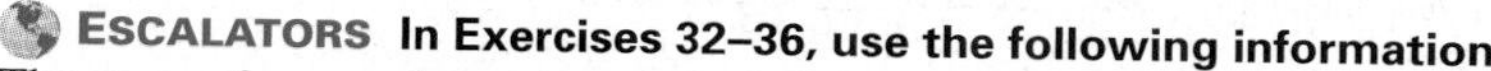

ESCALATORS **In Exercises 32–36, use the following information.**
The steps of an escalator are connected to a chain that runs around a drive wheel, which moves continuously. When a step on an up-escalator reaches the top, it flips over and goes back down to the bottom. Each step is shaped like a wedge, as shown at the right. On each step, let plane *A* be the plane you stand on.

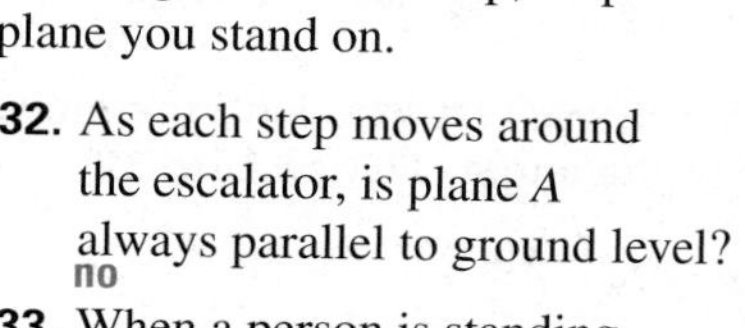

32. As each step moves around the escalator, is plane *A* always parallel to ground level? no
33. When a person is standing on plane *A*, is it parallel to ground level? yes
34. Is line ℓ on any step always parallel to ℓ on any other step? yes
35. Is plane *A* on any step always parallel to plane *A* on any other step? no
36. As each step moves around the escalator, how many positions are there at which plane *A* is perpendicular to ground level? 2

APPLICATION NOTE

EXERCISES 32–36 The axles of all the stairs on an escalator are joined by a heavy chain. Each step also has four wheels that run in tracks and cause the steps to remain level while they carry passengers.

MATHEMATICAL REASONING

If two lines are cut by a transversal, four interior angles are formed. If one pair of alternate interior angles measures 90°, explain why all four interior angles must measure 90°. The transversal forms a pair of supplementary angles at each intersection. Since one of the supplementary angles in each pair measures 90°, both angles must measure 90°.

39.–40.

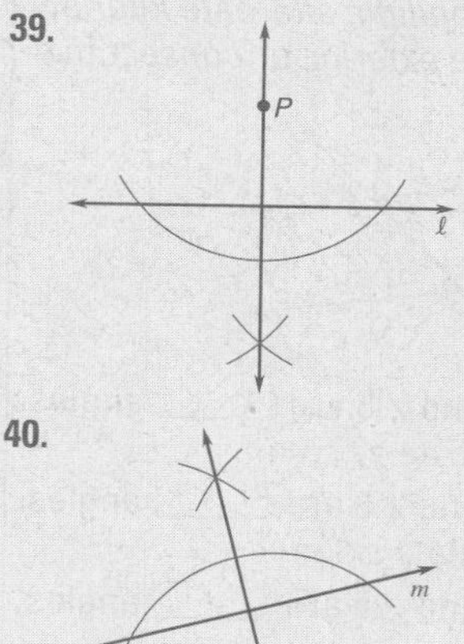

60–62. See Additional Answers beginning on page AA1.

ADDITIONAL PRACTICE AND RETEACHING

For Lesson 3.1:
- Practice Levels A, B, and C (*Chapter 3 Resource Book*, p. 13)
- Reteaching with Practice (*Chapter 3 Resource Book*, p. 16)
- See Lesson 3.1 of the *Personal Student Tutor*

For more Mixed Review:
- Search the *Test and Practice Generator* for key words or specific lessons.

4 ASSESS

DAILY HOMEWORK QUIZ

Transparency Available

Use the figure below. Fill in the blank with *parallel, skew,* or *perpendicular.*

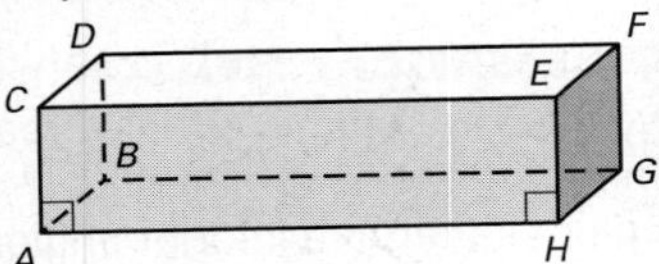

1. $\overline{CE}$ and $\overline{AC}$ are ______. perpendicular
2. $\overline{EH}$ and $\overline{AB}$ are ______. skew
3. Plane DBG and plane AHE are ______. parallel

Complete the statement with *corresponding, alternate interior, alternate exterior,* or *consecutive interior.*

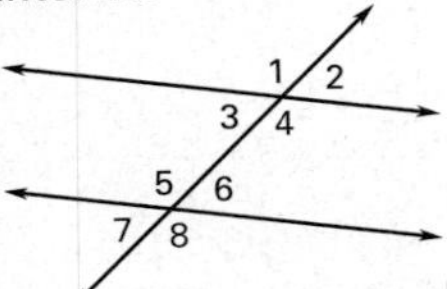

4. $\angle 3$ and $\angle 6$ are ______ angles. alternate interior
5. $\angle 1$ and $\angle 8$ are ______ angles. alternate exterior
6. $\angle 2$ and $\angle 6$ are ______ angles. corresponding
7. $\angle 3$ and $\angle 5$ are ______ angles. consecutive interior

39, 40, 60–62. See Additional Answers beginning on page AA1.

EXTRA CHALLENGE NOTE

Challenge problems for Lesson 3.1 are available in **blackline** format in the *Chapter 3 Resource Book,* p. 20 and at **www.mcdougallittell.com.**

ADDITIONAL TEST PREPARATION

1. **OPEN ENDED** Sketch a stop sign. Then extend three of its sides in both directions, two of which are opposite sides. Show a pair of corresponding angles. How many of the sides, when extended, could be a transversal for a pair of opposite sides? 8

---

37. *Sample answer:* The two lines of intersection are coplanar, since they are both in the third plane. The two lines do not intersect, because they are in parallel planes. Since they are coplanar and do not intersect, they are parallel.

37. **LOGICAL REASONING** If two parallel planes are cut by a third plane, explain why the lines of intersection are parallel.

38. *Writing* What does "two lines intersect" mean? *Sample answer:* There is one point that lies on both lines.

39. **CONSTRUCTION** Draw a horizontal line ℓ and a point P above ℓ. Construct a line through P perpendicular to ℓ. See margin.

40. **CONSTRUCTION** Draw a diagonal line m and a point Q below m. Construct a line through Q perpendicular to m. See margin.

Test Preparation

41. **MULTIPLE CHOICE** In the diagram at the right, how many lines can be drawn through point P that are perpendicular to line ℓ? B

Ⓐ 0 Ⓑ 1 Ⓒ 2 Ⓓ 3 Ⓔ More than 3

42. **MULTIPLE CHOICE** If two lines intersect, then they must be __?__. C

Ⓐ perpendicular Ⓑ parallel Ⓒ coplanar Ⓓ skew Ⓔ None of these

★ Challenge

ANGLE RELATIONSHIPS Complete each statement. List all possible correct answers.

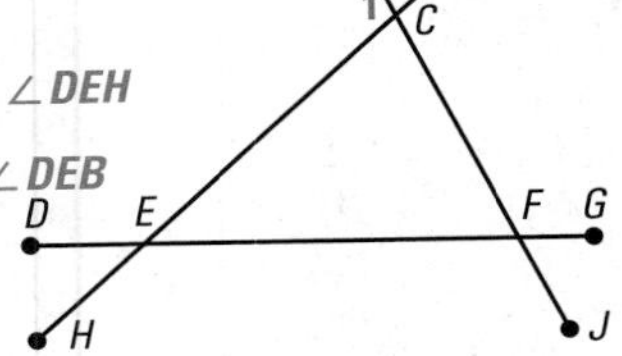

43. $\angle 1$ and __?__ are corresponding angles. $\angle DFA$, $\angle DEH$
44. $\angle 1$ and __?__ are consecutive interior angles. $\angle DEB$, $\angle BEG$
45. $\angle 1$ and __?__ are alternate interior angles. $\angle GFJ$
46. $\angle 1$ and __?__ are alternate exterior angles.

EXTRA CHALLENGE
www.mcdougallittell.com

MIXED REVIEW

47. **ANGLE BISECTOR** The ray $\overrightarrow{BD}$ bisects $\angle ABC$, as shown at the right. Find $m\angle ABD$ and $m\angle ABC$. (Review 1.5 for 3.2) $m\angle ABD = 80°$, $m\angle ABC = 160°$

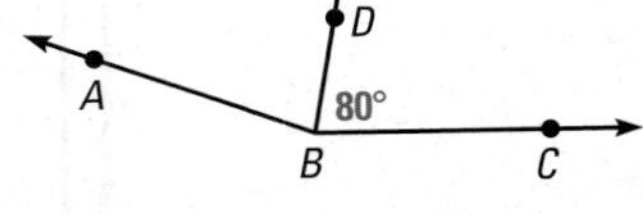

COMPLEMENTS AND SUPPLEMENTS Find the measures of a complement and a supplement of the angle. (Review 1.6 for 3.2)

48. 71° 19°, 109°
49. 13° 77°, 167°
50. 56° 34°, 124°
51. 88° 2°, 92°
52. 27° 63°, 153°
53. 68° 22°, 112°
54. 1° 89°, 179°
55. 60° 30°, 120°
56. 45° 45°, 135°

WRITING REASONS Solve the equation and state a reason for each step. (Review 2.4 for 3.2) 57–62. See margin.

57. $x + 13 = 23$
58. $x - 8 = 17$
59. $4x + 11 = 31$
60. $2x + 9 = 4x - 29$
61. $2(x - 1) + 3 = 17$
62. $5x + 7(x - 10) = -94$

57. $x + 13 - 13 = 23 - 13$ Subtraction property of equality, $x = 10$ Simplify

58. $x - 8 + 8 = 17 + 8$ Addition property of equality, $x = 25$ Simplify

59. $4x + 11 - 11 = 31 - 11$ Subtraction property of equality, $4x = 20$ Simplify $\frac{4x}{4} = \frac{20}{4}$ Division property of equality, $x = 5$ Simplify

Forming a Flow Proof

GROUP ACTIVITY
Work with a partner.

MATERIALS
- slips of paper
- large piece of paper
- tape
- pencils

▶ QUESTION How can you show the logical flow of a proof?

A *flow proof* is like a two-column proof, but the statements are connected by arrows to show how each statement comes from the ones before it.

GIVEN ▶ $\angle 1$ and $\angle 2$ are a linear pair.
$\angle 2$ and $\angle 3$ are a linear pair.

PROVE ▶ $\angle 1 \cong \angle 3$

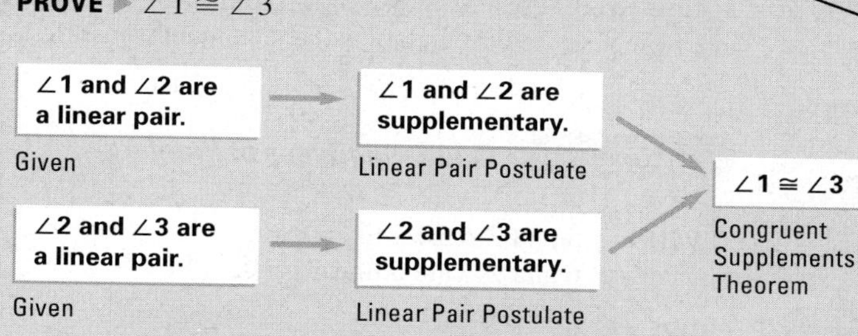

▶ EXPLORING THE CONCEPT

1. Copy the statements at the right. Then draw arrows to show the logical flow of the proof.

   GIVEN ▶ $x + y = 60$, $x = 5$

   PROVE ▶ $y = 55$

   $x + y = 60$ | $5 + y = 60$ | $x = 5$ | $y = 55$

2. Copy the statements below onto slips of paper. Put the slips of paper with given information on the left and put the statement you want to prove on the right. Rearrange the other statements logically to fill in the middle of the proof.

   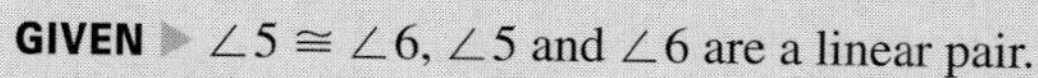

   GIVEN ▶ $\angle 5 \cong \angle 6$, $\angle 5$ and $\angle 6$ are a linear pair.

   PROVE ▶ $j \perp k$

   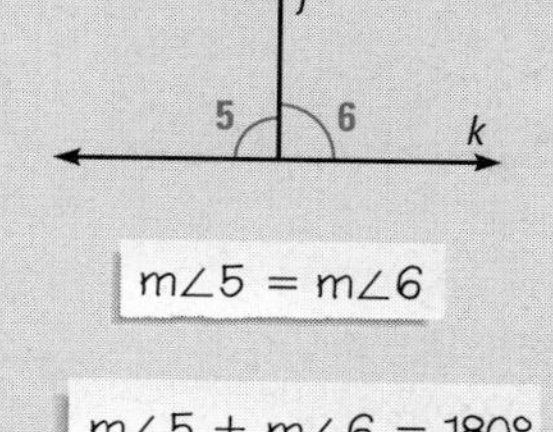

   $\angle 5 \cong \angle 6$ | $j \perp k$ | $m\angle 5 = 90°$ | $m\angle 5 = m\angle 6$ | $\angle 5$ & $\angle 6$ are a linear pair. | $2(m\angle 5) = 180°$ | $m\angle 5 + m\angle 6 = 180°$ | $\angle 5$ & $\angle 6$ are supplementary. | $\angle 5$ is a right angle. | $m\angle 5 + m\angle 5 = 180°$

3. In the flow proof at the top of the page, notice that each statement has a reason written below it. Add reasons to your flow proof from Exercise 2.

▶ DRAWING CONCLUSIONS

CRITICAL THINKING How are two-column proofs and flow proofs alike?

1. $x + y = 60$ → $x = 5$; $x = 5$ ↗ $5 + y = 60$ → $y = 55$

   $x + y = 60$ and $x = 5 \rightarrow 5 + y = 60 \rightarrow y = 55$

1 Planning the Activity

PURPOSE
To model a two-column deductive proof with a flow proof.

MATERIALS
- slips of paper
- large piece of paper
- tape
- pencils
- Activity Support Master (*Chapter 3 Resource Book*, p. 24)

PACING
- Exploring the Concept — 5 min
- Drawing Conclusions — 15 min

▶ LINK TO LESSON
Students should recall how a flow proof is created when they study Example 1 on page 136.

2 Managing the Activity

COOPERATIVE LEARNING
One student in each pair should arrange the statements in order and the other student should supply the reasons and point out any illogical flow in the proof. Students should alternate their tasks.

3 Closing the Activity

★ KEY DISCOVERY
In a flow proof, when one statement follows from another, an arrow is used to show that the statements are connected. The reasons for each statement, written below each statement, show the logical flow of the proof.

ACTIVITY ASSESSMENT
Represent this statement in a flow proof: If $\triangle ABC$ is a right triangle with hypotenuse $\overline{AB}$, then $(AC)^2 + (BC)^2 = (AB)^2$.
See sample answer at left.

2–3. See Additional Answers beginning on page AA1.

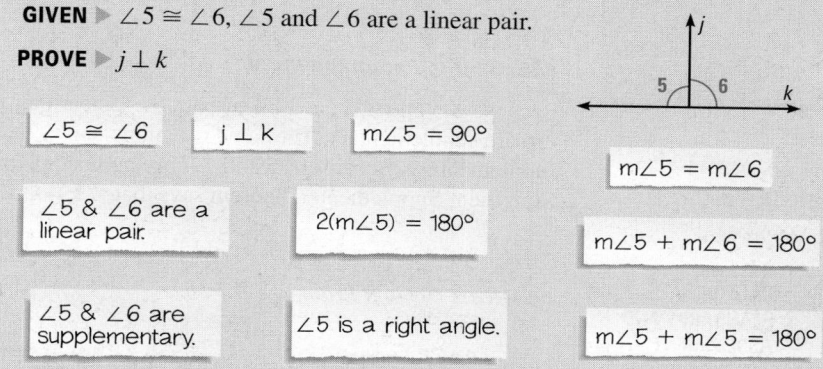

Activity Assessment *Sample answer:*

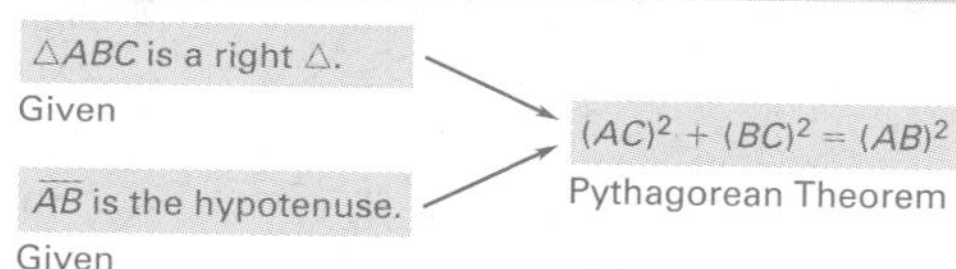

1 PLAN

PACING
Basic: 1 day
Average: 1 day
Advanced: 1 day
Block Schedule: 0.5 block with 3.3

LESSON OPENER
GEOMETRY SOFTWARE
An alternative way to approach Lesson 3.2 is to use the Geometry Software Lesson Opener:

- Blackline Master (*Chapter 3 Resource Book*, p. 25)
- Transparency (p. 15)

MEETING INDIVIDUAL NEEDS

- ***Chapter 3 Resource Book***
  Prerequisite Skills Review (p. 5)
  Practice Level A (p. 26)
  Practice Level B (p. 27)
  Practice Level C (p. 28)
  Reteaching with Practice (p. 29)
  Absent Student Catch-Up (p. 31)
  Challenge (p. 33)
- ***Resources in Spanish***
-  ***Personal Student Tutor***

NEW-TEACHER SUPPORT
See the Tips for New Teachers on pp. 1–2 of the *Chapter 3 Resource Book* for additional notes about Lesson 3.2.

WARM-UP EXERCISES
Transparency Available
State the postulate or theorem that justifies each statement.

1. If 3 + 4 = 7, then 7 = 3 + 4.
   symmetric prop. of equality
2. If $\angle A$ and $\angle B$ are vertical angles, then $\angle A \cong \angle B$.
   Vertical Angles Theorem
3. If $2x + 5 = 17$, then $2x = 12$.
   subtraction prop. of equality
4. If $\overleftrightarrow{AB}$ is a line, then $\overleftrightarrow{AB}$ contains more points than just A.
   A line contains at least 2 pts.

3.2 Proof and Perpendicular Lines

What you should learn

GOAL 1 Write different types of proofs.

GOAL 2 Prove results about perpendicular lines.

Why you should learn it

▼ Make conclusions from things you see in **real life**, such as the reflection in **Ex. 28**.

CALIFORNIA STANDARDS AND ASSESSMENT
CA Standards: 2, 4
SAT9 Task 2: Obj. 28

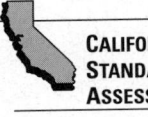

GOAL 1 COMPARING TYPES OF PROOFS

There is more than one way to write a proof. The two-column proof below is from Lesson 2.6. It can also be written as a paragraph proof or as a *flow* proof. A **flow proof** uses arrows to show the flow of the logical argument. Each reason in a flow proof is written below the statement it justifies.

EXAMPLE 1 Comparing Types of Proof

GIVEN ▶ $\angle 5$ and $\angle 6$ are a linear pair.
$\angle 6$ and $\angle 7$ are a linear pair.

PROVE ▶ $\angle 5 \cong \angle 7$

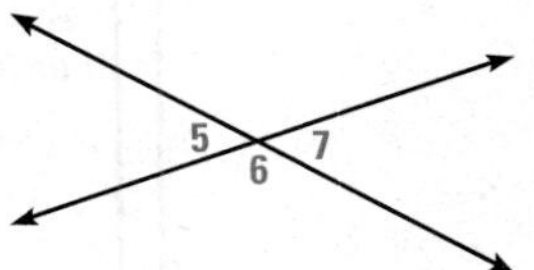

Method 1 *Two-column Proof*

Statements	Reasons
1. $\angle 5$ and $\angle 6$ are a linear pair. $\angle 6$ and $\angle 7$ are a linear pair.	1. Given
2. $\angle 5$ and $\angle 6$ are supplementary. $\angle 6$ and $\angle 7$ are supplementary.	2. Linear Pair Postulate
3. $\angle 5 \cong \angle 7$	3. Congruent Supplements Theorem

Method 2 *Paragraph Proof*

Because $\angle 5$ and $\angle 6$ are a linear pair, the Linear Pair Postulate says that $\angle 5$ and $\angle 6$ are supplementary. The same reasoning shows that $\angle 6$ and $\angle 7$ are supplementary. Because $\angle 5$ and $\angle 7$ are both supplementary to $\angle 6$, the Congruent Supplements Theorem says that $\angle 5 \cong \angle 7$.

Method 3 *Flow Proof*

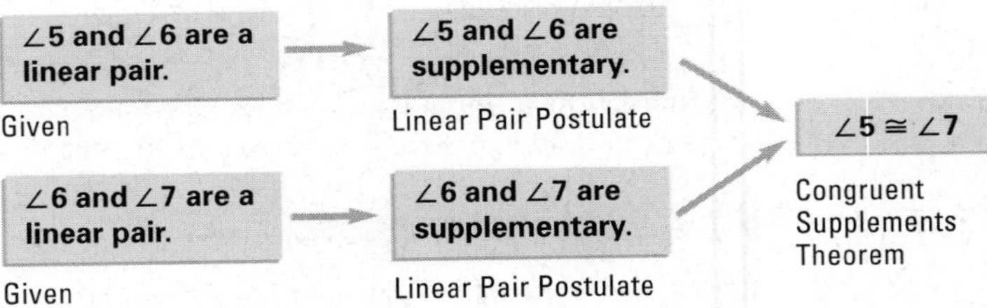

GOAL 2 PROVING RESULTS ABOUT PERPENDICULAR LINES

THEOREMS

THEOREM 3.1

If two lines intersect to form a linear pair of congruent angles, then the lines are perpendicular.

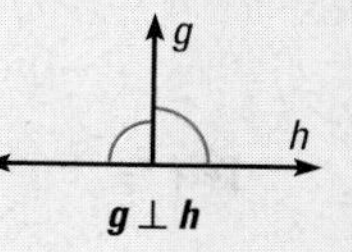

THEOREM 3.2

If two sides of two adjacent acute angles are perpendicular, then the angles are complementary.

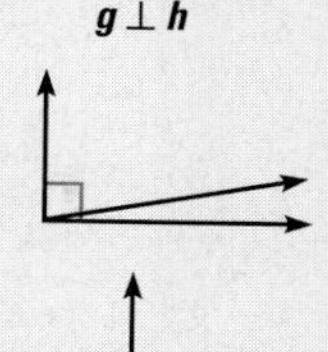

THEOREM 3.3

If two lines are perpendicular, then they intersect to form four right angles.

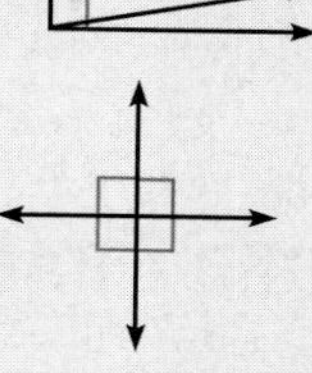

You will prove Theorem 3.2 and Theorem 3.3 in Exercises 17–19.

EXAMPLE 2 *Proof of Theorem 3.1*

Write a proof of Theorem 3.1.

SOLUTION

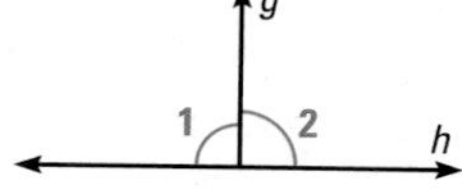

GIVEN ▶ $\angle 1 \cong \angle 2$, $\angle 1$ and $\angle 2$ are a linear pair.

PROVE ▶ $g \perp h$

Plan for Proof Use $m\angle 1 + m\angle 2 = 180°$ and $m\angle 1 = m\angle 2$ to show $m\angle 1 = 90°$.

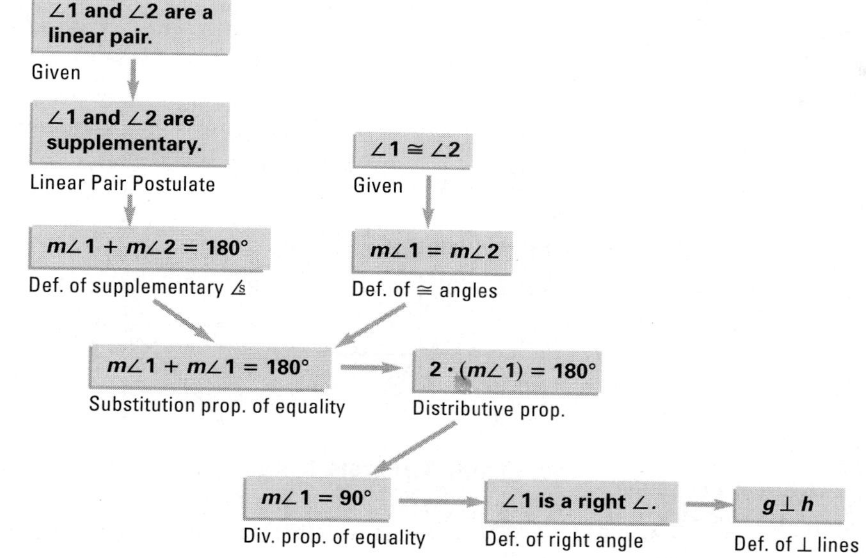

STUDENT HELP

Study Tip
When you write a complicated proof, it may help to write a plan first. The plan will also help others to understand your proof.

Extra Example 1 Method 3: Flow proof.

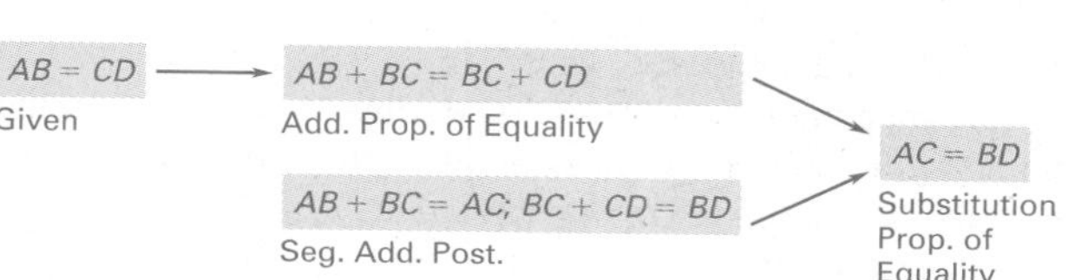

2 TEACH

EXTRA EXAMPLE 1

Given: $AB = CD$

Prove: $AC = BD$

Method 1: Two-column proof

Statements (Reasons)

1. $AB = CD$ (Given)
2. $AB + BC = BC + CD$ (addition prop. of equality)
3. $AB + BC = AC$ and $BC + CD = BD$ (segment addition post.)
4. $AC = BD$ (substitution prop. of equality)

Method 2: Paragraph proof

Because $AC = BD$, the addition property of equality says that $AB + BC = BC + CD$. Since $AB + BC = AC$ and $BC + CD = BD$ by the segment addition post., it follows from the substitution prop. of equality that $AC = BD$.

See margin for Method 3.

EXTRA EXAMPLE 2

Write a two-column proof.

Given: $BA \perp BC$

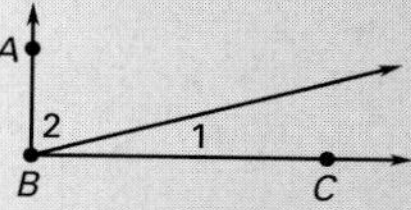

Prove: $\angle 1$ and $\angle 2$ are complementary

Statements (Reasons)

1. $BA \perp BC$ (Given)
2. $\angle ABC$ is a right angle (definition of perpendicular lines)
3. $m\angle ABC = 90°$ (definition of right angle)
4. $m\angle 1 + m\angle 2 = m\angle ABC$ (Angle Addition Post.)
5. $m\angle 1 + m\angle 2 = 90°$ (substitution prop. of equality)
6. $\angle 1$ and $\angle 2$ are complementary (definition of comp. angles)

Checkpoint Exercises for Examples 1 and 2 on next page.

✓ CHECKPOINT EXERCISES

For use after Examples 1 and 2:

1. Write a proof of the Congruent Supplements Theorem.

Given: $\angle 2 \cong \angle 4$
$\angle 1$ is supplementary to $\angle 2$.
$\angle 3$ is supplementary to $\angle 4$.

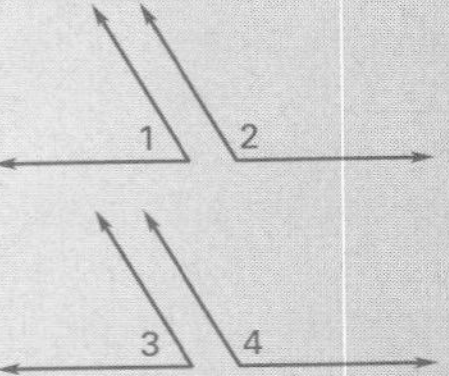

Prove: $\angle 1 \cong \angle 3$

Since $\angle 1$ is supplementary to $\angle 2$ and $\angle 3$ is supplementary to $\angle 4$, $m\angle 1 + m\angle 2 = 180°$ and $m\angle 3 + m\angle 4 = 180°$ by the definition of supplementary angles. Therefore the symmetric and transitive properties of equality say that $m\angle 1 + m\angle 2 = m\angle 3 + m\angle 4$. It is given that $\angle 2 \cong \angle 4$, so by the definition of congruent angles, $m\angle 2 = m\angle 4$. The subtraction prop. of equality allows the statement $m\angle 1 = m\angle 3$. Finally, by the definition of congruent angles, $\angle 1 \cong \angle 3$.

FOCUS ON VOCABULARY

How is a flow proof different from a two-column proof? See margin.

CLOSURE QUESTION

In a two-column proof, what can be written under the reasons column? definitions, postulates, or theorems

DAILY PUZZLER

Digits displayed on a digital clock form a series of perpendicular segments. Determine which digit is being described. *I am constructed from more than 4 distinct segments. I contain four different pairs of parallel segments. I contain six different pairs of perpendicular segments. I am an odd number.* 9

10. See Additional Answers beginning on page AA1.

CONCEPT SUMMARY — TYPES OF PROOFS

You have now studied three types of proofs.

1. **TWO-COLUMN PROOF** This is the most formal type of proof. It lists numbered statements in the left column and a reason for each statement in the right column.
2. **PARAGRAPH PROOF** This type of proof describes the logical argument with sentences. It is more conversational than a two-column proof.
3. **FLOW PROOF** This type of proof uses the same statements and reasons as a two-column proof, but the logical flow connecting the statements is indicated by arrows.

GUIDED PRACTICE

Vocabulary Check ✓

1. Define *perpendicular lines.*
   Two lines are perpendicular if and only if they meet to form right angles.

Concept Check ✓

2. Which postulate or theorem guarantees that there is only one line that can be constructed perpendicular to a given line from a given point not on the line?
   Postulate 14, Perpendicular Postulate

Skill Check ✓

Write the postulate or theorem that justifies the statement about the diagram.

3. $\angle 1 \cong \angle 2$ Vertical Angles Theorem

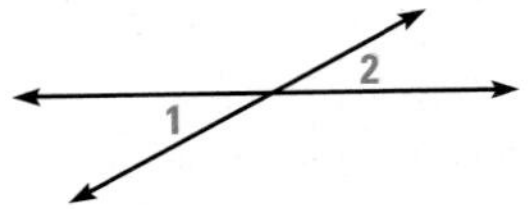

4. $j \perp k$ Theorem 3.1

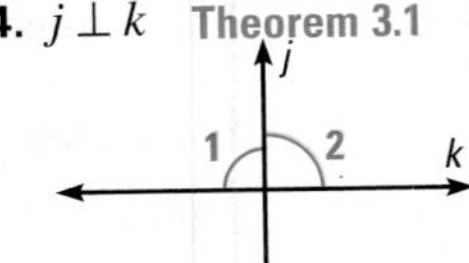

Write the postulate or theorem that justifies the statement, given that $g \perp h$.

5. $m\angle 5 + m\angle 6 = 90°$ Theorem 3.2

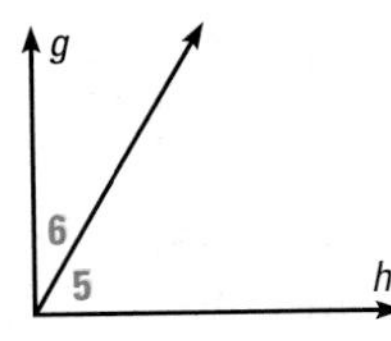

6. $\angle 3$ and $\angle 4$ are right angles.
   Theorem 3.3

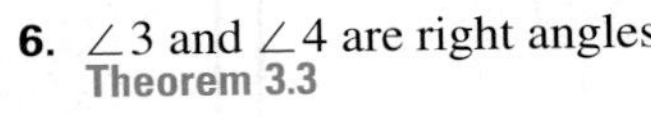

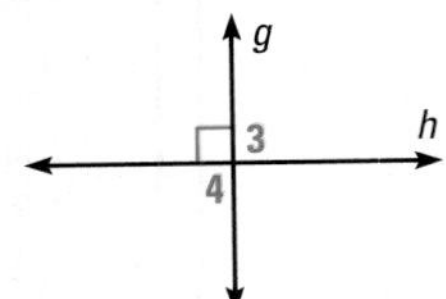

Find the value of *x*.

7. 90
8. 45
9. 20

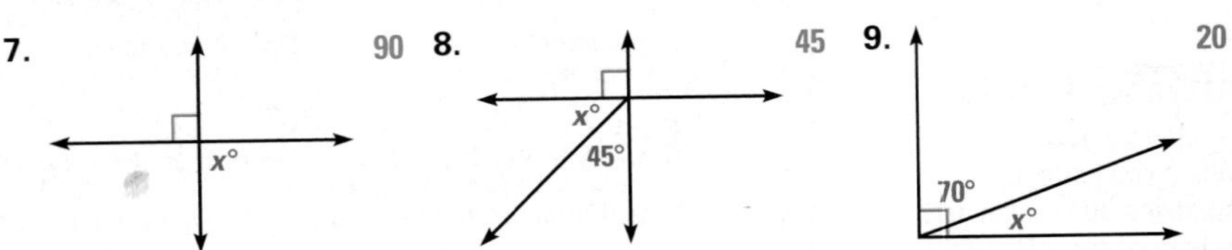

10. **ERROR ANALYSIS** It is given that $\angle ABC \cong \angle CBD$. A student concludes that because $\angle ABC$ and $\angle CBD$ are congruent adjacent angles, $\overleftrightarrow{AB} \perp \overleftrightarrow{CB}$. What is wrong with this reasoning? Draw a diagram to support your answer.

10. *Sample answer:* It is not stated that $\angle ABC$ and $\angle CBD$ form a linear pair; see margin for counterexample.

Focus on Vocabulary *Sample answer:*
The reason for each statement in a flow proof is written below the statement rather than in a column to the right of the statement. Instead of listing all of the statements in a single column, the statements in a flow proof may be in one or more columns with arrows to show the flow of logic between statements.

PRACTICE AND APPLICATIONS

STUDENT HELP

Extra Practice to help you master skills is on p. 807.

USING ALGEBRA **Find the value of *x*.**

11. 90 **12.** 30 **13.** 35

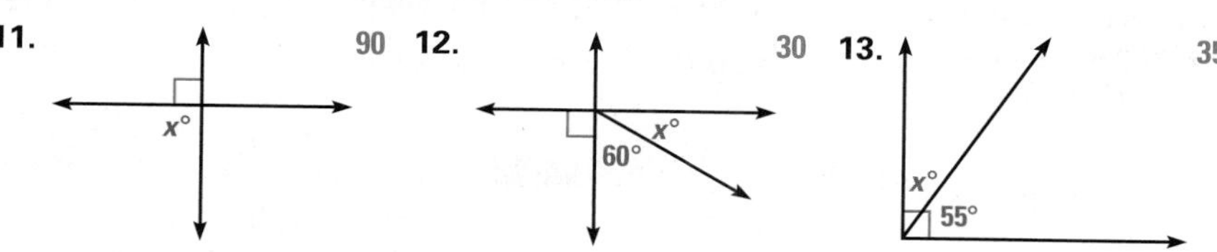

LOGICAL REASONING **What can you conclude about the labeled angles?**

14. $\overline{AB} \perp \overline{CB}$

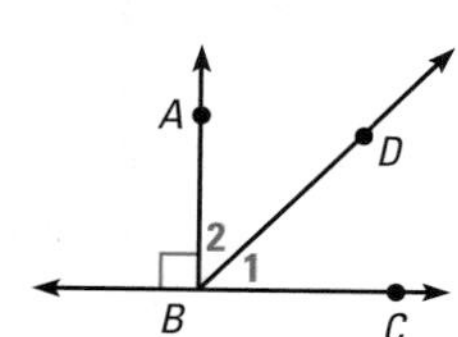

15. $n \perp m$

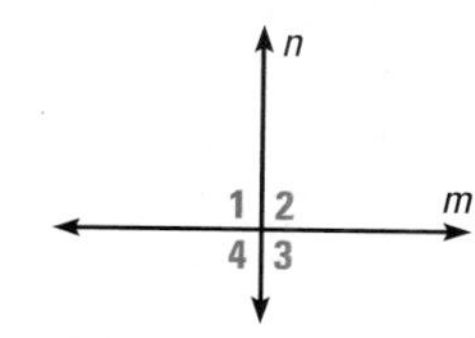

16. $h \perp k$

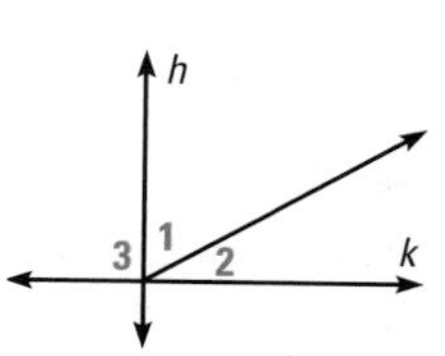

14. *Sample answer:* ∠1 and ∠2 are complementary.

15. *Sample answer:* ∠1, ∠2, ∠3, and ∠4 are right angles.

16. *Sample answer:* ∠3 is a right angle, ∠1 and ∠2 are complementary.

18. (a) ∠1 and ∠2 are supplementary (b) Definition of supplementary ∠s (c) Definition of right ∠s (d) Substitution property (e) $m\angle 2 = 90°$ (f) Definition of right ∠

17. **DEVELOPING PARAGRAPH PROOF** Fill in the lettered blanks to complete the proof of Theorem 3.2.

GIVEN ▶ $\overrightarrow{BA} \perp \overrightarrow{BC}$ (a) right angle (b) 90° (c) Angle Addition (d) $m\angle 3$ (e) $m\angle 4$ (f) 90°

PROVE ▶ ∠3 and ∠4 are complementary.

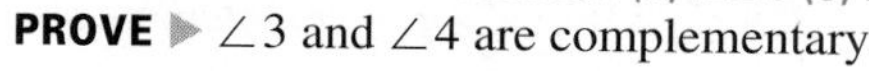

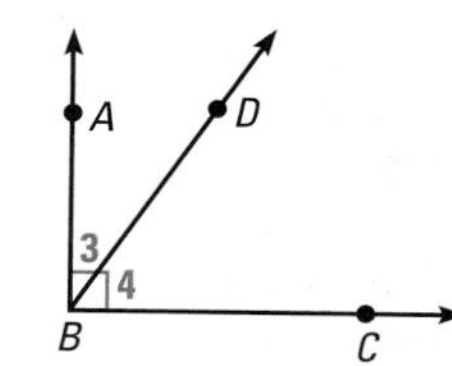

Because $\overrightarrow{BA} \perp \overrightarrow{BC}$, $\angle ABC$ is a __**a.**__ and $m\angle ABC =$ __**b.**__. According to the __**c.**__ Postulate, $m\angle 3 + m\angle 4 = m\angle ABC$. So, by the substitution property of equality, __**d.**__ + __**e.**__ = __**f.**__. By definition, ∠3 and ∠4 are complementary.

18. **DEVELOPING FLOW PROOF** Fill in the lettered blanks to complete the proof of part of Theorem 3.3. Because the lines are perpendicular, they intersect to form a right angle. Call that ∠1. See margin.

GIVEN ▶ $j \perp k$, ∠1 and ∠2 are a linear pair.

PROVE ▶ ∠2 is a right angle.

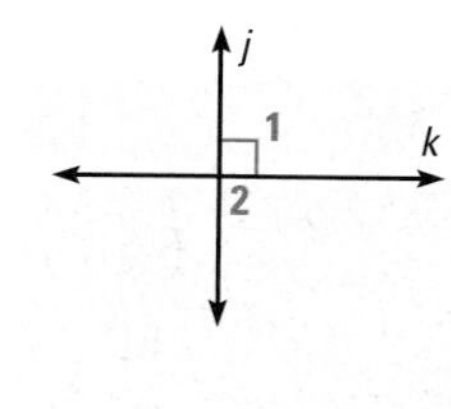

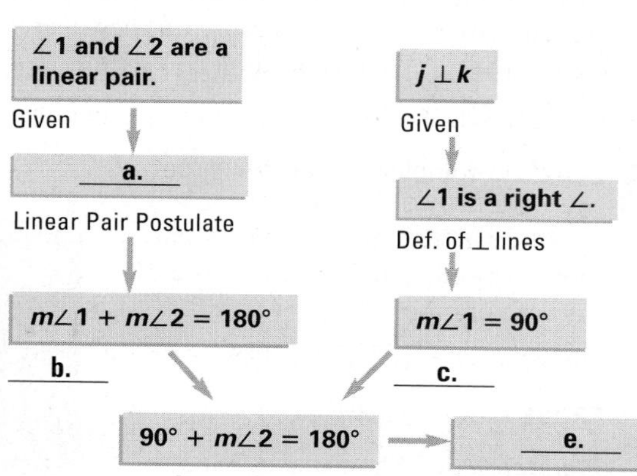

STUDENT HELP

HOMEWORK HELP
Example 1: Exs. 17–23
Example 2: Exs. 11–19, 24, 25

3 APPLY

ASSIGNMENT GUIDE

BASIC
Day 1: pp. 139–141 Exs. 11–23, 26, 27, 29–36

AVERAGE
Day 1: pp. 139–141 Exs. 11–23, 26, 27, 29–36

ADVANCED
Day 1: pp. 139–141 Exs. 11–36

BLOCK SCHEDULE WITH 3.3
pp. 139–141 Exs. 11–23, 26, 27, 29–36

EXERCISE LEVELS

Level A: ***Easier***
11–16

Level B: ***More Difficult***
17–23, 26, 27

Level C: ***Most Difficult***
24, 25, 28

HOMEWORK CHECK

To quickly check student understanding of key concepts, go over the following exercises: Exs. 12, 16, 17, 18, 19, 23. See also the Daily Homework Quiz:

- Blackline Master (*Chapter 3 Resource Book*, p. 36)
- Transparency (p. 19)

STUDENT HELP NOTES

Homework Help Students can find help for Exs. 17–24 at **www.mcdougallittell.com.** The information can be printed out for students who don't have access to the Internet.

! COMMON ERROR

EXERCISE 19 Students often interchange congruence and equality. Make sure that students understand whether a theorem or postulate that they are using defines a congruence or equality relation.

APPLICATION NOTE

EXERCISE 25 A carpenter can use a T-square to tell if an angle is a right angle. The converse of the Pythagorean Theorem can also be used.

19. 3. If two angles are congruent, then their measures are equal.

24. *Sample answer:* It is given that $\overline{AB} \perp \overline{BC}$ and $\overline{BC} \perp \overline{CD}$, so $\angle 7$ and $\angle 8$ are right angles because perpendicular lines form right angles. Then $\angle 7 \cong \angle 8$ because all right angles are congruent.

ADDITIONAL PRACTICE AND RETEACHING

For Lesson 3.2:

- Practice Levels A, B, and C (*Chapter 3 Resource Book,* p. 26)
- Reteaching with Practice (*Chapter 3 Resource Book,* p. 29)
- See Lesson 3.2 of the *Personal Student Tutor*

For more Mixed Review:

- Search the *Test and Practice Generator* for key words or specific lessons.

STUDENT HELP

HOMEWORK HELP Visit our Web site www.mcdougallittell.com for help with writing proofs in Exs. 17–24.

19. **DEVELOPING TWO-COLUMN PROOF** Fill in the blanks to complete the proof of part of Theorem 3.3. **See margin.**

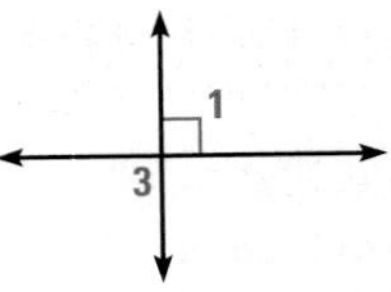

GIVEN ▶ $\angle 1$ is a right angle.

PROVE ▶ $\angle 3$ is a right angle.

Statements	Reasons
1. $\angle 1$ and $\angle 3$ are vertical angles.	1. Definition of vertical angles
2. ___?___ $\angle 1 \cong \angle 3$	2. Vertical Angles Theorem
3. $m\angle 1 = m\angle 3$	3. ___?___ See margin.
4. $\angle 1$ is a right angle.	4. ___?___ Given.
5. ___?___ $m\angle 1 = 90°$	5. Definition of right angle
6. ___?___ $90° = m\angle 3$	6. Substitution prop. of equality
7. ___?___ $\angle 3$ is a right angle.	7. Definition of right angle

20. If the exterior sides of two adjacent angles are perpendicular, then the angles are complementary; given; Vertical angles are congruent.

21. If $\angle 4 \cong \angle 6$, then $\angle 5 \cong \angle 6$ because $\angle 5 \cong \angle 4$ and because of the Transitive Property of Congruence for angles.

22. Both $\angle 4$ and $\angle 6$ are complementary to $\angle 3$, so $\angle 4 \cong \angle 6$ because if two angles are complementary to the same angle, then they are congruent.

DEVELOPING PROOF **In Exercises 20–23, use the following information.** Dan is trying to figure out how to prove that $\angle 5 \cong \angle 6$ below. First he wrote everything that he knew about the diagram, as shown below in **blue**.

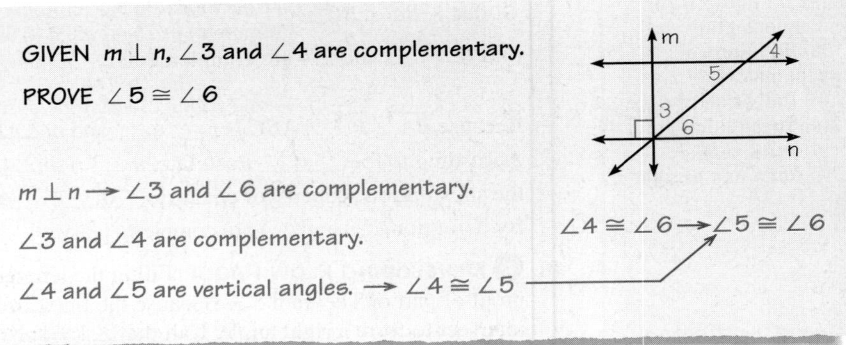

GIVEN m ⊥ n, ∠3 and ∠4 are complementary.
PROVE ∠5 ≅ ∠6
m
n
3
4
5
6
m ⊥ n → ∠3 and ∠6 are complementary.
∠3 and ∠4 are complementary.
∠4 ≅ ∠6 → ∠5 ≅ ∠6
∠4 and ∠5 are vertical angles. → ∠4 ≅ ∠5

20–24. See margin.

20. Write a justification for each statement Dan wrote in blue.

21. After writing all he knew, Dan wrote what he was supposed to prove in **red**. He also wrote $\angle 4 \cong \angle 6$ because he knew that if $\angle 4 \cong \angle 6$ and $\angle 4 \cong \angle 5$, then $\angle 5 \cong \angle 6$. Write a justification for this step.

22. How can you use Dan's blue statements to prove that $\angle 4 \cong \angle 6$?

23. Copy and complete Dan's flow proof.

FOCUS ON APPLICATIONS

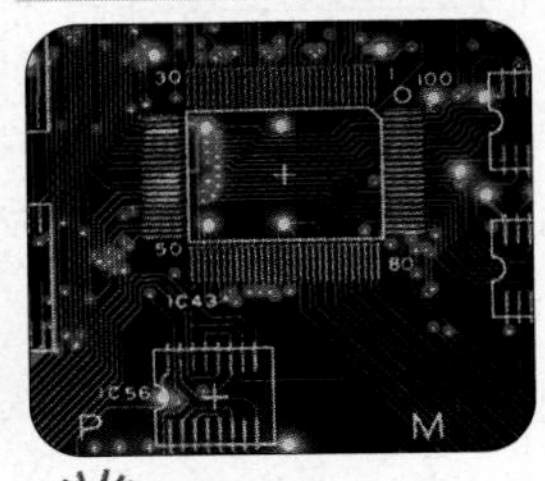

CIRCUIT BOARDS The lines on circuit boards are made of metal and carry electricity. The lines must not touch each other or the electricity will flow to the wrong place, creating a *short circuit.*

24. **CIRCUIT BOARDS** The diagram shows part of a circuit board. Write any type of proof.

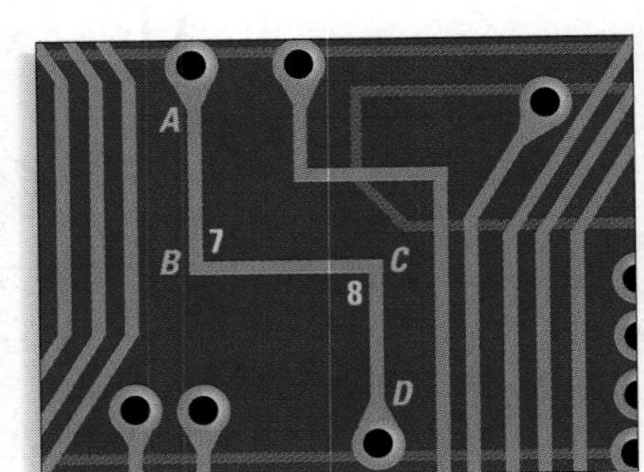

GIVEN ▶ $\overline{AB} \perp \overline{BC}$, $\overline{BC} \perp \overline{CD}$

PROVE ▶ $\angle 7 \cong \angle 8$

Plan for Proof Show that $\angle 7$ and $\angle 8$ are both right angles.

23.

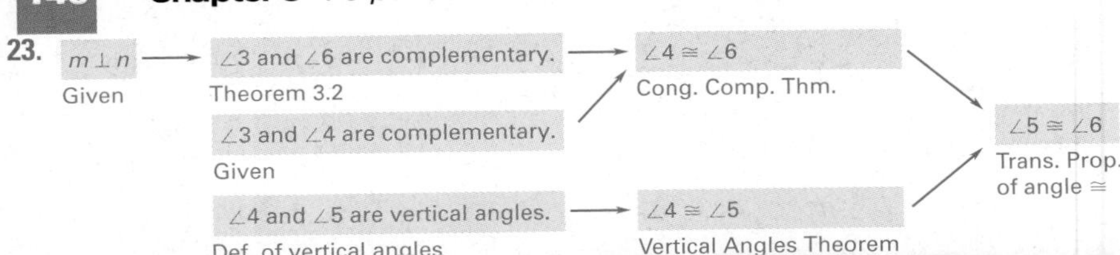

25. No. *Sample answer:* If one of the angles is a right angle, then the cross pieces are perpendicular, so all four angles will be right angles.

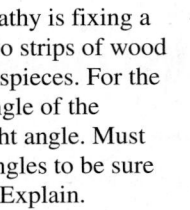

25. **WINDOW REPAIR** Cathy is fixing a window frame. She fit two strips of wood together to make the crosspieces. For the glass panes to fit, each angle of the crosspieces must be a right angle. Must Cathy measure all four angles to be sure they are all right angles? Explain.

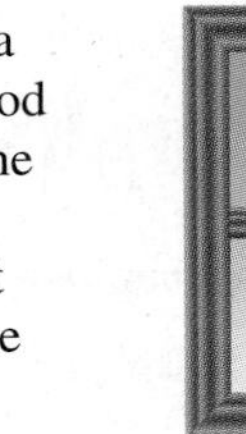

Test Preparation

26. **MULTIPLE CHOICE** Which of the following is true if $g \perp h$? B

Ⓐ $m\angle 1 + m\angle 2 > 180°$

Ⓑ $m\angle 1 + m\angle 2 < 180°$

Ⓒ $m\angle 1 + m\angle 2 = 180°$

Ⓓ Cannot be determined

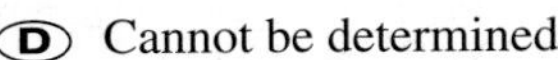

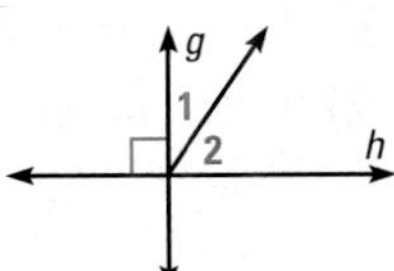

27. **MULTIPLE CHOICE** Which of the following must be true if $m\angle ACD = 90°$? B

I. $\angle BCE$ is a right angle.

II. $\overleftrightarrow{AE} \perp \overleftrightarrow{BD}$

III. $\angle BCA$ and $\angle BCE$ are complementary.

Ⓐ I only Ⓑ I and II only Ⓒ III only

Ⓓ I, II, and III Ⓔ None of these

28. *Sample answer:* The angles formed by the mirror and the floor and by the mirror and the reflection of the floor are congruent. If the sum of the measures of the two angles is not 180°, then each angle is not 90°, or the mirror is not perpendicular to the floor.

★ Challenge

28. **REFLECTIONS** Ann has a full-length mirror resting against the wall of her room. Ann notices that the floor and its reflection do not form a straight angle. She concludes that the mirror is not perpendicular to the floor. Explain her reasoning.

See margin.

EXTRA CHALLENGE

www.mcdougallittell.com

MIXED REVIEW

ANGLE MEASURES Complete the statement given that $s \perp t$. (Review 2.6 for 3.3)

29. If $m\angle 1 = 38°$, then $m\angle 4 =$ ___?___. 38°

30. $m\angle 2 =$ ___?___ 90°

31. If $m\angle 6 = 51°$, then $m\angle 1 =$ ___?___. 39°

32. If $m\angle 3 = 42°$, then $m\angle 1 =$ ___?___. 48°

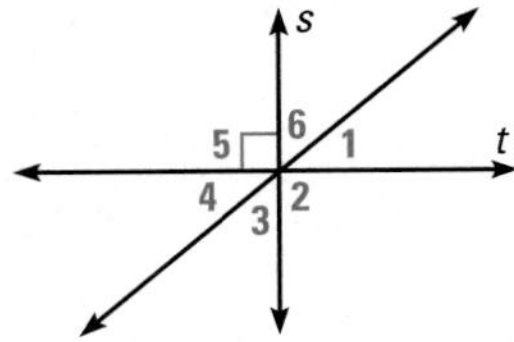

ANGLES List all pairs of angles that fit the description. (Review 3.1)

33. ∠1 and ∠5, ∠3 and ∠7, ∠2 and ∠6, ∠4 and ∠8

33. Corresponding angles

34. Alternate interior angles
∠3 and ∠6, ∠4 and ∠5

35. Alternate exterior angles
∠1 and ∠8, ∠2 and ∠7

36. Consecutive interior angles
∠3 and ∠5, ∠4 and ∠6

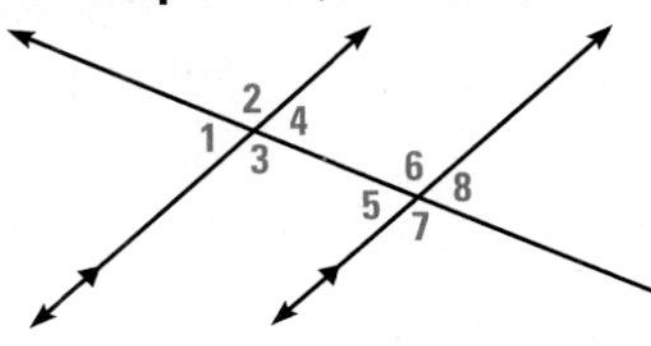

4 ASSESS

DAILY HOMEWORK QUIZ

Transparency Available

1. Find the value of *x*.

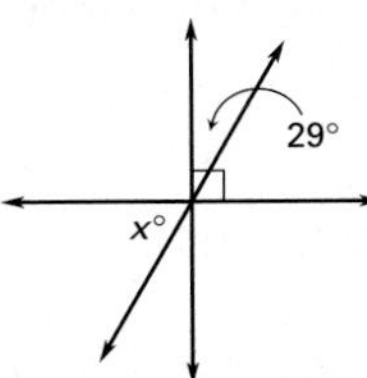

61°

2. What can you conclude about the labeled angles?

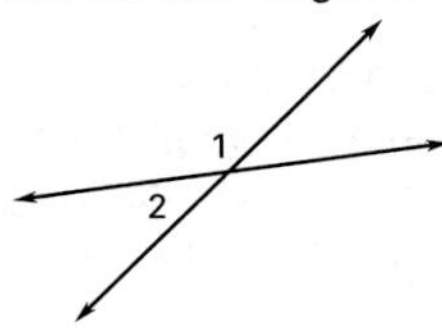

∠1 and ∠2 are linear pairs and are supplementary.

3. Which of the following must *not* be true if $m\angle 2 = 90°$ in Exercise 2?
   a. The lines are perpendicular.
   b. ∠1 is a right angle.
   c. The unlabeled angles are congruent.
   d. ∠1 and ∠2 are complementary. d

EXTRA CHALLENGE NOTE

Challenge problems for Lesson 3.2 are available in **blackline** format in the *Chapter 3 Resource Book,* p. 33 and at **www.mcdougallittell.com.**

ADDITIONAL TEST PREPARATION

1. **OPEN ENDED** Find an example in the classroom or draw a picture of a piece of furniture that demonstrates Theorem 3.1, *If two lines intersect to form a linear pair of congruent angles, then the lines are perpendicular.* *Sample answer:* A shelf on a bookcase has a divider that is perpendicular to the horizontal lines of the top and bottom of the shelf.

1 Planning the Activity

PURPOSE
To use geometry software to investigate the relationships between two corresponding angles and between two alternate interior angles.

MATERIALS
- Geometry software
- Software Help (*Chapter 3 Resource Book,* p. 38)

PACING
- Activity — 25 min

LINK TO LESSON
Students should recall the results of this activity when studying the theorems on page 143.

2 Managing the Activity

ALTERNATIVE APPROACH
Have students draw one or more figures on paper and measure the angles with a protractor.

3 Closing the Activity

★ **KEY DISCOVERY**
If two parallel lines are cut by a transversal the pairs of corresponding angles and alternate interior angles are congruent.

ACTIVITY ASSESSMENT
JOURNAL What kind of angles are ∠1 and ∠2? Explain how you can use the diagram to find the measures of ∠1 and ∠2?

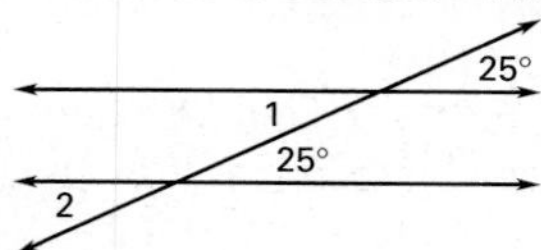

∠1 and ∠2 are vertical angles to the angles measuring 25°. Therefore $m\angle 1 = m\angle 2 = 25°$.

ACTIVITY 3.3
Using Technology

Parallel Lines and Angles

You can use geometry software to explore the properties of parallel lines.

STUDENT HELP

Visit our Web site www.mcdougallittell.com to see instructions for several software applications.

CONSTRUCT

Steps 1–6. Check drawings.

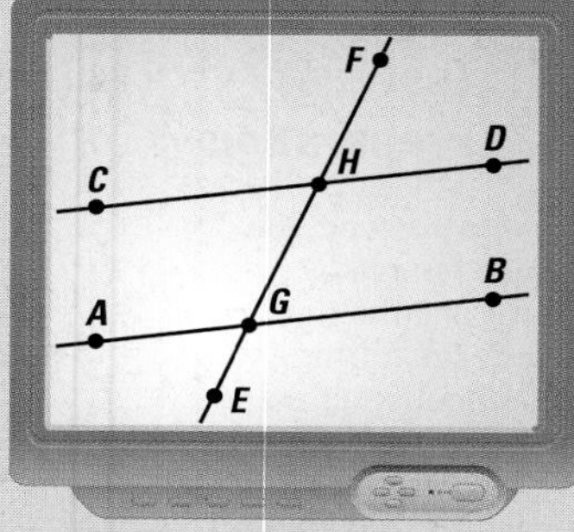

1. Draw two points. Label them A and B. Draw $\overleftrightarrow{AB}$.
2. Draw a point not on $\overleftrightarrow{AB}$. Label it C.
3. Use your software's *construct parallel line* feature to construct a line through C parallel to $\overleftrightarrow{AB}$.
4. Draw a point on the line you constructed. Label it D. Move A, B, C, and D to the edges of the screen, as shown.
5. Draw two points outside the parallel lines. Label them E and F. Draw transversal $\overleftrightarrow{EF}$.
6. Find the intersection of $\overleftrightarrow{AB}$ and $\overleftrightarrow{EF}$. Label it G. Find the intersection of $\overleftrightarrow{CD}$ and $\overleftrightarrow{EF}$. Label it H.

1. Answers will vary. *Sample answers:* See art at right. The corresponding angles are congruent. The alternate interior angles are congruent.

3. *Sample answer:* If two parallel lines are cut by a transversal, then the pairs of corresponding angles are congruent.

INVESTIGATE

1. Measure all eight angles formed by the three lines. What do you notice?
2. Drag point E or F to change the angle the transversal makes with the parallel lines. Be sure E and F stay outside the parallel lines. What do you notice?
   Answers will vary. *Sample answers:* The corresponding angles are always congruent. The alternate interior angles are always congruent.

MAKE A CONJECTURE

3. Make a conjecture about the measures of corresponding angles when two parallel lines are cut by a transversal.
   See margin.
4. Make a conjecture about the measures of alternate interior angles when two parallel lines are cut by a transversal.
   Sample answer: If two parallel lines are cut by a transversal, then the pairs of alternate interior angles are congruent.

EXTENSION

CRITICAL THINKING Calculate the sum of two consecutive interior angles. Make and test a conjecture about the sum.
Sample conjecture: If two parallel lines are cut by a transversal, then the sum of two consecutive interior angles is 180°.

3.3 Parallel Lines and Transversals

What you should learn

GOAL 1 Prove and use results about parallel lines and transversals.

GOAL 2 Use properties of parallel lines to solve **real-life** problems, such as estimating Earth's circumference in **Example 5**.

Why you should learn it

▼ Properties of parallel lines help you understand how rainbows are formed, as in **Ex. 30**.

REAL LIFE

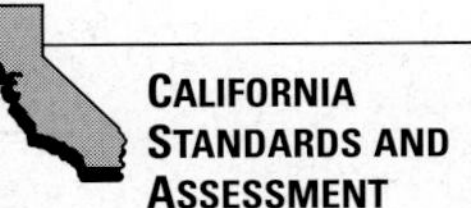

CALIFORNIA STANDARDS AND ASSESSMENT

CA Standards: 4, 7
SAT9 Task 1: Obj. 1
SAT9 Task 2: Objs. 1, 28

GOAL 1 PROPERTIES OF PARALLEL LINES

In the activity on page 142, you may have discovered the following results.

POSTULATE

POSTULATE 15 ***Corresponding Angles Postulate***

If two parallel lines are cut by a transversal, then the pairs of corresponding angles are congruent.

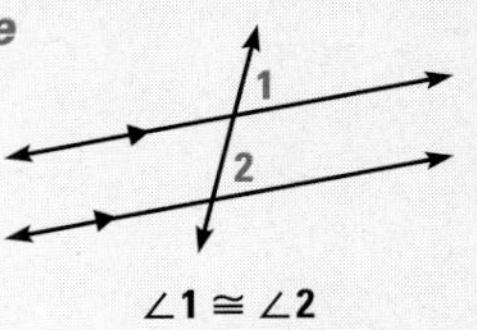

You are asked to prove Theorems 3.5, 3.6, and 3.7 in Exercises 27–29.

THEOREMS ABOUT PARALLEL LINES

THEOREM 3.4 ***Alternate Interior Angles***

If two parallel lines are cut by a transversal, then the pairs of alternate interior angles are congruent.

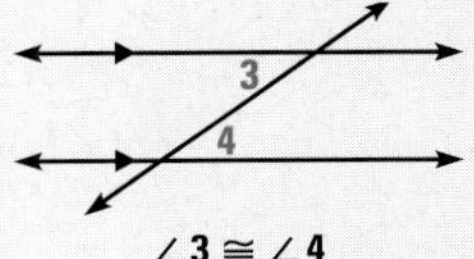

THEOREM 3.5 ***Consecutive Interior Angles***

If two parallel lines are cut by a transversal, then the pairs of consecutive interior angles are supplementary.

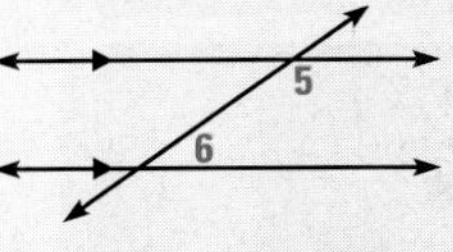

THEOREM 3.6 ***Alternate Exterior Angles***

If two parallel lines are cut by a transversal, then the pairs of alternate exterior angles are congruent.

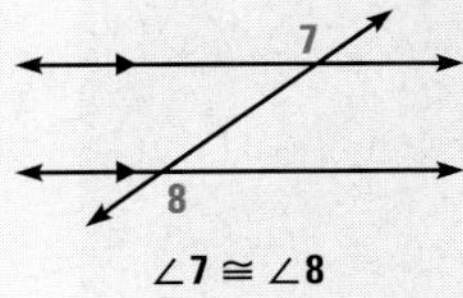

THEOREM 3.7 ***Perpendicular Transversal***

If a transversal is perpendicular to one of two parallel lines, then it is perpendicular to the other.

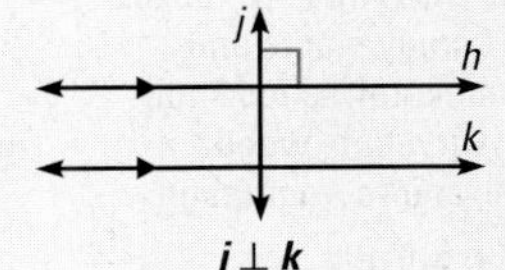

1 PLAN

PACING
Basic: 2 days
Average: 2 days
Advanced: 2 days
Block Schedule: 0.5 block with 3.2
0.5 block with 3.4

LESSON OPENER
APPLICATION
An alternative way to approach Lesson 3.3 is to use the Application Lesson Opener:

- Blackline Master (*Chapter 3 Resource Book*, p. 37)
- Transparency (p. 16)

MEETING INDIVIDUAL NEEDS

- ***Chapter 3 Resource Book***
  Prerequisite Skills Review (p. 5)
  Practice Level A (p. 40)
  Practice Level B (p. 41)
  Practice Level C (p. 42)
  Reteaching with Practice (p. 43)
  Absent Student Catch-Up (p. 45)
  Challenge (p. 47)
- ***Resources in Spanish***
- ***Personal Student Tutor***

NEW-TEACHER SUPPORT
See the Tips for New Teachers on pp. 1–2 of the *Chapter 3 Resource Book* for additional notes about Lesson 3.3.

WARM-UP EXERCISES

Transparency Available

State the definition, theorem, or postulate that justifies each statement.

1. If ∠1 and ∠2 are vertical angles, then ∠1 ≅ ∠2.
   Vertical Angles Thm.
2. If ∠1 ≅ ∠2 and ∠2 ≅ ∠3, then ∠1 ≅ ∠3.
   Transitive Prop. of Cong.
3. If ∠1 and ∠2 form a linear pair, then $m\angle 1 + m\angle 2 = 180°$.
   Linear Pair Postulate

2 TEACH

MOTIVATING THE LESSON
Creating a landscape that is appealing to the eye often requires the use of geometry. Landscape architects can use parallel lines and transversals to create designs having congruent and supplementary angles.

EXTRA EXAMPLE 1
Given: $p \parallel q$
Prove: $m\angle 1 + m\angle 2 = 180°$

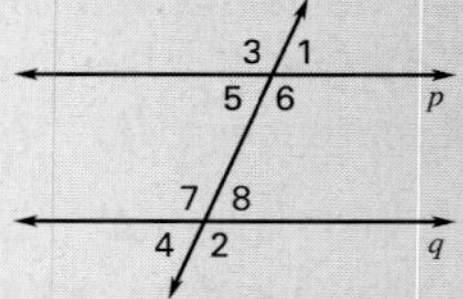

Statements (Reasons)
1. $p \parallel q$ (Given)
2. $\angle 1 \cong \angle 4$ (Alternate Exterior Angles Thm.)
3. $\angle 2$ and $\angle 4$ are supplementary (Linear Pair Postulate)
4. $\angle 1$ and $\angle 2$ are supplementary ($\cong$ Supplements Thm.)

EXTRA EXAMPLE 2
Use the diagram in Extra Example 1. Given that $m\angle 2 = 110°$, find each measure. Give the postulate or theorem.
a. $m\angle 8$ 70°; Linear Pair Postulate
b. $m\angle 1$ 70°; Corresponding Angles Postulate
c. $m\angle 3$ 110°; Alternate Exterior Angle Theorem or Linear Pair Postulate
d. $m\angle 4$ 70°; Alternate Exterior Angle Theorem or Linear Pair Postulate or Vertical Angles Theorem

CHECKPOINT EXERCISES
For use after Examples 1 and 2:
1. If $\overleftrightarrow{AB} \parallel \overleftrightarrow{CD}$, and $\overleftrightarrow{AC} \parallel \overleftrightarrow{BD}$ find $m\angle 1$, $m\angle 2$, and $m\angle 3$.

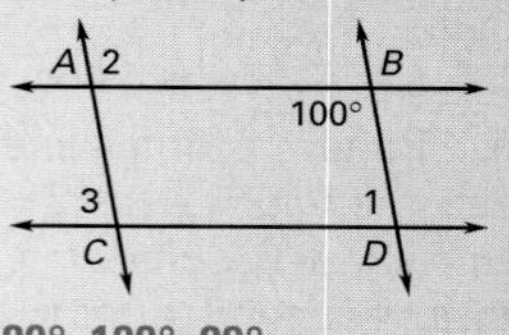

80°, 100°, 80°

STUDENT HELP
Study Tip
When you prove a theorem, the hypotheses of the theorem becomes the GIVEN, and the conclusion is what you must PROVE.

EXAMPLE 1 *Proving the Alternate Interior Angles Theorem*

Prove the Alternate Interior Angles Theorem.

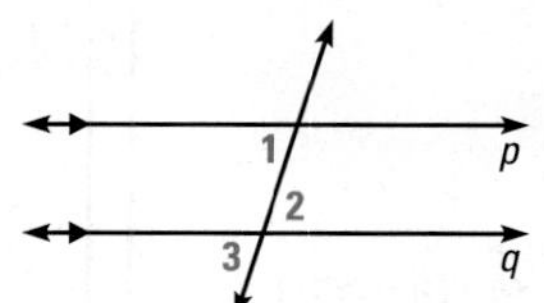

SOLUTION

GIVEN ▶ $p \parallel q$

PROVE ▶ $\angle 1 \cong \angle 2$

Statements	Reasons
1. $p \parallel q$	**1.** Given
2. $\angle 1 \cong \angle 3$	**2.** Corresponding Angles Postulate
3. $\angle 3 \cong \angle 2$	**3.** Vertical Angles Theorem
4. $\angle 1 \cong \angle 2$	**4.** Transitive Property of Congruence

EXAMPLE 2 *Using Properties of Parallel Lines*

Given that $m\angle 5 = 65°$, find each measure. Tell which postulate or theorem you use.

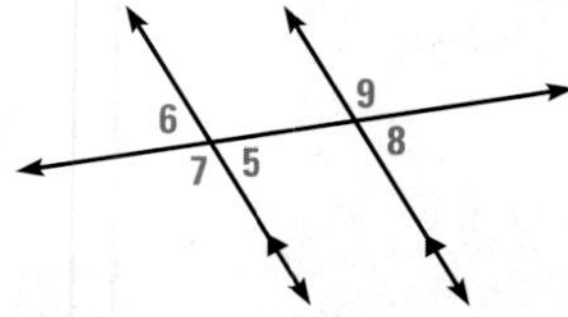

a. $m\angle 6$ **b.** $m\angle 7$

c. $m\angle 8$ **d.** $m\angle 9$

SOLUTION

a. $m\angle 6 = m\angle 5 = 65°$ **Vertical Angles Theorem**

b. $m\angle 7 = 180° - m\angle 5 = 115°$ **Linear Pair Postulate**

c. $m\angle 8 = m\angle 5 = 65°$ **Corresponding Angles Postulate**

d. $m\angle 9 = m\angle 7 = 115°$ **Alternate Exterior Angles Theorem**

FOCUS ON CAREERS

BOTANY Botanists study plants and environmental issues such as conservation, weed control, and re-vegetation.

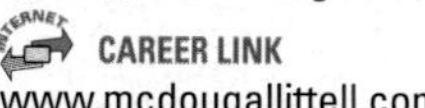

CAREER LINK
www.mcdougallittell.com

EXAMPLE 3 *Classifying Leaves*

BOTANY Some plants are classified by the arrangement of the veins in their leaves. In the diagram of the leaf, $j \parallel k$. What is $m\angle 1$?

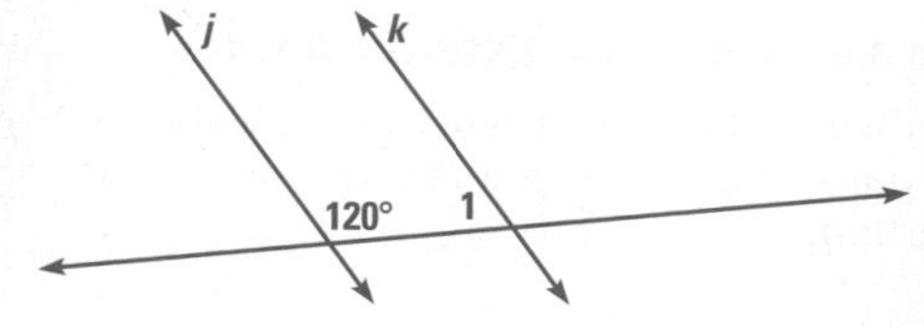

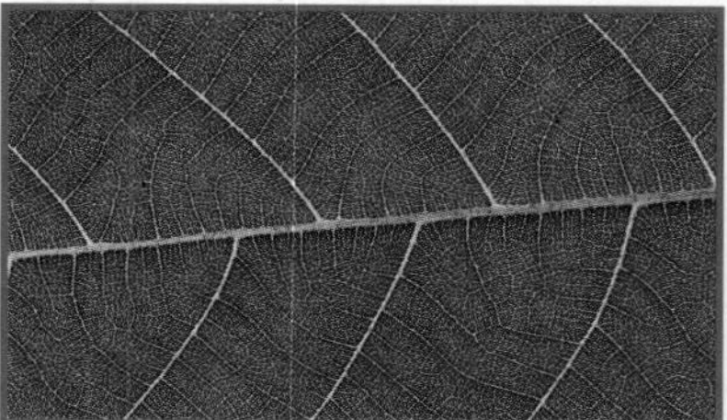

SOLUTION

$m\angle 1 + 120° = 180°$ **Consecutive Interior Angles Theorem**

$m\angle 1 = 60°$ **Subtract.**

 **PROPERTIES OF SPECIAL PAIRS OF ANGLES**

EXAMPLE 4 ***Using Properties of Parallel Lines***

Use properties of parallel lines to find the value of x.

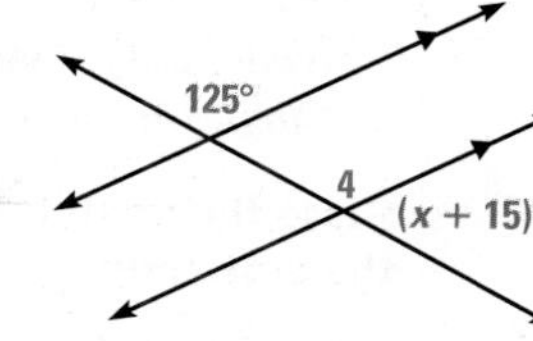

SOLUTION

$m\angle 4 = 125°$	**Corresponding Angles Postulate**
$m\angle 4 + (x + 15)° = 180°$	**Linear Pair Postulate**
$125° + (x + 15)° = 180°$	**Substitute.**
$x = 40$	**Subtract.**

EXAMPLE 5 ***Estimating Earth's Circumference***

HISTORY CONNECTION Eratosthenes was a Greek scholar. Over 2000 years ago, he estimated Earth's circumference by using the fact that the Sun's rays are parallel.

Eratosthenes chose a day when the Sun shone exactly down a vertical well in Syene at noon. On that day, he measured the angle the Sun's rays made with a vertical stick in Alexandria at noon. He discovered that

$$m\angle 2 \approx \frac{1}{50} \text{ of a circle.}$$

By using properties of parallel lines, he knew that $m\angle 1 = m\angle 2$. So he reasoned that

$$m\angle 1 \approx \frac{1}{50} \text{ of a circle.}$$

At the time, the distance from Syene to Alexandria was believed to be 575 miles.

$$\frac{1}{50} \text{ of a circle} \approx \frac{575 \text{ miles}}{\text{Earth's circumference}}$$

$$\text{Earth's circumference} \approx 50(575 \text{ miles}) \quad \leftarrow \textbf{Use cross product property.}$$

$$\approx 29{,}000 \text{ miles}$$

How did Eratosthenes know that $m\angle 1 = m\angle 2$?

SOLUTION

Because the Sun's rays are parallel, $\ell_1 \parallel \ell_2$. Angles 1 and 2 are alternate interior angles, so $\angle 1 \cong \angle 2$. By the definition of congruent angles, $m\angle 1 = m\angle 2$.

STUDENT HELP

APPLICATION LINK
Visit our Web site www.mcdougallittell.com for more information about Eratosthenes' estimate in Example 5.

EXTRA EXAMPLE 3
Refer to the diagram in the Checkpoint Exercises for use after Examples 1 and 2. How many other angles have a measure of 100°? **seven**

EXTRA EXAMPLE 4
Use properties of parallel lines to find the value of x.

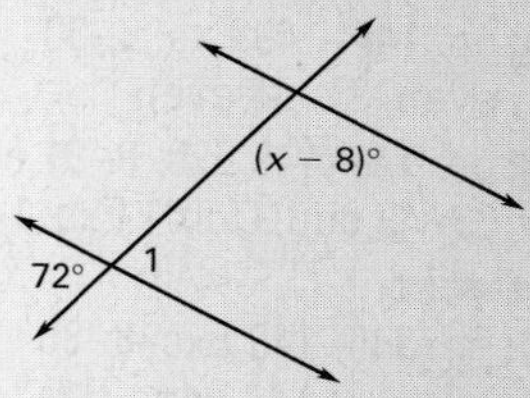

116

EXTRA EXAMPLE 5
Refer to Example 5. We now know that the diameter of Earth is about 7973 mi. Recalculate the distance between Syene and Alexandria using this figure. **about 501 mi.**

CHECKPOINT EXERCISES

For use after Examples 3–5:

1. Use properties of parallel lines to find the value of x.

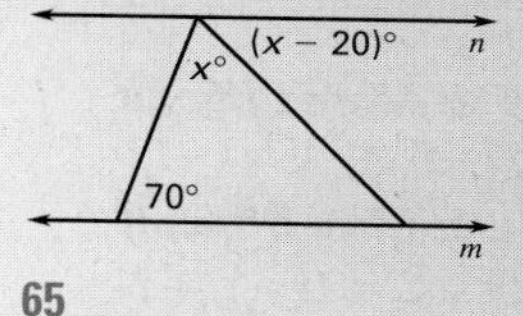

65

FOCUS ON VOCABULARY
The relationship between corresponding angles is stated as a postulate, but the relationships between alternate interior angles, consecutive interior angles, and alternate exterior angles are stated as theorems. Explain the difference. **The Corresponding Angles Postulate is accepted as true without proof. The theorems for the other three relationships have been proven true.**

CLOSURE QUESTION
If a transversal is perpendicular to one of two parallel lines, then what is the measure of all the angles formed? **90°**

3 APPLY

ASSIGNMENT GUIDE

BASIC

Day 1: pp. 146–149 Exs. 8–30 even, 34–44 even

Day 2: pp. 146–149 Exs. 9–31 odd, 33–43 odd, Quiz 1 Exs. 1–9

AVERAGE

Day 1: pp. 146–149 Exs. 8–30 even, 34–44 even

Day 2: pp. 146–149 Exs. 9–31 odd, 33–43 odd, Quiz 1 Exs. 1–9

ADVANCED

Day 1: pp. 146–149 Exs. 8–30 even, 34–44 even

Day 2: pp. 146–149 Exs. 9–31 odd, 32, 33–43 odd, Quiz 1 Exs. 1–9

BLOCK SCHEDULE

pp. 146–149 Exs. 8–30, 34–44 even (with 3.2)
pp. 146–149 Exs. 9–31 odd, 33–43 odd, Quiz 1 Exs. 1–9 (with 3.4)

EXERCISE LEVELS

Level A: *Easier*
8–10

Level B: *More Difficult*
11–27, 30, 31

Level C: *Most Difficult*
28, 29, 32

✓ HOMEWORK CHECK

To quickly check student understanding of key concepts, go over the following exercises: Exs. 10, 12, 18, 24, 28. See also the Daily Homework Quiz:

- Blackline Master (*Chapter 3 Resource Book*, p. 51)
- Transparency (p. 20)

GUIDED PRACTICE

Vocabulary Check ✓

1. Sketch two parallel lines cut by a transversal. Label a pair of consecutive interior angles. *Sample answer:* See margin.

Concept Check ✓

2. In the figure at the right, $j \parallel k$. How many angle measures must be given in order to find the measure of every angle? Explain your reasoning. See margin.

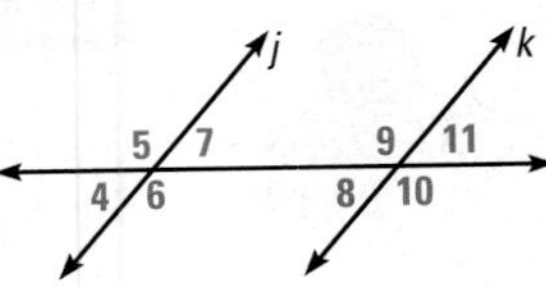

Skill Check ✓

State the postulate or theorem that justifies the statement. See margin.

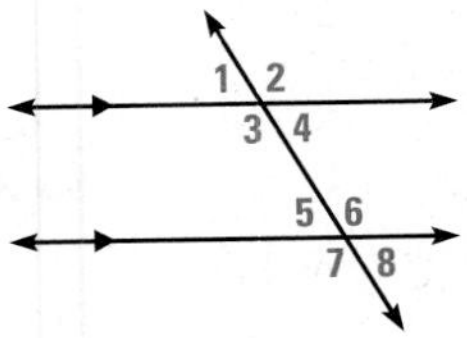

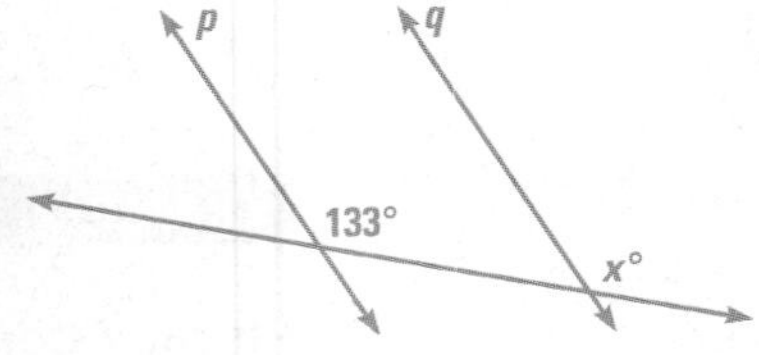

3. $\angle 2 \cong \angle 7$
4. $\angle 4 \cong \angle 5$
5. $m\angle 3 + m\angle 5 = 180°$
6. $\angle 2 \cong \angle 6$
7. In the diagram of the feather below, lines p and q are parallel. What is the value of x? 133

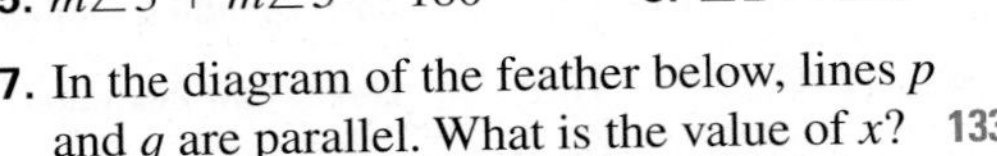

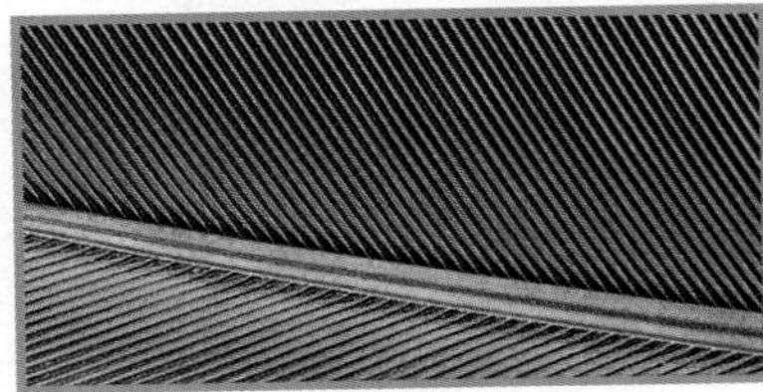

2. 1; *Sample answer:* Each angle is either congruent to the given angle or supplementary to it.
3. Alternate Exterior Angles Theorem
4. Alternate Interior Angles Theorem
5. Consecutive Interior Angles Theorem
6. Corresponding Angles Postulate

PRACTICE AND APPLICATIONS

STUDENT HELP

Extra Practice to help you master skills is on p. 808.

USING PARALLEL LINES Find $m\angle 1$ and $m\angle 2$. Explain your reasoning. 8–10. See margin.

8. 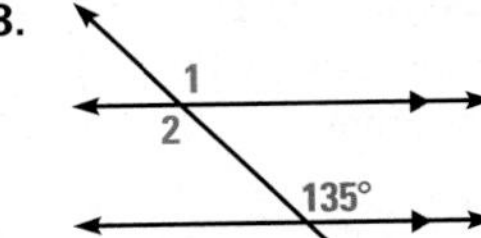

9. 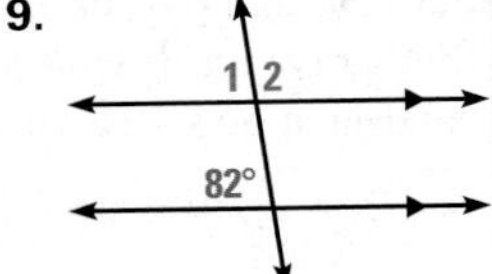

10. 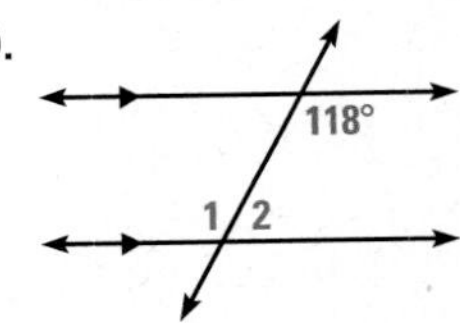

8. $m\angle 1 = 135°$. *Sample answer:* by the Corresponding Angles Postulate; $m\angle 2 = 135°$. *Sample answer:* by the Vertical Angles Theorem

USING PARALLEL LINES Find the values of x and y. Explain your reasoning. 11–16. See margin.

11. 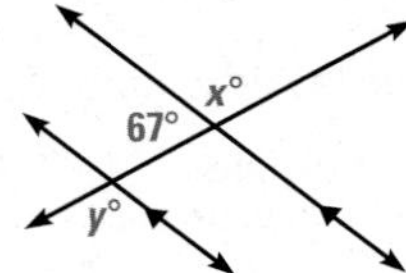

12. 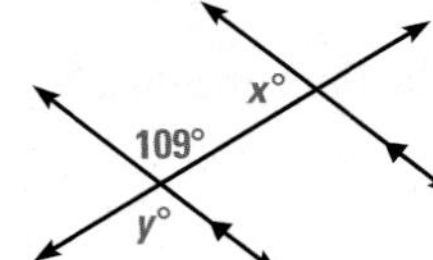

13. 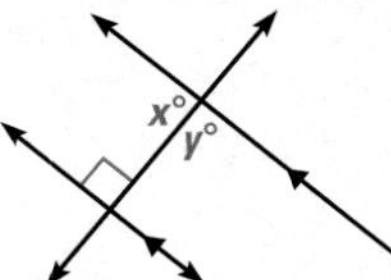

14.

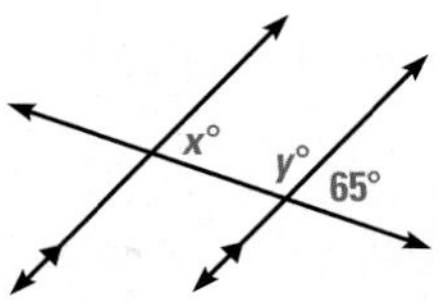

15. 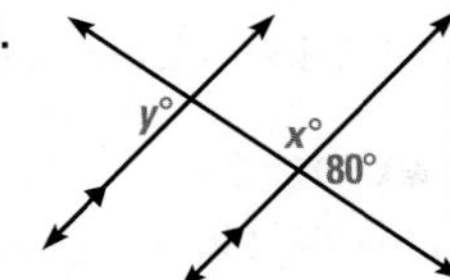

16. 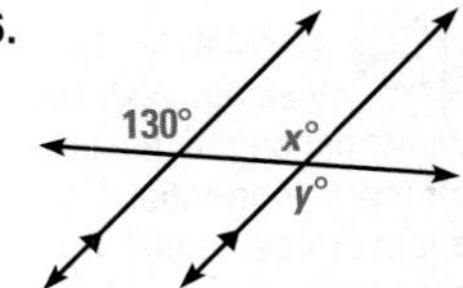

STUDENT HELP

HOMEWORK HELP
Example 1: Exs. 27–29
Example 2: Exs. 8–17
Example 3: Exs. 8–17
Example 4: Exs. 18–26
Example 5: Ex. 30

17. USING PROPERTIES OF PARALLEL LINES Use the given information to find the measures of the other seven angles in the figure at the right.

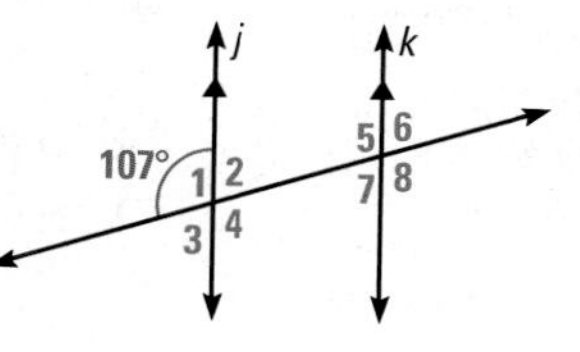

GIVEN ▶ $j \parallel k$, $m\angle 1 = 107°$

$m\angle 2 = m\angle 3 = m\angle 6 = m\angle 7 = 73°$,
$m\angle 4 = m\angle 5 = m\angle 8 = 107°$

USING ALGEBRA **Find the value of *y*.**

18. 35

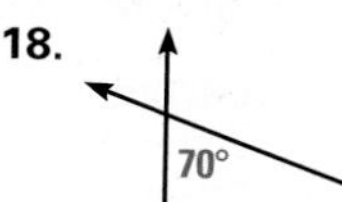

19. 23

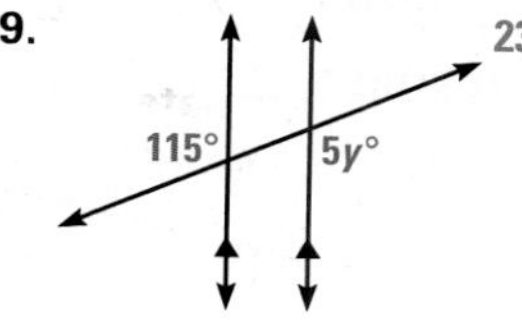

20. 10

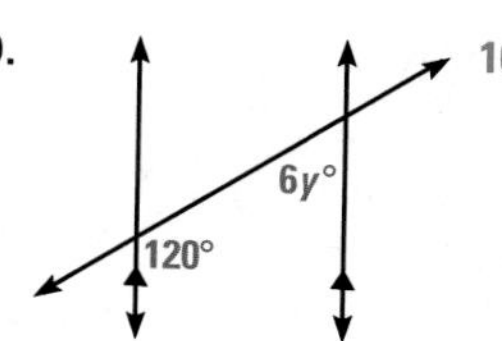

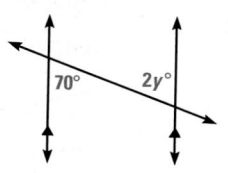

USING ALGEBRA **Find the value of *x*.**

21. 28

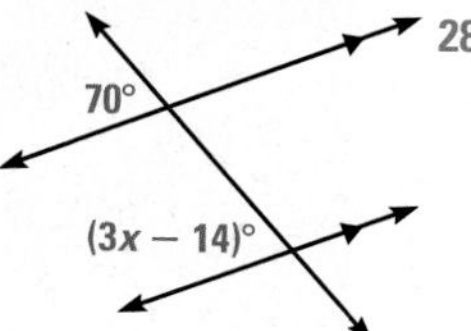

22. 40

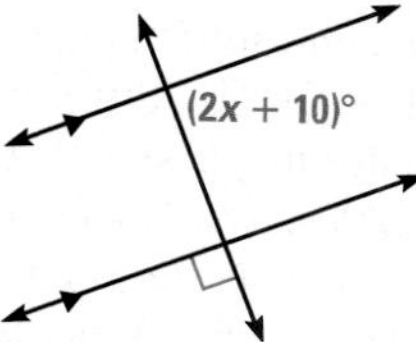

23. 12

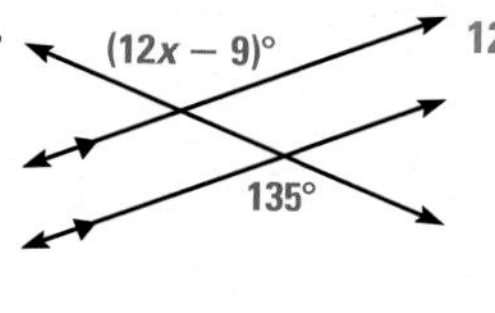

24. 23

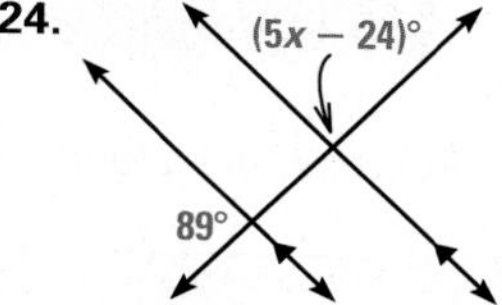

25. 7

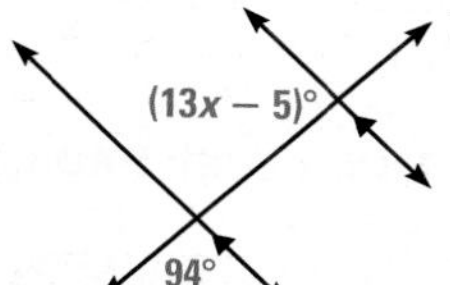

26. 25

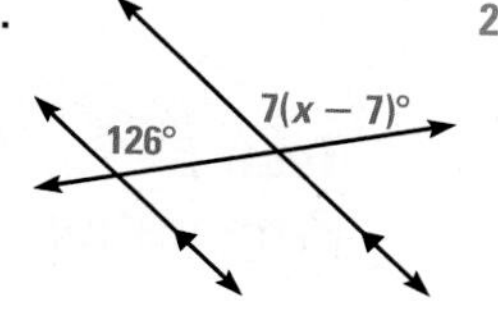

STUDENT HELP

HOMEWORK HELP Visit our Web site www.mcdougallittell.com for help with proving theorems in Exs. 27–29.

27. DEVELOPING PROOF Complete the proof of the Consecutive Interior Angles Theorem.

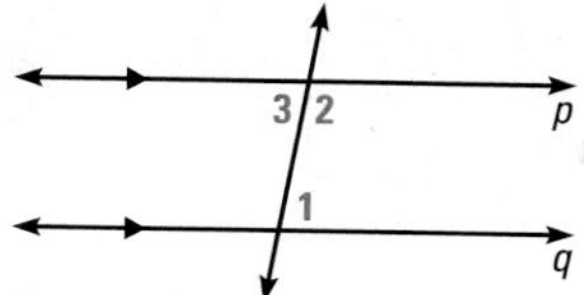

GIVEN ▶ $p \parallel q$

PROVE ▶ $\angle 1$ and $\angle 2$ are supplementary.

Statements	Reasons
1. __?__ $p \parallel q$	1. Given
2. $\angle 1 \cong \angle 3$	2. __?__ Alternate Interior Angles Theorem
3. __?__ $m\angle 1 = m\angle 3$	3. Definition of congruent angles
4. __?__ $\angle 2$ and $\angle 3$ form a linear pair.	4. Definition of linear pair
5. $m\angle 3 + m\angle 2 = 180°$	5. __?__ Linear Pair Postulate
6. __?__ $m\angle 1 + m\angle 2 = 180°$	6. Substitution prop. of equality
7. $\angle 1$ and $\angle 2$ are supplementary.	7. __?__ Definition of supplementary ⦣s

STUDENT HELP NOTES

Homework Help Students can find help for Exs. 27–29 at **www.mcdougallittell.com.** The information can be printed out for students who don't have access to the Internet.

1. ***Sample answer:***

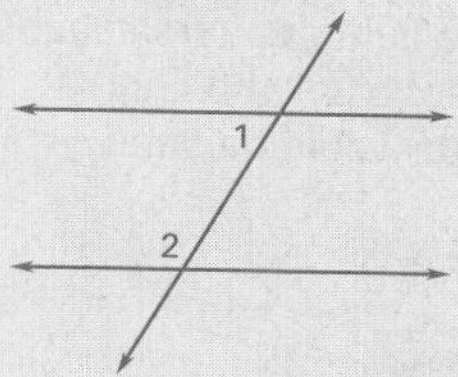

9. $m\angle 1 = 82°$. ***Sample answer:*** by the Corresponding Angles Postulate; $m\angle 2 = 98°$. ***Sample answer:*** $\angle 1$ and $\angle 2$ form a linear pair.

10. $m\angle 1 = 118°$. ***Sample answer:*** Alternate Interior Angles Theorem; $m\angle 2 = 62°$. ***Sample answer:*** Consecutive Interior Angles Theorem

11. $x = 113$ by the Linear Pair Postulate; $y = 113$ by the Alternate Exterior Angles Theorem

12. $x = 71$. ***Sample answer:*** by the Consecutive Interior Angles Theorem; $y = 109$. ***Sample answer:*** by the Vertical Angles Theorem

13. $x = 90$, $y = 90$. ***Sample answer:*** by the Perpendicular Transversal Theorem

14. $x = 65$. ***Sample answer:*** by the Corresponding Angles Postulate; $y = 115$. ***Sample answer:*** by the Linear Pair Postulate

15. $x = 100$. ***Sample answer:*** by the Linear Pair Postulate; $y = 80$. ***Sample answer:*** by the Alternate Exterior Angles Theorem

16. $x = 130$. ***Sample answer:*** by the Corresponding Angles Theorem; $y = 130$. ***Sample answer:*** by the Alternate Exterior Angles Theorem

APPLICATION NOTE

EXERCISES 30 Every color in the visible spectrum is emitted from each raindrop. However, depending upon the angle between the raindrop and your eye, you see only one color from each raindrop. But the observer can look at this angle in many directions from horizon to horizon. Thus the light appears as a bow. If Earth did not block the light, a circle of color would be seen.

29. ***Sample answer:*** **It is given that $p \perp q$, so $\angle 1$ is a right angle because perpendicular lines form right angles. It is given that $q \parallel r$, so $\angle 1 \cong \angle 2$ by the Corresponding Angles Postulate. Then $\angle 2$ is a right angle because it is congruent to a right angle. Finally, $p \perp r$ because the sides of a right angle are perpendicular.**

32. **$m\angle 2 = 132°$ (Linear Pair Postulate); $m\angle 3 = 48°$ (Vertical Angles Theorem); $m\angle 4 = 48°$ (Corresponding Angles Postulate); $m\angle 5 = 42°$ (If the exterior sides of two adjacent angles are perpendicular, then the angles are complementary.); $m\angle 6 = 42°$ (Corresponding Angles Postulate); $m\angle 7 = 138°$ (Linear Pair Postulate)**

ADDITIONAL PRACTICE AND RETEACHING

For Lesson 3.3:

- Practice Levels A, B, and C (*Chapter 3 Resource Book*, p. 40)
- Reteaching with Practice (*Chapter 3 Resource Book*, p. 43)
- See Lesson 3.3 of the *Personal Student Tutor*

For more Mixed Review:

- Search the *Test and Practice Generator* for key words or specific lessons.

STUDENT HELP

Study Tip
When you prove a theorem you may use any previous theorem, but you may not use the one you're proving.

PROVING THEOREMS 3.6 AND 3.7 In Exercises 28 and 29, complete the proof.

28. To prove the Alternate Exterior Angles Theorem, first show that $\angle 1 \cong \angle 3$. Then show that $\angle 3 \cong \angle 2$. Finally, show that $\angle 1 \cong \angle 2$.

GIVEN ▶ $j \parallel k$

PROVE ▶ $\angle 1 \cong \angle 2$

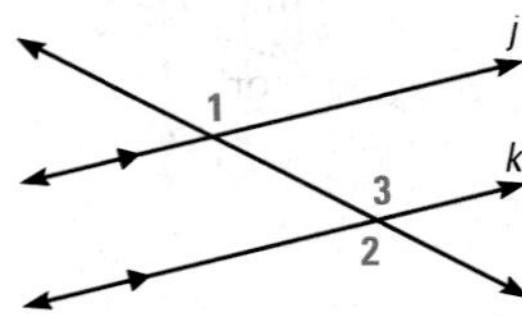

28. ***Sample answer:*** **$\angle 2 \cong \angle 3$ by the Vertical Angles Theorem. It is given that $j \parallel k$, so $\angle 1 \cong \angle 3$ by the Corresponding Angles Postulate. Then $\angle 1 \cong \angle 2$ by the Transitive Property of Angle Congruence.**

29. To prove the Perpendicular Transversal Theorem, show that $\angle 1$ is a right angle, $\angle 1 \cong \angle 2$, $\angle 2$ is a right angle, and finally that $p \perp r$. **See margin.**

GIVEN ▶ $p \perp q$, $q \parallel r$

PROVE ▶ $p \perp r$

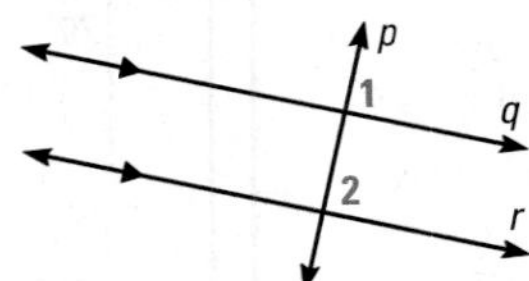

30. **FORMING RAINBOWS** When sunlight enters a drop of rain, different colors leave the drop at different angles. That's what makes a rainbow. For red light, $m\angle 2 = 42°$. What is $m\angle 1$? How do you know? **42°; Alternate Interior Angles Theorem**

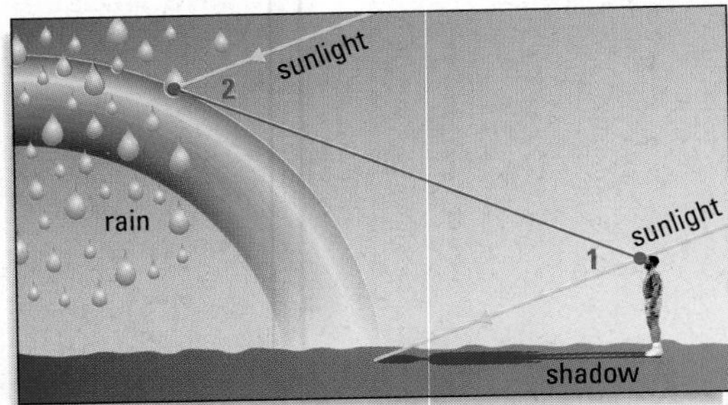

Test Preparation

31. **MULTI-STEP PROBLEM** You are designing a lunch box like the one below.

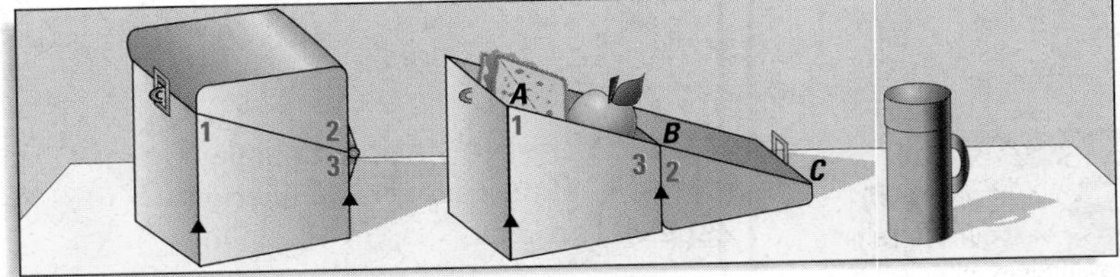

a. The measure of $\angle 1$ is 70°. What is the measure of $\angle 2$? What is the measure of $\angle 3$?

b. *Writing* Explain why $\angle ABC$ is a straight angle.

31. **a. 70°; 110°**

b. *Sample answer:* $\angle 3$ and $\angle 2$ are supplementary so they form a linear pair, and the exterior sides of a linear pair form a straight angle.

★ Challenge

32. **USING PROPERTIES OF PARALLEL LINES** Use the given information to find the measures of the other labeled angles in the figure. For each angle, tell which postulate or theorem you used. **See margin.**

GIVEN ▶ $\overline{PQ} \parallel \overline{RS}$, $\overline{LM} \perp \overline{NK}$, $m\angle 1 = 48°$

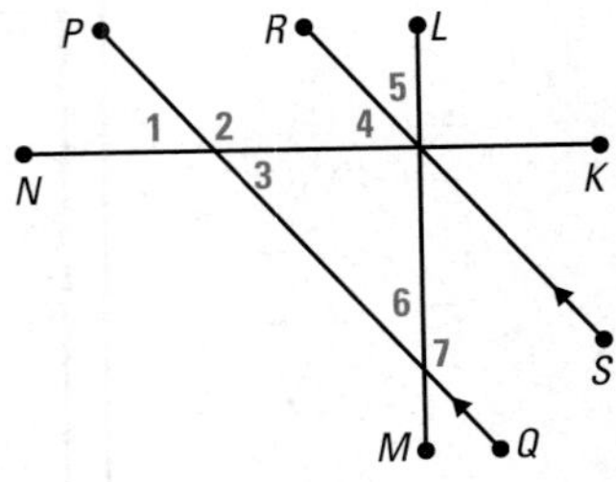

EXTRA CHALLENGE
www.mcdougallittell.com

Mixed Review

ANGLE MEASURES $\angle 1$ and $\angle 2$ are supplementary. Find $m\angle 2$. (Review 1.6)

33. $m\angle 1 = 50°$ 130°
34. $m\angle 1 = 73°$ 107°
35. $m\angle 1 = 101°$ 79°
36. $m\angle 1 = 107°$ 73°
37. $m\angle 1 = 111°$ 69°
38. $m\angle 1 = 118°$ 62°

CONVERSES Write the converse of the statement. (Review 2.1 for 3.4)

39. If the measure of an angle is 19°, then the angle is acute.
If an angle is acute, then the measure of the angle is 19°.
40. I will go to the park if you go with me.
If I go to the park, then you will go with me.
41. I will go fishing if I do not have to work.
If I go fishing, then I do not have to work.

FINDING ANGLES Complete the statement, given that $\overrightarrow{DE} \perp \overrightarrow{DG}$ and $\overleftrightarrow{AB} \perp \overrightarrow{DC}$. (Review 2.6)

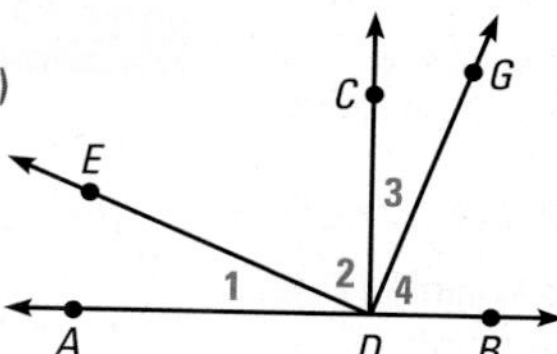

42. If $m\angle 1 = 23°$, then $m\angle 2 =$ __?__. 67°
43. If $m\angle 4 = 69°$, then $m\angle 3 =$ __?__. 21°
44. If $m\angle 2 = 70°$, then $m\angle 4 =$ __?__. 70°

Quiz 1

Self-Test for Lessons 3.1–3.3

Complete the statement. (Lesson 3.1)

1. $\angle 2$ and __?__ are corresponding angles. $\angle 6$
2. $\angle 3$ and __?__ are consecutive interior angles. $\angle 5$
3. $\angle 3$ and __?__ are alternate interior angles. $\angle 6$
4. $\angle 2$ and __?__ are alternate exterior angles. $\angle 7$

5. **PROOF** Write a plan for a proof. (Lesson 3.2)

GIVEN ▶ $\angle 1 \cong \angle 2$

PROVE ▶ $\angle 3$ and $\angle 4$ are right angles.

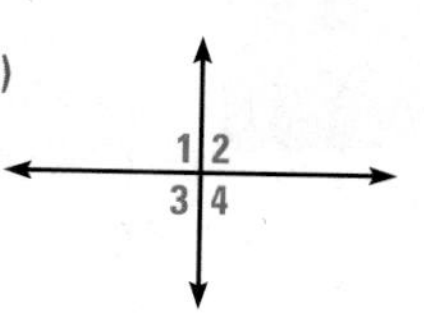

5. *Sample answer:* Since $\angle 1$ and $\angle 2$ are congruent angles that form a linear pair, this shows that $m\angle 1$ and $m\angle 2$ are both 90°. This shows that the two lines are perpendicular so that $\angle 3$ and $\angle 4$ are right angles.

Find the value of *x*. (Lesson 3.3)

6. 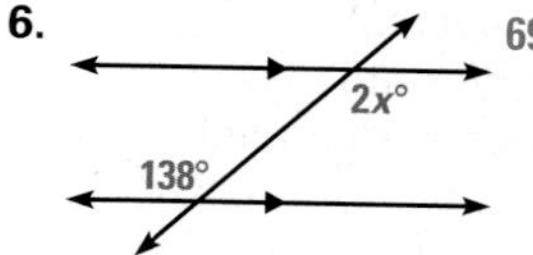

69

7. 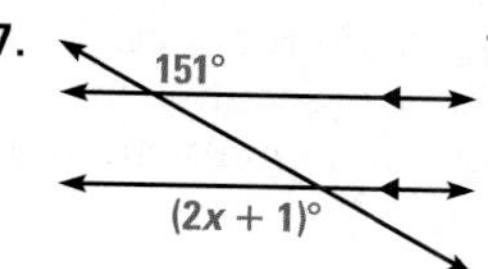

75

8. 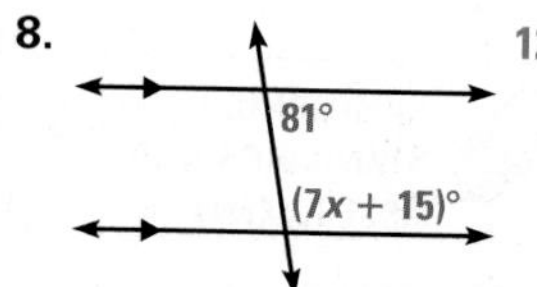

12

9. **FLAG OF PUERTO RICO** Sketch the flag of Puerto Rico shown at the right. Given that $m\angle 3 = 55°$, determine the measure of $\angle 1$. Justify each step in your argument. (Lesson 3.3)

9. 35°; The top left corner is assumed to be a right angle; $\angle 3$ and $\angle 2$ are complementary, Definition of complementary angles; $m\angle 3 + m\angle 2 = 90°$, Definition of complementary angles; $m\angle 2 = 90° - 55° = 35°$, substitute; $m\angle 1 = m\angle 2$, Corresponding Angles Postulate

4 ASSESS

Daily Homework Quiz

Transparency Available

1. Find $m\angle 1$ and $m\angle 2$. Explain your reasoning.

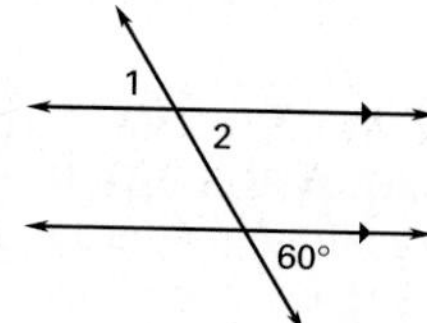

$m\angle 2 = 60°$ by the Corresponding Angles Postulate; $m\angle 1 = 60°$ by the Vertical Angles Theorem

2. Find the values of *x* and *y*. Explain your reasoning.

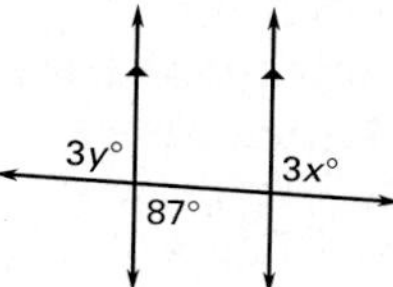

$y = 29$, Vertical Angles Theorem; $x = 31$, Vertical Angles theorem and Consecutive Interior Angles Theorem

Extra Challenge Note

Challenge problems for Lesson 3.3 are available in **blackline** format in the *Chapter 3 Resource Book*, p. 47 and at **www.mcdougallittell.com.**

Additional Test Preparation

1. **WRITING** Transversal *m* is perpendicular to line *p*, but not to line *q*. What assumption can be made about the relationship between *p* and *q*? Explain.
The lines are not parallel. According to the Perp. Trans. Thm., if *p* is parallel to *q*, transversal *m* is perpendicular to both. Since *m* is not perpendicular to *q*, *p* and *q* are not parallel.

Additional Resources

An additional Quiz for Lessons 3.1–3.3 is available in the *Chapter Resource 3 Book*, p. 48.

1 PLAN

PACING
Basic: 1 day
Average: 1 day
Advanced: 1 day
Block Schedule: 0.5 block with 3.3

LESSON OPENER
VISUAL APPROACH
An alternative way to approach Lesson 3.4 is to use the Visual Approach Lesson Opener:

- Blackline Master (*Chapter 3 Resource Book*, p. 52)
- Transparency (p. 17)

MEETING INDIVIDUAL NEEDS
- ***Chapter 3 Resource Book***
  Prerequisite Skills Review (p. 5)
  Practice Level A (p. 57)
  Practice Level B (p. 58)
  Practice Level C (p. 59)
  Reteaching with Practice (p. 60)
  Absent Student Catch-Up (p. 62)
  Challenge (p. 65)
- ***Resources in Spanish***
- 

NEW-TEACHER SUPPORT
See the Tips for New Teachers on pp. 1–2 of the *Chapter 3 Resource Book* for additional notes about Lesson 3.4.

WARM-UP EXERCISES
Transparency Available
State the converse of each statement.

1. If $\angle 1$ is a right angle, then $m\angle 1 = 90°$. **If $m\angle 1 = 90°$, then $\angle 1$ is a right angle.**

2. If $m\angle 1 + m\angle 2 = 180°$, then $\angle 1$ and $\angle 2$ are supplementary. **If $\angle 1$ and $\angle 2$ are supplementary, then $m\angle 1 + m\angle 2 = 180°$.**

3. State the hypothesis and the conclusion of the Alternate Exterior Angles Theorem. **Hypothesis: Two parallel lines are cut by a transversal; Conclusion: the pairs of alternate exterior angles are congruent.**

3.4 Proving Lines are Parallel

What you should learn

GOAL 1 Prove that two lines are parallel.

GOAL 2 Use properties of parallel lines to solve **real-life** problems, such as proving that prehistoric mounds are parallel in **Ex. 19**.

Why you should learn it

▼ Properties of parallel lines help you predict the paths of boats sailing into the wind, as in **Example 4**.

REAL LIFE

CALIFORNIA STANDARDS AND ASSESSMENT

CA Standards: 4, 7
SAT9 Task 1: Obj. 1
SAT9 Task 2: Objs. 1, 28

GOAL 1 PROVING LINES ARE PARALLEL

To use the theorems you learned in Lesson 3.3, you must first know that two lines are parallel. You can use the following postulate and theorems to prove that two lines are parallel.

POSTULATE

POSTULATE 16 ***Corresponding Angles Converse***
If two lines are cut by a transversal so that corresponding angles are congruent, then the lines are parallel.

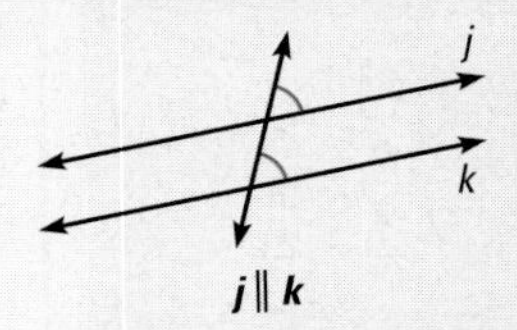

The following theorems are converses of those in Lesson 3.3. Remember that the converse of a true conditional statement is not necessarily true. Thus, each of the following must be proved to be true. Theorems 3.8 and 3.9 are proved in Examples 1 and 2. You are asked to prove Theorem 3.10 in Exercise 30.

THEOREMS ABOUT TRANSVERSALS

THEOREM 3.8 ***Alternate Interior Angles Converse***
If two lines are cut by a transversal so that alternate interior angles are congruent, then the lines are parallel.

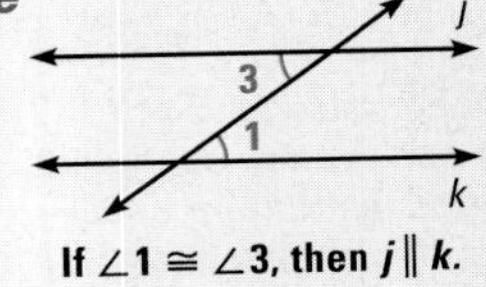

If $\angle 1 \cong \angle 3$, then $j \parallel k$.

THEOREM 3.9 ***Consecutive Interior Angles Converse***
If two lines are cut by a transversal so that consecutive interior angles are supplementary, then the lines are parallel.

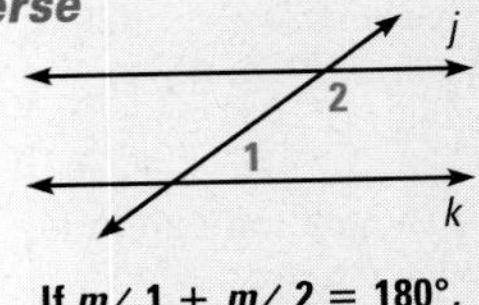

If $m\angle 1 + m\angle 2 = 180°$, then $j \parallel k$.

THEOREM 3.10 ***Alternate Exterior Angles Converse***
If two lines are cut by a transversal so that alternate exterior angles are congruent, then the lines are parallel.

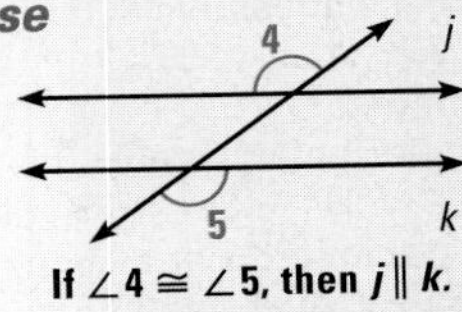

If $\angle 4 \cong \angle 5$, then $j \parallel k$.

EXAMPLE 1 Proof of the Alternate Interior Angles Converse

Prove the Alternate Interior Angles Converse.

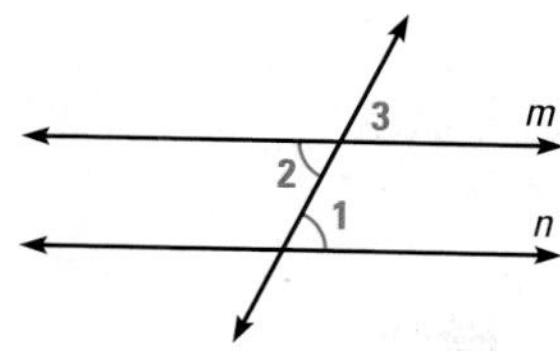

SOLUTION

GIVEN ▶ $\angle 1 \cong \angle 2$

PROVE ▶ $m \parallel n$

Statements	Reasons
1. $\angle 1 \cong \angle 2$	**1.** Given
2. $\angle 2 \cong \angle 3$	**2.** Vertical Angles Theorem
3. $\angle 1 \cong \angle 3$	**3.** Transitive Property of Congruence
4. $m \parallel n$	**4.** Corresponding Angles Converse

When you prove a theorem you may use only earlier results. For example, to prove Theorem 3.9, you may use Theorem 3.8 and Postulate 16, but you may not use Theorem 3.9 itself or Theorem 3.10.

EXAMPLE 2 Proof of the Consecutive Interior Angles Converse

Prove the Consecutive Interior Angles Converse.

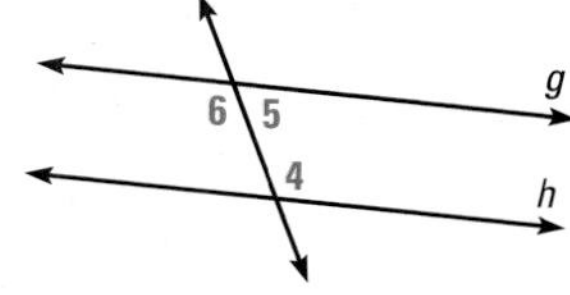

SOLUTION

GIVEN ▶ $\angle 4$ and $\angle 5$ are supplementary.

PROVE ▶ $g \parallel h$

Paragraph Proof You are given that $\angle 4$ and $\angle 5$ are supplementary. By the Linear Pair Postulate, $\angle 5$ and $\angle 6$ are also supplementary because they form a linear pair. By the Congruent Supplements Theorem, it follows that $\angle 4 \cong \angle 6$. Therefore, by the Alternate Interior Angles Converse, g and h are parallel.

EXAMPLE 3 Applying the Consecutive Interior Angles Converse

Find the value of x that makes $j \parallel k$.

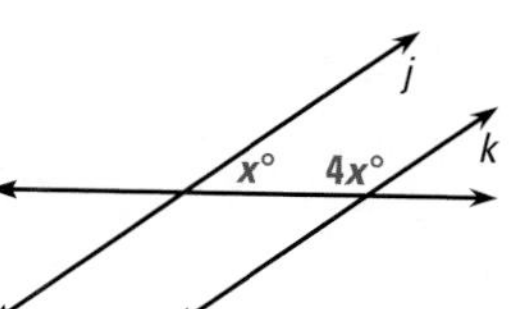

SOLUTION

Lines j and k will be parallel if the marked angles are supplementary.

$$x° + 4x° = 180°$$

$$5x = 180$$

$$x = 36$$

▶ So, if $x = 36$, then $j \parallel k$.

2 TEACH

EXTRA EXAMPLE 1

Given: $m \perp p$; $m \perp q$

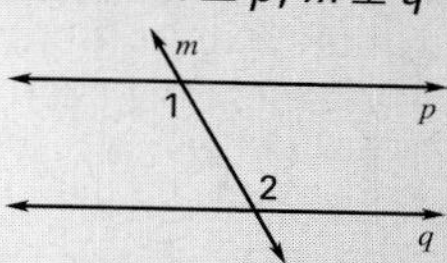

Prove: $p \parallel q$

Statements (Reasons)

1. $m \perp p$; $m \perp q$ (Given)
2. $\angle 1$ is a rt. $\angle$. $\angle 2$ is a rt. $\angle$. (If 2 lines are $\perp$, then they form 4 rt. $\angle$s.)
3. $\angle 1 \cong \angle 2$ (All right $\angle$s are $\cong$.)
4. $p \parallel q$ (Alternate Interior Angles Converse)

EXTRA EXAMPLE 2

Given: $\angle 5 \cong \angle 6$; $\angle 6 \cong \angle 4$

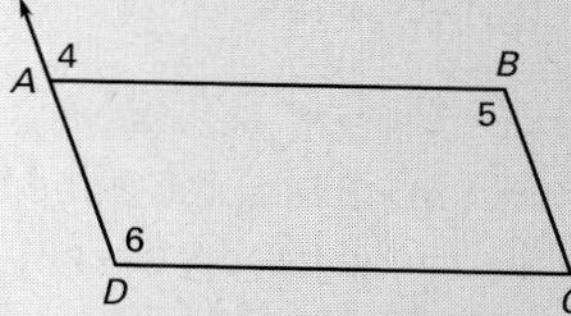

Prove: $\overline{AD} \parallel \overline{BC}$

It is given that $\angle 5 \cong \angle 6$ and $\angle 6 \cong \angle 4$. By the Transitive Property of Congruence $\angle 5 \cong \angle 4$. From the Alternate Interior Angles Converse, it follows that $\overline{AD} \parallel \overline{BC}$.

EXTRA EXAMPLE 3

Find the value of x that makes $m \parallel n$. 6

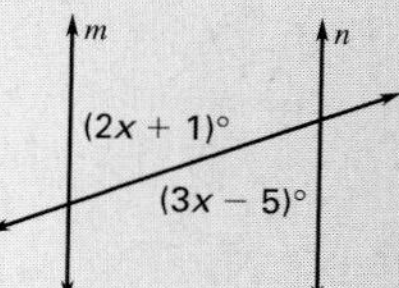

CHECKPOINT EXERCISES

For use after Examples 1–3:

1. Given: $\angle 1$ and $\angle 5$ are supplementary; $\angle 1$ and $\angle 4$ are supplementary.

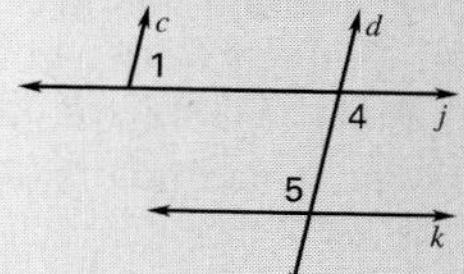

Prove: $j \parallel k$

See margin.

Checkpoint Exercises *Sample answer:*

1. It is given that $\angle 1$ and $\angle 5$ are supplementary and that $\angle 1$ and $\angle 4$ are supplementary. By the Congruent Supplements Theorem $\angle 5 \cong \angle 4$. From the Alternate Interior Angles Converse, it follows that $j \parallel k$.

EXTRA EXAMPLE 4

You notice that when your windshield wipers on your car stopped they each made a 30° angle with the bottom of the windshield. If the wipers were long enough, would they ever cross each other? Explain. **Because the 30° angles are corresponding angles, the wipers are parallel to each other. Since parallel lines do not intersect, the wipers will never cross.**

EXTRA EXAMPLE 5

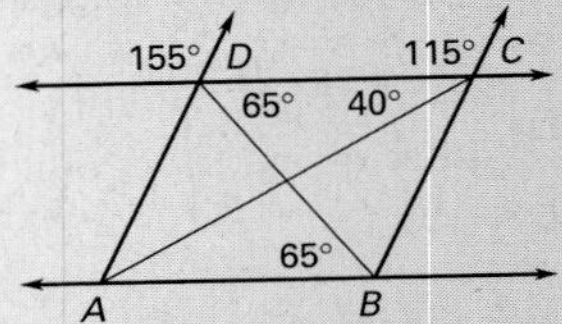

a. Is $AB \parallel DC$? **Yes.**

b. Is $BC \parallel AD$? **No.**

CHECKPOINT EXERCISES

For use after Examples 4 and 5:

1. When lines r and s are cut by a transversal, $\angle 1$ and $\angle 2$ are same side interior angles. If $m\angle 1$ is three times $m\angle 2$, can line r be parallel to line s? Explain. **Yes, if $m\angle 2 = 45$.**

FOCUS ON VOCABULARY

How is a converse of a statement related to the statement. **The hypothesis of the statement is the conclusion of the converse and the conclusion of the statement is the hypothesis of the converse.**

CLOSURE QUESTION

Two lines are cut by a transversal. How can you prove the lines are parallel? **See margin.**

DAILY PUZZLER

If you want to draw three distinct parallel lines through the three vertices of a triangle, how can you guarantee that the lines are parallel? **Draw them all perpendicular to one of the sides.**

GOAL 2 USING THE PARALLEL CONVERSES

STUDENT HELP

HOMEWORK HELP Visit our Web site www.mcdougallittell.com for extra examples.

EXAMPLE 4 *Using the Corresponding Angles Converse*

SAILING If two boats sail at a 45° angle to the wind as shown, and the wind is constant, will their paths ever cross? Explain.

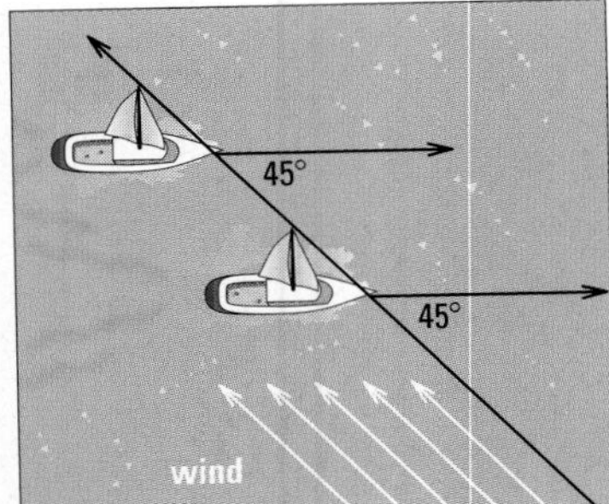

SOLUTION

Because corresponding angles are congruent, the boats' paths are parallel. Parallel lines do not intersect, so the boats' paths will not cross.

EXAMPLE 5 *Identifying Parallel Lines*

Decide which rays are parallel.

a. Is $\overrightarrow{EB}$ parallel to $\overrightarrow{HD}$?

b. Is $\overrightarrow{EA}$ parallel to $\overrightarrow{HC}$?

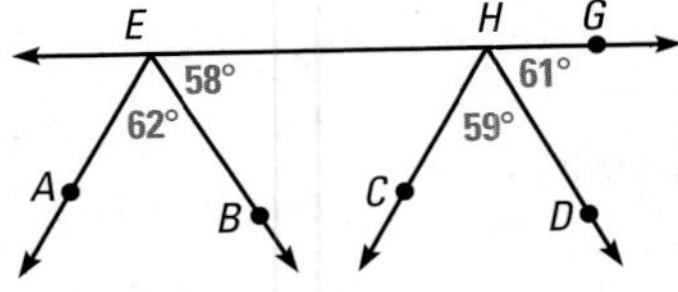

SOLUTION

a. Decide whether $\overrightarrow{EB} \parallel \overrightarrow{HD}$.

$m\angle BEH = 58°$

$m\angle DHG = 61°$

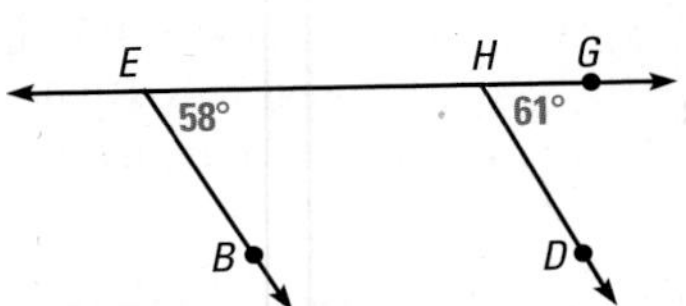

▶ $\angle BEH$ and $\angle DHG$ are corresponding angles, but they are not congruent, so $\overrightarrow{EB}$ and $\overrightarrow{HD}$ are not parallel.

b. Decide whether $\overrightarrow{EA} \parallel \overrightarrow{HC}$.

$m\angle AEH = 62° + 58°$

$= 120°$

$m\angle CHG = 59° + 61°$

$= 120°$

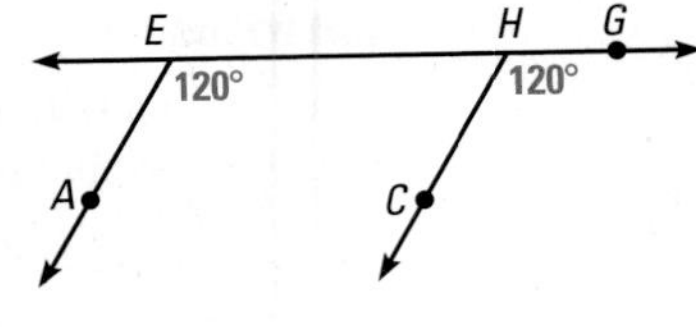

▶ $\angle AEH$ and $\angle CHG$ are congruent corresponding angles, so $\overrightarrow{EA} \parallel \overrightarrow{HC}$.

Closure Question ***Sample answer:*** **Show that either a pair of alternate interior angles, or a pair of corresponding angles, or a pair of alternate exterior angles is congruent, or show that a pair of consecutive interior angles is supplementary.**

GUIDED PRACTICE

Vocabulary Check ✓

Concept Check ✓

Skill Check ✓

1. What are *parallel lines*? coplanar lines that do not intersect

2. Write the converse of Theorem 3.8. Is the converse true? See margin.

2. If two parallel lines are cut by a transversal, then the alternate interior angles are congruent; yes.

3. yes; Alternate Exterior Angles Converse

6. yes; Alternate Interior Angles Converse

7. yes; Corresponding Angles Converse

8. yes; Consecutive Interior Angles Converse

9. 45; Consecutive Interior Angles Converse

Can you prove that lines *p* and *q* are parallel? If so, describe how.

3.

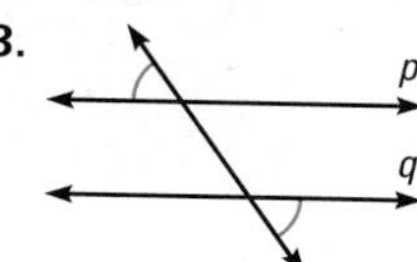

4. no

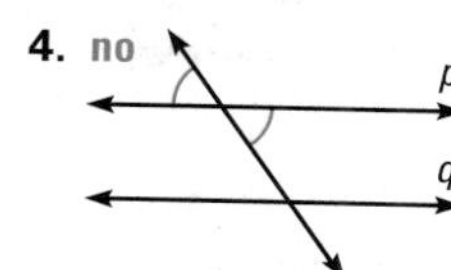

5. no

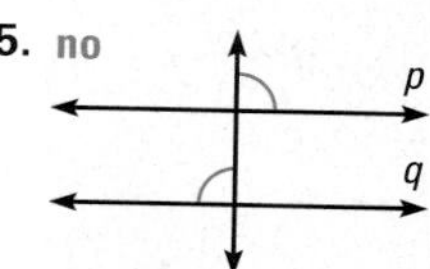

6.

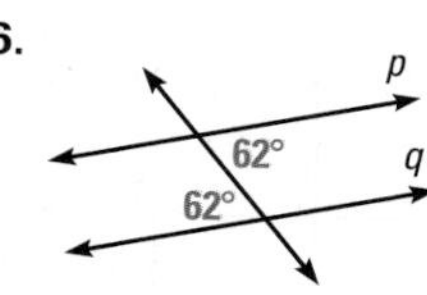

7.

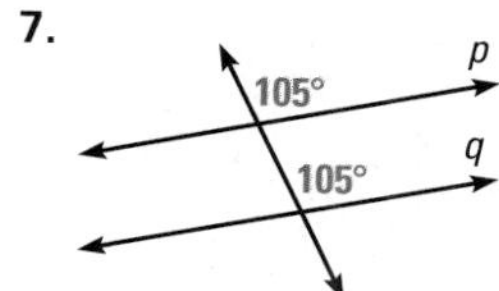

8.

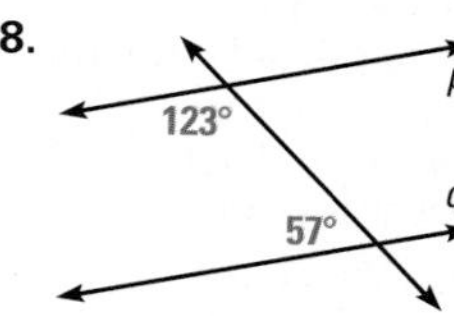

9. Find the value of x that makes $j \parallel k$. Which postulate or theorem about parallel lines supports your answer?

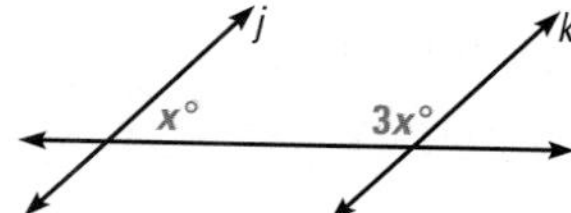

PRACTICE AND APPLICATIONS

STUDENT HELP

Extra Practice to help you master skills is on p. 808.

10. yes; Alternate Interior Angles Converse

11. yes; Alternate Exterior Angles Converse

12. yes; Corresponding Angles Converse

14. yes; Alternate Exterior Angles Converse

 **LOGICAL REASONING** **Is it possible to prove that lines *m* and *n* are parallel? If so, state the postulate or theorem you would use.**

10.

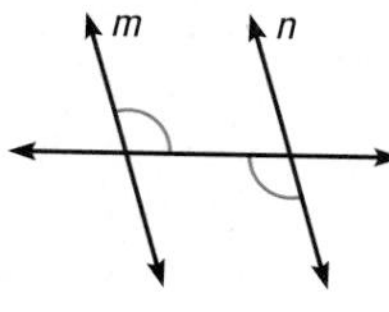

11.

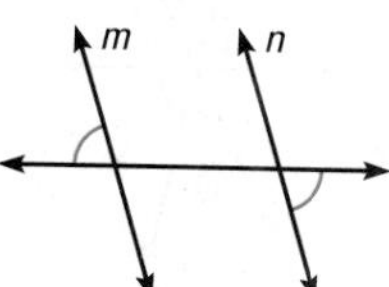

12.

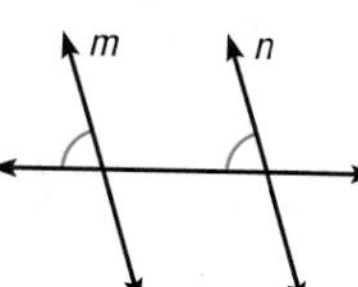

13. no

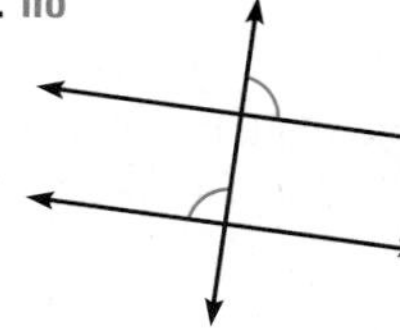

14.

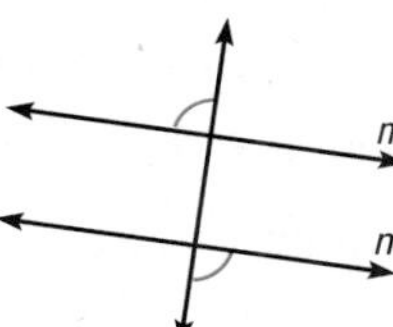

15. no

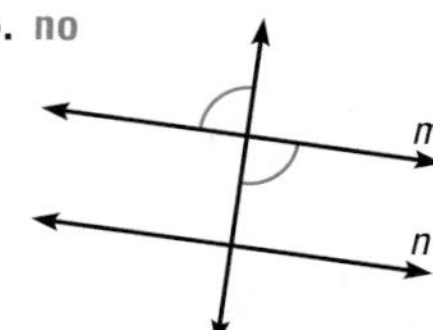

STUDENT HELP

HOMEWORK HELP

Example 1: Exs. 28, 30
Example 2: Exs. 28, 30
Example 3: Exs. 10–18
Example 4: Exs. 19, 29, 31
Example 5: Exs. 20–27

USING ALGEBRA **Find the value of *x* that makes $r \parallel s$.**

16. 60

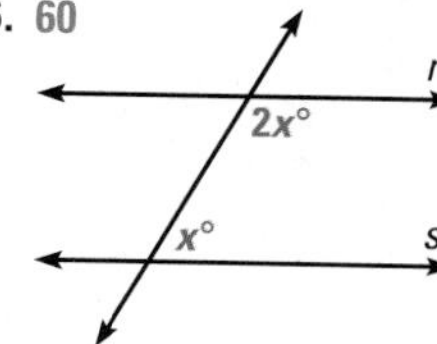

17. 45

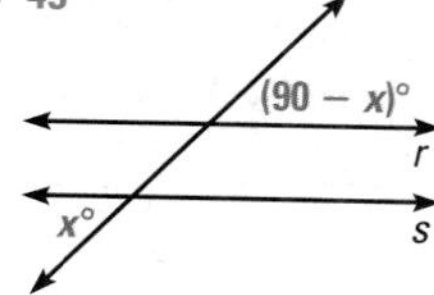

18. 20

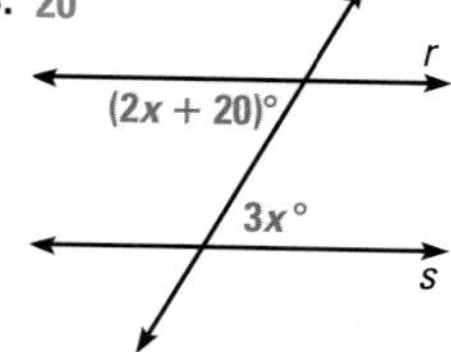

3 APPLY

ASSIGNMENT GUIDE

BASIC
Day 1: pp. 153–156 Exs. 10–35, 37, 38, 40–48 even

AVERAGE
Day 1: pp. 153–156 Exs. 10–35, 37, 38, 40–48 even

ADVANCED
Day 1: pp. 153–156 Exs. 10–35, 37–39, 40–48 even

BLOCK SCHEDULE WITH 3.3
pp. 153–156 Exs. 10–35, 37, 38, 40–48 even

EXERCISE LEVELS

Level A: *Easier*
10–15

Level B: *More Difficult*
16–33, 36–38

Level C: *Most Difficult*
34, 35, 39

✓ HOMEWORK CHECK

To quickly check student understanding of key concepts, go over the following exercises: Exs. 12, 18, 22, 26, 28, 34. See also the Daily Homework Quiz:

- Blackline Master (*Chapter 3 Resource Book,* p. 68)
- Transparency (p. 21)

APPLICATION NOTE

EXERCISE 19 Additional information about The Great Serpent Mound can be found at **www.mcdougallittell.com.**

MATHEMATICAL REASONING

EXERCISE 28 ∠1 and ∠2 are same-side exterior angles. Write a general statement in if-then form for this proof. **If two lines are cut by a transversal so that same-side exterior angles are supplementary, then the lines are parallel.**

34. *Sample answer:* $m\angle 7 + m\angle 8 = 125° + 55° = 180°$, so ∠7 and ∠8 are supplementary and $j \parallel k$ by the Consecutive Interior Angles Converse.

35. *Sample answer:* It is given that $a \parallel b$, so ∠1 and ∠3 are supplementary by the Consecutive Interior Angles Theorem. Then $m\angle 1 + m\angle 3 = 180°$ by the definition of supplementary angles. $\angle 1 \cong \angle 2$, so $m\angle 1 = m\angle 2$. Then $m\angle 2 + m\angle 3 = 180°$ by substitution, and $c \parallel d$ by the Consecutive Interior Angles Converse.

36. *Sample answer:*

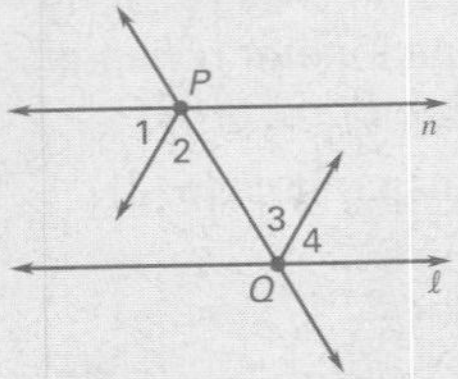

Conjecture: If two parallel lines are cut by a transversal, then the bisectors of the alternate interior angles are parallel. Plan for proof: Show that $m\angle 1 = m\angle 2$, $m\angle 3 = m\angle 4$, and $m\angle 1 + m\angle 2 = m\angle 3 + m\angle 4$. Then show that $2m\angle 2 = 2m\angle 3$ so $m\angle 2 = m\angle 3$. Finally, show that the angle bisectors are parallel.

FOCUS ON APPLICATIONS

THE GREAT SERPENT MOUND, an archaeological mound near Hillsboro, Ohio, is 2 to 5 feet high, and is nearly 20 feet wide. It is over $\frac{1}{4}$ mile long.

APPLICATION LINK
www.mcdougallittell.com

20. yes; Consecutive Interior Angles Converse

23. yes; Angle Addition Postulate and Alternate Exterior Angles Converse

24. yes; Angle Addition Postulate and Consecutive Interior Angles Converse

26. none. *Sample answer:* $m\angle EAB = 115°$ and $m\angle CBA = 66°$, so the consecutive interior angles are not supplementary.

19. **ARCHAEOLOGY** A farm lane in Ohio crosses two long, straight earthen mounds that may have been built about 2000 years ago. The mounds are about 200 feet apart, and both form a 63° angle with the lane, as shown. Are the mounds parallel? How do you know?
yes; Corresponding Angles Converse

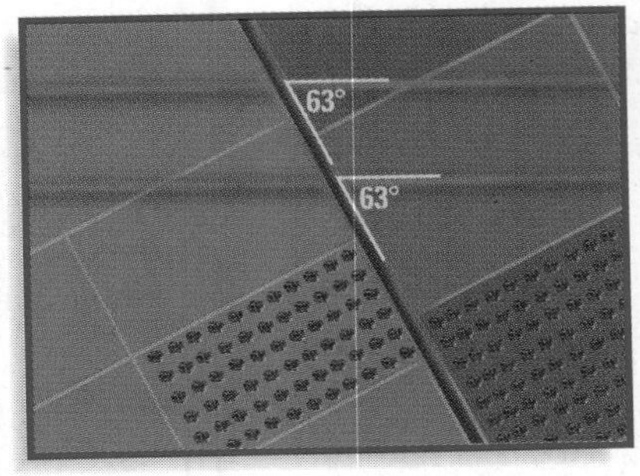

LOGICAL REASONING **Is it possible to prove that lines *a* and *b* are parallel? If so, explain how.**

20.

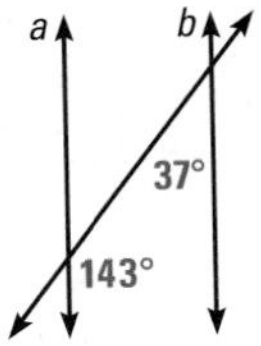

21. no

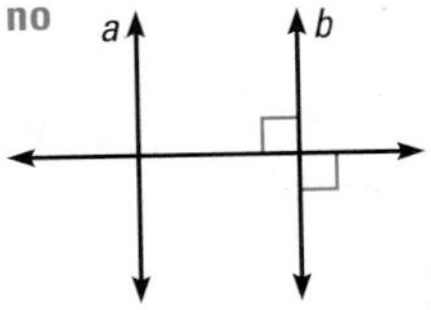

22. no

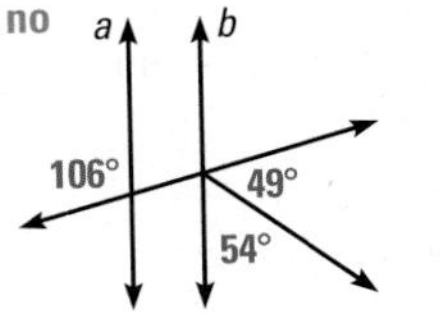

23.

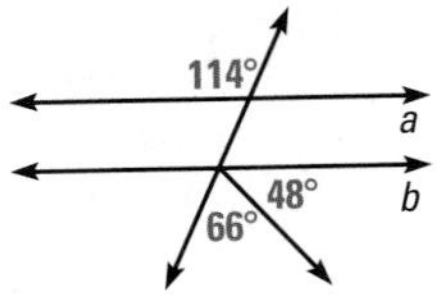

24.

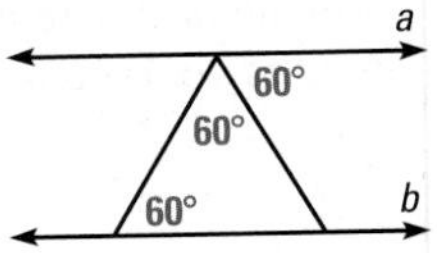

25. no

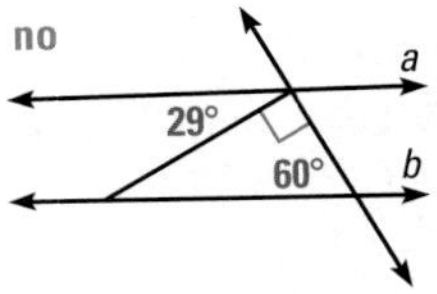

LOGICAL REASONING **Which lines, if any, are parallel? Explain.**

26.

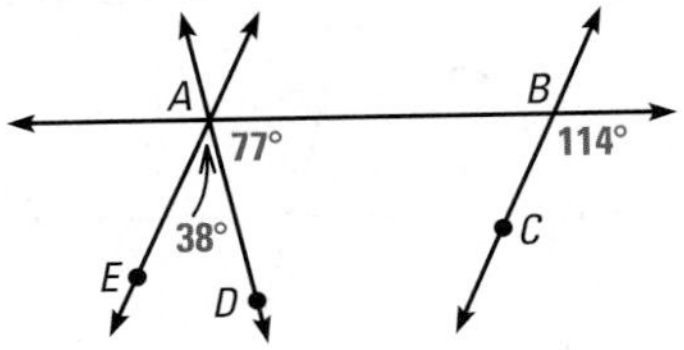

27.

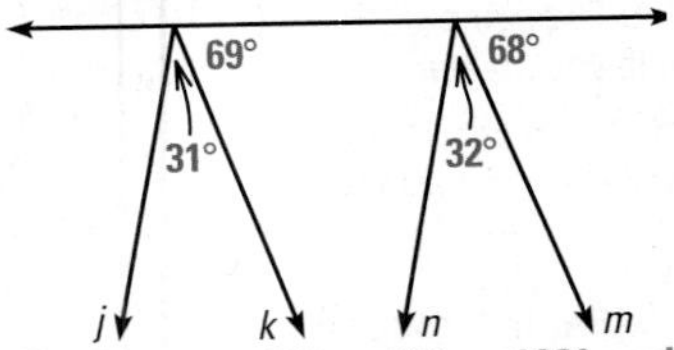

$j \parallel n$ because $31° + 69° = 100°$ and $32° + 68° = 100°$.

28. **PROOF** Complete the proof.

GIVEN ▶ ∠1 and ∠2 are supplementary.

PROVE ▶ $\ell_1 \parallel \ell_2$

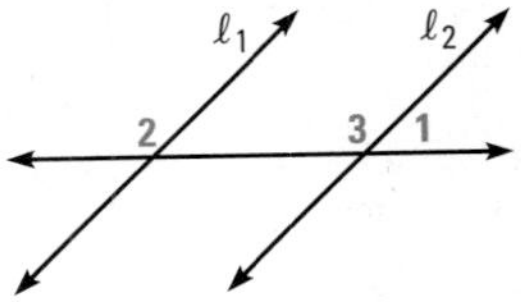

Statements	Reasons
1. ∠1 and ∠2 are supplementary.	1. ___?___ Given
2. ∠1 and ∠3 are a linear pair.	2. Definition of linear pair
3. ___?___ ∠1 and ∠3 are supplementary.	3. Linear Pair Postulate
4. ___?___ ∠2 ≅ ∠3	4. Congruent Supplements Theorem
5. $\ell_1 \parallel \ell_2$	5. ___?___ Corresponding Angles Convers

30. *Sample answer:* 1. ∠4 ≅ ∠5 (Given); 2. ∠4 ≅ ∠6 (Vertical Angles Theorem); 3. ∠5 ≅ ∠6 (Transitive Property of Angle Congruence); 4. $g \parallel h$ (Corresponding Angles Converse)

31. *Sample answer:* ∠5 and ∠6 are alternate interior angles. They have the same measure, so they are congruent. Then the lines *p* and *q* are parallel because of the Alternate Interior Angles Converse.

32. $\overline{AB} \parallel \overline{CD}$; ∠B ≅ ∠BEA, ∠BEA ≅ ∠CED by the Vertical Angles Theorem, and ∠CED ≅ ∠C. So ∠B ≅ ∠C by the Transitive Property of Angle Congruence, and $\overline{AB} \parallel \overline{CD}$ by the Alternate Interior Angles Converse.

33. ∠1 ≅ ∠4 and ∠2 ≅ ∠3. *Sample answer:* The angles marked as congruent are alternate interior angles, so $r \parallel s$ by the Alternate Interior Angles Converse. Then ∠1 ≅ ∠4 by the Alternate Interior Angles Theorem and ∠2 ≅ ∠3 by the Vertical Angles Theorem.

29. **BUILDING STAIRS** One way to build stairs is to attach triangular blocks to an angled support, as shown at the right. If the support makes a 32° angle with the floor, what must $m\angle 1$ be so the step will be parallel to the floor? The sides of the angled support are parallel. 32°

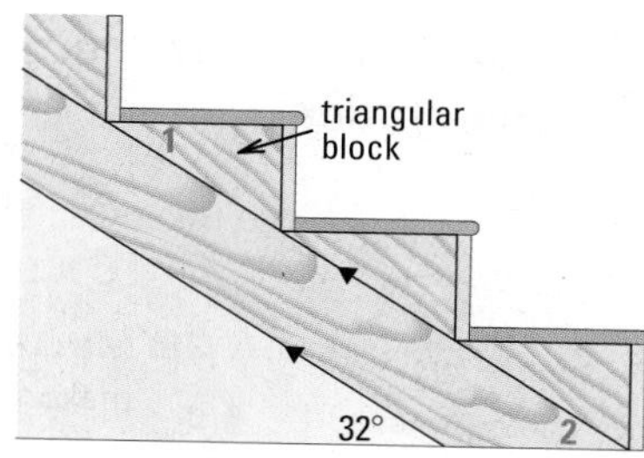

30. **PROVING THEOREM 3.10** Write a two-column proof for the Alternate Exterior Angles Converse: If two lines are cut by a transversal so that alternate exterior angles are congruent, then the lines are parallel.

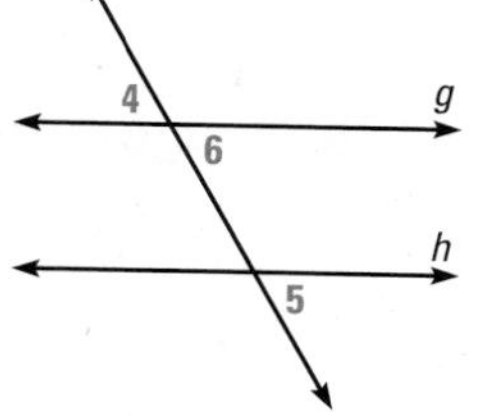

GIVEN ▶ ∠4 ≅ ∠5

PROVE ▶ $g \parallel h$

Plan for Proof Show that ∠4 is congruent to ∠6, show that ∠6 is congruent to ∠5, and then use the Corresponding Angles Converse. See margin.

31. *Writing* In the diagram at the right, $m\angle 5 = 110°$ and $m\angle 6 = 110°$. Explain why $p \parallel q$. See margin.

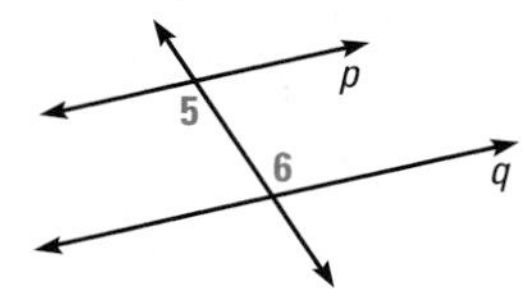

LOGICAL REASONING **Use the information given in the diagram.**

32. What can you prove about $\overline{AB}$ and $\overline{CD}$? Explain.

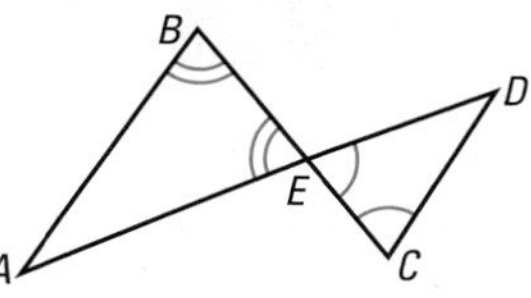

33. What can you prove about ∠1, ∠2, ∠3, and ∠4? Explain.

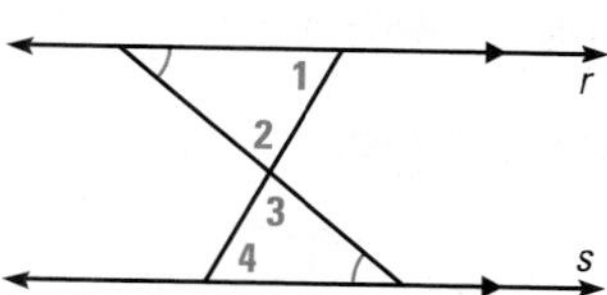

PROOF **Write a proof.**

34. **GIVEN** ▶ $m\angle 7 = 125°$, $m\angle 8 = 55°$

PROVE ▶ $j \parallel k$ See margin.

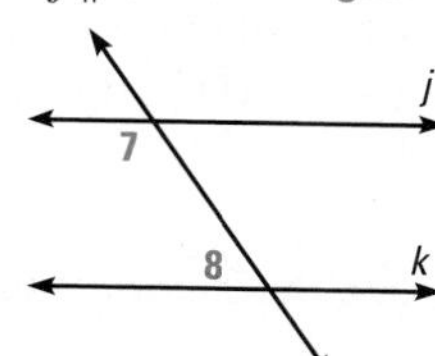

35. **GIVEN** ▶ $a \parallel b$, ∠1 ≅ ∠2

PROVE ▶ $c \parallel d$ See margin.

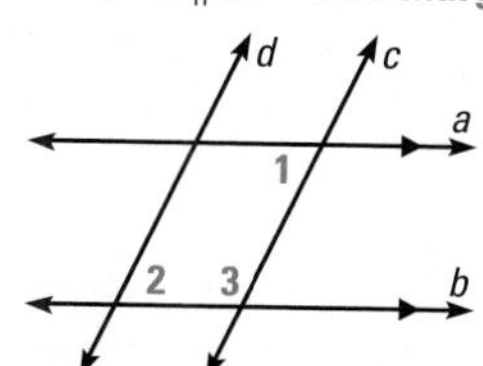

36. **TECHNOLOGY** Use geometry software to construct a line ℓ, a point *P* not on ℓ, and a line *n* through *P* parallel to ℓ. Construct a point *Q* on ℓ and construct $\overleftrightarrow{PQ}$. Choose a pair of alternate interior angles and construct their angle bisectors. Are the bisectors parallel? Make a conjecture. Write a plan for a proof of your conjecture. See margin.

STUDENT HELP

SOFTWARE HELP Visit our Web site www.mcdougallittell.com to see instructions for several software applications.

APPLICATION NOTE

EXERCISE 29 The blocks and angled support are referred to as the stringer. The stair treads and risers are secured to the stringer. To build a stairway that is easy to ascend and safe to descend, it is recommended that the riser be between 7 in. and 7.5 in. and the run be between 10 in. and 11 in. Thus, the angle of a stairway is a function of the riser to tread ratio. The ideal angle is between 30° and 35°. If the stairs in the diagram have a rise of 7 in., the tread is approximately 11 in.

ENGLISH LEARNERS

EXERCISE 29 Keep in mind that the language contained in word problems is often specialized, and can be difficult for English learners. In Exercise 29, students may not recognize which part is the *angled support.* You may want to point out this part on the diagram.

STUDENT HELP NOTES

Software Help Instructions for several software packages are available in **blackline** format in the *Chapter 3 Resource Book,* p. 56 and at **www.mcdougallittell.com.**

ADDITIONAL PRACTICE AND RETEACHING

For Lesson 3.4:

- Practice Levels A, B, and C (*Chapter 3 Resource Book,* p. 57)
- Reteaching with Practice (*Chapter 3 Resource Book,* p. 60)
- See Lesson 3.4 of the *Personal Student Tutor*

For more Mixed Review:

- Search the *Test and Practice Generator* for key words or specific lessons.

4 ASSESS

DAILY HOMEWORK QUIZ

Transparency Available

1. Is it possible to prove $m \parallel n$? If so, state the postulate or theorem.

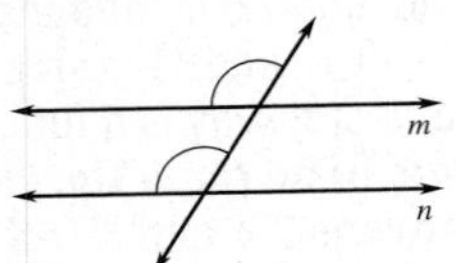

yes; Corresponding Angles Converse

2. Find x so $r \parallel s$.

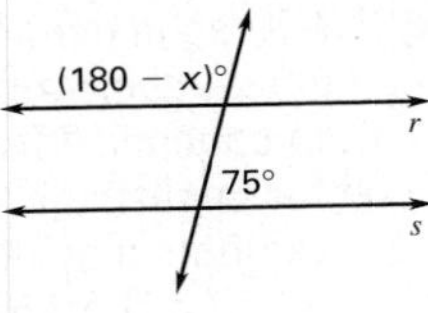

75

3. Which lines are parallel, if any? Explain.

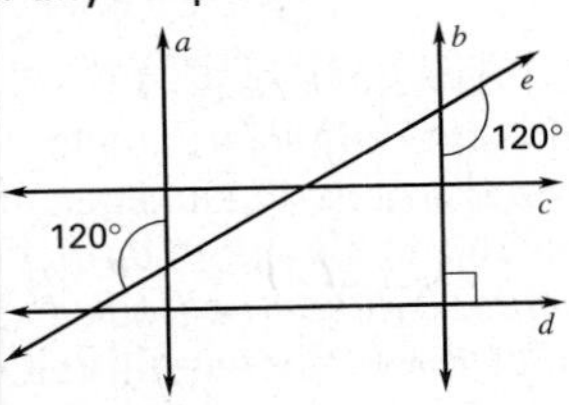

$a \parallel b$, Alternate Exterior Angles Converse

EXTRA CHALLENGE NOTE

Challenge problems for Lesson 3.4 are available in **blackline** format in the *Chapter 3 Resource Book,* p. 65 and at **www.mcdougallittell.com.**

ADDITIONAL TEST PREPARATION

1. **WRITING** State the *given* and *to prove* of the converse of the statement "If the opposite angles of quadrilateral *ABCD* are congruent, then the quadrilateral is a parallelogram." **See margin.**

40–43. See Additional Answers beginning on page AA1.

Test Preparation

37. **MULTIPLE CHOICE** What is the converse of the following statement? **C**

If $\angle 1 \cong \angle 2$, then $n \parallel m$.

Ⓐ $\angle 1 \cong \angle 2$ if and only if $n \parallel m$. Ⓑ If $\angle 2 \cong \angle 1$, then $m \parallel n$.

Ⓒ $\angle 1 \cong \angle 2$ if $n \parallel m$. Ⓓ $\angle 1 \cong \angle 2$ only if $n \parallel m$.

38. **MULTIPLE CHOICE** What value of x would make lines ℓ_1 and ℓ_2 parallel? **C**

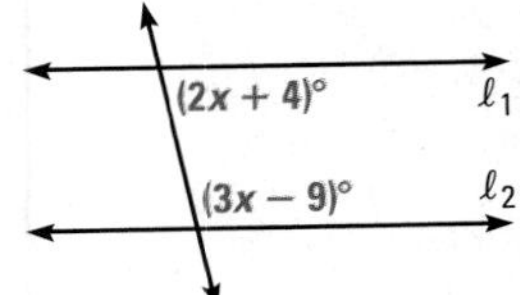

Ⓐ 13 Ⓑ 35 Ⓒ 37

Ⓓ 78 Ⓔ 102

★ Challenge

39. ***Sample answer:*** **$\ell_1 \parallel \ell_2$, so $m\angle BCA = m\angle A$ by the Alternate Interior Angles Theorem. $m\angle BCA = m\angle B$, so $j \parallel k$ by the Alternate Interior Angles Converse.**

39. **SNOW MAKING** To shoot the snow as far as possible, each snowmaker below is set at a 45° angle. The axles of the snowmakers are all parallel. It is possible to prove that the barrels of the snowmakers are also parallel, but the proof is difficult in 3 dimensions. To simplify the problem, think of the illustration as a flat image on a piece of paper. The axles and barrels are represented in the diagram on the right. Lines j and ℓ_2 intersect at C.

GIVEN ▶ $\ell_1 \parallel \ell_2$, $m\angle A = m\angle B = 45°$

PROVE ▶ $j \parallel k$

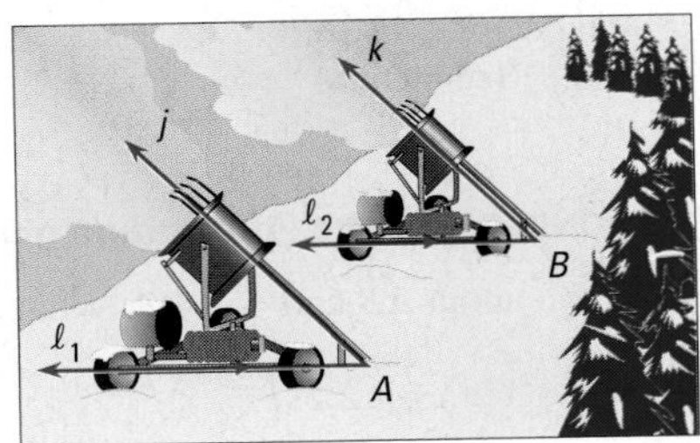

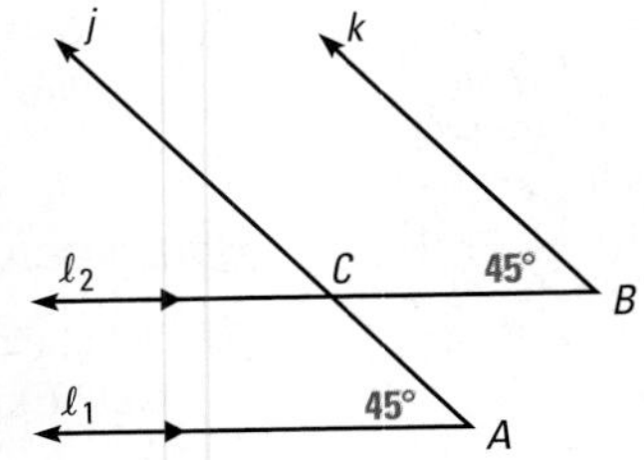

EXTRA CHALLENGE

www.mcdougallittell.com

MIXED REVIEW

FINDING THE MIDPOINT **Use a ruler to draw a line segment with the given length. Then use a compass and straightedge to construct the midpoint of the line segment.** **(Review 1.5 for 3.5)** **40–44. See margin.**

40. 3 inches **41.** 8 centimeters **42.** 5 centimeters **43.** 1 inch

44. **CONGRUENT SEGMENTS** Find the value of x if $\overline{AB} \cong \overline{AD}$ and $\overline{CD} \cong \overline{AD}$. Explain your steps. **(Review 2.5)**

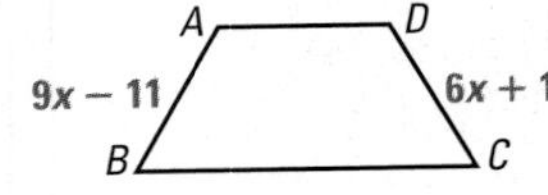

44. 4; $\overline{AB} \cong \overline{AD}$, $\overline{AD} \cong \overline{DC}$ (given), so $\overline{AB} \cong \overline{DC}$ by the Transitive Property of Segment Congruence. Then $9x - 11 = 6x + 1$ by substitution, $3x = 12$ by the Addition Property of Equality (add $-6x$ to each side, add 11 to each side), and $x = 4$ by the Multiplication property of equality.

IDENTIFYING ANGLES **Use the diagram to complete the statement.** **(Review 3.1)**

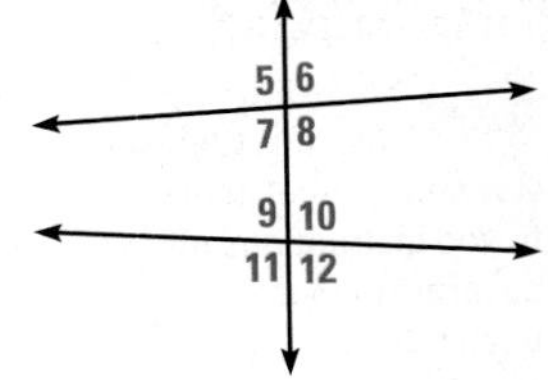

45. $\angle 12$ and __?__ are alternate exterior angles. **$\angle 5$**

46. $\angle 10$ and __?__ are corresponding angles. **$\angle 6$**

47. $\angle 10$ and __?__ are alternate interior angles. **$\angle 7$**

48. $\angle 9$ and __?__ are consecutive interior angles. **$\angle 7$**

Additional Test Preparation *Sample answer:*
1. Given: *ABCD* is a parallelogram.
Prove: $\angle A \cong \angle C$ and $\angle B \cong \angle D$

3.5 Using Properties of Parallel Lines

What you should learn

GOAL 1 Use properties of parallel lines in **real-life** situations, such as building a CD rack in **Example 3**.

GOAL 2 Construct parallel lines using straightedge and compass.

Why you should learn it

▼ To understand how light bends when it passes through glass or water, as in **Ex. 42**.

REAL LIFE

GOAL 1 USING PARALLEL LINES IN REAL LIFE

When a team of rowers competes, each rower keeps his or her oars parallel to the adjacent rower's oars. If any two *adjacent* oars on the same side of the boat are parallel, does this imply that *any two* oars on that side are parallel? This question is examined below.

Example 1 justifies Theorem 3.11, and you will prove Theorem 3.12 in Exercise 38.

EXAMPLE 1 *Proving Two Lines are Parallel*

Lines m, n, and k represent three of the oars above. $m \parallel n$ and $n \parallel k$. Prove that $m \parallel k$.

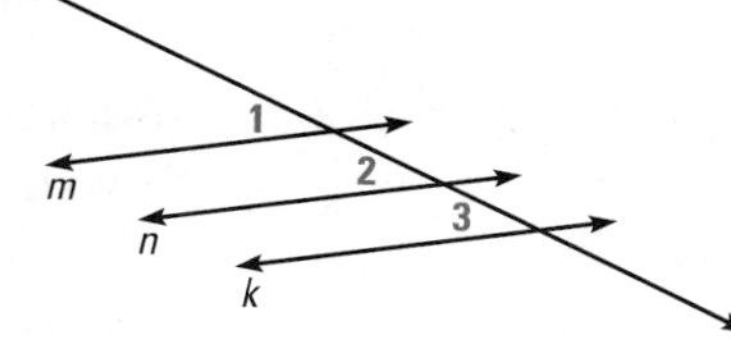

SOLUTION

GIVEN ▶ $m \parallel n$, $n \parallel k$

PROVE ▶ $m \parallel k$

Statements	Reasons
1. $m \parallel n$	**1.** Given
2. $\angle 1 \cong \angle 2$	**2.** Corresponding Angles Postulate
3. $n \parallel k$	**3.** Given
4. $\angle 2 \cong \angle 3$	**4.** Corresponding Angles Postulate
5. $\angle 1 \cong \angle 3$	**5.** Transitive Property of Congruence
6. $m \parallel k$	**6.** Corresponding Angles Converse

THEOREMS ABOUT PARALLEL AND PERPENDICULAR LINES

THEOREM 3.11

If two lines are parallel to the same line, then they are parallel to each other.

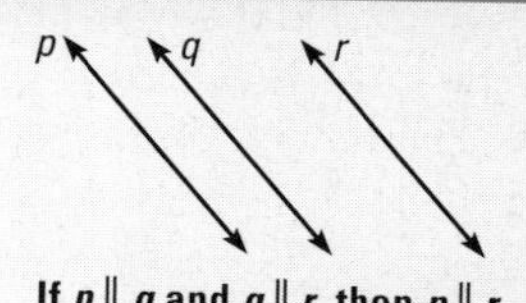

If $p \parallel q$ and $q \parallel r$, then $p \parallel r$.

THEOREM 3.12

In a plane, if two lines are perpendicular to the same line, then they are parallel to each other.

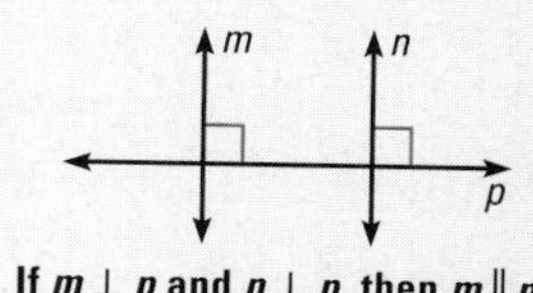

If $m \perp p$ and $n \perp p$, then $m \parallel n$.

CALIFORNIA STANDARDS AND ASSESSMENT

CA Standards: 7, 16
SAT9 Task 2: Obj. 28

1 PLAN

PACING

Basic: 2 days
Average: 2 days
Advanced: 2 days
Block Schedule: 1 block

LESSON OPENER
GEOMETRY SOFTWARE

An alternative way to approach Lesson 3.5 is to use the Geometry Software Lesson Opener:

- Blackline Master (*Chapter 3 Resource Book*, p. 69)
- Transparency (p. 18)

MEETING INDIVIDUAL NEEDS

- ***Chapter 3 Resource Book***
  Prerequisite Skills Review (p. 5)
  Practice Level A (p. 70)
  Practice Level B (p. 71)
  Practice Level C (p. 72)
  Reteaching with Practice (p. 73)
  Absent Student Catch-Up (p. 75)
  Challenge (p. 78)
- ***Resources in Spanish***
- ***Personal Student Tutor***

NEW-TEACHER SUPPORT

See the Tips for New Teachers on pp. 1–2 of the *Chapter 3 Resource Book* for additional notes about Lesson 3.5.

WARM-UP EXERCISES

Transparency Available

Give the name of the postulate or theorem.

1. If two parallel lines are cut by a transversal, then the pairs of corresponding angles are congruent. **Corresponding Angles Postulate**

2. If a transversal is perpendicular to one of two parallel lines, then it is perpendicular to the other. **Perpendicular Transversal Theorem**

2 TEACH

EXTRA EXAMPLE 1

Given: $r \parallel s$ and $s \parallel t$

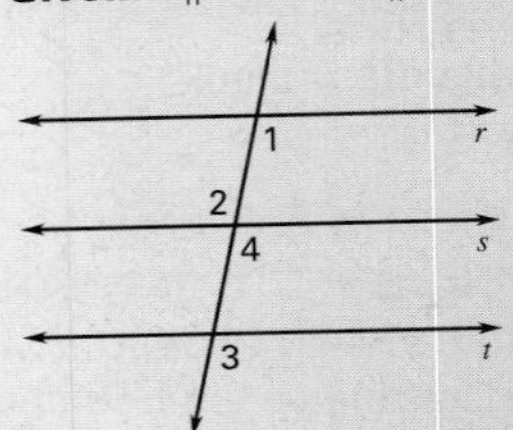

Prove: $r \parallel t$

Statements (Reasons)

1. $r \parallel s$ (Given)
2. $\angle 1 \cong \angle 2$ (Alternate Interior Angles Theorem)
3. $s \parallel t$ (Given)
4. $\angle 2 \cong \angle 3$ (Alternate Exterior Angles Theorem)
5. $\angle 1 \cong \angle 3$ (Transitive Prop. of Cong.)
6. $r \parallel t$ (Corresponding Angles Converse)

CHECKPOINT EXERCISES

For use after Example 1:

1. Use the figure in Extra Example 1 to write a paragraph proof of Theorem 3.11. **See margin.**

EXTRA EXAMPLE 2

The flag of the United States has 13 alternating red and white stripes. Each stripe is parallel to the stripe immediately above it. Explain why the top stripe is parallel to the bottom stripe. **Label the top stripe s_1, the second stripe s_2, the third stripe s_3, and so on. The bottom stripe is s_{13}. Given that $s_1 \parallel s_2$ and $s_2 \parallel s_3$, by the transitivity of parallel lines, $s_1 \parallel s_3$. Since $s_3 \parallel s_4$, it follows that $s_1 \parallel s_4$. Continuing this reasoning, $s_1 \parallel s_{13}$. Therefore, the top stripe is parallel to the bottom stripe.**

Checkpoint Exercises for Example 2 on next page.

Logical Reasoning

EXAMPLE 2 *Explaining Why Steps are Parallel*

In the diagram at the right, each step is parallel to the step immediately below it and the bottom step is parallel to the floor. Explain why the top step is parallel to the floor.

SOLUTION

You are given that $k_1 \parallel k_2$ and $k_2 \parallel k_3$.
By transitivity of parallel lines, $k_1 \parallel k_3$.
Since $k_1 \parallel k_3$ and $k_3 \parallel k_4$, it follows that $k_1 \parallel k_4$.
So, the top step is parallel to the floor.

EXAMPLE 3 *Building a CD Rack*

You are building a CD rack. You cut the sides, bottom, and top so that each corner is composed of two 45° angles. Prove that the top and bottom front edges of the CD rack are parallel.

SOLUTION

GIVEN ▶ $m\angle 1 = 45°, m\angle 2 = 45°$
$m\angle 3 = 45°, m\angle 4 = 45°$

PROVE ▶ $\overline{BA} \parallel \overline{CD}$

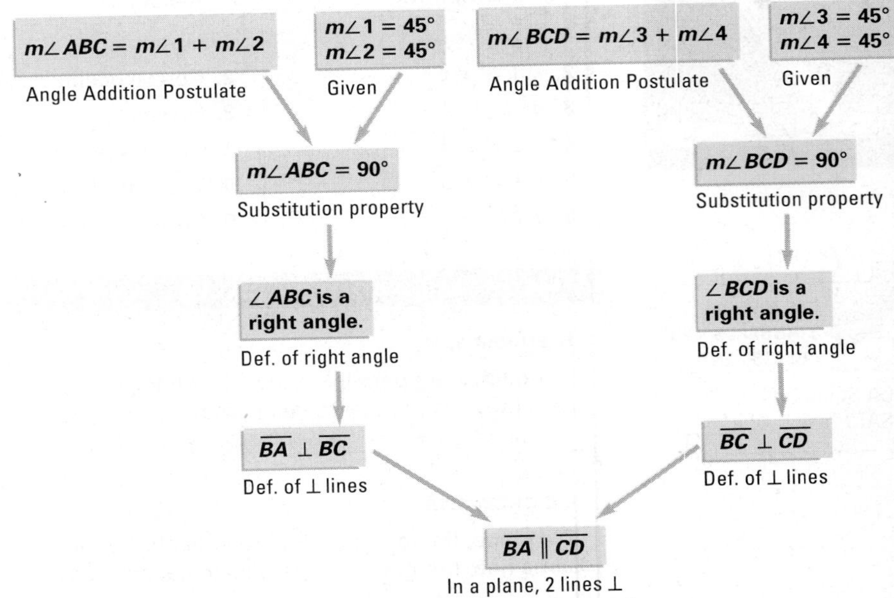

Checkpoint Exercises *Sample answer:*
1. It is given that $r \parallel s$ and $s \parallel t$. From the Corresponding Angles Postulate it follows that $\angle 1 \cong \angle 4$ and $\angle 4 \cong \angle 3$. Then $\angle 1 \cong \angle 3$ by the Transitive Property of Congruence. According to the Corresponding Angle Converse, $r \parallel t$.

GOAL 2 CONSTRUCTING PARALLEL LINES

To construct parallel lines, you first need to know how to copy an angle.

ACTIVITY Construction

Copying an Angle

Use these steps to construct an angle that is congruent to a given $\angle A$.

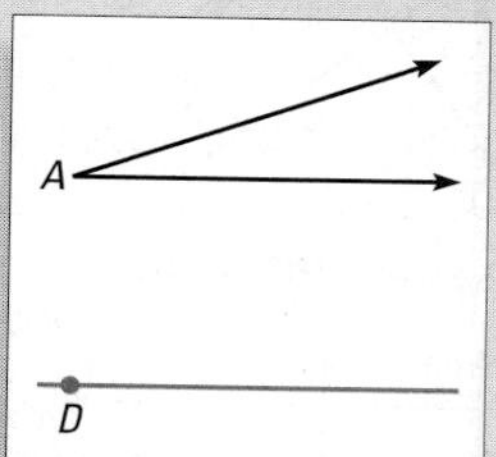

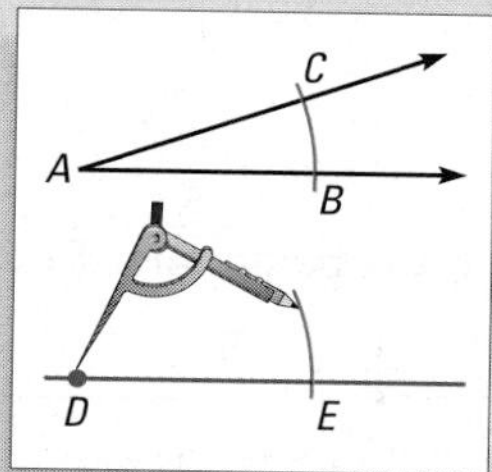

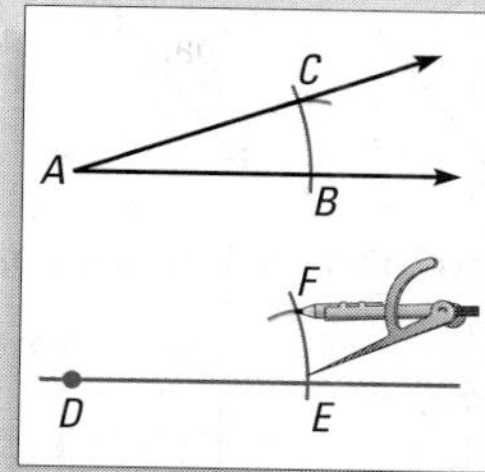

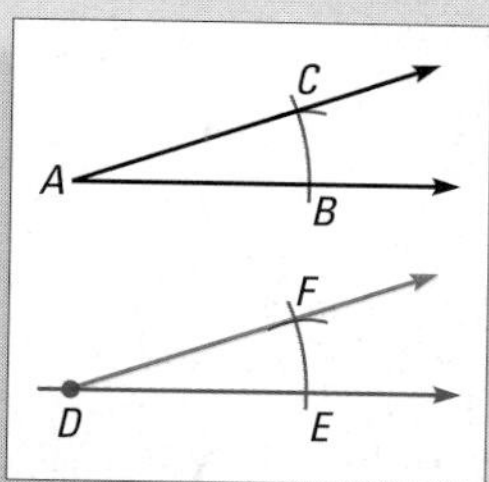

1. Draw a line. Label a point on the line D.
2. Draw an arc with center A. Label B and C. With the same radius, draw an arc with center D. Label E.
3. Draw an arc with radius BC and center E. Label the intersection F.
4. Draw $\overrightarrow{DF}$. $\angle EDF \cong \angle BAC$.

In Chapter 4, you will learn why the *Copying an Angle* construction works. You can use the *Copying an Angle* construction to construct two congruent corresponding angles. If you do, the sides of the angles will be parallel.

ACTIVITY Construction

Parallel Lines

Use these steps to construct a line that passes through a given point P and is parallel to a given line m.

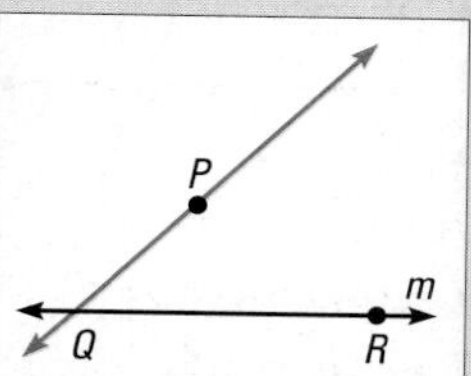

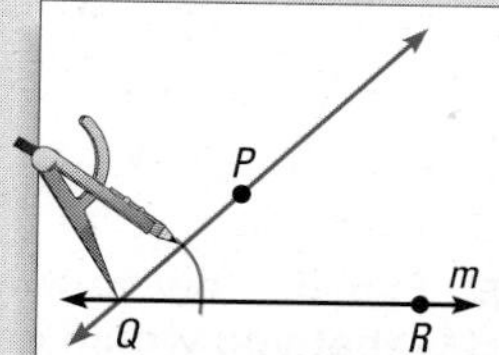

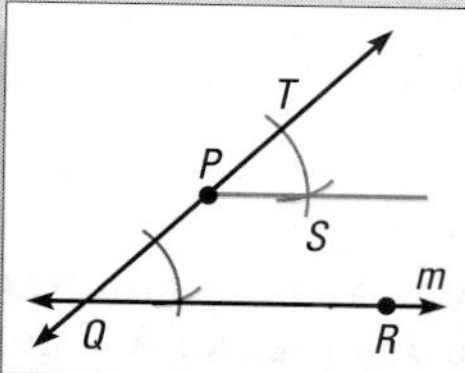

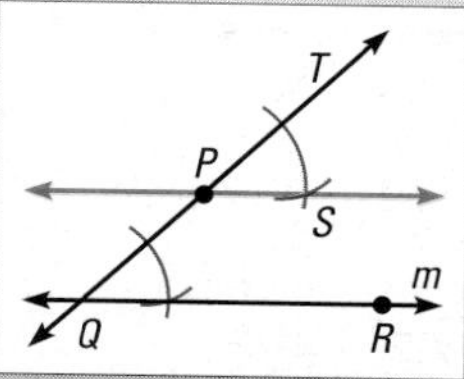

1. Draw points Q and R on m. Draw $\overleftrightarrow{PQ}$.
2. Draw an arc with the compass point at Q so that it crosses $\overrightarrow{QP}$ and $\overrightarrow{QR}$.
3. Copy $\angle PQR$ on $\overleftrightarrow{QP}$ as shown. Be sure the two angles are corresponding. Label the new angle $\angle TPS$ as shown.
4. Draw $\overleftrightarrow{PS}$. Because $\angle TPS$ and $\angle PQR$ are congruent corresponding angles, $\overleftrightarrow{PS} \parallel \overleftrightarrow{QR}$.

EXTRA EXAMPLE 3

You are constructing a garden. The diagonal plantings make 25° and 65° angles at each corner. Prove that the opposite sides of the garden are parallel.

You are given $m\angle 2 = m\angle 3 = m\angle 6 = m\angle 7 = 25°$ and that $m\angle 1 = m\angle 4 = m\angle 5 = m\angle 8 = 65°$. By the Angle Addition Post. and the Substitution prop., $m\angle DAB = m\angle 1 + m\angle 2 = 90°$, $m\angle ADC = m\angle 7 + m\angle 8 = 90°$, $m\angle ABC = m\angle 3 + m\angle 4 = 90°$, and $m\angle BCD = m\angle 5 + m\angle 6 = 90°$. Therefore $\angle DAB$, $\angle ADC$, $\angle ABC$, and $\angle BCD$ are right angles by the definition of rt. angles. From this it follows that $\overline{AB}$ and $\overline{DC}$ are both perpendicular to $\overline{AD}$ and that $\overline{AD}$ and $\overline{BC}$ are both perpendicular to $\overline{AB}$. Thus, because two lines perpendicular to the same line are parallel, $\overline{AB} \parallel \overline{DC}$ and $\overline{AD} \parallel \overline{BC}$.

CHECKPOINT EXERCISES

For use after Examples 2 and 3:

1. How can you show that the first horizontal line on a piece of graph paper is parallel to the last horizontal line if the center vertical line is perpendicular to all horizontal lines? **Since all the horizontal lines are perpendicular to the center line, they are parallel to each other by Theorem 3.12.**

CLOSURE QUESTION

What can you conclude about two coplanar lines that are perpendicular to the same line? **They are parallel to each other.**

3 APPLY

ASSIGNMENT GUIDE

BASIC

Day 1: pp. 160–163 Exs. 8–28 even, 34–40 even, 41, 44–52 even

Day 2: pp. 160–164 Exs. 9–29 odd, 33, 35, 37, Quiz 2 Exs. 1–5

AVERAGE

Day 1: pp. 160–163 Exs. 8–28 even, 34–40 even, 41, 44–52 even

Day 2: pp. 160–164 Exs. 9–29 odd, 30, 31–37 odd, Quiz 2 Exs. 1–5

ADVANCED

Day 1: pp. 160–163 Exs. 8–28 even, 34–40 even, 41, 42–52 even

Day 2: pp. 160–164 Exs. 9–29 odd, 30, 31–39 odd, Quiz 2 Exs. 1–5

BLOCK SCHEDULE

pp. 160–164 Exs. 8–31 , 33–38, 40, 41, 44–52 even, Quiz 2 Exs. 1–5

EXERCISE LEVELS

Level A: ***Easier***
8–10

Level B: ***More Difficult***
11–38, 40, 41

Level C: ***Most Difficult***
39, 42

✔ HOMEWORK CHECK

To quickly check student understanding of key concepts, go over the following exercises: Exs. 10, 12, 16, 20, 24, 28. See also the Daily Homework Quiz:

- Blackline Master (*Chapter 3 Resource Book,* p. 82)
- Transparency (p. 22)

6. *Sample answer:*

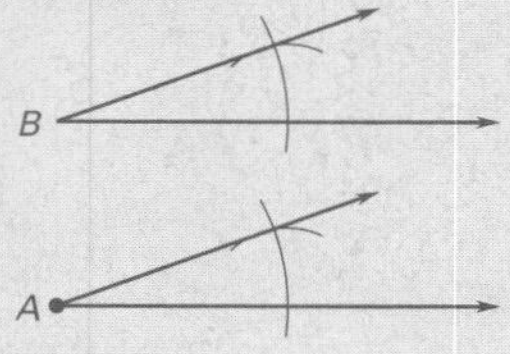

GUIDED PRACTICE

Concept Check ✔ **1.** Name two ways, from this lesson, to prove that two lines are parallel. **if they are || to the same line, if they are ⊥ to the same line**

Skill Check ✔ **State the theorem that you can use to prove that r is parallel to s.**

2. GIVEN ▶ $r \parallel t, t \parallel s$ **Theorem 3.11**

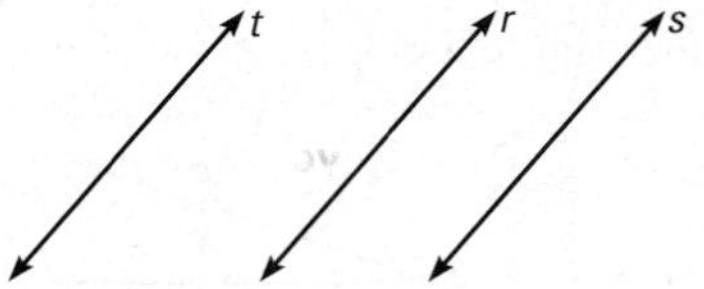

3. GIVEN ▶ $r \perp t, t \perp s$ **Theorem 3.12**

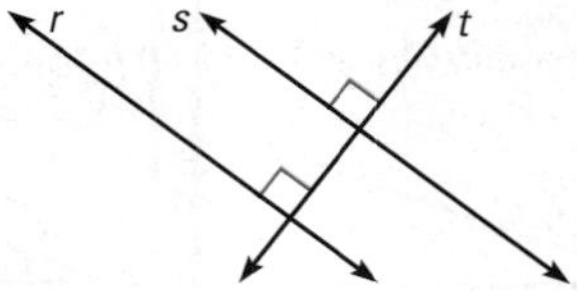

Determine which lines, if any, must be parallel. Explain your reasoning.

4.

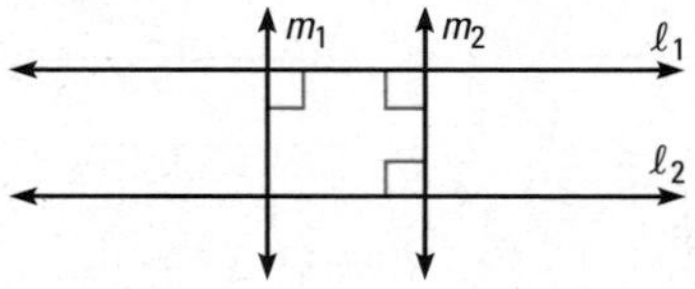

5.

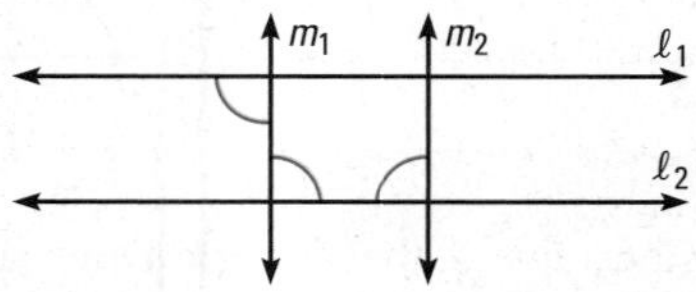

4. **$m_1 \parallel m_2$ because both are perpendicular to ℓ_1, $\ell_1 \parallel \ell_2$ because both are perpendicular to m_2.**

5. **$\ell_1 \parallel \ell_2$ because of the Alternate Interior Angles Converse.**

6. Draw any angle $\angle A$. Then construct $\angle B$ congruent to $\angle A$. **See margin.**

7. Given a line ℓ and a point P not on ℓ, describe how to construct a line through P parallel to ℓ. ***Sample answer:*** **Given line ℓ and exterior point P, draw any line n through P that intersects ℓ. Label one of the four angles where ℓ and n intersect as $\angle 1$. Copy $\angle 1$ at P. Be sure that $\angle 1$ and the new angle ($\angle 2$) are in corresponding positions. One of the sides of $\angle 2$ will lie on line n. Draw the line m that contains the other side of $\angle 2$. It will be parallel to ℓ.**

PRACTICE AND APPLICATIONS

STUDENT HELP

Extra Practice to help you master skills is on p. 808.

10. **Alternate Interior Angles Converse**

14. **Corresponding Angles Converse, Alternate Interior Angles Converse, Consecutive Interior Angles Converse, Alternate Exterior Angles Converse, if they are || to the same line, if they are ⊥ to the same line.**

STUDENT HELP

HOMEWORK HELP
Example 1: Exs. 8–24
Example 2: Exs. 8–24
Example 3: Exs. 8–24

LOGICAL REASONING **State the postulate or theorem that allows you to conclude that $j \parallel k$.**

8. GIVEN ▶ $j \parallel n, k \parallel n$

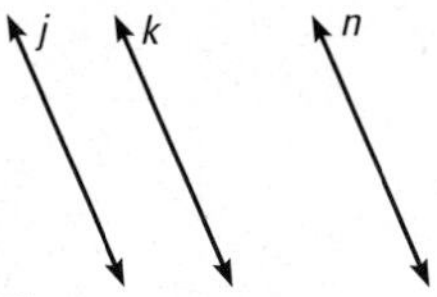

Theorem 3.11

9. GIVEN ▶ $j \perp n, k \perp n$

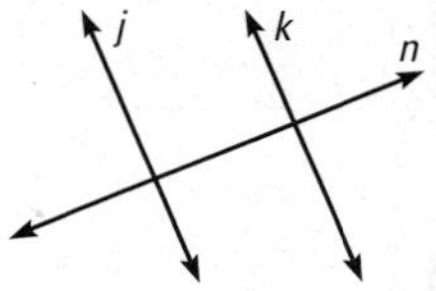

Theorem 3.12

10. GIVEN ▶ $\angle 1 \cong \angle 2$

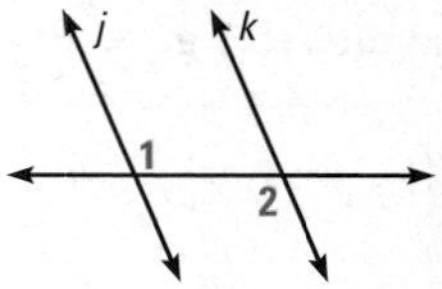

SHOWING LINES ARE PARALLEL **Explain how you would show that $k \parallel j$. State any theorems or postulates that you would use.**

11.

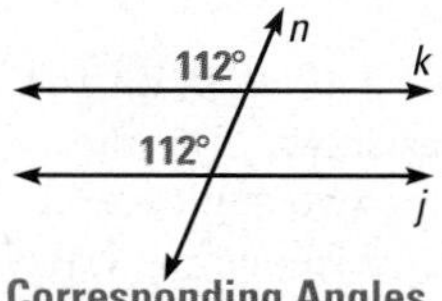

Corresponding Angles Converse

12.

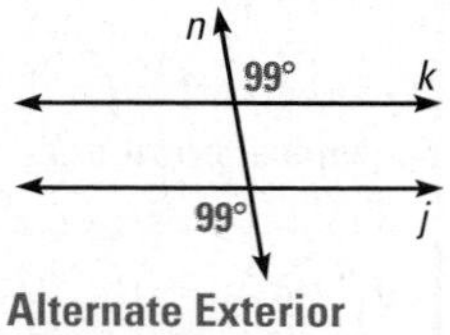

Alternate Exterior Angles Converse

13.

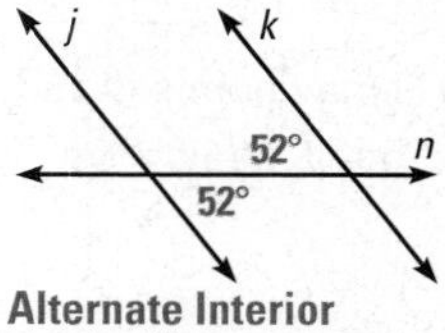

Alternate Interior Angles Converse

14. *Writing* Make a list of all the ways you know to prove that two lines are parallel. **See margin.**

15. $85° + 95° = 180°$, so $k \parallel j$ by the Consecutive Interior Angles Converse.

17. *Sample answer:* The measure of the obtuse exterior angle formed by n and k is $90° + \frac{90°}{2} = 135°$, so $k \parallel j$ by the Alternate Exterior Angles Converse.

18. *Sample answer:* The intersection of g and the transversal form two congruent angles that form a linear pair, so each is 90° and g is perpendicular to the transversal. Then $g \parallel h$ by Theorem 3.12.

19. *Sample answer:* The measure of the obtuse angle formed by g and the left transversal is $(180 - x)°$. Then, since $(180 - x)° + x° = 180°$, $g \parallel h$ by the Consecutive Interior Angles Converse.

20. *Sample answer:* The measure of the two obtuse vertical angles formed by g and the transversal is $(90 + x)°$. Then, since $(90 + x)° + (90 - x)° = 180°$, $g \parallel h$ by the Consecutive Interior Angles Converse.

21. $p \parallel q$ by the Corresponding Angles Converse; $q \parallel r$ by the Consecutive Interior Angles Converse. Then, because $p \parallel q$ and $q \parallel r$, $p \parallel r$.

23. See margin.

STUDENT HELP

HOMEWORK HELP Visit our Web site www.mcdougallittell.com for help with constructions in Exs. 25–29.

SHOWING LINES ARE PARALLEL Explain how you would show that $k \parallel j$.

15.

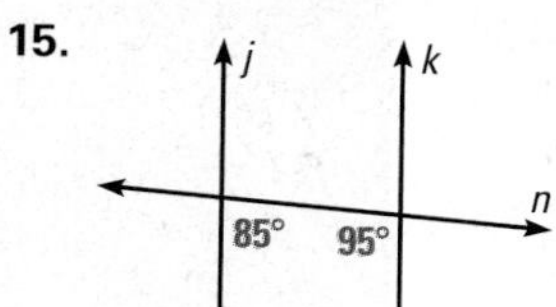

16.

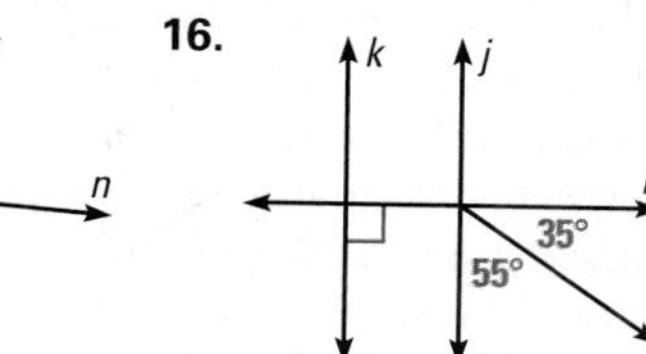

17.

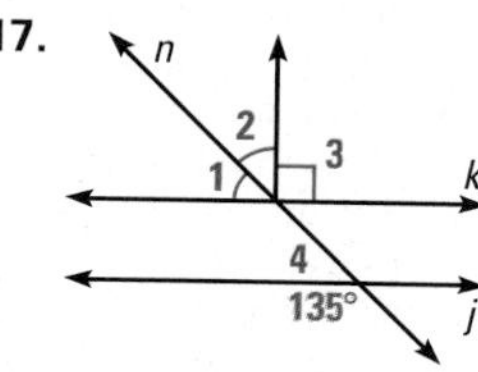

$35° + 55° = 90°$ so $n \perp j$, and $k \parallel j$ by Theorem 3.12.

USING ALGEBRA Explain how you would show that $g \parallel h$.

18.

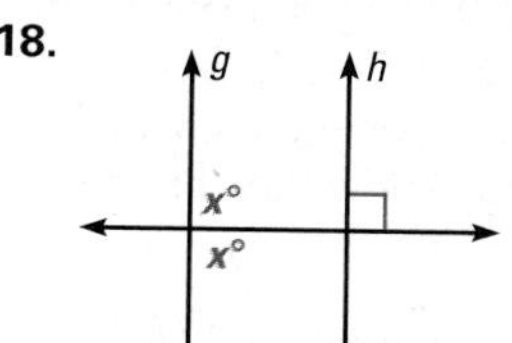

19.

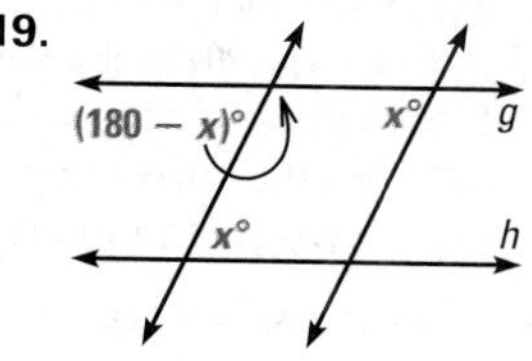

20.

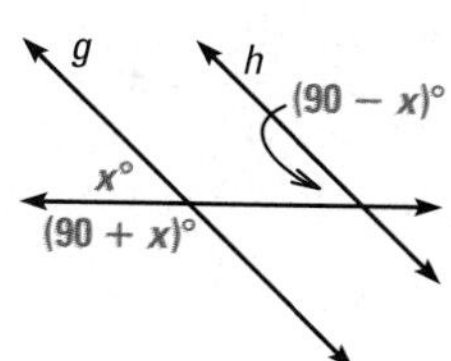

NAMING PARALLEL LINES Determine which lines, if any, must be parallel. Explain your reasoning.

21.

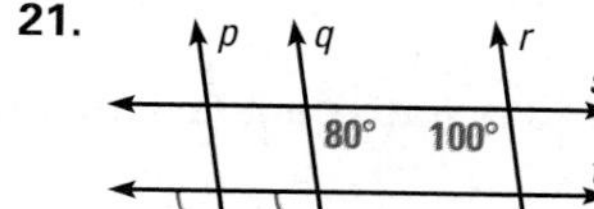

22.

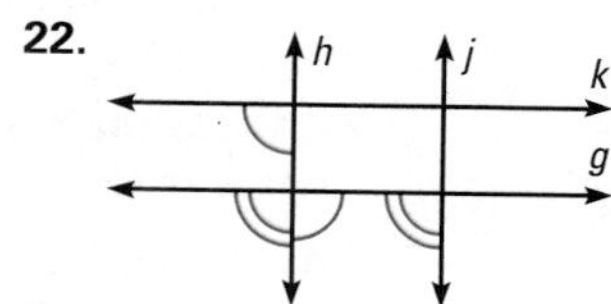

$h \parallel j$ by the Corresponding Angles Converse.

23.

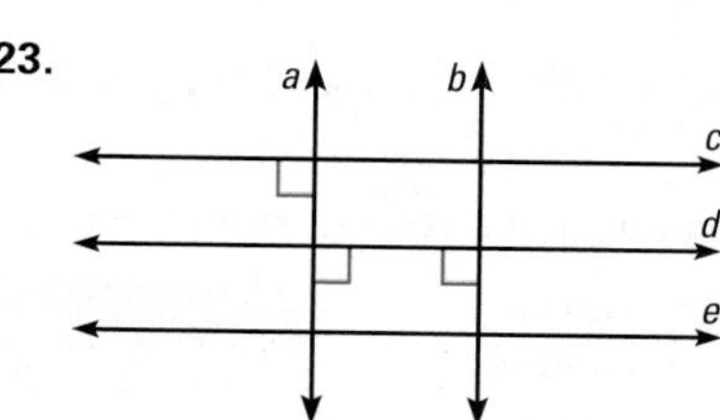

24.

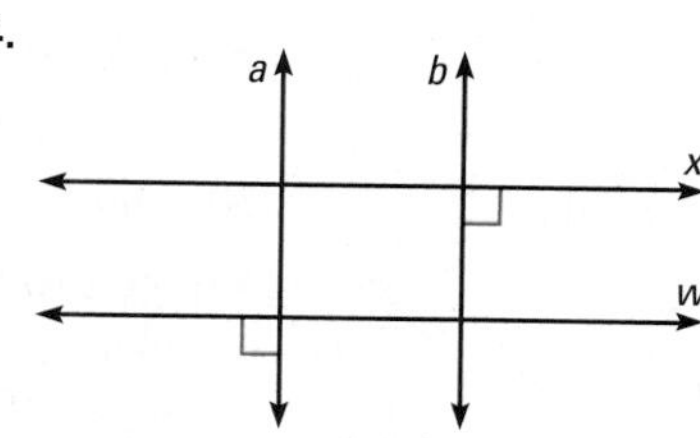

No pairs of lines must be parallel.

CONSTRUCTIONS Use a straightedge to draw an angle that fits the description. Then use the *Copying an Angle* construction on page 159 to copy the angle. 25–28. See margin.

25. An acute angle

26. An obtuse angle

27. **CONSTRUCTING PARALLEL LINES** Draw a horizontal line and construct a line parallel to it through a point above the line.

28. **CONSTRUCTING PARALLEL LINES** Draw a diagonal line and construct a line parallel to it through a point to the right of the line.

29. **JUSTIFYING A CONSTRUCTION** Explain why the lines in Exercise 28 are parallel. Use a postulate or theorem from Lesson 3.4 to support your answer. *Sample answer:* The two angles that are congruent are corresponding angles, so the two lines are parallel by the Corresponding Angles Converse.

STUDENT HELP NOTES

Homework Help Students can find help for Exs. 25–29 at **www.mcdougallittell.com.** The information can be printed out for students who don't have access to the Internet.

! COMMON ERROR

EXERCISES 25–26 Students often use the same radius to construct the second point on an angle that they used to construct the first point. Remind them that the first point locates a position on one ray of the angle. The second point makes the angle the same size as the given angle, so the radius used to locate this point must be equal to the distance between the two points on the given angle.

23. a and b are each perpendicular to d, so $a \parallel b$ by Theorem 3.12; c and d are each perpendicular to a so $c \parallel d$ by Theorem 3.12.

25. *Sample answer:*

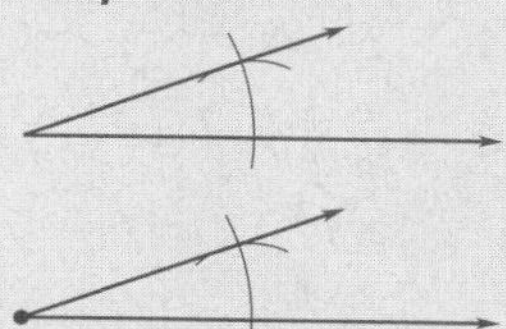

26. *Sample answer:*

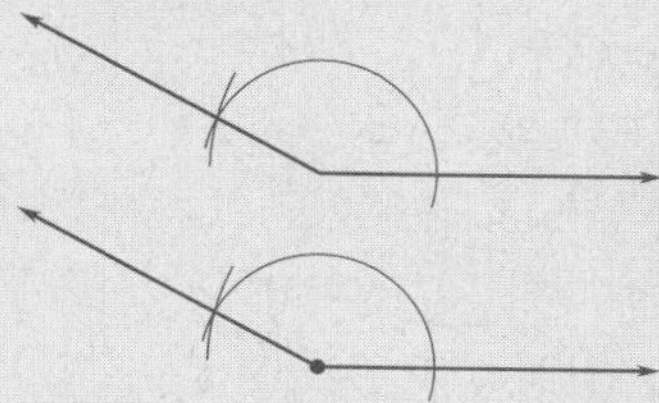

27. *Sample answer:*

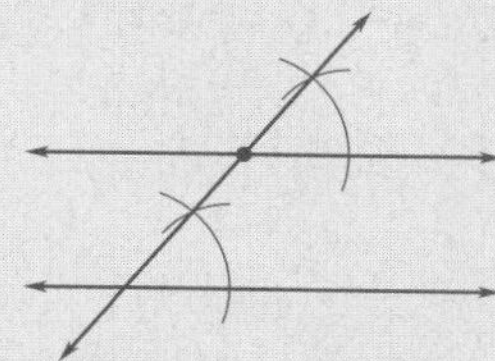

28. *Sample answer:*

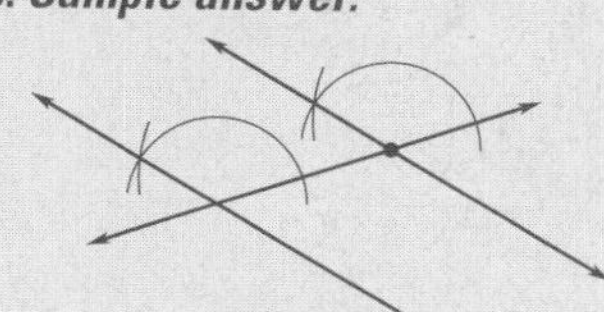

APPLICATION NOTE

EXERCISE 31 A plumb line is a basic leveling tool for a carpenter, who must make sure that all vertical surfaces are *plumb,* that is, that they are perpendicular to the horizontal. A plumb line is simply a string with a vertical weight, called a plumb bob, attached to its end. It uses gravity to gauge whether a vertical surface is plumb. When the string end is fixed and the weight hangs freely, the line of the string shows perfect plumb.

32.

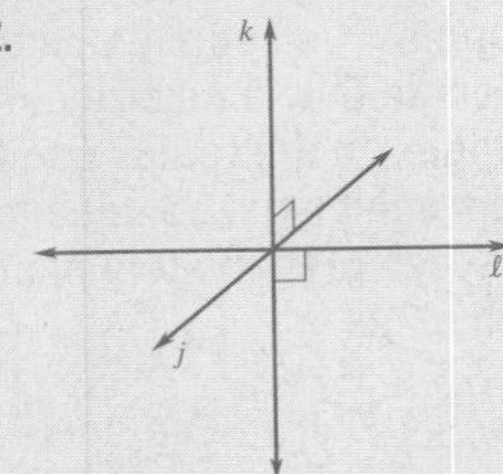

30. *Sample answer:* All the yard lines are perpendicular to the same line (the sideline), so *each pair* of yard lines are parallel by Theorem 3.12 and *all* the yard lines are parallel by Theorem 3.11.

31. *Sample answer:* Each edge is parallel to the previous edge, so all the strips are parallel by Theorem 3.11.

30. **FOOTBALL FIELD** The white lines along the long edges of a football field are called *sidelines. Yard lines* are perpendicular to the sidelines and cross the field every five yards. Explain why you can conclude that the yard lines are parallel.

31. **HANGING WALLPAPER** When you hang wallpaper, you use a tool called a *plumb line* to make sure one edge of the first strip of wallpaper is vertical. If the edges of each strip of wallpaper are parallel and there are no gaps between the strips, how do you know that the rest of the strips of wallpaper will be parallel to the first?

32. **ERROR ANALYSIS** It is given that $j \perp k$ and $k \perp \ell$. A student reasons that lines j and ℓ must be parallel. What is wrong with this reasoning? Sketch a counterexample to support your answer.
It is not given that j, k, and ℓ are in the same plane; See margin for counterexample.

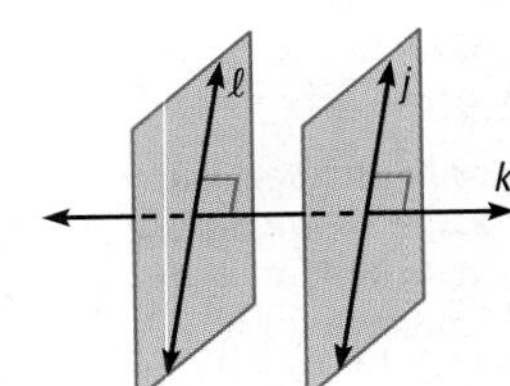

CATEGORIZING **Tell whether the statement is *sometimes, always,* or *never* true.**

33. Two lines that are parallel to the same line are parallel to each other. **always**

34. *In a plane*, two lines that are perpendicular to the same line are parallel to each other. **always**

35. Two *noncoplanar* lines that are perpendicular to the same line are parallel to each other. **never**

36. Through a point not on a line you can construct a parallel line. **always**

37. **LATTICEWORK** You are making a lattice fence out of pieces of wood called slats. You want the top of each slat to be parallel to the bottom. At what angle should you cut $\angle 1$?
50°

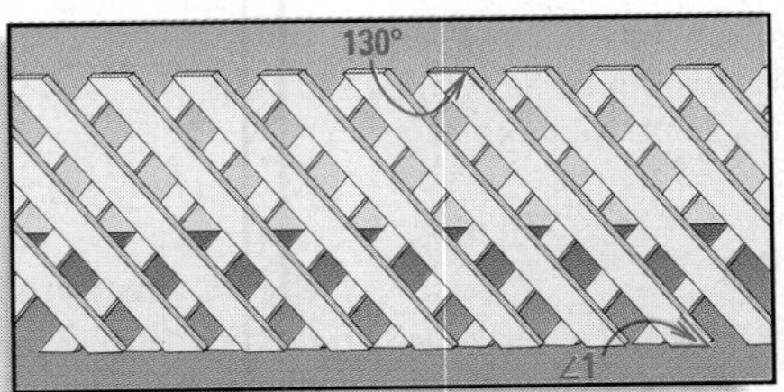

38. **PROVING THEOREM 3.12** Rearrange the statements to write a flow proof of Theorem 3.12. Remember to include a reason for each statement. **See margin.**

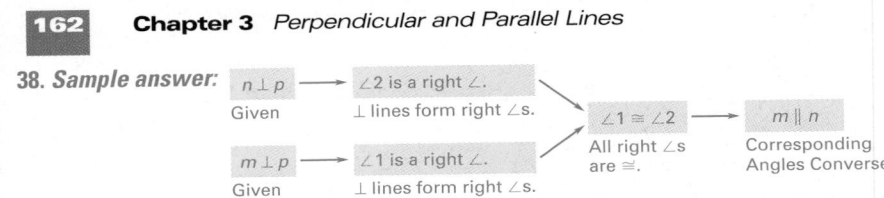

GIVEN ▶ $m \perp p$, $n \perp p$

PROVE ▶ $m \parallel n$

$\angle 1 \cong \angle 2$	$n \perp p$	$\angle 1$ is a right $\angle$.
$m \parallel n$	$m \perp p$	$\angle 2$ is a right $\angle$.

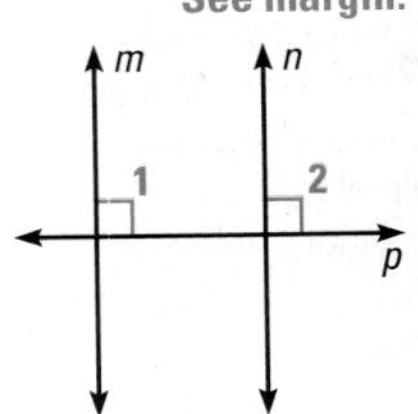

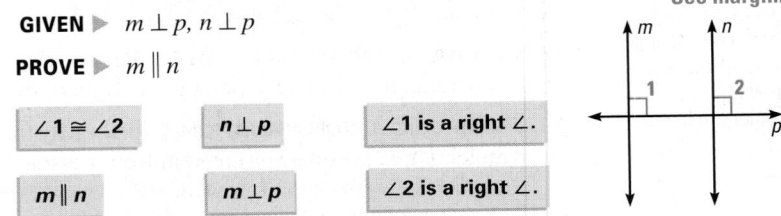

38. *Sample answer:* $n \perp p$ (Given) → $\angle 2$ is a right $\angle$. ($\perp$ lines form right $\angle$s.); $m \perp p$ (Given) → $\angle 1$ is a right $\angle$. ($\perp$ lines form right $\angle$s.) → $\angle 1 \cong \angle 2$ (All right $\angle$s are $\cong$.) → $m \parallel n$ (Corresponding Angles Converse)

39. a. *Sample answer:* Hold the straightedge next to each red line and see if the red lines are straight.

b. *Sample answer:* Measure the angles formed by the red lines and the top horizontal line, and see if corresponding angles are congruent.

Test Preparation

41. a. Corresponding Angles Converse

b. Consecutive Interior Angles Converse

★ Challenge

49. Converse: If an angle is acute, then its measure is 42°. Counterexample: a 41° angle (or any acute angle whose measure is not 42°)

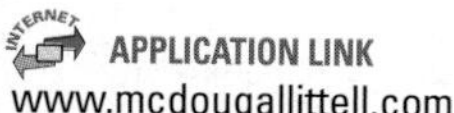

APPLICATION LINK
www.mcdougallittell.com

39. OPTICAL ILLUSION The radiating lines make it hard to tell if the red lines are straight. Explain how you can answer the question using only a straightedge and a protractor.

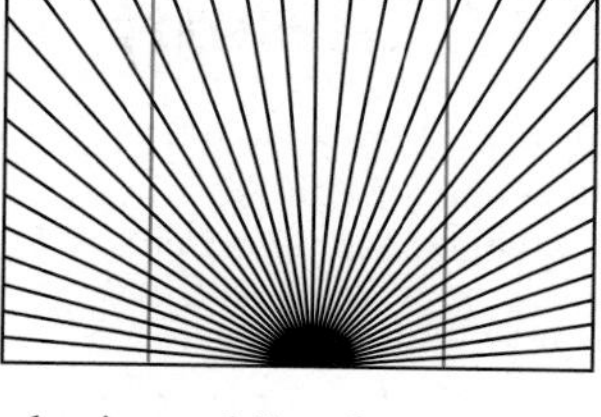

a. Are the red lines straight?

b. Are the red lines parallel?

40. CONSTRUCTING WITH PERPENDICULARS Draw a horizontal line ℓ and a point P not on ℓ. Construct a line m through P perpendicular to ℓ. Draw a point Q not on m or ℓ. Construct a line n through Q perpendicular to m. What postulate or theorem guarantees that the lines ℓ and n are parallel?

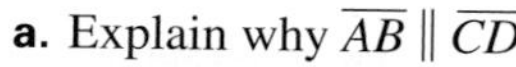

Theorem 3.12. *Sample answer:* See margin.

41. MULTI-STEP PROBLEM Use the information given in the diagram at the right.

a. Explain why $\overline{AB} \parallel \overline{CD}$.

b. Explain why $\overline{CD} \parallel \overline{EF}$.

c. *Writing* What is $m\angle 1$? How do you know? See margin.

42. SCIENCE CONNECTION When light enters glass, the light bends. When it leaves glass, it bends again. If both sides of a pane of glass are parallel, light leaves the pane at the same angle at which it entered. Prove that the path of the exiting light is parallel to the path of the entering light.

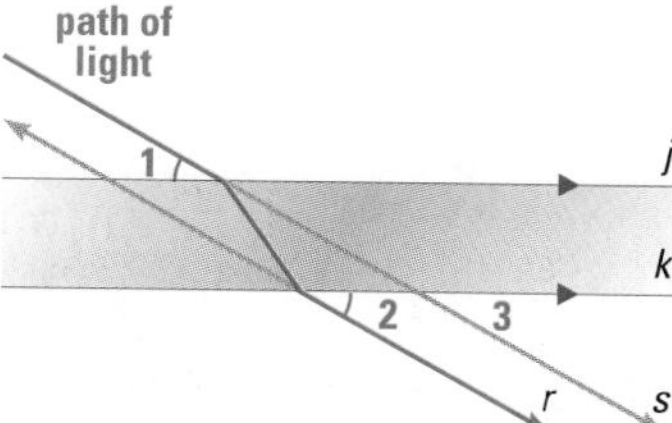

GIVEN ▶ $\angle 1 \cong \angle 2, j \parallel k$

PROVE ▶ $r \parallel s$

See margin.

MIXED REVIEW

50. Converse: If two angles are supplementary, then their measures are 150° and 30°. Counterexample: two angles with measures 151° and 29° (or any two supplementary angles whose measures are not 150° and 30°)

51. Converse: If a polygon contains four right angles, then it is a rectangle; See margin for counterexample.

USING THE DISTANCE FORMULA Find the distance between the two points. (Review 1.3 for 3.6)

43. $A(0, -6), B(14, 0)$ $2\sqrt{58}$, or about 15.23	**44.** $A(-3, -8), B(2, -1)$ $\sqrt{74}$, or about 8.60	**45.** $A(0, -7), B(6, 3)$ $2\sqrt{34}$, or about 11.66
46. $A(-9, -5), B(-1, 11)$ $8\sqrt{5}$, or about 17.89	**47.** $A(5, -7), B(-11, 6)$ $5\sqrt{17}$, or about 20.62	**48.** $A(4, 4), B(-3, -3)$ $7\sqrt{2}$, or about 9.90

FINDING COUNTEREXAMPLES Give a counterexample that demonstrates that the converse of the statement is false. (Review 2.2) 49–51. See margin.

49. If an angle measures 42°, then it is acute.

50. If two angles measure 150° and 30°, then they are supplementary.

51. If a polygon is a rectangle, then it contains four right angles.

52. USING PROPERTIES OF PARALLEL LINES Use the given information to find the measures of the other seven angles in the figure shown at the right. (Review 3.3)

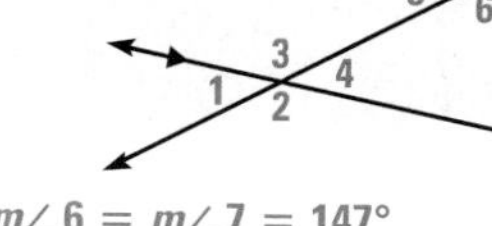

GIVEN ▶ $j \parallel k, m\angle 1 = 33°$

$m\angle 4 = m\angle 5 = m\angle 8 = 33°, m\angle 2 = m\angle 3 = m\angle 6 = m\angle 7 = 147°$

APPLICATION NOTE

EXERCISE 42 Both glass and water allow visible light to pass through. Therefore, they are said to be transparent to all frequencies of visible light. Glass however, blocks infrared and ultraviolet light.

40. *Sample answer:*

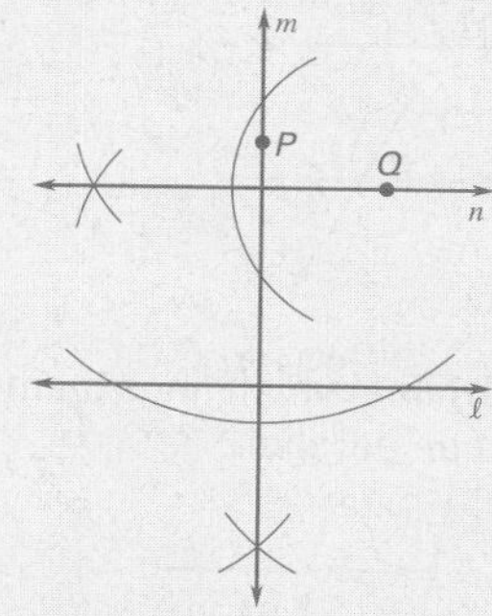

41c. 90°; $AB \parallel EF$, Interior angles are supplementary; $\angle 1$ and $\angle AEF$ are also supplementary interior angles, and since $m\angle AEF = 90°$, $m\angle 1 = 180 - 90 = 90°$.

42. 1. $\angle 1 \cong \angle 2$ (Given);
2. $j \parallel k$ (Given);
3. $\angle 1 \cong \angle 3$ (Alternate Exterior Angles Thm);
4. $\angle 3 \cong \angle 2$ (Transitive Property);
5. $r \parallel s$ (Corresponding Angles Converse)

51.

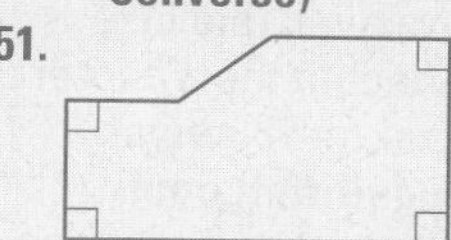

ADDITIONAL PRACTICE AND RETEACHING

For Lesson 3.5:

- Practice Levels A, B, and C (*Chapter 3 Resource Book*, p. 70)
- Reteaching with Practice (*Chapter 3 Resource Book*, p. 73)
- See Lesson 3.5 of the *Personal Student Tutor*

For more Mixed Review:

- Search the *Test and Practice Generator* for key words or specific lessons.

4 ASSESS

DAILY HOMEWORK QUIZ

Transparency Available

1. Explain how you would show that $s \parallel t$.

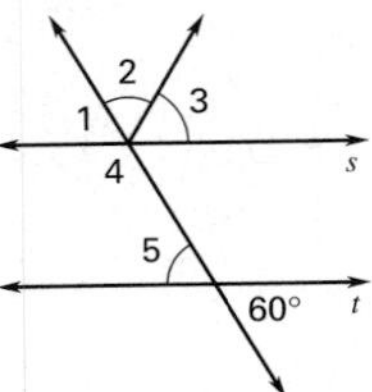

See margin.

2. Determine which lines if any must be parallel.

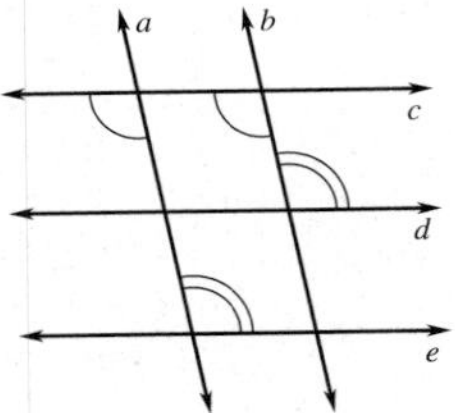

$a \parallel b$ by the Corresponding Angles Converse

EXTRA CHALLENGE NOTE

Challenge problems for Lesson 3.5 are available in **blackline** format in the *Chapter 3 Resource Book,* p. 78 and at **www.mcdougallittell.com**.

ADDITIONAL TEST PREPARATION

1. **WRITING** Describe how to construct an angle congruent to a given angle.
See activity at top of page 159.

ADDITIONAL RESOURCES

An alternative Quiz for Lessons 3.4 and 3.5 is available in the *Chapter 3 Resource Book,* p. 79.

A **blackline** master with additional Math & History exercises is available in the *Chapter 3 Resource Book,* p. 77.

QUIZ 2

Self-Test for Lessons 3.4 and 3.5

5. Sample answer: First it is given that $\angle ABC$ is supplementary to $\angle DEF$. Next, note that $\angle ABC$ and $\angle CBE$ are a linear pair; therefore, by the Linear Pair Postulate $\angle ABC$ and $\angle CBE$ are supplementary. By the Congruent Supplements Theorem, $\angle CBE \cong \angle DEF$. Finally, the left and right edges of the chimney are parallel by the Corresponding Angles Converse.

1. In the diagram shown at the right, determine whether you can prove that lines j and k are parallel. If you can, state the postulate or theorem that you would use. **(Lesson 3.4)**
yes; Consecutive Interior Angles Converse

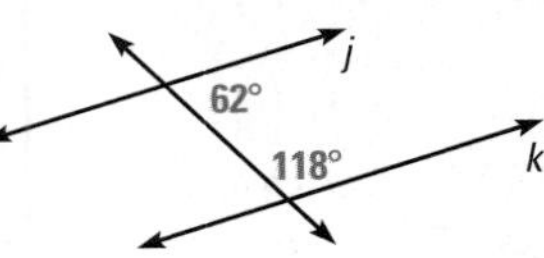

Use the given information and the diagram to determine which lines must be parallel. (Lesson 3.5)

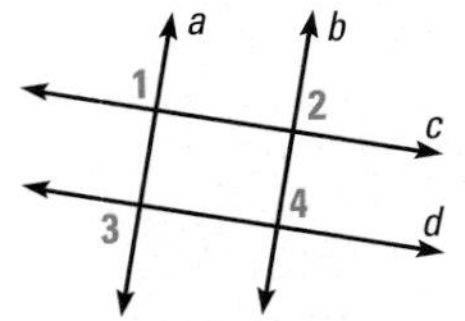

2. $\angle 1$ and $\angle 2$ are right angles. $a \parallel b$
3. $\angle 4 \cong \angle 3$ $a \parallel b$
4. $\angle 2 \cong \angle 3$, $\angle 3 \cong \angle 4$. $a \parallel b$, $c \parallel d$
5. **FIREPLACE CHIMNEY** In the illustration at the right, $\angle ABC$ and $\angle DEF$ are supplementary. Explain how you know that the left and right edges of the chimney are parallel. **(Lesson 3.4)**
See margin.

MATH & History

Measuring Earth's Circumference

APPLICATION LINK www.mcdougallittell.com

THEN **AROUND 230 B.C.,** the Greek scholar Eratosthenes estimated Earth's circumference. In the late 15th century, Christopher Columbus used a smaller estimate to convince the king and queen of Spain that his proposed voyage to India would take only 30 days.

NOW **TODAY,** satellites and other tools are used to determine Earth's circumference with great accuracy.

1. The actual distance from Syene to Alexandria is about 500 miles. Use this value and the information on page 145 to estimate Earth's circumference. How close is your value to the modern day measurement in the table at the right?

about 25,000 miles; the value is quite close to the modern day measurement of the Earth's circumference at 24,902 miles.

Measuring Earth's Circumference	
Circumference estimated by Eratosthenes (230 B.C.)	About 29,000 mi
Circumference assumed by Columbus (about 1492)	About 17,600 mi
Modern day measurement	24,902 mi

Eratosthenes becomes the head of the library in Alexandria.

235 B.C.

1492

A replica of one of the ships used by Christopher Columbus.

1999

Photograph of Earth from space.

Daily Homework Quiz *Sample answer:*

1. Since $m\angle 5 = 60°$, by the Vertical Angles Theorem, then $m\angle 2$ and $m\angle 3$ also equal 60°. Therefore $m\angle 2 + m\angle 3 = 120°$, by the Angle Addition Postulate. So, $m\angle 4 = 120°$ by the Vertical Angles Theorem. Since $m\angle 4 + m\angle 5 = 180°$, $s \parallel t$ by the Consecutive Interior Angles Converse.

3.6 Parallel Lines in the Coordinate Plane

What you should learn

GOAL 1 Find slopes of lines and use slope to identify parallel lines in a coordinate plane.

GOAL 2 Write equations of parallel lines in a coordinate plane.

Why you should learn it

▼ To describe steepness in **real-life**, such as the cog railway in **Example 1** and the zip line in **Ex. 46**.

California Standards and Assessment

CA Standards: 17
SAT9 Task 2: Obj. 28

GOAL 1 Slope of Parallel Lines

In algebra, you learned that the slope of a nonvertical line is the ratio of the vertical change (the rise) to the horizontal change (the run). If the line passes through the points (x_1, y_1) and (x_2, y_2), then the slope is given by

$$\text{Slope} = \frac{\text{rise}}{\text{run}}$$

$$m = \frac{y_2 - y_1}{x_2 - x_1}.$$

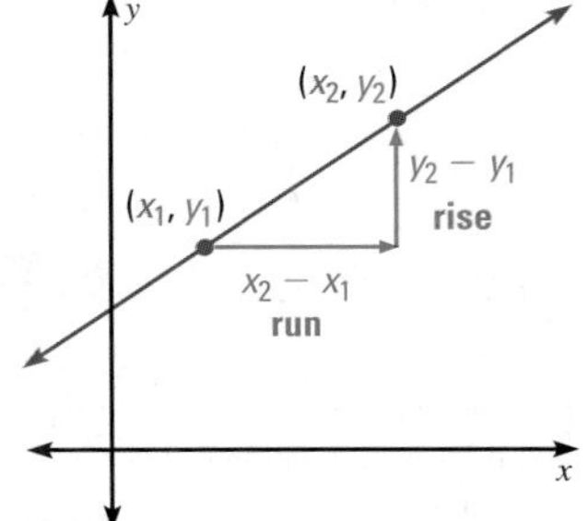

Slope is usually represented by the variable m.

EXAMPLE 1 Finding the Slope of Train Tracks

Cog Railway A cog railway goes up the side of Mount Washington, the tallest mountain in New England. At the steepest section, the train goes up about 4 feet for each 10 feet it goes forward. What is the slope of this section?

Solution

$$\text{slope} = \frac{\text{rise}}{\text{run}} = \frac{4 \text{ feet}}{10 \text{ feet}} = 0.4$$

EXAMPLE 2 Finding the Slope of a Line

Find the slope of the line that passes through the points (0, 6) and (5, 2).

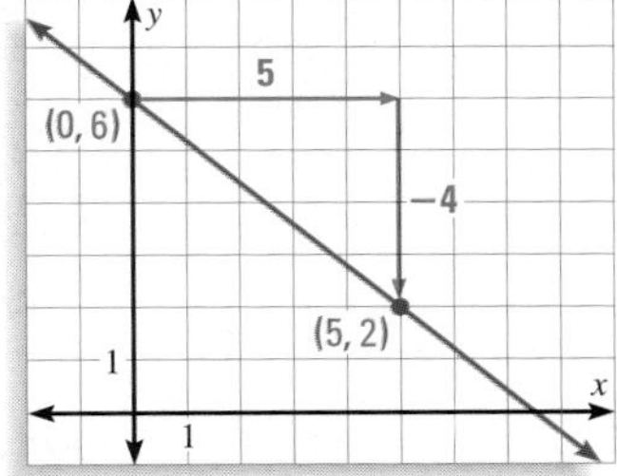

Solution

Let $(x_1, y_1) = (0, 6)$ and $(x_2, y_2) = (5, 2)$.

$$m = \frac{y_2 - y_1}{x_2 - x_1}$$

$$= \frac{2 - 6}{5 - 0}$$

$$= -\frac{4}{5}$$

▶ The slope of the line is $-\frac{4}{5}$.

1 PLAN

Pacing
Basic: 1 day
Average: 1 day
Advanced: 1 day
Block Schedule: 0.5 block with 3.7

Lesson Opener Application
An alternative way to approach Lesson 3.6 is to use the Application Lesson Opener:

- Blackline Master (*Chapter 3 Resource Book,* p. 83)
- Transparency (p. 19)

Meeting Individual Needs

- ***Chapter 3 Resource Book***
  Prerequisite Skills Review (p. 5)
  Practice Level A (p. 85)
  Practice Level B (p. 86)
  Practice Level C (p. 87)
  Reteaching with Practice (p. 88)
  Absent Student Catch-Up (p. 90)
  Challenge (p. 92)
- ***Resources in Spanish***
- ***Personal Student Tutor***

New-Teacher Support
See the Tips for New Teachers on pp. 1–2 of the *Chapter 3 Resource Book* for additional notes about Lesson 3.6.

Warm-Up Exercises

Transparency Available

State whether the slope of the line is positive, negative, undefined, or zero.

1. Rises from left to right **positive**
2. vertical **undefined**
3. horizontal **zero**
4. Falls from left to right **negative**

English Learners
Stack several books and place a ruler so it forms an incline. Use this model to review the terms *slope, rise,* and *run.*

2 TEACH

Motivating the Lesson

Civil engineers use computer software that allows them to examine the paths of rivers and roadways. For instance they may want to analyze roads that could be built parallel to existing roads or rivers.

Extra Example 1

The Cog Railway covers about 3.1 miles and gains about 3600 feet of altitude. What is the average slope of the track? about 0.22

Extra Example 2

Find the slope of a line that passes through the points (–3, 0) and (4, 7). 1

Extra Example 3

Find the slope of each line. Is $m_1 \parallel m_2$?

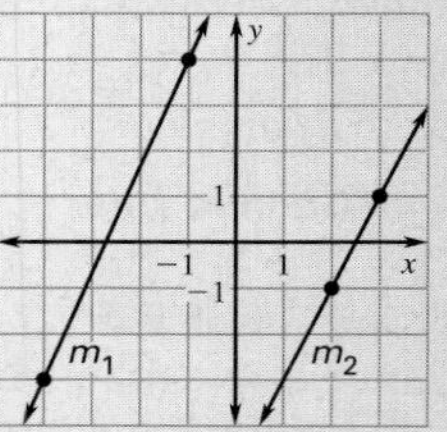

The slope of m_1 is $\frac{7}{3}$. The slope of m_2 is 2. The lines are not parallel.

Extra Example 4

Line p_1 passes through (0, –3) and (1, –2). Line p_2 passes through (5, 4) and (–4, –4). Line p_3 passes through (–6, –1) and (3, 7). Find the slope of each line. Which lines are parallel?
1, $\frac{8}{9}$, $\frac{8}{9}$; $p_2 \parallel p_3$

Checkpoint Exercises

For use after Examples 1–4:

1. Line k_1 passes through (8, –1) and (–5, –9). Line k_2 passes through (–6, –5) and (7, 3). Line k_3 passes through (10, –4) and (–3, –4). Find the slope of each line. Which lines are parallel?
$\frac{8}{13}$, $\frac{8}{13}$, 0; $k_1 \parallel k_2$

You can use the slopes of two lines to tell whether the lines are parallel.

POSTULATE

POSTULATE 17 ***Slopes of Parallel Lines***

In a coordinate plane, two nonvertical lines are parallel if and only if they have the same slope. Any two vertical lines are parallel.

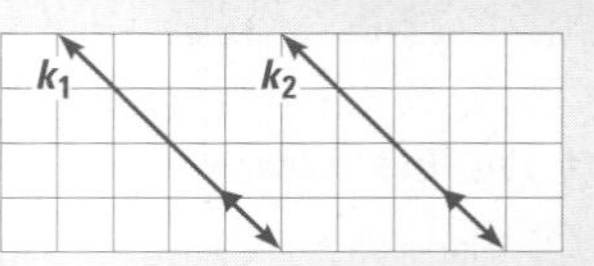

Lines k_1 and k_2 have the same slope.

STUDENT HELP

Study Tip
To find the slope in Example 3, you can either use the slope formula or you can count units on the graph.

EXAMPLE 3 *Deciding Whether Lines are Parallel*

Find the slope of each line. Is $j_1 \parallel j_2$?

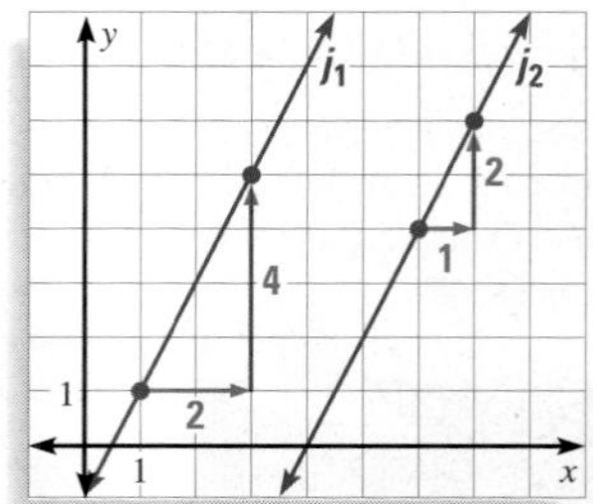

Solution

Line j_1 has a slope of

$$m_1 = \frac{4}{2} = 2$$

Line j_2 has a slope of

$$m_2 = \frac{2}{1} = 2$$

▶ Because the lines have the same slope, $j_1 \parallel j_2$.

Using Algebra

EXAMPLE 4 *Identifying Parallel Lines*

Find the slope of each line. Which lines are parallel?

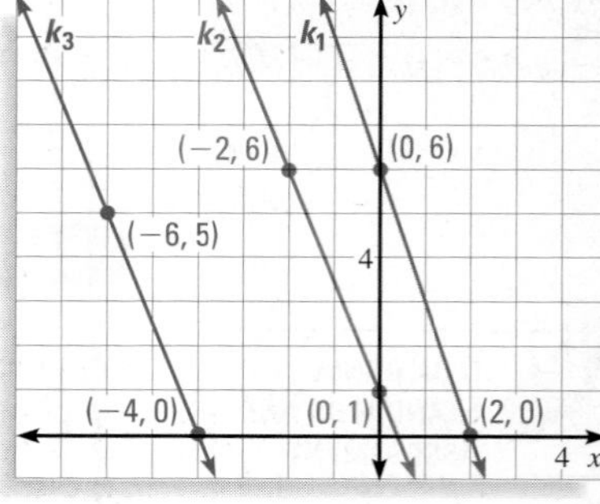

Solution

Find the slope of k_1. Line k_1 passes through (0, 6) and (2, 0).

$$m_1 = \frac{0-6}{2-0} = \frac{-6}{2} = -3$$

Find the slope of k_2. Line k_2 passes through $(-2, 6)$ and (0, 1).

$$m_2 = \frac{1-6}{0-(-2)} = \frac{-5}{0+2} = -\frac{5}{2}$$

Find the slope of k_3. Line k_3 passes through $(-6, 5)$ and $(-4, 0)$.

$$m_3 = \frac{0-5}{-4-(-6)} = \frac{-5}{-4+6} = -\frac{5}{2}$$

▶ Compare the slopes. Because k_2 and k_3 have the same slope, they are parallel. Line k_1 has a different slope, so it is not parallel to either of the other lines.

GOAL 2 WRITING EQUATIONS OF PARALLEL LINES

In algebra, you learned that you can use the slope m of a nonvertical line to write an equation of the line in *slope-intercept form.*

$$y = mx + b$$
(slope: m; y-intercept: b)

The y-intercept is the y-coordinate of the point where the line crosses the y-axis.

EXAMPLE 5 *Writing an Equation of a Line*

Using Algebra

Write an equation of the line through the point (2, 3) that has a slope of 5.

SOLUTION

Solve for b. Use $(x, y) = (2, 3)$ and $m = 5$.

$y = mx + b$	Slope-intercept form
$3 = 5(2) + b$	Substitute 2 for x, 3 for y, and 5 for m.
$3 = 10 + b$	Simplify.
$-7 = b$	Subtract.

▶ Write an equation. Since $m = 5$ and $b = -7$, an equation of the line is $y = 5x - 7$.

EXAMPLE 6 *Writing an Equation of a Parallel Line*

Line n_1 has the equation $y = -\frac{1}{3}x - 1$.
Line n_2 is parallel to n_1 and passes through the point (3, 2). Write an equation of n_2.

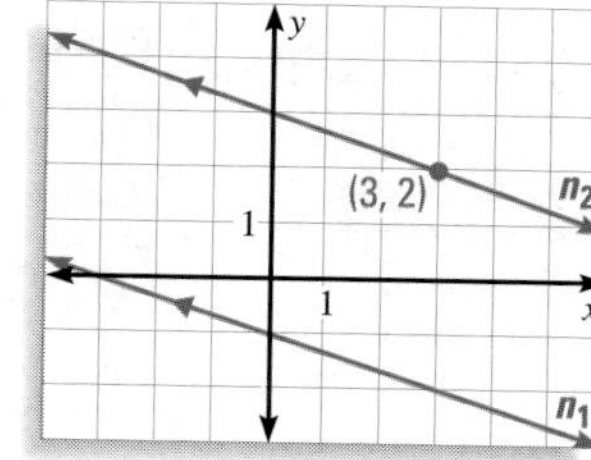

SOLUTION

Find the slope.

The slope of n_1 is $-\frac{1}{3}$. Because parallel lines have the same slope, the slope of n_2 is also $-\frac{1}{3}$.

Solve for b. Use $(x, y) = (3, 2)$ and $m = -\frac{1}{3}$.

$y = mx + b$

$2 = -\frac{1}{3}(3) + b$

$2 = -1 + b$

$3 = b$

Write an equation.

▶ Because $m = -\frac{1}{3}$ and $b = 3$, an equation of n_2 is $y = -\frac{1}{3}x + 3$.

STUDENT HELP

HOMEWORK HELP
Visit our Web site www.mcdougallittell.com for extra examples.

EXTRA EXAMPLE 5
Write an equation of the line through the point (4, 9) that has a slope of –2. $y = -2x + 17$

EXTRA EXAMPLE 6
Line k_1 has the equation $y = \frac{2}{5}x + 3$. Line k_2 is parallel to k_1 and passes through the point (–5, 0). Write an equation of k_2.
$y = \frac{2}{5}x + 2$

CHECKPOINT EXERCISES

For use after Example 5:

1. Write an equation of the line through the point (20, 5) that has a slope of $\frac{3}{10}$. $y = \frac{3}{10}x - 1$

For use after Example 6:

2. Line m_1 has the equation $y = 3x - 7$. Line m_2 is parallel to m_1 and passes through the point (–2, 1). Write an equation of m_2. $y = 3x + 7$

FOCUS ON VOCABULARY
What information is contained in the equation of a line written in slope-intercept form? the slope of the line and the y-intercept

CLOSURE QUESTION
If you know two points on line p and two points on line q how could you tell if $p \parallel q$? Find the slope of each line using the slope formula. If the slopes are equal, the lines are parallel.

DAILY PUZZLER
How can you make two parallel cuts through a square so that the square is divided into three parts with the ratio of their areas being 1:2:1? Neither of the cuts can be parallel to a side of the square.
One line connects the midpoint of the top of the square to the square's right lower vertex. The other line connects the square's upper left vertex with the midpoint of the bottom of the square.

3 APPLY

ASSIGNMENT GUIDE

BASIC
Day 1: pp. 168–171 Exs. 8–44 even, 45–48, 55, 56, 64–72 even

AVERAGE
Day 1: pp. 168–171 Exs. 8–22 even, 23, 24–44 even, 45–48, 55, 56, 64–72 even

ADVANCED
Day 1: pp. 168–171 Exs. 8–22 even, 23, 24–44 even, 45–52, 55–58, 64–72 even

BLOCK SCHEDULE WITH 3.7
pp. 168–171 Exs. 8–22 even, 23, 24–44 even, 45–48, 55, 56, 64–72 even

EXERCISE LEVELS

Level A: *Easier*
11–16

Level B: *More Difficult*
17–48, 53–56

Level C: *Most Difficult*
49–52, 57, 58

✔ HOMEWORK CHECK

To quickly check student understanding of key concepts, go over the following exercises: Exs. 12, 14, 16, 20, 24, 28, 34, 38, 42. See also the Daily Homework Quiz:

- Blackline Master (*Chapter 3 Resource Book,* p. 95)
- Transparency (p. 23)

GUIDED PRACTICE

Vocabulary Check ✔

1. What does *intercept* mean in the expression *slope-intercept form*? The y-coordinate of the point where the line crosses the y-axis.

Concept Check ✔

2. The slope of line j is 2 and $j \parallel k$. What is the slope of line k? 2

3. What is the slope of a horizontal line? What is the slope of a vertical line? 0; undefined or no slope

Skill Check ✔

Find the slope of the line that passes through the labeled points.

4. $\frac{4}{3}$

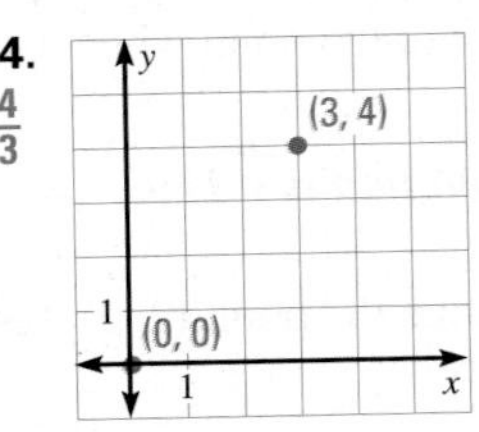

5. -2

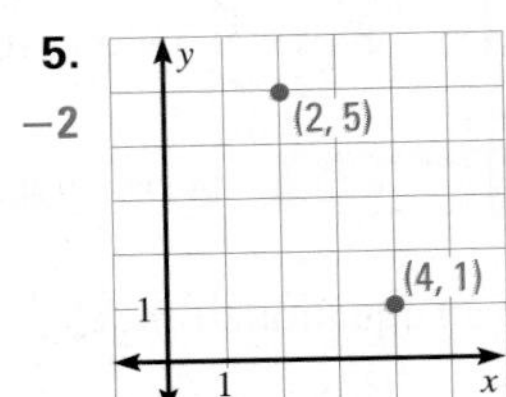

6. $\frac{5}{4}$

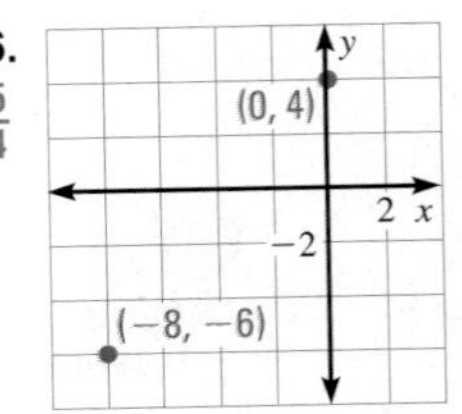

Determine whether the two lines shown in the graph are parallel. If they are parallel, explain how you know.

7. parallel; both have slope $\frac{1}{3}$

8. not parallel

9. parallel; both have slope $\frac{1}{2}$

7. 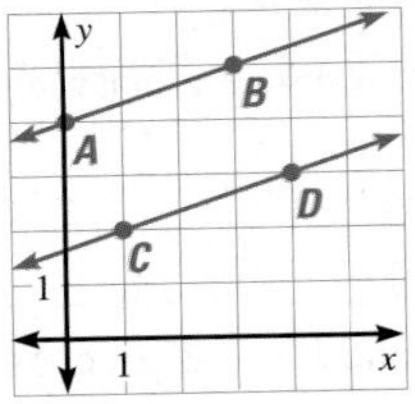
8.

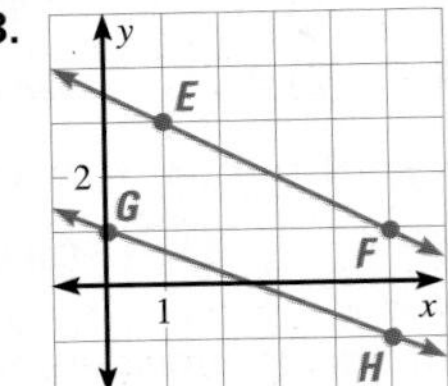

9.

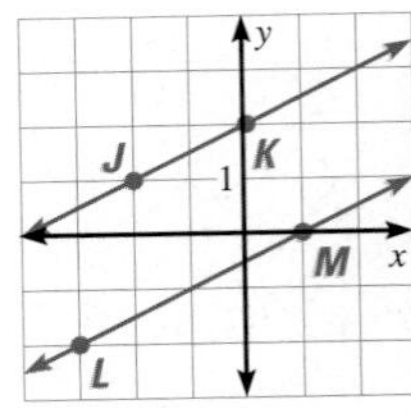

10. Write an equation of the line that passes through the point $(2, -3)$ and has a slope of -1. $y = -x - 1$

PRACTICE AND APPLICATIONS

STUDENT HELP
Extra Practice to help you master skills is on p. 808.

CALCULATING SLOPE **What is the slope of the line?**

11. $\frac{3}{2}$

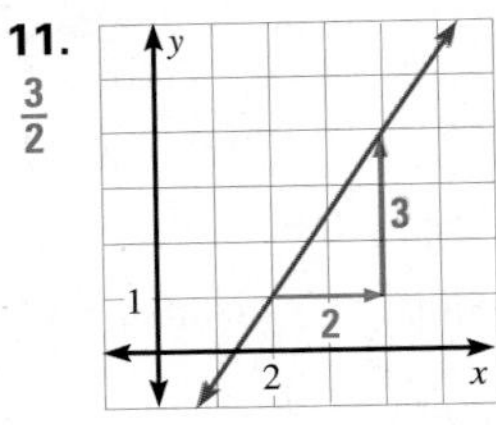

12. -1

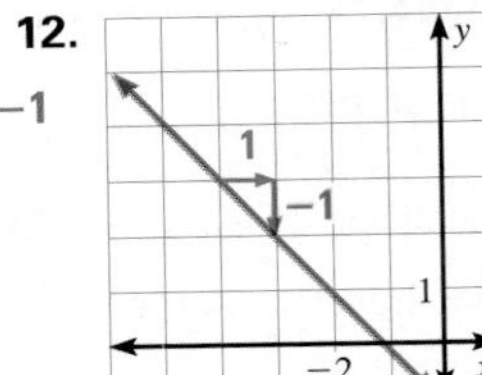

13. $\frac{1}{2}$

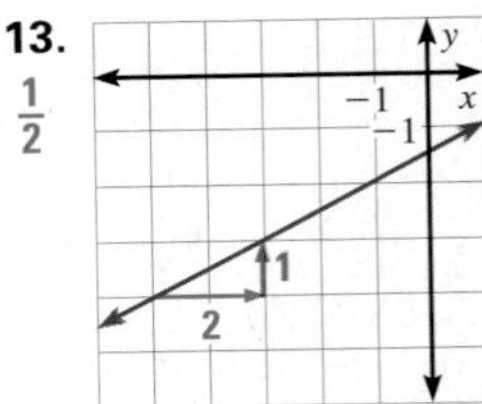

CALCULATING SLOPE **Find the slope of the line that passes through the labeled points on the graph.**

STUDENT HELP
HOMEWORK HELP
Example 1: Exs. 11–16, 23, 46, 49–52
Example 2: Exs. 11–16

14. 0

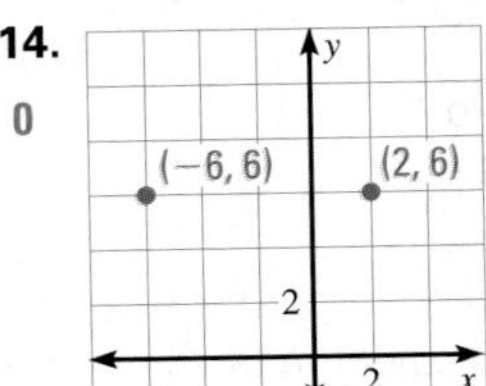

15. -1

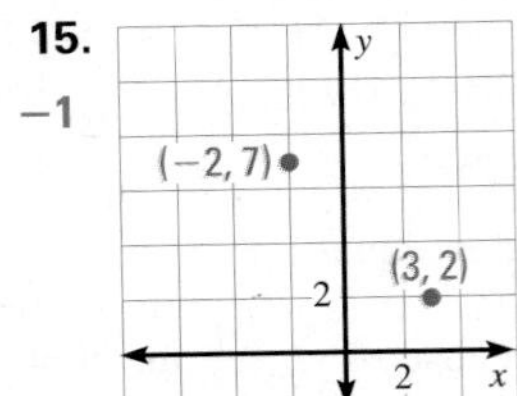

16. $\frac{16}{9}$

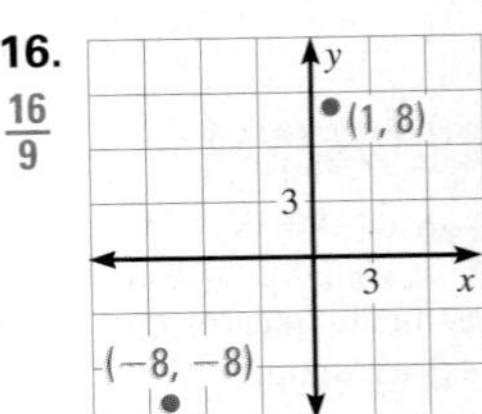

STUDENT HELP

HOMEWORK HELP
Example 3: Exs. 17–22
Example 4: Exs. 24–26, 47, 48
Example 5: Exs. 27–41
Example 6: Exs. 42–45

20. $\frac{1}{2}, \frac{1}{2}$; parallel

21. $\frac{5}{6}, \frac{5}{7}$; not parallel

22. $-\frac{3}{4}, -\frac{7}{8}$; not parallel

24. slope of $\overleftrightarrow{AB}$: $\frac{1}{2}$; slope of $\overleftrightarrow{CD}$: $\frac{1}{2}$; slope of $\overleftrightarrow{EF}$: -3; $\overleftrightarrow{AB} \parallel \overleftrightarrow{CD}$

25. slope of $\overleftrightarrow{AB}$: $\frac{1}{2}$; slope of $\overleftrightarrow{CD}$: $\frac{1}{2}$; slope of $\overleftrightarrow{EF}$: $\frac{3}{4}$; $\overleftrightarrow{AB} \parallel \overleftrightarrow{CD}$

26. slope of $\overleftrightarrow{AB}$: $\frac{3}{4}$; slope of $\overleftrightarrow{CD}$: -1; slope of $\overleftrightarrow{EF}$: -1; $\overleftrightarrow{CD} \parallel \overleftrightarrow{EF}$

IDENTIFYING PARALLELS Find the slope of each line. Are the lines parallel?

17.

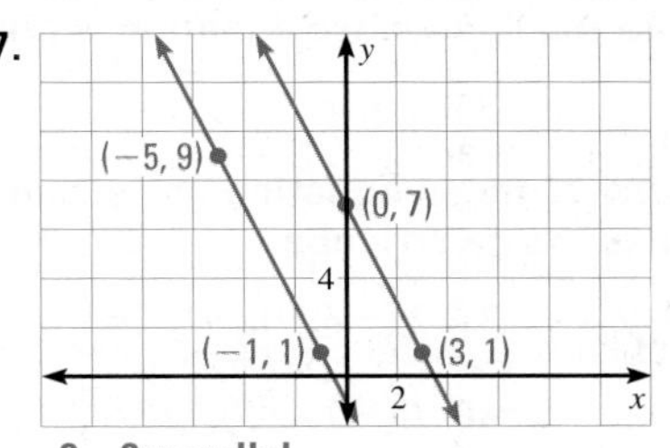

−2, −2; parallel

18.

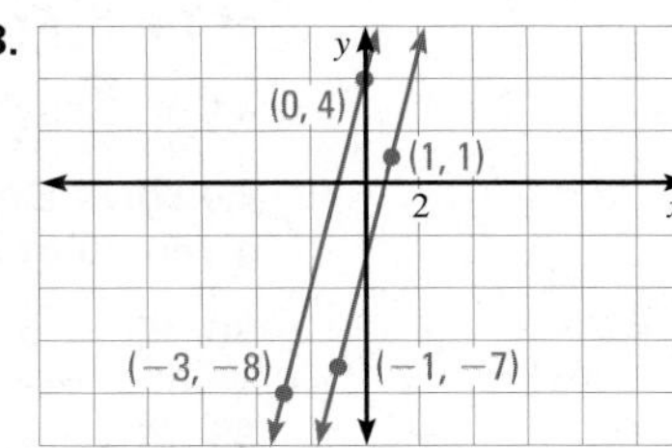

4, 4; parallel

19.

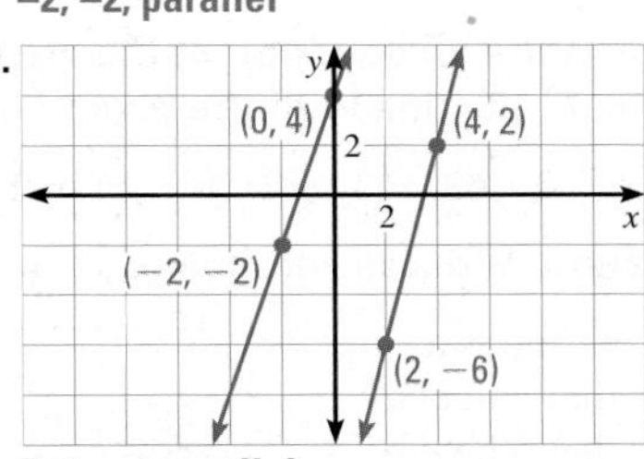

3, 4; not parallel

20.

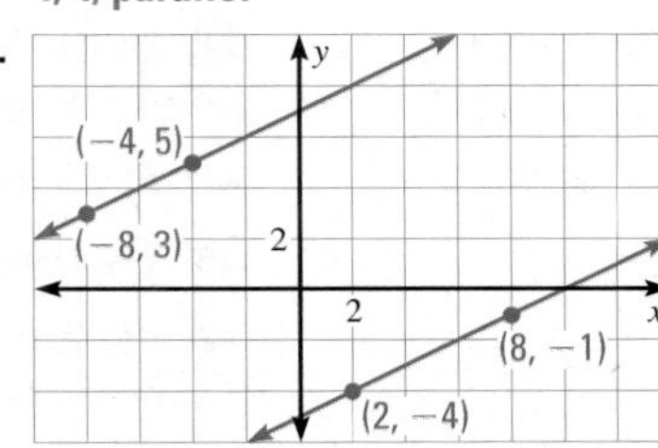

21.

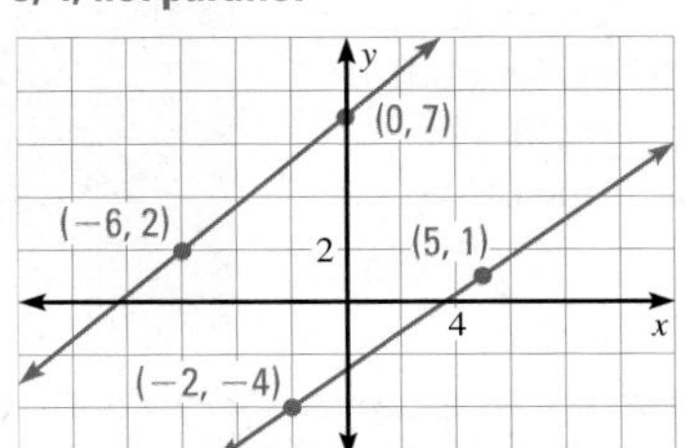

22.

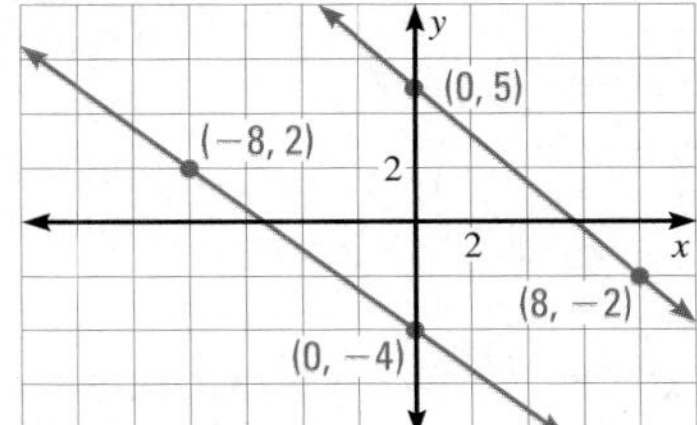

23. **UNDERGROUND RAILROAD** The photo at the right shows a monument in Oberlin, Ohio, that is dedicated to the Underground Railroad. The slope of each of the rails is about $-\frac{3}{5}$ and the sculpture is about 12 feet long. What is the height of the ends of the rails? Explain how you found your answer. **See margin.**

IDENTIFYING PARALLELS Find the slopes of $\overleftrightarrow{AB}$, $\overleftrightarrow{CD}$, and $\overleftrightarrow{EF}$. Which lines are parallel, if any? **24–26. See margin.**

24. $A(0, -6), B(4, -4)$
$C(0, 2), D(2, 3)$
$E(0, -4), F(1, -7)$

25. $A(2, 6), B(4, 7)$
$C(0, -1), D(6, 2)$
$E(4, -5), F(8, -2)$

26. $A(-4, 10), B(-8, 7)$
$C(-5, 7), D(-2, 4)$
$E(2, -3), F(6, -7)$

WRITING EQUATIONS Write an equation of the line.

27. slope $= 3$ **$y = 3x + 2$**
y-intercept $= 2$

28. slope $= \frac{1}{3}$ **$y = \frac{1}{3}x - 4$**
y-intercept $= -4$

29. slope $= -\frac{2}{9}$ **$y = -\frac{2}{9}x$**
y-intercept $= 0$

30. slope $= \frac{1}{2}$
y-intercept $= 6$
$y = \frac{1}{2}x + 6$

31. slope $= 0$
y-intercept $= -3$
$y = -3$

32. slope $= -\frac{2}{9}$
y-intercept $= -\frac{3}{5}$
$y = -\frac{2}{9}x - \frac{3}{5}$

FOCUS ON PEOPLE

UNDERGROUND RAILROAD is the name given to the network of people who helped some slaves to freedom. Harriet Tubman, a former slave, helped about 300 escape.

! COMMON ERROR

EXERCISES 14–16 Students calculating the slope by counting the units of rise and run may forget to consider the direction of the rise of the line. Tell them to count from one point to the other, assigning negative numbers to the count when they move down or left.

APPLICATION NOTE

EXERCISE 23 The Underground Railroad was, in fact, not underground. Rather than a physical entity whose slope could be measured, it was a loose network of volunteers who guided slaves to freedom. Their routes took them through swamps, along rivers, and across mountains to the northern states and Canada. The National Park Service, under a directive from Congress, has studied how to best interpret and commemorate the Underground Railroad. One of the suggestions was to construct a commemorative monument.

23. about 7.2 feet, *Sample answer:* Using x for the height, a proportion is $\frac{3}{5} = \frac{x}{12}$. Then $5x = 36$ and $x = 7.2$.

CAREER NOTE

EXERCISES 49–52 The warning signs posted by the U.S. Department of Transportation particularly benefit drivers of large trucks. In cases where long, steep grades end at busy intersections, runaway truck ramps can be constructed parallel to the road. A driver who expects difficulty at the bottom of the grade from mechanical failures, such as failed brakes, can exit the road and stop more safely on the runaway ramp. Additional information about civil engineering is available at **www.mcdougallittell.com.**

47.

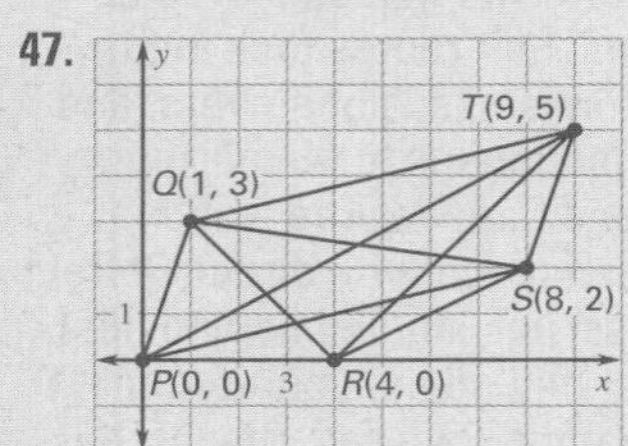

38. $y = \frac{1}{2}x + \frac{13}{4}$

40. $y = \frac{3}{4}x + \frac{1}{4}$

42. $y = -x + 3$

43. $y = \frac{5}{4}x - \frac{13}{4}$

44. $y = 7$

45. *Sample answer:* $y = \frac{1}{3}x$

48. $\overline{PQ} \parallel \overline{ST}$, $\overline{PS} \parallel \overline{QT}$. The slopes are: $\overline{PQ}$, 3; $\overline{PR}$, 0; $\overline{PT}$, $\frac{5}{9}$; $\overline{PS}$, $\frac{1}{4}$; $\overline{QR}$, −1; $\overline{QS}$, $-\frac{1}{7}$; $\overline{QT}$, $\frac{1}{4}$; $\overline{RS}$, $\frac{1}{2}$; $\overline{RT}$, 1; $\overline{ST}$, 3

ADDITIONAL PRACTICE AND RETEACHING

For Lesson 3.6:

- Practice Levels A, B, and C (*Chapter 3 Resource Book,* p. 85)
- Reteaching with Practice (*Chapter 3 Resource Book,* p. 88)
- See Lesson 3.6 of the *Personal Student Tutor*

For more Mixed Review:

- Search the *Test and Practice Generator* for key words or specific lessons.

WRITING EQUATIONS Write an equation of the line that has a *y*-intercept of 3 and is parallel to the line whose equation is given.

33. $y = -6x + 2$ $y = -6x + 3$ **34.** $y = x - 8$ $y = x + 3$ **35.** $y = -\frac{4}{3}x$ $y = -\frac{4}{3}x + 3$

WRITING EQUATIONS Write an equation of the line that passes through the given point *P* and has the given slope.

36. $P(0, -6), m = -2$ $y = -2x - 6$ **37.** $P(-3, 9), m = -1$ $y = -x + 6$ **38.** $P\left(\frac{3}{2}, 4\right), m = \frac{1}{2}$

39. $P(2, -4), m = 0$ $y = -4$ **40.** $P(-7, -5), m = \frac{3}{4}$ **41.** $P(6, 1)$, undefined slope $x = 6$

USING ALGEBRA Write an equation of the line that passes through point *P* and is parallel to the line with the given equation.

42. $P(-3, 6), y = -x - 5$ **43.** $P(1, -2), y = \frac{5}{4}x - 8$ **44.** $P(8, 7), y = 3$

45. **USING ALGEBRA** Write an equation of a line parallel to $y = \frac{1}{3}x - 16$.

46. **ZIP LINE** A zip line is a taut rope or cable that you can ride down on a pulley. The zip line at the right goes from a 9 foot tall tower to a 6 foot tall tower. The towers are 20 feet apart. What is the slope of the zip line? $-\frac{3}{20}$

COORDINATE GEOMETRY In Exercises 47 and 48, use the five points: ***P*(0, 0), *Q*(1, 3), *R*(4, 0), *S*(8, 2), and *T*(9, 5).** 47, 48. See margin.

47. Plot and label the points. Connect every pair of points with a segment.

48. Which segments are parallel? How can you verify this?

FOCUS ON CAREERS

CIVIL ENGINEERING

Civil engineers design and supervise the construction of roads, buildings, tunnels, bridges, and water supply systems.

CAREER LINK
www.mcdougallittell.com

CIVIL ENGINEERING In Exercises 49–52, use the following information. The slope of a road is called the road's *grade*. Grades are measured in percents. For example, if the slope of a road is $\frac{1}{20}$, the grade is 5%. A warning sign is needed before any hill that fits one of the following descriptions.

5% grade and more than 3000 feet long
6% grade and more than 2000 feet long
7% grade and more than 1000 feet long
8% grade and more than 750 feet long
9% grade and more than 500 feet long

▶ Source: U.S. Department of Transportation

What is the grade of the hill to the nearest percent? Is a sign needed?

49. The hill is 1400 feet long and drops 70 feet. 5%; no

50. The hill is 2200 feet long and drops 140 feet. 6%; yes

51. The hill is 600 feet long and drops 55 feet. 9%; yes

52. The hill is 450 feet long and drops 40 feet. 9%; no.

 **TECHNOLOGY Using a square viewing screen on a graphing calculator, graph a line that passes through the origin and has a slope of 1.**

53. Write an equation of the line you graphed. Approximately what angle does the line form with the x-axis? $y = x$; 45°

54. Graph a line that passes through the origin and has a slope of 2. Write an equation of the line. When you doubled the slope, did the measure of the angle formed with the x-axis double? $y = 2x$; no (The angle is about 63°.)

Test Preparation 

55. MULTIPLE CHOICE If two different lines with equations $y = m_1x + b_1$ and $y = m_2x + b_2$ are parallel, which of the following must be true? C

(A) $b_1 = b_2$ and $m_1 \neq m_2$ (B) $b_1 \neq b_2$ and $m_1 \neq m_2$

(C) $b_1 \neq b_2$ and $m_1 = m_2$ (D) $b_1 = b_2$ and $m_1 = m_2$

(E) None of these

56. MULTIPLE CHOICE Which of the following is an equation of a line parallel to $y - 4 = -\frac{1}{2}x$? E

(A) $y = \frac{1}{2}x - 6$ (B) $y = 2x + 1$ (C) $y = -2x + 3$

(D) $y = \frac{7}{2}x - 1$ (E) $y = -\frac{1}{2}x - 8$

★ Challenge

57. USING ALGEBRA Find a value for k so that the line through $(4, k)$ and $(-2, -1)$ is parallel to $y = -2x + \frac{3}{2}$. −13

58. USING ALGEBRA Find a value for k so that the line through $(k, -10)$ and $(5, -6)$ is parallel to $y = -\frac{1}{4}x + 3$. 21

MIXED REVIEW

RECIPROCALS Find the reciprocal of the number. (Skills Review, p. 788)

59. 20 $\frac{1}{20}$ **60.** −3 $-\frac{1}{3}$ **61.** −11 $-\frac{1}{11}$ **62.** 340 $\frac{1}{340}$

63. $\frac{3}{7}$ $\frac{7}{3}$ **64.** $-\frac{13}{3}$ $-\frac{3}{13}$ **65.** $-\frac{1}{2}$ −2 **66.** 0.25 4

MULTIPLYING NUMBERS Evaluate the expression. (Skills Review, p. 785)

67. $\frac{3}{4} \cdot (-12)$ −9 **68.** $-\frac{3}{2} \cdot \left(-\frac{8}{3}\right)$ 4 **69.** $-10 \cdot \frac{7}{6}$ $-11\frac{2}{3}$ **70.** $-\frac{2}{9} \cdot (-33)$ $7\frac{1}{3}$

PROVING LINES PARALLEL Can you prove that lines m and n are parallel? If so, state the postulate or theorem you would use. (Review 3.4)

71.

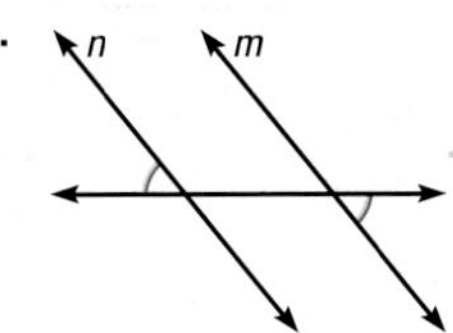

72.

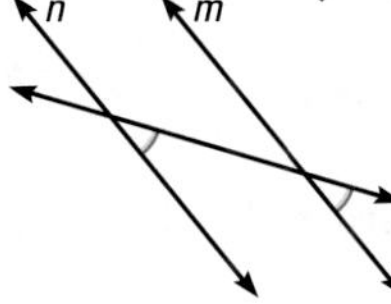

73.

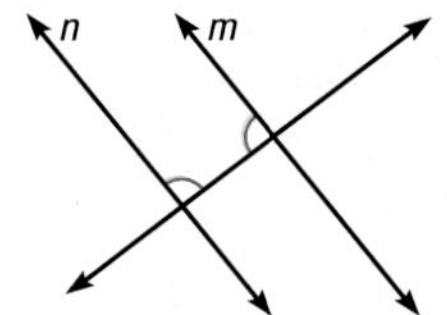

71. yes; Alternate Exterior Angles Converse

72. yes; Corresponding Angles Converse

73. no

4 ASSESS

DAILY HOMEWORK QUIZ

Transparency Available

1. What is the slope of the line that passes through the points (3, 4) and (−2, 6)? $-\frac{2}{5}$

2. Find the slope of each line. Are the lines parallel?

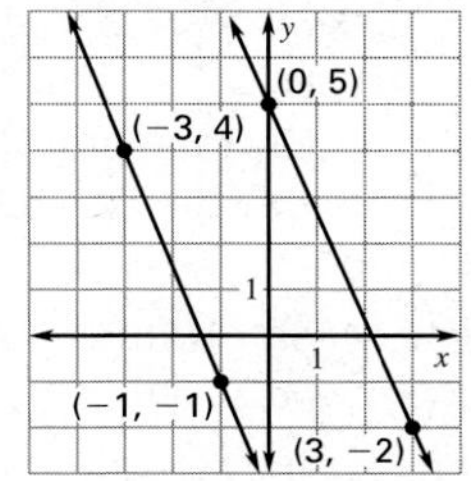

$-\frac{5}{2}, -\frac{7}{3}$; not parallel

3. Write an equation of the line whose slope is 2 and whose y-intercept is −1. $y = 2x - 1$

EXTRA CHALLENGE NOTE

Challenge problems for Lesson 3.6 are available in **blackline** format in the *Chapter 3 Resource Book,* p. 92 and at **www.mcdougallittell.com.**

ADDITIONAL TEST PREPARATION

1. WRITING Name five methods to prove two lines are parallel. Show that a pair of alternate interior angles, alternate exterior angles, or corresponding angles formed when a transversal cuts the lines is equal. Show that a pair of same-side interior angles formed when the lines are cut by a transversal is supplementary. Show that the lines are perpendicular to the same line. Show that the lines have the same slope but different y-intercepts.

2. OPEN ENDED Give the equations of two parallel lines. Any equations of the form $y = ax + b_1$ and $y = ax + b_2$, where $b_1 \neq b_2$ are parallel.

1 PLAN

PACING
Basic: 2 days
Average: 2 days
Advanced: 2 days
Block Schedule: 0.5 block with 3.6
0.5 block with Ch. Rev.

LESSON OPENER ACTIVITY

An alternative way to approach Lesson 3.7 is to use the Activity Lesson Opener:

- Blackline Master (*Chapter 3 Resource Book,* p. 96)
- Transparency (p. 20)

MEETING INDIVIDUAL NEEDS

- ***Chapter 3 Resource Book***
  Prerequisite Skills Review (p. 5)
  Practice Level A (p. 100)
  Practice Level B (p. 101)
  Practice Level C (p. 102)
  Reteaching with Practice (p. 103)
  Absent Student Catch-Up (p. 105)
  Challenge (p. 108)
- ***Resources in Spanish***
- ***Personal Student Tutor***

NEW-TEACHER SUPPORT

See the Tips for New Teachers on pp. 1–2 of the *Chapter 3 Resource Book* for additional notes about Lesson 3.7.

WARM-UP EXERCISES

Transparency Available

1. Line m is perpendicular to line n. If line m has a positive slope, what kind of slope does line n have? **a negative slope**
2. Find the slope of the line that passes through (5, 6) and (–9, 0). $\frac{3}{7}$
3. Write an equation of the line that passes through (3, –1) and (3, 5). $x = 3$
4. Write an equation of the line that has slope 4 and y-intercept 10. $y = 4x + 10$

3.7 Perpendicular Lines in the Coordinate Plane

What you should learn

GOAL 1 Use slope to identify perpendicular lines in a coordinate plane.

GOAL 2 Write equations of perpendicular lines, as applied in **Ex. 46**.

Why you should learn it

▼ Equations of perpendicular lines are used by ray tracing software to create realistic reflections, as in the illustration below and in **Example 6**.

CALIFORNIA STANDARDS AND ASSESSMENT

CA Standards: 17
SAT9 Task 2: Obj. 28

GOAL 1 SLOPE OF PERPENDICULAR LINES

In the activity below, you will trace a piece of paper to draw perpendicular lines on a coordinate grid. Points where grid lines cross are called *lattice points.*

ACTIVITY — Developing Concepts

Investigating Slopes of Perpendicular Lines

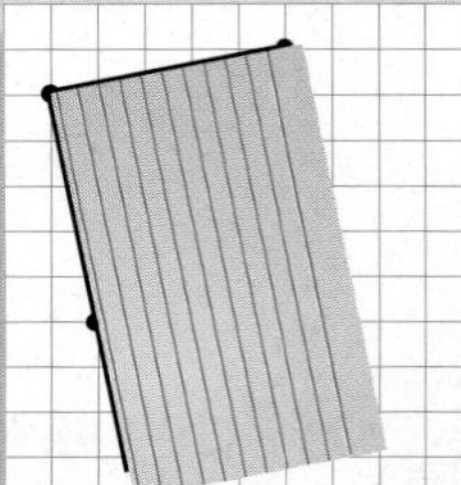

1. Put the corner of a piece of paper on a lattice point. Rotate the corner so each edge passes through another lattice point but neither edge is vertical. Trace the edges.
2. Find the slope of each line.
3. Multiply the slopes.
4. Repeat Steps 1–3 with the paper at a different angle.

In the activity, you may have discovered the following.

POSTULATE

POSTULATE 18 ***Slopes of Perpendicular Lines***

In a coordinate plane, two nonvertical lines are perpendicular if and only if the product of their slopes is –1.

Vertical and horizontal lines are perpendicular.

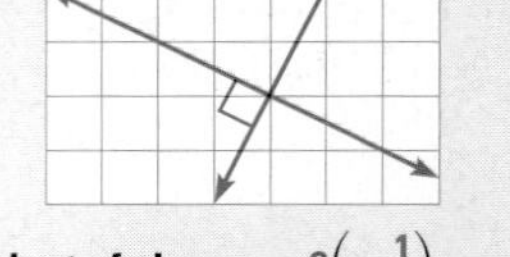

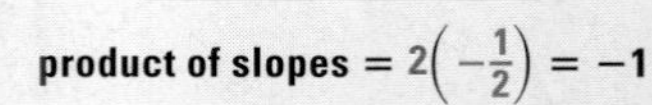

product of slopes $= 2\left(-\frac{1}{2}\right) = -1$

EXAMPLE 1 ***Deciding Whether Lines are Perpendicular***

Find each slope.

$$\text{Slope of } j_1 = \frac{3-1}{0-3} = -\frac{2}{3}$$

$$\text{Slope of } j_2 = \frac{3-(-3)}{0-(-4)} = \frac{6}{4} = \frac{3}{2}$$

Multiply the slopes.

The product is $\left(-\frac{2}{3}\right)\left(\frac{3}{2}\right) = -1$, so $j_1 \perp j_2$.

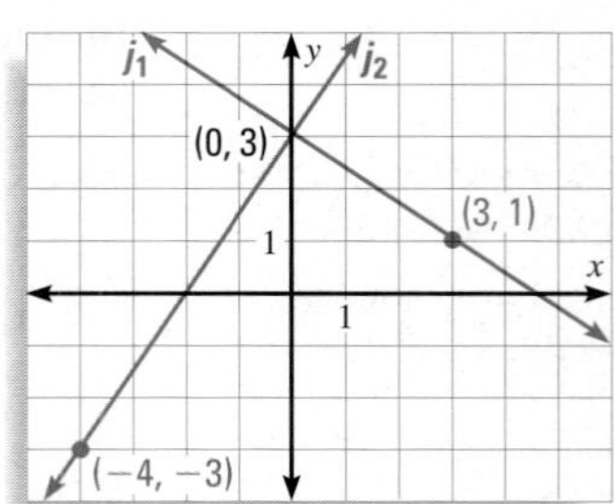

Logical Reasoning

EXAMPLE 2 Deciding Whether Lines are Perpendicular

Decide whether $\overleftrightarrow{AC}$ and $\overleftrightarrow{DB}$ are perpendicular.

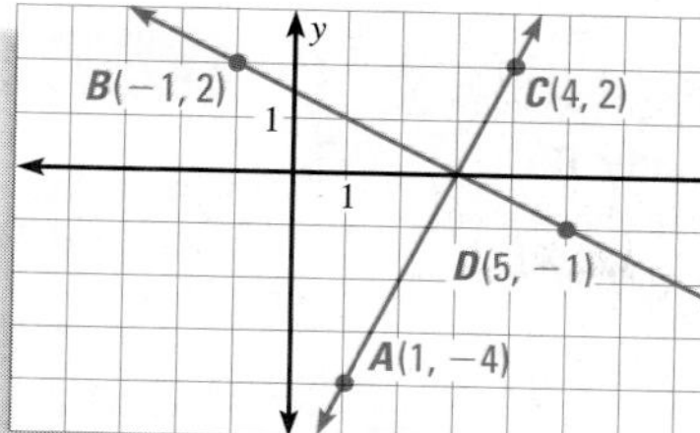

SOLUTION

$$\text{Slope of } \overleftrightarrow{AC} = \frac{2-(-4)}{4-1} = \frac{6}{3} = 2$$

$$\text{Slope of } \overleftrightarrow{DB} = \frac{2-(-1)}{-1-5} = \frac{3}{-6} = -\frac{1}{2}$$

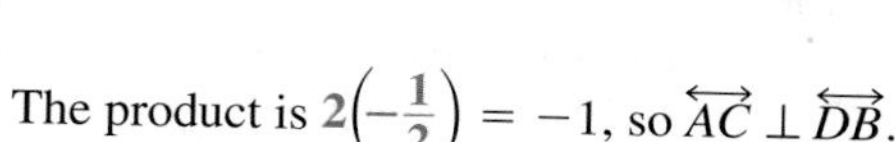

The product is $2\left(-\frac{1}{2}\right) = -1$, so $\overleftrightarrow{AC} \perp \overleftrightarrow{DB}$.

EXAMPLE 3 Deciding Whether Lines are Perpendicular

Decide whether the lines are perpendicular.

line h: $y = \frac{3}{4}x + 2$ **line j:** $y = -\frac{4}{3}x - 3$

SOLUTION

The slope of line h is $\frac{3}{4}$. The slope of line j is $-\frac{4}{3}$.

The product is $\left(\frac{3}{4}\right)\left(-\frac{4}{3}\right) = -1$, so the lines are perpendicular.

Using Algebra

EXAMPLE 4 Deciding Whether Lines are Perpendicular

Decide whether the lines are perpendicular.

line r: $4x + 5y = 2$ **line s:** $5x + 4y = 3$

SOLUTION

Rewrite each equation in slope-intercept form to find the slope.

line r:

$$4x + 5y = 2$$
$$5y = -4x + 2$$
$$y = -\frac{4}{5}x + \frac{2}{5}$$
$$\text{slope} = -\frac{4}{5}$$

line s:

$$5x + 4y = 3$$
$$4y = -5x + 3$$
$$y = -\frac{5}{4}x + \frac{3}{4}$$
$$\text{slope} = -\frac{5}{4}$$

Multiply the slopes to see if the lines are perpendicular.

$$\left(-\frac{4}{5}\right)\left(-\frac{5}{4}\right) = 1$$

▶ The product of the slopes is *not* -1. So, r and s are *not* perpendicular.

2 TEACH

EXTRA EXAMPLE 1

Find each slope. Then find the product of the slopes.

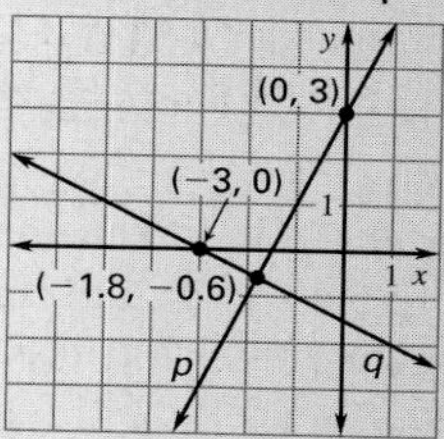

p: 2, q: $-\frac{1}{2}$; -1, $p \perp q$

EXTRA EXAMPLE 2

Decide whether $\overleftrightarrow{PQ}$ and $\overleftrightarrow{RS}$ are perpendicular.

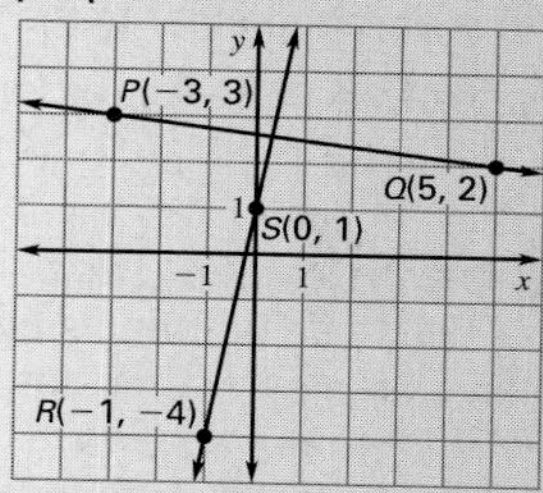

No.

EXTRA EXAMPLE 3

Decide whether the lines are perpendicular. line a: $y = -\frac{2}{3}x - 1$ line b: $y = -\frac{3}{2}x + 1$ **No.**

EXTRA EXAMPLE 4

Decide whether the lines are perpendicular. line e: $-2x + 7y = -4$ line f: $7x + 2y = 10$ **Yes.**

CHECKPOINT EXERCISES

For use after Examples 1 and 2:

1. Line r goes through $(-2, 2)$ and $(5, 8)$. Line s goes through $(-8, 7)$ and $(-2, 0)$. Is $r \perp s$? **Yes.**

For use after Examples 3 and 4:

2. An equation for line v is $y = -\frac{3}{8}x + \frac{5}{8}$. An equation for line w is $8x + 3y = 10$. Is $v \perp w$? **No.**

Extra Example 5

Line g has equation $y = 3x - 2$. Find the equation of the line h that passes through (3, 4) and is perpendicular to g. $y = -\frac{1}{3}x + 5$

Extra Example 6

The equation $y = \frac{5}{3}x - 4$ represents a mirror. A ray of light hits the mirror at (3, 1). What is the equation of the line, p, that is perpendicular to the mirror at this point? $y = -\frac{3}{5}x + \frac{14}{5}$

Checkpoint Exercises

For use after Examples 5 and 6:

1. Find an equation of the line that passes through $Q(-2, 0)$ and is perpendicular to the graph of $y = -2x + 4$. $y = \frac{1}{2}x + 1$

Focus on Vocabulary

Postulate 18 can be written using two if-then statements. One statement is *In a coordinate plane, if two vertical lines are perpendicular, then the product of their slopes is −1.* What is the other statement? In a coordinate plane, if the product of the slopes of two lines is −1, then the lines are perpendicular.

Closure Question

The slope of one of two perpendicular lines is $\frac{a}{b}$. What is the slope of the other line? $-\frac{b}{a}$

Daily Puzzler

You are building three houses. On a map, the coordinates of the three houses are $A(2, 5)$, $B(2, 1)$, and $C(6, 1)$. If the houses will share a well, what are the coordinates of the point where the well should be located to minimize the amount of pipe needed between the houses and the well? (4, 3)

GOAL 2 Writing Equations of Perpendicular Lines

STUDENT HELP

Study Tip

You can check m_2 by multiplying $m_1 \cdot m_2$.

$(-2)\left(\frac{1}{2}\right) = -1$ ✓

EXAMPLE 5 *Writing the Equation of a Perpendicular Line*

Line ℓ_1 has equation $y = -2x + 1$. Find an equation of the line ℓ_2 that passes through $P(4, 0)$ and is perpendicular to ℓ_1. First you must find the slope, m_2.

$m_1 \cdot m_2 = -1$ — The product of the slopes of ⊥ lines is −1.

$-2 \cdot m_2 = -1$ — The slope of ℓ_1 is −2.

$m_2 = \frac{1}{2}$ — Divide both sides by −2.

Then use $m = \frac{1}{2}$ and $(x, y) = (4, 0)$ to find b.

$y = mx + b$ — Slope-intercept form

$0 = \frac{1}{2}(4) + b$ — Substitute 0 for y, $\frac{1}{2}$ for m, and 4 for x.

$-2 = b$ — Simplify.

▶ So, an equation of ℓ_2 is $y = \frac{1}{2}x - 2$.

RAY TRACING Computer illustrators use *ray tracing* to make accurate reflections. To figure out what to show in the mirror, the computer traces a ray of light as it reflects off the mirror. This calculation has many steps. One of the first steps is to find the equation of a line perpendicular to the mirror.

EXAMPLE 6 *Writing the Equation of a Perpendicular Line*

The equation $y = \frac{3}{2}x + 3$ represents a mirror. A ray of light hits the mirror at $(-2, 0)$. What is the equation of the line p that is perpendicular to the mirror at this point?

SOLUTION

The mirror's slope is $\frac{3}{2}$, so the slope of p is $-\frac{2}{3}$.

Use $m = -\frac{2}{3}$ and $(x, y) = (-2, 0)$ to find b.

$$0 = -\frac{2}{3}(-2) + b$$

$$-\frac{4}{3} = b$$

▶ So, an equation for p is $y = -\frac{2}{3}x - \frac{4}{3}$.

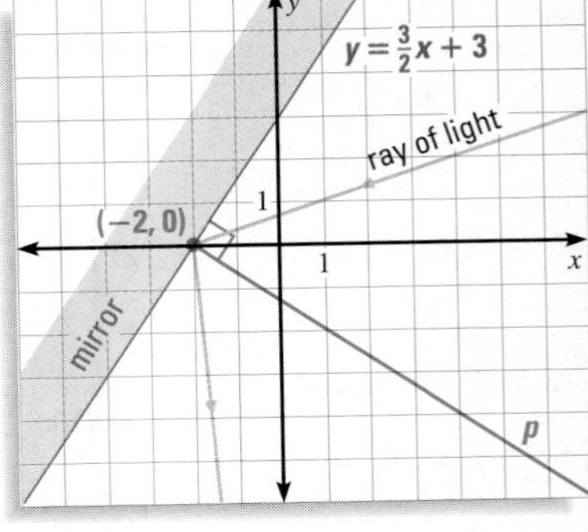

Top view of mirror

FOCUS ON CAREERS

GRAPHIC ARTS Many graphic artists use computer software to design images.

CAREER LINK www.mcdougallittell.com

GUIDED PRACTICE

Vocabulary Check ✓

Concept Check ✓

Skill Check ✓

1. Define *slope of a line.* $\frac{\text{rise}}{\text{run}}$

2. The slope of line m is $-\frac{1}{5}$. What is the slope of a line perpendicular to m? 5

3. In the coordinate plane shown at the right, is $\overleftrightarrow{AC}$ perpendicular to $\overleftrightarrow{BD}$? Explain.

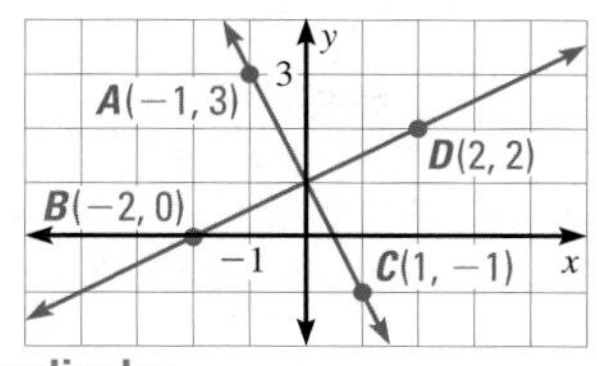

4. Decide whether the lines with the equations $y = 2x - 1$ and $y = -2x + 1$ are perpendicular. not perpendicular

5. Decide whether the lines with the equations $5y - x = 15$ and $y + 5x = 2$ are perpendicular. perpendicular

6. The line ℓ_1 has the equation $y = 3x$. The line ℓ_2 is perpendicular to ℓ_1 and passes through the point $P(0, 0)$. Write an equation of ℓ_2. $y = -\frac{1}{3}x$

3. yes. *Sample answer:* the slope of $\overleftrightarrow{AC}$ is −2, and the slope of $\overleftrightarrow{BD}$ is $\frac{1}{2}$, and $(-2)\left(\frac{1}{2}\right) = -1$.

PRACTICE AND APPLICATIONS

STUDENT HELP

Extra Practice to help you master skills is on p. 808.

SLOPES OF PERPENDICULAR LINES The slopes of two lines are given. Are the lines perpendicular?

7. $m_1 = 2, m_2 = -\frac{1}{2}$ yes

8. $m_1 = \frac{2}{3}, m_2 = \frac{3}{2}$ no

9. $m_1 = \frac{1}{4}, m_2 = -4$ yes

10. $m_1 = \frac{5}{7}, m_2 = -\frac{7}{5}$ yes

11. $m_1 = -\frac{1}{2}, m_2 = -\frac{1}{2}$ no

12. $m_1 = -1, m_2 = 1$ yes

SLOPES OF PERPENDICULAR LINES Lines *j* and *n* are perpendicular. The slope of line *j* is given. What is the slope of line *n*? Check your answer.

13. 2 $-\frac{1}{2}$

14. 5 $-\frac{1}{5}$

15. −3 $\frac{1}{3}$

16. −7 $\frac{1}{7}$

17. $\frac{2}{3}$ $-\frac{3}{2}$

18. $\frac{1}{5}$ −5

19. $-\frac{1}{3}$ 3

20. $-\frac{4}{3}$ $\frac{3}{4}$

IDENTIFYING PERPENDICULAR LINES Find the slope of $\overleftrightarrow{AC}$ and $\overleftrightarrow{BD}$. Decide whether $\overleftrightarrow{AC}$ is perpendicular to $\overleftrightarrow{BD}$. 21–24. See margin.

21.

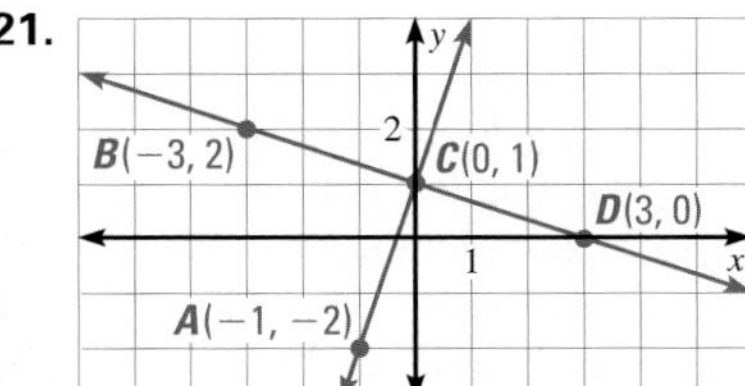

22.

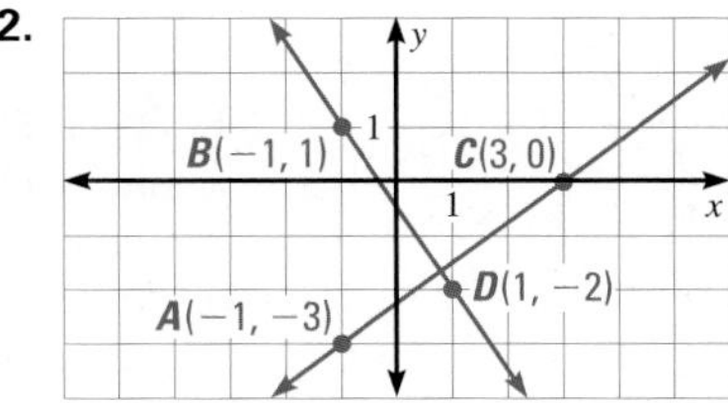

23.

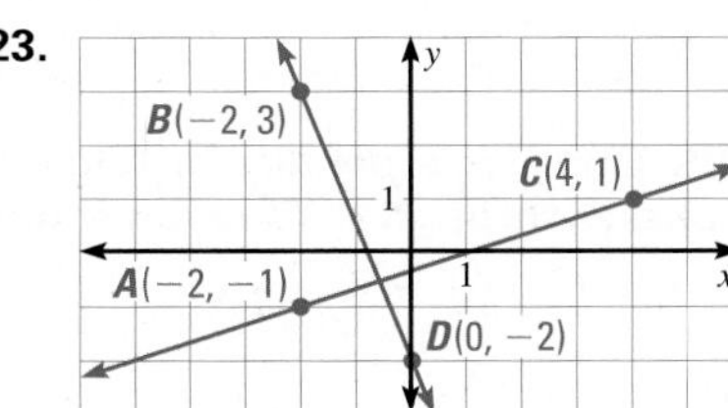

24.

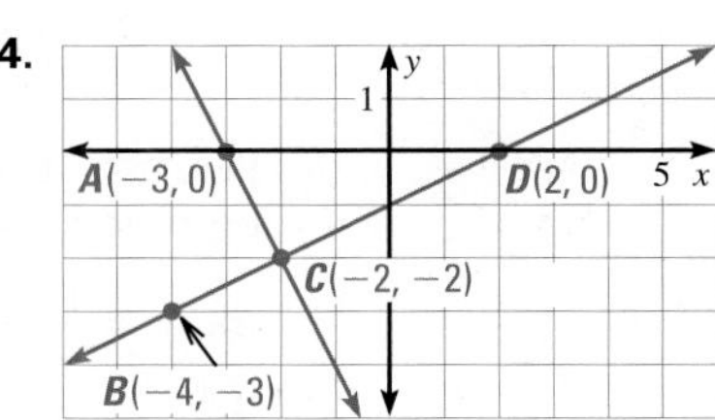

21. slope of $\overleftrightarrow{AC}$: 3; slope of $\overleftrightarrow{BD}$: $-\frac{1}{3}$; perpendicular

22. slope of $\overleftrightarrow{AC}$: $\frac{3}{4}$; slope of $\overleftrightarrow{BD}$: $-\frac{3}{2}$; not perpendicular

23. slope of $\overleftrightarrow{AC}$: $\frac{1}{3}$; slope of $\overleftrightarrow{BD}$: $-\frac{5}{2}$; not perpendicular

24. slope of $\overleftrightarrow{AC}$: −2; slope of $\overleftrightarrow{BD}$: $\frac{1}{2}$; perpendicular

STUDENT HELP

HOMEWORK HELP

Example 1: Exs. 7–20
Example 2: Exs. 21–24, 33–37
Example 3: Exs. 25–28, 47–50
Example 4: Exs. 29–32
Example 5: Exs. 38–41
Example 6: Exs. 42–46

3 APPLY

ASSIGNMENT GUIDE

BASIC

Day 1: pp. 175–178 Exs. 8–50 even, 51, 56–62 even

Day 2: pp. 175–178 Exs. 7–49 odd, 55–63 odd, Quiz 3 Exs. 1–7

AVERAGE

Day 1: pp. 175–178 Exs. 8–50 even, 51, 56–62 even

Day 2: pp. 175–178 Exs. 7–49 odd, 55–63 odd, Quiz 3 Exs. 1–7

ADVANCED

Day 1: pp. 175–178 Exs. 8–50 even, 51, 56–62 even

Day 2: pp. 175–178 Exs. 7–49 odd, 52–54, 55–63 odd, Quiz 3 Exs. 1–7

BLOCK SCHEDULE

pp. 175–178 Exs. 8–50 even 51, 56–62 even (with 3.6)
pp. 175–178 Exs. 7–49 odd, 55–63 odd, Quiz 3 Exs. 1–7 (with Ch. Rev.)

EXERCISE LEVELS

Level A: ***Easier***
7–20

Level B: ***More Difficult***
21–45, 47–51

Level C: ***Most Difficult***
46, 52–54

✓ HOMEWORK CHECK

To quickly check student understanding of key concepts, go over the following exercises: Exs. 8, 16, 22, 26, 30, 34, 38, 44, 46, 48. See also the Daily Homework Quiz:

- Blackline Master (*Chapter 4 Resource Book,* p. 11)
- Transparency (p. 25)

! COMMON ERROR

EXERCISES 29–32 Caution students who quickly make a determination of perpendicularity by examining the coefficients of *x* and *y*. Remind them to consider the signs of the coefficients. The slopes of two perpendicular lines are negative reciprocals of each other.

STUDENT HELP NOTES

Homework Help Students can find help for Exs. 33–36 at **www.mcdougallittell.com.** The information can be printed out for students who don't have access to the Internet.

APPLICATION NOTE

EXERCISE 37 Student should notice that the rise and run interchanged, and the lines go in opposite directions. Thus, showing that one line goes up 8 and right 4 while the other goes up 4 and left 8 also demonstrates that the lines are perpendicular.

USING ALGEBRA Decide whether lines k_1 and k_2 are perpendicular. Then graph the lines to check your answer.

25. line k_1: $y = 3x$ perpendicular
line k_2: $y = -\frac{1}{3}x - 2$

26. line k_1: $y = -\frac{4}{5}x - 2$ not perpendicular
line k_2: $y = \frac{1}{5}x + 4$

27. line k_1: $y = -\frac{3}{4}x + 2$ perpendicular
line k_2: $y = \frac{4}{3}x + 5$

28. line k_1: $y = \frac{1}{3}x - 10$ not perpendicular
line k_2: $y = 3x$

USING ALGEBRA Decide whether lines p_1 and p_2 are perpendicular.

29. line p_1: $3y - 4x = 3$ perpendicular
line p_2: $4y + 3x = -12$

30. line p_1: $y - 6x = 2$ not perpendicular
line p_2: $6y - x = 12$

31. line p_1: $3y + 2x = -36$
line p_2: $4y - 3x = 16$ not perpendicular

32. line p_1: $5y + 3x = -15$ perpendicular
line p_2: $3y - 5x = -33$

LINE RELATIONSHIPS Find the slope of each line. Identify any parallel or perpendicular lines.

33.

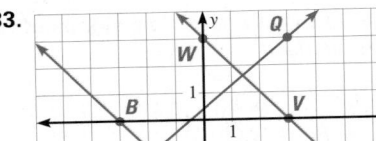

34.

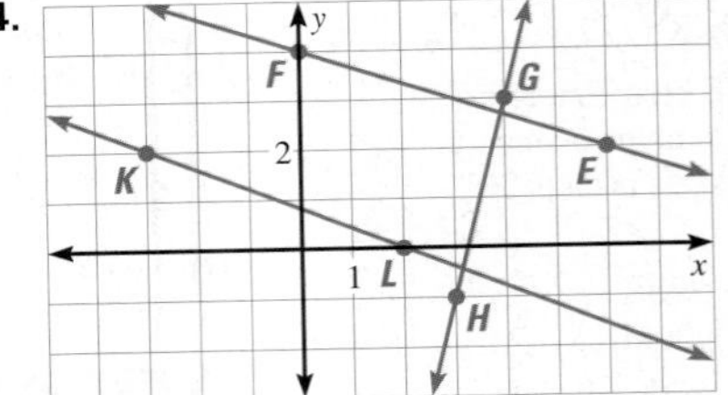

35.

36.

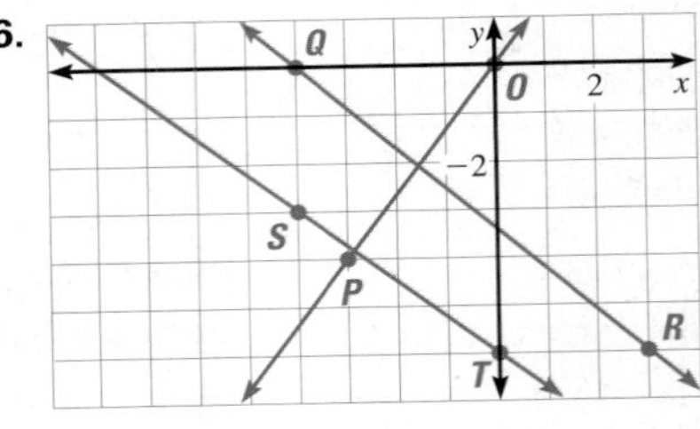

STUDENT HELP

HOMEWORK HELP Visit our Web site www.mcdougallittell.com for help with Exs. 33–36.

33. slope of $\overleftrightarrow{AB}$: -1; slope of $\overleftrightarrow{PQ}$: $\frac{6}{7}$; slope of $\overleftrightarrow{WV}$: -1; $\overleftrightarrow{AB} \parallel \overleftrightarrow{WV}$

34. slope of $\overleftrightarrow{FE}$: $-\frac{1}{3}$; slope of $\overleftrightarrow{GH}$: 4; slope of $\overleftrightarrow{KL}$: $-\frac{2}{5}$

35. slope of $\overleftrightarrow{AZ}$: $\frac{2}{3}$; slope of $\overleftrightarrow{CD}$: $-\frac{4}{3}$; slope of $\overleftrightarrow{RS}$: $\frac{3}{4}$; $\overleftrightarrow{CD} \perp \overleftrightarrow{RS}$

36. slope of $\overleftrightarrow{OP}$: $\frac{4}{3}$; slope of $\overleftrightarrow{ST}$: $-\frac{3}{4}$; slope of $\overleftrightarrow{QR}$: $-\frac{6}{7}$; $\overleftrightarrow{OP} \perp \overleftrightarrow{ST}$

37. *Sample answer:* the slopes are 2 and $-\frac{1}{2}$, and the product of the two slopes is -1.

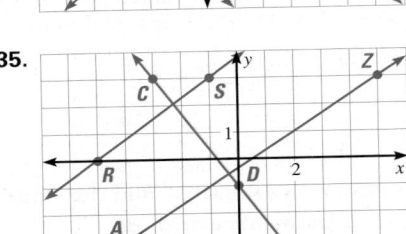

37. **NEEDLEPOINT** To check whether two stitched lines make a right angle, you can count the squares. For example, the lines at the right are perpendicular because one goes up 8 as it goes over 4, and the other goes over 8 as it goes down 4. Why does this mean the lines are perpendicular?

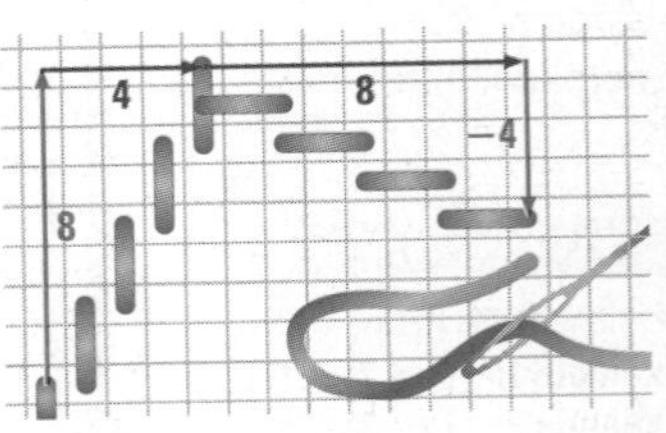

WRITING EQUATIONS Line *j* is perpendicular to the line with the given equation and line *j* passes through *P*. Write an equation of line *j*.

38. $y = \frac{1}{2}x - 1$, $P(0, 3)$ $y = -2x + 3$

39. $y = \frac{5}{3}x + 2$, $P(5, 1)$ $y = -\frac{3}{5}x + 4$

40. $y = -4x - 3$, $P(-2, 2)$ $y = \frac{1}{4}x + \frac{5}{2}$

41. $3y + 4x = 12$, $P(-3, -4)$ $y = \frac{3}{4}x - \frac{7}{4}$

FOCUS ON PEOPLE

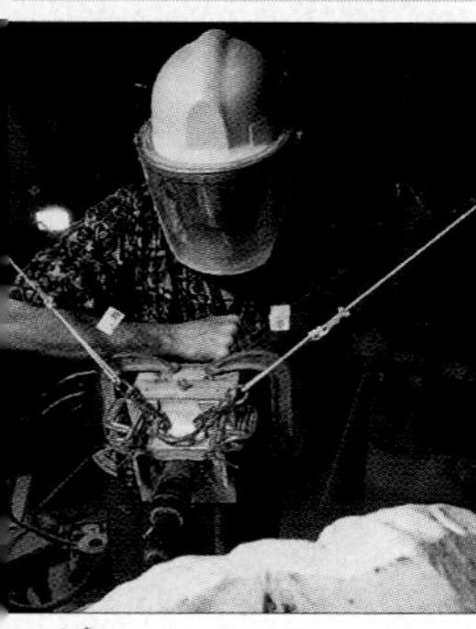

HELAMAN FERGUSON'S stone drill is suspended by six cables. The computer uses the lengths of the cables to calculate the coordinates of the drill tip.

WRITING EQUATIONS The line with the given equation is perpendicular to line *j* at point *R*. Write an equation of line *j*.

42. $y = -\frac{3}{4}x + 6, R(8, 0)$ $y = \frac{4}{3}x - \frac{32}{3}$

43. $y = \frac{1}{7}x - 11, R(7, -10)$ $y = -7x + 39$

44. $y = 3x + 5, R(-3, -4)$ $y = -\frac{1}{3}x - 5$

45. $y = -\frac{2}{5}x - 3, R(5, -5)$ $y = \frac{5}{2}x - \frac{35}{2}$

46. **SCULPTURE** Helaman Ferguson designs sculptures on a computer. The computer is connected to his stone drill and tells how far he should drill at any given point. The distance from the drill tip to the desired surface of the sculpture is calculated along a line perpendicular to the sculpture.

Suppose the drill tip is at $(-1, -1)$ and the equation $y = \frac{1}{4}x + 3$ represents the surface of the sculpture. Write an equation of the line that passes through the drill tip and is perpendicular to the sculpture. $y = -4x - 5$

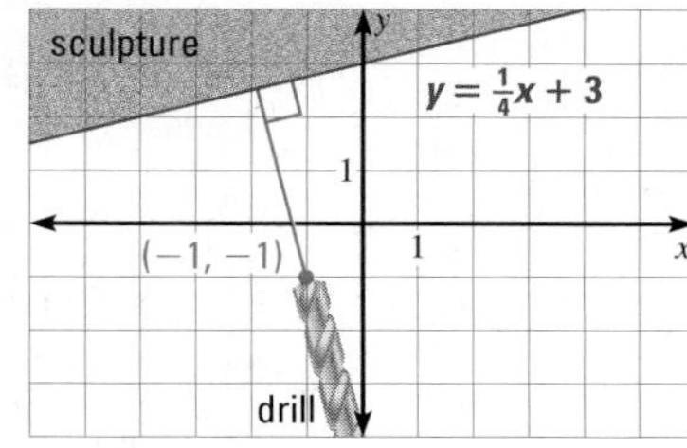

LINE RELATIONSHIPS Decide whether the lines with the given equations are *parallel, perpendicular,* or *neither*.

47. $y = -2x - 1$
$y = -2x - 3$
parallel

48. $y = -\frac{1}{2}x + 3$
$y = -\frac{1}{2}x + 5$
parallel

49. $y = -3x + 1$
$y = \frac{1}{3}x + 1$
perpendicular

50. $y = 4x + 10$
$y = -2x + 5$
neither

Test Preparation

51. MULTI-STEP PROBLEM Use the diagram at the right. 51. a. yes; both have slope $-\frac{3}{2}$.

a. Is $\ell_1 \parallel \ell_2$? How do you know?

b. Is $\ell_2 \perp n$? How do you know? b. yes; their slopes are $-\frac{3}{2}$ and $\frac{2}{3}$.

c. *Writing* Describe two ways to prove that $\ell_1 \perp n$. See margin.

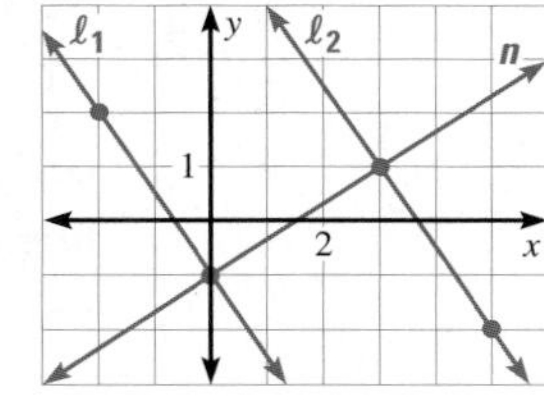

★ Challenge

51. c. *Sample answer:* Calculate the slopes of ℓ_1 and n and show that their product is -1; use the results of parts (a) and (b) and the result that if a line is perpendicular to one of two parallel lines, it is perpendicular to the other also.

DISTANCE TO A LINE In Exercises 52–54, use the following information.

The distance from a point to a line is defined to be the length of the perpendicular segment from the point to the line. In the diagram at the right, the distance d between point P and line ℓ is given by QP.

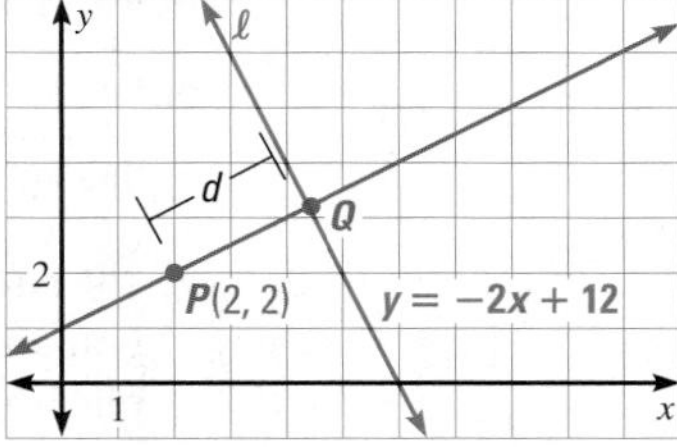

52. Find an equation of $\overleftrightarrow{QP}$. $y = \frac{1}{2}x + 1$

53. Solve a system of equations to find the coordinates of point Q, the intersection of the two lines. $\left(\frac{22}{5}, \frac{16}{5}\right)$

54. Use the Distance Formula to find QP. $\frac{6}{5}\sqrt{5}$, or about 2.68 units

EXTRA CHALLENGE
www.mcdougallittell.com

ADDITIONAL PRACTICE AND RETEACHING

For Lesson 3.7:

- Practice Levels A, B, and C (*Chapter 3 Resource Book*, p. 100)
- Reteaching with Practice (*Chapter 3 Resource Book*, p. 103)
- See Lesson 3.7 of the *Personal Student Tutor*

For more Mixed Review:

- Search the *Test and Practice Generator* for key words or specific lessons.

4 ASSESS

DAILY HOMEWORK QUIZ

Transparency Available

1. The slope of line r is 8 and the slope of line s is $-\frac{1}{8}$. Are the lines perpendicular? yes
2. Lines a and b are perpendicular. The slope of line a is $\frac{7}{5}$. What is the slope of line b? $-\frac{5}{7}$
3. Decide whether the lines with the equations $3y + 2x = 4$, and $2y - 3x = 3$ are perpendicular. perpendicular
4. The line m has the equation $y = 2x + 1$. The line n is perpendicular to m and passes through the point $A(2, 1)$. Write an equation of n. $y = -\frac{1}{2}x + 2$

EXTRA CHALLENGE NOTE

Challenge problems for Lesson 3.7 are available in **blackline** format in the *Chapter 3 Resource Book,* p. 108 and at **www.mcdougallittell.com.**

ADDITIONAL TEST PREPARATION

1. **WRITING** Explain how you can tell whether two lines are perpendicular. ***Sample answer:*** **Find the slopes of the lines. If the product of the slopes is –1, then the lines are perpendicular.**
2. **OPEN ENDED** Give an example of the equations of two perpendicular lines. **Any equations of the form $y = ax + b_1$, and $y = \left(-\frac{1}{a}\right)x + b_2$, with $a \neq 0$, are perpendicular.**

MIXED REVIEW

ANGLE MEASURES **Use the diagram to complete the statement.** **(Review 2.6 for 4.1)**

55. If $m\angle 5 = 38°$, then $m\angle 8 =$ __?__. 142°

56. If $m\angle 3 = 36°$, then $m\angle 4 =$ __?__. 144°

57. If $\angle 8 \cong \angle 4$ and $m\angle 2 = 145°$, then $m\angle 7 =$ __?__. 35°

58. If $m\angle 1 = 38°$ and $\angle 3 \cong \angle 5$, then $m\angle 6 =$ __?__. 142°

IDENTIFYING ANGLES **Use the diagram to complete the statement.** **(Review 3.1 for 4.1)**

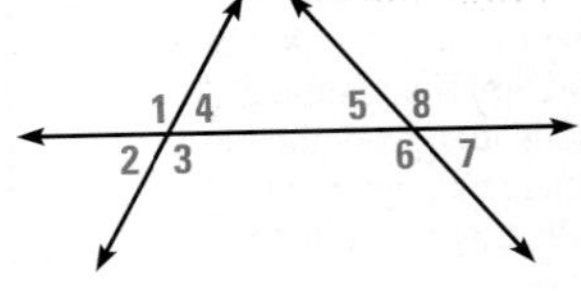

59. $\angle 3$ and __?__ are consecutive interior angles. $\angle 6$

60. $\angle 1$ and __?__ are alternate exterior angles. $\angle 7$

61. $\angle 4$ and __?__ are alternate interior angles. $\angle 6$

62. $\angle 1$ and __?__ are corresponding angles. $\angle 5$

63. ***Writing*** Describe the three types of proofs you have learned so far. **(Review 3.2)** ***Sample answer:*** **A paragraph proof presents statements and reasons in a string of sentences. A two-column proof presents a list of statements with a reason for each one. A flow proof shows a logical arrangement of statements with a reason for each one.**

QUIZ 3

Self-Test for Lessons 3.6 and 3.7

Find the slope of $\overleftrightarrow{AB}$. **(Lesson 3.6)**

1. $A(1, 2)$, $B(5, 8)$ $\frac{3}{2}$

2. $A(2, -3)$, $B(-1, 5)$ $-\frac{8}{3}$

Write an equation of line j_2 that passes through point P and is parallel to line j_1. **(Lesson 3.6)**

3. **line j_1:** $y = 3x - 2$ $y = 3x + 2$
   $P(0, 2)$

4. **line j_1:** $y = \frac{1}{2}x + 1$ $y = \frac{1}{2}x - 5$
   $P(2, -4)$

Decide whether k_1 and k_2 are perpendicular. **(Lesson 3.7)**

5. **line k_1:** $y = 2x - 1$ yes
   line k_2: $y = -\frac{1}{2}x + 2$

6. **line k_1:** $y - 3x = -2$ no
   line k_2: $3y - x = 12$

7. **ANGLE OF REPOSE** When a granular substance is poured into a pile, the slope of the pile depends only on the substance. For example, when barley is poured into piles, every pile has the same slope. A pile of barley that is 5 feet tall would be about 10 feet wide. What is the slope of a pile of barley? **(Lesson 3.6)** 1

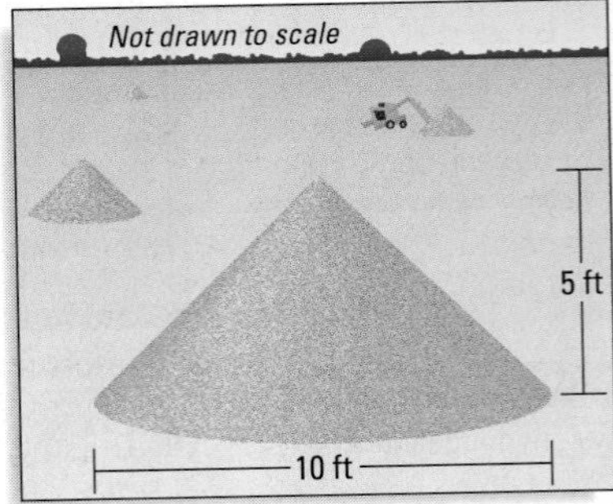

CHAPTER 3

Chapter Summary

WHAT did you learn?	*WHY did you learn it?*
Identify relationships between lines. **(3.1)**	Describe lines and planes in real-life objects, such as escalators. **(p. 133)**
Identify angles formed by coplanar lines intersected by a transversal. **(3.1)**	Lay the foundation for work with angles and proof.
Prove and use results about perpendicular lines. **(3.2)**	Solve real-life problems, such as deciding how many angles of a window frame to measure. **(p. 141)**
Write flow proofs and paragraph proofs. **(3.2)**	Learn to write and use different types of proof.
Prove and use results about parallel lines and transversals. **(3.3)**	Understand the world around you, such as how rainbows are formed. **(p. 148)**
Prove that lines are parallel. **(3.4)**	Solve real-life problems, such as predicting paths of sailboats. **(p. 152)**
Use properties of parallel lines. **(3.4, 3.5)**	Analyze light passing through glass. **(p. 163)**
Use slope to decide whether lines in a coordinate plane are parallel. **(3.6)**	Use coordinate geometry to show that two segments are parallel. **(p. 170)**
Write an equation of a line parallel to a given line in a coordinate plane. **(3.6)**	Prepare to write coordinate proofs.
Use slope to decide whether lines in a coordinate plane are perpendicular. **(3.7)**	Solve real-life problems, such as deciding whether two stitched lines form a right angle. **(p. 176)**
Write an equation of a line perpendicular to a given line. **(3.7)**	Find the distance from a point to a line. **(p. 177)**

How does Chapter 3 fit into the BIGGER PICTURE of geometry?

In this chapter, you learned about properties of perpendicular and parallel lines. You also learned to write flow proofs and learned some important skills related to coordinate geometry. This work will prepare you to reach conclusions about triangles and other figures and to solve real-life problems in areas such as carpentry, engineering, and physics.

STUDY STRATEGY

How did your study questions help you learn?

The study questions you wrote, following the study strategy on page 128, may resemble this one.

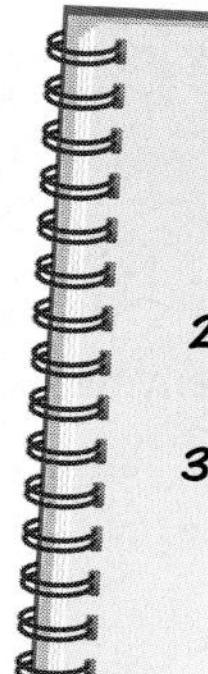

Lines and Angles

1. If two lines do not intersect, can you conclude they are parallel?
2. What is the slope of a line perpendicular to $2x - 3y = 6$?
3. If a transversal intersects two parallel lines, which angles are supplementary?

179

Chapter Review

ADDITIONAL RESOURCES

The following resources are available to help review the material in this chapter.

- Chapter Review Games and Activities (*Chapter 3 Resource Book,* p. 109)
- *Geometry in Motion video*
- *Personal Student Tutor*
- Cumulative Review, Chs. 1–3 (*Chapter 3 Resource Book,* p. 121)

3. $\overleftrightarrow{BF}$, $\overleftrightarrow{CG}$, or $\overleftrightarrow{AE}$

4. *Sample answers:* $\overleftrightarrow{EF}$, $\overleftrightarrow{AB}$, $\overleftrightarrow{AC}$, or $\overleftrightarrow{EG}$

5. *Sample answers:* $\overleftrightarrow{CG}$, $\overleftrightarrow{AB}$, $\overleftrightarrow{AC}$, $\overleftrightarrow{AE}$, $\overleftrightarrow{EG}$, $\overleftrightarrow{GH}$

VOCABULARY

- parallel lines, p. 129
- skew lines, p. 129
- parallel planes, p. 129
- transversal, p. 131
- corresponding angles, p. 131
- alternate interior angles, p. 131
- alternate exterior angles, p. 131
- consecutive interior angles, p. 131
- same side interior angles, p. 131
- flow proof, p. 136

3.1 LINES AND ANGLES

Examples on pp. 129–131

EXAMPLES In the figure, $j \parallel k$, h is a transversal, and $h \perp k$.

$\angle 1$ and $\angle 5$ are corresponding angles.

$\angle 3$ and $\angle 6$ are alternate interior angles.

$\angle 1$ and $\angle 8$ are alternate exterior angles.

$\angle 4$ and $\angle 6$ are consecutive interior angles.

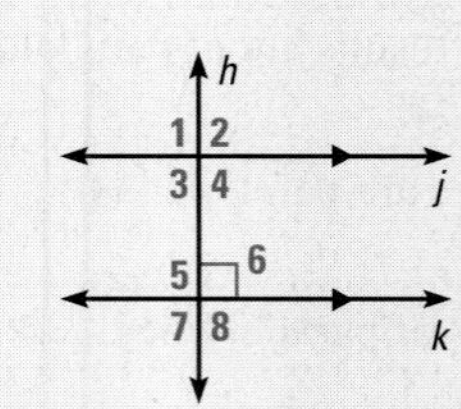

Complete the statement. Use the figure above.

1. $\angle 2$ and $\angle 7$ are __?__ angles. alternate exterior

2. $\angle 4$ and $\angle 5$ are __?__ angles. alternate interior

Use the figure at the right. 3–5. See margin.

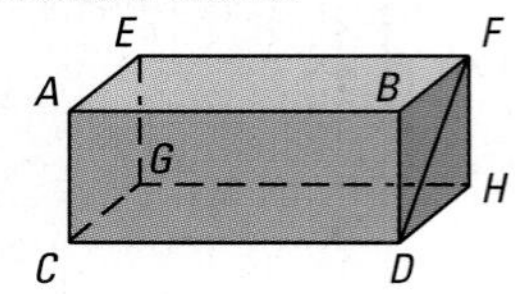

3. Name a line parallel to $\overleftrightarrow{DH}$.

4. Name a line perpendicular to $\overleftrightarrow{AE}$.

5. Name a line skew to $\overleftrightarrow{FD}$.

3.2 PROOF AND PERPENDICULAR LINES

Examples on pp. 136–138

EXAMPLE **GIVEN** ▶ $\angle 1$ and $\angle 2$ are complements.

PROVE ▶ $\overrightarrow{GH} \perp \overrightarrow{GJ}$

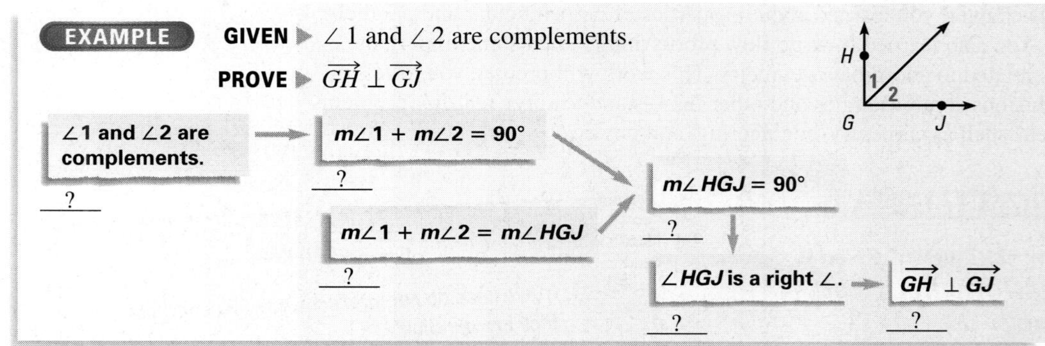

6. Copy the flow proof and add a reason for each statement.

a. Given; b. Def. of complements; c. Angle Addition Postulate; d. Transitive Prop. of Equality; e. Def. of a right angle; f. Def. of Perpendicular Lines

3.3 PARALLEL LINES AND TRANSVERSALS

Examples on pp. 143–145

EXAMPLE In the diagram, $m\angle 1 = 75°$. By the Alternate Exterior Angles Theorem, $m\angle 8 = m\angle 1 = 75°$. Because $\angle 8$ and $\angle 7$ are a linear pair, $m\angle 8 + m\angle 7 = 180°$. So, $m\angle 7 = 180° - 75° = 105°$.

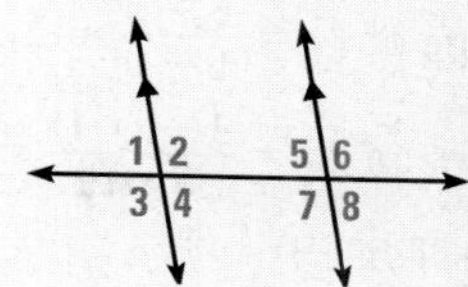

7. Find the measures of the other five angles in the diagram above.
$m\angle 2 = 105°$; $m\angle 3 = 105°$, $m\angle 4 = 75°$; $m\angle 5 = 75°$, $m\angle 6 = 105°$

Find the value of x. Explain your reasoning.
8–10. See margin.

8.

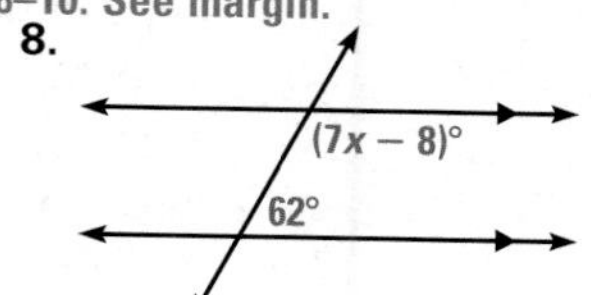

9.

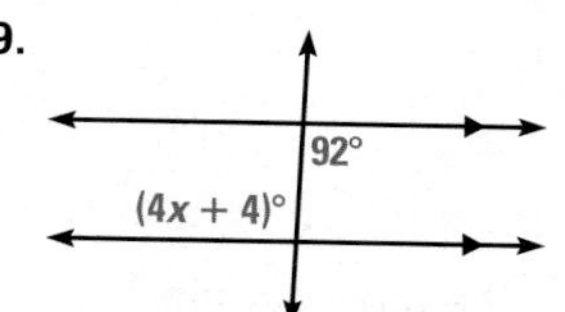

10.

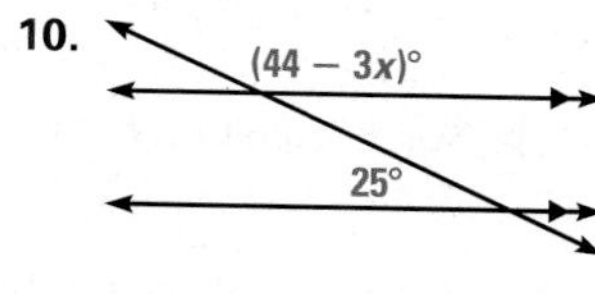

3.4 PROVING LINES ARE PARALLEL

Examples on pp. 150–152

EXAMPLE **GIVEN** ▶ $m\angle 3 = 125°$, $m\angle 6 = 125°$

PROVE ▶ $\ell \parallel m$

Plan for Proof: $m\angle 3 = 125° = m\angle 6$, so $\angle 3 \cong \angle 6$. So, $\ell \parallel m$ by the Alternate Exterior Angles Converse.

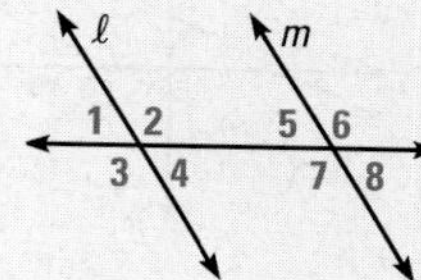

Use the diagram above to write a proof.
11 and 12. See margin.

11. GIVEN ▶ $m\angle 4 = 60°$, $m\angle 7 = 120°$

PROVE ▶ $\ell \parallel m$

12. GIVEN ▶ $\angle 1$ and $\angle 7$ are supplementary.

PROVE ▶ $\ell \parallel m$

3.5 USING PROPERTIES OF PARALLEL LINES

Examples on pp. 157–159

EXAMPLE In the diagram, $\ell \perp t$, $m \perp t$, and $m \parallel n$. Because ℓ and m are coplanar and perpendicular to the same line, $\ell \parallel m$. Then, because $\ell \parallel m$ and $m \parallel n$, $\ell \parallel n$.

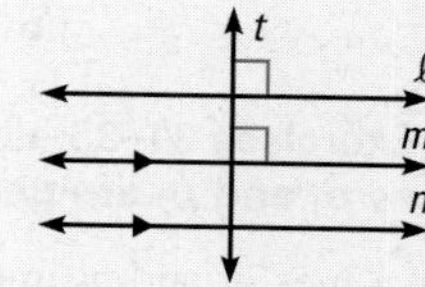

Which lines must be parallel? Explain.
13–16. See margin.

13. $\angle 1$ and $\angle 2$ are right angles.

14. $\angle 3 \cong \angle 6$

15. $\angle 3$ and $\angle 4$ are supplements.

16. $\angle 1 \cong \angle 2$, $\angle 3 \cong \angle 5$

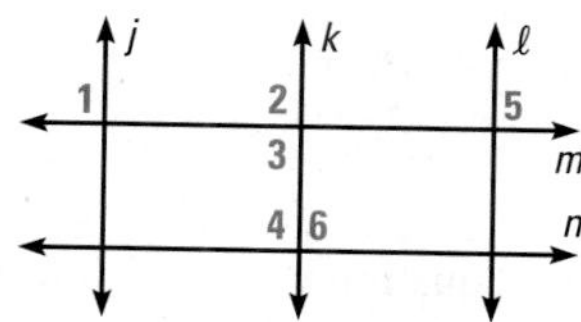

8. 18; By the Consecutive Interior Angles Thm, $(7x - 8)° + 62° = 180°$. So, $x = \frac{180 - 54}{7} = 18$.
9. 22; Alternate Interior Angles Postulate, $(4x + 4)° = 92°$. So, $x = \frac{92 - 4}{4} = 22$.
10. −37; By the Corresponding Angles Postulate, the angle adjacent to the angle labeled $(44 - 3x)°$ has measure 25°. Since the two angles are supplementary, $(44 - 3x)° + 25° = 180°$. So, $x = \frac{180 - 69}{-3} = -37$.
11. Since $m\angle 4 = 60°$ and $m\angle 7 = 120°$, they are supplementary because their measures add up to 180°. By the Consecutive Interior Angles Converse, $l \parallel m$.
12. Given: $\angle 1$ and $\angle 7$ are supplementary. $\angle 5$ and $\angle 7$ are supplementary because they form a linear pair. By the ≅ Supplements Theorem, $\angle 5 \cong \angle 1$. By Corresponding Angles Converse, $l \parallel m$.
13. $j \parallel k$; Corresponding Angles Converse
14. $m \parallel n$; Alternate Interior Angles Converse
15. $m \parallel n$; Consecutive Interior Angles Converse
16. $j \parallel k$, $k \parallel l$, $j \parallel l$; Corresponding Angles Converse, Alternate Exterior Angles Converse, Theorem 3.11

17. Slope of $\overleftrightarrow{AB}$ and $\overleftrightarrow{CD}$ is $\frac{1}{2}$; yes

18. Slope of $\overleftrightarrow{EF}$ and $\overleftrightarrow{GH}$ is -1; yes

19. Slope of $\overleftrightarrow{JK} = 3$; slope of $\overleftrightarrow{MN} = \frac{5}{2}$; no

3.6 PARALLEL LINES IN THE COORDINATE PLANE

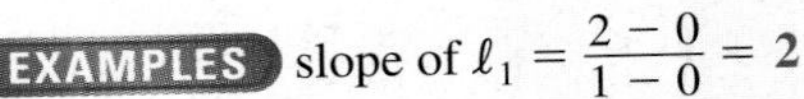

Examples on pp. 165–167

EXAMPLES slope of $\ell_1 = \frac{2-0}{1-0} = 2$

slope of $\ell_2 = \frac{3-(-1)}{5-3} = \frac{4}{2} = 2$

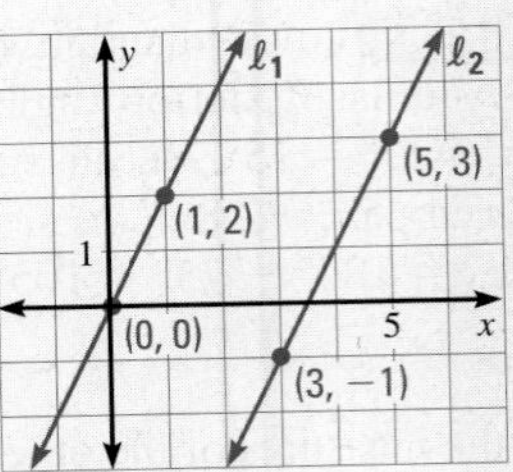

The slopes are the same, so $\ell_1 \parallel \ell_2$.

To write an equation for ℓ_2, substitute $(x, y) = (5, 3)$ and $m = 2$ into the slope-intercept form.

$y = mx + b$	**Slope-intercept form.**
$3 = (2)(5) + b$	**Substitute 5 for *x*, 3 for *y*, and 2 for *m*.**
$-7 = b$	**Solve for *b*.**

▶ So, an equation for ℓ_2 is $y = 2x - 7$.

Find the slope of each line. Are the lines parallel? 17–19. See margin.

17.

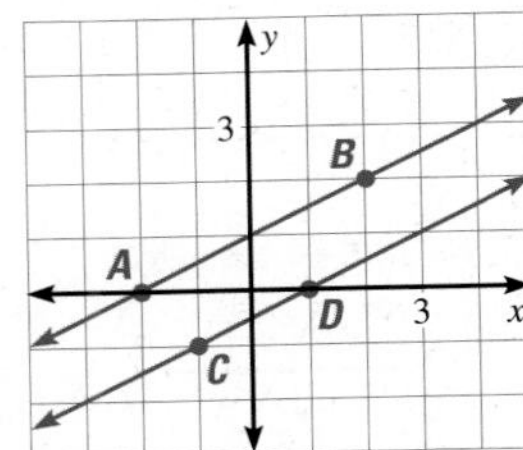

18.

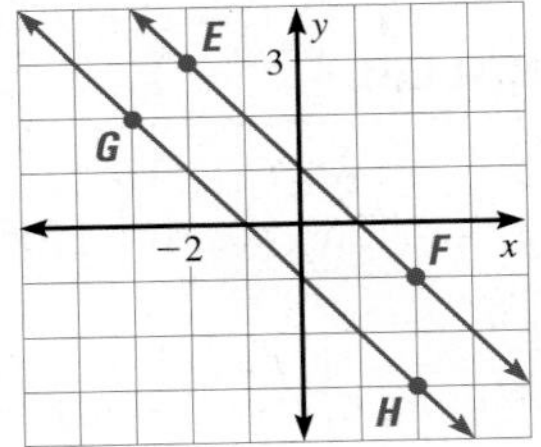

19.

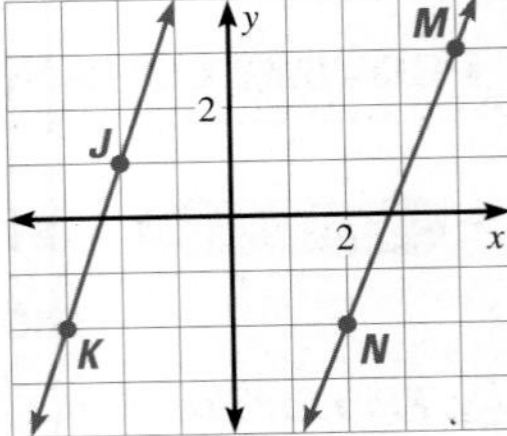

20. Find an equation of the line that is parallel to the line with equation $y = -2x + 5$ and passes through the point $(-1, -4)$. $y = -2x - 6$

3.7 PERPENDICULAR LINES IN THE COORDINATE PLANE

Examples on pp. 172–174

EXAMPLE The slope of line j is 3. The slope of line k is $-\frac{1}{3}$.

$$3\left(-\frac{1}{3}\right) = -1, \text{ so } j \perp k.$$

In Exercises 21–23, decide whether lines p_1 and p_2 are perpendicular.

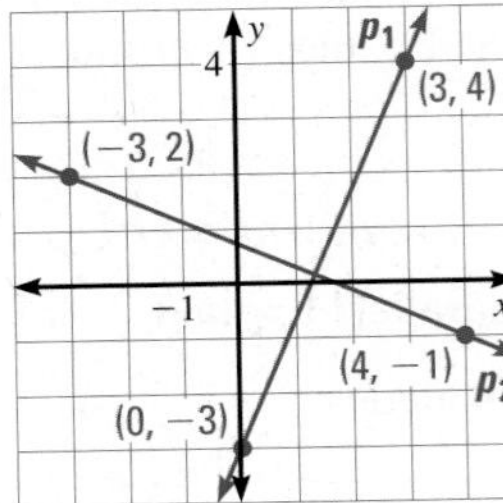

21. Lines p_1 and p_2 in the diagram.
yes

22. p_1: $y = \frac{3}{5}x + 2$; p_2: $y = \frac{5}{3}x - 1$
no

23. p_1: $2y - x = 2$; p_2: $y + 2x = 4$
yes

24. Line ℓ_1 has equation $y = -3x + 5$. Write an equation of line ℓ_2 which is perpendicular to ℓ_1 and passes through $(-3, 6)$. $y = \frac{1}{3}x + 7$

CHAPTER 3

Chapter Test

In Exercises 1–6, identify the relationship between the angles in the diagram at the right.

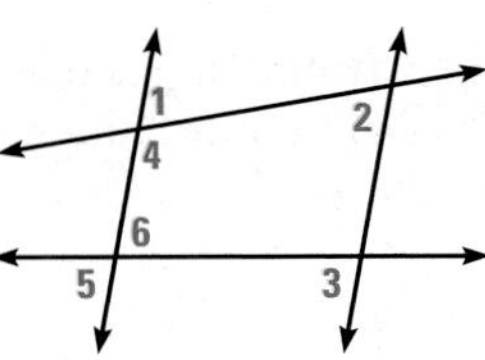

1. $\angle 1$ and $\angle 2$ **alternate interior angles** **2.** $\angle 1$ and $\angle 4$ **supplementary angles**

3. $\angle 2$ and $\angle 3$ **corresponding angles** **4.** $\angle 1$ and $\angle 5$ **alternate ext. angles**

5. $\angle 4$ and $\angle 2$ **consecutive int. angles** **6.** $\angle 5$ and $\angle 6$ **vertical angles**

7. Write a flow proof. **See margin.**

GIVEN ▶ $m\angle 1 = m\angle 3 = 37°$, $\overrightarrow{BA} \perp \overrightarrow{BC}$

PROVE ▶ $m\angle 2 = 16°$

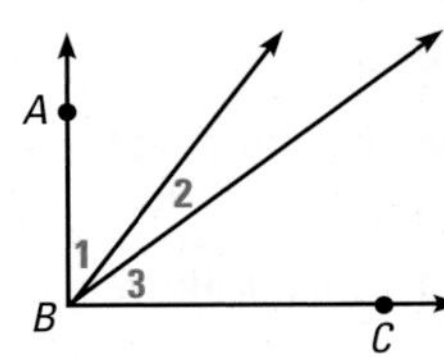

8. If $\ell \parallel m$, which angles are **∠2, ∠4, ∠6, ∠8** supplementary to $\angle 1$?

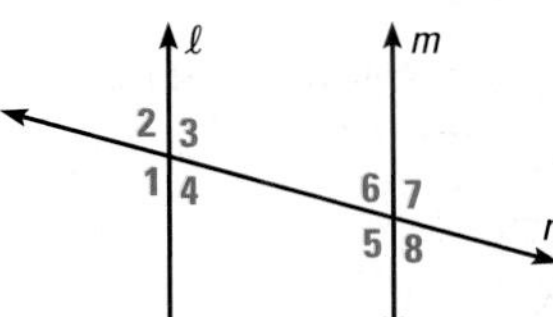

Use the given information and the diagram at the right to determine which lines must be parallel.

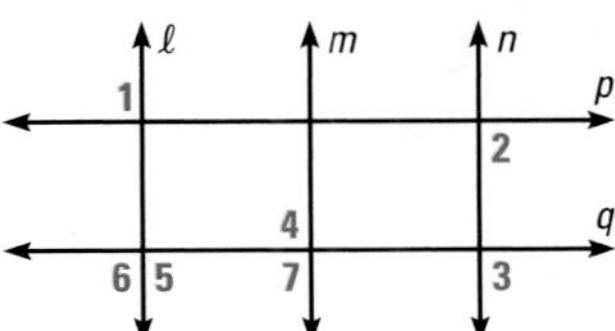

9. $\angle 1 \cong \angle 2$ **$\ell \parallel n$**

10. $\angle 3$ and $\angle 4$ are right angles. **$m \parallel n$**

11. $\angle 1 \cong \angle 5$; $\angle 5$ and $\angle 7$ are supplementary. **$p \parallel q$; $\ell \parallel m$**

In Exercises 12 and 13, write an equation of the line described.

12. The line parallel to $y = -\frac{1}{3}x + 5$ and with a y-intercept of 1 **$y = -\frac{1}{3}x + 1$**

13. The line perpendicular to $y = -2x + 4$ and that passes through the point $(-1, 2)$ **$y = \frac{1}{2}x + \frac{5}{2}$**

14. *Writing* Describe a real-life object that has edges that are straight lines. Are any of the lines skew? If so, describe a pair. **See margin.**

15. A carpenter wants to cut two boards to fit snugly together. The carpenter's squares are aligned along $\overline{EF}$, as shown. Are $\overline{AB}$ and $\overline{CD}$ parallel? State the theorem that justifies your answer. **See margin.**

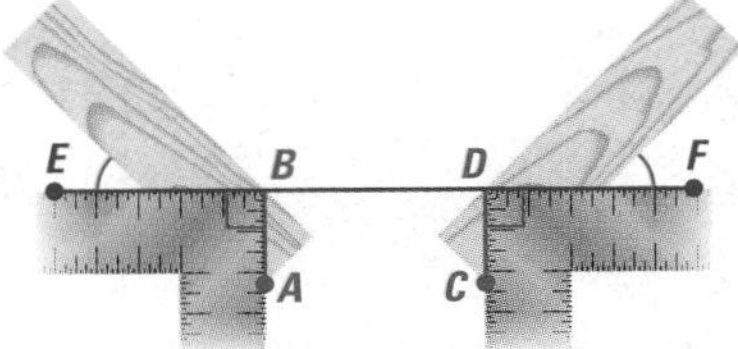

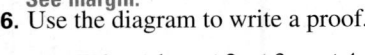

16. Use the diagram to write a proof.

GIVEN ▶ $\angle 1 \cong \angle 2$, $\angle 3 \cong \angle 4$

PROVE ▶ $n \parallel p$

See margin.

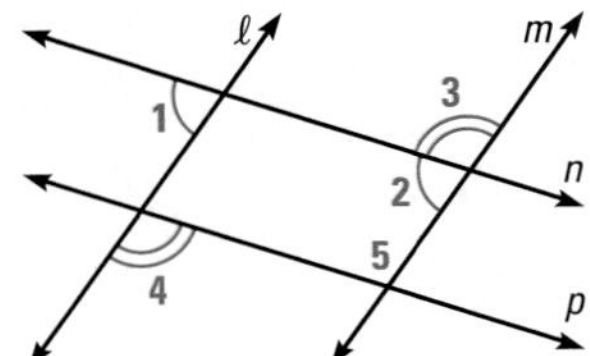

ADDITIONAL RESOURCES

- ***Chapter 3 Resource Book***
  Chapter Test (3 levels) (p. 110)
  SAT/ACT Chapter Test (p. 116)
  Alternative Assessment (p. 117)
- ***Test and Practice Generator***

7. 1. $m\angle 1 = m\angle 3 = 37°$ (Given);
2. $\overrightarrow{BA} \perp \overrightarrow{BC}$ (Given);
3. $m\angle 1 + m\angle 2 + m\angle 3 = m\angle ABC$ (Angle Addition Postulate);
4. $\angle ABC$ is a right angle. (Def. of perpendicular lines);
5. $m\angle ABC = 90°$ (Definition of right angle);
6. $m\angle 1 + m\angle 2 + m\angle 3 = 90°$ (Transitive Property of Equality);
7. $37° + m\angle 2 + 37° = 90°$ (Substitution);
8. $m\angle 2 = 16°$ (Subtraction Property of Equality)

14. *Sample answer:* on a cereal box, the line which is the front lower edge is skew to the line which is the left edge of the top of the box.

15. yes; If two coplanar lines are perpendicular to the same line then they are parallel to each other.

16. Given: $\angle 1 \cong \angle 2$, $\angle 3 \cong \angle 4$. $l \parallel m$ by Corresponding Angles Converse. If $l \parallel m$, then $\angle 5$ must be congruent to $\angle 4$ by Alternate Interior Angles Theorem. $\angle 5 \cong \angle 3$ by Transitive Property of Congruence. Therefore, $n \parallel p$ by Corresponding Angles Converse.

ADDITIONAL RESOURCES

- ***Chapter 3 Resource Book***
  Chapter Test (3 levels) (p. 110)
  SAT/ACT Chapter Test (p. 116)
  Alternative Assessment (p. 117)
- ***Test and Practice Generator***

CHAPTER 3

Chapter Standardized Test

TEST-TAKING STRATEGY The mathematical portion of the SAT is based on the material taught in your high school mathematics courses. One of the best ways to prepare for the SAT is to keep up with your regular studies and do your homework assignments.

1. **MULTIPLE CHOICE** In the diagram, how many lines can be drawn through point Q parallel to line n? **B**

Ⓐ 0 Ⓑ 1
Ⓒ 2 Ⓓ More than 2
Ⓔ Cannot be determined

2. **MULTIPLE CHOICE** In the diagram, if $a \parallel b$ and $m\angle 7 = 62°$, what is $m\angle 1$? **C**

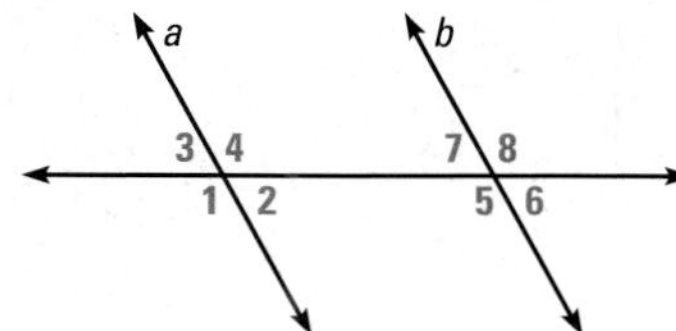

Ⓐ 28° Ⓑ 62°
Ⓒ 118° Ⓓ 124°
Ⓔ 128°

3. **MULTIPLE CHOICE** In the diagram, $j \parallel k$. Find the value of x. **C**

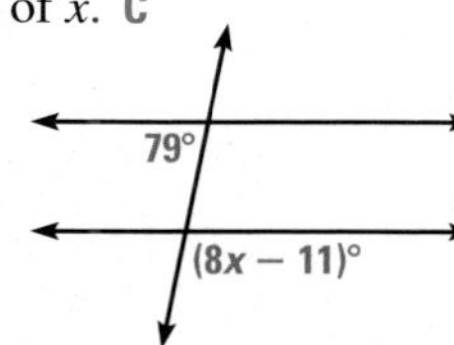

Ⓐ 11 Ⓑ 11.25
Ⓒ 14 Ⓓ 15.25
Ⓔ 23

4. **MULTIPLE CHOICE** Which line passes through the point $(10, -1)$ and has a slope of -2? **D**

Ⓐ $y = -2x - 19$ Ⓑ $y = 2x - 19$
Ⓒ $y = 2x + 19$ Ⓓ $y = -2x + 19$
Ⓔ $y = -2x - 21$

5. **QUANTITATIVE COMPARISON**

Column A	Column B
The slope of the line through $(-2, -4)$ and $(8, 3)$	The slope of the line perpendicular to $y = \frac{10}{7}x + \frac{1}{7}$

Choose the statement that is true. **A**

Ⓐ The quantity in column A is greater.
Ⓑ The quantity in column B is greater.
Ⓒ The two quantities are equal.
Ⓓ The relationship cannot be determined from the information given.

6. **MULTIPLE CHOICE** Which of the following lines is parallel to $y = -\frac{5}{7}x + 2$? **A**

Ⓐ $y + \frac{5}{7}x = -5$ Ⓑ $y = \frac{5}{7}x + 6$
Ⓒ $y = -\frac{7}{5}x - 3$ Ⓓ $y - \frac{5}{7}x = 9$
Ⓔ $y = \frac{7}{5}x + 1$

7. **MULTIPLE CHOICE** A line j has equation $y = -\frac{1}{4}x - 6$. If $k \perp j$ and k passes through point $(5, -2)$, what is an equation of k? **D**

Ⓐ $y = 4x + 22$ Ⓑ $y = \frac{1}{4}x - 22$
Ⓒ $y = -\frac{1}{4}x - 22$ Ⓓ $y = 4x - 22$
Ⓔ $y = -4x + 18$

8. **MULTIPLE CHOICE** Which lines are parallel? **D**

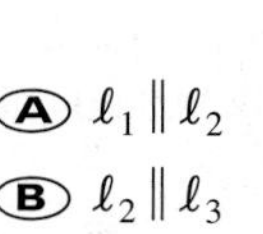

Ⓐ $\ell_1 \parallel \ell_2$
Ⓑ $\ell_2 \parallel \ell_3$
Ⓒ $\ell_1 \parallel \ell_3$

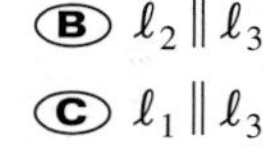

Ⓓ None
Ⓔ All 3

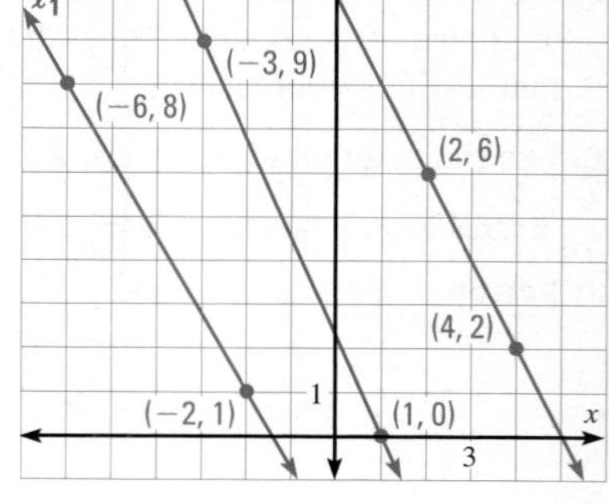

9. MULTIPLE CHOICE In the diagram, which two angles are alternate interior angles? A

Ⓐ ∠6 and ∠3

Ⓑ ∠10 and ∠5

Ⓒ ∠12 and ∠8

Ⓓ ∠2 and ∠6

Ⓔ ∠10 and ∠11

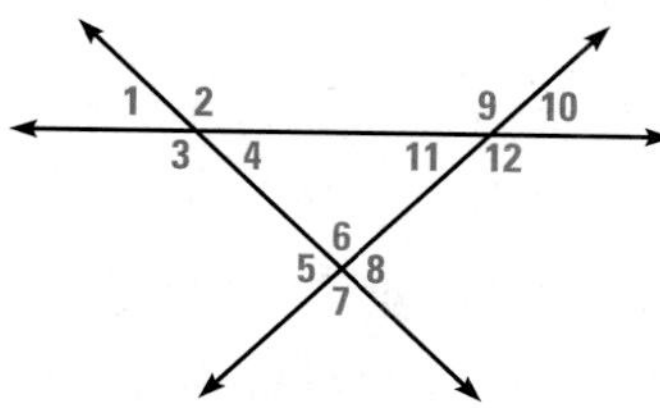

MULTI-STEP PROBLEM In Exercises 10 and 11, use the diagram at the right.

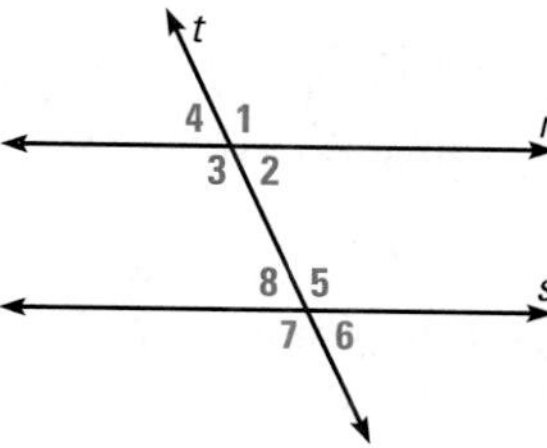

10. Suppose $r \parallel s$. Complete each statement with the word *always*, *sometimes*, or *never*.

a. If $r \perp t$, then s is __?__ perpendicular to t. always

b. ∠3 and ∠8 are __?__ both acute angles. never

c. ∠1 and ∠6 are __?__ supplementary angles. always

d. ∠2 and ∠7 are __?__ congruent angles. sometimes

11. Given $m\angle 4 = 65°$ and $m\angle 5 = 115°$, write two different paragraph proofs to show that $r \parallel s$. See margin.

MULTI-STEP PROBLEM Line j has equation $y = 3x - 2$.

12. Write an equation for line k that is perpendicular to line j and passes through point (1, 1). $y = -\frac{1}{3}x + \frac{4}{3}$

13. Write an equation for a line n that is perpendicular to line k and passes through point (4, 0). $y = 3x - 12$

14. Describe two different ways you could show that $j \parallel n$. *Sample answer:* Check to see if they have the same slope, solve them as a system of equations.

15. Graph lines j, k, and n in a coordinate plane. See margin.

MULTI-STEP PROBLEM In Exercises 16 and 17, use the following information.

Suppose you are constructing a wheelchair ramp. The building code requires the slope of the ramp to be no greater than $\frac{1}{12}$. The diagram at the right shows a side view of the ramp in a coordinate plane, where each unit represents one inch.

▶ Source: *Uniform Federal Accessibility Standards*

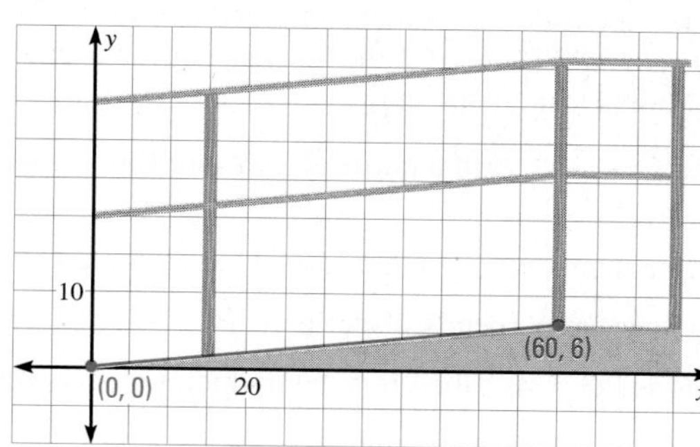

16. *Writing* Explain what is wrong with the slope of the ramp in the diagram. The slope of the ramp is greater than $\frac{1}{12}$ and therefore too steep.

17. Keeping the height of the ramp at 6 inches, how much longer must the base of the ramp be in order to meet the slope specification of $\frac{1}{12}$? 12 inches longer so that the slanted part stops at (72, 6).

11. *Sample answers:*

- Since $m\angle 4 = 65°$ and $m\angle 5 = 115°$, they are supplementary because their measures add up to 180°. ∠3 and ∠4 are supplementary because they form a linear pair. By the Congruent Supplements Thm, it follows that $\angle 3 \cong \angle 5$. Therefore, by the Alternate Interior Angles Converse, $r \parallel s$.
- Since $m\angle 4 = 65°$ and $m\angle 5 = 115°$, they are supplementary because their measures add up to 180°. ∠5 and ∠6 are supplementary because they form a linear pair. By the Congruent Supplement Thm, it follows that $\angle 4 \cong \angle 6$. Therefore, by the Alternate Exterior Angle Converse, $r \parallel s$.

15.

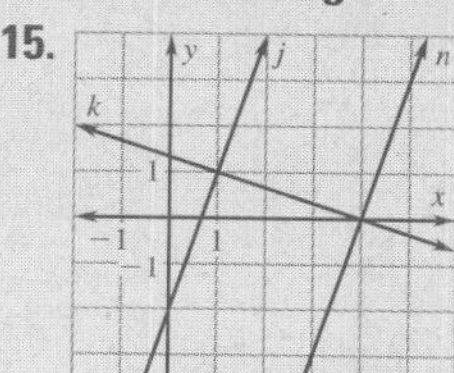

ADDITIONAL RESOURCES
A Cumulative Review covering Chapters 1–3 is available in the *Chapter 3 Resource Book*, p. 121.

8.

9.

10.

CHAPTER 3 Cumulative Practice

1. Describe a pattern in the sequence 10, 12, 15, 19, 24, ... Predict the next number. (1.1) You add 2, then 3, then 4, and so on; 30.

In the diagram at the right, $\overleftrightarrow{AB}$, $\overleftrightarrow{AC}$, and $\overleftrightarrow{BC}$ are in plane *M*.

2. Name a point that is collinear with points *A* and *D*. (1.2) B
3. Name a line skew to $\overleftrightarrow{BC}$. (3.1) $\overleftrightarrow{DT}$
4. Name the ray that is opposite to $\overrightarrow{GC}$. (1.2) $\overrightarrow{GB}$
5. How many planes contain *A*, *B*, and *C*? Explain. (2.1)
Exactly one; through any three noncollinear points there is exactly one plane.

$\overline{MN}$ has endpoints $M(7, -5)$ and $N(-3, -1)$.

6. Find the length of $\overline{MN}$. (1.3) $2\sqrt{29} \approx 10.8$
7. If *N* is the midpoint of $\overline{MP}$, find the coordinates of point *P*. (1.5) (−13, 3)

In a coordinate plane, plot the points and sketch ∠*ABC*. Classify the angle as *acute, right,* or *obtuse*. (1.4)

8. $A(-6, 6)$, $B(-2, 2)$, $C(4, 2)$ obtuse
9. $A(2, 1)$, $B(4, 7)$, $C(10, 5)$ right
10. $A(2, 5)$, $B(2, -2)$, $C(5, 4)$ acute

Find the values of *x* and *y*. (1.5, 1.6, 3.2)

11. 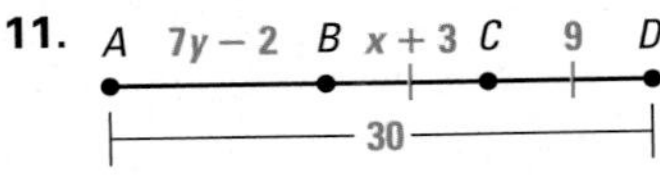

$x = 6$, $y = 2$

12. 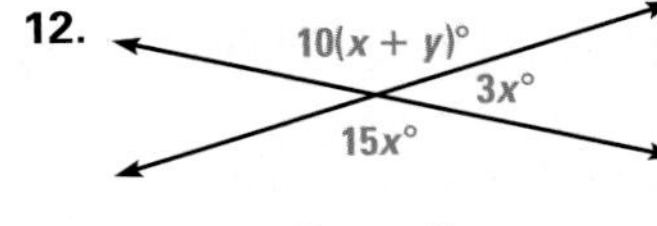

$x = 10$, $y = 5$

13. 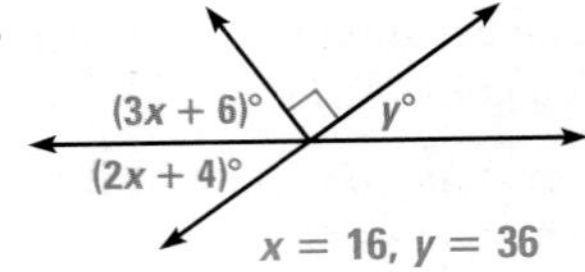

$x = 16$, $y = 36$

In Exercises 14 and 15, find the area of each figure. (1.7)

14. Square with a perimeter of 40 cm $100\ cm^2$
15. Triangle defined by $R(0, 0)$, $S(6, 8)$, and $T(10, 0)$ 40 square units
16. Construct two perpendicular lines. Bisect one of the angles formed. (1.5, 3.1) Check drawings.
17. Rewrite the following statement in if-then form: *The measure of a straight angle is 180°.* Then write the inverse, converse, and contrapositive of the conditional statement. (2.1) See margin.

In Exercises 18–21, find a counterexample that shows the statement is false.

18. If a line intersects two other lines, then all three lines are coplanar. (2.1) For example, consider the three lines at a corner of a room.
19. Two lines are perpendicular if they intersect. (2.2) Two lines can intersect to form acute and obtuse angles.
20. If $AB + BC = AC$, then *B* is the midpoint of $\overline{AC}$. (2.5) *Sample answer:* If $AB = 2$, $BC = 6$, and $AC = 8$ then $AB + BC = AC$ but *B* is not the midpoint of $\overline{AC}$.
21. If ∠1 and ∠2 are supplementary, then ∠1 and ∠2 form a linear pair. (2.6) See margin.
22. Solve the equation $3(s - 2) = 15$ and write a reason for each step. (2.4) See margin.
23. Draw a diagram of intersecting lines *j* and *k*. Label each angle with a number. Use the Linear Pair Postulate and the Vertical Angles Theorem to write true statements about the angles formed by the intersecting lines. (2.6) See margin.

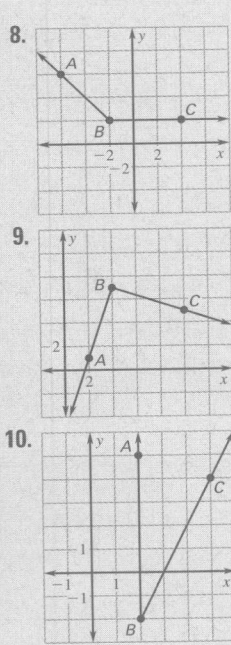

Let p represent "$x = 0$" and let q represent "$x + x = x$."

24. Write the biconditional $p \longleftrightarrow q$ in words. Decide whether the biconditional is true. (2.2, 2.3) $x = 0$ if and only if $x + x = x$; true.

25. If the statement $p \rightarrow q$ is true and p is true, does it follow that q is true? Explain. (2.3) Yes, by the law of Detachment.

Use the diagram at the right.

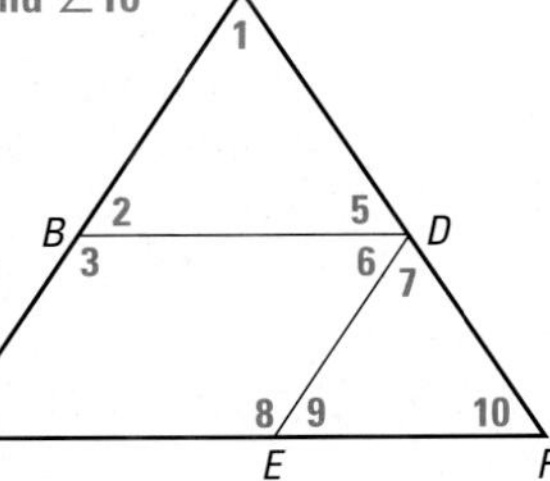

26. Name four pairs of corresponding angles. (3.1) $\angle 1$ and $\angle 7$, $\angle 4$ and $\angle 9$, $\angle 2$ and $\angle 4$, $\angle 5$ and $\angle 10$

27. If $\overleftrightarrow{AC} \parallel \overleftrightarrow{DE}$ and $m\angle 2 = 55°$, find $m\angle 6$. (3.3) 55°

28. If $\overleftrightarrow{BD} \parallel \overleftrightarrow{CF}$ and $m\angle 3 = 140°$, find $m\angle 4$. (3.3) 40°

29. Which lines must be parallel if $m\angle 3 + m\angle 6 = 180°$? Explain. (3.4) $\overleftrightarrow{DE} \parallel \overleftrightarrow{AC}$ by the Consecutive Interior Angles Converse

30. **PROOF** Write a proof. See margin.

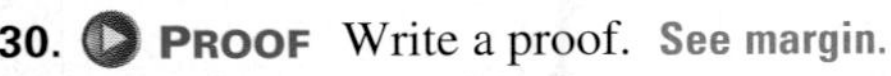

GIVEN ▶ $\angle 6 \cong \angle 9$

PROVE ▶ $\angle 3$ and $\angle 4$ are supplements. (3.3, 3.4)

In Exercises 31–33, use $A(2, 10)$, $B(22, -5)$, $C(-1, 6)$, and $D(25, -1)$.

31. Show that $\overleftrightarrow{AD}$ is parallel to $\overleftrightarrow{BC}$. (3.6) the slope of $\overleftrightarrow{AD}$ is $-\frac{11}{23}$; the slope of $\overleftrightarrow{BC}$ is $-\frac{11}{23}$

32. Use slopes to show that $\angle BAC$ is a right angle. (3.7) See margin.

33. Write an equation for a line through the point C and parallel to $\overleftrightarrow{AB}$. (3.6) $y = -\frac{3}{4}x + \frac{21}{4}$

34. **RUNNING TRACK** The inside of the running track in the diagram is formed by a rectangle and two half circles. Find the distance, to the nearest yard, around the inside of the track. Then find the area enclosed by the track. (Use $\pi \approx 3.14$.) (1.7)
about 377 yd; about 7462.5 yd^2

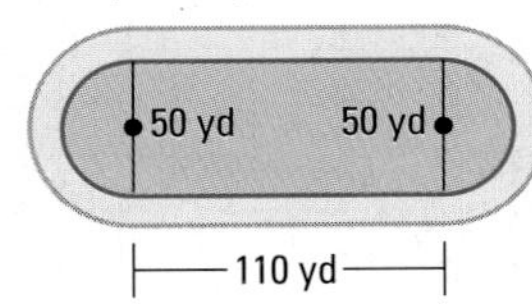

35. **PHOTO ENLARGEMENT** A photographer took a 4-inch-by-6-inch photo and enlarged each side to 150% of the original size.

    a. Find the dimensions of the enlarged photo. 6 in. by 9 in.

    b. Describe the relationship between $\angle 1$ and $\angle 3$. (1.6, 3.2) $\angle 1$ and $\angle 3$ are complementary.

    c. Make an accurate diagram of the original photo and the enlargement, as shown. Draw $\overline{DB}$ and $\overline{BQ}$. Make a conjecture about the relationship between $\angle 1$ and $\angle 2$. Measure the angles in your diagram to test your conjecture. (1.1, 1.6) $\angle 1$ and $\angle 2$ are supplementary.

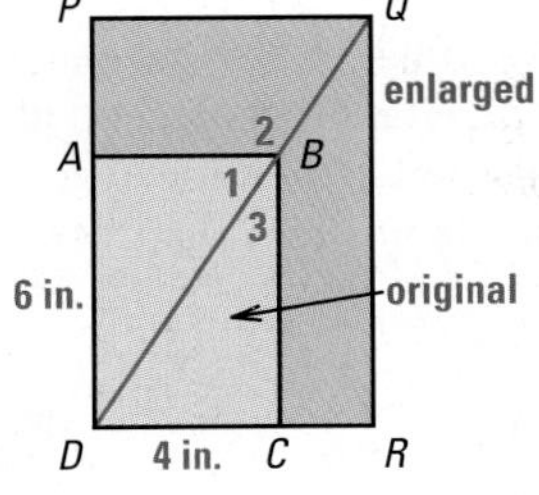

36. **CONSTRUCTION** Two posts support a raised deck. The posts have two parallel braces, as shown.

    a. If $m\angle 1 = 35°$, find $m\angle 2$. (3.3) 145°

    b. If $m\angle 3 = 40°$, what other angle has a measure of 40°? (3.3) $\angle 1$

    c. Each post is perpendicular to the deck. Explain how this can be used to show that the posts are parallel to each other. (3.5) In a plane, if two lines are perpendicular to the same line, then they are parallel to each other.

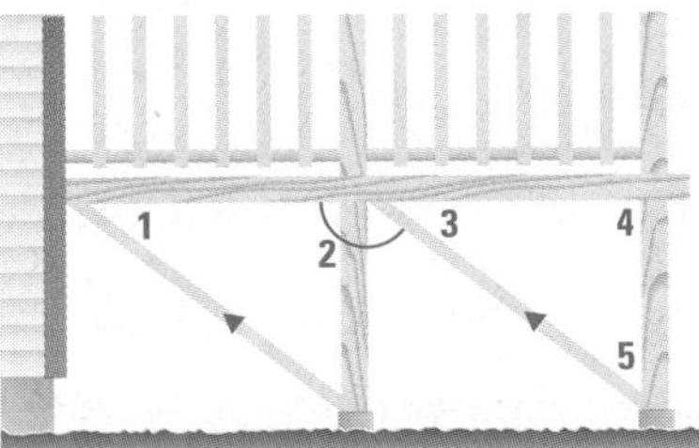

17. If an angle is a straight angle, then its measure is 180°. If an angle is not a straight angle, then its measure is not 180°. If an angle measure is 180°, then it is a straight angle. If an angle measure is not 180°, then it is not a straight angle.

21. If the angles are same side interior angles of two parallel lines they would be supplementary but not a linear pair.

22. $3s - 6 = 15$ (Distributive property);
$3s - 6 + 6 = 15 + 6$
(Addition property of equality);
$3s = 21$ (Simplify);
$\frac{3s}{3} = \frac{21}{3}$
(Division property of equality);
$s = 7$ (Simplify)

23.

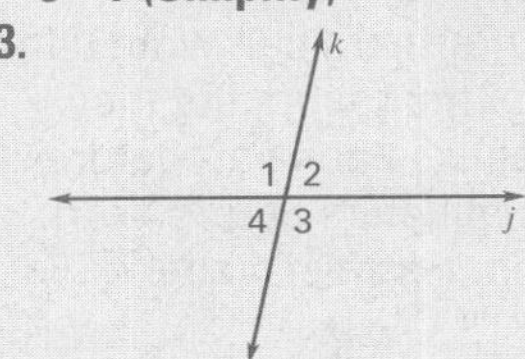

$\angle 1$ and $\angle 2$ are supplementary;
$\angle 1$ and $\angle 4$ are supplementary;
$\angle 2$ and $\angle 3$ are supplementary;
$\angle 3$ and $\angle 4$ are supplementary;
$\angle 1$ and $\angle 3$ are vertical angles;
$\angle 2$ and $\angle 4$ are vertical angles;

30. 1. $\angle 6 \cong \angle 9$ (Given);
2. $\overline{BD} \parallel \overline{CE}$ (Alternate Interior Angles Converse);
3. $\angle 3$ and $\angle 4$ are supplements (Consecutive Interior Angles Thm)

32. Slope $\overrightarrow{AB} = -\frac{3}{4}$, slope $\overrightarrow{AC} = \frac{4}{3}$; the product of the slopes is -1.

PROJECT OVERVIEW

PROJECT GOALS

- Use orthographic projections to represent real-life objects.
- Use isometric drawings to represent real-life objects.
- identify parallel and perpendicular lines in isometric drawings.

MANAGING THE PROJECT

CLASSROOM MANAGEMENT
The Chapter 3 Project may be completed by students working alone or with a partner. If students work with a partner, they should work on Questions 1–3 together. Each partner can work on one of the new drawings. Partners can write different parts of the report, but they should discuss each part beforehand and edit each others' work before a final draft is made.

ALTERNATIVE APPROACH
Students may need additional hands-on practice with the concepts in this project. Have students use wooden blocks to make objects and then practice making orthographic projections and isometric drawings of the objects. Then have students trade drawings and see if they can create the object from the drawing.

CONCLUDING THE PROJECT

Have each student or group of students discuss part of their finished project. Ask that each presenter try to add something that has not been said previously.

Ask a parent or other member of the community to come and talk about how they use technical drawing or CAD in their field.

PROJECT *for Chapters 2 and 3*

Technical Drawing

OBJECTIVE **Make technical drawings of objects, including orthographic projections and isometric drawings.**

Materials: ruler, graph paper, isometric dot paper, colored pencils, file folder

Technical drawings are drawings that show different viewpoints of an object. Engineers and architects create technical drawings of products and buildings before actually constructing the objects in real life.

Technical drawings may include an *orthographic projection*. This is a two-dimensional drawing of the front, top, and side views of an object. *Isometric drawings* look three-dimensional, and can be created on a grid of dots using three axes that intersect to form 120° angles.

CREATING ORTHOGRAPHIC PROJECTIONS AND ISOMETRIC DRAWINGS

Follow these steps to make a technical drawing of a set of stairs.

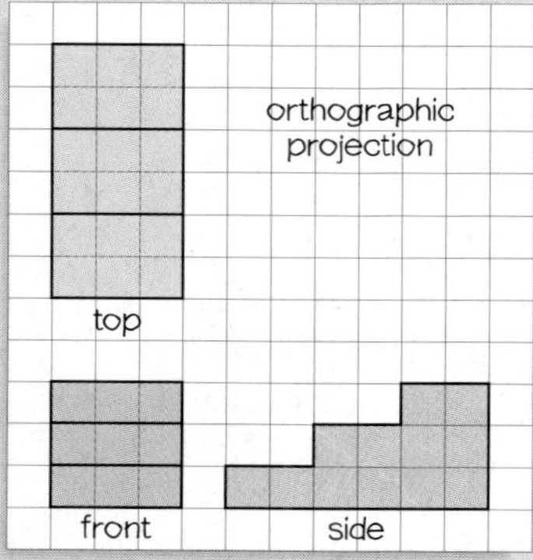

1 On graph paper, draw an orthographic projection of the stairs. Your drawing should include top, front, and side views.

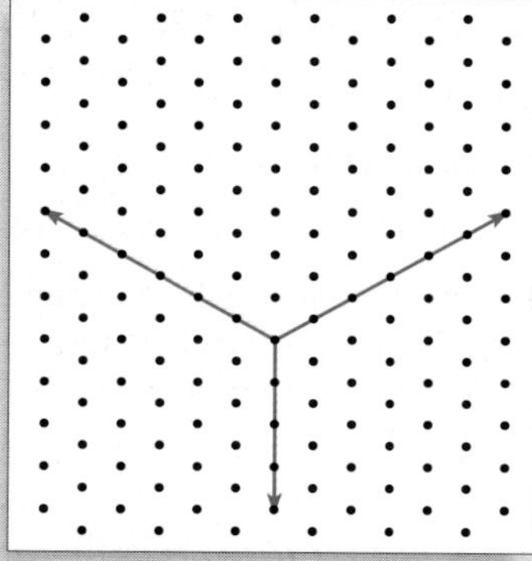

2 Sketch three axes on isometric dot paper. The lines in your isometric drawing will be parallel to these three axes.

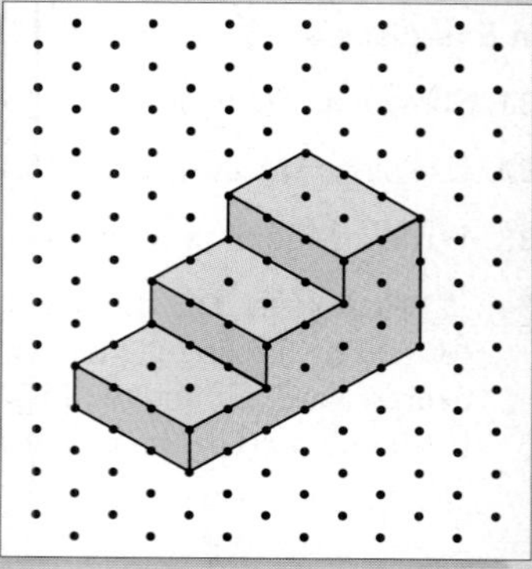

3 Copy the isometric drawing of the stairs. You can add depth by shading the top, front, and side of the stairs.

INVESTIGATION

Use your technical drawing to answer the questions below. See margin.

1. *Isometric lines* are drawn parallel to one of the isometric axes. Identify a pair of parallel isometric lines in your drawing. Mark them as parallel.
2. Identify two lines on your isometric drawing that represent perpendicular lines. Mark the right angle. What is the actual measure of the angle you marked? Explain why this angle can represent a right angle in your drawing.
3. Is there another angle in your isometric drawing that could represent a right angle between perpendicular lines? Explain why or why not.

1. Check drawings.
2. Check drawings. Either 120° or 60°.
3. Yes. Sample explanation: All four angles in the shape that represents the top of the stairs represent right angles.

CREATE YOUR OWN

Choose two objects at your school or home that have simple shapes. Use objects that already exist, or create your own using wooden blocks. For each object, make an orthographic projection and an isometric drawing. The measurements should be approximately proportional to the actual distances they represent. **Check drawings.**

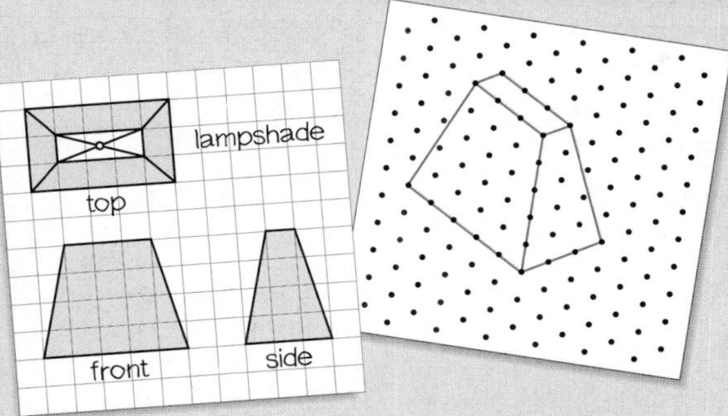

PRESENT YOUR RESULTS

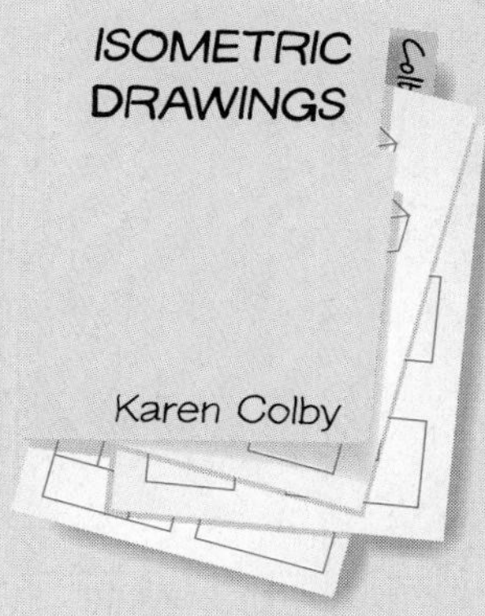

Gather your drawings and present them in a file folder.

- Include your answers to the Investigation Exercises 1–3.
- Include your technical drawings of the three stairs and two other objects.
- Summarize what you have learned about technical drawing. Include an explanation of the change in appearance of parallel and perpendicular lines as you switch from an orthographic projection to an isometric drawing.

EXTENSION

Research a career that involves technical drawing. Write a job description for an open position to be advertised in the classified section of the newspaper. Include required education, skills, responsibilities, and salary. Is this a job you think you might like? Explain why or why not.

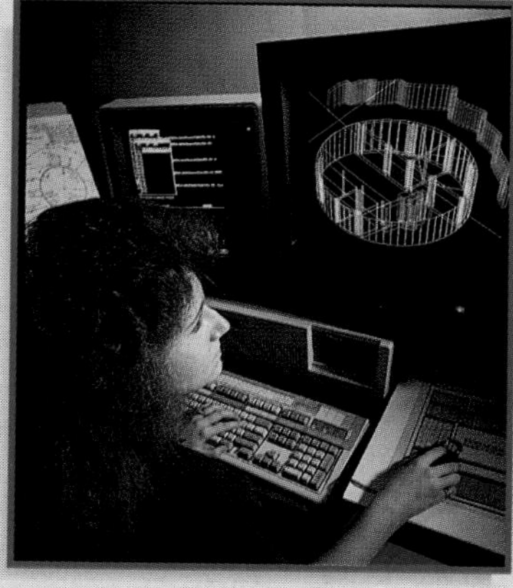

Computer-Aided Design (CAD) software allows designers to develop models and generate drawings of them.

GRADING THE PROJECT RUBRIC FOR CHAPTER PROJECT

4 Students' answers to the Investigation Exercises are correct and complete. The drawings are correct and neatly done. The written report demonstrates an understanding of the project and the mathematics involved.

3 Students' answers to the Investigation Exercises are included but may be lacking in some details. Some of the drawings are incorrect or are poorly done. The written report contains all the required elements but may not explain each part well.

2 The Investigation Exercise answers or the graphs contain serious errors or are incomplete. Not all of the questions are answered in the report.

1 The answers to the Investigation Exercises show that the student does not have an understanding of the method presented. The drawings are missing or are incorrectly marked. The report is incomplete or not understandable. The project should be returned with a new deadline for completion. The student should speak with the teacher as soon as possible so that he/she understands the purpose and format of the project.

CHAPTER 4

PLANNING THE CHAPTER

Congruent Triangles

GOALS

LESSON	GOALS	NCTM	ITED	SAT9 (TASK 1)	Terra-Nova	Local
4.1 *pp. 193–201*	CONCEPT ACTIVITY: 4.1 *Investigate angles of triangles.* GOAL 1 Classify triangles by their sides and angles. GOAL 2 Find angle measures in triangles.	1, 3, 4	MIM, MIGE		11, 13, 14, 49	12, 13
4.2 *pp. 202–210*	GOAL 1 Identify congruent figures and corresponding parts. GOAL 2 Prove that two triangles are congruent.	3, 7, 8, 9, 10	MIGE	24, 26	14, 17, 18	5
4.3 *pp. 211–219*	CONCEPT ACTIVITY: 4.3 *Investigate congruent triangles.* GOAL 1 Prove that triangles are congruent using the SSS and SAS Congruence Postulates. GOAL 2 Use congruence postulates in real-life problems.	3, 6, 7, 8, 9, 10	MIGE, RQGE	1, 24, 26, 27	14, 17, 18	2, 5, 16
4.4 *pp. 220–228*	GOAL 1 Prove that triangles are congruent using the ASA Congruence Postulate and the AAS Congruence Theorem. GOAL 2 Use congruence postulates and theorems in real-life problems. TECHNOLOGY ACTIVITY: 4.4 *Use geometry software to investigate triangles and congruence.*	3, 7, 8, 9, 10	MIGE	24, 26, 27	14, 17, 18	2, 5
4.5 *pp. 229–235*	GOAL 1 Use congruent triangles to plan and write proofs. GOAL 2 Use congruent triangles to prove constructions are valid.	3, 7, 8, 9, 10	MIGE	24, 26, 27	14, 17, 18	2, 5
4.6 *pp. 236–242*	GOAL 1 Use properties of isosceles and equilateral triangles. GOAL 2 Use properties of right triangles.	3, 9, 10	MIGE	24, 26, 27	14	5, 12, 13
4.7 *pp. 243–250*	GOAL 1 Place geometric figures in a coordinate plane. GOAL 2 Write a coordinate proof.	2, 3, 7, 8, 9, 10	MIG, MIGE		14, 16, 17, 18	2, 5, 17

RESOURCES

CHAPTER RESOURCE BOOKLETS

CHAPTER SUPPORT

Tips for New Teachers	p. 1	Prerequisite Skills Review	p. 5
Parent Guide for Student Success	p. 3	Strategies for Reading Mathematics	p. 7

LESSON SUPPORT

	4.1	4.2	4.3	4.4	4.5	4.6	4.7
Lesson Plans (regular and block)	p. 9	p. 23	p. 40	p. 53	p. 68	p. 81	p. 94
Warm-Up Exercises and Daily Quiz	p. 11	p. 25	p. 42	p. 55	p. 70	p. 83	p. 96
Activity Support Masters	p. 12						
Lesson Openers	p. 13	p. 26	p. 43	p. 56	p. 71	p. 84	p. 97
Technology Activities & Keystrokes	p. 14	p. 27	p. 44	p. 57			p. 98
Practice (3 levels)	p. 15	p. 30	p. 45	p. 59	p. 72	p. 85	p. 102
Reteaching with Practice	p. 18	p. 33	p. 48	p. 62	p. 75	p. 88	p. 105
Quick Catch-Up for Absent Students	p. 20	p. 35	p. 50	p. 64	p. 77	p. 90	p. 107
Cooperative Learning Activities					p. 78	p. 91	
Interdisciplinary Applications		p. 36		p. 65		p. 92	
Real-Life Applications	p. 21		p. 51		p. 79		p. 108
Math & History Applications		p. 37					
Challenge: Skills and Applications	p. 22	p. 38	p. 52	p. 66	p. 80	p. 93	p. 109

REVIEW AND ASSESSMENT

Quizzes	pp. 39, 67	Alternative Assessment with Math Journal	p. 118
Chapter Review Games and Activities	p. 110	Project with Rubric	p. 120
Chapter Test (3 levels)	pp. 111–116	Cumulative Review	p. 122
SAT/ACT Chapter Test	p. 117	Resource Book Answers	p. A1

TRANSPARENCIES

	4.1	4.2	4.3	4.4	4.5	4.6	4.7
Warm-Up Exercises and Daily Quiz	p. 25	p. 26	p. 27	p. 28	p. 29	p. 30	p. 31
Alternative Lesson Opener Transparencies	p. 21	p. 22	p. 23	p. 24	p. 25	p. 26	p. 27
Examples/Standardized Test Practice	✓	✓	✓	✓	✓	✓	✓
Answer Transparencies	✓	✓	✓	✓	✓	✓	✓

TECHNOLOGY

- Electronic Teaching Tools
- Online Lesson Planner
- Internet Support
- Personal Student Tutor
- Test and Practice Generator
- Geometry in Motion video
- Electronic Lesson Presentations (Lesson 4.3)

ADDITIONAL RESOURCES

- Basic Skills Workbook: Diagnosis and Remediation
- Worked-Out Solution Key
- Resources in Spanish
- Standardized Test Practice Workbook
- Practice Workbook with Examples

CORRELATIONS TO THE CALIFORNIA CURRICULUM

Correlations to California Standards
See Teacher's Edition pp. CA9–CA11

Correlations to SAT9
Task 1: See Teacher's Edition pp. CA12–CA14
Task 2: See Teacher's Edition pp. CA15–CA17

CHAPTER 4 PACING THE CHAPTER

Resource Key
- Student Edition
- Chapter 4 Resource Book
- Teacher's Edition

REGULAR SCHEDULE

Day 1

4.1

Starting Options
- Prereq. Skills Review
- Strategies for Reading
- Homework Check
- Warm-Up or Daily Quiz

Teaching Options
- Concept Act. & Wksht.
- Les. Opener (Activity)
- Examples 1–4
- Guided Practice Exs.

Apply/Homework
- See Assignment Guide.
- See the CRB: Practice, Reteach, Apply, Extend

Assessment Options
- Checkpoint Exercises

Day 2

4.1 *(cont.)*

Starting Options
- Homework Check

Teaching Options
- Examples 1–4
- Closure Question

Apply/Homework
- See Assignment Guide.
- See the CRB: Practice, Reteach, Apply, Extend

Assessment Options
- Checkpoint Exercises
- Daily Quiz (4.1)
- Stand. Test Practice

Day 3

4.2

Starting Options
- Homework Check
- Warm-Up or Daily Quiz

Teaching Options
- Les. Opener (Visual)
- Technology Activity
- Examples 1–5
- Guided Practice Exs.

Apply/Homework
- See Assignment Guide.
- See the CRB: Practice, Reteach, Apply, Extend

Assessment Options
- Checkpoint Exercises

Day 4

4.2 *(cont.)*

Starting Options
- Homework Check

Teaching Options
- Examples 1–5
- Closure Question

Apply/Homework
- See Assignment Guide.
- See the CRB: Practice, Reteach, Apply, Extend

Assessment Options
- Checkpoint Exercises
- Daily Quiz (4.2)
- Stand. Test Practice
- Quiz (4.1–4.2)

Day 5

4.3

Starting Options
- Homework Check
- Warm-Up or Daily Quiz

Teaching Options
- Concept Activity
- Les. Opener (Application)
- Examples 1–4
- Guided Practice Exs.

Apply/Homework
- See Assignment Guide.
- See the CRB: Practice, Reteach, Apply, Extend

Assessment Options
- Checkpoint Exercises, pp. 213–214

Day 6

4.3 *(cont.)*

Starting Options
- Homework Check

Teaching Options
- Examples 5–6
- Closure Question

Apply/Homework
- See Assignment Guide.
- See the CRB: Practice, Reteach, Apply, Extend

Assessment Options
- Checkpoint Exercises, p. 215
- Daily Quiz (4.3)
- Stand. Test Practice

Day 9

4.5

Starting Options
- Homework Check
- Warm-Up or Daily Quiz

Teaching Options
- Les. Opener (Visual)
- Examples 1–4
- Closure Question
- Guided Practice Exs.

Apply/Homework
- See Assignment Guide.
- See the CRB: Practice, Reteach, Apply, Extend

Assessment Options
- Checkpoint Exercises
- Daily Quiz (4.5)
- Stand. Test Practice

Day 10

4.6

Starting Options
- Homework Check
- Warm-Up or Daily Quiz

Teaching Options
- Motivating the Lesson
- Les. Opener (Software)
- Examples 1–3
- Guided Practice Exs.

Apply/Homework
- See Assignment Guide.
- See the CRB: Practice, Reteach, Apply, Extend

Assessment Options
- Checkpoint Exercises

Day 11

4.6 *(cont.)*

Starting Options
- Homework Check

Teaching Options
- Examples 1–3
- Closure Question

Apply/Homework
- See Assignment Guide.
- See the CRB: Practice, Reteach, Apply, Extend

Assessment Options
- Checkpoint Exercises
- Daily Quiz (4.6)
- Stand. Test Practice

Day 12

4.7

Starting Options
- Homework Check
- Warm-Up or Daily Quiz

Teaching Options
- Les. Opener (Activity)
- Technology Activity
- Examples 1–3
- Guided Practice Exs. 2–3

Apply/Homework
- See Assignment Guide.
- See the CRB: Practice, Reteach, Apply, Extend

Assessment Options
- Checkpoint Exercises, p. 244

Day 13

4.7 *(cont.)*

Starting Options
- Homework Check

Teaching Options
- Examples 4–6
- Closure Question
- Guided Practice Exs. 1, 4–5

Apply/Homework
- See Assignment Guide.
- See the CRB: Practice, Reteach, Apply, Extend

Assessment Options
- Checkpoint Exercises, pp. 245–246
- Daily Quiz (4.7)
- Stand. Test Practice
- Quiz (4.5–4.7)

Day 14

Review

Day 14 Start Options
- Homework Check

Reviewing Options
- Chapter 4 Summary
- Chapter 4 Review
- Chapter Review Games and Activities

Apply/Homework
- Chapter 4 Test (practice)
- Ch. Standardized Test (practice)

Day 7

4.4

Starting Options
- Homework Check
- Warm-Up or Daily Quiz

Teaching Options
- Les. Opener (Application)
- Examples 1–3
- Guided Practice Exs.

Apply/Homework
- See Assignment Guide.
- See the CRB: Practice, Reteach, Apply, Extend

Assessment Options
- Checkpoint Exercises

Day 8

4.4 *(cont.)*

Starting Options
- Homework Check

Teaching Options
- Examples 1–3
- Technology Activity
- Closure Question

Apply/Homework
- See Assignment Guide.
- See the CRB: Practice, Reteach, Apply, Extend

Assessment Options
- Checkpoint Exercises
- Daily Quiz (4.4)
- Stand. Test Practice
- Quiz (4.3–4.4)

Day 15

Assess

Day 15 Start Options
- Homework Check

Assessment Options
- Chapter 4 Test
- SAT/ACT Ch. 4 Test
- Alternative Assessment

Apply/Homework
- Skill Review, p. 262

BLOCK SCHEDULE

Day 1

Assess & 4.1

(Day 1 = Ch. 3 Day 7)

Assessment Options
- Chapter 3 Test
- SAT/ACT Ch. 3 Test
- Alternative Assessment

Ch. 4 Start Options
- Skills Review, p. 192
- Prereq. Skills Review
- Strategies for Reading

Beginning 4.1 Options
- Warm-Up (Les. 4.1)
- Concept Act. & Wksht.
- Les. Opener (Activity)
- Examples 1–4
- Guided Practice Exs.

Apply/Homework
- See Assignment Guide.
- See the CRB: Practice, Reteach, Apply, Extend

Assessment Options
- Checkpoint Exercises

Day 2

4.1 & 4.2

Day 2 Start Options
- Homework Check

Finishing 4.1 Options
- Examples 1–4
- Closure Question

Beginning 4.2 Options
- Warm-Up (Les. 4.2)
- Les. Opener (Visual)
- Technology Activity
- Examples 1–5
- Guided Practice Exs.

Apply/Homework
- See Assignment Guide.
- See the CRB: Practice, Reteach, Apply, Extend

Assessment Options
- Checkpoint Exercises
- Daily Quiz (Les. 4.1)
- Stand. Test Prac. (4.1)

Day 3

4.2 & 4.3

Day 3 Start Options
- Homework Check
- Daily Quiz (Les. 4.1)

Finishing 4.2 Options
- Examples 1–5
- Closure Question

Beginning 4.3 Options
- Warm-Up (Les. 4.3)
- Concept Activity
- Les. Opener (Appl.)
- Examples 1–4
- Guided Practice Exs.

Apply/Homework
- See Assignment Guide.
- See the CRB: Practice, Reteach, Apply, Extend

Assessment Options
- Checkpoint Exercises
- Daily Quiz (Les. 4.2)
- Stand. Test Prac. (4.2)
- Quiz (4.1–4.2)

Day 4

4.3 & 4.4

Day 4 Start Options
- Homework Check
- Daily Quiz (Les. 4.2)

Finishing 4.3 Options
- Examples 5–6
- Closure Question

Beginning 4.4 Options
- Warm-Up (Les. 4.4)
- Les. Opener (Appl.)
- Examples 1–3
- Guided Practice Exs.

Apply/Homework
- See Assignment Guide.
- See the CRB: Practice, Reteach, Apply, Extend

Assessment Options
- Checkpoint Exercises
- Daily Quiz (Les. 4.3)
- Stand. Test Prac. (4.3)

Day 5

4.4 & 4.5

Day 5 Start Options
- Homework Check
- Daily Quiz (Les. 4.3)

Finishing 4.4 Options
- Examples 1–3
- Technology Activity
- Closure Question

Teaching 4.5 Options
- Warm-Up (Les. 4.5)
- Les. Opener (Visual)
- Examples 1–4
- Closure Question
- Guided Practice Exs.

Apply/Homework
- See Assignment Guide.
- See the CRB: Practice, Reteach, Apply, Extend

Assessment Options
- Checkpoint Exercises
- Daily Quiz (Les. 4.4, 4.5)
- Stand. Test Practice
- Quiz (4.3–4.4)

Day 6

4.6

Day 6 Start Options
- Homework Check
- Warm-Up or Daily Quiz

Teaching 4.6 Options
- Motivating the Lesson
- Les. Opener (Software)
- Examples 1–3
- Closure Question
- Guided Practice Exs.

Apply/Homework
- See Assignment Guide.
- See the CRB: Practice, Reteach, Apply, Extend

Assessment Options
- Checkpoint Exercises
- Daily Quiz (Les. 4.6)
- Stand. Test Practice

Day 7

4.7

Day 7 Start Options
- Homework Check
- Warm-Up or Daily Quiz

Teaching 4.7 Options
- Les. Opener (Activity)
- Technology Activity
- Examples 1–6
- Closure Question
- Guided Practice Exs.

Apply/Homework
- See Assignment Guide.
- See the CRB: Practice, Reteach, Apply, Extend

Assessment Options
- Checkpoint Exercises
- Daily Quiz (Les. 4.7)
- Stand. Test Practice
- Quiz (4.5–4.7)

Day 8

Review/Assess

Day 8 Start Options
- Homework Check

Reviewing Options
- Chapter 4 Summary
- Chapter 4 Review
- Chapter Review Games and Activities
- Chapter 4 Test (practice)
- Ch. Standardized Test (practice)

Assessment Options
- Chapter 4 Test
- SAT/ACT Ch. 4 Test
- Alternative Assessment

Apply/Homework
- Skill Review, p. 262

CHAPTER 4

MEETING INDIVIDUAL NEEDS

BEFORE THE CHAPTER

The *Chapter 4 Resource Book* has the following materials to distribute and use before the chapter:

- **Parent Guide for Student Success**
- **Prerequisite Skills Review (pictured below)**
- **Strategies for Reading Mathematics**

PREREQUISITE SKILLS *Pages 5–6*

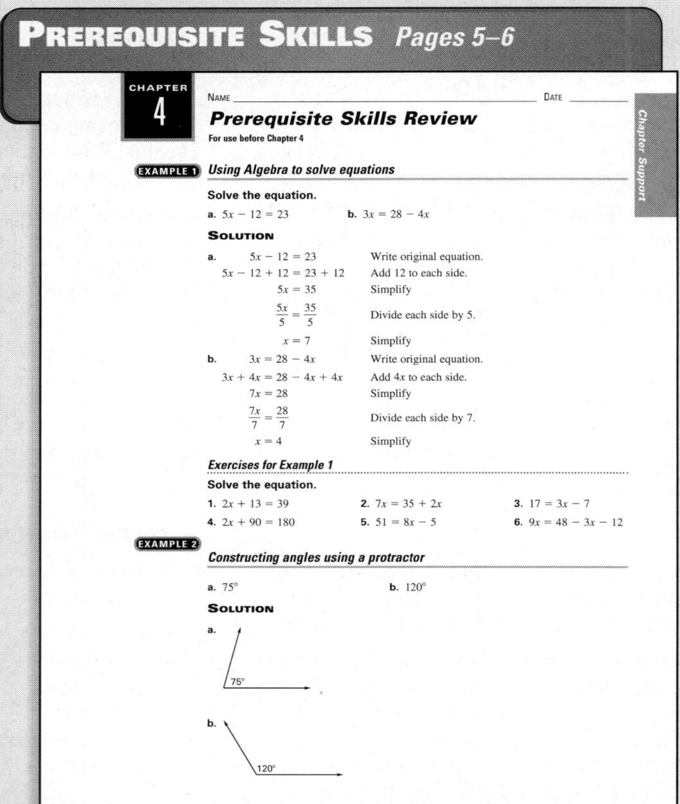

CHAPTER 4 NAME ______ DATE ______

Prerequisite Skills Review

For use before Chapter 4

Chapter Support

EXAMPLE 1 *Using Algebra to solve equations*

Solve the equation.

a. $5x - 12 = 23$ b. $3x = 28 - 4x$

SOLUTION

a. $5x - 12 = 23$ Write original equation.
$5x - 12 + 12 = 23 + 12$ Add 12 to each side.
$5x = 35$ Simplify
$\frac{5x}{5} = \frac{35}{5}$ Divide each side by 5.
$x = 7$ Simplify

b. $3x = 28 - 4x$ Write original equation.
$3x + 4x = 28 - 4x + 4x$ Add $4x$ to each side.
$7x = 28$ Simplify
$\frac{7x}{7} = \frac{28}{7}$ Divide each side by 7.
$x = 4$ Simplify

Exercises for Example 1

Solve the equation.

1. $2x + 13 = 39$ 2. $7x = 35 + 2x$ 3. $17 = 3x - 7$
4. $2x + 90 = 180$ 5. $51 = 8x - 5$ 6. $9x = 48 - 3x - 12$

EXAMPLE 2 *Constructing angles using a protractor*

a. 75° b. 120°

SOLUTION

a. 75°

b. 120°

PREREQUISITE SKILLS REVIEW These two pages support the Study Guide on page 192. They help students prepare for Chapter 4 by providing worked-out examples and practice for the following skills needed in the chapter:

- **Use algebra to solve equations.**
- **Construct angles.**
- **Use theorems or postulates to support statements about congruent angles.**

TECHNOLOGY RESOURCE

Students can use the Personal Student Tutor to find additional reteaching and practice for skills from earlier chapters that are used in Chapter 4.

DURING EACH LESSON

The *Chapter 4 Resource Book* has the following alternatives for introducing the lesson:

- **Lesson Openers (pictured below)**
- **Technology Activities with Keystrokes**

LESSON OPENER *Page 56*

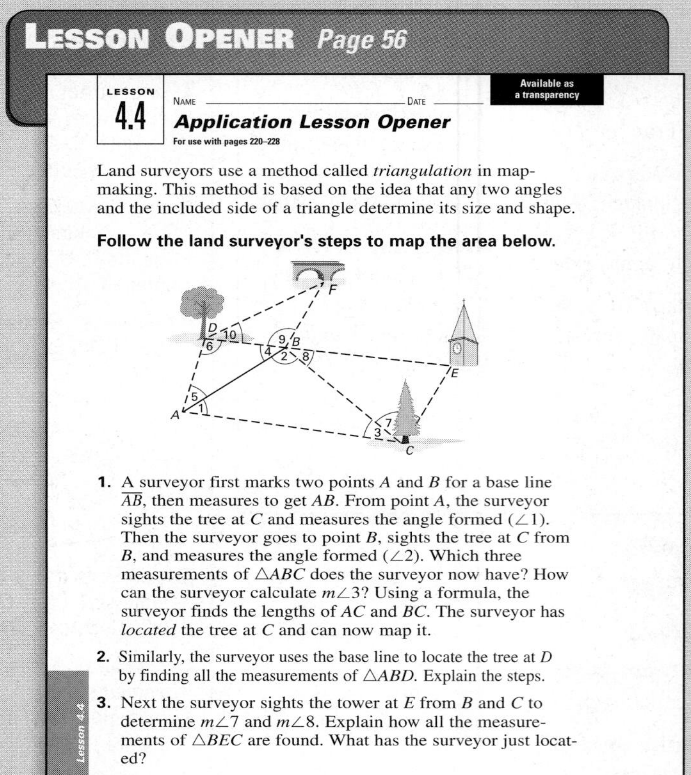

LESSON 4.4 NAME ______ DATE ______ Available as a transparency

Application Lesson Opener

For use with pages 220–228

Land surveyors use a method called *triangulation* in map-making. This method is based on the idea that any two angles and the included side of a triangle determine its size and shape.

Follow the land surveyor's steps to map the area below.

1. A surveyor first marks two points A and B for a base line $\overline{AB}$, then measures to get AB. From point A, the surveyor sights the tree at C and measures the angle formed ($\angle 1$). Then the surveyor goes to point B, sights the tree at C from B, and measures the angle formed ($\angle 2$). Which three measurements of $\triangle ABC$ does the surveyor now have? How can the surveyor calculate $m\angle 3$? Using a formula, the surveyor finds the lengths of AC and BC. The surveyor has *located* the tree at C and can now map it.
2. Similarly, the surveyor uses the base line to locate the tree at D by finding all the measurements of $\triangle ABD$. Explain the steps.
3. Next the surveyor sights the tower at E from B and C to determine $m\angle 7$ and $m\angle 8$. Explain how all the measurements of $\triangle BEC$ are found. What has the surveyor just located?
4. Now the surveyor locates the bridge at F. Explain the steps.

Lesson 4.4

APPLICATION LESSON OPENER This Lesson Opener provides an alternative way to start Lesson 4.4 in the form of a real-life application. Students see how dimensions of triangles relate to land surveying.

TECHNOLOGY RESOURCE

The Geometry in Motion video can be used to give dynamic presentations of selected material in Chapter 4.

FOLLOWING EACH LESSON

The *Chapter 4 Resource Book* has a variety of materials to follow-up each lesson. They include the following:

- **Practice (3 levels)**
- **Reteaching with Practice**
- **Quick Catch-Up for Absent Students**
- **Interdisciplinary Applications**
- **Real-Life Applications (pictured below)**

APPLICATION *Page 51*

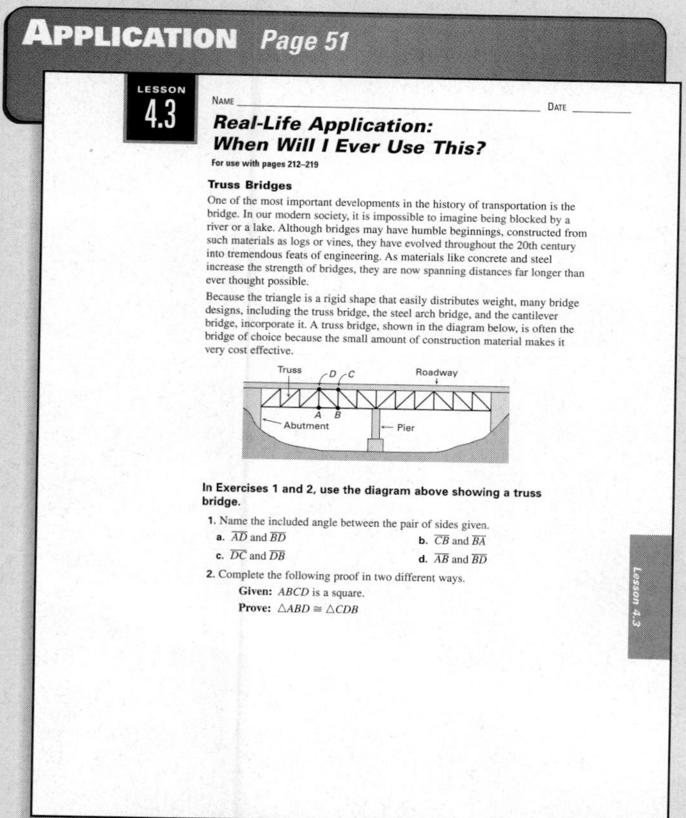
LESSON 4.3

NAME ______________________ DATE ________

Real-Life Application: When Will I Ever Use This?

For use with pages 212–219

Truss Bridges

One of the most important developments in the history of transportation is the bridge. In our modern society, it is impossible to imagine being blocked by a river or a lake. Although bridges may have humble beginnings, constructed from such materials as logs or vines, they have evolved throughout the 20th century into tremendous feats of engineering. As materials like concrete and steel increase the strength of bridges, they are now spanning distances far longer than ever thought possible.

Because the triangle is a rigid shape that easily distributes weight, many bridge designs, including the truss bridge, the steel arch bridge, and the cantilever bridge, incorporate it. A truss bridge, shown in the diagram below, is often the bridge of choice because the small amount of construction material makes it very cost effective.

In Exercises 1 and 2, use the diagram above showing a truss bridge.

1. Name the included angle between the pair of sides given.
   a. $\overline{AD}$ and $\overline{BD}$ b. $\overline{CB}$ and $\overline{BA}$
   c. $\overline{DC}$ and $\overline{DB}$ d. $\overline{AB}$ and $\overline{BD}$
2. Complete the following proof in two different ways.
   Given: *ABCD* is a square.
   Prove: $\triangle ABD \cong \triangle CDB$

Lesson 4.3

REAL-LIFE APPLICATION When students ask "When will I ever use proofs of congruent triangles?," you can have them work through this Real-Life Application in which they apply the content of Lesson 4.3 to a truss bridge.

ASSESSING THE CHAPTER

The *Chapter 4 Resource Book* has the following review and assessment materials:

- **Quizzes**
- **Chapter Review Games and Activities**
- **Chapter Test (3 levels)**
- **SAT/ACT Chapter Test (pictured below)**
- **Alternative Assessment with Rubric and Math Journal**
- **Project with Rubric**
- **Cumulative Review**

SAT/ACT CHAPTER TEST *Page 117*

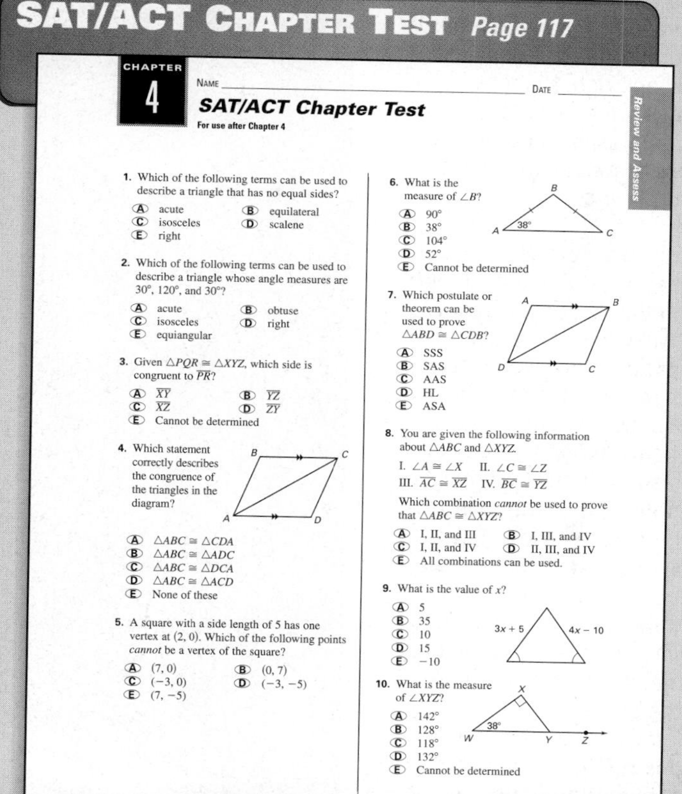
CHAPTER 4

NAME ______________________ DATE ________

SAT/ACT Chapter Test

For use after Chapter 4

1. Which of the following terms can be used to describe a triangle that has no equal sides?
   (A) acute (B) equilateral
   (C) isosceles (D) scalene
   (E) right
2. Which of the following terms can be used to describe a triangle whose angle measures are 30°, 120°, and 30°?
   (A) acute (B) obtuse
   (C) isosceles (D) right
   (E) equiangular
3. Given $\triangle PQR \cong \triangle XYZ$, which side is congruent to $\overline{PR}$?
   (A) $\overline{XY}$ (B) $\overline{YZ}$
   (C) $\overline{XZ}$ (D) $\overline{ZY}$
   (E) Cannot be determined
4. Which statement correctly describes the congruence of the triangles in the diagram?
   (A) $\triangle ABC \cong \triangle CDA$
   (B) $\triangle ABC \cong \triangle ADC$
   (C) $\triangle ABC \cong \triangle DCA$
   (D) $\triangle ABC \cong \triangle ACD$
   (E) None of these
5. A square with a side length of 5 has one vertex at (2, 0). Which of the following points *cannot* be a vertex of the square?
   (A) (7, 0) (B) (0, 7)
   (C) (−3, 0) (D) (−3, −5)
   (E) (7, −5)
6. What is the measure of $\angle B$?
   (A) 90°
   (B) 38°
   (C) 104°
   (D) 52°
   (E) Cannot be determined
7. Which postulate or theorem can be used to prove $\triangle ABD \cong \triangle CDB$?
   (A) SSS
   (B) SAS
   (C) AAS
   (D) HL
   (E) ASA
8. You are given the following information about $\triangle ABC$ and $\triangle XYZ$.
   I. $\angle A \cong \angle X$ II. $\angle C \cong \angle Z$
   III. $\overline{AC} \cong \overline{XZ}$ IV. $\overline{BC} \cong \overline{YZ}$
   Which combination *cannot* be used to prove that $\triangle ABC \cong \triangle XYZ$?
   (A) I, II, and III (B) I, III, and IV
   (C) I, II, and IV (D) II, III, and IV
   (E) All combinations can be used.
9. What is the value of x?
   (A) 5
   (B) 35
   (C) 10
   (D) 15
   (E) −10
10. What is the measure of $\angle XYZ$?
    (A) 142°
    (B) 128°
    (C) 118°
    (D) 132°
    (E) Cannot be determined

Review and Assess

SAT/ACT CHAPTER TEST This test covers the material in Chapter 4 in a standardized test format. Students taking this form of the test should be reminded to read all of the answer choices before deciding which is the correct one.

CHAPTER OVERVIEW

CHAPTER GOALS

Chapter 4 introduces students to proving triangles congruent and using congruent triangles in real-life problems. Students first classify triangles and find angle measures. They identify congruent figures and corresponding parts of figures, and learn to correctly name angles and triangles. Students prove triangles are congruent using SSS, SAS, ASA, and AAS. They use congruence postulates to solve real-life problems. They use congruent triangles to plan and write proofs and to prove the validity of constructions. They use properties of isosceles, equilateral, and right triangles. Finally they learn how to place geometric figures in a coordinate plane to prove statements about the figures.

APPLICATION NOTE

Have students stand and hold their arms out at their sides horizontally. Students will feel their muscles holding up their arms. Now provide students a few lengths of rope or string, about five feet long. Have students help each other tie each end of the string to their elbows and lay the middle of the string across the top of the heads. Now they should be able to feel some of the weight being supported by their heads. Cable-stayed bridges work on the same principle. The towers support the weight of the bridge through the cables.

Additional information about bridge construction is available at **www.mcdougallittell.com.**

CONGRUENT TRIANGLES

How does a cable-stayed bridge work?

CHAPTER 4

APPLICATION: Bridges

On a cable-stayed bridge, **the cables attached to the sides of each tower transfer the weight of the roadway to the tower.**

You can see from the diagram below that the cables balance the weight of the roadway on both sides of each tower.

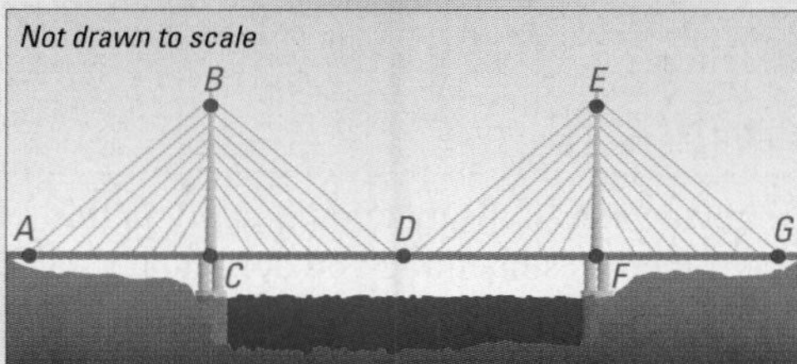

Think & Discuss

1. In the diagram above, what type of angle does each tower of the bridge make with the roadway? **right angle**
2. Use the diagram above. Find at least one pair of acute angles that appear to be congruent and one pair of obtuse angles that appear to be congruent. **See margin.**

Learn More About It

You will prove that triangles formed by the cables and towers of a cable-stayed bridge are congruent in Exercise 16 on p. 234.

APPLICATION LINK Visit www.mcdougallittell.com for more information about bridge construction.

PROJECTS

A project covering Chapters 4–5 appears on pages 316–317 of the Student Edition. An additional project for Chapter 4 is available in the *Chapter 4 Resource Book,* p. 120.

TECHNOLOGY

Software

- *Electronic Teaching Tools*
- *Online Lesson Planner*
- *Personal Student Tutor*
- *Test and Practice Generator*
- *Electronic Lesson Presentations (Lesson 4.3)*

Video

- *Geometry in Motion*

Internet Connections
www.mcdougallittell.com

- **Application Links**
  191, 210, 241
- **Student Help**
  199, 203, 217, 218, 228, 230, 237, 243, 245
- **Career Links**
  200, 234
- **Extra Challenge**
  201, 209, 219, 226, 235, 242, 249

2. ***Sample answers:***
Acute: $\angle BAC$ and $\angle BDC$, $\angle BDC$ and $\angle EDF$, $\angle EDF$ and $\angle EGF$, $\angle BAC$ and $\angle EDF$, $\angle BDC$ and $\angle EGF$, or $\angle BAC$ and $\angle EGF$; Obtuse: $\angle ABD$ and $\angle DEG$

PREPARE

DIAGNOSTIC TOOLS
The **Skill Review** exercises can help you diagnose whether students have the following skills needed in Chapter 4:

- Solve equations containing variables.
- Draw angles using protractors.
- Name angle theorems.

The following resources are available for students who need additional help with these skills:

- Prerequisite Skills Review (*Chapter 4 Resource Book,* p. 5; *Warm-Up Transparencies,* p. 24)
- *Personal Student Tutor*

ADDITIONAL RESOURCES
The following resources are provided to help you prepare for the upcoming chapter and customize review materials:

- ***Chapter 4 Resource Book***
  Tips for New Teachers (p. 1)
  Parent Guide (p. 3)
  Lesson Plans (every lesson)
  Lesson Plans for Block Scheduling (every lesson)
- ***Electronic Teaching Tools***
- ***Online Lesson Planner***
- ***Test and Practice Generator***

7–9. See Additional Answers beginning on page AA1.

CHAPTER 4

Study Guide

PREVIEW

What's the chapter about?

Chapter 4 is about **congruent triangles**. Congruent triangles are triangles that are the same size and shape. In Chapter 4 you'll learn

- to prove triangles are congruent given information about their sides and angles.
- how to use congruent triangles to solve real-life problems.

KEY VOCABULARY

▶ **Review**
- congruent segments, p. 19
- acute angle, p. 28
- right angle, p. 28
- midpoint, p. 34
- vertical angles, p. 44
- alternate interior angles, p. 131

▶ **New**
- isosceles triangle, p. 194
- right triangle, p. 194
- legs and hypotenuse of a right triangle, p. 195
- interior angle, p. 196
- exterior angle, p. 196
- corollary, p. 197
- congruent figures, p. 202
- corresponding sides and angles, p. 202
- coordinate proof, p. 243

PREPARE

Are you ready for the chapter?

SKILL REVIEW Do these exercises to review key skills that you'll apply in this chapter. See the given **reference page** if there is something you don't understand.

STUDENT HELP
Study Tip
"Student Help" boxes throughout the chapter give you study tips and tell you where to look for extra help in this book and on the Internet.

USING ALGEBRA **Solve the equation.** (Skills Review, pp. 789 and 790)

1. $180 = 90 + x + 60$ 30 **2.** $6 = 2x + 2$ 2 **3.** $2x = 4x - 6$ 3

4. $180 = 30 + 2x$ 75 **5.** $90 = 3x - 90$ 60 **6.** $3x = 27 - 6x$ 3

Use a protractor to draw an angle that has the given measure. Check your results by measuring the angle. (Review p. 27) 7–9. See margin.

7. 30° **8.** 135° **9.** 72°

Use the diagram at the right. Write the theorem that supports each statement. (Review pp. 112 and 143)

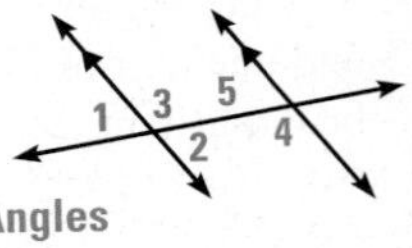

10. $\angle 1 \cong \angle 2$ Vertical Angles **11.** $\angle 3 \cong \angle 4$ Alternate Interior Angles **12.** $\angle 1 \cong \angle 5$ Corresponding Angles Postulate

STUDY STRATEGY

Here's a study strategy!

Remembering Theorems

In this chapter you will learn many theorems that you will use throughout the rest of the book.

- Keep a list of theorems in your math notebook.
- Make up a helpful name for each theorem, or draw a sketch to help you recognize it.

ACTIVITY 4.1

Developing Concepts

GROUP ACTIVITY
Work in a small group.

MATERIALS
- paper
- scissors
- ruler

Investigating Angles of Triangles

QUESTION **What is the sum of the measures of the *interior angles* of a triangle? How is the measure of an *exterior angle* of a triangle related to the measures of its interior angles?**

EXPLORING THE CONCEPT: INTERIOR ANGLES

1. With other students in your group, draw and cut out several different triangles.
2. For each triangle, tear off the three corners and place them adjacent to each other, as shown in the diagram at the right. Check figures.
3. What do you observe about the measures of the three interior angles of a triangle?
The sum of the measures of the angles is 180°.

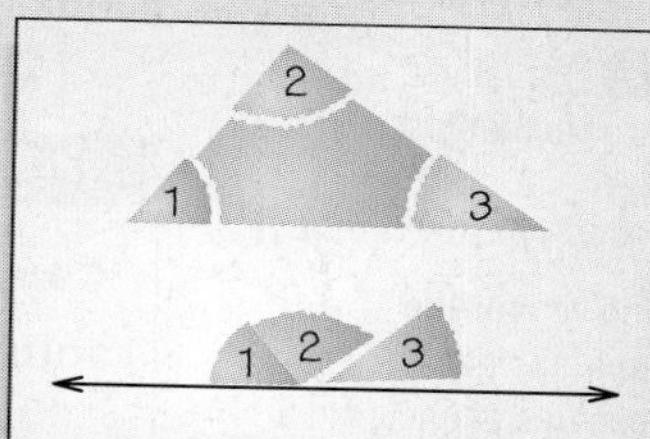

∠1, ∠2, and ∠3 are *interior angles*.

EXPLORING THE CONCEPT: EXTERIOR ANGLES

4. With the other students in your group, draw and cut out several different triangles.
5. Place each triangle on a piece of paper and extend one side to form an exterior angle, as shown in the diagram at the right.
6. Tear off the corners that are not adjacent to the exterior angle. Use them to fill the exterior angle, as shown. Check figures.
7. What do you observe about the measure of an exterior angle of a triangle?
The measure of an exterior angle is equal to the sum of the measures of the nonadjacent interior angles.

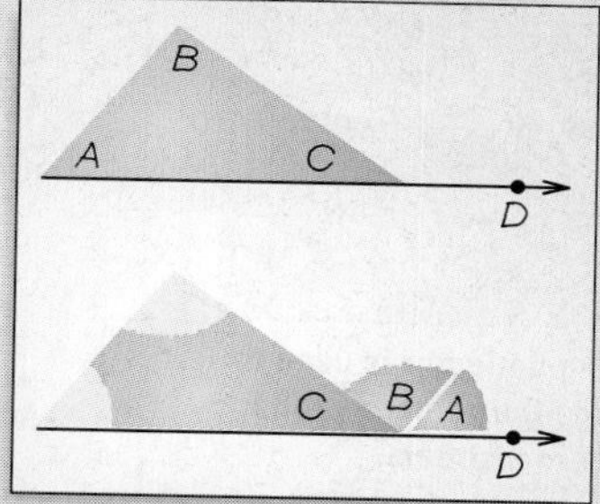

In the top figure, ∠*BCD* is an *exterior angle*.

DRAWING CONCLUSIONS

1. Make a conjecture about the sum of the measures of the interior angles of a triangle. The sum of the measures of the interior angles of a triangle is 180°.
2. Make a conjecture about the relationship between the measure of an exterior angle of a triangle and the measures of the nonadjacent interior angles.
3. **CRITICAL THINKING** If you know the measures of two interior angles of a triangle, how can you find the measure of the third interior angle?
Subtract the sum of the two measures from 180°.

2. The measure of an exterior angle of a triangle is equal to the sum of the measures of the nonadjacent interior angles.

1 Planning the Activity

PURPOSE
To investigate the measures of exterior angles and interior angles of a triangle.

MATERIALS
- scissors
- ruler
- Activity Support Master (*Chapter 4 Resource Book*, p. 12)

PACING
- Exploring the Concept — 10 min
- Drawing Conclusions — 5 min

LINK TO LESSON
As students study the Triangle Sum Theorem and the Exterior Angle Theorem on pages 196 and 197, have them recall the results of this activity.

2 Managing the Activity

CLASSROOM MANAGEMENT
You can have ready-made triangles available for students to use. The triangles should be of different types and sizes to emphasize the fact that the results are the same no matter what type or size triangle is used.

ALTERNATIVE APPROACH
This activity could be performed as a demonstration using an overhead projector. Students can make conjectures as a class.

3 Closing the Activity

KEY DISCOVERY
The sum of the measures of the interior angles of a triangle is 180°. The measure of an exterior angle of a triangle is equal to the sum of the nonadjacent interior angles.

ACTIVITY ASSESSMENT
If one angle of a triangle measures 78°, what is the sum of the measures of the other interior angles? 102°

1 PLAN

PACING
Basic: 2 days
Average: 2 days
Advanced: 2 days
Block Schedule: 0.5 block with Ch. 3 Assess.
0.5 block with 4.2

LESSON OPENER ACTIVITY
An alternative way to approach Lesson 4.1 is to use the Activity Lesson Opener:
- Blackline Master (*Chapter 4 Resource Book*, p. 13)
- Transparency (p. 21)

MEETING INDIVIDUAL NEEDS
- ***Chapter 4 Resource Book***
  Prerequisite Skills Review (p. 5)
  Practice Level A (p. 15)
  Practice Level B (p. 16)
  Practice Level C (p. 17)
  Reteaching with Practice (p. 18)
  Absent Student Catch-Up (p. 20)
  Challenge (p. 22)
- ***Resources in Spanish***
- ***Personal Student Tutor***

NEW-TEACHER SUPPORT
See the Tips for New Teachers on pp. 1–2 of the *Chapter 4 Resource Book* for additional notes about Lesson 4.1.

WARM-UP EXERCISES
Transparency Available
State the number of sides in each geometric figure.
1. trapezoid 4
2. equilateral triangle 3
3. rhombus 4
4. parallelogram 4
5. scalene triangle 3

4.1 Triangles and Angles

What you should learn

GOAL 1 Classify triangles by their sides and angles, as applied in **Example 2.**

GOAL 2 Find angle measures in triangles.

Why you should learn it

▼ To solve **real-life** problems, such as finding the measures of angles in a wing deflector in **Exs. 45 and 46.**

REAL LIFE

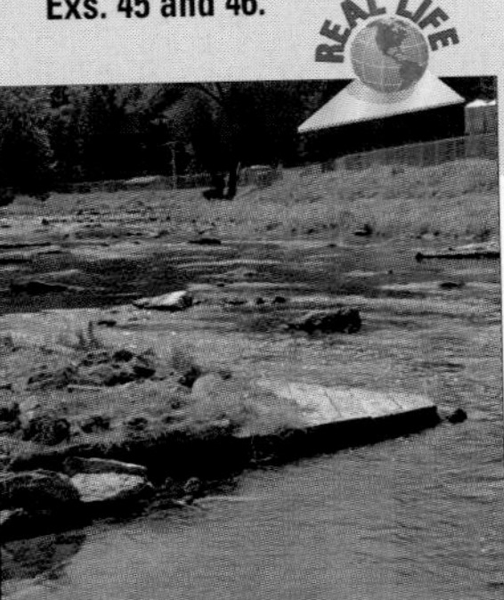

A wing deflector is used to change the velocity of the water in a stream.

CALIFORNIA STANDARDS AND ASSESSMENT
CA Standards: 12, 13

GOAL 1 CLASSIFYING TRIANGLES

A **triangle** is a figure formed by three segments joining three noncollinear points. A triangle can be classified by its sides and by its angles, as shown in the definitions below.

NAMES OF TRIANGLES

Classification by Sides

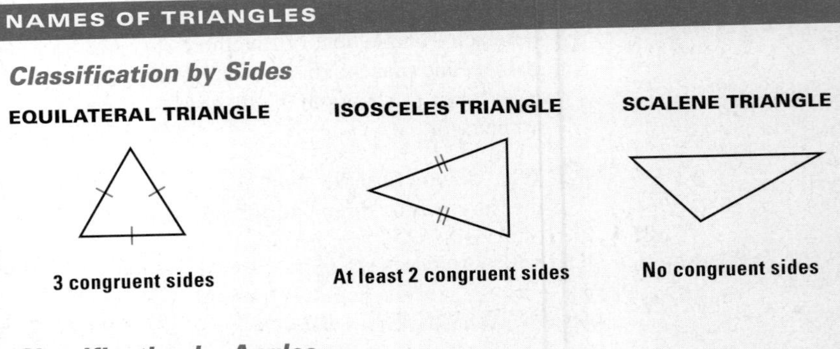

EQUILATERAL TRIANGLE	ISOSCELES TRIANGLE	SCALENE TRIANGLE
3 congruent sides	At least 2 congruent sides	No congruent sides

Classification by Angles

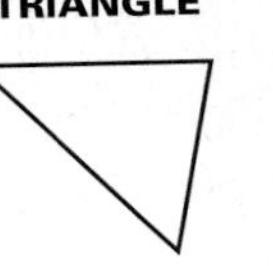
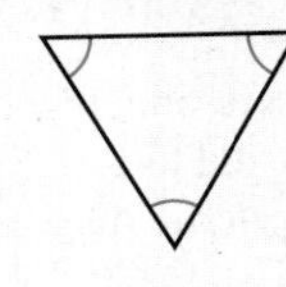
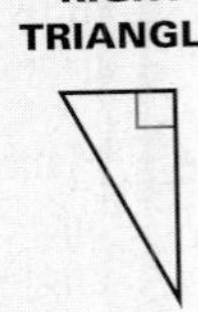
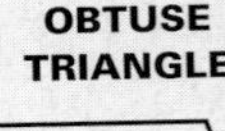

ACUTE TRIANGLE	EQUIANGULAR TRIANGLE	RIGHT TRIANGLE	OBTUSE TRIANGLE
3 acute angles	3 congruent angles	1 right angle	1 obtuse angle

Note: An equiangular triangle is also acute.

EXAMPLE 1 ***Classifying Triangles***

When you classify a triangle, you need to be as specific as possible.

a. $\triangle ABC$ has three acute angles and no congruent sides. It is an acute scalene triangle. ($\triangle ABC$ is read as "triangle ABC.")

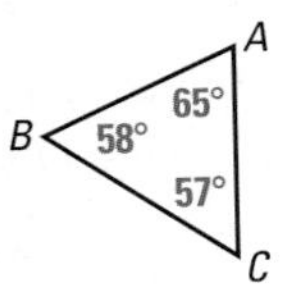

b. $\triangle DEF$ has one obtuse angle and two congruent sides. It is an obtuse isosceles triangle.

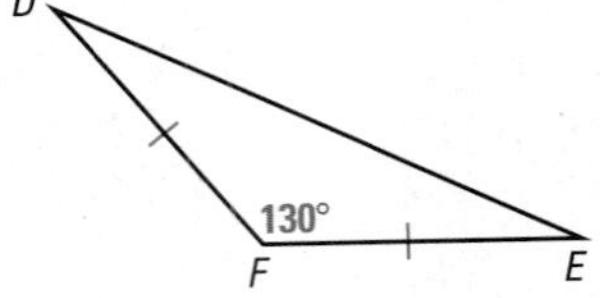

Each of the three points joining the sides of a triangle is a **vertex**. (The plural of vertex is *vertices*.) For example, in $\triangle ABC$, points A, B, and C are vertices.

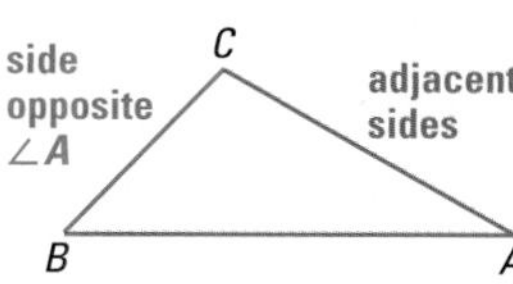

In a triangle, two sides sharing a common vertex are **adjacent sides**. In $\triangle ABC$, $\overline{CA}$ and $\overline{BA}$ are adjacent sides. The third side, $\overline{BC}$, is the side *opposite* $\angle A$.

RIGHT AND ISOSCELES TRIANGLES The sides of right triangles and isosceles triangles have special names. In a right triangle, the sides that form the right angle are the **legs** of the right triangle. The side opposite the right angle is the **hypotenuse** of the triangle.

An isosceles triangle can have three congruent sides, in which case it is equilateral. When an isosceles triangle has only two congruent sides, then these two sides are the **legs** of the isosceles triangle. The third side is the **base** of the isosceles triangle.

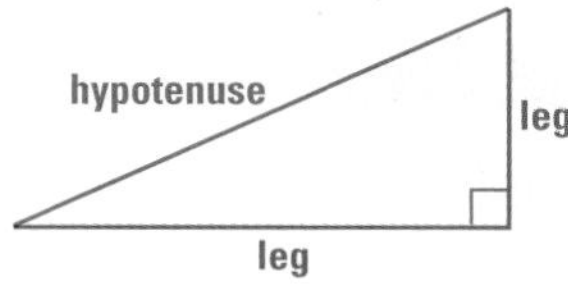

Right triangle

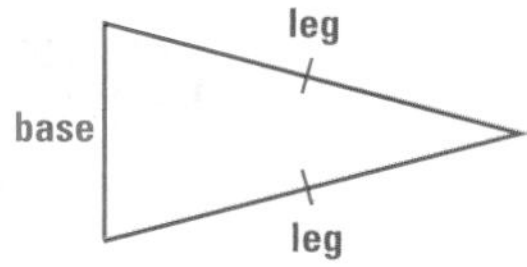

Isosceles triangle

EXAMPLE 2 *Identifying Parts of an Isosceles Right Triangle*

The diagram shows a triangular loom.

a. Explain why $\triangle ABC$ is an isosceles right triangle.

b. Identify the legs and the hypotenuse of $\triangle ABC$. Which side is the base of the triangle?

A about 7 ft B
5 ft 5 ft
C

SOLUTION

a. In the diagram, you are given that $\angle C$ is a right angle. By definition, $\triangle ABC$ is a right triangle. Because $AC = 5$ ft and $BC = 5$ ft, $\overline{AC} \cong \overline{BC}$. By definition, $\triangle ABC$ is also an isosceles triangle.

b. Sides $\overline{AC}$ and $\overline{BC}$ are adjacent to the right angle, so they are the legs. Side $\overline{AB}$ is opposite the right angle, so it is the hypotenuse. Because $\overline{AC} \cong \overline{BC}$, side $\overline{AB}$ is also the base.

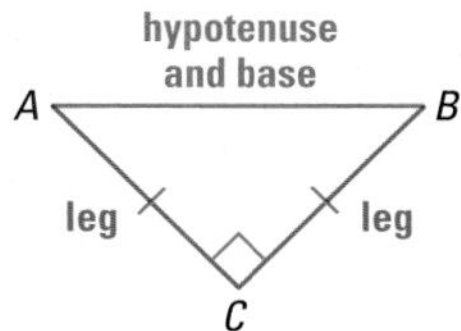

WEAVING Most looms are used to weave rectangular cloth. The loom shown in the photo is used to weave triangular pieces of cloth. A piece of cloth woven on the loom can use about 550 yards of yarn.

2 TEACH

EXTRA EXAMPLE 1

Classify the triangle.

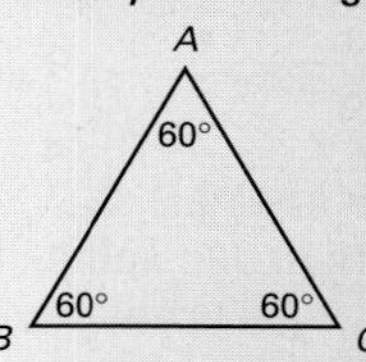

equilateral equiangular

EXTRA EXAMPLE 2

The diagram shows a bridge.

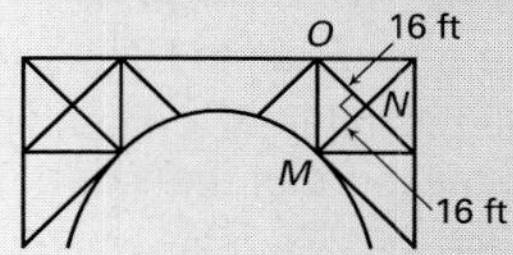

a. Explain why $\triangle MNO$ is an isosceles right triangle. **$\angle MNO$ is a right angle; $NO = MN = 16$ ft; by definition, $\triangle MNO$ is an isosceles right triangle**

b. Identify the legs and the hypotenuse of $\triangle MNO$. Which side is the base of the triangle? **legs: $\overline{MN}$ and $\overline{NO}$; hypotenuse: $\overline{MO}$; base: $\overline{MO}$**

CHECKPOINT EXERCISES

For use after Example 1:

1. Classify the triangle.

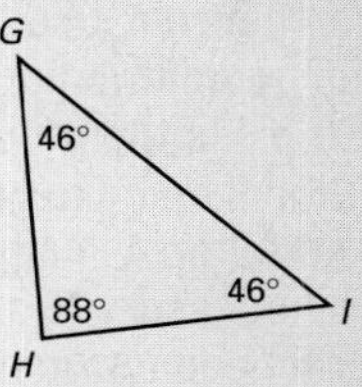

acute isosceles

For use after Example 2:

2. Use the given triangle.

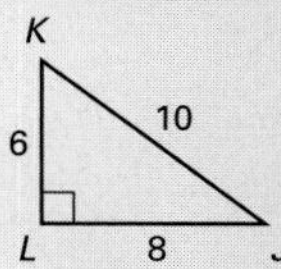

a. Explain why the triangle is a scalene right triangle. **It has one right angle and the side lengths are different.**

b. Explain why there is no base in the triangle. **The triangle is not isosceles.**

EXTRA EXAMPLE 3

Find the value of x. Then find the measure of the exterior angle. $x = 83$; 155°

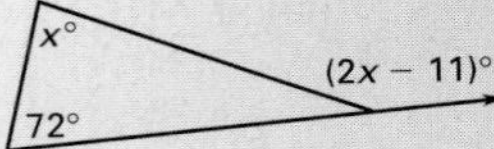

EXTRA EXAMPLE 4

The measure of one acute angle of a right triangle is one-fourth the measure of the other acute angle. Find the measure of each acute angle. 72°, 18°

CHECKPOINT EXERCISES

For use after Example 3:

1. Find the value of x. Then find the measure of the exterior angle. $x = 39$; 149°

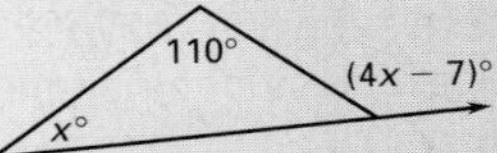

For use after Example 4:

2. The measure of one acute angle of a right triangle is five times the measure of the other acute angle. Find the measure of each acute angle. 15°, 75°

MULTIPLE REPRESENTATIONS

The proof of Theorem 4.1, the Triangle Sum Theorem, uses both algebraic and geometric notation. Step 3 and Step 4 of the proof are equivalent, Step 3 being in geometric notation and Step 4 in algebraic notation. It is necessary to make this switch from geometric notation to algebraic notation because what we are attempting to prove requires an algebraic statement.

GOAL 2 USING ANGLE MEASURES OF TRIANGLES

When the sides of a triangle are extended, other angles are formed. The three original angles are the **interior angles**. The angles that are adjacent to the interior angles are the **exterior angles**. Each vertex has a *pair* of congruent exterior angles. It is common to show only *one* exterior angle at each vertex.

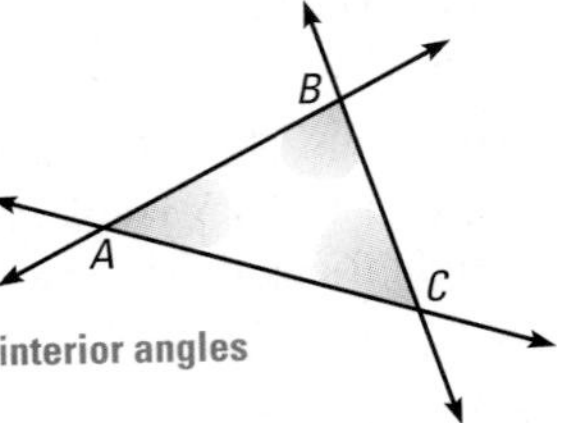

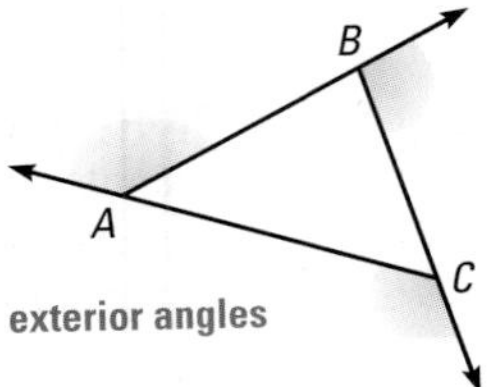

In Activity 4.1 on page 193, you may have discovered the *Triangle Sum Theorem*, shown below, and the *Exterior Angle Theorem*, shown on page 197.

THEOREM

THEOREM 4.1 ***Triangle Sum Theorem***

The sum of the measures of the interior angles of a triangle is 180°.

$m\angle A + m\angle B + m\angle C = 180°$

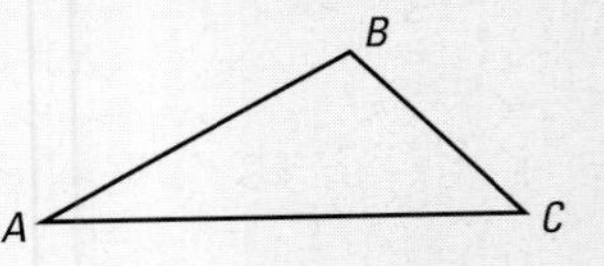

To prove some theorems, you may need to add a line, a segment, or a ray to the given diagram. Such an *auxiliary line* is used to prove the Triangle Sum Theorem.

GIVEN ▶ $\triangle ABC$

PROVE ▶ $m\angle 1 + m\angle 2 + m\angle 3 = 180°$

Plan for Proof By the Parallel Postulate, you can draw an auxiliary line through point B and parallel to $\overline{AC}$. Because $\angle 4$, $\angle 2$, and $\angle 5$ form a straight angle, the sum of their measures is 180°. You also know that $\angle 1 \cong \angle 4$ and $\angle 3 \cong \angle 5$ by the Alternate Interior Angles Theorem.

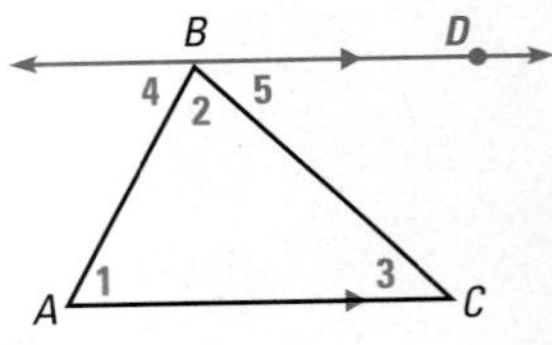

Statements	Reasons
1. Draw $\overleftrightarrow{BD}$ parallel to $\overline{AC}$.	1. Parallel Postulate
2. $m\angle 4 + m\angle 2 + m\angle 5 = 180°$	2. Angle Addition Postulate and definition of straight angle
3. $\angle 1 \cong \angle 4$ and $\angle 3 \cong \angle 5$	3. Alternate Interior Angles Theorem
4. $m\angle 1 = m\angle 4$ and $m\angle 3 = m\angle 5$	4. Definition of congruent angles
5. $m\angle 1 + m\angle 2 + m\angle 3 = 180°$	5. Substitution property of equality

STUDENT HELP

Study Tip
An auxiliary line, segment, or ray used in a proof must be justified with a reason.

THEOREM

THEOREM 4.2 ***Exterior Angle Theorem***

The measure of an exterior angle of a triangle is equal to the sum of the measures of the two nonadjacent interior angles.

$m\angle 1 = m\angle A + m\angle B$

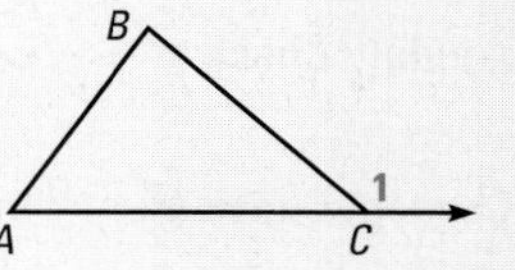

EXAMPLE 3 *Finding an Angle Measure*

You can apply the Exterior Angle Theorem to find the measure of the exterior angle shown. First write and solve an equation to find the value of x:

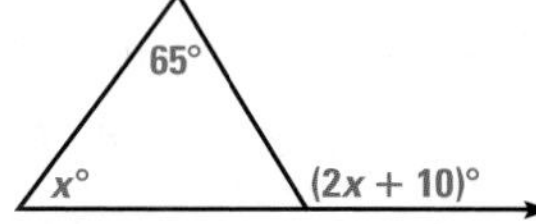

$x° + 65° = (2x + 10)°$ **Apply the Exterior Angles Theorem.**

$55 = x$ **Solve for *x*.**

▶ So, the measure of the exterior angle is $(2 \cdot 55 + 10)°$, or $120°$.

STUDENT HELP

Skills Review
For help with solving equations, see p. 790.

A **corollary to a theorem** is a statement that can be proved easily using the theorem. The corollary below follows from the Triangle Sum Theorem.

COROLLARY

COROLLARY TO THE TRIANGLE SUM THEOREM

The acute angles of a right triangle are complementary.

$m\angle A + m\angle B = 90°$

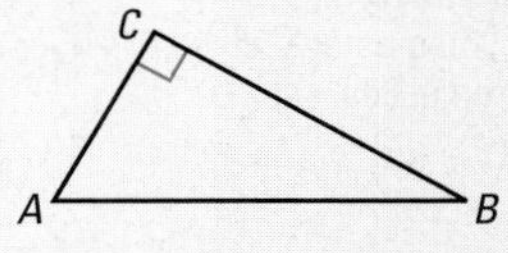

EXAMPLE 4 *Finding Angle Measures*

The measure of one acute angle of a right triangle is two times the measure of the other acute angle. Find the measure of each acute angle.

SOLUTION

Make a sketch. Let $x° = m\angle A$.
Then $m\angle B = 2x°$.

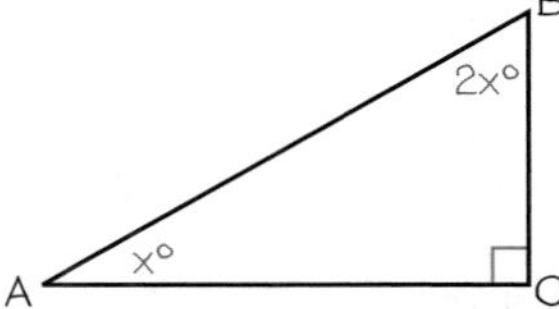

$x° + 2x° = 90°$ **The acute angles of a right triangle are complementary.**

$x = 30$ **Solve for *x*.**

▶ So, $m\angle A = 30°$ and $m\angle B = 2(30°) = 60°$.

STUDENT HELP NOTES

Skill Review As students review solving equations on p. 790, remind them that the goal is to find a value for the variable in the equation. All numeric values go on one side of the equation and all terms containing the variable go on the other side of the equation.

MATHEMATICAL REASONING

Knowing that the sum of the two acute angles of a right triangle sum to 90° will help students when they study trigonometric identities. The identities $\sin\theta = \cos(90° - \theta)$ and $\cos\theta = \sin(90° - \theta)$ are both connected to this corollary.

FOCUS ON VOCABULARY

Ask questions such as the following to test students' understanding: Can a scalene triangle be equiangular? Can an isosceles triangle be obtuse? Can a right triangle be equilateral? **no; yes; no**

CLOSURE QUESTION

What are some ways to classify a triangle by sides? by angles? **sides: equilateral, isosceles, scalene; angles: acute, obtuse, right, equiangular**

DAILY PUZZLER

The ratio of the measures of the angles in a triangle is 3:2:1. Find the measures. **90°, 60°, 30°**

3 APPLY

ASSIGNMENT GUIDE

BASIC
Day 1: pp. 198–201 Exs. 10–15, 16–38 even, 42, 49, 50
Day 2: pp. 198–201 Exs. 17–43 odd, 45–47, 52–68

AVERAGE
Day 1: pp. 198–201 Exs. 10–15, 16–38 even, 42, 49, 50
Day 2: pp. 198–201 Exs. 17–43 odd, 45–47, 52–68

ADVANCED
Day 1: pp. 198–201 Exs. 10–15, 16–38 even, 42, 49–51
Day 2: pp. 198–201 Exs. 17–43 odd, 45–48, 52–68

BLOCK SCHEDULE
pp. 198–201 Exs. 10–15, 16–38 even, 42, 49, 50 (with Ch. 3 Assess.)
pp. 198–201 Exs. 17–43 odd, 45–47, 52–68 (with 4.2)

EXERCISE LEVELS

Level A: *Easier*
10–21

Level B: *More Difficult*
22–39, 41–47, 49, 50

Level C: *Most Difficult*
40, 48, 51

✓ HOMEWORK CHECK

To quickly check student understanding of key concepts, go over the following exercises: Exs. 16, 24, 30, 32, 34, 38, 42, 47. See also the Daily Homework Quiz:

- Blackline Master (*Chapter 4 Resource Book*, p. 25)
- Transparency (p. 26)

GUIDED PRACTICE

Vocabulary Check ✓

1. Sketch an obtuse scalene triangle. Label its interior angles 1, 2, and 3. Then draw its exterior angles. Shade the exterior angles. See margin.

Concept Check ✓

In the figure, $\overline{PQ} \cong \overline{PS}$ and $\overline{PR} \perp \overline{QS}$. Complete the sentence.

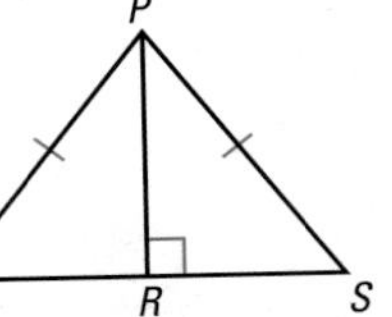

2. $\overline{PQ}$ is the __?__ of the right triangle $\triangle PQR$. hypotenuse
3. In $\triangle PQR$, $\overline{PQ}$ is the side opposite angle __?__. PRQ
4. $\overline{QS}$ is the __?__ of the isosceles triangle $\triangle PQS$. base
5. The legs of $\triangle PRS$ are __?__ and __?__. $\overline{PR}$ and $\overline{RS}$

Skill Check ✓

In Exercises 6–8, classify the triangle by its angles and by its sides.

6. 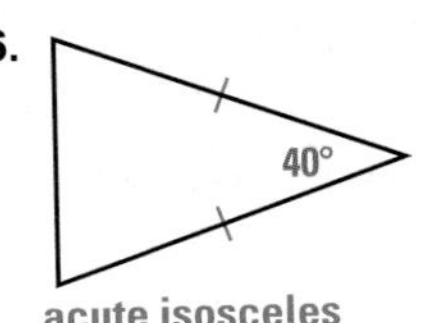

acute isosceles

7. 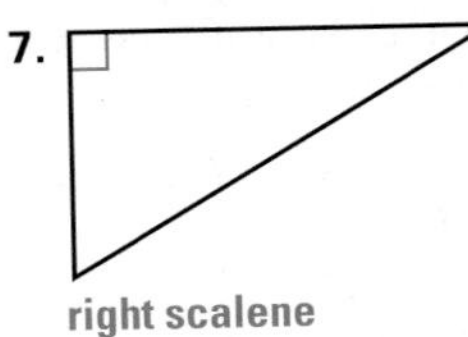
right scalene

8. 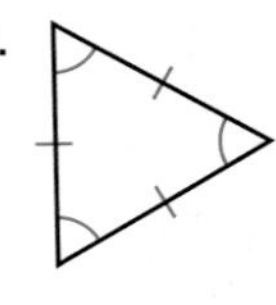

8. equiangular (or acute); equilateral (or isosceles)

9. The measure of one interior angle of a triangle is 25°. The other interior angles are congruent. Find the measures of the other interior angles. 77.5°

PRACTICE AND APPLICATIONS

STUDENT HELP
Extra Practice to help you master skills is on p. 809.

MATCHING TRIANGLES **In Exercises 10–15, match the triangle description with the most specific name.**

10. Side lengths: 2 cm, 3 cm, 4 cm B
11. Side lengths: 3 cm, 2 cm, 3 cm E
12. Side lengths: 4 cm, 4 cm, 4 cm A
13. Angle measures: 60°, 60°, 60° D
14. Angle measures: 30°, 60°, 90° F
15. Angle measures: 20°, 145°, 15° C

A. Equilateral
B. Scalene
C. Obtuse
D. Equiangular
E. Isosceles
F. Right

CLASSIFYING TRIANGLES **Classify the triangle by its angles and by its sides.**

16. 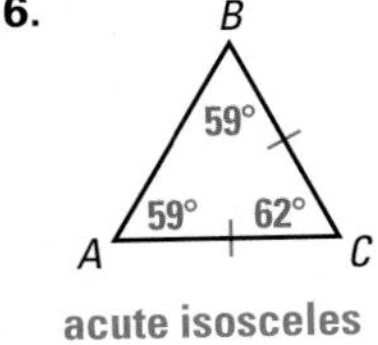

acute isosceles

17.  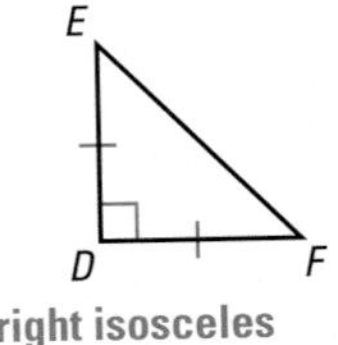

right isosceles

18. 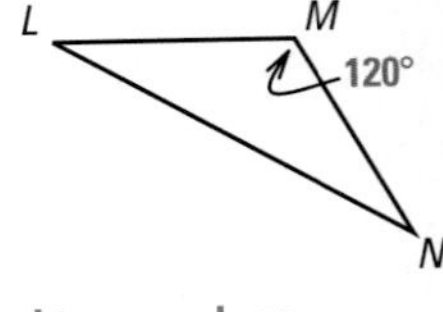

obtuse scalene

19. 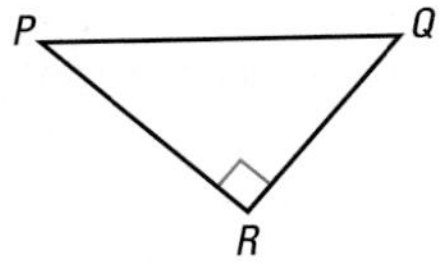 P Q R
right scalene

20. 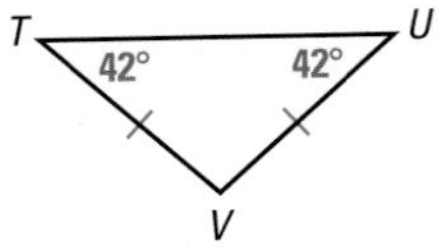 T U V 42° 42°
obtuse isosceles

21. 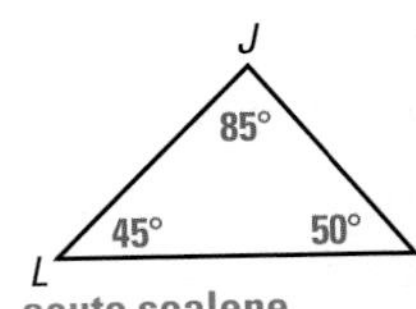

acute scalene

STUDENT HELP
HOMEWORK HELP
Example 1: Exs. 10–26, 34–36
Example 2: Exs. 27, 28, 45
Example 3: Exs. 31–39
Example 4: Exs. 41–44

LOGICAL REASONING Complete the statement using *always, sometimes,* or *never.*

22. An isosceles triangle is __?__ an equilateral triangle. sometimes

23. An obtuse triangle is __?__ an isosceles triangle. sometimes

24. An interior angle of a triangle and one of its adjacent exterior angles are __?__ supplementary. always

25. The acute angles of a right triangle are __?__ complementary. always

26. A triangle __?__ has a right angle and an obtuse angle. never

IDENTIFYING PARTS OF TRIANGLES Refer to the triangles in Exercises 16–21.

27. Identify the legs and the hypotenuse of any right triangles.

28. Identify the legs and the base of any isosceles triangles. Which isosceles triangle has a base that is also the hypotenuse of a right triangle?

27. (Ex. 17) legs: $\overline{DE}$, $\overline{DF}$, hypotenuse: $\overline{EF}$; (Ex. 19) legs: $\overline{RP}$, $\overline{RQ}$, hypotenuse: $\overline{PQ}$

28. (Ex. 16) legs: $\overline{CA}$, $\overline{CB}$, base: $\overline{AB}$; (Ex. 17) legs: $\overline{DE}$, $\overline{DF}$, base: $\overline{EF}$; (Ex. 20) legs: $\overline{VT}$, $\overline{VU}$, base: $\overline{TU}$; $\triangle DEF$ (Ex. 17)

USING ALGEBRA Use the graph. The segment $\overline{AB}$ is a leg of an isosceles right triangle.

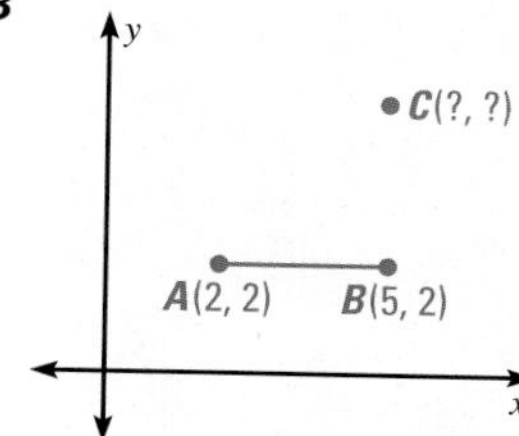

29. Find the coordinates of point C. Copy the graph and sketch $\triangle ABC$. C(5, 5); Check sketches.

30. Find the coordinates of a point D that forms a different isosceles right triangle with leg $\overline{AB}$. Include a sketch with your answer.
Sample answer: D(2, –1); Check sketches.

STUDENT HELP

HOMEWORK HELP
Visit our Web site www.mcdougallittell.com for help with Exs. 31–33.

FINDING ANGLE MEASURES Find the measure of the numbered angles.

31.
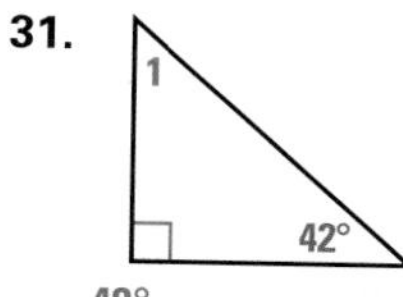

48°

32.
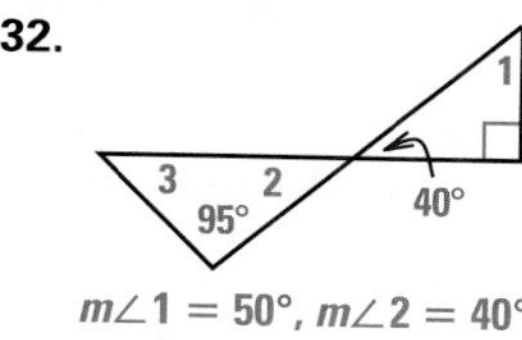

$m\angle 1 = 50°$, $m\angle 2 = 40°$, $m\angle 3 = 45°$

33.
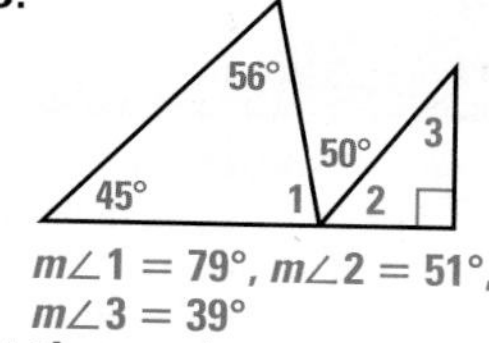

$m\angle 1 = 79°$, $m\angle 2 = 51°$, $m\angle 3 = 39°$

USING ALGEBRA The variable expressions represent the angle measures of a triangle. Find the measure of each angle. Then classify the triangle by its angles. 34–36. See margin.

34. $m\angle A = x°$
$m\angle B = 2x°$
$m\angle C = (2x + 15)°$

35. $m\angle R = x°$
$m\angle S = 7x°$
$m\angle T = x°$

36. $m\angle W = (x - 15)°$
$m\angle Y = (2x - 165)°$
$m\angle Z = 90°$

34. $m\angle A = 33°$, $m\angle B = 66°$, $m\angle C = 81°$; acute

35. $m\angle R = 20°$, $m\angle S = 140°$, $m\angle T = 20°$; obtuse

36. $m\angle W = 75°$, $m\angle Y = 15°$, $m\angle Z = 90°$; right

EXTERIOR ANGLES Find the measure of the exterior angle shown.

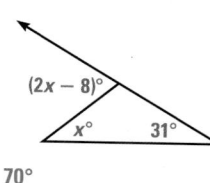

37.
(2x – 8)°
x°
31°
70°

38.
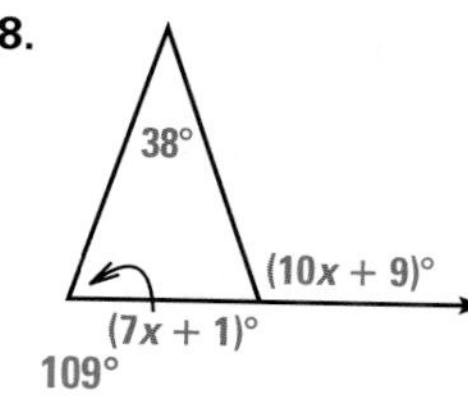

109°

39.
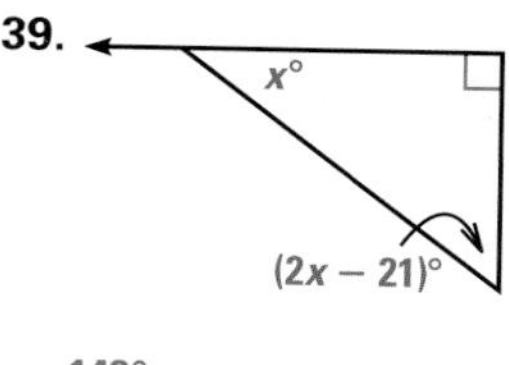

143°

40. **TECHNOLOGY** Use geometry software to demonstrate the Triangle Sum Theorem or the Exterior Angle Theorem. Describe your procedure.
See margin.

TEACHING TIPS

EXERCISE 8 Point out that an equilateral triangle is also isosceles; however, the term *equilateral* is more specific and therefore the better term to describe a triangle with three congruent sides.

COMMON ERROR

EXERCISES 27–28 Students may incorrectly identify sides of isosceles triangles and right triangles. The hypotenuse of a right triangle is always the side opposite the right angle and is the longest side. The legs of an isosceles triangle are always the sides that are congruent.

STUDENT HELP NOTES

Homework Help Students can find help for Exs. 31–33 at **www.mcdougallittell.com.** The information can be printed out for students who don't have access to the Internet.

ENGLISH LEARNERS

EXERCISES 1–8 The large number of geometric terms used in this chapter may make learning concepts more difficult for English learners. Students may benefit from discussions of phrases containing several geometric terms before they work on these exercises.

1. *Sample answer:*

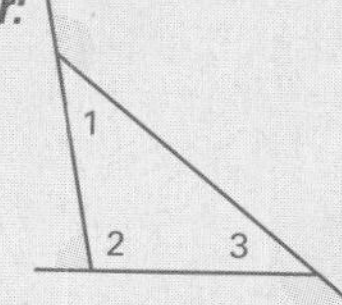

40. *Sample answer:* To demonstrate the Triangle Sum Theorem, draw a triangle, measure its three interior angles, and verify that their sum is 180°. To demonstrate the Exterior Angle Theorem, extend one side of the triangle to form an exterior angle, measure the exterior angle and its two remote interior angles, and verify that the measure of the exterior angle equals the sum of the measures of the two remote interior angles.

CAREER NOTE
EXERCISES 45–46
Additional information about hydrology is available at **www.mcdougallittell.com.**

44.

20 cm

$18\frac{1}{2}$ cm $18\frac{1}{2}$ cm

31 cm

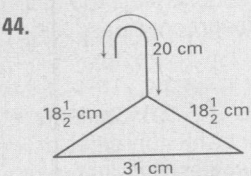

48. Given: $\triangle ABC$ with $m\angle C = 90°$
Prove: $m\angle A + m\angle B = 90°$
Statements (Reasons)
1. $m\angle C = 90°$ (Given)
2. $m\angle A + m\angle B + m\angle C = 180°$ (Triangle Sum Theorem)
3. $m\angle A + m\angle B + 90° = 180°$ (Substitution property of equality)
4. $m\angle A + m\angle B = 90°$ (Subtraction property of equality)

ADDITIONAL PRACTICE AND RETEACHING

For Lesson 4.1:
- Practice Levels A, B, and C (*Chapter 4 Resource Book,* p. 15)
- Reteaching with Practice (*Chapter 4 Resource Book,* p. 18)
- See Lesson 4.1 of the *Personal Student Tutor*

For more Mixed Review:
- Search the *Test and Practice Generator* for key words or specific lessons.

41. **USING ALGEBRA** In $\triangle PQR$, the measure of $\angle P$ is 36°. The measure of $\angle Q$ is five times the measure of $\angle R$. Find $m\angle Q$ and $m\angle R$. **120°, 24°**

42. **USING ALGEBRA** The measure of an exterior angle of a triangle is 120°. The interior angles that are not adjacent to this exterior angle are congruent. Find the measures of the interior angles of the triangle. **60°, 60°, 60°**

43. **BILLIARD RACK** You want to make a wooden billiard rack. The rack will be an equilateral triangle whose side length is 33.5 centimeters. You have a strip of wood that is 100 centimeters long. Do you need more wood? Explain.

43. Yes; the total length needed is 3×33.5 or 100.5 cm.

44. **COAT HANGER** You are bending a wire to make a coat hanger. The length of the wire is 88 centimeters, and 20 centimeters are needed to make the hook portion of the hanger. The triangular portion of the hanger is an isosceles triangle. The length of one leg of this triangle is $\frac{3}{5}$ the length of the base. Sketch the hanger. Give the dimensions of the triangular portion. **See margin.**

FOCUS ON CAREERS

HYDROLOGY
A hydrologist studies how water circulates in the atmosphere, on the ground, and under the ground. A hydrologist might use a wing deflector to minimize the effects of erosion on the bank of a stream.

CAREER LINK
www.mcdougallittell.com

WING DEFLECTORS **In Exercises 45 and 46, use the information about wing deflectors.**
A wing deflector is a structure built with rocks to redirect the flow of water in a stream and increase the rate of the water's flow. Its shape is a right triangle.

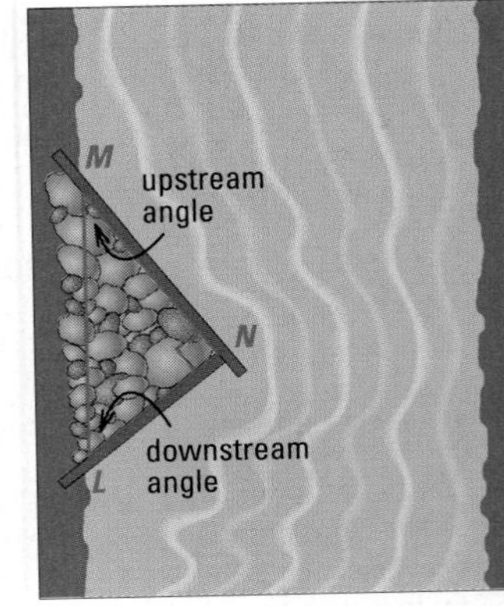

45. Identify the legs and the hypotenuse of the right triangle formed by the wing deflector. $\overline{MN}$ **and** $\overline{LN}$; $\overline{ML}$

46. It is generally recommended that the upstream angle should range from 30° to 45°. Give a range of angle measures for the downstream angle. **60° to 45°**

47. **DEVELOPING PROOF** Fill in the missing steps in the two-column proof of the Exterior Angle Theorem. **See margin.**

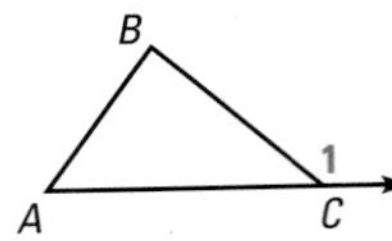

GIVEN ▶ $\angle 1$ is an exterior angle of $\triangle ABC$.

PROVE ▶ $m\angle 1 = m\angle A + m\angle B$

Statements	Reasons
1. $\angle 1$ is an exterior angle of $\triangle ABC$.	1. Given
2. $\angle ACB$ and $\angle 1$ are a linear pair.	2. Definition of exterior angle
3. $m\angle ACB + m\angle 1 = 180°$	3. __?__ **Linear Pair Postulate**
4. __?__ $m\angle A + m\angle B + m\angle ACB = 180°$	4. Triangle Sum Theorem
5. $m\angle ACB + m\angle 1 = m\angle A + m\angle B + m\angle ACB$	5. __?__ **Substitution property of equality**
6. $m\angle 1 = m\angle A + m\angle B$	6. __?__ **Subtraction property of equality**

48. **TWO-COLUMN PROOF** Write a two-column proof of the Corollary to the Triangle Sum Theorem on page 197. **See margin.**

Test Preparation

49. **MULTIPLE CHOICE** The lengths of the two legs of an isosceles triangle are represented by the expressions $(2x - 5)$ and $(x + 7)$. The perimeter of the triangle is 50 cm. Find the length of the base of the triangle. **C**

Ⓐ 11 cm Ⓑ 19 cm Ⓒ 12 cm Ⓓ 26 cm Ⓔ 32 cm

50. **MULTIPLE CHOICE** Which of the terms below can be used to describe a triangle with two 45° interior angles? **B**

Ⓐ Acute Ⓑ Right Ⓒ Scalene Ⓓ Obtuse Ⓔ Equilateral

★ Challenge

51. **ALTERNATIVE PROOFS** There is often more than one way to prove a theorem. In the diagram, $\overline{SP}$ is constructed parallel to $\overline{QR}$. This construction is the first step of a proof of the Triangle Sum Theorem. Use the diagram to prove the Triangle Sum Theorem. See margin.

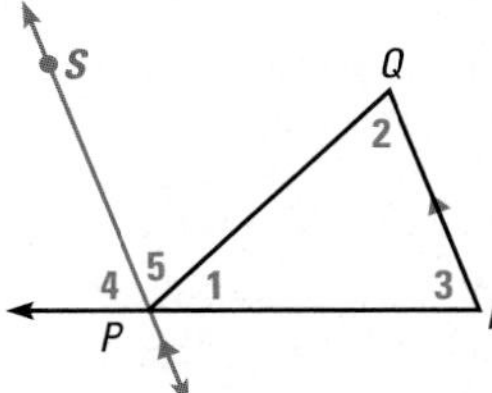

GIVEN ▶ $\triangle PQR$

PROVE ▶ $m\angle 1 + m\angle 2 + m\angle 3 = 180°$

EXTRA CHALLENGE
www.mcdougallittell.com

MIXED REVIEW

EVALUATING STATEMENTS Use the figure to determine whether the statement is *true* or *false*. (Review 1.5 for 4.2)

52. $\overline{AE} \cong \overline{BA}$ true

53. $\angle CAD \cong \angle EAD$ true

54. $m\angle CAD + m\angle EAB = 86°$ false

55. $\overline{CD} \cong \overline{AC}$ false

56. $\overrightarrow{AD}$ bisects $\angle CAE$. true

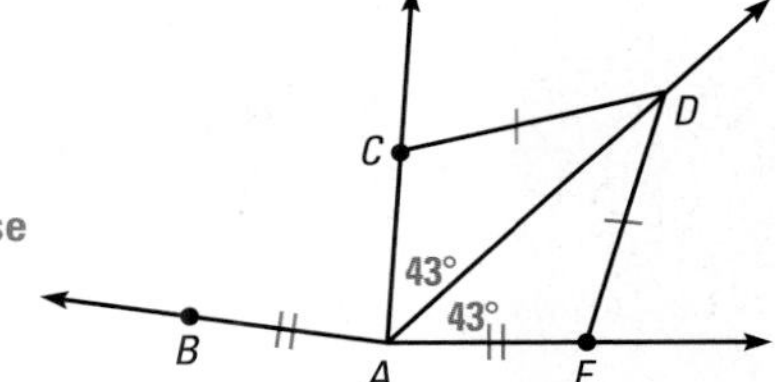

DEVELOPING PROOF Is it possible to prove that lines *p* and *q* are parallel? If so, state the postulate or theorem you would use. (Review 3.4)

57. 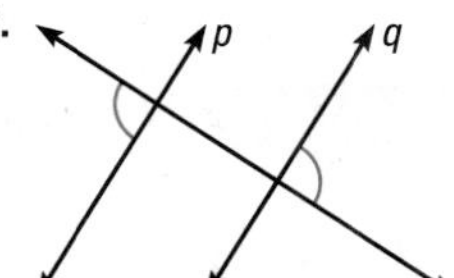

58. 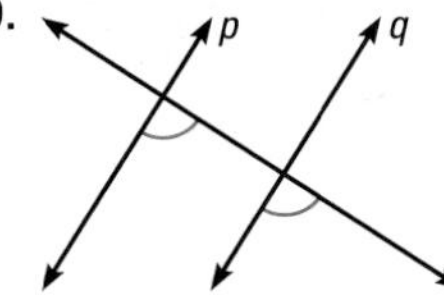

59. 

57. yes; Alternate Interior Angles Converse

58. yes; Alternate Exterior Angles Converse

59. yes; Corresponding Angles Converse

WRITING EQUATIONS Write an equation of the line that passes through the given point *P* and has the given slope. (Review 3.6)

60. $P(0, -2), m = 0$ $y = -2$

61. $P(4, 7), m = 1$ $y = x + 3$

62. $P(-3, -5), m = -1$ $y = -x - 8$

63. $P(9, -1), m = \frac{2}{3}$

64. $P(-1, -1), m = \frac{3}{4}$

65. $P(-2, -3), m = -\frac{7}{2}$

66. $P(5, 2), m = 0$ $y = 2$

67. $P(8, 3), m = -\frac{3}{2}$ $y = -\frac{3}{2}x + 15$

68. $P(-6, -4), m = -\frac{1}{3}$ $y = -\frac{1}{3}x - 6$

63. $y = \frac{2}{3}x - 7$

64. $y = \frac{3}{4}x - \frac{1}{4}$

65. $y = -\frac{7}{2}x - 10$

4 ASSESS

DAILY HOMEWORK QUIZ

Transparency Available

The variable expressions represent the angle measures of a triangle. Find the measure of each angle. Then classify the triangle by its angles and by its sides.

1. $m\angle A = (2x + 5)°$; $m\angle B = (3x - 15)°$; $m\angle C = (4x + 10)°$
$m\angle A = 45°$; $m\angle B = 45°$; $m\angle C = 90°$; right isosceles

2. $m\angle K = 10(x + 1)°$; $m\angle L = (9x - 3)°$; $m\angle M = (7x - 9)°$
$m\angle K = 80°$; $m\angle L = 60°$; $m\angle M = 40°$; acute scalene

Find the measure of the exterior angle shown.

3. 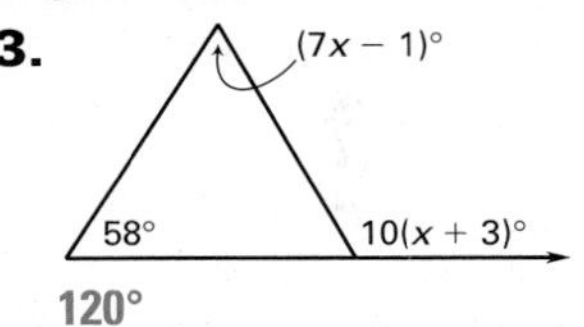

120°

EXTRA CHALLENGE NOTE
Challenge problems for Lesson 4.1 are available in **blackline** format in the *Chapter 4 Resource Book,* p. 22 and at **www.mcdougallittell.com.**

ADDITIONAL TEST PREPARATION

1. **WRITING** Explain why the two other angles of a right triangle must be acute angles.
Sample answer: Because if one angle is a right or obtuse angle, then the sum of the two angle measures is 180° or greater. This means the other angle has a measure of 0° or has a negative angle measure, which is not possible in a triangle.

51. See Additional Answers beginning on page AA1.

1 PLAN

PACING
Basic: 2 days
Average: 2 days
Advanced: 2 days
Block Schedule: 0.5 block with 4.1
0.5 block with 4.3

LESSON OPENER
VISUAL APPROACH
An alternative way to approach Lesson 4.2 is to use the Visual Approach Lesson Opener:
- Blackline Master (*Chapter 4 Resource Book,* p. 26)
- Transparency (p. 22)

MEETING INDIVIDUAL NEEDS
- ***Chapter 4 Resource Book***
  Prerequisite Skills Review (p. 5)
  Practice Level A (p. 30)
  Practice Level B (p. 31)
  Practice Level C (p. 32)
  Reteaching with Practice (p. 33)
  Absent Student Catch-Up (p. 35)
  Challenge (p. 38)
- ***Resources in Spanish***
- ***Personal Student Tutor***

NEW-TEACHER SUPPORT
See the Tips for New Teachers on pp. 1–2 of the *Chapter 4 Resource Book* for additional notes about Lesson 4.2.

WARM-UP EXERCISES
Transparency Available
Tell whether it is possible to draw each triangle.
1. acute scalene triangle yes
2. obtuse equilateral triangle no
3. right isosceles triangle yes
4. scalene equiangular triangle no
5. right scalene triangle yes

4.2 Congruence and Triangles

What *you should learn*

GOAL 1 Identify congruent figures and corresponding parts.

GOAL 2 Prove that two triangles are congruent.

Why *you should learn it*

▼ To identify and describe congruent figures in **real-life** objects, such as the sculpture described in **Example 1**.

REAL LIFE

***Two Open Triangles Up Gyratory II* by George Rickey**

STUDENT HELP
Study Tip
Notice that single, double, and triple arcs are used to show congruent angles.

GOAL 1 IDENTIFYING CONGRUENT FIGURES

Two geometric figures are *congruent* if they have exactly the same size and shape. Each of the red figures is congruent to the other red figures. None of the blue figures is congruent to another blue figure.

Congruent

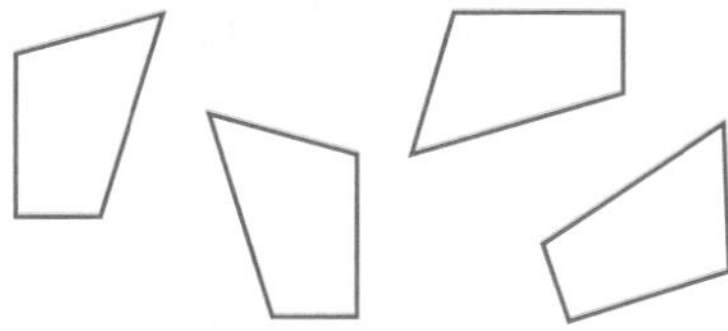

Not congruent

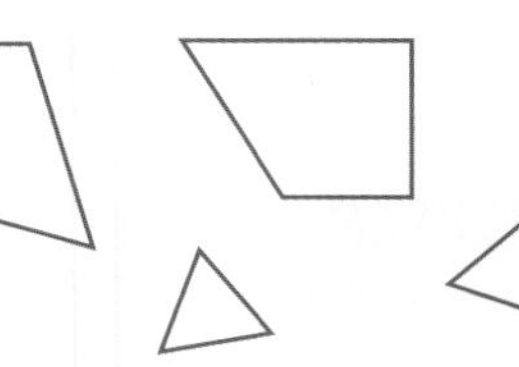

When two figures are **congruent**, there is a correspondence between their angles and sides such that **corresponding angles** are congruent and **corresponding sides** are congruent. For the triangles below, you can write $\triangle ABC \cong \triangle PQR$, which is read "triangle ABC is congruent to triangle PQR." The notation shows the congruence and the correspondence.

Corresponding angles	Corresponding sides
$\angle A \cong \angle P$	$\overline{AB} \cong \overline{PQ}$
$\angle B \cong \angle Q$	$\overline{BC} \cong \overline{QR}$
$\angle C \cong \angle R$	$\overline{CA} \cong \overline{RP}$

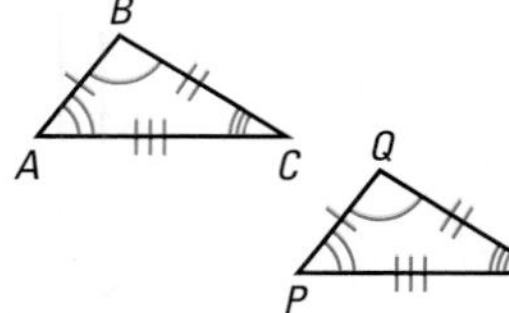

There is more than one way to write a congruence statement, but it is important to list the corresponding angles in the same order. For example, you can also write $\triangle BCA \cong \triangle QRP$.

EXAMPLE 1 *Naming Congruent Parts*

The congruent triangles represent the triangles in the photo above. Write a congruence statement. Identify all pairs of congruent corresponding parts.

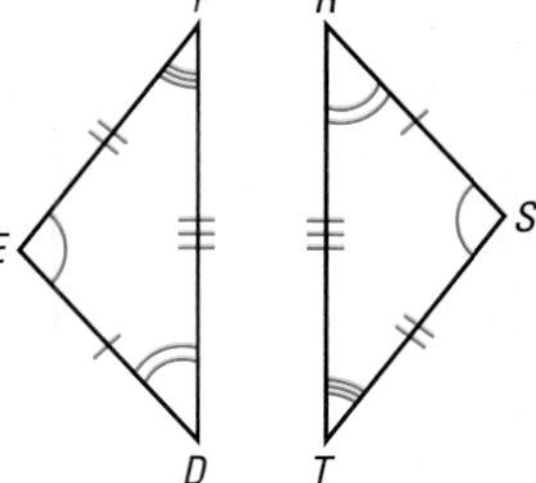

SOLUTION

The diagram indicates that $\triangle DEF \cong \triangle RST$. The congruent angles and sides are as follows.

Angles: $\angle D \cong \angle R$, $\angle E \cong \angle S$, $\angle F \cong \angle T$

Sides: $\overline{DE} \cong \overline{RS}$, $\overline{EF} \cong \overline{ST}$, $\overline{FD} \cong \overline{TR}$

CALIFORNIA STANDARDS AND ASSESSMENT
CA Standards: 5
SAT9 Task 1: Objs. 22, 26
SAT9 Task 2: Objs. 24, 26

EXAMPLE 2 Using Properties of Congruent Figures

In the diagram, $NPLM \cong EFGH$.

a. Find the value of x.

b. Find the value of y.

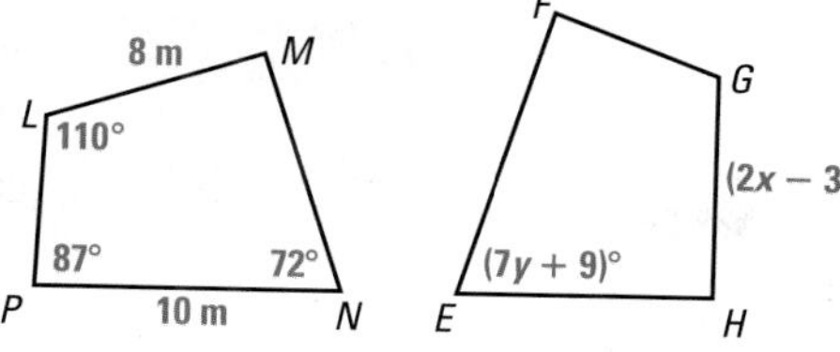

SOLUTION

a. You know that $\overline{LM} \cong \overline{GH}$.
So, $LM = GH$.

$8 = 2x - 3$

$11 = 2x$

$5.5 = x$

b. You know that $\angle N \cong \angle E$.
So, $m\angle N = m\angle E$.

$72° = (7y + 9)°$

$63 = 7y$

$9 = y$

. . . .

The Third Angles Theorem below follows from the Triangle Sum Theorem. You are asked to prove the Third Angles Theorem in Exercise 35.

THEOREM

THEOREM 4.3 ***Third Angles Theorem***

If two angles of one triangle are congruent to two angles of another triangle, then the third angles are also congruent.

If $\angle A \cong \angle D$ and $\angle B \cong \angle E$, then $\angle C \cong \angle F$.

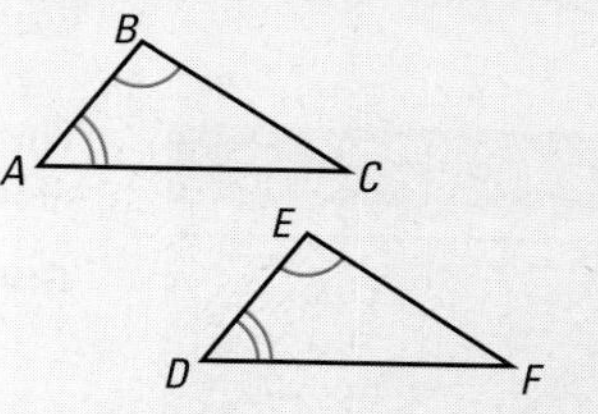

EXAMPLE 3 Using the Third Angles Theorem

Find the value of x.

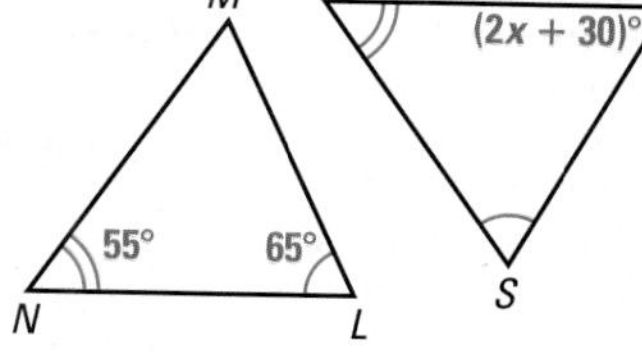

SOLUTION

In the diagram, $\angle N \cong \angle R$ and $\angle L \cong \angle S$. From the Third Angles Theorem, you know that $\angle M \cong \angle T$. So, $m\angle M = m\angle T$. From the Triangle Sum Theorem, $m\angle M = 180° - 55° - 65° = 60°$.

$m\angle M = m\angle T$	Third Angles Theorem
$60° = (2x + 30)°$	Substitute.
$30 = 2x$	Subtract 30 from each side.
$15 = x$	Divide each side by 2.

STUDENT HELP

INTERNET **HOMEWORK HELP** Visit our Web site www.mcdougallittell.com for extra examples.

Extra Example 1 ***Sample answer:***
$\triangle XYZ \cong \triangle HKJ$; $\angle X \cong \angle H$; $\angle Y \cong \angle K$; $\angle Z \cong \angle J$; $\overline{XY} \cong \overline{HK}$; $\overline{YZ} \cong \overline{KJ}$; $\overline{XZ} \cong \overline{HJ}$

2 TEACH

EXTRA EXAMPLE 1

Write a congruence statement for the triangles below. Identify all pairs of congruent corresponding parts. See below.

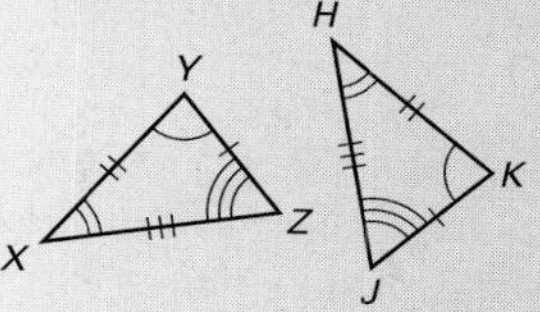

EXTRA EXAMPLE 2

In the diagram, $ABCD \cong KJHL$.

a. Find the value of x. 3

b. Find the value of y. 25

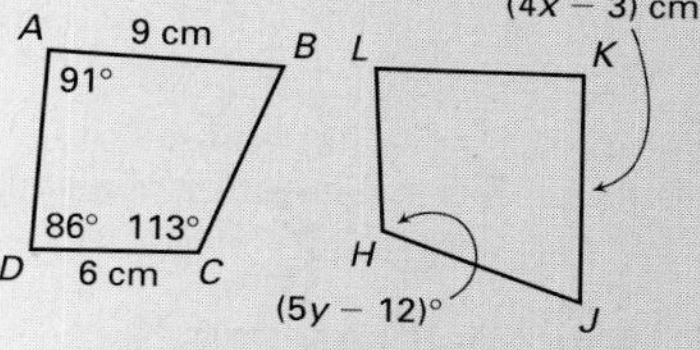

EXTRA EXAMPLE 3

Find the value of x. 14

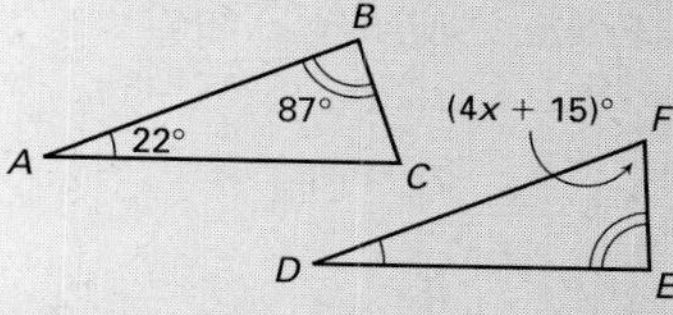

CHECKPOINT EXERCISES

For use after Example 1:

1. Identify all pairs of congruent corresponding parts.
$\angle A \cong \angle R$; $\angle B \cong \angle Q$; $\angle C \cong \angle P$; $\overline{AB} \cong \overline{RQ}$; $\overline{BC} \cong \overline{QP}$; $\overline{AC} \cong \overline{RP}$

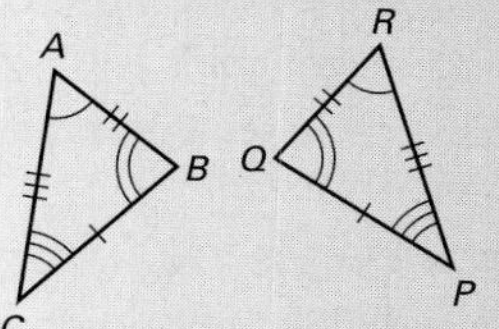

For use after Examples 2 and 3:

2. Find the value of x. 11

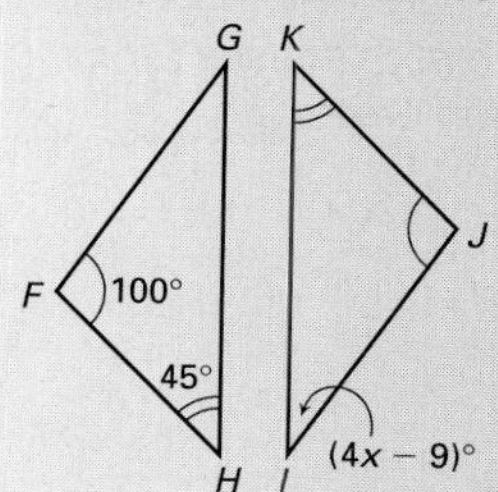

EXTRA EXAMPLE 4

Decide whether the triangles are congruent. Justify your reasoning.

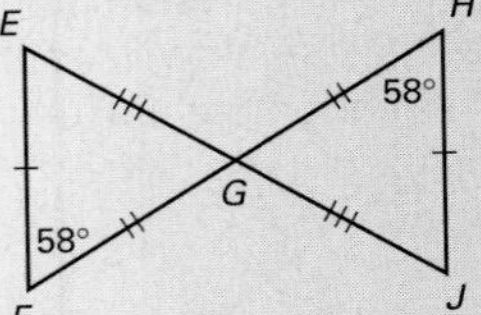

From the diagram, you are given that all three pairs of corresponding sides are congruent: $\overline{EF} \cong \overline{JH}$, $\overline{EG} \cong \overline{JG}$, $\overline{FG} \cong \overline{HG}$. Because $\angle F$ and $\angle H$ have the same measure, $\angle F \cong \angle H$. By the Vertical Angles Theorem, you know that $\angle EGF \cong \angle JGH$. By the Third Angles Theorem, $\angle E \cong \angle J$. So all three sides and all three angles are congruent. By the definition of congruent triangles, $\triangle EFG \cong \triangle JHG$.

EXTRA EXAMPLE 5

Given: $\overline{MN} \cong \overline{QP}$, $\overline{MN} \parallel \overline{PQ}$, O is the midpoint of $\overline{MQ}$ and $\overline{PN}$.

Prove: $\triangle MNO \cong \triangle QPO$

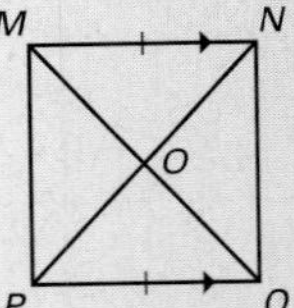

Statements (Reasons)

1. $\overline{MN} \cong \overline{QP}$, $\overline{MN} \parallel \overline{PQ}$, (Given)
2. $\angle OMN \cong \angle OQP$, $\angle MNO \cong \angle QPO$ (Alternate Interior Angles Theorem)
3. $\angle MON \cong \angle QOP$ (Vertical Angles Theorem)
4. O is the midpoint of $\overline{MQ}$ and $\overline{PN}$. (Given)
5. $\overline{MO} \cong \overline{QO}$, $\overline{PO} \cong \overline{NO}$ (Def. of midpoint)
6. $\triangle MNO \cong \triangle QPO$ (Def. of $\cong$ $\triangle$s)

Checkpoint Exercises for Examples 4 and 5 on next page.

GOAL 2 PROVING TRIANGLES ARE CONGRUENT

EXAMPLE 4 *Determining Whether Triangles are Congruent*

Decide whether the triangles are congruent. Justify your reasoning.

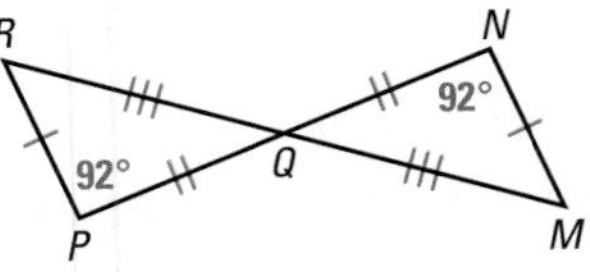

Proof

SOLUTION

Paragraph Proof From the diagram, you are given that all three pairs of corresponding sides are congruent.

$$\overline{RP} \cong \overline{MN},\ \overline{PQ} \cong \overline{NQ}, \text{ and } \overline{QR} \cong \overline{QM}$$

Because $\angle P$ and $\angle N$ have the same measure, $\angle P \cong \angle N$. By the Vertical Angles Theorem, you know that $\angle PQR \cong \angle NQM$. By the Third Angles Theorem, $\angle R \cong \angle M$.

▶ So, all three pairs of corresponding sides and all three pairs of corresponding angles are congruent. By the definition of congruent triangles, $\triangle PQR \cong \triangle NQM$.

EXAMPLE 5 *Proving Two Triangles are Congruent*

FOCUS ON APPLICATIONS

TRIANGULAR STAMP When these stamps were issued in 1997, Postmaster General Marvin Runyon said, "Since 1847, when the first U.S. postage stamps were issued, stamps have been rectangular in shape. We want the American public to know stamps aren't 'square.'"

The diagram represents the triangular stamps shown in the photo. Prove that $\triangle AEB \cong \triangle DEC$.

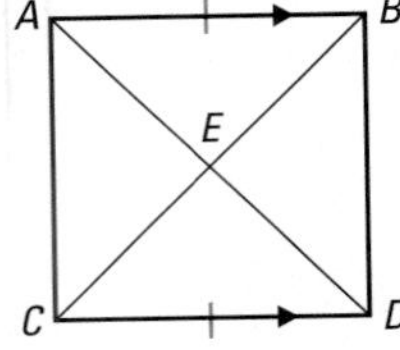

GIVEN ▶ $\overline{AB} \parallel \overline{DC}$, $\overline{AB} \cong \overline{DC}$, E is the midpoint of $\overline{BC}$ and $\overline{AD}$.

PROVE ▶ $\triangle AEB \cong \triangle DEC$

Plan for Proof Use the fact that $\angle AEB$ and $\angle DEC$ are vertical angles to show that those angles are congruent. Use the fact that $\overline{BC}$ intersects parallel segments $\overline{AB}$ and $\overline{DC}$ to identify other pairs of angles that are congruent.

SOLUTION

Statements	Reasons
1. $\overline{AB} \parallel \overline{DC}$, $\overline{AB} \cong \overline{DC}$	1. Given
2. $\angle EAB \cong \angle EDC$, $\angle ABE \cong \angle DCE$	2. Alternate Interior Angles Theorem
3. $\angle AEB \cong \angle DEC$	3. Vertical Angles Theorem
4. E is the midpoint of $\overline{AD}$, E is the midpoint of $\overline{BC}$.	4. Given
5. $\overline{AE} \cong \overline{DE}$, $\overline{BE} \cong \overline{CE}$	5. Definition of midpoint
6. $\triangle AEB \cong \triangle DEC$	6. Definition of congruent triangles

In this lesson, you have learned to prove that two triangles are congruent by the *definition of congruence*—that is, by showing that all pairs of corresponding angles and corresponding sides are congruent. In upcoming lessons, you will learn more efficient ways of proving that triangles are congruent. The properties below will be useful in such proofs.

THEOREM

THEOREM 4.4 ***Properties of Congruent Triangles***

REFLEXIVE PROPERTY OF CONGRUENT TRIANGLES

Every triangle is congruent to itself.

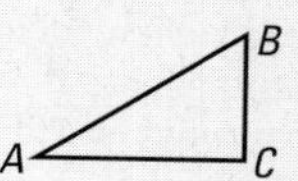

SYMMETRIC PROPERTY OF CONGRUENT TRIANGLES

If $\triangle ABC \cong \triangle DEF$, then $\triangle DEF \cong \triangle ABC$.

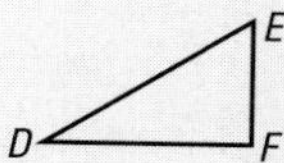

TRANSITIVE PROPERTY OF CONGRUENT TRIANGLES

If $\triangle ABC \cong \triangle DEF$ and $\triangle DEF \cong \triangle JKL$, then $\triangle ABC \cong \triangle JKL$.

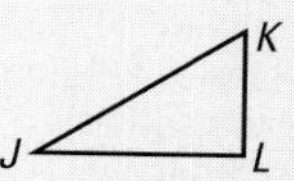

GUIDED PRACTICE

Vocabulary Check ✓

1. Copy the congruent triangles shown at the right. Then label the vertices of your triangles so that $\triangle JKL \cong \triangle RST$. Identify all pairs of congruent *corresponding angles* and *corresponding sides*. $\angle J$ and $\angle R$, $\angle K$ and $\angle S$, $\angle L$ and $\angle T$, $\overline{JK}$ and $\overline{RS}$, $\overline{KL}$ and $\overline{ST}$, $\overline{JL}$ and $\overline{RT}$.

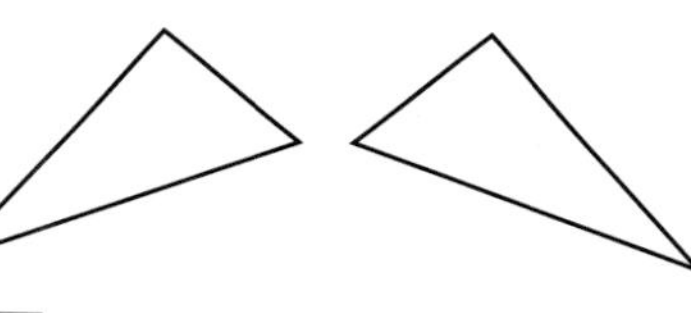

Concept Check ✓

ERROR ANALYSIS Use the information and the diagram below.

On an exam, a student says that $\triangle ABC \cong \triangle ADE$ because the corresponding angles of the triangles are congruent.

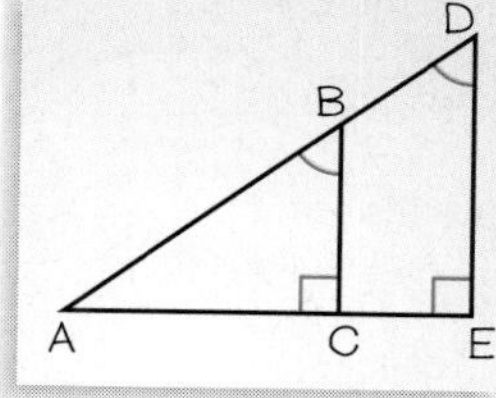

2. How does the student know that the corresponding angles are congruent?

3. Is $\triangle ABC \cong \triangle ADE$? Explain your answer.

2. Third Angles Theorem

3. No; corresponding sides are not congruent.

Skill Check ✓

Use the diagram at the right, where $\triangle LMN \cong \triangle PQR$.

4. What is the measure of $\angle P$? 105°

5. What is the measure of $\angle M$? 45°

6. What is the measure of $\angle R$? 30°

7. What is the measure of $\angle N$? 30°

8. Which side is congruent to $\overline{QR}$? $\overline{MN}$

9. Which side is congruent to $\overline{LN}$? $\overline{PR}$

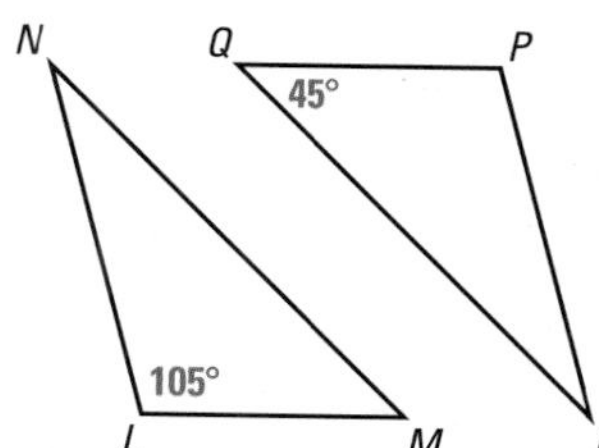

CHECKPOINT EXERCISES

For use after Examples 4 and 5:

1. Decide whether the triangles are congruent. Justify your reasoning.

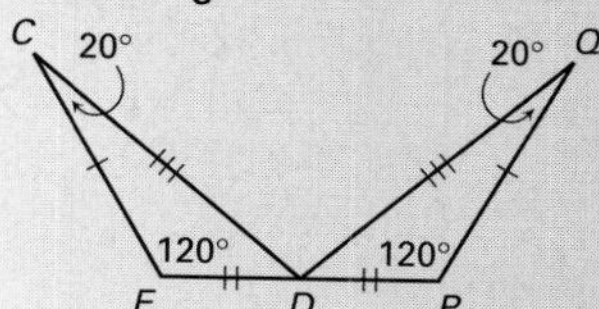

From the diagram, you are given that all three pairs of corresponding sides are congruent: $\overline{CE} \cong \overline{QP}$, $\overline{ED} \cong \overline{PD}$, $\overline{CD} \cong \overline{QD}$. Because $\angle C$ and $\angle Q$ have the same measure, and $\angle E$ and $\angle P$ have the same measure, $\angle C \cong \angle Q$ and $\angle E \cong \angle P$. By the Third Angles Theorem, $\angle CDE \cong \angle QDP$. So all three sides and all three angles are congruent. By the definition of congruent triangles, $\triangle CED \cong \triangle QPD$.

FOCUS ON VOCABULARY

Draw two figures that are similar but not congruent. Point out that these figures have corresponding sides. Make sure students understand that the term *corresponding sides* does not imply that the sides are necessarily congruent.

CLOSURE QUESTION

If $\triangle GHJ \cong \triangle MNP$, what corresponding angles and sides are congruent? $\angle G \cong \angle M$, $\angle H \cong \angle N$, $\angle J \cong \angle P$, $\overline{GH} \cong \overline{MN}$, $\overline{HJ} \cong \overline{NP}$, $\overline{GJ} \cong \overline{MP}$

DAILY PUZZLER

The design shown is created entirely from congruent triangles. If the area of the design is 96 square units, what is the area of one triangle?
3 square units

3 APPLY

ASSIGNMENT GUIDE

BASIC

Day 1: pp. 206–210 Exs. 10–28 even, 39, 42–56 even

Day 2: pp. 206–210 Exs. 11–29 odd, 30–33, 35, 53, 55, 57, Quiz 1 Exs. 1–6

AVERAGE

Day 1: pp. 206–210 Exs. 10–28 even, 39, 42–56 even

Day 2: pp. 206–210 Exs. 11–29 odd, 30–35, 53, 55, 57, Quiz 1 Exs. 1–6

ADVANCED

Day 1: pp. 206–210 Exs. 10–28 even, 36–40, 42–56 even

Day 2: pp. 206–210 Exs. 11–29 odd, 30–35, 53, 55, 57, Quiz 1 Exs. 1–6

BLOCK SCHEDULE

pp. 206–210 Exs. 10–28 even, 39, 42–56 even (with 4.1)
pp. 206–210 Exs. 11–29 odd, 30–35, 53, 55, 57, Quiz 1 Exs. 1–6 (with 4.3)

EXERCISE LEVELS

Level A: *Easier*
10–15

Level B: *More Difficult*
16–37, 39

Level C: *Most Difficult*
38, 40

✔ HOMEWORK CHECK

To quickly check student understanding of key concepts, go over the following exercises: Exs. 14, 20, 24, 26, 32, 35. See also the Daily Homework Quiz:

- Blackline Master (*Chapter 4 Resource Book*, p. 42)
- Transparency (p. 27)

1. See Additional Answers beginning on page AA1.

PRACTICE AND APPLICATIONS

STUDENT HELP

Extra Practice to help you master skills is on p. 809.

16. $\triangle ABD \cong \triangle CDB$; $\overline{BD} \cong \overline{BD}$ by the Reflexive Property of Congruence, so the triangles are congruent by the definition of congruence

17. $\triangle FGH \cong \triangle JKH$; $\angle FHG \cong \angle JHK$ by the Vertical Angles Theorem, so the triangles are congruent by the definition of congruence

18. $ABCD \cong PSRQ$; definition of congruence

19. $VWXYZ \cong MNJKL$; definition of congruence

20. $EFJK \cong HJFG$; In a plane, if two lines are perpendicular to the same line, then they are parallel to each other, so $\overline{EG} \parallel \overline{KH}$, so $\angle EFJ \cong \angle HJF$ and $\angle KJF \cong \angle GFJ$ by the Alternate Interior Angles Theorem. $\overline{FJ} \cong \overline{FJ}$ by the Reflexive Property of Congruence, so the trapezoids are congruent by the definition of congruence

DESCRIBING CONGRUENT TRIANGLES **In the diagram, $\triangle ABC \cong \triangle TUV$. Complete the statement.**

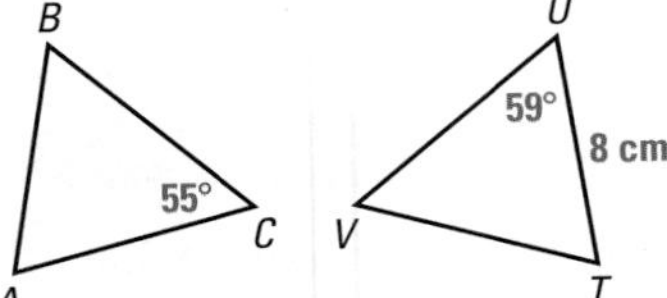

10. $\angle A \cong$? $\angle T$
11. $\overline{VT} \cong$? $\overline{CA}$
12. $\triangle VTU \cong$? $\triangle CAB$
13. $BC =$? UV
14. $m\angle A = m\angle$? $=$?° T; 66

15. Which of the statements below can be used to describe the congruent triangles in Exercises 10–14? (There may be more than one answer.) B, C, D

A. $\triangle CBA \cong \triangle TUV$ **B.** $\triangle CBA \cong \triangle VUT$
C. $\triangle UTV \cong \triangle BAC$ **D.** $\triangle TVU \cong \triangle ACB$

NAMING CONGRUENT FIGURES **Identify any figures that can be proved congruent. Explain your reasoning. For those that can be proved congruent, write a congruence statement.** 16–21. See margin.

16.
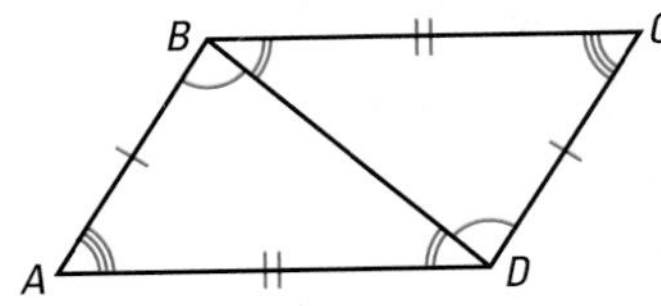

17.
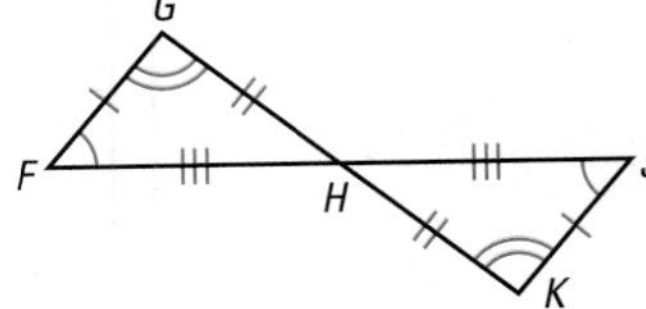

18.
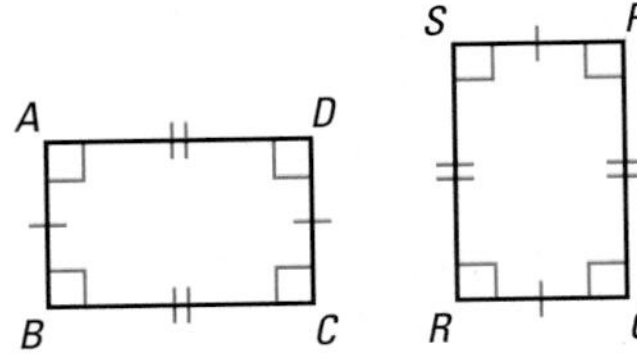

19.
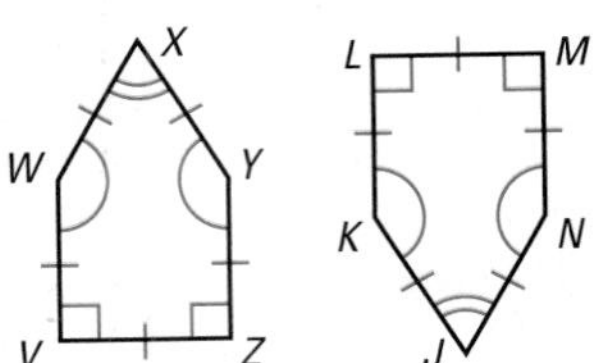

20.
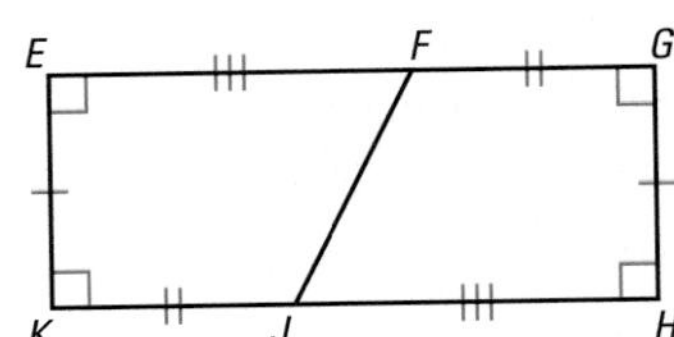

21.
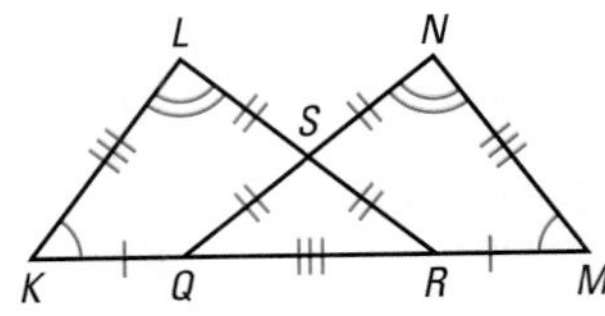

STUDENT HELP

HOMEWORK HELP
Example 1: Exs. 10–22
Example 2: Exs. 14, 24, 25
Example 3: Exs. 26–29
Example 4: Exs. 16–21, 23
Example 5: Ex. 38

22. **IDENTIFYING CORRESPONDING PARTS** Use the triangles shown in Exercise 17 above. Identify all pairs of congruent corresponding angles and corresponding sides. See margin.

23. **CRITICAL THINKING** Use the triangles shown at the right. How many pairs of angles are congruent? Are the triangles congruent? Explain your reasoning. See margin.

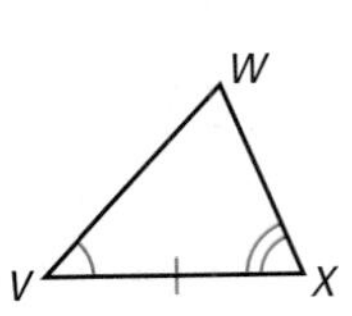

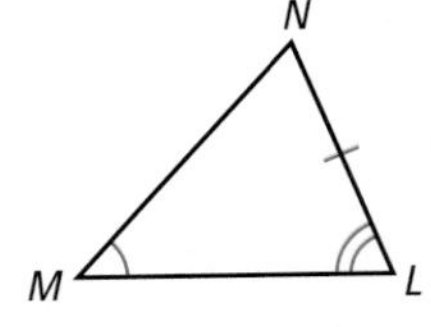

USING ALGEBRA Use the given information to find the indicated values.

24. Given $ABCD \cong EFGH$, find the values of x and y.
$x = 7, y = 8$

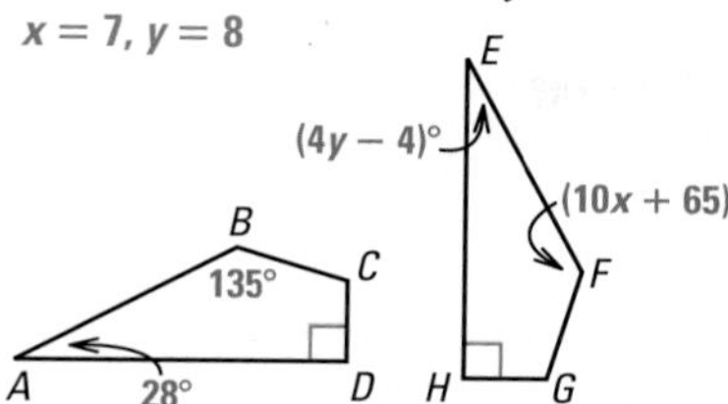

25. Given $\triangle XYZ \cong \triangle RST$, find the values of a and b.
$a = 13, b = 13$

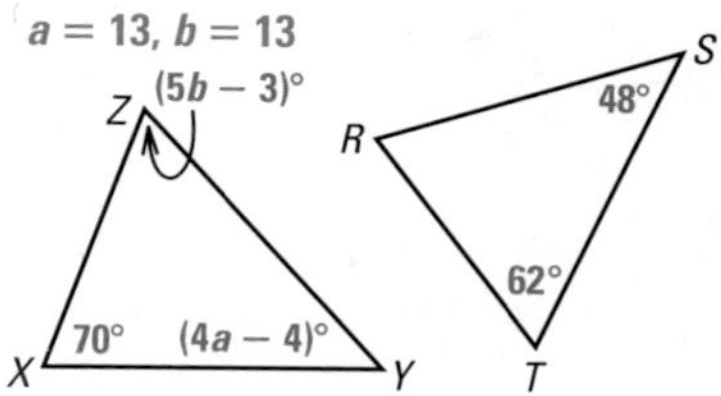

USING ALGEBRA Use the given information to find the indicated value.

26. Given $\angle M \cong \angle G$ and $\angle N \cong \angle H$, find the value of x. 32

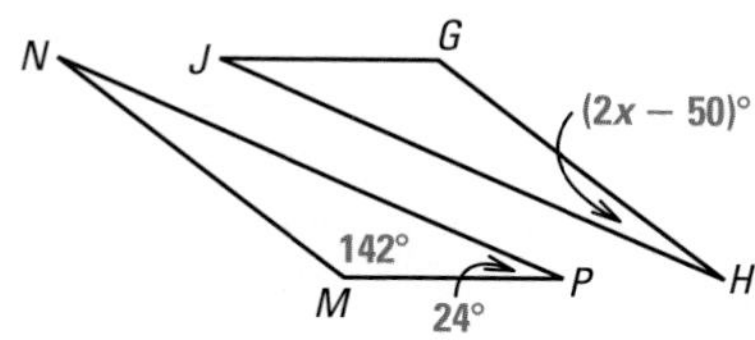

27. Given $\angle P \cong \angle S$ and $\angle Q \cong \angle T$, find the value of m. 12

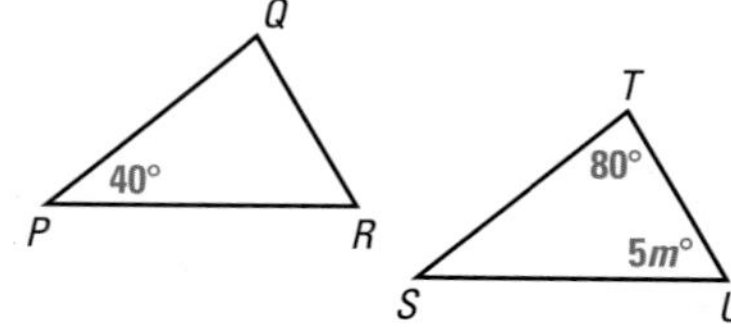

28. Given $\angle K \cong \angle D$ and $\angle J \cong \angle C$, find the value of s. 25

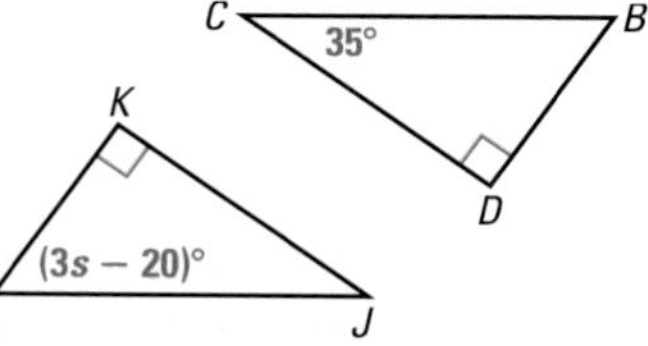

29. Given $\angle A \cong \angle X$ and $\angle C \cong \angle Z$, find the value of r. 65

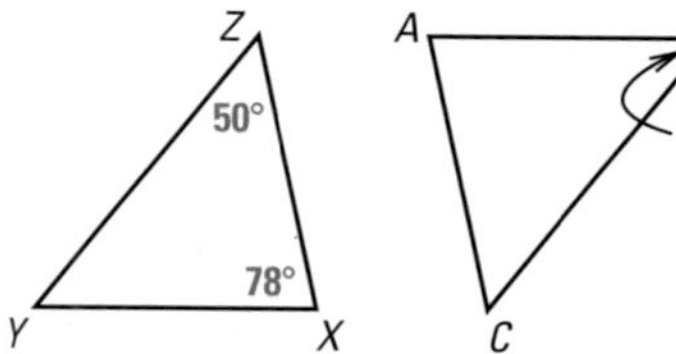

CROP CIRCLES Use the diagram based on the photo. The small triangles, $\triangle ADB$, $\triangle CDA$, and $\triangle CDB$, are congruent.

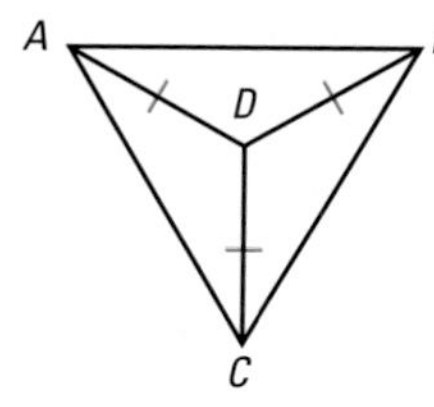

This pattern was made by mowing a field in England.

30–33. See margin.

30. Explain why $\triangle ABC$ is equilateral.

31. The sum of the measures of $\angle ADB$, $\angle CDA$, and $\angle CDB$ is 360°. Find $m\angle BDC$.

32. Each of the small isosceles triangles has two congruent acute angles. Find $m\angle DBC$ and $m\angle DCB$.

33. LOGICAL REASONING Explain why $\triangle ABC$ is equiangular.

30. $\overline{AB}$, $\overline{BC}$, and $\overline{AC}$ are corresponding sides of congruent triangles and are congruent.
31. 120°
32. $m\angle DBC = m\angle DCB = 30°$
33. The measure of each of the congruent angles in each small triangle is 30°. By the Angle Addition Postulate, the measure of each angle of $\triangle ABC$ is 60°.

TEACHING TIPS

EXERCISES 24–29 Students may feel they are lacking enough information to find the indicated values. Have pairs of students describe to each other what they know and what they can find using the information they have. They may also want to make quick sketches of the figures and add the information they have and can find to the figure. These techniques will help them plan how to find the values needed.

21. Triangles LKR and NMQ and quadrilaterals $LKQS$ and $NMRS$; $\overline{LR}$ and $\overline{NQ}$ are congruent by the addition property of equality, the Segment Addition Postulate, and the definition of congruence and $\angle NQM$ and $\angle LRK$ are congruent by the Third Angles Theorem, so the triangles are congruent by the definition of congruence; $\angle LSQ \cong \angle NSR$ by the Vertical Angles Theorem and $\angle KQS \cong \angle MRS$ by the Congruent Supplements Theorem, so the quadrilaterals are congruent by the definition of congruence; $\triangle LKR \cong \triangle NMQ$, $LKQS \cong NMRS$.
22. $\angle F$ and $\angle J$, $\angle G$ and $\angle K$, $\angle FHG$ and $\angle JHK$, $\overline{FG}$ and $\overline{JK}$, $\overline{GH}$ and $\overline{KH}$, $\overline{FH}$ and $\overline{JH}$
23. Three pairs; congruence cannot be determined from the figure; $\overline{VX}$ and $\overline{NL}$ are not corresponding sides, so no corresponding congruent sides are shown.

38. Statements (Reasons)

1. $\overline{DB} \perp \overline{FG}$, E is the midpoint of $\overline{FG}$, $\overline{BF} \cong \overline{BG}$, $\overrightarrow{BD}$ bisects $\angle GBF$. (Given)
2. $\angle BEF$ and $\angle BEG$ are right angles. (If two lines are perpendicular, then they intersect to form four right angles.)
3. $\angle BEF \cong \angle BEG$ (Right Angle Congruence Theorem)
4. $\overline{EF} \cong \overline{EG}$ (Definition of midpoint)
5. $\angle FBE \cong \angle GBE$ (Definition of angle bisector)
6. $\angle BFE \cong \angle BGE$ (Third Angles Theorem)
7. $\overline{BE} \cong \overline{BE}$ (Reflexive Property of Congruence)
8. $\triangle FEB \cong \triangle GEB$ (Definition of congruent triangles)

39a. They are corresponding sides of congruent figures.

b. They are corresponding angles of congruent figures.

c. Linear Pair Postulate and Congruent Supplements Theorem

d. $\angle GEB$ is a right angle because if 2 lines are $\perp$, then they form 4 right angles. So $\angle GEB \cong \angle GED$ because all right angles are congruent.

e. Yes. By a–d and the figure we have two pairs of congruent sides and two pairs of congruent angles, $\angle BGE \cong \angle DGE$ by the Third Angles Theorem, and $\overline{EG} \cong \overline{EG}$ by the Reflexive Property of Congruence, so $\triangle BEG \cong \triangle DEG$ by the definition of congruent triangles.

Additional Practice and Reteaching

For Lesson 4.2:

- Practice Levels A, B, and C (*Chapter 4 Resource Book*, p. 30)
- Reteaching with Practice (*Chapter 4 Resource Book*, p. 33)
- See Lesson 4.2 of the *Personal Student Tutor*

For more Mixed Review:

- Search the *Test and Practice Generator* for key words or specific lessons.

FOCUS ON PEOPLE

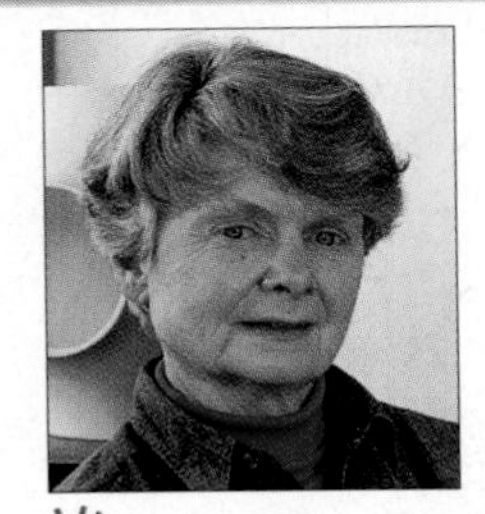

HARRIET BRISSON is an artist who has created many works of art that rely on or express mathematical principles. The pattern used to arrange the triangles in her sculpture shown at the right can be extended indefinitely.

34. SCULPTURE The sculpture shown in the photo is made of congruent triangles cut from transparent plastic. Suppose you use one triangle as a pattern to cut all the other triangles. Which property guarantees that all the triangles are congruent to each other?
Transitive Property of Congruent Triangles

35. DEVELOPING PROOF Complete the proof of the Third Angles Theorem.

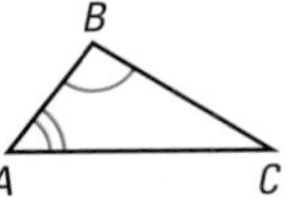

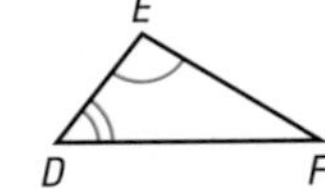

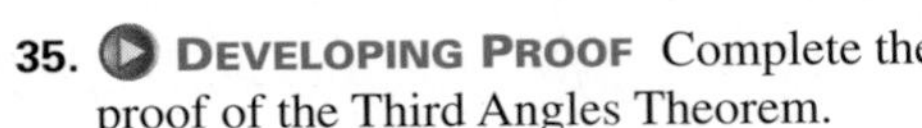

GIVEN ▶ $\angle A \cong \angle D$, $\angle B \cong \angle E$

PROVE ▶ $\angle C \cong \angle F$

Statements	Reasons
1. $\angle A \cong \angle D$, $\angle B \cong \angle E$	1. ? Given
2. $m\angle$? $= m\angle$?, $m\angle$? $= m\angle$? A, D, B, E	2. ? Definition of congruent angles
3. $m\angle A + m\angle B + m\angle C = 180°$, $m\angle D + m\angle E + m\angle F = 180°$	3. ? Triangle Sum Theorem
4. $m\angle A + m\angle B + m\angle C = m\angle D + m\angle E + m\angle F$	4. ? Substitution property of equality or transitive property of equality
5. $m\angle D + m\angle E + m\angle C = m\angle D + m\angle E + m\angle F$	5. ? Substitution property of equality
6. $m\angle C = m\angle F$	6. ? Subtraction property of equality
7. ? $\angle C \cong \angle F$	7. Def. of $\cong$ $\angle$s.

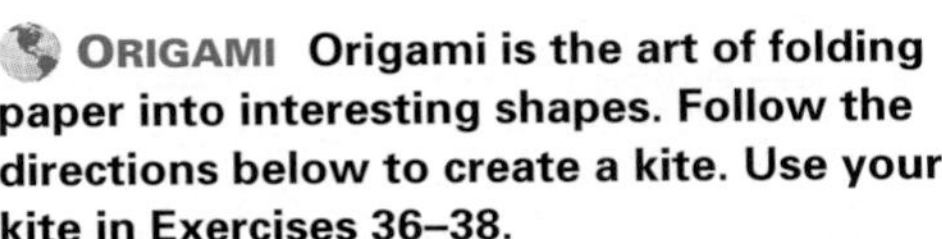

ORIGAMI Origami is the art of folding paper into interesting shapes. Follow the directions below to create a kite. Use your kite in Exercises 36–38.

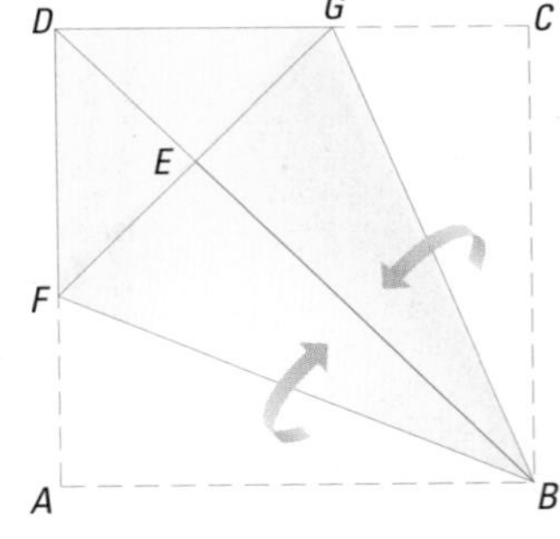

1. Fold a square piece of paper in half diagonally to create $\overline{DB}$.
2. Next fold the paper so that side $\overline{AB}$ lies directly on $\overline{DB}$.
3. Then fold the paper so that side $\overline{CB}$ lies directly on $\overline{DB}$.

36. Is $\overline{EB}$ congruent to $\overline{AB}$? Is $\overline{EF}$ congruent to $\overline{AF}$? Explain.

37. **LOGICAL REASONING** From folding, you know that $\overrightarrow{BF}$ bisects $\angle EBA$ and $\overrightarrow{FB}$ bisects $\angle AFE$. Given these facts and your answers to Exercise 36, which triangles can you conclude are congruent? Explain.

38. **PROOF** Write a proof. See margin.

GIVEN ▶ $\overline{DB} \perp \overline{FG}$, E is the midpoint of $\overline{FG}$, $\overline{BF} \cong \overline{BG}$, and $\overrightarrow{BD}$ bisects $\angle GBF$.

PROVE ▶ $\triangle FEB \cong \triangle GEB$

36. Yes; when the paper is folded, $\overline{EB}$ and $\overline{AB}$ coincide, as do $\overline{EF}$ and $\overline{AF}$.

37. $\triangle ABF$ and $\triangle EBF$; $\overline{BF} \cong \overline{BF}$ by the Reflexive Property of Congruence, and $\angle A$ and $\angle BEF$ are congruent by the Third Angles Theorem, so the triangles are congruent by the definition of congruence.

40. See Additional Answers beginning on page AA1.

Test Preparation

39. MULTI-STEP PROBLEM Use the diagram, in which $ABEF \cong CDEF$. See margin.

a. Explain how you know that $\overline{BE} \cong \overline{DE}$.

b. Explain how you know that $\angle ABE \cong \angle CDE$.

c. Explain how you know that $\angle GBE \cong \angle GDE$.

d. Explain how you know that $\angle GEB \cong \angle GED$.

e. *Writing* Do you have enough information to prove that $\triangle BEG \cong \triangle DEG$? Explain.

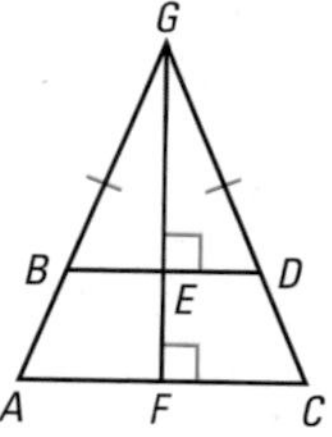

★ Challenge

40. ORIGAMI REVISITED Look back at Exercises 36–38 on page 208. Suppose the following statements are also true about the diagram.

$\overrightarrow{BD}$ bisects $\angle ABC$ and $\overrightarrow{DB}$ bisects $\angle ADC$.
$\angle ABC$ and $\angle ADC$ are right angles.

Find all of the unknown angle measures in the figure. Use a sketch to show your answers. See margin.

www.mcdougallittell.com

MIXED REVIEW

DISTANCE FORMULA **Find the distance between each pair of points.** (Review 1.3 for 4.3)

41. $A(3, 8)$ $B(-1, -4)$ $4\sqrt{10}$

42. $C(3, -8)$ $D(-13, 7)$ $\sqrt{481}$

43. $E(-2, -6)$ $F(3, -5)$ $\sqrt{26}$

44. $G(0, 5)$ $H(-5, 2)$ $\sqrt{34}$

45. $J(0, -4)$ $K(9, 2)$ $3\sqrt{13}$

46. $L(7, -2)$ $M(0, 9)$ $\sqrt{170}$

FINDING THE MIDPOINT **Find the coordinates of the midpoint of a segment with the given endpoints.** (Review 1.5)

47. $N(-1, 5)$ $P(-3, -9)$ $(-2, -2)$

48. $Q(5, 7)$ $R(-1, 4)$ $\left(2, 5\frac{1}{2}\right)$

49. $S(-6, -2)$ $T(8, 2)$ $(1, 0)$

50. $U(0, -7)$ $V(-6, 4)$ $\left(-3, -1\frac{1}{2}\right)$

51. $W(12, 0)$ $Z(8, 6)$ $(10, 3)$

52. $A(-5, -7)$ $B(0, 4)$ $\left(-2\frac{1}{2}, -1\frac{1}{2}\right)$

FINDING COMPLEMENTARY ANGLES **In Exercises 53–55, $\angle 1$ and $\angle 2$ are complementary. Find $m\angle 2$.** (Review 1.6)

53. $m\angle 1 = 8°$ $m\angle 2 = \underline{\ ?\ }$ 82°

54. $m\angle 1 = 73°$ $m\angle 2 = \underline{\ ?\ }$ 17°

55. $m\angle 1 = 62°$ $m\angle 2 = \underline{\ ?\ }$ 28°

IDENTIFYING PARALLELS **Find the slope of each line. Are the lines parallel?** (Review 3.6)

56.

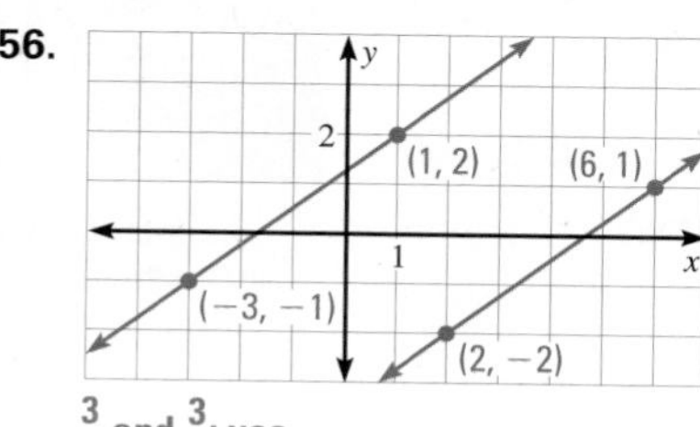

$\frac{3}{4}$ and $\frac{3}{4}$; yes

57.

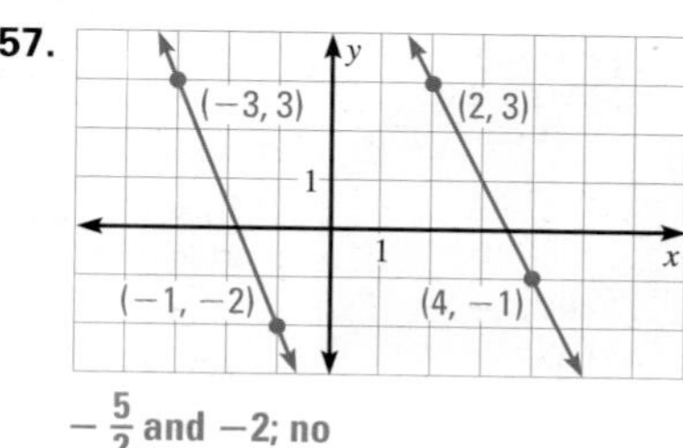

$-\frac{5}{2}$ and -2; no

4 ASSESS

DAILY HOMEWORK QUIZ

Transparency Available

$\triangle DEF \cong \triangle MNO$. Complete the statements.

1. $m\angle E = m\angle$ _____ N

2. $DF =$ _____ MO

Use the given information to find the indicated values.

3. Given $\triangle ABC \cong \triangle PQR$, find the values of x and y.

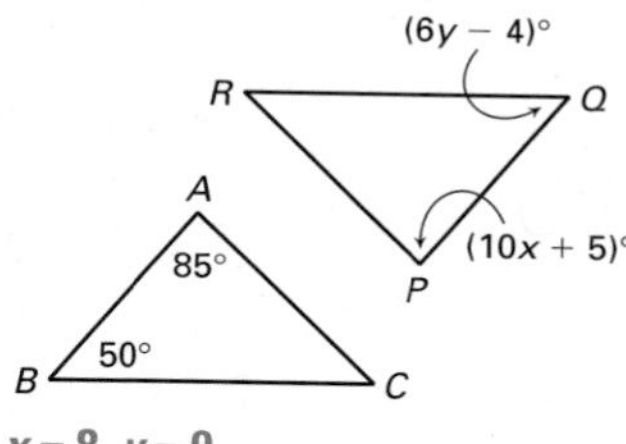

$x = 8$, $y = 9$

4. Given $\triangle JKL \cong \triangle XYZ$, find the value of a.

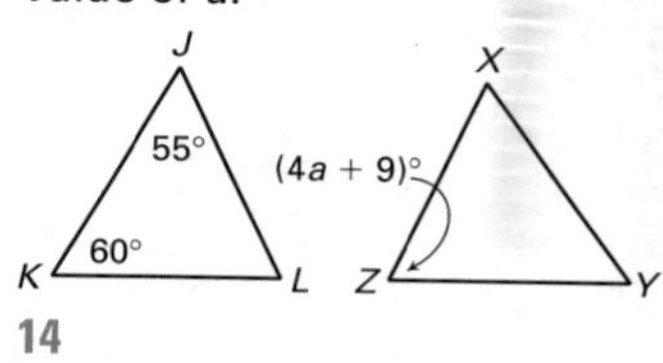

14

EXTRA CHALLENGE NOTE

Challenge problems for Lesson 4.2 are available in **blackline** format in the *Chapter 4 Resource Book,* p. 38 and at **www.mcdougallittell.com.**

ADDITIONAL TEST PREPARATION

1. OPEN ENDED Draw a rectangle and its two diagonals. Name all pairs of congruent triangles in your drawing. Check work.

ADDITIONAL RESOURCES

An alternative Quiz for Lessons 4.1–4.2 is available in the *Chapter 4 Resource Book,* p. 39.

A **blackline** master with additional Math & History exercises is available in the *Chapter 4 Resource Book,* p. 37.

QUIZ 1

Self-Test for Lessons 4.1 and 4.2

Classify the triangle by its angles and by its sides. (Lesson 4.1)

1. 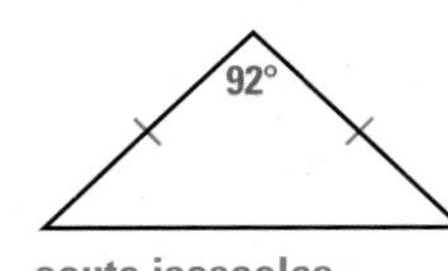

acute isosceles

2. 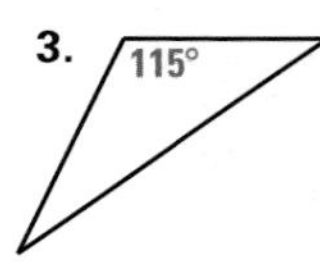

acute isosceles

3. 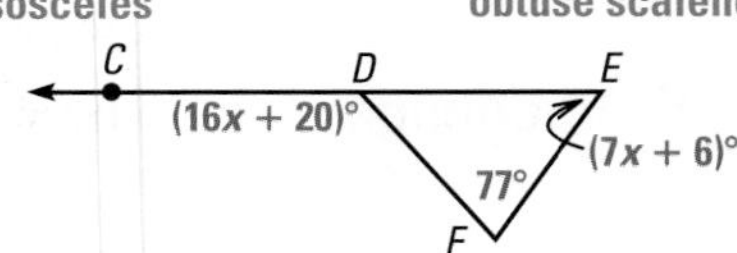

obtuse scalene

4. Find the value of x in the figure at the right. Then give the measure of each interior angle and the measure of the exterior angle shown. (Lesson 4.1)

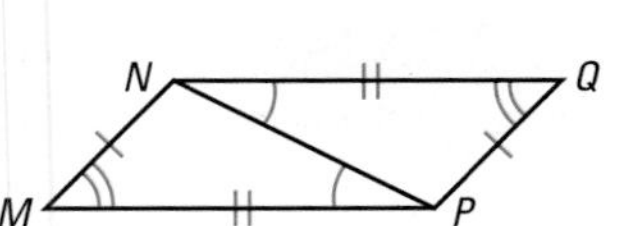

4. 7; $m\angle F = 77°$, $m\angle E = 55°$, $m\angle EDF = 48°$, $m\angle CDF = 132°$

Use the diagram at the right. (Lesson 4.2)

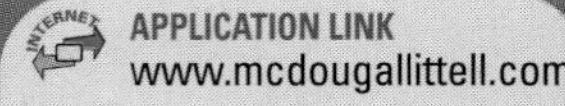

5. Write a congruence statement. Identify all pairs of congruent corresponding parts.

5. $\triangle MNP \cong \triangle QPN$; $\angle M$ and $\angle Q$, $\angle MNP$ and $\angle QPN$, $\angle MPN$ and $\angle QNP$, $\overline{MN}$ and $\overline{QP}$, $\overline{NP}$ and $\overline{PN}$, $\overline{MP}$ and $\overline{QN}$

6. You are given that $m\angle NMP = 46°$ and $m\angle PNQ = 27°$. Find $m\angle MNP$. 107°

MATH & History — Triangles In Architecture

APPLICATION LINK www.mcdougallittell.com

THEN **AROUND 2600 B.C.,** construction of the Great Pyramid of Khufu began. It took the ancient Egyptians about 30 years to transform 6.5 million tons of stone into a pyramid with a square base and four congruent triangular faces.

NOW **TODAY,** triangles are still used in architecture. They are even being used in structures designed to house astronauts on long-term space missions.

1. The original side lengths of a triangular face on the Great Pyramid of Khufu were about 219 meters, 230 meters, and 219 meters. The measure of one of the interior angles was about 63°. The other two interior angles were congruent. Find the measures of the other angles. Then classify the triangle by its angles and sides.

58.5°, 58.5°; acute isosceles

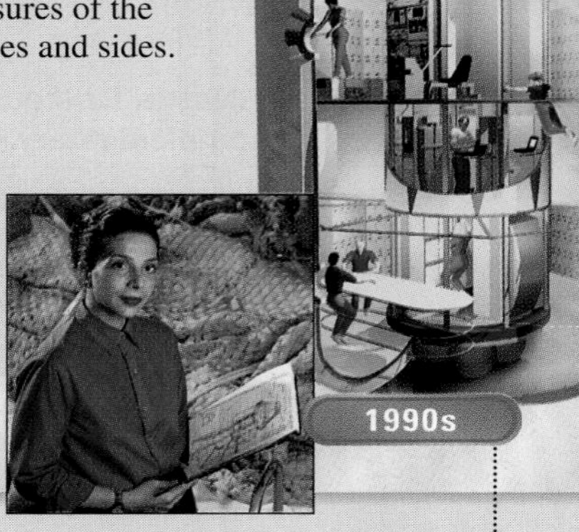

Construction on the Great Pyramid of Khufu begins.

c. 2600 B.C.

1825

Moscow's Bolshoi Theater uses triangles in its design.

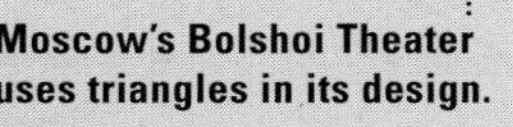

1990s

Architect Constance Adams uses triangles in the design of a space module.

ACTIVITY 4.3

Developing Concepts

Investigating Congruent Triangles

GROUP ACTIVITY
Work with a partner.

MATERIALS
- 3 pencils
- protractor
- ruler

▶ QUESTION **How much information do you need to know to tell whether two triangles are congruent?**

▶ EXPLORING THE CONCEPT: SSS

Steps 1–3. Check drawings.

1. On a piece of paper, place three pencils of different lengths so they make a triangle.
2. Mark each vertex of your triangle by pressing the pencil points to the paper.
3. Remove the pencils and draw the sides of your triangle.
4. Have your partner repeat **Steps 1–3** using the same three pencils. Try to make a triangle that is *not* congruent to the one you drew.

Step 4. It is not possible to do so.

▶ EXPLORING THE CONCEPT: SAS

Steps 5–7. Check drawings.

5. On a piece of paper, place two pencils so their erasers are at the center of a protractor. Arrange them to form a 45° angle.
6. Mark two vertices of a triangle by pressing the pencil points to the paper. Mark the center of the protractor as the third vertex.
7. Remove the pencils and protractor and draw the sides of your triangle.
8. Have your partner repeat **Steps 5–7** using the same two pencils. Try to make a triangle that has a 45° angle but is *not* congruent to the one you drew. It is not possible to do so.

▶ DRAWING CONCLUSIONS

1. What do you notice about the triangles you made with three pencils? What do you notice about the triangles you made with two pencils and a 45° angle between them?
2. **CRITICAL THINKING** If you know that two sides of a triangle are congruent to two sides of another triangle, what other information do you need to tell whether the triangles are congruent?

1. All triangles made with three pencils appear to be congruent; All triangles made with two pencils and a 45° angle appear to be congruent.
2. the length of the third side or the measure of the angle between the sides whose lengths are known

1 Planning the Activity

PURPOSE
To find how much information is needed to prove two triangles are congruent.

MATERIALS
- 3 pencils
- protractor
- ruler

PACING
- Exploring the Concept — 10 min
- Drawing Conclusions — 5 min

▶ *LINK TO LESSON*
As students study SSS and SAS on pages 212 and 213, have them recall the results of this activity.

2 Managing the Activity

CLASSROOM MANAGEMENT
For both Steps 4 and 8, the task described is impossible. Give students a few minutes to reach this conclusion.

ALTERNATIVE APPROACH
The activity can be done as a demonstration using an overhead projector, colored rods, and a clear protractor.

3 Closing the Activity

★ ***KEY DISCOVERY***
If you are given the lengths of all three sides of a triangle or the lengths of two sides and their included angle, then this is enough information to prove that two triangles are congruent.

ACTIVITY ASSESSMENT
JOURNAL Describe what you learned in this activity about proving pairs of triangles congruent.
Sample answer: To prove whether two triangles are congruent, you need to know the lengths of all three sides or the lengths of two sides and the included angle.

1 PLAN

PACING
Basic: 2 days
Average: 2 days
Advanced: 2 days
Block Schedule: 0.5 block with 4.2
0.5 block with 4.4

LESSON OPENER
APPLICATION
An alternative way to approach Lesson 4.3 is to use the Application Lesson Opener:

- Blackline Master (*Chapter 4 Resource Book,* p. 43)
- Transparency (p. 23)

MEETING INDIVIDUAL NEEDS

- ***Chapter 4 Resource Book***
  Prerequisite Skills Review (p. 5)
  Practice Level A (p. 45)
  Practice Level B (p. 46)
  Practice Level C (p. 47)
  Reteaching with Practice (p. 48)
  Absent Student Catch-Up (p. 50)
  Challenge (p. 52)
- ***Resources in Spanish***
- ***Personal Student Tutor***

NEW-TEACHER SUPPORT
See the Tips for New Teachers on pp. 1–2 of the *Chapter 4 Resource Book* for additional notes about Lesson 4.3.

WARM-UP EXERCISES

Transparency Available

Tell whether each statement is needed to show congruence.

1. The figures must have exactly the same size. **yes**
2. The figures must have exactly the same shape. **yes**
3. The figures must be triangles. **no**
4. The figures must be polygons. **no**

4.3 Proving Triangles are Congruent: SSS and SAS

What you should learn

GOAL 1 Prove that triangles are congruent using the SSS and SAS Congruence Postulates.

GOAL 2 Use congruence postulates in **real-life** problems, such as bracing a structure in **Example 5**.

Why you should learn it

▼ Congruence postulates help you see why triangles make things stable, such as the seaplane's wing below and the objects in **Exs. 30 and 31**.

REAL LIFE

CALIFORNIA STANDARDS AND ASSESSMENT

CA Standards: 2, 5, 16
SAT9 Task 1: Objs. 1, 22, 24, 26
SAT9 Task 2: Objs. 1, 24, 26, 27

GOAL 1 SSS AND SAS CONGRUENCE POSTULATES

How much do you need to know about two triangles to prove that they are congruent? In Lesson 4.2, you learned that if all six pairs of corresponding parts (sides and angles) are congruent, then the triangles are congruent.

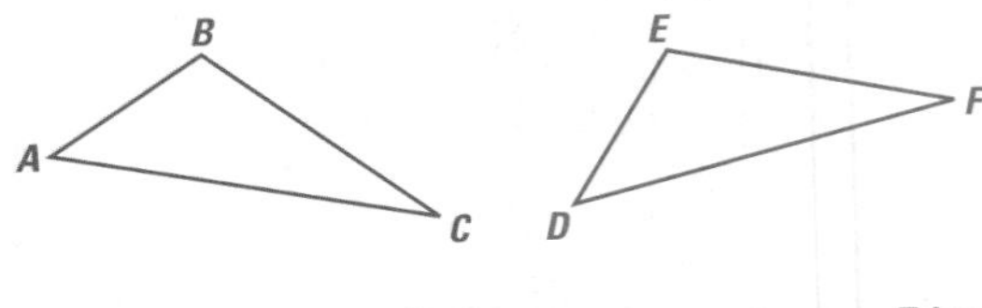

If	Sides are congruent	and	Angles are congruent	then	Triangles are congruent
	1. $\overline{AB} \cong \overline{DE}$		**4.** $\angle A \cong \angle D$		$\triangle ABC \cong \triangle DEF$
	2. $\overline{BC} \cong \overline{EF}$		**5.** $\angle B \cong \angle E$		
	3. $\overline{AC} \cong \overline{DF}$		**6.** $\angle C \cong \angle F$		

In this lesson and the next, you will learn that you do not need all six of the pieces of information above to prove that the triangles are congruent. For example, if all three pairs of corresponding sides are congruent, then the *SSS Congruence Postulate* guarantees that the triangles are congruent.

POSTULATE

POSTULATE 19 ***Side-Side-Side (SSS) Congruence Postulate***

If three sides of one triangle are congruent to three sides of a second triangle, then the two triangles are congruent.

If Side $\overline{MN} \cong \overline{QR}$,
Side $\overline{NP} \cong \overline{RS}$, and
Side $\overline{PM} \cong \overline{SQ}$,
then $\triangle MNP \cong \triangle QRS$.

EXAMPLE 1 *Using the SSS Congruence Postulate*

Prove that $\triangle PQW \cong \triangle TSW$.

Paragraph Proof The marks on the diagram show that $\overline{PQ} \cong \overline{TS}$, $\overline{PW} \cong \overline{TW}$, and $\overline{QW} \cong \overline{SW}$.

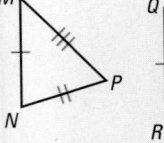

▶ So, by the SSS Congruence Postulate, you know that $\triangle PQW \cong \triangle TSW$.

ACTIVITY

Construction

Copying a Triangle

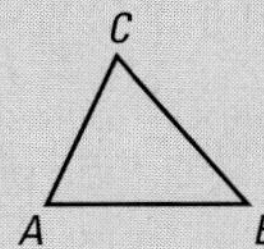

Follow the steps below to construct a triangle that is congruent to a given $\triangle ABC$.

1–4. Check drawings.

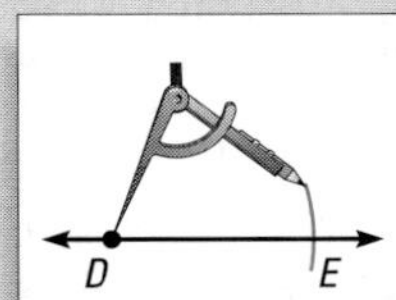

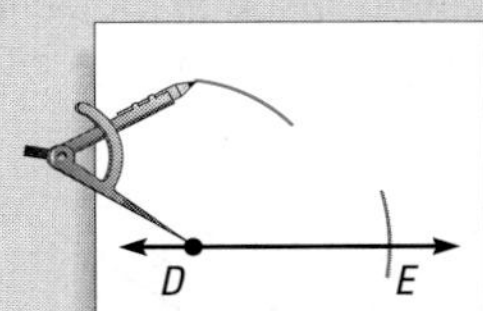

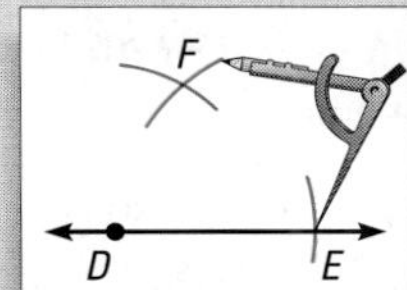

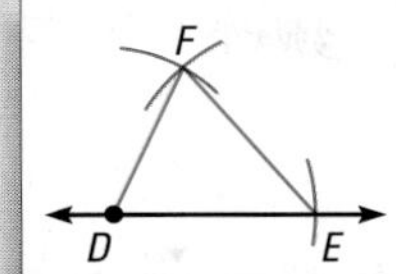

1. Construct $\overline{DE}$ so that it is congruent to $\overline{AB}$. (See page 104 for the construction.)
2. Open your compass to the length AC. Use this length to draw an arc with the compass point at D.
3. Draw an arc with radius BC and center E that intersects the arc from **Step 2.** Label the intersection point F.
4. Draw $\triangle DEF$. By the SSS Congruence Postulate, $\triangle ABC \cong \triangle DEF$.

The SSS Congruence Postulate is a shortcut for proving two triangles are congruent without using all six pairs of corresponding parts. The postulate below is a shortcut that uses two sides and the angle that is *included* between the sides.

STUDENT HELP

Study Tip

In the triangle, $\angle B$ is the **included angle** between sides $\overline{AB}$ and $\overline{BC}$.

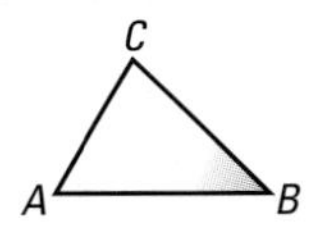

POSTULATE

POSTULATE 20 ***Side-Angle-Side (SAS) Congruence Postulate***

If two sides and the included angle of one triangle are congruent to two sides and the included angle of a second triangle, then the two triangles are congruent.

If Side $\overline{PQ} \cong \overline{WX}$,
Angle $\angle Q \cong \angle X$, and
Side $\overline{QS} \cong \overline{XY}$,
then $\triangle PQS \cong \triangle WXY$.

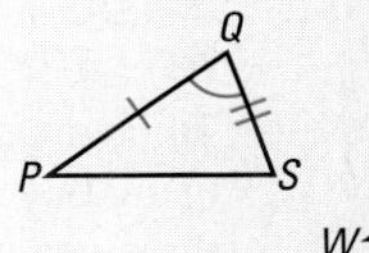

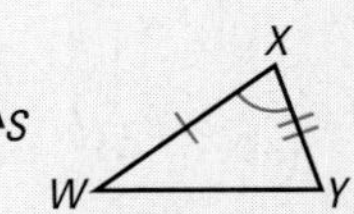

EXAMPLE 2 *Using the SAS Congruence Postulate*

Prove that $\triangle AEB \cong \triangle DEC$.

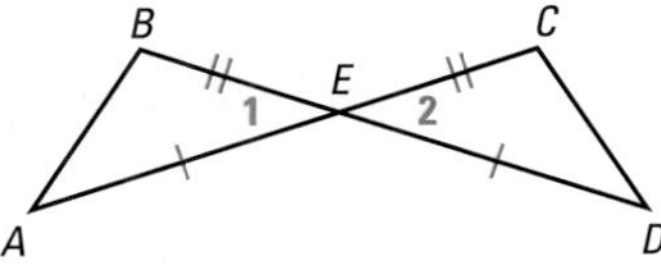

Statements	Reasons
1. $\overline{AE} \cong \overline{DE}$, $\overline{BE} \cong \overline{CE}$	**1.** Given
2. $\angle 1 \cong \angle 2$	**2.** Vertical Angles Theorem
3. $\triangle AEB \cong \triangle DEC$	**3.** SAS Congruence Postulate

2 TEACH

EXTRA EXAMPLE 1

Prove $\triangle KLM \cong \triangle NMP$.

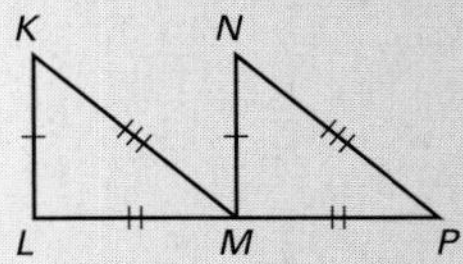

The marks show that $\overline{KL} \cong \overline{NM}$, $\overline{LM} \cong \overline{MP}$, and $\overline{KM} \cong \overline{NP}$. So by SSS, $\triangle KLM \cong \triangle NMP$.

EXTRA EXAMPLE 2

Prove that $\triangle VWZ \cong \triangle YWX$.

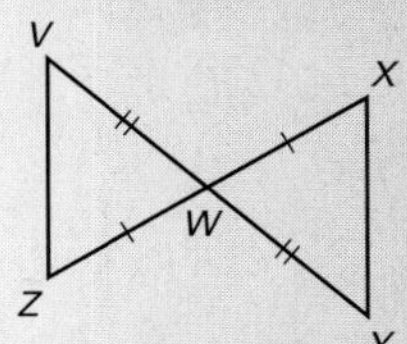

Statements (Reasons)

1. $\overline{VW} \cong \overline{YW}$ (Given)
2. $\angle VWZ \cong \angle YWX$ (Vertical Angles Theorem)
3. $\overline{ZW} \cong \overline{XW}$ (Given)
4. $\triangle VWZ \cong \triangle YWX$ (SAS)

CHECKPOINT EXERCISES

For use after Example 1:

1. Prove $\triangle ABC \cong \triangle FDE$.

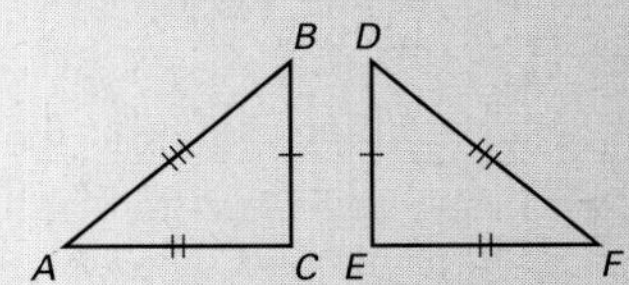

The marks show that $\overline{BC} \cong \overline{DE}$, $\overline{AB} \cong \overline{FD}$, and $\overline{AC} \cong \overline{FE}$. So by SSS, $\triangle ABC \cong \triangle FDE$.

For use after Example 2:

2. Prove $\triangle GHJ \cong \triangle KHL$.

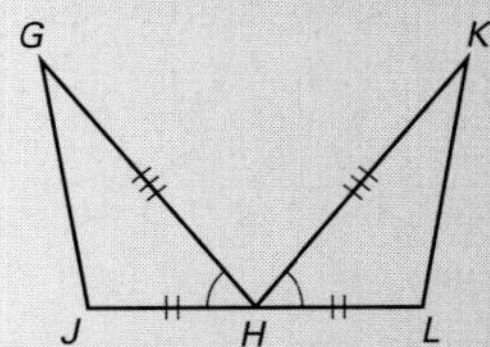

Statements (Reasons)

1. $\overline{GH} \cong \overline{KH}$ (Given)
2. $\angle GHJ \cong \angle KHL$ (Given)
3. $\overline{JH} \cong \overline{LH}$ (Given)
4. $\triangle GHJ \cong \triangle KHL$ (SAS)

Extra Example 3

Is enough information given to prove that $\triangle LMP \cong \triangle NPM$?

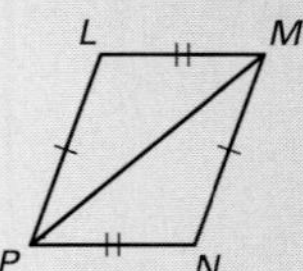

The marks show $\overline{LM} \cong \overline{NP}$ and $\overline{LP} \cong \overline{NM}$. By the Reflexive Property, $\overline{PM} \cong \overline{PM}$. Because the sides of $\triangle LMP$ are congruent to the corresponding sides of $\triangle NPM$, you can use SSS.

Extra Example 4

Given: $AB \cong PB$, $\overline{MB} \perp \overline{AP}$
Prove: $\triangle MBA \cong \triangle MBP$

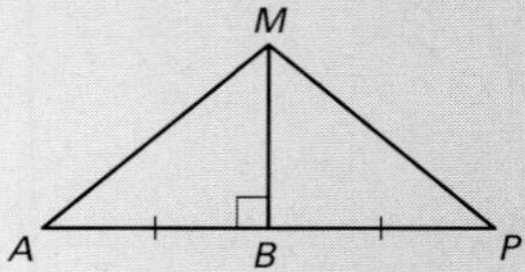

Statements (Reasons)

1. $\overline{MB} \perp \overline{AP}$ (Given)
2. $\angle MBA$ and $\angle MBP$ are right $\angle$s ($\perp$ lines form right $\angle$s)
3. $\angle MBA \cong \angle MBP$ (Right $\angle$s are $\cong$)
4. $\overline{AB} \cong \overline{PB}$ (Given)
5. $\overline{MB} \cong \overline{MB}$ (Reflexive Prop.)
6. $\triangle MBA \cong \triangle MBP$ (SAS)

Checkpoint Exercises

For use after Examples 3 and 4:

1. Is enough information given to prove that $\triangle STU \cong \triangle PUT$?

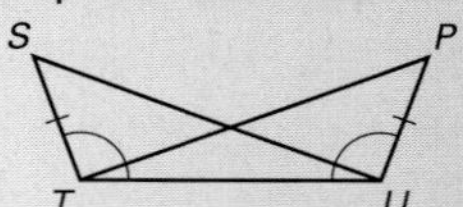

The marks show that $\overline{ST} \cong \overline{PU}$ and that $\angle STU \cong \angle PUT$. By the Reflexive Property, $\overline{TU} \cong \overline{TU}$. Because two sides and the included angle of $\triangle STU$ are congruent to the corresponding two sides and included angle of $\triangle PUT$, you can use SAS.

214

GOAL 2 Modeling a Real-Life Situation

EXAMPLE 3 *Choosing Which Congruence Postulate to Use*

Logical Reasoning

Decide whether enough information is given in the diagram to prove that $\triangle PQR \cong \triangle PSR$. If there is enough information, state the congruence postulate you would use.

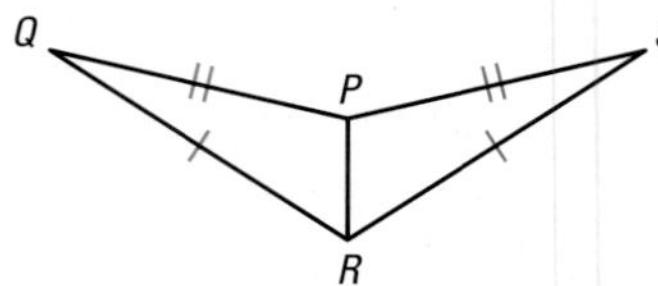

Solution

Paragraph Proof The marks on the diagram show that $\overline{PQ} \cong \overline{PS}$ and $\overline{QR} \cong \overline{SR}$. By the Reflexive Property of Congruence, $\overline{RP} \cong \overline{RP}$. Because the sides of $\triangle PQR$ are congruent to the corresponding sides of $\triangle PSR$, you can use the SSS Congruence Postulate to prove that the triangles are congruent.

EXAMPLE 4 *Proving Triangles Congruent*

REAL LIFE **Architecture** You are designing the window shown in the photo. You want to make $\triangle DRA$ congruent to $\triangle DRG$. You design the window so that $\overline{DR} \perp \overline{AG}$ and $\overline{RA} \cong \overline{RG}$. Can you conclude that $\triangle DRA \cong \triangle DRG$?

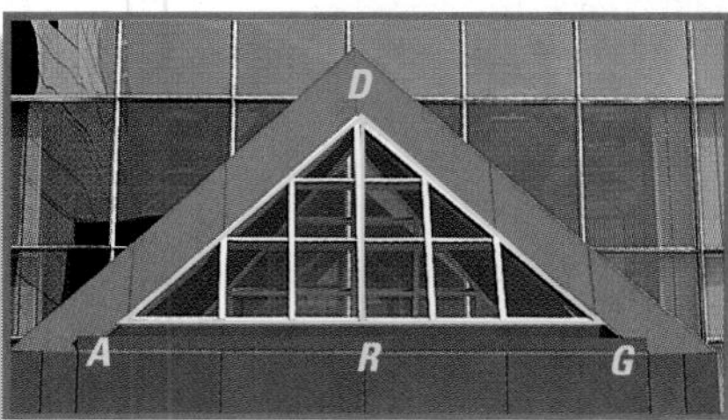

Solution

To begin, copy the diagram and label it using the given information. Then write the given information and the statement you need to prove.

Proof

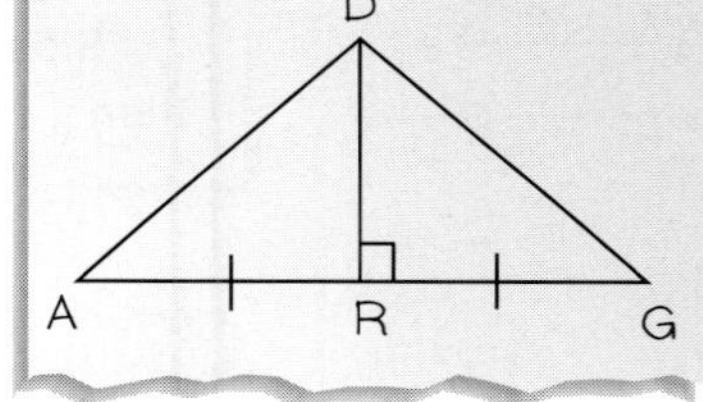

GIVEN ▶ $\overline{DR} \perp \overline{AG}$,
$\overline{RA} \cong \overline{RG}$

PROVE ▶ $\triangle DRA \cong \triangle DRG$

Statements	Reasons
1. $\overline{DR} \perp \overline{AG}$	**1.** Given
2. $\angle DRA$ and $\angle DRG$ are right angles.	**2.** If 2 lines are $\perp$, then they form 4 rt. $\angle$s.
3. $\angle DRA \cong \angle DRG$	**3.** Right Angle Congruence Theorem
4. $\overline{RA} \cong \overline{RG}$	**4.** Given
5. $\overline{DR} \cong \overline{DR}$	**5.** Reflexive Property of Congruence
6. $\triangle DRA \cong \triangle DRG$	**6.** SAS Congruence Postulate

EXAMPLE 5 Triangular Frameworks are Rigid

STRUCTURAL SUPPORT To prevent a doorway from collapsing after an earthquake, you can reinforce it. Explain why the doorway with the diagonal brace is more stable, while the one without the brace can collapse.

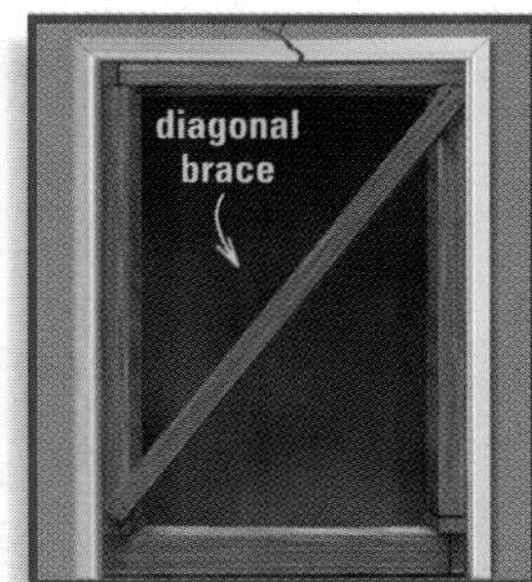

SOLUTION

In the doorway with the diagonal brace, the wood forms triangles whose sides have fixed lengths. The SSS Congruence Postulate guarantees that these triangles are rigid, because a triangle with given side lengths has only one possible size and shape. The doorway without the brace is unstable because there are many possible shapes for a four-sided figure with the given side lengths.

EXAMPLE 6 Congruent Triangles in a Coordinate Plane

Use the SSS Congruence Postulate to show that $\triangle ABC \cong \triangle FGH$.

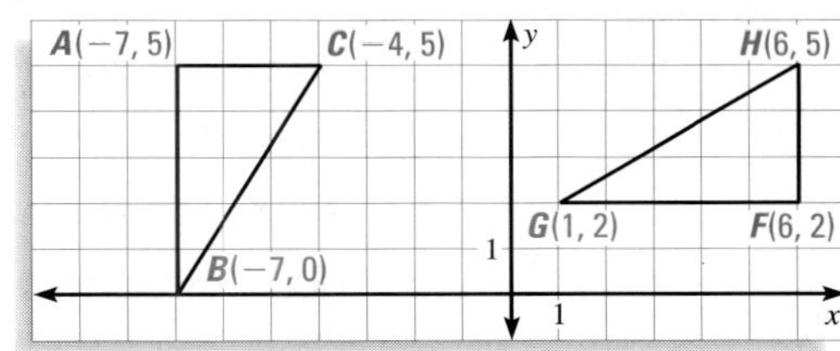

SOLUTION

Because $AC = 3$ and $FH = 3$, $\overline{AC} \cong \overline{FH}$. Because $AB = 5$ and $FG = 5$, $\overline{AB} \cong \overline{FG}$. Use the Distance Formula to find the lengths BC and GH.

STUDENT HELP

Look Back
For help with the Distance Formula, see page 19.

$$d = \sqrt{(x_2 - x_1)^2 + (y_2 - y_1)^2} \qquad d = \sqrt{(x_2 - x_1)^2 + (y_2 - y_1)^2}$$

$$BC = \sqrt{(-4-(-7))^2 + (5-0)^2} \qquad GH = \sqrt{(6-1)^2 + (5-2)^2}$$

$$= \sqrt{3^2 + 5^2} \qquad = \sqrt{5^2 + 3^2}$$

$$= \sqrt{34} \qquad = \sqrt{34}$$

▶ Because $BC = \sqrt{34}$ and $GH = \sqrt{34}$, $\overline{BC} \cong \overline{GH}$. All three pairs of corresponding sides are congruent, so $\triangle ABC \cong \triangle FGH$ by the SSS Congruence Postulate.

EXTRA EXAMPLE 5

A picture frame is assembled with a diagonal brace along the back. Explain why the frame with a brace is more stable than a frame without the brace. **In the frame with the brace, the sides form triangles whose sides have fixed lengths. SSS guarantees that these triangles are rigid. The frame without the brace is unstable because there are many possible shapes for a four-sided figure.**

EXTRA EXAMPLE 6

Use SSS to show that $\triangle NPM \cong \triangle DFE$.

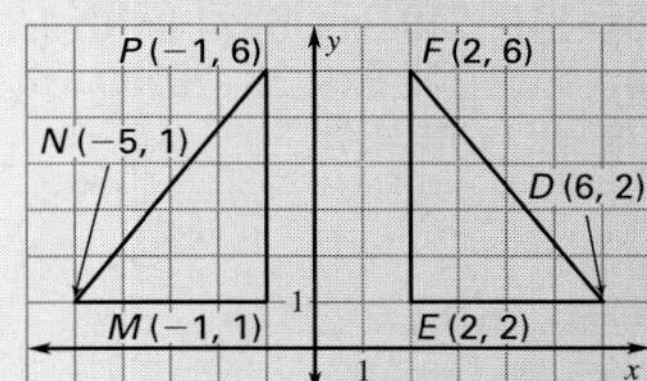

Because $NM = 4$ and $DE = 4$, $\overline{NM} \cong \overline{DE}$. Because $PM = 5$ and $FE = 5$, $\overline{PM} \cong \overline{FE}$. Because $NP = \sqrt{41}$ and $DF = \sqrt{41}$, $\overline{NP} \cong \overline{DF}$. All three pairs of corresponding sides are congruent, so $\triangle NPM \cong \triangle DFE$ by SSS.

CHECKPOINT EXERCISES

For use after Examples 5 and 6:

1. Explain why the crossed legs of a picnic table give it more support than if the legs go straight down, as in a dinner table. **The triangle formed by the legs can only have one shape so the picnic table is rigid. The four-sided figure formed by the legs, tabletop, and ground under a dinner table can have more than one shape so it is less rigid.**

CLOSURE QUESTION

Which congruence postulate would be used to prove the triangles congruent? **SAS**

3 APPLY

ASSIGNMENT GUIDE

BASIC
Day 1: pp. 216–219 Exs. 6–21
Day 2: pp. 217–219 Exs. 22–28, 32–37, 39–46

AVERAGE
Day 1: pp. 216–219 Exs. 6–21
Day 2: pp. 217–219 Exs. 22–28, 32–37, 39–46

ADVANCED
Day 1: pp. 216–219 Exs. 6–21
Day 2: pp. 217–219 Exs. 22–28, 30–46

BLOCK SCHEDULE
pp. 216–219 Exs. 6–21 (with 4.2)
pp. 216–219 Exs. 22–28, 30–37, 39–46 (with 4.4)

EXERCISE LEVELS

Level A: *Easier*
6–17

Level B: *More Difficult*
18–37

Level C: *Most Difficult*
38

✔ HOMEWORK CHECK

To quickly check student understanding of key concepts, go over the following exercises: Exs. 8, 16, 18, 20, 26, 28, 32, 34. See also the Daily Homework Quiz:

- Blackline Master (*Chapter 4 Resource Book,* p. 55)
- Transparency (p. 28)

216

GUIDED PRACTICE

Vocabulary Check ✓

1. Sketch a triangle and label its vertices. Name two sides and the included angle between the sides. **See margin.**

Concept Check ✓

2. **ERROR ANALYSIS** Henry believes he can use the information given in the diagram and the SAS Congruence Postulate to prove the two triangles are congruent. Explain Henry's mistake.

2. The congruent angles are not the angles included between the congruent sides.

Skill Check ✓

LOGICAL REASONING **Decide whether enough information is given to prove that the triangles are congruent. If there is enough information, tell which congruence postulate you would use.**

3. $\triangle ABC$, $\triangle DEC$

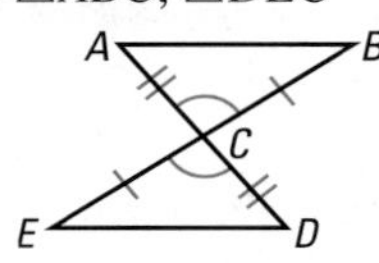

yes; SAS Congruence Postulate

4. $\triangle FGH$, $\triangle JKH$

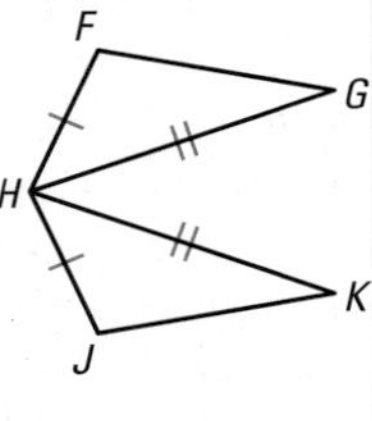

no

5. $\triangle PQR$, $\triangle SRQ$

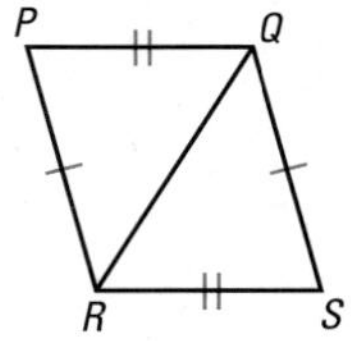

yes; SSS Congruence Postulate

PRACTICE AND APPLICATIONS

STUDENT HELP
Extra Practice to help you master skills is on p. 809.

NAMING SIDES AND INCLUDED ANGLES **Use the diagram. Name the included angle between the pair of sides given.**

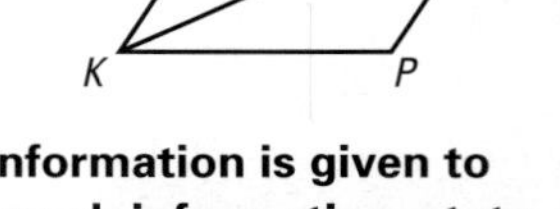

6. $\overline{JK}$ and $\overline{KL}$ $\angle JKL$
7. $\overline{PK}$ and $\overline{LK}$ $\angle LKP$
8. $\overline{LP}$ and $\overline{LK}$ $\angle KLP$
9. $\overline{JL}$ and $\overline{JK}$ $\angle KJL$
10. $\overline{KL}$ and $\overline{JL}$ $\angle JLK$
11. $\overline{KP}$ and $\overline{PL}$ $\angle KPL$

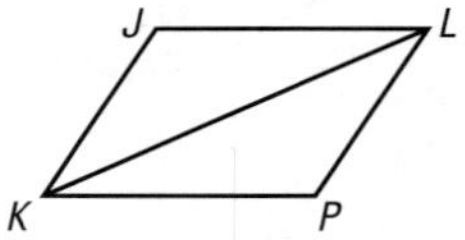

LOGICAL REASONING **Decide whether enough information is given to prove that the triangles are congruent. If there is enough information, state the congruence postulate you would use.** 12–17. See margin.

12. no
13. yes; SAS Congruence Postulate
14. yes; SSS Congruence Postulate
15. yes; SAS Congruence Postulate
16. no
17. yes; SSS Congruence Postulate

12. $\triangle UVT$, $\triangle WVT$

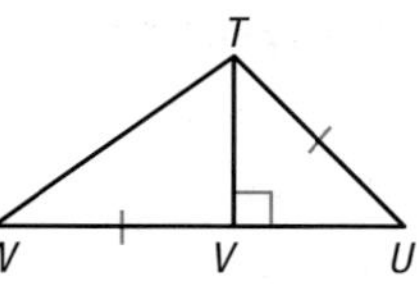

13. $\triangle LMN$, $\triangle TNM$

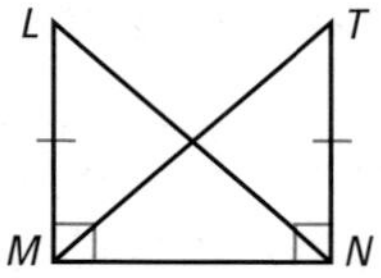

14. $\triangle YZW$, $\triangle YXW$

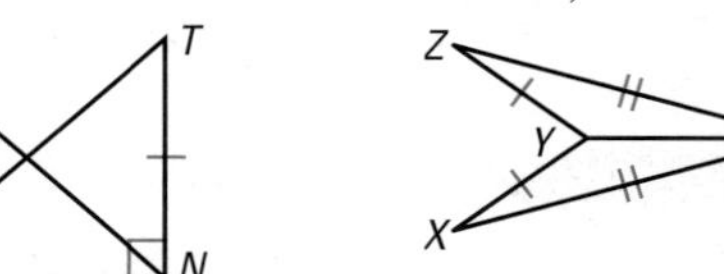

15. $\triangle ACB$, $\triangle ECD$

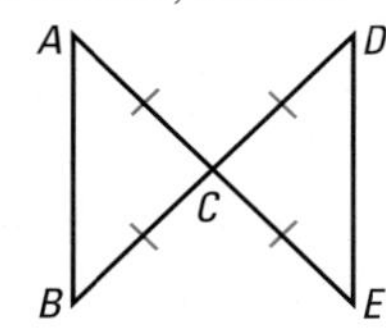

16. $\triangle RST$, $\triangle WVU$

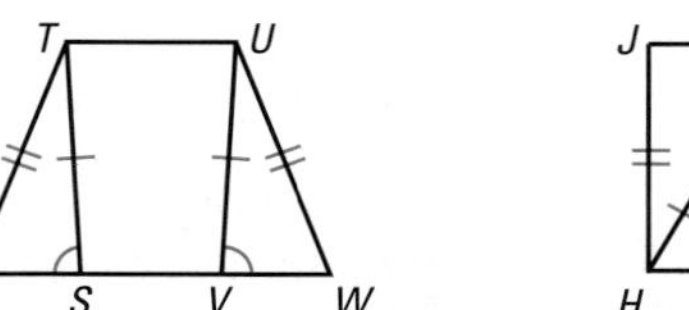

17. $\triangle GJH$, $\triangle HLK$

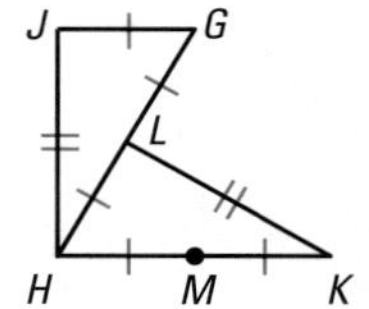

STUDENT HELP
HOMEWORK HELP
Example 1: Exs. 18, 20–28
Example 2: Exs. 19–28
Example 3: Exs. 12–17
Example 4: Exs. 20–28
Example 5: Exs. 30, 31
Example 6: Exs. 33–35

DEVELOPING PROOF In Exercises 18 and 19, use the photo of the Navajo rug. Assume that $\overline{BC} \cong \overline{DE}$ and $\overline{AC} \cong \overline{CE}$.

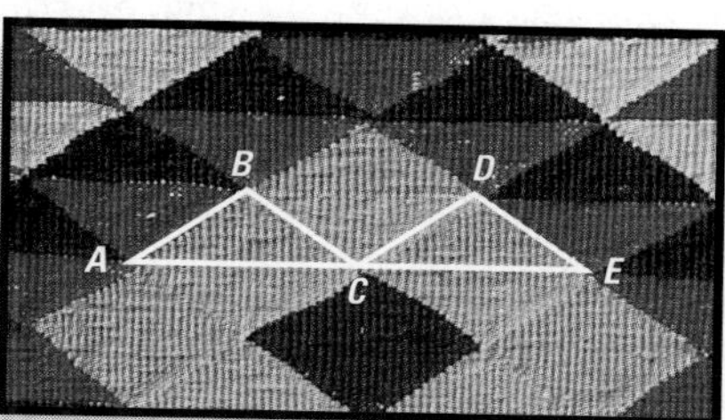

18. What other piece of information is needed to prove that $\triangle ABC \cong \triangle CDE$ using the SSS Congruence Postulate? $\overline{AB} \cong \overline{CD}$

19. What other piece of information is needed to prove that $\triangle ABC \cong \triangle CDE$ using the SAS Congruence Postulate? $\angle ACB \cong \angle CED$

20. **DEVELOPING PROOF** Complete the proof by supplying the reasons.

GIVEN ▶ $\overline{EF} \cong \overline{GH}$, $\overline{FG} \cong \overline{HE}$

PROVE ▶ $\triangle EFG \cong \triangle GHE$

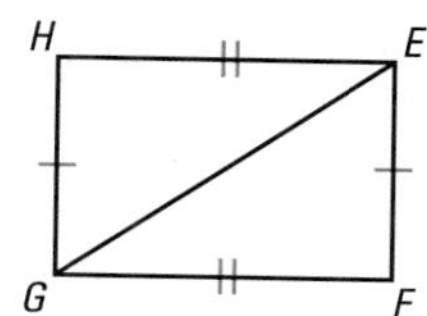

Statements	Reasons
1. $\overline{EF} \cong \overline{GH}$	1. ? Given
2. $\overline{FG} \cong \overline{HE}$	2. ? Given
3. $\overline{GE} \cong \overline{GE}$	3. ? Reflexive Property of Congruence
4. $\triangle EFG \cong \triangle GHE$	4. ? SSS Congruence Postulate

TWO-COLUMN PROOF Write a two-column proof. 21, 22. See margin.

21. GIVEN ▶ $\overline{NP} \cong \overline{QN} \cong \overline{RS} \cong \overline{TR}$, $\overline{PQ} \cong \overline{ST}$

PROVE ▶ $\triangle NPQ \cong \triangle RST$

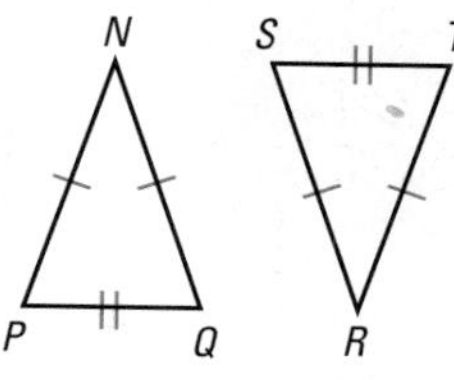

22. GIVEN ▶ $\overline{AB} \cong \overline{CD}$, $\overline{AB} \parallel \overline{CD}$

PROVE ▶ $\triangle ABC \cong \triangle CDA$

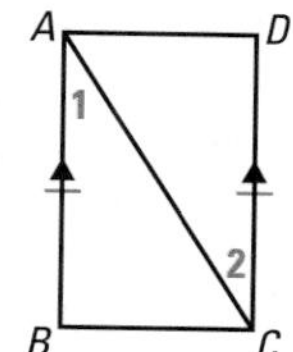

PARAGRAPH PROOF Write a paragraph proof. 23, 24. See margin.

23. GIVEN ▶ $\overrightarrow{PQ}$ bisects $\angle SPT$, $\overline{SP} \cong \overline{TP}$

PROVE ▶ $\triangle SPQ \cong \triangle TPQ$

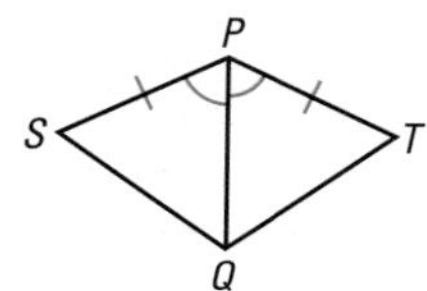

24. GIVEN ▶ $\overline{PT} \cong \overline{RT}$, $\overline{QT} \cong \overline{ST}$

PROVE ▶ $\triangle PQT \cong \triangle RST$

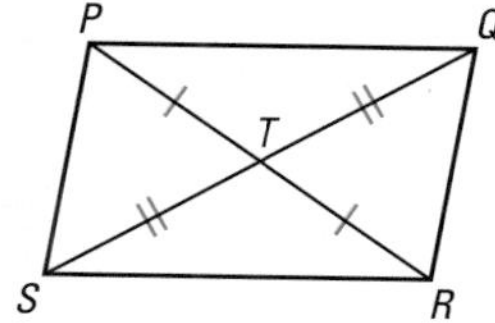

23. It is given that $\overline{SP} \cong \overline{TP}$ and that $\overrightarrow{PQ}$ bisects $\angle SPT$. Then, by the definition of angle bisector, $\angle SPQ \cong \angle TPQ$. $\overline{PQ} \cong \overline{PQ}$ by the Reflexive Property of Congruence, so $\triangle SPQ \cong \triangle TPQ$ by the SAS Congruence Postulate.

24. It is given that $\overline{PT} \cong \overline{RT}$ and $\overline{QT} \cong \overline{ST}$. $\angle PTQ \cong \angle RTS$ by the Vertical Angles Theorem. Then $\triangle PQT \cong \triangle RST$ by the SAS Congruence Postulate.

STUDENT HELP

HOMEWORK HELP Visit our Web site www.mcdougallittell.com for help with paragraph proofs.

COMMON ERROR

EXERCISE 2 Students may incorrectly say that two triangles can be proven congruent using the SAS Congruence Postulate when they are given two pairs of corresponding congruent sides and the corresponding nonincluded angles. Demonstrate that SSA is not a congruence postulate.

STUDENT HELP NOTES

Homework Help Students can find help for Exs. 23–24 at **www.mcdougallittell.com.** The information can be printed out for students who don't have access to the Internet.

1. *Sample answer:*

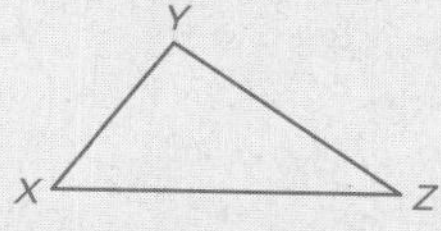

$\angle X$ is included between $\overline{XY}$ and $\overline{XZ}$, $\angle Y$ is included between $\overline{XY}$ and $\overline{YZ}$, and $\angle Z$ is included between $\overline{XZ}$ and $\overline{YZ}$.

21. Statements (Reasons)

1. $\overline{NP} \cong \overline{QN} \cong \overline{RS} \cong \overline{TR}$, $\overline{PQ} \cong \overline{ST}$ (Given)
2. $\triangle NPQ \cong \triangle RST$ (SSS Congruence Postulate)

22. See Additional Answers beginning on page AA1.

STUDENT HELP NOTES

Software Help Instructions for several software packages are available in **blackline** format in the *Chapter 4 Resource Book,* p. 44 and at **www.mcdougallittell.com.**

25. Statements (Reasons)
1. $\overline{AC} \cong \overline{BC}$, M is the midpoint of $\overline{AB}$. (Given)
2. $\overline{AM} \cong \overline{BM}$ (Definition of midpoint)
3. $\overline{CM} \cong \overline{CM}$ (Reflexive Property of Congruence)
4. $\triangle ACM \cong \triangle BCM$ (SSS Congruence Postulate)

26. Statements (Reasons)
1. $\overline{BC} \cong \overline{AE}$, $\overline{BD} \cong \overline{AD}$, $\overline{DE} \cong \overline{DC}$ (Given)
2. $BD = AD$, $DE = DC$ (Definition of congruent segments)
3. $BD + DE = AD + DC$ (Addition property of equality)
4. $BD + DE = BE$, $AD + DC = AC$ (Segment Addition Postulate)
5. $BE = AC$ (Substitution property)
6. $\overline{BE} \cong \overline{AC}$ (Definition of congruent segments)
7. $\overline{AB} \cong \overline{AB}$ (Reflexive Property of Congruence)
8. $\triangle ABC \cong \triangle BAE$ (SSS Congruence Postulate)

33–35, 38, 46. See Additional Answers beginning on page AA1.

ADDITIONAL PRACTICE AND RETEACHING

For Lesson 4.3:

- Practice Levels A, B, and C (*Chapter 4 Resource Book,* p. 45)
- Reteaching with Practice (*Chapter 4 Resource Book,* p. 48)
- See Lesson 4.3 of the *Personal Student Tutor*

For more Mixed Review:

- Search the *Test and Practice Generator* for key words or specific lessons.

27. Since it is given that $\overline{PA} \cong \overline{PB} \cong \overline{PC}$ and $\overline{AB} \cong \overline{BC}$, $\triangle PAB \cong \triangle PBC$ by the SSS Congruence Postulate.

28. It is given that $\overline{CR} \cong \overline{CS}$ and that $\overline{QC}$ is perpendicular to both $\overline{CR}$ and $\overline{CS}$. If two lines are perpendicular, then they intersect to form four right angles, so $\angle QCR$ and $\angle QCS$ are right angles. By the Right Angle Congruence Theorem, $\angle QCR \cong \angle QCS$. By the Reflexive Property of Congruence, $\overline{QC} \cong \overline{QC}$. Then $\triangle QCR \cong \triangle QCS$ by the SAS Congruence Postulate.

29. The new triangle and the original triangle are congruent.

STUDENT HELP

INTERNET SOFTWARE HELP
Visit our Web site www.mcdougallittell.com to see instructions for several software applications.

30, 31. Sample answers are given.

30. The cross pieces form triangles which are rigid, ensuring that the supports keep their shape.

31. The struts that go from the body of the plane to the wing form triangles, making the wing structure rigid.

32. Use the method described in the activity on page 213. Note, however, that the same compass setting will be used to construct the legs of the triangle.

PROOF **Write a two-column proof or a paragraph proof.** 25–28. See margin.

25. **GIVEN** ▶ $\overline{AC} \cong \overline{BC}$, M is the midpoint of $\overline{AB}$.

PROVE ▶ $\triangle ACM \cong \triangle BCM$

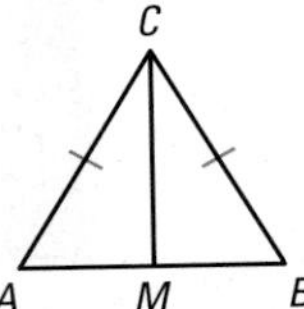

26. **GIVEN** ▶ $\overline{BC} \cong \overline{AE}$, $\overline{BD} \cong \overline{AD}$, $\overline{DE} \cong \overline{DC}$

PROVE ▶ $\triangle ABC \cong \triangle BAE$

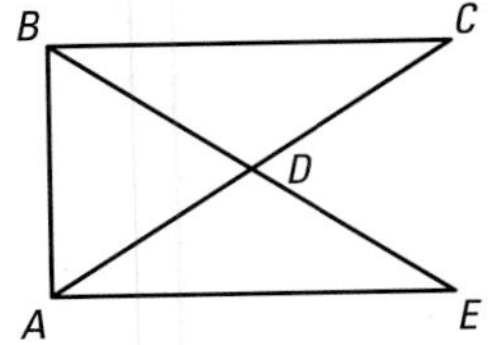

27. **GIVEN** ▶ $\overline{PA} \cong \overline{PB} \cong \overline{PC}$, $\overline{AB} \cong \overline{BC}$

PROVE ▶ $\triangle PAB \cong \triangle PBC$

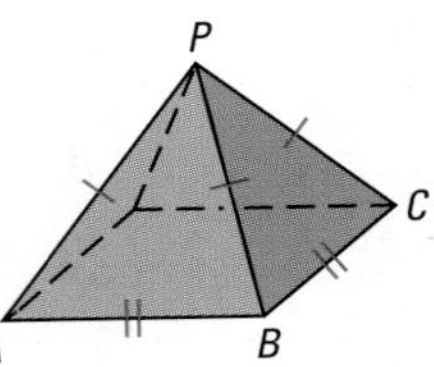

28. **GIVEN** ▶ $\overline{CR} \cong \overline{CS}$, $\overline{QC} \perp \overline{CR}$, $\overline{QC} \perp \overline{CS}$

PROVE ▶ $\triangle QCR \cong \triangle QCS$

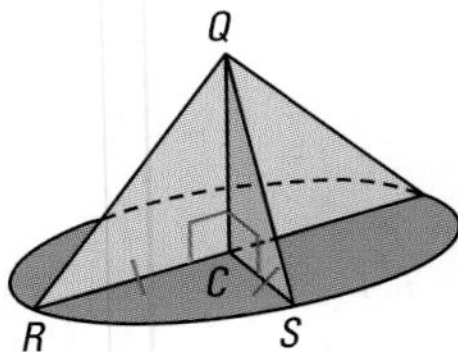

29. **TECHNOLOGY** Use geometry software to draw a triangle. Draw a line and reflect the triangle across the line. Measure the sides and the angles of the new triangle and tell whether it is congruent to the original one. See margin.

Writing **Explain how triangles are used in the object shown to make it more stable.**

30.

31.

32. **CONSTRUCTION** Draw an isosceles triangle with vertices A, B, and C. Use a compass and straightedge to construct $\triangle DEF$ so that $\triangle DEF \cong \triangle ABC$. See margin.

USING ALGEBRA **Use the Distance Formula and the SSS Congruence Postulate to show that $\triangle ABC \cong \triangle DEF$.** 33–35. See margin.

33.

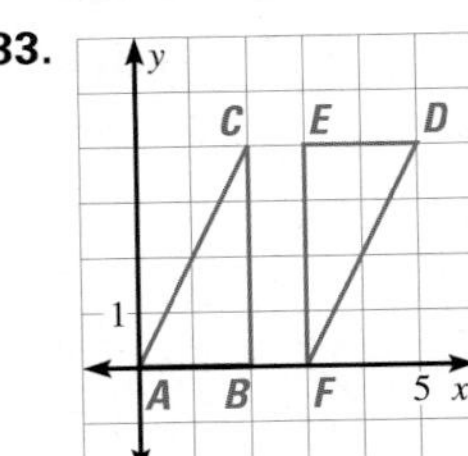

34.

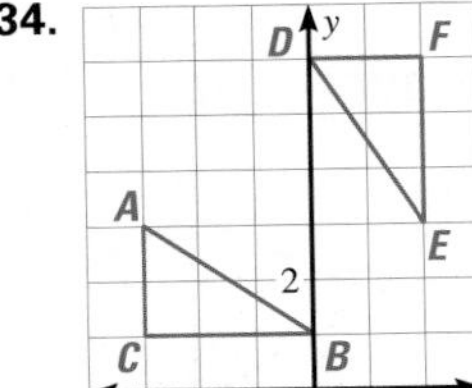

35.

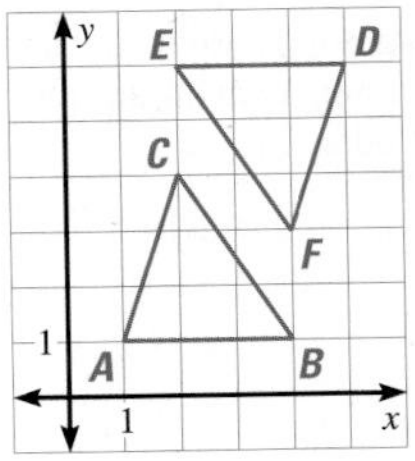

Test Preparation

36. MULTIPLE CHOICE In $\triangle RST$ and $\triangle ABC$, $\overline{RS} \cong \overline{AB}$, $\overline{ST} \cong \overline{BC}$, and $\overline{TR} \cong \overline{CA}$. Which angle is congruent to $\angle T$? **C**

Ⓐ $\angle R$ Ⓑ $\angle A$ Ⓒ $\angle C$ Ⓓ cannot be determined

37. MULTIPLE CHOICE In equilateral $\triangle DEF$, a segment is drawn from point F to G, the midpoint of $\overline{DE}$. Which of the statements below is *not* true? **B**

Ⓐ $\overline{DF} \cong \overline{EF}$ Ⓑ $\overline{DG} \cong \overline{DF}$ Ⓒ $\overline{DG} \cong \overline{EG}$ Ⓓ $\triangle DFG \cong \triangle EFG$

★ Challenge

38. CHOOSING A METHOD Describe how to show that $\triangle PMO \cong \triangle PMN$ using the SSS Congruence Postulate. Then find a way to show that the triangles are congruent using the SAS Congruence Postulate. You may not use a protractor to measure any angles. Compare the two methods. Which do you prefer? Why? **See margin.**

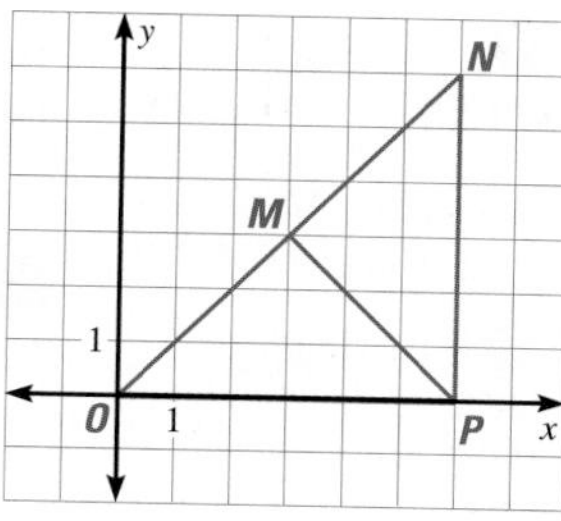

EXTRA CHALLENGE

www.mcdougallittell.com

MIXED REVIEW

SCIENCE CONNECTION **Find an important angle in the photo. Copy the angle, extend its sides, and use a protractor to measure it to the nearest degree.** (Review 1.4)

39.

40.

USING PARALLEL LINES **Find $m\angle 1$ and $m\angle 2$. Explain your reasoning.** (Review 3.3 for 4.4)

41.

42.

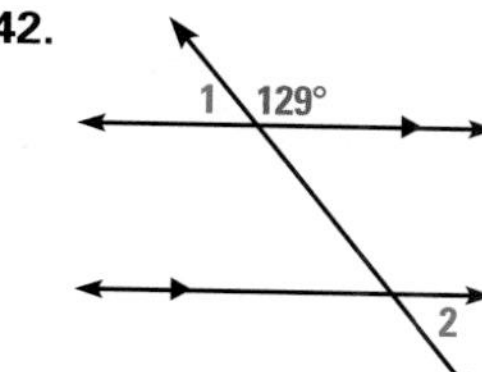

43.

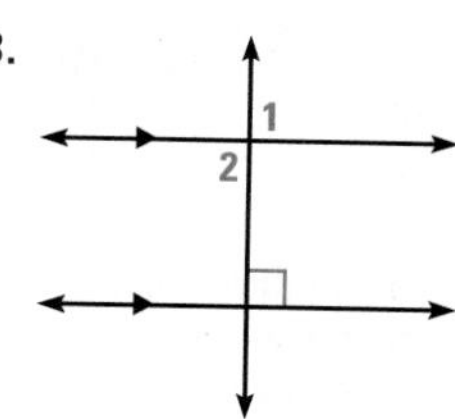

LINE RELATIONSHIPS **Find the slope of each line. Identify any parallel or perpendicular lines.** (Review 3.7) **44–46. See margin.**

44.

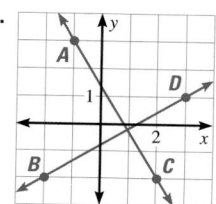

45.

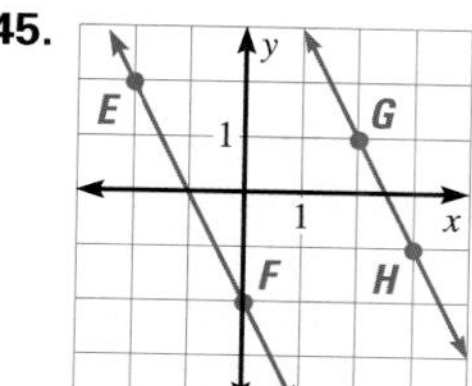

46.

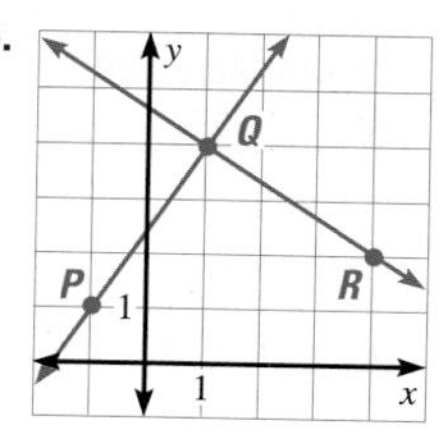

39, 40. Sample answers are given.

39. The measure of each of the angles formed by two adjacent "spokes" is about 60°.

40. The measure of each of the angles formed by two adjacent sides of a cell of the honeycomb is about 120°.

41. $m\angle 2 = 57°$ (Vertical Angles Theorem), $m\angle 1 = 180° - m\angle 2 = 123°$ (Consecutive Interior Angles Theorem)

42. $m\angle 1 = 180° - 129° = 51°$ (Linear Pair Postulate), $m\angle 2 = m\angle 1 = 51°$ (Alternate Exterior Angles Theorem)

43. $m\angle 1 = 90°$ (Corresponding Angles Postulate), $m\angle 2 = 90°$ (Alternate Interior Angles Theorem or Vertical Angles Theorem)

44. slope of $\overleftrightarrow{AC} = -\frac{5}{3}$, slope of $\overleftrightarrow{BD} = \frac{3}{5}$; $\overleftrightarrow{AC} \perp \overleftrightarrow{BD}$

45. slope of $\overleftrightarrow{EF} = -2$, slope of $\overleftrightarrow{GH} = -2$, $\overleftrightarrow{EF} \parallel \overleftrightarrow{GH}$

4 ASSESS

DAILY HOMEWORK QUIZ

Transparency Available

Use the diagram. Name the included angle between the pairs of sides given.

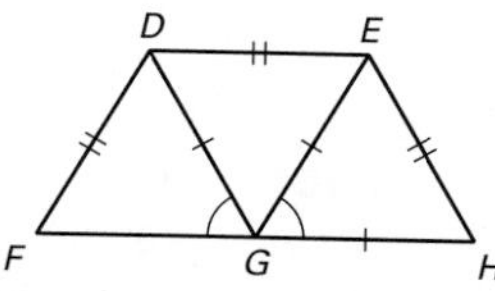

1. $\overline{DG}$ and $\overline{GE}$ **$\angle DGE$**
2. $\overline{EH}$ and $\overline{GH}$ **$\angle EHG$**

Using the diagram above, decide whether enough information is given to prove that the triangles are congruent. If there is enough information, state the congruence postulate you would use.

3. $\triangle DGF$, $\triangle EGH$ **no**
4. $\triangle DGE$, $\triangle EGH$ **yes; SSS Congruence Postulate**

EXTRA CHALLENGE NOTE

Challenge problems for Lesson 4.3 are available in **blackline** format in the *Chapter 4 Resource Book*, p. 52 and at **www.mcdougallittell.com.**

ADDITIONAL TEST PREPARATION

1. **WRITING** Explain the difference between the SSS Congruence Postulate and the SAS Congruence Postulate.
Sample answer: **Both are used to prove triangles congruent. SSS is used when three sides of one triangle are congruent to three sides of a second triangle. SAS is used when two sides and the included angle of one triangle are congruent to two sides and the included angle of a second triangle.**

1 PLAN

PACING
Basic: 2 days
Average: 2 days
Advanced: 2 days
Block Schedule: 0.5 block with 4.3
0.5 block with 4.5

LESSON OPENER APPLICATION
An alternative way to approach Lesson 4.4 is to use the Application Lesson Opener:
- Blackline Master (*Chapter 4 Resource Book*, p. 56)
- Transparency (p. 24)

MEETING INDIVIDUAL NEEDS
- ***Chapter 4 Resource Book***
  Prerequisite Skills Review (p. 5)
  Practice Level A (p. 59)
  Practice Level B (p. 60)
  Practice Level C (p. 61)
  Reteaching with Practice (p. 62)
  Absent Student Catch-Up (p. 64)
  Challenge (p. 66)
- ***Resources in Spanish***
- ***Personal Student Tutor***

NEW-TEACHER SUPPORT
See the Tips for New Teachers on pp. 1–2 of the *Chapter 4 Resource Book* for additional notes about Lesson 4.4.

WARM-UP EXERCISES
Transparency Available
If SSS represents side-side-side and SAS represents side-angle-side, describe the meaning of the following.
1. AAA angle-angle-angle
2. AAS angle-angle-side
3. SSA side-side-angle
4. ASA angle-side-angle

4.4 Proving Triangles are Congruent: ASA and AAS

What you should learn

GOAL 1 Prove that triangles are congruent using the ASA Congruence Postulate and the AAS Congruence Theorem.

GOAL 2 Use congruence postulates and theorems in **real-life** problems, such as taking measurements for a map in **Exs. 24 and 25**.

Why you should learn it

▼ To solve **real-life** problems, such as finding the location of a meteorite in **Example 3**.

REAL LIFE

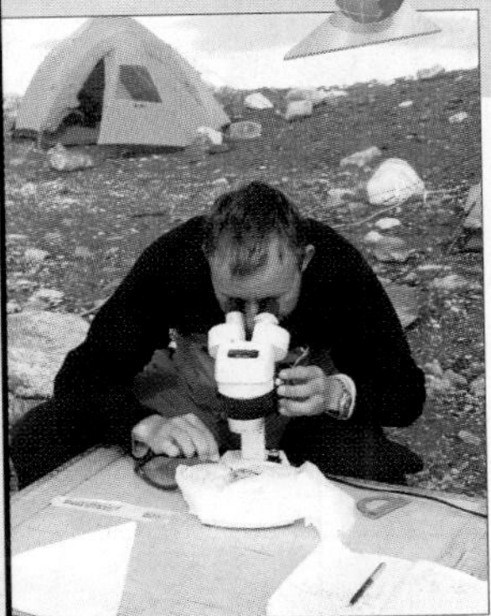

Lars Lindberg Christensen is an astronomer who participated in a search for a meteorite in Greenland.

CALIFORNIA STANDARDS AND ASSESSMENT
CA Standards: 2, 5
SAT9 Task 1: Objs. 22, 24, 26
SAT9 Task 2: Objs. 24, 26, 27

GOAL 1 USING THE ASA AND AAS CONGRUENCE METHODS

In Lesson 4.3, you studied the SSS and the SAS Congruence Postulates. Two additional ways to prove two triangles are congruent are listed below.

MORE WAYS TO PROVE TRIANGLES ARE CONGRUENT

POSTULATE 21 ***Angle-Side-Angle (ASA) Congruence Postulate***

If two angles and the included side of one triangle are congruent to two angles and the included side of a second triangle, then the two triangles are congruent.

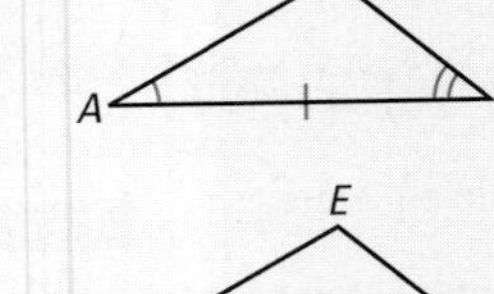

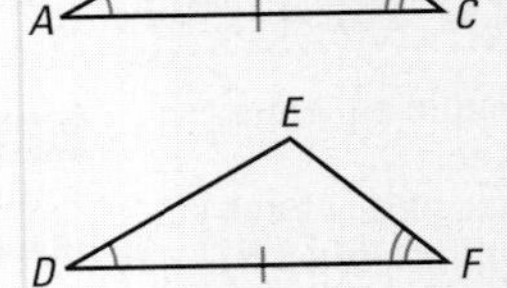

If Angle $\angle A \cong \angle D$,
Side $\overline{AC} \cong \overline{DF}$, and
Angle $\angle C \cong \angle F$,
then $\triangle ABC \cong \triangle DEF$.

THEOREM 4.5 ***Angle-Angle-Side (AAS) Congruence Theorem***

If two angles and a nonincluded side of one triangle are congruent to two angles and the corresponding nonincluded side of a second triangle, then the two triangles are congruent.

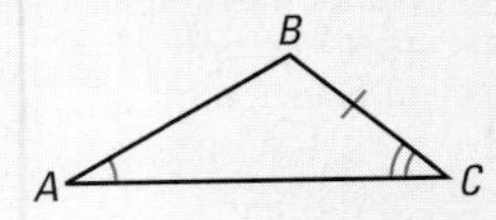

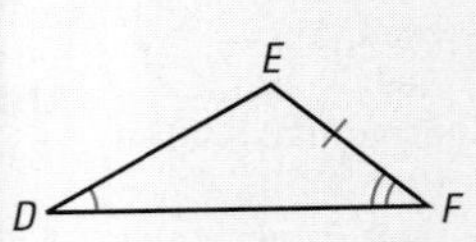

If Angle $\angle A \cong \angle D$,
Angle $\angle C \cong \angle F$, and
Side $\overline{BC} \cong \overline{EF}$,
then $\triangle ABC \cong \triangle DEF$.

A proof of the Angle-Angle-Side (AAS) Congruence Theorem is given below.

GIVEN ▶ $\angle A \cong \angle D$, $\angle C \cong \angle F$, $\overline{BC} \cong \overline{EF}$

PROVE ▶ $\triangle ABC \cong \triangle DEF$

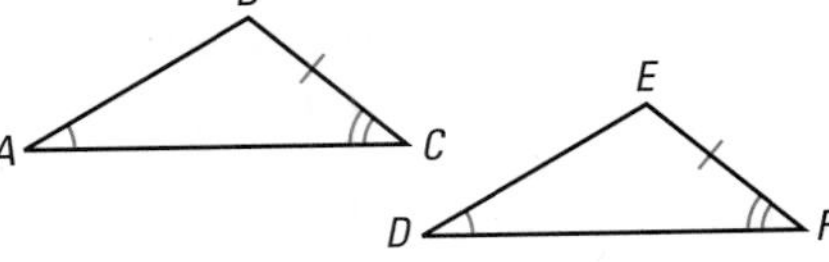

Paragraph Proof You are given that two angles of $\triangle ABC$ are congruent to two angles of $\triangle DEF$. By the Third Angles Theorem, the third angles are also congruent. That is, $\angle B \cong \angle E$. Notice that $\overline{BC}$ is the side included between $\angle B$ and $\angle C$, and $\overline{EF}$ is the side included between $\angle E$ and $\angle F$. You can apply the ASA Congruence Postulate to conclude that $\triangle ABC \cong \triangle DEF$.

EXAMPLE 1 *Developing Proof*

Is it possible to prove that the triangles are congruent? If so, state the postulate or theorem you would use. Explain your reasoning.

a.

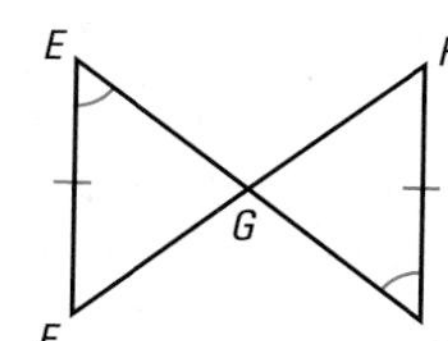

b.

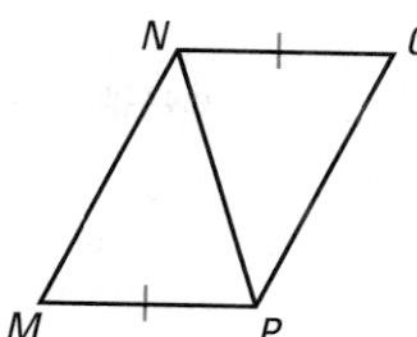

c.

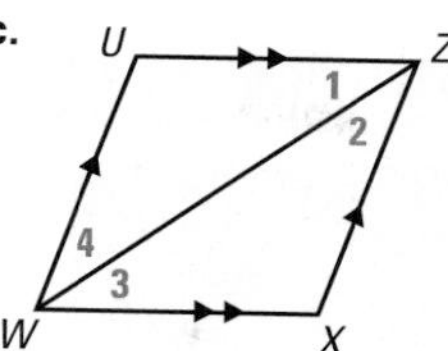

> **STUDENT HELP**
>
> **Study Tip**
> In addition to the information that is marked on a diagram, you need to consider other pairs of angles or sides that may be congruent. For instance, look for vertical angles or a side that is shared by two triangles.

SOLUTION

a. In addition to the angles and segments that are marked, $\angle EGF \cong \angle JGH$ by the Vertical Angles Theorem. Two pairs of corresponding angles and one pair of corresponding sides are congruent. You can use the AAS Congruence Theorem to prove that $\triangle EFG \cong \triangle JHG$.

b. In addition to the congruent segments that are marked, $\overline{NP} \cong \overline{NP}$. Two pairs of corresponding sides are congruent. This is not enough information to prove that the triangles are congruent.

c. The two pairs of parallel sides can be used to show $\angle 1 \cong \angle 3$ and $\angle 2 \cong \angle 4$. Because the included side $\overline{WZ}$ is congruent to itself, $\triangle WUZ \cong \triangle ZXW$ by the ASA Congruence Postulate.

EXAMPLE 2 *Proving Triangles are Congruent*

GIVEN ▶ $\overline{AD} \parallel \overline{EC}$, $\overline{BD} \cong \overline{BC}$

PROVE ▶ $\triangle ABD \cong \triangle EBC$

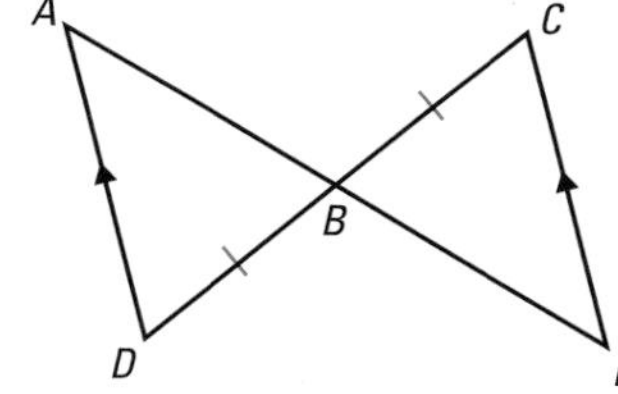

Plan for Proof Notice that $\angle ABD$ and $\angle EBC$ are congruent. You are given that $\overline{BD} \cong \overline{BC}$. Use the fact that $\overline{AD} \parallel \overline{EC}$ to identify a pair of congruent angles.

Statements	Reasons
1. $\overline{BD} \cong \overline{BC}$	**1.** Given
2. $\overline{AD} \parallel \overline{EC}$	**2.** Given
3. $\angle D \cong \angle C$	**3.** Alternate Interior Angles Theorem
4. $\angle ABD \cong \angle EBC$	**4.** Vertical Angles Theorem
5. $\triangle ABD \cong \triangle EBC$	**5.** ASA Congruence Postulate

....

You can often use more than one method to prove a statement. In Example 2, you can use the parallel segments to show that $\angle D \cong \angle C$ and $\angle A \cong \angle E$. Then you can use the AAS Congruence Theorem to prove that the triangles are congruent.

2 TEACH

EXTRA EXAMPLE 1
Is it possible to prove that the triangles are congruent? If so, state the postulate or theorem.

a. **No**

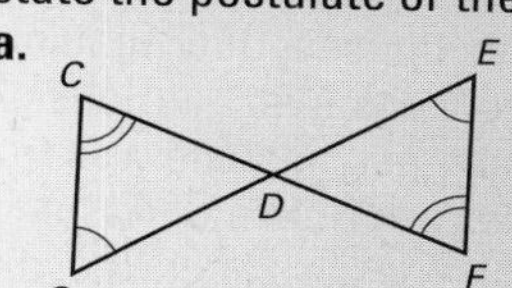

b. **Yes; ASA**

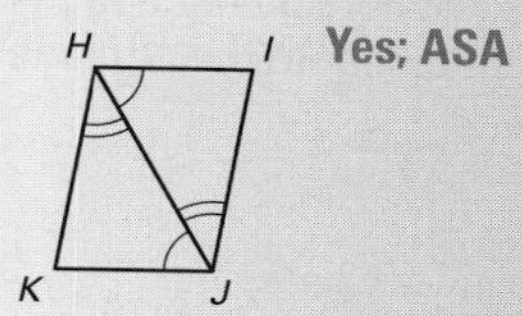

EXTRA EXAMPLE 2
Given: $\angle B \cong \angle C$, $\angle D \cong \angle F$; M is the midpoint of $\overline{DF}$.
Prove: $\triangle BDM \cong \triangle CFM$

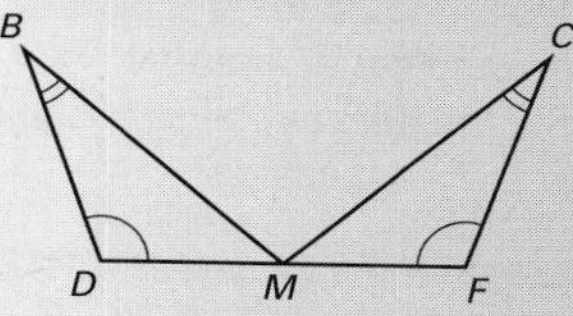

Statements (Reasons)
1. $\angle B \cong \angle C$, $\angle D \cong \angle F$ (Given)
2. M is the midpoint of $\overline{DF}$. (Given)
3. $\overline{DM} \cong \overline{FM}$ (Def. of midpoint)
4. $\triangle BDM \cong \triangle CFM$ (AAS)

CHECKPOINT EXERCISES

For use after Example 1:

1. Is it possible to prove that the triangles are congruent? **No**

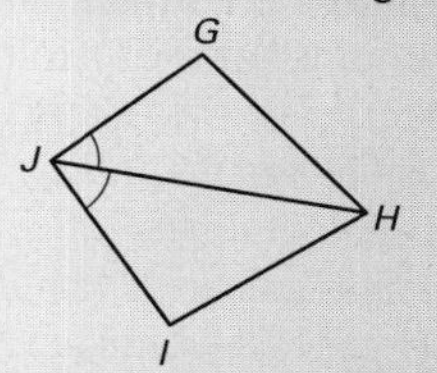

For use after Example 2:

2. Given: $\overline{WZ}$ bisects $\angle XZY$ and $\angle XWY$
Prove: $\triangle WZX \cong \triangle WZY$

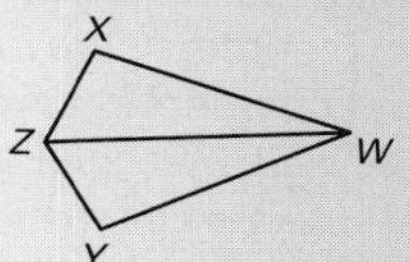

See answer at left.

Checkpoint Exercises ***Sample answer:***
2. Statements (Reasons)
1. $\overline{WZ}$ bisects $\angle XZY$ and $\angle XWY$ (Given)
2. $\angle WZX \cong \angle WZY$ (Def. of angle bisector)
3. $\angle XWZ \cong \angle YWZ$ (Def. of angle bisector)
4. $\overline{WZ} \cong \overline{WZ}$ (Reflexive Property of Congruence)
5. $\triangle WZX \cong \triangle WZY$ (ASA)

EXTRA EXAMPLE 3

When searching for a missing airplane, searchers used observations from people in two different areas of a city. As shown, the observers were able to describe sight lines from observers in different houses. One sightline was from observers in House A and the other sightline was from observers in House B. Assuming the sightlines are accurate, did the searchers have enough information to locate the airplane?

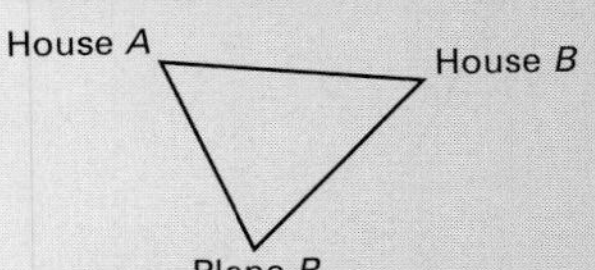

Yes; Because the searchers knew $m\angle A$ and $m\angle B$, and they knew the length of $\overline{AB}$. From the ASA Congruence Postulate the searchers could conclude that this is the only possible triangle with these measures.

CHECKPOINT EXERCISES

For use after Example 3:

1. A July 4th firework is launched at an angle of 80° with the ground. The firework flies straight for a distance of 300 feet, then explodes at 250 feet in the air. The shell does not fall straight to the ground because of a strong wind. Is there enough information to locate the shell of the firework after it exploded? **No; You know the lengths of two sides and the measure of a nonincluded angle. This is not enough information to know where the shell landed.**

CLOSURE QUESTION

What information do you need to know in order to use the AAS Congruence Theorem to prove two triangles are congruent? **that two corresponding pairs of angles and a nonincluded side are congruent to each other**

USING CONGRUENCE POSTULATES AND THEOREMS

EXAMPLE 3 *Using Properties of Congruent Triangles*

FOCUS ON APPLICATIONS

METEORITES When a *meteoroid* (a piece of rocky or metallic matter from space) enters Earth's atmosphere, it heats up, leaving a trail of burning gases called a *meteor.* Meteoroid fragments that reach Earth without burning up are called *meteorites.*

METEORITES On December 9, 1997, an extremely bright meteor lit up the sky above Greenland. Scientists attempted to find meteorite fragments by collecting data from eyewitnesses who had seen the meteor pass through the sky. As shown, the scientists were able to describe sightlines from observers in different towns. One sightline was from observers in Paamiut (Town P) and another was from observers in Narsarsuaq (Town N).

Assuming the sightlines were accurate, did the scientists have enough information to locate any meteorite fragments? Explain.

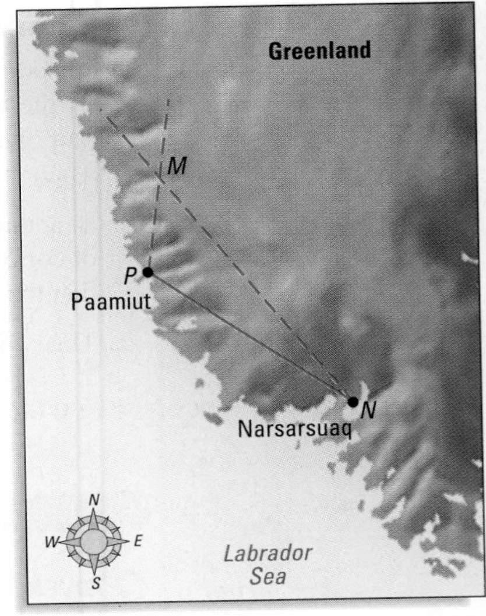

SOLUTION

Think of Town P and Town N as two vertices of a triangle. The meteorite's position M is the other vertex. The scientists knew $m\angle P$ and $m\angle N$. They also knew the length of the included side $\overline{PN}$.

From the ASA Congruence Postulate, the scientists could conclude that any two triangles with these measurements are congruent. In other words, there is only one triangle with the given measurements and location.

▶ Assuming the sightlines were accurate, the scientists did have enough information to locate the meteorite fragments.

ACCURACY IN MEASUREMENT The conclusion in Example 3 depends on the assumption that the sightlines were accurate. If, however, the sightlines based on that information were only approximate, then the scientists could only narrow the meteorite's location to a region near point M.

For instance, if the angle measures for the sightlines were off by 2° in either direction, the meteorite's location would be known to lie within a region of about 25 square miles, which is a very large area to search.

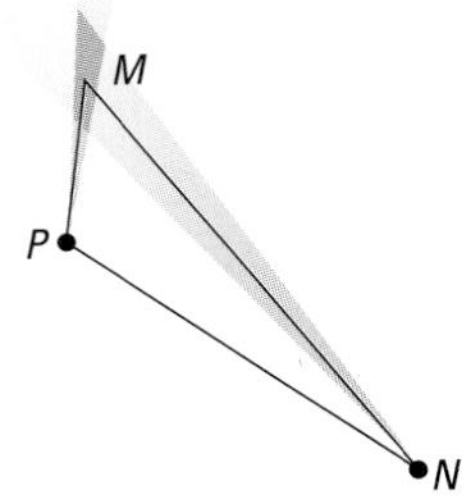

In fact, the scientists looking for the meteorite searched over 1150 square miles of rough, icy terrain without finding any meteorite fragments.

GUIDED PRACTICE

Vocabulary Check ✓

1. Name the four methods you have learned for proving triangles congruent. Only one of these is called a *theorem*. Why is it called a theorem? See margin.

Concept Check ✓

Is it possible to prove that the triangles are congruent? If so, state the postulate or theorem you would use. Explain your reasoning. 2–4. See margin.

2. $\triangle RST$ and $\triangle TQR$

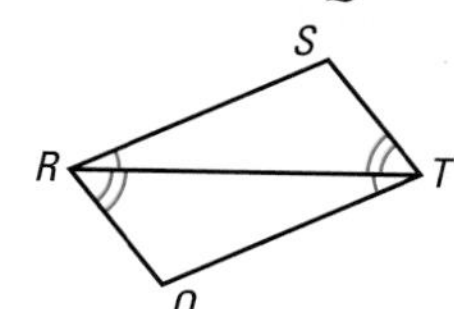

3. $\triangle JKL$ and $\triangle NML$

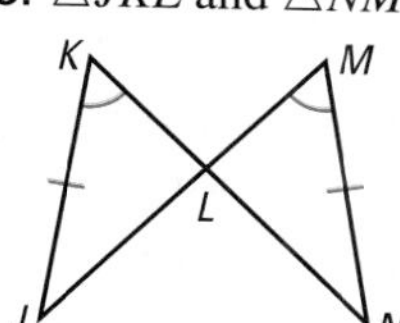

4. $\triangle DFE$ and $\triangle JGH$

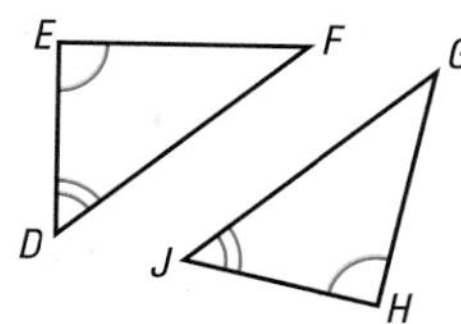

1. SSS Congruence Postulate, SAS Congruence Postulate, ASA Congruence Postulate, and AAS Congruence Theorem; because it is proved, unlike a postulate, which is accepted without proof

Skill Check ✓

State the third congruence that must be given to prove that $\triangle ABC \cong \triangle DEF$ using the indicated postulate or theorem.

5. ASA Congruence Postulate $\overline{AB} \cong \overline{DE}$

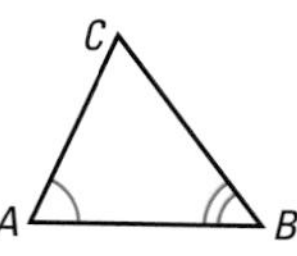

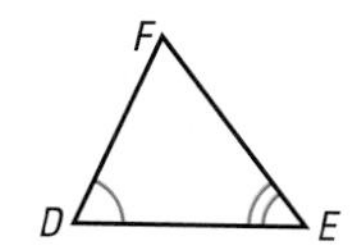

6. AAS Congruence Theorem $\angle A \cong \angle D$

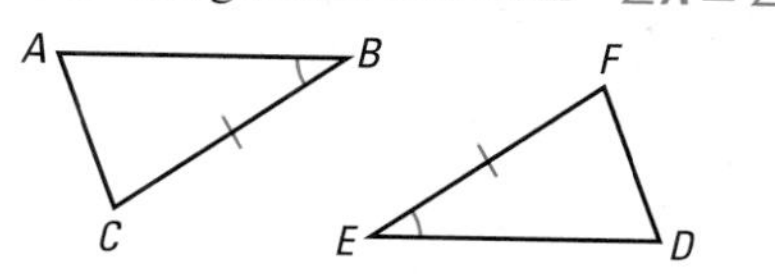

7. **RELAY RACE** A course for a relay race is marked on the gymnasium floor. Your team starts at *A*, goes to *B*, then *C*, then returns to *A*. The other team starts at *C*, goes to *D*, then *A*, then returns to *C*. Given that $\overline{AD} \parallel \overline{BC}$ and $\angle B$ and $\angle D$ are right angles, explain how you know the two courses are the same length. See margin.

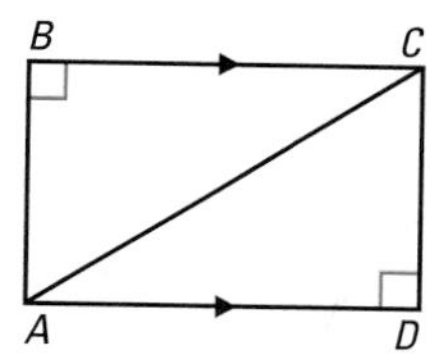

2. Yes; ASA Congruence Postulate; two pairs of corresponding angles and the corresponding included sides are congruent.
3. Yes; AAS Congruence Theorem; two pairs of corresponding angles and corresponding nonincluded sides are congruent.
4. No; two pairs of angles are congruent; that is insufficient to prove triangle congruence.

PRACTICE AND APPLICATIONS

STUDENT HELP

Extra Practice to help you master skills is on pp. 809 and 810.

LOGICAL REASONING **Is it possible to prove that the triangles are congruent? If so, state the postulate or theorem you would use. Explain your reasoning.** 8–13. See margin.

8.

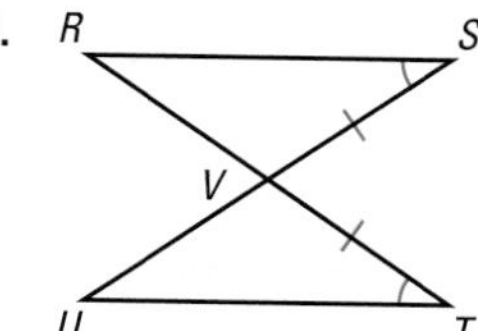

9.

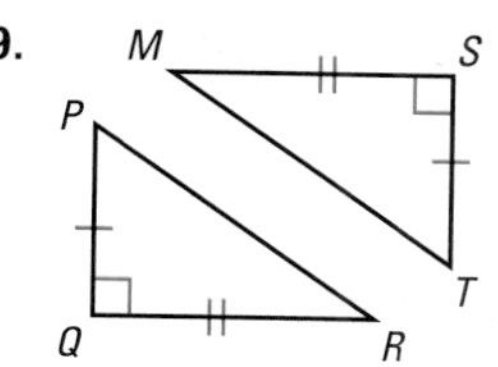

10.

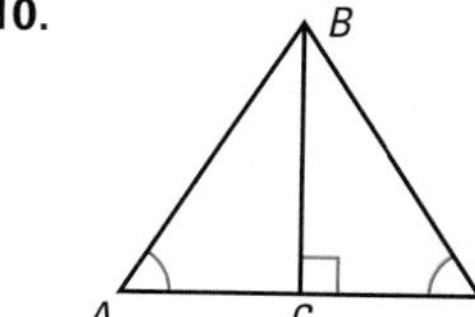

11.

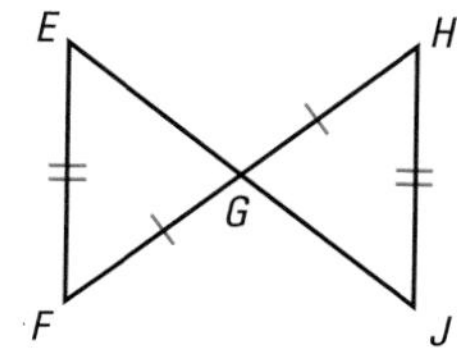

12.

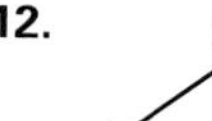

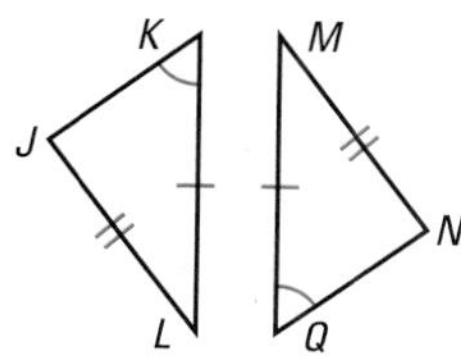

13.

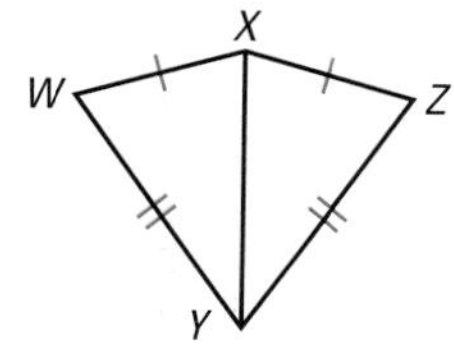

STUDENT HELP

HOMEWORK HELP
Example 1: Exs. 8–13
Example 2: Exs. 14–22
Example 3: Exs. 23–25, 28

3 APPLY

ASSIGNMENT GUIDE

BASIC
Day 1: p. 223 Exs. 8–20
Day 2: pp. 224–227 Exs. 21, 22, 26, 27, 29, 32–38, Quiz 2 Exs. 1–7

AVERAGE
Day 1: p. 223 Exs. 8–20
Day 2: pp. 224–227 Exs. 21–27, 29, 32–38, Quiz 2 Exs. 1–7

ADVANCED
Day 1: p. 223 Exs. 8–20
Day 2: pp. 224–227 Exs. 21–27, 29–38, Quiz 2 Exs. 1–7

BLOCK SCHEDULE
p. 223 Exs. 8–20 (with 4.3)
pp. 224–227 Exs. 21–27, 29, 32–38, Quiz 2 Exs. 1–7 (with 4.5)

EXERCISE LEVELS
Level A: *Easier*
8–13
Level B: *More Difficult*
14–29
Level C: *Most Difficult*
30, 31

✓ HOMEWORK CHECK
To quickly check student understanding of key concepts, go over the following exercises: Exs. 8, 12, 14, 18, 20, 22, 26. See also the Daily Homework Quiz:

- Blackline Master (*Chapter 4 Resource Book,* p. 70)
- Transparency (p. 29)

7–13. See Additional Answers beginning on page AA1.

! COMMON ERROR

EXERCISES 18 AND 22 Students tend to have trouble with overlapping triangles. Refer them to the study tip on this page. You may want to demonstrate how to redraw the triangles in Ex. 18 as an example.

TEACHING TIPS

EXERCISES 19–22 Students can work together to examine the logic behind the proofs. Saying aloud the reasons for specific statements can help them develop a deeper understanding for the flow of a proof and the main ideas behind the proofs.

19. Statements (Reasons)
1. $\overline{FH} \parallel \overline{LK}$, $\overline{GF} \cong \overline{GL}$ (Given)
2. $\angle F \cong \angle L$, $\angle H \cong \angle K$ (Alternate Interior Angles Theorem)
3. $\triangle FGH \cong \triangle LGK$ (AAS Congruence Theorem)

20. Statements (Reasons)
1. $\overline{AB} \perp \overline{AD}$, $\overline{DE} \perp \overline{AD}$, $\overline{BC} \cong \overline{EC}$ (Given)
2. $\angle A$ and $\angle D$ are right angles. (If two lines are perpendicular, then they form four right angles.)
3. $\angle A \cong \angle D$ (Right Angle Congruence Theorem)
4. $\angle ACB \cong \angle DCE$ (Vertical Angles Theorem)
5. $\triangle ABC \cong \triangle DEC$ (AAS Congruence Theorem)

25.

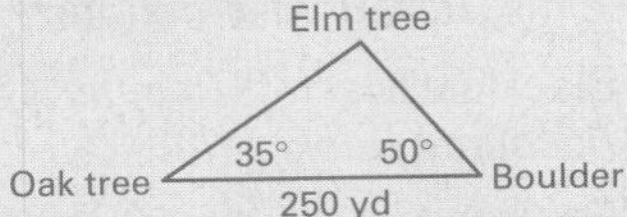

Yes; the measures of two angles and the length of the included side are known and only one such triangle is possible.

STUDENT HELP

Study Tip
When a proof involves overlapping triangles, such as the ones in Exs. 18 and 22, you may find it helpful to sketch the triangles separately.

DEVELOPING PROOF **State the third congruence that must be given to prove that $\triangle PQR \cong \triangle STU$ using the indicated postulate or theorem. (*Hint:* First sketch $\triangle PQR$ and $\triangle STU$. Mark the triangles with the given information.)**

14. **GIVEN** ▶ $\angle Q \cong \angle T$, $\overline{PQ} \cong \overline{ST}$
Use the AAS Congruence Theorem. $\angle R \cong \angle U$

15. **GIVEN** ▶ $\angle R \cong \angle U$, $\overline{PR} \cong \overline{SU}$
Use the ASA Congruence Postulate. $\angle P \cong \angle S$

16. **GIVEN** ▶ $\angle R \cong \angle U$, $\angle P \cong \angle S$
Use the ASA Congruence Postulate. $\overline{PR} \cong \overline{SU}$

17. **GIVEN** ▶ $\overline{PR} \cong \overline{SU}$, $\angle R \cong \angle U$
Use the SAS Congruence Postulate. $\overline{QR} \cong \overline{TU}$

18. **DEVELOPING PROOF** Complete the proof that $\triangle XWV \cong \triangle ZWU$.

GIVEN ▶ $\overline{VW} \cong \overline{UW}$
$\angle X \cong \angle Z$

PROVE ▶ $\triangle XWV \cong \triangle ZWU$

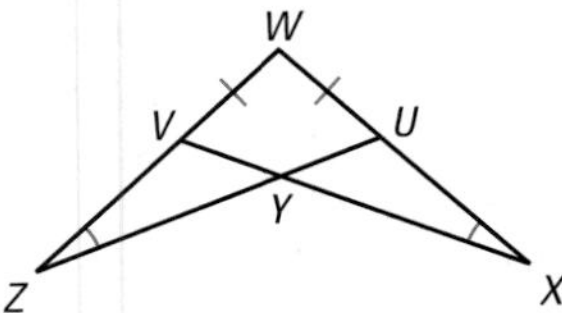

Statements	Reasons
1. $\overline{VW} \cong \overline{UW}$	1. ___?___ Given
2. $\angle X \cong \angle Z$	2. ___?___ Given
3. ___?___ $\angle W \cong \angle W$	3. Reflexive Property of Congruence
4. $\triangle XWV \cong \triangle ZWU$	4. ___?___ AAS Congruence Theorem

PROOF **Write a two-column proof or a paragraph proof.** 19–22. See margin.

19. **GIVEN** ▶ $\overline{FH} \parallel \overline{LK}$, $\overline{GF} \cong \overline{GL}$

PROVE ▶ $\triangle FGH \cong \triangle LGK$

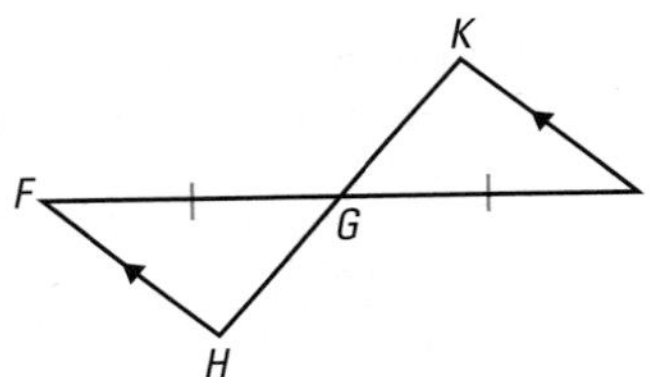

20. **GIVEN** ▶ $\overline{AB} \perp \overline{AD}$, $\overline{DE} \perp \overline{AD}$, $\overline{BC} \cong \overline{EC}$

PROVE ▶ $\triangle ABC \cong \triangle DEC$

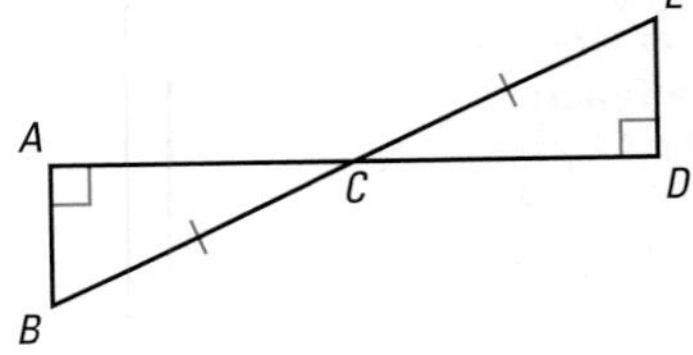

21. **GIVEN** ▶ $\overline{VX} \cong \overline{XY}$, $\overline{XW} \cong \overline{YZ}$, $\overline{XW} \parallel \overline{YZ}$

PROVE ▶ $\triangle VXW \cong \triangle XYZ$

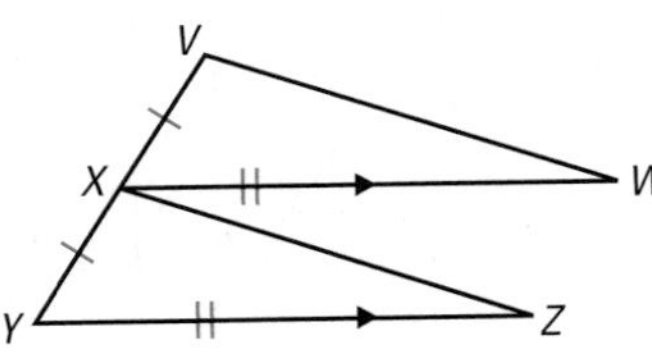

21. It is given that $\overline{VX} \cong \overline{XY}$, $\overline{XW} \cong \overline{YZ}$, and that $\overline{XW} \parallel \overline{YZ}$. Then $\angle VXW \cong \angle Y$ by the Corresponding Angles Postulate and $\triangle VXW \cong \triangle XYZ$ by the SAS Congruence Postulate.

22. **GIVEN** ▶ $\angle TQS \cong \angle RSQ$, $\angle R \cong \angle T$

PROVE ▶ $\triangle TQS \cong \triangle RSQ$

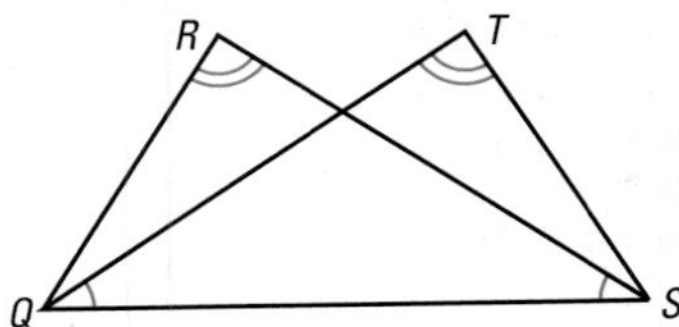

22. It is given that $\angle TQS \cong \angle RSQ$ and $\angle R \cong \angle T$. By the Reflexive Property of Congruence, $\overline{QS} \cong \overline{QS}$. Then $\triangle TQS \cong \triangle RSQ$ by the AAS Congruence Theorem.

23. Yes; two sides of the triangle are north-south and east-west lines, which are perpendicular, so the measures of two angles and the length of a nonincluded side are known and only one such triangle is possible.

24. Assuming that all three streets can be represented by straight segments, a surveyor needs to measure the bearing of Ellis Avenue with respect to either Green Street (which would give a unique triangle by the AAS Congruence Theorem) or Plain Steeet (which would give a unique triangle by the SAS or the ASA Congruence Postulate). The length of the portion of Green Street between Plain Street and Ellis Avenue could also be measured, giving a unique triangle by the SAS Congruence Postulate or the SSS Congruence Postulate.

FOCUS ON APPLICATIONS

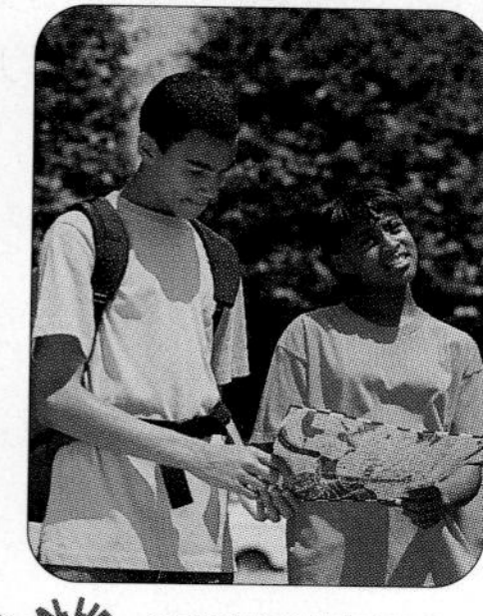

REAL LIFE **ORIENTEERING** In the sport of orienteering, participants use a map and a compass to navigate a course. Along the way, they travel to various points marked on the map.

BEARINGS Use the information about bearings in Exercises 23–25. In surveying and orienteering, bearings convey information about direction. For example, the bearing W 53.1° N means 53.1° to the north of west. To find this bearing, face west. Then turn 53.1° to the north. 23–25. See margin.

23. You want to describe the boundary lines of a triangular piece of property to a friend. You fax the note and the sketch below to your friend. Have you provided enough information to determine the boundary lines of the property? Explain.

The southern border is a line running east from the apple tree, and the western border is the north-south line running from the cherry tree to the apple tree. The bearing from the easternmost point to the northernmost point is W 53.1° N. The distance between these points is 250 feet.

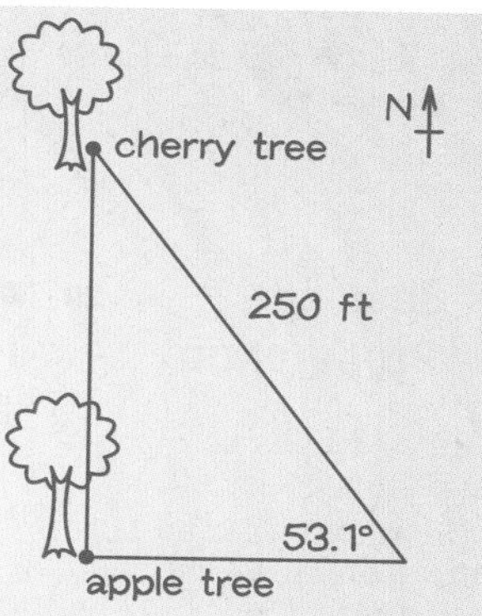

24. A surveyor wants to make a map of several streets in a village. The surveyor finds that Green Street is on an east-west line. Plain Street is at a bearing of E 55° N from its intersection with Green Street. It runs 120 yards before intersecting Ellis Avenue. Ellis Avenue runs 100 yards between Green Street and Plain Street.

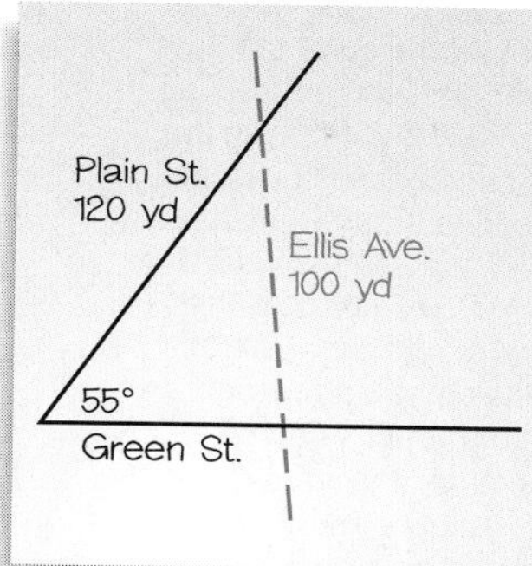

Assuming these measurements are accurate, what additional measurements, if any, does the surveyor need to make to draw Ellis Avenue correctly? Explain your reasoning.

25. You are creating a map for an orienteering race. Participants start out at a large oak tree, find a boulder that is 250 yards east of the oak tree, and then find an elm tree that is W 50° N of the boulder and E 35° N of the oak tree. Use this information to sketch a map. Do you have enough information to mark the position of the elm tree? Explain.

USING ALGEBRA Graph the equations in the same coordinate plane. Label the vertices of the two triangles formed by the lines. Show that the triangles are congruent. 26, 27. See margin.

26. $y = 0; y = x; y = -x + 3; y = 3$

27. $y = 2; y = 6; x = 3; x = 5; y = 2x - 4$

MATHEMATICAL REASONING

EXERCISE 24 When given SSA for a triangle it is possible to draw 0, 1, or 2 triangles. The drawings below illustrate examples of the three possibilities.

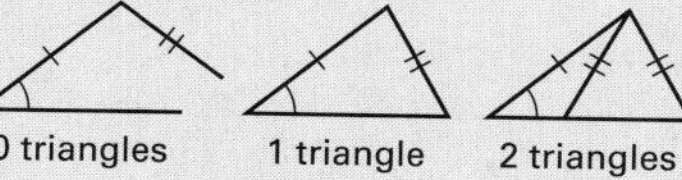

ENGLISH LEARNERS

EXERCISES 23–25 Direction words are a class of words that frequently cause confusion for English learners. You may wish to point out the directions north, east, south, and west, and then have volunteers use this information to indicate directions as they explain the meanings of *to the north of west*, *east-west* (line), *north-south* (line), *face west*, and *turn to the north*.

26.

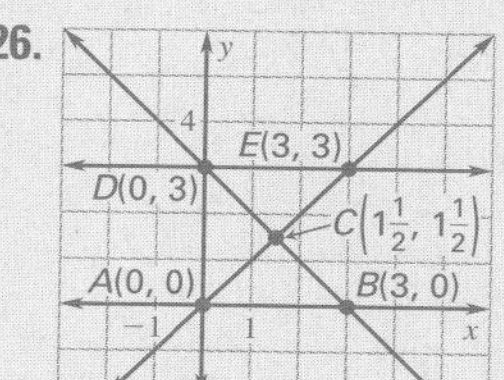

Sample answer: $AB = ED = 3$, so one pair of corresponding sides are congruent. $\angle ACB$ and $\angle ECD$ are congruent by the Vertical Angles Theorem, and, since $\overline{AB} \parallel \overline{DE}$, $\angle CBA \cong \angle CDE$ by the Alternate Interior Angles Theorem. So $\triangle ABC \cong \triangle EDC$ by the AAS Congruence Theorem.

27.

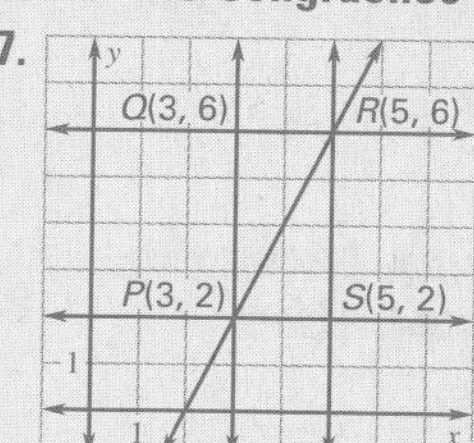

$\angle PQR \cong \angle RSP$ since they are both right angles, and, since, $\overline{QR} \parallel \overline{PS}$, $\angle PRQ \cong \angle RPS$ by the Alternate Interior Angles Theorem. $QR = SP = 2$ so $\overline{QR} \cong \overline{SP}$. Then two pairs of corresponding angles and a pair of included sides are congruent and so $\triangle PQR \cong \triangle RSP$ by the ASA Congruence Postulate.

7. Statements (Reasons)

1. M is the midpoint of $\overline{NL}$, $\overline{NL} \perp \overline{NQ}$, $\overline{NL} \perp \overline{MP}$, $\overline{QM} \parallel \overline{PL}$ (Given)
2. $\angle N$ and $\angle PML$ are right angles. (If two lines are perpendicular, they form four right angles.)
3. $\angle N \cong \angle PML$ (Right Angle Congruence Theorem)
4. $\overline{NM} \cong \overline{ML}$ (Definition of midpoint)
5. $\angle QMN \cong \angle PLM$ (Corresponding Angles Postulate)
6. $\triangle NQM \cong \triangle MPL$ (ASA Congruence Postulate)

ADDITIONAL PRACTICE AND RETEACHING

For Lesson 4.4:

- Practice Levels A, B, and C (*Chapter 4 Resource Book*, p. 59)
- Reteaching with Practice (*Chapter 4 Resource Book*, p. 62)
- See Lesson 4.4 of the *Personal Student Tutor*

For more Mixed Review:

- Search the *Test and Practice Generator* for key words or specific lessons.

29. a. $\overline{AB} \cong \overline{AB}$, $\angle ABC \cong \angle ABD$, $\angle BAC \cong \angle BAD$.
b. ASA Congruence Postulate
c. By parts a and b, $\triangle ABC \cong \triangle ABD$, so $\overline{BC} \cong \overline{BD}$ since they are corresponding sides of congruent triangles. That is, the distance across the stream is the same as the length of $\overline{BD}$.

30. Since only the pair of corresponding sides $\overline{MQ}$ and $\overline{MQ}$ are known to be congruent, Alicia would have to use the ASA Congruence Postulate or the AAS Congruence Theorem. In the first case, she would need to know that $NMQ \cong \angle PQM$ and $\angle NQM \cong \angle PMQ$. In the second case, she would need to know that either $\angle N \cong \angle P$ and $\angle NQM \cong \angle PMQ$ or that $\angle N \cong \angle P$ and $\angle NMQ \cong \angle PQM$. None of the necessary congruences can be deduced from the postulates and theorems concerning parallel lines and transversals.

28. **QUILTING** You are making a quilt block out of congruent right triangles. Before cutting out each fabric triangle, you mark a right angle and the length of each leg, as shown. What theorem or postulate guarantees that the fabric triangles are congruent? **SAS Congruence Postulate**

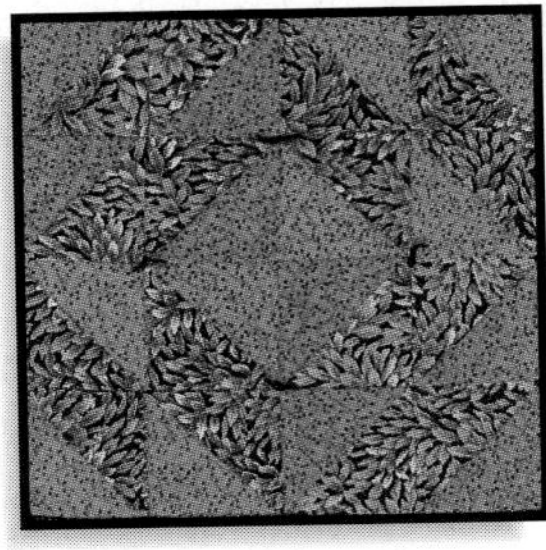

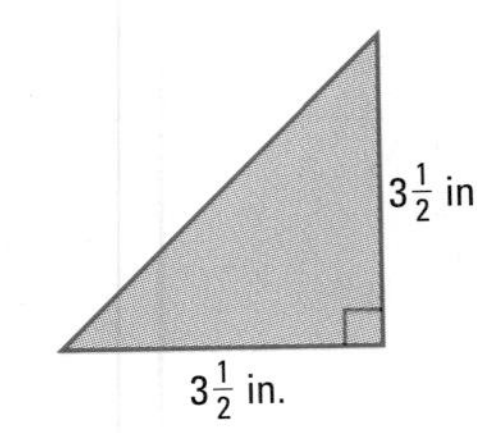

Test Preparation

29. MULTI-STEP PROBLEM You can use the method described below to approximate the distance across a stream without getting wet. As shown in the diagrams, you need a cap with a visor. **See margin.**

- Stand on the edge of the stream and look straight across to a point on the other edge of the stream. Adjust the visor of your cap so that it is in line with that point.
- Without changing the inclination of your neck and head, turn sideways until the visor is in line with a point on your side of the stream.
- Measure the distance BD between your feet and that point.

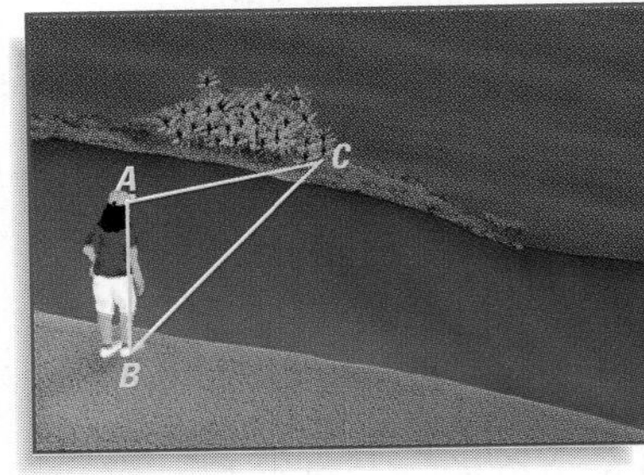

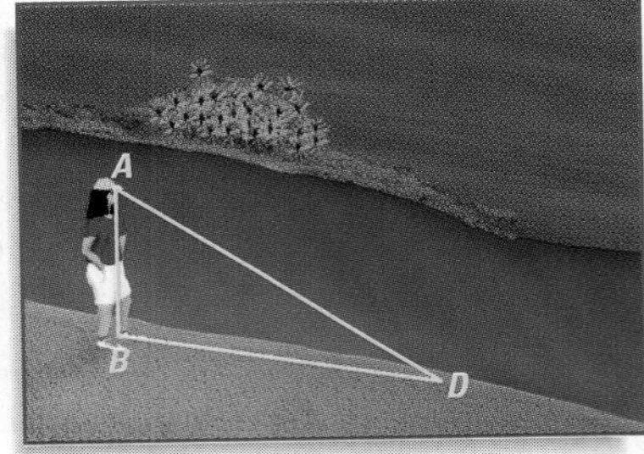

a. From the description of the measuring method, what corresponding parts of the two triangles can you assume are congruent?

b. What theorem or postulate can be used to show that the two triangles are congruent?

c. *Writing* Explain why the length of $\overline{BD}$ is also the distance across the stream.

★ Challenge

PROOF **Use the diagram.**

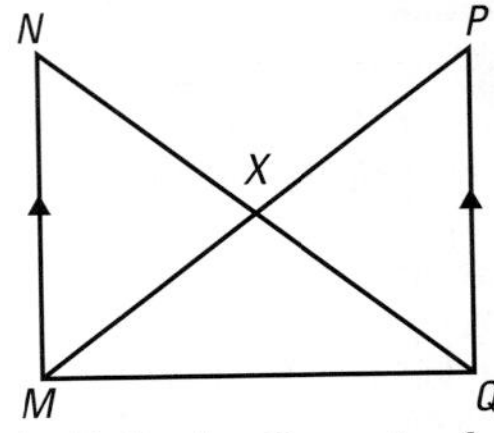

30. Alicia thinks that she can prove that $\triangle MNQ \cong \triangle QPM$ based on the information in the diagram. Explain why she cannot. **See margin.**

31. Suppose you are given that $\angle XMQ \cong \angle XQM$ and that $\angle N \cong \angle P$. Prove that $\triangle MNQ \cong \triangle QPM$.
It is given that $\angle XMQ \cong \angle XQM$ and $\angle N \cong \angle P$. $\overline{MQ} \cong \overline{MQ}$ by the Reflexive Property of Congruence, so $\triangle MNQ \cong \triangle QPM$ by the AAS Congruence Theorem.

EXTRA CHALLENGE
www.mcdougallittell.com

MIXED REVIEW

35. $m\angle DBC = 42°$, $m\angle ABC = 84°$

36. $m\angle ABD = m\angle DBC = 27.5°$

37. $m\angle ABD = 75°$, $m\angle ABC = 150°$

FINDING ENDPOINTS **Find the coordinates of the other endpoint of a segment with the given endpoint and midpoint M.** (Review 1.5)

32. $B(5, 7)$, $M(-1, 0)$ $(-7, -7)$
33. $C(0, 9)$, $M(6, -2)$ $(12, -13)$
34. $F(8, -5)$, $M(-1, -3)$ $(-10, -1)$

USING ANGLE BISECTORS $\overrightarrow{BD}$ **is the angle bisector of $\angle ABC$. Find the two angle measures not given in the diagram.** (Review 1.5 for 4.5) 35–37. See margin.

35.
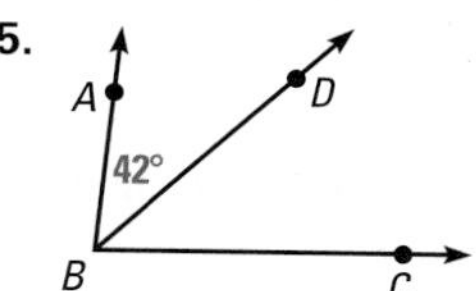

36.
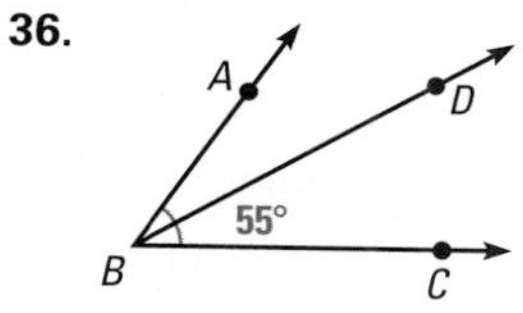

37.
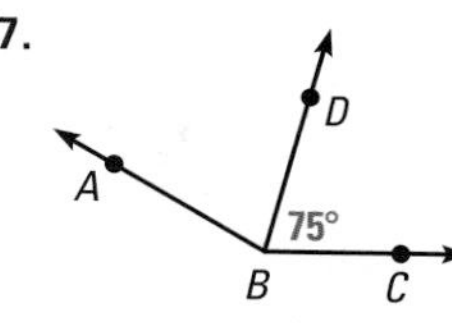

38. **BARN DOOR** You are making a brace for a barn door, as shown. The top and bottom pieces are parallel. To make the middle piece, you cut off the ends of a board at the same angle. What postulate or theorem guarantees that the cuts are parallel? (Review 3.4)

Corresponding Angles Converse

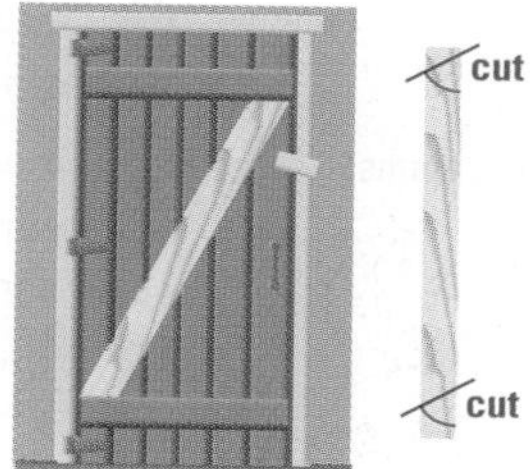

1. Yes; SAS Congruence Postulate; $\overline{BD} \cong \overline{BD}$, by the Reflexive Property of Congruence, so two pairs of corresponding sides and the corresponding included angles are congruent.
2. Yes; SSS Congruence Postulate; $\overline{SQ} \cong \overline{SQ}$ by the Reflexive Property of Congruence, so three pairs of corresponding sides are congruent.

QUIZ 2

Self-Test for Lessons 4.3 and 4.4

3. No; two pairs of corresponding sides and one pair of corresponding nonincluded angles are congruent; that is insufficient to prove triangle congruence.
4. Yes; ASA Congruence Postulate; $\overline{MK} \cong \overline{MK}$ by the Reflexive Property of Congruence, so two pairs of corresponding angles and the corresponding included sides are congruent.
5. No; $\overline{ZB} \cong \overline{ZB}$ by the Reflexive Property of Congruence, so two pairs of corresponding sides are congruent; that is insufficient to prove triangle congruence.
6. Yes; AAS Congruence Theorem; $\angle STR \cong \angle VTU$ by the Vertical Angles Theorem, so two pairs of corresponding angles and corresponding nonincluded sides are congruent.

In Exercises 1–6, decide whether it is possible to prove that the triangles are congruent. If it is possible, state the theorem or postulate you would use. Explain your reasoning. (Lessons 4.3 and 4.4) 1–6. See margin.

1.
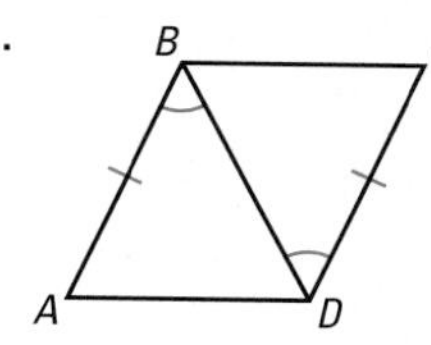

2.
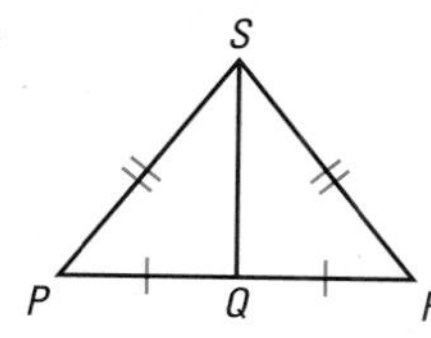

3.
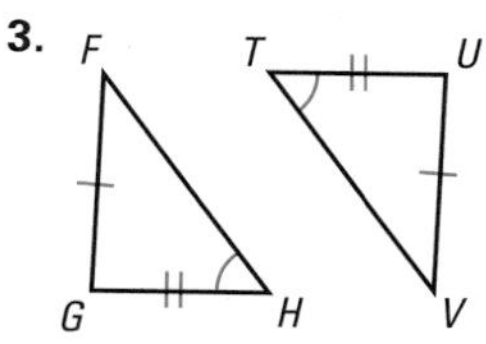

4.
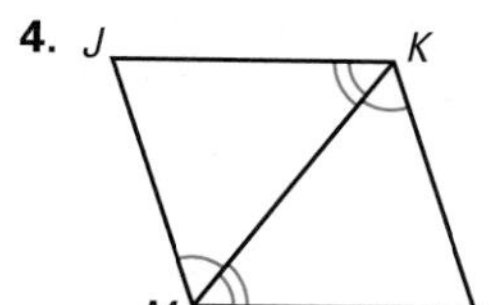

5.
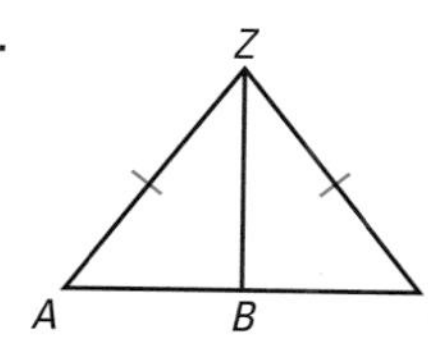

6.
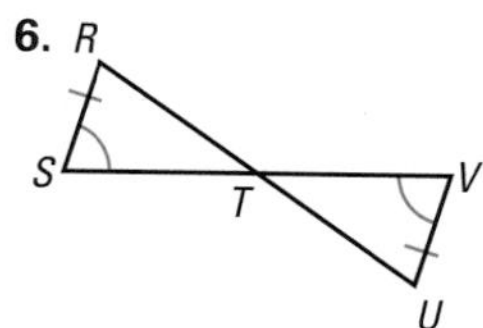

7. **PROOF** Write a two-column proof. (Lesson 4.4) See margin.

GIVEN ▶ M is the midpoint of $\overline{NL}$, $\overline{NL} \perp \overline{NQ}$, $\overline{NL} \perp \overline{MP}$, $\overline{QM} \parallel \overline{PL}$

PROVE ▶ $\triangle NQM \cong \triangle MPL$

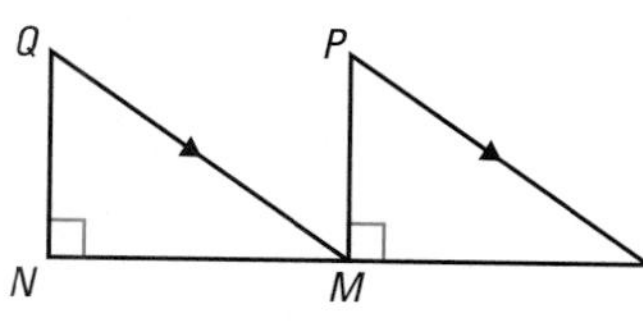

Additional Test Preparation *Sample answer:*

1. They are alike in that they both require two angles and one side of two triangles to be congruent. They are both ways to prove two triangles are congruent. They are different in that the ASA Congruence Postulate uses two angles and the included side of two triangles where the AAS Congruence Theorem uses two angles and a nonincluded side.

DAILY HOMEWORK QUIZ

Transparency Available

Is it possible to prove that the triangles are congruent? If so, state the postulate or theorem you would use. Explain your reasoning.

1.
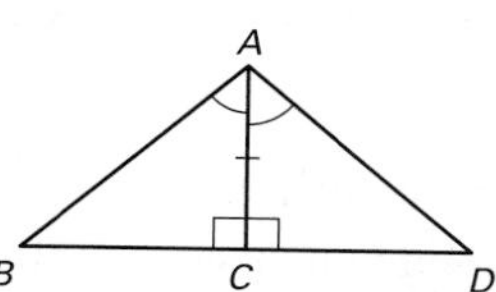

Yes; ASA Congruence Postulate; since all right angles are congruent, two pairs of corresponding angles and the corresponding included side are congruent

2.
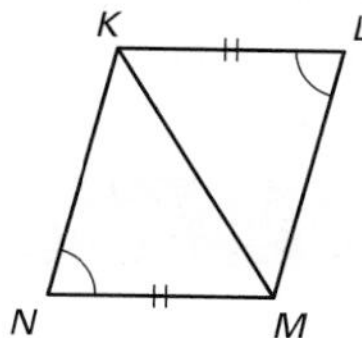

No; two pairs of corresponding sides are congruent and corresponding nonincluded angles $\angle KNM$ and $\angle MLK$ are congruent; that is insufficient to prove triangle congruence

EXTRA CHALLENGE NOTE

Challenge problems for Lesson 4.4 are available in **blackline** format in the *Chapter 4 Resource Book,* p. 66 and at **www.mcdougallittell.com.**

ADDITIONAL TEST PREPARATION

1. **WRITING** Compare and contrast the ASA Congruence Postulate and the AAS Congruence Theorem. How are they alike? How are they different? See left.

ADDITIONAL RESOURCES

An alternative Quiz for Lessons 4.3–4.4 is available in the *Chapter 4 Resource Book,* p. 67.

1 Planning the Activity

PURPOSE
To explore triangles with pairs of corresponding congruent sides and a congruent nonincluded angle.

MATERIALS
- geometry software
- Software Help (*Chapter 4 Resource Book,* p. 57)

PACING
- Exploring the Concept — 10 min
- Drawing Conclusions — 15 min

LINK TO LESSON
Exercises 11 and 12 on page 223 show an SSA relationship. Students should realize why these two sets of triangles cannot be shown to be congruent.

2 Managing the Activity

COOPERATIVE LEARNING
Pairs of students can work together to discuss and complete the steps in the activity. Make sure both students have the opportunity to use the software. Encourage students to use the correct geometry terms as they discuss their work.

CLASSROOM MANAGEMENT
Watch for students who get the wrong angle measurements because they confuse angles. Have pairs of students read the angle label quietly aloud and carefully trace between the three points to find the angle they should be working with.

3 Closing the Activity

KEY DISCOVERY
Two triangles with pairs of corresponding congruent sides and a pair of congruent nonincluded angles may not be congruent.

ACTIVITY ASSESSMENT
Can SSA be used to prove two triangles are congruent? Explain.
See sample answer at right.

ACTIVITY 4.4
Using Technology

Investigating Triangles and Congruence

You can use geometry software to show that if two sides and a nonincluded angle of one triangle are congruent to two sides and a nonincluded angle of another triangle, the triangles are not necessarily congruent.

STUDENT HELP
INTERNET SOFTWARE HELP
Visit our Web site www.mcdougallittell.com to see instructions for several different software applications.

CONSTRUCT

Steps 1–4. Check drawings.

Follow the steps below to construct $\triangle ABG$ and $\triangle ABH$.

1. Draw a segment and label it $\overline{AB}$, as shown in the diagram.
2. Draw another point not on $\overline{AB}$. Label this point E and draw $\overleftrightarrow{AE}$.
3. Draw a circle with center at point B that intersects $\overleftrightarrow{AE}$ in two points. Label the intersection points G and H.
4. Draw $\overline{BG}$ and $\overline{BH}$.

INVESTIGATE

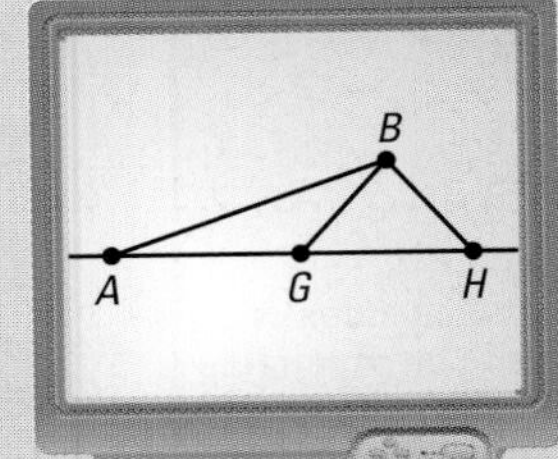

1. Measure the lengths of $\overline{AB}$, $\overline{BH}$, $\overline{BG}$, $\overline{AG}$, and $\overline{AH}$. Answers will vary, but $BH = BG$.
2. Measure $\angle ABG$, $\angle BAG$, $\angle AGB$, $\angle ABH$, $\angle BAH$, and $\angle AHB$. Answers will vary.

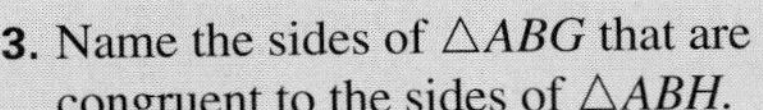

3. Name the sides of $\triangle ABG$ that are congruent to the sides of $\triangle ABH$.

3. $\overline{AB}$ and $\overline{AB}$, $\overline{BG}$ and $\overline{BH}$

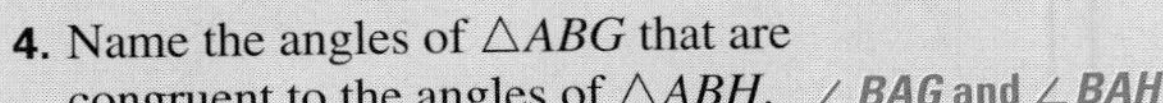

4. Name the angles of $\triangle ABG$ that are congruent to the angles of $\triangle ABH$. $\angle BAG$ and $\angle BAH$
5. Explain why the following conjecture is false.

   If two sides and a nonincluded angle of one triangle are congruent to two sides and a nonincluded angle of the other triangle, then the triangles are congruent. $\triangle ABG$ and $\triangle ABH$ provide a counterexample.

EXTENSION

CRITICAL THINKING If you know that three angles of one triangle are congruent to three angles of another triangle, can you prove that the triangles are congruent? In other words, is there an Angle-Angle-Angle Congruence Postulate or Theorem? Make a conjecture. Then test your conjecture by drawing a triangle with angle measures of 40°, 60°, and 80°. Compare your triangle with those of others in your class. Is your conjecture true or false? Explain.
It is possible to have two noncongruent triangles in which three angles of one are congruent to three angles of the other. (Consider two equilateral triangles, one with sides 3 cm long, the other with sides 3 m long.) There is no AAA Congruence Postulate or Theorem.

Activity Assessment *Sample answer:*
No; it is not enough information to ensure that the triangles are congruent.

4.5 Using Congruent Triangles

What you should learn

GOAL 1 Use congruent triangles to plan and write proofs.

GOAL 2 Use congruent triangles to prove constructions are valid.

Why you should learn it

▼ Congruent triangles are important in **real-life** problems, such as in designing and constructing bridges like the one in **Ex. 16**.

REAL LIFE

CALIFORNIA STANDARDS AND ASSESSMENT

CA Standards: 2, 5
SAT9 Task 1: Objs. 22, 24, 26
SAT9 Task 2: Objs. 24, 26, 27

GOAL 1 Planning a Proof

Knowing that all pairs of corresponding parts of congruent triangles are congruent can help you reach conclusions about congruent figures.

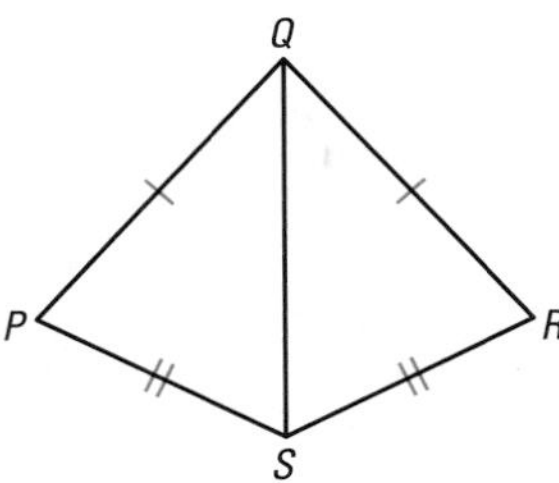

For instance, suppose you want to prove that $\angle PQS \cong \angle RQS$ in the diagram shown at the right. One way to do this is to show that $\triangle PQS \cong \triangle RQS$ by the SSS Congruence Postulate. Then you can use the fact that corresponding parts of congruent triangles are congruent to conclude that $\angle PQS \cong \angle RQS$.

EXAMPLE 1 *Planning and Writing a Proof*

GIVEN ▶ $\overline{AB} \parallel \overline{CD}$, $\overline{BC} \parallel \overline{DA}$

PROVE ▶ $\overline{AB} \cong \overline{CD}$

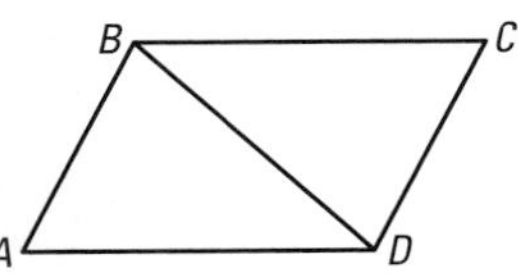

Plan for Proof Show that $\triangle ABD \cong \triangle CDB$. Then use the fact that corresponding parts of congruent triangles are congruent.

Solution

First copy the diagram and mark it with the given information. Then mark any additional information that you can deduce. Because $\overline{AB}$ and $\overline{CD}$ are parallel segments intersected by a transversal, and $\overline{BC}$ and $\overline{DA}$ are parallel segments intersected by a transversal, you can deduce that two pairs of alternate interior angles are congruent.

Mark given information.

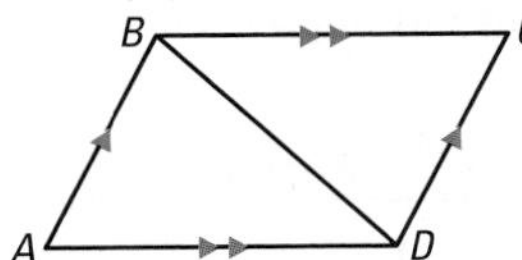

Add deduced information.

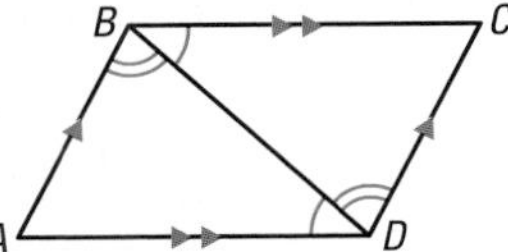

Paragraph Proof Because $\overline{AB} \parallel \overline{CD}$, it follows from the Alternate Interior Angles Theorem that $\angle ABD \cong \angle CDB$. For the same reason, $\angle ADB \cong \angle CBD$ because $\overline{BC} \parallel \overline{DA}$. By the Reflexive Property of Congruence, $\overline{BD} \cong \overline{BD}$. You can use the ASA Congruence Postulate to conclude that $\triangle ABD \cong \triangle CDB$. Finally, because corresponding parts of congruent triangles are congruent, it follows that $\overline{AB} \cong \overline{CD}$.

1 PLAN

Pacing

Basic: 1 day
Average: 1 day
Advanced: 1 day
Block Schedule: 0.5 block with 4.4

Lesson Opener
Visual Approach

An alternative way to approach Lesson 4.5 is to use the Visual Approach Lesson Opener:

- Blackline Master (*Chapter 4 Resource Book,* p. 71)
- Transparency (p. 25)

Meeting Individual Needs

- ***Chapter 4 Resource Book***
  Prerequisite Skills Review (p. 5)
  Practice Level A (p. 72)
  Practice Level B (p. 73)
  Practice Level C (p. 74)
  Reteaching with Practice (p. 75)
  Absent Student Catch-Up (p. 77)
  Challenge (p. 80)
- ***Resources in Spanish***
- ***Personal Student Tutor***

New-Teacher Support

See the Tips for New Teachers on pp. 1–2 of the *Chapter 4 Resource Book* for additional notes about Lesson 4.5.

Warm-Up Exercises

Transparency Available

State whether or not you can use the following information to prove two triangles are congruent.

1. ASA yes
2. SSA no
3. SAS yes
4. SSS yes
5. AAS yes
6. AAA no

2 TEACH

EXTRA EXAMPLE 1

Given: $\overline{HJ} \parallel \overline{LK}$, $\overline{JK} \parallel \overline{HL}$
Prove: $\angle LHJ \cong \angle JKL$

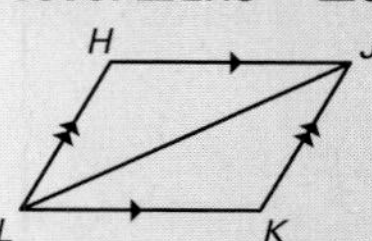

Because $\overline{HJ} \parallel \overline{KL}$, it follows from the Alternate Interior Angles Theorem that $\angle HJL \cong \angle KLJ$. For the same reason, $\angle HLJ \cong \angle KJL$ because $\overline{JK} \parallel \overline{HL}$. Because $\overline{JL} \cong \overline{JL}$, you can use ASA to conclude that $\triangle HJL \cong \triangle KLJ$. Since corresponding parts of congruent triangles are congruent $\angle LHJ \cong \angle JKL$.

EXTRA EXAMPLE 2

Given: $\overline{MS} \parallel \overline{TR}$, $\overline{MS} \cong \overline{TR}$
Prove: A is the midpoint of $\overline{MT}$.

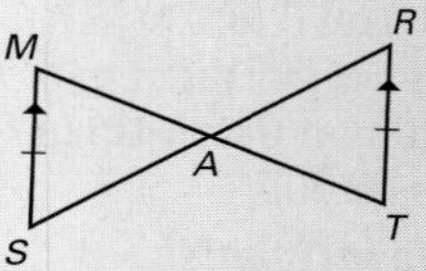

Statements (Reasons)

1. $\overline{MS} \parallel \overline{TR}$ (Given)
2. $\angle M \cong \angle T$, $\angle S \cong \angle R$ (Alternate Interior Angles Theorem)
3. $\overline{MS} \cong \overline{TR}$ (Given)
4. $\triangle MSA \cong \triangle TRA$ (ASA)
5. $\overline{MA} \cong \overline{TA}$ (Corresp. parts of ≅ ▲ are ≅)
6. A is the midpoint of $\overline{MT}$ (Def. of midpoint)

EXTRA EXAMPLE 3

Given: $\overline{QT}$ is the ⊥ bisector of $\overline{US}$, $\overline{QV} \cong \overline{QR}$, $\angle VQU \cong \angle RQS$
Prove: $\triangle QUV \cong \triangle QSR$

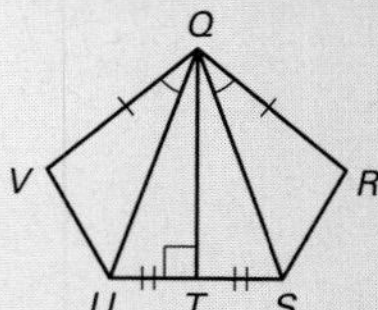

See answer at right.

Checkpoint Exercises for Examples 1–3 on next page.

EXAMPLE 2 Planning and Writing a Proof

GIVEN ▶ A is the midpoint of $\overline{MT}$,
A is the midpoint of $\overline{SR}$.

PROVE ▶ $\overline{MS} \parallel \overline{TR}$

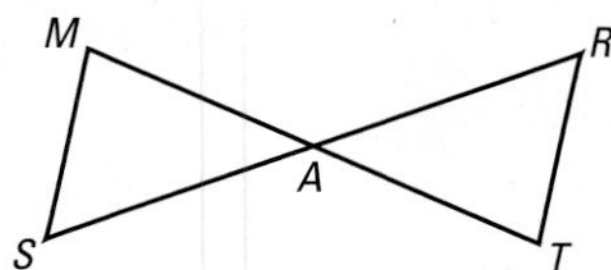

Plan for Proof Prove that $\triangle MAS \cong \triangle TAR$. Then use the fact that corresponding parts of congruent triangles are congruent to show that $\angle M \cong \angle T$. Because these angles are formed by two segments intersected by a transversal, you can conclude that $\overline{MS} \parallel \overline{TR}$.

STUDENT HELP

HOMEWORK HELP
Visit our Web site at www.mcdougallittell.com for extra examples.

Statements	Reasons
1. A is the midpoint of $\overline{MT}$, A is the midpoint of $\overline{SR}$.	**1.** Given
2. $\overline{MA} \cong \overline{TA}$, $\overline{SA} \cong \overline{RA}$	**2.** Definition of midpoint
3. $\angle MAS \cong \angle TAR$	**3.** Vertical Angles Theorem
4. $\triangle MAS \cong \triangle TAR$	**4.** SAS Congruence Postulate
5. $\angle M \cong \angle T$	**5.** Corresp. parts of ≅ ▲ are ≅.
6. $\overline{MS} \parallel \overline{TR}$	**6.** Alternate Interior Angles Converse

EXAMPLE 3 Using More than One Pair of Triangles

GIVEN ▶ $\angle 1 \cong \angle 2$
$\angle 3 \cong \angle 4$

PROVE ▶ $\triangle BCE \cong \triangle DCE$

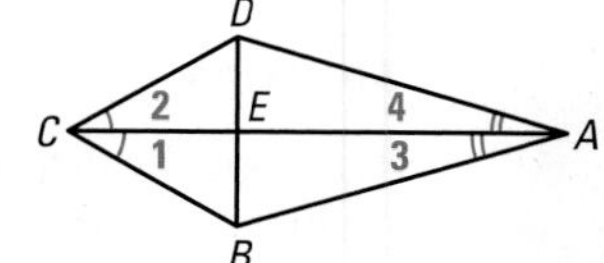

Plan for Proof The only information you have about $\triangle BCE$ and $\triangle DCE$ is that $\angle 1 \cong \angle 2$ and that $\overline{CE} \cong \overline{CE}$. Notice, however, that sides $\overline{BC}$ and $\overline{DC}$ are also sides of $\triangle ABC$ and $\triangle ADC$. If you can prove that $\triangle ABC \cong \triangle ADC$, you can use the fact that corresponding parts of congruent triangles are congruent to get a third piece of information about $\triangle BCE$ and $\triangle DCE$.

Statements	Reasons
1. $\angle 1 \cong \angle 2$, $\angle 3 \cong \angle 4$	**1.** Given
2. $\overline{AC} \cong \overline{AC}$	**2.** Reflexive Property of Congruence
3. $\triangle ABC \cong \triangle ADC$	**3.** ASA Congruence Postulate
4. $\overline{BC} \cong \overline{DC}$	**4.** Corresp. parts of ≅ ▲ are ≅.
5. $\overline{CE} \cong \overline{CE}$	**5.** Reflexive Property of Congruence
6. $\triangle BCE \cong \triangle DCE$	**6.** SAS Congruence Postulate

Extra Example 3 *Sample answer:*
Statements (Reasons)

1. $\overline{QT}$ is the ⊥ bisector of $\overline{US}$ (Given)
2. $\overline{UT} \cong \overline{ST}$ (Def. of ⊥ bisector)
3. $\angle QTU \cong \angle QTS$ (Right ▲ are ≅)
4. $\overline{QT} \cong \overline{QT}$ (Reflexive Prop.)
5. $\triangle QTU \cong \triangle QTS$ (SAS)
6. $\overline{QU} \cong \overline{QS}$ (Corresp. parts of ≅ ▲ are ≅)
7. $\angle VQU \cong \angle RQS$ (Given)
8. $\overline{QV} \cong \overline{QR}$ (Given)
9. $\triangle QUV \cong \triangle QSR$ (SAS)

GOAL 2 PROVING CONSTRUCTIONS ARE VALID

STUDENT HELP

Look Back
For help with copying an angle, see p. 159.

In Lesson 3.5, you learned how to copy an angle using a compass and a straightedge. The construction is summarized below. You can use congruent triangles to prove that this (and other) constructions are valid.

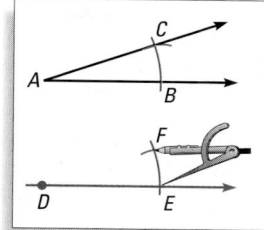

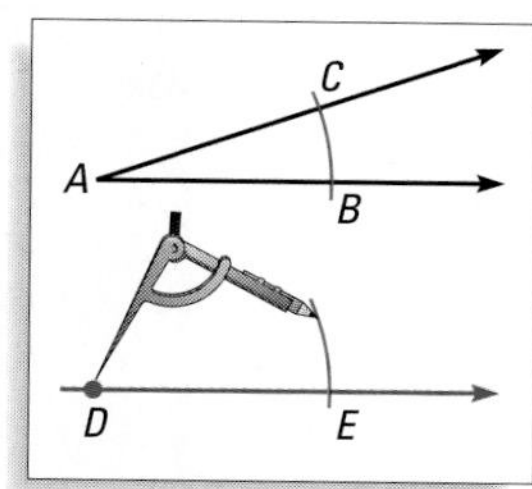

1 To copy $\angle A$, first draw a ray with initial point D. Then use the same compass setting to draw an arc with center A and an arc with center D. Label points B, C, and E.

2 Draw an arc with radius BC and center E. Label the intersection F.

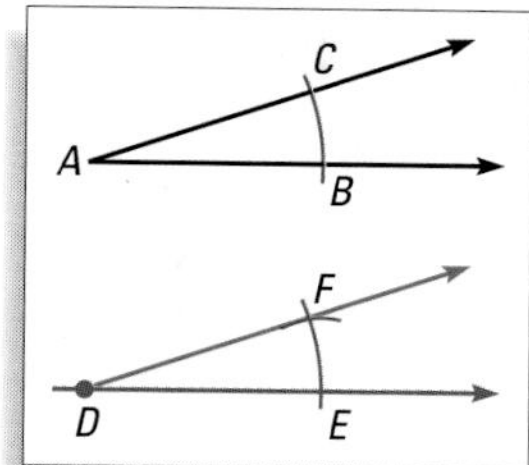

3 Draw $\overrightarrow{DF}$. $\angle FDE \cong \angle CAB$

EXAMPLE 4 *Proving a Construction*

Using the construction summarized above, you can copy $\angle CAB$ to form $\angle FDE$. Write a proof to verify that the construction is valid.

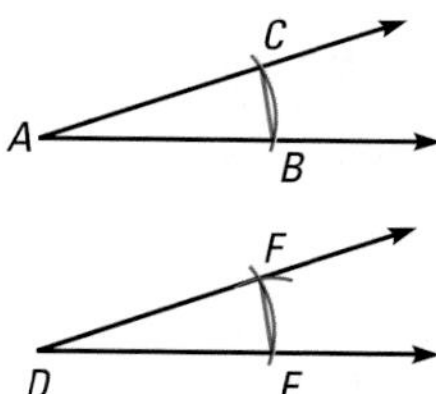

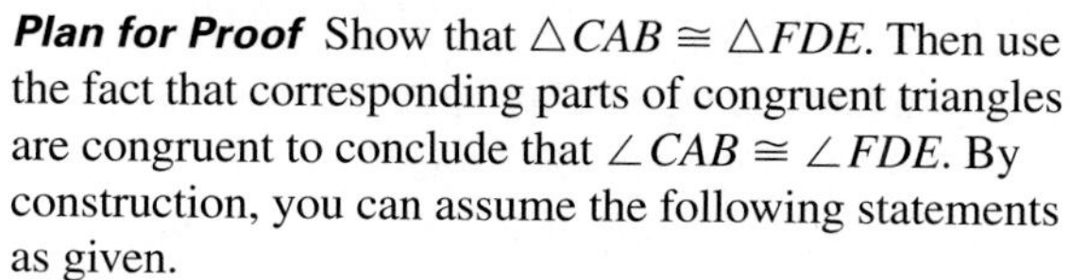

Plan for Proof Show that $\triangle CAB \cong \triangle FDE$. Then use the fact that corresponding parts of congruent triangles are congruent to conclude that $\angle CAB \cong \angle FDE$. By construction, you can assume the following statements as given.

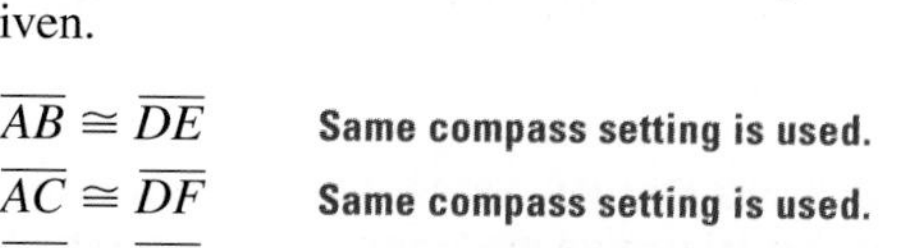

$\overline{AB} \cong \overline{DE}$ **Same compass setting is used.**

$\overline{AC} \cong \overline{DF}$ **Same compass setting is used.**

$\overline{BC} \cong \overline{EF}$ **Same compass setting is used.**

SOLUTION

Statements	Reasons
1. $\overline{AB} \cong \overline{DE}$	**1.** Given
2. $\overline{AC} \cong \overline{DF}$	**2.** Given
3. $\overline{BC} \cong \overline{EF}$	**3.** Given
4. $\triangle CAB \cong \triangle FDE$	**4.** SSS Congruence Postulate
5. $\angle CAB \cong \angle FDE$	**5.** Corresp. parts of $\cong$ $\triangle$s are $\cong$.

CHECKPOINT EXERCISES

For use after Examples 1–3:

1. Given: $\overline{MP}$ bisects $\angle LMN$, $\overline{LM} \cong \overline{NM}$
Prove: $\overline{LP} \cong \overline{NP}$

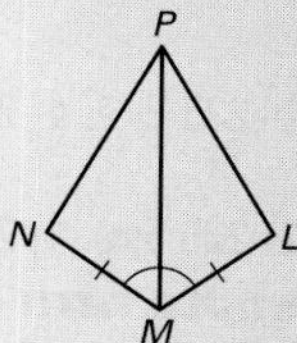

Statements (Reasons)
1. **$\overline{MP}$ bisects $\angle LMN$ (Given)**
2. **$\angle LMP \cong \angle NMP$ (Def. of angle bisector)**
3. **$\overline{MP} \cong \overline{MP}$ (Reflexive Prop.)**
4. **$\overline{LM} \cong \overline{NM}$ (Given)**
5. **$\triangle LMP \cong \triangle NMP$ (SAS)**
6. **$\overline{LP} \cong \overline{NP}$ (Corresp. parts of $\cong$ $\triangle$s are $\cong$.)**

EXTRA EXAMPLE 4

Write a proof to verify that the construction is valid.

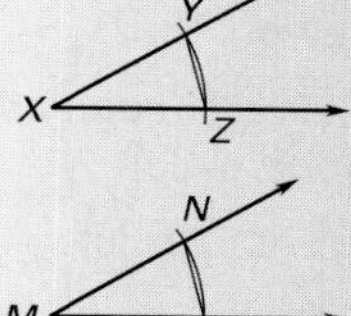

1. **$\overline{MN} \cong \overline{XY}$ (Given)**
2. **$\overline{MP} \cong \overline{XZ}$ (Given)**
3. **$\overline{NP} \cong \overline{YZ}$ (Given)**
4. **$\triangle MNP \cong \triangle XYZ$ (SSS)**
5. **$\angle NMP \cong \angle YXZ$ (Corresp. parts of $\cong$ $\triangle$s are $\cong$)**

CHECKPOINT EXERCISES

For use after Example 4:

1. What two triangles can be formed to show the construction is valid?
$\triangle ABD$ and $\triangle ACD$

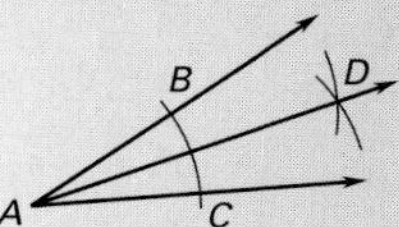

CLOSURE QUESTION

What's the first step in planning a proof? **List given information.**

3 APPLY

ASSIGNMENT GUIDE

BASIC
Day 1: pp. 232–235 Exs. 4–18, 22, 23

AVERAGE
Day 1: pp. 232–235 Exs. 4–23

ADVANCED
Day 1: pp. 232–235 Exs. 4–24

BLOCK SCHEDULE WITH 4.4
pp. 232–235 Exs. 4–23

EXERCISE LEVELS

Level A: ***Easier***
4–10

Level B: ***More Difficult***
11–16, 19–23

Level C: ***Most Difficult***
17, 18, 24

✓ HOMEWORK CHECK

To quickly check student understanding of key concepts, go over the following exercises: Exs. 6, 8, 12, 14, 16, 18. See also the Daily Homework Quiz:

- Blackline Master (*Chapter 4 Resource Book*, p. 83)
- Transparency (p. 30)

GUIDED PRACTICE

Concept Check ✓

In Exercises 1–3, use the photo of the eagle ray.

1. To prove that $\angle PQT \cong \angle RQT$, which triangles might you prove to be congruent?
$\triangle PSQ$ and $\triangle RSQ$ or $\triangle PTQ$ and $\triangle RTQ$

2. If you know that the opposite sides of figure $PQRS$ are parallel, can you prove that $\triangle PQT \cong \triangle RST$? Explain.

2. Yes; prove that $\triangle PQS \cong \triangle RSQ$ or $\triangle PQR \cong \triangle RSP$ by ASA, to get $\overline{PQ} \cong \overline{RS}$. Then $\triangle PQT \cong \triangle RST$ by ASA.

Skill Check ✓

3. The statements listed below are not in order. Use the photo to order them as statements in a two-column proof. Write a reason for each statement.
See margin.

GIVEN ▶ $\overline{QS} \perp \overline{RP}$, $\overline{PT} \cong \overline{RT}$

PROVE ▶ $\overline{PS} \cong \overline{RS}$

A. $\overline{QS} \perp \overline{RP}$ **B.** $\triangle PTS \cong \triangle RTS$ **C.** $\angle PTS \cong \angle RTS$

D. $\overline{PS} \cong \overline{RS}$ **E.** $\overline{PT} \cong \overline{RT}$ **F.** $\overline{TS} \cong \overline{TS}$

G. $\angle PTS$ and $\angle RTS$ are right angles.

PRACTICE AND APPLICATIONS

STUDENT HELP
Extra Practice to help you master skills is on p. 810.

STAINED GLASS WINDOW **The eight window panes in the diagram are isosceles triangles. The bases of the eight triangles are congruent.**
4–7. See margin.

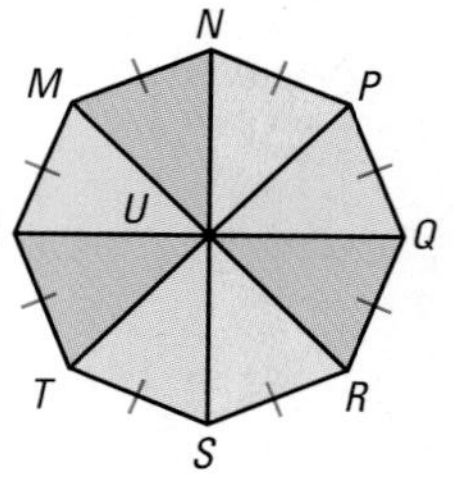

4. Explain how you know that $\triangle NUP \cong \triangle PUQ$.

5. Explain how you know that $\triangle NUP \cong \triangle QUR$.

6. Do you have enough information to prove that all the triangles are congruent? Explain.

7. Explain how you know that $\angle UNP \cong \angle UPQ$.

4. $\triangle NUP$ and $\triangle PUQ$ are both isosceles, so $\overline{UN} \cong \overline{UP} \cong \overline{UQ}$. Then since $\overline{NP}$ and $\overline{PQ}$ are also congruent, $\triangle NUP \cong \triangle PUQ$ by the SSS Congruence Postulate.

5. You can use the method in the answer to Ex. 4 to show that $\triangle QUR \cong \triangle PUQ$, so by the Transitive Property of Congruent Triangles, $\triangle NUP \cong \triangle QUR$. (You could instead use the Transitive Property of Congruence to show that $\overline{UN} \cong \overline{UP} \cong \overline{UQ} \cong \overline{UR}$.)

DEVELOPING PROOF **State which postulate or theorem you can use to prove that the triangles are congruent. Then explain how proving that the triangles are congruent proves the given statement.** 8–10. See margin.

8. **PROVE** ▶ $\overline{ML} \cong \overline{QL}$

9. **PROVE** ▶ $\angle STV \cong \angle UVT$

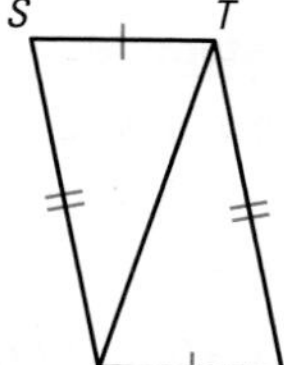

10. **PROVE** ▶ $KL = NL$

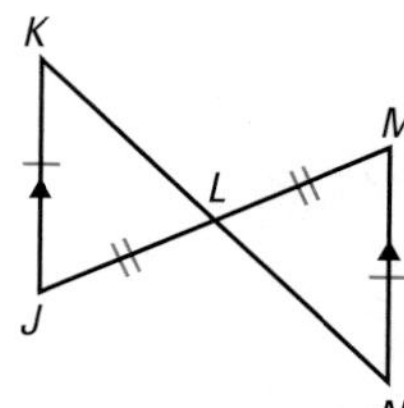

STUDENT HELP
HOMEWORK HELP
Example 1: Exs. 4–14, 17, 18
Example 2: Exs. 14, 17, 18
Example 3: Exs. 15, 16
Example 4: Exs. 19–21

CAT'S CRADLE Use the diagram of the string game Cat's Cradle and the information given below. 11–13. See margin.

GIVEN ▶ $\triangle EDA \cong \triangle BCF$
$\triangle AGD \cong \triangle FHC$
$\triangle BFC \cong \triangle ECF$

11. PROVE ▶ $\overline{GD} \cong \overline{HC}$

12. PROVE ▶ $\angle CBH \cong \angle FEH$

13. PROVE ▶ $\overline{AE} \cong \overline{FB}$

14. **DEVELOPING PROOF** Complete the proof that $\angle BAC \cong \angle DBE$.

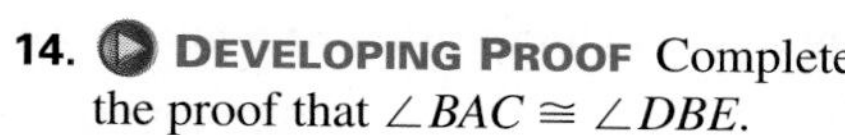

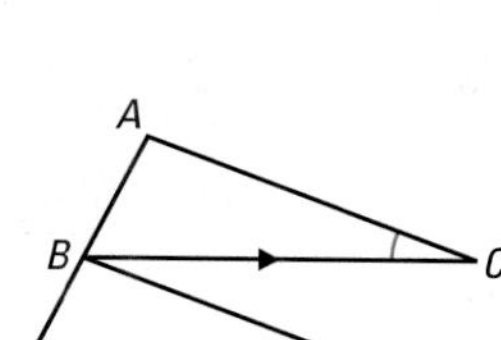

GIVEN ▶ B is the midpoint of $\overline{AD}$, $\angle C \cong \angle E$, $\overline{BC} \parallel \overline{DE}$

PROVE ▶ $\angle BAC \cong \angle DBE$

Statements	Reasons
1. B is the midpoint of $\overline{AD}$.	**1.** Given
2. $\overline{AB} \cong \overline{BD}$	**2.** ? Definition of midpoint
3. $\angle C \cong \angle E$	**3.** Given
4. $\overline{BC} \parallel \overline{DE}$	**4.** Given
5. $\angle EDB \cong \angle CBA$	**5.** ? Corresponding Angles Postulate
6. ? $\triangle BAC \cong \triangle DBE$	**6.** AAS Congruence Theorem
7. $\angle BAC \cong \angle DBE$	**7.** ? Corresponding parts of congruent triangles are congruent.

15. **DEVELOPING PROOF** Complete the proof that $\triangle AFB \cong \triangle EFD$.

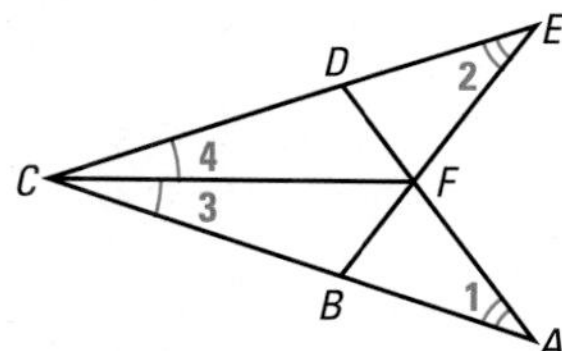

GIVEN ▶ $\angle 1 \cong \angle 2$
$\angle 3 \cong \angle 4$

PROVE ▶ $\angle AFB \cong \angle EFD$

Statements	Reasons
1. $\angle 1 \cong \angle 2$	**1.** ? Given
2. $\angle 3 \cong \angle 4$	**2.** ? Given
3. ? $\overline{CF} \cong \overline{CF}$	**3.** Reflexive Property of Congruence
4. $\triangle AFC \cong \triangle EFC$	**4.** ? AAS Congruence Theorem
5. $\overline{AF} \cong \overline{EF}$	**5.** ? Corresp. parts of ≅ ▵ are ≅.
6. ? $\angle AFB \cong \angle EFD$	**6.** Vertical Angles Theorem
7. $\triangle AFB \cong \triangle EFD$	**7.** ? ASA Congruence Postulate

11–13. See Additional Answers beginning on page AA1.

! COMMON ERROR

EXERCISE 15 When figures contain more than one pair of triangles, students may not see all the possible triangles they can use. For instance, students may use $\triangle CEF$ and $\triangle CAF$, but may miss $\triangle CDF$ and $\triangle CBF$. Suggest that if students feel they do not have sufficient information to complete the proof, they should make sure they have examined all the possible triangles in the figure.

3. *Sample answer:* A, G, C, F, E, B, D
   Statements (Reasons)
   1. $\overline{QS} \perp \overline{RP}$ (Given)
   2. $\angle PTS$ and $\angle RTS$ are right angles (If two lines are perpendicular, then they form four right angles.)
   3. $\angle PTS \cong \angle RTS$ (Right Angle Congruence Theorem)
   4. $\overline{TS} \cong \overline{TS}$ (Reflexive Property of Congruence)
   5. $\overline{PT} \cong \overline{RT}$ (Given)
   6. $\triangle PTS \cong \triangle RTS$ (SAS Congruence Postulate)
   7. $\overline{PS} \cong \overline{RS}$ (Corresp. parts of ≅ ▵ are ≅.)
6. Yes; you can use either the Transitive Property of Congruent Triangles or the Transitive Property of Congruence as described in the answer to Ex. 5 above.
7. $\triangle NUP$ and $\triangle PUQ$ are congruent by Ex. 4 above. Since corresponding parts of congruent triangles are congruent, $\angle UNP \cong \angle UPQ$.
8. AAS Congruence Theorem; if $\triangle LNM \cong \triangle LPQ$, then $\overline{ML} \cong \overline{QL}$ because corresponding parts of congruent triangles are congruent.
9. SSS Congruence Postulate; if $\triangle STV \cong \triangle UVT$, then $\angle STV \cong \angle UVT$ because corresponding parts of congruent triangles are congruent.
10. SAS Congruence Postulate, ASA Congruence Postulate, or AAS Congruence Theorem; if $\triangle LKJ \cong \triangle LNM$, then $\overline{KL} \cong \overline{NL}$ because corresponding parts of congruent triangles are congruent and $KL = NL$ by the definition of congruent segments.

STUDENT HELP NOTES

Look Back As students look back to page 36, remind them that they must use the same compass setting to draw the two intersecting arcs.

16. Statements (Reasons)
 1. L is the midpoint of $\overline{JN}$, $\overline{PJ} \cong \overline{QN}$, $\overline{PL} \cong \overline{QL}$, $\angle PKJ$ and $\angle QMN$ are right angles. (Given)
 2. $\overline{JL} \cong \overline{NL}$ (Definition of midpoint)
 3. $\triangle JPL \cong \triangle NQL$ (SSS Congruence Postulate)
 4. $\angle J \cong \angle N$ (Corresp. parts of $\cong$ ⚠ are $\cong$.)
 5. $\angle PKJ \cong \angle QMN$ (Right Angle Congruence Theorem)
 6. $\triangle PKJ \cong \triangle QMN$ (AAS Congruence Theorem)

17. Statements (Reasons)
 1. $\overline{UR} \parallel \overline{ST}$, $\angle R$ and $\angle T$ are right angles. (Given)
 2. $\angle R \cong \angle T$ (Right Angle Congruence Theorem)
 3. $\angle RUS \cong \angle TSU$ (Alternate Interior Angles Theorem)
 4. $\overline{US} \cong \overline{US}$ (Reflexive Property of Congruence)
 5. $\triangle RSU \cong \triangle TUS$ (AAS Congruence Theorem)
 6. $\angle RSU \cong \angle TUS$ (Corresp. parts of $\cong$ ⚠ are $\cong$.)

18–21, 24, 31–33. See Additional Answers beginning on page AA1.

ADDITIONAL PRACTICE AND RETEACHING

For Lesson 4.5:

- Practice Levels A, B, and C (*Chapter 4 Resource Book,* p. 72)
- Reteaching with Practice (*Chapter 4 Resource Book,* p. 75)
- See Lesson 4.5 of the *Personal Student Tutor*

For more Mixed Review:

- Search the *Test and Practice Generator* for key words or specific lessons.

FOCUS ON CAREER

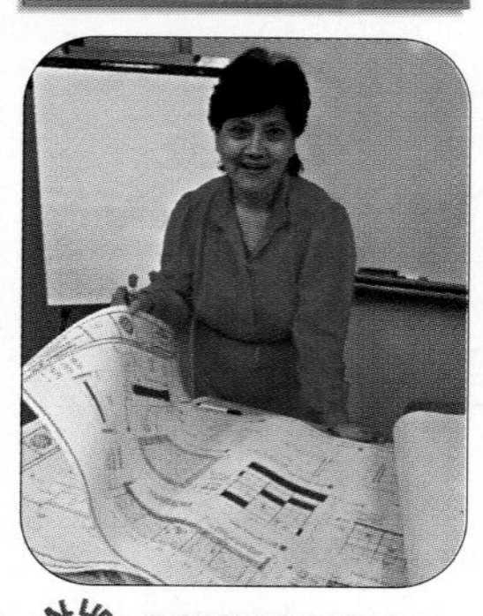

REAL LIFE CONSTRUCTION MANAGER

A construction manager plans and directs the work at a building site. Among other things, the manager reviews engineering specifications and architectural drawings to make sure that a project is proceeding according to plan.

CAREER LINK
www.mcdougallittell.com

16. **BRIDGES** The diagram represents a section of the framework of the Kap Shui Mun Bridge shown in the photo on page 229. Write a two-column proof to show that $\triangle PKJ \cong \triangle QMN$. See margin.

GIVEN ▶ L is the midpoint of $\overline{JN}$, $\overline{PJ} \cong \overline{QN}$, $\overline{PL} \cong \overline{QL}$, $\angle PKJ$ and $\angle QMN$ are right angles.

PROVE ▶ $\triangle PKJ \cong \triangle QMN$

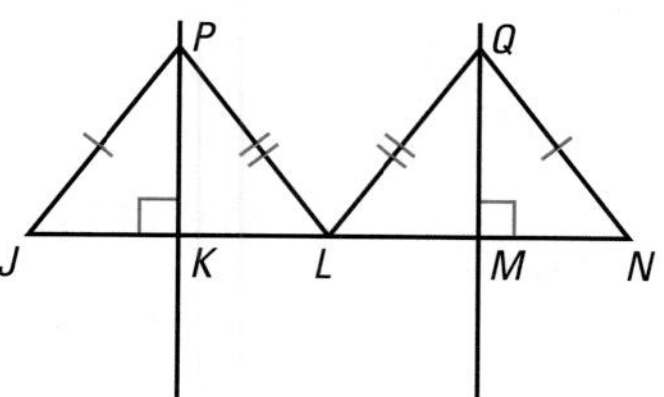

PROOF **Write a two-column proof or a paragraph proof.** 17, 18. See margin.

17. GIVEN ▶ $\overline{UR} \parallel \overline{ST}$, $\angle R$ and $\angle T$ are right angles.

PROVE ▶ $\angle RSU \cong \angle TUS$

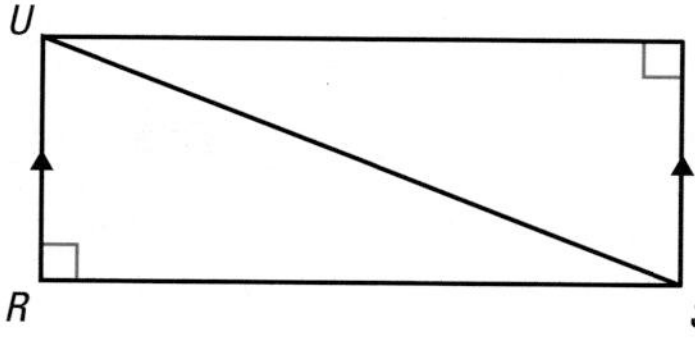

18. GIVEN ▶ $\overline{BD} \perp \overline{AC}$, $\overline{BD}$ bisects $\overline{AC}$.

PROVE ▶ $\angle ABD$ and $\angle BCD$ are complementary angles.

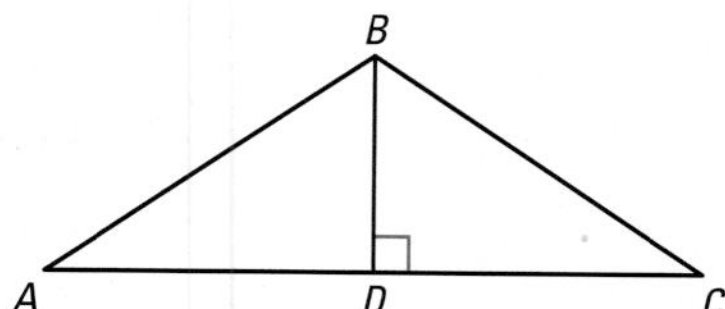

19. **PROVING A CONSTRUCTION** The diagrams below summarize the construction used to bisect $\angle A$. By construction, you can assume that $\overline{AB} \cong \overline{AC}$ and $\overline{BD} \cong \overline{CD}$. Write a proof to verify that $\overrightarrow{AD}$ bisects $\angle A$. See margin.

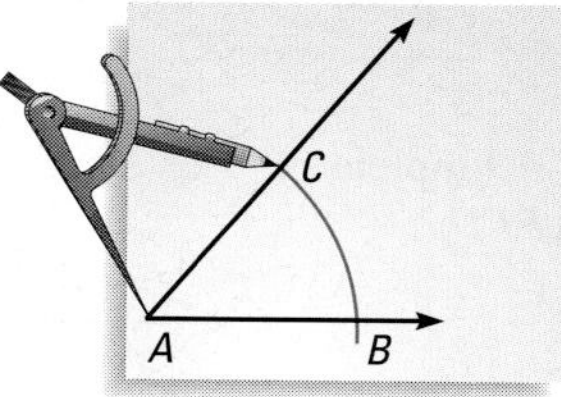

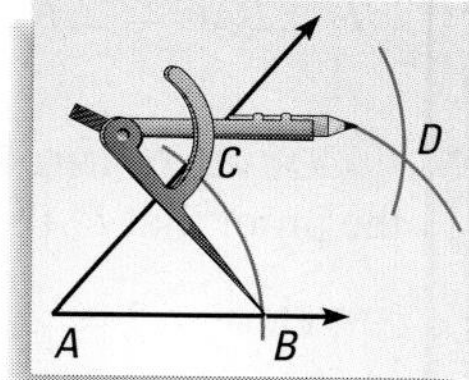

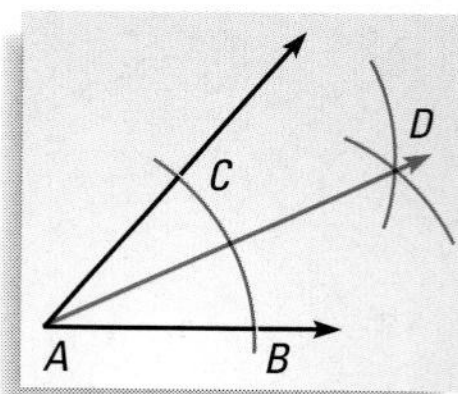

1. First draw an arc with center A. Label the points where the arc intersects the sides of the angle points B and C.
2. Draw an arc with center C. Using the same compass setting, draw an arc with center B. Label the intersection point D.
3. Draw $\overrightarrow{AD}$. $\angle CAD \cong \angle BAD$

PROVING A CONSTRUCTION **Use a straightedge and a compass to perform the construction. Label the important points of your construction. Then write a flow proof to verify the results.** 20, 21. See margin.

20. Bisect an obtuse angle.

21. Copy an obtuse angle.

STUDENT HELP

Look Back
For help with bisecting an angle, see p. 36.

Test Preparation

22. **MULTIPLE CHOICE** Suppose $\overline{PQ} \parallel \overline{RS}$. You want to prove that $\overline{PR} \cong \overline{SQ}$. Which of the reasons below would *not* appear in your two-column proof? **A**

Ⓐ SAS Congruence Postulate

Ⓑ Reflexive Property of Congruence

Ⓒ AAS Congruence Theorem

Ⓓ Right Angle Congruence Theorem

Ⓔ Alternate Interior Angles Theorem

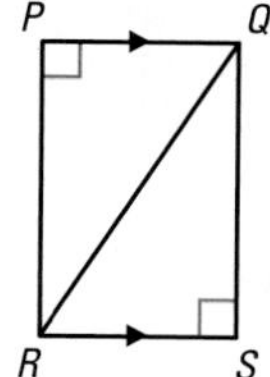

23. **MULTIPLE CHOICE** Which statement correctly describes the congruence of the triangles in the diagram in Exercise 22? **D**

Ⓐ $\triangle SRQ \cong \triangle RQP$ Ⓑ $\triangle PRQ \cong \triangle SRQ$

Ⓒ $\triangle QRS \cong \triangle PQR$ Ⓓ $\triangle SRQ \cong \triangle PQR$

★ Challenge

24. **PROVING A CONSTRUCTION** Use a straightedge and a compass to bisect a segment. (For help with this construction, look back at page 34.) Then write a proof to show that the construction is valid.
See margin.

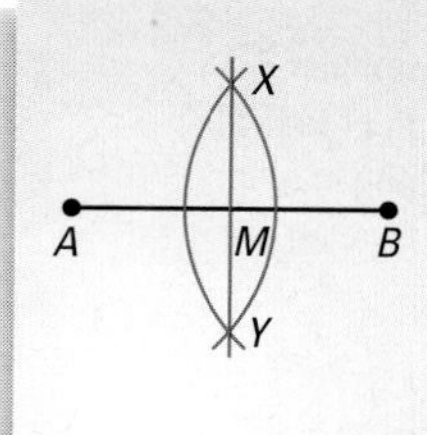

MIXED REVIEW

FINDING PERIMETER, CIRCUMFERENCE, AND AREA **Find the perimeter (or circumference) and area of the figure. (Where necessary, use $\pi \approx 3.14$.)** (Review 1.7)

25.

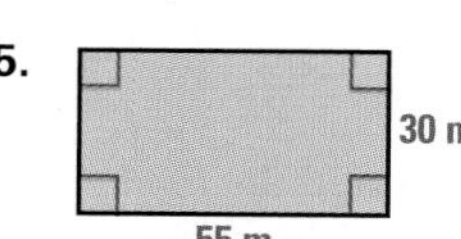

170 m; 1650 m²

26.

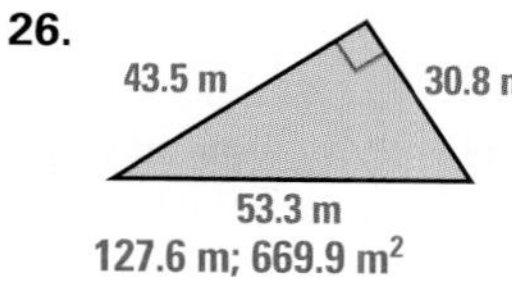

127.6 m; 669.9 m²

27.

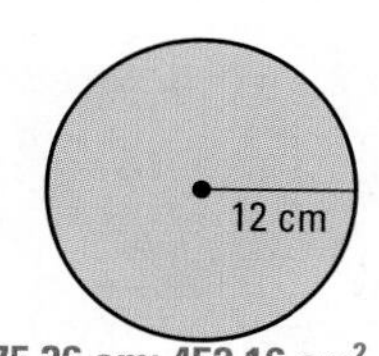

75.36 cm; 452.16 cm²

SOLVING EQUATIONS **Solve the equation and state a reason for each step.** (Review 2.4) **28–33. See margin.**

28. $x - 2 = 10$ 29. $x + 11 = 21$ 30. $9x + 2 = 29$

31. $8x + 13 = 3x + 38$ 32. $3(x - 1) = 16$ 33. $6(2x - 1) + 15 = 69$

IDENTIFYING PARTS OF TRIANGLES **Classify the triangle by its angles and by its sides. Identify the legs and the hypotenuse of any right triangles. Identify the legs and the base of any isosceles triangles.** (Review 4.1 for 4.6)

34.

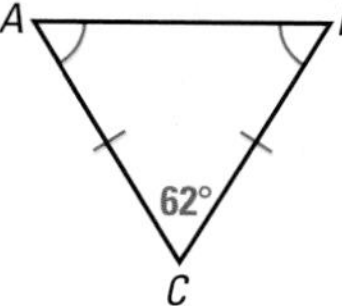

35.

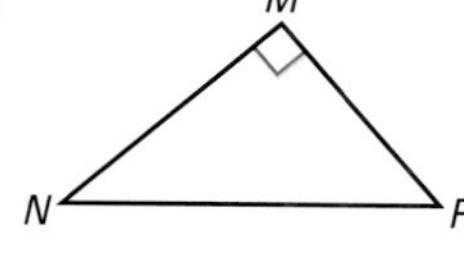

36.

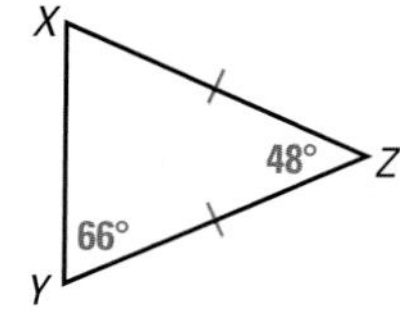

28. $x - 2 = 10$
$x = 12$ **Addition property of equality**

29. $x + 11 = 21$
$x = 10$ **Subtraction property of equality**

30. $9x + 2 = 29$
$9x = 27$ **Subtraction property of equality**
$x = 3$ **Division property of equality**

34. acute isosceles; legs: $\overline{AC}$ and $\overline{BC}$, base: $\overline{AB}$

35. right scalene; legs: $\overline{MN}$ and $\overline{MP}$, hypotenuse: $\overline{NP}$

36. acute isosceles; legs: $\overline{XZ}$ and $\overline{YZ}$, base: $\overline{XY}$

Additional Test Preparation *Sample answer:*

1. Knowing the three angles measures of the two triangles are congruent ensures that the triangles have the same shape, but it does not ensure that they have the same size. You need to know that at least one pair of sides are congruent in order to prove the triangles are congruent.

4 ASSESS

DAILY HOMEWORK QUIZ

Transparency Available

State which postulate or theorem you can use to prove that the triangles are congruent. Then explain how proving that the triangles are congruent proves the given statement.

1. $\overline{LK} \cong \overline{NK}$

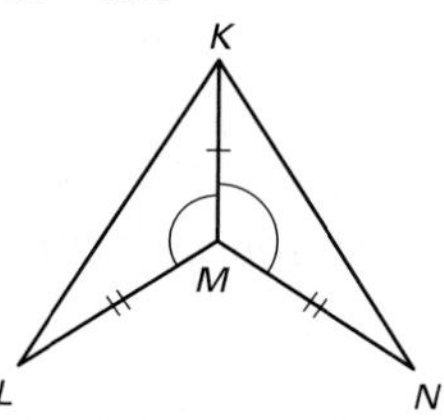

SAS Congruence Postulate; if $\angle KML \cong \angle KMN$, then $\overline{LK} \cong \overline{NK}$ because corresponding parts of congruent triangles are congruent

Use the diagram of the string game Cat's Cradle and the information given on page 233 for Exercises 11–13.

2. Prove $\angle BFC \cong \angle EAD$
$\triangle EDA \cong \triangle BCF$ (Given); $\angle BFC \cong \angle EAD$ (Corresp. parts of ≅ ▲ are ≅.)

EXTRA CHALLENGE NOTE

Challenge problems for Lesson 4.5 are available in **blackline** format in the *Chapter 4 Resource Book*, p. 80 and at **www.mcdougallittell.com.**

ADDITIONAL TEST PREPARATION

1. **WRITING** Congruent figures must have the same size and the same shape. Using this idea, explain why knowing only that the three angle measures of two triangles are congruent cannot be used to show that the triangles are congruent.
See answer at left.

1 PLAN

PACING
Basic: 2 days
Average: 2 days
Advanced: 2 days
Block Schedule: 1 block

LESSON OPENER
GEOMETRY SOFTWARE
An alternative way to approach Lesson 4.6 is to use the Geometry Software Lesson Opener:

- Blackline Master (*Chapter 4 Resource Book,* p. 84)
- Transparency (p. 26)

MEETING INDIVIDUAL NEEDS
- ***Chapter 4 Resource Book***
  Prerequisite Skills Review (p. 5)
  Practice Level A (p. 85)
  Practice Level B (p. 86)
  Practice Level C (p. 87)
  Reteaching with Practice (p. 88)
  Absent Student Catch-Up (p. 90)
  Challenge (p. 93)
- ***Resources in Spanish***
-  ***Personal Student Tutor***

NEW-TEACHER SUPPORT
See the Tips for New Teachers on pp. 1–2 of the *Chapter 4 Resource Book* for additional notes about Lesson 4.6.

WARM-UP EXERCISES
Transparency Available
Tell how many obtuse, acute, and right angles each triangle has.

1. acute triangle
   0 obtuse, 0 right, 3 acute
2. right triangle
   0 obtuse, 1 right, 2 acute
3. obtuse triangle
   1 obtuse, 0 right, 2 acute
4. equilateral triangle
   0 obtuse, 0 right, 3 acute

4.6 Isosceles, Equilateral, and Right Triangles

What you should learn

GOAL 1 Use properties of isosceles and equilateral triangles.

GOAL 2 Use properties of right triangles.

Why you should learn it

▼ Isosceles, equilateral, and right triangles are commonly used in the design of **real-life** objects, such as the exterior structure of the building in **Exs. 29–32**.

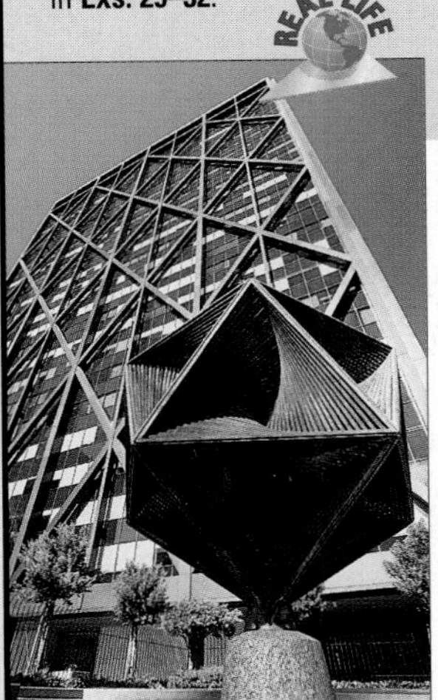

CALIFORNIA STANDARDS AND ASSESSMENT
CA Standards: 5, 12, 13
SAT9 Task 1: Objs. 22, 24, 26
SAT9 Task 2: Objs. 24, 26, 27

GOAL 1 USING PROPERTIES OF ISOSCELES TRIANGLES

In Lesson 4.1, you learned that a triangle is isosceles if it has at least two congruent sides. If it has exactly two congruent sides, then they are the legs of the triangle and the noncongruent side is the base. The two angles adjacent to the base are the **base angles**. The angle opposite the base is the **vertex angle**.

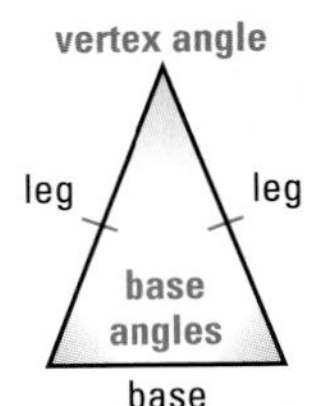

ACTIVITY Developing Concepts

Investigating Isosceles Triangles

1, 2. Check constructions.

1. Use a straightedge and a compass to construct an acute isosceles triangle. Then fold the triangle along a line that bisects the vertex angle, as shown.
2. Repeat the procedure for an obtuse isosceles triangle.
3. What observations can you make about the base angles of an isosceles triangle? Write your observations as a conjecture.
   The base angles of an isosceles triangle are congruent.

In the activity, you may have discovered the *Base Angles Theorem*, which is proved in Example 1. The converse of this theorem is also true. You are asked to prove the converse in Exercise 26.

THEOREMS

THEOREM 4.6 ***Base Angles Theorem***
If two sides of a triangle are congruent, then the angles opposite them are congruent.
If $\overline{AB} \cong \overline{AC}$, then $\angle B \cong \angle C$.

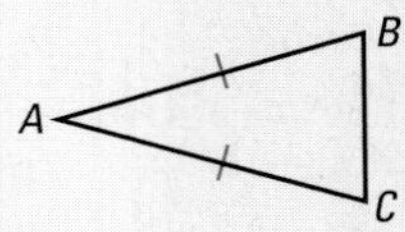

THEOREM 4.7 ***Converse of the Base Angles Theorem***
If two angles of a triangle are congruent, then the sides opposite them are congruent.
If $\angle B \cong \angle C$, then $\overline{AB} \cong \overline{AC}$.

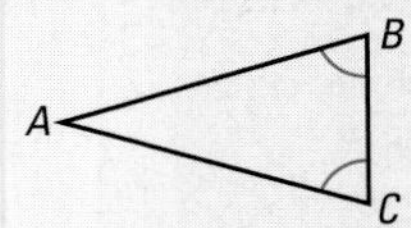

EXAMPLE 1 Proof of the Base Angles Theorem

Use the diagram of $\triangle ABC$ to prove the Base Angles Theorem.

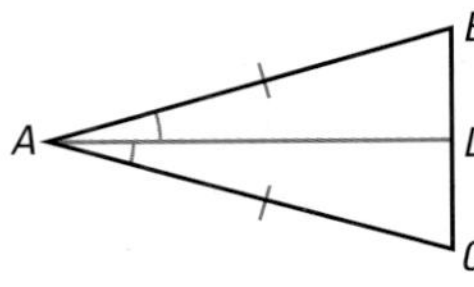

GIVEN ▶ $\triangle ABC$, $\overline{AB} \cong \overline{AC}$

PROVE ▶ $\angle B \cong \angle C$

Paragraph Proof Draw the bisector of $\angle CAB$. By construction, $\angle CAD \cong \angle BAD$. You are given that $\overline{AB} \cong \overline{AC}$. Also, $\overline{DA} \cong \overline{DA}$ by the Reflexive Property of Congruence. Use the SAS Congruence Postulate to conclude that $\triangle ADB \cong \triangle ADC$. Because corresponding parts of congruent triangles are congruent, it follows that $\angle B \cong \angle C$.

....

Recall that an *equilateral* triangle is a special type of isosceles triangle. The corollaries below state that a triangle is equilateral if and only if it is equiangular.

COROLLARIES

COROLLARY TO THEOREM 4.6

If a triangle is equilateral, then it is equiangular.

COROLLARY TO THEOREM 4.7

If a triangle is equiangular, then it is equilateral.

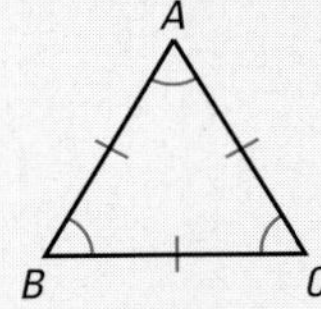

EXAMPLE 2 Using Equilateral and Isosceles Triangles

a. Find the value of x.

b. Find the value of y.

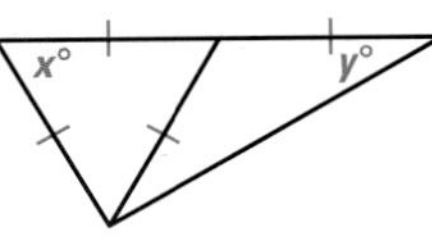

SOLUTION

a. Notice that x represents the measure of an angle of an equilateral triangle. From the corollary above, this triangle is also equiangular.

$3x° = 180°$ **Apply the Triangle Sum Theorem.**

$x = 60$ **Solve for x.**

b. Notice that y represents the measure of a base angle of an isosceles triangle. From the Base Angles Theorem, the other base angle has the same measure. The vertex angle forms a linear pair with a 60° angle, so its measure is 120°.

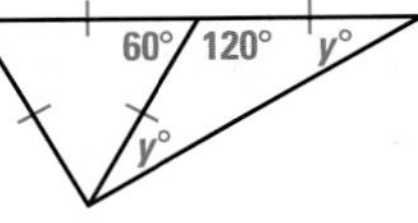

$120° + 2y° = 180°$ **Apply the Triangle Sum Theorem.**

$y = 30$ **Solve for y.**

STUDENT HELP

HOMEWORK HELP
Visit our Web site www.mcdougallittell.com for extra examples.

2 TEACH

MOTIVATING THE LESSON
Draw an isosceles, an equilateral, and a right triangle. Have volunteers write facts about each kind of triangle beneath the corresponding drawing. Once the three types of triangles have been reviewed, introduce the properties associated with each.

ACTIVITY NOTE
Check students' constructions to ensure that their triangles are isosceles. They will not make accurate conjectures if they are examining base angles that are obviously not congruent.

EXTRA EXAMPLE 1
Use the diagram of $\triangle WXY$ to prove the Base Angles Theorem.

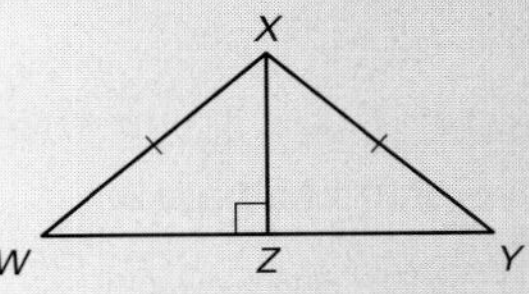

See below.

EXTRA EXAMPLE 2
a. Find the value of x. 65
b. Find the value of y. 32.5

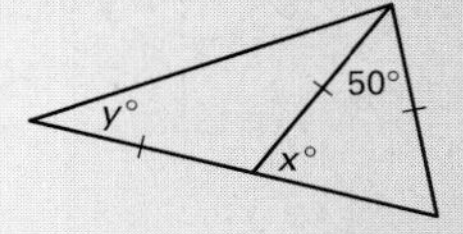

CHECKPOINT EXERCISES
For use after Examples 1 and 2:
1. a. Find the value of x. 40
b. Find the value of y. 80

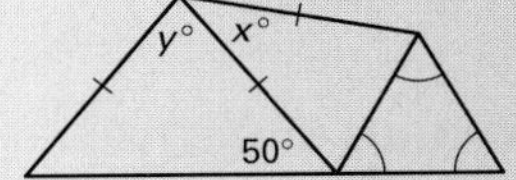

STUDENT HELP NOTES
Homework Help Students can find extra examples at **www.mcdougallittell.com** that parallel the examples in the student edition.

Extra Example 1 ***Sample answer:***
Draw $\overline{XZ}$ so that it bisects $\overline{WY}$. You are given $\overline{WX} \cong \overline{YX}$. Also, $\overline{XZ} \cong \overline{XZ}$ by the Reflexive Property of Congruence. Use the SSS Congruence Postulate to conclude that $\triangle XWZ \cong \triangle XYZ$. Because corresponding parts of congruent triangles are congruent, it follows that $\angle W \cong \angle Y$.

EXTRA EXAMPLE 3

Given: $\overline{TS} \perp \overline{PS}$, $\overline{TS} \perp \overline{QS}$, $\overline{TS} \perp \overline{RS}$; $\overline{TP} \cong \overline{TQ} \cong \overline{TR}$

Prove: $\triangle TPS \cong \triangle TQS \cong \triangle TRS$

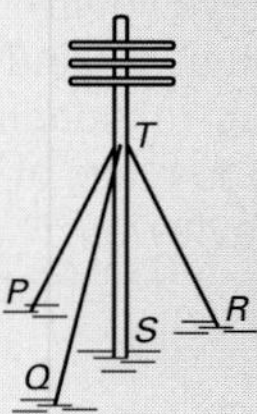

$\overline{TS} \perp \overline{PS}$ and $\overline{TS} \perp \overline{QS}$, which implies $\angle TSP$ and $\angle TSQ$ are right angles. By definition, $\triangle TSP$ and $\triangle TSQ$ are right triangles. The hypotenuses of these triangles, $\overline{TP}$ and $\overline{TQ}$, are congruent. Also, $\overline{TS}$ is a leg for both triangles, and $\overline{TS} \cong \overline{TS}$ by the Reflexive Property. Thus, by HL, $\triangle TPS \cong \triangle TQS$. Similar reasoning can be used to prove that $\triangle TPS \cong \triangle TRS$. So, by the Transitive Property, $\triangle TPS \cong \triangle TQS \cong \triangle TRS$.

CHECKPOINT EXERCISES

For use after Example 3:

1. Given: $\overline{AB} \cong \overline{DE}$, $\overline{BC} \cong \overline{EF}$; $\angle ABC$ and $\angle DEF$ are right angles
Prove: $\triangle ABC \cong \triangle DEF$

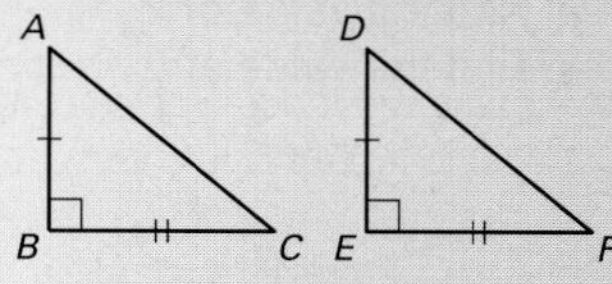

Statements (Reasons)
1. **$\overline{AB} \cong \overline{DE}$, $\overline{BC} \cong \overline{EF}$ (Given)**
2. **$\angle ABC$ and $\angle DEF$ are right angles (Given)**
3. **$\angle ABC \cong \angle DEF$ (Rt. $\angle$s are $\cong$)**
4. **$\triangle ABC \cong \triangle DEF$ (SAS)**

CLOSURE QUESTION

Could you use the HL Congruence Theorem to prove two isosceles triangles congruent? **only if they are right triangles**

GOAL 2 USING PROPERTIES OF RIGHT TRIANGLES

You have learned four ways to prove that triangles are congruent.

- Side-Side-Side (SSS) Congruence Postulate (p. 212)
- Side-Angle-Side (SAS) Congruence Postulate (p. 213)
- Angle-Side-Angle (ASA) Congruence Postulate (p. 220)
- Angle-Angle-Side (AAS) Congruence Theorem (p. 220)

The Hypotenuse-Leg Congruence Theorem below can be used to prove that two *right* triangles are congruent. A proof of this theorem appears on page 837.

THEOREM

THEOREM 4.8 ***Hypotenuse-Leg (HL) Congruence Theorem***

If the hypotenuse and a leg of a right triangle are congruent to the hypotenuse and a leg of a second right triangle, then the two triangles are congruent.

If $\overline{BC} \cong \overline{EF}$ and $\overline{AC} \cong \overline{DF}$, then $\triangle ABC \cong \triangle DEF$.

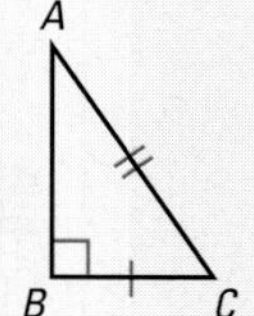

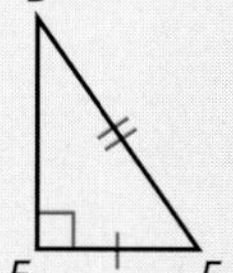

EXAMPLE 3 ***Proving Right Triangles Congruent***

The television antenna is perpendicular to the plane containing the points *B*, *C*, *D*, and *E*. Each of the stays running from the top of the antenna to *B*, *C*, and *D* uses the same length of cable. Prove that $\triangle AEB$, $\triangle AEC$, and $\triangle AED$ are congruent.

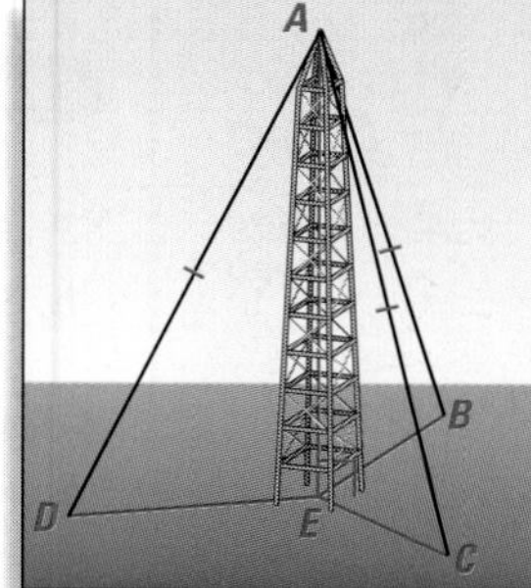

GIVEN ▶ $\overline{AE} \perp \overline{EB}$, $\overline{AE} \perp \overline{EC}$, $\overline{AE} \perp \overline{ED}$, $\overline{AB} \cong \overline{AC} \cong \overline{AD}$

PROVE ▶ $\triangle AEB \cong \triangle AEC \cong \triangle AED$

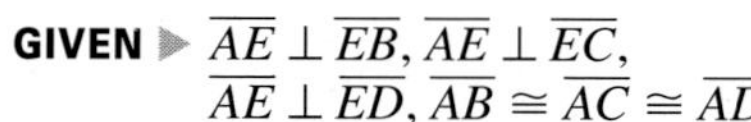

SOLUTION

Paragraph Proof You are given that $\overline{AE} \perp \overline{EB}$ and $\overline{AE} \perp \overline{EC}$, which implies that $\angle AEB$ and $\angle AEC$ are right angles. By definition, $\triangle AEB$ and $\triangle AEC$ are right triangles. You are given that the hypotenuses of these two triangles, $\overline{AB}$ and $\overline{AC}$, are congruent. Also, $\overline{AE}$ is a leg for both triangles, and $\overline{AE} \cong \overline{AE}$ by the Reflexive Property of Congruence. Thus, by the Hypotenuse-Leg Congruence Theorem, $\triangle AEB \cong \triangle AEC$.

▶ Similar reasoning can be used to prove that $\triangle AEC \cong \triangle AED$. So, by the Transitive Property of Congruent Triangles, $\triangle AEB \cong \triangle AEC \cong \triangle AED$.

STUDENT HELP

Study Tip
Before you use the HL Congruence Theorem in a proof, you need to prove that the triangles are right triangles.

GUIDED PRACTICE

Vocabulary Check ✓

1. Describe the meaning of *equilateral* and *equiangular*.
Sample answers: having all sides equal in length; having all angles equal in measure

Concept Check ✓

Find the unknown measure(s). Tell what theorems you used.

2. 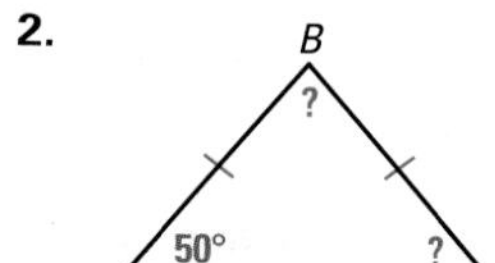

3. 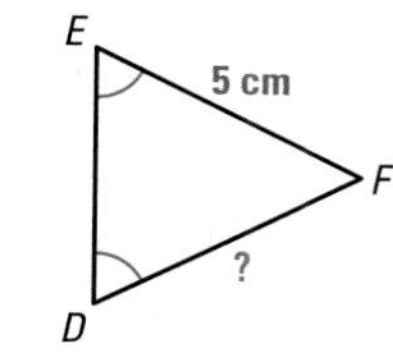

4. 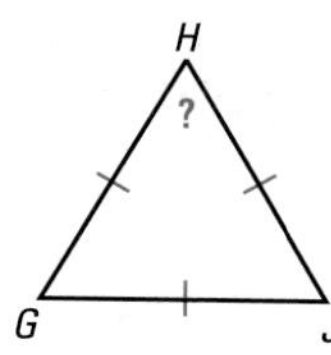

2. $m\angle C = 50°$ (Base Angles Theorem), $m\angle B = 80°$ (Triangle Sum Theorem)

3. 5 cm (Converse of the Base Angles Theorem)

4. 60° (Corollary to the Base Angles Theorem)

Skill Check ✓

Determine whether you are given enough information to prove that the triangles are congruent. Explain your answer.

5. 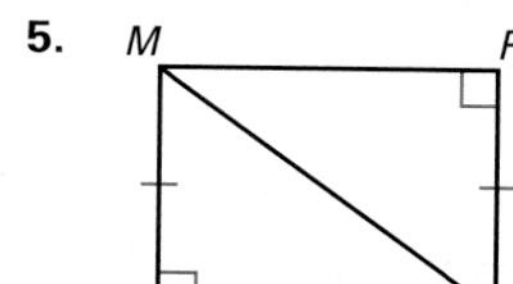

6. 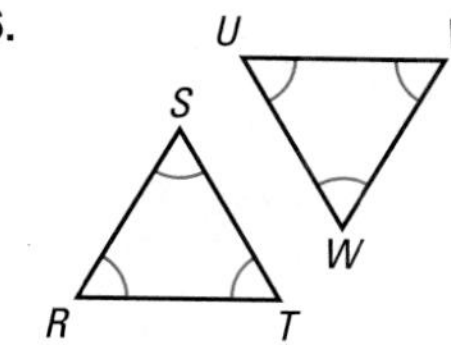

7. 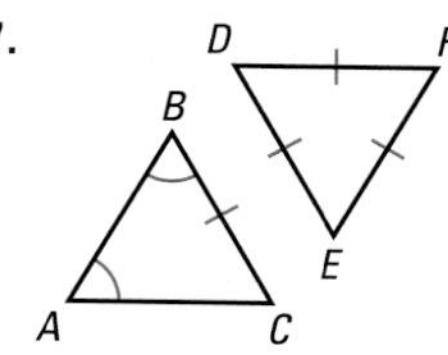

No; it cannot be shown that $\triangle ABC$ is equilateral.

5. Yes; the hypotenuse and one leg of one right triangle are congruent to the hypotenuse and one leg of the other.

6. No; both triangles are equilateral and equiangular, but it cannot be determined whether the sides of one triangle are congruent to the sides of the other.

PRACTICE AND APPLICATIONS

STUDENT HELP

Extra Practice to help you master skills is on p. 810.

USING ALGEBRA Solve for *x* and *y*.

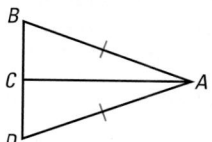

8. 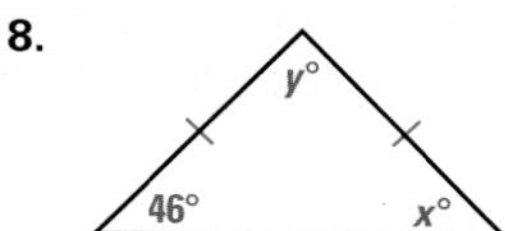
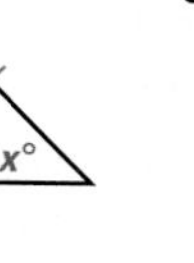

$x = 46, y = 88$

9. 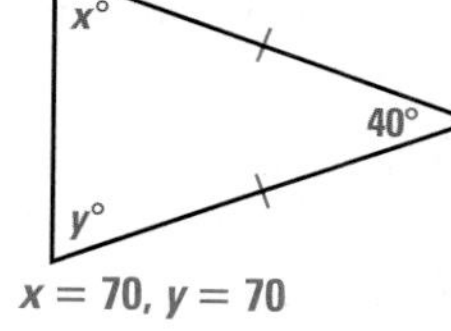

$x = 70, y = 70$

10. 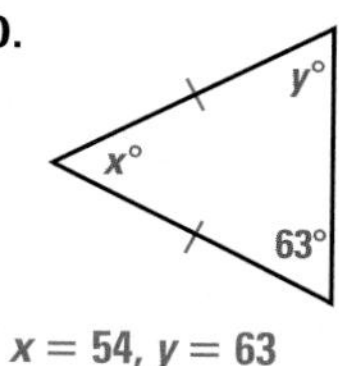

$x = 54, y = 63$

LOGICAL REASONING Decide whether enough information is given to prove that the triangles are congruent. Explain your answer. 11–16. See margin.

11. 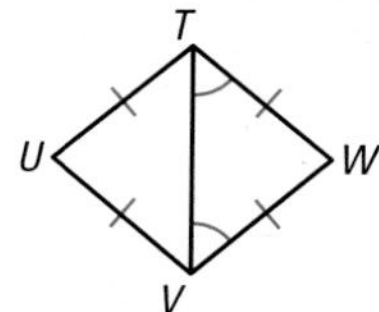

12.

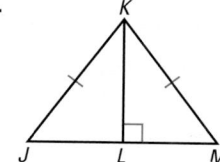

13. 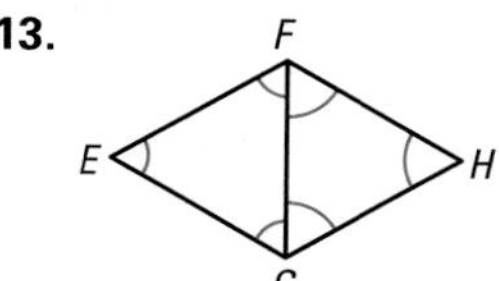

14. 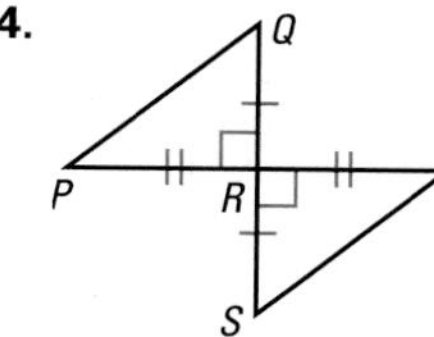

15.

16. 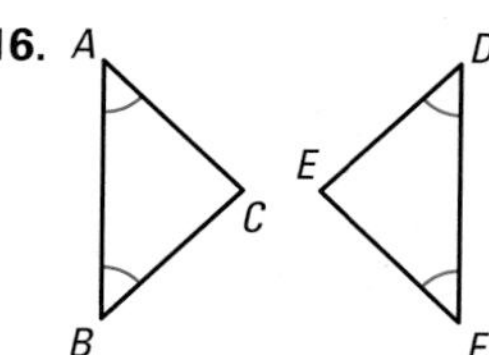

11. Yes; the triangles can be proved congruent using the SSS Congruence Postulate.

12. No; there are two pairs of corresponding congruent sides, but no angles can be shown to be congruent.

STUDENT HELP

HOMEWORK HELP
Example 1: Exs. 26–28
Example 2: Exs. 8–10, 17–25
Example 3: Exs. 31, 33, 34, 39

3 APPLY

ASSIGNMENT GUIDE

BASIC
Day 1: pp. 239–242 Exs. 8–28 even, 29–33
Day 2: pp. 239–242 Exs. 9–27 odd, 34, 42, 43, 46–56 even

AVERAGE
Day 1: pp. 239–242 Exs. 8–28 even, 29–33
Day 2: pp. 239–242 Exs. 9–27 odd, 34–38, 42, 43, 46–56 even

ADVANCED
Day 1: pp. 239–242 Exs. 8–28 even, 29–33
Day 2: pp. 239–242 Exs. 9–27 odd, 34–44, 46–56 even

BLOCK SCHEDULE
pp. 239–242 Exs. 8–38, 42, 43, 46–56 even

EXERCISE LEVELS

Level A: *Easier*
8–16

Level B: *More Difficult*
17–38, 42, 43

Level C: *Most Difficult*
39–41, 44

✓ HOMEWORK CHECK

To quickly check student understanding of key concepts, go over the following exercises: Exs. 10, 16, 18, 20, 24, 26, 28, 34. See also the Daily Homework Quiz:

- Blackline Master (*Chapter 4 Resource Book,* p. 96)
- Transparency (p. 31)

13–16. See Additional Answers beginning on page AA1.

! COMMON ERROR
EXERCISES 17–25 Watch for students who assume triangles are right, isosceles, or equilateral because of the way they look and not because of the way they are labeled or because of their measures. Remind students that they cannot assume a figure has any special characteristics unless that information is given.

MATHEMATICAL REASONING
EXERCISE 26 The Base Angles Theorem and its converse can be used to illustrate if-and-only-if statements. When both a statement and its converse are true, an if-and-only-if statement can be made. For the Base Angles Theorem and its converse, an if-and-only-if statement is "Two angles of a triangle are congruent if and only if the sides opposite them are congruent."

31. Since $\triangle ABD$ and $\triangle CBD$ are congruent equilateral triangles, $\overline{AB} \cong \overline{BC}$ and $\angle ABD \cong \angle CBD$. By the Base Angles Theorem, $\angle BAE \cong \angle BCE$. Then $\triangle ABE \cong \triangle CBE$ by the AAS Congruence Theorem. Moreover, by the Linear Pair Postulate, $m\angle AEB + m\angle CEB = 180°$. But $\angle AEB$ and $\angle CEB$ are corresponding parts of congruent triangles, so they are congruent, that is, $m\angle AEB = m\angle CEB$. Then by the Substitution Property, $2m\angle AEB = 180°$ and $m\angle AEB = 90°$. So $\angle AEB$ and $\angle CEB$ are both right angles, and $\triangle AEB$ and $\triangle CEB$ are congruent right triangles.

26. GIVEN: $\angle B \cong \angle C$
PROVE: $\overline{AB} \cong \overline{AC}$
Proof: Draw $\overrightarrow{AD}$, the bisector of $\angle BAC$. By construction, $\angle BAD \cong \angle CAD$. It is given that $\angle B \cong \angle C$, and $\overline{AD} \cong \overline{AD}$ by the Reflexive Property of Congruence. Then $\triangle ABD \cong \triangle ACD$ by the AAS Congruence Theorem and $\overline{AB} \cong \overline{AC}$ because corresponding parts of congruent triangles are congruent.

27. GIVEN: $\overline{AB} \cong \overline{AC} \cong \overline{BC}$
PROVE: $\angle A \cong \angle B \cong \angle C$
Since $\overline{AB} \cong \overline{AC}$, $\angle B \cong \angle C$ by the Base Angles Theorem. Since $\overline{AB} \cong \overline{BC}$, $\angle A \cong \angle C$ by the Base Angles Theorem. Then by the Transitive Property of Congruence, $\angle A \cong \angle B \cong \angle C$ and $\triangle ABC$ is equiangular.

28. GIVEN: $\angle A \cong \angle B \cong \angle C$
PROVE: $\overline{AB} \cong \overline{AC} \cong \overline{BC}$
Since $\angle B \cong \angle C$, $\overline{AB} \cong \overline{AC}$ by the Converse of the Base Angles Theorem. Since $\angle A \cong \angle C$, $\overline{AB} \cong \overline{BC}$ by the Converse of the Base Angles Theorem. Then by the Transitive Property of Congruence, $\overline{AB} \cong \overline{AC} \cong \overline{BC}$ and $\triangle ABC$ is equilateral.

29. $\triangle ABD$ and $\triangle CBD$ are congruent equilateral triangles so $\overline{AB} \cong \overline{CB}$ and therefore $\triangle ABC$ is isosceles by definition.

USING ALGEBRA **Find the value of x.**

17. (x + 13) ft, 24 ft
11

18.
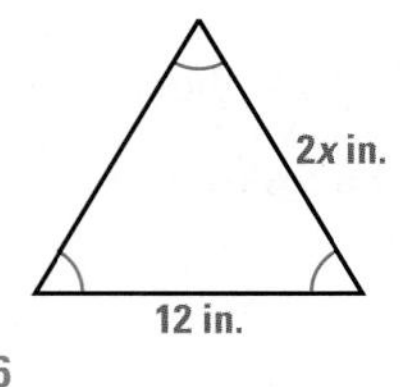

6

19.
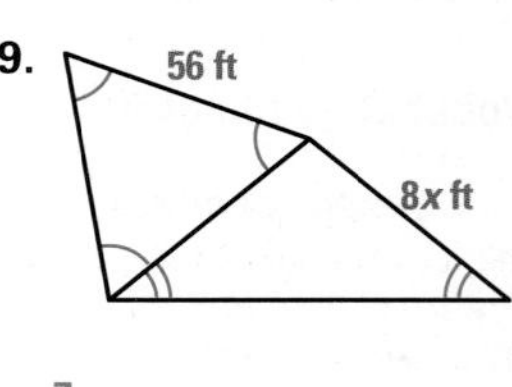

7

USING ALGEBRA **Find the values of x and y.**

20.
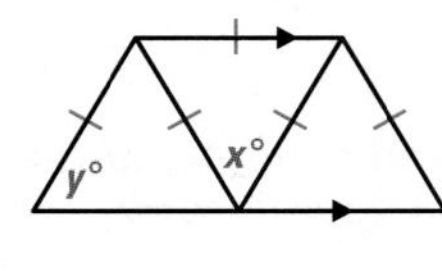

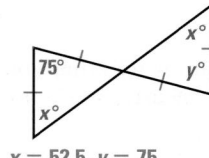

$x = 60$, $y = 60$

21. 75°, x°, y°, x°
$x = 52.5$, $y = 75$

22.
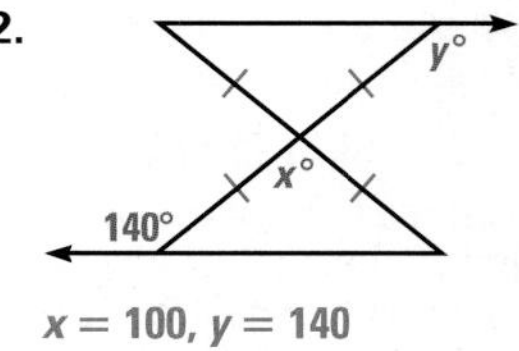

$x = 100$, $y = 140$

23. x°, y°
$x = 30$, $y = 120$

24.
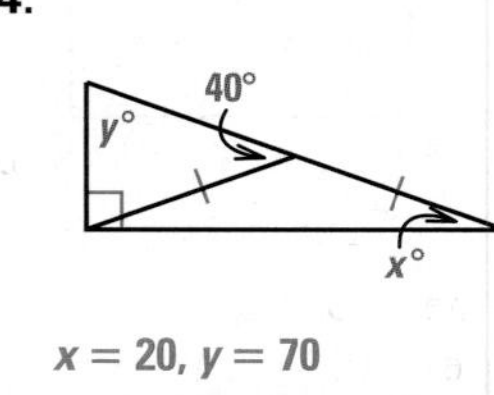

$x = 20$, $y = 70$

25.
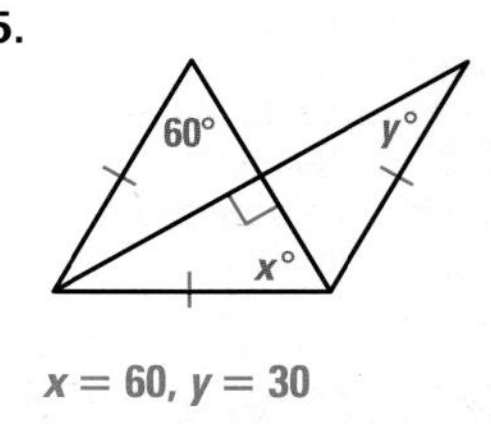

$x = 60$, $y = 30$

PROOF **In Exercises 26–28, use the diagrams that accompany the theorems on pages 236 and 237.** 26–28. See margin.

26. The Converse of the Base Angles Theorem on page 236 states, "If two angles of a triangle are congruent, then the sides opposite them are congruent." Write a proof of this theorem.

27. The Corollary to Theorem 4.6 on page 237 states, "If a triangle is equilateral, then it is equiangular." Write a proof of this corollary.

28. The Corollary to Theorem 4.7 on page 237 states, "If a triangle is equiangular, then it is equilateral." Write a proof of this corollary.

ARCHITECTURE **The diagram represents part of the exterior of the building in the photograph. In the diagram, $\triangle ABD$ and $\triangle CBD$ are congruent equilateral triangles.**

29. Explain why $\triangle ABC$ is isosceles.

30. Explain why $\angle BAE \cong \angle BCE$. Base Angles Theorem

31. **PROOF** Prove that $\triangle ABE$ and $\triangle CBE$ are congruent right triangles. See margin.

32. Find the measure of $\angle BAE$. 30°

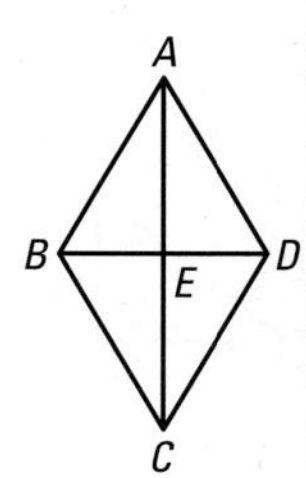

34. It is given that $\overline{VW} \parallel \overline{ZY}$ and that $\overline{VZ}$ and $\overline{WY}$ are both $\perp$ to $\overline{VW}$. By the Perpendicular Transversal Theorem, it follows that $\overline{VZ}$ and $\overline{WY}$ are both $\perp$ to $\overline{ZY}$. Then $\angle UZV$ and $\angle XYW$ are both rt. $\angle$s and $\triangle UZV$ and $\triangle XYW$ are both rt. $\triangle$s. Since $\overline{UV} \cong \overline{XW}$ and $\overline{UZ} \cong \overline{XY}$, $\triangle UZV \cong \triangle XYW$ by the HL Cong. Thm. Thus $\angle U \cong \angle X$ because corresp. parts of $\cong$ $\triangle$s are $\cong$.

FOCUS ON PEOPLE

ISAAC NEWTON The English scientist Isaac Newton (1642–1727) observed that light is made up of a spectrum of colors. Newton was the first person to arrange the colors of the spectrum in a "color wheel."

APPLICATION LINK www.mcdougallittell.com

38. red, yellow, blue; red-orange, yellow-green, blue-purple; purple, orange, green; red-purple, yellow-orange, blue-green

41. No; the measure of $\angle ADB$ will decrease, as will the measure of $\angle CDB$ and the amount of reflection will remain the same.

PROOF **Write a two-column proof or a paragraph proof.** 33, 34. See margin.

33. **GIVEN** ▶ D is the midpoint of $\overline{CE}$, $\angle BCD$ and $\angle FED$ are right angles, and $\overline{BD} \cong \overline{FD}$.

PROVE ▶ $\triangle BCD \cong \triangle FED$

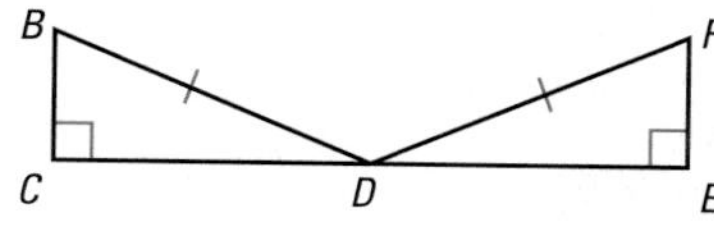

34. **GIVEN** ▶ $\overline{VW} \parallel \overline{ZY}$, $\overline{UV} \cong \overline{XW}$, $\overline{UZ} \cong \overline{XY}$, $\overline{VW} \perp \overline{VZ}$, $\overline{VW} \perp \overline{WY}$

PROVE ▶ $\angle U \cong \angle X$

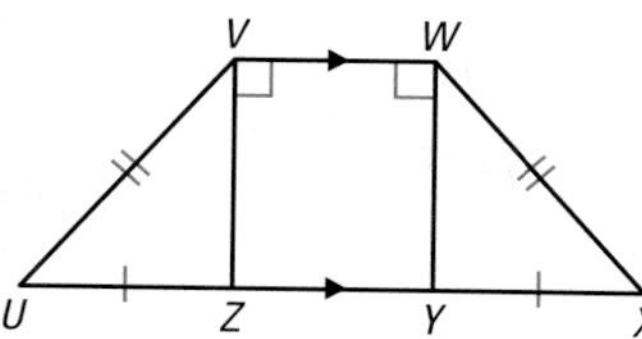

COLOR WHEEL **Artists use a color wheel to show relationships between colors. The 12 triangles in the diagram are isosceles triangles with congruent vertex angles.**

35. Complementary colors lie directly opposite each other on the color wheel. Explain how you know that the yellow triangle is congruent to the purple triangle. See margin.

36. The measure of the vertex angle of the yellow triangle is 30°. Find the measures of the base angles. 75°

yellow-green yellow yellow-orange green orange blue-green red-orange blue red blue-purple purple red-purple

37. Trace the color wheel. Then form a triangle whose vertices are the midpoints of the bases of the red, yellow, and blue triangles. (These colors are the *primary colors.*) What type of triangle is this? equilateral

38. Form other triangles that are congruent to the triangle in Exercise 37. The colors of the vertices are called *triads*. What are the possible triads? See margin.

PHYSICS **Use the information below.**

When a light ray from an object meets a mirror, it is reflected back to your eye. For example, in the diagram, a light ray from point C is reflected at point D and travels back to point A. The *law of reflection* states that the angle of incidence $\angle CDB$ is equal to the angle of reflection $\angle ADB$.

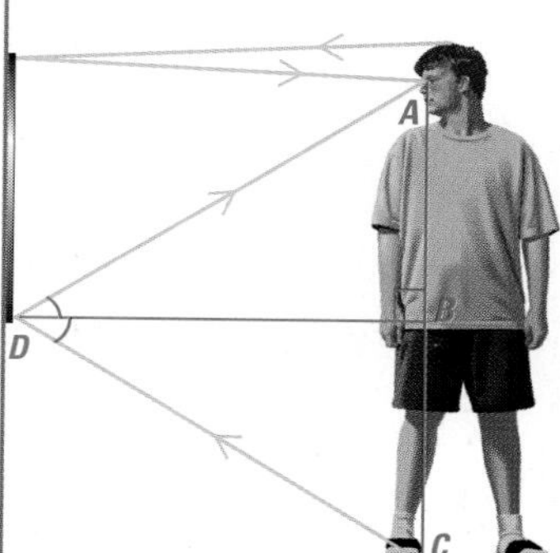

For a person to see his or her complete reflection, the mirror must be at least one half the person's height.

39. **GIVEN** ▶ $\angle CDB \cong \angle ADB$, $\overline{DB} \perp \overline{AC}$

PROVE ▶ $\triangle ABD \cong \triangle CBD$ See margin.

40. Verify that $\triangle ACD$ is isosceles. See margin.

41. Does moving away from the mirror have any effect on the amount of his or her reflection the person sees?

APPLICATION NOTE
EXERCISES 35–38
Additional information about Isaac Newton is available at **www.mcdougallittell.com**.

33. Statements (Reasons)
1. D is the midpoint of $\overline{CE}$, $\angle BCD$ and $\angle FED$ are rt. $\angle$s. (Given)
2. $\angle BCD \cong \angle FED$ (Right Angle Congruence Theorem)
3. $\overline{CD} \cong \overline{ED}$ (Definition of midpoint)
4. $\overline{BD} \cong \overline{FD}$ (Given)
5. $\triangle BCD \cong \triangle FED$ (HL Congruence Theorem)

35. Each of the triangles is isosceles and every pair of adjacent triangles have a common side, so the legs of all the triangles are congruent by the Transitive Property of Congruence. The common vertex angles are congruent, so any two of the triangles are congruent by the SAS Congruence Postulate.

39, 40. See Additional Answers beginning on page AA1.

ADDITIONAL PRACTICE AND RETEACHING

For Lesson 4.6:
- Practice Levels A, B, and C (*Chapter 4 Resource Book*, p. 85)
- Reteaching with Practice (*Chapter 4 Resource Book*, p. 88)
-  See Lesson 4.6 of the *Personal Student Tutor*

For more Mixed Review:
- Search the *Test and Practice Generator* for key words or specific lessons.

4 ASSESS

DAILY HOMEWORK QUIZ

 *Transparency Available*

Solve for x and y.

1.

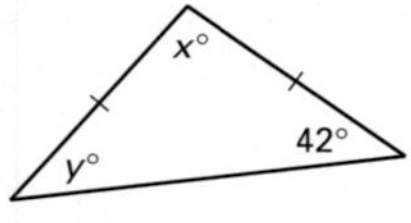

$x = 96$, $y = 42$

2.

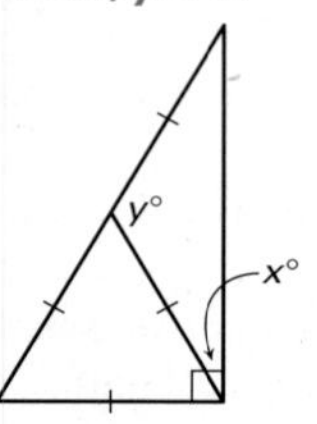

$x = 30$, $y = 120$

Decide whether enough information is given to prove that the triangles are congruent. Explain your answer.

3.

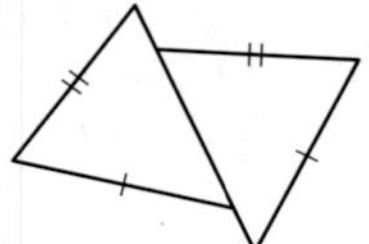

No; there are two pairs of corresponding congruent sides, but no angles can be shown to be congruent.

EXTRA CHALLENGE NOTE

Challenge problems for Lesson 4.5 are available in **blackline** format in the *Chapter 4 Resource Book,* p. 93 and at **www.mcdougallittell.com.**

ADDITIONAL TEST PREPARATION

1. WRITING Tell whether the statement below is true or false. Explain your reasoning. *An equilateral triangle is also an isosceles triangle.*
true; *Sample answer:* By definition, an isosceles triangle has at least two congruent sides so an equilateral triangle can also be considered isosceles.

44. See Additional Answers beginning on page AA1.

Test Preparation

QUANTITATIVE COMPARISON **In Exercises 42 and 43, refer to the figures below. Choose the statement that is true about the given values.**

Ⓐ The value in column A is greater.

Ⓑ The value in column B is greater.

Ⓒ The two values are equal.

Ⓓ The relationship cannot be determined from the given information.

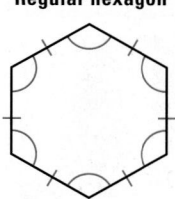

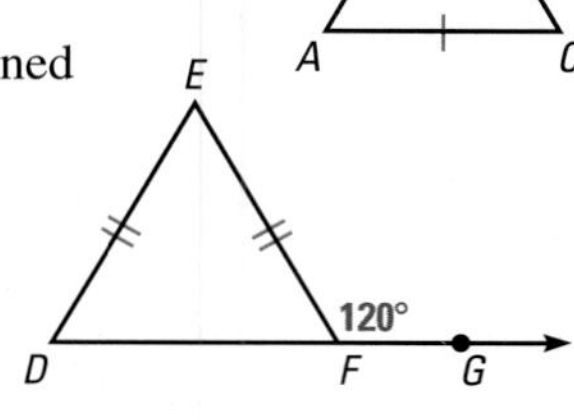

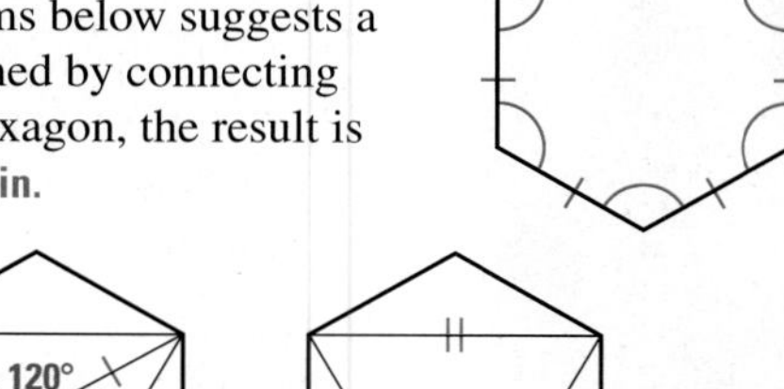

	Column A	Column B	
42.	$\angle D$	$\angle EFD$	C
43.	$\angle B$	$\angle EFD$	C

★ Challenge

44. **LOGICAL REASONING** A *regular hexagon* has six congruent sides and six congruent interior angles. It can be divided into six equilateral triangles. Explain how the series of diagrams below suggests a proof that when a triangle is formed by connecting every other vertex of a regular hexagon, the result is an equilateral triangle. See margin.

Regular hexagon

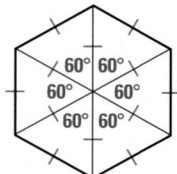

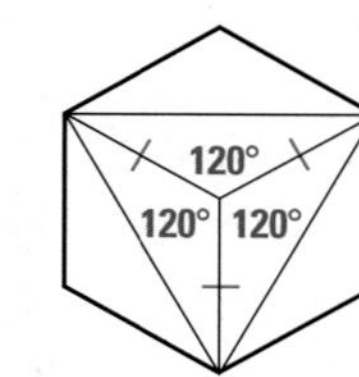

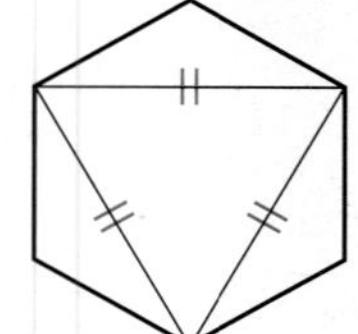

EXTRA CHALLENGE
www.mcdougallittell.com

MIXED REVIEW

CONGRUENCE **Use the Distance Formula to decide whether $\overline{AB} \cong \overline{AC}$.** (Review 1.3 for 4.7)

45. $A(0, -4)$
$B(5, 8)$
$C(-12, 1)$
congruent

46. $A(0, 0)$
$B(-6, -10)$
$C(6, 10)$
congruent

47. $A(1, -1)$
$B(-8, 7)$
$C(8, 7)$
not congruent

FINDING THE MIDPOINT **Find the coordinates of the midpoint of a segment with the given endpoints.** (Review 1.5 for 4.7)

48. $C(4, 9)$, $D(10, 7)$ (7, 8)
49. $G(0, 11)$, $H(8, -3)$ (4, 4)
50. $L(1, 7)$, $M(-5, -5)$ (−2, 1)
51. $C(-2, 3)$, $D(5, 6)$
52. $G(0, -13)$, $H(2, -1)$ (1, −7)
53. $L(-3, -5)$, $M(0, -20)$

51. $\left(1\frac{1}{2}, 4\frac{1}{2}\right)$

53. $\left(-1\frac{1}{2}, -12\frac{1}{2}\right)$

WRITING EQUATIONS **Line j is perpendicular to the line with the given equation and line j passes through point P. Write an equation of line j.** (Review 3.7)

54. $y = -3x - 4$; $P(1, 1)$ $y = \frac{1}{3}x + \frac{2}{3}$
55. $y = x - 7$; $P(0, 0)$ $y = -x$
56. $y = -\frac{10}{9}x + 3$; $P(5, -12)$
57. $y = \frac{2}{3}x + 4$; $P(-3, 4)$ $y = -\frac{3}{2}x - \frac{1}{2}$

56. $y = \frac{9}{10}x - \frac{33}{2}$

GOAL 2 WRITING COORDINATE PROOFS

Once a figure is placed in a coordinate plane, you may be able to prove statements about the figure.

EXAMPLE 4 Writing a Plan for a Coordinate Proof

Proof

Write a plan to prove that $\overrightarrow{SO}$ bisects $\angle PSR$.

GIVEN ▶ Coordinates of vertices of $\triangle POS$ and $\triangle ROS$

PROVE ▶ $\overrightarrow{SO}$ bisects $\angle PSR$

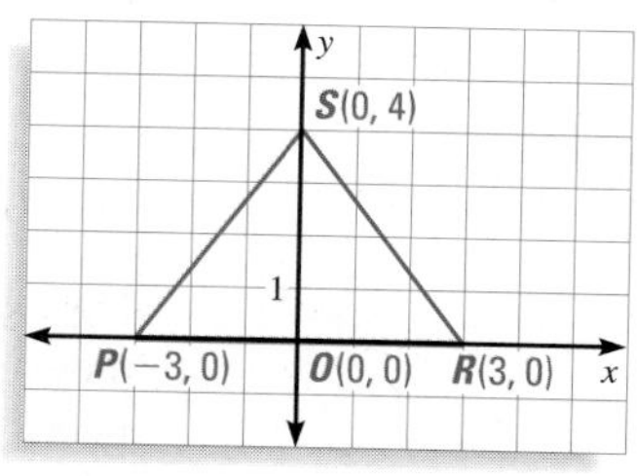

SOLUTION

Plan for Proof Use the Distance Formula to find the side lengths of $\triangle POS$ and $\triangle ROS$. Then use the SSS Congruence Postulate to show that $\triangle POS \cong \triangle ROS$. Finally, use the fact that corresponding parts of congruent triangles are congruent to conclude that $\angle PSO \cong \angle RSO$, which implies that $\overrightarrow{SO}$ bisects $\angle PSR$.

....

The coordinate proof in Example 4 applies to a specific triangle. When you want to prove a statement about a more general set of figures, it is helpful to use variables as coordinates.

For instance, you can use variable coordinates to duplicate the proof in Example 4. Once this is done, you can conclude that $\overrightarrow{SO}$ bisects $\angle PSR$ for *any* triangle whose coordinates fit the given pattern.

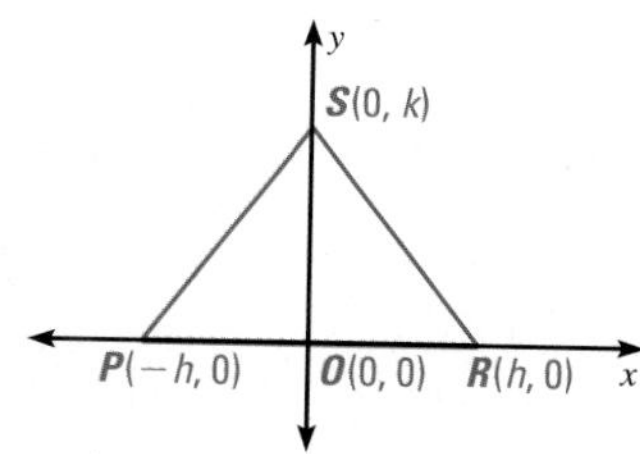

EXAMPLE 5 Using Variables as Coordinates

Right $\triangle OBC$ has leg lengths of h units and k units. You can find the coordinates of points B and C by considering how the triangle is placed in the coordinate plane.

Point B is h units horizontally from the origin, so its coordinates are $(h, 0)$. Point C is h units horizontally from the origin and k units vertically from the origin, so its coordinates are (h, k).

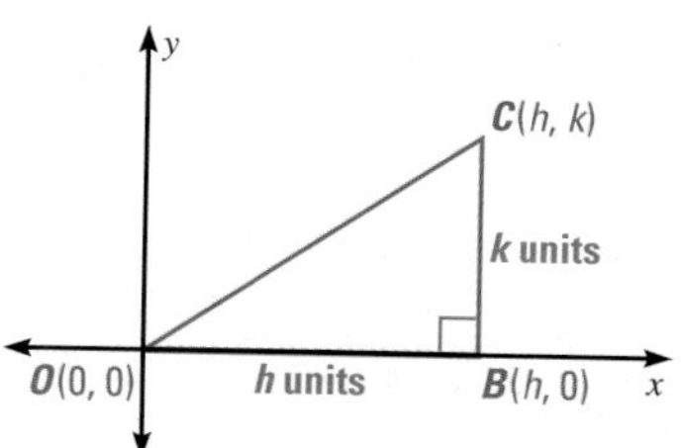

You can use the Distance Formula to find the length of the hypotenuse $\overline{OC}$.

$$OC = \sqrt{(h-0)^2 + (k-0)^2} = \sqrt{h^2 + k^2}$$

STUDENT HELP

INTERNET HOMEWORK HELP
Visit our Web site www.mcdougallittell.com for extra examples.

EXTRA EXAMPLE 4

Write a plan to prove that $\overline{OU}$ bisects $\angle TOV$.

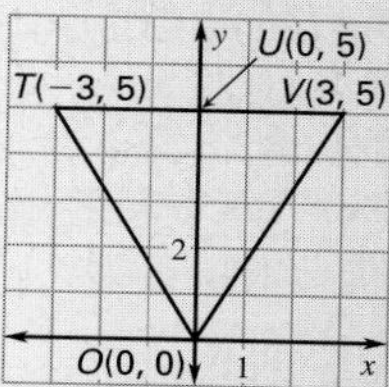

Use the Distance Formula to find the sides of $\triangle TUO$ and $\triangle VUO$. Then use SSS to show $\triangle TUO \cong \triangle VUO$. Finally, use corresponding parts of congruent figures are congruent to show $\angle TOU \cong \angle VOU$, which implies $\overline{OU}$ bisects $\angle TOV$.

EXTRA EXAMPLE 5

Find the coordinates of P. **(h, k)**

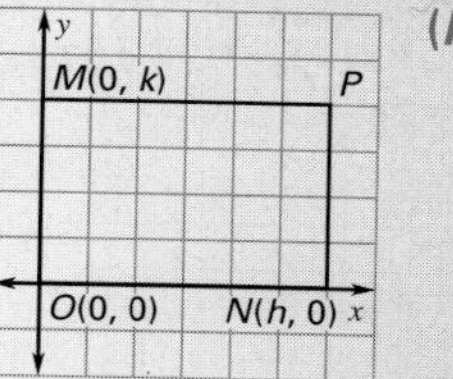

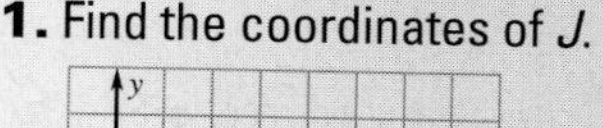

CHECKPOINT EXERCISES

For use after Examples 4 and 5:

1. Find the coordinates of J.

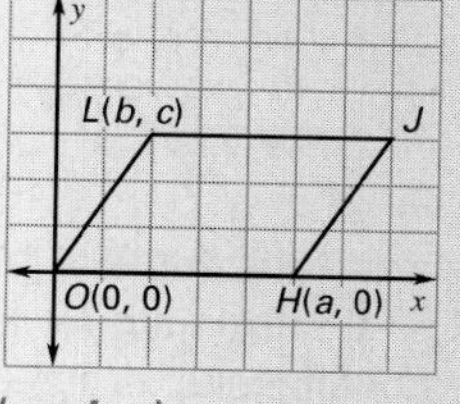

$(a + b, c)$

EXTRA EXAMPLE 6

Prove: $\triangle OPQ \cong \triangle QRO$

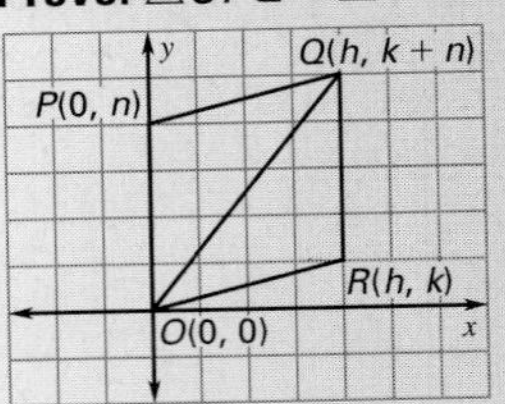

$OR = \sqrt{h^2 + k^2}$; $PQ = \sqrt{h^2 + k^2}$; $OP = n$; $QR = n$. By the Reflexive Property, $\overline{OQ} \cong \overline{OQ}$, so by SSS, $\triangle OPQ \cong \triangle QRO$

CHECKPOINT EXERCISES

For use after Example 6:

1. Given: Coordinates of figure *ABCD*
Prove: $\triangle ABC \cong \triangle CDA$.

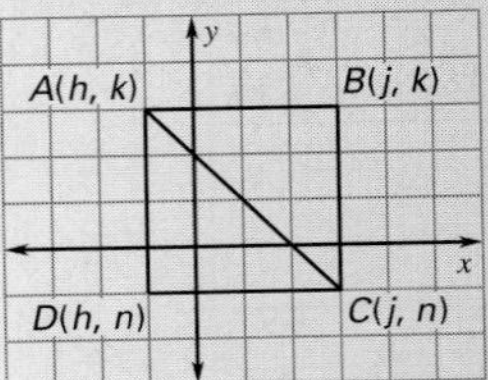

$AB = \sqrt{(j-h)^2}$; $CD = \sqrt{(j-h)^2}$; $AD = \sqrt{(k-n)^2}$; $BC = \sqrt{(k-n)^2}$; By the Reflexive Property of Congruence, $\overline{AC} \cong \overline{AC}$, so by the SSS Congruence Postulate, $\triangle ABC \cong \triangle CDA$.

FOCUS ON VOCABULARY

A proof uses coordinates in a plane to prove conclusions. What kind of proof is this? **coordinate proof**

CLOSURE QUESTION

How is a coordinate proof different from a two-column proof?
Sample answer: **A coordinate proof uses equations and specific points or coordinates. A two-column proof uses statements involving angles and line segments.**

DAILY PUZZLER

The hypotenuse of a right triangle in the coordinate plane extends from the origin to $(3a, 6b)$. One leg is parallel to the y-axis and the other is along the x-axis. What is the area of the triangle? **$9ab$**

Proof

EXAMPLE 6 *Writing a Coordinate Proof*

GIVEN ▶ Coordinates of figure *OTUV*

PROVE ▶ $\triangle OTU \cong \triangle UVO$

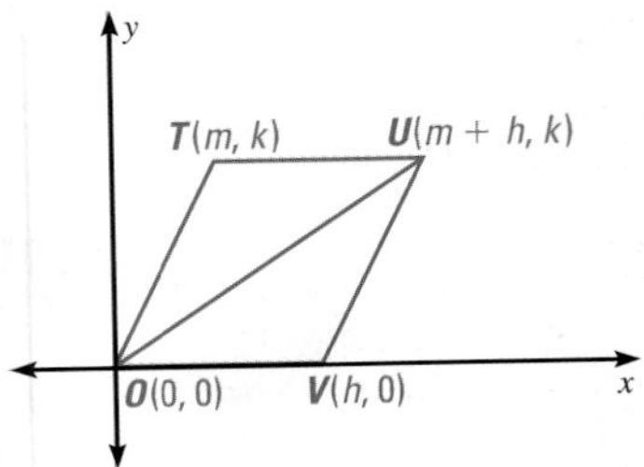

SOLUTION

COORDINATE PROOF Segments $\overline{OV}$ and $\overline{UT}$ have the same length.

$$OV = \sqrt{(h-0)^2 + (0-0)^2} = h$$

$$UT = \sqrt{(m+h-m)^2 + (k-k)^2} = h$$

Horizontal segments $\overline{UT}$ and $\overline{OV}$ each have a slope of 0, which implies that they are parallel. Segment $\overline{OU}$ intersects $\overline{UT}$ and $\overline{OV}$ to form congruent alternate interior angles $\angle TUO$ and $\angle VOU$. Because $\overline{OU} \cong \overline{OU}$, you can apply the SAS Congruence Postulate to conclude that $\triangle OTU \cong \triangle UVO$.

GUIDED PRACTICE

Vocabulary Check ✓

1. Prior to this section, you have studied two-column proofs, paragraph proofs, and flow proofs. How is a *coordinate proof* different from these other types of proof? How is it the same? **See margin.**

Concept Check ✓

2. Two different ways to place the same right triangle in a coordinate plane are shown. Which placement is more convenient for finding the side lengths? Explain your thinking. Then sketch a third placement that also makes it convenient to find the side lengths.
The first; each vertex has at least one coordinate that is 0; See margin for sketch.

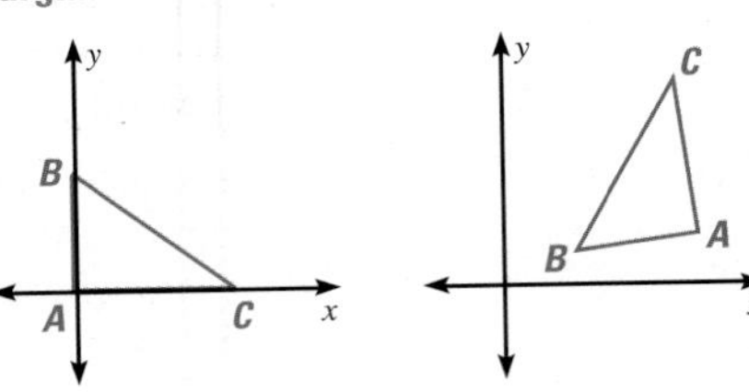

1. ***Sample answer:*** **Coordinate proof involves placing geometric figures in a coordinate plane; all the methods involve providing a logical argument that shows that the given information leads to that which is to be proved.**

Skill Check ✓

3. A right triangle with legs of 7 units and 4 units has one vertex at (0, 0) and another at (0, 7). Give possible coordinates of the third vertex.
(4, 0), (4, 7), (−4, 7), (−4, 0)

DEVELOPING PROOF **Describe a plan for the proof.**

4. **GIVEN** ▶ $\overrightarrow{GJ}$ bisects $\angle OGH$.
PROVE ▶ $\triangle GJO \cong \triangle GJH$

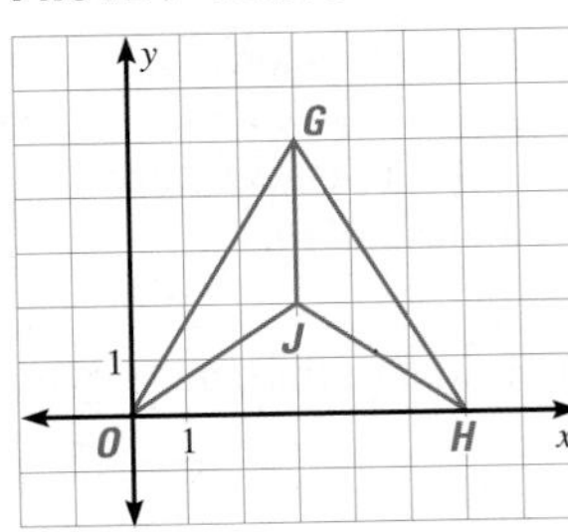

5. **GIVEN** ▶ Coordinates of vertices of $\triangle ABC$
PROVE ▶ $\triangle ABC$ is isosceles.

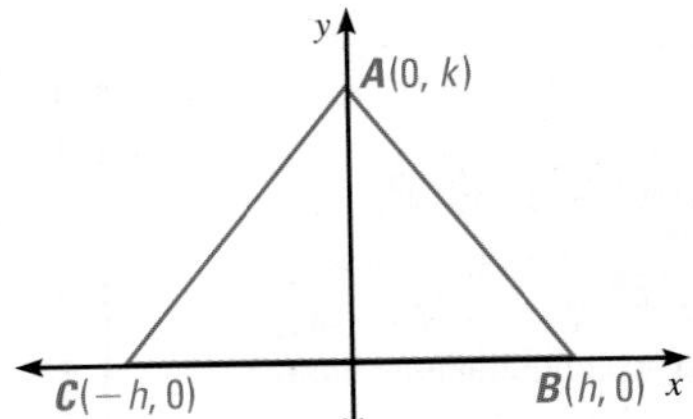

4. Use the Distance Formula to show $\overline{OG} \cong \overline{HG}$. Then show that, since $\overline{GJ}$ bisects $\angle OGH$, $\angle OGJ \cong \angle HGJ$ and that $\overline{GJ} \cong \overline{GJ}$ by the Reflexive Property of Congruence. Then $\triangle GJO \cong \triangle GJH$ by the SAS Congruence Postulate.

5. Use the Distance Formula to show that $\overline{AB} \cong \overline{AC}$.

Practice and Applications

STUDENT HELP

Extra Practice to help you master skills is on p. 810.

PLACING FIGURES IN A COORDINATE PLANE Place the figure in a coordinate plane. Label the vertices and give the coordinates of each vertex. 6–8. See margin.

6. A 5-unit by 8-unit rectangle with one vertex at (0, 0)
7. An 8-unit by 6-unit rectangle with one vertex at (0, −4)
8. A square with side length s and one vertex at $(s, 0)$

CHOOSING A GOOD PLACEMENT Place the figure in a coordinate plane. Label the vertices and give the coordinates of each vertex. Explain the advantages of your placement. 9–11. See margin for figures; good placements should include vertices for which at least one coordinate is 0.

9. A right triangle with legs of 3 units and 8 units
10. An isosceles right triangle with legs of 20 units
11. A rectangle with length h and width k

FINDING AND USING COORDINATES In the diagram, $\triangle ABC$ is isosceles. Its base is 60 units and its height is 50 units.

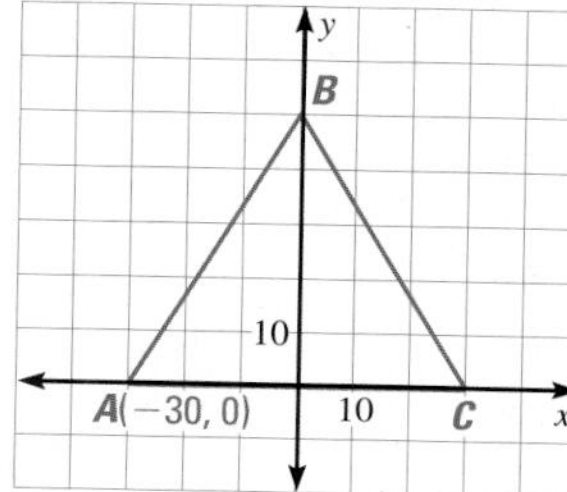

12. Give the coordinates of points B and C. B(0, 50), C(30, 0)
13. Find the length of a leg of $\triangle ABC$. Round your answer to the nearest hundredth. 58.31

USING THE DISTANCE FORMULA Place the figure in a coordinate plane and find the given information.

14. A right triangle with legs of 7 and 9 units; find the length of the hypotenuse. $\sqrt{130}$
15. A rectangle with length 5 units and width 4 units; find the length of a diagonal. $\sqrt{41}$
16. An isosceles right triangle with legs of 3 units; find the length of the hypotenuse. $3\sqrt{2}$
17. A 3-unit by 3-unit square; find the length of a diagonal. $3\sqrt{2}$

USING THE MIDPOINT FORMULA Use the given information and diagram to find the coordinates of H.

18. $\triangle FOH \cong \triangle FJH$ (40, 40)

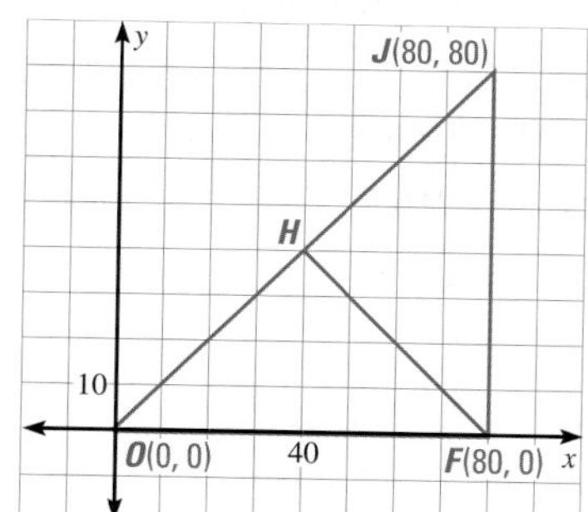

19. $\triangle OCH \cong \triangle HNM$ (45, 35)

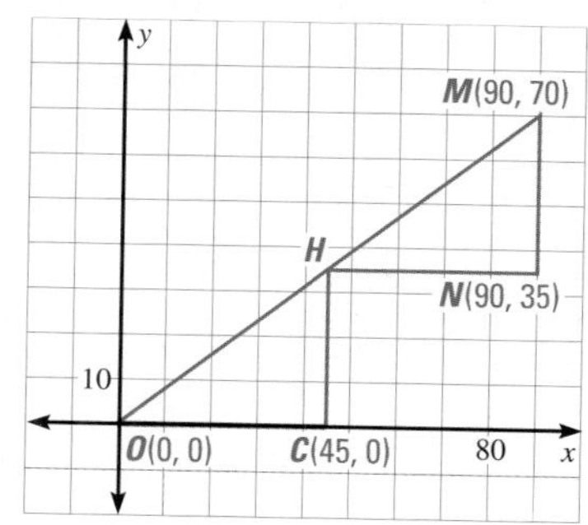

STUDENT HELP

HOMEWORK HELP
Example 1: Exs. 6–11
Example 2: Exs. 12–17
Example 3: Exs. 18, 19
Example 4: Exs. 20, 21
Example 5: Exs. 22–25
Example 6: Exs. 26, 27

3 APPLY

Assignment Guide

BASIC
Day 1: p. 247 Exs. 6–19
Day 2: pp. 248–250 Exs. 20–27, 32, 33, 35–43, Quiz 3 Exs. 1–3

AVERAGE
Day 1: p. 247 Exs. 6–19
Day 2: pp. 248–250 Exs. 20–28, 32, 33, 35–43, Quiz 3 Exs. 1–3

ADVANCED
Day 1: p. 247 Exs. 6–19
Day 2: pp. 248–250 Exs. 20–28, 32–43, Quiz 3 Exs. 1–3

BLOCK SCHEDULE
pp. 247–250 Exs. 6–28, 32, 33, 35–43, Quiz 3 Exs. 1–3

Exercise Levels

Level A: *Easier*
6–8

Level B: *More Difficult*
9–33

Level C: *Most Difficult*
34

✓ Homework Check

To quickly check student understanding of key concepts, go over the following exercises: Exs. 6, 10, 13, 16, 18, 20, 24, 26. See also the Daily Homework Quiz:

- Blackline Master (*Chapter 5 Resource Book,* p. 11)
- Transparency (p. 33)

2, 6–11. See Additional Answers beginning on page AA1.

! COMMON ERROR

EXERCISES 22–25 Students often have difficulty using variables as coordinates. Suggest that students try replacing variables with numbers to help in their understanding, and then repeat the problem with variables.

20. Use the Distance Formula to show that $\overline{OR} \cong \overline{OT}$. Then show that since $\angle R \cong \angle T$ by the Base Angles Theorem and $\angle OSR \cong \angle OST$ (Right Angle Congruence Theorem), $\triangle OSR \cong \triangle OST$ (AAS Congruence Theorem). Then $\angle ROS \cong \angle TOS$ and $\overrightarrow{OS}$ bisects $\angle TOR$.

21. Show that, since $\overline{HJ}$ and $\overline{OF}$ both have slope 0, they are parallel, so that alternate interior angles $\angle H$ and $\angle F$ are congruent. $\overline{HG} \cong \overline{FG}$ by the definition of midpoint. Then use the Distance Formula to show that $\overline{HJ} \cong \overline{OF}$ so that $\triangle GHJ \cong \triangle GFO$ by the SAS Congruence Postulate.

26. Since $OP = 2h$ and $OM = 2h$, $\overline{OP} \cong \overline{OM}$. According to the Midpoint Formula, N is the midpoint of $\overline{PM}$, so $\overline{PN} \cong \overline{MN}$. By the Reflexive Property of Congruence, $\overline{ON} \cong \overline{ON}$. Then $\triangle NPO \cong \triangle NMO$ by the SSS Congruence Postulate.

27. Since $OC = \sqrt{h^2 + k^2}$ and $EC = \sqrt{h^2 + k^2}$, $\overline{OC} \cong \overline{EC}$ and since $BC = k$ and $DC = k$, $\overline{BC} \cong \overline{DC}$. Then since vertical angles $\angle OCB$ and $\angle ECD$ are congruent, $\triangle OBC \cong \triangle EDC$ by the SAS Congruence Postulate.

DEVELOPING PROOF **Write a plan for a proof.**

20. GIVEN ▶ $\overline{OS} \perp \overline{RT}$

PROVE ▶ $\overrightarrow{OS}$ bisects $\angle TOR$.

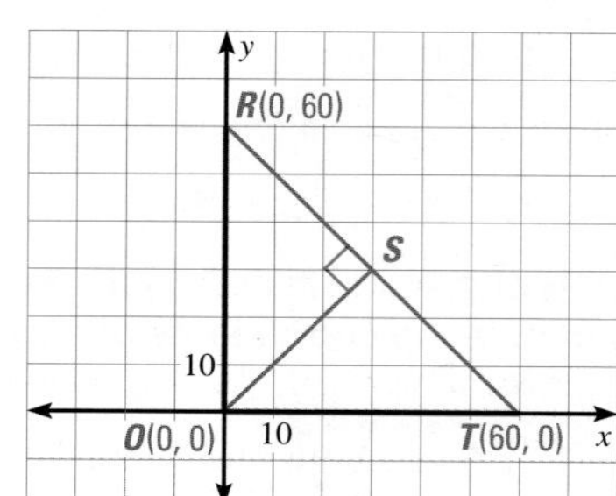

21. GIVEN ▶ G is the midpoint of $\overline{HF}$.

PROVE ▶ $\triangle GHJ \cong \triangle GFO$

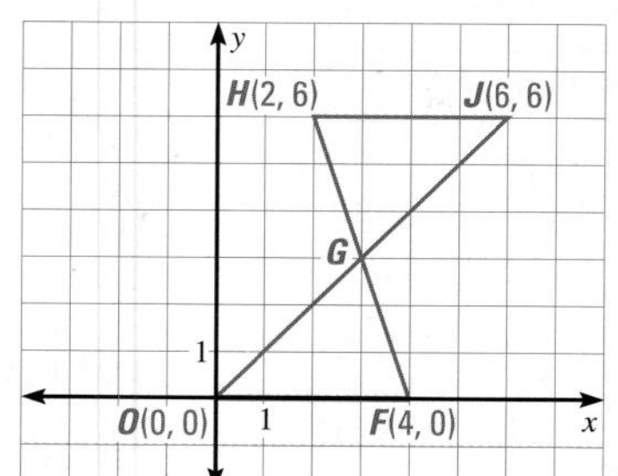

USING VARIABLES AS COORDINATES **Find the coordinates of any unlabeled points. Then find the requested information.**

22. Find MP. $M(0, k)$, $N(h, k)$, $P(h, 0)$; $\sqrt{h^2 + k^2}$

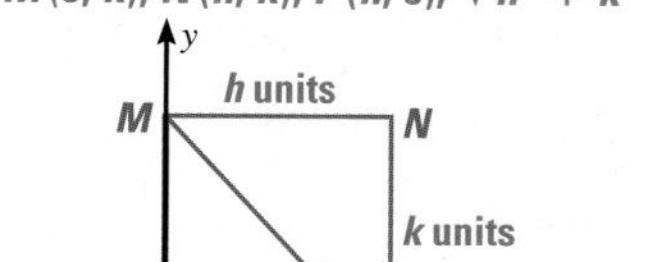

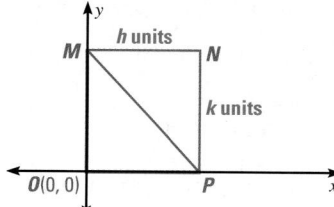

23. Find OE. $F(2h, 0)$, $E(2h, h)$; $h\sqrt{5}$

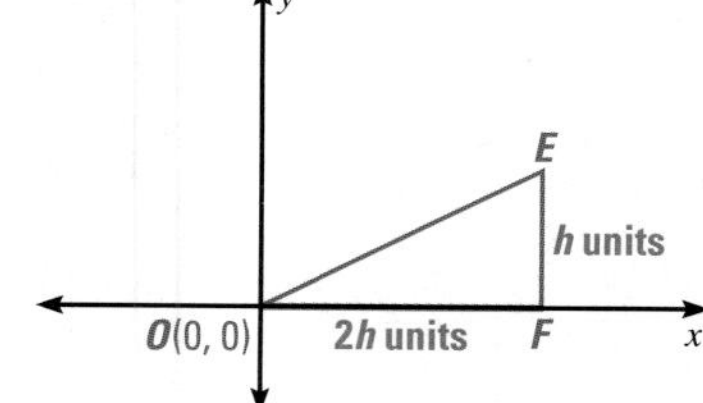

24. Find ON and MN. $N(h, k)$; $ON = MN = \sqrt{h^2 + k^2}$

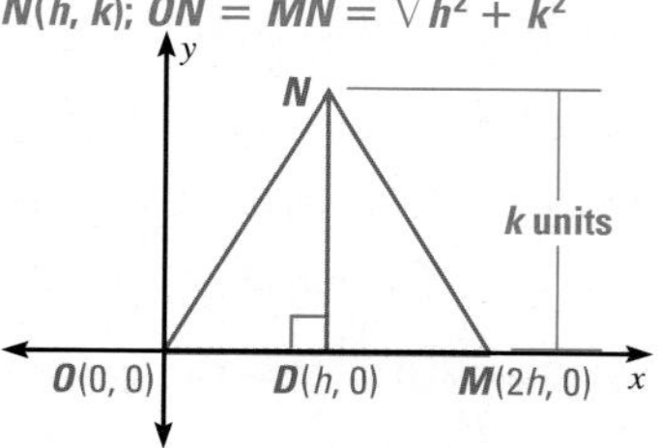

25. Find OT. $O(0, 0)$, $R(k, k)$, $S(k, 2k)$, $T(2k, 2k)$, $U(k, 0)$; $2k\sqrt{2}$

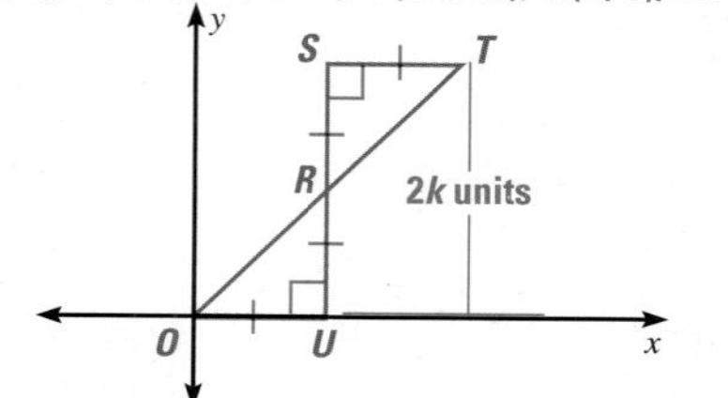

COORDINATE PROOF **Write a coordinate proof.** 26, 27. See margin.

26. GIVEN ▶ Coordinates of $\triangle NPO$ and $\triangle NMO$

PROVE ▶ $\triangle NPO \cong \triangle NMO$

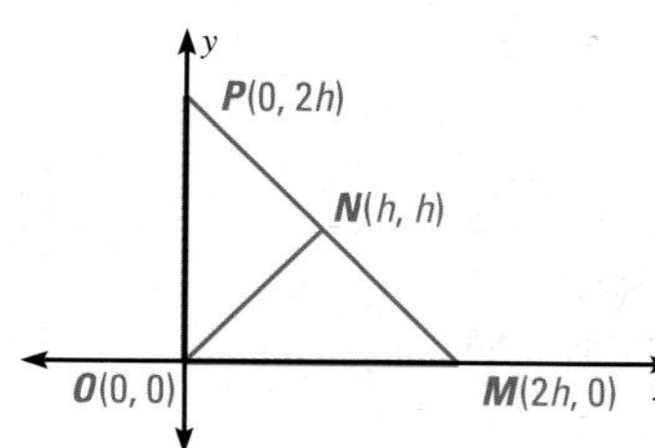

27. GIVEN ▶ Coordinates of $\triangle OBC$ and $\triangle EDC$

PROVE ▶ $\triangle OBC \cong \triangle EDC$

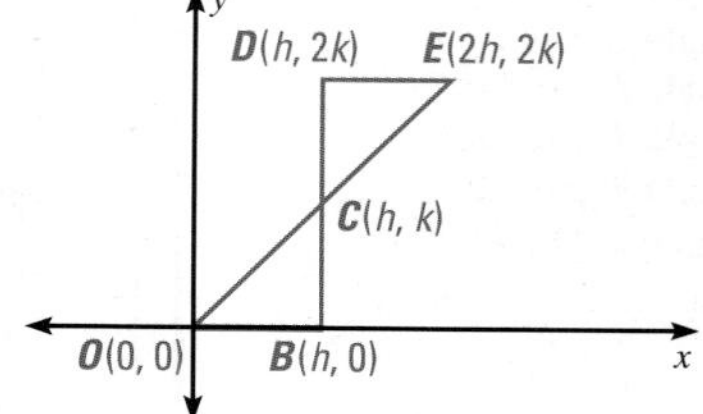

30. They are equal; they remain equal; they remain equal.

31. The triangle in Exercise 5 has vertices which can be used to describe $\triangle ABC$. Point A is on the y-axis and points B and C are on the x-axis, equidistant from the origin. The proof shows that any such triangle is isosceles.

34. $AD = 2\sqrt{h^2 + k^2}$ and $AE = 2\sqrt{h^2 + k^2}$ so $\overline{AD} \cong \overline{AE}$. H is the midpoint of $\overline{AD}$, so $AH = \frac{1}{2}AD = \sqrt{h^2 + k^2}$. Similarly, G is the midpoint of $\overline{AE}$, so $AG = \sqrt{h^2 + k^2}$. Then $\overline{AH} \cong \overline{AG}$. By the Reflexive Property of Congruence, $\angle HAG \cong \angle HAG$. Then $\triangle HAE \cong \triangle GAD$ by the SAS Congruence Postulate. Since $\overline{DG}$ and $\overline{EH}$ are corresponding parts of congruent triangles, $\overline{DG} \cong \overline{EH}$.

28. **PLANT STAND** You buy a tall, three-legged plant stand. When you place a plant on the stand, the stand appears to be unstable under the weight of the plant. The diagram at the right shows a coordinate plane superimposed on one pair of the plant stand's legs. The legs are extended to form $\triangle OBC$. Is $\triangle OBC$ an isosceles triangle? Explain why the plant stand may be unstable. See margin.

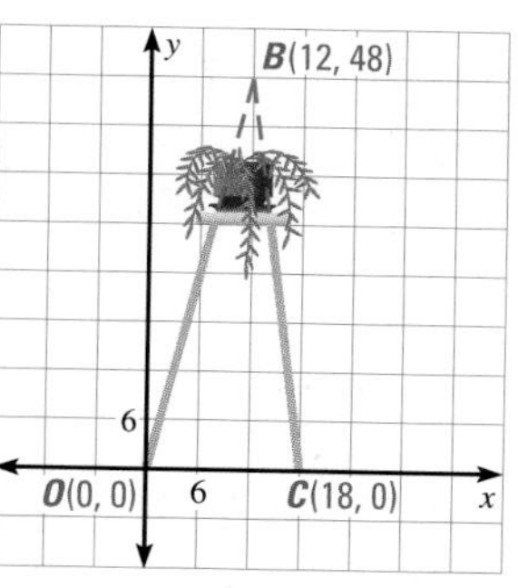

28. No; $OB = 12\sqrt{17} \approx 49.5$ and $BC = 6\sqrt{65} \approx 48.4$. $\overline{OB}$ is longer so the plant stand is leaning to the right.

TECHNOLOGY Use geometry software for Exercises 29–31. Follow the steps below to construct $\triangle ABC$.

- Create a pair of axes. Construct point A on the y-axis so that the y-coordinate is positive. Construct point B on the x-axis.
- Construct a circle with a center at the origin that contains point B. Label the other point where the circle intersects the x-axis C.
- Connect points A, B, and C to form $\triangle ABC$. Find the coordinates of each vertex.

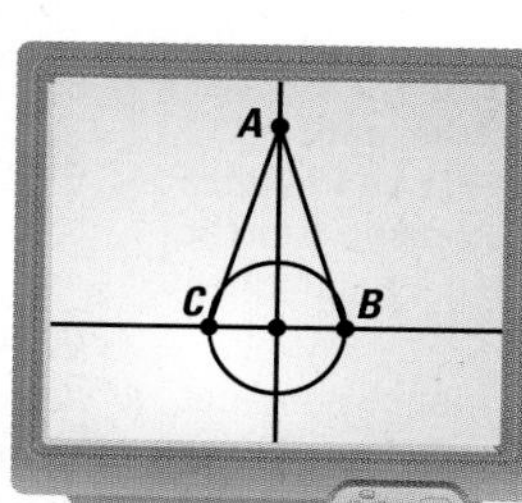

29. What type of triangle does $\triangle ABC$ appear to be? Does your answer change if you drag point A? If you drag point B? isosceles; no; no

30. Measure and compare AB and AC. What happens to these lengths as you drag point A? What happens as you drag point B? See margin.

31. Look back at the proof described in Exercise 5 on page 246. How does that proof help explain your answers to Exercises 29 and 30? See margin.

Test Preparation

32. **MULTIPLE CHOICE** A square with side length 4 has one vertex at (0, 2). Which of the points below *could* be a vertex of the square? A

Ⓐ $(0, -2)$ Ⓑ $(2, -2)$ Ⓒ $(0, 0)$ Ⓓ $(2, 2)$

33. **MULTIPLE CHOICE** A rectangle with side lengths $2h$ and k has one vertex at $(-h, k)$. Which of the points below *could not* be a vertex of the rectangle? A

Ⓐ $(0, k)$ Ⓑ $(-h, 0)$ Ⓒ (h, k) Ⓓ $(h, 0)$

★ Challenge

34. **COORDINATE PROOF** Use the diagram and the given information to write a proof. See margin.

GIVEN ▶ Coordinates of $\triangle DEA$, H is the midpoint of $\overline{DA}$, G is the midpoint of $\overline{EA}$.

PROVE ▶ $\overline{DG} \cong \overline{EH}$

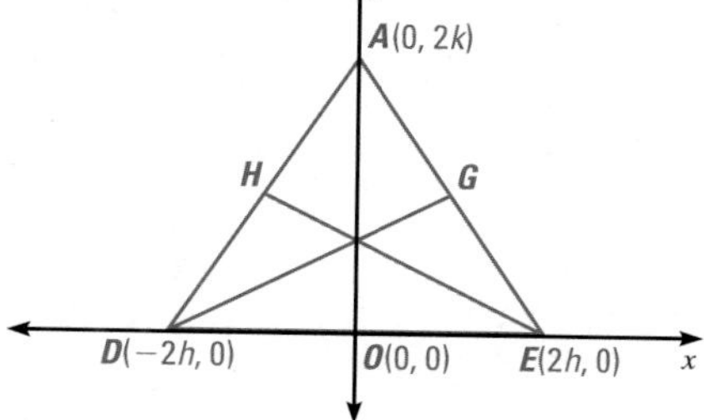

EXTRA CHALLENGE
www.mcdougallittell.com

ADDITIONAL PRACTICE AND RETEACHING

For Lesson 4.7:

- Practice Levels A, B, and C (*Chapter 4 Resource Book,* p. 102)
- Reteaching with Practice (*Chapter 4 Resource Book,* p. 105)
- See Lesson 4.7 of the *Personal Student Tutor*

For more Mixed Review:

- Search the *Test and Practice Generator* for key words or specific lessons.

4 ASSESS

DAILY HOMEWORK QUIZ

Transparency Available

Place the figure in a coordinate plane and find the given information.

1. An isosceles right triangle with legs of 4 units; find the length of the hypotenuse. $4\sqrt{2}$
2. A rectangle with length 8 units and width 3 units; find the length of the diagonal. $\sqrt{73}$

Find the coordinates of any unlabeled points. Then find the requested information.

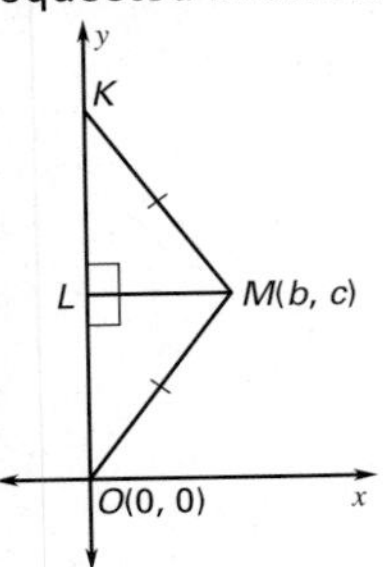

3. Find *KM*. $K(0, 2c)$, $L(0, c)$, $KM = \sqrt{b^2 + c^2}$

EXTRA CHALLENGE NOTE

Challenge problems for Lesson 4.7 are available in **blackline** format in the *Chapter 4 Resource Book,* p. 109 and at **www.mcdougallittell.com.**

ADDITIONAL TEST PREPARATION

1. **WRITING** How would you prove that a triangle is isosceles using a coordinate proof? **Place the triangle on a coordinate plane, use the Distance Formula to find the lengths of the three sides, and show that two of the sides have the same length.**

MIXED REVIEW

USING ALGEBRA In the diagram, $\overrightarrow{GR}$ bisects $\angle CGF$. (Review 1.5 for 5.1)

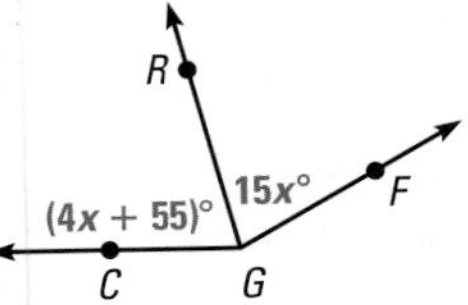

35. Find the value of x. 5

36. Find $m\angle CGF$. 150°

PERPENDICULAR LINES AND SEGMENT BISECTORS Use the diagram to determine whether the statement is *true* or *false*. (Review 1.5, 2.2 for 5.1)

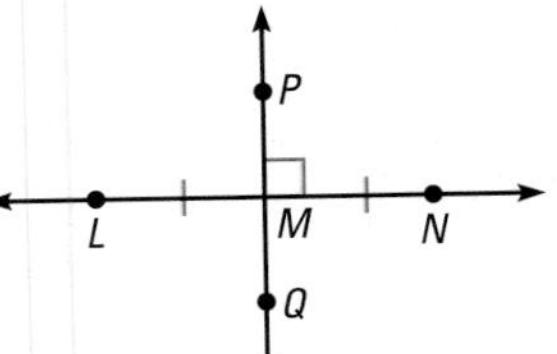

37. $\overleftrightarrow{PQ}$ is perpendicular to $\overleftrightarrow{LN}$. true

38. Points L, Q, and N are collinear. false

39. $\overleftrightarrow{PQ}$ bisects $\overline{LN}$. true

40. $\angle LMQ$ and $\angle PMN$ are supplementary. true

WRITING STATEMENTS Let p be "two triangles are congruent" and let q be "the corresponding angles of the triangles are congruent." Write the symbolic statement in words. Decide whether the statement is true. (Review 2.3) 42, 43. See margin.

41. $p \rightarrow q$ If two triangles are congruent, then the corresponding angles of the triangles are congruent; true.

42. $q \rightarrow p$

43. $\sim p \rightarrow \sim q$

42. If the corresponding angles of two triangles are congruent, then the triangles are congruent; false.

43. If two triangles are not congruent, then the corresponding angles of the triangles are not congruent; false.

QUIZ 3

Self-Test for Lessons 4.5–4.7

PROOF Write a two-column proof or a paragraph proof. (Lessons 4.5 and 4.6) 1, 2. See margin.

1. **GIVEN** ▶ $\overline{DF} \cong \overline{DG}$, $\overline{ED} \cong \overline{HD}$

   PROVE ▶ $\angle EFD \cong \angle HGD$

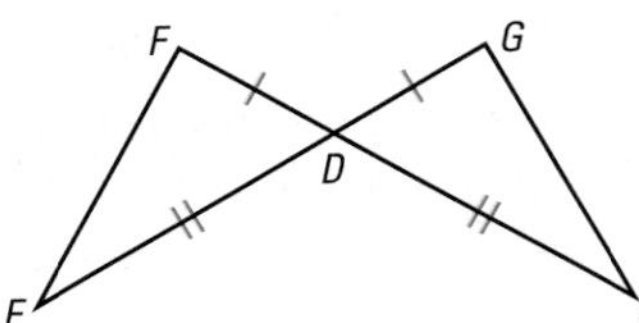

2. **GIVEN** ▶ $\overline{ST} \cong \overline{UT} \cong \overline{VU}$, $\overline{SU} \parallel \overline{TV}$

   PROVE ▶ $\triangle STU \cong \triangle TUV$

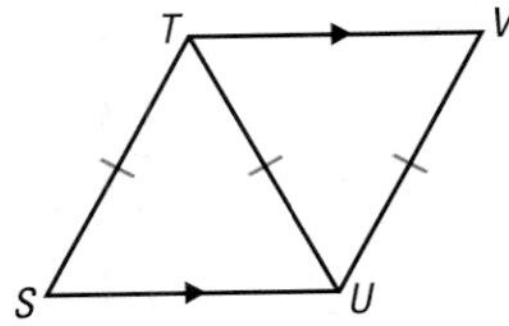

3. **COORDINATE PROOF** Write a plan for a coordinate proof. (Lesson 4.7)

   GIVEN ▶ Coordinates of vertices of $\triangle OPM$ and $\triangle ONM$

   PROVE ▶ $\triangle OPM$ and $\triangle ONM$ are congruent isosceles triangles.

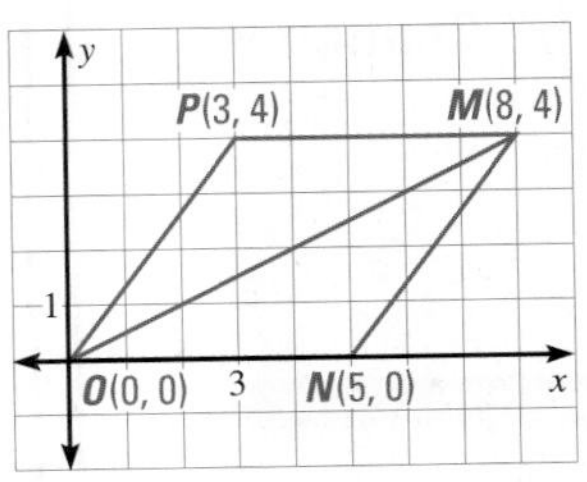

3. Use the Distance Formula to show that *OP, PM, NM,* and *ON* are all equal, so that $\overline{OP} \cong \overline{PM} \cong \overline{NM} \cong \overline{ON}$. Since $\overline{OM} \cong \overline{OM}$ by the Reflexive Property of Congruence, $\triangle OPM \cong \triangle ONM$ by the SSS Congruence Postulate and both triangles are isosceles by definition.

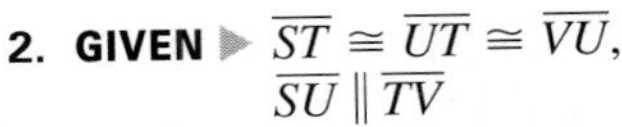

CHAPTER 4

Chapter Summary

WHAT did you learn?	*WHY did you learn it?*
Classify triangles by their sides and angles. **(4.1)**	Lay the foundation for work with triangles.
Find angle measures in triangles. **(4.1)**	Find the angle measures in triangular objects, such as a wing deflector. **(p. 200)**
Identify congruent figures and corresponding parts. **(4.2)**	Analyze patterns, such as those made by the folds of an origami kite. **(p. 208)**
Prove that triangles are congruent	
• using corresponding sides and angles. **(4.2)**	Learn to work with congruent triangles.
• using the SSS and SAS Congruence Postulates. **(4.3)**	Explain why triangles are used in structural supports for buildings. **(p. 215)**
• using the ASA Congruence Postulate and the AAS Congruence Theorem. **(4.4)**	Understand how properties of triangles are applied in surveying. **(p. 225)**
• using the HL Congruence Theorem. **(4.6)**	Prove that right triangles are congruent.
• using coordinate geometry. **(4.7)**	Plan and write coordinate proofs.
Use congruent triangles to plan and write proofs. **(4.5)**	Prove that triangular parts of the framework of a bridge are congruent. **(p. 234)**
Prove that constructions are valid. **(4.5)**	Develop understanding of geometric constructions.
Use properties of isosceles, equilateral, and right triangles. **(4.6)**	Apply a law from physics, the law of reflection. **(p. 241)**

How does Chapter 4 fit into the BIGGER PICTURE of geometry?

The ways you have learned to prove triangles are congruent will be used to prove theorems about *polygons*, as well as in other topics throughout the book. Knowing the properties of triangles will help you solve real-life problems in fields such as art, architecture, and engineering.

STUDY STRATEGY

How did you use your list of theorems?

The list of theorems you made, following the **Study Strategy** on page 192, may resemble this one.

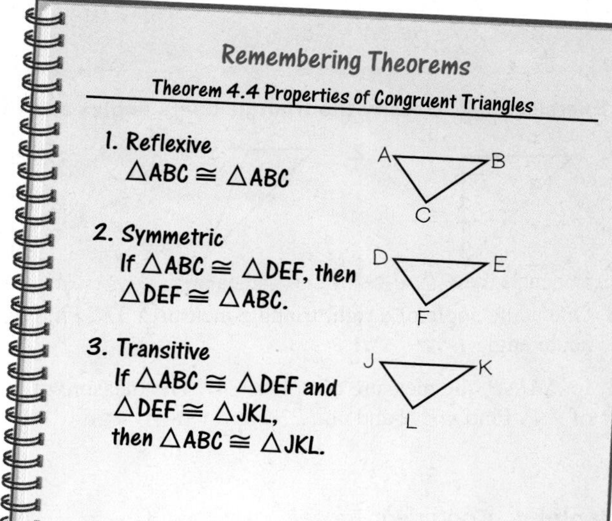

Remembering Theorems
Theorem 4.4 Properties of Congruent Triangles
1. Reflexive
△ABC ≅ △ABC
A
B
C
2. Symmetric
If △ABC ≅ △DEF, then
△DEF ≅ △ABC.
D
E
F
3. Transitive
If △ABC ≅ △DEF and
△DEF ≅ △JKL,
then △ABC ≅ △JKL.
J
K
L

1. Statements (Reasons)
   1. $\overline{DF} \cong \overline{DG}$, $\overline{ED} \cong \overline{HD}$ (Given)
   2. $\angle EDF \cong \angle HDG$ (Vertical Angles Theorem)
   3. $\triangle EDF \cong \triangle HDG$ (SAS Congruence Postulate)
   4. $\angle EFD \cong \angle HGD$ (Corresp. parts of ≅ △s are ≅.)
2. Statements (Reasons)
   1. $\overline{ST} \cong \overline{UT} \cong \overline{VU}$, $\overline{SU} \parallel \overline{TV}$ (Given)
   2. $\angle S \cong \angle SUT$, $\angle UTV \cong \angle V$ (Base Angles Theorem)
   3. $\angle SUT \cong \angle UTV$ (Alternate Interior Angles Theorem)
   4. $\angle S \cong \angle SUT \cong \angle UTV \cong \angle V$ (Transitive Property of Congruence)
   5. $\triangle STU \cong \triangle TUV$ (AAS Congruence Theorem)

ADDITIONAL RESOURCES

The following resources are available to help review the material in this chapter.

- Chapter Review Games and Activities (*Chapter 4 Resource Book,* p. 110)
- *Geometry in Motion video*
- *Personal Student Tutor*
- Cumulative Review, Chs. 1–4 (*Chapter 4 Resource Book,* p. 122)

252

CHAPTER 4

Chapter Review

VOCABULARY

- equilateral triangle, p. 194
- isosceles triangle, p. 194
- scalene triangle, p. 194
- acute triangle, p. 194
- equiangular triangle, p. 194
- right triangle, p. 194
- obtuse triangle, p. 194
- vertex of a triangle, p. 195
- adjacent sides of a triangle, p. 195
- legs of a right triangle, p. 195
- hypotenuse, p. 195
- legs of an isosceles triangle, p. 195
- base of an isosceles triangle, p. 195
- interior angle, p. 196
- exterior angle, p. 196
- corollary, p. 197
- congruent, p. 202
- corresponding angles, p. 202
- corresponding sides, p. 202
- base angles, p. 236
- vertex angle, p. 236
- coordinate proof, p. 243

4.1 TRIANGLES AND ANGLES

Examples on pp. 194–197

EXAMPLES You can classify triangles by their sides and by their angles.

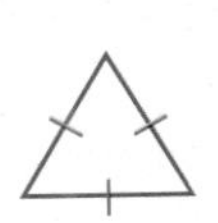
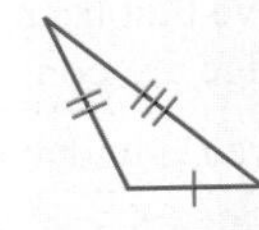
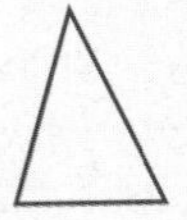
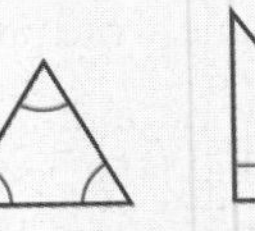
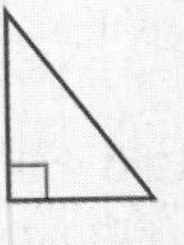

equilateral isosceles scalene acute equiangular right obtuse

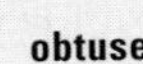

Note that an equilateral triangle is also isosceles and acute.

You can apply the Triangle Sum Theorem to find unknown angle measures in triangles.

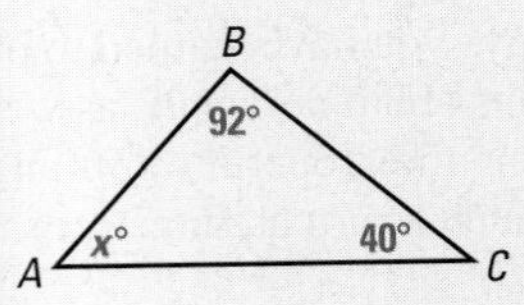

$m\angle A + m\angle B + m\angle C = 180°$ **Triangle Sum Theorem**

$x° + 92° + 40° = 180°$ **Substitute.**

$x + 132 = 180$ **Simplify.**

$x = 48$ **Subtract 132 from each side.**

$m\angle A = 48°$

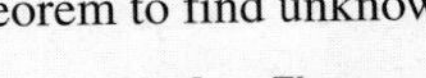

In Exercises 1–4, classify the triangle by its angles and by its sides.

1. 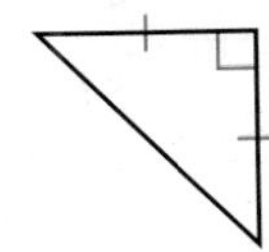 isosceles right
2. 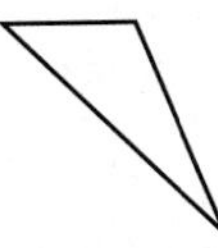 obtuse scalene
3. 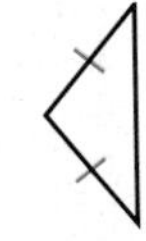 obtuse isosceles
4. 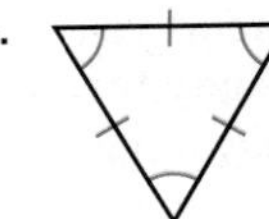 equiangular (or acute); equilate(ral) (or isosceles)
5. One acute angle of a right triangle measures 37°. Find the measure of the other acute angle. 53°
6. In $\triangle MNP$, the measure of $\angle M$ is 24°. The measure of $\angle N$ is five times the measure of $\angle P$. Find $m\angle N$ and $m\angle P$. $m\angle N = 130°$, $m\angle P = 26°$

4.2 CONGRUENCE AND TRIANGLES

Examples on pp. 202–205

EXAMPLE When two figures are congruent, their corresponding sides and corresponding angles are congruent. In the diagram, $\triangle ABC \cong \triangle XYZ$.

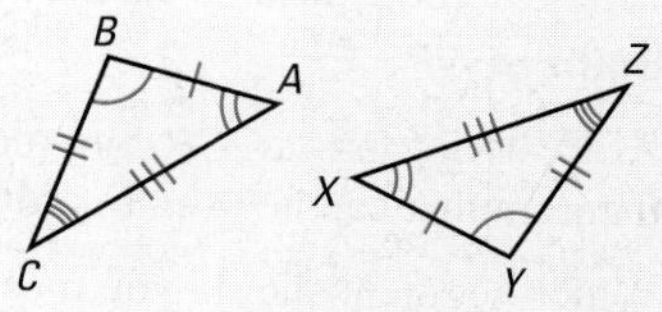

Use the diagram above of $\triangle ABC$ and $\triangle XYZ$.

7. Identify the congruent corresponding parts of the triangles. $\angle A$ and $\angle X$, $\angle B$ and $\angle Y$, $\angle C$ and $\angle Z$, $\overline{AB}$ and $\overline{XY}$, $\overline{BC}$ and $\overline{YZ}$, $\overline{AC}$ and $\overline{XZ}$

8. Given $m\angle A = 48°$ and $m\angle Z = 37°$, find $m\angle Y$. 95°

4.3 & 4.4 PROVING TRIANGLES ARE CONGRUENT: SSS, SAS, ASA, AND AAS

Examples on pp. 212–215, 220–222

EXAMPLES You can prove triangles are congruent using congruence postulates and theorems.

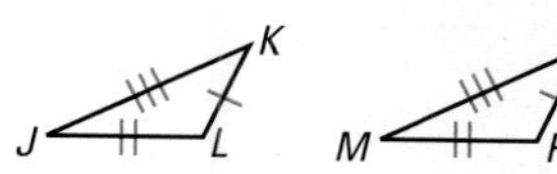

$\overline{JK} \cong \overline{MN}$, $\overline{KL} \cong \overline{NP}$, $\overline{JL} \cong \overline{MP}$, so $\triangle JKL \cong \triangle MNP$ by the SSS Congruence Postulate.

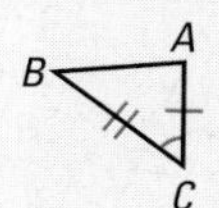

$\overline{DE} \cong \overline{AC}$, $\angle E \cong \angle C$, and $\overline{EF} \cong \overline{CB}$, so $\triangle DEF \cong \triangle ACB$ by the SAS Congruence Postulate.

Decide whether it is possible to prove that the triangles are congruent. If it is possible, tell which postulate or theorem you would use. Explain your reasoning. 9–11. See margin.

9.

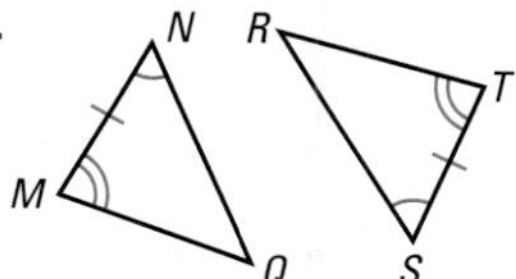

10.

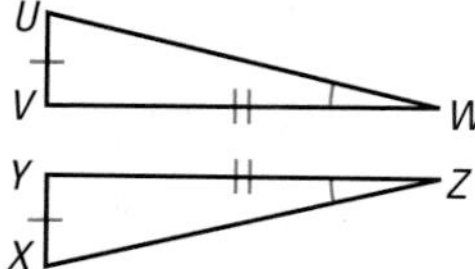

11.

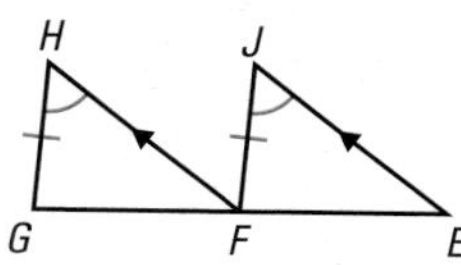

4.5 USING CONGRUENT TRIANGLES

Examples on pp. 229–231

EXAMPLE You can use congruent triangles to write proofs.

GIVEN ▶ $\overline{PQ} \cong \overline{PS}$, $\overline{RQ} \cong \overline{RS}$

PROVE ▶ $\overline{PR} \perp \overline{QS}$

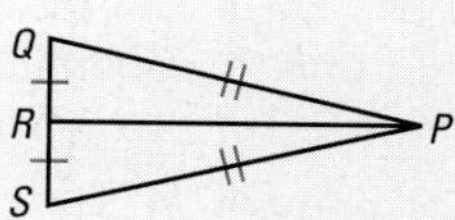

Plan for Proof Use the SSS Congruence Postulate to show that $\triangle PRQ \cong \triangle PRS$. Because corresponding parts of congruent triangles are congruent, you can conclude that $\angle PRQ \cong \angle PRS$. These angles form a linear pair, so $\overline{PR} \perp \overline{QS}$.

9. Yes; ASA Congruence Postulate; two pairs of corresponding angles are congruent and the corresponding included sides are congruent.
10. No; two pairs of corresponding sides are congruent and two nonincluded angles are congruent; that is insufficient to prove triangle congruence.
11. Yes; AAS Congruence Theorem; because $\overline{HF} \parallel \overline{JE}$, $\angle HFG \cong \angle E$ (Corresponding Angles Postulate) so two pairs of corresponding angles are congruent and two nonincluded sides are congruent.

4.5 continued

SURVEYING **You want to determine the width of a river beside a camp. You place stakes so that $\overline{MN} \perp \overline{NP}$, $\overline{PQ} \perp \overline{NP}$, and C is the midpoint of $\overline{NP}$.**

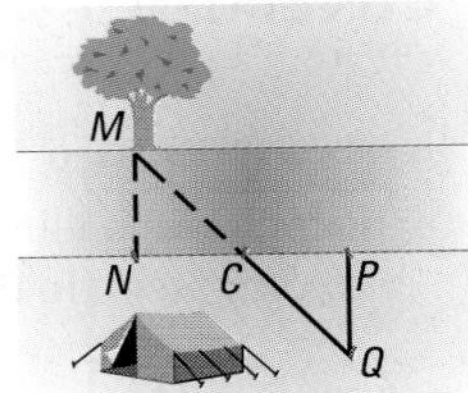

12. Are $\triangle MCN$ and $\triangle QCP$ congruent? If so, state the postulate or theorem that can be used to prove they are congruent.
Yes; AAS Congruence Theorem (or ASA Congruence Postulate)

13. Which segment should you measure to find the width of the river?
$\overline{PQ}$

4.6 ISOSCELES, EQUILATERAL, AND RIGHT TRIANGLES

Examples on pp. 236–238

EXAMPLE To find the value of x, notice that $\triangle ABC$ is an isosceles right triangle. By the Base Angles Theorem, $\angle B \cong \angle C$. Because $\angle B$ and $\angle C$ are complementary, their sum is $90°$. The measure of each must be $45°$. So $x = 45°$.

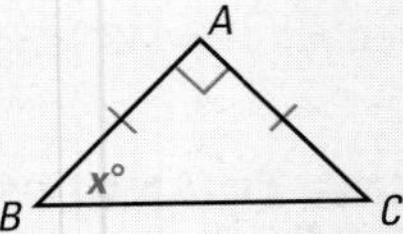

Find the value of *x*.

14.

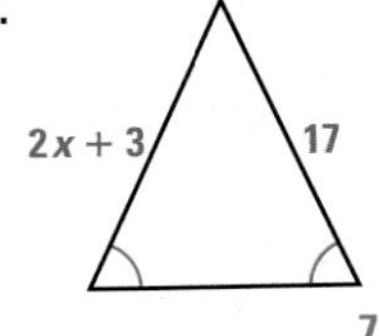

7

15.

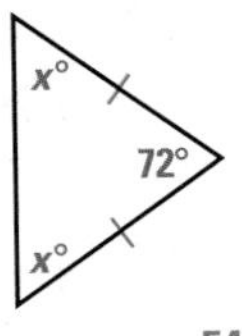

54

16.

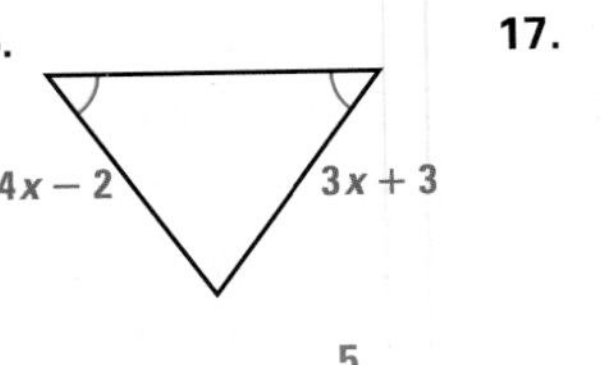

5

17. 35° x°

110

4.7 TRIANGLES AND COORDINATE PROOF

Examples on pp. 243–246

EXAMPLE You can use a coordinate proof to prove that $\triangle OPQ$ is isosceles. Use the Distance Formula to show that $\overline{OP} \cong \overline{QP}$.

$$OP = \sqrt{(2-0)^2 + (3-0)^2} = \sqrt{13}$$

$$QP = \sqrt{(2-4)^2 + (3-0)^2} = \sqrt{13}$$

Because $\overline{OP} \cong \overline{QP}$, $\triangle OPQ$ is isosceles.

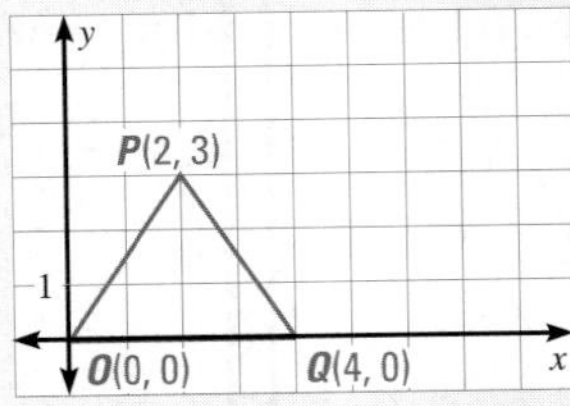

18. Write a coordinate proof.

GIVEN ▶ Coordinates of vertices of $\triangle OAC$ and $\triangle BCA$

PROVE ▶ $\triangle OAC \cong \triangle BCA$

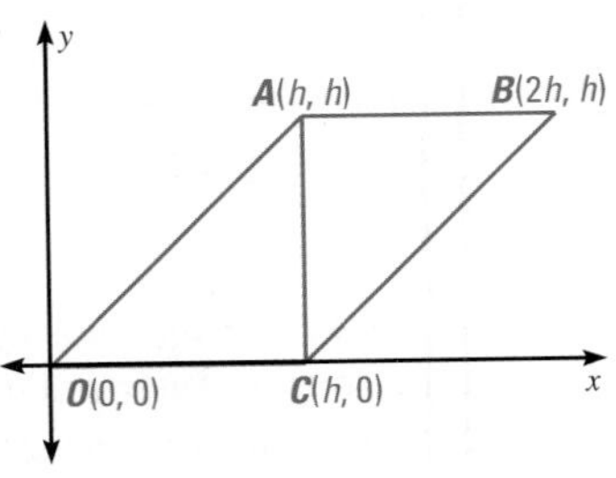

Since both $\overline{AB}$ and $\overline{OC}$ have slope 0, $\overline{AB} \parallel \overline{OC}$. Then $\angle OCA \cong \angle BAC$ by the Alternate Interior Angles Theorem. Since $OC = h$ and $AB = h$, $\overline{OC} \cong \overline{AB}$. Also, $\overline{AC} \cong \overline{AC}$ by the Reflexive Property of Congruence, so $\triangle OAC \cong \triangle BCA$ by the SAS Congruence Postulate.

Chapter Test

In Exercises 1–6, identify all triangles in the figure that fit the given description.

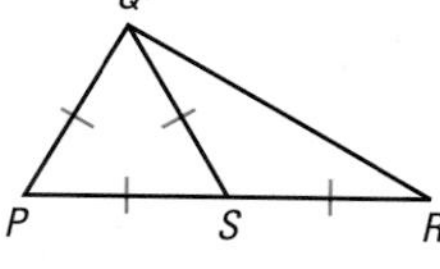

1. isosceles $\triangle QPS$, $\triangle QSR$ **2.** equilateral $\triangle QPS$ **3.** scalene $\triangle QPR$

4. acute $\triangle QPS$ **5.** obtuse $\triangle QSR$ **6.** right $\triangle QPR$

7. In $\triangle ABC$, the measure of $\angle A$ is $116°$. The measure of $\angle B$ is three times the measure of $\angle C$. Find $m\angle B$ and $m\angle C$. $m\angle B = 48°$, $m\angle C = 16°$

Decide whether it is possible to prove that the triangles are congruent. If it is possible, tell which congruence postulate or theorem you would use. Explain your reasoning. 8–13. See margin.

8.

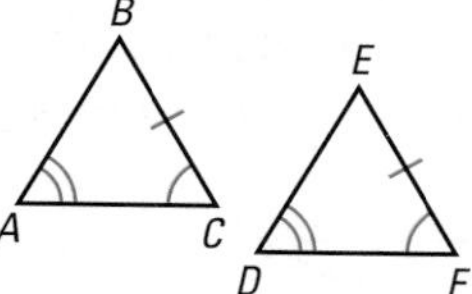

9.

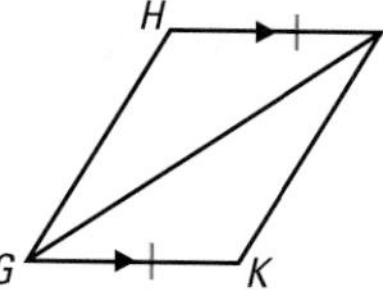

10.

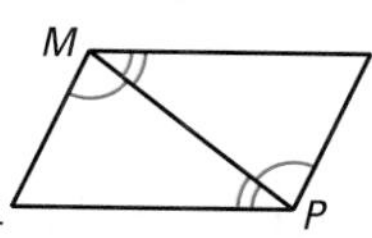

11.

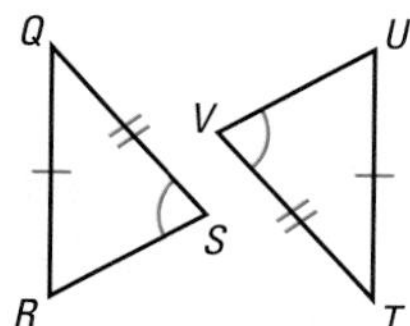

12.

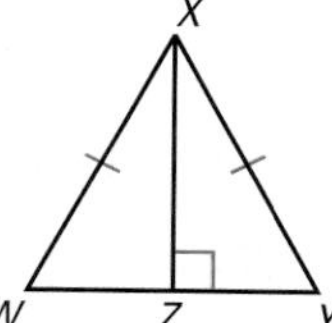

13.

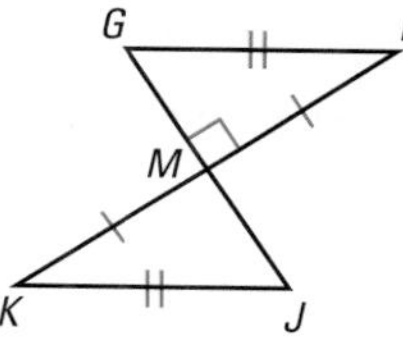

Find the value of *x*.

14. 55

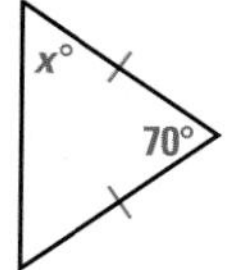

15. 5

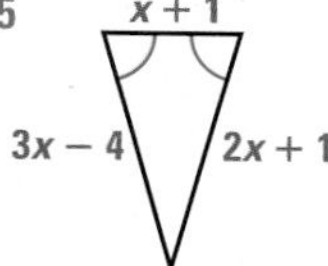

16. 50

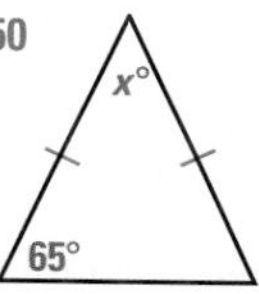

PROOF Write a two-column proof or a paragraph proof. 17, 18. See margin.

17. GIVEN ▶ $\overline{BD} \cong \overline{EC}$, $\overline{AC} \cong \overline{AD}$

PROVE ▶ $\overline{AB} \cong \overline{AE}$

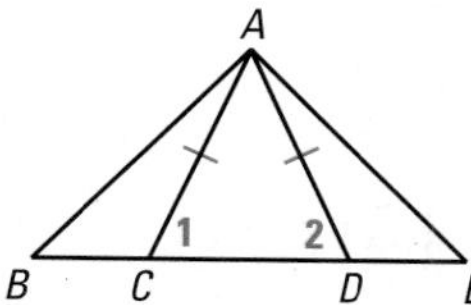

18. GIVEN ▶ $\overline{XY} \parallel \overline{WZ}$, $\overline{XZ} \parallel \overline{WY}$

PROVE ▶ $\angle X \cong \angle W$

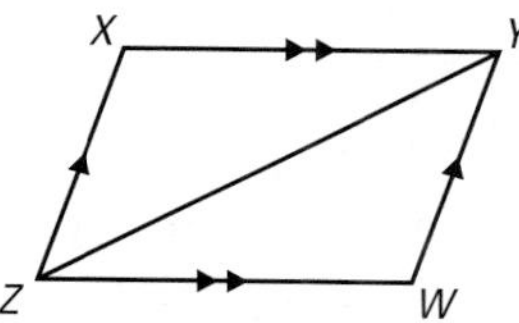

Place the figure in a coordinate plane and find the requested information.

19. A right triangle with leg lengths of 4 units and 7 units; find the length of the hypotenuse. $\sqrt{65}$

20. A square with side length s and vertices at $(0, 0)$ and (s, s); find the coordinates of the midpoint of a diagonal. $\frac{s}{2}, \frac{s}{2}$

ADDITIONAL RESOURCES

- ***Chapter 4 Resource Book***
  Chapter Test (3 levels) (p. 111)
  SAT/ACT Chapter Test (p. 117)
  Alternative Assessment (p. 118)
- ***Test and Practice Generator***

8. Yes; AAS Congruence Theorem; two pairs of corresponding angles are congruent, and one pair of corresponding nonincluded sides are congruent.

9. Yes; SAS Congruence Postulate; since $\overline{HJ} \parallel \overline{GK}$, $\angle HJG \cong \angle KGJ$, so two pairs of corresponding sides and the corresponding included angles are congruent.

10. Yes; ASA Congruence Postulate; two pairs of corresponding angles and the corresponding included sides are congruent.

11. No; two pairs of corresponding sides are congruent, and one pair of corresponding nonincluded angles are congruent; that is insufficient to show triangle congruence.

12. Yes; HL Theorem; by the Linear Pair Postulate, $\angle XZW$ is a right angle, so both triangles are right triangles. The hypotenuses are congruent and one pair of legs ($\overline{XZ}$ and $\overline{XZ}$) are congruent.

13. Yes; HL Theorem; by the Vertical Angles Theorem, $\angle JMK$ is a right angle, so both triangles are right triangles. The hypotenuses and one pair of corresponding legs ($\overline{MH}$ and $\overline{MK}$) are congruent.

17. Statements (Reasons)

1. $\overline{BD} \cong \overline{EC}$, $\overline{AC} \cong \overline{AD}$ (Given)
2. $\angle 1 \cong \angle 2$ (Base Angles Theorem)
3. $\triangle ABD \cong \triangle AEC$ (SAS Congruence Postulate)
4. $\overline{AB} \cong \overline{AE}$ (Corresp. parts of $\cong$ △ are $\cong$.)

18. Since it is given that $\overline{XY} \parallel \overline{WZ}$ and $\overline{XZ} \parallel \overline{WY}$, $\angle XYZ \cong \angle WZY$ and $\angle XZY \cong \angle WYZ$ by the Alternate Interior Angles Theorem. By the Reflexive Property of Congruence, $\overline{YZ} \cong \overline{YZ}$, so $\triangle XYZ \cong \triangle WZY$ by the ASA Congruence Postulate. Thus $\angle X \cong \angle W$ since corresponding parts of congruent triangles are congruent.

ADDITIONAL RESOURCES

- ***Chapter 4 Resource Book***
  Chapter Test (3 levels) (p. 111)
  SAT/ACT Chapter Test (p. 117)
  Alternative Assessment (p. 118)
- ***Test and Practice Generator***

10. Because $\overline{RU} \perp \overline{QS}$, $\angle RUS$ and $\angle RUQ$ are right angles, and $\triangle RUS$ and $\triangle RUQ$ are right triangles. It is given that $\overline{RQ} \cong \overline{RS}$. Also, $\overline{RU} \cong \overline{RU}$ by the Reflexive Property of Congruence. So $\triangle RUS \cong \triangle RUQ$ by the HL Congruence Theorem.
11. Because $\overline{QT} \perp \overline{PS}$, $\angle QTP$ and $\angle QTS$ are right angles. They are also congruent because all right angles are congruent. It is given that $\overline{PT} \cong \overline{ST}$, and $\overline{QT} \cong \overline{QT}$ by the Reflexive Property of Congruence. So, $\triangle QTP \cong \triangle QTS$ by the SAS Congruence Postulate.
12. In Exercise 10, it was proved that $\triangle RUQ \cong \triangle RUS$. You can use the HL Congruence Theorem to prove that $\triangle QTP$ is congruent to $\triangle RUS$. Then, by the Transitive Property of Congruence, $\triangle QTP \cong \triangle RUQ$. In Exercise 11, it was proved that $\triangle QTP \cong \triangle QTS$. By the Transitive Property of Congruence, $\triangle QTS$ is also congruent to $\triangle RUQ$ and $\triangle RUS$. Because corresponding parts of congruent triangles are congruent, $\angle QPT \cong \angle RQU$ and $\angle QST \cong \angle RSU$. It is given that $\overline{PQ} \cong \overline{QR}$. So, by the AAS Congruence Theorem, $\triangle PQS \cong \triangle QRS$.

CHAPTER 4

Chapter Standardized Test

TEST-TAKING STRATEGY Avoid spending too much time on one question. Skip questions that are too difficult for you, and spend no more than a few minutes on each question.

1. MULTIPLE CHOICE What is the measure of $\angle J$? C

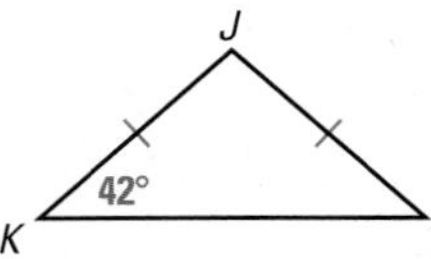

(A) 42°
(B) 90°
(C) 96°
(D) 138°
(E) cannot be determined

2. MULTIPLE CHOICE What is the measure of $\angle BCD$? D

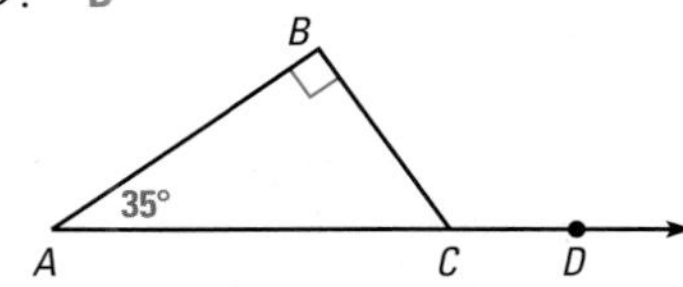

(A) 35°
(B) 55°
(C) 90°
(D) 125°
(E) cannot be determined

3. QUANTITATIVE COMPARISON Four congruent equilateral triangles form the figures below.

Column A	Column B
perimeter	perimeter

Choose the statement that is true. B

(A) The perimeter in column A is greater.
(B) The perimeter in column B is greater.
(C) The two perimeters are equal.
(D) The relationship cannot be determined from the given information.

4. MULTIPLE CHOICE Which postulate or theorem can be used to prove that $\triangle JML \cong \triangle LKJ$? B

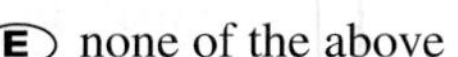

(A) SSS
(B) SAS
(C) ASA
(D) AAS
(E) none of the above

5. MULTIPLE CHOICE In figure $JKLM$, $\overline{JM} \parallel \overline{KL}$, $\overline{JK} \parallel \overline{ML}$, and N is the midpoint of $\overline{JL}$ and $\overline{MK}$. Which statement or statements can be proved to be true? B

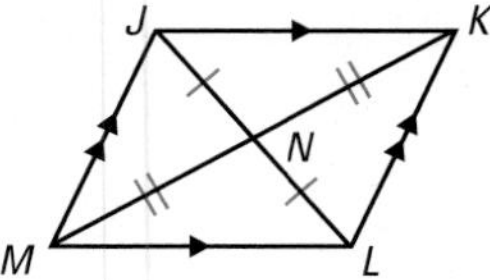

I. $\triangle JNM \cong \triangle LNK$ II. $\triangle JNK \cong \triangle LNM$

III. $\triangle JMK \cong \triangle JKL$

(A) I only (B) I and II only
(C) II and III only (D) I, II, and III
(E) None are true.

6. MULTIPLE CHOICE You are given the following information about $\triangle PQR$ and $\triangle XYZ$.

I. $\angle P \cong \angle X$ II. $\angle Q \cong \angle Y$

III. $\overline{PQ} \cong \overline{XY}$ IV. $\overline{QR} \cong \overline{YZ}$

Which combination *cannot* be used to prove that $\triangle PQR \cong \triangle XYZ$? C

(A) I, II, and III
(B) II, III, and IV
(C) I, III, and IV
(D) I, II, and IV
(E) All combinations can be used.

7. MULTIPLE CHOICE What is the value of x? B

(A) $\frac{3}{5}$ (B) 3
(C) 6 (D) 8
(E) 55

$2x + 5$, $x + 3$, $3x + 2$

8. **MULTIPLE CHOICE** You want to prove that $\overline{DB} \cong \overline{DF}$. As a first step, which pair of triangles would you prove congruent? **D**

Ⓐ $\triangle ADB$ and $\triangle GFD$

Ⓑ $\triangle ADB$ and $\triangle EDF$

Ⓒ $\triangle BDC$ and $\triangle FDG$

Ⓓ $\triangle ADC$ and $\triangle EDG$

Ⓔ $\triangle ABD$ and $\triangle EFD$

9. **MULTIPLE CHOICE** Use the diagram to determine which statement is true. **A**

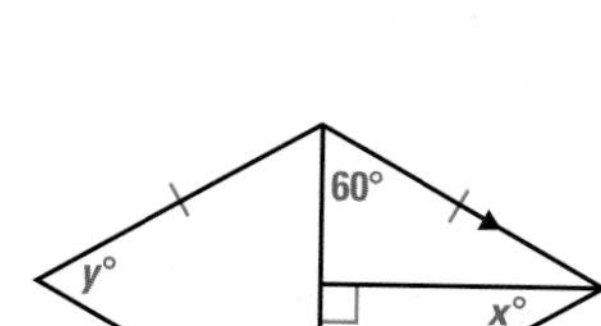

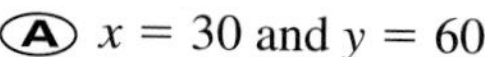

Ⓐ $x = 30$ and $y = 60$

Ⓑ $x = 60$ and $y = 60$

Ⓒ $x = 30$ and $y = 30$

Ⓓ $x = 60$ and $y = 30$

Ⓔ $x = 60$ and $y = 90$

MULTI-STEP PROBLEM In Exercises 10–13, use the diagram and the information below. **10–13. See margin.**

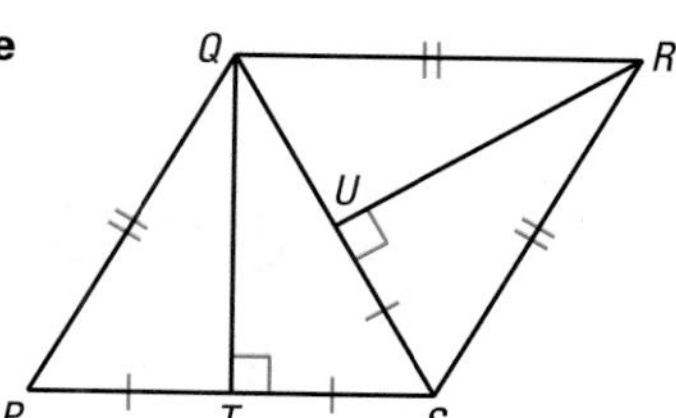

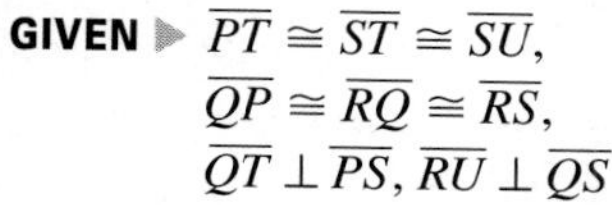

GIVEN ▶ $\overline{PT} \cong \overline{ST} \cong \overline{SU}$,
$\overline{QP} \cong \overline{RQ} \cong \overline{RS}$,
$\overline{QT} \perp \overline{PS}$, $\overline{RU} \perp \overline{QS}$

10. Show that $\triangle RUS \cong \triangle RUQ$.

11. Show that $\triangle QTP \cong \triangle QTS$.

12. Use your answers to Exercises 10 and 11 to show that $\triangle PQS \cong \triangle QRS$.

13. Classify $\triangle RQS$ and $\triangle PQS$, using the most specific names you can. Explain your answers.

MULTI-STEP PROBLEM In Exercises 14–19, use figure *ABCD*.

14. On graph paper, sketch figure $ABCD$. **Check drawing.**

15. Draw diagonal $\overline{AC}$. **Check drawing.**

16. Is $\triangle ABC \cong \triangle CDA$? Justify your answer. **See margin.**

17. What kind of triangles are $\triangle ABC$ and $\triangle CDA$? **isosceles**

18. Sketch diagonal $\overline{BD}$. What kind of triangles are $\triangle BCD$ and $\triangle DAB$? **isosceles**

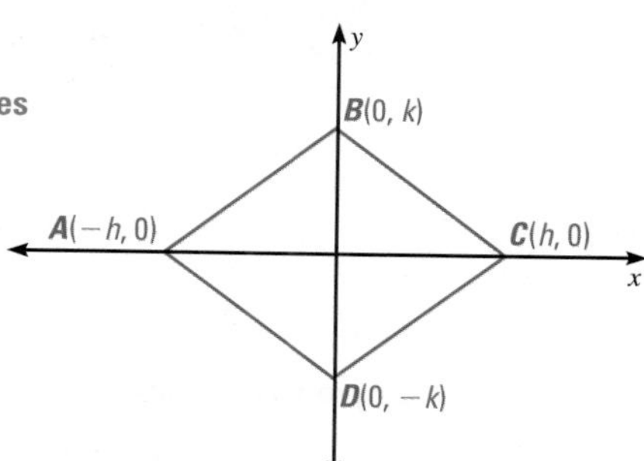

19. *Writing* A *rhombus* is a figure with four congruent sides. Figure $ABCD$ is an example of a rhombus. Can you *always* draw a diagonal in any given rhombus so that the two triangles formed are isosceles? Explain.
Yes; the triangles will always be isosceles because either diagonal will give you a pair of triangles each with two congruent sides.

13. Both triangles are equilateral equiangular triangles. In Exercise 11, it was proved that $\triangle QTP \cong \triangle QTS$. Because corresponding parts of congruent triangles are congruent, $\overline{QP} \cong \overline{QS}$. It is given that $\overline{QP} \cong \overline{RQ} \cong \overline{RS}$, so by the Transitive Property of Congruence, side $\overline{QS}$ is also congruent to sides $\overline{RQ}$ and $\overline{RS}$. Thus, all three sides of $\triangle QRS$ are congruent, so $\triangle RQS$ is equilateral. It is also equiangular because all equilateral triangles are equiangular. In Exercise 12, it was proved that $\triangle PQS \cong \triangle QRS$. Therefore $\triangle PQS$ is also equilateral and equiangular.

16. Yes; *Sample answer:* By the Distance Formula $\overline{BC} \cong \overline{DA}$ and $\overline{AB} \cong \overline{CD}$. By the Reflexive Property of Congruence, $\overline{AC} \cong \overline{AC}$, so $\triangle ABC \cong \triangle CDA$ by the SSS Congruence Postulate.

EXTRA EXAMPLE 1
Find the distance between the points (3, –9) and (–1, –4). $\sqrt{41}$

EXTRA EXAMPLE 2
Simplify $6m^2p - 3m^2 - 7m^2p$.
$-m^2p - 3m^2$

EXTRA EXAMPLE 3
Solve $-5x + 11 = 9x - 3$. 1

CHECKPOINT EXERCISES

For use after Example 1:

1. Find the distance between (4, –1) and (–3, 1). $\sqrt{53}$

For use after Example 2:

2. Simplify $5xy - 3x^2 + 3xy + y^2$.
$-3x^2 + 8xy + y^2$

For use after Example 3:

3. Solve $5 - 2d = 5d - 9$. 2

CHAPTER 4

Algebra Review

EXAMPLE 1 *Distance Formula*

Find the distance between the points (−4, 3) and (−7, 8).

$$d = \sqrt{(x_2 - x_1)^2 + (y_2 - y_1)^2}$$
$$= \sqrt{(-7 - (-4))^2 + (8 - 3)^2}$$
$$= \sqrt{(-3)^2 + (5)^2}$$
$$= \sqrt{34}$$

EXERCISES

Find the distance between the points.

1. (3, 6), (0, −2) $\sqrt{73}$
2. (5, −2), (−6, 5) $\sqrt{170}$
3. (−3, 4), (1, 4) 4
4. (−6, −6), (−3, −2) 5
5. (8, −2), (−3, −6) $\sqrt{137}$
6. (−8, 5), (−1, 1) $\sqrt{65}$

EXAMPLE 2 *Combining Like Terms*

Simplify.

$8x^2 + 16xy - 3x^2 + 3xy - 3x$

$8x^2 - 3x^2 + 16xy + 3xy - 3x$ **Group like terms.**

$5x^2 - 3x + 19xy$ **Simplify.**

EXERCISES

Simplify.

7. $6x + 11y - 4x + y$ $2x + 12y$
8. $-5m + 3q + 4m - q$ $-m + 2q$
9. $-3p - 4t - 5t - 2p$ $-5p - 9t$
10. $9x - 22y + 18x - 3y$ $27x - 25y$
11. $3x^2y - 5xy^2 + 6x^2y$ $9x^2y - 5xy^2$
12. $5x^2 + 2xy - 7x^2 + xy$ $-2x^2 + 3xy$

EXAMPLE 3 *Solving Equations with Variables on Both Sides*

Solve.

$6a - 12 = 5a + 9$

$a - 12 = 9$ **Subtract 5*a* from each side.**

$a = 21$ **Add 12 to each side.**

EXERCISES

Solve the equation.

13. $3x + 5 = 2x + 11$ 6
14. $-14 + 3a = 10 - a$ 6
15. $8m + 1 = 7m - 9$ −10
16. $y - 18 = 6y + 7$ −5
17. $2s + 1 = 7s + 1$ 0
18. $3a - 12 = -6a - 12$ 0
19. $-2t + 10 = -t$ 10
20. $11q - 6 = 3q + 8q$ No solution
21. $-7x + 7 = 2x - 11$ 2

EXAMPLE 4 Solving Inequalities

Solve.

a. $5x - 4 \geq 4x + 6$ **b.** $10 - 7x < 24$

When you multiply or divide each side of an inequality by a *negative* number, you must *reverse* the inequality symbol to maintain a true statement.

a. $5x - 4 \geq 4x + 6$
$x - 4 \geq 6$
$x \geq 10$

b. $10 - 7x < 24$
$-7x < 14$
$x > -2$

EXERCISES

Solve the inequality.

22. $-x + 2 > 7$ $x < -5$

23. $c - 18 < 10$ $c < 28$

24. $-5 + m < 21$ $m < 26$

25. $x - 5 < 4$ $x < 9$

26. $z + 6 > -2$ $z > -8$

27. $-3x + 4 \leq -5$ $x \geq 3$

28. $5 - 2x < -3x - 6$ $x < -11$

29. $-m + 3 \geq -4m + 6$ $m \geq 1$

30. $2b + 4 > -3b + 7$ $b > \frac{3}{5}$

31. $13 - 6x > 10 + 4x$ $x < \frac{3}{10}$

32. $4z + 8 \leq 12$ $z \leq 1$

33. $14 - 5t \geq 28$ $t \leq -\frac{14}{5}$

34. $6 - 3r < 24$ $r > -6$

35. $16 - 12x \leq 28$ $x \geq -1$

36. $-3x + 11 \geq 32$ $x \leq -7$

EXAMPLE 5 Absolute Value Equations and Inequalities

Solve.

a. $|x + 8| = 4$
$x + 8 = 4$ *or*
$x + 8 = -4$
$x = -4$ *or* $x = -12$

b. $|x - 5| \geq 20$
$x - 5 \geq 20$ *or*
$x - 5 \leq -20$
$x \geq 25$ *or* $x \leq -15$

c. $|x + 1| < 3$
$x + 1 < 3$ *and*
$x + 1 > -3$
$x < 2$ *and* $x > -4$
$-4 < x < 2$

EXERCISES

Solve. 37–66. See margin.

37. $|x + 5| = 12$ **38.** $|x - 2| = 10$ **39.** $|5 - x| = 3$

40. $|1 - x| = 6$ **41.** $|x + 3| = 17$ **42.** $|-5x + 2| = 7$

43. $|2x - 3| = 11$ **44.** $|7x + 8| = 20$ **45.** $|-4x + 5| = 13$

46. $|3x + 8| = 4$ **47.** $|x + 13| \geq 23$ **48.** $|x - 6| > 8$

49. $|x - 2| \leq 8$ **50.** $|15 - x| \geq 7$ **51.** $|16 - x| < 4$

52. $|6x - 4| < 8$ **53.** $|-2x + 4| \leq 10$ **54.** $|9x - 6| \leq 21$

55. $|11x - 11| \geq 33$ **56.** $|2x + 3| > 13$ **57.** $|10x + 20| < 40$

58. $|4x - 6| > 14$ **59.** $|x + 2| \geq 4$ **60.** $|5x - 9| < 14$

61. $|11x + 1| > 21$ **62.** $|-7x - 2| \leq -21$ **63.** $|3x - 2| > 10$

64. $|12x + 16| \leq 20$ **65.** $|5x + 8| \geq -32$ **66.** $7 + |x + 1| \leq 8$

EXTRA EXAMPLE 4

Solve.

a. $2x + 5 > 5x$ $x < \frac{5}{3}$

b. $21 \leq 3 - 6d$ $d \leq -3$

EXTRA EXAMPLE 5

Solve.

a. $|x - 4| = 6$ $x = 10$ or -2

b. $|2x + 1| > 9$ $x < -5$ or $x > 4$

c. $|x - 7| \leq 11$ $-4 \leq x \leq 18$

CHECKPOINT EXERCISES

For use after Example 4:

1. Solve $-4y - 6 > 4 + 9y$. $y < -\frac{10}{13}$

For use after Example 5:

2. Solve $|1 - 3t| \geq 4$. $t \leq -1$ or $t \geq \frac{5}{3}$

37. $x = 7$ or -17
38. $x = 12$ or -8
39. $x = 2$ or 8
40. $x = 7$ or -5
41. $x = 14$ or -20
42. $x = -1$ or $\frac{9}{5}$
43. $x = 7$ or -4
44. $x = \frac{12}{7}$ or -4
45. $x = -2$ or $\frac{9}{2}$
46. $x = -\frac{4}{3}$ or -4
47. $x \geq 10$ or $x \leq -36$
48. $x > 14$ or $x < -2$
49. $-6 \leq x \leq 10$
50. $x \leq 8$ or $x \geq 22$
51. $12 < x < 20$
52. $-\frac{2}{3} < x < 2$
53. $-3 \leq x \leq 7$
54. $-\frac{5}{3} \leq x \leq 3$
55. $x \leq -2$ or $x \geq 4$
56. $x < -8$ or $x > 5$
57. $-6 < x < 2$
58. $x < -2$ or $x > 5$
59. $x \leq -6$ or $x \geq 2$
60. $-1 < x < \frac{23}{5}$
61. $x < -2$ or $x > \frac{20}{11}$
62. No solution
63. $x < -\frac{8}{3}$ or $x > 4$
64. $-3 \leq x \leq \frac{1}{3}$
65. All real numbers
66. $-2 \leq x \leq 0$

CHAPTER 5

PLANNING THE CHAPTER

Properties of Triangles

GOALS

LESSON	GOALS	NCTM	ITED	SAT9 (TASK 1)	Terra-Nova	Local
5.1 *pp. 263–271*	CONCEPT ACTIVITY: 5.1 *Investigate perpendicular bisectors.* GOAL 1 Use properties of perpendicular bisectors. GOAL 2 Use properties of angle bisectors to identify equal distances.	1, 2, 3, 4, 8, 9, 10	MIM, MIGE		11, 13, 14, 16, 18, 49, 51	16
5.2 *pp. 272–278*	GOAL 1 Use properties of perpendicular bisectors of a triangle. GOAL 2 Use properties of angle bisectors of a triangle.	3, 4, 10	MIM, MIGE		13, 14	16, 21
5.3 *pp. 279–286*	GOAL 1 Use properties of medians of a triangle. GOAL 2 Use properties of altitudes of a triangle. TECHNOLOGY ACTIVITY: 5.3 *Explore concurrent lines using geometry software.*	3, 4, 10	MIM, MIGE		13, 14	16
5.4 *pp. 287–293*	GOAL 1 Identify the midsegments of a triangle. GOAL 2 Use properties of midsegments of a triangle.	3, 4, 10	MIM, MIGE		13, 14	17
5.5 *pp. 294–301*	TECHNOLOGY ACTIVITY: 5.5 *Decide which sides and angles are the smallest and largest in a triangle using geometry software.* GOAL 1 Use triangle measurements to decide which side is longest or which angle is largest. GOAL 2 Use the Triangle Inequality.	1, 2, 3, 4, 9, 10	MCWN, MIM, MIGE	2, 3, 26, 27	11, 13, 14, 16, 49, 51	6, 13
5.6 *pp. 302–308*	GOAL 1 Read and write an indirect proof. GOAL 2 Use the Hinge Theorem and its converse to compare side lengths and angle measures.	1, 2, 3, 4, 7, 8, 9, 10	MCWN, MIM, MIGE	2, 26, 27	11, 13, 14, 16, 17, 18, 49, 51	2, 6, 13

RESOURCES

Chapter Resource Booklets

Chapter Support

Tips for New Teachers	p. 1	Prerequisite Skills Review	p. 5
Parent Guide for Student Success	p. 3	Strategies for Reading Mathematics	p. 7

Lesson Support

Lesson Support	5.1	5.2	5.3	5.4	5.5	5.6
Lesson Plans (regular and block)	p. 9	p. 25	p. 37	p. 53	p. 67	p. 81
Warm-Up Exercises and Daily Quiz	p. 11	p. 27	p. 39	p. 55	p. 69	p. 83
Activity Support Masters						
Lesson Openers	p. 12	p. 28	p. 40	p. 56	p. 70	p. 84
Technology Activities & Keystrokes	p. 13		p. 41		p. 71	p. 85
Practice (3 levels)	p. 17	p. 29	p. 43	p. 58	p. 73	p. 88
Reteaching with Practice	p. 20	p. 32	p. 46	p. 61	p. 76	p. 91
Quick Catch-Up for Absent Students	p. 22	p. 34	p. 48	p. 63	p. 78	p. 93
Cooperative Learning Activities				p. 64		
Interdisciplinary Applications	p. 23		p. 49		p. 79	
Real-Life Applications		p. 35		p. 65		p. 94
Math & History Applications			p. 50			
Challenge: Skills and Applications	p. 24	p. 36	p. 51	p. 66	p. 80	p. 95

Review and Assessment

Quizzes	pp. 52, 96	Alternative Assessment with Math Journal	p. 105
Chapter Review Games and Activities	p. 97	Project with Rubric	p. 107
Chapter Test (3 levels)	pp. 98–103	Cumulative Review	p. 109
SAT/ACT Chapter Test	p. 104	Resource Book Answers	p. A1

Transparencies

	5.1	5.2	5.3	5.4	5.5	5.6
Warm-Up Exercises and Daily Quiz	p. 33	p. 34	p. 35	p. 36	p. 37	p. 38
Alternative Lesson Opener Transparencies	p. 28	p. 29	p. 30	p. 31	p. 32	p. 33
Examples/Standardized Test Practice	✓	✓	✓	✓	✓	✓
Answer Transparencies	✓	✓	✓	✓	✓	✓

Technology

- Electronic Teaching Tools
- Online Lesson Planner
- Internet Support
- Personal Student Tutor
- Test and Practice Generator
- Geometry in Motion video
- Electronic Lesson Presentations (Lesson 5.3)

Additional Resources

- Basic Skills Workbook: Diagnosis and Remediation
- Worked-Out Solution Key
- Resources in Spanish
- Standardized Test Practice Workbook
- Practice Workbook with Examples

Correlations to the California Curriculum

Correlations to California Standards
See Teacher's Edition pp. CA9–CA11

Correlations to SAT9
Task 1: See Teacher's Edition pp. CA12–CA14
Task 2: See Teacher's Edition pp. CA15–CA17

CHAPTER 5

Pacing the Chapter

Resource Key
- Student Edition
- Chapter 5 Resource Book
- Teacher's Edition

Regular Schedule

Day 1

5.1

Starting Options
- Prereq. Skills Review
- Strategies for Reading
- Homework Check
- Warm-Up or Daily Quiz

Teaching Options
- Motivating the Lesson
- Concept Activity
- Les. Opener (Activity)
- Technology Activity
- Examples 1–3
- Guided Practice Exs.

Apply/Homework
- See Assignment Guide.
- See the CRB: Practice, Reteach, Apply, Extend

Assessment Options
- Checkpoint Exercises

Day 2

5.1 *(cont.)*

Starting Options
- Homework Check

Teaching Options
- Examples 1–3
- Closure Question

Apply/Homework
- See Assignment Guide.
- See the CRB: Practice, Reteach, Apply, Extend

Assessment Options
- Checkpoint Exercises
- Daily Quiz (5.1)
- Stand. Test Practice

Day 3

5.2

Starting Options
- Homework Check
- Warm-Up or Daily Quiz

Teaching Options
- Les. Opener (Software)
- Examples 1–2
- Guided Practice Exs.

Apply/Homework
- See Assignment Guide.
- See the CRB: Practice, Reteach, Apply, Extend

Assessment Options
- Checkpoint Exercises

Day 4

5.2 *(cont.)*

Starting Options
- Homework Check

Teaching Options
- Examples 1–2
- Closure Question

Apply/Homework
- See Assignment Guide.
- See the CRB: Practice, Reteach, Apply, Extend

Assessment Options
- Checkpoint Exercises
- Daily Quiz (5.2)
- Stand. Test Practice

Day 5

5.3

Starting Options
- Homework Check
- Warm-Up or Daily Quiz

Teaching Options
- Motivating the Lesson
- Les. Opener (Application)
- Examples 1–3
- Guided Practice Exs.

Apply/Homework
- See Assignment Guide.
- See the CRB: Practice, Reteach, Apply, Extend

Assessment Options
- Checkpoint Exercises

Day 6

5.3 *(cont.)*

Starting Options
- Homework Check

Teaching Options
- Examples 1–3
- Technology Activity
- Closure Question

Apply/Homework
- See Assignment Guide.
- See the CRB: Practice, Reteach, Apply, Extend

Assessment Options
- Checkpoint Exercises
- Daily Quiz (5.3)
- Stand. Test Practice
- Quiz (5.1–5.3)

Day 9

5.5 *(cont.)*

Starting Options
- Homework Check

Teaching Options
- Example 4
- Technology Activity
- Closure Question
- Guided Practice Ex. 5

Apply/Homework
- See Assignment Guide.
- See the CRB: Practice, Reteach, Apply, Extend

Assessment Options
- Checkpoint Exercises, p. 297
- Daily Quiz (5.5)
- Stand. Test Practice

Day 10

5.6

Starting Options
- Homework Check
- Warm-Up or Daily Quiz

Teaching Options
- Les. Opener (Application)
- Technology Activity
- Examples 1–3
- Guided Practice Exs.

Apply/Homework
- See Assignment Guide.
- See the CRB: Practice, Reteach, Apply, Extend

Assessment Options
- Checkpoint Exercises, pp. 303–304

Day 11

5.6 *(cont.)*

Starting Options
- Homework Check

Teaching Options
- Example 4
- Closure Question

Apply/Homework
- See Assignment Guide.
- See the CRB: Practice, Reteach, Apply, Extend

Assessment Options
- Checkpoint Exercises, p. 304
- Daily Quiz (5.6)
- Stand. Test Practice
- Quiz (5.4–5.6)

Day 12

Review

Day 12 Start Options
- Homework Check

Reviewing Options
- Chapter 5 Summary
- Chapter 5 Review
- Chapter Review Games and Activities

Apply/Homework
- Chapter 5 Test (practice)
- Ch. Standardized Test (practice)

Day 13

Assess

Day 13 Start Options
- Homework Check

Assessment Options
- Chapter 5 Test
- SAT/ACT Ch. 5 Test
- Alternative Assessment

Apply/Homework
- Skill Review, p. 320

BLOCK SCHEDULE

Day 7

5.4

Starting Options
- Homework Check
- Warm-Up or Daily Quiz

Teaching Options
- Les. Opener (Visual)
- Examples 1–5
- Closure Question
- Guided Practice Exs.

Apply/Homework
- See Assignment Guide.
- See the CRB: Practice, Reteach, Apply, Extend

Assessment Options
- Checkpoint Exercises
- Daily Quiz (5.4)
- Stand. Test Practice

Day 8

5.5

Starting Options
- Homework Check
- Warm-Up or Daily Quiz

Teaching Options
- Les. Opener (Activity)
- Examples 1–3
- Guided Practice Exs. 1–4

Apply/Homework
- See Assignment Guide.
- See the CRB: Practice, Reteach, Apply, Extend

Assessment Options
- Checkpoint Exercises, pp. 296–297

Day 1

5.1

Day 1 Start Options
- Prereq. Skills Review
- Strategies for Reading
- Homework Check
- Warm-Up or Daily Quiz

Teaching 5.1 Options
- Motivating the Lesson
- Concept Activity
- Les. Opener (Activity)
- Technology Activity
- Examples 1–3
- Closure Question
- Guided Practice Exs.

Apply/Homework
- See Assignment Guide.
- See the CRB: Practice, Reteach, Apply, Extend

Assessment Options
- Checkpoint Exercises
- Daily Quiz (Les. 5.1)
- Stand. Test Practice

Day 2

5.2

Day 2 Start Options
- Homework Check
- Warm-Up or Daily Quiz

Teaching 5.2 Options
- Les. Opener (Software)
- Examples 1–2
- Closure Question
- Guided Practice Exs.

Apply/Homework
- See Assignment Guide.
- See the CRB: Practice, Reteach, Apply, Extend

Assessment Options
- Checkpoint Exercises
- Daily Quiz (Les. 5.2)
- Stand. Test Practice

Day 3

5.3

Day 3 Start Options
- Homework Check
- Warm-Up or Daily Quiz

Teaching 5.3 Options
- Motivating the Lesson
- Les. Opener (Appl.)
- Examples 1–3
- Technology Activity
- Closure Question
- Guided Practice Exs.

Apply/Homework
- See Assignment Guide.
- See the CRB: Practice, Reteach, Apply, Extend

Assessment Options
- Checkpoint Exercises
- Daily Quiz (Les. 5.3)
- Stand. Test Practice
- Quiz (5.1–5.3)

Day 4

5.4 & 5.5

Day 4 Start Options
- Homework Check
- Warm-Up (Les. 5.4) or Daily Quiz (Les. 5.3)

Teaching 5.4 Options
- Les. Opener (Visual)
- Examples 1–5
- Closure Question
- Guided Practice Exs.

Beginning 5.5 Options
- Warm-Up (Les. 5.5)
- Les. Opener (Activity)
- Examples 1–3
- Guided Practice Exs. 1–4

Apply/Homework
- See Assignment Guide.
- See the CRB: Practice, Reteach, Apply, Extend

Assessment Options
- Checkpoint Exercises
- Daily Quiz (Les. 5.4)
- Stand. Test Prac. (5.4)

Day 5

5.5 & 5.6

Day 5 Start Options
- Homework Check
- Daily Quiz (Les. 5.4)

Finishing 5.5 Options
- Example 4
- Technology Activity
- Closure Question
- Guided Practice Ex. 5

Beginning 5.6 Options
- Warm-Up (Les. 5.6)
- Les. Opener (Appl.)
- Technology Activity
- Examples 1–3
- Guided Practice Exs.

Apply/Homework
- See Assignment Guide.
- See the CRB: Practice, Reteach, Apply, Extend

Assessment Options
- Checkpoint Exercises
- Daily Quiz (Les. 5.5)
- Stand. Test Prac. (5.5)

Day 6

5.6 & Review

Day 6 Start Options
- Homework Check
- Daily Quiz (Les. 5.5)

Finishing 5.6 Options
- Example 4
- Closure Question

Reviewing Options
- Chapter 5 Summary
- Chapter 5 Review
- Chapter Review Games and Activities

Apply/Homework
- See Assignment Guide.
- See the CRB: Practice, Reteach, Apply, Extend
- Chapter 5 Test (practice)
- Ch. Standardized Test (practice)

Assessment Options
- Checkpoint Exercises
- Daily Quiz (5.6)
- Stand. Test Practice
- Quiz (5.4–5.6)

Day 7

Assess & 6.1

(Day 7 = Ch. 6 Day 1)

Assessment Options
- Chapter 5 Test
- SAT/ACT Ch. 5 Test
- Alternative Assessment

Ch. 6 Start Options
- Skills Review, p. 320
- Prereq. Skills Review
- Strategies for Reading

Beginning 6.1 Options
- Warm-Up (Les. 6.1)
- Motivating the Lesson
- Concept Activity
- Les. Opener (Application)
- Examples 1–4
- Guided Practice Exs.

Apply/Homework
- See Assignment Guide.
- See the CRB: Practice, Reteach, Apply, Extend

Assessment Options
- Checkpoint Exercises

MEETING INDIVIDUAL NEEDS

BEFORE THE CHAPTER

The *Chapter 5 Resource Book* has the following materials to distribute and use before the chapter:

- **Parent Guide for Student Success**
- **Prerequisite Skills Review**
- **Strategies for Reading Mathematics (pictured below)**

STRATEGIES FOR READING *Pages 7–8*

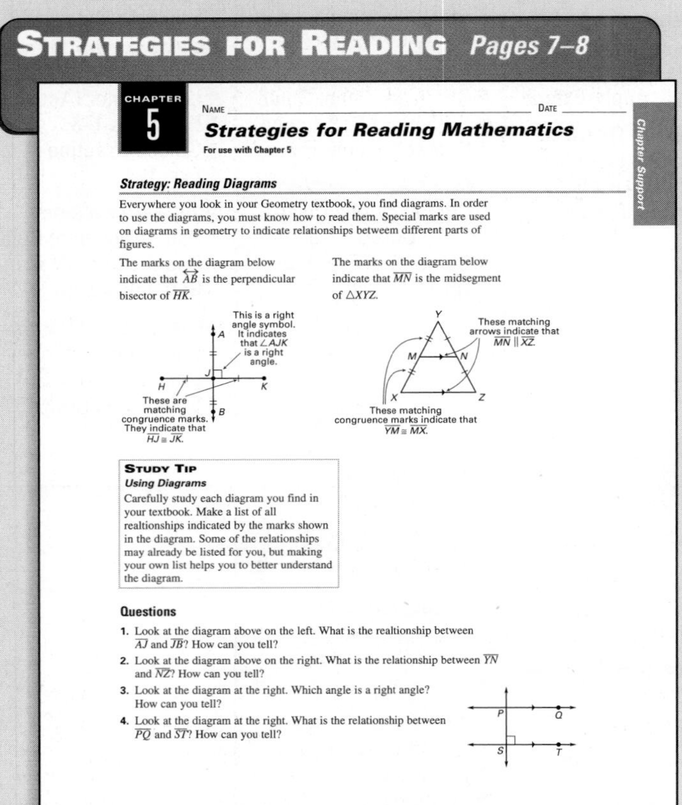

CHAPTER 5 NAME ______ DATE ______

Strategies for Reading Mathematics

For use with Chapter 5

Chapter Support

Strategy: Reading Diagrams

Everywhere you look in your Geometry textbook, you find diagrams. In order to use the diagrams, you must know how to read them. Special marks are used on diagrams in geometry to indicate relationships betweem different parts of figures.

The marks on the diagram below indicate that $\overleftrightarrow{AB}$ is the perpendicular bisector of $\overline{HK}$.

The marks on the diagram below indicate that $\overline{MN}$ is the midsegment of $\triangle XYZ$.

STUDY TIP

Using Diagrams

Carefully study each diagram you find in your textbook. Make a list of all realtionships indicated by the marks shown in the diagram. Some of the relationships may already be listed for you, but making your own list helps you to better understand the diagram.

Questions

1. Look at the diagram above on the left. What is the realtionship between $\overline{AJ}$ and $\overline{JB}$? How can you tell?
2. Look at the diagram above on the right. What is the relationship between $\overline{YN}$ and $\overline{NZ}$? How can you tell?
3. Look at the diagram at the right. Which angle is a right angle? How can you tell?
4. Look at the diagram at the right. What is the relationship between $\overline{PQ}$ and $\overline{ST}$? How can you tell?

STRATEGIES FOR READING MATHEMATICS These two pages give students tips about reading and using diagrams as they prepare for Chapter 5 and provide a visual glossary of key vocabulary words in the chapter, such as angle bisector of a triangle and altitude of a triangle.

DURING EACH LESSON

The *Chapter 5 Resource Book* has the following alternatives for introducing the lesson:

- **Lesson Openers (pictured below)**
- **Technology Activities with Keystrokes**

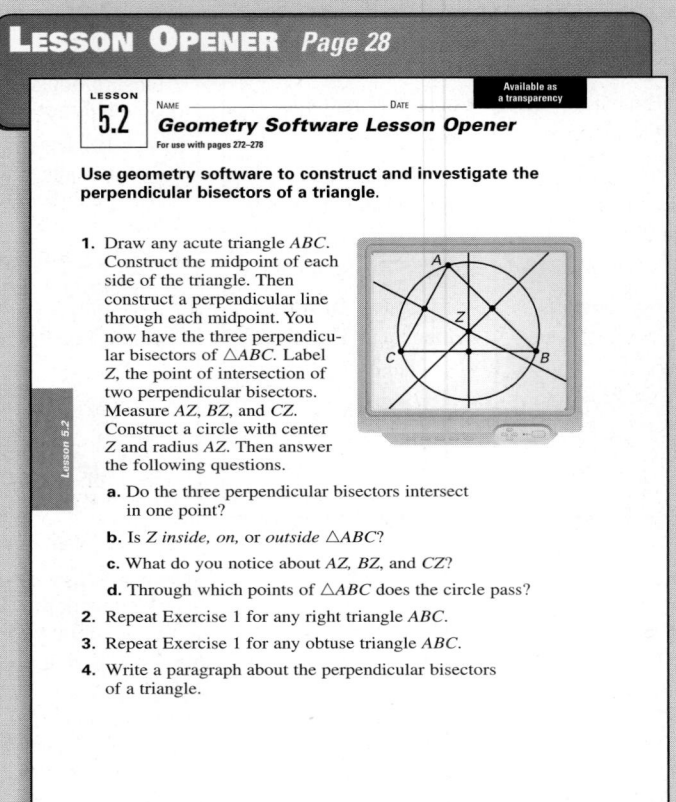

LESSON OPENER *Page 28*

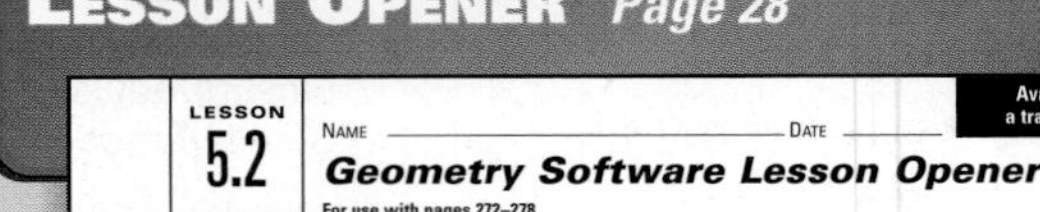

LESSON 5.2 NAME ______ DATE ______

Available as a transparency

Geometry Software Lesson Opener

For use with pages 272–278

Use geometry software to construct and investigate the perpendicular bisectors of a triangle.

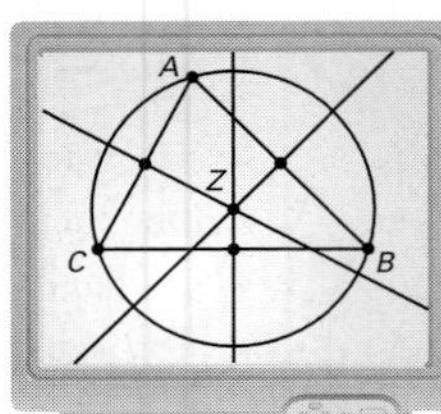

1. Draw any acute triangle ABC. Construct the midpoint of each side of the triangle. Then construct a perpendicular line through each midpoint. You now have the three perpendicular bisectors of $\triangle ABC$. Label Z, the point of intersection of two perpendicular bisectors. Measure AZ, BZ, and CZ. Construct a circle with center Z and radius AZ. Then answer the following questions.
   a. Do the three perpendicular bisectors intersect in one point?
   b. Is Z *inside*, *on*, or *outside* $\triangle ABC$?
   c. What do you notice about AZ, BZ, and CZ?
   d. Through which points of $\triangle ABC$ does the circle pass?
2. Repeat Exercise 1 for any right triangle ABC.
3. Repeat Exercise 1 for any obtuse triangle ABC.
4. Write a paragraph about the perpendicular bisectors of a triangle.

Lesson 5.2

GEOMETRY SOFTWARE LESSON OPENER This Lesson Opener provides an alternative way to start Lesson 5.2 through the use of geometry software. Students construct a circle using a triangle to develop an understanding of perpendicular bisectors.

TECHNOLOGY RESOURCE

Students and teachers can look to the Application Links and the Career Links at www.mcdougallittell.com for more information about selected applications in Chapter 5.

Following Each Lesson

The *Chapter 5 Resource Book* has a variety of materials to follow-up each lesson. They include the following:

- **Practice (3 levels)**
- **Reteaching with Practice**
- **Quick Catch-Up for Absent Students**
- **Interdisciplinary Applications**
- **Real-Life Applications (pictured below)**

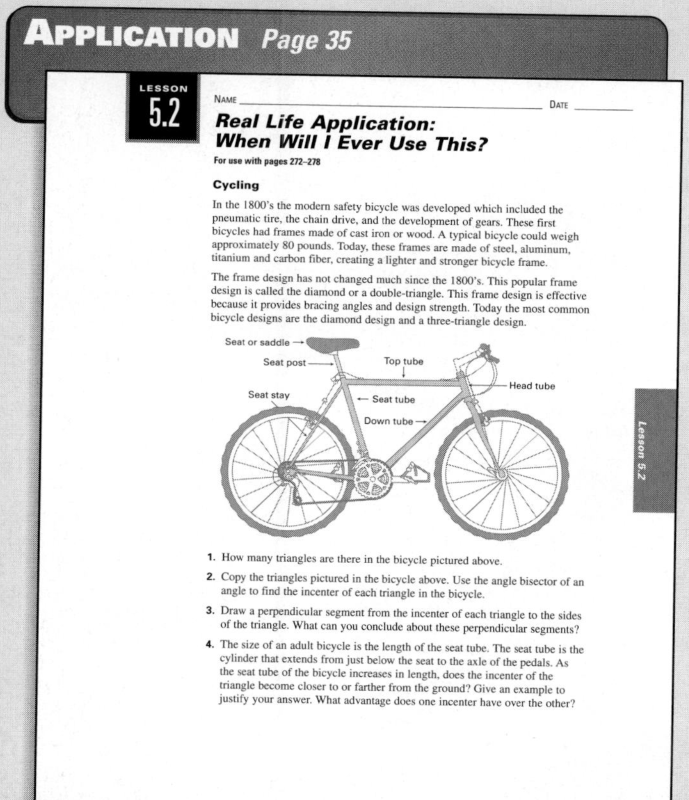

Application *Page 35*

Lesson 5.2

Name ______________ Date ______

Real Life Application: When Will I Ever Use This?

For use with pages 272–278

Cycling

In the 1800's the modern safety bicycle was developed which included the pneumatic tire, the chain drive, and the development of gears. These first bicycles had frames made of cast iron or wood. A typical bicycle could weigh approximately 80 pounds. Today, these frames are made of steel, aluminum, titanium and carbon fiber, creating a lighter and stronger bicycle frame.

The frame design has not changed much since the 1800's. This popular frame design is called the diamond or a double-triangle. This frame design is effective because it provides bracing angles and design strength. Today the most common bicycle designs are the diamond design and a three-triangle design.

Seat or saddle
Seat post
Top tube
Head tube
Seat stay
Seat tube
Down tube

1. How many triangles are there in the bicycle pictured above.
2. Copy the triangles pictured in the bicycle above. Use the angle bisector of an angle to find the incenter of each triangle in the bicycle.
3. Draw a perpendicular segment from the incenter of each triangle to the sides of the triangle. What can you conclude about these perpendicular segments?
4. The size of an adult bicycle is the length of the seat tube. The seat tube is the cylinder that extends from just below the seat to the axle of the pedals. As the seat tube of the bicycle increases in length, does the incenter of the triangle become closer to or farther from the ground? Give an example to justify your answer. What advantage does one incenter have over the other?

Lesson 5.2

Real-Life Application When students ask "When will I ever use angle bisectors and perpendicular segments?," you can have them work through this Real-Life Application in which they apply the content of Lesson 5.2 to bicycle safety.

Assessing the Chapter

The *Chapter 5 Resource Book* has the following review and assessment materials:

- **Quizzes**
- **Chapter Review Games and Activities**
- **Chapter Test (3 levels)**
- **SAT/ACT Chapter Test**
- **Alternative Assessment with Rubric and Math Journal**
- **Project with Rubric (pictured below)**
- **Cumulative Review**

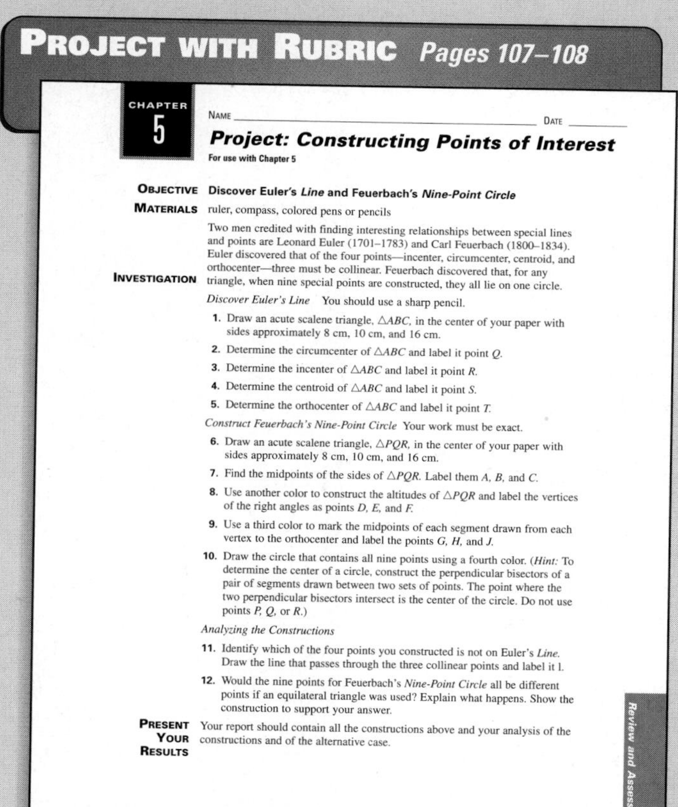

Project with Rubric *Pages 107–108*

Chapter 5

Name ______________ Date ______

Project: Constructing Points of Interest

For use with Chapter 5

Objective Discover Euler's *Line* and Feuerbach's *Nine-Point Circle*

Materials ruler, compass, colored pens or pencils

Investigation Two men credited with finding interesting relationships between special lines and points are Leonard Euler (1701–1783) and Carl Feuerbach (1800–1834). Euler discovered that of the four points—incenter, circumcenter, centroid, and orthocenter—three must be collinear. Feuerbach discovered that, for any triangle, when nine special points are constructed, they all lie on one circle.

Discover Euler's Line You should use a sharp pencil.

1. Draw an acute scalene triangle, $\triangle ABC$, in the center of your paper with sides approximately 8 cm, 10 cm, and 16 cm.
2. Determine the circumcenter of $\triangle ABC$ and label it point Q.
3. Determine the incenter of $\triangle ABC$ and label it point R.
4. Determine the centroid of $\triangle ABC$ and label it point S.
5. Determine the orthocenter of $\triangle ABC$ and label it point T.

Construct Feuerbach's Nine-Point Circle Your work must be exact.

6. Draw an acute scalene triangle, $\triangle PQR$, in the center of your paper with sides approximately 8 cm, 10 cm, and 16 cm.
7. Find the midpoints of the sides of $\triangle PQR$. Label them A, B, and C.
8. Use another color to construct the altitudes of $\triangle PQR$ and label the vertices of the right angles as points D, E, and F.
9. Use a third color to mark the midpoints of each segment drawn from each vertex to the orthocenter and label the points G, H, and J.
10. Draw the circle that contains all nine points using a fourth color. (*Hint:* To determine the center of a circle, construct the perpendicular bisectors of a pair of segments drawn between two sets of points. The point where the two perpendicular bisectors intersect is the center of the circle. Do not use points P, Q, or R.)

Analyzing the Constructions

11. Identify which of the four points you constructed is not on Euler's *Line*. Draw the line that passes through the three collinear points and label it l.
12. Would the nine points for Feuerbach's *Nine-Point Circle* all be different points if an equilateral triangle was used? Explain what happens. Show the construction to support your answer.

Present Your Results Your report should contain all the constructions above and your analysis of the constructions and of the alternative case.

Review and Assess

Project with Rubric The Project for Chapter 5 provides students with the opportunity to apply the concepts they have learned in the chapter in a new way. In this project, students use what they have learned about triangle geometry to investigate Euler's Line and Feuerbach's Nine-Point Circle. Teacher's notes and a scoring rubric are provided on a separate sheet.

CHAPTER OVERVIEW

CHAPTER GOALS

Chapter 5 covers various properties of triangles. Students begin by studying perpendicular bisectors and angle bisectors in general and then they relate these to triangles in particular. Students learn that the perpendicular bisectors of a triangle are concurrent, as are its angle bisectors. Students then study medians and altitudes and learn that these three segments associated with a triangle are also concurrent. Students study the Midsegment Theorem and learn about various triangle inequalities. The chapter concludes with a lesson on indirect proof.

APPLICATION NOTE

The game of soccer is the most popular international sport. It is played with 11 players on each team and is distinguished from other sports in that only one player, the goalkeeper, can use his or her hands. The object of the game is to propel the ball past the opponent's goalkeeper into the net. In every nation other than the United States, the sport is called *football.* The U.S. altered the name to *soccer* to distinguish this game from American football.

A soccer ball has a circumference of 27–28 inches and weighs about 14–16 ounces. The game is played on a field that is between 100–130 yards long and between 50–100 yards wide. Normally, a field is longer than it is wide. The game itself is divided into 2 halves, each of which is 45 minutes long.

Additional information about soccer angles and goalkeeping is available at **www.mcdougallittell.com.**

PROPERTIES OF TRIANGLES

How can a goalkeeper best defend the goal?

CHAPTER

5

APPLICATION: Goalkeeping

Soccer goalkeepers use triangle relationships to help block goal attempts.

An opponent can shoot the ball from many different angles. The goalkeeper determines the best defensive position by imagining a triangle formed by the goal posts and the opponent.

Think & Discuss

Use the diagram for Exercises 1 and 2.

1. The opponent at X is trying to score a goal. Which position do you think is best for the goalkeeper, A, B, or C? Why? **See margin.**
2. Estimate the measure of $\angle X$, known as the *shooting angle*. How could the opponent change positions to increase the shooting angle? **About 40°; move closer to the goal.**

Learn More About It

You will learn more about strategies of goalkeeping in Exercises 33–35 on p. 270.

APPLICATION LINK Visit www.mcdougallittell.com for more information about angles and goalkeeping.

PROJECTS

A project covering Chapters 4 and 5 appears on pages 316–317 of the Student Edition. An additional project for Chapter 5 is available in the *Chapter 5 Resource Book,* p. 107.

TECHNOLOGY

Software

- *Electronic Teaching Tools*
- *Online Lesson Planner*
- *Personal Student Tutor*
- *Test and Practice Generator*
- *Electronic Lesson Presentations (Lesson 5.3)*

Video

- *Geometry in Motion*

Internet Connections
www.mcdougallittell.com

- **Application Links**
  261, 285, 291
- **Student Help**
  273, 280, 286, 291, 294, 300, 306
- **Career Links**
  267, 283, 304
- **Extra Challenge**
  271, 278, 284, 293, 301, 307

1. *B*; at position *B*, the goalkeeper is closer to *both* sides of the imaginary triangle formed by the goal posts and the opponent. The goalkeeper has an equal space to defend to the left and to the right and so has a greater chance of catching or deflecting a ball shot to either side than she would have at position *A* or position *C*.

PREPARE

DIAGNOSTIC TOOLS

The **Skill Review** exercises can help you diagnose whether students have the following skills needed in Chapter 5:

- Construct a segment bisector and label its midpoint.
- Construct an angle bisector.
- Locate and find the coordinates of a midpoint.
- Use the distance formula.
- Find the slope of a line or line segment.
- Find the slope of the line perpendicular to a given line.

The following resources are available for students who need additional help with these skills:

- Prerequisite Skills Review (*Chapter 5 Resource Book,* p. 5; *Warm-Up Transparencies,* p. 32)
- Reteaching with Practice (Chapter Resource Books for Lessons 1.3, 1.5, 3.6, and 3.7)
- *Personal Student Tutor*

ADDITIONAL RESOURCES

The following resources are provided to help you prepare for the upcoming chapter and customize review materials:

- ***Chapter 5 Resource Book***
  Tips for New Teachers (p. 1)
  Parent Guide (p. 3)
  Lesson Plans (every lesson)
  Lesson Plans for Block Scheduling (every lesson)
- ***Electronic Teaching Tools***
- ***Online Lesson Planner***
- ***Test and Practice Generator***

CHAPTER 5

Study Guide

PREVIEW

What's the chapter about?

Chapter 5 is about **properties of triangles**. In Chapter 5, you'll learn how to

- use properties of special lines and segments related to triangles.
- compare side lengths and angle measures in one or more triangles.

KEY VOCABULARY

▶ **Review**
- **intersect, p. 12**
- **midpoint, p. 34**
- **angle bisector, p. 36**
- **perpendicular lines, p. 79**

▶ **New**
- **perpendicular bisector, p. 264**
- **perpendicular bisector of a triangle, p. 272**
- **concurrent lines, p. 272**
- **circumcenter of a triangle, p. 273**
- **angle bisector of a triangle, p. 274**
- **incenter of a triangle, p. 274**
- **median of a triangle, p. 279**
- **centroid of a triangle, p. 279**
- **altitude of a triangle, p. 281**
- **orthocenter of a triangle, p. 281**
- **midsegment of a triangle, p. 287**
- **indirect proof, p. 302**

PREPARE

Are you ready for the chapter?

SKILL REVIEW Do these exercises to review key skills that you'll apply in this chapter. See the given **reference page** if there is something you don't understand.

1. Draw a segment and label it $\overline{AB}$. Construct a bisector of $\overline{AB}$. Label its midpoint M. **(Review p. 34)** Check drawings.
2. Draw an angle and label it $\angle P$. Construct an angle bisector of $\angle P$. **(Review p. 36)** Check drawings.

Use the diagram at the right.

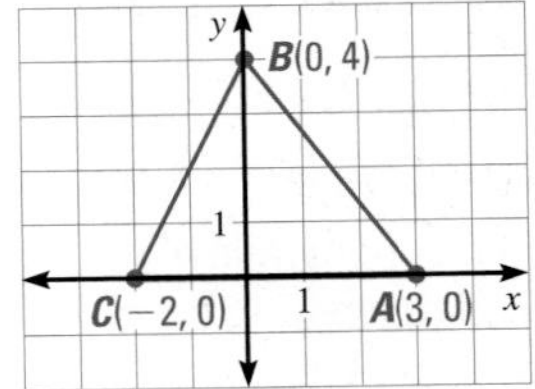

3. Find the coordinates of the midpoint of $\overline{BC}$. **(Review p. 35)** (−1, 2)
4. Find the length of $\overline{AB}$. **(Review p. 19)** 5
5. Find the slope of $\overline{BC}$. **(Review p. 165)** 2
6. Find the slope of a line perpendicular to $\overline{BC}$. **(Review p. 174)** $-\frac{1}{2}$

STUDY STRATEGY

Here's a study strategy!

Check Your Memory

Without looking at your book or your notes, write a list of important vocabulary terms and skills. Then look through the chapter and your notes as you compare them with your list. Did you miss anything?

ACTIVITY 5.1

Developing Concepts

Investigating Perpendicular Bisectors

Group Activity for use with Lesson 5.1

GROUP ACTIVITY
Work with a partner.

MATERIALS
- paper
- pencils
- ruler
- protractor

▶ **QUESTION** **What is true about any point on the perpendicular bisector of a segment?**

▶ **EXPLORING THE CONCEPT**

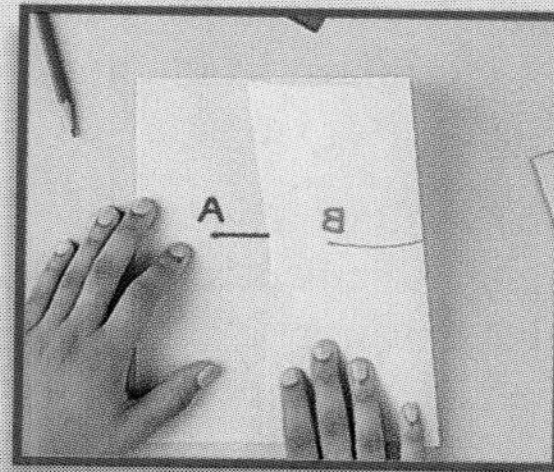

1. On a piece of paper, draw $\overline{AB}$. Fold the paper so that point B lies directly on point A.

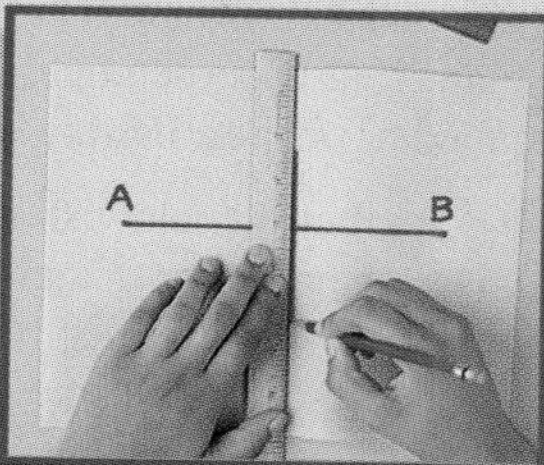

2. Draw a line along the crease in the paper. Label the point where the line intersects $\overline{AB}$ as point M.

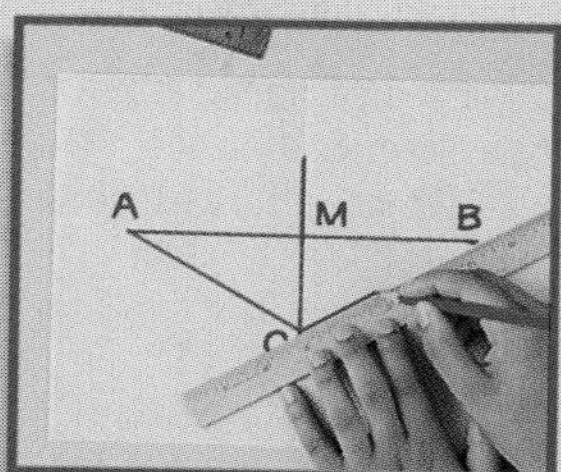

3. Label another point on the line as point C. Draw $\overline{CA}$ and $\overline{CB}$.

Steps 1–3. Check drawings.

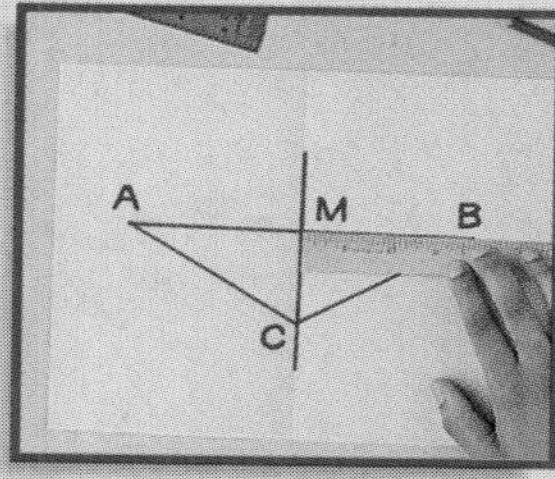

4. Measure $\overline{MA}$ and $\overline{MB}$.

Step 4. $MA = MB = \frac{1}{2}AB$

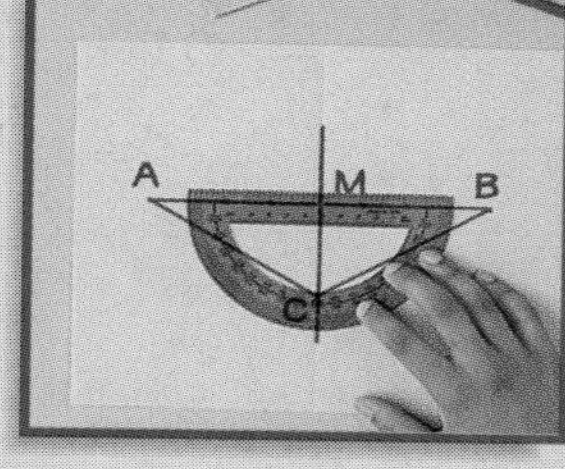

5. Measure $\angle CMA$.

Step 5. 90°

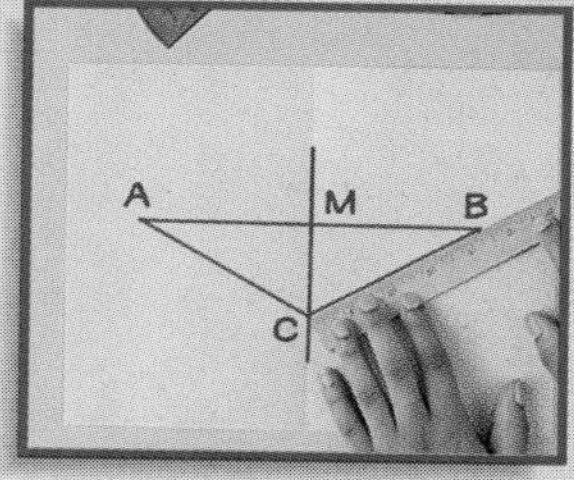

6. Measure $\overline{CA}$ and $\overline{CB}$.

Step 6. $CA = CB$

▶ **DRAWING CONCLUSIONS**

1. $\overleftrightarrow{CM}$ is called the *perpendicular bisector* of $\overline{AB}$. Explain why. $\overleftrightarrow{CM}$ is $\perp$ to $\overline{AB}$ because $m\angle CMA = 90°$ and $\overleftrightarrow{CM}$ intersects $\overline{AB}$ at its midpoint.

2. Choose four other points on $\overleftrightarrow{CM}$. Label the points as D, E, F, and G.

3. Copy and complete the table by measuring the length of each segment. What do you notice? Answers will vary, but $DA = DB$, $EA = EB$, $FA = FB$, and $GA = GB$.

Point D	Point E	Point F	Point G
$DA =$?	$EA =$?	$FA =$?	$GA =$?
$DB =$?	$EB =$?	$FB =$?	$GB =$?

4. **CRITICAL THINKING** What is true about any point on the perpendicular bisector of a segment? Any point on the perpendicular bisector of a segment is the same distance from either of the endpoints of the segment.

1 Planning the Activity

PURPOSE
To investigate perpendicular bisectors.

MATERIALS
- ruler for each pair of students
- protractor for each pair of students

PACING
- Exploring the Concept — 5 min
- Drawing Conclusions — 10 min

▶ ***LINK TO LESSON***
Lesson 5.1 introduces two theorems about perpendicular bisectors. The theorems relate to the property of perpendicular bisectors investigated in this activity.

2 Managing the Activity

COOPERATIVE LEARNING
Encourage students to discuss and compare their findings and drawings with those of other groups. Also, remind them that they can pick points on the perpendicular bisector that are both above and below the line segment.

3 Closing the Activity

★ ***KEY DISCOVERY***
Any point on the perpendicular bisector of a segment will be equidistant from both endpoints of the segment.

ACTIVITY ASSESSMENT
JOURNAL Describe what is true about two segments drawn from any point on the perpendicular bisector of a line segment to the endpoints of the segment. Draw a sketch. Check students' drawings. The segments will be equal in length.

1 PLAN

PACING
Basic: 2 days
Average: 2 days
Advanced: 2 days
Block Schedule: 1 block

LESSON OPENER ACTIVITY
An alternative way to approach Lesson 5.1 is to use the Activity Lesson Opener:
- Blackline Master (*Chapter 5 Resource Book,* p. 12)
- Transparency (p. 28)

MEETING INDIVIDUAL NEEDS
- ***Chapter 5 Resource Book***
  Prerequisite Skills Review (p. 5)
  Practice Level A (p. 17)
  Practice Level B (p. 18)
  Practice Level C (p. 19)
  Reteaching with Practice (p. 20)
  Absent Student Catch-Up (p. 22)
  Challenge (p. 24)
- ***Resources in Spanish***
-  ***Personal Student Tutor***

NEW-TEACHER SUPPORT
See the Tips for New Teachers on pp. 1–2 of the *Chapter 5 Resource Book* for additional notes about Lesson 5.1.

WARM-UP EXERCISES
Transparency Available
Copy the figure and label the information on the figure.

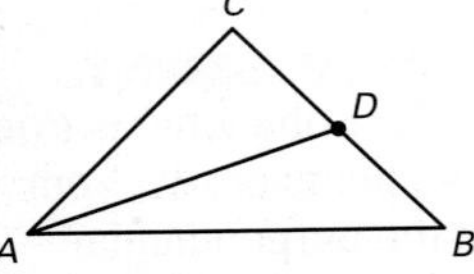

1. $\angle C$ is a right angle.
2. $\angle A \cong \angle B$
3. $AB = 8$
4. $\overline{AD}$ bisects $\overline{CB}$. See right.

5.1 Perpendiculars and Bisectors

What you should learn

GOAL 1 Use properties of perpendicular bisectors.

GOAL 2 Use properties of angle bisectors to identify equal distances, such as the lengths of beams in a roof truss in **Example 3**.

Why you should learn it

▼ To solve **real-life** problems, such as deciding where a hockey goalie should be positioned in **Exs. 33–35**.

CALIFORNIA STANDARDS AND ASSESSMENT
CA Standards: 16

GOAL 1 USING PROPERTIES OF PERPENDICULAR BISECTORS

In Lesson 1.5, you learned that a segment bisector intersects a segment at its midpoint. A segment, ray, line, or plane that is perpendicular to a segment at its midpoint is called a **perpendicular bisector**.

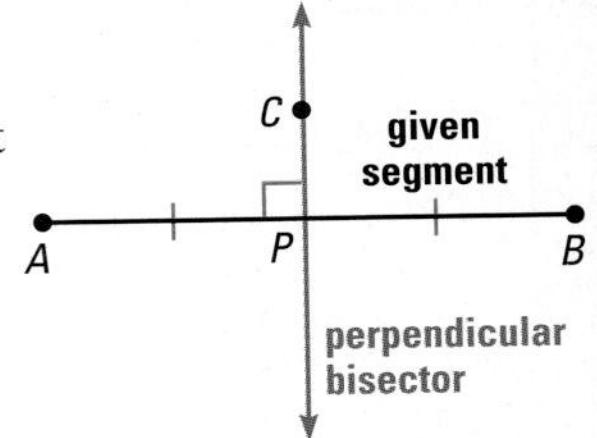

$\overleftrightarrow{CP}$ is a $\perp$ bisector of $\overline{AB}$.

The construction below shows how to draw a line that is perpendicular to a given line or segment at a point P. You can use this method to construct a perpendicular bisector of a segment, as described below the activity.

ACTIVITY
Construction
Perpendicular Through a Point on a Line

Use these steps to construct a line that is perpendicular to a given line m and that passes through a given point P on m.

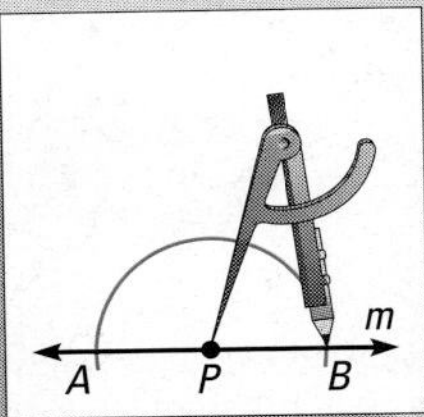

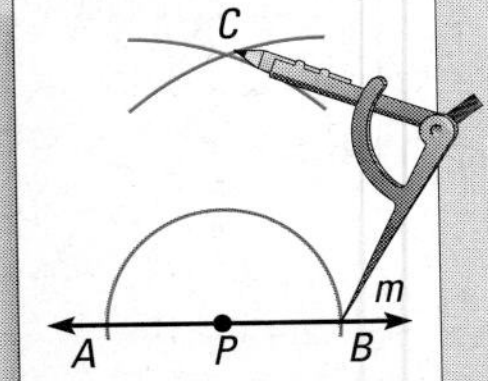

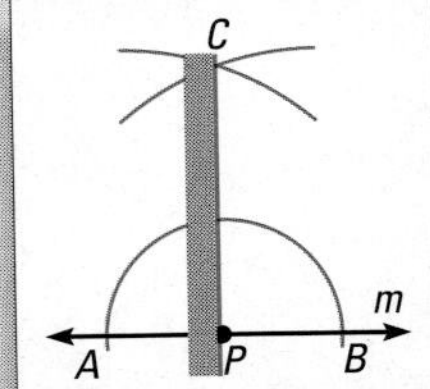

1 Place the compass point at P. Draw an arc that intersects line m twice. Label the intersections as A and B.

2 Use a compass setting greater than AP. Draw an arc from A. With the same setting, draw an arc from B. Label the intersection of the arcs as C.

3 Use a straightedge to draw $\overleftrightarrow{CP}$. This line is perpendicular to line m and passes through P.

1–3. Check drawings.

You can measure $\angle CPA$ on your construction to verify that the constructed line is perpendicular to the given line m. In the construction, $\overleftrightarrow{CP} \perp \overline{AB}$ and $PA = PB$, so $\overleftrightarrow{CP}$ is the perpendicular bisector of $\overline{AB}$.

A point is **equidistant from two points** if its distance from each point is the same. In the construction above, C is equidistant from A and B because C was drawn so that $CA = CB$.

STUDENT HELP

Look Back
For a construction of a perpendicular to a line through a point not on the given line, see p. 130.

4.
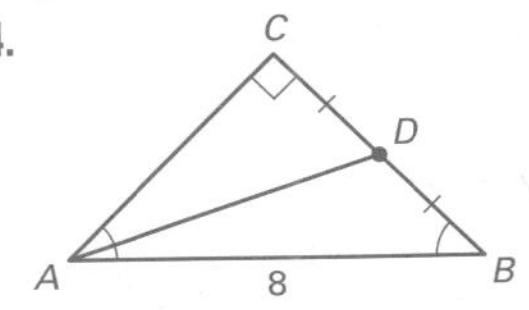

Theorem 5.1 below states that *any* point on the perpendicular bisector $\overleftrightarrow{CP}$ in the construction is equidistant from A and B, the endpoints of the segment. The converse helps you prove that a given point lies on a perpendicular bisector.

THEOREMS

THEOREM 5.1 ***Perpendicular Bisector Theorem***

If a point is on the perpendicular bisector of a segment, then it is equidistant from the endpoints of the segment.

If $\overleftrightarrow{CP}$ is the perpendicular bisector of $\overline{AB}$, then $CA = CB$.

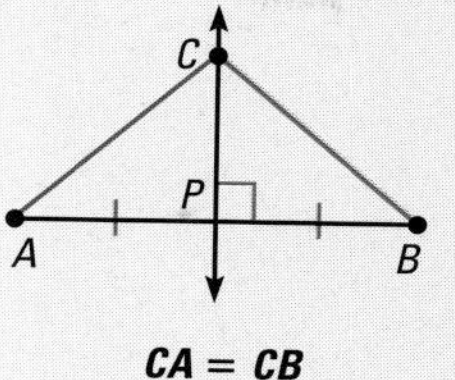

$CA = CB$

THEOREM 5.2 ***Converse of the Perpendicular Bisector Theorem***

If a point is equidistant from the endpoints of a segment, then it is on the perpendicular bisector of the segment.

If $DA = DB$, then D lies on the perpendicular bisector of $\overline{AB}$.

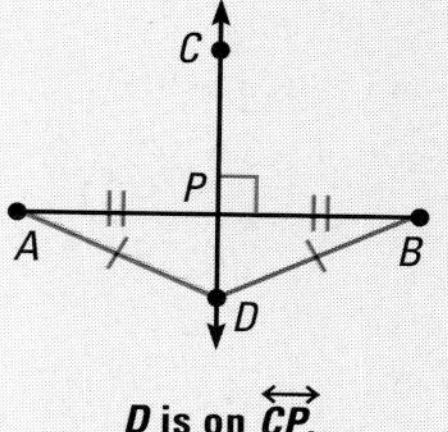

D is on $\overleftrightarrow{CP}$.

Plan for Proof of Theorem 5.1 Refer to the diagram for Theorem 5.1 above. Suppose that you are given that $\overleftrightarrow{CP}$ is the perpendicular bisector of $\overline{AB}$. Show that right triangles $\triangle APC$ and $\triangle BPC$ are congruent using the SAS Congruence Postulate. Then show that $\overline{CA} \cong \overline{CB}$.

Exercise 28 asks you to write a two-column proof of Theorem 5.1 using this plan for proof. Exercise 29 asks you to write a proof of Theorem 5.2.

EXAMPLE 1 *Using Perpendicular Bisectors*

In the diagram shown, $\overleftrightarrow{MN}$ is the perpendicular bisector of $\overline{ST}$.

a. What segment lengths in the diagram are equal?

b. Explain why Q is on $\overleftrightarrow{MN}$.

T, M, N, Q, S, 12, 12

SOLUTION

a. $\overleftrightarrow{MN}$ bisects $\overline{ST}$, so $NS = NT$. Because M is on the perpendicular bisector of $\overline{ST}$, $MS = MT$ (by Theorem 5.1). The diagram shows that $QS = QT = 12$.

b. $QS = QT$, so Q is equidistant from S and T. By Theorem 5.2, Q is on the perpendicular bisector of $\overline{ST}$, which is $\overleftrightarrow{MN}$.

2 TEACH

MOTIVATING THE LESSON

Ask students to imagine a telephone pole on level ground. Tell them that the pole has support wires on either side of it attached at the same height. If the two wires are the same length, ask students what they think about the distances from the places where the wires hit the ground to the bottom of the pole. **They are the same.**

EXTRA EXAMPLE 1

In the diagram shown, $\overleftrightarrow{PQ}$ is the perpendicular bisector of $\overline{CD}$.

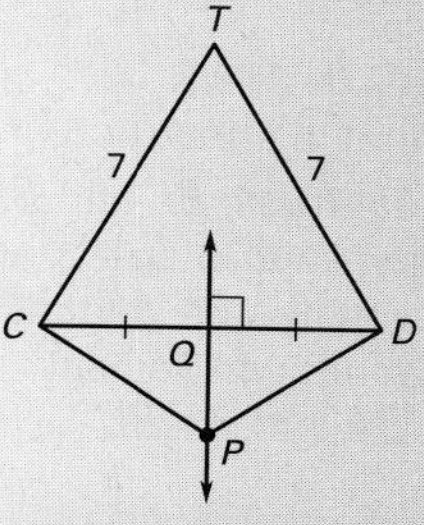

a. What segment lengths in the diagram are equal? ***QC = QD, PC = PD, and TC = TD***

b. Explain why T is on $\overleftrightarrow{PQ}$. ***CT = DT, so T is equidistant from C and D. By Theorem 5.2, T is on the perpendicular bisector of the segment.***

CHECKPOINT EXERCISES

For use after Example 1:

1. Explain why $FA = FB$.

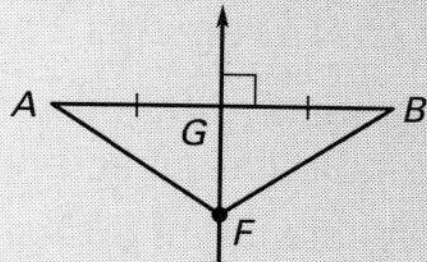

Because $\overleftrightarrow{FG}$ is the perpendicular bisector of $\overline{AB}$, $FA = FB$ by Theorem 5.1.

Extra Example 2

Given: R is on the bisector of $\angle QPS$. $\overline{RQ} \perp \overrightarrow{PQ}$, $\overline{RS} \perp \overrightarrow{PS}$

Prove: $\overline{RQ} \cong \overline{RS}$

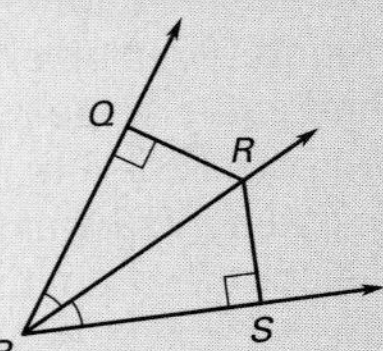

Statements (Reasons)

1. $\angle QPR \cong \angle SPR$ (Def. of $\angle$ bisector.)
2. $\angle PQR \cong \angle PSR$ (All rt. $\angle$s are $\cong$.)
3. $\overline{PR} = \overline{PR}$ (Reflexive Property)
4. $\triangle PRQ \cong \triangle PRS$ (AAS Cong. Thm.)
5. $\overline{RQ} \cong \overline{RS}$ (Corresp. parts of $\cong$ $\triangle$s are $\cong$.)

Extra Example 3

Suppose that in constructing a wooden roof truss, $\overline{BC}$ and $\overline{BD}$ are installed so that $\angle ACB$ and $\angle ADB$ are right angles and that $AC = AD$. What can you say about $\angle CBA$ and $\angle ABD$?

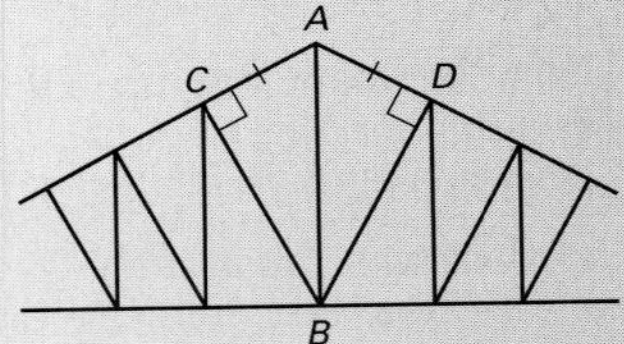

A is in the interior of $\angle CBD$ and is equidistant from the sides of the angle. By Theorem 5.4, *A* is on the bisector of $\angle CBD$, so $m\angle CBA = m\angle ABD$.

Checkpoint Exercises

For use after Examples 2 and 3:

1. In the figure, $\overleftrightarrow{CD}$ is the perpendicular bisector of $\overline{AB}$. What kind of triangle is $\triangle ABC$?

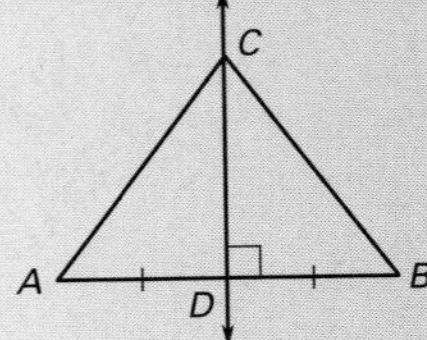

isosceles

GOAL 2 Using Properties of Angle Bisectors

The **distance from a point to a line** is defined as the length of the perpendicular segment from the point to the line. For instance, in the diagram shown, the distance between the point Q and the line m is QP.

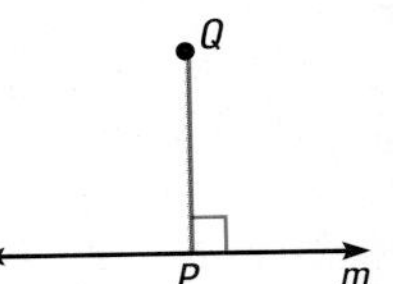

When a point is the same distance from one line as it is from another line, then the point is **equidistant from the two lines** (or rays or segments). The theorems below show that a point in the interior of an angle is equidistant from the sides of the angle if and only if the point is on the bisector of the angle.

THEOREMS

THEOREM 5.3 ***Angle Bisector Theorem***

If a point is on the bisector of an angle, then it is equidistant from the two sides of the angle.

If $m\angle BAD = m\angle CAD$, then $DB = DC$.

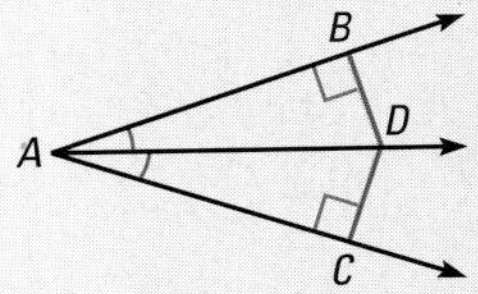

$DB = DC$

THEOREM 5.4 ***Converse of the Angle Bisector Theorem***

If a point is in the interior of an angle and is equidistant from the sides of the angle, then it lies on the bisector of the angle.

If $DB = DC$, then $m\angle BAD = m\angle CAD$.

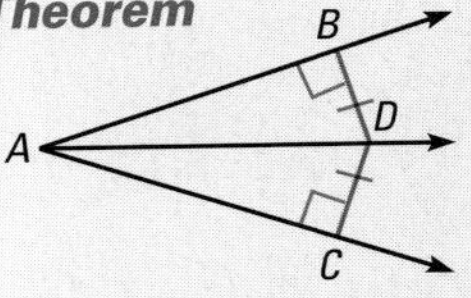

$m\angle BAD = m\angle CAD$

A paragraph proof of Theorem 5.3 is given in Example 2. Exercise 32 asks you to write a proof of Theorem 5.4.

EXAMPLE 2 *Proof of Theorem 5.3*

GIVEN ▶ D is on the bisector of $\angle BAC$. $\overline{DB} \perp \overrightarrow{AB}$, $\overline{DC} \perp \overrightarrow{AC}$

PROVE ▶ $DB = DC$

Plan for Proof Prove that $\triangle ADB \cong \triangle ADC$. Then conclude that $\overline{DB} \cong \overline{DC}$, so $DB = DC$.

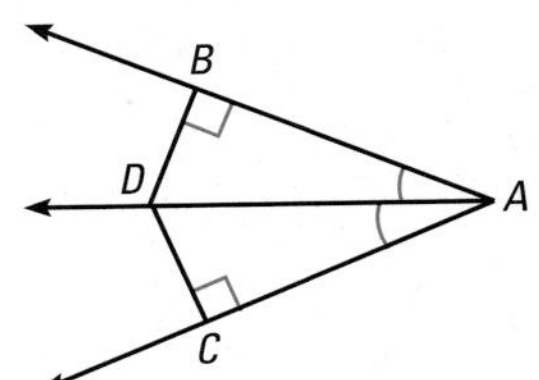

Solution

Paragraph Proof By the definition of an angle bisector, $\angle BAD \cong \angle CAD$. Because $\angle ABD$ and $\angle ACD$ are right angles, $\angle ABD \cong \angle ACD$. By the Reflexive Property of Congruence, $\overline{AD} \cong \overline{AD}$. Then $\triangle ADB \cong \triangle ADC$ by the AAS Congruence Theorem. Because corresponding parts of congruent triangles are congruent, $\overline{DB} \cong \overline{DC}$. By the definition of congruent segments, $DB = DC$.

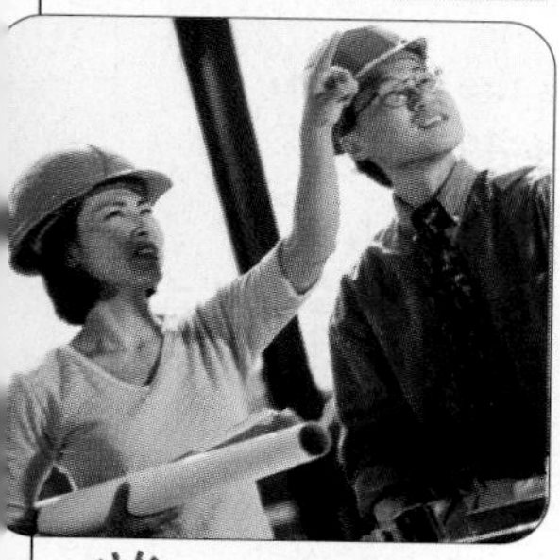

ENGINEERING TECHNICIAN

In manufacturing, engineering technicians prepare specifications for products such as roof trusses, and devise and run tests for quality control.

CAREER LINK
www.mcdougallittell.com

EXAMPLE 3 ***Using Angle Bisectors***

ROOF TRUSSES Some roofs are built with wooden trusses that are assembled in a factory and shipped to the building site. In the diagram of the roof truss shown below, you are given that $\overrightarrow{AB}$ bisects $\angle CAD$ and that $\angle ACB$ and $\angle ADB$ are right angles. What can you say about $\overline{BC}$ and $\overline{BD}$?

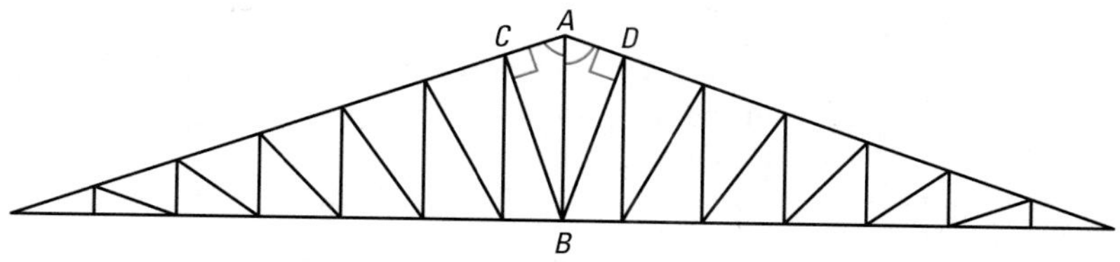

SOLUTION

Because $\overline{BC}$ and $\overline{BD}$ meet $\overline{AC}$ and $\overline{AD}$ at right angles, they are perpendicular segments to the sides of $\angle CAD$. This implies that their lengths represent the distances from the point B to $\overrightarrow{AC}$ and $\overrightarrow{AD}$. Because point B is on the bisector of $\angle CAD$, it is equidistant from the sides of the angle.

▶ So, $BC = BD$, and you can conclude that $\overline{BC} \cong \overline{BD}$.

GUIDED PRACTICE

Vocabulary Check ✓

1. If D is on the __?__ of $\overline{AB}$, then D is *equidistant* from A and B. ⊥ bisector

Concept Check ✓

2. Point G is in the interior of $\angle HJK$ and is equidistant from the sides of the angle, $\overrightarrow{JH}$ and $\overrightarrow{JK}$. What can you conclude about G? Use a sketch to support your answer. Check drawings; G is on the bisector of $\angle HJK$.

Skill Check ✓

In the diagram, $\overleftrightarrow{CD}$ is the perpendicular bisector of $\overline{AB}$.

3. What is the relationship between $\overline{AD}$ and $\overline{BD}$? $\overline{AD} \cong \overline{BD}$
4. What is the relationship between $\angle ADC$ and $\angle BDC$? $\angle ADC \cong \angle BDC$ and $m\angle ADC = m\angle BDC = 90°$.
5. What is the relationship between $\overline{AC}$ and $\overline{BC}$? Explain your answer. $\overline{AC} \cong \overline{BC}$; C is on the ⊥ bisector of $\overline{AB}$.

In the diagram, $\overrightarrow{PM}$ is the bisector of $\angle LPN$.

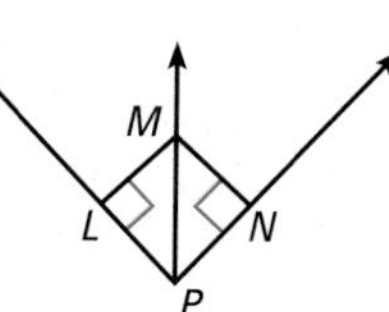

6. What is the relationship between $\angle LPM$ and $\angle NPM$? $\angle LPM \cong \angle NPM$
7. How is the distance between point M and $\overrightarrow{PL}$ related to the distance between point M and $\overrightarrow{PN}$? The distance from M to $\overrightarrow{PL}$ is equal to the distance from M to $\overrightarrow{PN}$.

CAREER NOTE
Additional information about engineering technicians is available at **www.mcdougallittell.com.**

FOCUS ON VOCABULARY
Ask students to make sketches to illustrate "equidistant from two points" and "equidistant from two intersecting lines."

CLOSURE QUESTION
What does the Perpendicular Bisector Theorem allow you to show? What does the Angle Bisector Theorem allow you to show? A point on the perpendicular bisector is equidistant from the endpoints of the segment; a point on the bisector of an angle is equidistant from the two sides of the angle.

DAILY PUZZLER
How many triangles are in the figure below? 28

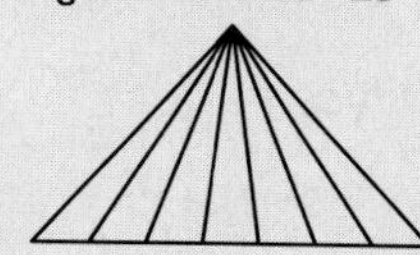

3 APPLY

ASSIGNMENT GUIDE

BASIC
Day 1: pp. 268–270 Exs. 8–32 even
Day 2: pp. 268–271 Exs. 9–31 odd, 33–35, 41–52

AVERAGE
Day 1: pp. 268–270 Exs. 8–32 even
Day 2: pp. 268–271 Exs. 9–31 odd, 33–35, 37, 41–52

ADVANCED
Day 1: pp. 268–270 Exs. 8–32 even
Day 2: pp. 268–271 Exs. 9–31 odd, 33–35, 37–52

BLOCK SCHEDULE
pp. 268–271 Exs. 8–35, 37, 41–52

EXERCISE LEVELS

Level A: ***Easier***
8–13

Level B: ***More Difficult***
14–37

Level C: ***Most Difficult***
38–40

✔ HOMEWORK CHECK

To quickly check student understanding of key concepts, go over the following exercises: Exs. 8, 12, 14, 16, 20, 22, 28, 30. See also the Daily Homework Quiz:

- Blackline Master (*Chapter 5 Resource Book,* p. 27)
- Transparency (p. 34)

PRACTICE AND APPLICATIONS

STUDENT HELP

Extra Practice to help you master skills is on p. 811.

8. No; since $CA \neq CB$, C is not on the $\perp$ bisector of $\overline{AB}$.
9. No; the diagram does not show that $CA = CB$.
10. No; the diagram does not show that $CA = CB$.
11. No; since P is not equidistant from the sides of $\angle A$, P is not on the bisector of $\angle A$.
12. No; the diagram does not show that both of the segments with equal length are perpendicular segments.
13. No; the diagram does not show that the segments with equal length are perpendicular segments.

LOGICAL REASONING **Tell whether the information in the diagram allows you to conclude that C is on the perpendicular bisector of $\overline{AB}$. Explain your reasoning.**

8.

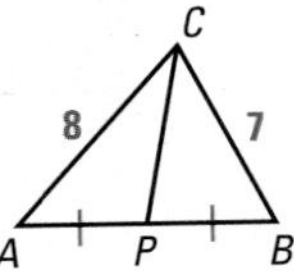

9. A P B C

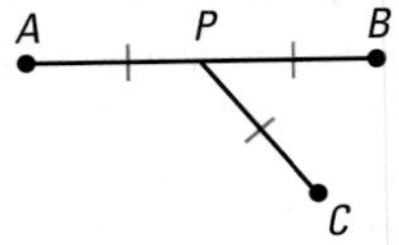

10.

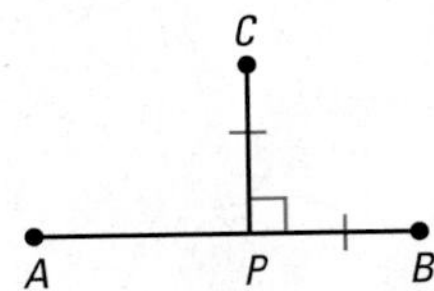

LOGICAL REASONING **In Exercises 11–13, tell whether the information in the diagram allows you to conclude that P is on the bisector of $\angle A$. Explain.**

11.

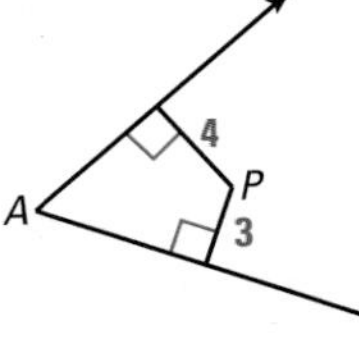

12.

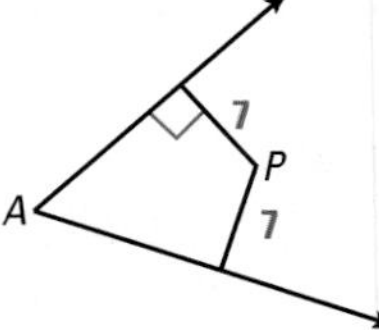

13.

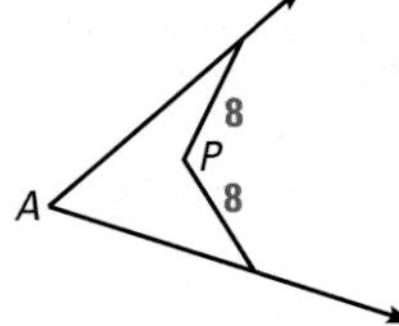

14. **CONSTRUCTION** Draw $\overline{AB}$ with a length of 8 centimeters. Construct a perpendicular bisector and draw a point D on the bisector so that the distance between D and $\overline{AB}$ is 3 centimeters. Measure $\overline{AD}$ and $\overline{BD}$. $AD = BD = 5$ cm

15. **CONSTRUCTION** Draw a large $\angle A$ with a measure of 60°. Construct the angle bisector and draw a point D on the bisector so that $AD = 3$ inches. Draw perpendicular segments from D to the sides of $\angle A$. Measure these segments to find the distance between D and the sides of $\angle A$.
D is $1\frac{1}{2}$ in. from each side of $\angle A$.

USING PERPENDICULAR BISECTORS **Use the diagram shown.**

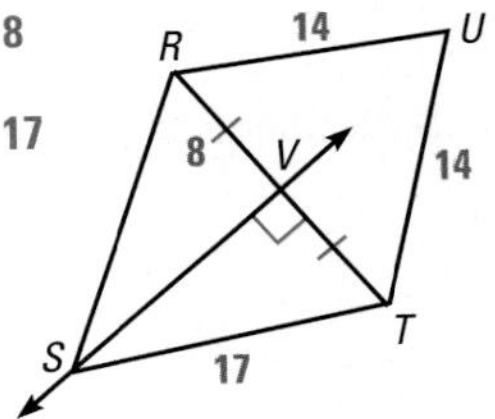

16. In the diagram, $\overleftrightarrow{SV} \perp \overline{RT}$ and $\overline{VR} \cong \overline{VT}$. Find VT. 8

17. In the diagram, $\overleftrightarrow{SV} \perp \overline{RT}$ and $\overline{VR} \cong \overline{VT}$. Find SR. 17

18. In the diagram, $\overleftrightarrow{SV}$ is the perpendicular bisector of $\overline{RT}$. Because $UR = UT = 14$, what can you conclude about point U?
U is on $\overleftrightarrow{SV}$, the $\perp$ bisector of $\overline{RT}$.

STUDENT HELP

HOMEWORK HELP
Example 1: Exs. 8–10, 14, 16–18, 21–26
Example 2: Exs. 11–13, 15, 19, 20, 21–26
Example 3: Exs. 31, 33–35

USING ANGLE BISECTORS **Use the diagram shown.**

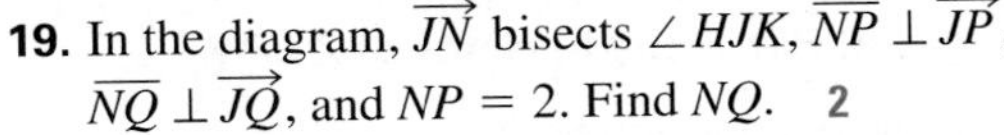

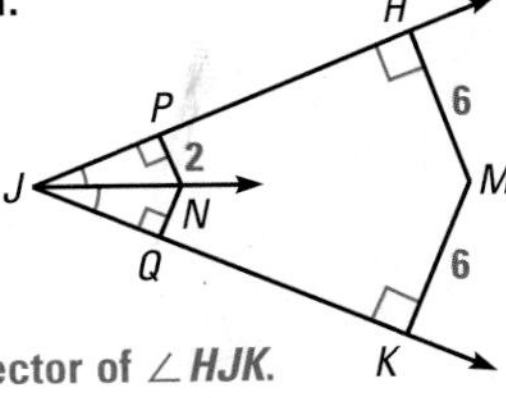

19. In the diagram, $\overrightarrow{JN}$ bisects $\angle HJK$, $\overline{NP} \perp \overrightarrow{JP}$, $\overline{NQ} \perp \overrightarrow{JQ}$, and $NP = 2$. Find NQ. 2

20. In the diagram, $\overrightarrow{JN}$ bisects $\angle HJK$, $\overline{MH} \perp \overrightarrow{JH}$, $\overline{MK} \perp \overrightarrow{JK}$, and $MH = MK = 6$. What can you conclude about point M? M is on $\overrightarrow{JN}$, the bisector of $\angle HJK$.

USING BISECTOR THEOREMS In Exercises 21–26, match the angle measure or segment length described with its correct value.

A. 60° B. 8

C. 40° D. 4

E. 50° F. 3.36

21. SW B 22. $m\angle XTV$ A

23. $m\angle VWX$ C 24. VU F

25. WX D 26. $m\angle WVX$ E

27. **PROVING A CONSTRUCTION** Write a proof to verify that $\overleftrightarrow{CP} \perp \overline{AB}$ in the construction on page 264. **See margin.**

28. **PROVING THEOREM 5.1** Write a proof of Theorem 5.1, the Perpendicular Bisector Theorem. You may want to use the plan for proof given on page 265. **See margin.**

GIVEN ▶ $\overleftrightarrow{CP}$ is the perpendicular bisector of $\overline{AB}$.

PROVE ▶ C is equidistant from A and B.

29. **PROVING THEOREM 5.2** Use the diagram shown to write a two-column proof of Theorem 5.2, the Converse of the Perpendicular Bisector Theorem. **See margin.**

GIVEN ▶ C is equidistant from A and B.

PROVE ▶ C is on the perpendicular bisector of $\overline{AB}$.

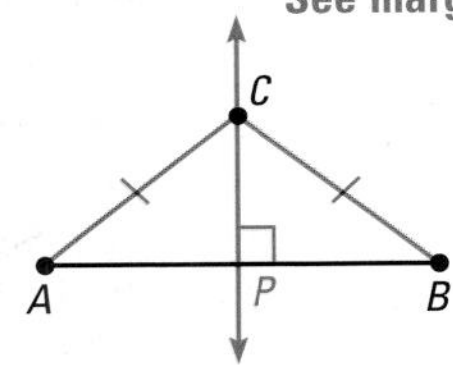

Plan for Proof Use the Perpendicular Postulate to draw $\overleftrightarrow{CP} \perp \overleftrightarrow{AB}$. Show that $\triangle APC \cong \triangle BPC$ by the HL Congruence Theorem. Then $\overline{AP} \cong \overline{BP}$, so $AP = BP$.

30. **PROOF** Use the diagram shown.

GIVEN ▶ $\overline{GJ}$ is the perpendicular bisector of $\overline{HK}$.

PROVE ▶ $\triangle GHM \cong \triangle GKM$ **See margin.**

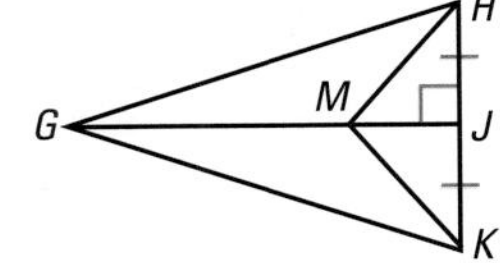

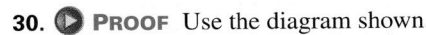

31. **EARLY AIRCRAFT** On many of the earliest airplanes, wires connected vertical posts to the edges of the wings, which were wooden frames covered with cloth. Suppose the lengths of the wires from the top of a post to the edges of the frame are the same and the distances from the bottom of the post to the ends of the two wires are the same. What does that tell you about the post and the section of frame between the ends of the wires?
The post is the ⊥ bisector of the segment between the ends of the wires.

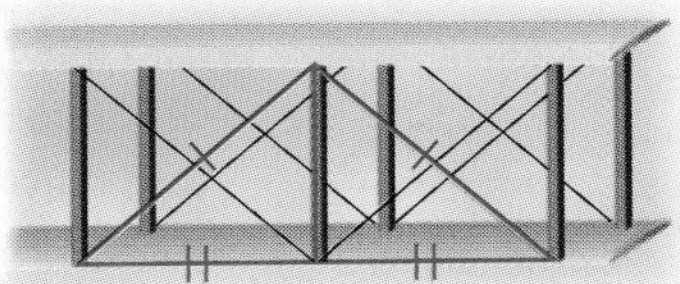

27. $\overline{PA} \cong \overline{PB}$ **and** $\overline{CA} \cong \overline{CB}$ **by construction. By the Reflexive Prop. of Cong.,** $\overline{CP} \cong \overline{CP}$**. Then** $\triangle CPA \cong \triangle CPB$ **by the SSS Cong. Post. Corresp. ∠s** CPA **and** CPB **are ≅. Then** $\overleftrightarrow{CP} \perp \overline{AB}$**. (If 2 lines form a linear pair of ≅ ∠s, then the lines are ⊥.)**

STUDENT HELP

Look Back
For help with proving that constructions are valid, see p. 231.

28. Since $\overleftrightarrow{CP}$ **is the ⊥ bisector of** $\overline{AB}$**,** $\overleftrightarrow{CP} \perp \overline{AB}$**, ∠CPA and ∠CPB are right ∠s. (Def. of ⊥ lines) Also,** $\overline{PA} \cong \overline{PB}$**. Then, since** $\overline{CP} \cong \overline{CP}$ **by the Reflexive Prop. of Cong.,** $\triangle CPA \cong \triangle CPB$ **by the SAS Cong. Post. Corresp. parts of ≅ △s are ≅, so** $\overline{CA} \cong \overline{CB}$**. Then** $CA = CB$ **(Def. of ≅ segments) and** C **is equidistant from** A **and** B**. (Def. of equidistant)**

FOCUS ON PEOPLE

THE WRIGHT BROTHERS
In Kitty Hawk, North Carolina, on December 17, 1903, Orville and Wilbur Wright became the first people to successfully fly an engine-driven, heavier-than-air machine.

! COMMON ERROR
EXERCISES 14 AND 15 Since measurements are given in these exercises, students may measure to draw the perpendicular bisector and the angle bisector. Remind students that in doing a construction they are not to measure and that a construction is done using a compass and straightedge only.

TEACHING TIPS
EXERCISES 27–30 When students are completing proofs, always encourage them to copy a given figure, as in Exs. 29 and 30, or draw a picture using the given information if one does not exist, as in Exs. 27 and 28. This practice allows them to refer to the drawing frequently when completing the proofs.

! COMMON ERROR
EXERCISES 28 AND 29 When students are proving a theorem and its converse, remind them that the "if" part of the theorem contains the given information, and the "then" part of the theorem is the part that they are trying to prove. Students may incorrectly switch the hypothesis and the conclusion.

29. Statements (Reasons)
1. **Draw a line through** $C \perp$ **to** $\overline{AB}$ **intersecting** $\overline{AB}$ **at a point** P**. (Through a point not on a line there is exactly one line ⊥ to a given line.)**
2. **∠CPA and ∠CPB are right ∠s. (Def. of ⊥ lines)**
3. **△CPA and △CPB are right △s. (Def. of right △)**
4. $CA = CB$**, or** $\overline{CA} \cong \overline{CB}$ **(Given; def. of cong.)**
5. $\overline{CP} \cong \overline{CP}$ **(Reflexive Prop. of Cong.)**
6. $\triangle CPA \cong \triangle CPB$ **(HL Cong. Thm.)**
7. $\overline{PA} \cong \overline{PB}$ **(Corresp. parts of ≅ △s are ≅.)**
8. $\overleftrightarrow{CP}$ **is the ⊥ bisector of** $\overline{AB}$ **and** C **is on the ⊥ bisector of** $\overline{AB}$**. (Def. of ⊥ bisector)**

30. See Additional Answers beginning on page AA1.

ENGLISH LEARNERS

EXERCISES 33–35 The sport of hockey may be unfamiliar to some English learners. Before students begin Exercises 33–35, you might ask a volunteer familiar with hockey and its terminology to explain how the sport is played and define the terms *rink, puck, goalie,* and *goal.*

38. slope of $\overline{WS} = -\frac{1}{3}$ and slope of $\overleftrightarrow{YX} = 3$, so $\overline{WS} \perp \overleftrightarrow{YX}$; slope of $\overline{WT} = 3$ and slope of $\overleftrightarrow{YZ} = -\frac{1}{3}$, so $\overline{WT} \perp \overleftrightarrow{YZ}$. (Nonvertical lines are $\perp$ if and only their the product of their slopes is -1.)

40. Converse of the Angle Bisector Theorem

ADDITIONAL PRACTICE AND RETEACHING

For Lesson 5.1:

- Practice Levels A, B, and C (*Chapter 5 Resource Book,* p. 17)
- Reteaching with Practice (*Chapter 5 Resource Book,* p. 20)
- See Lesson 5.1 of the *Personal Student Tutor*

For more Mixed Review:

- Search the *Test and Practice Generator* for key words or specific lessons.

32. (1) Given (2) equidistant (3) DA, DC (4) $\overrightarrow{BA}$, $\overrightarrow{DC}$ (5) $\angle BAD$ and $\angle BCD$ are right $\angle$s. (6) $\triangle DAB$ and $\triangle DCB$ are right $\triangle$s. (7) Reflexive Prop. of Cong. (8) $\triangle DAB \cong \triangle DCB$ (9) Corresp. parts of $\cong$ $\triangle$s are $\cong$. (10) Def. of $\angle$ bisector

32. **DEVELOPING PROOF** Use the diagram to complete the proof of Theorem 5.4, the Converse of the Angle Bisector Theorem.

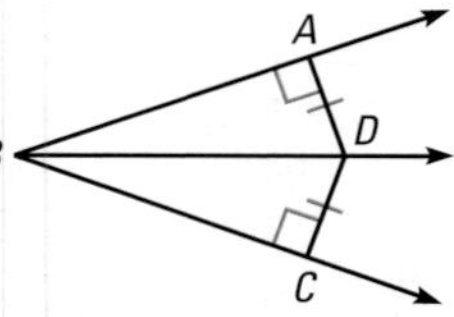

GIVEN ▶ D is in the interior of $\angle ABC$ and is equidistant from $\overrightarrow{BA}$ and $\overrightarrow{BC}$.

PROVE ▶ D lies on the angle bisector of $\angle ABC$.

Statements	Reasons
1. D is in the interior of $\angle ABC$.	**1.** ___?___
2. D is ___?___ from $\overrightarrow{BA}$ and $\overrightarrow{BC}$.	**2.** Given
3. ___?___ = ___?___	**3.** Definition of equidistant
4. $\overline{DA} \perp$ ___?___, ___?___ $\perp \overrightarrow{BC}$	**4.** Definition of distance from a point to a line
5. ___?___	**5.** If 2 lines are $\perp$, then they form 4 rt. $\angle$s.
6. ___?___	**6.** Definition of right triangle
7. $\overline{BD} \cong \overline{BD}$	**7.** ___?___
8. ___?___	**8.** HL Congruence Thm.
9. $\angle ABD \cong \angle CBD$	**9.** ___?___
10. $\overrightarrow{BD}$ bisects $\angle ABC$ and point D is on the bisector of $\angle ABC$.	**10.** ___?___

ICE HOCKEY **In Exercises 33–35, use the following information.** In the diagram, the goalie is at point G and the puck is at point P. The goalie's job is to prevent the puck from entering the goal.

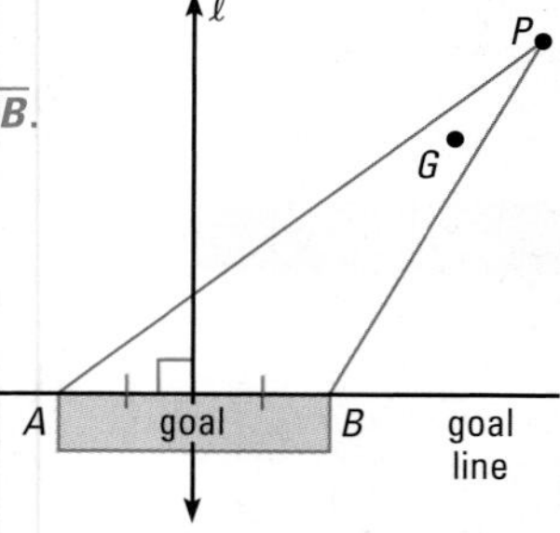

33. When the puck is at the other end of the rink, the goalie is likely to be standing on line ℓ. How is ℓ related to $\overline{AB}$? **ℓ is the $\perp$ bisector of $\overline{AB}$.**

34. As an opposing player with the puck skates toward the goal, the goalie is likely to move from line ℓ to other places on the ice. What should be the relationship between $\overrightarrow{PG}$ and $\angle APB$? **$\overrightarrow{PG}$ should bisect $\angle APB$.**

35. How does $m\angle APB$ change as the puck gets closer to the goal? Does this change make it easier or more difficult for the goalie to defend the goal? Explain.

35. $m\angle APB$ increases; more difficult; the goalie has a greater area to defend because the distances from the goalie to the sides of $\angle APB$ (the shooting angle) increase.

36. **TECHNOLOGY** Use geometry software to construct $\overline{AB}$. Find the midpoint C. Draw the perpendicular bisector of $\overline{AB}$ through C. Construct a point D along the perpendicular bisector and measure $\overline{DA}$ and $\overline{DB}$. Move D along the perpendicular bisector. What theorem does this construction demonstrate?

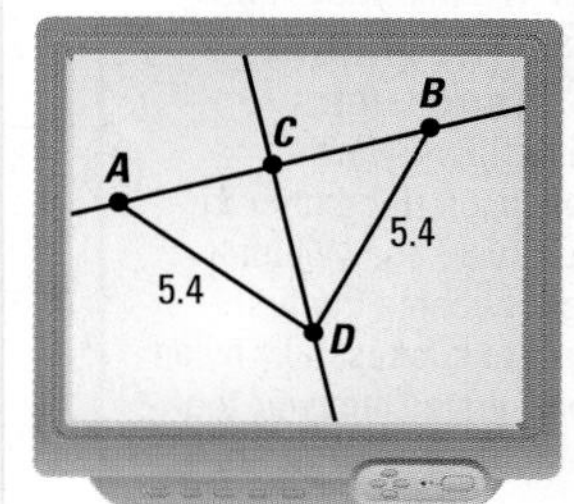

36. As D moves along the $\perp$ bisector, DA and DB change, but are always equal; Theorem 5.1.

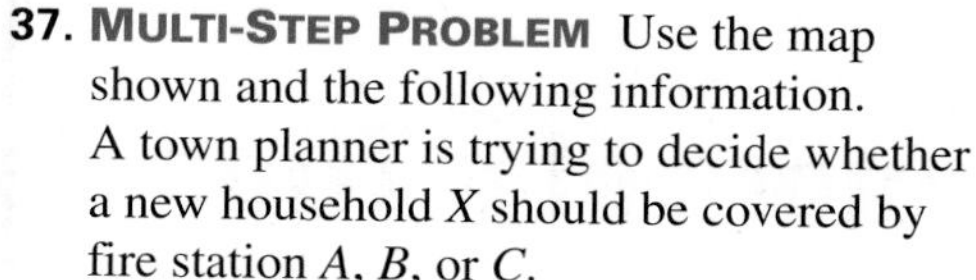

Test Preparation

38. slope of $\overrightarrow{WS} = -\frac{1}{3}$ and slope of $\overrightarrow{YX} = 3$, so $\overrightarrow{WS} \perp \overrightarrow{YX}$; slope of $\overrightarrow{WT} = 3$ and slope of $\overrightarrow{YZ} = -\frac{1}{3}$, so $\overrightarrow{WT} \perp \overrightarrow{YZ}$. (Nonvertical lines are ⊥ if and only if the product of their slopes is −1.)

40. $\overline{WS}$ and $\overline{WT}$ are perpendicular segments to the sides of ∠XYZ. Because $WS = WT$, W is equidistant from the sides of the angle. By Theorem 5.4, W is on the angle bisector so $\overrightarrow{YW}$ bisects ∠XYZ.

37. **MULTI-STEP PROBLEM** Use the map shown and the following information. A town planner is trying to decide whether a new household X should be covered by fire station A, B, or C.

a. Trace the map and draw the segments $\overline{AB}$, $\overline{BC}$, and $\overline{CA}$. **Check drawings.**

b. Construct the perpendicular bisectors of $\overline{AB}$, $\overline{BC}$, and $\overline{CA}$. Do the perpendicular bisectors meet at a point? **Check drawings; yes.**

c. The perpendicular bisectors divide the town into regions. Shade the region closest to fire station A red. Shade the region closest to fire station B blue. Shade the region closest to fire station C gray. **Check drawings.**

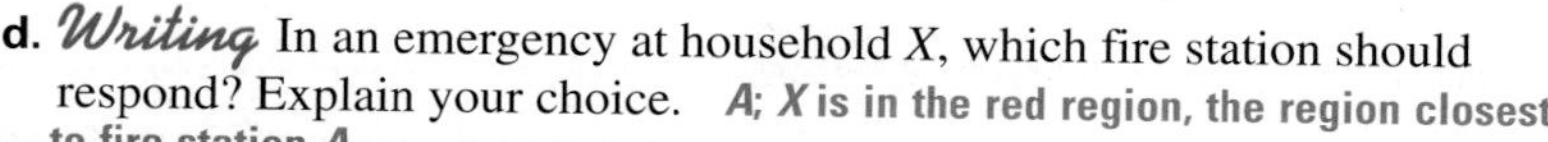

d. *Writing* In an emergency at household X, which fire station should respond? Explain your choice. **A; X is in the red region, the region closest to fire station A.**

★ **Challenge**

USING ALGEBRA Use the graph at the right.

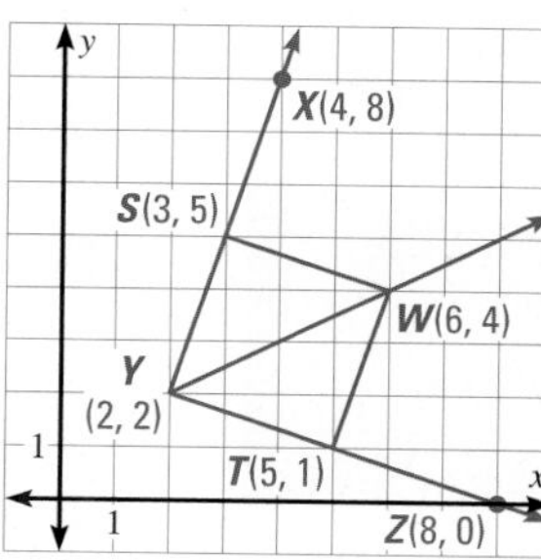

38. Use slopes to show that $\overrightarrow{WS} \perp \overrightarrow{YX}$ and that $\overrightarrow{WT} \perp \overrightarrow{YZ}$. **See margin.**

39. Find WS and WT. $WS = WT = \sqrt{10}$

40. Explain how you know that $\overrightarrow{YW}$ bisects ∠XYZ. **See margin.**

EXTRA CHALLENGE
www.mcdougallittell.com

MIXED REVIEW

CIRCLES Find the missing measurement for the circle shown. Use 3.14 as an approximation for π. (Review 1.7 for 5.2)

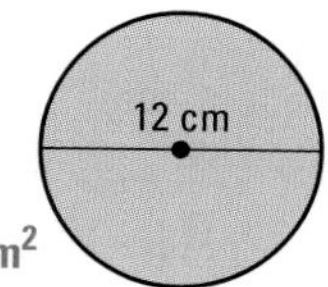

41. radius **6 cm**
42. circumference **about 37.68 cm**
43. area **about 113.04 cm²**

CALCULATING SLOPE Find the slope of the line that passes through the given points. (Review 3.6)

44. $A(-1, 5)$, $B(-2, 10)$ **−5**
45. $C(4, -3)$, $D(-6, 5)$ $-\frac{4}{5}$
46. $E(4, 5)$, $F(9, 5)$ **0**
47. $G(0, 8)$, $H(-7, 0)$ $\frac{8}{7}$
48. $J(3, 11)$, $K(-10, 12)$ $-\frac{1}{13}$
49. $L(-3, -8)$, $M(8, -8)$ **0**

USING ALGEBRA Find the value of x. (Review 4.1)

50. **59**

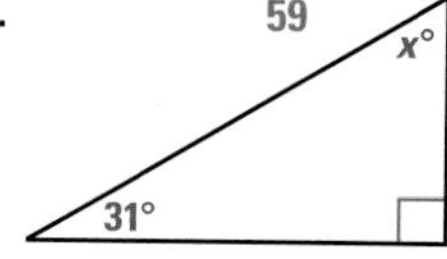

51. **34**

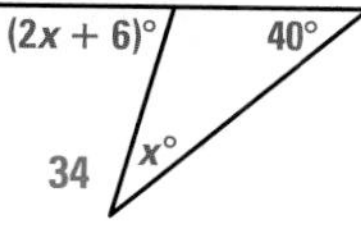

52. **8**

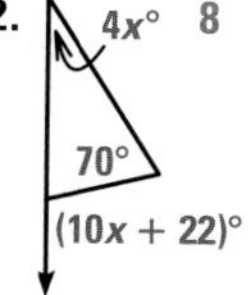

DAILY HOMEWORK QUIZ

Transparency Available

Use the diagram for Exercises 1–4.

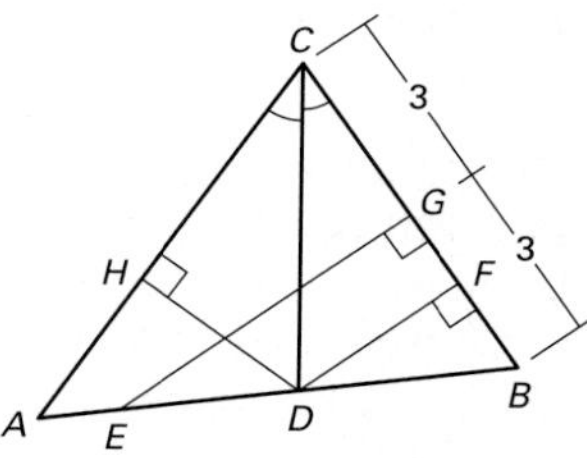

1. Which segment is the perpendicular bisector of $\overline{BC}$? $\overline{EG}$
2. Which segment is on the bisector of ∠ACB? $\overline{CD}$
3. If $m\angle ACD = 35°$, what is $m\angle ACB$? **70°**
4. If $DF = 4$, what is DH? **4**

EXTRA CHALLENGE NOTE

Challenge problems for Lesson 5.1 are available in **blackline** format in the *Chapter 5 Resource Book,* p. 24 and at **www.mcdougallittell.com.**

ADDITIONAL TEST PREPARATION

1. **WRITING** Explain how to construct a perpendicular to a given line through a point on the line. **See the activity box on page 264.**

1 PLAN

PACING
Basic: 2 days
Average: 2 days
Advanced: 2 days
Block Schedule: 1 block

LESSON OPENER
GEOMETRY SOFTWARE
An alternative way to approach Lesson 5.2 is to use the Geometry Software Lesson Opener:
- Blackline Master (*Chapter 5 Resource Book,* p. 28)
- Transparency (p. 29)

MEETING INDIVIDUAL NEEDS
- ***Chapter 5 Resource Book***
  Prerequisite Skills Review (p. 5)
  Practice Level A (p. 29)
  Practice Level B (p. 30)
  Practice Level C (p. 31)
  Reteaching with Practice (p. 32)
  Absent Student Catch-Up (p. 34)
  Challenge (p. 36)
- ***Resources in Spanish***
-  ***Personal Student Tutor***

NEW-TEACHER SUPPORT
See the Tips for New Teachers on pp. 1–2 of the *Chapter 5 Resource Book* for additional notes about Lesson 5.2.

WARM-UP EXERCISES
Transparency Available
Tell if the geometric figure can have a bisector.
1. angle yes
2. ray no
3. line no
4. segment yes
5. point no

5.2 Bisectors of a Triangle

What you should learn

GOAL 1 Use properties of perpendicular bisectors of a triangle, as applied in **Example 1**.

GOAL 2 Use properties of angle bisectors of a triangle.

Why you should learn it

▼ To solve **real-life** problems, such as finding the center of a mushroom ring in **Exs. 24–26**.

CALIFORNIA STANDARDS AND ASSESSMENT
CA Standards: 16, 21
SAT9 Task 1: Obj. 25

GOAL 1 USING PERPENDICULAR BISECTORS OF A TRIANGLE

In Lesson 5.1, you studied properties of perpendicular bisectors of segments and angle bisectors. In this lesson, you will study the special cases in which the segments and angles being bisected are parts of a triangle.

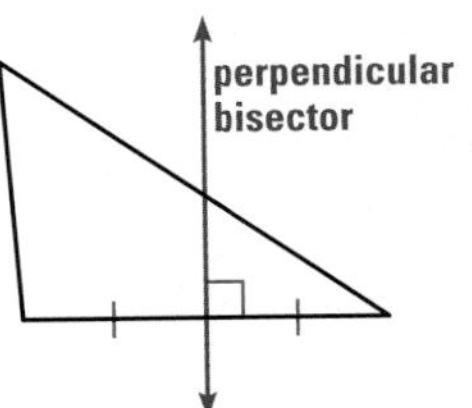

A **perpendicular bisector of a triangle** is a line (or ray or segment) that is perpendicular to a side of the triangle at the midpoint of the side.

ACTIVITY Developing Concepts: Perpendicular Bisectors of a Triangle

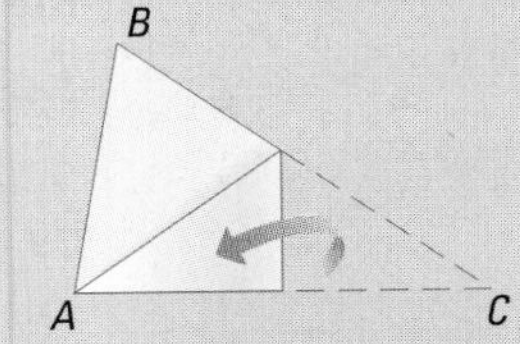

1. Cut four large acute scalene triangles out of paper. Make each one different.
2. Choose one triangle. Fold the triangle to form the perpendicular bisectors of the sides. Do the three bisectors intersect at the same point? yes
3. Repeat the process for the other three triangles. What do you observe? Write your observation in the form of a conjecture. For any △, the ⊥ bisectors of the 3 sides intersect at the same point.
4. Choose one triangle. Label the vertices A, B, and C. Label the point of intersection of the perpendicular bisectors as P. Measure $\overline{AP}$, $\overline{BP}$, and $\overline{CP}$. What do you observe? $\overline{AP}$, $\overline{BP}$, and $\overline{CP}$ are ≅.

When three or more lines (or rays or segments) intersect in the same point, they are called **concurrent lines** (or rays or segments). The point of intersection of the lines is called the **point of concurrency**.

The three perpendicular bisectors of a triangle are concurrent. The point of concurrency can be *inside* the triangle, *on* the triangle, or *outside* the triangle.

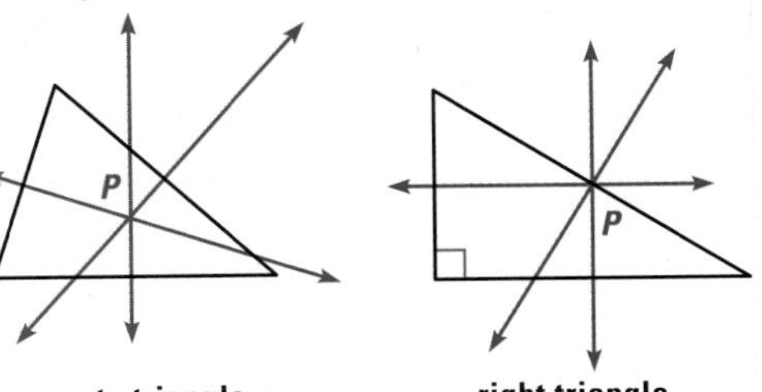

acute triangle   right triangle

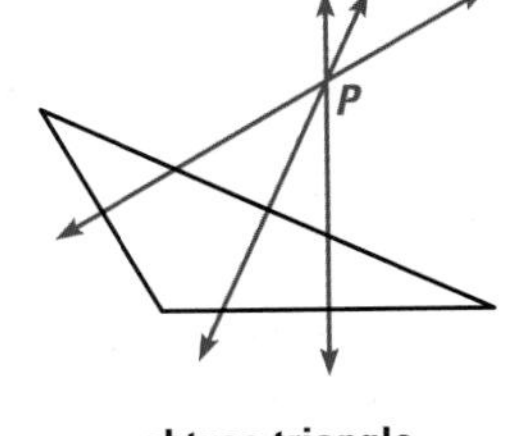

obtuse triangle

The point of concurrency of the perpendicular bisectors of a triangle is called the **circumcenter of the triangle.** In each triangle at the bottom of page 272, the circumcenter is at P. The circumcenter of a triangle has a special property, as described in Theorem 5.5. You will use coordinate geometry to illustrate this theorem in Exercises 29–31. A proof appears on page 835.

THEOREM

THEOREM 5.5 ***Concurrency of Perpendicular Bisectors of a Triangle***

The perpendicular bisectors of a triangle intersect at a point that is equidistant from the vertices of the triangle.

$$PA = PB = PC$$

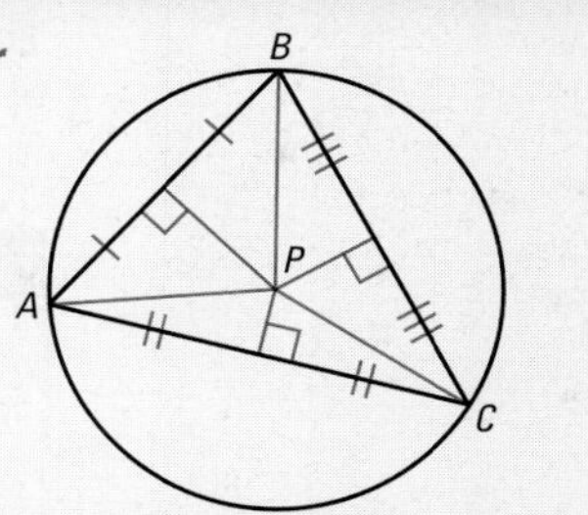

The diagram for Theorem 5.5 shows that the circumcenter is the center of the circle that passes through the vertices of the triangle. The circle is *circumscribed* about $\triangle ABC$. Thus, the radius of this circle is the distance from the center to any of the vertices.

EXAMPLE 1 *Using Perpendicular Bisectors*

FACILITIES PLANNING A company plans to build a distribution center that is convenient to three of its major clients. The planners start by roughly locating the three clients on a sketch and finding the circumcenter of the triangle formed.

a. Explain why using the circumcenter as the location of a distribution center would be convenient for all the clients.

b. Make a sketch of the triangle formed by the clients. Locate the circumcenter of the triangle. Tell what segments are congruent.

Client F
Client E
Client G

SOLUTION

a. Because the circumcenter is equidistant from the three vertices, each client would be equally close to the distribution center.

b. Label the vertices of the triangle as E, F, and G. Draw the perpendicular bisectors. Label their intersection as D.

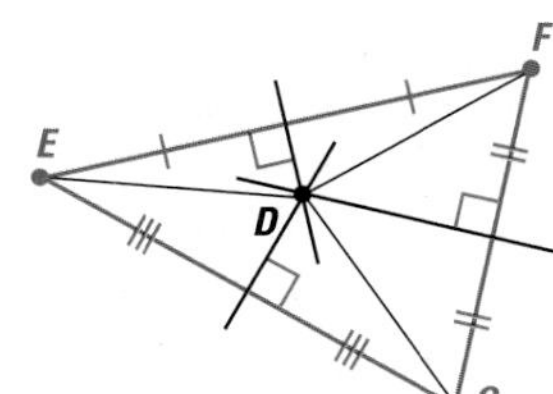

▶ By Theorem 5.5, $DE = DF = DG$.

STUDENT HELP

INTERNET HOMEWORK HELP Visit our Web site www.mcdougallittell.com for extra examples.

2 TEACH

EXTRA EXAMPLE 1

Three people need to decide on a location to hold a monthly meeting. They will all be coming from different places in the city, and they want to make the meeting location the same distance from each person.

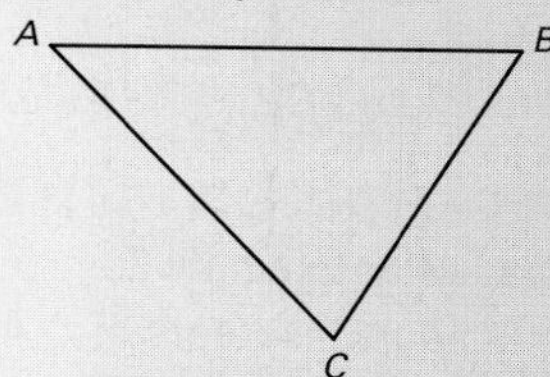

a. Explain why using the circumcenter as the location for the meeting would be the fairest for all. **Because the circumcenter is equidistant from the three vertices, so each person will be equally distant from the point.**

b. Copy the triangle and locate the circumcenter. Tell what segments are congruent. ***PA = PB = PC***

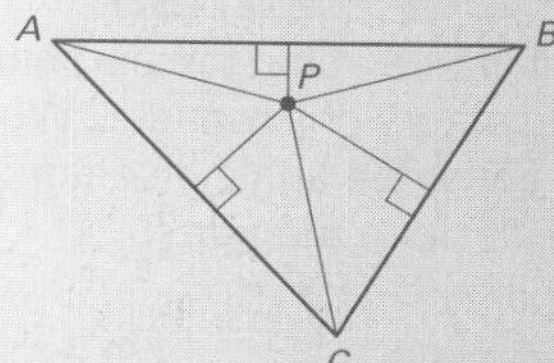

CHECKPOINT EXERCISES

For use after Example 1:

1. a. Which point is the best spot for placing a sprinkler to water the plants located at point X, Y, and Z?

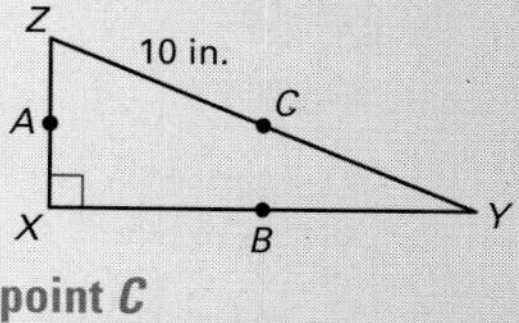

point *C*

b. If the sprinkler covers a circular region with a radius of 15. in., will the water reach all three plants? **yes**

EXTRA EXAMPLE 2

The angle bisectors of $\triangle XYZ$ meet at point P.

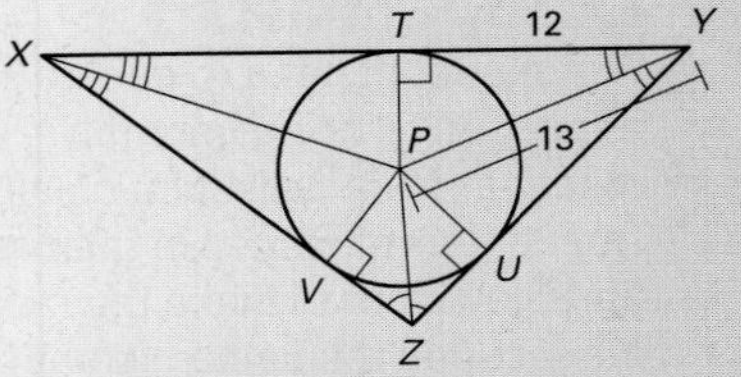

a. What segments are congruent? $\overline{PT} \cong \overline{PV} \cong \overline{PU}$

b. Find PT and PV. $PT = PV = 5$

CHECKPOINT EXERCISES

For use after Example 2:

1. The angle bisectors of $\triangle ABC$ meet at point L. Find AL and FL. $AL = 10$; $FL = 6$

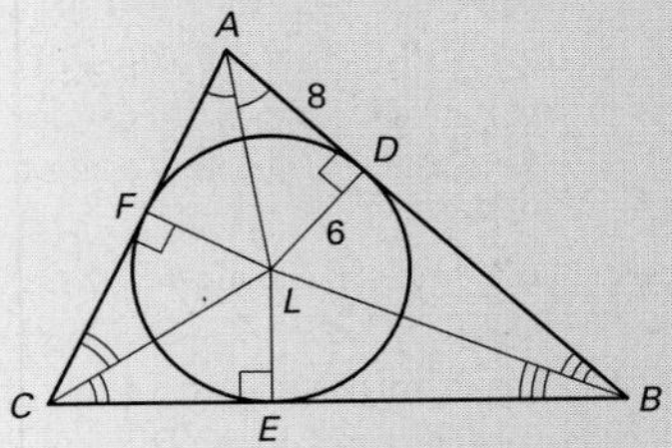

CLOSURE QUESTION

What is true about the perpendicular bisectors of a triangle? What is true about the angle bisectors of the sides of a triangle?

The perpendicular bisectors meet at a point of concurrency that is equidistant from the vertices of the triangle. This point may or may not be inside the triangle. The angle bisectors meet at a point of concurrency inside the triangle that is equidistant from the sides of the triangle.

GOAL 2 USING ANGLE BISECTORS OF A TRIANGLE

An **angle bisector of a triangle** is a bisector of an angle of the triangle. The three angle bisectors are concurrent. The point of concurrency of the angle bisectors is called the **incenter of the triangle,** and it always lies inside the triangle. The incenter has a special property that is described below in Theorem 5.6. Exercise 22 asks you to write a proof of this theorem.

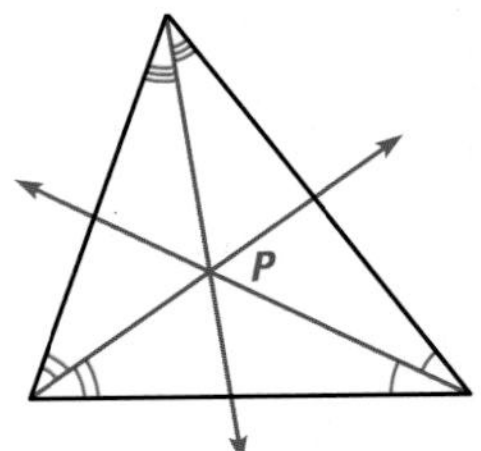

THEOREM

THEOREM 5.6 ***Concurrency of Angle Bisectors of a Triangle***

The angle bisectors of a triangle intersect at a point that is equidistant from the sides of the triangle.

$$PD = PE = PF$$

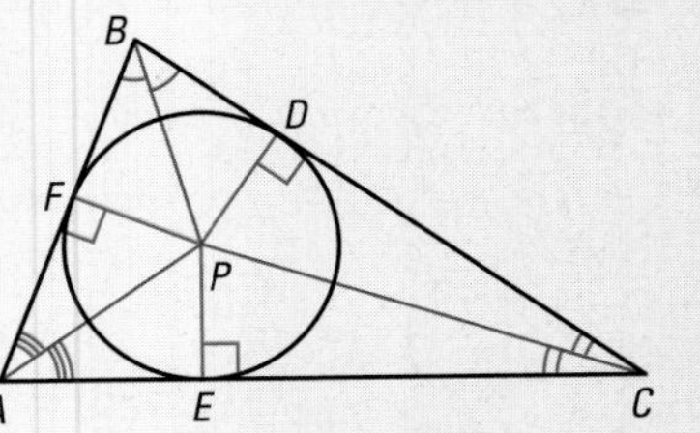

The diagram for Theorem 5.6 shows that the incenter is the center of the circle that touches each side of the triangle once. The circle is *inscribed* within $\triangle ABC$. Thus, the radius of this circle is the distance from the center to any of the sides.

EXAMPLE 2 *Using Angle Bisectors*

The angle bisectors of $\triangle MNP$ meet at point L.

a. What segments are congruent?

b. Find LQ and LR.

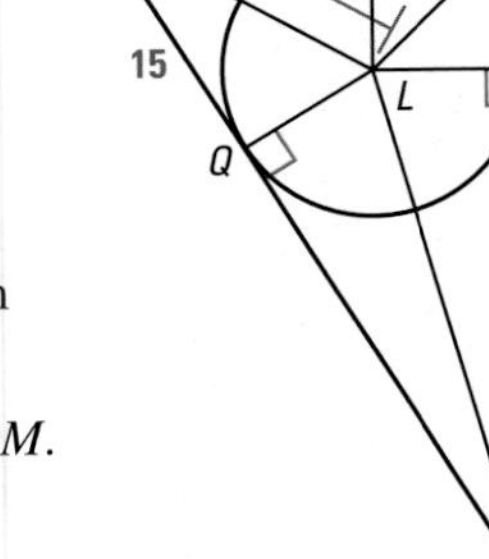

SOLUTION

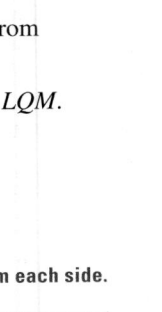

a. By Theorem 5.6, the three angle bisectors of a triangle intersect at a point that is equidistant from the sides of the triangle. So, $\overline{LR} \cong \overline{LQ} \cong \overline{LS}$.

b. Use the Pythagorean Theorem to find LQ in $\triangle LQM$.

$(LQ)^2 + (MQ)^2 = (LM)^2$

$(LQ)^2 + 15^2 = 17^2$ **Substitute.**

$(LQ)^2 + 225 = 289$ **Multiply.**

$(LQ)^2 = 64$ **Subtract 225 from each side.**

$LQ = 8$ **Find the positive square root.**

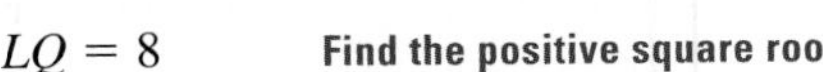

▶ So, $LQ = 8$ units. Because $\overline{LR} \cong \overline{LQ}$, $LR = 8$ units.

STUDENT HELP

Look Back

For help with the Pythagorean Theorem, see p. 20.

GUIDED PRACTICE

Vocabulary Check ✓

1. If three or more lines intersect at the same point, the lines are ___?___. concurrent

Concept Check ✓

2. Think of something about the words *incenter* and *circumcenter* that you can use to remember which special parts of a triangle meet at each point.

2. *Sample answer:* I will remember that the ∠ bisectors of a △ always intersect *inside* the circle, so their intersection point is the *incenter.* The ⊥ bisectors of the sides of a △ can intersect *outside* the △. The circle circumscribed about a △ is around (or outside) the △, so I will remember that the ⊥ bisectors intersect at the *circumcenter.*

Skill Check ✓

Use the diagram and the given information to find the indicated measure.

3. The perpendicular bisectors of △*ABC* meet at point *G*. Find *GC*. 7

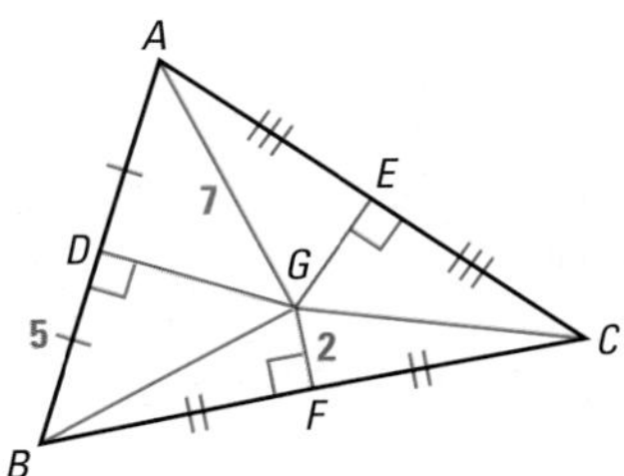

4. The angle bisectors of △*XYZ* meet at point *M*. Find *MK*. 5

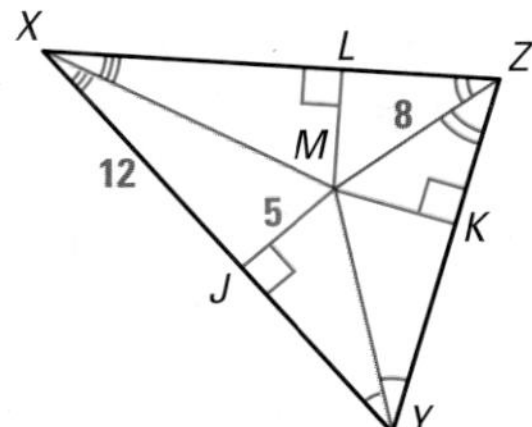

PRACTICE AND APPLICATIONS

STUDENT HELP

Extra Practice to help you master skills is on p. 811.

CONSTRUCTION **Draw a large example of the given type of triangle. Construct perpendicular bisectors of the sides. (See page 264.) For the type of triangle, do the bisectors intersect *inside, on,* or *outside* the triangle?**

5–7. Check constructions.

5. obtuse triangle outside

6. acute triangle inside

7. right triangle on

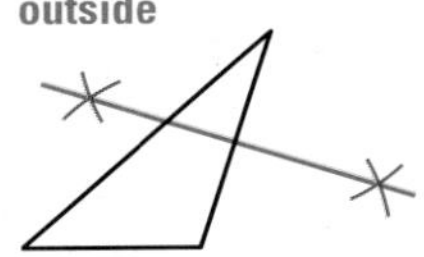

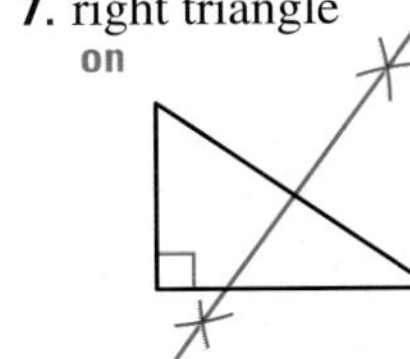

DRAWING CONCLUSIONS **Draw a large △*ABC*.**

8. Construct the angle bisectors of △*ABC*. Label the point where the angle bisectors meet as *D*. Check constructions.

9. Construct perpendicular segments from *D* to each of the sides of the triangle. Measure each segment. What do you notice? Which theorem have you just confirmed? The segments are ≅; Thm. 5.6.

LOGICAL REASONING **Use the results of Exercises 5–9 to complete the statement using *always, sometimes,* or *never.***

10. A perpendicular bisector of a triangle ___?___ passes through the midpoint of a side of the triangle. always

11. The angle bisectors of a triangle ___?___ intersect at a single point. always

12. The angle bisectors of a triangle ___?___ meet at a point outside the triangle. never

13. The circumcenter of a triangle ___?___ lies outside the triangle. sometimes

STUDENT HELP

HOMEWORK HELP

Example 1: Exs. 5–7, 10–13, 14, 17, 20, 21

Example 2: Exs. 8, 9, 10–13, 15, 16, 22

3 APPLY

ASSIGNMENT GUIDE

BASIC

Day 1: pp. 275–276 Exs. 6–18 even

Day 2: pp. 275–278 Exs. 5–19 odd, 20–22, 24–28, 32–40

AVERAGE

Day 1: pp. 275–276 Exs. 6–18 even

Day 2: pp. 275–278 Exs. 5–19 odd, 20–28, 32–40

ADVANCED

Day 1: pp. 275–276 Exs. 6–18 even

Day 2: pp. 275–278 Exs. 5–19 odd, 20–40

BLOCK SCHEDULE

pp. 275–278 Exs. 5–28, 32–40

EXERCISE LEVELS

Level A: *Easier* 5–7, 10–13

Level B: *More Difficult* 8, 9, 14–28

Level C: *Most Difficult* 29–31

HOMEWORK CHECK

To quickly check student understanding of key concepts, go over the following exercises: Exs. 6, 8, 10, 14, 18, 20, 22, 26. See also the Daily Homework Quiz:

- Blackline Master (*Chapter 5 Resource Book,* p. 39)
- Transparency (p. 35)

COMMON ERROR

EXERCISES 10–13 Students may confuse the circumcenter of a triangle with the incenter of a triangle. Use the idea that "incenter" contains the word "in" so it must be inside the triangle. The circumcenter need not be inside the triangle.

! COMMON ERROR

EXERCISES 18 AND 19

Students have a tendency to confuse the results of Theorems 5.5 and 5.6. These exercises should serve as an indicator as to which students are having this problem. Refer these students back to pages 273 and 274.

21. 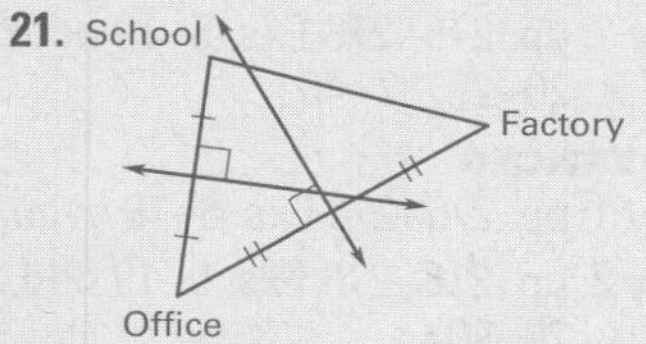

BISECTORS **In each case, find the indicated measure.**

14. The perpendicular bisectors of $\triangle RST$ meet at point D. Find DR. **9**

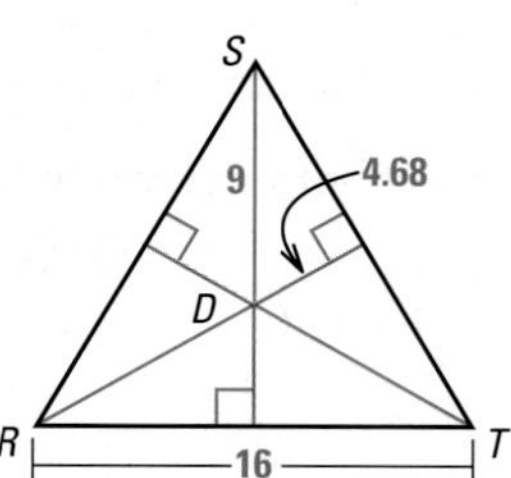

15. The angle bisectors of $\triangle XYZ$ meet at point W. Find WB. **20**

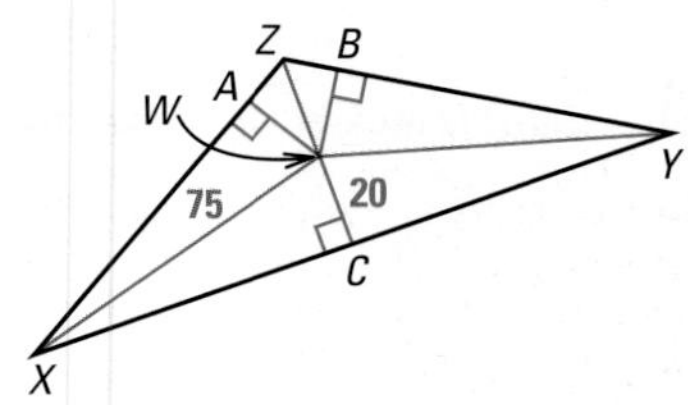

16. The angle bisectors of $\triangle GHJ$ meet at point K. Find KB. **3**

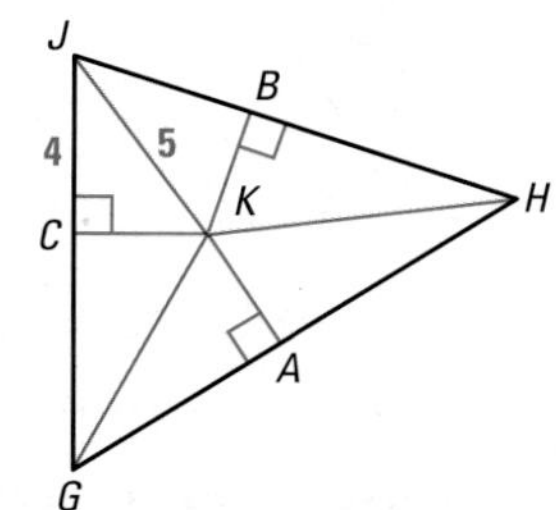

17. The perpendicular bisectors of $\triangle MNP$ meet at point Q. Find QN. **25**

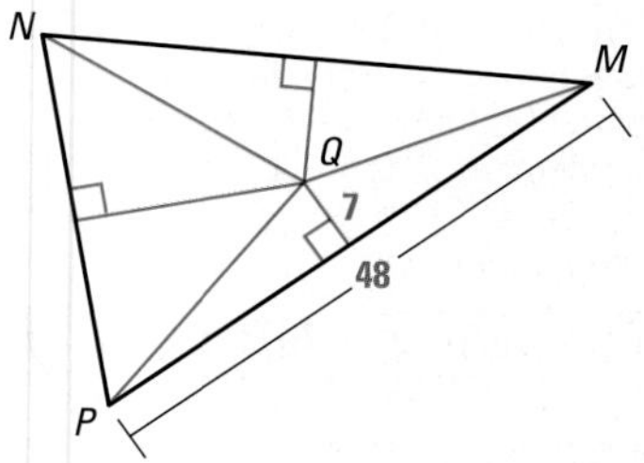

ERROR ANALYSIS **Explain why the student's conclusion is *false*. Then state a correct conclusion that can be deduced from the diagram.**

18.

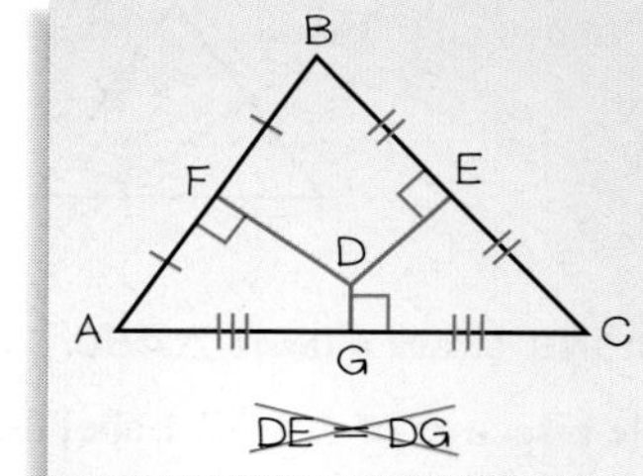

19.

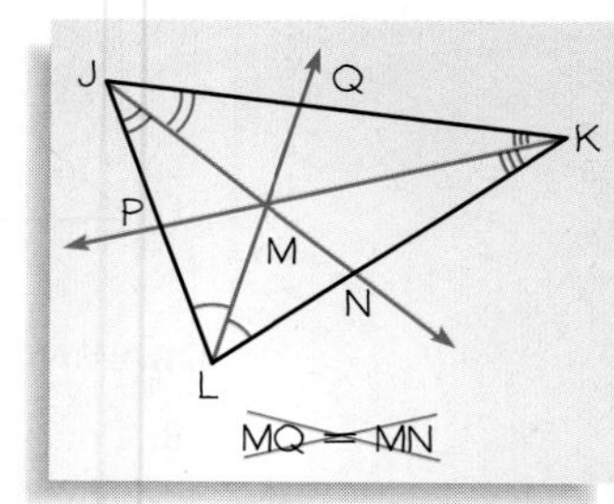

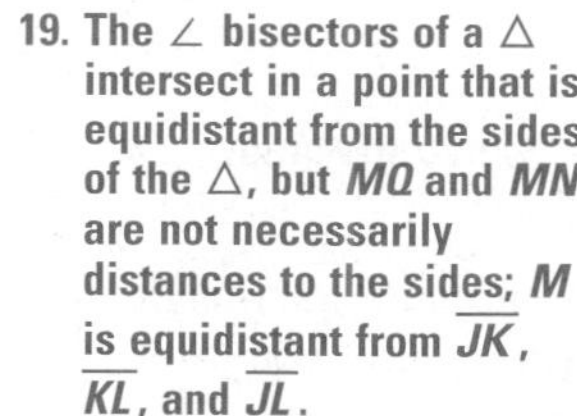

18. The ⊥ bisectors of a △ intersect in a point that is equidistant from the vertices of the △, not the sides; *D* is equidistant from *A*, *B*, and *C*.

19. The ∠ bisectors of a △ intersect in a point that is equidistant from the sides of the △, but *MQ* and *MN* are not necessarily distances to the sides; *M* is equidistant from $\overline{JK}$, $\overline{KL}$, and $\overline{JL}$.

20. Construct 2 of the ⊥ bisectors of the △; the point where the ⊥ bisectors of a △ intersect is equidistant from the vertices, so the point constructed is equidistant from the two workplaces and the school.

LOGICAL REASONING **In Exercises 20 and 21, use the following information and map.**

Your family is considering moving to a new home. The diagram shows the locations of where your parents work and where you go to school. The locations form a triangle.

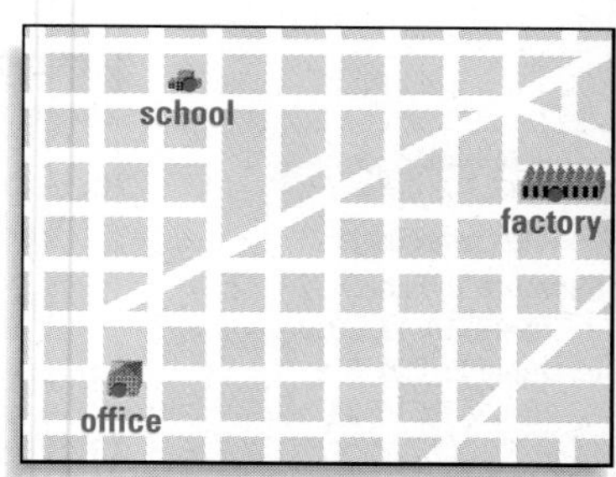

20. In the diagram, how could you find a point that is equidistant from each location? Explain your answer.

21. Make a sketch of the situation. Find the best location for the new home. **See margin.**

22. (2) $\overline{DE}$; equidistant

(3) $\overrightarrow{BD}$ bisects $\angle ABC$, so D is equidistant from the sides of $\angle ABC$.

(4) Trans. prop. of equality

(5) bisector

(6) D is equidistant from the sides of $\triangle ABC$; 2–4.

23. According to this lesson, the perpendicular bisectors of a right triangle meet at a point on the hypotenuse. Because this point lies on $\overline{RS}$ and on the perpendicular bisector of $\overline{RS}$, it is the midpoint of $\overline{RS}$. Call this point Q. Point Q is on the perpendicular bisector of $\overline{RT}$, so $QR = QT$ (by Theorem 5.1). Also, Q is on the perpendicular bisector of $\overline{ST}$, so $QS = QT$ (by Theorem 5.1). By transitivity, $QR = QS = QT$, so Q is equidistant from all three vertices of the triangle.

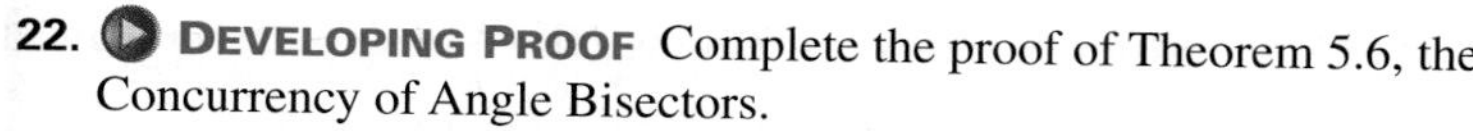

22. **DEVELOPING PROOF** Complete the proof of Theorem 5.6, the Concurrency of Angle Bisectors.

GIVEN ▶ $\triangle ABC$, the bisectors of $\angle A$, $\angle B$, and $\angle C$, $\overline{DE} \perp \overline{AB}$, $\overline{DF} \perp \overline{BC}$, $\overline{DG} \perp \overline{CA}$

PROVE ▶ The angle bisectors intersect at a point that is equidistant from $\overline{AB}$, $\overline{BC}$, and $\overline{CA}$.

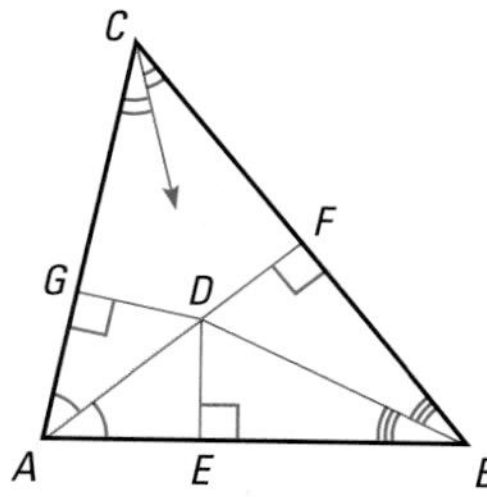

Plan for Proof Show that D, the point of intersection of the bisectors of $\angle A$ and $\angle B$, also lies on the bisector of $\angle C$. Then show that D is equidistant from the sides of the triangle.

Statements	Reasons
1. $\triangle ABC$, the bisectors of $\angle A$, $\angle B$, and $\angle C$, $\overline{DE} \perp \overline{AB}$, $\overline{DF} \perp \overline{BC}$, $\overline{DG} \perp \overline{CA}$	1. Given
2. __?__ $= DG$	2. $\overrightarrow{AD}$ bisects $\angle BAC$, so D is __?__ from the sides of $\angle BAC$.
3. $DE = DF$	3. __?__
4. $DF = DG$	4. __?__
5. D is on the __?__ of $\angle C$.	5. Converse of the Angle Bisector Theorem
6. __?__	6. Givens and Steps __?__

23. *Writing* Joannie thinks that the midpoint of the hypotenuse of a right triangle is equidistant from the vertices of the triangle. Explain how she could use perpendicular bisectors to verify her conjecture.

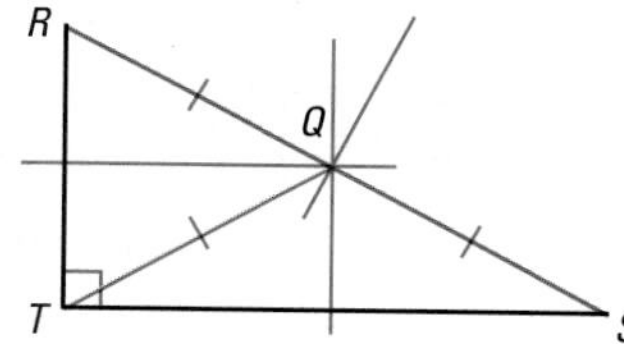

FOCUS ON APPLICATIONS

REAL LIFE **MUSHROOMS** live for only a few days. As the mycelium spreads outward, new mushroom rings are formed. A mushroom ring in France is almost half a mile in diameter and is about 700 years old.

SCIENCE CONNECTION **In Exercises 24–26, use the following information.**
A *mycelium* fungus grows underground in all directions from a central point. Under certain conditions, mushrooms sprout up in a ring at the edge. The radius of the mushroom ring is an indication of the mycelium's age.

24. Suppose three mushrooms in a mushroom ring are located as shown. Make a large copy of the diagram and draw $\triangle ABC$. Each unit on your coordinate grid should represent 1 foot. Check drawings.

25. Draw perpendicular bisectors on your diagram to find the center of the mushroom ring. Estimate the radius of the ring. about $2\frac{1}{2}$ feet

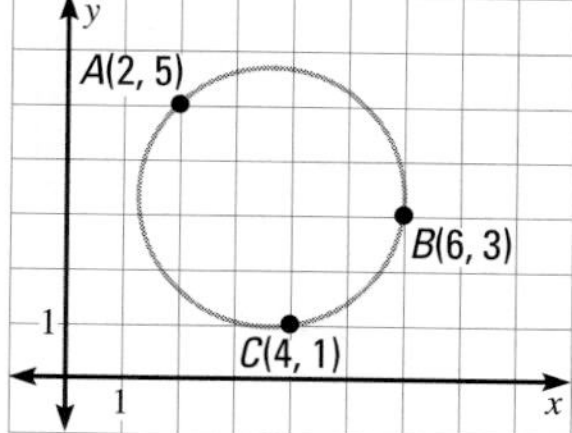

26. Suppose the radius of the mycelium increases at a rate of about 8 inches per year. Estimate its age. about $3\frac{3}{4}$ years

TEACHING TIPS

EXERCISE 23 After students have written their explanations, you may wish to have them write a formal proof of this conjecture.

ADDITIONAL PRACTICE AND RETEACHING

For Lesson 5.2:

- Practice Levels A, B, and C (*Chapter 5 Resource Book*, p. 29)
- Reteaching with Practice (*Chapter 5 Resource Book*, p. 32)
- See Lesson 5.2 of the *Personal Student Tutor*

For more Mixed Review:

- Search the *Test and Practice Generator* for key words or specific lessons.

4 ASSESS

DAILY HOMEWORK QUIZ

Transparency Available

1. The perpendicular bisectors of $\triangle PQR$ meet at point M.

a. What is a name for point M? **circumcenter**

b. What kind of triangle is $\triangle PMQ$? **isosceles**

2. The angle bisectors of $\triangle DEF$ meet at point G.

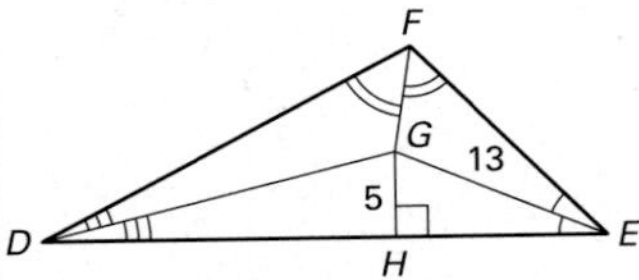

a. What is the radius of the inscribed circle of $\triangle DEF$? **5**

b. Find EH. **12**

EXTRA CHALLENGE NOTE

Challenge problems for Lesson 5.2 are available in **blackline** format in the *Chapter 5 Resource Book,* p. 36 and at **www.mcdougallittell.com.**

ADDITIONAL TEST PREPARATION

1. WRITING In the isosceles triangle below, point P is the incenter of $\triangle LMN$ and $LM = LN$. On which line will the circumcenter of the triangle lie? Explain.

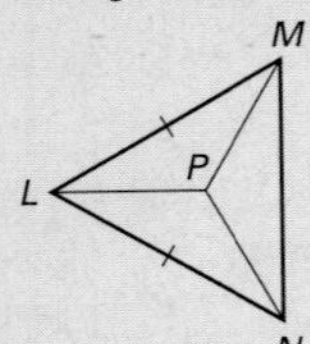

$\overleftrightarrow{LP}$; in an isosceles triangle, the bisector of the vertex angle is also the perpendicular bisector of the base. Thus, the circumcenter must lie somewhere on $\overleftrightarrow{LP}$.

Test Preparation

MULTIPLE CHOICE Choose the correct answer from the list given.

27. $\overline{AD}$ and $\overline{CD}$ are angle bisectors of $\triangle ABC$ and $m\angle ABC = 100°$. Find $m\angle ADC$. **E**

(A) 80° (B) 90° (C) 100° (D) 120° (E) 140°

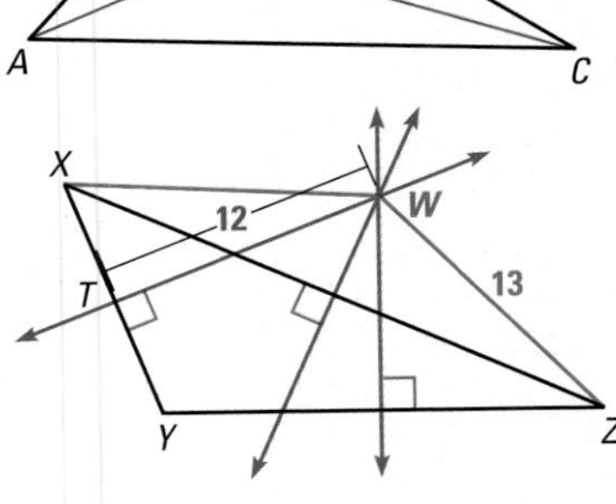

28. The perpendicular bisectors of $\triangle XYZ$ intersect at point W, $WT = 12$, and $WZ = 13$. Find XY. **C**

(A) 5 (B) 8 (C) 10 (D) 12 (E) 13

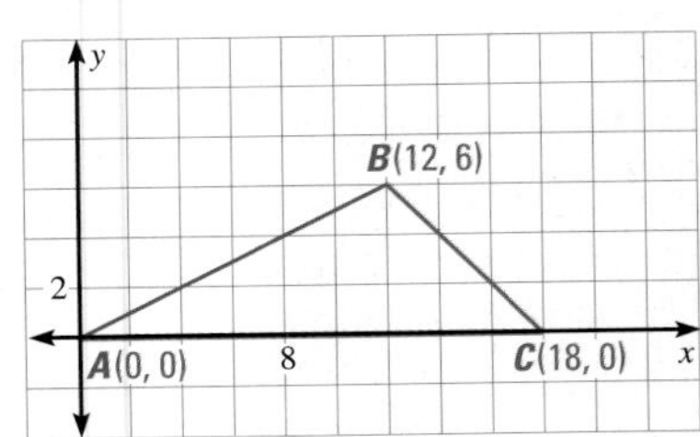

★ Challenge

29. $\overline{AC}$: (9, 0), $x = 9$; $\overline{AB}$: (6, 3), $y = -2x + 15$; $\overline{BC}$: (15, 3), $y = x - 12$

30. Let $P = (9, -3)$; $9 = 9$, so P is on $\overline{AC}$, $-3 = -2(9) + 15$, so P is on $\overline{AB}$; $-3 = 9 - 12$, so P is on $\overline{BC}$.

EXTRA CHALLENGE
www.mcdougallittell.com

USING ALGEBRA Use the graph of $\triangle ABC$ to illustrate Theorem 5.5, the Concurrency of Perpendicular Bisectors.

29. Find the midpoint of each side of $\triangle ABC$. Use the midpoints to find the equations of the perpendicular bisectors of $\triangle ABC$.

30. Using your equations from Exercise 29, find the intersection of two of the lines. Show that the point is on the third line.

31. Show that the point in Exercise 30 is equidistant from the vertices of $\triangle ABC$.
Let $P = (9, -3)$; $PA = PB = PC = 3\sqrt{10}$

MIXED REVIEW

FINDING AREAS Find the area of the triangle described. (Review 1.7 for 5.3)

32. base = 9, height = 5 **22.5 square units**

33. base = 22, height = 7 **77 square units**

WRITING EQUATIONS The line with the given equation is perpendicular to line j at point P. Write an equation of line j. (Review 3.7)

34. $y = 3x - 2$, $P(1, 4)$ $\quad y = -\frac{1}{3}x + \frac{13}{3}$

35. $y = -2x + 5$, $P(7, 6)$ $\quad y = \frac{1}{2}x + \frac{5}{2}$

36. $y = -\frac{2}{3}x - 1$, $P(2, 8)$ $\quad y = \frac{3}{2}x + 5$

37. $y = \frac{10}{11}x + 3$, $P(-2, -9)$ $\quad y = -\frac{11}{10}x - \frac{56}{5}$

LOGICAL REASONING Decide whether enough information is given to prove that the triangles are congruent. If there is enough information, tell which congruence postulate or theorem you would use. (Review 4.3, 4.4, and 4.6)

38.

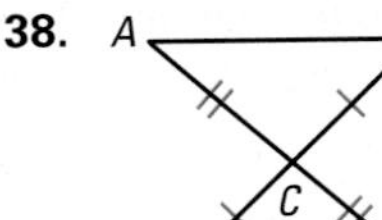

yes; SAS Cong. Post.

39.

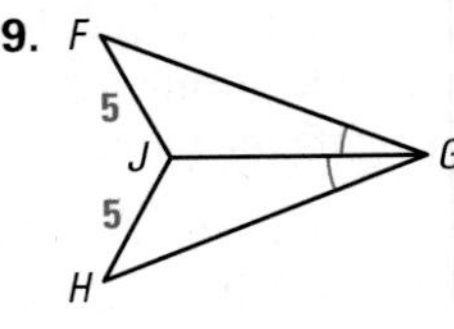

no

40.

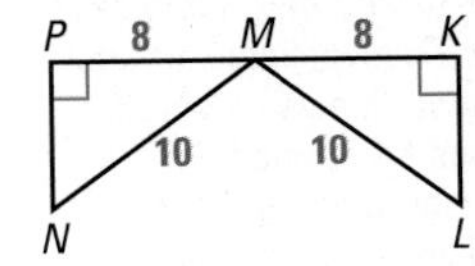

yes; HL Cong. Thm.

5.3 Medians and Altitudes of a Triangle

What you should learn

GOAL 1 Use properties of medians of a triangle.

GOAL 2 Use properties of altitudes of a triangle.

Why you should learn it

▼ To solve **real-life** problems, such as locating points in a triangle used to measure a person's heart fitness as in **Exs. 30–33**.

REAL LIFE

CALIFORNIA STANDARDS AND ASSESSMENT

CA Standards: 16

GOAL 1 USING MEDIANS OF A TRIANGLE

In Lesson 5.2, you studied two special types of segments of a triangle: perpendicular bisectors of the sides and angle bisectors. In this lesson, you will study two other special types of segments of a triangle: *medians* and *altitudes*.

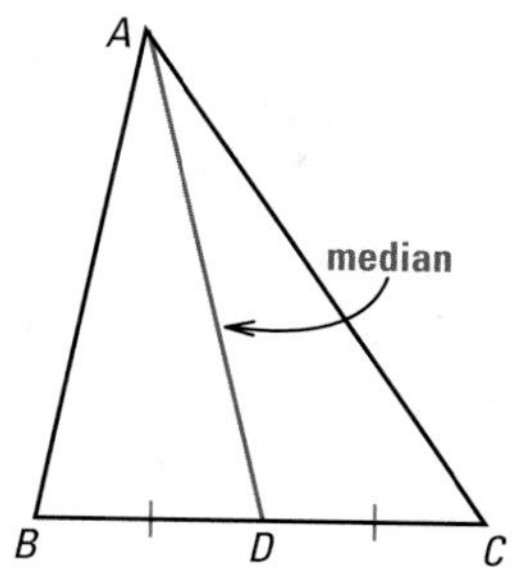

A **median of a triangle** is a segment whose endpoints are a vertex of the triangle and the midpoint of the opposite side. For instance, in $\triangle ABC$ shown at the right, D is the midpoint of side $\overline{BC}$. So, $\overline{AD}$ is a median of the triangle.

The three medians of a triangle are concurrent. The point of concurrency is called the **centroid of the triangle**. The centroid, labeled P in the diagrams below, is always inside the triangle.

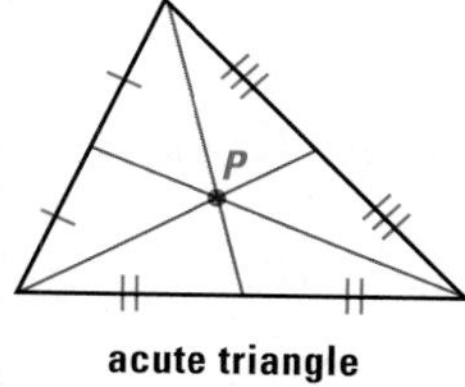

acute triangle

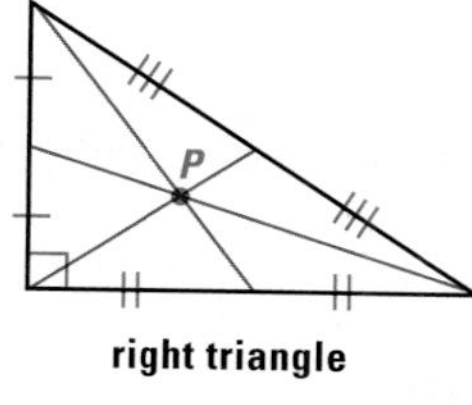

right triangle

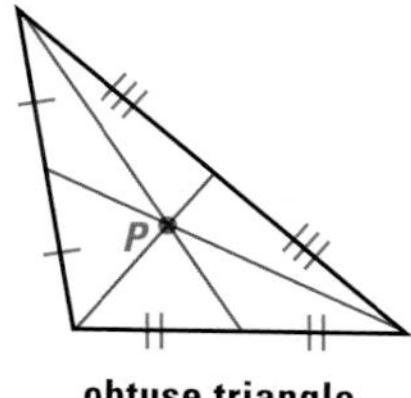

obtuse triangle

The medians of a triangle have a special concurrency property, as described in Theorem 5.7. Exercises 13–16 ask you to use paper folding to demonstrate the relationships in this theorem. A proof appears on pages 836–837.

THEOREM

THEOREM 5.7 ***Concurrency of Medians of a Triangle***

The medians of a triangle intersect at a point that is two thirds of the distance from each vertex to the midpoint of the opposite side.

If P is the centroid of $\triangle ABC$, then

$AP = \frac{2}{3}AD$, $BP = \frac{2}{3}BF$, and $CP = \frac{2}{3}CE$.

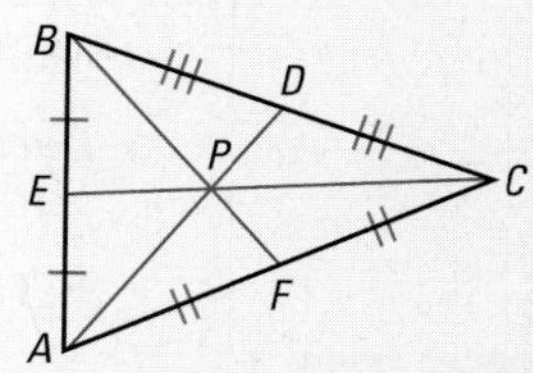

The centroid of a triangle can be used as its balancing point, as shown on the next page.

1 PLAN

PACING

Basic: 2 days
Average: 2 days
Advanced: 2 days
Block Schedule: 1 block

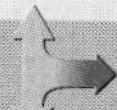

LESSON OPENER APPLICATION

An alternative way to approach Lesson 5.3 is to use the Application Lesson Opener:

- Blackline Master (*Chapter 5 Resource Book*, p. 40)
- Transparency (p. 30)

MEETING INDIVIDUAL NEEDS

- ***Chapter 5 Resource Book***
  Prerequisite Skills Review (p. 5)
  Practice Level A (p. 43)
  Practice Level B (p. 44)
  Practice Level C (p. 45)
  Reteaching with Practice (p. 46)
  Absent Student Catch-Up (p. 48)
  Challenge (p. 51)
- ***Resources in Spanish***
- ***Personal Student Tutor***

NEW-TEACHER SUPPORT

See the Tips for New Teachers on pp. 1–2 of the *Chapter 5 Resource Book* for additional notes about Lesson 5.3.

WARM-UP EXERCISES

Transparency Available

Find the product.

1. $\frac{5}{3}(12)$ 20
2. $\frac{2}{3} \cdot \frac{6}{11}$ $\frac{4}{11}$
3. $6\left(\frac{3}{4}\right)$ $\frac{9}{2}$

Simplify.

4. $\frac{6+9}{2}$ $\frac{15}{2}$
5. $\frac{10+8}{13-7}$ 3

2 TEACH

Motivating the Lesson

Cut out a cardboard triangle and try to balance it on the tip of a pencil. Once the balancing point is found, ask students if they think every triangle has a balancing point. Explain that they will find out in this lesson and that they will learn how to find this point for a triangle.

Extra Example 1

C is the centroid of $\triangle GHJ$ and $CM = 8$. Find *HM* and *CH*.

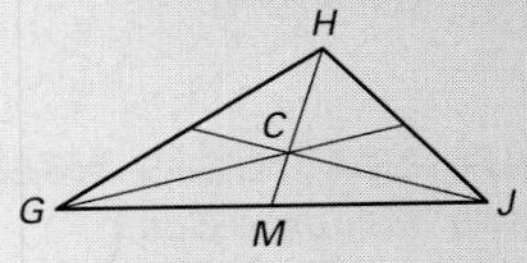

HM = 24; *CH* = 16

Extra Example 2

Find the coordinates of the centroid *P* of $\triangle DEF$. $\left(\frac{14}{3}, 3\right)$

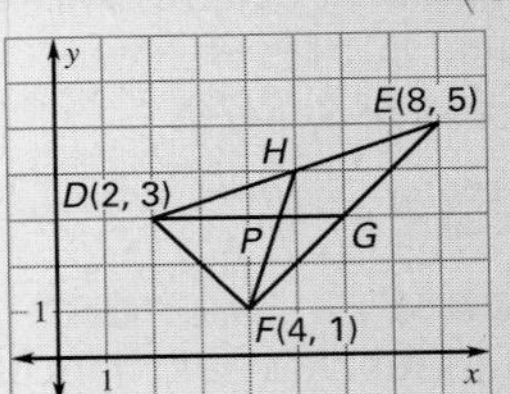

Checkpoint Exercises

For use after Examples 1 and 2:

Point *C* is the centroid of $\triangle VWX$.

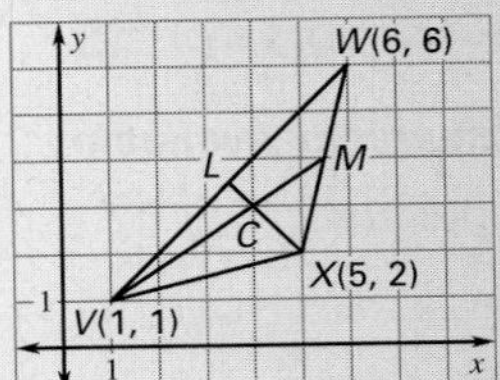

1. Find the coordinates of point *C*. (4, 3)

2. If $CL = \frac{\sqrt{2}}{2}$, find *CX*. $CX = \sqrt{2}$

Student Help Notes

Homework Help Students can find extra examples at **www.mcdougallittell.com** that parallel the examples in the student edition.

Focus on Applications

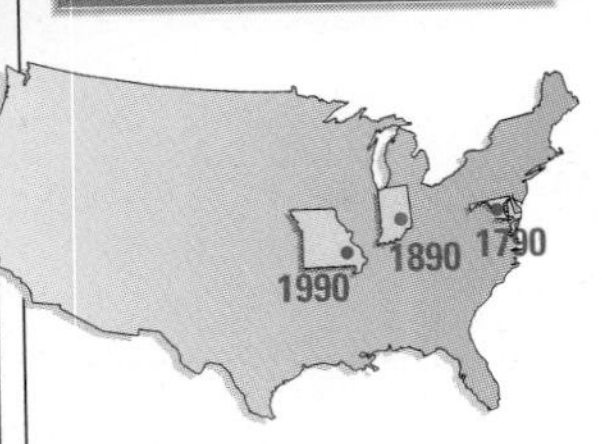

CENTER OF POPULATION

Suppose the location of each person counted in a census is identified by a weight placed on a flat, weightless map of the United States. The map would balance at a point that is the center of the population. This center has been moving westward over time.

A triangular model of uniform thickness and density will balance at the centroid of the triangle. For instance, in the diagram shown at the right, the triangular model will balance if the tip of a pencil is placed at its centroid.

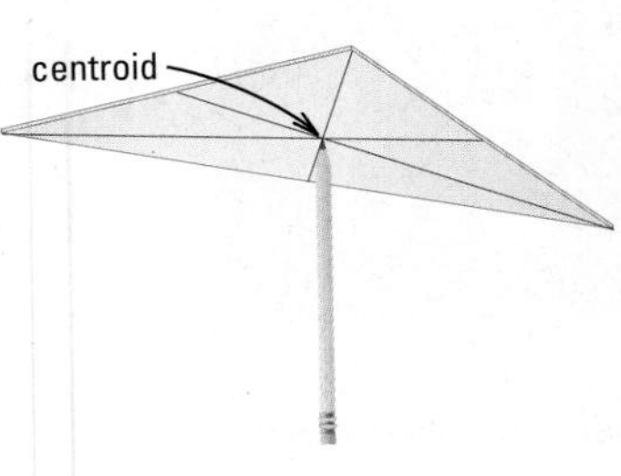

EXAMPLE 1 Using the Centroid of a Triangle

P is the centroid of $\triangle QRS$ shown below and $PT = 5$. Find *RT* and *RP*.

Solution

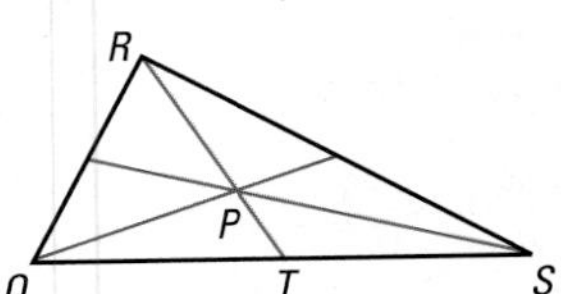

Because *P* is the centroid, $RP = \frac{2}{3}RT$.

Then $PT = RT - RP = \frac{1}{3}RT$.

Substituting 5 for *PT*, $5 = \frac{1}{3}RT$, so $RT = 15$.

Then $RP = \frac{2}{3}RT = \frac{2}{3}(15) = 10$.

▶ So, $RP = 10$ and $RT = 15$.

EXAMPLE 2 Finding the Centroid of a Triangle

Find the coordinates of the centroid of $\triangle JKL$.

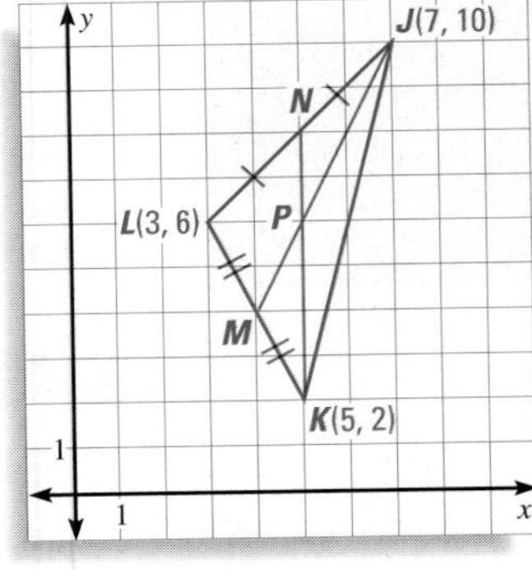

Solution

You know that the centroid is two thirds of the distance from each vertex to the midpoint of the opposite side.

Choose the median $\overline{KN}$. Find the coordinates of *N*, the midpoint of $\overline{JL}$. The coordinates of *N* are

$$\left(\frac{3+7}{2}, \frac{6+10}{2}\right) = \left(\frac{10}{2}, \frac{16}{2}\right) = (5, 8).$$

Find the distance from vertex *K* to midpoint *N*. The distance from *K*(5, 2) to *N*(5, 8) is 8 − 2, or 6 units.

Determine the coordinates of the centroid, which is $\frac{2}{3} \cdot 6$, or 4 units up from vertex *K* along the median $\overline{KN}$.

▶ The coordinates of centroid *P* are (5, 2 + 4), or (5, 6).

....

Exercises 21–23 ask you to use the Distance Formula to confirm that the distance from vertex *J* to the centroid *P* in Example 2 is two thirds of the distance from *J* to *M*, the midpoint of the opposite side.

Student Help

HOMEWORK HELP
Visit our Web site www.mcdougallittell.com for extra examples.

GOAL 2 USING ALTITUDES OF A TRIANGLE

An **altitude of a triangle** is the perpendicular segment from a vertex to the opposite side or to the line that contains the opposite side. An altitude can lie inside, on, or outside the triangle.

Every triangle has three altitudes. The lines containing the altitudes are concurrent and intersect at a point called the **orthocenter of the triangle.**

EXAMPLE 3 *Drawing Altitudes and Orthocenters*

Where is the orthocenter located in each type of triangle?

a. Acute triangle **b.** Right triangle **c.** Obtuse triangle

SOLUTION

Draw an example of each type of triangle and locate its orthocenter.

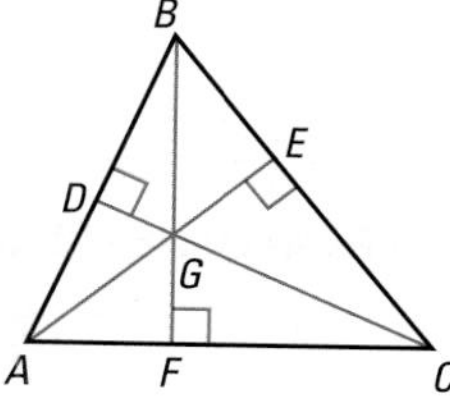

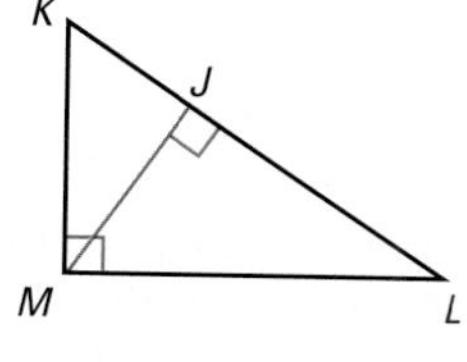

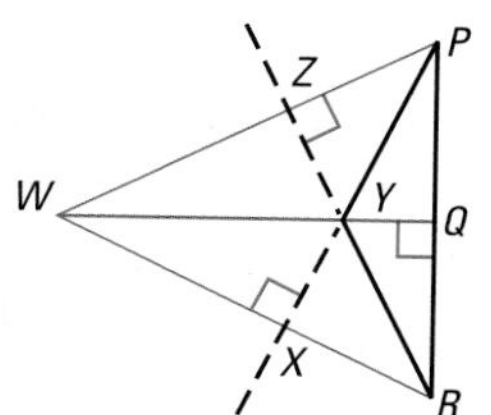

a. $\triangle ABC$ is an acute triangle. The three altitudes intersect at G, a point *inside* the triangle.

b. $\triangle KLM$ is a right triangle. The two legs, $\overline{LM}$ and $\overline{KM}$, are also altitudes. They intersect at the triangle's right angle. This implies that the orthocenter is *on* the triangle at M, the vertex of the right angle of the triangle.

c. $\triangle YPR$ is an obtuse triangle. The three lines that contain the altitudes intersect at W, a point that is *outside* the triangle.

THEOREM

THEOREM 5.8 ***Concurrency of Altitudes of a Triangle***

The lines containing the altitudes of a triangle are concurrent.

If $\overline{AE}$, $\overline{BF}$, and $\overline{CD}$ are the altitudes of $\triangle ABC$, then the lines $\overleftrightarrow{AE}$, $\overleftrightarrow{BF}$, and $\overleftrightarrow{CD}$ intersect at some point H.

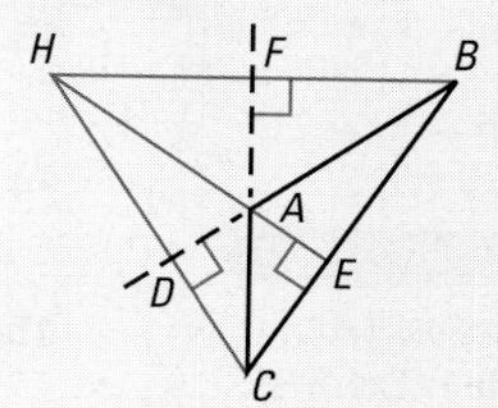

Exercises 24–26 ask you to use construction to verify Theorem 5.8. A proof appears on page 838.

EXTRA EXAMPLE 3

Where is the orthocenter located in $\triangle ABC$

a. if $m\angle A = m\angle B = m\angle C$? **inside**

b. if $m\angle A = m\angle B = 45°$? **on**

c. if $m\angle A = 110°$? **outside**

CHECKPOINT EXERCISES

For use after Example 3:

1. Draw an example of an obtuse scalene triangle and locate its orthocenter. **Check student drawings. The orthocenter should be outside the triangle.**

FOCUS ON VOCABULARY

How are the medians and the centroid of a triangle related? How are the altitudes and the orthocenter of a triangle related? **The medians of a triangle intersect at the point of concurrency called the centroid. The altitudes of a triangle intersect at the point of concurrency called the orthocenter.**

CLOSURE QUESTION

Where can the centroid of a triangle be located? Where can the orthocenter of a triangle be located? **The centroid must be inside the triangle. The orthocenter can be inside the triangle if it is acute, on the triangle if it is right, and outside the triangle if it is obtuse.**

DAILY PUZZLER

A pattern in a woodworking project requires congruent isosceles right triangles with 2-foot legs. To fit in the finished design, the triangles must be cut with a 3-inch border all the way around. How long is the leg of the triangle that forms the outside border? **about 2.85 ft**

3 APPLY

ASSIGNMENT GUIDE

BASIC
Day 1: pp. 282–283 Exs. 8–26 even
Day 2: pp. 282–284 Exs. 9–25 odd, 34, 39–45, Quiz 1 Exs. 1–5

AVERAGE
Day 1: pp. 282–283 Exs. 8–26 even
Day 2: pp. 282–284 Exs. 9–25 odd, 30–34, 39–45, Quiz 1 Exs. 1–5

ADVANCED
Day 1: pp. 282–283 Exs. 8–26 even
Day 2: pp. 282–284 Exs. 9–25 odd, 30–45, Quiz 1 Exs. 1–5

BLOCK SCHEDULE
pp. 282–284 Exs. 8–26, 30–34, 39–45, Quiz 1 Exs. 1–5

EXERCISE LEVELS

Level A: ***Easier***
8–11
Level B: ***More Difficult***
12–34
Level C: ***Most Difficult***
35–38

✔ HOMEWORK CHECK

To quickly check student understanding of key concepts, go over the following exercises: Exs. 8, 12, 14, 18, 20, 22, 24. See also the Daily Homework Quiz:

- Blackline Master (*Chapter 5 Resource Book,* p. 55)
- Transparency (p. 36)

GUIDED PRACTICE

Vocabulary Check ✔

1. The *centroid* of a triangle is the point where the three __?__ intersect. **medians**

Concept Check ✔

2. In Example 3 on page 281, explain why the two legs of the right triangle in part (b) are also altitudes of the triangle.

Skill Check ✔

Use the diagram shown and the given information to decide in each case whether $\overline{EG}$ is a *perpendicular bisector*, an *angle bisector*, a *median*, or an *altitude* of $\triangle DEF$.

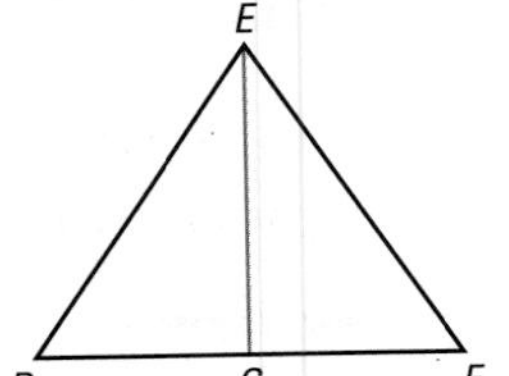

3. $\overline{DG} \cong \overline{FG}$ **median**
4. $\overline{EG} \perp \overline{DF}$ **altitude**
5. $\angle DEG \cong \angle FEG$ **angle bisector**
6. $\overline{EG} \perp \overline{DF}$ and $\overline{DG} \cong \overline{FG}$
7. $\triangle DGE \cong \triangle FGE$
⊥ bisector, ∠ bisector, median, altitude

2. An altitude is the ⊥ segment from a vertex to the opp. side; since $\overline{KM}$ is the ⊥ segment from K to $\overline{LM}$, $\overline{KM}$ is an altitude. Similarly, $\overline{LM}$ is an altitude.

6. ⊥ bisector, median, angle bisector, altitude

PRACTICE AND APPLICATIONS

STUDENT HELP
Extra Practice
to help you master skills is on p. 811.

USING MEDIANS OF A TRIANGLE In Exercises 8–12, use the figure below and the given information.
P is the centroid of $\triangle DEF$, $\overline{EH} \perp \overline{DF}$, $DH = 9$, $DG = 7.5$, $EP = 8$, and $DE = FE$.

8. Find the length of $\overline{FH}$. **9**
9. Find the length of $\overline{EH}$. **12**
10. Find the length of $\overline{PH}$. **4**
11. Find the perimeter of $\triangle DEF$. **48**

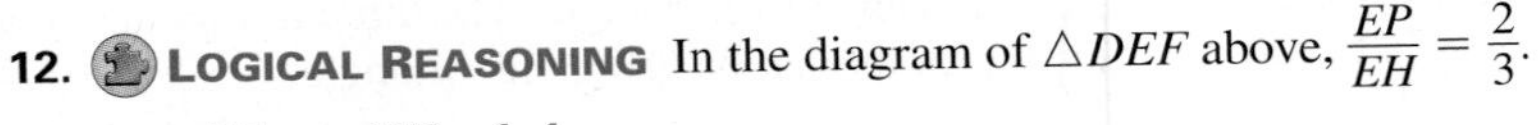

12. **LOGICAL REASONING** In the diagram of $\triangle DEF$ above, $\frac{EP}{EH} = \frac{2}{3}$.
Find $\frac{PH}{EH}$ and $\frac{PH}{EP}$. $\frac{1}{3}, \frac{1}{2}$

PAPER FOLDING Cut out a large acute, right, or obtuse triangle. Label the vertices. Follow the steps in Exercises 13–16 to verify Theorem 5.7.

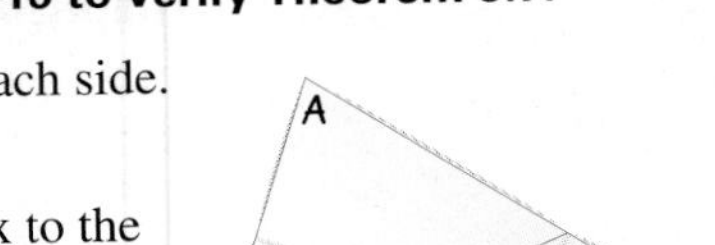

13. Fold the sides to locate the midpoint of each side. Label the midpoints. **Check results.**
14. Fold to form the median from each vertex to the midpoint of the opposite side. **Check results.**
15. Did your medians meet at about the same point? If so, label this centroid point. **yes**
16. Verify that the distance from the centroid to a vertex is two thirds of the distance from that vertex to the midpoint of the opposite side. **See margin.**

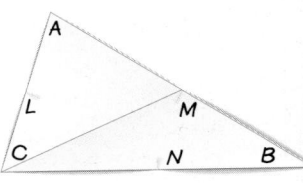

16. Label the $\triangle ABC$ and let $\overline{CM}$ be a median and P be the centroid. Fold the △ so C is directly over the centroid. Unfold and label Q, the point where $\overline{CM}$ crosses the crease that was just made. Then fold the △ again so that M overlaps Q. (That crease should cross $\overline{CM}$ at P.) Then $CQ = QP = PM$, so $CP = \frac{2}{3}CM$.

STUDENT HELP
HOMEWORK HELP
Example 1: Exs. 8–11, 13–16
Example 2: Exs. 17–23
Example 3: Exs. 24–26

USING ALGEBRA **Use the graph shown.**

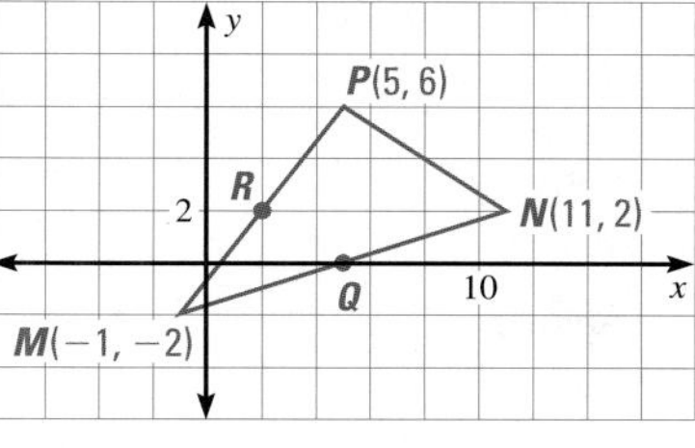

17. Find the coordinates of Q, the midpoint of $\overline{MN}$. **(5, 0)**

18. Find the length of the median $\overline{PQ}$. **6 units**

19. Find the coordinates of the centroid. Label this point as T. **(5, 2)**

20. Find the coordinates of R, the midpoint of $\overline{MP}$. Show that the quotient $\frac{NT}{NR}$ is $\frac{2}{3}$. **(2, 2); $NR = 11 - 2 = 9$, $NT = 11 - 5 = 6$; $\frac{NT}{NR} = \frac{6}{9} = \frac{2}{3}$**

USING ALGEBRA **Refer back to Example 2 on page 280.**

21. Find the coordinates of M, the midpoint of $\overline{KL}$. **(4, 4)**

22. Use the Distance Formula to find the lengths of $\overline{JP}$ and $\overline{JM}$.

23. Verify that $JP = \frac{2}{3}JM$.

22. $JP = 2\sqrt{5}$, $JM = 3\sqrt{5}$

23. $\frac{JP}{JM} = \frac{2\sqrt{5}}{3\sqrt{5}} = \frac{2}{3}$, so $JP = \frac{2}{3}JM$.

STUDENT HELP

Look Back
To construct an altitude, use the construction of a perpendicular to a line through a point not on the line, as shown on p. 130.

CONSTRUCTION **Draw and label a large scalene triangle of the given type and construct the altitudes. Verify Theorem 5.8 by showing that the lines containing the altitudes are concurrent, and label the orthocenter.**
24–26. Check drawings.

24. an acute $\triangle ABC$

25. a right $\triangle EFG$ with right angle at G

26. an obtuse $\triangle KLM$

TECHNOLOGY **Use geometry software to draw a triangle. Label the vertices as *A*, *B*, and *C*.**

27. Construct the altitudes of $\triangle ABC$ by drawing perpendicular lines through each side to the opposite vertex. Label them $\overline{AD}$, $\overline{BE}$, and $\overline{CF}$. **Check results.**

28. Find and label G and H, the intersections of $\overline{AD}$ and $\overline{BE}$ and of $\overline{BE}$ and $\overline{CF}$. **Check results.**

29. Prove that the altitudes are concurrent by showing that $GH = 0$.

29. Measure GH. Because $GH = 0$, G and H must be the same point; therefore, the lines containing the three altitudes intersect at one point.

ELECTROCARDIOGRAPH **In Exercises 30–33, use the following information about electrocardiographs.**
The equilateral triangle $\triangle BCD$ is used to plot electrocardiograph readings. Consider a person who has a left shoulder reading (S) of -1, a right shoulder reading (R) of 2, and a left leg reading (L) of 3. **30–32. See margin.**

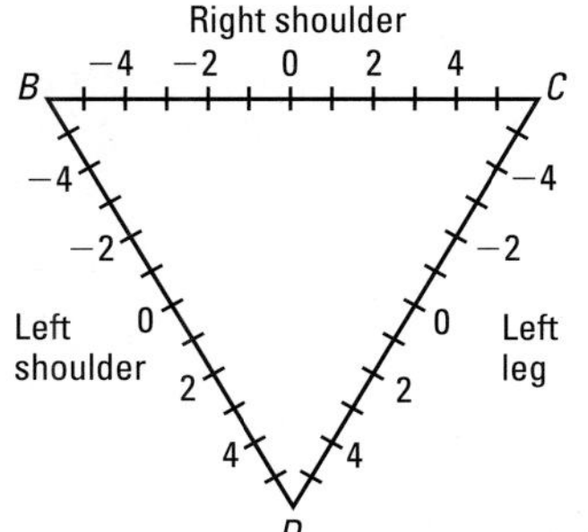

30. On a large copy of $\triangle BCD$, plot the reading to form the vertices of $\triangle SRL$. (This triangle is an *Einthoven's Triangle*, named for the inventor of the electrocardiograph.)

31. Construct the circumcenter M of $\triangle SRL$.

32. Construct the centroid P of $\triangle SRL$. Draw line r through P parallel to $\overline{BC}$.

33. Estimate the measure of the acute angle between line r and $\overline{MP}$. Cardiologists call this the angle of a person's heart. **about 20°**

FOCUS ON CAREERS

CARDIOLOGY TECHNICIAN
Technicians use equipment like electrocardiographs to test, monitor, and evaluate heart function.

CAREER LINK
www.mcdougallittell.com

TEACHING TIPS
Review the meanings of circumcenter, incenter, centroid, and orthocenter with students so that they are able to distinguish among them. Have them define and describe these terms in their journal or notebook, along with an illustrative diagram.

ENGLISH LEARNERS
EXERCISES 24–26 Unfamiliar phrases in instructions can cause confusion for English learners. Here students may not understand that *of the given type* means "the type of triangle specified in each of the three items below."

COMMON ERROR
EXERCISES 24–29 Students may confuse an altitude of a triangle with the perpendicular bisector of a side of the triangle. Remind students that altitudes are drawn from a vertex of the triangle and are perpendicular to the opposite side of the triangle, or the line that contains the opposite side. A perpendicular bisector of a side of a triangle *does not* have to go through the opposite vertex of the triangle.

CAREER NOTE
EXERCISES 30–33 Additional information about cardiology technicians is available at **www.mcdougallittell.com.**

30–32.

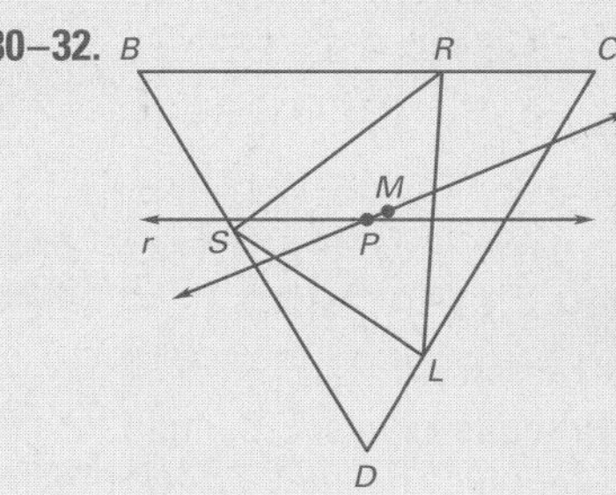

APPLICATION NOTE
Additional information about optimization is available at **www.mcdougallittell.com.**

36. The medians to the legs are altitudes if and only if the △ is equilateral; if the △ is equilateral, the proof for Ex. 35 could be used to show that all the medians are altitudes. Suppose that $\overline{AE}$, $\overline{BD}$, and $\overline{CF}$ are the medians of △ABC and all the medians are altitudes. Each of the segments form a pair of ≅ △s that can be used to show that all the sides of △ABC are ≅.

ADDITIONAL PRACTICE AND RETEACHING

For Lesson 5.3:

- Practice Levels A, B, and C (*Chapter 5 Resource Book,* p. 43)
- Reteaching with Practice (*Chapter 5 Resource Book,* p. 46)
- See Lesson 5.3 of the *Personal Student Tutor*

For more Mixed Review:

- Search the *Test and Practice Generator* for key words or specific lessons.

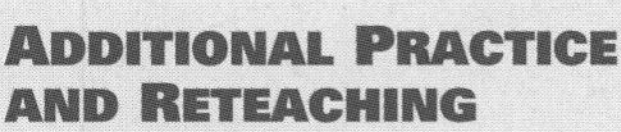

Test Preparation

34. MULTI-STEP PROBLEM Recall the formula for the area of a triangle, $A = \frac{1}{2}bh$, where b is the length of the base and h is the height. The height of a triangle is the length of an altitude.

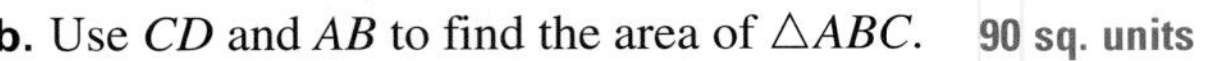

a. Make a sketch of $\triangle ABC$. Find CD, the height of the triangle (the length of the altitude to side $\overline{AB}$). **9**

b. Use CD and AB to find the area of $\triangle ABC$. **90 sq. units**

c. Draw $\overline{BE}$, the altitude to the line containing side $\overline{AC}$. **Check drawings.**

d. Use the results of part (b) to find the length of $\overline{BE}$. **12**

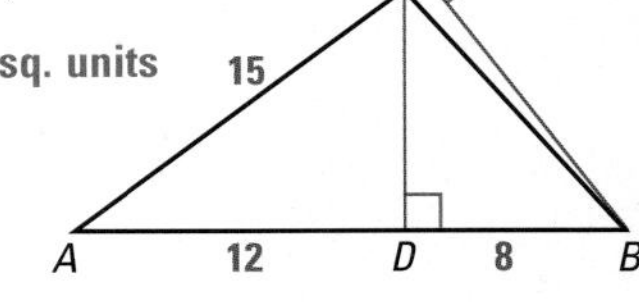

e. *Writing* Write a formula for the length of an altitude in terms of the base and the area of the triangle. Explain.

34. e. $h = \frac{2A}{b}$; let h = the length of an altitude; $A = \frac{1}{2}bh$, so $h = \frac{2A}{b}$.

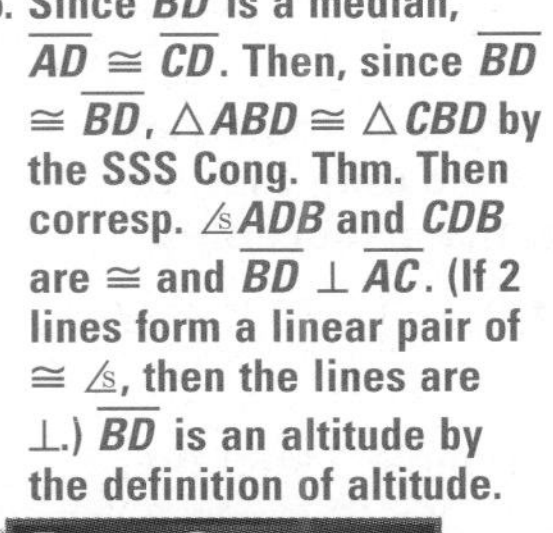

★ Challenge

35. Since $\overline{BD}$ is a median, $\overline{AD} \cong \overline{CD}$. Then, since $\overline{BD} \cong \overline{BD}$, $\triangle ABD \cong \triangle CBD$ by the SSS Cong. Thm. Then corresp. ∠s ADB and CDB are ≅ and $\overline{BD} \perp \overline{AC}$. (If 2 lines form a linear pair of ≅ ∠s, then the lines are ⊥.) $\overline{BD}$ is an altitude by the definition of altitude.

EXTRA CHALLENGE
www.mcdougallittell.com

SPECIAL TRIANGLES Use the diagram at the right.

35. GIVEN ▶ $\triangle ABC$ is isosceles.
$\overline{BD}$ is a median to base $\overline{AC}$.

PROVE ▶ $\overline{BD}$ is also an altitude.

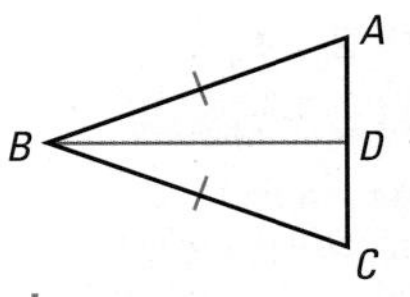

36. Are the medians to the *legs* of an isosceles triangle also altitudes? Explain your reasoning. **See margin.**

37. Are the medians of an *equilateral* triangle also altitudes? Are they contained in the angle bisectors? Are they contained in the perpendicular bisectors? **yes; yes; yes**

38. LOGICAL REASONING In a proof, if you are given a median of an equilateral triangle, what else can you conclude about the segment? **That the median is also an altitude, an ∠ bisector, and a ⊥ bisector.**

MIXED REVIEW

36. No; the medians to the legs of an isosceles △ are not ⊥ to the legs.

USING ALGEBRA Write an equation of the line that passes through point *P* and is parallel to the line with the given equation. (Review 3.6 for 5.4)

39. $P(1, 7)$, $y = -x + 3$ **$y = -x + 8$**

40. $P(-3, -8)$, $y = -2x - 3$ **$y = -2x - 14$**

41. $P(4, -9)$, $y = 3x + 5$ **$y = 3x - 21$**

42. $P(4, -2)$, $y = -\frac{1}{2}x - 1$ **$y = -\frac{1}{2}x$**

DEVELOPING PROOF In Exercises 43 and 44, state the third congruence that must be given to prove that △DEF ≅ △GHJ using the indicated postulate or theorem. (Review 4.4)

43. GIVEN ▶ $\angle D \cong \angle G$, $\overline{DF} \cong \overline{GJ}$
AAS Congruence Theorem **∠E ≅ ∠H**

44. GIVEN ▶ $\angle E \cong \angle H$, $\overline{EF} \cong \overline{HJ}$
ASA Congruence Postulate **∠F ≅ ∠J**

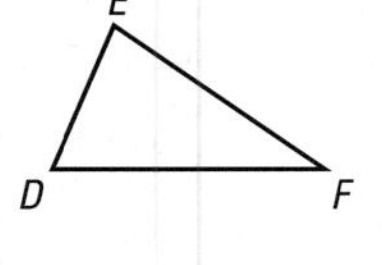

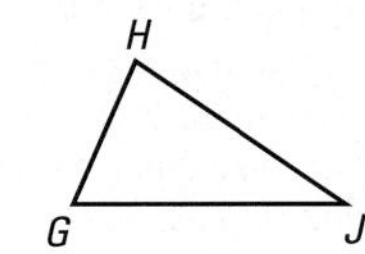

45. USING THE DISTANCE FORMULA Place a right triangle with legs of length 9 units and 13 units in a coordinate plane and use the Distance Formula to find the length of the hypotenuse. (Review 4.7) **$5\sqrt{10}$**

Quiz 1

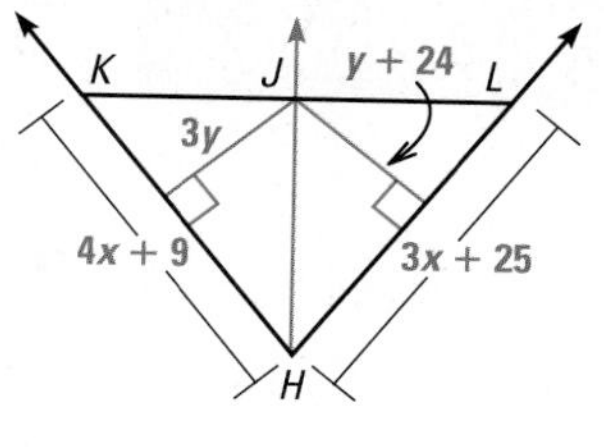

Use the diagram shown and the given information. (Lesson 5.1)

$\overline{HJ}$ is the perpendicular bisector of $\overline{KL}$.

$\overrightarrow{HJ}$ bisects $\angle KHL$.

1. Find the value of x. 16
2. Find the value of y. 12

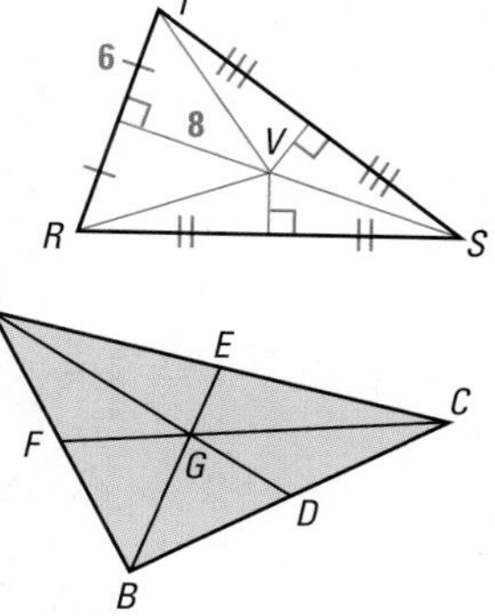

In the diagram shown, the perpendicular bisectors of $\triangle RST$ meet at V. (Lesson 5.2)

3. Find the length of $\overline{VT}$. 10
4. What is the length of $\overline{VS}$? Explain.

4. 10; the ⊥ bisectors intersect at a point equidistant from the vertices of the △.

5. **BUILDING A MOBILE** Suppose you want to attach the items in a mobile so that they hang horizontally. You would want to find the balancing point of each item. For the triangular metal plate shown, describe where the balancing point would be located. (Lesson 5.3)
at G, the intersection of the medians of $\triangle ABC$, 8 in. from C on $\overline{CF}$

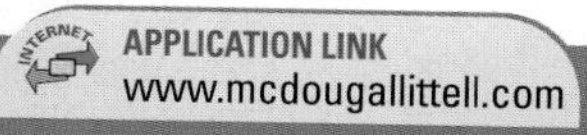

$\overline{AD}$, $\overline{BE}$, and $\overline{CF}$ are medians. $CF = 12$ in.

4 ASSESS

Daily Homework Quiz

Transparency Available

Use the triangle shown for Exercises 1–4.

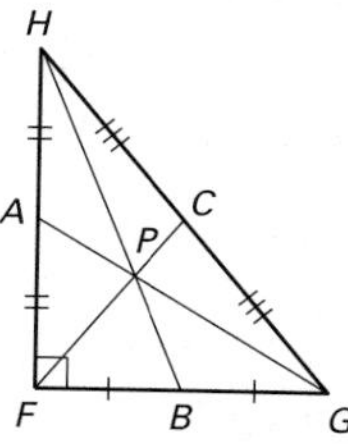

1. What point is the centroid of $\triangle FGH$? point P
2. If $FP = 6$, what is FC? 9
3. If $HB = 9$, what is PB? 3
4. Where is the orthocenter of $\triangle FGH$ located? at point F

Math & History

Optimization

APPLICATION LINK www.mcdougallittell.com

THEN **THROUGHOUT HISTORY**, people have faced problems involving minimizing resources or maximizing output, a process called optimization. The use of mathematics in solving these types of problems has increased greatly since World War II, when mathematicians found the optimal shape for naval convoys to avoid enemy fire.

NOW **TODAY**, with the help of computers, optimization techniques are used in many industries, including manufacturing, economics, and architecture.

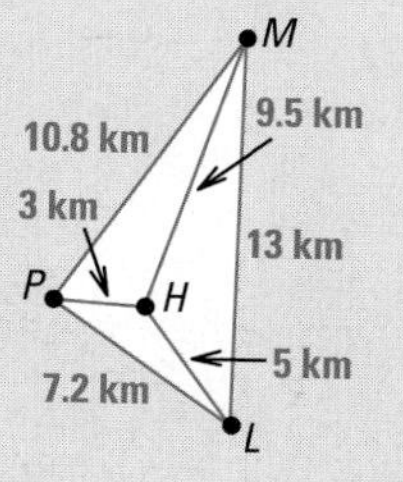

1. Your house is located at point H in the diagram. You need to do errands at the post office (P), the market (M), and the library (L). In what order should you do your errands to minimize the distance traveled?
2. Look back at Exercise 34 on page 270. Explain why the goalie's position on the angle bisector optimizes the chances of blocking a scoring shot. See margin.

1. post office, market, library, home (H, P, M, L, H) or library, market, post office, home (H, L, M, P, H).

1611

Johannes Kepler proposes the optimal way to stack cannonballs.

WWII naval convoy

1942

1972

This Olympic stadium roof uses a minimum of materials.

1997

Thomas Hales proves Kepler's cannonball conjecture.

Extra Challenge Note

Challenge problems for Lesson 5.3 are available in **blackline** format in the *Chapter 5 Resource Book*, p. 51 and at **www.mcdougallittell.com.**

Additional Test Preparation

1. **OPEN ENDED** Draw a triangle whose centroid and orthocenter are the same point.
Sample answer:

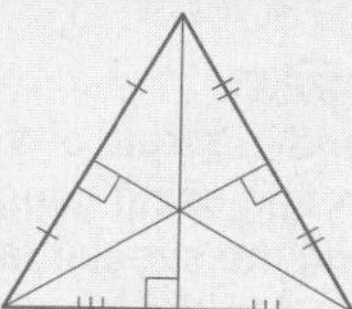

Additional Resources

An alternative Quiz for Lessons 5.1–5.3 is available in the *Chapter 5 Resource Book*, p. 52.

A **blackline** master with additional Math & History exercises is available in the *Chapter 5 Resource Book*, p. 50.

2. The goalie must travel an equal distance to protect against a shot to the left or right corner of the goal.

1 Planning the Activity

PURPOSE
To explore concurrent lines in a triangle.

MATERIALS
- geometry software
- Software Help (*Chapter 5 Resource Book*, p. 41)

PACING
- Activity — 30 min

LINK TO LESSON
Students use software in this activity to verify Theorem 5.6 of Lesson 5.2 and Theorem 5.7 of Lesson 5.3.

2 Managing the Activity

COOPERATIVE LEARNING
Students can work together to complete the activity. Individual students or groups of students can compare different drawings.

CLASSROOM MANAGEMENT
Use a computer that is connected to an overhead monitor and work through the activity with the students.

3 Closing the Activity

KEY DISCOVERY
The incenter and centroid of a triangle can be found using geometric software and the special ratio of lengths related to the location of the centroid can be verified.

ACTIVITY ASSESSMENT
What is true about both the angle bisectors of a triangle and the medians of a triangle? Both have points of concurrency inside the triangle.

ACTIVITY 5.3

Using Technology

Investigating Concurrent Lines

You can use geometry software to explore concurrent lines.

STUDENT HELP

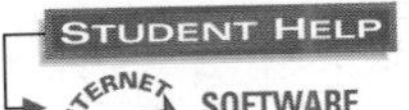

Visit our Web site www.mcdougallittell.com to see instructions for several software applications.

CONSTRUCT **Construct the angle bisectors of a triangle.**

1. Draw any triangle *ABC*.
2. Draw the bisector $\overrightarrow{BD}$ of $\angle ABC$. Then draw the bisector $\overrightarrow{CE}$ of $\angle BCA$.
3. Label the intersection point of the two angle bisectors as *F*.
4. Draw the ray from *A* that passes through *F*.

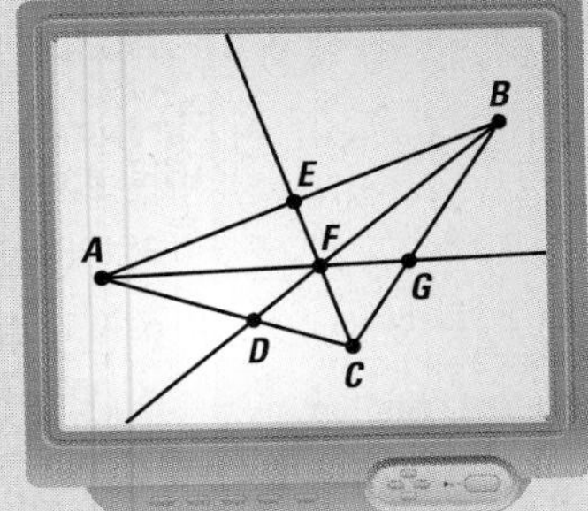

INVESTIGATE

1. Measure $\angle BAF$ and $\angle CAF$ to show that $\overrightarrow{AF}$ is an angle bisector. $m\angle BAF = m\angle CAF$
2. Explain how the results of Exercise 1 can be used to verify that the angle bisectors of a triangle are concurrent. Because angle bisector $\overrightarrow{AF}$ passes through the intersection point, *F*, of $\overrightarrow{BD}$ and $\overrightarrow{CE}$ the three angle bisectors are concurrent.

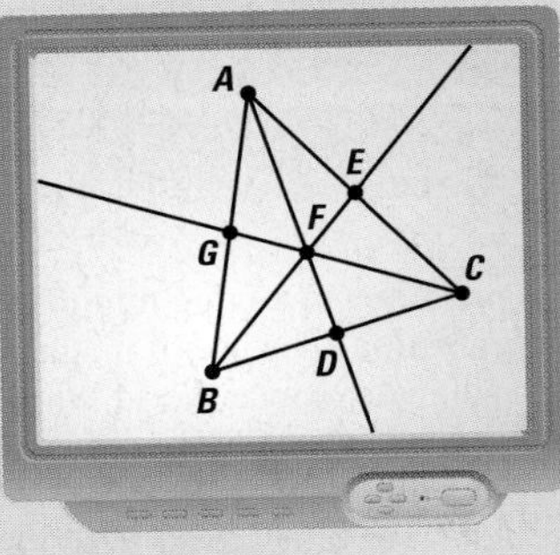

CONSTRUCT **Construct the medians of a triangle.**

5. Draw any triangle *ABC*.
6. Locate the midpoint of $\overline{BC}$ and label it *D*. Locate the midpoint of $\overline{AC}$ and label it *E*.
7. Draw the medians $\overline{AD}$ and $\overline{BE}$.
8. Label the intersection of the two medians as *F*.
9. Draw the ray from *C* that passes through *F*. Label the intersection of $\overrightarrow{CF}$ and $\overline{AB}$ as *G*.

INVESTIGATE

3. Measure $\overline{AG}$ and $\overline{BG}$. What do you notice? Is $\overline{CG}$ a median? $\overline{AG} \cong \overline{BG}$; yes
4. Explain how the results of Exercise 3 can be used to verify that the medians of a triangle are concurrent.
5. Measure $\overline{AD}$ and $\overline{AF}$. Calculate $\frac{AD}{AF}$. Is $AF = \frac{2}{3}AD$? yes
6. Drag point *A* to change the triangle. Does the quotient $\frac{AD}{AF}$ change? no

4. A ray from *C* through *F* bisects $\overline{AB}$, that is, intersects $\overline{AB}$ at its midpoint. Since there is only one line through any two points, the ray is contained in the same line as the median of $\overline{AB}$. Then the medians of the △ are concurrent.

Extension: isosceles △, equilateral △; the bisector of the vertex ∠ of an isosceles △ is contained in a median, an altitude, and a ⊥ bisector. The same is true for the bisector of each angle of an equilateral △.

EXTENSION

CRITICAL THINKING Find examples of triangles in which an angle bisector is contained in the same line as a median. Do the lines also contain an *altitude* and a *perpendicular bisector* of the triangle as well? Explain.

5.4 Midsegment Theorem

What you should learn

GOAL 1 Identify the midsegments of a triangle.

GOAL 2 Use properties of midsegments of a triangle.

Why you should learn it

▼ To solve **real-life** problems involving midsegments, as applied in **Exs. 32 and 35.**

The roof of the Cowles Conservatory in Minneapolis, Minnesota, shows the midsegments of a triangle.

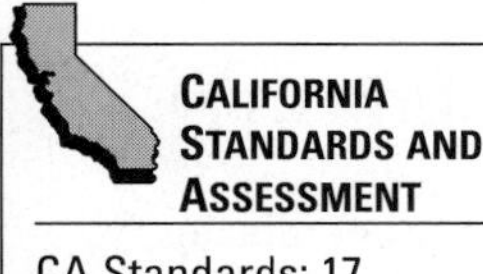

CALIFORNIA STANDARDS AND ASSESSMENT

CA Standards: 17

GOAL 1 USING MIDSEGMENTS OF A TRIANGLE

In Lessons 5.2 and 5.3, you studied four special types of segments of a triangle: perpendicular bisectors, angle bisectors, medians, and altitudes. Another special type of segment is called a *midsegment.* A **midsegment of a triangle** is a segment that connects the midpoints of two sides of a triangle.

You can form the three midsegments of a triangle by tracing the triangle on paper, cutting it out, and folding it, as shown below.

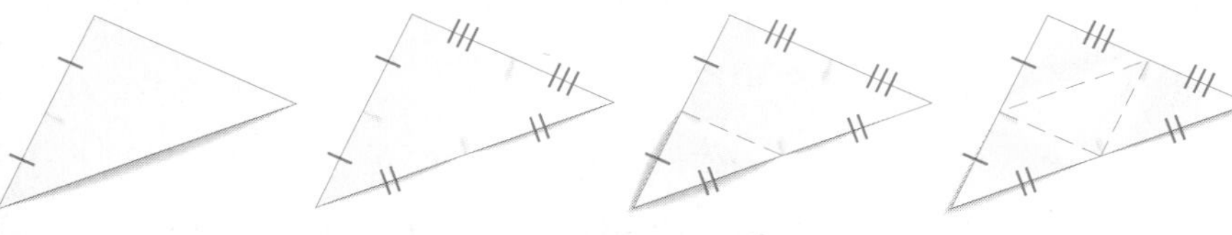

1. Fold one vertex onto another to find one midpoint.
2. Repeat the process to find the other two midpoints.
3. Fold a segment that contains two of the midpoints.
4. Fold the remaining two midsegments of the triangle.

The midsegments and sides of a triangle have a special relationship, as shown in Example 1 and Theorem 5.9 on the next page.

EXAMPLE 1 *Using Midsegments*

Show that the midsegment $\overline{MN}$ is parallel to side $\overline{JK}$ and is half as long.

SOLUTION

Use the Midpoint Formula to find the coordinates of M and N.

$$M = \left(\frac{-2+6}{2}, \frac{3+(-1)}{2}\right) = (2, 1)$$

$$N = \left(\frac{4+6}{2}, \frac{5+(-1)}{2}\right) = (5, 2)$$

Next, find the slopes of $\overline{JK}$ and $\overline{MN}$.

$$\text{Slope of } \overline{JK} = \frac{5-3}{4-(-2)} = \frac{2}{6} = \frac{1}{3} \qquad \text{Slope of } \overline{MN} = \frac{2-1}{5-2} = \frac{1}{3}$$

▶ Because their slopes are equal, $\overline{JK}$ and $\overline{MN}$ are parallel. You can use the Distance Formula to show that $MN = \sqrt{10}$ and $JK = \sqrt{40} = 2\sqrt{10}$. So, $\overline{MN}$ is half as long as $\overline{JK}$.

1 PLAN

PACING

Basic: 1 day
Average: 1 day
Advanced: 1 day
Block Schedule: 0.5 block with 5.5

LESSON OPENER
VISUAL APPROACH

An alternative way to approach Lesson 5.4 is to use the Visual Approach Lesson Opener:

- Blackline Master (*Chapter 5 Resource Book,* p. 56)
- Transparency (p. 31)

MEETING INDIVIDUAL NEEDS

- ***Chapter 5 Resource Book***
  - Prerequisite Skills Review (p. 5)
  - Practice Level A (p. 58)
  - Practice Level B (p. 59)
  - Practice Level C (p. 60)
  - Reteaching with Practice (p. 61)
  - Absent Student Catch-Up (p. 63)
  - Challenge (p. 66)
- ***Resources in Spanish***
- ***Personal Student Tutor***

NEW-TEACHER SUPPORT

See the Tips for New Teachers on pp. 1–2 of the *Chapter 5 Resource Book* for additional notes about Lesson 5.4.

WARM-UP EXERCISES

Transparency Available

Find the coordinates of the midpoint.

1. (2, 0) and (0, 2) (1, 1)
2. (5, 8) and (–3, –4) (1, 2)

Find the slope of the line through the given points.

3. (3, 11) and (3, 4) undefined
4. (–2, –6) and (4, –9) $-\frac{1}{2}$
5. (4, 3) and (8, 3) 0

2 TEACH

EXTRA EXAMPLE 1

Show that midsegment $\overline{PQ}$ is parallel to $\overline{DE}$ and half as long.

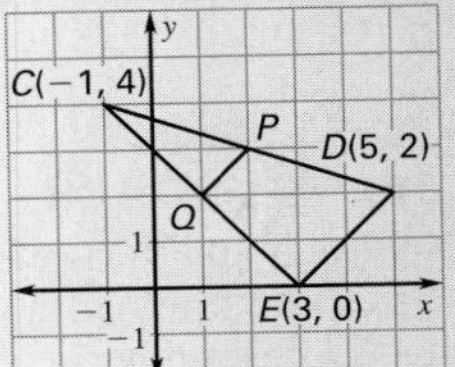

$P = (2, 3)$; $Q = (1, 2)$; slope of $\overline{DE} = 1 =$ slope of $\overline{PQ}$: $DE = 2\sqrt{2}$ and $PQ = \sqrt{2}$

EXTRA EXAMPLE 2

$\overline{JK}$ and $\overline{KL}$ are midsegments of $\triangle ABC$. Find JK and AB.

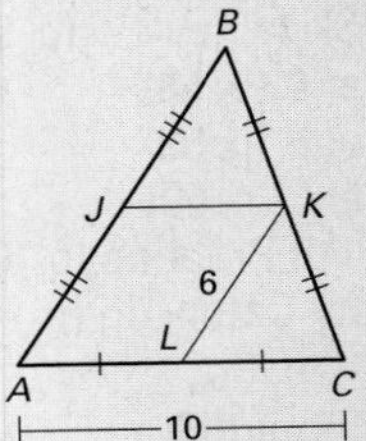

$JK = 5$; $AB = 12$

EXTRA EXAMPLE 3

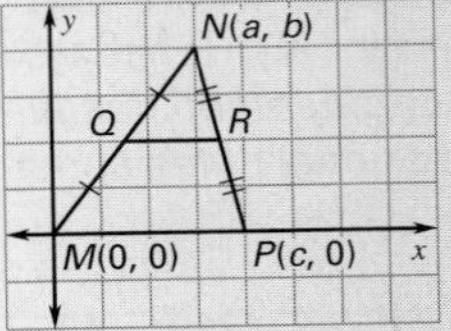

a. What are the coordinates of Q? of R? $\left(\frac{a}{2}, \frac{b}{2}\right)$; $\left(\frac{a+c}{2}, \frac{b}{2}\right)$

b. Why is $\overline{QR} \parallel \overline{MP}$? Both have slope 0.

c. What is MP? What is QR? c; $\frac{c}{2}$

CHECKPOINT EXERCISES

For use after Examples 1–3:

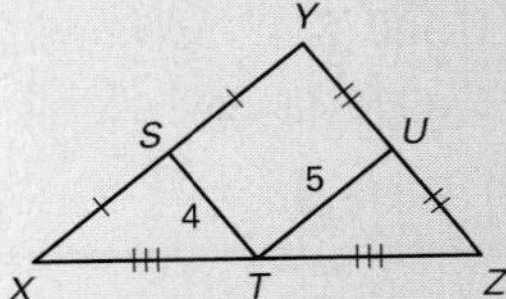

1. In $\triangle XYZ$, which segment is parallel to $\overline{XY}$? $\overline{TU}$

2. If $\overline{ST} \parallel \overline{YZ}$, what is YZ? 8

THEOREM

THEOREM 5.9 ***Midsegment Theorem***

The segment connecting the midpoints of two sides of a triangle is parallel to the third side and is half as long.

$\overline{DE} \parallel \overline{AB}$ and $DE = \frac{1}{2}AB$

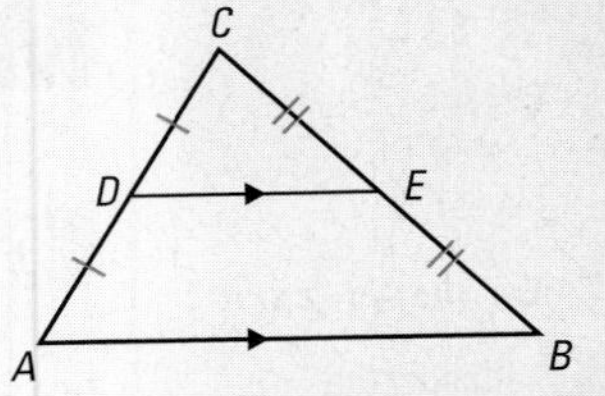

EXAMPLE 2 Using the Midsegment Theorem

$\overline{UW}$ and $\overline{VW}$ are midsegments of $\triangle RST$. Find UW and RT.

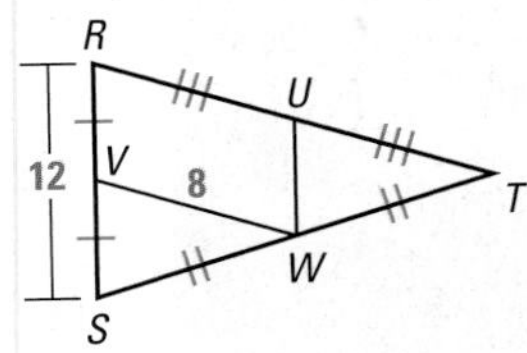

SOLUTION

$$UW = \frac{1}{2}(RS) = \frac{1}{2}(12) = 6$$

$$RT = 2(VW) = 2(8) = 16$$

A coordinate proof of Theorem 5.9 for one midsegment of a triangle is given below. Exercises 23–25 ask for proofs about the other two midsegments. To set up a coordinate proof, remember to place the figure in a convenient location.

EXAMPLE 3 Proving Theorem 5.9

Proof

Write a coordinate proof of the Midsegment Theorem.

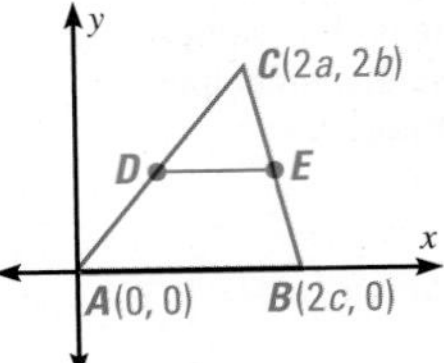

SOLUTION

Place points A, B, and C in convenient locations in a coordinate plane, as shown. Use the Midpoint Formula to find the coordinates of the midpoints D and E.

$$D = \left(\frac{2a+0}{2}, \frac{2b+0}{2}\right) = (a, b) \qquad E = \left(\frac{2a+2c}{2}, \frac{2b+0}{2}\right) = (a+c, b)$$

Find the slope of midsegment $\overline{DE}$. Points D and E have the same y-coordinates, so the slope of $\overline{DE}$ is zero.

▶ $\overline{AB}$ also has a slope of zero, so the slopes are equal and $\overline{DE}$ and $\overline{AB}$ are parallel.

Calculate the lengths of $\overline{DE}$ and $\overline{AB}$. The segments are both horizontal, so their lengths are given by the absolute values of the differences of their x-coordinates.

$$AB = |2c - 0| = 2c \qquad DE = |a + c - a| = c$$

▶ The length of $\overline{DE}$ is half the length of $\overline{AB}$.

> STUDENT HELP
>
> **Study Tip**
> In Example 3, it is convenient to locate a vertex at (0, 0) and it also helps to make one side horizontal. To use the Midpoint Formula, it is helpful for the coordinates to be multiples of 2.

GOAL 2 USING PROPERTIES OF MIDSEGMENTS

Suppose you are given only the three midpoints of the sides of a triangle. Is it possible to draw the original triangle? Example 4 shows one method.

EXAMPLE 4 Using Midpoints to Draw a Triangle

The midpoints of the sides of a triangle are $L(4, 2)$, $M(2, 3)$, and $N(5, 4)$. What are the coordinates of the vertices of the triangle?

SOLUTION

Plot the midpoints in a coordinate plane.

Connect these midpoints to form the midsegments $\overline{LN}$, $\overline{MN}$, and $\overline{ML}$.

Find the slopes of the midsegments. Use the slope formula as shown.

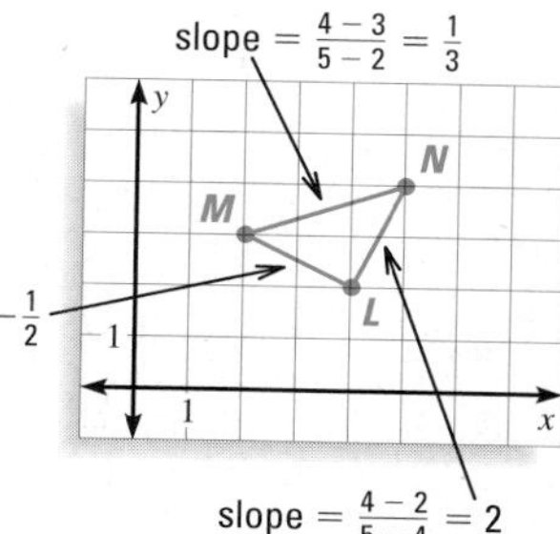

Each midsegment contains two of the unknown triangle's midpoints and is parallel to the side that contains the third midpoint. So, you know a point on each side of the triangle and the slope of each side.

Draw the lines that contain the three sides.

▶ The lines intersect at $A(3, 5)$, $B(7, 3)$, and $C(1, 1)$, which are the vertices of the triangle.

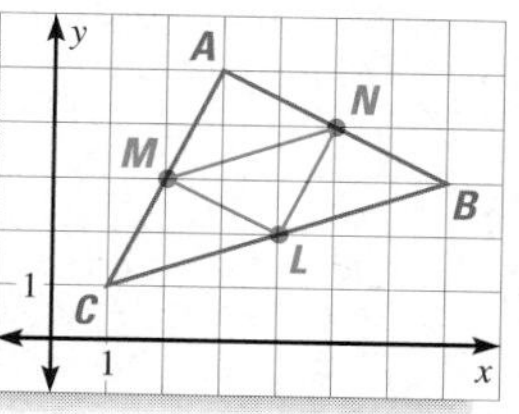

The perimeter of the triangle formed by the three midsegments of a triangle is *half* the perimeter of the original triangle, as shown in Example 5.

EXAMPLE 5 Perimeter of Midsegment Triangle

ORIGAMI $\overline{DE}$, $\overline{EF}$, and $\overline{DF}$ are midsegments in $\triangle ABC$. Find the perimeter of $\triangle DEF$.

SOLUTION The lengths of the midsegments are half the lengths of the sides of $\triangle ABC$.

$$DF = \frac{1}{2}AB = \frac{1}{2}(10) = 5$$

$$EF = \frac{1}{2}AC = \frac{1}{2}(10) = 5$$

$$ED = \frac{1}{2}BC = \frac{1}{2}(14.2) = 7.1$$

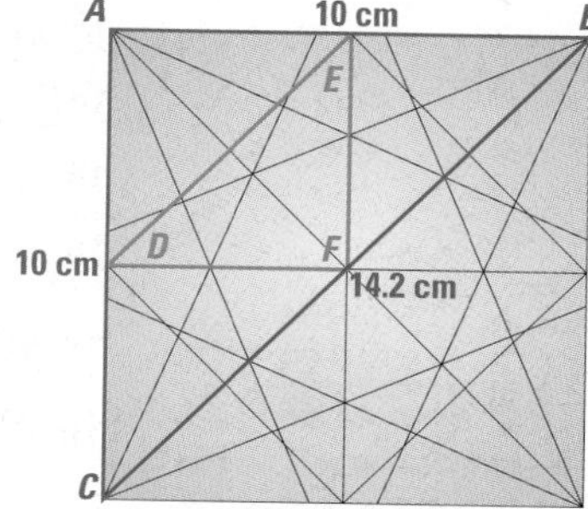

Crease pattern of origami flower

▶ The perimeter of $\triangle DEF$ is $5 + 5 + 7.1$, or 17.1. The perimeter of $\triangle ABC$ is $10 + 10 + 14.2$, or 34.2, so the perimeter of the triangle formed by the midsegments is half the perimeter of the original triangle.

FOCUS ON APPLICATIONS

ORIGAMI is an ancient method of paper folding. The pattern of folds for a number of objects, such as the flower shown, involve midsegments.

EXTRA EXAMPLE 4
The midpoints of the sides of a triangle are $S(1, 5)$, $T(3, 3)$ and $V(4, 6)$. What are the coordinates of the vertices of the triangle? **(6, 4), (2, 8), and (0, 2)**

EXTRA EXAMPLE 5
$\overline{RS}$, $\overline{ST}$, and $\overline{RT}$ are midsegments in $\triangle XYZ$. Find the perimeter of $\triangle XYZ$. **36 units**

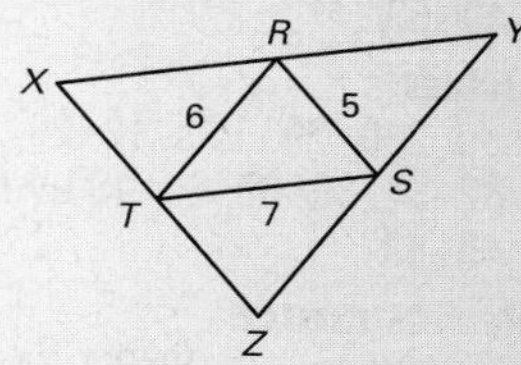

CHECKPOINT EXERCISES
For use after Examples 4 and 5:

1. The midpoints of the sides of a triangle are $A(2, 5)$, $B(2, 2)$ and $C(6, 5)$.
   a. What are the coordinates of the vertices of the triangle? **(6, 2), (6, 8), and (−2, 2)**
   b. Find the perimeter of the triangle. **24 units**

FOCUS ON VOCABULARY
Define midsegment of a triangle. **A midsegment of a triangle is a segment that connects the midpoints of two sides of the triangle.**

CLOSURE QUESTION
How is a midsegment related to the side it does not intersect? **It is parallel to that side and half as long.**

DAILY PUZZLER
The diagram below is drawn on centimeter grid paper. Find the perimeter of the triangle exactly and to the nearest hundredth.

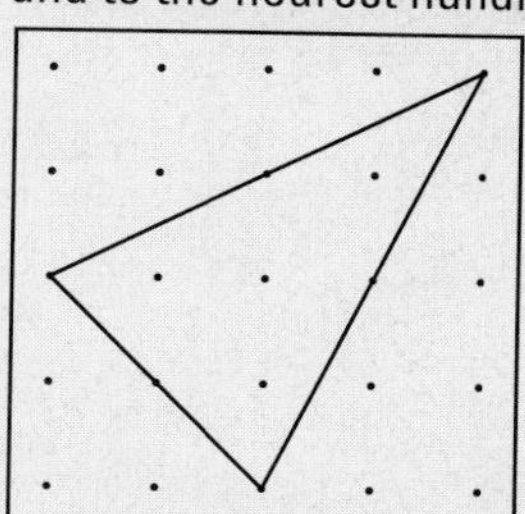

$2\sqrt{2} + 4\sqrt{5} \approx 11.77$ cm

3 APPLY

ASSIGNMENT GUIDE

BASIC
Day 1: pp. 290–293 Exs. 12–29, 33, 34, 36, 40–48 even, 49–53

AVERAGE
Day 1: pp. 290–293 Exs. 12–29, 32–34, 36, 40–48 even, 49–53

ADVANCED
Day 1: pp. 290–293 Exs. 12–29, 32–34, 36–38, 40–48 even, 49–53

BLOCK SCHEDULE
pp. 290–293 Exs. 12–29, 32–34, 36, 40–48 even, 49–53 (with 5.5)

EXERCISE LEVELS

Level A: *Easier*
12–16

Level B: *More Difficult*
17–36

Level C: *Most Difficult*
37, 38

✔ HOMEWORK CHECK

To quickly check student understanding of key concepts, go over the following exercises: Exs. 16, 18, 20, 22, 24, 26, 28, 34. See also the Daily Homework Quiz:

- Blackline Master (*Chapter 5 Resource Book,* p. 69)
- Transparency (p. 37)

22. slope of $\overline{DF} = \frac{4-0}{5-2\frac{1}{2}} = \frac{8}{5}$ and slope of $\overline{BC} = \frac{6-(-2)}{10-5} = \frac{8}{5}$, so $\overline{DF} \parallel \overline{BC}$; $DF = \sqrt{\left(5-2\frac{1}{2}\right)^2 + (4-0)^2} = \frac{\sqrt{89}}{2}$ and $BC = \sqrt{(10-5)^2 + (6-(-2))^2} = \sqrt{89}$, so $DF = \frac{1}{2}BC$.

19. $\angle BLN$, $\angle A$, and $\angle NMC$ are ≅ by the Corresp. Angles Post., as are $\angle BNL$, $\angle C$, and $\angle LMA$. By the Alternate Interior Angles Thm., $\angle LNM \cong \angle NMC$ and $\angle NLM \cong \angle LMA$, so by the Transitive Prop. of Cong., $\angle BLN$, $\angle A$, $\angle NMC$, and $\angle LNM$ are ≅, as are $\angle BNL$, $\angle C$, $\angle LMA$, and $\angle NLM$. Then $\angle B$, $\angle ALM$, $\angle LMN$, and $\angle MNC$ are all ≅ by the Third Angles Thm. and the Transitive Prop. of Cong.

GUIDED PRACTICE

Vocabulary Check ✔

1. In △*ABC*, if *M* is the midpoint of $\overline{AB}$, *N* is the midpoint of $\overline{AC}$, and *P* is the midpoint of $\overline{BC}$, then $\overline{MN}$, $\overline{NP}$, and $\overline{PN}$ are __?__ of △*ABC*. **midsegments**

Concept Check ✔

2. In Example 3 on page 288, why was it convenient to position one of the sides of the triangle along the *x*-axis? **One vertex has 0 for both coordinates and another has 0 for one coordinate. One side of the △ also has a slope of 0.**

Skill Check ✔

In Exercises 3–9, $\overline{GH}$, $\overline{HJ}$, and $\overline{JG}$ are midsegments of △*DEF*.

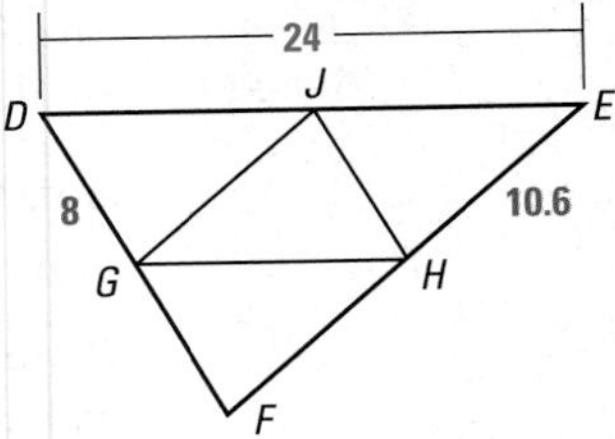

3. $\overline{JH} \parallel$ __?__ $\overline{DF}$

4. __?__ $\parallel \overline{DE}$ $\overline{GH}$

5. $EF =$ __?__ 21.2

6. $GH =$ __?__ 12

7. $DF =$ __?__ 16

8. $JH =$ __?__ 8

9. Find the perimeter of △*GHJ*. **30.6**

WALKWAYS **The triangle below shows a section of walkways on a college campus.**

10. The midsegment $\overline{AB}$ represents a new walkway that is to be constructed on the campus. What are the coordinates of points *A* and *B*? **A(1, 4), B(6, 6)**

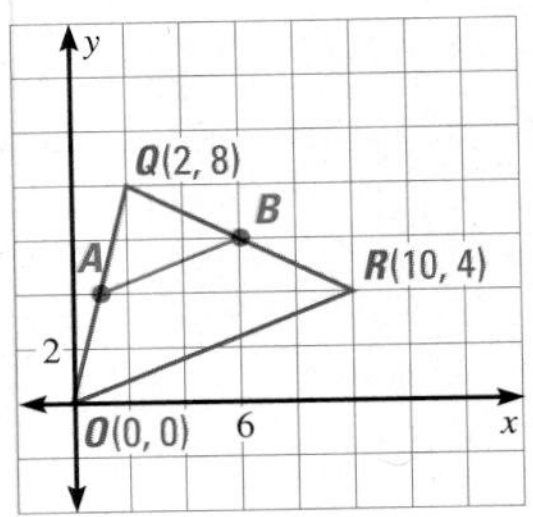

11. Each unit in the coordinate plane represents 10 yards. Use the Distance Formula to find the length of the new walkway. **about 54 yd**

PRACTICE AND APPLICATIONS

STUDENT HELP
Extra Practice to help you master skills is on p. 812.

COMPLETE THE STATEMENT **In Exercises 12–19, use △*ABC*, where *L*, *M*, and *N* are midpoints of the sides.**

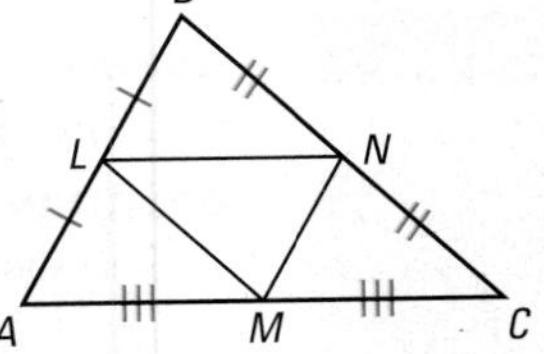

12. $\overline{LM} \parallel$ __?__ $\overline{BC}$

13. $\overline{AB} \parallel$ __?__ $\overline{MN}$

14. If $AC = 20$, then $LN =$ __?__. 10

15. If $MN = 7$, then $AB =$ __?__. 14

16. If $NC = 9$, then $LM =$ __?__. 9

17. **USING ALGEBRA** If $LM = 3x + 7$ and $BC = 7x + 6$, then $LM =$ __?__. 31

18. **USING ALGEBRA** If $MN = x - 1$ and $AB = 6x - 18$, then $AB =$ __?__. 6

STUDENT HELP
HOMEWORK HELP
Example 1: Exs. 21, 22
Example 2: Exs. 12–16
Example 3: Exs. 23–25
Example 4: Exs. 26, 27
Example 5: Exs. 28, 29

19. **LOGICAL REASONING** Which angles in the diagram are congruent? Explain your reasoning. **See margin.**

20. **CONSTRUCTION** Use a straightedge to draw a triangle. Then use the straightedge and a compass to construct the three midsegments of the triangle. **Check drawings.**

21. $D\left(2\frac{1}{2}, 0\right)$, $E\left(7\frac{1}{2}, 2\right)$, $F(5, 4)$

USING ALGEBRA **Use the diagram.**

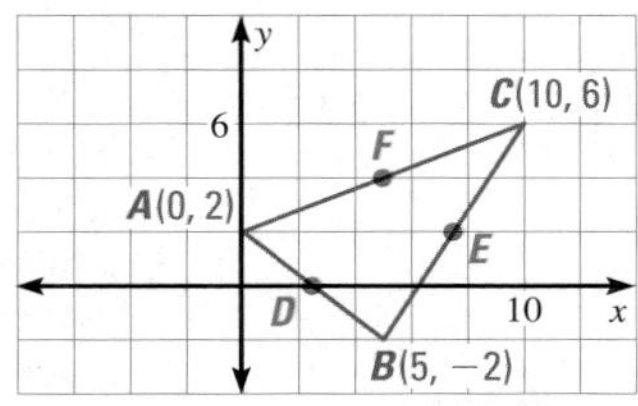

21. Find the coordinates of the endpoints of each midsegment of $\triangle ABC$.

22. Use slope and the Distance Formula to verify that the Midsegment Theorem is true for $\overline{DF}$. See margin.

USING ALGEBRA **Copy the diagram in Example 3 on page 288 to complete the proof of Theorem 5.9, the Midsegment Theorem.**

23. Locate the midpoint of $\overline{AB}$ and label it F. What are the coordinates of F? Draw midsegments $\overline{DF}$ and $\overline{EF}$. $(c, 0)$

24. slope of $\overline{DF}$ = slope of $\overline{CB} = \frac{b}{a-c}$; slope of $\overline{EF}$ = slope of $\overline{CA} = \frac{b}{a}$

24. Use slopes to show that $\overline{DF} \parallel \overline{CB}$ and $\overline{EF} \parallel \overline{CA}$.

25. Use the Distance Formula to find DF, EF, CB, and CA. Verify that $DF = \frac{1}{2}CB$ and $EF = \frac{1}{2}CA$. See margin.

STUDENT HELP

HOMEWORK HELP Visit our Web site www.mcdougallittell.com for help with Exs. 26 and 27.

USING ALGEBRA **In Exercises 26 and 27, you are given the midpoints of the sides of a triangle. Find the coordinates of the vertices of the triangle.**

26. $L(1, 3)$, $M(5, 9)$, $N(4, 4)$
$(0, -2)$, $(2, 8)$, $(8, 10)$

27. $L(7, 1)$, $M(9, 6)$, $N(5, 4)$
$(3, -1)$, $(11, 3)$, $(7, 9)$

FINDING PERIMETER **In Exercises 28 and 29, use the diagram shown.**

28. Given $CD = 14$, $GF = 8$, and $GC = 5$, find the perimeter of $\triangle BCD$. 40

29. Given $PQ = 20$, $SU = 12$, and $QU = 9$, find the perimeter of $\triangle STU$. 31

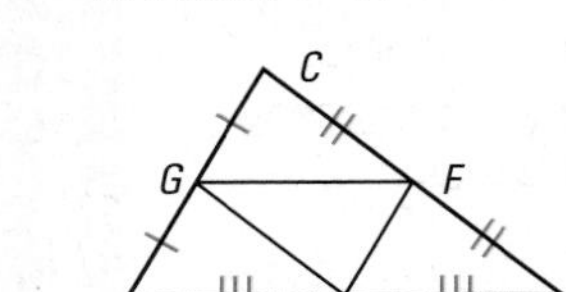

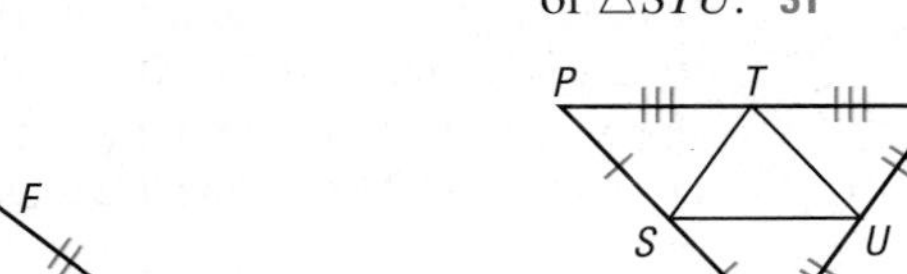

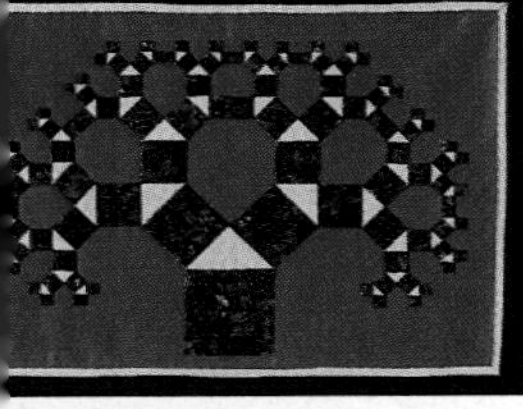

FRACTALS are shapes that look the same at many levels of magnification. Take a small part of the image above and you will see that it looks about the same as the whole image.

APPLICATION LINK www.mcdougallittell.com

30. **TECHNOLOGY** Use geometry software to draw any $\triangle ABC$. Construct the midpoints of $\overline{AB}$, $\overline{BC}$, and $\overline{CA}$. Label them as D, E, and F. Construct the midpoints of $\overline{DE}$, $\overline{EF}$, and $\overline{FD}$. Label them as G, H, and I. What is the relationship between the perimeters of $\triangle ABC$ and $\triangle GHI$?
The perimeter of $\triangle GHI$ is one fourth of the perimeter of $\triangle ABC$.

31. **FRACTALS** The design below, which approximates a *fractal*, is created with midsegments. Beginning with any triangle, shade the triangle formed by the three midsegments. Continue the process for each unshaded triangle. Suppose the perimeter of the original triangle is 1. What is the perimeter of the triangle that is shaded in Stage 1? What is the total perimeter of all the triangles that are shaded in Stage 2? in Stage 3? $\frac{1}{2}$; $1\frac{1}{4}$; $2\frac{3}{8}$

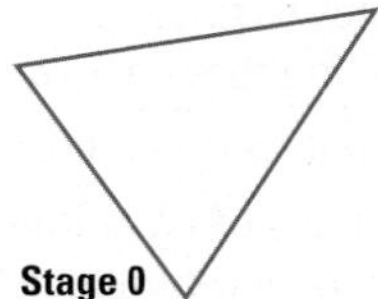
Stage 0

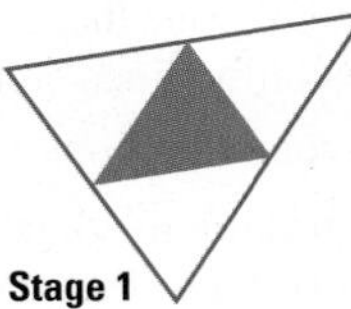
Stage 1

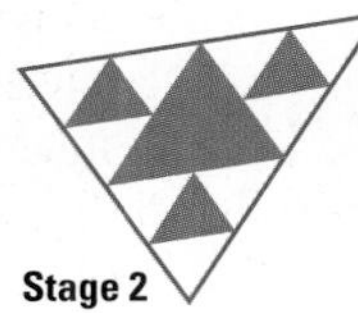
Stage 2

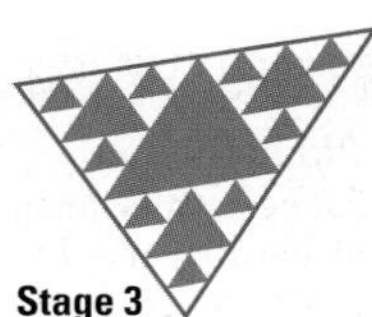
Stage 3

TEACHING TIPS

EXERCISES 23–25 As students complete the proof of the Midsegment Theorem, have them write down the given information and what they need to prove.

COMMON ERROR

EXERCISES 26 AND 27 Students may incorrectly draw a triangle using given midsegments. The sides of the triangles are parallel to the midsegments, but figuring out on which side of the midsegment to draw the parallel segment may be difficult. Point out that each side of the triangle must contain one of the endpoints of the triangle formed by the midsegments because these are the midpoints of the original triangle. Therefore, the parallel side should go through the midpoint not contained in the parallel midsegment.

STUDENT HELP NOTES

Homework Help Students can find help for Exs. 26 and 27 at **www.mcdougallittell.com.** The information can be printed out for students who don't have access to the Internet.

APPLICATION NOTE

Additional information about fractals is available at **www.mcdougallittell.com.**

25. $DF = \sqrt{(a-c)^2 + (b-0)^2} = \sqrt{(a-c)^2 + b^2}$ and $CB = \sqrt{(2a-2c)^2 + (2b-0)^2} = 2\sqrt{(a-c)^2 + b^2}$, so $DF = \frac{1}{2}CB$; $EF = \sqrt{(a+c-c)^2 + (b-0)^2} = \sqrt{a^2 + b^2}$ and $CA = \sqrt{(2a-0)^2 + (2b-0)^2} = 2\sqrt{a^2+b^2}$, so $EF = \frac{1}{2}CA$.

STUDENT HELP NOTES

Skills Review As students review writing an equation of a line on p. 795, remind them that a linear equation in two variables can be written in either point-slope form, $y - y_1 = m(x - x_1)$, or in slope-intercept form, $y = mx + b$.

36d. slope of $\overline{DF} = \frac{1}{2}$, slope of $\overline{FE} = 3$;
$\overleftrightarrow{AB}$: $y - 2 = \frac{1}{2}(x - 3)$,
$\overleftrightarrow{AC}$: $y - 4 = 3(x - 2)$
e. $\overleftrightarrow{BC}$: $y = -2x + 13$,
$\overleftrightarrow{AB}$: $y = \frac{1}{2}x + \frac{1}{2}$,
$\overleftrightarrow{AC}$: $y = 3x - 2$

ADDITIONAL PRACTICE AND RETEACHING

For Lesson 5.4:

- Practice Levels A, B, and C (*Chapter 5 Resource Book*, p. 58)
- Reteaching with Practice (*Chapter 5 Resource Book*, p. 61)
- See Lesson 5.4 of the *Personal Student Tutor*

For more Mixed Review:

- Search the *Test and Practice Generator* for key words or specific lessons.

32. 60 in.; each crossbar is a midsegment that is || to the base, and must be half as long as the base.

33. $\overline{DE}$ is a midsegment of $\triangle ABC$, so D is the midpoint of $\overline{AB}$ and $\overline{AD} \cong \overline{DB}$. $\overline{DE}$ is also a midsegment of $\triangle ABC$, so by the Midsegment Thm., $\overline{DE} \parallel \overline{BC}$ and $DE = \frac{1}{2}BC$. But F is the midpoint of $\overline{BC}$, so $BF = \frac{1}{2}BC$. Then by the transitive prop. of equality and the def. of cong., $\overline{DE} \cong \overline{BF}$. Corresp. ∠s ADE and ABC are ≅, so $\triangle ADE \cong \triangle DBF$ by the SAS Cong. Post.

34. Use the method of Ex. 33 to show that $\overline{AD} \cong \overline{DB}$ and $\overline{DE} \cong \overline{BF}$. Then use the same method used to prove that $\overline{DE} \cong \overline{BF}$ to show that $\overline{AE} \cong \overline{DF}$.

32. **PORCH SWING** You are assembling the frame for a porch swing. The horizontal crossbars in the kit you purchased are each 30 inches long. You attach the crossbars at the midpoints of the legs. At each end of the frame, how far apart will the bottoms of the legs be when the frame is assembled? Explain.

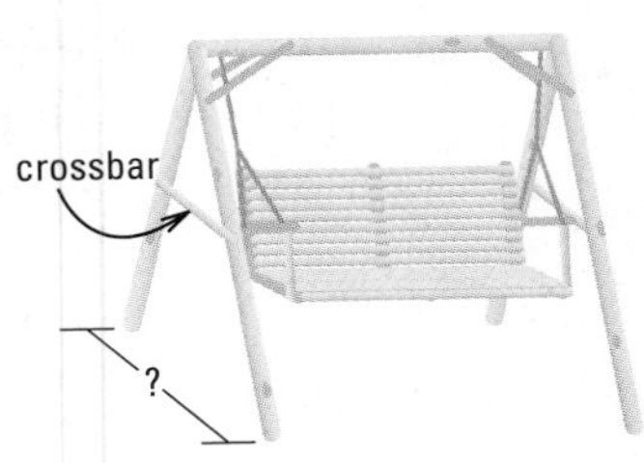

33. **WRITING A PROOF** Write a paragraph proof using the diagram shown and the given information.

GIVEN ▶ $\triangle ABC$ with midsegments $\overline{DE}$, $\overline{EF}$, and $\overline{FD}$

PROVE ▶ $\triangle ADE \cong \triangle DBF$

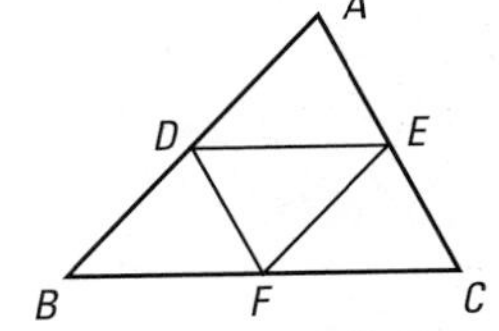

Plan for Proof Use the SAS Congruence Postulate. Show that $\overline{AD} \cong \overline{DB}$. Show that because $DE = BF = \frac{1}{2}BC$, then $\overline{DE} \cong \overline{BF}$. Use parallel lines to show that $\angle ADE \cong \angle ABC$.

34. **WRITING A PLAN** Using the information from Exercise 33, write a plan for a proof showing how you could use the SSS Congruence Postulate to prove that $\triangle ADE \cong \triangle DBF$.

35. **A-FRAME HOUSE** In the A-frame house shown, the floor of the second level, labeled $\overline{PQ}$, is closer to the first floor, $\overline{RS}$, than midsegment $\overline{MN}$ is. If $\overline{RS}$ is 24 feet long, can $\overline{PQ}$ be 10 feet long? 12 feet long? 14 feet long? 24 feet long? Explain.
See margin.

Test Preparation

35. no, no, yes, no; if you imagine "sliding" a segment parallel to $\overline{RS}$ up the triangle, then its length decreases as the segment slides upward (can be shown with a coordinate argument). So $MN < PQ < RS$, or $12 < PQ < 24$.

36. **MULTI-STEP PROBLEM** The diagram below shows the points $D(2, 4)$, $E(3, 2)$, and $F(4, 5)$, which are midpoints of the sides of $\triangle ABC$. The directions below show how to use equations of lines to reconstruct the original $\triangle ABC$.

a. Plot D, E, and F in a coordinate plane. Check drawings.

b. Find the slope m_1 of one midsegment, say $\overline{DE}$. slope of $\overline{DE} = -2$

c. The line containing side $\overline{CB}$ will have the same slope as $\overline{DE}$. Because $\overline{CB}$ contains $F(4, 5)$, an equation of $\overleftrightarrow{CB}$ in *point-slope form* is $y - 5 = m_1(x - 4)$. Write an equation of $\overleftrightarrow{CB}$. $y - 5 = -2(x - 4)$

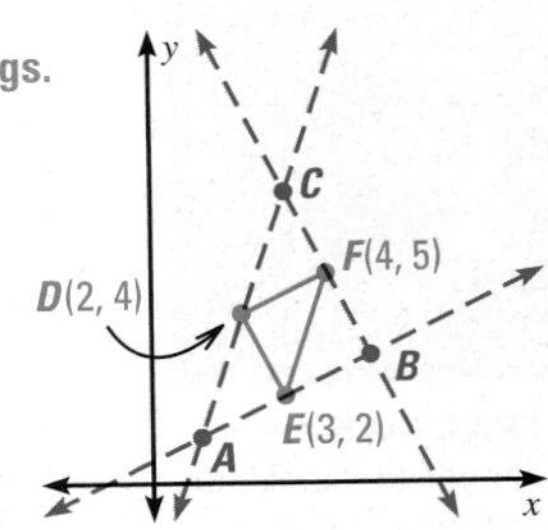

d. Find the slopes m_2 and m_3 of the other two midsegments. Use these slopes to find equations of the lines containing the other two sides of $\triangle ABC$. See margin.

e. Rewrite your equations from parts (c) and (d) in *slope-intercept form*. See margin.

f. Use substitution to solve systems of equations to find the intersection of each pair of lines. Plot these points A, B, and C on your graph. $A(1, 1)$, $B(5, 3)$, $C(3, 7)$

STUDENT HELP

Skills Review For help with writing an equation of a line, see page 795.

★ Challenge

37. FINDING A PATTERN In $\triangle ABC$, the length of $\overline{AB}$ is 24. In the triangle, a succession of midsegments are formed. See margin.

- At Stage 1, draw the midsegment of $\triangle ABC$. Label it $\overline{DE}$.
- At Stage 2, draw the midsegment of $\triangle DEC$. Label it $\overline{FG}$.
- At Stage 3, draw the midsegment of $\triangle FGC$. Label it $\overline{HJ}$.

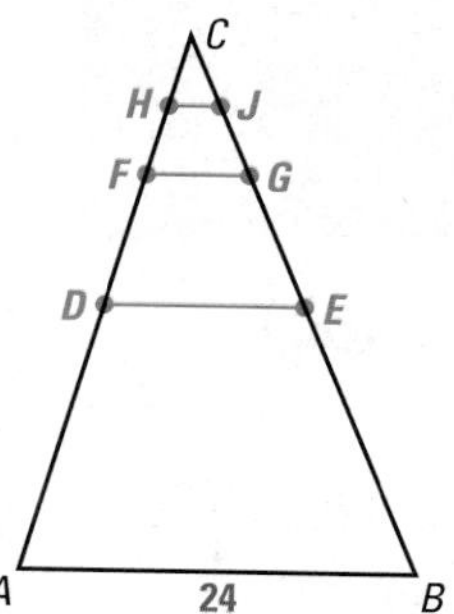

Copy and complete the table showing the length of the midsegment at each stage.

Stage n	0	1	2	3	4	5
Midsegment length	24	?	?	?	?	?

www.mcdougallittell.com

38. **USING ALGEBRA** In Exercise 37, let y represent the length of the midsegment at Stage n. Construct a scatter plot for the data given in the table. Then find a function that gives the length of the midsegment at Stage n.
See margin for graph. $y = \frac{24}{2^n}$

MIXED REVIEW

SOLVING EQUATIONS Solve the equation and state a reason for each step. (Review 2.4) 39–46. See margin.

39. $x - 3 = 11$

40. $3x + 13 = 46$

41. $8x - 1 = 2x + 17$

42. $5x + 12 = 9x - 4$

43. $2(4x - 1) = 14$

44. $9(3x + 10) = 27$

45. $-2(x + 1) + 3 = 23$

46. $3x + 2(x + 5) = 40$

USING ALGEBRA Find the value of x. (Review 4.1 for 5.5)

47. 23

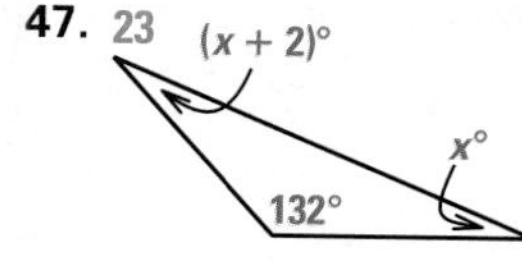

48. 7

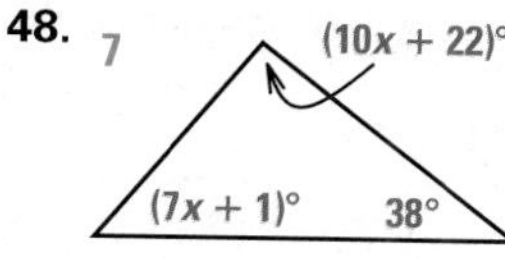

49. 18

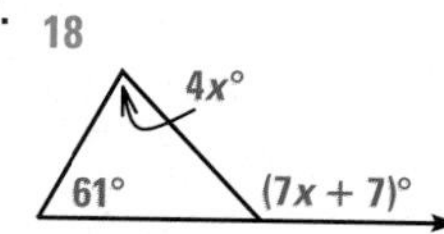

ANGLE BISECTORS $\overrightarrow{AD}$, $\overrightarrow{BD}$, and $\overrightarrow{CD}$ **are angle bisectors of $\triangle ABC$.** (Review 5.2)

50. Explain why $\angle CAD \cong \angle BAD$ and $\angle BCD \cong \angle ACD$. def. of ∠ bisector

51. Is point D the *circumcenter* or *incenter* of $\triangle ABC$? incenter

52. Explain why $\overline{DE} \cong \overline{DG} \cong \overline{DF}$.

53. Suppose $CD = 10$ and $EC = 8$. Find DF. 6

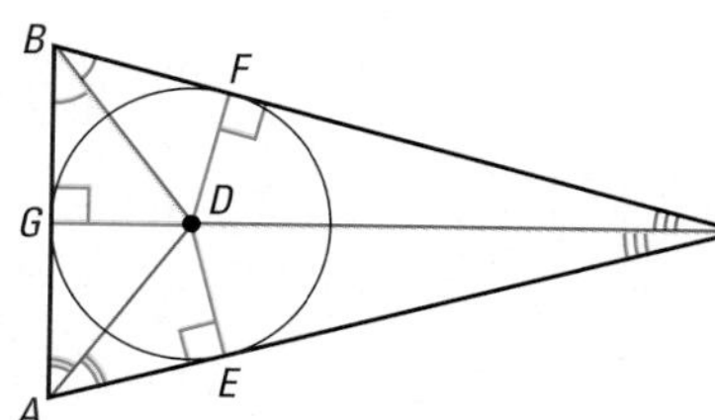

52. The ∠ bisectors of a △ intersect at a point equidistant from the sides of the △. Because $\overline{DE}$, $\overline{DF}$, and $\overline{DG}$ are ⊥ segments to the sides of the △s, their lengths are = distances and $DE = DG = DF$. By the def. of ≅ segments, $\overline{DE} \cong \overline{DG} \cong \overline{DF}$.

4 ASSESS

DAILY HOMEWORK QUIZ

Transparency Available

In $\triangle DEF$, G, H, and J are the midpoints of the sides.

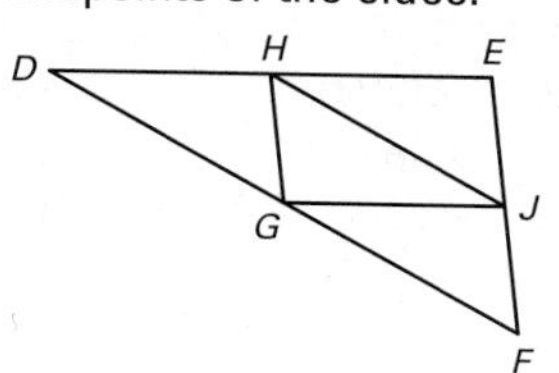

1. Which segment is parallel to $\overline{EF}$? $\overline{GH}$

2. If $GJ = 3$, what is HE? 3

3. If $DF = 5$, what is HJ? 2.5

4. $\triangle ABC$ has its vertices at $A(2, 2)$, $B(8, 4)$, and $C(6, -2)$. What is the perimeter of its midsegment triangle?
$2\sqrt{10} + 2\sqrt{2}$

EXTRA CHALLENGE NOTE

Challenge problems for Lesson 5.4 are available in **blackline** format in the *Chapter 5 Resource Book*, p. 66 and at **www.mcdougallittell.com.**

ADDITIONAL TEST PREPARATION

1. WRITING Describe how to draw the original triangle if you are given the midpoints of the three sides of the triangle.
Sample answer: Connect the midpoints to form a midsegment triangle. Then draw a line segment parallel to one side of the midsegment triangle and through the other vertex of the midsegment triangle. Then do the same thing for the other two sides of the midsegment triangle. The vertices of the original triangle are the intersection points of the drawn segments.

37–46. See Additional Answers beginning on page AA1.

1 Planning the Activity

PURPOSE
To decide which sides and angles of a triangle are the smallest and which are the largest.

MATERIALS
- geometry software
- Software Help (*Chapter 5 Resource Book*, p. 71)

PACING
- Activity — 15 min

LINK TO LESSON
Students can use this activity to verify the theorems in Lesson 5.5.

2 Managing the Activity

CLASSROOM MANAGEMENT
Work through the activity with students so that they understand what each question is asking. Use a computer to demonstrate the software.

ALTERNATIVE APPROACH
Students can complete the activity using paper, pencil, a ruler, and a protractor.

3 Closing the Activity

KEY DISCOVERY
The side opposite the largest angle of a triangle will be the longest side of the triangle and vice versa. The side opposite the smallest angle of a triangle will be the shortest side of the triangle and vice versa.

ACTIVITY ASSESSMENT
What happens to the side lengths as the angles of the triangle you draw all get close to 60°? **The side lengths get close to being equal.**

ACTIVITY 5.5
Using Technology

Side Lengths and Angle Measures

You can use geometry software to decide which sides and angles are the smallest and largest in a triangle.

STUDENT HELP

SOFTWARE HELP
Visit our Web site www.mcdougallittell.com to see instructions for several software applications.

CONSTRUCT Construct a triangle.

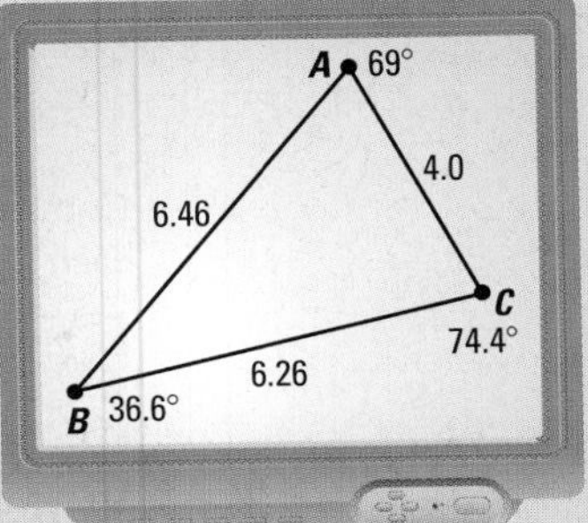

1. Draw any scalene triangle. Label the vertices as A, B, and C. **Check drawings.**
2. Find the measure of each angle of the triangle. **Answers will vary.**
3. Find the length of each side of the triangle. **Answers will vary.**

INVESTIGATE

1. In $\triangle ABC$, is the longest side *adjacent to* or *opposite* the largest angle? **opposite**

2. In $\triangle ABC$, is the shortest side *adjacent to* or *opposite* the smallest angle? **opposite**

3. Drag point A to change the shape and size of $\triangle ABC$. Answer the questions in Exercises 1 and 2 for the new triangle. **opposite; opposite**

MAKE A CONJECTURE

4. Make a conjecture about how the positions of sides of different lengths in a triangle are related to the positions of the angles of different measures. **In a △, the longest side is opp. the largest angle and the shortest side is opp. the smallest angle.**

EXTENSION

CRITICAL THINKING Use the triangle measurements from the activity above. Complete the following expressions.

$$\frac{\text{measure of smallest angle}}{\text{measure of largest angle}} = \frac{?}{?} = \underline{\ ?\ }$$ **Answers will vary.**

$$\frac{\text{length of shortest side}}{\text{length of longest side}} = \frac{?}{?} = \underline{\ ?\ }$$ **Answers will vary.**

Tell whether this statement is *true* or *false*: **false**

"The quotient of the measures of two angles in a triangle is always the same as the quotient of the lengths of the sides opposite those angles."

5.5 Inequalities in One Triangle

What you should learn

GOAL 1 Use triangle measurements to decide which side is longest or which angle is largest, as applied in **Example 2**.

GOAL 2 Use the Triangle Inequality.

Why you should learn it

▼ To solve **real-life** problems, such as describing the motion of a crane as it clears the sediment from the mouth of a river in **Exs. 29–31**.

CALIFORNIA STANDARDS AND ASSESSMENT

CA Standards: 6, 13
SAT9 Task 1: Objs. 3, 6, 24, 26
SAT9 Task 2: Objs. 2, 3, 26, 27

GOAL 1 COMPARING MEASUREMENTS OF A TRIANGLE

In Activity 5.5, you may have discovered a relationship between the positions of the longest and shortest sides of a triangle and the positions of its angles.

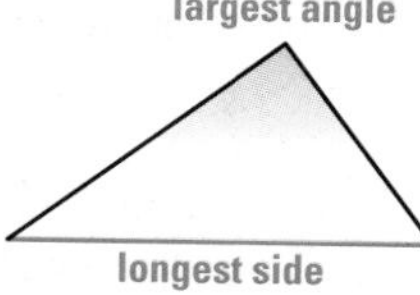

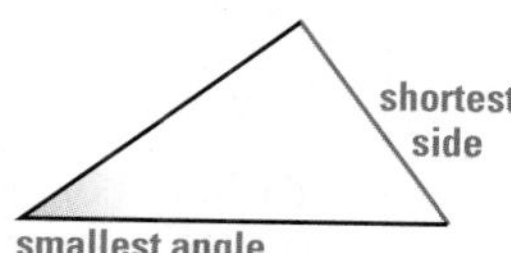

The diagrams illustrate the results stated in the theorems below.

THEOREMS

THEOREM 5.10

If one side of a triangle is longer than another side, then the angle opposite the longer side is larger than the angle opposite the shorter side.

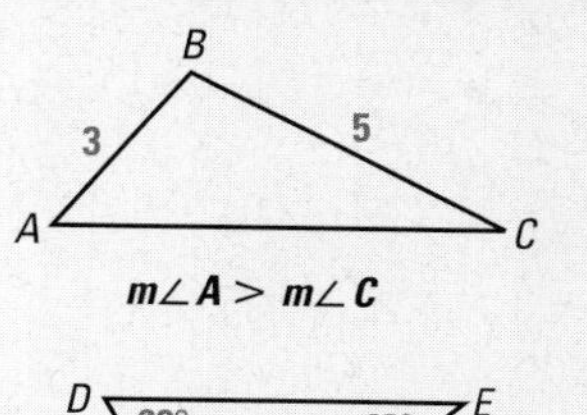

$m\angle A > m\angle C$

THEOREM 5.11

If one angle of a triangle is larger than another angle, then the side opposite the larger angle is longer than the side opposite the smaller angle.

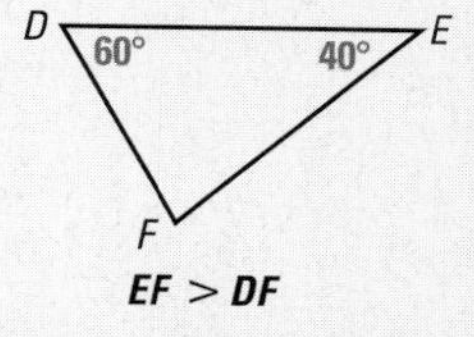

$EF > DF$

You can write the measurements of a triangle in order from least to greatest.

EXAMPLE 1 ***Writing Measurements in Order from Least to Greatest***

Write the measurements of the triangles in order from least to greatest.

a.

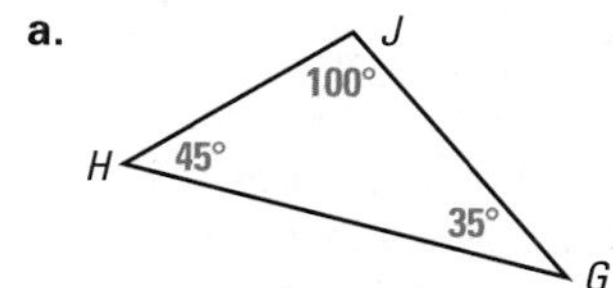

b. (Triangle QRP with $QR = 8$, $PR = 7$, $QP = 5$)

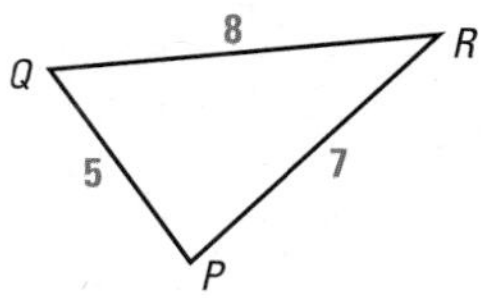

SOLUTION

a. $m\angle G < m\angle H < m\angle J$
$JH < JG < GH$

b. $QP < PR < QR$
$m\angle R < m\angle Q < m\angle P$

1 PLAN

PACING
Basic: 2 days
Average: 2 days
Advanced: 2 days
Block Schedule: 0.5 block with 5.4
0.5 block with 5.6

LESSON OPENER ACTIVITY

An alternative way to approach Lesson 5.5 is to use the Activity Lesson Opener:

- Blackline Master (*Chapter 5 Resource Book*, p. 70)
- Transparency (p. 31)

MEETING INDIVIDUAL NEEDS

- ***Chapter 5 Resource Book***
  Prerequisite Skills Review (p. 5)
  Practice Level A (p. 73)
  Practice Level B (p. 74)
  Practice Level C (p. 75)
  Reteaching with Practice (p. 76)
  Absent Student Catch-Up (p. 78)
  Challenge (p. 80)
- ***Resources in Spanish***
- ***Personal Student Tutor***

NEW-TEACHER SUPPORT

See the Tips for New Teachers on pp. 1–2 of the *Chapter 5 Resource Book* for additional notes about Lesson 5.5.

WARM-UP EXERCISES

Transparency Available

Solve the inequality.

1. $x + 3 < 14$ $x < 11$
2. $12 > 10 - x$ $x > -2$
3. $2x + 3 < 4x - 9$ $x > 6$

Find the measure of the third angle of a triangle with the two given angle measures.

4. 28°, 59° 93°
5. $x°$, $2x°$ $180° - 3x°$

2 TEACH

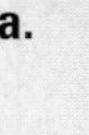

EXTRA EXAMPLE 1
Write the measures in the triangles in order from least to greatest.

a.

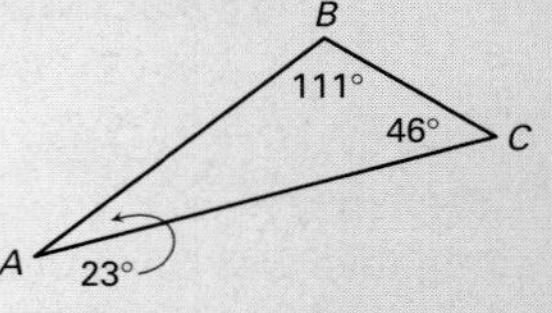

$m\angle A < m\angle C < m\angle B$; $BC < AB < AC$

b.

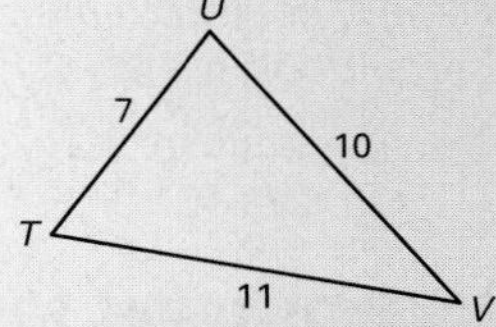

$TU < UV < TV$; $m\angle V < m\angle T < m\angle U$

EXTRA EXAMPLE 2
The figure below shows the side view of an Adirondack chair. In the figure, $\overline{JL} \cong \overline{LK}$ and $JK < JL$. What can you conclude about the angles in $\triangle JKL$?

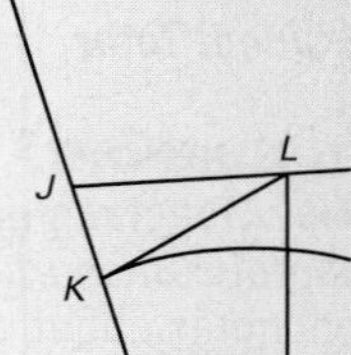

$m\angle KJL = m\angle JKL$; $m\angle JLK < m\angle KJL$; $m\angle JLK < m\angle JKL$

CHECKPOINT EXERCISES
For use after Examples 1 and 2:

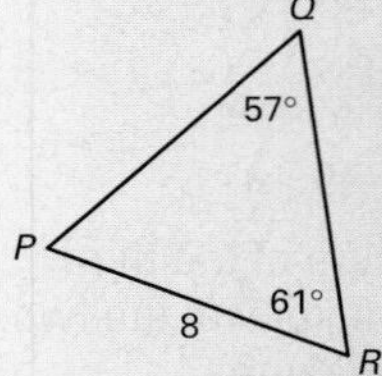

1. Name the smallest and largest angles of $\triangle PQR$. *$\angle Q$; $\angle P$*

2. Is $QR \geq 8$? Is $PQ < 8$? *yes; no*

Theorem 5.11 will be proved in Lesson 5.6, using a technique called *indirect proof*. Theorem 5.10 can be proved using the diagram shown below.

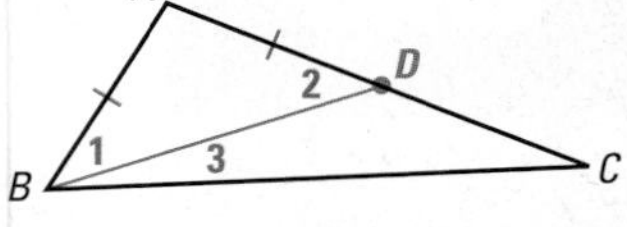

GIVEN ▶ $AC > AB$

PROVE ▶ $m\angle ABC > m\angle C$

Paragraph Proof Use the Ruler Postulate to locate a point D on $\overline{AC}$ such that $DA = BA$. Then draw the segment $\overline{BD}$. In the isosceles triangle $\triangle ABD$, $\angle 1 \cong \angle 2$. Because $m\angle ABC = m\angle 1 + m\angle 3$, it follows that $m\angle ABC > m\angle 1$. Substituting $m\angle 2$ for $m\angle 1$ produces $m\angle ABC > m\angle 2$. Because $m\angle 2 = m\angle 3 + m\angle C$, $m\angle 2 > m\angle C$. Finally, because $m\angle ABC > m\angle 2$ and $m\angle 2 > m\angle C$, you can conclude that $m\angle ABC > m\angle C$.

The proof of Theorem 5.10 above uses the fact that $\angle 2$ is an exterior angle for $\triangle BDC$, so its measure is the sum of the measures of the two nonadjacent interior angles. Then $m\angle 2$ must be greater than the measure of either nonadjacent interior angle. This result is stated below as Theorem 5.12.

THEOREM

THEOREM 5.12 ***Exterior Angle Inequality***

The measure of an exterior angle of a triangle is greater than the measure of either of the two nonadjacent interior angles.

$m\angle 1 > m\angle A$ and $m\angle 1 > m\angle B$

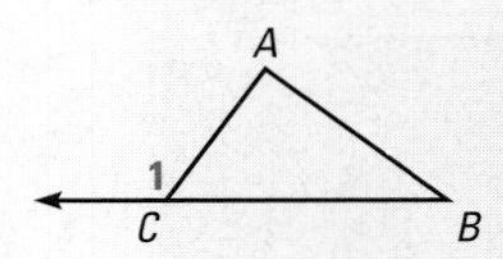

You can use Theorem 5.10 to determine possible angle measures in a chair or other real-life object.

EXAMPLE 2 *Using Theorem 5.10*

REAL LIFE **DIRECTOR'S CHAIR** In the director's chair shown, $\overline{AB} \cong \overline{AC}$ and $BC > AB$. What can you conclude about the angles in $\triangle ABC$?

SOLUTION

Because $\overline{AB} \cong \overline{AC}$, $\triangle ABC$ is isosceles, so $\angle B \cong \angle C$. Therefore, $m\angle B = m\angle C$. Because $BC > AB$, $m\angle A > m\angle C$ by Theorem 5.10. By substitution, $m\angle A > m\angle B$. In addition, you can conclude that $m\angle A > 60°$, $m\angle B < 60°$, and $m\angle C < 60°$.

GOAL 2 USING THE TRIANGLE INEQUALITY

Not every group of three segments can be used to form a triangle. The lengths of the segments must fit a certain relationship.

EXAMPLE 3 *Constructing a Triangle*

Construct a triangle with the given group of side lengths, if possible.

a. 2 cm, 2 cm, 5 cm **b.** 3 cm, 2 cm, 5 cm **c.** 4 cm, 2 cm, 5 cm

SOLUTION

Try drawing triangles with the given side lengths. Only group (c) is possible. The sum of the first and second lengths must be greater than the third length.

a.
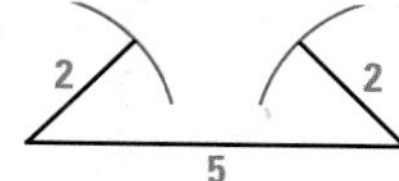

b.
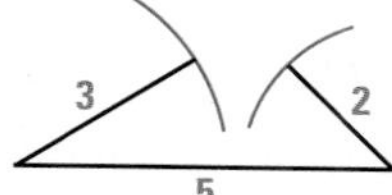

c.
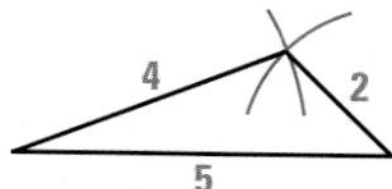

The result of Example 3 is summarized as Theorem 5.13. Exercise 34 asks you to write a proof of this theorem.

THEOREM

THEOREM 5.13 *Triangle Inequality*

The sum of the lengths of any two sides of a triangle is greater than the length of the third side.

$AB + BC > AC$

$AC + BC > AB$

$AB + AC > BC$

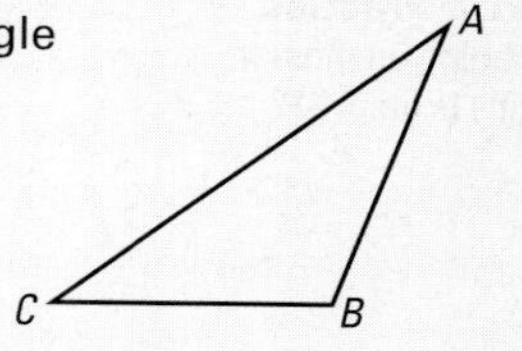

EXAMPLE 4 *Finding Possible Side Lengths*

A triangle has one side of 10 centimeters and another of 14 centimeters. Describe the possible lengths of the third side.

SOLUTION

Let x represent the length of the third side. Using the Triangle Inequality, you can write and solve inequalities.

$x + 10 > 14$ $\qquad$ $10 + 14 > x$

$x > 4$ $\qquad$ $24 > x$

▶ So, the length of the third side must be greater than 4 centimeters and less than 24 centimeters.

STUDENT HELP

Skills Review
For help with solving inequalities, see p. 791.

EXTRA EXAMPLE 3

Construct a triangle with the given side lengths, if possible.

a. 3 in., 3 in., 8 in. **not possible**

b. 6 in., 6 in., 12 in. **not possible**

c. 9 in., 5 in., 11 in.

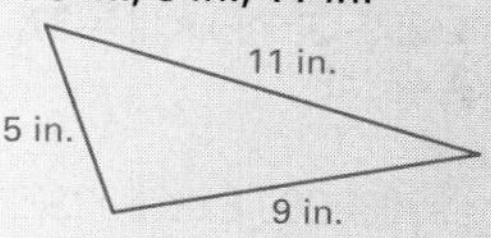

EXTRA EXAMPLE 4

A triangle has one side of 8 cm and another of 17 cm. Describe the possible lengths of the third side. **The length of the third side must be greater than 9 cm and less than 25 cm.**

CHECKPOINT EXERCISES

For use after Examples 3 and 4:

A triangle has one side of 11 in. and another side of 16 in.

1. Describe the possible lengths of the third side. **The length of the third side must be greater than 5 in. and less than 27 in.**

2. Construct a possible triangle with the two given side lengths. ***Sample answer:***

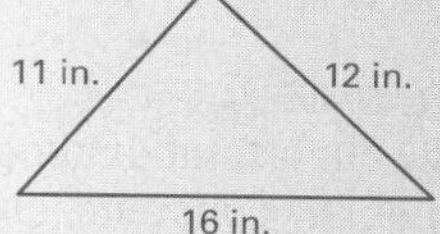

FOCUS ON VOCABULARY

What angles of a triangle are used in the Exterior Angle inequality? **one exterior angle and the two nonadjacent interior angles**

CLOSURE QUESTION

In $\triangle ABC$, $\angle B$ is obtuse and $m\angle A < m\angle C$. State what you know about the lengths of the sides of $\triangle ABC$. **$AC > AB > BC$, $AB + BC > AC$, $AC + BC > AB$, and $AB + AC > BC$.**

3 APPLY

ASSIGNMENT GUIDE

BASIC
Day 1: pp. 298–299 Exs. 6–23
Day 2: pp. 299–301 Exs. 24–37, 39–46, 48

AVERAGE
Day 1: pp. 298–299 Exs. 6–23
Day 2: pp. 299–301 Exs. 24–37, 39–46, 48

ADVANCED
Day 1: pp. 298–299 Exs. 6–23
Day 2: pp. 299–301 Exs. 24–46, 48

BLOCK SCHEDULE
pp. 298–299 Exs. 6–23 (with 5.4)
pp. 299–301 Exs. 24–37, 39–46, 48 (with 5.6)

EXERCISE LEVELS

Level A: *Easier*
6–19

Level B: *More Difficult*
20–37

Level C: *Most Difficult*
38

HOMEWORK CHECK

To quickly check student understanding of key concepts, go over the following exercises: Exs. 8, 10, 12, 16, 18, 22, 24, 28, 32, 34. See also the Daily Homework Quiz:

- Blackline Master (*Chapter 5 Resource Book,* p. 83)
- Transparency (p. 38)

GUIDED PRACTICE

Vocabulary Check ✓

1. $\triangle ABC$ has side lengths of 1 inch, $1\frac{7}{8}$ inches, and $2\frac{1}{8}$ inches and angle measures of 90°, 28°, and 62°. Which side is *opposite* each angle? **See margin.**

1. The $2\frac{1}{8}$ in. side is opp. the 90°∠, the $1\frac{7}{8}$ in. side is opp. the 62°∠, and the 1 in. side is opp. the 28°∠.

Concept Check ✓

2. Is it possible to draw a triangle with side lengths of 5 inches, 2 inches, and 8 inches? Explain why or why not. **No; 5 + 2 is not greater than 8.**

Skill Check ✓

In Exercises 3 and 4, use the figure shown at the right.

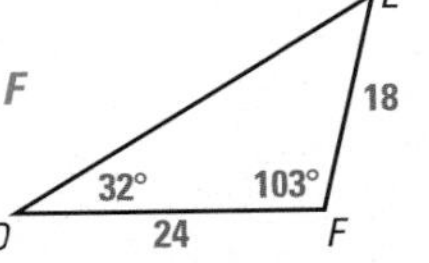

3. Name the smallest and largest angles of $\triangle DEF$. **∠D, ∠F**
4. Name the shortest and longest sides of $\triangle DEF$. $\overline{EF}$, $\overline{DE}$

5. **GEOGRAPHY** Suppose you know the following information about distances between cities in the Philippine Islands:

   Cadiz to Masbate: 99 miles

   Cadiz to Guiuan: 165 miles

   Describe the range of possible distances from Guiuan to Masbate.
   greater than 66 mi and less than 264 mi

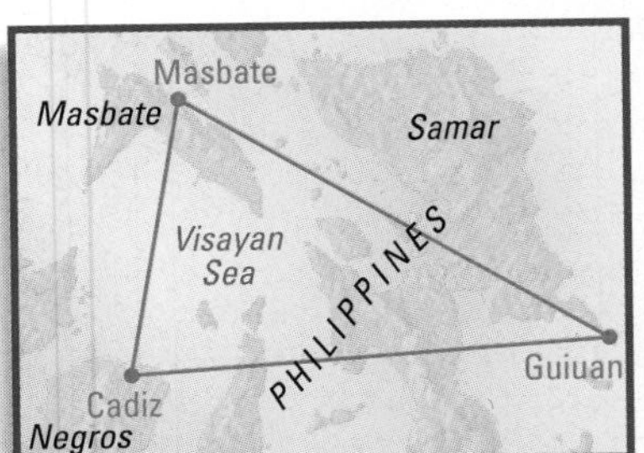

PRACTICE AND APPLICATIONS

STUDENT HELP
Extra Practice to help you master skills is on p. 812.

COMPARING SIDE LENGTHS Name the shortest and longest sides of the triangle.

6. 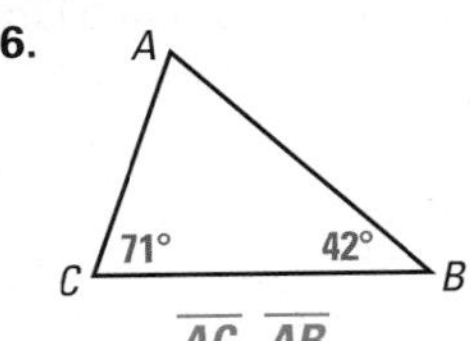

$\overline{AC}$, $\overline{AB}$

7. 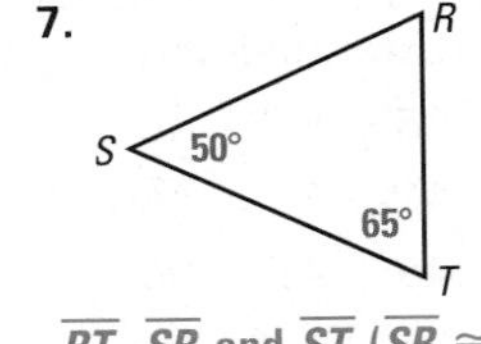

$\overline{RT}$, $\overline{SR}$ and $\overline{ST}$ ($\overline{SR} \cong \overline{ST}$)

8. 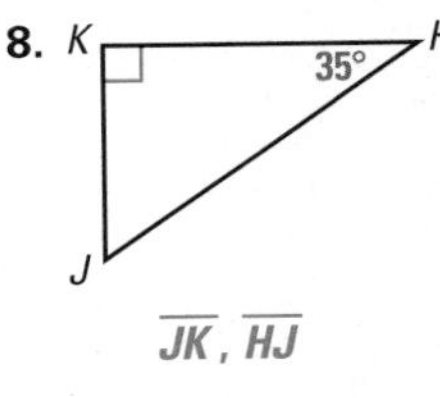

$\overline{JK}$, $\overline{HJ}$

COMPARING ANGLE MEASURES Name the smallest and largest angles of the triangle.

9. 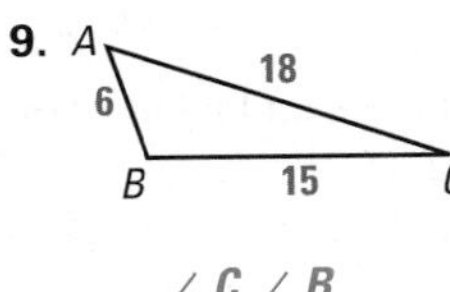

∠C, ∠B

10. 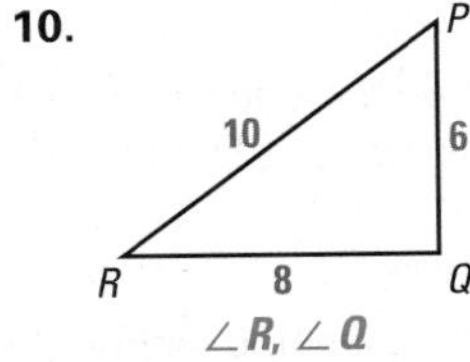

∠R, ∠Q

11. 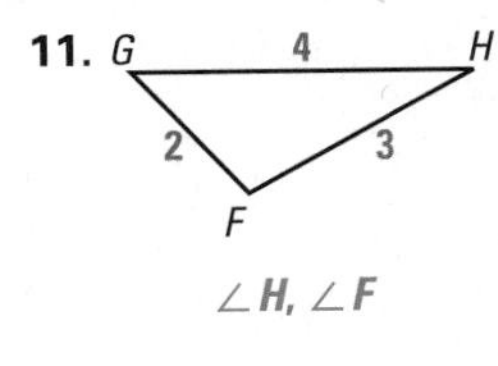

∠H, ∠F

STUDENT HELP
HOMEWORK HELP
Example 1: Exs. 6–19
Example 2: Exs. 6–19
Example 3: Exs. 20–23
Example 4: Exs. 24, 25

USING ALGEBRA Use the diagram of $\triangle RST$ with exterior angle $\angle QRT$.

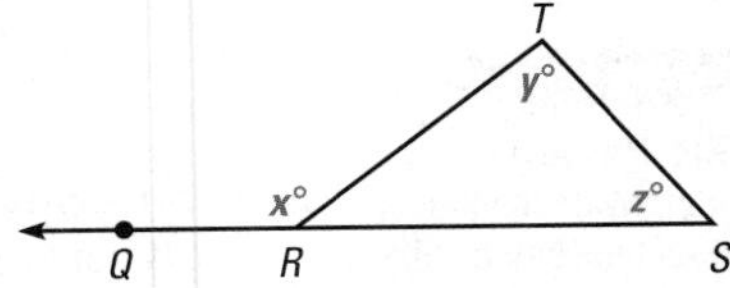

12. Write an equation about the angle measures labeled in the diagram. $x = y + z$
13. Write two inequalities about the angle measures labeled in the diagram. $x > y$, $x > z$

ORDERING SIDES List the sides in order from shortest to longest.

14.

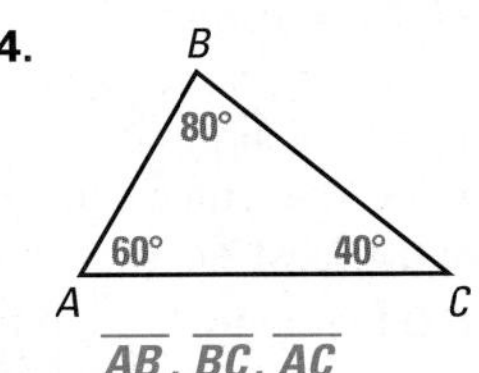

$\overline{AB}, \overline{BC}, \overline{AC}$

15.

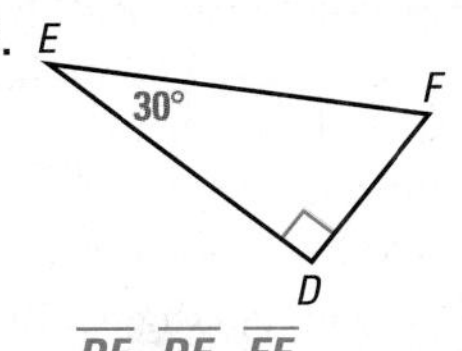

$\overline{DF}, \overline{DE}, \overline{EF}$

16.

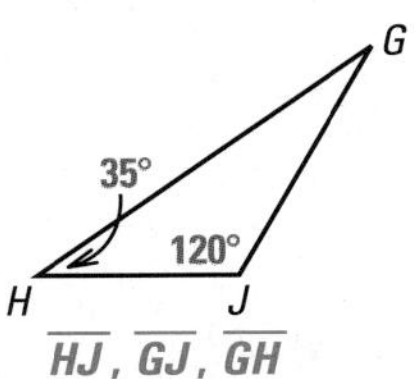

$\overline{HJ}, \overline{GJ}, \overline{GH}$

ORDERING ANGLES List the angles in order from smallest to largest.

17.

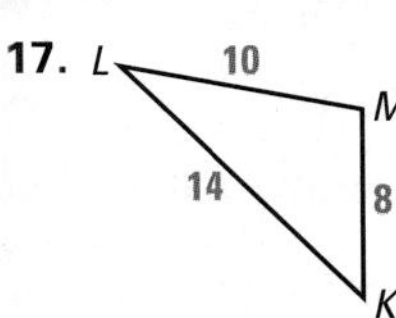

$\angle L, \angle K, \angle M$

18. P, 18, 12, N, 24, Q

$\angle N, \angle Q, \angle P$

19. T, 6, 9, R, 5, S

$\angle T, \angle S, \angle R$

FORMING TRIANGLES In Exercises 20–23, you are given an 18 inch piece of wire. You want to bend the wire to form a triangle so that the length of each side is a whole number. 20–22. Sample answers are given. See margin.

20. Sketch four possible isosceles triangles and label each side length.

21. Sketch a possible acute scalene triangle.

22. Sketch a possible obtuse scalene triangle.

23. List three combinations of segment lengths that will not produce triangles.
Sample answer: 4 in., 5 in., 9 in.; 4 in., 4 in., 10 in.; 3 in., 6 in., 9 in.

USING ALGEBRA In Exercises 24 and 25, solve the inequality $AB + AC > BC$.

24. $x < 7$

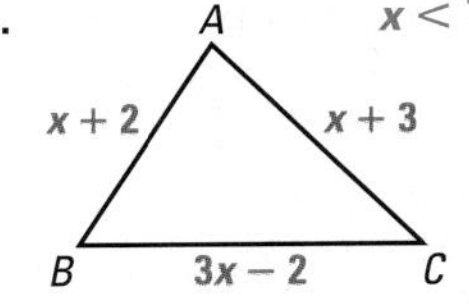

25. $x < 7$

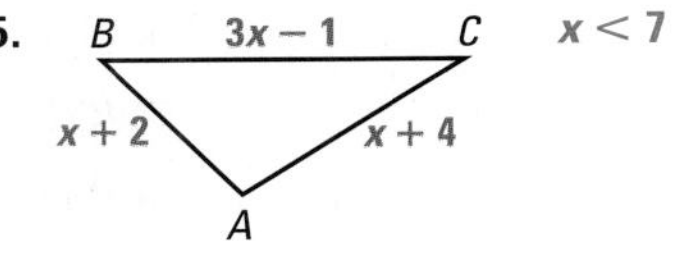

26. **TAKING A SHORTCUT** Look at the diagram shown. Suppose you are walking south on the sidewalk of Pine Street. When you reach Pleasant Street, you cut across the empty lot to go to the corner of Oak Hill Avenue and Union Street. Explain why this route is shorter than staying on the sidewalks. See margin.

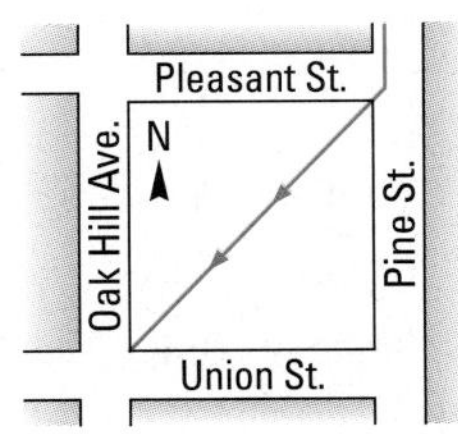

KITCHEN TRIANGLE In Exercises 27 and 28, use the following information.

The term "kitchen triangle" refers to the imaginary triangle formed by three kitchen appliances: the refrigerator, the sink, and the range. The distances shown are measured in feet.

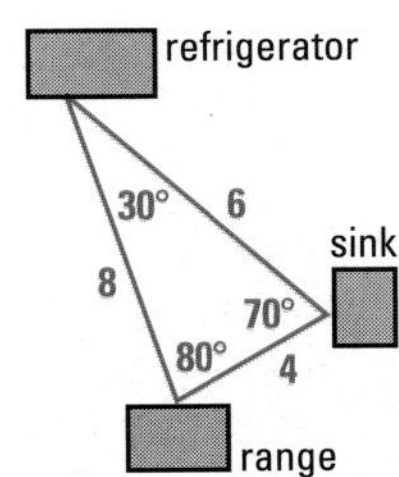

27. What is wrong with the labels on the kitchen triangle? See margin.

28. Can a kitchen triangle have the following side lengths: 9 feet, 3 feet, and 5 feet? Explain why or why not. No; 3 + 5 is not greater than 9.

26. The diagonal and the sidewalks from Pine to Union and from Union to Oak Hill form a △. The walk along the diagonal is shorter by the △ Inequality Thm.

27. The sides and ⦟s could not be positioned as they are labeled; for example, the longest side is not opposite the largest ∠.

FOCUS ON APPLICATIONS

WORK TRIANGLES For ease of movement among appliances, the perimeter of an ideal kitchen work triangle should be less than 22 ft and more than 15 ft.

MATHEMATICAL REASONING
EXERCISES 17–19 Write a statement about angle measures of a triangle that corresponds to the Triangle Inequality for side lengths. Is the statement you wrote *true* or *false*? Explain. The sum of the measures of any two angles of a triangle is greater than the measure of the third angle; false; in a right triangle, the sum of the measures of the two acute angles equals the measure of the right angle and in an obtuse triangle, the sum is less than the measure of the obtuse angle.

! COMMON ERROR
EXERCISE 28 Students may check the side lengths of a triangle by using just one set of two side lengths, finding their sum, and checking to see if the sum is greater than the length of the third side. This method is not valid, because it does not ensure that all inequalities of the triangle inequality hold. Remind students to check all three sums to ensure that a triangle exists.

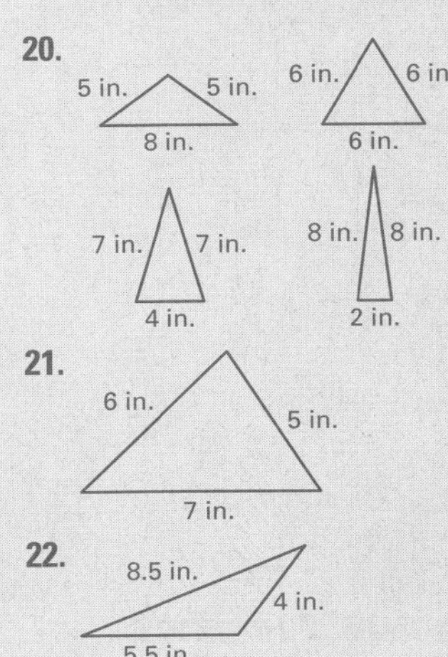

22. 8.5 in., 4 in., 5.5 in.

ENGLISH LEARNERS

EXERCISES 29–31 Diagrams that illuminate the meanings of the vocabulary, such as the one of the crane, can be very helpful to English learners. To help them connect the vocabulary with the process described, you might ask students questions about dredging and about the functions of a crane; for example, "What part of a river is its mouth? What does a crane do when it dredges a river mouth? How does it do this?"

STUDENT HELP NOTES

→ **Homework Help** Students can find help for Exs. 33 and 34 at **www.mcdougallittell.com.** The information can be printed out for students who don't have access to the Internet.

ADDITIONAL PRACTICE AND RETEACHING

For Lesson 5.5:

- Practice Levels A, B, and C (*Chapter 5 Resource Book*, p. 73)
- Reteaching with Practice (*Chapter 5 Resource Book*, p. 76)
- See Lesson 5.5 of the *Personal Student Tutor*

For more Mixed Review:

- Search the *Test and Practice Generator* for key words or specific lessons.

CHANNEL DREDGING In Exercises 29–31, use the figure shown and the given information.
The crane is used in dredging mouths of rivers to clear out the collected debris. By adjusting the length of the boom lines from A to B, the operator of the crane can raise and lower the boom. Suppose the mast $\overline{AC}$ is 50 feet long and the boom $\overline{BC}$ is 100 feet long.

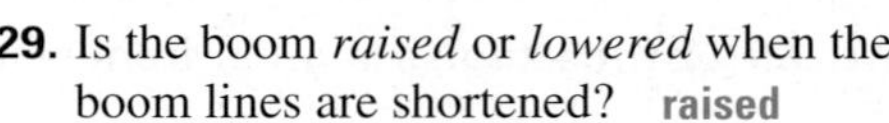

29. Is the boom *raised* or *lowered* when the boom lines are shortened? raised

30. AB must be less than _?_ feet. 150 ft

31. As the boom and shovel are raised or lowered, is $\angle ACB$ ever larger than $\angle BAC$? Explain. Yes; when the boom is lowered and $AB > 100$ (and so $AB > BC$), then $\angle ACB$ will be larger than $\angle BAC$.

32. **LOGICAL REASONING** In Example 4 on page 297, only two inequalities were needed to solve the problem. Write the third inequality. Why is that inequality not helpful in determining the range of values of x? $x + 14 > 10$; since x is positive, $x + 14 > 10$ is true for any value of x.

33. **PROOF** Prove that a perpendicular segment is the shortest line segment from a point to a line. Prove that $\overline{MJ}$ is the shortest line segment from M to $\overleftrightarrow{JN}$. See margin.

GIVEN ▶ $\overline{MJ} \perp \overleftrightarrow{JN}$

PROVE ▶ $MN > MJ$

Plan for Proof Show that $m\angle MJN > m\angle MNJ$, so $MN > MJ$.

33. $\overline{MJ} \perp \overline{JN}$, so $\triangle MJN$ is a right $\triangle$. The largest $\angle$ in a right $\triangle$ is the right $\angle$, so $m\angle MJN > m\angle MNJ$, so $MN > MJ$. (If one $\angle$ of a $\triangle$ is larger than another $\angle$, then the side opp. the larger $\angle$ is longer than the side opp. the smaller $\angle$.)

STUDENT HELP
HOMEWORK HELP Visit our Web site www.mcdougallittell.com for help with proof.

34. **DEVELOPING PROOF** Complete the proof of Theorem 5.13, the Triangle Inequality.

GIVEN ▶ $\triangle ABC$

PROVE ▶ (1) $AB + BC > AC$
(2) $AC + BC > AB$
(3) $AB + AC > BC$

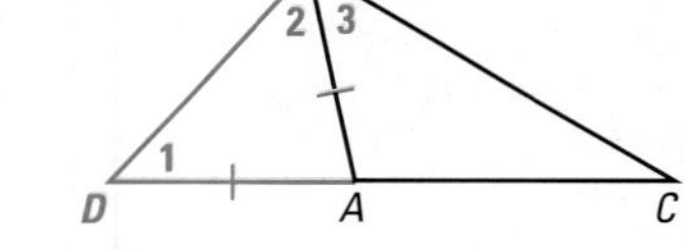

Plan for Proof One side, say $\overline{BC}$, is longer than or is at least as long as each of the other sides. Then (1) and (2) are true. The proof for (3) is as follows.

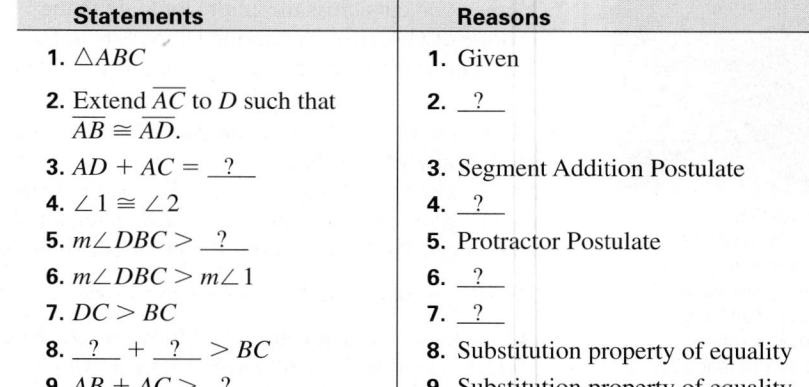

Statements	Reasons
1. $\triangle ABC$	1. Given
2. Extend $\overline{AC}$ to D such that $\overline{AB} \cong \overline{AD}$.	2. _?_
3. $AD + AC =$ _?_	3. Segment Addition Postulate
4. $\angle 1 \cong \angle 2$	4. _?_
5. $m\angle DBC >$ _?_	5. Protractor Postulate
6. $m\angle DBC > m\angle 1$	6. _?_
7. $DC > BC$	7. _?_
8. _?_ + _?_ $> BC$	8. Substitution property of equality
9. $AB + AC >$ _?_	9. Substitution property of equality

34. (2) Ruler Post.
(3) DC
(4) Base Angles Thm.
(5) $m\angle 2$
(6) Substitution prop.
(7) If one $\angle$ of a $\triangle$ is larger than another $\angle$, then the side opp. the larger $\angle$ is longer than the side opp. the smaller $\angle$.
(8) AD, AC
(9) BC

Test Preparation

QUANTITATIVE COMPARISON In Exercises 35–37, use the diagram to choose the statement that is true about the given quantities.

Ⓐ The quantity in column A is greater.

Ⓑ The quantity in column B is greater.

Ⓒ The two quantities are equal.

Ⓓ The relationship cannot be determined from the given information.

	Column A	Column B	
35.	x	y	A
36.	x	z	B
37.	m	n	D

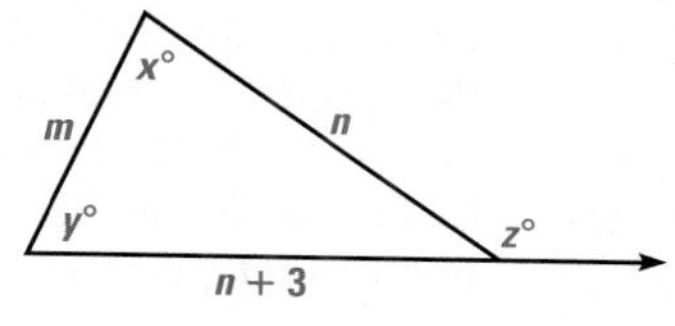

★ Challenge

38. **PROOF** Use the diagram shown to prove that a perpendicular segment is the shortest segment from a point to a plane.

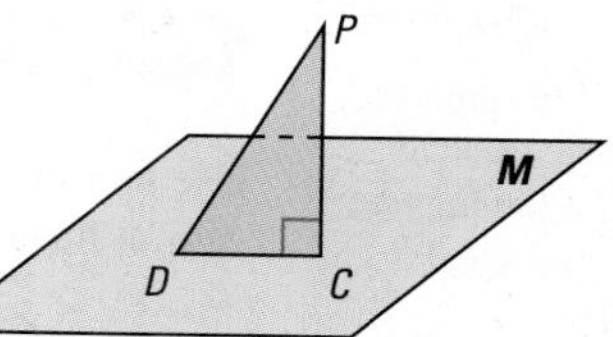

GIVEN ▸ $\overline{PC} \perp$ plane M

PROVE ▸ $PD > PC$

$\overline{PC}$ is $\perp$ to plane M so $\overline{PC} \perp \overline{DC}$ and $\triangle PCD$ is a right $\triangle$. The largest $\angle$ in a right $\triangle$ is the right $\angle$, so $m\angle C > m\angle D$, so $PD > PC$. (If one $\angle$ of a $\triangle$ is larger than another $\angle$, then the side opp. the larger $\angle$ is longer than the side opp. the smaller $\angle$.)

EXTRA CHALLENGE

www.mcdougallittell.com

MIXED REVIEW

RECOGNIZING PROOFS In Exercises 39–41, look through your textbook to find an example of the type of proof. (Review Chapters 2–5 for 5.6)

39–41. Sample answers are given.

39. two-column proof **proof of Theorem 4.1, page 196**

40. paragraph proof **proof of Theorem 5.10, page 296**

41. flow proof **Example 1, page 136**

ANGLE RELATIONSHIPS Complete each statement. (Review 3.1)

42. $\angle 5$ and __?__ are corresponding angles. So are $\angle 5$ and __?__. **$\angle 1$; $\angle 9$**

43. $\angle 12$ and __?__ are vertical angles. **$\angle 9$**

44. $\angle 6$ and __?__ are alternate interior angles. So are $\angle 6$ and __?__. **$\angle 3$; $\angle 11$**

45. $\angle 7$ and __?__ are alternate exterior angles. So are $\angle 7$ and __?__. **$\angle 2$; $\angle 10$**

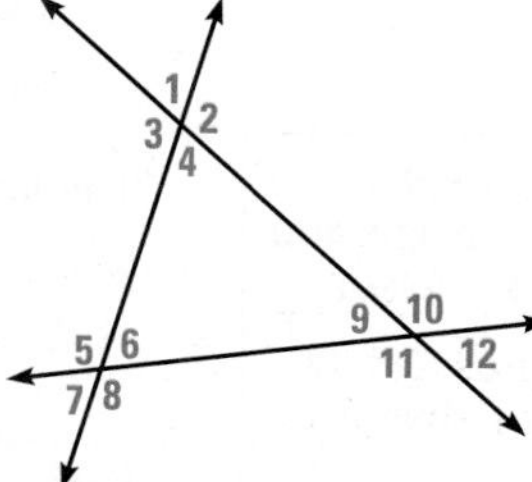

USING ALGEBRA In Exercises 46–49, you are given the coordinates of the midpoints of the sides of a triangle. Find the coordinates of the vertices of the triangle. (Review 5.4)

46. $L(-2, 1)$, $M(2, 3)$, $N(3, -1)$ **(−1, −3), (−3, 5), (7, 1)**

47. $L(-3, 5)$, $M(-2, 2)$, $N(-6, 0)$ **(−7, 3), (−5, −3), (1, 7)**

48. $L(3, 6)$, $M(9, 5)$, $N(8, 1)$ **(2, 2), (14, 0), (4, 10)**

49. $L(3, -2)$, $M(0, -4)$, $N(3, -6)$ **(0, 0), (6, −4), (0, −8)**

4 ASSESS

DAILY HOMEWORK QUIZ

Transparency Available

Use the diagrams for Exercises 1–3.

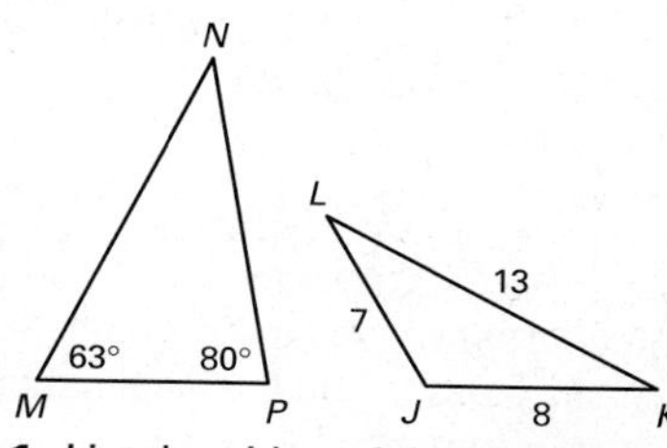

1. List the sides of $\triangle MNP$ in order from shortest to longest. **$\overline{MP}$, $\overline{NP}$, $\overline{MN}$**

2. List the angles of $\triangle JKL$ in order from smallest to largest. **$\angle K$, $\angle L$, $\angle J$**

3. In $\triangle MNP$, $MP = 5$ and $NP = 8$. What are the possible lengths of $\overline{MN}$? **MN must be greater than 3 and less than 13.**

EXTRA CHALLENGE NOTE

Challenge problems for Lesson 5.5 are available in **blackline** format in the *Chapter 5 Resource Book,* p. 80 and at **www.mcdougallittell.com.**

ADDITIONAL TEST PREPARATION

1. WRITING Using $\triangle BCD$ below, fill in the blanks with side lengths to make the inequalities true.

____ + ____ > ____

____ + ____ > ____

____ + ____ > ____

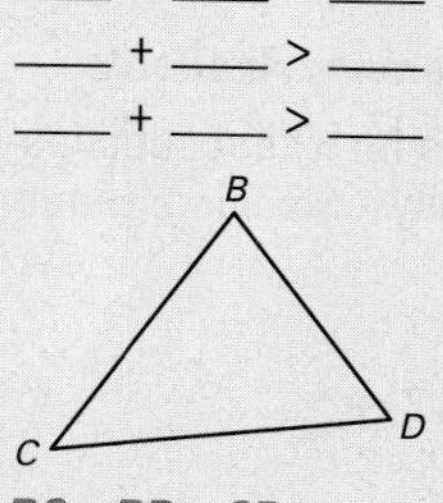

$BC + BD > CD$; $CD + BD > BC$; $BC + CD > BD$

1 PLAN

PACING
Basic: 2 days
Average: 2 days
Advanced: 2 days
Block Schedule: 0.5 block with 5.5
0.5 block with Ch. Rev.

LESSON OPENER APPLICATION
An alternative way to approach Lesson 5.6 is to use the Application Lesson Opener:

- Blackline Master (*Chapter 5 Resource Book*, p. 84)
- Transparency (p. 33)

MEETING INDIVIDUAL NEEDS

- ***Chapter 5 Resource Book***
  Prerequisite Skills Review (p. 5)
  Practice Level A (p. 88)
  Practice Level B (p. 89)
  Practice Level C (p. 90)
  Reteaching with Practice (p. 91)
  Absent Student Catch-Up (p. 93)
  Challenge (p. 95)
- ***Resources in Spanish***
- ***Personal Student Tutor***

NEW-TEACHER SUPPORT
See the Tips for New Teachers on pp. 1–2 of the *Chapter 5 Resource Book* for additional notes about Lesson 5.6.

WARM-UP EXERCISES

Transparency Available

Give a value for x that satisfies the inequality. **Sample answers are given.**

1. $x > 6$ 9
2. $-2 \leq x \leq 3$ 0
3. $x \leq 8$ 8
4. $3x - 8 \leq 2x + 4$ 10
5. $2 - 2x > 5 + 3x$ −2

5.6 Indirect Proof and Inequalities in Two Triangles

What you should learn

GOAL 1 Read and write an indirect proof.

GOAL 2 Use the Hinge Theorem and its converse to compare side lengths and angle measures.

Why you should learn it

▼ To solve **real-life** problems, such as deciding which of two planes is farther from an airport in **Example 4** and **Exs. 28 and 29.**

CALIFORNIA STANDARDS AND ASSESSMENT
CA Standards: 2, 6, 13
SAT9 Task 1: Objs. 3, 24, 26
SAT9 Task 2: Objs. 2, 26, 27

GOAL 1 USING INDIRECT PROOF

Up to now, all of the proofs in this textbook have used the Laws of Syllogism and Detachment to obtain conclusions directly. In this lesson, you will study *indirect proofs*. An **indirect proof** is a proof in which you prove that a statement is true by first assuming that its opposite is true. If this assumption leads to an impossibility, then you have proved that the original statement is true.

EXAMPLE 1 *Using Indirect Proof*

Use an indirect proof to prove that a triangle cannot have more than one obtuse angle.

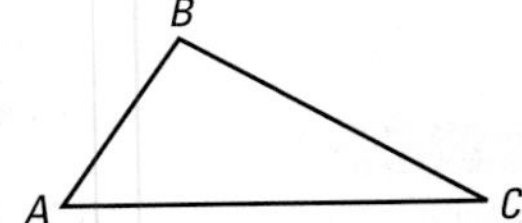

SOLUTION

GIVEN ▶ $\triangle ABC$

PROVE ▶ $\triangle ABC$ does not have more than one obtuse angle.

Begin by assuming that $\triangle ABC$ *does* have more than one obtuse angle.

$m\angle A > 90°$ and $m\angle B > 90°$ — **Assume $\triangle ABC$ has two obtuse angles.**

$m\angle A + m\angle B > 180°$ — **Add the two given inequalities.**

You know, however, that the sum of the measures of all *three* angles is 180°.

$m\angle A + m\angle B + m\angle C = 180°$ — **Triangle Sum Theorem**

$m\angle A + m\angle B = 180° - m\angle C$ — **Subtraction property of equality**

So, you can substitute $180° - m\angle C$ for $m\angle A + m\angle B$ in $m\angle A + m\angle B > 180°$.

$180° - m\angle C > 180°$ — **Substitution property of equality**

$0° > m\angle C$ — **Simplify.**

The last statement is *not possible*; angle measures in triangles cannot be negative.

▶ So, you can conclude that the original assumption must be false. That is, $\triangle ABC$ cannot have more than one obtuse angle.

CONCEPT SUMMARY — GUIDELINES FOR WRITING AN INDIRECT PROOF

1. Identify the statement that you want to prove is true.
2. Begin by assuming the statement is false; assume its opposite is true.
3. Obtain statements that logically follow from your assumption.
4. If you obtain a contradiction, then the original statement must be true.

GOAL 2 USING THE HINGE THEOREM

In the two triangles shown, notice that $\overline{AB} \cong \overline{DE}$ and $\overline{BC} \cong \overline{EF}$, but $m\angle B$ is greater than $m\angle E$.

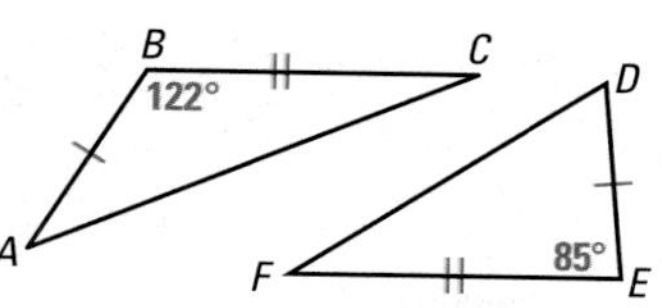

It appears that the side opposite the 122° angle is longer than the side opposite the 85° angle. This relationship is guaranteed by the Hinge Theorem below.

Exercise 31 asks you to write a proof of Theorem 5.14. Theorem 5.15 can be proved using Theorem 5.14 and indirect proof, as shown in Example 2.

THEOREMS

THEOREM 5.14 ***Hinge Theorem***

If two sides of one triangle are congruent to two sides of another triangle, and the included angle of the first is larger than the included angle of the second, then the third side of the first is longer than the third side of the second.

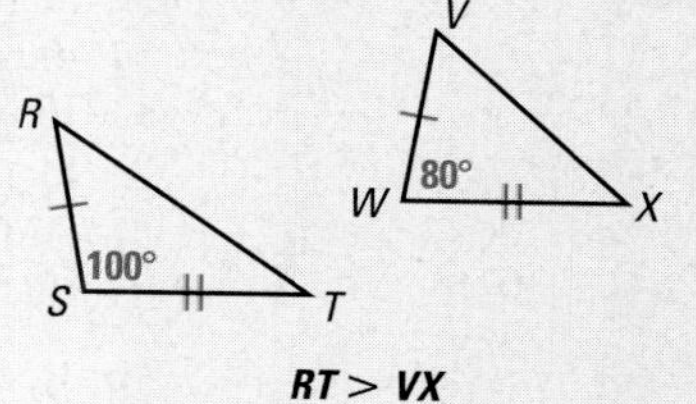

THEOREM 5.15 ***Converse of the Hinge Theorem***

If two sides of one triangle are congruent to two sides of another triangle, and the third side of the first is longer than the third side of the second, then the included angle of the first is larger than the included angle of the second.

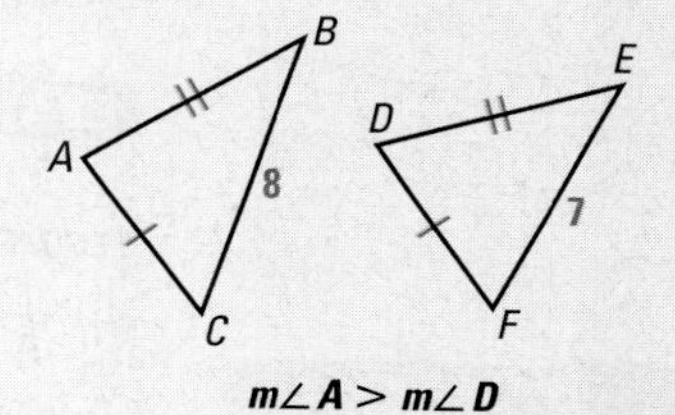

EXAMPLE 2 *Indirect Proof of Theorem 5.15*

GIVEN ▶ $\overline{AB} \cong \overline{DE}$
$\overline{BC} \cong \overline{EF}$
$AC > DF$

PROVE ▶ $m\angle B > m\angle E$

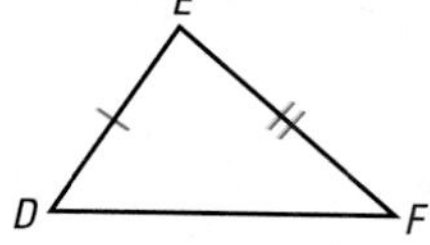

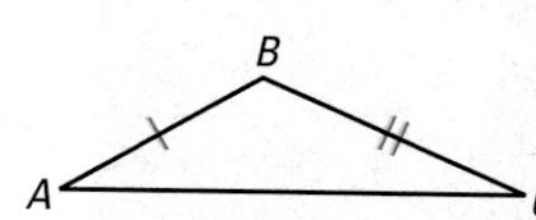

SOLUTION Begin by assuming that $m\angle B \ngtr m\angle E$. Then, it follows that either $m\angle B = m\angle E$ or $m\angle B < m\angle E$.

Case 1 If $m\angle B = m\angle E$, then $\angle B \cong \angle E$. So, $\triangle ABC \cong \triangle DEF$ by the SAS Congruence Postulate and $AC = DF$.

Case 2 If $m\angle B < m\angle E$, then $AC < DF$ by the Hinge Theorem.

Both conclusions contradict the given information that $AC > DF$. So the original assumption that $m\angle B \ngtr m\angle E$ cannot be correct. Therefore, $m\angle B > m\angle E$.

STUDENT HELP

Study Tip
The symbol $\ngtr$ is read as "is not greater than."

2 TEACH

EXTRA EXAMPLES 1–2

Use an indirect proof to prove that a triangle cannot have more than one right angle.

Given: rt. $\triangle ABC$

Prove: $\triangle ABC$ does not have more than one rt. $\angle$.

Assume that $\triangle ABC$ *does* have more than one right angle. Since $m\angle A = 90°$ and $m\angle B = 90°$, $m\angle A + m\angle B = 180°$. But the sum of the three measures of all *three* angles is 180°; that is, $m\angle A + m\angle B + m\angle C = 180°$. This implies that $m\angle C = 0°$. But this is impossible, since angle measures in triangles must be greater than 0°. So you can conclude that the original assumption must be false. That is, $\triangle ABC$ cannot have more than one right angle.

CHECKPOINT EXERCISES

For use after Examples 1 and 2:

1. Use the Extra Example to write an indirect proof that through a point P on a line t, there is at most one line perpendicular to t.

Given: Point P not on line t.

Prove: There is at most one line through P that is perpendicular to t.

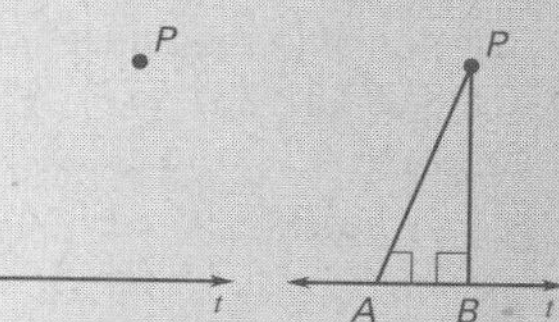

Assume that there are two lines through P perpendicular to t at points A and B. Since P, A, and B are three non-collinear points, they form $\triangle PAB$. Thus, $\triangle PAB$ contains two right angles. Since this contradicts the statement proved in the Extra Example, it follows that there is at most one line through P that is perpendicular to line t.

EXTRA EXAMPLE 3

a. In $\triangle ABC$ and $\triangle DEF$, $\overline{AC} \cong \overline{DF}$, $\overline{BC} \cong \overline{EF}$, $AB = 11$ in., $ED = 15$ in., and $m\angle F = 58°$. Which of the following is a possible measure for $\angle C$: 45°, 58°, 80°, or 90°? **45°**

b. In $\triangle GHI$ and $\triangle JKL$, $\overline{GH} \cong \overline{JK}$, $\overline{HI} \cong \overline{KL}$, $GI = 9$ cm, $m\angle H = 45°$, and $m\angle K = 65°$. Which of the following is a possible length for $\overline{JL}$: 5 cm, 7 cm, 9 cm, or 11 cm? **11 cm**

EXTRA EXAMPLE 4

You and a friend are flying separate planes. You leave the airport and fly 200 miles due north. You then change direction and fly W 60° N for 90 miles. Your friend leaves the airport and flies 200 miles due south. She then changes direction and flies E 15° S for 90 miles. Each of you has flown 290 miles, but which plane is further from the airport? **Your plane is farther from the airport.**

CHECKPOINT EXERCISES

For use after Examples 3 and 4:

1. In $\triangle RST$ and $\triangle XYZ$, $\overline{RT} \cong \overline{XZ}$, $\overline{ST} \cong \overline{YZ}$, $RS = 24$ cm, $XY = 18$ cm, and $m\angle Z = 62°$, Which of the following is a possible measure for $\angle T$: 34°, 48°, 56°, 77°? **77°**
2. In $\triangle ABC$ and $\triangle DEF$, $\overline{AB} \cong \overline{DE}$, $\overline{BC} \cong \overline{EF}$, $AC = 14$ in., $m\angle B = 70°$, and $m\angle E = 40°$. Which of the following is a possible length for $\overline{DF}$: 8 in., 16 in., 20 in., 25 in.? **8 in.**

CLOSURE QUESTION

What is the first step in writing an indirect proof? **Assume that the opposite of what you are trying to prove is true.**

FOCUS ON CAREERS

AIR TRAFFIC CONTROLLERS help ensure the safety of airline passengers and crews by developing air traffic flight paths that keep planes a safe distance apart.

CAREER LINK
www.mcdougallittell.com

EXAMPLE 3 *Finding Possible Side Lengths and Angle Measures*

You can use the Hinge Theorem and its converse to choose possible side lengths or angle measures from a given list.

a. $\overline{AB} \cong \overline{DE}$, $\overline{BC} \cong \overline{EF}$, $AC = 12$ inches, $m\angle B = 36°$, and $m\angle E = 80°$. Which of the following is a possible length for $\overline{DF}$: 8 in., 10 in., 12 in., or 23 in.?

b. In a $\triangle RST$ and a $\triangle XYZ$, $\overline{RT} \cong \overline{XZ}$, $\overline{ST} \cong \overline{YZ}$, $RS = 3.7$ centimeters, $XY = 4.5$ centimeters, and $m\angle Z = 75°$. Which of the following is a possible measure for $\angle T$: 60°, 75°, 90°, or 105°?

SOLUTION

a. Because the included angle in $\triangle DEF$ is larger than the included angle in $\triangle ABC$, the third side $\overline{DF}$ must be longer than $\overline{AC}$. So, of the four choices, the only possible length for $\overline{DF}$ is 23 inches. A diagram of the triangles shows that this is plausible.

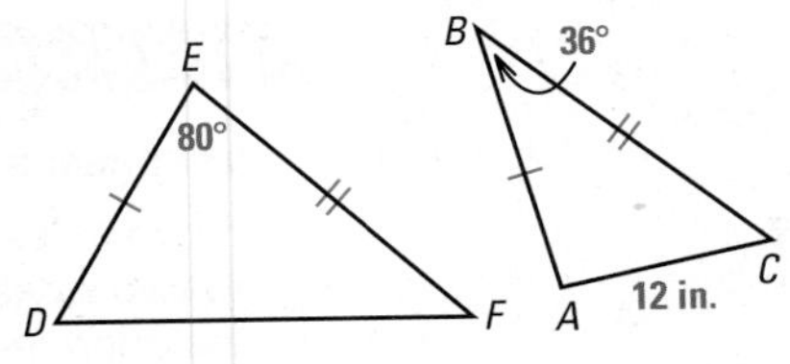

b. Because the third side in $\triangle RST$ is shorter than the third side in $\triangle XYZ$, the included angle $\angle T$ must be smaller than $\angle Z$. So, of the four choices, the only possible measure for $\angle T$ is 60°.

EXAMPLE 4 *Comparing Distances*

TRAVEL DISTANCES You and a friend are flying separate planes. You leave the airport and fly 120 miles due west. You then change direction and fly W 30° N for 70 miles. (W 30° N indicates a north-west direction that is 30° north of due west.) Your friend leaves the airport and flies 120 miles due east. She then changes direction and flies E 40° S for 70 miles. Each of you has flown 190 miles, but which plane is farther from the airport?

SOLUTION

Begin by drawing a diagram, as shown below. Your flight is represented by $\triangle PQR$ and your friend's flight is represented by $\triangle PST$.

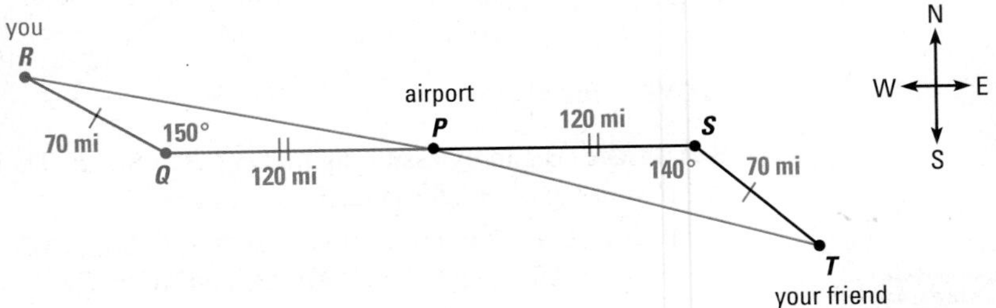

Because these two triangles have two sides that are congruent, you can apply the Hinge Theorem to conclude that $\overline{RP}$ is longer than $\overline{TP}$.

▶ So, your plane is farther from the airport than your friend's plane.

GUIDED PRACTICE

Vocabulary Check ✓

1. Explain why an indirect proof might also be called a *proof by contradiction*. See margin.

Concept Check ✓

2. To use an indirect proof to show that two lines m and n are parallel, you would first make the assumption that __?__. lines m and n are not $\parallel$

Skill Check ✓

In Exercises 3–5, complete with $<$, $>$, or $=$.

3. $m\angle 1$ _?_ $m\angle 2$ $>$

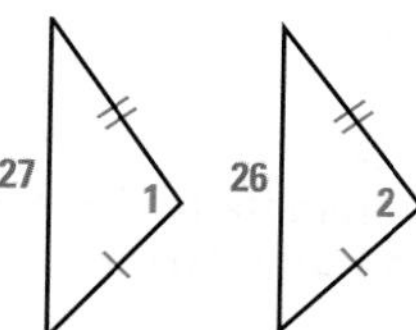

4. KL _?_ NQ $<$

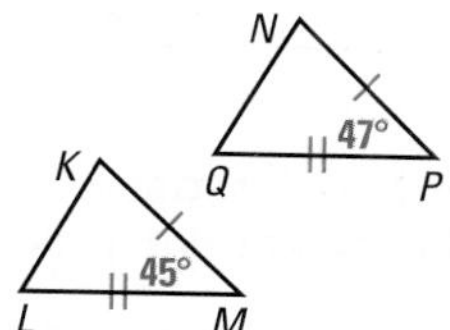

5. DC _?_ FE $<$

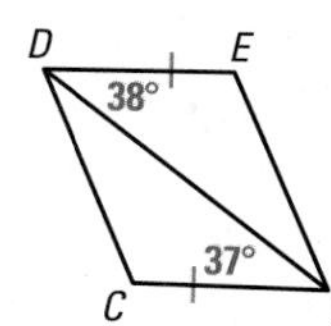

6. Suppose that in a $\triangle ABC$, you want to prove that $BC > AC$. What are the two cases you would use in an indirect proof? Case 1: Assume that $BC = AC$; Case 2: Assume that $BC < AC$.

PRACTICE AND APPLICATIONS

Extra Practice to help you master skills is on p. 812.

USING THE HINGE THEOREM AND ITS CONVERSE Complete with $<$, $>$, or $=$.

7. RS _?_ TU $<$

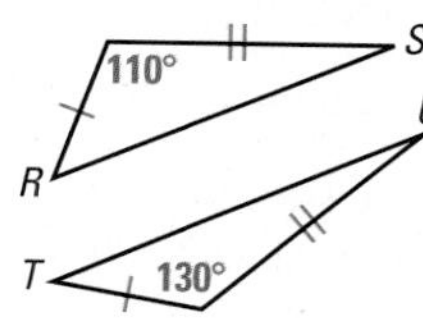

8. $m\angle 1$ _?_ $m\angle 2$ $=$

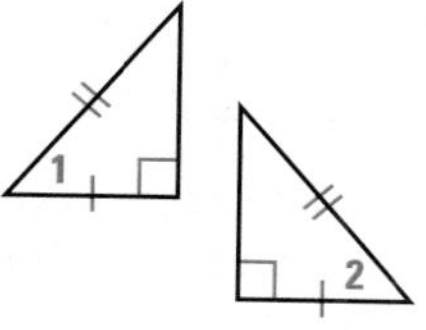

9. $m\angle 1$ _?_ $m\angle 2$ $>$

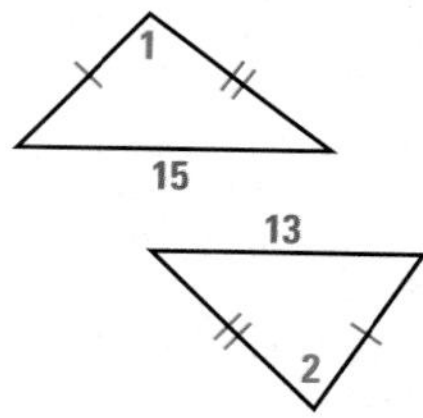

10. XY _?_ ZY $>$

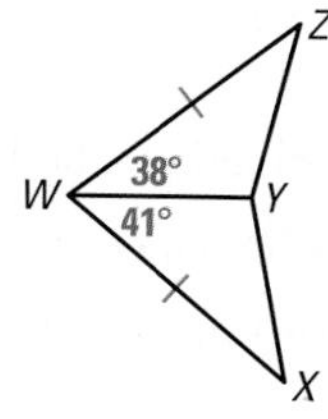

11. $m\angle 1$ _?_ $m\angle 2$ $=$

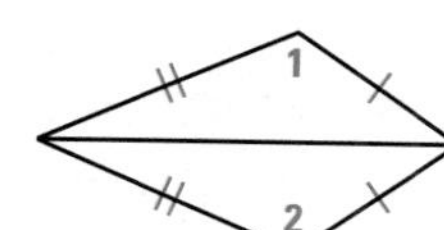
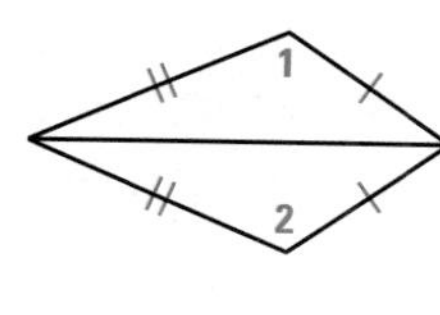

12. $m\angle 1$ _?_ $m\angle 2$ $<$

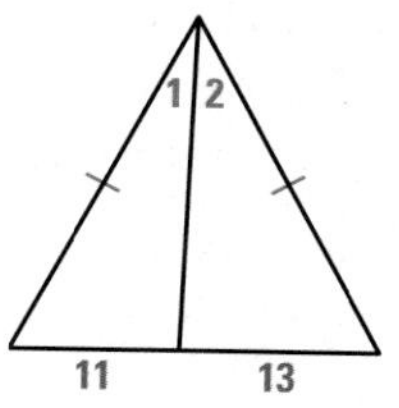

13. AB _?_ CB $>$

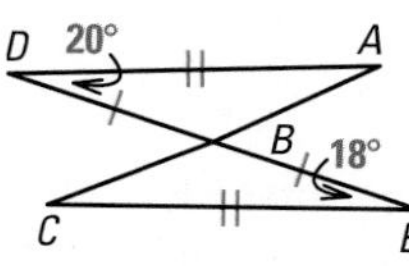

14. UT _?_ SV $>$

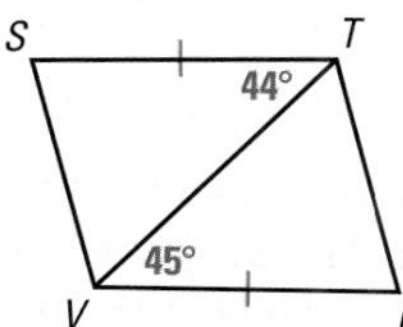

15. $m\angle 1$ _?_ $m\angle 2$ $>$

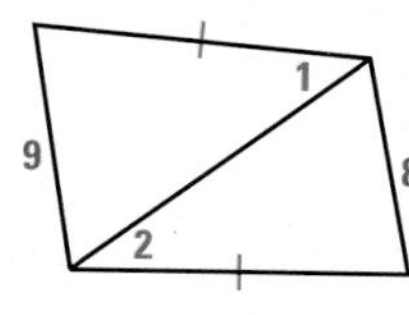

STUDENT HELP

HOMEWORK HELP
Example 1: Exs. 21–24
Example 2: Exs. 25–27
Example 3: Exs. 7–17
Example 4: Exs. 28, 29

3 APPLY

ASSIGNMENT GUIDE

BASIC
Day 1: pp. 305–307 Exs. 8–26 even
Day 2: pp. 305–308 Exs. 7–27 odd, 30–36 even, 38–42, Quiz 2 Exs. 1–8

AVERAGE
Day 1: pp. 305–307 Exs. 8–26 even
Day 2: pp. 305–308 Exs. 7–27 odd, 28–30, 32, 34, 36, 38–42, Quiz 2 Exs. 1–8

ADVANCED
Day 1: pp. 305–307 Exs. 8–26 even
Day 2: pp. 305–308 Exs. 7–27 odd, 28–32, 34, 36, 38–42, Quiz 2 Exs. 1–8

BLOCK SCHEDULE
pp. 305–307 Exs. 8–26 even (with 5.5)
pp. 305–308 Exs. 7–27 odd, 28–30, 32, 34, 36, 38–42, Quiz 2 Exs. 1–8 (with Ch. Rev.)

EXERCISE LEVELS

Level A: *Easier*
7–15
Level B: *More Difficult*
16–25, 28–30
Level C: *Most Difficult*
26, 27, 31

✓ HOMEWORK CHECK

To quickly check student understanding of key concepts, go over the following exercises: Exs. 10, 14, 16, 20, 22, 24, 26. See also the Daily Homework Quiz:

- Blackline Master (*Chapter 6 Resource Book*, p. 11)
- Transparency (p. 40)

1. ***Sample answer:*** **Indirect proof involves assuming something is true and showing that the assumption leads to a contradiction of information that is given or known to be true.**

STUDENT HELP NOTES

Homework Help Students can find help for Exs. 21–23 at **www.mcdougallittell.com.** The information can be printed out for students who don't have access to the Internet.

COMMON ERROR

EXERCISES 24–27 Students may have difficulty understanding the flow and logic of an indirect proof. Students may not know how to assume the opposite of a statement or may not use all of the information that they know or that is given to create a contradiction. To help avoid this problem, work through several examples with students so that they can get an understanding of indirect proof.

LOGICAL REASONING In Exercises 16 and 17, match the given information with conclusion A, B, or C. Explain your reasoning.

A. $AD > CD$ **B.** $AC > BD$ **C.** $m\angle 4 < m\angle 5$

16. $AC > AB$, $BD = CD$

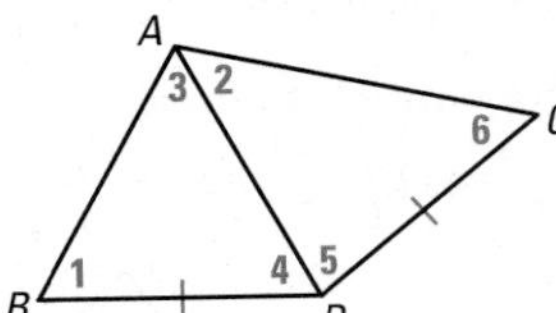

16. C; $AD = AD$, $BD = CD$, and $AC > AB$, so by the Converse of the Hinge Thm., $m\angle 4 < m\angle 5$.

17. $AB = DC$, $m\angle 3 < m\angle 5$

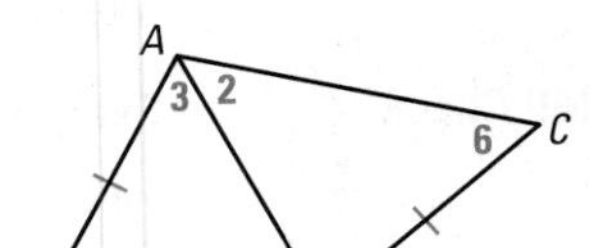

17. B; $AD = AD$, $AB = DC$, and $m\angle 3 < m\angle 5$, so by the Hinge Thm., $AC > BD$.

USING ALGEBRA Use an inequality to describe a restriction on the value of x as determined by the Hinge Theorem or its converse.

18.

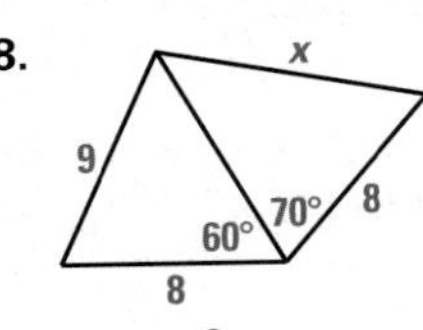

$x > 9$

19.

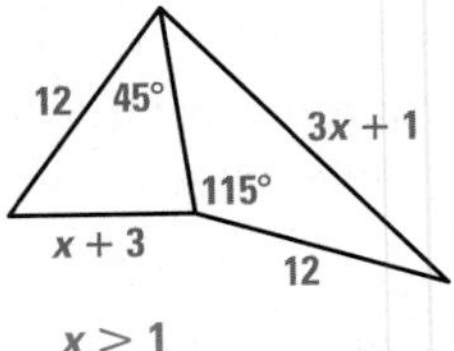

$x > 1$

20.

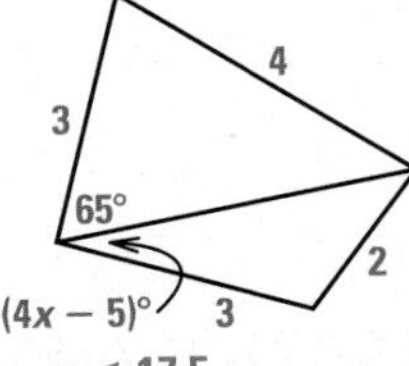

$x < 17.5$

ASSUMING THE NEGATION OF THE CONCLUSION In Exercises 21–23, write the first statement for an indirect proof of the situation.

21. If $RS + ST \neq 12$ in. and $ST = 5$ in., then $RS \neq 7$ in.

21. Given that $RS + ST \neq 12$ in. and $ST = 5$ in., assume that $RS = 7$ in.

22. In $\triangle MNP$, if Q is the midpoint of $\overline{NP}$, then $\overline{MQ}$ is a median.

22. Given $\triangle MNP$ with Q the midpoint of $\overline{NP}$, assume that $\overline{MQ}$ is not a median.

23. In $\triangle ABC$, if $m\angle A + m\angle B = 90°$, then $m\angle C = 90°$. Given $\triangle ABC$ with $m\angle A + m\angle B = 90°$, assume $m\angle C \neq 90°$. (That is, assume that either $m\angle C < 90°$ or $m\angle C > 90°$.)

STUDENT HELP

HOMEWORK HELP Visit our Web site www.mcdougallittell.com for help with negations in Exs. 21–23.

24. DEVELOPING PROOF Arrange statements A–D in correct order to write an indirect proof of Postulate 7 from page 73: *If two lines intersect, then their intersection is exactly one point.* C, B, A, D

GIVEN ▶ line m, line n

PROVE ▶ Lines m and n intersect in exactly one point.

A. But this contradicts Postulate 5, which states that there is exactly one line through any two points.

B. Then there are two lines (m and n) through points P and Q.

C. Assume that there are two points, P and Q, where m and n intersect.

D. It is false that m and n can intersect in two points, so they must intersect in exactly one point.

25. PROOF Write an indirect proof of Theorem 5.11 on page 295.

GIVEN ▶ $m\angle D > m\angle E$

PROVE ▶ $EF > DF$

D E F

Plan for Proof In Case 1, assume that $EF < DF$. In Case 2, assume that $EF = DF$. Show that neither case can be true, so $EF > DF$.

25. Case 1: Assume that $EF < DF$. If one side of a △ is longer than another side, then the ∠ opp. the longer side is larger than the ∠ opp. the shorter side, so $m\angle D < m\angle E$. But this contradicts the given information that $m\angle D > m\angle E$.

Case 2: Assume that $EF = DF$. By the Converse of the Base Angles Thm., $m\angle E = m\angle D$. But this contradicts the given information that $m\angle D > m\angle E$.

Since both cases produce a contradiction, the assumption that EF is not greater than DF must be incorrect and $EF > DF$.

26. Assume that m and n are not ∥. Then m and n must intersect in some point, say, P. Let Q and R be the points where t intersects m and n, respectively. Since ∠1 and ∠2 are supplementary and $m\angle QPR > 0$, $m\angle 1 + m\angle 2 + m\angle QPR > 180°$. This contradicts the △ Sum Theorem. Then the assumption that m and n are not ∥ must be incorrect and $m \parallel n$.

PROOF **Write an indirect proof in paragraph form. The diagrams, which illustrate negations of the conclusions, may help you.** 26, 27. See margin.

26. **GIVEN** ▶ ∠1 and ∠2 are supplementary.

PROVE ▶ $m \parallel n$

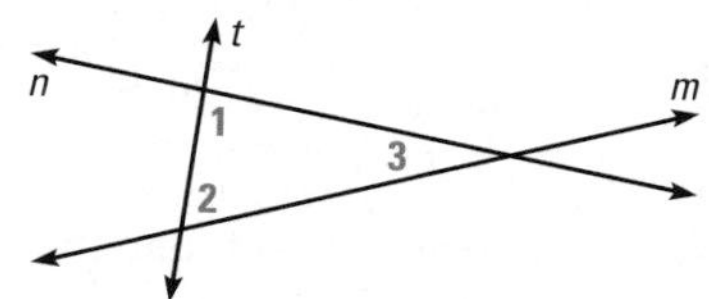

Begin by assuming that $m \nparallel n$.

27. **GIVEN** ▶ $\overline{RU}$ is an altitude, $\overrightarrow{RU}$ bisects ∠SRT.

PROVE ▶ △RST is isosceles.

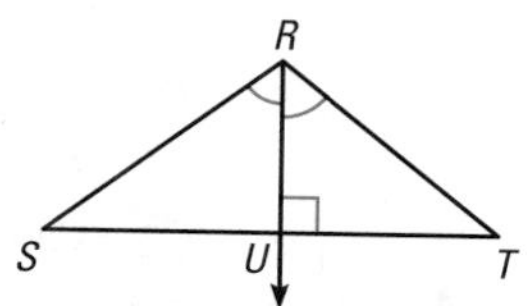

Begin by assuming that $RS > RT$.

COMPARING DISTANCES **In Exercises 28 and 29, consider the flight paths described. Explain how to use the Hinge Theorem to determine who is farther from the airport.** 28, 29. See margin.

28. *Your flight:* 100 miles due west, then 50 miles N 20° W
Friend's flight: 100 miles due north, then 50 miles N 30° E

29. *Your flight:* 210 miles due south, then 80 miles S 70° W
Friend's flight: 80 miles due north, then 210 miles N 50° E

Test Preparation

27. Assume that $RS > RT$. Then $m\angle T > m\angle S$. But $\triangle RUS \cong \triangle RUT$ by the ASA Congruence Postulate, so $\angle S \cong \angle T$, or $m\angle T = m\angle S$. This is a contradiction, so $RS \le RT$. We get a similar contradiction if we assume $RT > RS$; therefore $RS = RT$, and △RST is isosceles by definition.

30. **MULTI-STEP PROBLEM** Use the diagram of the tank cleaning system's expandable arm shown below.

a. As the cleaning system arm expands, $\overline{ED}$ gets longer. As ED increases, what happens to $m\angle EBD$? What happens to $m\angle DBA$?
$m\angle EBD$ increases; $m\angle DBA$ decreases

b. Name a distance that decreases as ED gets longer. *AD*

c. *Writing* Explain how the cleaning arm illustrates the Hinge Theorem.
In △EBD and △ABD, $\overline{BE} \cong \overline{BD} \cong \overline{BA}$. The included angle in △EBD, ∠EBD, is larger than the included angle in △ABD, ∠ABD. So $\overline{ED}$ is longer than $\overline{AD}$.

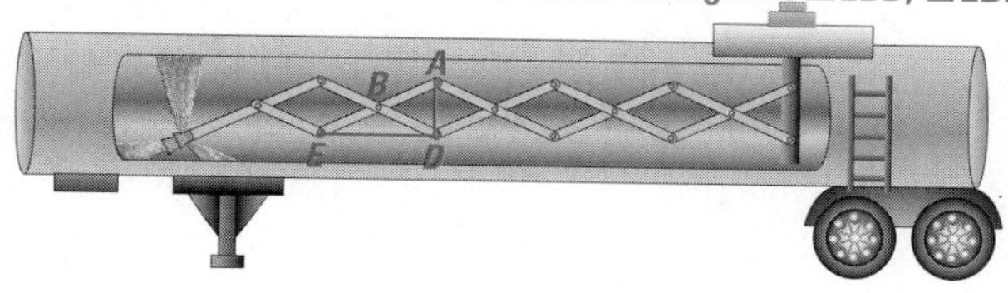

★ Challenge

28, 29. The paths are described by two △ in which two sides of one △ are ≅ to two sides of another △, but the included ∠ in your friend's △ is larger than the included ∠ in yours, so the side representing the distance from the airport is longer in your friend's △.

EXTRA CHALLENGE
www.mcdougallittell.com

31. **PROOF** Prove Theorem 5.14, the Hinge Theorem. See margin.

GIVEN ▶ $\overline{AB} \cong \overline{DE}$, $\overline{BC} \cong \overline{EF}$, $m\angle ABC > m\angle DEF$

PROVE ▶ $AC > DF$

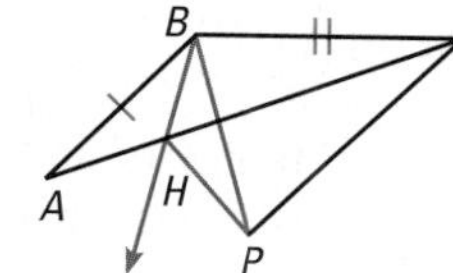

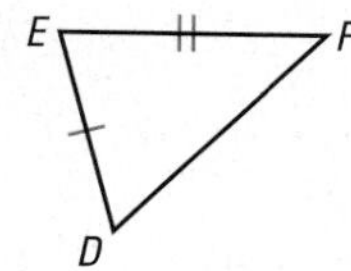

Plan for Proof

1. Locate a point P outside △ABC so you can construct △PBC ≅ △DEF.

2. Show that △PBC ≅ △DEF by the SAS Congruence Postulate.

3. Because $m\angle ABC > m\angle DEF$, locate a point H on $\overline{AC}$ so that $\overrightarrow{BH}$ bisects ∠PBA.

4. Give reasons for each equality or inequality below to show that $AC > DF$.

$$AC = AH + HC = PH + HC > PC = DF$$

31. Locate point P outside △ABC so that ∠PBC ≅ ∠E and $\overline{BP} \cong \overline{ED}$. △PBC ≅ △DEF by the SAS Cong. Thm. and corresp. sides $\overline{PC}$ and $\overline{DF}$ are ≅. Construct the bisector of ∠PBA, intersecting $\overline{AC}$ at H. Since $\overline{BP} \cong \overline{ED}$ and $\overline{ED} \cong \overline{AB}$, $\overline{BP} \cong \overline{AB}$ by the Transitive Prop. of Cong. $\overline{BH} \cong \overline{BH}$, and ∠ABH ≅ ∠PBH, so △ABH ≅ △PBH by the SAS Cong. Thm. and corresp. sides $\overline{AH}$ and $\overline{PH}$ are ≅. So $AC = AH + HC$ by the Segment Addition Post. and $AH = PH$ by the def. of cong. By the △ Inequality Thm., $PH + HC > PC$. But $PC = DF$, so $AC = AH + HC = PH + HC > PC = DF$ and $AC > DF$.

ADDITIONAL PRACTICE AND RETEACHING

For Lesson 5.6:

- Practice Levels A, B, and C (*Chapter 5 Resource Book,* p. 88)
- Reteaching with Practice (*Chapter 5 Resource Book,* p. 91)
- See Lesson 5.6 of the *Personal Student Tutor*

For more Mixed Review:

- Search the *Test and Practice Generator* for key words or specific lessons.

4 ASSESS

DAILY HOMEWORK QUIZ

Transparency Available

In Exercises 1–4, complete with <, >, or =.

1. *AB* ____ *DE* >

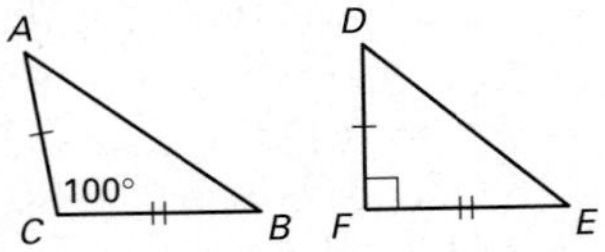

2. $m\angle 1$ ____ $m\angle 2$ >

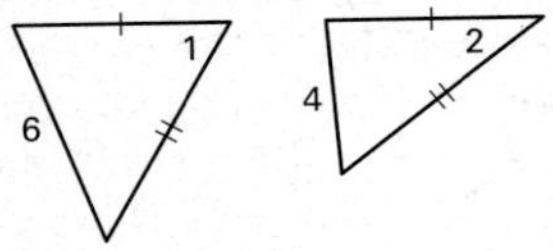

3. $m\angle 1$ ____ $m\angle 2$ =

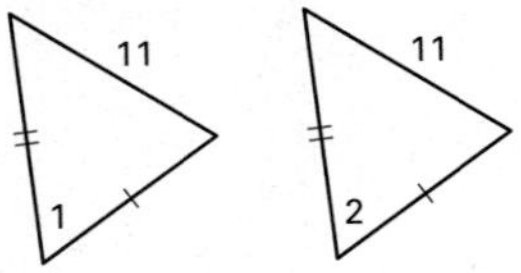

4. *AB* ____ *CD* >

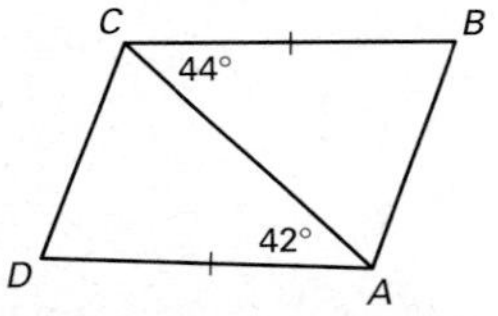

EXTRA CHALLENGE NOTE

Challenge problems for Lesson 5.6 are available in **blackline** format in the *Chapter 5 Resource Book,* p. 95 and at **www.mcdougallittell.com.**

ADDITIONAL TEST PREPARATION

1. OPEN ENDED Explain how the Hinge Theorem applies when you use kitchen tongs. ***Sample answer:*** **When you use the tongs to pick up food, you open them wider — that is, make a bigger angle — to pick up larger pieces of food.**

ADDITIONAL RESOURCES

An alternative Quiz for Lessons 5.4–5.6 is available in the *Chapter 5 Resource Book,* p. 96.

MIXED REVIEW

CLASSIFYING TRIANGLES State whether the triangle described is *isosceles, equiangular, equilateral,* or *scalene.* **(Review 4.1 for 6.1)**

32. Side lengths: 3 cm, 5 cm, 3 cm **isosceles**

33. Side lengths: 5 cm, 5 cm, 5 cm **isosceles, equiangular, equilateral**

34. Side lengths: 5 cm, 6 cm, 8 cm **scalene**

35. Angle measures: 30°, 30°, 120° **isosceles**

36. Angle measures: 60°, 60°, 60° **isosceles, equiangular, equilateral**

37. Angle measures: 65°, 50°, 65° **isosceles**

USING ALGEBRA In Exercises 38–41, use the diagram shown at the right. **(Review 4.1 for 6.1)**

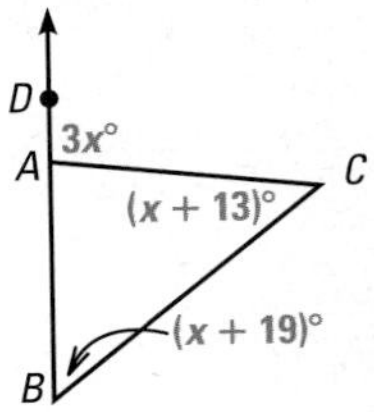

38. Find the value of x. **32**

39. Find $m\angle B$. **51°**

40. Find $m\angle C$. **45°**

41. Find $m\angle BAC$. **84°**

42. DESCRIBING A SEGMENT Draw any equilateral triangle $\triangle RST$. Draw a line segment from vertex R to the midpoint of side $\overline{ST}$. State everything that you know about the line segment you have drawn. **(Review 5.3)**
The segment is a median, an ∠ bisector, a ⊥ bisector, and an altitude. It divides △*RST* into two ≅ △. It is shorter than each of the sides of △*RST*.

QUIZ 2

Self-Test for Lessons 5.4–5.6

In Exercises 1–3, use the triangle shown at the right. The midpoints of the sides of △*CDE* are *F, G,* and *H.* **(Lesson 5.4)**

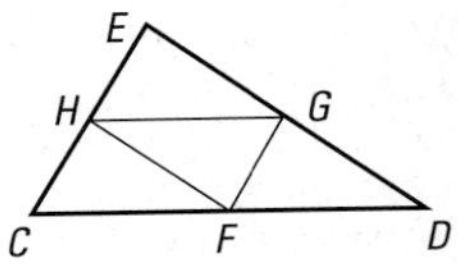

1. $\overline{FG} \parallel$ ___?___ $\overline{CE}$

2. If $FG = 8$, then $CE =$ ___?___. **16**

3. If the perimeter of $\triangle CDE = 42$, then the perimeter of $\triangle GHF =$ ___?___. **21**

In Exercises 4–6, list the sides in order from shortest to longest. **(Lesson 5.5)**

4.

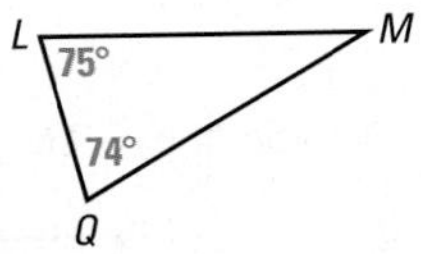

$\overline{LQ}, \overline{LM}, \overline{MQ}$

5.

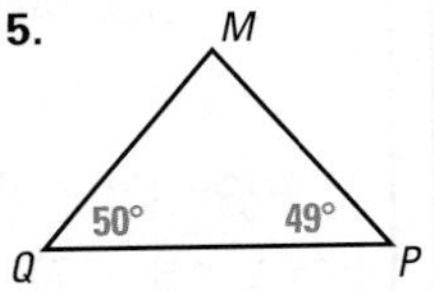

$\overline{QM}, \overline{PM}, \overline{QP}$

6.

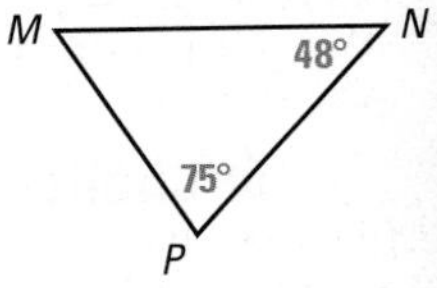

$\overline{MP}, \overline{NP}, \overline{MN}$

7. In $\triangle ABC$ and $\triangle DEF$ shown at the right, which is longer, $\overline{AB}$ or $\overline{DE}$? **(Lesson 5.6)** $\overline{DE}$

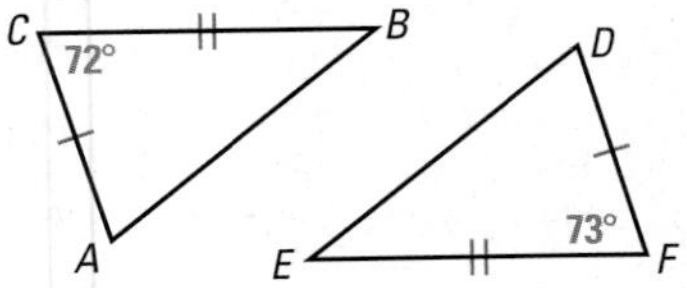

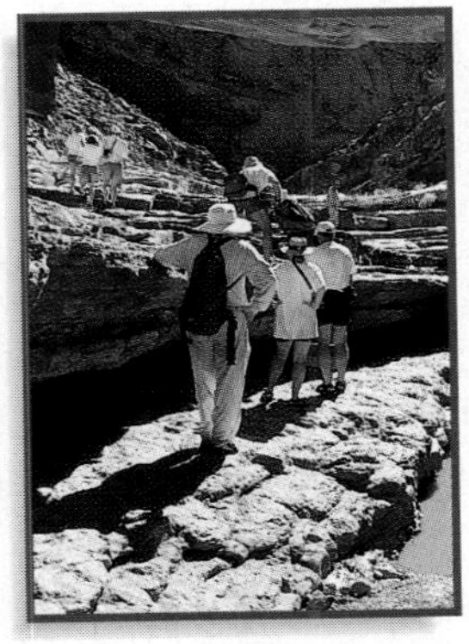

Hikers in the Grand Canyon

8. HIKING Two groups of hikers leave from the same base camp and head in opposite directions. The first group walks 4.5 miles due east, then changes direction and walks E 45° N for 3 miles. The second group walks 4.5 miles due west, then changes direction and walks W 20° S for 3 miles. Each group has walked 7.5 miles, but which is farther from the base camp? **(Lesson 5.6)**
the second group

CHAPTER 5

Chapter Summary

WHAT did you learn?	WHY did you learn it?
Use properties of perpendicular bisectors and angle bisectors. (5.1)	Decide where a hockey goalie should be positioned to defend the goal. (p. 270)
Use properties of perpendicular bisectors and angle bisectors of a triangle. (5.2)	Find the center of a mushroom ring. (p. 277)
Use properties of medians and altitudes of a triangle. (5.3)	Find points in a triangle used to measure a person's heart fitness. (p. 283)
Use properties of midsegments of a triangle. (5.4)	Determine the length of the crossbar of a swing set. (p. 292)
Compare the lengths of the sides or the measures of the angles of a triangle. (5.5)	Determine how the lengths of the boom lines of a crane affect the position of the boom. (p. 300)
Understand and write indirect proofs. (5.6)	Prove theorems that cannot be easily proved directly.
Use the Hinge Theorem and its converse to compare side lengths and angle measures of triangles. (5.6)	Decide which of two airplanes is farther from an airport. (p. 304)

How does Chapter 5 fit into the BIGGER PICTURE of geometry?

In this chapter, you studied properties of special segments of triangles, which are an important building block for more complex figures that you will explore in later chapters. The special segments of a triangle have applications in many areas such as demographics (p. 280), medicine (p. 283), and room design (p. 299).

STUDY STRATEGY

Did you test your memory?

The list of important vocabulary terms and skills you made, following the **Study Strategy** on page 262, may resemble this one.

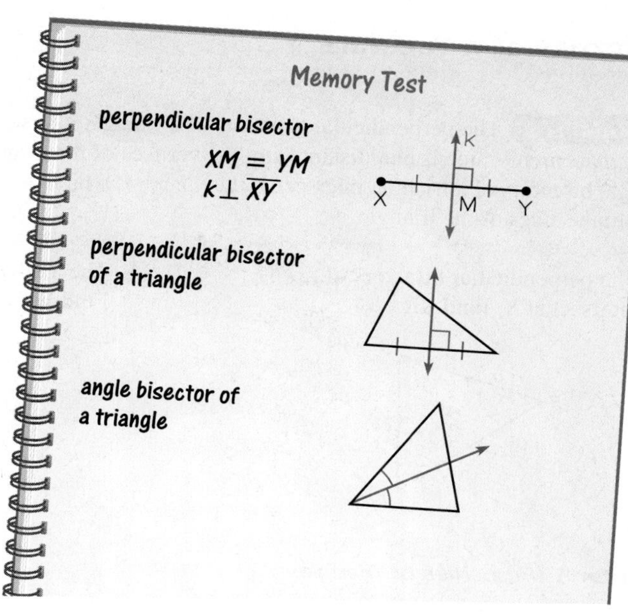

Memory Test
perpendicular bisector
XM = YM
k ⊥ XY
k
X
M
Y
perpendicular bisector of a triangle
angle bisector of a triangle

ADDITIONAL RESOURCES

The following resources are available to help review the material in this chapter.

- Chapter Review Games and Activities (*Chapter 5 Resource Book,* p. 97)
- *Geometry in Motion video*
- *Personal Student Tutor*
- Cumulative Review, Chs. 1–5 (*Chapter 5 Resource Book,* p. 109)

CHAPTER 5

Chapter Review

- **perpendicular bisector, p. 264**
- **equidistant from two points, p. 264**
- **distance from a point to a line, p. 266**
- **equidistant from two lines, p. 266**
- **perpendicular bisector of a triangle, p. 272**
- **concurrent lines, p. 272**
- **point of concurrency, p. 272**
- **circumcenter of a triangle, p. 273**
- **angle bisector of a triangle, p. 274**
- **incenter of a triangle, p. 274**
- **median of a triangle, p. 279**
- **centroid of a triangle, p. 279**
- **altitude of a triangle, p. 281**
- **orthocenter of a triangle, p. 281**
- **midsegment of a triangle, p. 287**
- **indirect proof, p. 302**

5.1 PERPENDICULARS AND BISECTORS

Examples on pp. 264–267

EXAMPLES In the figure, $\overrightarrow{AD}$ is the angle bisector of $\angle BAC$ and the perpendicular bisector of $\overline{BC}$. You know that $BE = CE$ by the definition of perpendicular bisector and that $AB = AC$ by the Perpendicular Bisector Theorem. Because $\overline{DP} \perp \overrightarrow{AP}$ and $\overline{DQ} \perp \overrightarrow{AQ}$, then DP and DQ are the distances from D to the sides of $\angle PAQ$ and you know that $DP = DQ$ by the Angle Bisector Theorem.

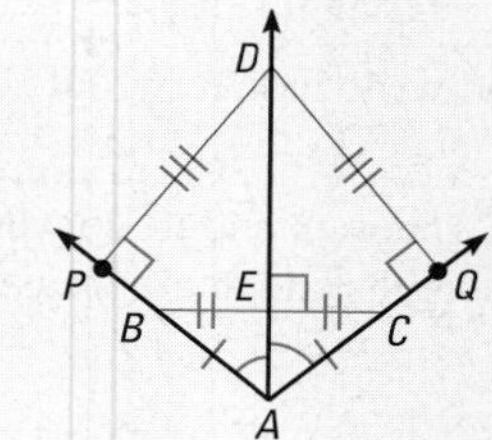

In Exercises 1–3, use the diagram.

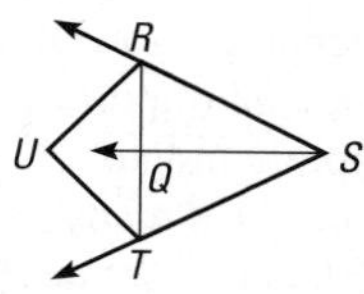

1. If $\overrightarrow{SQ}$ is the perpendicular bisector of $\overline{RT}$, explain how you know that $\overline{RQ} \cong \overline{TQ}$ and $\overline{RS} \cong \overline{TS}$. **If a point is on the ⊥ bisector of a segment, then it is equidistant from the endpoints of the segment.**

2. If $\overline{UR} \cong \overline{UT}$, what can you conclude about U? **U is on the ⊥ bisector of $\overline{RT}$.**

3. If Q is equidistant from $\overrightarrow{SR}$ and $\overrightarrow{ST}$, what can you conclude about Q? **Q is on the bisector of $\angle RST$.**

5.2 BISECTORS OF A TRIANGLE

Examples on pp. 272–274

EXAMPLES The perpendicular bisectors of a triangle intersect at the *circumcenter*, which is equidistant from the vertices of the triangle. The angle bisectors of a triangle intersect at the *incenter*, which is equidistant from the sides of the triangle.

4. The perpendicular bisectors of $\triangle RST$ intersect at K. Find KR. **20**

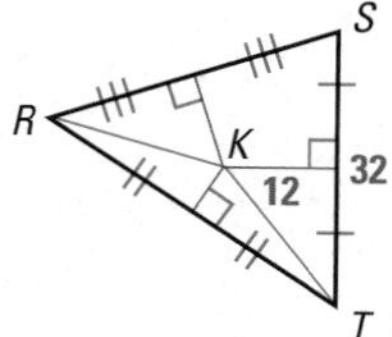

5. The angle bisectors of $\triangle XYZ$ intersect at W. Find WB. **6**

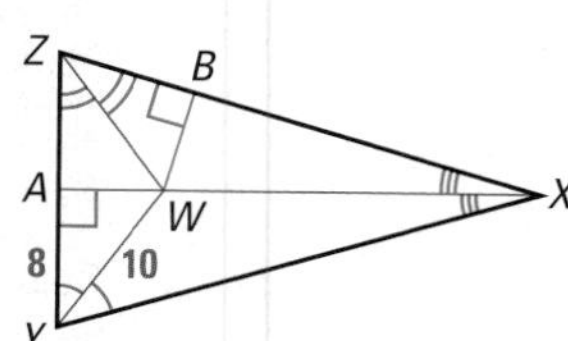

5.3

MEDIANS AND ALTITUDES OF A TRIANGLE

Examples on pp. 279–281

EXAMPLES The medians of a triangle intersect at the centroid. The lines containing the altitudes of a triangle intersect at the orthocenter.

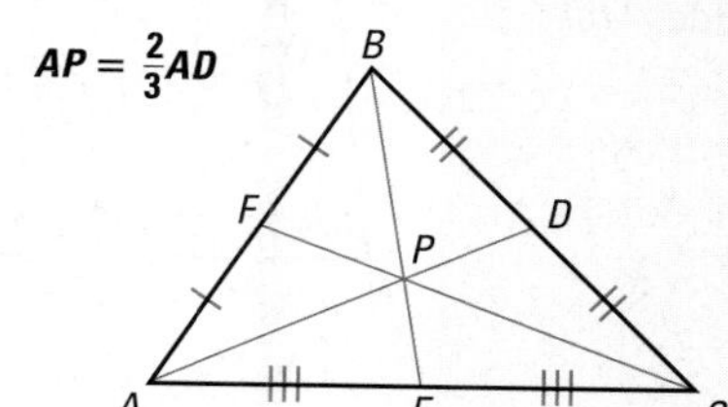

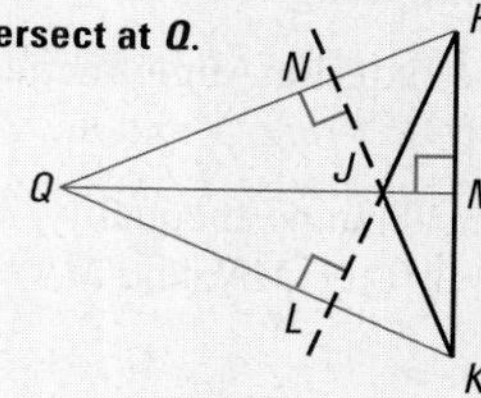

Name the special segments and point of concurrency of the triangle.

6. 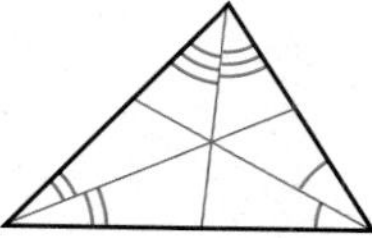
∠ bisectors; incenter

7. 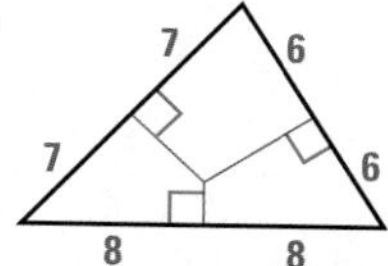

⊥ bisectors; circumcenter

8. 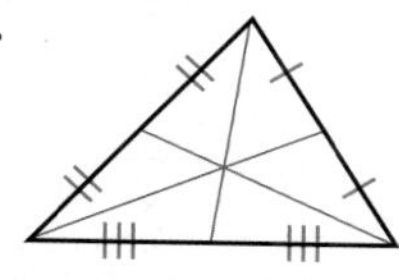
medians; centroid

9. 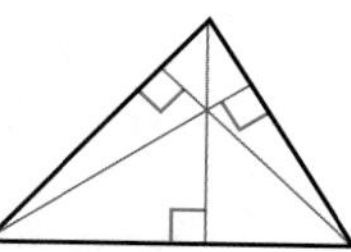
altitudes; orthocenter

$\triangle XYZ$ has vertices $X(0, 0)$, $Y(-4, 0)$, and $Z(0, 6)$. Find the coordinates of the indicated point.

10. the centroid of $\triangle XYZ$ $\left(-\frac{4}{3}, 2\right)$

11. the orthocenter of $\triangle XYZ$ (0, 0)

5.4

MIDSEGMENT THEOREM

Examples on pp. 287–289

EXAMPLES A midsegment of a triangle connects the midpoints of two sides of the triangle. By the Midsegment Theorem, a midsegment of a triangle is parallel to the third side and its length is half the length of the third side.

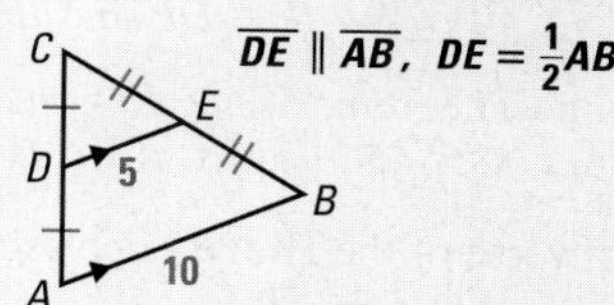

In Exercises 12 and 13, the midpoints of the sides of $\triangle HJK$ are $L(4, 3)$, $M(8, 3)$, and $N(6, 1)$.

12. Find the coordinates of the vertices of the triangle. (2, 1), (6, 5), (10, 1)

13. Show that each midsegment is parallel to a side of the triangle. See margin.

14. Find the perimeter of $\triangle BCD$. 64

15. Find the perimeter of $\triangle STU$. 31

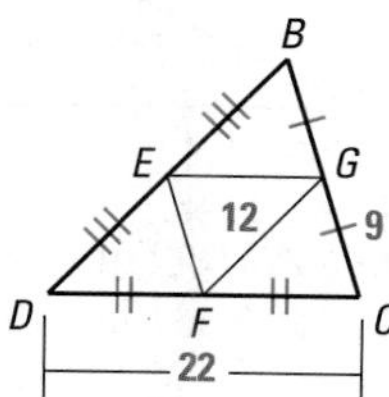

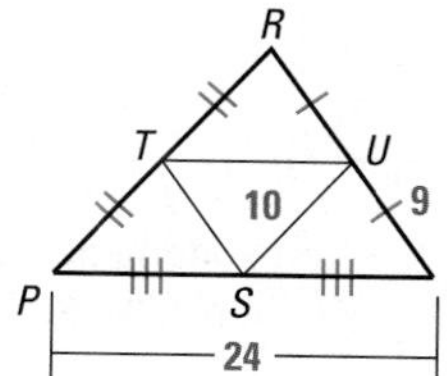

13. Let L be the midpoint of $\overline{HJ}$, M the midpoint of $\overline{JK}$, and N the midpoint of $\overline{HK}$; slope of $\overline{LM} = 0 =$ slope of $\overline{HK}$, so $\overline{LM} \parallel \overline{HK}$; slope of $\overline{LN} = -1 =$ slope of $\overline{JK}$, so $\overline{LN} \parallel \overline{JK}$; slope of $\overline{MN} = 1 =$ slope of $\overline{HJ}$, so $\overline{MN} \parallel \overline{HJ}$.

25. **Assume that there is a $\triangle ABC$ with 2 right $\angle$s, say $m\angle A = 90°$ and $m\angle B = 90°$. Then $m\angle A + m\angle B = 180°$ and, since $m\angle C > 0°$, $m\angle A + m\angle B + m\angle C > 180°$. This contradicts the $\triangle$ Sum Theorem. Then the assumption that there is such a $\triangle ABC$ must be incorrect and no $\triangle$ has 2 right $\angle$s.**

5.5 INEQUALITIES IN ONE TRIANGLE

Examples on pp. 295–297

EXAMPLES In a triangle, the side and the angle of greatest measurement are always opposite each other. In the diagram, the largest angle, $\angle MNQ$, is opposite the longest side, $\overline{MQ}$.

By the Exterior Angle Inequality, $m\angle MQP > m\angle N$ and $m\angle MQP > m\angle M$.

By the Triangle Inequality, $MN + NQ > MQ$, $NQ + MQ > MN$, and $MN + MQ > NQ$.

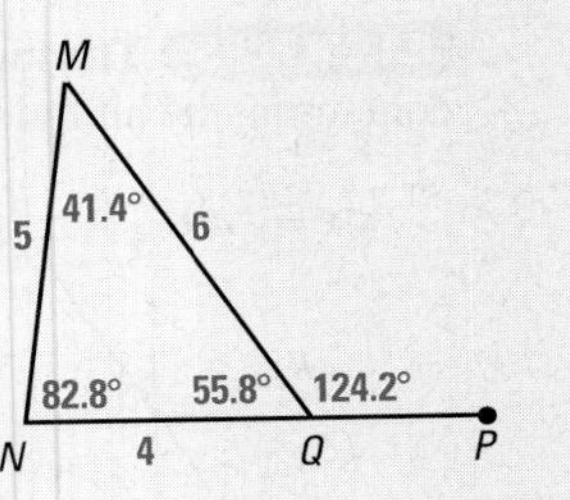

In Exercises 16–19, write the angle and side measurements in order from least to greatest.

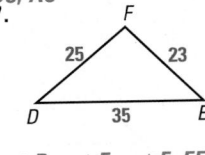

16. *$m\angle C$, $m\angle A$, $m\angle B$; AB, BC, AC*

17.

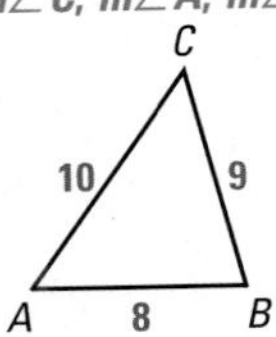

$m\angle D$, $m\angle E$, $m\angle F$; EF, DF, DE

18. *$m\angle H$, $m\angle J$, $m\angle G$; JG, GH, JH*

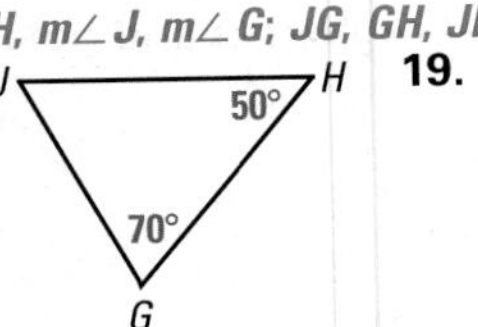

19.

$m\angle L$, $m\angle K$, $m\angle M$; KM, LM, KL

20. **FENCING A GARDEN** You are enclosing a triangular garden region with a fence. You have measured two sides of the garden to be 100 feet and 200 feet. What is the maximum length of fencing you need? Explain. **600 feet; the third side must be less than 300 ft long (100 ft + 200 ft = 300 ft), so the total fencing is less than 100 ft + 200 ft + 300 ft = 600 ft.**

5.6 INDIRECT PROOF AND INEQUALITIES IN TWO TRIANGLES

Examples on pp. 302–304

EXAMPLES $\overline{AB} \cong \overline{DE}$ and $\overline{BC} \cong \overline{EF}$

Hinge Theorem: If $m\angle E > m\angle B$, then $DF > AC$.

Converse of the Hinge Theorem: If $DF > AC$, then $m\angle E > m\angle B$.

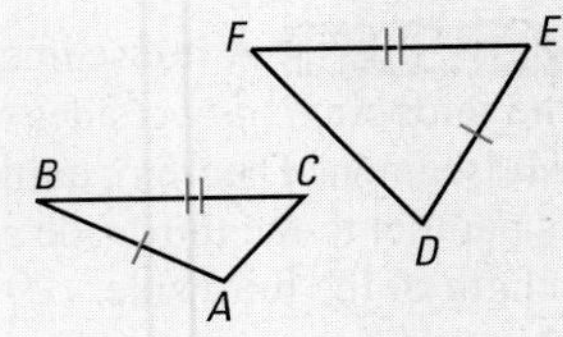

In Exercises 21–23, complete with <, >, or =.

21. AB _?_ CB **<**

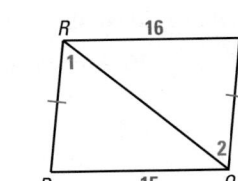

22. $m\angle 1$ _?_ $m\angle 2$ **<**

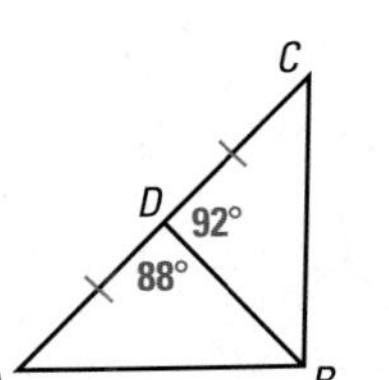

23. TU _?_ VS **=**

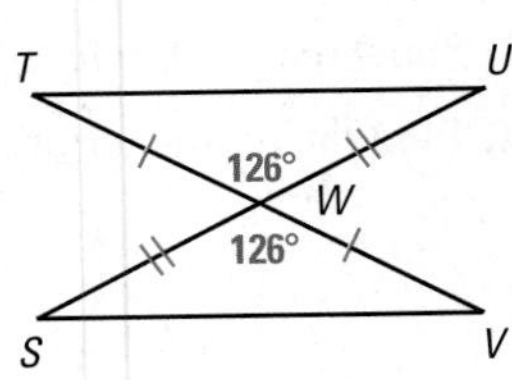

24. Write the first statement for an indirect proof of this situation: In a $\triangle MPQ$, if $\angle M \cong \angle Q$, then $\triangle MPQ$ is isosceles. **Given that $\angle M \cong \angle Q$ in $\triangle MPQ$, assume that $MP \neq QP$.**

25. Write an indirect proof to show that no triangle has two right angles. **See margin.**

CHAPTER 5

Chapter Test

In Exercises 1–5, complete the statement with the word *always, sometimes,* or *never*.

1. If P is the circumcenter of $\triangle RST$, then PR, PS, and PT are __?__ equal. always
2. If $\overrightarrow{BD}$ bisects $\angle ABC$, then $\overline{AD}$ and $\overline{CD}$ are __?__ congruent. sometimes
3. The incenter of a triangle __?__ lies outside the triangle. never
4. The length of a median of a triangle is __?__ equal to the length of a midsegment. sometimes
5. If $\overline{AM}$ is the altitude to side $\overline{BC}$ of $\triangle ABC$, then $\overline{AM}$ is __?__ shorter than $\overline{AB}$. always

In Exercises 6–10, use the diagram.

6. Find each length.

   a. HC 12 **b.** HB 10 **c.** HE 5 **d.** BC 19.8
7. Point H is the __?__ of the triangle. centroid
8. $\overline{CG}$ is a(n) __?__, __?__, __?__, and __?__ of $\triangle ABC$. 8. a median, an altitude, an ∠ bisector, and a ⊥ bisector
9. EF = __?__ and $\overline{EF} \parallel$ __?__ by the __?__ Theorem. $\frac{1}{2}AB = 8$; $\overline{AB}$; Midsegment
10. Compare the measures of $\angle ACB$ and $\angle BAC$. Justify your answer. See margin.

C E F H 9.9 6 A G 8 B

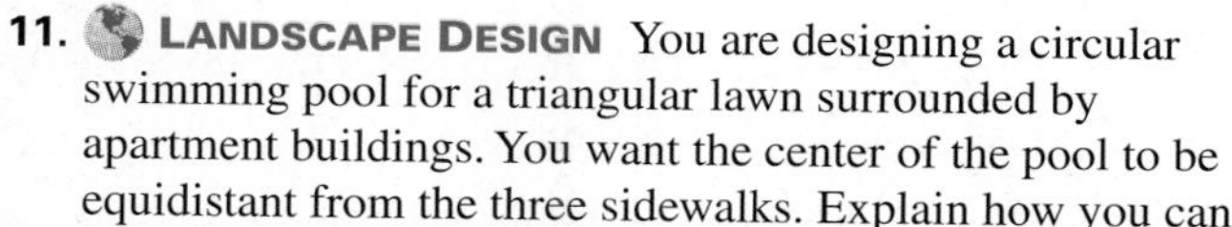

11. **LANDSCAPE DESIGN** You are designing a circular swimming pool for a triangular lawn surrounded by apartment buildings. You want the center of the pool to be equidistant from the three sidewalks. Explain how you can locate the center of the pool. Construct the bisectors of 2 of the △s. The point where they intersect is the incenter of the △ and is equidistant from the 3 sides.

In Exercises 12–14, use the photo of the three-legged tripod.

12. As the legs of a tripod are spread apart, which theorem guarantees that the angles between each pair of legs get larger? Converse of the Hinge Thm.
13. Each leg of a tripod can extend to a length of 5 feet. What is the maximum possible distance between the ends of two legs? 10 ft
14. Let $\overline{OA}$, $\overline{OB}$, and $\overline{OC}$ represent the legs of a tripod. Draw and label a sketch. Suppose the legs are congruent and $m\angle AOC > m\angle BOC$. Compare the lengths of $\overline{AC}$ and $\overline{BC}$. $AC > BC$

In Exercises 15 and 16, use the diagram at the right.

15. Write a two-column proof.

    GIVEN ▶ $AC = BC$

    PROVE ▶ $BE < AE$

Statements	Reasons
1. $AC + CE = AE$	1. Segment Addition Post.
2. $AC = BC$	2. Given
3. $BC + CE = AE$	3. Substitution prop.
4. $BE < BC + CE$	4. △ Inequality Thm.
5. $BE < AE$	5. Substitution prop.

16. Write an indirect proof.

    GIVEN ▶ $AD \neq AB$

    PROVE ▶ $m\angle D \neq m\angle ABC$

    See margin.

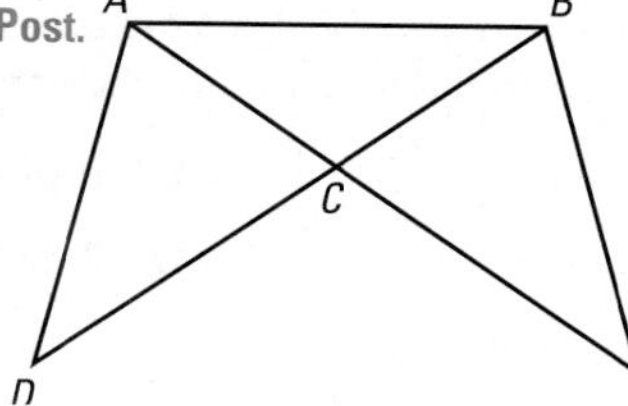

ADDITIONAL RESOURCES
- ***Chapter 5 Resource Book***
  Chapter Test (3 levels) (p. 98)
  SAT/ACT Chapter Test (p. 104)
  Alternative Assessment (p. 105)
- ***Test and Practice Generator***

10. $m\angle ACB < m\angle BAC$ because the side opposite $\angle ACB$, $\overline{AB}$, is shorter than the side opp. $\angle BAC$, $\overline{BC}$. (If one side of a △ is longer than another side, then the ∠ opp. the longer side is larger than the ∠ opp. the shorter side.)

16. Assume that $m\angle D = m\angle ABC$. Then, by the Converse of the Base Angles Thm., $\overline{AD} \cong \overline{AB}$. But this contradicts the given information that $AD \neq AB$. Then the assumption that $m\angle D = m\angle ABC$ must be incorrect and $m\angle D \neq m\angle ABC$.

ADDITIONAL RESOURCES

- ***Chapter 5 Resource Book***
  Chapter Test (3 levels) (p. 98)
  SAT/ACT Chapter Test (p. 104)
  Alternative Assessment (p. 105)
- ***Test and Practice Generator***

CHAPTER 5

Chapter Standardized Test

TEST-TAKING STRATEGY If you find yourself spending too much time on one test question and getting frustrated, move on to the next question. You can revisit a difficult problem later with a fresh perspective.

1. **MULTIPLE CHOICE** In the diagram below, $\overleftrightarrow{PQ}$ is the perpendicular bisector of $\overline{FG}$. What are the values of x and y? B

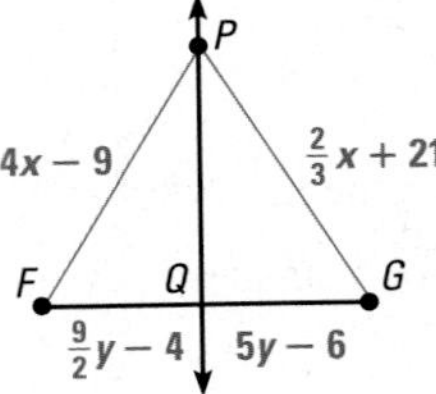

Ⓐ $x = 9, y = 1$ Ⓑ $x = 9, y = 4$
Ⓒ $x = 4, y = 9$ Ⓓ $x = \frac{1}{2}, y = 9$
Ⓔ $x = 9, y = 6$

2. **MULTIPLE CHOICE** In the diagram, $\overrightarrow{ST}$ bisects $\angle RSU$. Which segments do you know are congruent? D

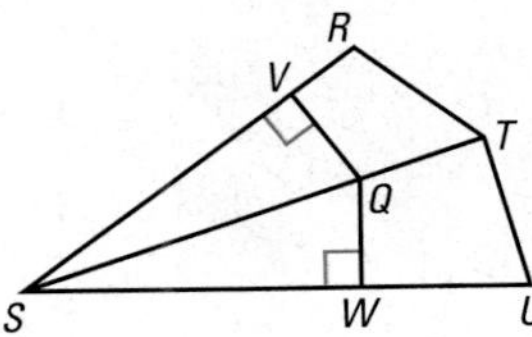

Ⓐ $\overline{SR} \cong \overline{SU}$ Ⓑ $\overline{VR} \cong \overline{WU}$ Ⓒ $\overline{RT} \cong \overline{UT}$
Ⓓ $\overline{QV} \cong \overline{QW}$ Ⓔ $\overline{SQ} \cong \overline{QT}$

3. **MULTIPLE CHOICE** Which of the following statements are true about the circumcenter P of an isosceles triangle? B

   I. Point P is equidistant from the sides.

   II. Point P is equidistant from the vertices.

   III. Point P is two thirds of the distance from each vertex to the midpoint of the opposite side.

Ⓐ I only Ⓑ II only
Ⓒ III only Ⓓ I and II
Ⓔ none of these

4. **MULTIPLE CHOICE** What are the coordinates of the centroid C of a triangle whose vertices are $F(-12, 1)$, $G(-2, 1)$, and $H(-7, -11)$? E

Ⓐ $(-7, -7)$ Ⓑ $\left(-7, -\frac{9}{2}\right)$
Ⓒ $\left(-7, -\frac{5}{4}\right)$ Ⓓ $\left(-7, -\frac{7}{2}\right)$
Ⓔ $(-7, -3)$

5. **MULTIPLE CHOICE** Use the diagram to find the perimeter of $\triangle NPL$. C

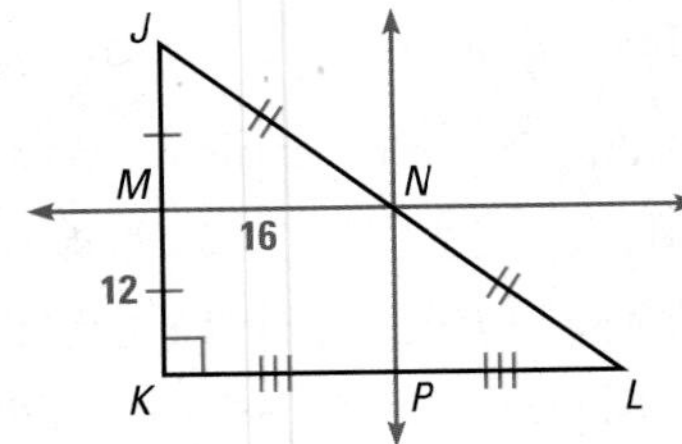

Ⓐ 28 Ⓑ 36 Ⓒ 48
Ⓓ 88 Ⓔ 96

6. **MULTIPLE CHOICE** Points D, E, and F are the midpoints of the sides of $\triangle ABC$. Which of the following statements is false? A

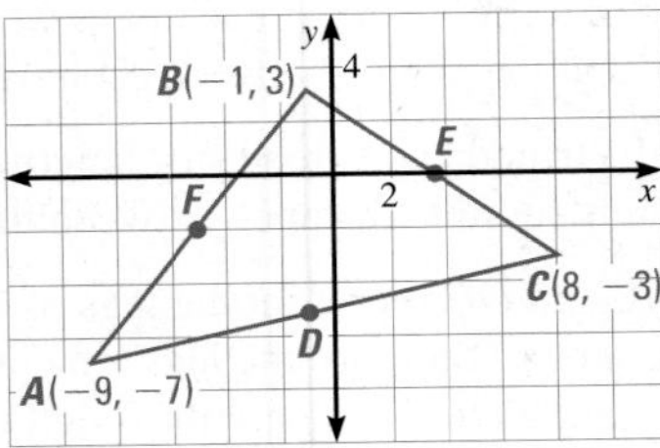

Ⓐ The intersection of $\overline{AE}$ and $\overline{BD}$ is the orthocenter of $\triangle ABC$.

Ⓑ $\overline{EF} \parallel \overline{CA}$

Ⓒ $m\angle A < m\angle C$

Ⓓ $DE = \frac{1}{2}AB$

Ⓔ $\overline{BD}$ is a median of $\triangle ABC$.

7. MULTIPLE CHOICE A triangle has two sides that have lengths of 16 inches and 28 inches. Which of the following lengths could *not* represent the length of the third side? **A**

Ⓐ 12 in. Ⓑ 26 in. Ⓒ 33 in. Ⓓ 40 in. Ⓔ 43 in.

8. QUANTITATIVE COMPARISON Two quantities are described below.

Column A	Column B
K, L, J, 75°	P, Q, R, 42°
KL	*PR*

Choose the statement that is true. **A**

Ⓐ The quantity in column A is greater.

Ⓑ The quantity in column B is greater.

Ⓒ The two quantities are equal.

Ⓓ The relationship cannot be determined from the given information.

MULTI-STEP PROBLEM In Exercises 9–12, use △*GHJ* at the right.

9. What is the sum of x and y? **90**

10. Which measure is greater, $x°$ or $y°$? **$x°$**

11. Which of the following is true? **C**

Ⓐ $x = 45$ Ⓑ $x < 45$ Ⓒ $x > 45$

12. Describe the location of the intersection point of the perpendicular bisectors of △*GHJ*. **the midpoint of hypotenuse $\overline{GH}$**

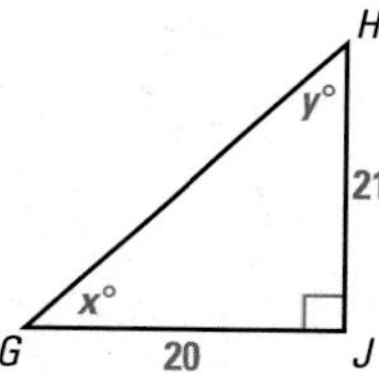

MULTI-STEP PROBLEM In Exercises 13–15, use the following information.

In 1765, a Swiss mathematician, Leonhard Euler, proved that the centroid, orthocenter, and circumcenter of a triangle are all collinear. The line containing these three points is called the *Euler Line*. Euler also proved that the centroid of a triangle is one third the distance from the circumcenter to the orthocenter.

13. Find equations of the lines that contain the medians. Use the equations to find the coordinates of the centroid of △*ABC*.

13. $y = 2x - 18$, $y = \frac{1}{5}x$, $y = -\frac{1}{4}x + \frac{9}{2}$; (10, 2)

14. Find equations of the lines that contain the altitudes of △*ABC*. Use the equations to find the coordinates of the orthocenter. **$x = 12$, $y = x$, $y = -2x + 36$; (12, 12)**

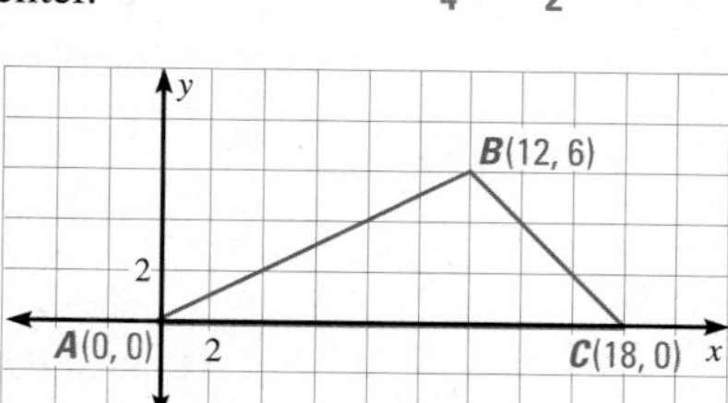

15. In Exercise 30 on page 278, you found that the circumcenter of a △*ABC* with the given vertices is the point (9, −3).

a. Verify that the centroid and the orthocenter you found in Exercises 13 and 14 and the circumcenter above are all collinear. **See margin.**

b. Verify that the distance from the circumcenter to the centroid is one third the distance from the circumcenter to the orthocenter. **See margin.**

15a. ***Sample answer:*** **The line through (10, 2) (the centroid) and (12, 12) (the orthocenter) has equation $y = 5x - 48$. Since the coordinates (9, −3) satisfy that equation, the centroid, the orthocenter, and the circumcenter are collinear.**

b. The distance from the circumcenter to the centroid is $\sqrt{(-3-2)^2 + (9-10)^2} = \sqrt{26}$ and the distance from the circumcenter to the orthocenter is $\sqrt{(-3-12)^2 + (9-12)^2} = 3\sqrt{26}$.

PROJECT OVERVIEW

Mathematical Goals

- Understand and use the median and centroid of a triangle.
- Identify the balance point of a triangle as the centroid.
- Identify the balance point of a square, rectangle, parallelogram, or rhombus as the intersection of the diagonals.
- Make and test conjectures.

Managing the Project

Classroom Management

The Chapter 5 Project may be completed by students working with a partner or in small groups. Group members should work together to complete the steps and answer the Investigation Questions. The other questions should be discussed as a group. Group members can work on different parts of the report, but they should discuss each part beforehand and edit each others' work before a final draft is made.

Guiding Student's Work

Encourage students to draw different types of triangles. Some groups may want to use more than one triangle. They should feel confident that the centroid is the balancing point of any triangle. Also, try to get at least one group to do one of each of the four types of shapes in Question 3. A thinner type of cardboard will be easier to cut than a thick corrugated cardboard.

Concluding the Project

Have each group pick one representative to share their results with the class. Then discuss the following questions.

- Is the balance point different for different types of triangles?
- How does the balance point compare for squares, rectangles, parallelograms, and rhombuses?
- How were the conjectures tested in this investigation?

PROJECT for Chapters 4 and 5

Balancing Shapes

OBJECTIVE **Explore the balancing points of triangles and other shapes.**

Materials: cardboard, straightedge, scissors, hole punch, string, paper clip, pencil with eraser

HOW TO FIND A BALANCING POINT

1 Draw a large triangle on cardboard and cut it out. Punch holes in the triangle near the vertices.

2 Tie a weight to a string and attach the string to a paper clip. Hang your triangle from the paper clip. Mark the vertical line the string makes on the triangle.

3 Repeat Step 2 with the other holes in the triangle. The three lines should intersect near the same point. Balance the triangle by placing this point on a pencil eraser.

INVESTIGATION

1. Are the lines you drew in **Steps 2 and 3** *perpendicular bisectors*, *angle bisectors*, *medians*, or *altitudes* of the triangle? medians
2. Is the balancing point of the triangle the *orthocenter*, *incenter*, *circumcenter*, or *centroid*? centroid
3. Choose one of the following special shapes: *square, rectangle, parallelogram,* or *rhombus*.

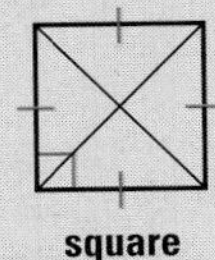

square

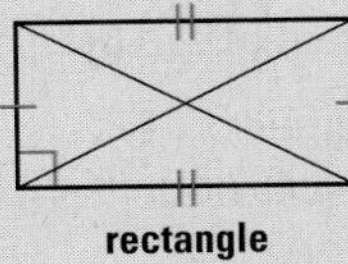

rectangle

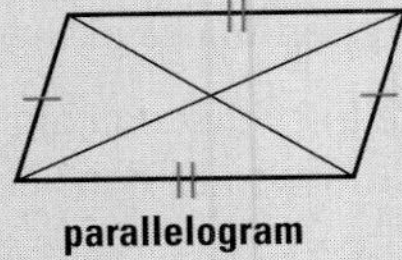

parallelogram

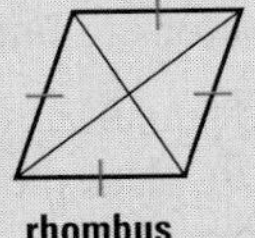

rhombus

Draw and cut out a large example of the shape you have chosen. Follow the steps above to find its balancing point. Check students' points.

4. Make a conjecture about the location of the balancing point in relation to the *diagonals* of the shape. The balancing point is at the intersection of the diagonals.
5. Test your conjecture. Then explain how you tested your conjecture and describe the results of the test. Check students' work.

PRESENT YOUR RESULTS

Write a report to present your results.

- Include your answers to Investigation Exercises 1–5 on the previous page.
- Include your cut-out shapes or sketches of them. Mark the balancing point of each shape.
- Describe the conjectures that you made and your reasons for believing them to be true.
- What advice would you give to someone else who is going to do this project?
- Which geometric facts did this project help you to understand better?

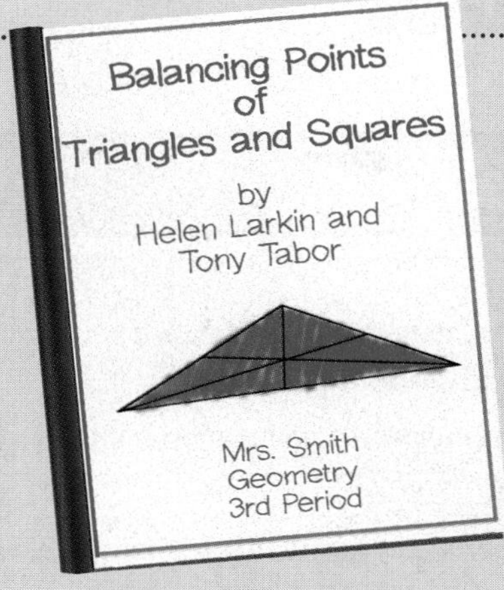

You may wish to display your cut-out shapes on a poster or as a mobile. Here are some hints for creating a mobile.

- Punch a small hole at the balancing point of each shape.
- Tie a knot in a string and thread the string through the hole until the string stops at the knot.
- You can hang all of your shapes from one string, or you can hang them from several strings tied to a stick.

EXTENSION

Do you think your conjecture about balancing points of certain four-sided shapes is true for *all* four-sided shapes? Cut out and test more shapes to find out. In your report, describe your investigation and the results.

No, the balancing point of a four-sided shape is not always at the intersection of its diagonals.

This mobile includes horizontal red and yellow plates that hang from their balancing points.

For the Extension, students might try the following method for determining the balancing point of a four-sided shape:

Draw one diagonal of the shape, dividing the shape into two triangles. Draw three medians for each triangle and locate the centroids of the triangles. The shape should balance at the point halfway between these centroids.

GRADING THE PROJECT

4 Students' answers to the Investigation Exercises are correct and complete. The cut-out shapes or sketches of them are included with the balancing points marked. Conjectures are clear and well supported. The written report demonstrates an understanding of the project and the mathematics involved.

3 Students' answers to the Investigation Exercises are included but may be lacking in some details. Some of the cut-out shapes or sketches may not have the correct balancing points marked. Conjectures are given but may not be fully supported. The written report contains all the required elements but may not explain each part well.

2 The Investigation Exercise answers or the cut-out shapes or sketches contain serious errors or are incomplete. Not all of the questions are answered in the report.

1 The answers to the Investigation Exercises show that the student does not have an understanding of the method presented. The cut-out shapes or sketches are missing or are incorrectly marked. The report is incomplete or not understandable. The project should be returned with a new deadline for completion. The student should speak with the teacher as soon as possible so that they understand the purpose and format of the project.

CHAPTER 6

PLANNING THE CHAPTER

Quadrilaterals

GOALS

LESSON	GOALS	NCTM	ITED	SAT9 (TASK 1)	Terra-Nova	Local
6.1 *pp. 321–328*	CONCEPT ACTIVITY: 6.1 *Investigate shapes to determine if they are polygons.* GOAL 1 Identify, name, and describe polygons. GOAL 2 Use the sum of the measures of the interior angles of a quadrilateral.	1, 2, 3, 4, 8, 10	MCWN, MIM, MIGE	27	11, 13, 14, 16, 18, 49, 51	7, 12, 13
6.2 *pp. 329–337*	TECHNOLOGY ACTIVITY: 6.2 *Explore the properties of parallelograms using geometry software.* GOAL 1 Use some properties of parallelograms. GOAL 2 Use properties of parallelograms in real-life situations.	3, 8, 9, 10	MIGE		14, 18	4, 7, 12, 13, 16, 17
6.3 *pp. 338–346*	GOAL 1 Prove that a quadrilateral is a parallelogram. GOAL 2 Use coordinate geometry with parallelograms.	2, 3, 7, 8, 9, 10	MIGE	33	14, 16, 17, 18, 51	4, 7, 12, 17
6.4 *pp. 347–355*	GOAL 1 Use properties of sides and angles of rhombuses, rectangles, and squares. GOAL 2 Use properties of diagonals of rhombuses, rectangles, and squares.	3, 10	MIGE		14	4, 7, 12, 17
6.5 *pp. 356–363*	GOAL 1 Use properties of trapezoids. GOAL 2 Use properties of kites.	3, 10	MIGE		14	4, 7, 12
6.6 *pp. 364–370*	GOAL 1 Identify special quadrilaterals based on limited information. GOAL 2 Prove that a quadrilateral is a special type of quadrilateral.	3, 7, 8, 9, 10	MIGE		14, 17, 18	7, 12
6.7 *pp. 371–380*	CONCEPT ACTIVITY: 6.7 *Investigate areas of quadrilaterals.* GOAL 1 Find the areas of squares, rectangles, parallelograms, and triangles. GOAL 2 Find the areas of trapezoids, kites, and rhombuses.	1, 2, 3, 4	MCWN, MIM, MIGE	29	10, 11, 13, 14, 16, 49, 51	7, 8, 10

RESOURCES

Chapter Resource Booklets

Chapter Support

Tips for New Teachers	p. 1
Parent Guide for Student Success	p. 3
Prerequisite Skills Review	p. 5
Strategies for Reading Mathematics	p. 7

Lesson Support

	6.1	6.2	6.3	6.4	6.5	6.6	6.7
Lesson Plans (regular and block)	p. 9	p. 22	p. 36	p. 50	p. 66	p. 80	p. 93
Warm-Up Exercises and Daily Quiz	p. 11	p. 24	p. 38	p. 52	p. 68	p. 82	p. 95
Activity Support Masters							p. 96
Lesson Openers	p. 12	p. 25	p. 39	p. 53	p. 69	p. 83	p. 98
Technology Activities & Keystrokes	p. 13	p. 26		p. 54	p. 70		p. 99
Practice (3 levels)	p. 14	p. 28	p. 40	p. 58	p. 71	p. 84	p. 102
Reteaching with Practice	p. 17	p. 31	p. 43	p. 61	p. 74	p. 87	p. 105
Quick Catch-Up for Absent Students	p. 19	p. 33	p. 45	p. 63	p. 76	p. 89	p. 107
Cooperative Learning Activities						p. 90	
Interdisciplinary Applications	p. 20		p. 46		p. 77		p. 108
Real-Life Applications		p. 34		p. 64		p. 91	
Math & History Applications			p. 47				
Challenge: Skills and Applications	p. 21	p. 35	p. 48	p. 65	p. 78	p. 92	p. 109

Review and Assessment

Quizzes	pp. 49, 79
Chapter Review Games and Activities	p. 110
Chapter Test (3 levels)	pp. 111–116
SAT/ACT Chapter Test	p. 117
Alternative Assessment with Math Journal	p. 118
Project with Rubric	p. 120
Cumulative Review	p. 122
Resource Book Answers	p. A1

Transparencies

	6.1	6.2	6.3	6.4	6.5	6.6	6.7
Warm-Up Exercises and Daily Quiz	p. 40	p. 41	p. 42	p. 43	p. 44	p. 45	p. 46
Alternative Lesson Opener Transparencies	p. 34	p. 35	p. 36	p. 37	p. 38	p. 39	p. 40
Examples/Standardized Test Practice	✓	✓	✓	✓	✓	✓	✓
Answer Transparencies	✓	✓	✓	✓	✓	✓	✓

Technology

- Electronic Teaching Tools
- Online Lesson Planner
- Internet Support
- Personal Student Tutor
- Test and Practice Generator
- Geometry in Motion video
- Electronic Lesson Presentations (Lesson 6.4)

Additional Resources

- Basic Skills Workbook: Diagnosis and Remediation
- Worked-Out Solution Key
- Resources in Spanish
- Standardized Test Practice Workbook
- Practice Workbook with Examples

Correlations to the California Curriculum

Correlations to California Standards
See Teacher's Edition pp. CA9–CA11

Correlations to SAT9
Task 1: See Teacher's Edition pp. CA12–CA14
Task 2: See Teacher's Edition pp. CA15–CA17

CHAPTER 6

PACING THE CHAPTER

Resource Key
- ● STUDENT EDITION
- ● CHAPTER 6 RESOURCE BOOK
- ● TEACHER'S EDITION

REGULAR SCHEDULE

Day 1

6.1

STARTING OPTIONS
- Prereq. Skills Review
- Strategies for Reading
- Homework Check
- Warm-Up or Daily Quiz

TEACHING OPTIONS
- Motivating the Lesson
- Concept Activity
- Les. Opener (Application)
- Examples 1–4
- Guided Practice Exs.

APPLY/HOMEWORK
- See Assignment Guide.
- See the CRB: Practice, Reteach, Apply, Extend

ASSESSMENT OPTIONS
- Checkpoint Exercises

Day 2

6.1 *(cont.)*

STARTING OPTIONS
- Homework Check

TEACHING OPTIONS
- Examples 1–4
- Closure Question

APPLY/HOMEWORK
- See Assignment Guide.
- See the CRB: Practice, Reteach, Apply, Extend

ASSESSMENT OPTIONS
- Checkpoint Exercises
- Daily Quiz (6.1)
- Stand. Test Practice

Day 3

6.2

STARTING OPTIONS
- Homework Check
- Warm-Up or Daily Quiz

TEACHING OPTIONS
- Motivating the Lesson
- Les. Opener (Activity)
- Examples 1–6
- Guided Practice Exs.

APPLY/HOMEWORK
- See Assignment Guide.
- See the CRB: Practice, Reteach, Apply, Extend

ASSESSMENT OPTIONS
- Checkpoint Exercises

Day 4

6.2 *(cont.)*

STARTING OPTIONS
- Homework Check

TEACHING OPTIONS
- Examples 1–6
- Technology Activity
- Closure Question

APPLY/HOMEWORK
- See Assignment Guide.
- See the CRB: Practice, Reteach, Apply, Extend

ASSESSMENT OPTIONS
- Checkpoint Exercises
- Daily Quiz (6.2)
- Stand. Test Practice

Day 5

6.3

STARTING OPTIONS
- Homework Check
- Warm-Up or Daily Quiz

TEACHING OPTIONS
- Les. Opener (Activity)
- Examples 1–4
- Guided Practice Exs.

APPLY/HOMEWORK
- See Assignment Guide.
- See the CRB: Practice, Reteach, Apply, Extend

ASSESSMENT OPTIONS
- Checkpoint Exercises

Day 6

6.3 *(cont.)*

STARTING OPTIONS
- Homework Check

TEACHING OPTIONS
- Examples 1–4
- Closure Question

APPLY/HOMEWORK
- See Assignment Guide.
- See the CRB: Practice, Reteach, Apply, Extend

ASSESSMENT OPTIONS
- Checkpoint Exercises
- Daily Quiz (6.3)
- Stand. Test Practice
- Quiz (6.1–6.3)

Day 9

6.5

STARTING OPTIONS
- Homework Check
- Warm-Up or Daily Quiz

TEACHING OPTIONS
- Motivating the Lesson
- Les. Opener (Application)
- Examples 1–5
- Guided Practice Exs.

APPLY/HOMEWORK
- See Assignment Guide.
- See the CRB: Practice, Reteach, Apply, Extend

ASSESSMENT OPTIONS
- Checkpoint Exercises

Day 10

6.5 *(cont.)*

STARTING OPTIONS
- Homework Check

TEACHING OPTIONS
- Examples 1–5
- Closure Question

APPLY/HOMEWORK
- See Assignment Guide.
- See the CRB: Practice, Reteach, Apply, Extend

ASSESSMENT OPTIONS
- Checkpoint Exercises
- Daily Quiz (6.5)
- Stand. Test Practice
- Quiz (6.4–6.5)

Day 11

6.6

STARTING OPTIONS
- Homework Check
- Warm-Up or Daily Quiz

TEACHING OPTIONS
- Motivating the Lesson
- Les. Opener (Visual)
- Examples 1–5
- Closure Question
- Guided Practice Exs.

APPLY/HOMEWORK
- See Assignment Guide.
- See the CRB: Practice, Reteach, Apply, Extend

ASSESSMENT OPTIONS
- Checkpoint Exercises
- Daily Quiz (6.6)
- Stand. Test Practice

Day 12

6.7

STARTING OPTIONS
- Homework Check
- Warm-Up or Daily Quiz

TEACHING OPTIONS
- Motivating the Lesson
- Concept Act. & Wksht.
- Les. Opener (Visual)
- Technology Activity
- Examples 1–5
- Guided Practice Exs.

APPLY/HOMEWORK
- See Assignment Guide.
- See the CRB: Practice, Reteach, Apply, Extend

ASSESSMENT OPTIONS
- Checkpoint Exercises, pp. 373–375

Day 13

6.7 *(cont.)*

STARTING OPTIONS
- Homework Check

TEACHING OPTIONS
- Example 6
- Closure Question

APPLY/HOMEWORK
- See Assignment Guide.
- See the CRB: Practice, Reteach, Apply, Extend

ASSESSMENT OPTIONS
- Checkpoint Exercises, p. 375
- Daily Quiz (6.7)
- Stand. Test Practice
- Quiz (6.6–6.7)

Day 14

Review

DAY 14 START OPTIONS
- Homework Check

REVIEWING OPTIONS
- Chapter 6 Summary
- Chapter 6 Review
- Chapter Review Games and Activities

APPLY/HOMEWORK
- Chapter 6 Test (practice)
- Ch. Standardized Test (practice)

Day 7

6.4

Starting Options
- Homework Check
- Warm-Up or Daily Quiz

Teaching Options
- Motivating the Lesson
- Les. Opener (Software)
- Technology Activity
- Examples 1–3
- Guided Practice Exs. 1, 3–8, 10–11

Apply/Homework
- See Assignment Guide.
- See the CRB: Practice, Reteach, Apply, Extend

Assessment Options
- Checkpoint Exercises, p. 348

Day 8

6.4 *(cont.)*

Starting Options
- Homework Check

Teaching Options
- Examples 4–6
- Closure Question
- Guided Practice Exs. 2, 9

Apply/Homework
- See Assignment Guide.
- See the CRB: Practice, Reteach, Apply, Extend

Assessment Options
- Checkpoint Exercises, pp. 349–350
- Daily Quiz (6.4)
- Stand. Test Practice

Day 15

Assess

Day 15 Start Options
- Homework Check

Assessment Options
- Chapter 6 Test
- SAT/ACT Ch. 6 Test
- Alternative Assessment

Apply/Homework
- Skill Review, p. 394

BLOCK SCHEDULE

Day 1

Assess & 6.1

(Day 1 = Ch. 5 Day 7)

Assessment Options
- Chapter 5 Test
- SAT/ACT Ch. 5 Test
- Alternative Assessment

Ch. 6 Start Options
- Skills Review, p. 320
- Prereq. Skills Review
- Strategies for Reading

Beginning 6.1 Options
- Warm-Up (Les. 6.1)
- Motivating the Lesson
- Concept Activity
- Les. Opener (Appl.)
- Examples 1–4
- Guided Practice Exs.

Apply/Homework
- See Assignment Guide.
- See the CRB: Practice, Reteach, Apply, Extend

Assessment Options
- Checkpoint Exercises

Day 2

6.1 & 6.2

Day 2 Start Options
- Homework Check

Finishing 6.1 Options
- Examples 1–4
- Closure Question

Beginning 6.2 Options
- Warm-Up (Les. 6.2)
- Motivating the Lesson
- Les. Opener (Activity)
- Examples 1–6
- Guided Practice Exs.

Apply/Homework
- See Assignment Guide.
- See the CRB: Practice, Reteach, Apply, Extend

Assessment Options
- Checkpoint Exercises
- Daily Quiz (Les. 6.1)
- Stand. Test Prac. (6.1)

Day 3

6.2 & 6.3

Day 3 Start Options
- Homework Check
- Daily Quiz (Les. 6.1)

Finishing 6.2 Options
- Examples 1–6
- Technology Activity
- Closure Question

Beginning 6.3 Options
- Warm-Up (Les. 6.3)
- Les. Opener (Activity)
- Examples 1–4
- Guided Practice Exs.

Apply/Homework
- See Assignment Guide.
- See the CRB: Practice, Reteach, Apply, Extend

Assessment Options
- Checkpoint Exercises
- Daily Quiz (Les. 6.2)
- Stand. Test Prac. (6.2)

Day 4

6.3 & 6.4

Day 4 Start Options
- Homework Check
- Daily Quiz (Les. 6.2)

Finishing 6.3 Options
- Examples 1–4
- Closure Question

Beginning 6.4 Options
- Warm-Up (Les. 6.4)
- Motivating the Lesson
- Les. Opener (Software)
- Technology Activity
- Examples 1–3
- Guided Practice Exs. 1, 3–8, 10–11

Apply/Homework
- See Assignment Guide.
- See the CRB: Practice, Reteach, Apply, Extend

Assessment Options
- Checkpoint Exercises
- Daily Quiz (Les. 6.3)
- Stand. Test Prac. (6.3)
- Quiz (6.1–6.3)

Day 5

6.4 & 6.5

Day 5 Start Options
- Homework Check
- Daily Quiz (Les. 6.3)

Finishing 6.4 Options
- Examples 4–6
- Closure Question
- Guided Practice Exs. 2, 9

Beginning 6.5 Options
- Warm-Up (Les. 6.5)
- Motivating the Lesson
- Les. Opener (Appl.)
- Examples 1–5
- Guided Practice Exs.

Apply/Homework
- See Assignment Guide.
- See the CRB: Practice, Reteach, Apply, Extend

Assessment Options
- Checkpoint Exercises
- Daily Quiz (Les. 6.4)
- Stand. Test Prac. (6.4)

Day 6

6.5 & 6.6

Day 6 Start Options
- Homework Check
- Daily Quiz (Les. 6.4)

Finishing 6.5 Options
- Examples 1–5
- Closure Question

Teaching 6.6 Options
- Warm-Up (Les. 6.6)
- Motivating the Lesson
- Les. Opener (Visual)
- Examples 1–5
- Closure Question
- Guided Practice Exs.

Apply/Homework
- See Assignment Guide.
- See the CRB: Practice, Reteach, Apply, Extend

Assessment Options
- Checkpoint Exercises
- Daily Quiz (Les. 6.5, 6.6)
- Stand. Test Practice
- Quiz (6.4–6.5)

Day 7

6.7

Day 7 Start Options
- Homework Check
- Warm-Up or Daily Quiz

Teaching 6.7 Options
- Motivating the Lesson
- Concept Act. & Wksht.
- Les. Opener (Visual)
- Technology Activity
- Examples 1–6
- Closure Question
- Guided Practice Exs.

Apply/Homework
- See Assignment Guide.
- See the CRB: Practice, Reteach, Apply, Extend

Assessment Options
- Checkpoint Exercises
- Daily Quiz (Les. 6.7)
- Stand. Test Practice
- Quiz (6.6–6.7)

Day 8

Review/Assess

Day 8 Start Options
- Homework Check

Reviewing Options
- Chapter 6 Summary
- Chapter 6 Review
- Chapter Review Games and Activities
- Chapter 6 Test (practice)
- Ch. Standardized Test (practice)

Assessment Options
- Chapter 6 Test
- SAT/ACT Ch. 6 Test
- Alternative Assessment

Apply/Homework
- Skill Review, p. 394

MEETING INDIVIDUAL NEEDS

BEFORE THE CHAPTER

The *Chapter 6 Resource Book* has the following materials to distribute and use before the chapter:

- **Parent Guide for Student Success (pictured below)**
- **Prerequisite Skills Review**
- **Strategies for Reading Mathematics**

PARENT GUIDE *Pages 3–4*

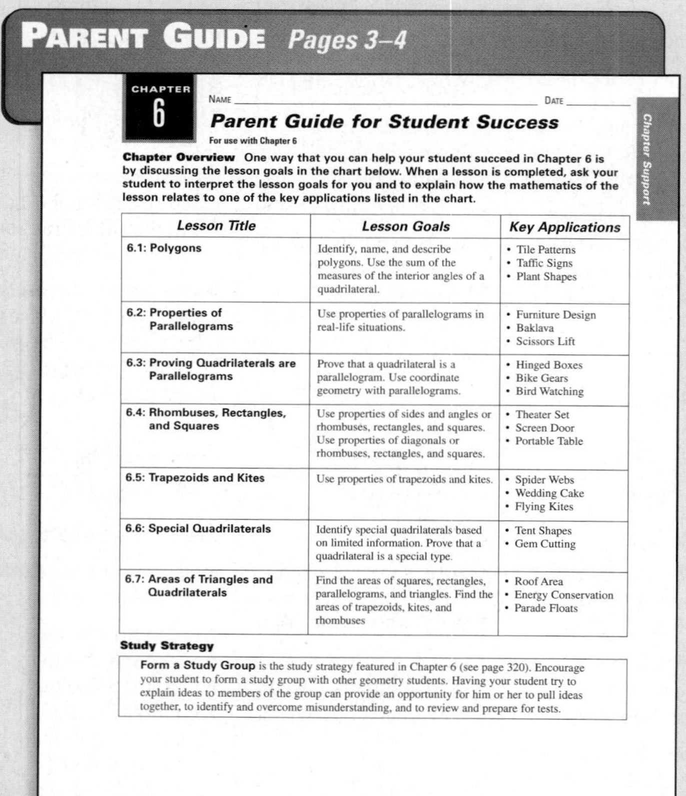

CHAPTER 6

NAME ______________________ DATE __________

Parent Guide for Student Success

For use with Chapter 6

Chapter Support

Chapter Overview **One way that you can help your student succeed in Chapter 6 is by discussing the lesson goals in the chart below. When a lesson is completed, ask your student to interpret the lesson goals for you and to explain how the mathematics of the lesson relates to one of the key applications listed in the chart.**

Lesson Title	*Lesson Goals*	*Key Applications*
6.1: Polygons	Identify, name, and describe polygons. Use the sum of the measures of the interior angles of a quadrilateral.	• Tile Patterns • Taffic Signs • Plant Shapes
6.2: Properties of Parallelograms	Use properties of parallelograms in real-life situations.	• Furniture Design • Baklava • Scissors Lift
6.3: Proving Quadrilaterals are Parallelograms	Prove that a quadrilateral is a parallelogram. Use coordinate geometry with parallelograms.	• Hinged Boxes • Bike Gears • Bird Watching
6.4: Rhombuses, Rectangles, and Squares	Use properties of sides and angles or rhombuses, rectangles, and squares. Use properties of diagonals or rhombuses, rectangles, and squares.	• Theater Set • Screen Door • Portable Table
6.5: Trapezoids and Kites	Use properties of trapezoids and kites.	• Spider Webs • Wedding Cake • Flying Kites
6.6: Special Quadrilaterals	Identify special quadrilaterals based on limited information. Prove that a quadrilateral is a special type.	• Tent Shapes • Gem Cutting
6.7: Areas of Triangles and Quadrilaterals	Find the areas of squares, rectangles, parallelograms, and triangles. Find the areas of trapezoids, kites, and rhombuses	• Roof Area • Energy Conservation • Parade Floats

Study Strategy

Form a Study Group is the study strategy featured in Chapter 6 (see page 320). Encourage your student to form a study group with other geometry students. Having your student try to explain ideas to members of the group can provide an opportunity for him or her to pull ideas together, to identify and overcome misunderstanding, and to review and prepare for tests.

PARENT GUIDE FOR STUDENT SUCCESS The first page summarizes the content of Chapter 6. Parents are encouraged to have their students explain how the material relates to key applications in the chapter, such as energy conservation. The second page (not shown) provides exercises and an activity that parents can do with their students. In the activity, parents and students conduct a quadrilateral scavenger hunt.

DURING EACH LESSON

The *Chapter 6 Resource Book* has the following alternatives for introducing the lesson:

- **Lesson Openers (pictured below)**
- **Technology Activities with Keystrokes**

LESSON OPENER *Page 39*

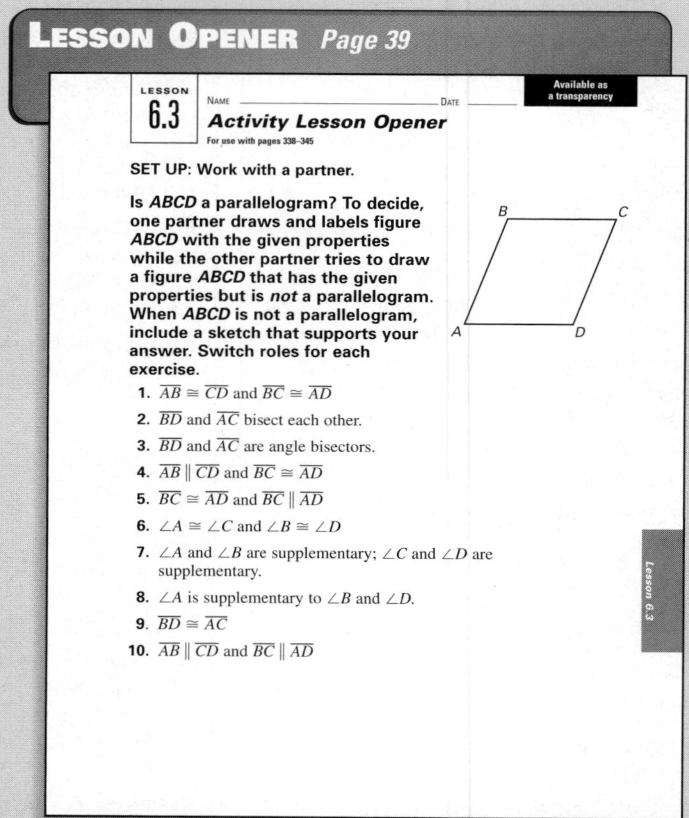

LESSON 6.3

NAME ______________________ DATE __________

Available as a transparency

Activity Lesson Opener

For use with pages 338–345

SET UP: Work with a partner.

Is *ABCD* a parallelogram? To decide, one partner draws and labels figure *ABCD* with the given properties while the other partner tries to draw a figure *ABCD* that has the given properties but is *not* a parallelogram. When *ABCD* is not a parallelogram, include a sketch that supports your answer. Switch roles for each exercise.

1. $\overline{AB} \cong \overline{CD}$ and $\overline{BC} \cong \overline{AD}$
2. $\overline{BD}$ and $\overline{AC}$ bisect each other.
3. $\overline{BD}$ and $\overline{AC}$ are angle bisectors.
4. $\overline{AB} \parallel \overline{CD}$ and $\overline{BC} \cong \overline{AD}$
5. $\overline{BC} \cong \overline{AD}$ and $\overline{BC} \parallel \overline{AD}$
6. $\angle A \cong \angle C$ and $\angle B \cong \angle D$
7. $\angle A$ and $\angle B$ are supplementary; $\angle C$ and $\angle D$ are supplementary.
8. $\angle A$ is supplementary to $\angle B$ and $\angle D$.
9. $\overline{BD} \cong \overline{AC}$
10. $\overline{AB} \parallel \overline{CD}$ and $\overline{BC} \parallel \overline{AD}$

Lesson 6.3

ACTIVITY LESSON OPENER This Lesson Opener provides an alternative way to start Lesson 6.3 in the form of an activity. In this activity, students work with a partner to sketch quadrilaterals as they learn about identifying parallelograms.

Following Each Lesson

The *Chapter 6 Resource Book* has a variety of materials to follow-up each lesson. They include the following:

- **Practice (3 levels)**
- **Reteaching with Practice (pictured below)**
- **Quick Catch-Up for Absent Students**
- **Interdisciplinary Applications**
- **Real-Life Applications**

Reteaching with Practice *Pages 74–75*

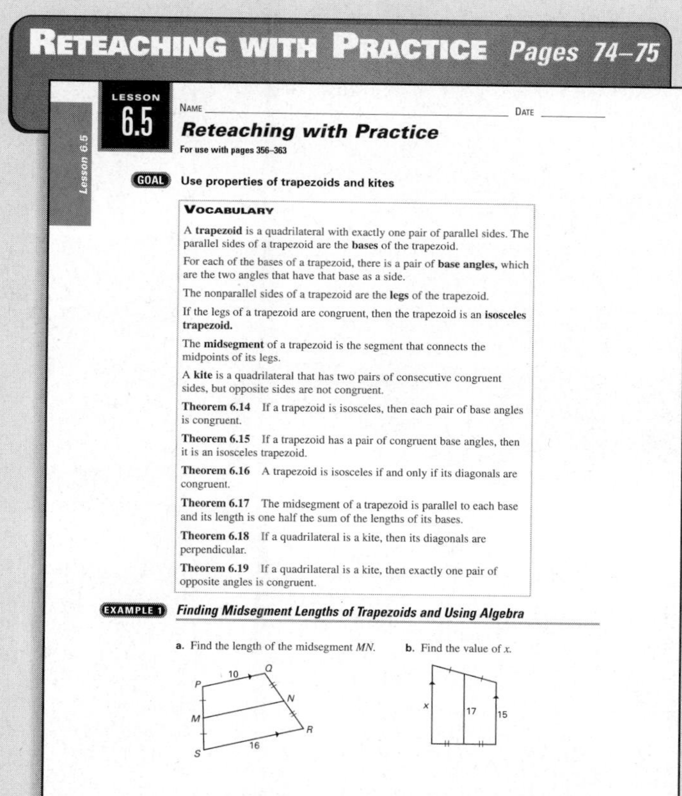

LESSON 6.5 NAME ______ DATE ______

Reteaching with Practice

For use with pages 356–363

GOAL Use properties of trapezoids and kites

Vocabulary

A **trapezoid** is a quadrilateral with exactly one pair of parallel sides. The parallel sides of a trapezoid are the **bases** of the trapezoid.

For each of the bases of a trapezoid, there is a pair of **base angles,** which are the two angles that have that base as a side.

The nonparallel sides of a trapezoid are the **legs** of the trapezoid.

If the legs of a trapezoid are congruent, then the trapezoid is an **isosceles trapezoid.**

The **midsegment** of a trapezoid is the segment that connects the midpoints of its legs.

A **kite** is a quadrilateral that has two pairs of consecutive congruent sides, but opposite sides are not congruent.

Theorem 6.14 If a trapezoid is isosceles, then each pair of base angles is congruent.

Theorem 6.15 If a trapezoid has a pair of congruent base angles, then it is an isosceles trapezoid.

Theorem 6.16 A trapezoid is isosceles if and only if its diagonals are congruent.

Theorem 6.17 The midsegment of a trapezoid is parallel to each base and its length is one half the sum of the lengths of its bases.

Theorem 6.18 If a quadrilateral is a kite, then its diagonals are perpendicular.

Theorem 6.19 If a quadrilateral is a kite, then exactly one pair of opposite angles is congruent.

EXAMPLE 1 *Finding Midsegment Lengths of Trapezoids and Using Algebra*

a. Find the length of the midsegment MN.

b. Find the value of x.

Reteaching with Practice On this two-page worksheet, additional examples and practice reinforce the key concepts of Lesson 6.5: finding midsegment lengths of trapezoids and using properties of kites.

Technology Resource

Students can use the Personal Student Tutor to find additional reteaching and practice for the skills in Lesson 6.5 and in the rest of Chapter 6.

Assessing the Chapter

The *Chapter 6 Resource Book* has the following review and assessment materials:

- **Quizzes**
- **Chapter Review Games and Activities**
- **Chapter Test (3 levels)**
- **SAT/ACT Chapter Test**
- **Alternative Assessment with Rubric and Math Journal**
- **Project with Rubric**
- **Cumulative Review (pictured below)**

Cumulative Review *Pages 122–123*

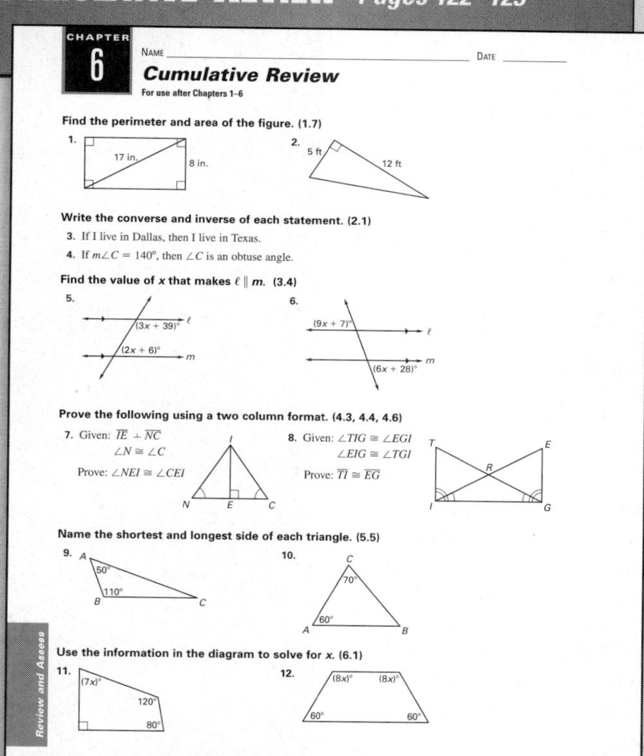

CHAPTER 6 NAME ______ DATE ______

Cumulative Review

For use after Chapters 1–6

Find the perimeter and area of the figure. (1.7)

1.

2.

Write the converse and inverse of each statement. (2.1)

3. If I live in Dallas, then I live in Texas.

4. If $m\angle C = 140°$, then $\angle C$ is an obtuse angle.

Find the value of x that makes $\ell \parallel m$. (3.4)

5.

6.

Prove the following using a two column format. (4.3, 4.4, 4.6)

7. Given: $\overline{IE} \perp \overline{NC}$, $\angle N \cong \angle C$
Prove: $\angle NEI \cong \angle CEI$

8. Given: $\angle TIG \cong \angle EGI$, $\angle EIG \cong \angle TGI$
Prove: $\overline{TI} \cong \overline{EG}$

Name the shortest and longest side of each triangle. (5.5)

9.

10.

Use the information in the diagram to solve for x. (6.1)

11.

12.

Cumulative Review The content of Chapters 1–6 is reviewed in this two-page cumulative review. Lesson references with each cluster of exercises guide students to the places in the textbook where they can go to review each concept.

Technology Resource

Teachers can use the Time-Saving Test and Practice Generator to create customized review materials covering Chapters 1–6.

CHAPTER OVERVIEW

Chapter Goals

Students will study quadrilaterals and their properties in this chapter. They will identify convex, concave, and regular polygons, and will examine properties of interior angles of quadrilaterals. Students will use the properties of parallelograms and algebra to solve problems involving side lengths and angle measures, and will formally prove properties of parallelograms, including the conditions for which quadrilaterals are parallelograms. Students will use the distance and slope formulas with coordinate geometry to show figures are parallelograms. They will examine properties of the sides, angles, and diagonals of special parallelograms such as rhombuses, rectangles, and squares. They will use properties of trapezoids and kites. Students will identify special quadrilaterals based on limited information, and will use both formal proof and coordinate geometry to prove that a quadrilateral is a special quadrilateral. Finally, students will learn and apply formulas for the areas of squares, rectangles, parallelograms, triangles, trapezoids, kites, and rhombuses.

Application Note

Scissors lifts can allow a movie scene to be filmed with more than one camera, and from different heights and perspectives. When the various shots are then spliced together, the result can be an enhanced sense of character movement.

Additional information about scissors lifts is available at **www.mcdougallittell.com.**

QUADRILATERALS

How are overhead shots taken for movies?

CHAPTER 6

APPLICATION: Scissors Lift

Scissors lifts are used to lift construction workers, movie crews, and other people who need to be up high.

The platform can be raised to different heights. The design of the lift ensures that as the platform is raised or lowered, it is always parallel to the ground.

In Chapter 6, you'll learn how machines and tools like the scissors lift work.

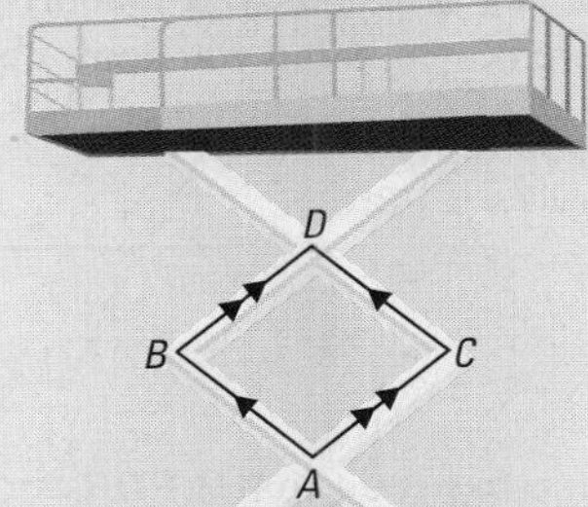

Think & Discuss

1. The lengths of $\overline{BA}$ and $\overline{BD}$ are constant. What happens to AD if $m\angle B$ increases? Explain. See margin.
2. What do you think happens to the platform of the scissors lift if $m\angle B$ increases? The platform will rise.

Learn More About It

You will learn more about scissors lifts in Exercises 51–54 on p. 336.

APPLICATION LINK Visit www.mcdougallittell.com for more information about scissors lifts.

PROJECTS

A project covering Chapters 6 and 7 appears on pages 452–453 of the Student Edition. An additional project for Chapter 6 is available in the *Chapter 6 Resource Book,* p. 120.

TECHNOLOGY

Software

- *Electronic Teaching Tools*
- *Online Lesson Planner*
- *Personal Student Tutor*
- *Test and Practice Generator*
- *Electronic Lesson Presentations (Lesson 6.4)*

Video

- *Geometry in Motion*

Internet Connections www.mcdougallittell.com

- **Application Links** 319, 346, 377
- **Student Help** 327, 329, 335, 341, 344, 354, 357, 361, 369
- **Career Links** 333, 361, 369
- **Extra Challenge** 328, 337, 345, 355, 362, 379

1. **AD will increase. *Sample answer:* The distance between A and D increases as $m\angle B$ increases.**

PREPARE

Diagnostic Tools

The **Skill Review** exercises can help you diagnose whether students have the following skills needed in Chapter 6:

- Identify the postulate or theorem that justifies a statement about angle measures.
- Identify the postulate or theorem that can be used to prove that two triangles are congruent.

The following resources are available for students who need additional help with these skills:

- Prerequisite Skills Review (*Chapter 6 Resource Book,* p. 5; *Warm-Up Transparencies,* p. 39)
- Reteaching with Practice (Chapter Resource Books for Lessons 1.3, 1.5, 3.3, 3.6, 4.3, and 4.4)
- *Personal Student Tutor*

Additional Resources

The following resources are provided to help you prepare for the upcoming chapter and customize review materials:

- ***Chapter 6 Resource Book***
  Tips for New Teachers (p. 1)
  Parent Guide (p. 3)
  Lesson Plans (every lesson)
  Lesson Plans for Block Scheduling (every lesson)
- ***Electronic Teaching Tools***
- ***Online Lesson Planner***
- ***Test and Practice Generator***

1. *If two ∥ lines are cut by a transversal, consecutive interior angles are supplementary.*
2. *If two ∥ lines are cut by a transversal, alternate interior angles are congruent.*

CHAPTER 6

Study Guide

PREVIEW

What's the chapter about?

Chapter 6 is about four-sided figures called **quadrilaterals** and their properties. In Chapter 6, you'll learn

- how to classify special quadrilaterals and how to use their properties.
- how to write proofs about special quadrilaterals.
- how to find areas of triangles and quadrilaterals.

KEY VOCABULARY

- polygon, p. 322
- sides and vertices of a polygon, p. 322
- convex, p. 323
- concave, p. 323
- equilateral, p. 323
- equiangular, p. 323
- regular, p. 323
- diagonal, p. 324
- parallelogram, p. 330
- rhombus, p. 347
- rectangle, p. 347
- square, p. 347
- trapezoid, p. 356
- isosceles trapezoid, p. 356
- midsegment of a trapezoid, p. 357
- kite, p. 358

PREPARE

Are you ready for the chapter?

SKILL REVIEW Do these exercises to review key skills that you'll apply in this chapter. See the given **reference page** if there is something you don't understand.

STUDENT HELP

Study Tip
"Student Help" boxes throughout the chapter give you study tips and tell you where to look for extra help in this book and on the Internet.

Use the diagram at the right. Write the postulate or theorem that justifies the statement. (Review p. 143)

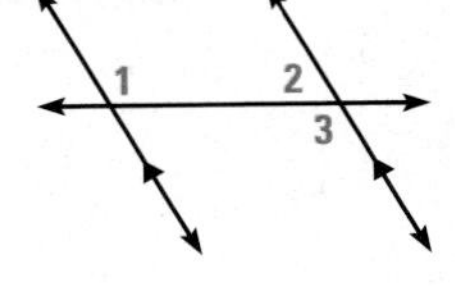

1, 2. See margin.

1. $\angle 1$ and $\angle 2$ are supplementary angles.

2. $\angle 1 \cong \angle 3$

Which postulate or theorem could you use to prove that $\triangle PQR \cong \triangle XYZ$? (Review pp. 212–215, 220–222)

3. $\angle Q \cong \angle Y$, $\angle R \cong \angle Z$, $\overline{PQ} \cong \overline{XY}$ AAS Cong. Theorem

4. $PQ = XY$, $QR = YZ$, $PR = XZ$ SSS Cong. Postulate

5. The endpoints of $\overline{AB}$ are $A(-3, 4)$ and $B(2, -8)$. Find the length and the slope of $\overline{AB}$. Then find the coordinates of the midpoint of $\overline{AB}$. **(Review pp. 19, 35, and 165)**
$13, -\frac{12}{5}, \left(-\frac{1}{2}, -2\right)$

STUDY STRATEGY

Here's a study strategy!

Form a study group

Form a study group with two or three of your friends. Each person should review a few sections of the chapter and prepare a summary of the important concepts and skills. At a group meeting, present and discuss your summaries.

ACTIVITY 6.1

Developing Concepts

Classifying Shapes

GROUP ACTIVITY
Work with a partner.

QUESTION Which shapes are polygons?

EXPLORING THE CONCEPT

The symbols at the right are used in meteorology to represent different weather elements such as storms, precipitation, and cloud formations.

You can classify the shapes based on the tests below.

Test 1 Is the symbol made up of straight line segments only?

Test 2 Does each line segment in the symbol intersect exactly two other line segments, one at each endpoint?

WEATHER SYMBOLS

squall | lightning | cumulus cloud
snow | altostratus cloud | hail
showers | haze | tropical storm

DRAWING CONCLUSIONS

1. Make a list of weather symbols that pass Test 1.
squall, lightning, snow, altostratus cloud, hail, showers
2. From your list in Exercise 1, which symbols pass Test 2?
squall, hail, showers
3. A shape that passes both Test 1 and Test 2 is called a *polygon*. The following symbols are used to write flow charts for computer programs. Which symbols are polygons? Explain your reasoning.

3. Process, input/output, manual operation, decision, extract; each figure passes both Test 1 and Test 2.

PROGRAMMING SYMBOLS

process | document | input/output | manual operation | collate
online storage | decision | extract | keying | connecter

4. **CRITICAL THINKING** What is the fewest number of sides a polygon can have? What is the greatest possible number of sides? Explain.

4. Three; there is no greatest number; for each line segment, there must be two others, one to connect at each endpoint. The smallest number of segments for which this is possible is three. There is no limit other than this on the number of sides.

1 Planning the Activity

PURPOSE
To identify polygons.

PACING
- Exploring the Concept — 5 min
- Drawing Conclusions — 10 min

LINK TO LESSON
Describing and identifying polygons is covered in Goal 1 of Lesson 6.1.

2 Managing the Activity

CLASSROOM MANAGEMENT
Have students explain why any of the weather symbols that fails either of the tests does so.

ALTERNATE APPROACH
The pairs of students can draw each of the nine symbols on a separate index card and place the cards face down. Have students take turns turning over the cards. As a card is turned over, the student tells whether or not the symbol is a polygon. If it is not, the student explains why not.

3 Closing the Activity

KEY DISCOVERY
A polygon is a plane figure whose sides are line segments that intersect only at their endpoints. Each segment intersects exactly two other segments.

ACTIVITY ASSESSMENT
Draw three different polygons. Draw three figures that are not polygons. Check students' work.

1 PLAN

PACING
Basic: 2 days
Average: 2 days
Advanced: 2 days
Block Schedule: 0.5 block with Ch. 5 Assess.
0.5 block with 6.2

LESSON OPENER APPLICATION
An alternative way to approach Lesson 6.1 is to use the Application Lesson Opener:
- Blackline Master (*Chapter 6 Resource Book*, p. 12)
- Transparency (p. 34)

MEETING INDIVIDUAL NEEDS
- ***Chapter 6 Resource Book***
  Prerequisite Skills Review (p. 5)
  Practice Level A (p. 14)
  Practice Level B (p. 15)
  Practice Level C (p. 16)
  Reteaching with Practice (p. 17)
  Absent Student Catch-Up (p. 19)
  Challenge (p. 21)
- ***Resources in Spanish***
- ***Personal Student Tutor***

NEW-TEACHER SUPPORT
See the Tips for New Teachers on pp. 1–2 of the *Chapter 6 Resource Book* for additional notes about Lesson 6.1.

WARM-UP EXERCISES
Transparency Available
1. What is the sum of the measures of the interior angles of a triangle? 180°
2. Two angles in a triangle measure 34° and 53°. The third angle measures $3x°$. What is x? 31
3. In which kind of triangle are all three sides congruent? equilateral
4. In which kind of triangle are all three angles congruent? equiangular

6.1 Polygons

What you should learn

GOAL 1 Identify, name, and describe polygons such as the building shapes in **Example 2**.

GOAL 2 Use the sum of the measures of the interior angles of a quadrilateral.

Why you should learn it

▼ To describe **real-life** objects, such as the parachute in **Exs. 21–23**.

CALIFORNIA STANDARDS AND ASSESSMENT
CA Standards: 7, 12, 13
SAT9 Task 1: Obj. 24
SAT9 Task 2: Obj. 27

GOAL 1 DESCRIBING POLYGONS

A **polygon** is a plane figure that meets the following conditions.

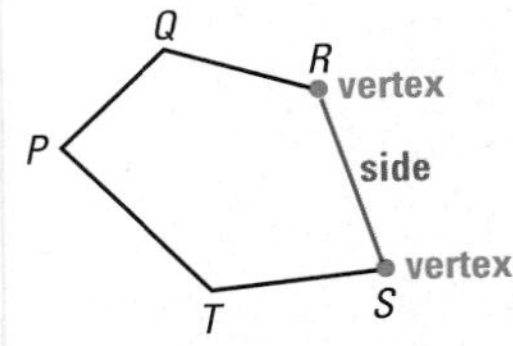

1. It is formed by three or more segments called **sides**, such that no two sides with a common endpoint are collinear.
2. Each side intersects exactly two other sides, one at each endpoint.

Each endpoint of a side is a **vertex** of the polygon. The plural of *vertex* is *vertices*. You can name a polygon by listing its vertices *consecutively*. For instance, *PQRST* and *QPTSR* are two correct names for the polygon above.

EXAMPLE 1 *Identifying Polygons*

State whether the figure is a polygon. If it is not, explain why.

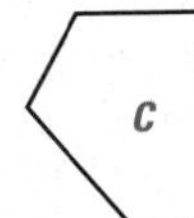

SOLUTION

Figures *A*, *B*, and *C are* polygons.

- Figure *D is not* a polygon because it has a side that is not a segment.
- Figure *E is not* a polygon because two of the sides intersect only one other side.
- Figure *F is not* a polygon because some of its sides intersect more than two other sides.

Polygons are named by the number of sides they have.

STUDENT HELP
Study Tip
To name a polygon not listed in the table, use the number of sides. For example, a polygon with 14 sides is a 14-gon.

Number of sides	Type of polygon
3	Triangle
4	Quadrilateral
5	Pentagon
6	Hexagon
7	Heptagon

Number of sides	Type of polygon
8	Octagon
9	Nonagon
10	Decagon
12	Dodecagon
n	n-gon

A polygon is **convex** if no line that contains a side of the polygon contains a point in the interior of the polygon. A polygon that is not convex is called **nonconvex** or **concave**.

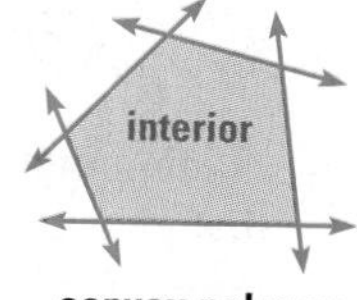

convex polygon

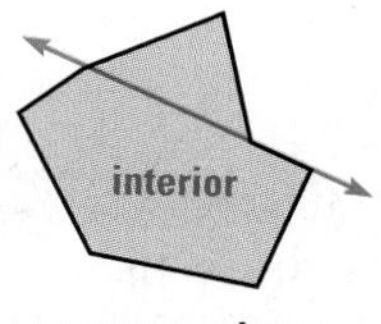

concave polygon

EXAMPLE 2 *Identifying Convex and Concave Polygons*

Identify the polygon and state whether it is convex or concave.

a.

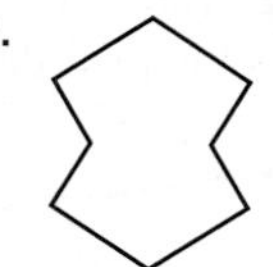

b.

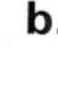

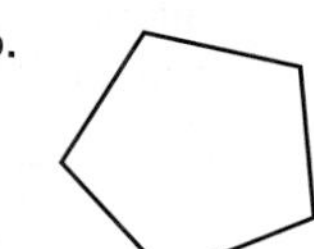

This tile pattern in Iran contains both convex and concave polygons.

SOLUTION

a. The polygon has 8 sides, so it is an octagon. When extended, some of the sides intersect the interior, so the polygon is concave.

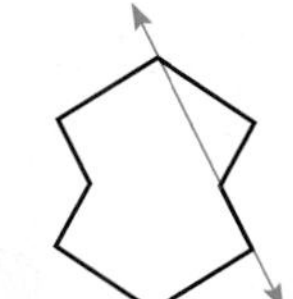

b. The polygon has 5 sides, so it is a pentagon. When extended, none of the sides intersect the interior, so the polygon is convex.

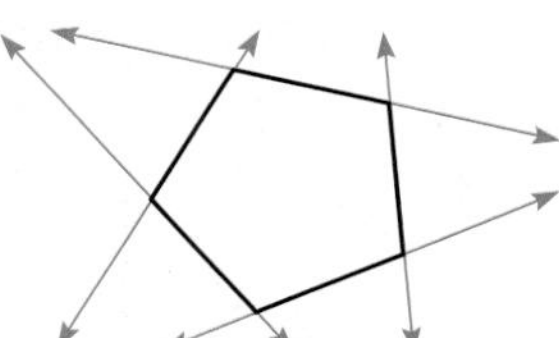

A polygon is **equilateral** if all of its sides are congruent. A polygon is **equiangular** if all of its interior angles are congruent. A polygon is **regular** if it is equilateral and equiangular.

EXAMPLE 3 *Identifying Regular Polygons*

Decide whether the polygon is regular.

a.

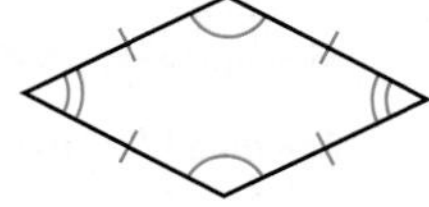

b.

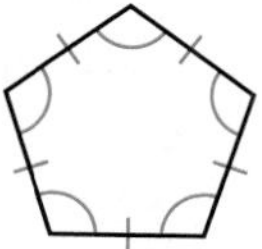

c.

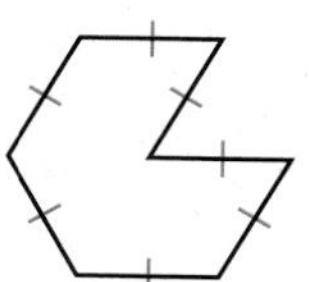

SOLUTION

a. The polygon is an equilateral quadrilateral, but not equiangular. So, it is not a regular polygon.

b. This pentagon is equilateral and equiangular. So, it is a regular polygon.

c. This heptagon is equilateral, but not equiangular. So, it is not regular.

2 TEACH

MOTIVATING THE LESSON

Ask students what geometric shapes are on any jewelry that they are wearing. Some of the most common of these shapes are *polygons*, which students will explore in this lesson.

EXTRA EXAMPLE 1

Identify the figures that are not polygons. Explain.

B: two sides intersect only one other side; C: the sides intersect more than two other sides, some at nonendpoints.

EXTRA EXAMPLE 2

Identify the polygon and state whether it is convex or concave.

a. **b.**

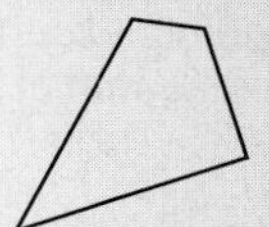

a. convex quadrilateral
b. concave pentagon

EXTRA EXAMPLE 3

Decide whether the polygon is regular.

a.

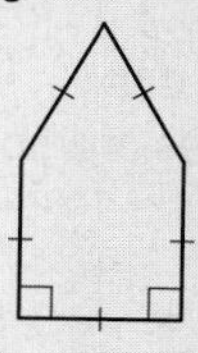

no

b.

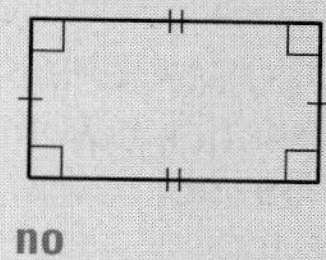

no

CHECKPOINT EXERCISES

For use after Examples 1–3:

1. State whether the figure is a polygon. If it is, state whether it is convex or concave. If it is not a polygon, explain why not.

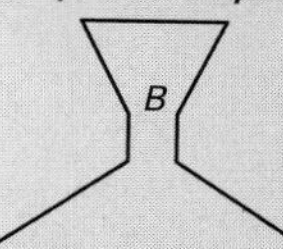

A: not a polygon because some sides are not segments; B: concave octagon

EXTRA EXAMPLE 4

Find $m\angle F$, $m\angle G$, and $m\angle H$.

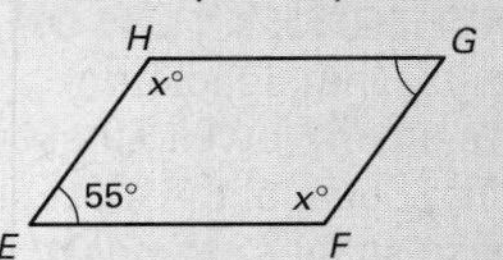

$m\angle F = 125°$, $m\angle G = 55°$, $m\angle H = 125°$

CHECKPOINT EXERCISES

For use after Example 4:

1. Find $m\angle K$, $m\angle L$, and $m\angle M$. Is quadrilateral $JKLM$ regular?

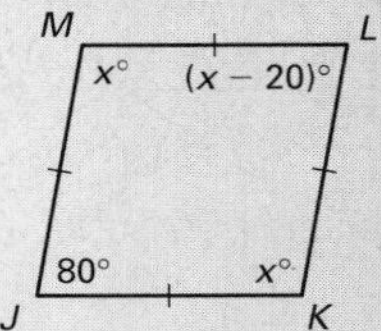

$m\angle K = 100°$, $m\angle L = 80°$, $m\angle M = 100°$; no

MATHEMATICAL REASONING

What is true of all points except the endpoints on a diagonal of a convex polygon? **They lie in the interior of the polygon.**

FOCUS ON VOCABULARY

What word describes a *regular* polygon by its side lengths? By its angle measures? **equilateral; equiangular**

CLOSURE QUESTION

Describe how the sides of a polygon intersect. **Each segment intersects exactly two others, and only at their endpoints.**

DAILY PUZZLER

A polygon has at least a pair each of supplementary angles and complementary angles. Can it be a quadrilateral? Explain or give an example. **a quadrilateral with angles of 140°, 40°, 50°, and 130°**

GOAL 2 INTERIOR ANGLES OF QUADRILATERALS

STUDENT HELP

Study Tip
Two vertices that are endpoints of the same side are called *consecutive vertices.* For example, P and Q are consecutive vertices.

A **diagonal** of a polygon is a segment that joins two *nonconsecutive* vertices. Polygon $PQRST$ has 2 diagonals from point Q, $\overline{QT}$ and $\overline{QS}$.

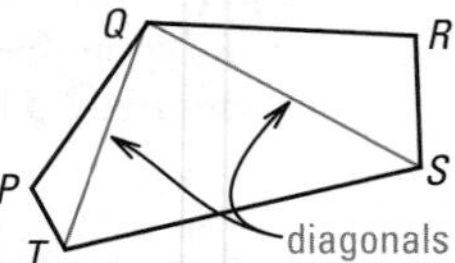

Like triangles, quadrilaterals have both *interior* and *exterior* angles. If you draw a diagonal in a quadrilateral, you divide it into two triangles, each of which has interior angles with measures that add up to 180°. So you can conclude that the sum of the measures of the interior angles of a quadrilateral is 2(180°), or 360°.

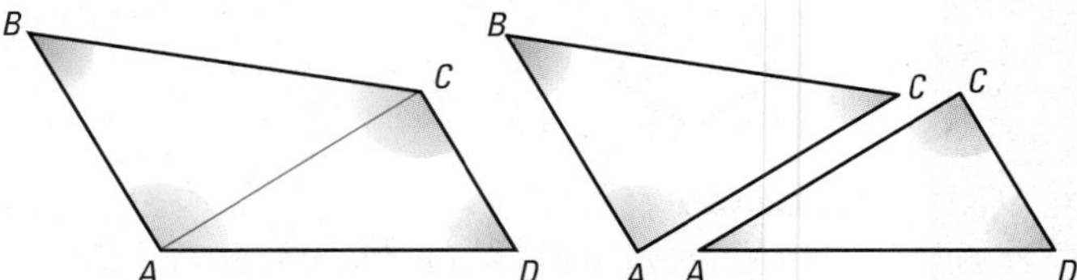

THEOREM

THEOREM 6.1 ***Interior Angles of a Quadrilateral***

The sum of the measures of the interior angles of a quadrilateral is 360°.

$m\angle 1 + m\angle 2 + m\angle 3 + m\angle 4 = 360°$

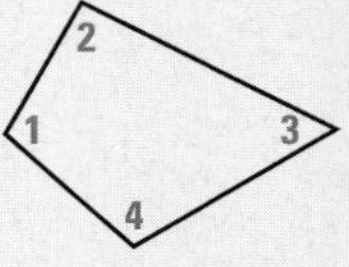

EXAMPLE 4 ***Interior Angles of a Quadrilateral***

Using Algebra

Find $m\angle Q$ and $m\angle R$.

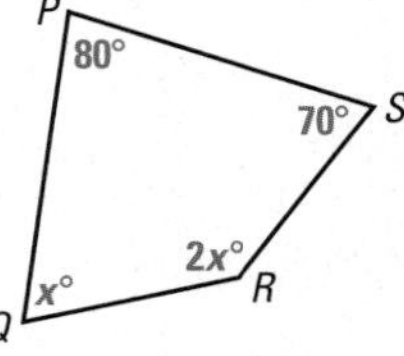

SOLUTION

Find the value of x. Use the sum of the measures of the interior angles to write an equation involving x. Then, solve the equation.

$x° + 2x° + 70° + 80° = 360°$	Sum of measures of int. ∠s of a quad. is 360°.
$3x + 150 = 360$	Combine like terms.
$3x = 210$	Subtract 150 from each side.
$x = 70$	Divide each side by 3.

Find $m\angle Q$ and $m\angle R$.

$m\angle Q = x° = 70°$

$m\angle R = 2x° = 140°$

▶ So, $m\angle Q = 70°$ and $m\angle R = 140°$.

GUIDED PRACTICE

Vocabulary Check ✓

1. What is the plural of *vertex*? vertices

2. What do you call a polygon with 8 sides? a polygon with 15 sides? octagon; 15-gon

Concept Check ✓

3. Suppose you could tie a string tightly around a convex polygon. Would the length of the string be equal to the perimeter of the polygon? What if the polygon were concave? Explain. See margin.

Skill Check ✓

3. Yes; no; if the polygon were convex, the string would wrap exactly around the polygon with no gaps. If the polygon were concave, there would be gaps and the length of the string would be less than the perimeter of the polygon.

6. Not a polygon; two sides intersect only one other side.

Decide whether the figure is a polygon. If it is not, explain why.

4. 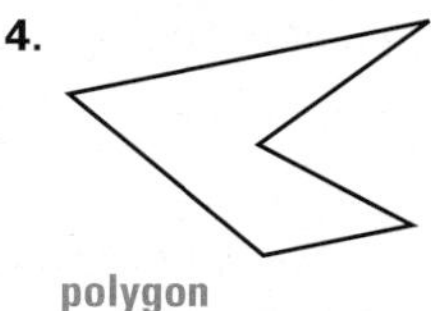
polygon

5. 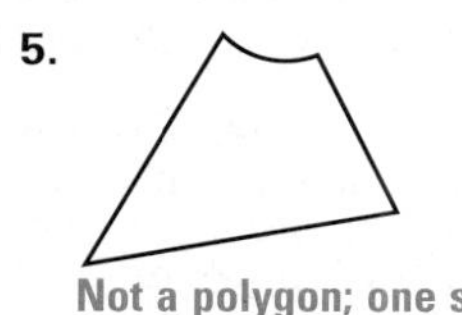
Not a polygon; one side is not a segment.

6. 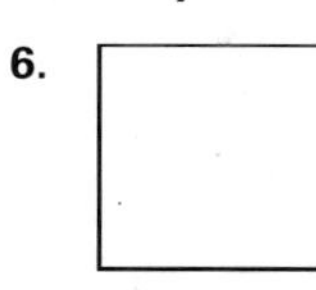
See margin.

Tell whether the polygon is best described as *equiangular, equilateral, regular,* or *none of these.*

7. 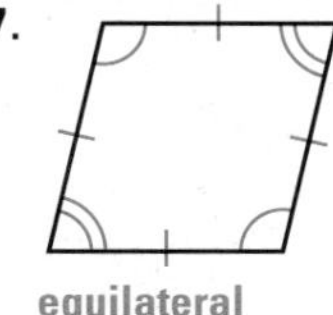
equilateral

8. 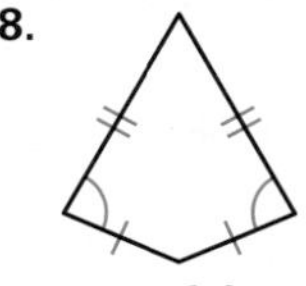
none of these

9. 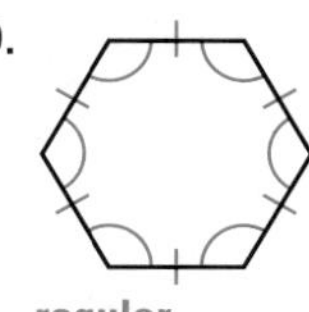
regular

Use the information in the diagram to find $m\angle A$.

10. 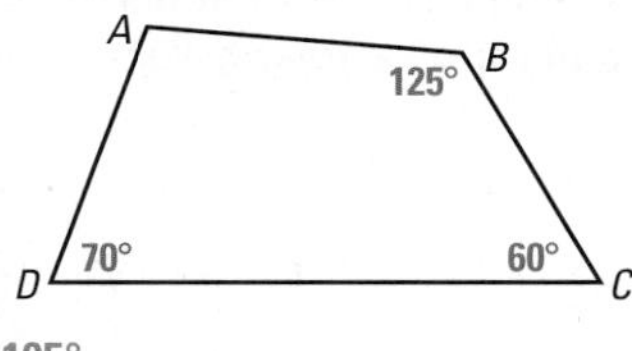

105°

11. 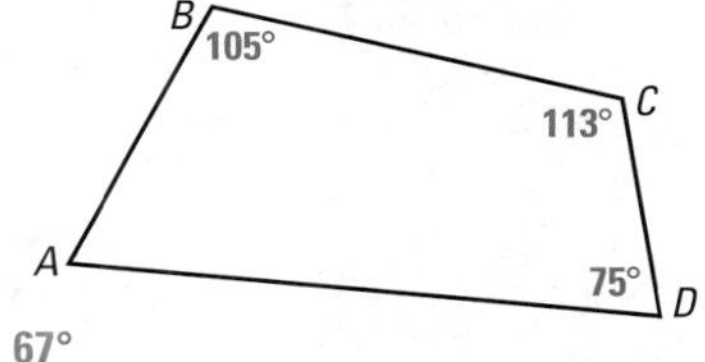

67°

PRACTICE AND APPLICATIONS

STUDENT HELP

Extra Practice to help you master skills is on p. 813.

RECOGNIZING POLYGONS **Decide whether the figure is a polygon.**

12. 
polygon

13. 
not a polygon

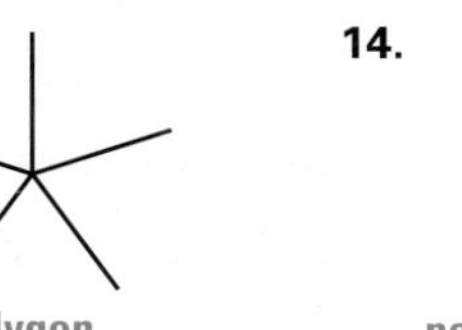

14. 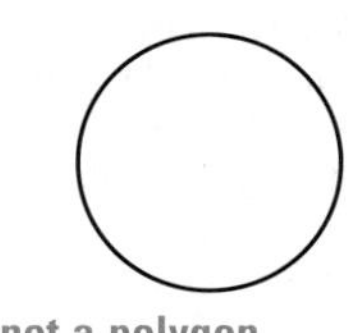
not a polygon

15. 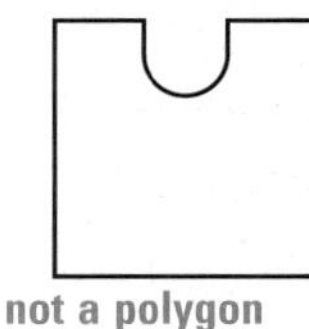
not a polygon

16. 
polygon

17. 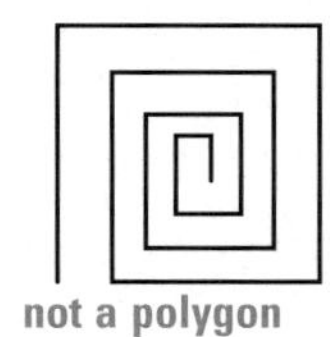
not a polygon

3 APPLY

ASSIGNMENT GUIDE

BASIC

Day 1: pp. 325–328 Exs. 12–20 even, 21–23, 24–38 even, 42–52 even

Day 2: pp. 325–328 Exs. 13–19 odd, 25–51 odd, 54–64 even

AVERAGE

Day 1: pp. 325–328 Exs. 12–20 even, 21–23, 24–38 even, 42–52 even

Day 2: pp. 325–328 Exs. 13–19 odd, 25–51 odd, 54–64 even

ADVANCED

Day 1: pp. 325–328 Exs. 12–20 even, 21–23, 24–38 even, 42–52 even

Day 2: pp. 325–328 Exs. 13–19 odd, 25–53 odd, 54–64 even

BLOCK SCHEDULE

pp. 325–328 Exs. 12–20 even, 21–23, 24–38 even, 42–52 even (with Ch. 5 Assess.)
pp. 325–328 Exs. 13–19 odd, 25–51 odd, 54–64 even (with 6.2)

EXERCISE LEVELS

Level A: *Easier*
12–20, 24–30, 54, 55

Level B: *More Difficult*
21–23, 31–52, 56–64

Level C: *Most Difficult*
53

✓ HOMEWORK CHECK

To quickly check student understanding of key concepts, go over the following exercises: Exs. 15, 20, 24, 34, 38, 42, 48. See also the Daily Homework Quiz:

- Blackline Master (*Chapter 6 Resource Book,* p. 24)
- Transparency (p. 41)

APPLICATION NOTE

EXERCISES 27–30 Students will notice that two of the signs are pictorial and two contain words. Pictorial signs can be universally understood. Where words are required, the color and shape of the sign can be universally understood. A red octagon with the words STOP or ARRÊT is understandable by both English and French speaking drivers.

TEACHING TIPS

EXERCISES 33–34 Students may not be sure how to approach finding the required figure. If they first draw a figure that meets the positive requirement (equilateral/equiangular), they can then adjust the figure so that it meets the negative requirement.

31–34. Sample figures are given.

31.

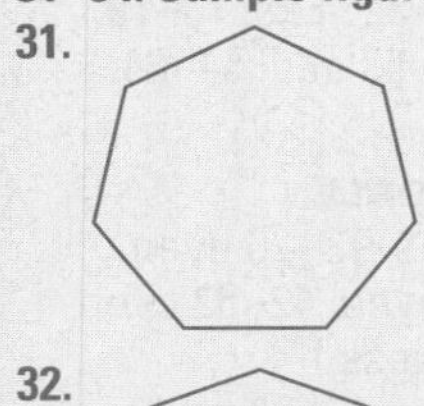

32.

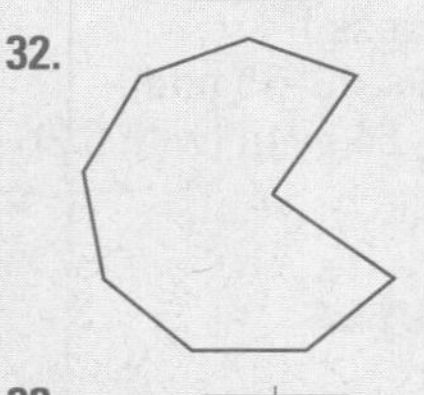

33.

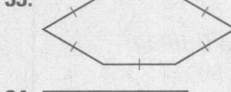

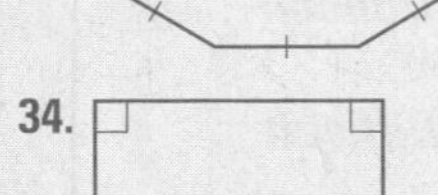

34.

STUDENT HELP

HOMEWORK HELP

Example 1: Exs. 12–17, 48–51
Example 2: Exs. 18–20, 48–51
Example 3: Exs. 24–30, 48–51
Example 4: Exs. 36–46

35. Yes; *Sample answer:* A polygon that is concave must include an ∠ with measure greater than 180°. By the Triangle Sum Theorem, every △ must be convex.

FOCUS ON APPLICATIONS

ROAD SIGNS The shape of a sign tells what it is for. For example, triangular signs like the one above are used internationally as warning signs.

36. 90°; the 4 ∠s have the same measure, say x°; since the sum of the measures of the interior ∠s of a quad. is 360°, $4x = 360$ and $x = 90$.

CONVEX OR CONCAVE **Use the number of sides to tell what kind of polygon the shape is. Then state whether the polygon is *convex* or *concave*.**

18.

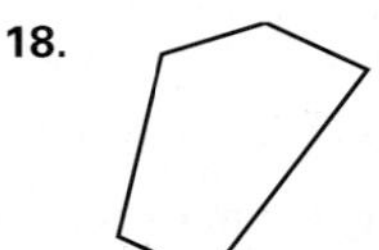

pentagon; convex

19.

heptagon; concave

20.

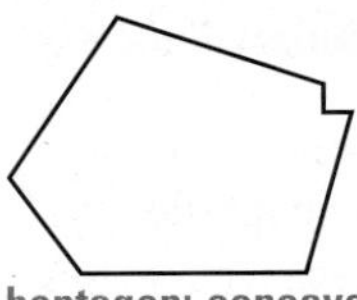

heptagon; concave

PARACHUTES **Some gym classes use parachutes that look like the polygon at the right.**

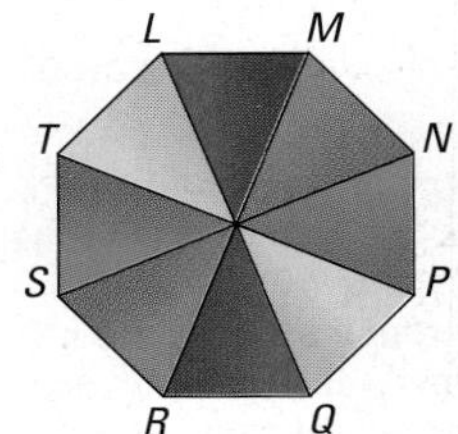

21. Is the polygon a *heptagon*, *octagon*, or *nonagon*? octagon

22. Polygon *LMNPQRST* is one name for the polygon. State two other names.
Sample answers: QPNMLTSR, LTSRQPNM

23. Name all of the diagonals that have vertex *M* as an endpoint. Not all of the diagonals are shown.
$\overline{MP}$, $\overline{MQ}$, $\overline{MR}$, $\overline{MS}$, $\overline{MT}$

RECOGNIZING PROPERTIES **State whether the polygon is best described as *equilateral, equiangular, regular,* or *none of these*.**

24.

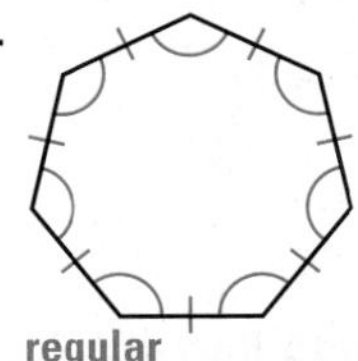

regular

25.

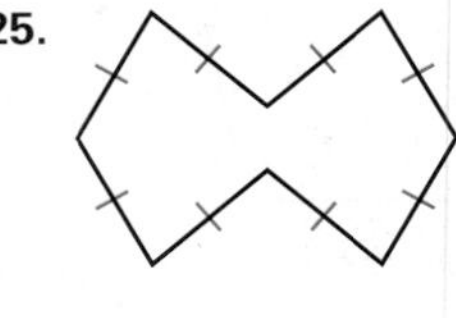

equilateral

26.

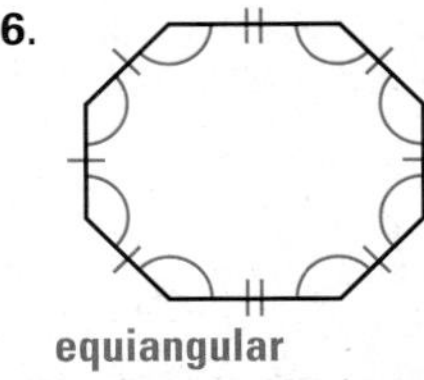

equiangular

TRAFFIC SIGNS **Use the number of sides of the traffic sign to tell what kind of polygon it is. Is it *equilateral, equiangular, regular,* or *none of these*?**

27.

quadrilateral; regular

28.

pentagon; none of these

29.

triangle; regular

30.

octagon; regular

DRAWING **Draw a figure that fits the description.** 31–34. See margin.

31. A convex heptagon

32. A concave nonagon

33. An equilateral hexagon that is not equiangular

34. An equiangular polygon that is not equilateral

35. **LOGICAL REASONING** Is every triangle convex? Explain your reasoning. See margin.

36. **LOGICAL REASONING** Quadrilateral *ABCD* is regular. What is the measure of ∠*ABC*? How do you know?

ANGLE MEASURES **Use the information in the diagram to find $m\angle A$.**

37. 75°

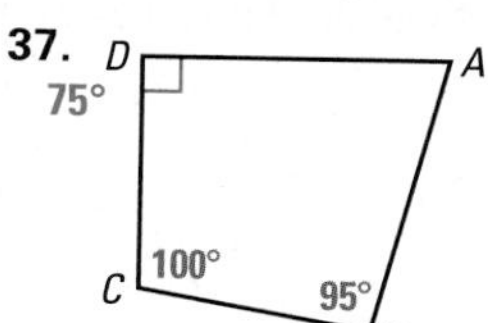

38. 71°

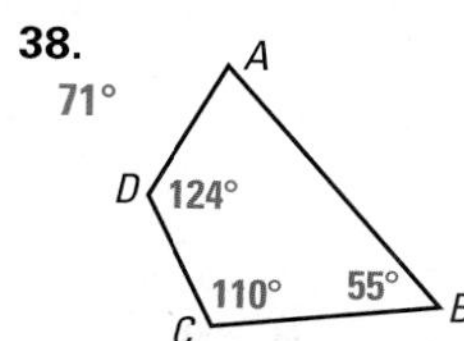

39. 125°

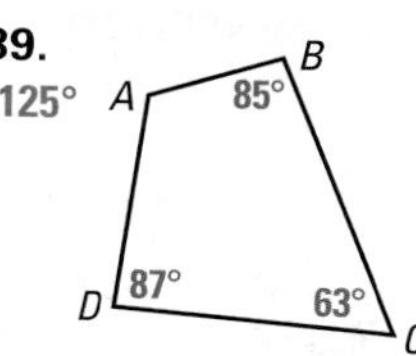

40. TECHNOLOGY Use geometry software to draw a quadrilateral. Measure each interior angle and calculate the sum. What happens to the sum as you drag the vertices of the quadrilateral? The sum is always 360°.

USING ALGEBRA **Use the information in the diagram to solve for x.**

41. 67

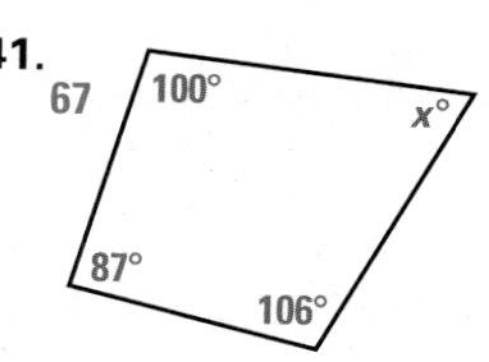

42. 20

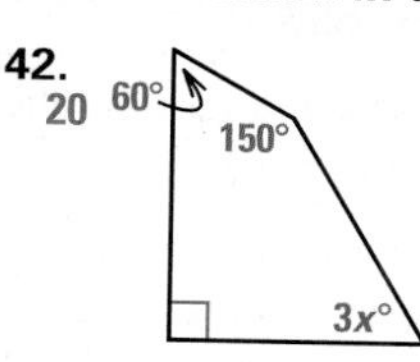

43. 44

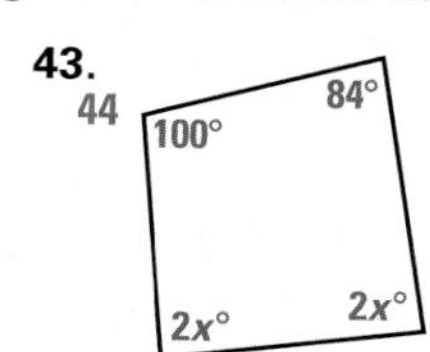

44. 25

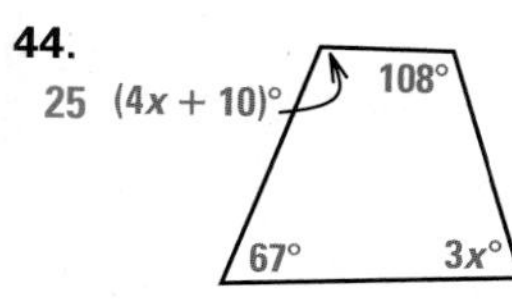

45. 4

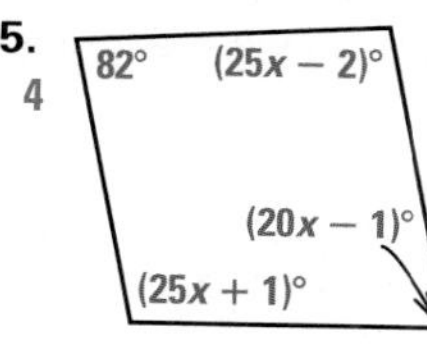

46. −9, 9

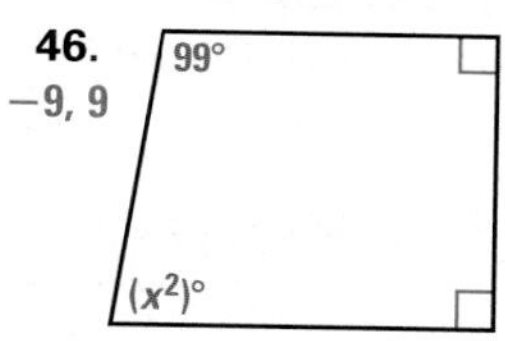

47. LANGUAGE CONNECTION A ***decagon*** has ten sides and a ***deca**de* has ten years. The prefix *deca-* comes from Greek. It means *ten*. What does the prefix *tri-* mean? List four words that use *tri-* and explain what they mean.

PLANT SHAPES **In Exercises 48–51, use the following information.** Cross sections of seeds and fruits often resemble polygons. Next to each cross section is the polygon it resembles. Describe each polygon. Tell what kind of polygon it is, whether it is *concave* or *convex*, and whether it appears to be *equilateral*, *equiangular*, *regular*, or *none of these*. ▶ Source: The History and Folklore of N. American Wildflowers

48. Virginia Snakeroot
hexagon; convex; regular

49. Caraway
octagon; concave, equilateral

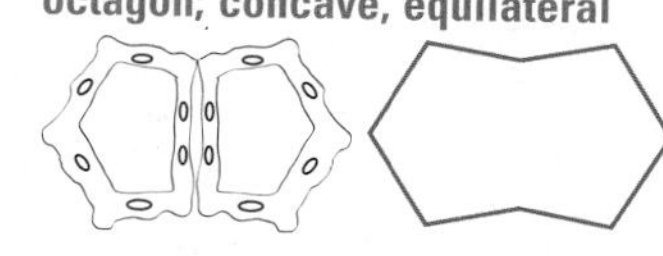

50. Fennel
pentagon; convex; none of these

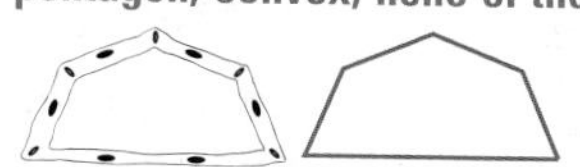

51. Poison Hemlock
17-gon; concave; none of these

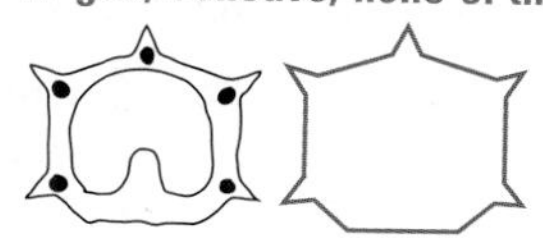

STUDENT HELP

INTERNET SOFTWARE HELP
Visit our Web site www.mcdougallittell.com to see instructions for several software applications.

47. three; *Sample answers:* triangle (a polygon with three sides), trilateral (having three sides) tricycle (a vehicle with three wheels), trio (a group of three)

FOCUS ON APPLICATIONS

REAL LIFE **CARAMBOLA,** or star fruit, has a cross section shaped like a 5 pointed star. The fruit comes from an evergreen tree whose leaflets may fold at night or when the tree is shaken.

STUDENT HELP NOTES

Software Help Instructions for several software packages are available in **blackline** format in the *Chapter 6 Resource Book*, p. 13 and at **www.mcdougallittell.com.**

APPLICATION NOTE

EXERCISE 47 Though the month of December includes the prefix *dec-*, it is, of course, not the tenth month of our calendar year. When the original Roman calendar was adopted, it included only ten months, beginning with March and ending with December. January and February were added to the calendar later.

ADDITIONAL PRACTICE AND RETEACHING

For Lesson 6.1:

- Practice Levels A, B, and C (*Chapter 6 Resource Book*, p. 14)
- Reteaching with Practice (*Chapter 6 Resource Book*, p. 17)
- See Lesson 6.1 of the *Personal Student Tutor*

For more Mixed Review:

- Search the *Test and Practice Generator* for key words or specific lessons.

4 ASSESS

DAILY HOMEWORK QUIZ

Transparency Available

1. Use the number of sides to identify the polygon. Is it *convex* or *concave*?

nonagon; concave

2. Draw an equilateral quadrilateral that is not regular. Students' drawings should show a rhombus.

3. Use the information in the diagram to find $m\angle N$.

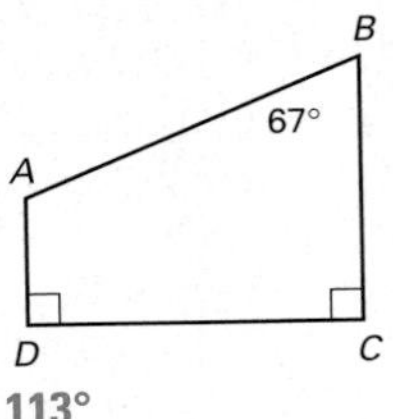

113°

4. Use the information in the diagram to solve for *x*.

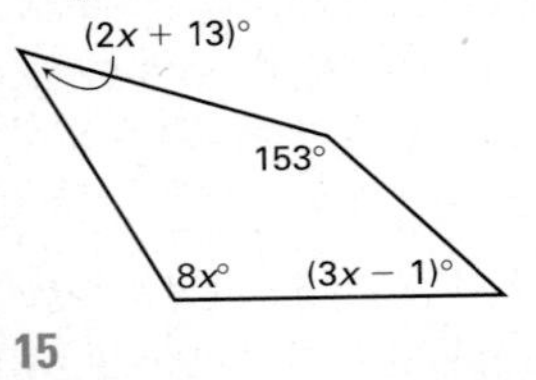

15

EXTRA CHALLENGE NOTE

Challenge problems for Lesson 6.1 are available in **blackline** format in the *Chapter 6 Resource Book*, p. 21 and at **www.mcdougallittell.com.**

ADDITIONAL TEST PREPARATION

1. OPEN ENDED Describe how you can use a circle to draw a regular octagon.
See sample answer at right.

53. See Additional Answers beginning on page AA1.

Test Preparation 

52. MULTI-STEP PROBLEM Envelope manufacturers fold a specially-shaped piece of paper to make an envelope, as shown below.

1 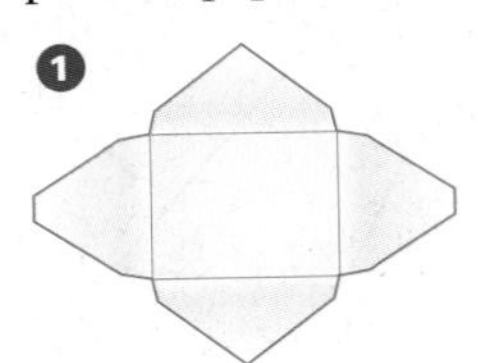 2 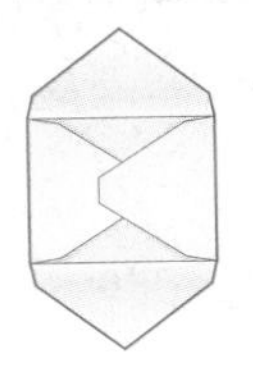 3 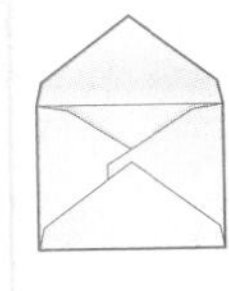 4 

a. What type of polygon is formed by the outside edges of the paper before it is folded? Is the polygon convex? 18-gon; no

b. Tell what type of polygon is formed at each step. Which of the polygons are convex?
18-gon (concave); decagon (convex); heptagon (convex); quad. (convex)

c. *Writing* Explain the reason for the V-shaped notches that are at the ends of the folds.
The notches allow the paper to be folded into right or straight ∠s without overlapping the paper.

★ Challenge

53. FINDING VARIABLES Find the values of *x* and *y* in the diagram at the right. Check your answer. Then copy the shape and write the measure of each angle on your diagram. $x = 15$, $y = 45$; *See margin for diagram.*

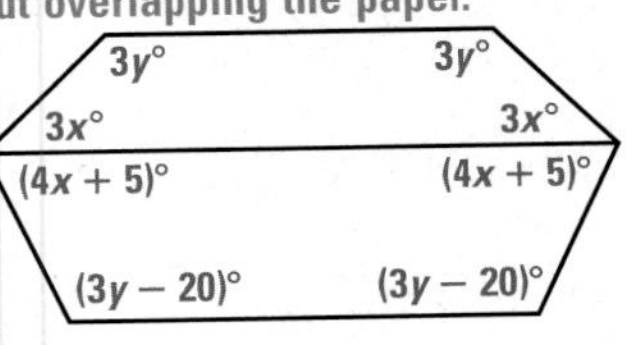

EXTRA CHALLENGE
www.mcdougallittell.com

MIXED REVIEW

PARALLEL LINES In the diagram, $j \parallel k$. Find the value of *x*. (Review 3.3 for 6.2)

54. 120

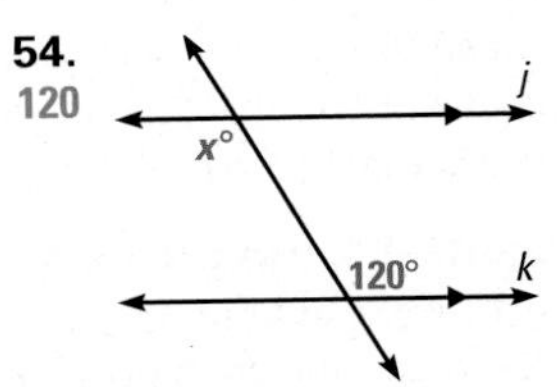

55. 63

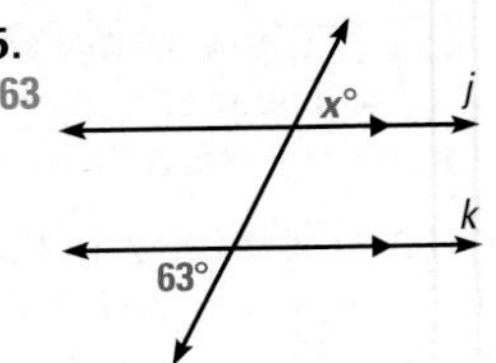

56. 60

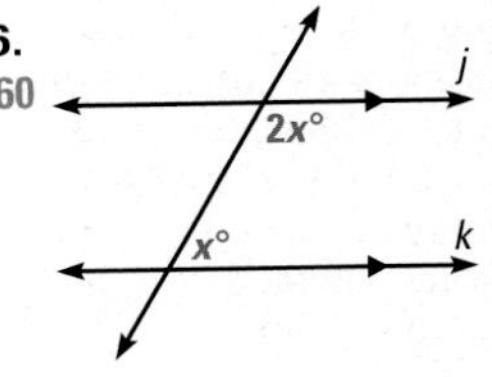

57. 6

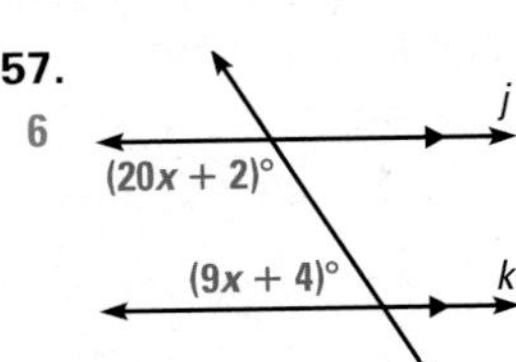

58. 90

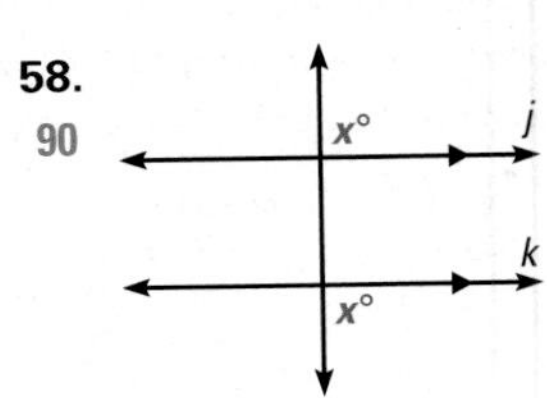

59. 5

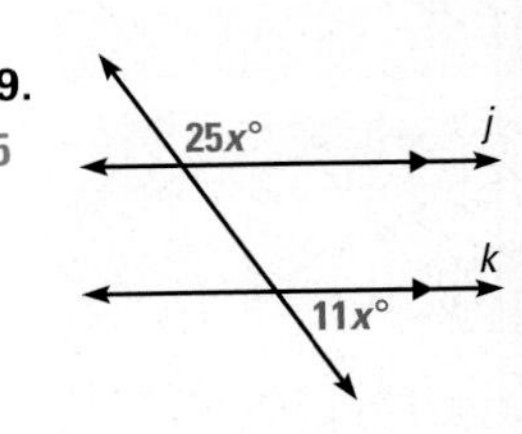

COORDINATE GEOMETRY You are given the midpoints of the sides of a triangle. Find the coordinates of the vertices of the triangle. (Review 5.4)

60. $L(-3, 7)$, $M(-5, 1)$, $N(-8, 8)$
(0, 0), (−10, 2), (−6, 14)

61. $L(-4, -1)$, $M(3, 6)$, $N(-2, -8)$
(1, 13), (5, −1), (−9, −15)

62. $L(2, 4)$, $M(-1, 2)$, $N(0, 7)$
(−3, 5), (3, 9), (1, −1)

63. $L(-1, 3)$, $M(6, 7)$, $N(3, -5)$
(2, 15), (−4, −9), (10, −1)

64.  **USING ALGEBRA** Use the Distance Formula to find the lengths of the diagonals of a polygon with vertices $A(0, 3)$, $B(3, 3)$, $C(4, 1)$, $D(0, -1)$, and $E(-2, 1)$. (Review 1.3) $AC = 2\sqrt{5}$, $AD = 4$, $BD = 5$, $BE = \sqrt{29}$, $CE = 6$

Additional Test Preparation *Sample answer:*
1. Mark the four compass points on a circle. Then mark the four points on the circle halfway between these points. Connect the points to form an octagon.

ACTIVITY 6.2

Using Technology

Geometry Software Activity for use with Lesson 6.2

Investigating Parallelograms

You can use geometry software to explore the properties of parallelograms. A parallelogram is a quadrilateral with both pairs of opposite sides parallel.

STUDENT HELP

SOFTWARE HELP

Visit our Web site www.mcdougallittell.com to see instructions for several software applications.

▶ CONSTRUCT Construct a parallelogram. Steps 1–5. Check constructions

1. To construct a parallelogram, draw a segment and label it $\overline{AB}$. From point A, draw another segment. Label it $\overline{AC}$.
2. Construct a line through B parallel to $\overline{AC}$.
3. Construct a line through C parallel to $\overline{AB}$.
4. Mark the intersection of these two lines F and hide the lines.
5. Draw $\overline{BF}$ and $\overline{CF}$ to form parallelogram $ABFC$.

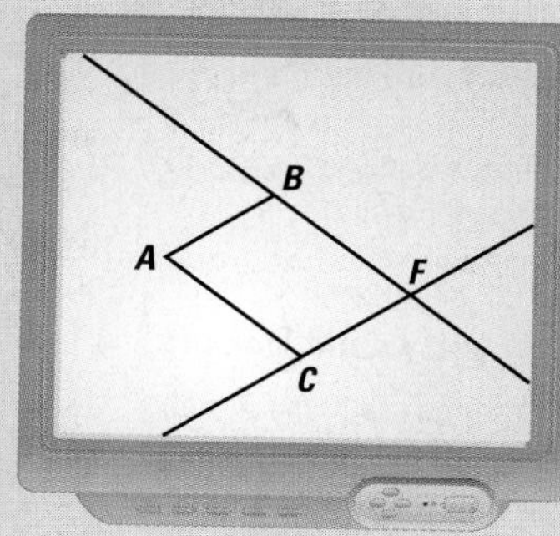

▶ INVESTIGATE

1. Drag points A, B, and C one at a time and notice how $ABFC$ changes. Is $ABFC$ always a parallelogram? How do you know? yes; $\overline{AB} \parallel \overline{CF}$, $\overline{AC} \parallel \overline{BF}$
2. Measure $\overline{AB}$, $\overline{BF}$, $\overline{CF}$, and $\overline{AC}$. What do you notice? $\overline{AB} \cong \overline{CF}$, $\overline{AC} \cong \overline{BF}$
3. Drag points A, B, and C one at a time, continuing to compare the side lengths. What do you notice? It is always true that $\overline{AB} \cong \overline{CF}$ and $\overline{AC} \cong \overline{BF}$.

▶ MAKE A CONJECTURE

4. Make a conjecture about the sides of a parallelogram. Opp. sides of a ▱ are ≅.

▶ INVESTIGATE

5. Measure $\angle A$, $\angle B$, $\angle C$, and $\angle F$. Drag points A, B, and C one at a time while comparing the angle measures. What do you notice? $\angle A \cong \angle F$, $\angle B \cong \angle C$

▶ MAKE A CONJECTURE

6. Make a conjecture about opposite angles of a parallelogram. Opp. ∠s of a ▱ are ≅.

EXTENSION

CRITICAL THINKING Draw the diagonals of parallelogram $ABFC$. Measure the distance from the intersection of the diagonals to each vertex of the parallelogram. Make and test a conjecture. The diags. of a ▱ bisect each other.

1 Planning the Activity

PURPOSE
To investigate the properties of parallelograms using geometry software.

MATERIALS
- Software Help (*Chapter 6 Resource Book,* p. 26)

PACING
- Activity — 25 min

▶ LINK TO LESSON
This investigation demonstrates Theorems 6.2–6.4 from Lesson 6.2.

2 Managing the Activity

CLASSROOM MANAGEMENT
If students work in groups, ask them to have one member record their observations. Have students repeat the investigation with a different parallelogram and compare the results to the recorded results.

ALTERNATE APPROACH
If geometry software is not available, students can draw a parallelogram on graph paper, using grid points to place the sides. They can then "drag" points one at a time while preserving parallel sides and use dashed lines to mark the results.

3 Closing the Activity

★ **KEY DISCOVERY**
Opposite sides of a parallelogram are congruent. Opposite angles of a parallelogram are congruent.

ACTIVITY ASSESSMENT
In parallelogram $WXYZ$, $WX = 15$. What is the measure of $\overline{YZ}$? If $XY = 12$, what is the measure of $\overline{WZ}$? Name two pairs of congruent angles. 15; 12; $\angle W$ and $\angle Y$; $\angle X$ and $\angle Z$

1 PLAN

PACING
Basic: 2 days
Average: 2 days
Advanced: 2 days
Block Schedule: 0.5 block with 6.1
0.5 block with 6.3

LESSON OPENER ACTIVITY
An alternative way to approach Lesson 6.2 is to use the Activity Lesson Opener:
- Blackline Master (*Chapter 6 Resource Book,* p. 25)
- Transparency (p. 35)

MEETING INDIVIDUAL NEEDS
- ***Chapter 6 Resource Book***
  Prerequisite Skills Review (p. 5)
  Practice Level A (p. 28)
  Practice Level B (p. 29)
  Practice Level C (p. 30)
  Reteaching with Practice (p. 31)
  Absent Student Catch-Up (p. 33)
  Challenge (p. 35)
- ***Resources in Spanish***
-  ***Personal Student Tutor***

NEW-TEACHER SUPPORT
See the Tips for New Teachers on pp. 1–2 of the *Chapter 6 Resource Book* for additional notes about Lesson 6.2.

WARM-UP EXERCISES
Transparency Available
Which property justifies the statement?
1. If $\angle A \cong \angle B$ and $\angle B \cong \angle C$, then $\angle A \cong \angle C$.
   Transitive Prop. of Cong.
2. If $\angle M \cong \angle N$, then $\angle N \cong \angle M$.
   Symmetric Prop. of Cong.
3. If $m\angle 1 = 80°$, and $m\angle 1 = m\angle 2$, then $m\angle 2 = 80°$.
   substitution prop. of equality

6.2 Properties of Parallelograms

What you should learn

GOAL 1 Use some properties of parallelograms.

GOAL 2 Use properties of parallelograms in **real-life** situations, such as the drafting table shown in **Example 6**.

Why you should learn it

▼ You can use properties of parallelograms to understand how a scissors lift works in **Exs. 51–54**. REAL LIFE

CALIFORNIA STANDARDS AND ASSESSMENT
CA Standards: 4, 7, 12, 13, 16, 17

GOAL 1 PROPERTIES OF PARALLELOGRAMS

In this lesson and in the rest of the chapter you will study special quadrilaterals. A **parallelogram** is a quadrilateral with both pairs of opposite sides parallel.

When you mark diagrams of quadrilaterals, use matching arrowheads to indicate which sides are parallel. For example, in the diagram at the right, $\overline{PQ} \parallel \overline{RS}$ and $\overline{QR} \parallel \overline{SP}$. The symbol $\square PQRS$ is read "parallelogram $PQRS$."

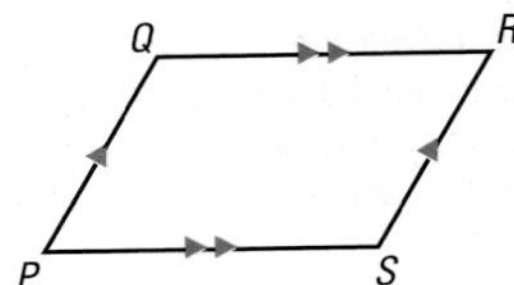

THEOREMS ABOUT PARALLELOGRAMS

THEOREM 6.2
If a quadrilateral is a parallelogram, then its **opposite sides** are congruent.
$\overline{PQ} \cong \overline{RS}$ and $\overline{SP} \cong \overline{QR}$

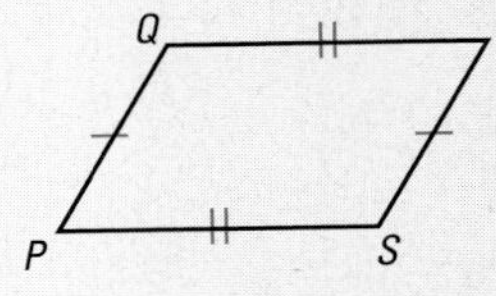

THEOREM 6.3
If a quadrilateral is a parallelogram, then its **opposite angles** are congruent.
$\angle P \cong \angle R$ and $\angle Q \cong \angle S$

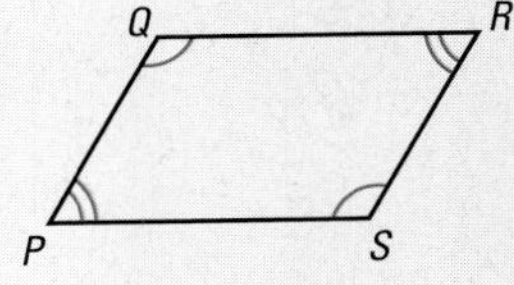

THEOREM 6.4
If a quadrilateral is a parallelogram, then its **consecutive angles** are supplementary.
$m\angle P + m\angle Q = 180°$, $m\angle Q + m\angle R = 180°$,
$m\angle R + m\angle S = 180°$, $m\angle S + m\angle P = 180°$

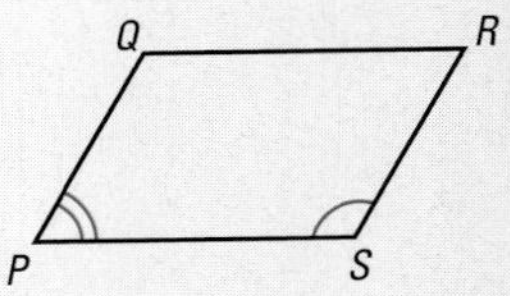

THEOREM 6.5
If a quadrilateral is a parallelogram, then its diagonals bisect each other.
$\overline{QM} \cong \overline{SM}$ and $\overline{PM} \cong \overline{RM}$

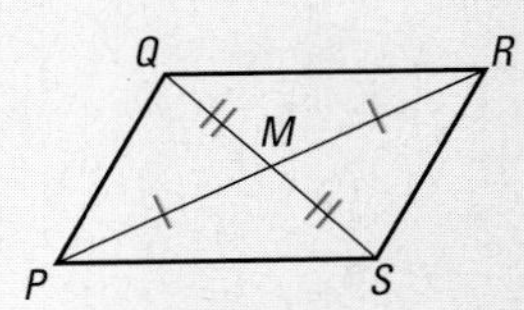

Theorem 6.2 is proved in Example 5. You are asked to prove Theorem 6.3, Theorem 6.4, and Theorem 6.5 in Exercises 38–44.

EXAMPLE 1 Using Properties of Parallelograms

FGHJ is a parallelogram. Find the unknown length. Explain your reasoning.

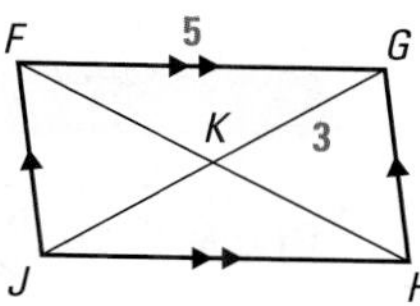

a. *JH*

b. *JK*

SOLUTION

a. $JH = FG$ — Opposite sides of a ▱ are ≅.

$JH = 5$ — Substitute 5 for *FG*.

b. $JK = GK$ — Diagonals of a ▱ bisect each other.

$JK = 3$ — Substitute 3 for *GK*.

EXAMPLE 2 Using Properties of Parallelograms

PQRS is a parallelogram. Find the angle measure.

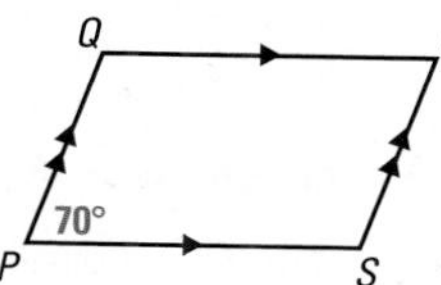

a. $m\angle R$

b. $m\angle Q$

SOLUTION

a. $m\angle R = m\angle P$ — Opposite angles of a ▱ are ≅.

$m\angle R = 70°$ — Substitute 70° for $m\angle P$.

b. $m\angle Q + m\angle P = 180°$ — Consecutive ∠s of a ▱ are supplementary.

$m\angle Q + 70° = 180°$ — Substitute 70° for $m\angle P$.

$m\angle Q = 110°$ — Subtract 70° from each side.

EXAMPLE 3 Using Algebra with Parallelograms

PQRS is a parallelogram. Find the value of *x*.

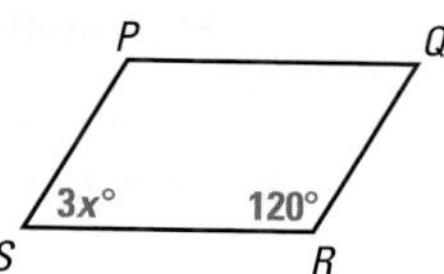

SOLUTION

$m\angle S + m\angle R = 180°$ — Consecutive angles of a ▱ are supplementary.

$3x + 120 = 180$ — Substitute $3x$ for $m\angle S$ and 120 for $m\angle R$.

$3x = 60$ — Subtract 120 from each side.

$x = 20$ — Divide each side by 3.

2 TEACH

MOTIVATING THE LESSON

Some school buses employ a *transverse parallelogram suspension,* which uses parallelograms, the topic of this lesson, to position the load directly over the springs. This system is designed to give riders more comfort and the driver more control.

EXTRA EXAMPLE 1

GHJK is a parallelogram. Find the unknown length.

a. *JH* 8 b. *LH* 6

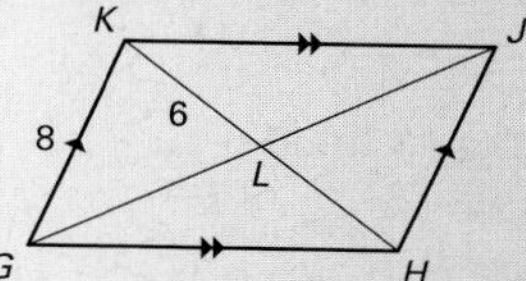

EXTRA EXAMPLE 2

In ▱*ABCD*, $m\angle C = 105°$. Find the angle measure.

a. $m\angle A$ 105° b. $m\angle D$ 75°

EXTRA EXAMPLE 3

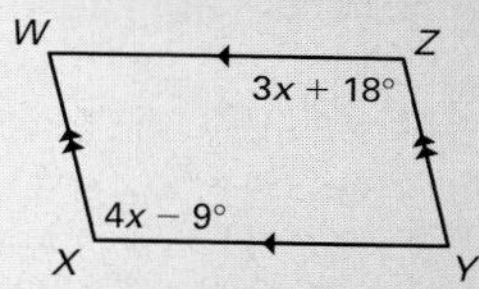

WXYZ is a parallelogram. Find the value of *x*. 27

CHECKPOINT EXERCISES

For use after Examples 1–3:

UVWX is a parallelogram.

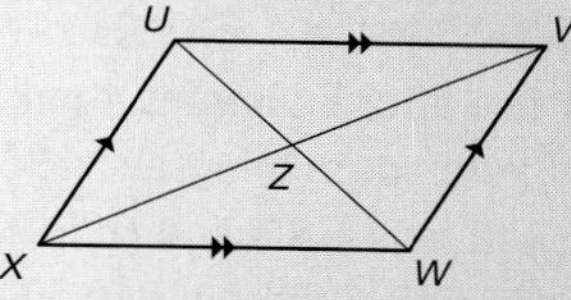

1. If $XU = 15$ and $UW = 28$, find *WZ*. 14
2. If $m\angle VWX = 120°$, find $m\angle WXU$. 60°
3. If $m\angle UVW = 55°$ and $m\angle VWX = 7x - 8$, find *x*. 19

Extra Example 4

Given: $ABCD$ is a ▱.
Prove: $\angle 2 \cong \angle 4$

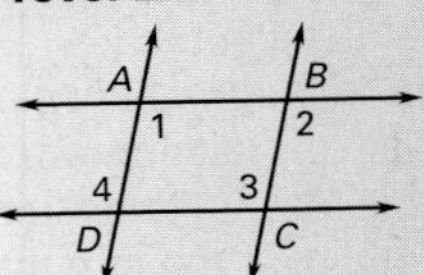

See below.

Extra Example 5

Given: $ACDF$ is a ▱.
$ABDE$ is a ▱.
Prove: $\triangle BCD \cong \triangle EFA$

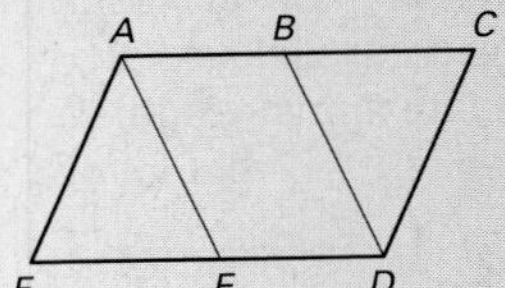

Statements (Reasons)
1. $ACDF$ is a ▱. $ABDE$ is a ▱. (Given)
2. $\overline{AC} \cong \overline{DF}$; $\overline{AB} \cong \overline{DE}$; $\overline{AF} \cong \overline{DC}$; $\overline{AE} \cong \overline{DB}$; (Opp. sides of a ▱ are ≅.)
3. $AC = DF$; $AB = DE$ (Def. of cong.)
4. $AC = AB + BC$; $DF = DE + EF$ (Seg. Addition Post.)
5. $AC = DE + EF$ (Substitution prop. of equality)
6. $AB + BC = DE + EF$ (Transitive prop. of equality)
7. $AB + BC = AB + EF$ (Substitution prop. of equality)
8. $BC = EF$ (Subtraction prop. of equality)
9. $\overline{BC} = \overline{EF}$ (Def. of cong.)
10. $\triangle BCD \cong \triangle EFA$ (SSS Cong. Post.)

Checkpoint Exercises

For use after Examples 4 and 5:

1. Sketch parallelogram $ABCD$ with rays $\overrightarrow{BAE}$ and $\overrightarrow{DCF}$. You can use linear pairs to show that $m\angle EAD + m\angle DAB = m\angle FCB + m\angle DCB$. What postulate or theorem can you then use with the substitution and subtraction properties of equality and the definition of congruence to show that $\angle EAD \cong m\angle FCB$?
Opposite ⦞ of a ▱ are ≅.

GOAL 2 Reasoning About Parallelograms

EXAMPLE 4 *Proving Facts about Parallelograms*

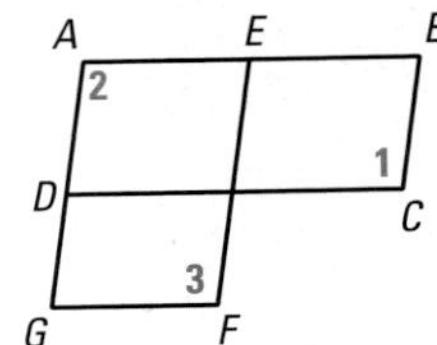

GIVEN ▶ $ABCD$ and $AEFG$ are parallelograms.

PROVE ▶ $\angle 1 \cong \angle 3$

Plan Show that both angles are congruent to $\angle 2$. Then use the Transitive Property of Congruence.

Solution

Method 1 Write a two-column proof.

Statements	Reasons
1. $ABCD$ is a ▱. $AEFG$ is a ▱.	1. Given
2. $\angle 1 \cong \angle 2$, $\angle 2 \cong \angle 3$	2. Opposite angles of a ▱ are ≅.
3. $\angle 1 \cong \angle 3$	3. Transitive Property of Congruence

Method 2 Write a paragraph proof.

$ABCD$ is a parallelogram, so $\angle 1 \cong \angle 2$ because opposite angles of a parallelogram are congruent. $AEFG$ is a parallelogram, so $\angle 2 \cong \angle 3$. By the Transitive Property of Congruence, $\angle 1 \cong \angle 3$.

EXAMPLE 5 *Proving Theorem 6.2*

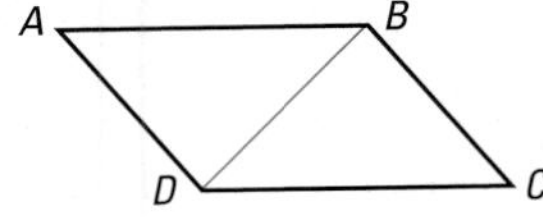

GIVEN ▶ $ABCD$ is a parallelogram.

PROVE ▶ $\overline{AB} \cong \overline{CD}$, $\overline{AD} \cong \overline{CB}$

Solution

Statements	Reasons
1. $ABCD$ is a ▱.	1. Given
2. Draw $\overline{BD}$.	2. Through any two points there exists exactly one line.
3. $\overline{AB} \parallel \overline{CD}$, $\overline{AD} \parallel \overline{CB}$	3. Definition of parallelogram
4. $\angle ABD \cong \angle CDB$, $\angle ADB \cong \angle CBD$	4. Alternate Interior Angles Theorem
5. $\overline{DB} \cong \overline{DB}$	5. Reflexive Property of Congruence
6. $\triangle ADB \cong \triangle CBD$	6. ASA Congruence Postulate
7. $\overline{AB} \cong \overline{CD}$, $\overline{AD} \cong \overline{CB}$	7. Corresponding parts of ≅ ⽰ are ≅.

Extra Example 4:
Statements (Reasons)
1. $ABCD$ is a ▱. (Given)
2. $\overline{AD} \parallel \overline{BC}$ (Def. of ▱)
3. $\angle 2 \cong \angle 1$ (Corresp. ⦞ Post.)
4. $\overline{AB} \parallel \overline{CD}$ (Def. of ▱)
5. $\angle 1 \cong \angle 4$ (Alt. Int. ⦞ Thm.)
6. $\angle 2 \cong \angle 4$ (Transitive Prop. of Cong.)

FOCUS ON CAREERS

FURNITURE DESIGN
Furniture designers use geometry, trigonometry, and other skills to create designs for furniture.

CAREER LINK
www.mcdougallittell.com

EXAMPLE 6 ***Using Parallelograms in Real Life***

FURNITURE DESIGN A drafting table is made so that the legs can be joined in different ways to change the slope of the drawing surface. In the arrangement below, the legs $\overline{AC}$ and $\overline{BD}$ do *not* bisect each other. Is *ABCD* a parallelogram?

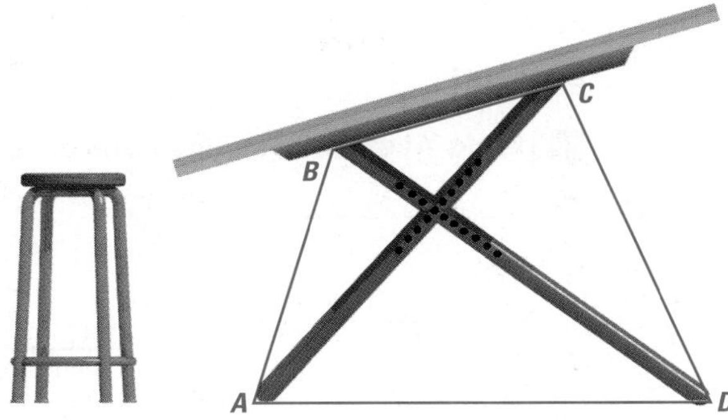

SOLUTION

No. If *ABCD* were a parallelogram, then by Theorem 6.5 $\overline{AC}$ would bisect $\overline{BD}$ and $\overline{BD}$ would bisect $\overline{AC}$.

GUIDED PRACTICE

Vocabulary Check ✓

1. Write a definition of *parallelogram*.
A ▱ is a quad. with both pairs of opp. sides ∥.

Concept Check ✓

Decide whether the figure is a parallelogram. If it is not, explain why not.

2. 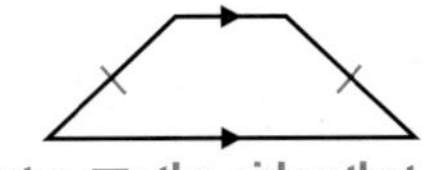
Not a ▱; the sides that are ≅ are not ∥.

3. parallelogram

Skill Check ✓

IDENTIFYING CONGRUENT PARTS Use the diagram of parallelogram *JKLM* at the right. Complete the statement, and give a reason for your answer.

4. $\overline{JK} \cong$ ___?___
$\overline{ML}$; opp. sides of a ▱ are ≅.

5. $\overline{MN} \cong$ ___?___
See margin.

6. $\angle MLK \cong$ ___?___
$\angle KJM$; opp. ∠s of a ▱ are ≅.

7. $\angle JKL \cong$ ___?___
See margin.

8. $\overline{JN} \cong$ ___?___ $\overline{LN}$; diags. of a ▱ bisect each other.

9. $\overline{KL} \cong$ ___?___ $\overline{JM}$; opp. sides of a ▱ are ≅.

10. $\angle MNL \cong$ ___?___
$\angle KNJ$; vertical ∠s are ≅.

11. $\angle MKL \cong$ ___?___
See margin.

Find the measure in parallelogram *LMNQ*. Explain your reasoning.
12–19. See margin.

12. *LM*
13. *LP*
14. *LQ*
15. *QP*
16. *m*∠*LMN*
17. *m*∠*NQL*
18. *m*∠*MNQ*
19. *m*∠*LMQ*

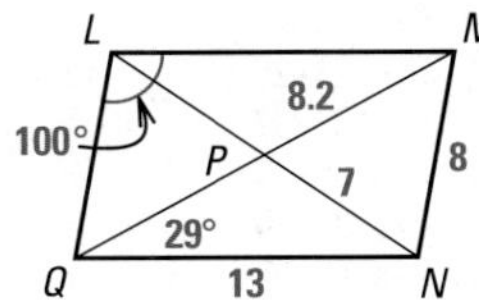

5. $\overline{KN}$; diags. of a ▱ bisect each other.

7. ∠*LMJ*; opp. ∠s of a ▱ are ≅.

11. ∠*KMJ*; if 2 ∥ lines are cut by a transversal, then alt. int. ∠s are ≅.

12. 13; since opp. sides of a ▱ are ≅, *LM* = *QN* = 13.

13. 7; since the diags. of a ▱ bisect each other, *LP* = *NP* = 7.

14. 8; since opp. sides of a ▱ are ≅, *LQ* = *MN* = 8.

15. 8.2; since the diags. of a ▱ bisect each other, *QP* = *MP* = 8.2.

EXTRA EXAMPLE 6
A four-sided concrete slab has consecutive angle measures of 85°, 94°, 85°, and 96°. Is the slab a parallelogram? Explain. No; if it were, then by Theorem 6.3 both pairs of opp. ∠s would be ≅, not just one pair.

CHECKPOINT EXERCISES
For use after Example 6:

1. Each circle in the crystal lattice shown represents a molecule. *ABED* and *BCFE* are parallelograms. *A*, *B*, and *C* are collinear, as are *D*, *E*, and *F*. Must *ACFD* be a parallelogram? Explain.

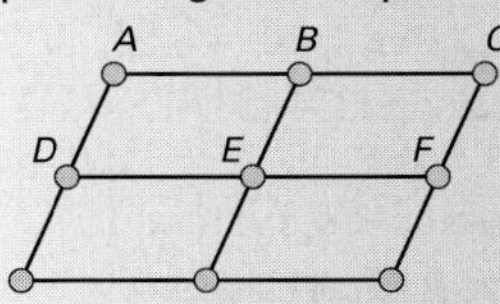

Yes; because $\overline{AB}$ and $\overline{DE}$ are ∥, the collinearity constraints mean $\overline{AC}$ and $\overline{DF}$ are ∥; $\overline{AD}$ and $\overline{CF}$ are ∥ because both are ∥ to $\overline{BE}$.

FOCUS ON VOCABULARY
True or *False*: A parallelogram is any polygon whose opposite sides are parallel. False.

CLOSURE QUESTION
Name five properties of parallelograms. opposite sides ∥; opposite sides ≅; opposite angles ≅; consecutive angles supplementary; diagonals bisect each other

DAILY PUZZLER
ABDE, *BCDG*, and *AGEF* are parallelograms. The product of the diagonals of *ABDE* is 128. Find the perimeter of *AGEF*. 24

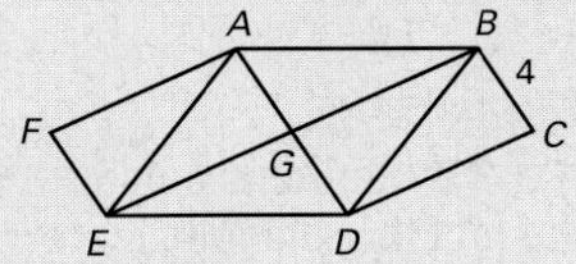

16–19. See Additional Answers beginning on page AA1.

3 APPLY

ASSIGNMENT GUIDE

BASIC

Day 1: pp. 334–336 Exs. 20–38 even, 40–44, 56, 58

Day 2: pp. 334–337 Exs. 21–39 odd, 45–50, 55, 57, 60, 61, 66–74 even

AVERAGE

Day 1: pp. 334–336 Exs. 20–38 even, 40–44, 56, 58

Day 2: pp. 334–337 Exs. 21–39 odd, 45–55, 57, 60, 61, 66–74 even

ADVANCED

Day 1: pp. 334–336 Exs. 20–38 even, 40–44, 56, 58

Day 2: pp. 334–337 Exs. 21–39 odd, 45–55, 57, 60–64, 66–74 even

BLOCK SCHEDULE

pp. 334–336 Exs. 20–38 even, 40–44, 56, 58 (with 6.1)
pp. 334–337 Exs. 21–39 odd, 45–50, 55, 57, 60, 61, 66–74 even (with 6.3)

EXERCISE LEVELS

Level A: ***Easier***
20–31, 68–74

Level B: ***More Difficult***
32–61, 65–67

Level C: ***Most Difficult***
62–64

✔ HOMEWORK CHECK

To quickly check student understanding of key concepts, go over the following exercises: Exs. 24, 28, 34, 37, 42, 46, 56. See also the Daily Homework Quiz:

- Blackline Master (*Chapter 6 Resource Book*, p. 38)
- Transparency (p. 42)

! COMMON ERROR

EXERCISE 33 Students could confuse the fact that diagonals are bisected in a parallelogram with the diagonals being congruent. Tell them that they will soon learn which parallelograms have congruent diagonals.

PRACTICE AND APPLICATIONS

STUDENT HELP

Extra Practice to help you master skills is on p. 813.

20. 10; since the diags. of a ▱ bisect each other, $DE = BE = 10$.

21. 11; since opp. sides of a ▱ are ≅, $BA = CD = 11$.

22. 12; since opp. sides of a ▱ are ≅, $BC = AD = 12$.

23. 60°; since consec. ∠s of a ▱ are supplementary, $m\angle CDA = 180° - m\angle BAD = 60°$.

24. 60°; since consec. ∠s of a ▱ are supplementary, $m\angle ABC = 180° - m\angle BAD = 60°$.

25. 120°; since opp. ∠s of a ▱ are ≅, $m\angle BCD = m\angle BAD = 120°$.

FINDING MEASURES **Find the measure in parallelogram *ABCD*. Explain your reasoning.** 20–25. See margin.

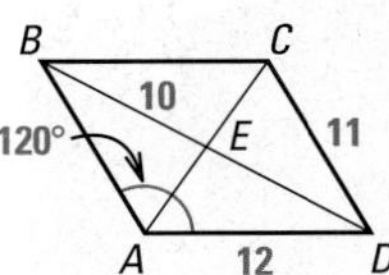

20. DE
21. BA
22. BC
23. $m\angle CDA$
24. $m\angle ABC$
25. $m\angle BCD$

USING ALGEBRA **Find the value of each variable in the parallelogram.**

26.
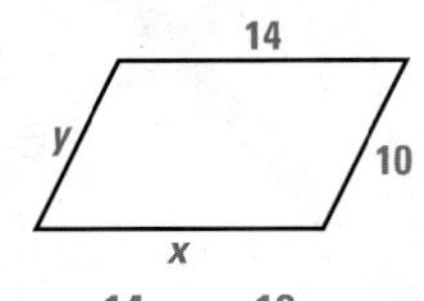

$x = 14, y = 10$

27.
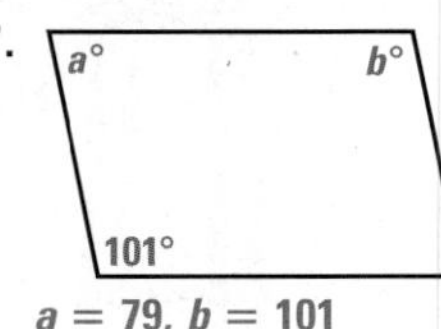

$a = 79, b = 101$

28.
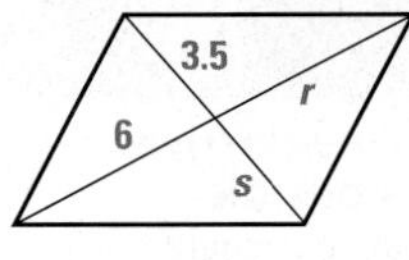

$r = 6, s = 3.5$

29.
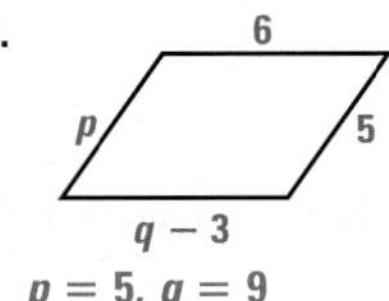

$p = 5, q = 9$

30.
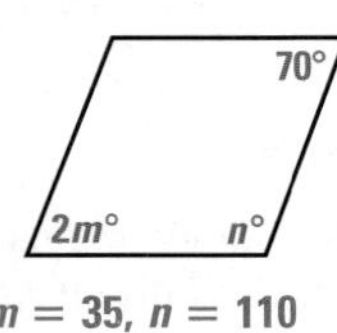

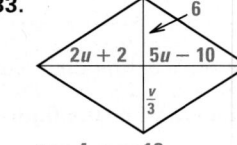

$m = 35, n = 110$

31.
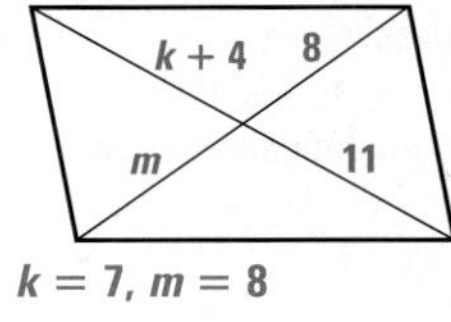

$k = 7, m = 8$

USING ALGEBRA **Find the value of each variable in the parallelogram.**

32.
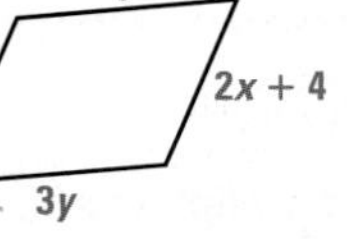

$x = 2, y = 3$

33.

$u = 4, v = 18$

34.
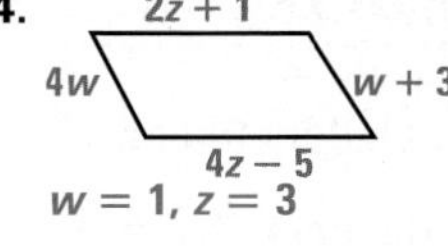

$w = 1, z = 3$

35.
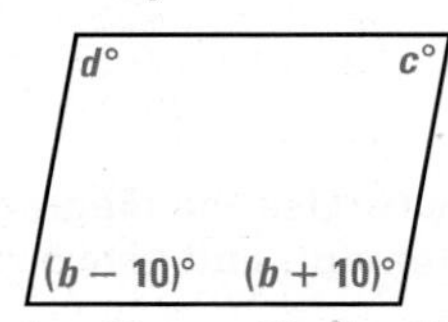

$b = 90, c = 80, d = 100$

36.
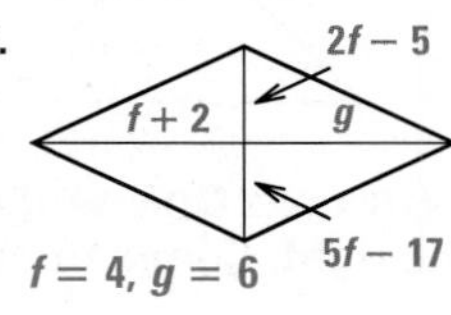

$f = 4, g = 6$

37.
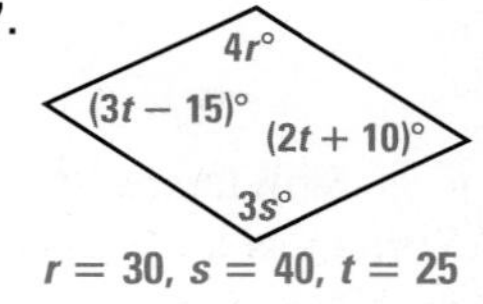

$r = 30, s = 40, t = 25$

38. **PROVING THEOREM 6.3** Copy and complete the proof of Theorem 6.3: If a quadrilateral is a parallelogram, then its opposite angles are congruent. See margin.

GIVEN ▶ $ABCD$ is a ▱.

PROVE ▶ $\angle A \cong \angle C$, $\angle B \cong \angle D$

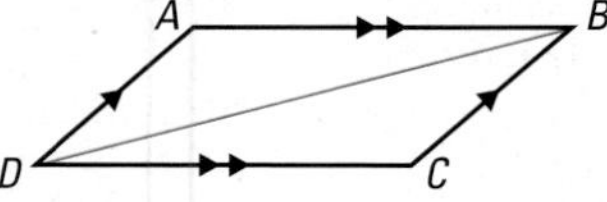

Paragraph Proof Opposite sides of a parallelogram are congruent, so ___**a.**___ and ___**b.**___. By the Reflexive Property of Congruence, ___**c.**___. $\triangle ABD \cong \triangle CDB$ because of the ___**d.**___ Congruence Postulate. Because ___**e.**___ parts of congruent triangles are congruent, $\angle A \cong \angle C$.

To prove that $\angle B \cong \angle D$, draw ___**f.**___ and use the same reasoning.

38. a. $\overline{AB} \cong \overline{DC}$
b. $\overline{AD} \cong \overline{BC}$
c. $\overline{BD} \cong \overline{BD}$
d. SSS
e. corresp.
f. $\overline{AC}$

STUDENT HELP

HOMEWORK HELP
Example 1: Exs. 20–22
Example 2: Exs. 23–25
Example 3: Exs. 26–37
Example 4: Exs. 55–58
Example 5: Exs. 38–44
Example 6: Exs. 45–54

39. **PROVING THEOREM 6.4** Copy and complete the two-column proof of Theorem 6.4: If a quadrilateral is a parallelogram, then its consecutive angles are supplementary.

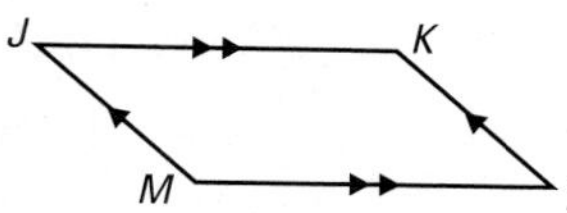

GIVEN ▶ $JKLM$ is a ▱.

PROVE ▶ $\angle J$ and $\angle K$ are supplementary.

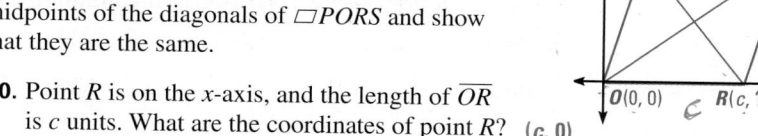

Statements	Reasons
1. ___?___ $JKLM$ is a ▱.	1. Given
2. $m\angle J = m\angle L$, $m\angle K = m\angle M$	2. ___?___ Opp. ∠s of a ▱ are ≅.
3. $m\angle J + m\angle L + m\angle K + m\angle M =$ ___?___ 360°	3. Sum of measures of int. ∠s of a quad. is 360°.
4. $m\angle J + m\angle J + m\angle K + m\angle K = 360°$	4. ___?___ Substitution prop. of equality
5. 2(___?___ + ___?___) = 360° $m\angle J$; $m\angle K$	5. Distributive property
6. $m\angle J + m\angle K = 180°$	6. ___?___ prop. of equality Division
7. $\angle J$ and $\angle K$ are supplementary.	7. ___?___ Def. of supplementary ∠s

You can use the same reasoning to prove any other pair of consecutive angles in ▱$JKLM$ are supplementary.

44. They have the same midpoint. Then, since $\overline{PR}$ intersects $\overline{OS}$ at its midpoint, $\overline{PR}$ bisects $\overline{OS}$ by the definition of a segment bisector. Similarly, $\overline{OS}$ bisects $\overline{PR}$.

45. $\angle 3$ and $\angle 7$ are supplementary by the Linear Pair Postulate, so $m\angle 3 + m\angle 7 = 180°$. Opp. ∠s of a ▱ are ≅, so $\angle 6 \cong \angle 7$, or $m\angle 6 = m\angle 7$. Then by the substitution prop. of equality, $m\angle 3 + m\angle 6 = 180°$ and $\angle 3$ and $\angle 6$ are supplementary.

DEVELOPING COORDINATE PROOF **Copy and complete the coordinate proof of Theorem 6.5.**

GIVEN ▶ $PORS$ is a ▱.

PROVE ▶ $\overline{PR}$ and $\overline{OS}$ bisect each other.

Plan for Proof Find the coordinates of the midpoints of the diagonals of ▱$PORS$ and show that they are the same.

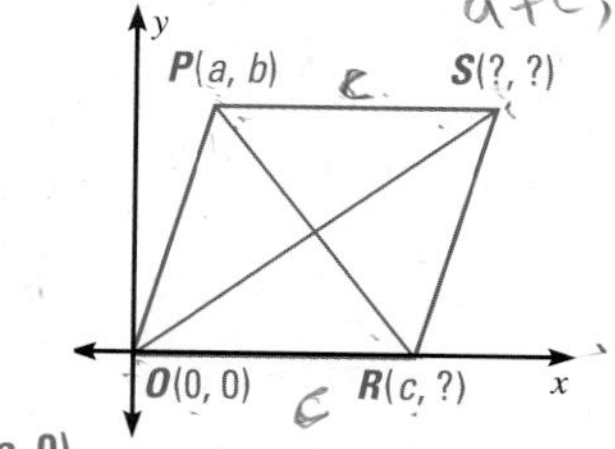

STUDENT HELP

INTERNET **HOMEWORK HELP** Visit our Web site www.mcdougallittell.com for help with the coordinate proof in Exs. 40–44.

40. Point R is on the x-axis, and the length of $\overline{OR}$ is c units. What are the coordinates of point R? **(c, 0)**

41. The length of $\overline{PS}$ is also c units, and $\overline{PS}$ is horizontal. What are the coordinates of point S? **(a + c, b)**

42. What are the coordinates of the midpoint of $\overline{PR}$? $\left(\frac{a+c}{2}, \frac{b}{2}\right)$

43. What are the coordinates of the midpoint of $\overline{OS}$? $\left(\frac{a+c}{2}, \frac{b}{2}\right)$

44. *Writing* How do you know that $\overline{PR}$ and $\overline{OS}$ bisect each other? **See margin.**

46. $\angle 2$ and $\angle 5$ are supplementary by the Linear Pair Postulate, so $m\angle 2 + m\angle 5 = 180°$. Opp. ∠s of a ▱ are ≅, so $\angle 4 \cong \angle 2$, or $m\angle 4 = m\angle 2$. Then by the substitution prop. of equality, $m\angle 4 + m\angle 5 = 180°$ and $\angle 4$ and $\angle 5$ are supplementary.

BAKING **In Exercises 45 and 46, use the following information.**
In a recipe for baklava, the pastry should be cut into triangles that form congruent parallelograms, as shown. Write a paragraph proof to prove the statement.

45. $\angle 3$ is supplementary to $\angle 6$. **See margin.**

46. $\angle 4$ is supplementary to $\angle 5$. **See margin.**

STUDENT HELP NOTES

Homework Help Students can find help for Exs. 40–44 at **www.mcdougallittell.com.** The information can be printed out for students who don't have access to the Internet.

APPLICATION NOTE

EXERCISES 45–46 A similar diagram can be drawn for cutting the baklava into diamond shapes. Because a diamond shape is a parallelogram with all sides equal, the same pairs of angles are still supplementary.

55. Statements (Reasons)
1. *ABCD* and *CEFD* are ▱s. (Given)
2. $\overline{AB} \cong \overline{CD}$; $\overline{CD} \cong \overline{EF}$ (Opp. sides of a ▱ are ≅.)
3. $\overline{AB} \cong \overline{EF}$ (Transitive Prop. of Cong.)

56. Statements (Reasons)
1. *PQRS* and *TUVS* are ▱s. (Given)
2. $\angle 1 \cong \angle 2$; $\angle 3 \cong \angle 2$ (Opp. ∠s of a ▱ are ≅.)
3. $\angle 1 \cong \angle 3$ (Transitive Prop. of Cong.)

57. Statements (Reasons)
1. *WXYZ* is a ▱. (Given)
2. $\overline{WZ} \cong \overline{XY}$ (Opp. sides of a ▱ are ≅.)
3. $\overline{WM} \cong \overline{YM}$; $\overline{ZM} \cong \overline{XM}$ (The diags. of a ▱ bisect each other.)
4. $\triangle WMZ \cong \triangle YMX$ (SSS Cong. Post.)

58. Statements (Reasons)
1. *ABCD*, *EBGF*, and *HJKD* are ▱s. (Given)
2. $\angle 1 \cong \angle 2$, $\angle 1 \cong \angle 4$ (Opp. ∠s of a ▱ are ≅.)
3. $\angle 2 \cong \angle 4$ (Transitive Prop. of Cong.)
4. $\angle 3 \cong \angle 4$ (Opp. ∠s of a ▱ are ≅.)
5. $\angle 2 \cong \angle 3$ (Transitive Prop. of Cong.)

ADDITIONAL PRACTICE AND RETEACHING

For Lesson 6.2:

- Practice Levels A, B, and C (*Chapter 6 Resource Book*, p. 28)
- Reteaching with Practice (*Chapter 6 Resource Book*, p. 31)
- See Lesson 6.2 of the *Personal Student Tutor*

For more Mixed Review:

- Search the *Test and Practice Generator* for key words or specific lessons.

STAIR BALUSTERS **In Exercises 47–50, use the following information.** In the diagram at the right, the slope of the handrail is equal to the slope of the stairs. The balusters (vertical posts) support the handrail.

47. Which angle in the red parallelogram is congruent to $\angle 1$? $\angle 4$

48. Which angles in the blue parallelogram are supplementary to $\angle 6$? $\angle 5$ and $\angle 8$

49. Which postulate can be used to prove that $\angle 1 \cong \angle 5$? Corresp. ∠s Postulate (If 2 ∥ lines are cut by a transv., then corresp. ∠s are ≅.)

50. *Writing* Is the red parallelogram congruent to the blue parallelogram? Explain your reasoning. No; the corresp. longer sides of the two ▱ are not ≅.

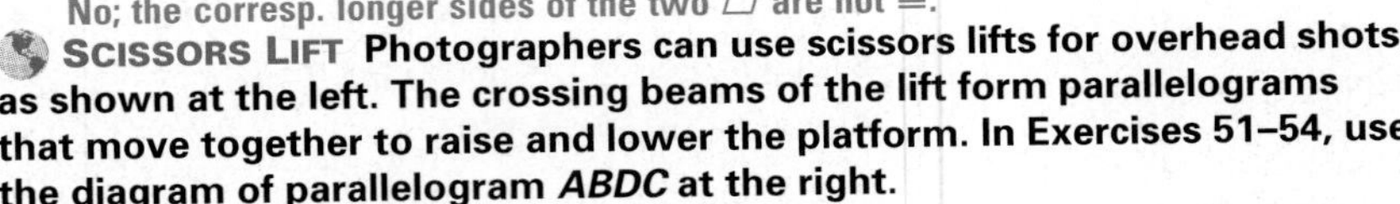

SCISSORS LIFT **Photographers can use scissors lifts for overhead shots, as shown at the left. The crossing beams of the lift form parallelograms that move together to raise and lower the platform. In Exercises 51–54, use the diagram of parallelogram *ABDC* at the right.**

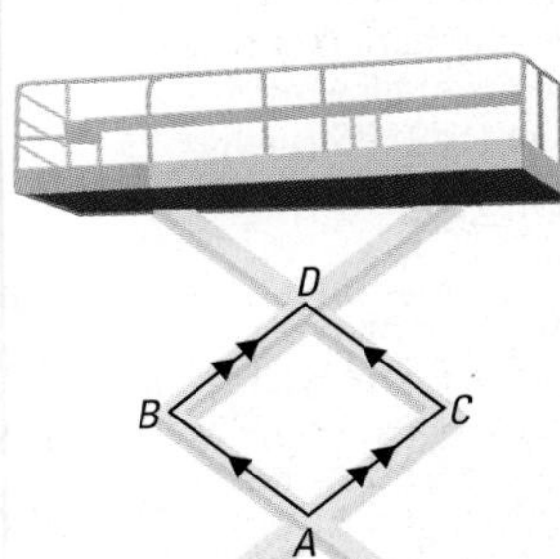

51. What is $m\angle B$ when $m\angle A = 120°$? 60°

52. Suppose you decrease $m\angle A$. What happens to $m\angle B$? $m\angle B$ increases.

53. Suppose you decrease $m\angle A$. What happens to AD? AD increases.

54. Suppose you decrease $m\angle A$. What happens to the overall height of the scissors lift? It increases.

TWO-COLUMN PROOF **Write a two-column proof.** 55–58. See margin.

55. GIVEN ▶ *ABCD* and *CEFD* are ▱s.

PROVE ▶ $\overline{AB} \cong \overline{FE}$

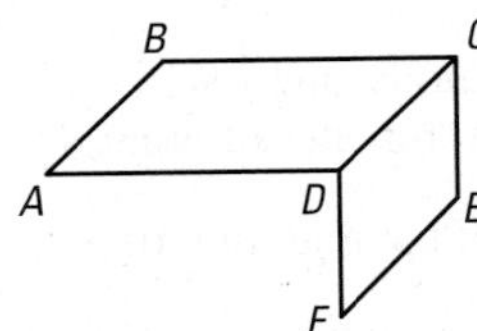

56. GIVEN ▶ *PQRS* and *TUVS* are ▱s.

PROVE ▶ $\angle 1 \cong \angle 3$

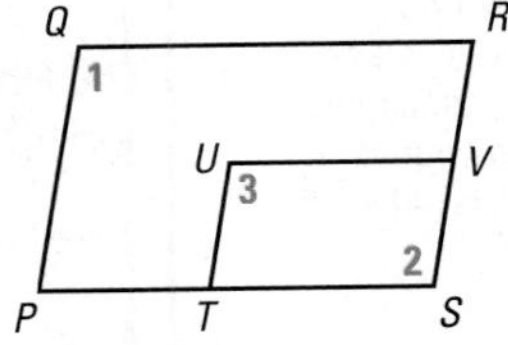

57. GIVEN ▶ *WXYZ* is a ▱.

PROVE ▶ $\triangle WMZ \cong \triangle YMX$

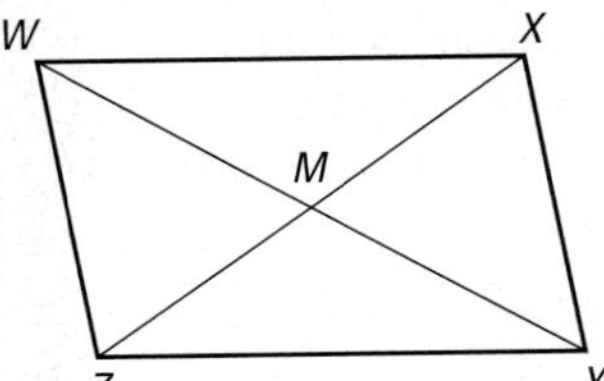

58. GIVEN ▶ *ABCD*, *EBGF*, *HJKD* are ▱s.

PROVE ▶ $\angle 2 \cong \angle 3$

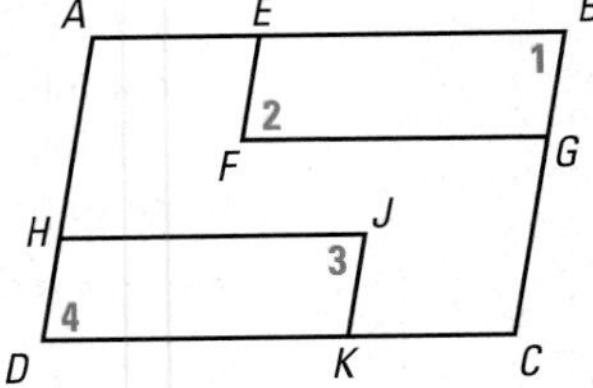

59. *Writing* In the diagram, $ABCG$, $CDEG$, and $AGEF$ are parallelograms. Copy the diagram and add as many other angle measures as you can. Then describe how you know the angle measures you added are correct. See margin.

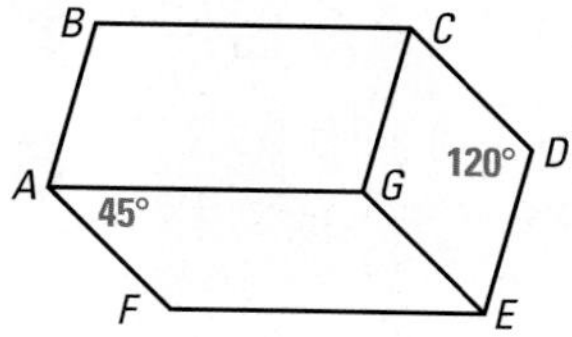

Test Preparation

60. MULTIPLE CHOICE In ▱$KLMN$, what is the value of s? B

Ⓐ 5 Ⓑ 20 Ⓒ 40
Ⓓ 52 Ⓔ 70

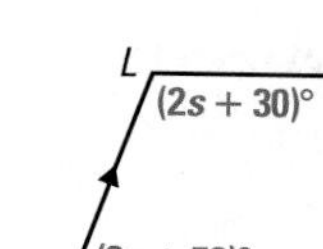

61. MULTIPLE CHOICE In ▱$ABCD$, point E is the intersection of the diagonals. Which of the following is *not* necessarily true? B

Ⓐ $AB = CD$ Ⓑ $AC = BD$ Ⓒ $AE = CE$ Ⓓ $AD = BC$ Ⓔ $DE = BE$

★ Challenge

USING ALGEBRA Suppose points $A(1, 2)$, $B(3, 6)$, and $C(6, 4)$ are three vertices of a parallelogram.

62. Give the coordinates of a point that could be the fourth vertex. Sketch the parallelogram in a coordinate plane. $(-2, 4)$, $(4, 0)$, or $(8, 8)$; check drawings.

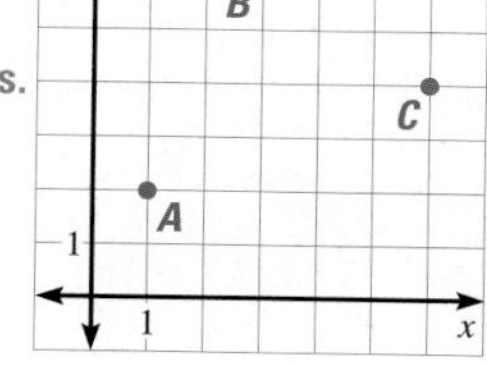

63. Explain how to check to make sure the figure you drew in Exercise 62 is a parallelogram.
Sample answer: Use slopes to show that opp. sides are ∥.

64. How many different parallelograms can be formed using A, B, and C as vertices? Sketch each parallelogram and label the coordinates of the fourth vertex.
Three; the possible fourth vertices are $(-2, 4)$, $(4, 0)$, and $(8, 8)$.

72. $\overline{AB}$, $\overline{AC}$; $m\angle B = 180° - (65° + 35°) = 80°$, so $\angle D$ is the smallest ∠ of △ABC and ∠B is the largest. If 1 ∠ of a △ is larger than another ∠, then the side opp. the larger ∠ is longer than the side opp. the smaller ∠.

EXTRA CHALLENGE
www.mcdougallittell.com

MIXED REVIEW

USING ALGEBRA Use the Distance Formula to find AB. (Review 1.3 for 6.3)

65. $A(2, 1)$, $B(6, 9)$ $4\sqrt{5}$ **66.** $A(-4, 2)$, $B(2, -1)$ $3\sqrt{5}$ **67.** $A(-8, -4)$, $B(-1, -3)$ $5\sqrt{2}$

USING ALGEBRA Find the slope of $\overline{AB}$. (Review 3.6 for 6.3)

68. $A(2, 1)$, $B(6, 9)$ 2 **69.** $A(-4, 2)$, $B(2, -1)$ $-\frac{1}{2}$ **70.** $A(-8, -4)$, $B(-1, -3)$ $\frac{1}{7}$

71. PARKING CARS In a parking lot, two guidelines are painted so that they are both perpendicular to the line along the curb. Are the guidelines parallel? Explain why or why not. (Review 3.5)
Yes; in a plane, 2 lines ⊥ to the same line are ∥.

Name the shortest and longest sides of the triangle. Explain. (Review 5.5)
72–74. See margin.

72. **73.** **74.**

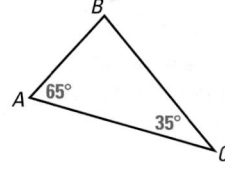

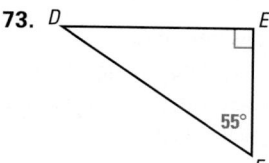

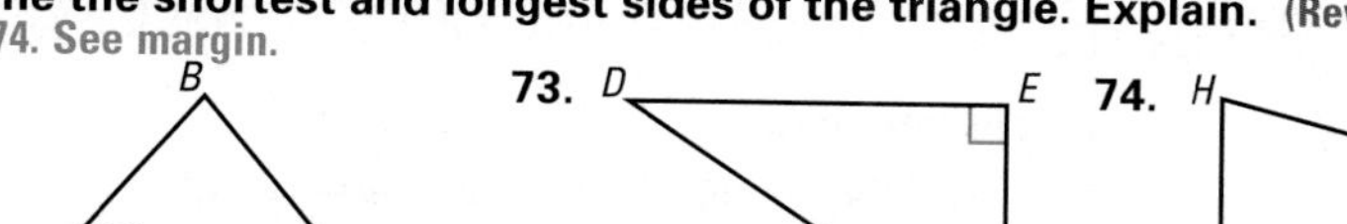

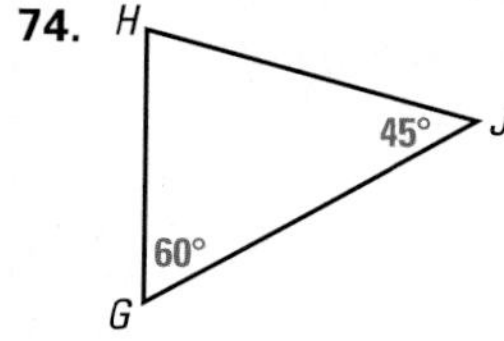

73. $\overline{EF}$, $\overline{DF}$; $m\angle D = 180° - (90° + 55°) = 35°$, so ∠$D$ is the smallest ∠ of △DEF and ∠E is the largest. If 1 ∠ of a △ is larger than another ∠, then the side opp. the larger ∠ is longer than the side opp. the smaller ∠.

74. $\overline{GH}$, $\overline{GJ}$; $m\angle H = 180° - (60° + 45°) = 75°$, so ∠$J$ is the smallest ∠ of △GHJ and ∠H is the largest. If 1 ∠ of a △ is larger than another ∠, then the side opp. the larger ∠ is longer than the side opp. the smaller ∠.

59. See Additional Answers beginning on page AA1.

4 ASSESS

DAILY HOMEWORK QUIZ

Transparency Available

1. Find the sum of the lengths of the diagonals in parallelogram $FGHJ$. Explain your reasoning.

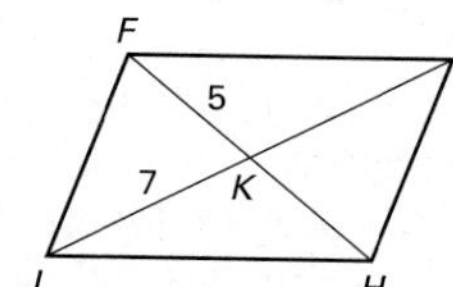

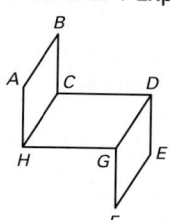

24; the diags. of a ▱ bisect each other, so $KH = 5$ and $KG = 7$. Then $FH = 5 + 5 = 10$ and $JG = 7 + 7 = 14$, so $FH + JG = 10 + 14 = 24$.

2. Each quadrilateral in the figure is a parallelogram. What is the relationship of $\overline{AB}$ and $\overline{EF}$? Explain.

They are ≅. Opp. sides of a ▱ are ≅, so $\overline{AB} \cong \overline{CH}$, $\overline{CH} \cong \overline{DG}$, and $\overline{DG} \cong \overline{EF}$. Using the Transitive Prop. of Cong. twice, $\overline{AB} \cong \overline{EF}$.

EXTRA CHALLENGE NOTE

Challenge problems for Lesson 6.2 are available in **blackline** format in the *Chapter 6 Resource Book*, p. 35 and at **www.mcdougallittell.com.**

ADDITIONAL TEST PREPARATION

1. WRITING In quadrilateral $ABCD$, $m\angle B = 110°$, $m\angle A = 70°$, and $m\angle C = 110°$. Explain why $ABCD$ cannot be a parallelogram.
∠A and ∠C are opp. ∠s but not ≅, and ∠B and ∠C are adjacent ∠s but not supplementary. Both facts violate the properties of parallelograms.

1 PLAN

PACING
Basic: 2 days
Average: 2 days
Advanced: 2 days
Block Schedule: 0.5 block with 6.2
0.5 block with 6.4

LESSON OPENER ACTIVITY
An alternative way to approach Lesson 6.3 is to use the Activity Lesson Opener:
- Blackline Master (*Chapter 6 Resource Book,* p. 39)
- Transparency (p. 36)

MEETING INDIVIDUAL NEEDS
- ***Chapter 6 Resource Book***
  Prerequisite Skills Review (p. 5)
  Practice Level A (p. 40)
  Practice Level B (p. 41)
  Practice Level C (p. 42)
  Reteaching with Practice (p. 43)
  Absent Student Catch-Up (p. 45)
  Challenge (p. 48)
- ***Resources in Spanish***
- ***Personal Student Tutor***

NEW-TEACHER SUPPORT
See the Tips for New Teachers on pp. 1–2 of the *Chapter 6 Resource Book* for additional notes about Lesson 6.3.

WARM-UP EXERCISES
Transparency Available
Give the definition, theorem, or postulate that justifies the statement.

1. If $\overline{AC} \cong \overline{A'C'}$, $\overline{AB} \cong \overline{A'B'}$, and $\overline{BC} \cong \overline{B'C'}$, then $\triangle ABC \cong \triangle A'B'C'$. **SSS Cong. Post.**
2. If $ABCD$ is a parallelogram, then $\overline{AB} \cong \overline{DC}$ and $\overline{AD} \cong \overline{BC}$. **Opposite sides of a ▱ are ≅.**
3. If $MNPQ$ is a parallelogram, then $\overline{MP}$ bisects $\overline{NQ}$. **Diagonals of a ▱ bisect each other.**

6.3 Proving Quadrilaterals are Parallelograms

What you should learn

GOAL 1 Prove that a quadrilateral is a parallelogram.

GOAL 2 Use coordinate geometry with parallelograms.

Why you should learn it

▼ To understand how **real-life** tools work, such as the bicycle derailleur in **Ex. 27**, which lets you change gears when you are biking uphill.

REAL LIFE

CALIFORNIA STANDARDS AND ASSESSMENT
CA Standards: 4, 7, 12, 17
SAT9 Task 1: Obj. 30
SAT9 Task 2: Obj. 33

GOAL 1 PROVING QUADRILATERALS ARE PARALLELOGRAMS

The activity illustrates one way to prove that a quadrilateral is a parallelogram.

ACTIVITY Developing Concepts

Investigating Properties of Parallelograms

1. Cut four straws to form two congruent pairs. **Check results.**
2. Partly unbend two paperclips, link their smaller ends, and insert the larger ends into two cut straws, as shown. Join the rest of the straws to form a quadrilateral with opposite sides congruent, as shown. **Check results.**
3. Change the angles of your quadrilateral. Is your quadrilateral always a parallelogram? **yes**

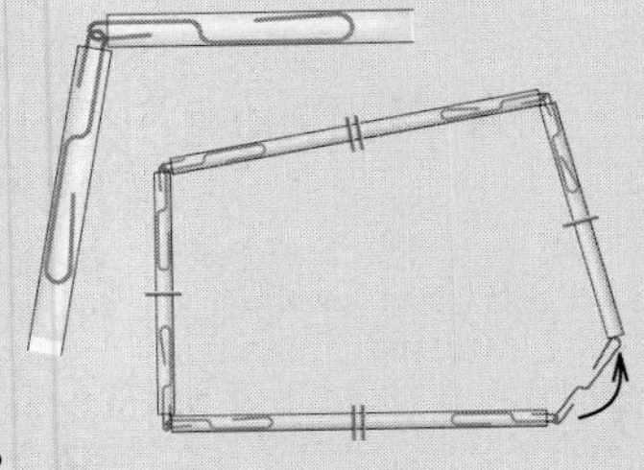

THEOREMS

THEOREM 6.6
If both pairs of opposite sides of a quadrilateral are congruent, then the quadrilateral is a parallelogram.

ABCD **is a parallelogram.**

THEOREM 6.7
If both pairs of opposite angles of a quadrilateral are congruent, then the quadrilateral is a parallelogram.

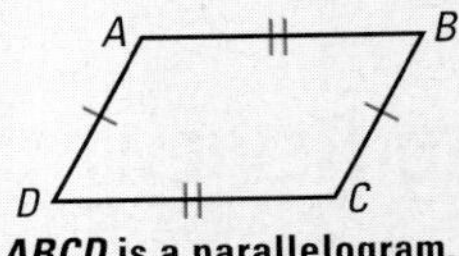

ABCD **is a parallelogram.**

THEOREM 6.8
If an angle of a quadrilateral is supplementary to both of its consecutive angles, then the quadrilateral is a parallelogram.

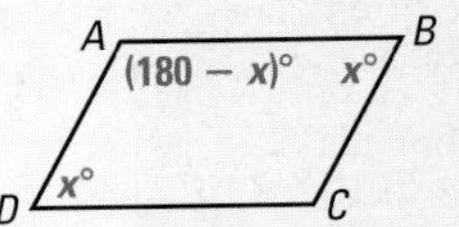

ABCD **is a parallelogram.**

THEOREM 6.9
If the diagonals of a quadrilateral bisect each other, then the quadrilateral is a parallelogram.

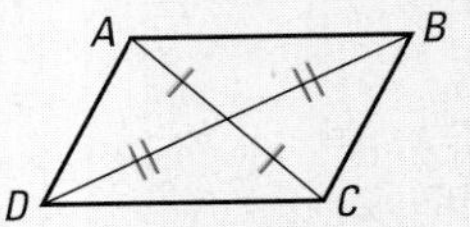

ABCD **is a parallelogram.**

The proof of Theorem 6.6 is given in Example 1. You will be asked to prove Theorem 6.7, Theorem 6.8, and Theorem 6.9 in Exercises 32–36.

EXAMPLE 1 ***Proof of Theorem 6.6***

Prove Theorem 6.6.

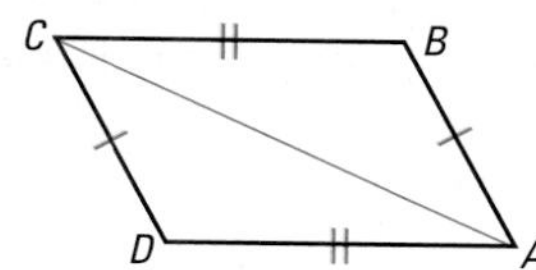

GIVEN ▶ $\overline{AB} \cong \overline{CD}, \overline{AD} \cong \overline{CB}$

PROVE ▶ $ABCD$ is a parallelogram.

Statements	Reasons
1. $\overline{AB} \cong \overline{CD}, \overline{AD} \cong \overline{CB}$	**1.** Given
2. $\overline{AC} \cong \overline{AC}$	**2.** Reflexive Property of Congruence
3. $\triangle ABC \cong \triangle CDA$	**3.** SSS Congruence Postulate
4. $\angle BAC \cong \angle DCA$, $\angle DAC \cong \angle BCA$	**4.** Corresponding parts of ≅ ▲ are ≅.
5. $\overline{AB} \parallel \overline{CD}, \overline{AD} \parallel \overline{CB}$	**5.** Alternate Interior Angles Converse
6. $ABCD$ is a ▱.	**6.** Definition of parallelogram

EXAMPLE 2 ***Proving Quadrilaterals are Parallelograms***

As the sewing box below is opened, the trays are always parallel to each other. Why?

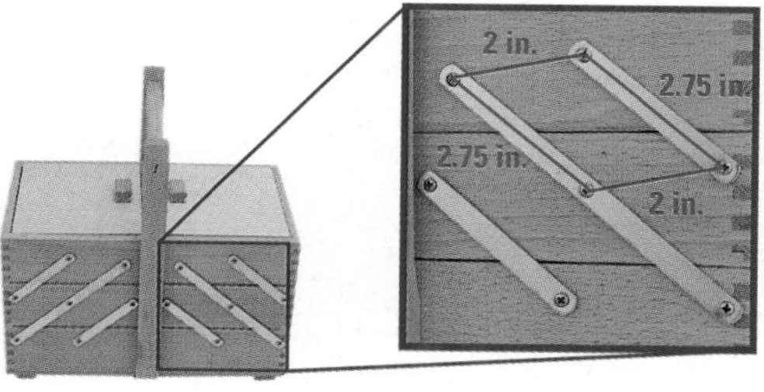

SOLUTION

Each pair of hinges are opposite sides of a quadrilateral. The 2.75 inch sides of the quadrilateral are opposite and congruent. The 2 inch sides are also opposite and congruent. Because opposite sides of the quadrilateral are congruent, it is a parallelogram. By the definition of a parallelogram, opposite sides are parallel, so the trays of the sewing box are always parallel.

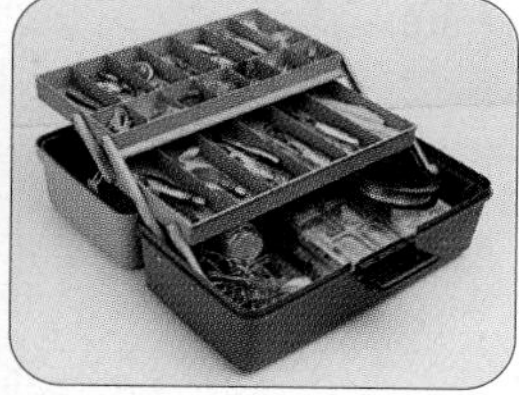

CONTAINERS Many containers, such as tackle boxes, jewelry boxes, and tool boxes, use parallelograms in their design to ensure that the trays stay level.

2 TEACH

EXTRA EXAMPLE 1

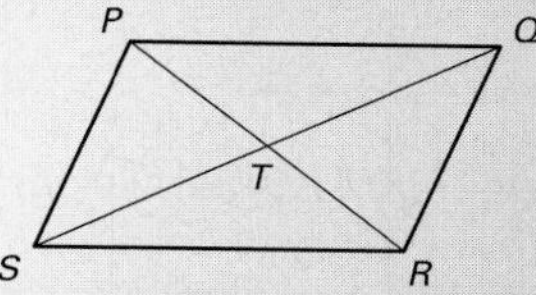

Given: $\triangle PQT \cong \triangle RST$
Prove: $PQRS$ is a parallelogram.
Statements (Reasons)
1. $\triangle PQT \cong \triangle RST$ (Given)
2. $\overline{PT} \cong \overline{RT}$ and $\overline{ST} \cong \overline{QT}$ (Corresp. parts of ≅ ▲ are ≅.)
3. $PT = RT$ and $ST = QT$ (Def. of cong.)
4. $\overline{PR}$ and $\overline{SQ}$ bisect each other. (Def. of bisect)
5. $PQRS$ is a ▱. (If the diags. of a quad. bisect each other, then it is a ▱.)

EXTRA EXAMPLE 2

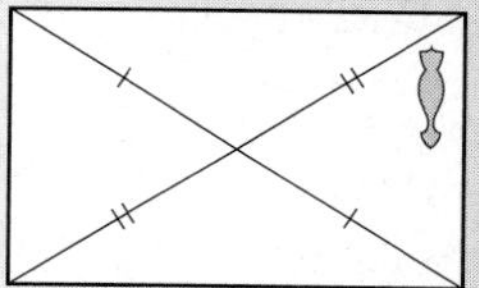

A gate is braced as shown. How do you know that the opposite sides of the gate are congruent?
The diagonals bisect each other, so the gate is a ▱. The opposite sides of a ▱ are ≅.

CHECKPOINT EXERCISES

For use after Examples 1 and 2:

1.

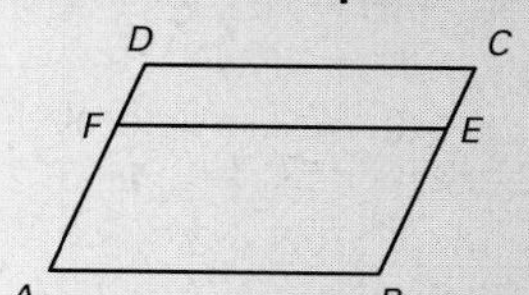

Given: $ABCD$ is a parallelogram; $\overline{FE} \parallel \overline{DC}$.
Prove: $ABEF$ is a parallelogram.
Statements (Reasons)
1. $ABCD$ is a ▱. (Given)
2. $\overline{AD} \parallel \overline{BC}$; $\overline{AB} \parallel \overline{DC}$ (Def. of ▱)
3. $\overline{AF} \parallel \overline{BE}$ (Def. of ∥ segments)
4. $\overline{FE} \parallel \overline{DC}$ (Given)
5. $\overline{AB} \parallel \overline{FE}$ (If 2 lines are ∥ to the same line, then they are ∥ to each other.)
6. $ABEF$ is a ▱. (Def. of ▱)

EXTRA EXAMPLE 3

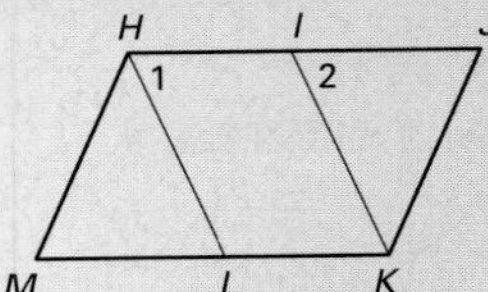

Given: *HJKM* is a parallelogram; $\triangle IJK \cong \triangle LMH$,
Prove: *HIKL* is a parallelogram.

Statements (Reasons)

1. *HJKM* is a ▱. (Given)
2. $\overline{HJ} \parallel \overline{KM}$ (Def. of ▱)
3. $\overline{HI} \parallel \overline{LK}$ (Def. of ∥ segments)
4. $\triangle IJK \cong \triangle LMH$ (Given)
5. $\overline{IJ} \cong \overline{LM}$ (Corresp. parts of ≅ ⊿s are ≅.)
6. $\overline{HJ} \cong \overline{KM}$ (Opp. sides of a ▱ are ≅.)
7. $IJ = LM$, $HJ = KM$ (Def. of cong.)
8. $HJ = HI + IJ$; $KM = KL + LM$ (Segment Addition Post.)
9. $HJ = KL + LM$ (Substitution prop. of equality)
10. $HI + IJ = KL + LM$ (Transitive prop. of equality)
11. $HI + IJ = KL + IJ$ (Substitution prop. of equality)
12. $HI = KL$ (Subtraction prop. of equality)
13. *HIKL* is a ▱. (If 1 pair of opp. sides of a quad. are ≅ and ∥, then the quad. is a ▱.)

CHECKPOINT EXERCISES

For use after Example 3:

1. Use the figure from Extra Example 3.
   Given: $\angle 1 \cong \angle 2$; $\triangle IJK \cong \triangle LMH$
   Prove: *HIKL* is a parallelogram.
   Statements (Reasons)
   1. $\angle 1 \cong \angle 2$; $\triangle IJK \cong \triangle LMH$ (Given)
   2. $\overline{HL} \parallel \overline{IK}$ (If 2 lines are cut by a transv. so that corres. ⊿s are ≅, then the lines are ∥.)
   3. $\overline{HL} \cong \overline{KI}$ (Corres. parts of ≅ triangles are ≅.)
   4. *HIKL* is a ▱. (If 1 pair of opp. sides of a quad. are ≅ and ∥, then the quad. is a ▱.)

340

Theorem 6.10 gives another way to prove a quadrilateral is a parallelogram.

THEOREM

THEOREM 6.10

If one pair of opposite sides of a quadrilateral are congruent and parallel, then the quadrilateral is a parallelogram.

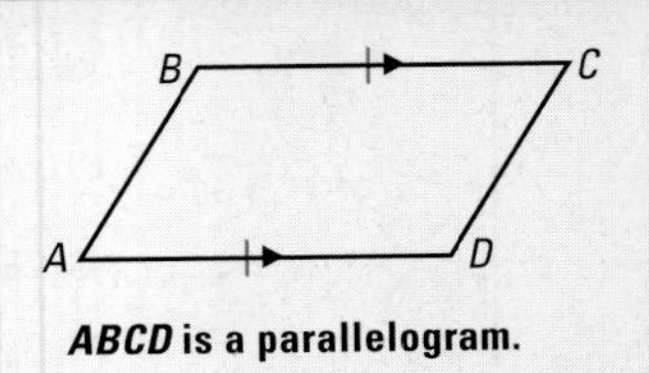

ABCD **is a parallelogram.**

EXAMPLE 3 *Proof of Theorem 6.10*

Proof

Prove Theorem 6.10.

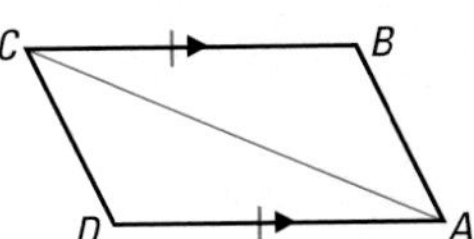

GIVEN ▶ $\overline{BC} \parallel \overline{DA}$, $\overline{BC} \cong \overline{DA}$

PROVE ▶ *ABCD* is a parallelogram.

Plan for Proof Show that $\triangle BAC \cong \triangle DCA$, so $\overline{AB} \cong \overline{CD}$. Use Theorem 6.6.

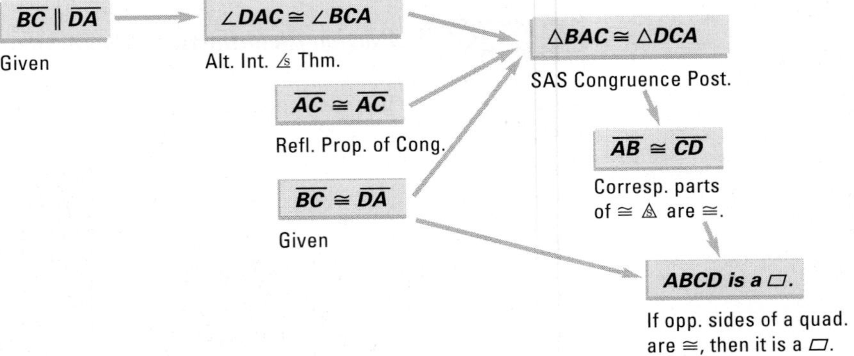

....

You have studied several ways to prove that a quadrilateral is a parallelogram. In the box below, the first way is also the definition of a parallelogram.

CONCEPT SUMMARY — PROVING QUADRILATERALS ARE PARALLELOGRAMS

- Show that both pairs of opposite sides are parallel.
- Show that both pairs of opposite sides are congruent.
- Show that both pairs of opposite angles are congruent.
- Show that one angle is supplementary to both consecutive angles.
- Show that the diagonals bisect each other.
- Show that one pair of opposite sides are congruent and parallel.

GOAL 2 USING COORDINATE GEOMETRY

When a figure is in the coordinate plane, you can use the Distance Formula to prove that sides are congruent and you can use the slope formula to prove that sides are parallel.

EXAMPLE 4 *Using Properties of Parallelograms*

Show that $A(2, -1)$, $B(1, 3)$, $C(6, 5)$, and $D(7, 1)$ are the vertices of a parallelogram.

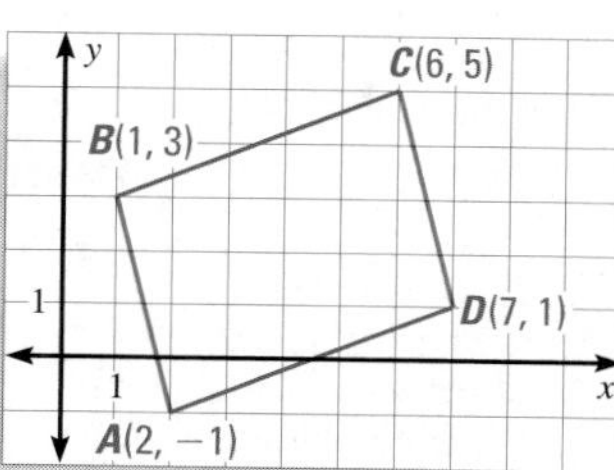

SOLUTION

There are many ways to solve this problem.

Method 1 Show that opposite sides have the same slope, so they are parallel.

$$\text{Slope of } \overline{AB} = \frac{3-(-1)}{1-2} = -4$$

$$\text{Slope of } \overline{CD} = \frac{1-5}{7-6} = -4$$

$$\text{Slope of } \overline{BC} = \frac{5-3}{6-1} = \frac{2}{5}$$

$$\text{Slope of } \overline{DA} = \frac{-1-1}{2-7} = \frac{2}{5}$$

$\overline{AB}$ and $\overline{CD}$ have the same slope so they are parallel. Similarly, $\overline{BC} \parallel \overline{DA}$.

▶ Because opposite sides are parallel, $ABCD$ is a parallelogram.

Method 2 Show that opposite sides have the same length.

$$AB = \sqrt{(1-2)^2 + [3-(-1)]^2} = \sqrt{17}$$

$$CD = \sqrt{(7-6)^2 + (1-5)^2} = \sqrt{17}$$

$$BC = \sqrt{(6-1)^2 + (5-3)^2} = \sqrt{29}$$

$$DA = \sqrt{(2-7)^2 + (-1-1)^2} = \sqrt{29}$$

▶ $\overline{AB} \cong \overline{CD}$ and $\overline{BC} \cong \overline{DA}$. Because both pairs of opposite sides are congruent, $ABCD$ is a parallelogram.

Method 3 Show that one pair of opposite sides is congruent and parallel.

Find the slopes and lengths of $\overline{AB}$ and $\overline{CD}$ as shown in Methods 1 and 2.

$$\text{Slope of } \overline{AB} = \text{Slope of } \overline{CD} = -4$$

$$AB = CD = \sqrt{17}$$

▶ $\overline{AB}$ and $\overline{CD}$ are congruent and parallel, so $ABCD$ is a parallelogram.

STUDENT HELP

Study Tip
Because you don't know the measures of the angles of *ABCD*, you can *not* use Theorems 6.7 or 6.8 in Example 4.

STUDENT HELP

INTERNET HOMEWORK HELP
Visit our Web site www.mcdougallittell.com for extra examples.

EXTRA EXAMPLE 4
Show that $A(-1, 2)$, $B(3, 2)$, $C(1, -2)$, and $D(-3, -2)$ are the vertices of a parallelogram.
Method 1: slopes of $\overline{AB}$, $\overline{DC} = 0$; slopes of $\overline{AD}$, $\overline{BC} = 2$; Method 2: $AB = DC = 4$ and $AD = BC = 2\sqrt{5}$; Method 3: slopes of $\overline{AB}$, $\overline{DC} = 0$ and $AB = DC = 4$.

CHECKPOINT EXERCISES
For use after Example 4:
1. Identify any quadrilateral that is a parallelogram.
a. $G(-3, 1)$, $H(4, 1)$, $I(3, 6)$, $J(-1, 6)$
b. $P(-2, 2)$, $Q(1, 1)$, $R(4, 4)$, $S(1, 4)$
c. $W(3, -1)$, $X(4, 2)$, $Y(1, 5)$, $Z(0, 2)$ **c**

! COMMON ERROR
EXAMPLE 4 Some students may want to measure the angles and apply Theorem 6.7. Remind them that a protractor gives only approximate measures.

STUDENT HELP NOTES
Homework Help Students can find extra examples at **www.mcdougallittell.com** that parallel the examples in the student edition.

CLOSURE QUESTION
State the six ways to prove that a quadrilateral ia a parallelogram. **See the property box at the bottom of page 340.**

DAILY PUZZLER
In ▱*ABCD*, the ratio of $m\angle A$ to $m\angle B$ is 4:5. What are the measures of all the angles? **$m\angle A = m\angle C = 80°$, and $m\angle B = m\angle D = 100°$**

3 APPLY

ASSIGNMENT GUIDE

BASIC

Day 1: pp. 342–345 Exs. 10–26 even, 30, 32, 34–37

Day 2: pp. 342–346 Exs. 9–25 odd, 29, 40, 42–47, Quiz 1 Exs. 1–4

AVERAGE

Day 1: pp. 342–345 Exs. 10–26 even, 30, 32, 34–37

Day 2: pp. 342–346 Exs. 9–31 odd, 40, 42–47, Quiz 1 Exs. 1–4

ADVANCED

Day 1: pp. 342–345 Exs. 10–26 even, 30, 32, 34–37

Day 2: pp. 342–346 Exs. 9–31 odd, 38, 40, 42–47, Quiz 1 Exs. 1–4

BLOCK SCHEDULE

pp. 342–345 Exs. 10–26 even, 30, 32, 34–37 (with 6.2)
pp. 342–346 Exs. 9–31 odd, 40, 42–47, Quiz 1 Exs. 1–4 (with 6.4)

EXERCISE LEVELS

Level A: ***Easier***
9–14, 39–43, 45–47

Level B: ***More Difficult***
15–37, 44

Level C: ***Most Difficult***
38

HOMEWORK CHECK

To quickly check student understanding of key concepts, go over the following exercises: Exs. 10, 16, 18, 22, 26, 29, 32, 36. See also the Daily Homework Quiz:

- Blackline Master (*Chapter 6 Resource Book*, p. 52)
- Transparency (p. 43)

6. Show that since alt. int. ∠s *BCA* and *DAC* are ≅, $\overline{BC} \parallel \overline{AD}$. Similarly, $\overline{AB} \parallel \overline{DC}$, and *ABCD* is a ▱ by the def. of a ▱.
7. See next page.
8, 12–14, 16. See Additional Answers beginning on page AA1.

GUIDED PRACTICE

Concept Check ✓

1. Is a hexagon with opposite sides parallel called a parallelogram? Explain.
No; a ▱ is a quad.

Skill Check ✓

Decide whether you are given enough information to determine that the quadrilateral is a parallelogram. Explain your reasoning.

2.

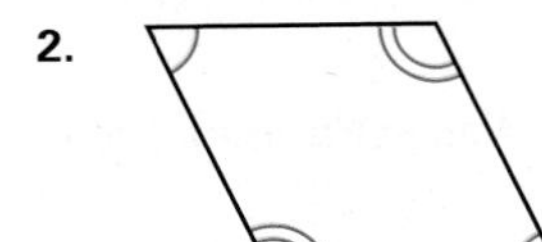

3.

4.

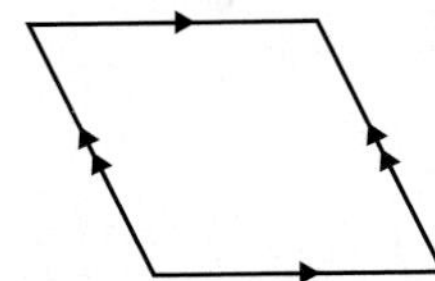

2. Yes; if opp. ∠s of a quad. are ≅, then it is a ▱.
3. Yes; if an ∠ of a quad. is supplementary to both of its consec. ∠s, then the quad. is a ▱.
4. Yes; the quad. is a ▱ by the def. of a ▱.

Describe how you would prove that *ABCD* is a parallelogram. 5–8. See margin.

5.

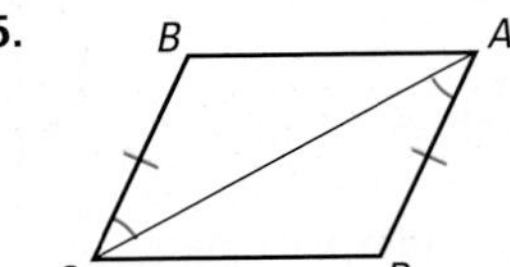

6.

7.

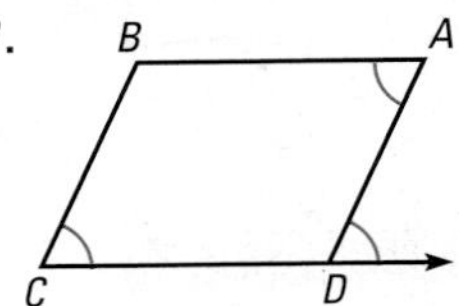

5. Show that since alternate interior ∠s *BCA* and *DAC* are ≅, $\overline{BC} \parallel \overline{AD}$. Then since one pair of opp. sides of *ABCD* is both ∥ and ≅, *ABCD* is a ▱.

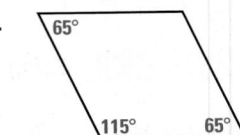

8. Describe at least three ways to show that $A(0, 0)$, $B(2, 6)$, $C(5, 7)$, and $D(3, 1)$ are the vertices of a parallelogram.

PRACTICE AND APPLICATIONS

STUDENT HELP

Extra Practice to help you master skills is on p. 813.

LOGICAL REASONING **Are you given enough information to determine whether the quadrilateral is a parallelogram? Explain.** 9–14. See margin.

9.

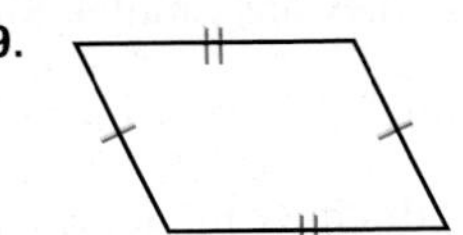

10.

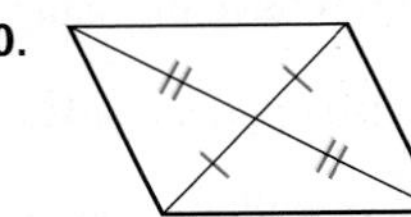

11.

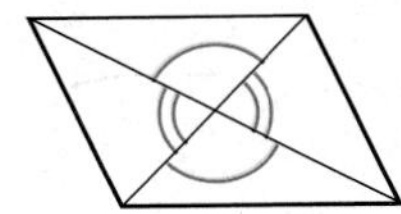

12.

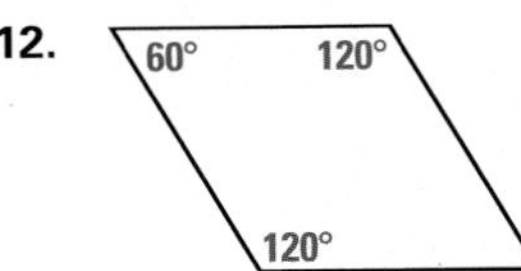

13.

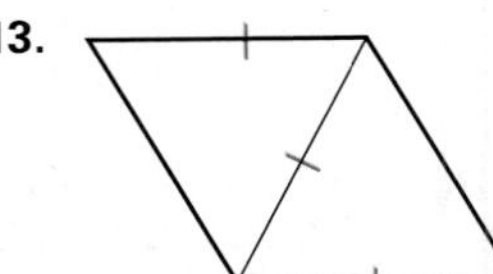

14.

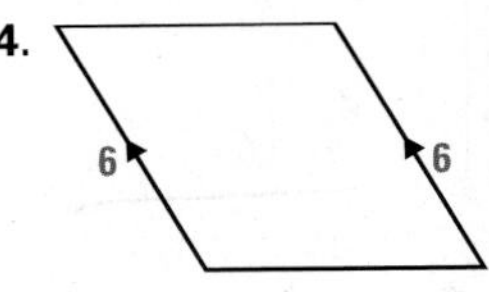

9. Yes; if opp. sides of a quad. are ≅, then it is a ▱.
10. Yes; if the diags. of a quad. bisect each other, then the quad. is a ▱.
11. No; according to the Vertical Angles Theorem, the given information is true for the diags. of any quad.

STUDENT HELP

HOMEWORK HELP

Example 1: Exs. 15, 16, 32, 33
Example 2: Exs. 21, 28, 31
Example 3: Exs. 32, 33
Example 4: Exs. 21–26, 34–36

LOGICAL REASONING **Describe how to prove that *ABCD* is a parallelogram. Use the given information.** 15, 16. Sample answers are given.

15. $\triangle ABC \cong \triangle CDA$

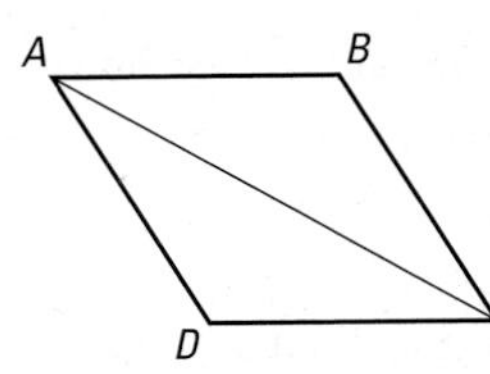

Since corresp. parts of ≅ △s are ≅, both pairs of opp. sides of *ABCD* are ≅, so *ABCD* is a ▱.

16. $\triangle AXB \cong \triangle CXD$

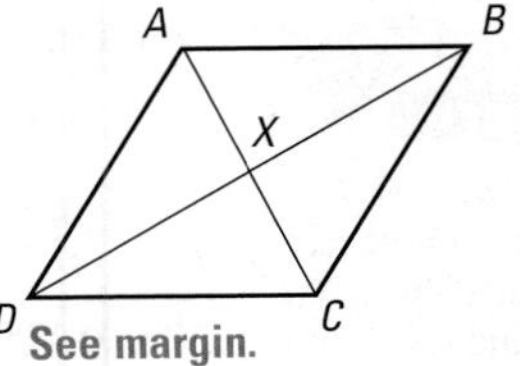

See margin.

USING ALGEBRA What value of *x* will make the polygon a parallelogram?

17. 70

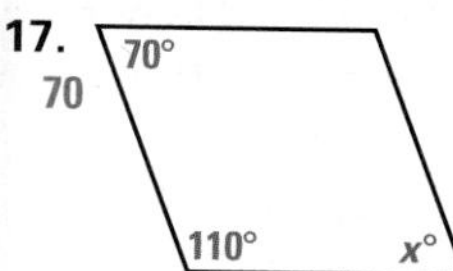

18. 60

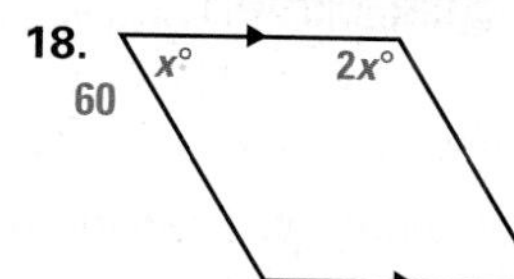

19. 90

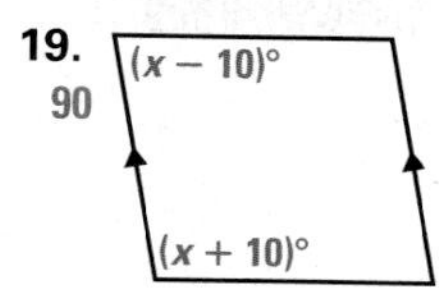

20. **VISUAL THINKING** Draw a quadrilateral that has one pair of congruent sides and one pair of parallel sides but that is not a parallelogram. **See margin.**

COORDINATE GEOMETRY Use the given definition or theorem to prove that *ABCD* is a parallelogram. Use $A(-1, 6)$, $B(3, 5)$, $C(5, -3)$, and $D(1, -2)$.

21–24. See margin.

21. Theorem 6.6
22. Theorem 6.9
23. definition of a parallelogram
24. Theorem 6.10

USING COORDINATE GEOMETRY Prove that the points represent the vertices of a parallelogram. Use a different method for each exercise.

25, 26. See margin.

25. $J(-6, 2)$, $K(-1, 3)$, $L(2, -3)$, $M(-3, -4)$
26. $P(2, 5)$, $Q(8, 4)$, $R(9, -4)$, $S(3, -3)$

27. **CHANGING GEARS** When you change gears on a bicycle, the *derailleur* moves the chain to the new gear. For the derailleur at the right, $AB = 1.8$ cm, $BC = 3.6$ cm, $CD = 1.8$ cm, and $DA = 3.6$ cm. Explain why $\overline{AB}$ and $\overline{CD}$ are always parallel when the derailleur moves. **See margin.**

28. **COMPUTERS** Many word processors have a feature that allows a regular letter to be changed to an oblique (slanted) letter. The diagram at the right shows some regular letters and their oblique versions. Explain how you can prove that the oblique I is a parallelogram. **See margin.**

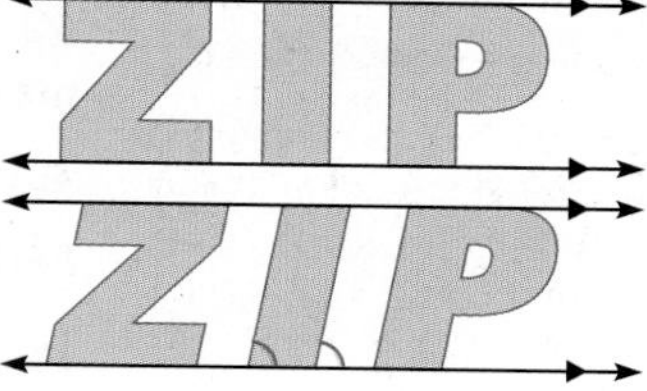

29. **VISUAL REASONING** Explain why the following method of drawing a parallelogram works. State a theorem to support your answer. **See margin.**

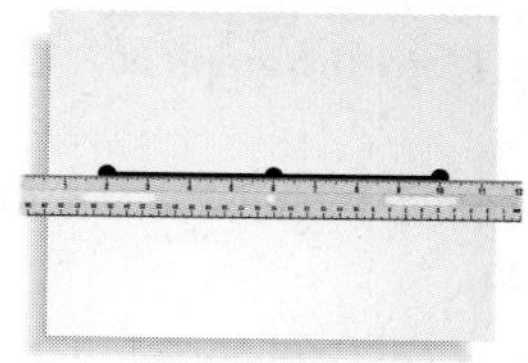

1. Use a ruler to draw a segment and its midpoint.

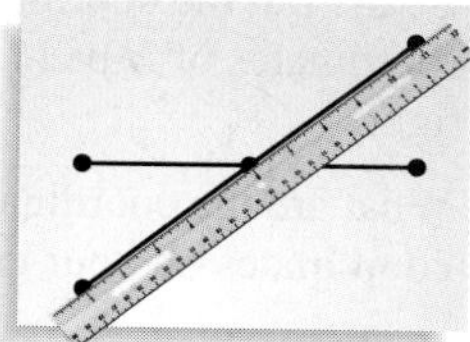

2. Draw another segment so the midpoints coincide.

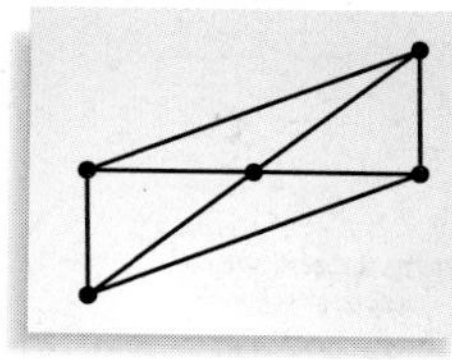

3. Connect the endpoints of the segments.

---

21. $AB = CD = \sqrt{17}$, so $\overline{AB} \cong \overline{CD}$. $AD = BC = 2\sqrt{17}$, so $\overline{AD} \cong \overline{BC}$. Since opp. sides of *ABCD* are ≅, *ABCD* is a ▱.

22. The midpoint of $\overline{AC}$ is $\left(2, \frac{3}{2}\right)$, which is also the midpoint of $\overline{BD}$. Since the diags. of *ABCD* bisect each other, *ABCD* is a ▱.

23. Slope of $\overline{AB}$ = slope of $\overline{CD} = -\frac{1}{4}$ and slope of $\overline{AD}$ = slope of $\overline{BC} = -4$, so $\overline{AB} \parallel \overline{CD}$ and $\overline{AD} \parallel \overline{BC}$. Then *ABCD* is a ▱ by the def. of a ▱.

FOCUS ON APPLICATIONS

DERAILLEURS (named from the French word meaning 'derail') move the chain among two to six sprockets of different diameters to change gears.

24. *Sample answer:* $AB = CD = \sqrt{17}$, so $\overline{AB} \cong \overline{CD}$. Slope of $\overline{AB}$ = slope of $\overline{CD} = -\frac{1}{4}$, so $\overline{AB} \parallel \overline{CD}$. Since 1 pair of sides of *ABCD* are both ≅ and ∥, *ABCD* is a ▱.

25. *Sample answer:* Slope of $\overline{JK}$ = slope of $\overline{LM} = \frac{1}{5}$ and slope of $\overline{JM}$ = slope of $\overline{KL} = -2$, so $\overline{JK} \parallel \overline{LM}$ and $\overline{JM} \parallel \overline{KL}$. Then *JKLM* is a ▱ by the def. of a ▱.

MATHEMATICAL REASONING
EXERCISES 25–26 Parallelogram *ABCD* has coordinates $A(a, b)$, $B(0, 0)$, and $C(c, 0)$. What are the coordinates of *D*? $(c + a, b)$

APPLICATION NOTE
EXERCISE 27 A bicycle has two derailleurs. The front derailleur moves the chain from one sprocket to another on the chainwheel, which is driven by the pedals. The chain transfers the energy to the freewheel, which drives the rear wheel. The rear derailleur moves the chain from one sprocket to another on the freewheel. The ratio of the number of teeth on the front sprocket to the number on the rear sprocket determines the gear ratio, which sets the number of wheel rotations that correspond to a given number of pedal rotations.

7. Use the Corresp. ∠s Converse to show that $\overline{BC} \parallel \overline{AD}$ and the Alt. Int. ∠s Converse to show that $\overline{AB} \parallel \overline{DC}$. Then *ABCD* is a ▱ by the def. of a ▱.

20. *Sample answer:*

26. *Sample answer:* Slope of $\overline{PQ}$ = slope of $\overline{RS} = -\frac{1}{6}$, so $\overline{PQ} \parallel \overline{RS}$, and $PQ = RS = \sqrt{37}$, so $\overline{PQ} \cong \overline{RS}$. Then a pair of opp. sides of *PQRS* are both ≅ and ∥, so *PQRS* is a ▱.

27. Since opp. sides of *ABCD* are ≅, *ABCD* is a ▱, so opp. sides $\overline{AB}$ and $\overline{CD}$ are ∥.

28. The corresponding ∠s are ≅, so the longer sides are parallel. Then both pairs of opposite sides are ∥ and the oblique I is a ▱ by the def. of a ▱.

29. The diags. of the figure that is drawn were drawn to bisect each other. Therefore, the figure is a ▱.

APPLICATION NOTE

EXERCISE 31 As the magnification of the binoculars increases, objects appear closer. But the more powerful the binoculars, the more they also magnify tremors, making the binoculars very difficult to hold steady. The parallelogram mount holds the binoculars steady.

STUDENT HELP NOTES

Homework Help Students can find help for Exs. 34–36 at **www.mcdougallittell.com.** The information can be printed out for students who don't have access to the Internet.

ENGLISH LEARNERS

EXERCISES 39–41

Remembering English-language mathematical terms can be even more challenging for English learners than for other students. Before assigning Exercises 39-41, you might review with the class the difference between a biconditional statement and a conditional statement.

30, 31, 36. See Additional Answers beginning on page AA1.

ADDITIONAL PRACTICE AND RETEACHING

For Lesson 6.3:

- Practice Levels A, B, and C (*Chapter 6 Resource Book*, p. 40)
- Reteaching with Practice (*Chapter 6 Resource Book*, p. 43)
- See Lesson 6.3 of the *Personal Student Tutor*

For more Mixed Review:

- Search the *Test and Practice Generator* for key words or specific lessons.

32. The sum of the measures of the interior ∆s of a quad. is 360°, so $m\angle R + m\angle S + m\angle T + m\angle U = 360°$. It is given that $\angle R \cong \angle T$ and $\angle S \cong \angle U$, so $m\angle R = m\angle T$ and $m\angle S = m\angle U$ and, by the substitution prop. of equality, $m\angle T + m\angle S + m\angle T + m\angle S = 360°$. Then $2(m\angle S) + 2(m\angle T) = 360°$ and $m\angle S + m\angle T = 180°$. By the Consecutive Interior Angles Converse, $\overline{ST} \parallel \overline{RU}$. Similarly, $\overline{SR} \parallel \overline{TU}$ and *RSTU* is a ▱ by the def. of a ▱.

33. Since $\angle P$ is supplementary to $\angle Q$, $\overline{QR} \parallel \overline{PS}$ by the Consecutive Interior Angles Converse. Similarly, $\overline{QP} \parallel \overline{RS}$ by the same theorem. Then *PQRS* is a ▱ by the def. of a ▱.

34. $(0, -a)$; the diags. of a ▱ bisect each other, so $(0, 0)$ is the midpoint of $\overline{MP}$. Let $P = (x, y)$. By the Midpoint Formula, $(0, 0) = \left(\frac{x+0}{2}, \frac{y+a}{2}\right)$ so $x = 0$ and $y = -a$.

35. $(-b, -c)$; the diags. of a ▱ bisect each other, so $(0, 0)$ is the midpoint of $\overline{QN}$. Let $Q = (x, y)$. By the Midpoint Formula, $(0, 0) = \left(\frac{x+b}{2}, \frac{y+c}{2}\right)$, so $x = -b$ and $y = -c$.

STUDENT HELP

HOMEWORK HELP Visit our Web site www.mcdougallittell.com for help with the coordinate proof in Exs. 34–36.

30. **CONSTRUCTION** There are many ways to use a compass and straightedge to construct a parallelogram. Describe a method that uses Theorem 6.6, Theorem 6.8, or Theorem 6.10. Then use your method to construct a parallelogram. **See margin.**

31. **BIRD WATCHING** You are designing a binocular mount that will keep the binoculars pointed in the same direction while they are raised and lowered for different viewers. If $\overline{BC}$ is always vertical, the binoculars will always point in the same direction. How can you design the mount so $\overline{BC}$ is always vertical? Justify your answer. **See margin.**

PROVING THEOREMS 6.7 AND 6.8 Write a proof of the theorem. **32, 33. See margin.**

32. Prove Theorem 6.7.

GIVEN ▶ $\angle R \cong \angle T$, $\angle S \cong \angle U$

PROVE ▶ *RSTU* is a parallelogram.

Plan for Proof Show that the sum $2(m\angle S) + 2(m\angle T) = 360°$, so $\angle S$ and $\angle T$ are supplementary and $\overline{SR} \parallel \overline{UT}$.

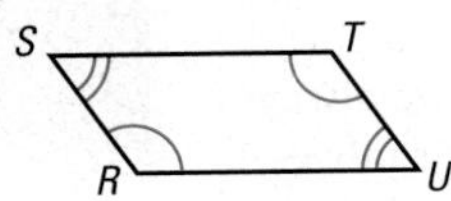

33. Prove Theorem 6.8.

GIVEN ▶ $\angle P$ is supplementary to $\angle Q$ and $\angle S$.

PROVE ▶ *PQRS* is a parallelogram.

Plan for Proof Show that opposite sides of *PQRS* are parallel.

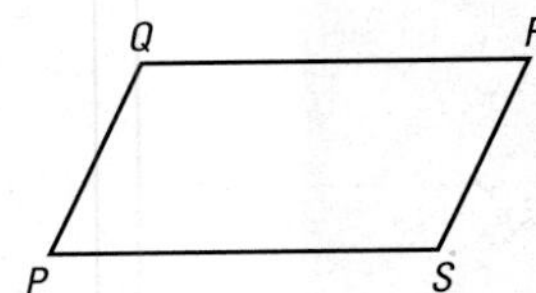

PROVING THEOREM 6.9 In Exercises 34–36, complete the coordinate proof of Theorem 6.9. **34–36. See margin.**

GIVEN ▶ Diagonals $\overline{MP}$ and $\overline{NQ}$ bisect each other.

PROVE ▶ *MNPQ* is a parallelogram.

Plan for Proof Show that opposite sides of *MNPQ* have the same slope.

Place *MNPQ* in the coordinate plane so the diagonals intersect at the origin and $\overline{MP}$ lies on the y-axis. Let the coordinates of M be $(0, a)$ and the coordinates of N be (b, c). Copy the graph at the right.

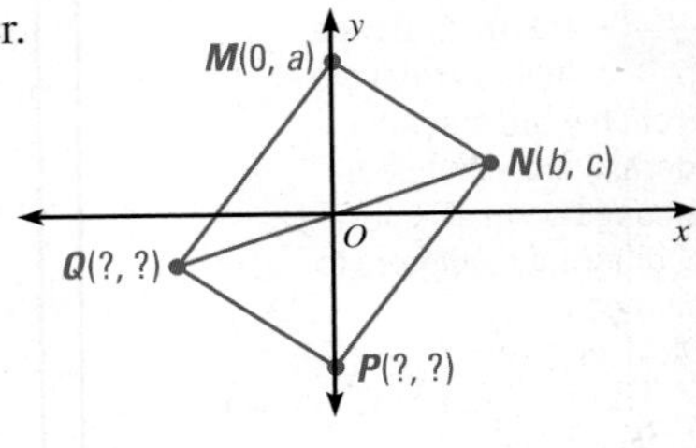

34. What are the coordinates of P? Explain your reasoning and label the coordinates on your graph.

35. What are the coordinates of Q? Explain your reasoning and label the coordinates on your graph.

36. Find the slope of each side of *MNPQ* and show that the slopes of opposite sides are equal.

Test Preparation

37. a. The acute ∠s of a right △ are complementary.

b. The ball bounces off each wall at the same ∠ at which it hit the wall, so $m\angle DFG = m\angle AFE$. Since △DFG is a right △ and the acute ∠s of a right △ are complementary, $m\angle FGD \approx 63°$.

d. $m\angle FEH = m\angle HGF \approx 54°$; $m\angle EFG = m\angle GHE \approx 126°$; ▱; if opp. ∠s of a quad. are ≅, then it is a ▱.

★ Challenge

EXTRA CHALLENGE

www.mcdougallittell.com

37. **MULTI-STEP PROBLEM** You shoot a pool ball as shown at the right and it rolls back to where it started. The ball bounces off each wall at the same angle at which it hit the wall. Copy the diagram and add each angle measure as you know it.

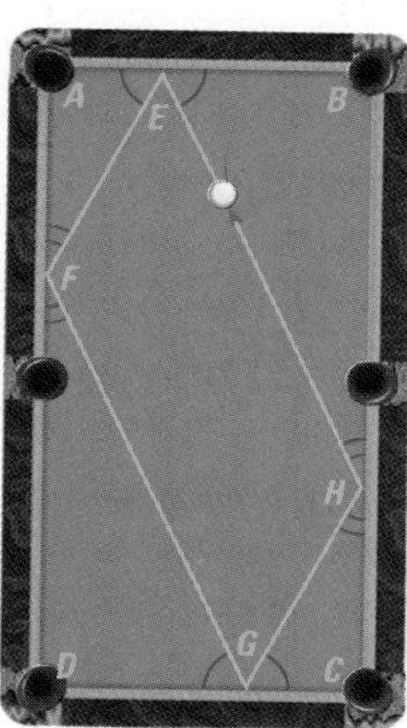

a. The ball hits the first wall at an angle of about 63°. So $m\angle AEF = m\angle BEH \approx 63°$. Explain why $m\angle AFE \approx 27°$.

b. Explain why $m\angle FGD \approx 63°$.

c. What is $m\angle GHC$? $m\angle EHB$? 27°; 27°

d. Find the measure of each interior angle of $EFGH$. What kind of shape is $EFGH$? How do you know?

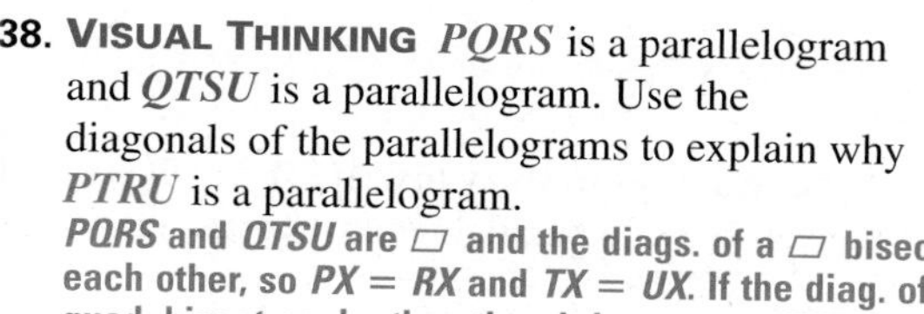

38. **VISUAL THINKING** $PQRS$ is a parallelogram and $QTSU$ is a parallelogram. Use the diagonals of the parallelograms to explain why $PTRU$ is a parallelogram.
PQRS and QTSU are ▱ and the diags. of a ▱ bisect each other, so $PX = RX$ and $TX = UX$. If the diag. of a quad. bisect each other, then it is a ▱, so PTRU is a ▱.

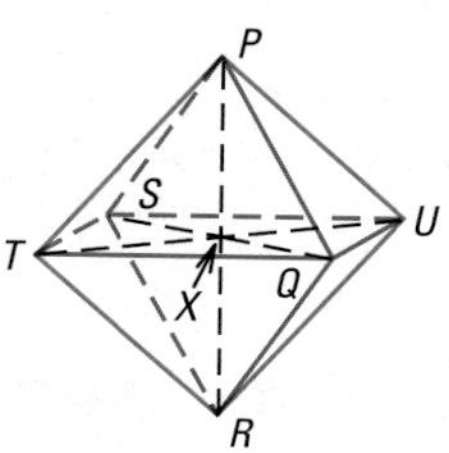

MIXED REVIEW

USING ALGEBRA Rewrite the biconditional statement as a conditional statement and its converse. (Review 2.2 for 6.4)

39. $x^2 + 2 = 2$ if and only if $x = 0$.
If $x^2 + 2 = 2$, then $x = 0$. If $x = 0$, then $x^2 + 2 = 2$.

40. $4x + 7 = x + 37$ if and only if $x = 10$.
If $4x + 7 = x + 37$, then $x = 10$. If $x = 10$, then $4x + 7 = x + 37$.

41. A quadrilateral is a parallelogram if and only if each pair of opposite sides are parallel.

41. If a quad. is a ▱, then each pair of opp. sides are ∥. If each pair of opp. sides of a quad. are ∥, then the quad. is a ▱.

WRITING BICONDITIONAL STATEMENTS Write the pair of theorems from Lesson 5.1 as a single biconditional statement. (Review 2.2, 5.1 for 6.4)

42. Theorems 5.1 and 5.2

43. Theorems 5.3 and 5.4

42. A point is on the ⊥ bisector of a segment if and only if the point is equidistant from the endpoints of the segment.

43. A point is on the bisector of an ∠ if and only if the point is equidistant from the two sides of the ∠.

44. Write an equation of the line that is perpendicular to $y = -4x + 2$ and passes through the point $(1, -2)$. (Review 3.7) $y = \frac{1}{4}x - \frac{9}{4}$

ANGLE MEASURES Find the value of *x*. (Review 4.1)

45. 60

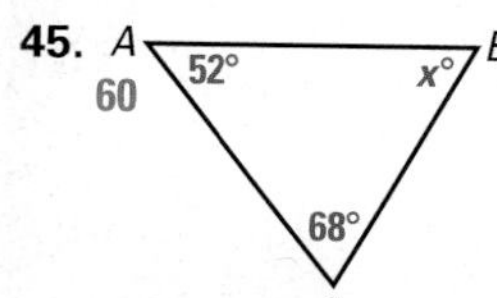

46. 48

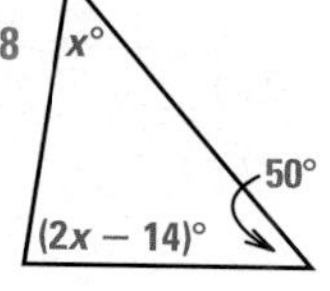

47. 35

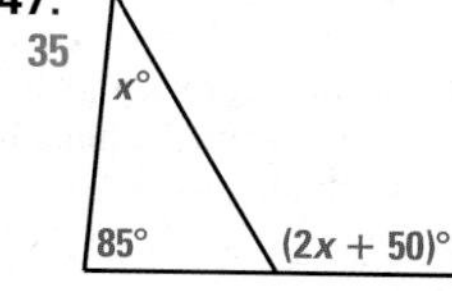

4 ASSESS

DAILY HOMEWORK QUIZ

Transparency Available

1. Describe how to prove that $ACEG$ is a parallelogram given that $\triangle BCD \cong \triangle FGH$ and $\triangle DEF \cong \triangle HAB$.

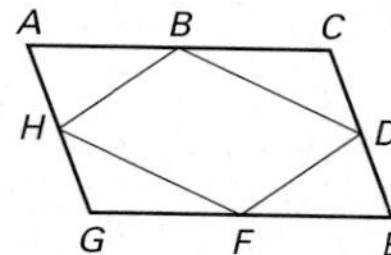

Since corresp. parts of ≅ △s are ≅, $\angle C \cong \angle G$ and $\angle E \cong \angle A$. Both pairs of opp. ∠s of ACEG are ≅, so ACEG is a ▱.

2. Prove that $EFGH$ is a parallelogram by showing that a pair of opposite sides are both congruent and parallel. Use $E(1, 2)$, $F(7, 9)$, $G(9, 8)$, and $H(3, 1)$. Using $\overline{EF}$ and $\overline{GH}$: $EF = GH = \sqrt{85}$, so $\overline{EF} \cong \overline{GH}$. Slope of $\overline{EF}$ = slope of $\overline{GH} = \frac{7}{6}$, so $\overline{EF} \parallel \overline{GH}$.

3. Prove that $JKLM$ is a parallelogram by showing that the diagonals bisect each other. Use $J(-4, 4)$, $K(-1, 5)$, $L(1, -1)$, and $M(-2, -2)$. The midpoints of diags. $\overline{JL}$ and $\overline{KM}$ are both $(-1.5, 1.5)$, so they bisect each other.

EXTRA CHALLENGE NOTE

Challenge problems for Lesson 6.3 are available in **blackline** format in the *Chapter 6 Resource Book*, p. 48 and at **www.mcdougallittell.com.**

ADDITIONAL TEST PREPARATION

1. **OPEN ENDED** Choose four coordinates that can represent the vertices of a parallelogram. See sample answer at left.

2. **WRITING** An ironing board has X-shaped legs that intersect at each other's midpoints. How do you know that the ironing surface is parallel to the floor? See sample answer at left.

Additional Test Preparation *Sample answers:*

1. $A(-4, 3)$, $B(3, 4)$, $C(4, -1)$, and $D(-3, -2)$

2. The legs form the diagonals of a quadrilateral, which is a parallelogram because the legs bisect each other. So, the opposite sides formed by the floor and ironing surface are parallel.

ADDITIONAL RESOURCES

An alternative Quiz for Lessons 6.1–6.3 is available in the *Chapter 6 Resource Book,* p. 49.

A **blackline** master with additional Math & History exercises is available in the *Chapter 6 Resource Book,* p. 47.

3. ***ABCG*** **and** ***CDEF*** **are ▱s so ∠*A* ≅ ∠*BCG* and ∠*DCF* ≅ ∠*E*. (Opp. ∠s of a ▱ are ≅.) ∠*BCG* ≅ ∠*DCF* by the Vert. ∠s Thm. Then ∠*A* ≅ ∠*E* by the Transitive Prop. of Cong.**

4. ***Sample answers:*** **Use slopes to show that both pairs of opp. sides are ∥, use the Distance Formula to show that both pairs of opp. sides are ≅, use slope and the Distance Formula to show that one pair of opp. sides are both ∥ and ≅, use the Midpoint Formula to show that the diags. bisect each other.**

QUIZ 1

1. Choose the words that describe the quadrilateral at the right: *concave, convex, equilateral, equiangular,* and *regular.* **(Lesson 6.1)**
convex, equilateral, equiangular, regular

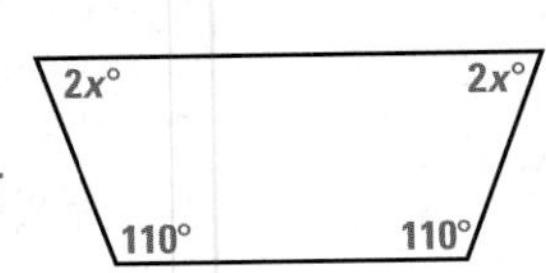

2. Find the value of x. Explain your reasoning. **(Lesson 6.1)**
35; the sum of the measures of the interior ∠s of a quad. is 360°, so $2x + 2x + 110 + 110 = 360$, $4x = 140$, and $x = 35$.

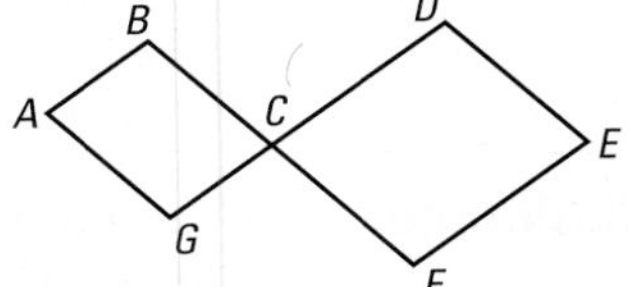

3. Write a proof. **(Lesson 6.2)** **See margin.**

GIVEN ▶ *ABCG* and *CDEF* are parallelograms.

PROVE ▶ ∠*A* ≅ ∠*E*

4. Describe two ways to show that $A(-4, 1)$, $B(3, 0)$, $C(5, -7)$, and $D(-2, -6)$ are the vertices of a parallelogram. **(Lesson 6.3)** **See margin.**

MATH & History — History of Finding Area

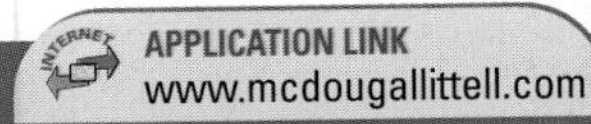

APPLICATION LINK www.mcdougallittell.com

THEN — THOUSANDS OF YEARS AGO, the Egyptians needed to find the area of the land they were farming. The mathematical methods they used are described in a papyrus dating from about 1650 B.C.

NOW — TODAY, satellites and aerial photographs can be used to measure the areas of large or inaccessible regions.

1. Find the area of the trapezoid outlined on the aerial photograph. The formula for the area of a trapezoid appears on page 374.
1,150,000 ft²

c.1650 B.C.

This Egyptian papyrus includes methods for finding area.

Methods for finding area are recorded in this Chinese manuscript.

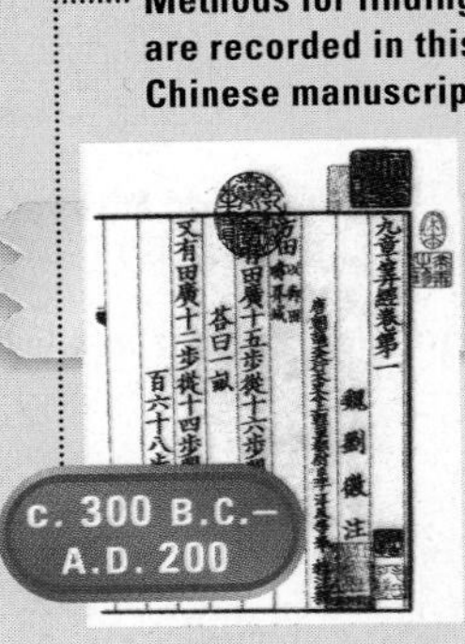

c. 300 B.C.–A.D. 200

Surveyors use signals from satellites to measure large areas.

1990s

6.4 Rhombuses, Rectangles, and Squares

What *you should learn*

GOAL 1 Use properties of sides and angles of rhombuses, rectangles, and squares.

GOAL 2 Use properties of diagonals of rhombuses, rectangles, and squares.

Why *you should learn it*

▼ To simplify **real-life** tasks, such as checking whether a theater flat is rectangular in **Example 6**.

REAL LIFE

GOAL 1 PROPERTIES OF SPECIAL PARALLELOGRAMS

In this lesson you will study three special types of parallelograms: *rhombuses*, *rectangles*, and *squares*.

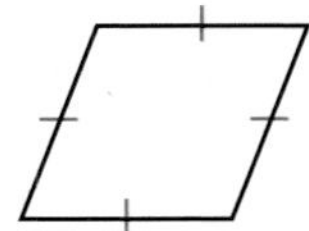

A **rhombus** is a parallelogram with four congruent sides.

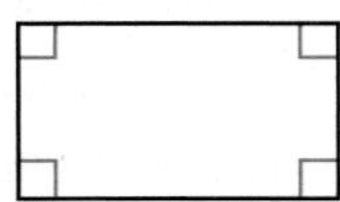

A **rectangle** is a parallelogram with four right angles.

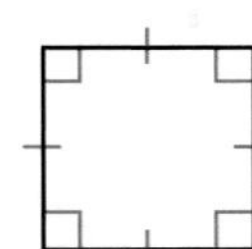

A **square** is a parallelogram with four congruent sides and four right angles.

The *Venn diagram* at the right shows the relationships among parallelograms, rhombuses, rectangles, and squares. Each shape has the properties of every group that it belongs to. For instance, a square is a rectangle, a rhombus, and a parallelogram, so it has all of the properties of each of those shapes.

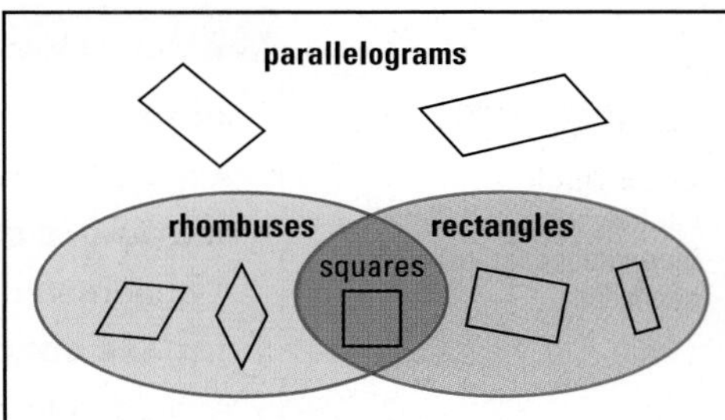

EXAMPLE 1 *Describing a Special Parallelogram*

Decide whether the statement is *always*, *sometimes*, or *never* true.

a. A rhombus is a rectangle.

b. A parallelogram is a rectangle.

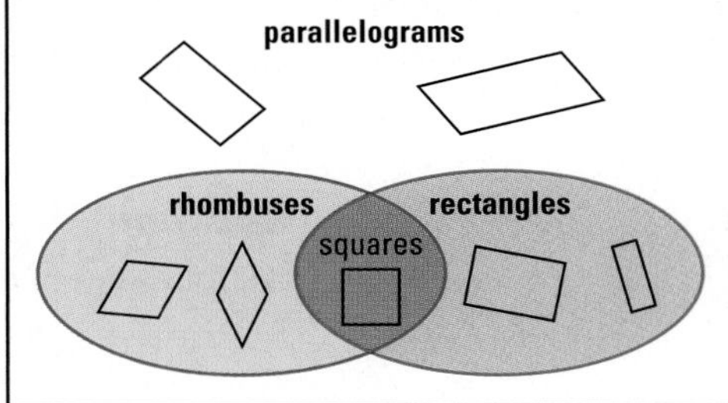

SOLUTION

a. The statement is *sometimes* true. In the Venn diagram, the regions for rhombuses and rectangles overlap. If the rhombus is a square, it is a rectangle.

b. The statement is *sometimes* true. Some parallelograms are rectangles. In the Venn diagram, you can see that some of the shapes in the parallelogram box are in the region for rectangles, but many aren't.

CALIFORNIA STANDARDS AND ASSESSMENT

CA Standards: 4, 7, 12, 17

1 PLAN

PACING

Basic: 2 days
Average: 2 days
Advanced: 2 days
Block Schedule: 0.5 block with 6.3
0.5 block with 6.5

LESSON OPENER
GEOMETRY SOFTWARE

An alternative way to approach Lesson 6.4 is to use the Geometry Software Lesson Opener:

- Blackline Master (*Chapter 6 Resource Book*, p. 53)
- Transparency (p. 37)

MEETING INDIVIDUAL NEEDS

- ***Chapter 6 Resource Book***
  Prerequisite Skills Review (p. 5)
  Practice Level A (p. 58)
  Practice Level B (p. 59)
  Practice Level C (p. 60)
  Reteaching with Practice (p. 61)
  Absent Student Catch-Up (p. 63)
  Challenge (p. 65)
- ***Resources in Spanish***
- ***Personal Student Tutor***

NEW-TEACHER SUPPORT

See the Tips for New Teachers on pp. 1–2 of the *Chapter 6 Resource Book* for additional notes about Lesson 6.4.

WARM-UP EXERCISES

Transparency Available

1. In $\square ABCD$, $m\angle A = 3x + 15$ and $m\angle C = 5x - 17$. What is the value of x? 16
2. Find the distance between $K(1, 3)$ and $M(3, 4)$ $\sqrt{5}$
3. In $\square KJLM$, $KJ = 10y - 5$ and $LM = -6y + 27$. What is the value of y? 2
4. The vertices of $PQRS$ are $P(-1, -3)$, $Q(2, -4)$, $R(5, -1)$, and $S(2, 0)$. Is $PQRS$ a parallelogram? yes

2 TEACH

MOTIVATING THE LESSON

Ask students where they have seen diamond shapes, such as in tile or upholstery designs. Point out that this shape is actually a *rhombus*, a special kind of parallelogram that they will learn about in this lesson.

EXTRA EXAMPLE 1

Decide whether the statement is *always, sometimes,* or *never* true.

a. A rectangle is a square. **sometimes**

b. A square is a rhombus. **always**

EXTRA EXAMPLE 2

QRST is a square. What else do you know about *QRST*? **It has four right ∠s and four ≅ sides. Its opp. sides are ∥. Its opp. angles are ≅. Its consec. ∠s are supplementary. Its diagonals bisect each other.**

EXTRA EXAMPLE 3

EFGH is a rectangle. *K* is the midpoint of *FH*. If $EG = 8z - 16$, what is $\overline{EK}$? $\overline{GK}$? **$4z - 8$; $4z - 8$**

CHECKPOINT EXERCISES

For use after Example 1:

1. Is the statement *A rectangle is a parallelogram* always, sometimes, or never true? **always**

For use after Examples 2 and 3:

2. *ABCD* is a rectangle and $m\angle B = 8x + 26$. What is the value of *x*? **8**

EXAMPLE 2 *Using Properties of Special Parallelograms*

ABCD is a rectangle. What else do you know about *ABCD*?

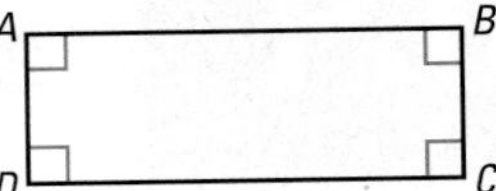

SOLUTION

Because *ABCD* is a rectangle, it has four right angles by the definition. The definition also states that rectangles are parallelograms, so *ABCD* has all the properties of a parallelogram:

- Opposite sides are parallel and congruent.
- Opposite angles are congruent and consecutive angles are supplementary.
- Diagonals bisect each other.

....

A rectangle is defined as a *parallelogram* with four right angles. But *any quadrilateral* with four right angles is a rectangle because any quadrilateral with four right angles is a parallelogram. In Exercises 48–50 you will justify the following corollaries to the definitions of rhombus, rectangle, and square.

STUDENT HELP

Look Back
For help with biconditional statements, see p. 80.

COROLLARIES ABOUT SPECIAL QUADRILATERALS

RHOMBUS COROLLARY
A quadrilateral is a rhombus if and only if it has four congruent sides.

RECTANGLE COROLLARY
A quadrilateral is a rectangle if and only if it has four right angles.

SQUARE COROLLARY
A quadrilateral is a square if and only if it is a rhombus and a rectangle.

You can use these corollaries to prove that a quadrilateral is a rhombus, rectangle, or square without proving first that the quadrilateral is a parallelogram.

EXAMPLE 3 *Using Properties of a Rhombus*

In the diagram at the right, *PQRS* is a rhombus. What is the value of *y*?

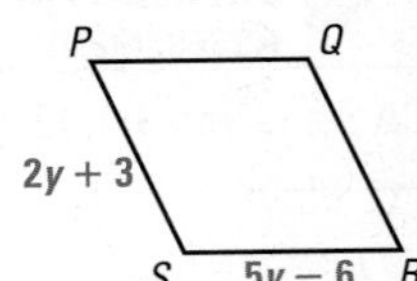

SOLUTION

All four sides of a rhombus are congruent, so $RS = PS$.

$5y - 6 = 2y + 3$	**Equate lengths of congruent sides.**
$5y = 2y + 9$	**Add 6 to each side.**
$3y = 9$	**Subtract 2*y* from each side.**
$y = 3$	**Divide each side by 3.**

GOAL 2 USING DIAGONALS OF SPECIAL PARALLELOGRAMS

The following theorems are about diagonals of rhombuses and rectangles. You are asked to prove Theorems 6.12 and 6.13 in Exercises 51, 52, 59, and 60.

THEOREMS

THEOREM 6.11

A parallelogram is a rhombus if and only if its diagonals are perpendicular.

ABCD is a rhombus if and only if $\overline{AC} \perp \overline{BD}$.

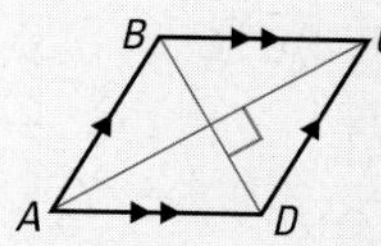

THEOREM 6.12

A parallelogram is a rhombus if and only if each diagonal bisects a pair of opposite angles.

ABCD is a rhombus if and only if $\overline{AC}$ bisects $\angle DAB$ and $\angle BCD$ and $\overline{BD}$ bisects $\angle ADC$ and $\angle CBA$.

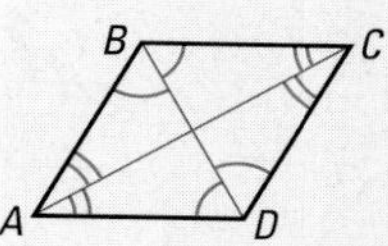

THEOREM 6.13

A parallelogram is a rectangle if and only if its diagonals are congruent.

ABCD is a rectangle if and only if $\overline{AC} \cong \overline{BD}$.

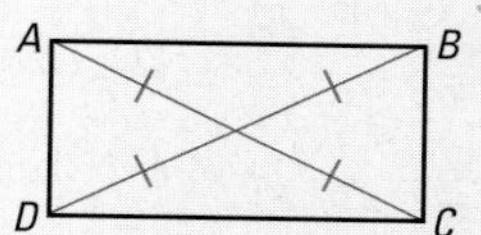

You can rewrite Theorem 6.11 as a conditional statement and its converse.

Conditional statement: If the diagonals of a parallelogram are perpendicular, then the parallelogram is a rhombus.

Converse: If a parallelogram is a rhombus, then its diagonals are perpendicular.

To prove the theorem, you must prove both statements.

EXAMPLE 4 *Proving Theorem 6.11*

Write a paragraph proof of the converse above.

GIVEN ▶ *ABCD* is a rhombus.

PROVE ▶ $\overline{AC} \perp \overline{BD}$

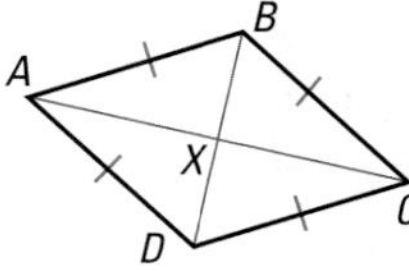

SOLUTION

Paragraph Proof *ABCD* is a rhombus, so $\overline{AB} \cong \overline{CB}$. Because *ABCD* is a parallelogram, its diagonals bisect each other so $\overline{AX} \cong \overline{CX}$ and $\overline{BX} \cong \overline{BX}$. Use the SSS Congruence Postulate to prove $\triangle AXB \cong \triangle CXB$, so $\angle AXB \cong \angle CXB$. Then, because $\overline{AC}$ and $\overline{BD}$ intersect to form congruent adjacent angles, $\overline{AC} \perp \overline{BD}$.

STUDENT HELP

INTERNET HOMEWORK HELP
Visit our Web site www.mcdougallittell.com for extra examples.

EXTRA EXAMPLE 4

Write a paragraph proof of this conditional of Theorem 6.13: If the diagonals of a parallelogram are congruent, then it is a rectangle.

Given: ▱*ABCD* with $\overline{AC} \cong \overline{BD}$
Prove: *ABCD* is a rectangle.
Solution: Because *ABCD* is a ▱, $\overline{AB} \cong \overline{CD}$. $\overline{AC} \cong \overline{BD}$ is given, and $\overline{BC} \cong \overline{BC}$ by the Reflexive Prop. of Cong., so $\triangle ABC \cong \triangle DCB$ by the SSS Cong. Post. Then $\angle ABC \cong \angle DCB$ because corresp. parts of ≅ △ are ≅. These ∠s are supplementary because they are consec. ∠s of a ▱. You can then use substitution ($m\angle ABC + m\angle ABC = 180$) and algebra to show that $\angle ABC$ and $\angle DCB$ are both right ∠s. The opp. ∠s of a ▱ are ≅, so $\angle DAB$ and $\angle ADC$ are also right ∠s. So, *ABCD* meets the definition of a rectangle.

CHECKPOINT EXERCISES

For use after Example 4:

1. In ▱*ABCD*, the diagonals meet at point *E*, and $AE = BE = 6$. Is *ABCD* a rectangle? Explain. **Yes; because the diags. of a ▱ bisect each other, $CE = DE = 6$. Then, $AC = AE + CE = 6 + 6 = 12$, and $BD = BE + DE = 6 + 6 + 12$. Because the diags. of *ABCD* are ≅, it is a ▱.**

MULTIPLE REPRESENTATIONS

Many proofs in geometry involve a labeled figure. The way in which you represent the figure often depends upon the type of proof you are doing. The proof in Example 4 on page 349 involves a simple diagram of a rhombus. For the proof in Example 5 on page 350, the rhombus must be drawn on a coordinate plane.

EXTRA EXAMPLE 5

Write a coordinate proof of the converse conditional from Theorem 6.11.

Given: *ABCD* is a rhombus.

Prove: $\overline{AC} \perp \overline{BD}$

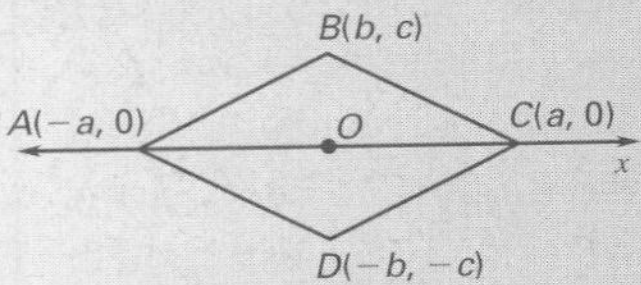

Choose a diagonal on the x-axis. Because the diagonals of a rhombus bisect each other, choosing $A(-a, 0)$ gives you $C(a, 0)$. $OB = OD$, so choosing $B(b, c)$ gives you $D(-b, -c)$. The sides of a rhombus are ≅, so $AB = BC$, which by the Distance Formula gives $\sqrt{(b-a)^2 + c^2} = \sqrt{(b+a)^2 + c^2}$. Algebra gives $-ab = ab$. This is true when $ab = 0$. But $a \neq 0$, so $b = 0$. This gives vertices $B(0, c)$ and $D(0, -c)$, so they lie on the y-axis. So, $\overline{AC} \perp \overline{BD}$.

EXTRA EXAMPLE 6

a. You cut out a parallelogram-shaped quilt piece and measure the diagonals to be congruent. What is the shape? **rectangle**

b. An angle formed by the diagonals of the quilt piece measures 90°. Is the shape a square? **yes**

CHECKPOINT EXERCISES

For use after Examples 5 and 6:

1. In ▱*RSTV*, the diagonals form a pair of congruent angles at each vertex. What kind of figure is *RSTU*? **rhombus**

CLOSURE QUESTION

What is true of the diagonals of a rectangle and a square, but not of those of every rhombus? **They are congruent.**

DAILY PUZZLER

How many *non-square* rhombuses can be formed by connecting vertices on a 4-by-4 square grid? **16 (14 of side $\sqrt{5}$, 2 of side $\sqrt{10}$)**

EXAMPLE 5 *Coordinate Proof of Theorem 6.11*

Proof

In Example 4, a paragraph proof was given for part of Theorem 6.11. Write a coordinate proof of the original conditional statement.

GIVEN ▸ *ABCD* is a parallelogram, $\overline{AC} \perp \overline{BD}$.

PROVE ▸ *ABCD* is a rhombus.

SOLUTION

Assign coordinates Because $\overline{AC} \perp \overline{BD}$, place *ABCD* in the coordinate plane so $\overline{AC}$ and $\overline{BD}$ lie on the axes and their intersection is at the origin.

Let $(0, a)$ be the coordinates of *A*, and let $(b, 0)$ be the coordinates of *B*.

Because *ABCD* is a parallelogram, the diagonals bisect each other and $OA = OC$. So, the coordinates of *C* are $(0, -a)$.

Similarly, the coordinates of *D* are $(-b, 0)$.

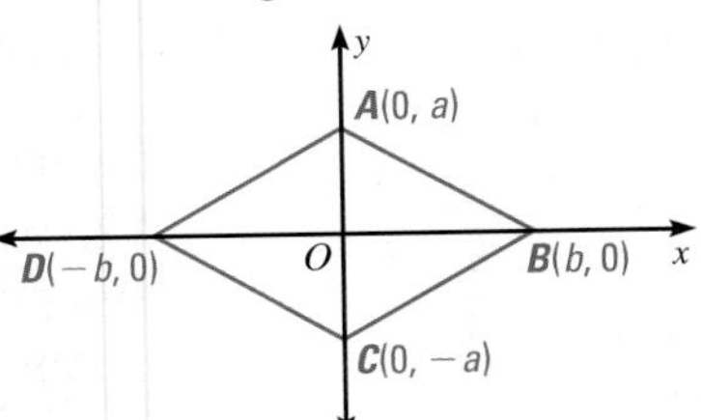

Find the lengths of the sides of *ABCD*. Use the Distance Formula.

$$AB = \sqrt{(b-0)^2 + (0-a)^2} = \sqrt{b^2 + a^2}$$

$$BC = \sqrt{(0-b)^2 + (-a-0)^2} = \sqrt{b^2 + a^2}$$

$$CD = \sqrt{(-b-0)^2 + [0-(-a)]^2} = \sqrt{b^2 + a^2}$$

$$DA = \sqrt{[0-(-b)]^2 + (a-0)^2} = \sqrt{b^2 + a^2}$$

▸ All of the side lengths are equal, so *ABCD* is a rhombus.

FOCUS ON APPLICATIONS

CARPENTRY If a screen door is not rectangular, you can use a piece of hardware called a *turnbuckle* to shorten the longer diagonal until the door is rectangular.

EXAMPLE 6 *Checking a Rectangle*

CARPENTRY You are building a rectangular frame for a theater set.

a. First, you nail four pieces of wood together, as shown at the right. What is the shape of the frame?

b. To make sure the frame is a rectangle, you measure the diagonals. One is 7 feet 4 inches and the other is 7 feet 2 inches. Is the frame a rectangle? Explain.

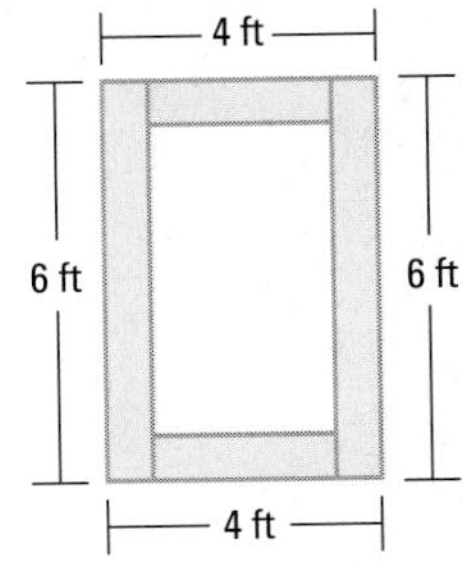

SOLUTION

a. Opposite sides are congruent, so the frame is a parallelogram.

b. The parallelogram is not a rectangle. If it were a rectangle, the diagonals would be congruent.

GUIDED PRACTICE

Vocabulary Check ✓

1. What is another name for an *equilateral quadrilateral*? rhombus

Concept Check ✓

2. Theorem 6.12 is a biconditional statement. Rewrite the theorem as a conditional statement and its converse, and tell what each statement means for parallelogram *PQRS*. See margin.

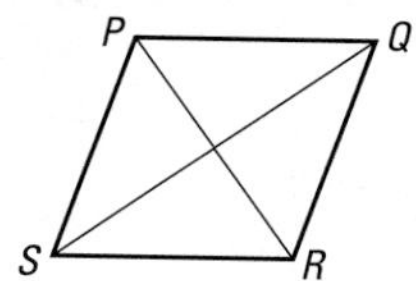

Skill Check ✓

Decide whether the statement is *sometimes, always,* or *never* true.

3. A rectangle is a parallelogram. always
4. A parallelogram is a rhombus. sometimes
5. A rectangle is a rhombus. sometimes
6. A square is a rectangle. always

Which of the following quadrilaterals have the given property?

7. All sides are congruent. C, D
8. All angles are congruent. B, D
9. The diagonals are congruent. B, D
10. Opposite angles are congruent. A, B, C, D

A. Parallelogram
B. Rectangle
C. Rhombus
D. Square

11. *MNPQ* is a rectangle. What is the value of *x*? 45

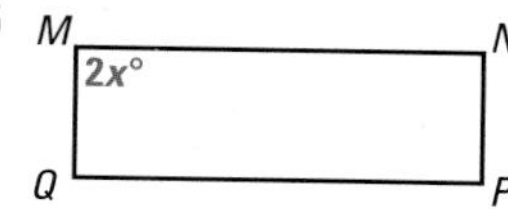

2. If a ▱ is a rhombus, then each diag. bisects a pair of opp. ∠s. If each diag. of a ▱ bisects a pair of opp. ∠s, then the ▱ is a rhombus; $\overline{PR}$ bisects ∠*QPS* and ∠*SRQ* and $\overline{QS}$ bisects ∠*PSR* and ∠*RQP*.

12. Always; all the ∠s of a rectangle are right ∠s and all right ∠s are ≅.

13. Sometimes; if rectangle *ABCD* is also a rhombus (a square), then $\overline{AB} \cong \overline{BC}$.

PRACTICE AND APPLICATIONS

STUDENT HELP

Extra Practice to help you master skills is on p. 814.

RECTANGLE **For any rectangle *ABCD*, decide whether the statement is *always, sometimes,* or *never* true. Draw a sketch and explain your answer.**
12–15. See margin.

12. $\angle A \cong \angle B$
13. $\overline{AB} \cong \overline{BC}$
14. $\overline{AC} \cong \overline{BD}$
15. $\overline{AC} \perp \overline{BD}$

14. Always; the diags. of a rectangle are ≅.

15. Sometimes; if rectangle *ABCD* is also a rhombus (a square), then the diags. of *ABCD* are ⊥.

PROPERTIES **List each quadrilateral for which the statement is true.**

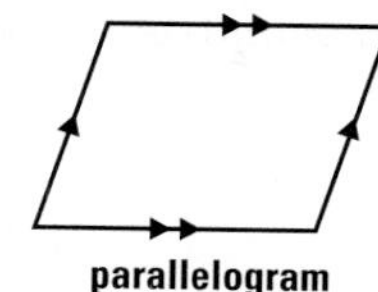
parallelogram

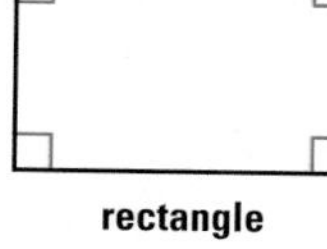
rectangle

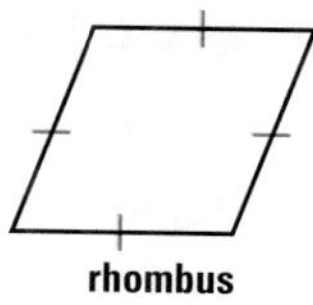
rhombus

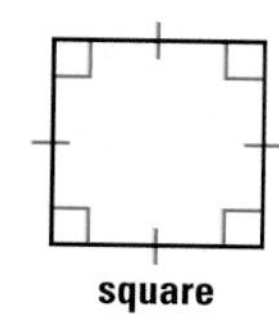
square

16. It is equiangular. rectangle, square
17. It is equiangular and equilateral. square
18. The diagonals are perpendicular. rhombus, square
19. Opposite sides are congruent. ▱, rectangle, rhombus, square
20. The diagonals bisect each other. ▱, rectangle, rhombus, square
21. The diagonals bisect opposite angles. rhombus, square

STUDENT HELP

HOMEWORK HELP

Example 1:	Exs. 12–15, 27–32
Example 2:	Exs. 27–32, 51
Example 3:	Exs. 33–43
Example 4:	Exs. 44–52
Example 5:	Exs. 55–60
Example 6:	Exs. 61, 62

PROPERTIES **Sketch the quadrilateral and list everything you know about it.**
22–24. Check sketches. See margin.

22. parallelogram *FGHI*
23. rhombus *PQRS*
24. square *ABCD*

3 APPLY

ASSIGNMENT GUIDE

BASIC
Day 1: pp. 351–352 Exs. 12–43
Day 2: pp. 353–355 Exs. 44–60, 66–68, 74–82 even, 83

AVERAGE
Day 1: pp. 351–352 Exs. 12–43
Day 2: pp. 353–355 Exs. 44–62, 66–68, 74–82 even, 83

ADVANCED
Day 1: pp. 351–352 Exs. 12–43
Day 2: pp. 353–355 Exs. 44–62, 66–72, 74–82 even, 83

BLOCK SCHEDULE
pp. 351–352 Exs. 12–43 (with 6.3)
pp. 353–355 Exs. 44–62, 66–68, 74–82 even, 83 (with 6.5)

EXERCISE LEVELS

Level A: ***Easier***
12–21

Level B: ***More Difficult***
22–45, 47–68, 73–83

Level C: ***Most Difficult***
46, 69–72

✓ HOMEWORK CHECK

To quickly check student understanding of key concepts, go over the following exercises: Exs. 14, 20, 36, 42, 46, 48, 54, 60. See also the Daily Homework Quiz:

- Blackline Master (*Chapter 6 Resource Book,* p. 68)
- Transparency (p. 44)

22. $\overline{FG} \parallel \overline{HI}$, $\overline{FI} \parallel \overline{GH}$, $\overline{FG} \cong \overline{HI}$, $\overline{FI} \cong \overline{GH}$, ∠*F* ≅ ∠*H*, ∠*G* ≅ ∠*I*, and $\overline{FH}$ and $\overline{GI}$ bisect each other.

23. $\overline{PQ} \parallel \overline{RS}$, $\overline{PS} \parallel \overline{QR}$, $\overline{PQ} \cong \overline{QR} \cong \overline{RS} \cong \overline{PS}$, ∠*P* ≅ ∠*R*, ∠*Q* ≅ ∠*S*, $\overline{PR}$ and $\overline{QS}$ bisect each other, $\overline{PR} \perp \overline{QS}$, $\overline{PR}$ bisects ∠*SPQ* and ∠*SRQ*, and $\overline{QS}$ bisects ∠*PSR* and ∠*PQR*.

24. See next page.

24. $\overline{AB} \parallel \overline{CD}$, $\overline{AD} \parallel \overline{BC}$, $\overline{AB} \cong \overline{BC} \cong \overline{CD} \cong \overline{AD}$, $\angle A \cong \angle B \cong \angle C \cong \angle D$ (and $m\angle A = m\angle B = m\angle C = m\angle D = 90°$), $\overline{AC}$ and $\overline{BD}$ bisect each other, $\overline{AC} \perp \overline{BD}$, $\overline{AC} \cong \overline{BD}$, $\overline{AC}$ bisects $\angle BAD$ and $\angle BCD$, and $\overline{BD}$ bisects $\angle ABC$ and $\angle ADC$.

28. Sometimes; if a rhombus is also a rectangle (a square), then all 4 ∠s are ≅.

29. Always; each diag. of a rhombus bisects a pair of opp. ∠s.

30. Always; a rhombus has 4 ≅ sides.

31. Sometimes; if a rhombus is also a rectangle (a square), then its diagonals are ≅.

LOGICAL REASONING **Give another name for the quadrilateral.**

25. equiangular quadrilateral rectangle

26. regular quadrilateral square

RHOMBUS **For any rhombus *ABCD*, decide whether the statement is *always, sometimes,* or *never* true. Draw a sketch and explain your answer.**

27–32. Check sketches.

27. $\angle A \cong \angle C$
Always; opp. ∠s of a ▱ are ≅.

28. $\angle A \cong \angle B$

29. $\angle ABD \cong \angle CBD$

30. $\overline{AB} \cong \overline{BC}$

31. $\overline{AC} \cong \overline{BD}$

32. $\overline{AD} \cong \overline{CD}$
Always; a rhombus has 4 ≅ sides.

USING ALGEBRA **Find the value of *x*.**

33. *ABCD* is a square. 18

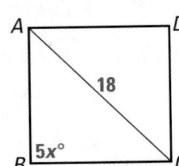

34. *EFGH* is a rhombus. 50

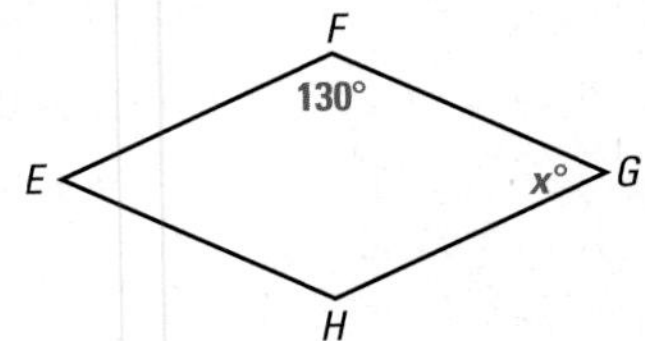

35. *KLMN* is a rectangle. 50

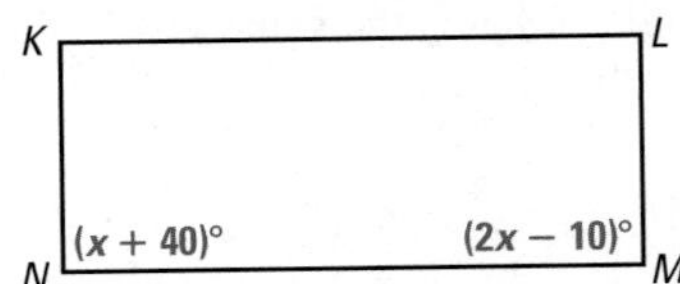

36. *PQRS* is a parallelogram. 5

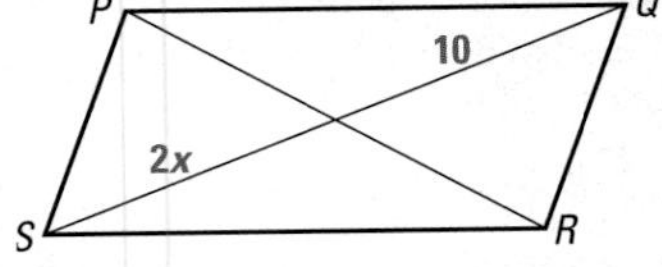

37. *TUWY* is a rhombus. 1

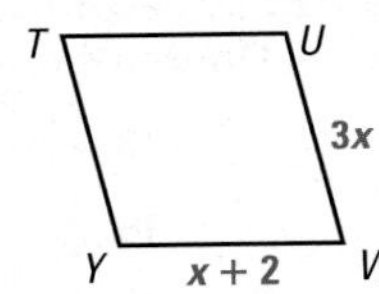

38. *CDEF* is a rectangle. 24

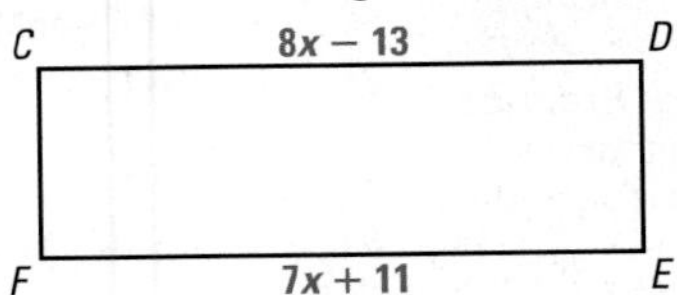

COMPLETING STATEMENTS ***GHJK* is a square with diagonals intersecting at *L*. Given that $GH = 2$ and $GL = \sqrt{2}$, complete the statement.**

39. $HK =$ __?__ $2\sqrt{2}$

40. $m\angle KLJ =$ __?__ 90°

41. $m\angle HJG =$ __?__ 45°

42. Perimeter of $\triangle HJK =$ __?__ $4 + 2\sqrt{2}$

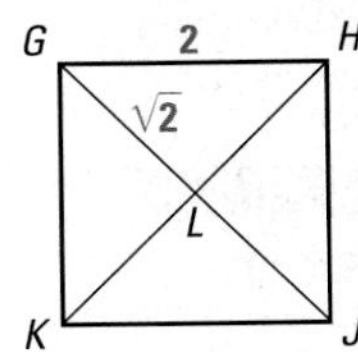

43. **USING ALGEBRA** *WXYZ* is a rectangle. The perimeter of $\triangle XYZ$ is 24. $XY + YZ = 5x - 1$ and $XZ = 13 - x$. Find *WY*. 10

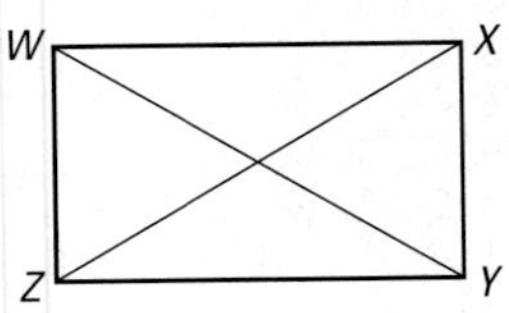

45. Assume temporarily that $\overline{MN} \parallel \overline{PQ}$, $\angle 1 \not\cong \angle 2$, and that $\overline{MQ} \parallel \overline{NP}$. By the def. of a ▱, $MNPQ$ is a ▱. This contradicts the given information that $\angle 1 \not\cong \angle 2$. It follows that $\overline{MQ}$ is not $\parallel \overline{NP}$.

46. $RSTU$ is a ▱ and $\overline{SU} \perp \overline{RT}$, so $RSTU$ is a rhombus. (A ▱ is a rhombus if and only if its diags. are ⊥.) Then $\angle STR \cong \angle UTR$, since each diag. of a rhombus bisects a pair of opp. ∠s.

48. If a quad. is a rhombus, then it has 4 ≅ sides (def. of rhombus); if a quad. has 4 ≅ sides, then it is a rhombus. (Both pairs of opp. sides are ≅, so the quad. is a ▱. A ▱ with 4 ≅ sides is a rhombus.)

49. If a quad. is a rectangle, then it has 4 right ∠s (def. of rectangle); if a quad. has 4 right ∠s, then it is a rectangle. (Both pairs of opp. ∠s are ≅, so the quad. is a ▱. By definition, a ▱ with 4 right ∠s is a rectangle.)

50. If a quad. is a square, then it is a rhombus and a rectangle. (A square is a ▱ that is equilateral (a rhombus) and equiangular (a rectangle).) If a quad. is a rhombus and a rectangle, then it is a square. (Since the quad. is a rhombus, it is an equilateral ▱. Since it is a rectangle, it is equiangular. Therefore it is a square.)

44. **LOGICAL REASONING** What additional information do you need to prove that $ABCD$ is a square?
Sample answers: $\overline{AC} \cong \overline{DB}$; the measure of $\angle A$ (or $\angle B$, $\angle C$, or $\angle D$) is 90°.

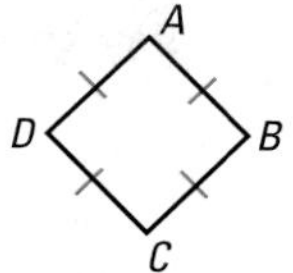

PROOF In Exercises 45 and 46, write any kind of proof. 45, 46. See margin.

45. **GIVEN ▸** $\overline{MN} \parallel \overline{PQ}$, $\angle 1 \not\cong \angle 2$

PROVE ▸ $\overline{MQ}$ is not parallel to $\overline{PN}$.

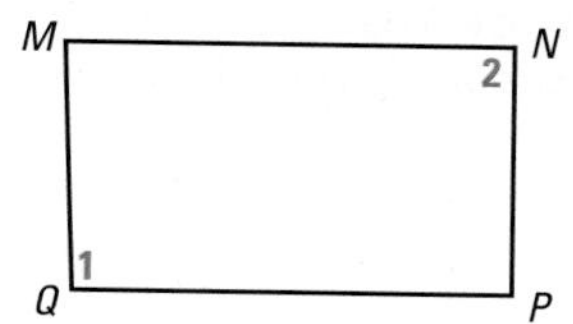

46. **GIVEN ▸** $RSTU$ is a ▱, $\overline{SU} \perp \overline{RT}$

PROVE ▸ $\angle STR \cong \angle UTR$

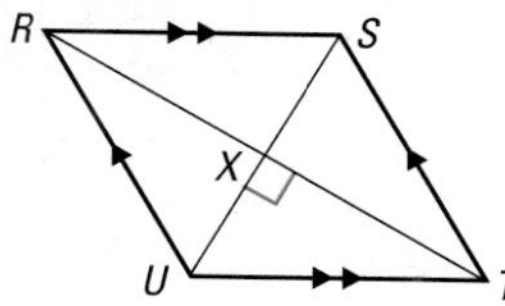

47. **BICONDITIONAL STATEMENTS** Rewrite Theorem 6.13 as a conditional statement and its converse. Tell what each statement means for parallelogram $JKLM$.
If a ▱ is a rectangle, then its diags. are ≅; if the diags. of a ▱ are ≅, then the ▱ is a rectangle; $JL \cong KM$.

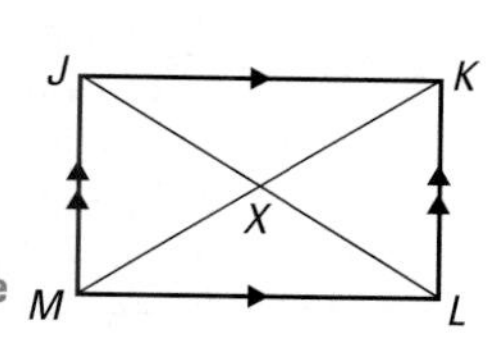

LOGICAL REASONING Write the corollary as a conditional statement and its converse. Then explain why each statement is true. 48–50. See margin.

48. Rhombus corollary

49. Rectangle corollary

50. Square corollary

PROVING THEOREM 6.12 Prove both conditional statements of Theorem 6.12. 51, 52. See margin.

51. **GIVEN ▸** $PQRT$ is a rhombus.

PROVE ▸ $\overline{PR}$ bisects $\angle TPQ$ and $\angle QRT$. $\overline{TQ}$ bisects $\angle PTR$ and $\angle RQP$.

Plan for Proof To prove that $\overline{PR}$ bisects $\angle TPQ$ and $\angle QRT$, first prove that $\triangle PRQ \cong \triangle PRT$.

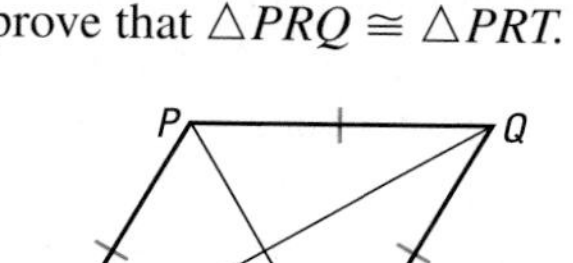

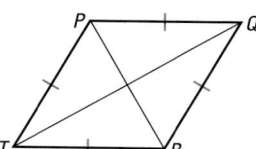

52. **GIVEN ▸** $FGHJ$ is a parallelogram. $\overline{FH}$ bisects $\angle JFG$ and $\angle GHJ$. $\overline{JG}$ bisects $\angle FJH$ and $\angle HGF$.

PROVE ▸ $FGHJ$ is a rhombus.

Plan for Proof Prove $\triangle FHJ \cong \triangle FHG$ so $\overline{JH} \cong \overline{GH}$. Then use the fact that $\overline{JH} \cong \overline{FG}$ and $\overline{GH} \cong \overline{FJ}$.

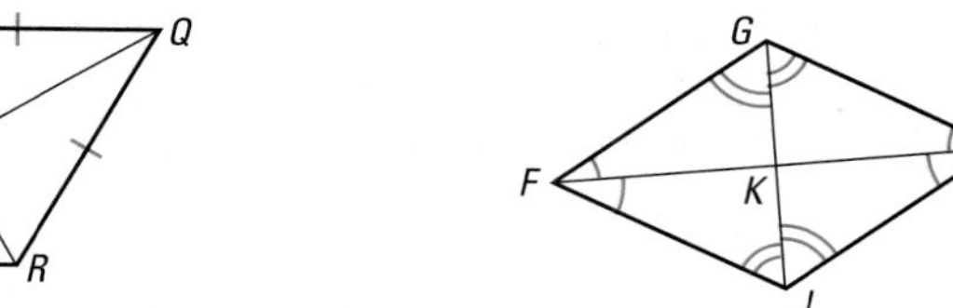

CONSTRUCTION Explain how to construct the figure using a straightedge and a compass. Use a definition or theorem from this lesson to explain why your method works. 53, 54. See margin.

53. a rhombus that is not a square

54. a rectangle that is not a square

! COMMON ERROR

EXERCISE 44 Some students may assume that the vertex angles are right angles because they look like right angles. Caution students not to make assumptions based on the looks of a diagram. Only clearly stated information can be regarded as given.

51. Statements (Reasons)
1. $PQRT$ is a rhombus. (Given)
2. $\overline{PQ} \cong \overline{QR} \cong \overline{RT} \cong \overline{PT}$ (A quad. is a rhombus if and only if it has 4 ≅ sides.)
3. $\overline{PR} \cong \overline{PR}$, $\overline{QT} \cong \overline{QT}$ (Reflexive Prop. of Cong.)
4. $\triangle PRQ \cong \triangle PRT$; $\triangle PTQ \cong \triangle RTQ$ (SSS Cong. Post.)
5. $\angle TPR \cong \angle QPR$, $\angle TRP \cong \angle QRP$, $\angle PTQ \cong \angle RTQ$, $\angle PQT \cong \angle RQT$ (Corresp. parts of ≅ ▵ are ≅.)
6. $\overline{PR}$ bisects $\angle TPQ$ and $\angle QRT$, $\overline{QT}$ bisects $\angle PTR$ and $\angle RQP$. (Def. of ∠ bisector)

52. It is given that $FGHJ$ is a ▱ and that $\overline{FH}$ bisects $\angle JFG$ and $\angle GHJ$, and that $\overline{JG}$ bisects $\angle FJH$ and $\angle HGF$. Opp. ∠s of a ▱ are ≅, so $m\angle FGH = m\angle FJH$ and $m\angle GFJ = m\angle GHJ$. It follows that $m\angle GFH = m\angle GHF = m\angle JFH = m\angle JHF$. $\overline{FH} \cong \overline{FH}$ by the Reflexive Prop. of Cong., so $\triangle FHJ \cong \triangle FHG$ by the ASA Cong. Post., and corresp. sides $\overline{JH}$ and $\overline{GH}$ are ≅. Since $FGHJ$ is a ▱, $\overline{JH} \cong \overline{FG}$ and $\overline{GH} \cong \overline{FJ}$. Then, by the Transitive Prop. of Cong., $\overline{FG} \cong \overline{GH} \cong \overline{JH} \cong \overline{FJ}$ and $FGHJ$ is a rhombus.

53. *Sample answer:* Draw $\overline{AB}$ and a line j (not ⊥ to $\overline{AB}$) intersecting $\overline{AB}$ at B. Construct $\overline{BC}$ on j so that $\overline{BC} \cong \overline{AB}$. Construct two arcs with radius AB and centers A and C, intersecting at D. Draw $\overline{AD}$ and $\overline{CD}$. Since all 4 sides of $ABCD$ are ≅, $ABCD$ is a rhombus. Since $\overline{AB}$ and $\overline{BC}$ are not ⊥, $ABCD$ is not a rectangle, and thus not a square.

54. See Additional Answers beginning on page AA1.

! COMMON ERROR

EXERCISE 59 Students may have trouble with general forms of coordinates. Suggest that they assign values to *a* and *b*, and then use these values and the model to determine specific coordinates of *M* before expressing general coordinates for *M*.

APPLICATION NOTE

EXERCISES 61 AND 62 It is not sufficient to know that the cross braces are the same length. To apply Theorem 6.13, the figure must be a parallelogram. That the diagonals bisect each other guarantees that the figure is a parallelogram.

STUDENT HELP NOTES

Software Help Instructions for several software packages are available in **blackline** format in the *Chapter 6 Resource Book*, p. 57 and at **www.mcdougallittell.com.**

61. *Sample answer:* Since cross braces $\overline{AD}$ and $\overline{BC}$ bisect each other, *ABDC* is a ▱. Since cross braces $\overline{AD}$ and $\overline{BC}$ also have the same length, *ABDC* is a rectangle. Since a rectangle has four right ∠s, $m\angle BAC = m\angle ABD = 90°$. Then $m\angle BAC = m\angle BAE$ and $m\angle ABD = m\angle ABF$, so $m\angle BAE = m\angle ABF = 90°$ by substitution. So tabletop $\overline{AB}$ is ⊥ to legs $\overline{AE}$ and $\overline{BF}$ by the def. of ⊥.

62, 64, 65. See Additional Answers beginning on page AA1.

ADDITIONAL PRACTICE AND RETEACHING

For Lesson 6.4:

- Practice Levels A, B, and C (*Chapter 6 Resource Book*, p. 58)
- Reteaching with Practice (*Chapter 6 Resource Book*, p. 61)
- See Lesson 6.4 of the *Personal Student Tutor*

For more Mixed Review:

- Search the *Test and Practice Generator* for key words or specific lessons.

COORDINATE GEOMETRY **It is given that *PQRS* is a parallelogram. Graph ▱*PQRS*. Decide whether it is a *rectangle*, a *rhombus*, a *square*, or *none of the above*. Justify your answer using theorems about quadrilaterals.** 55–58. See margin.

55. Rectangle; $PR = QS = \sqrt{41}$; since the diags. of *PQRS* are ≅, *PQRS* is a rectangle.

56. Rhombus; slope of $\overline{PR} = 0$, slope of $\overline{QS}$ is undefined. Therefore, $\overline{PR}$ is horizontal and $\overline{QS}$ is vertical. Since the diags. of *PQRS* are ⊥, *PQRS* is a rhombus.

57. Rectangle; $PR = QS = \sqrt{58}$; since the diags. of *PQRS* are ≅, *PQRS* is a rectangle.

58. Square; slope of $PR = 0$, slope of $\overline{QS}$ is undefined. Therefore, $\overline{PR}$ is horizontal and $\overline{QS}$ is vertical. Since the diags. of *PQRS* are ⊥, *PQRS* is a rhombus. $PR = QS = 6$, so the diags. of *PQRS* are ≅, and *PQRS* is a rectangle. A quad. that is both a rhombus and a rectangle is a square.

55. $P(3, 1)$	**56.** $P(5, 2)$	**57.** $P(-1, 4)$	**58.** $P(5, 2)$
$Q(3, -3)$	$Q(1, 9)$	$Q(-3, 2)$	$Q(2, 5)$
$R(-2, -3)$	$R(-3, 2)$	$R(2, -3)$	$R(-1, 2)$
$S(-2, 1)$	$S(1, -5)$	$S(4, -1)$	$S(2, -1)$

COORDINATE PROOF OF THEOREM 6.13 **In Exercises 59 and 60, you will complete a coordinate proof of one conditional statement of Theorem 6.13.**

GIVEN ▶ *KMNO* is a rectangle.

PROVE ▶ $\overline{OM} \cong \overline{KN}$

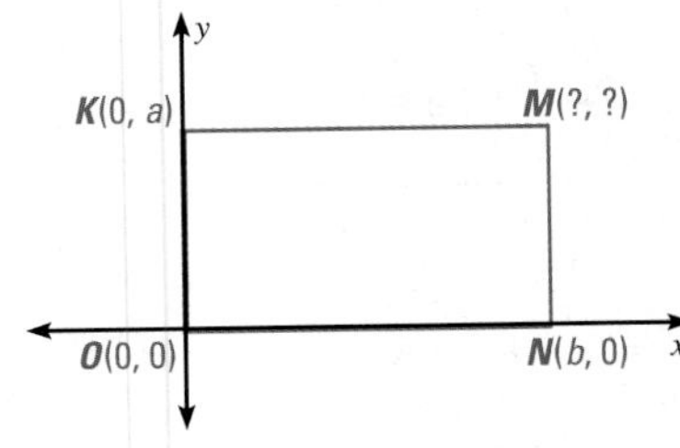

Because ∠*O* is a right angle, place *KMNO* in the coordinate plane so *O* is at the origin, $\overline{ON}$ lies on the *x*-axis and $\overline{OK}$ lies on the *y*-axis. Let the coordinates of *K* be $(0, a)$ and let the coordinates of *N* be $(b, 0)$.

59, 60. See margin.

59. What are the coordinates of *M*? Explain your reasoning.

60. Use the Distance Formula to prove that $\overline{OM} \cong \overline{KN}$.

PORTABLE TABLE **The legs of the table shown at the right are all the same length. The cross braces are all the same length and bisect each other.** 61, 62. See margin.

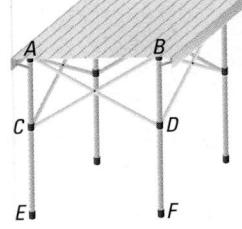

61. Show that the edge of the tabletop $\overline{AB}$ is perpendicular to legs $\overline{AE}$ and $\overline{BF}$.

62. Show that $\overline{AB}$ is parallel to $\overline{EF}$.

STUDENT HELP

SOFTWARE HELP Visit our Web site www.mcdougallittell.com to see instructions for several software applications.

59. (b, a); $\overline{KM} \cong \overline{ON}$, so $KM = b$ and $\overline{MN} \cong \overline{KO}$, so $MN = a$.

60. $OM = \sqrt{(b-0)^2 + (a-0)^2} = \sqrt{b^2 + a^2}$; $KN = \sqrt{(b-0)^2 + (0-a)^2} = \sqrt{b^2 + a^2}$

63. Rhombus; $\overline{AE} \cong \overline{CE} \cong \overline{AF} \cong \overline{CF}$; *AECF* remains a rhombus; *AECF* remains a rhombus.

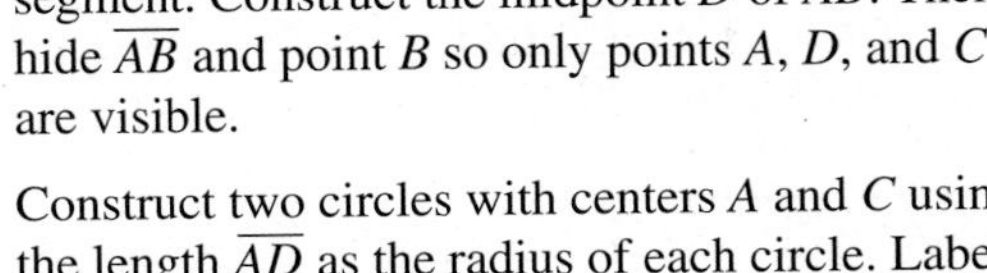

TECHNOLOGY **In Exercises 63–65, use geometry software.**

Draw a segment $\overline{AB}$ and a point *C* on the segment. Construct the midpoint *D* of $\overline{AB}$. Then hide $\overline{AB}$ and point *B* so only points *A*, *D*, and *C* are visible.

Construct two circles with centers *A* and *C* using the length *AD* as the radius of each circle. Label the points of intersection *E* and *F*. Draw $\overline{AE}$, $\overline{CE}$, $\overline{CF}$, and $\overline{AF}$. 63–65. See margin.

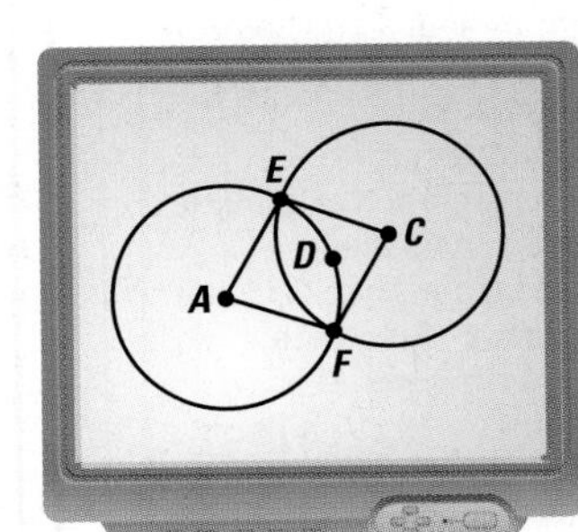

63. What kind of shape is *AECF*? How do you know? What happens to the shape as you drag *A*? drag *C*?

64. Hide the circles and point *D*, and draw diagonals $\overline{EF}$ and $\overline{AC}$. Measure ∠*EAC*, ∠*FAC*, ∠*AEF*, and ∠*CEF*. What happens to the measures as you drag *A*? drag *C*?

65. Which theorem does this construction illustrate?

Test Preparation

66. **MULTIPLE CHOICE** In rectangle $ABCD$, if $AB = 7x - 3$ and $CD = 4x + 9$, then $x = \underline{?}$. **D**

Ⓐ 1 Ⓑ 2 Ⓒ 3 Ⓓ 4 Ⓔ 5

67. **MULTIPLE CHOICE** In parallelogram $KLMN$, $KM = LN$, $m\angle KLM = 2xy$, and $m\angle LMN = 9x + 9$. Find the value of y. **B**

Ⓐ 9 Ⓑ 5 Ⓒ 18

Ⓓ 10 Ⓔ Cannot be determined.

68. *Writing* Explain why a parallelogram with one right angle is a rectangle. **See margin.**

★ Challenge

COORDINATE PROOF OF THEOREM 6.13 Complete the coordinate proof of one conditional statement of Theorem 6.13.

GIVEN ▸ $ABCD$ is a parallelogram, $\overline{AC} \cong \overline{DB}$.

PROVE ▸ $ABCD$ is a rectangle.

Place $ABCD$ in the coordinate plane so $\overline{DB}$ lies on the x-axis and the diagonals intersect at the origin. Let the coordinates of B be $(b, 0)$ and let the x-coordinate of A be a as shown. **69–72. See margin.**

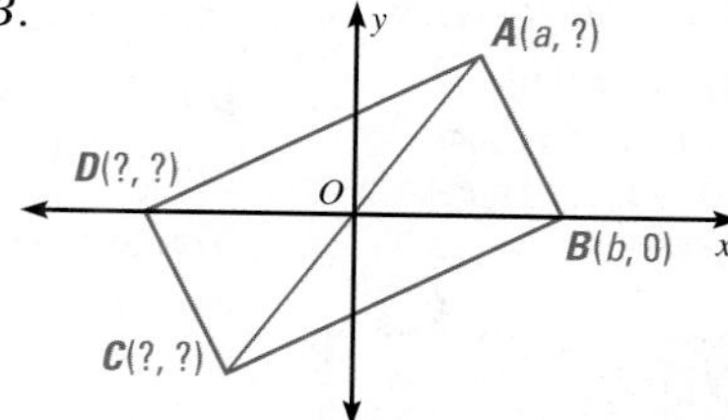

69. Explain why $OA = OB = OC = OD$.

70. Write the y-coordinate of A in terms of a and b. Explain your reasoning.

71. Write the coordinates of C and D in terms of a and b. Explain your reasoning.

72. Find and compare the slopes of the sides to prove that $ABCD$ is a rectangle.

EXTRA CHALLENGE
www.mcdougallittell.com

MIXED REVIEW

USING THE SAS CONGRUENCE POSTULATE Decide whether enough information is given to determine that $\triangle ABC \cong \triangle DEF$. (Review 4.3)

73. $\angle A \cong \angle D$, $\overline{AB} \cong \overline{DE}$, $\overline{AC} \cong \overline{DF}$ **yes**

74. $\overline{AB} \cong \overline{BC}$, $\overline{BC} \cong \overline{CA}$, $\angle A \cong \angle D$ **no**

75. $\angle B \cong \angle E$, $\overline{AC} \cong \overline{DF}$, $\overline{AB} \cong \overline{DE}$ **no**

76. $\overline{EF} \cong \overline{BC}$, $\overline{DF} \cong \overline{AB}$, $\angle A \cong \angle E$ **no**

77. $\angle C \cong \angle F$, $\overline{AC} \cong \overline{DF}$, $\overline{BC} \cong \overline{EF}$ **yes**

78. $\angle B \cong \angle E$, $\overline{AB} \cong \overline{DE}$, $\overline{BC} \cong \overline{EF}$ **yes**

CONCURRENCY PROPERTY FOR MEDIANS Use the information given in the diagram to fill in the blanks. (Review 5.3)

79. $AP = 1$, $PD = \underline{?}$ **$\frac{1}{2}$**

80. $PC = 6.6$, $PE = \underline{?}$ **3.3**

81. $PB = 6$, $FB = \underline{?}$ **9**

82. $AD = 39$, $PD = \underline{?}$ **13**

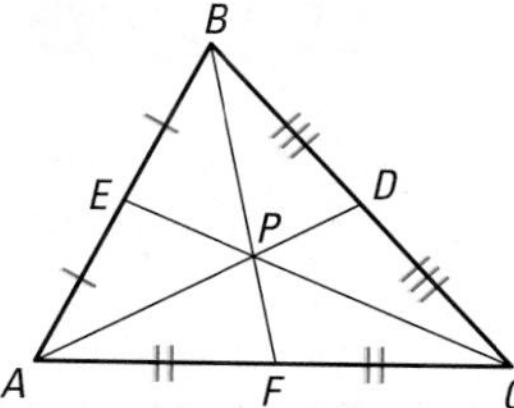

83. **INDIRECT PROOF** Write an indirect proof to show that there is no quadrilateral with four acute angles. (Review 6.1 for 6.5) **See margin.**

68. *Sample answer:* Let $ABCD$ be a ▱ with $\angle A$ a right $\angle$. Consec. ∠s of a ▱ are supplementary, so $\angle D$ and $\angle B$ are right ∠s. Opp. ∠s are ≅, so $\angle C$ is a right $\angle$. Then all 4 ∠s are right ∠s and $ABCD$ is a rectangle.

69. *Sample answer:* The diags. of a rectangle are ≅, so $AC = BD$. O is the midpoint of each diag., so $OA = \frac{1}{2}AC = \frac{1}{2}BD = OB$. Similarly, $OA = OB = OC = OD$.

70. Let $A = (a, y)$. $OA = OB$, so $\sqrt{(a-0)^2 + (y-0)^2} = b$ or $\sqrt{a^2 + y^2} = b$ and $y = \sqrt{b^2 - a^2}$. (The y-coordinate of A is positive.)

71. $D = (-b, 0)$ since $OD = OB = b$; $C = (-a, -\sqrt{b^2 - a^2})$ since $(0, 0)$ is the midpoint of $\overline{AC}$.

Additional Test Preparation *Sample answers:*

1. All sides are congruent. All angles are right angles. The diagonals are congruent, perpendicular, and bisect each other. Each diagonal bisects a pair of opposite angles.

2. Show that the diagonals are perpendicular; show that each diagonal bisects a pair of opposite angles; or show that all four sides are congruent.

4 ASSESS

DAILY HOMEWORK QUIZ

Transparency Available

For any rhombus $ABCD$, decide whether the statement in Exercises 1–3 is *always*, *sometimes*, or *never true*. If the answer is not *always*, explain.

1. $\overline{AC} \perp \overline{BD}$ **always**
2. $\overline{AC} \cong \overline{BD}$ **Sometimes; this is true if $ABCD$ is also a rectangle, which means that it must be a square.**
3. $\overline{AB} \parallel \overline{CD}$ **always**
4. For which parallelograms is it true both that the diagonals are congruent and that each diagonal bisects a pair of opposite angles? **squares**
5. Find the value of x in rectangle $PQRS$ if $PT = 5x + 1$ and $QT = 3x + 3$.

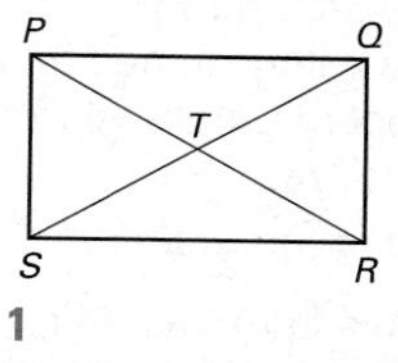

1

EXTRA CHALLENGE NOTE

Challenge problems for Lesson 6.4 are available in **blackline** format in the *Chapter 6 Resource Book*, p. 65 and at **www.mcdougallittell.com.**

ADDITIONAL TEST PREPARATION

1. **WRITING** Describe all the properties that you know about the sides, angles, and diagonals of a square. **See sample answer at left.**
2. **WRITING** Give three ways to show that a parallelogram is a rhombus. **See sample answer at left.**

72, 83. See Additional Answers beginning on page AA1.

1 PLAN

PACING
Basic: 2 days
Average: 2 days
Advanced: 2 days
Block Schedule: 0.5 block with 6.4
0.5 block with 6.6

LESSON OPENER APPLICATION
An alternative way to approach Lesson 6.5 is to use the Application Lesson Opener:

- Blackline Master (*Chapter 6 Resource Book,* p. 69)
- Transparency (p. 38)

MEETING INDIVIDUAL NEEDS

- ***Chapter 6 Resource Book***
  Prerequisite Skills Review (p. 5)
  Practice Level A (p. 71)
  Practice Level B (p. 72)
  Practice Level C (p. 73)
  Reteaching with Practice (p. 74)
  Absent Student Catch-Up (p. 76)
  Challenge (p. 78)
- ***Resources in Spanish***
- ***Personal Student Tutor***

NEW-TEACHER SUPPORT
See the Tips for New Teachers on pp. 1–2 of the *Chapter 6 Resource Book* for additional notes about Lesson 6.5.

WARM-UP EXERCISES

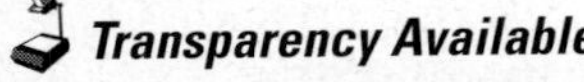

Find the slope of the line passing through the given points.

1. (3, 5) and (7, 1) –1

2. (–2, –2) and (0, 0) 1

Triangle ABC is a right triangle with hypotenuse $\overline{AB}$. Use the Pythagorean theorem to find each length.

3. AB, given that $AC = 8$ and $BC = 10$ $2\sqrt{41}$

4. BC, given that $AC = 5$ and $AB = 13$ 12

6.5 Trapezoids and Kites

What you should learn

GOAL 1 Use properties of trapezoids.

GOAL 2 Use properties of kites.

Why you should learn it

▼ To solve **real-life** problems, such as planning the layers of a layer cake in **Example 3**.

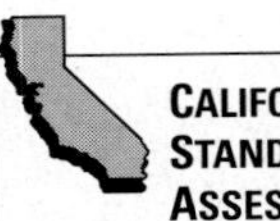

CALIFORNIA STANDARDS AND ASSESSMENT
CA Standards: 4, 7, 12

GOAL 1 USING PROPERTIES OF TRAPEZOIDS

A **trapezoid** is a quadrilateral with exactly one pair of parallel sides. The parallel sides are the **bases.** A trapezoid has two pairs of **base angles.** For instance, in trapezoid $ABCD$, $\angle D$ and $\angle C$ are one pair of base angles. The other pair is $\angle A$ and $\angle B$. The nonparallel sides are the **legs** of the trapezoid.

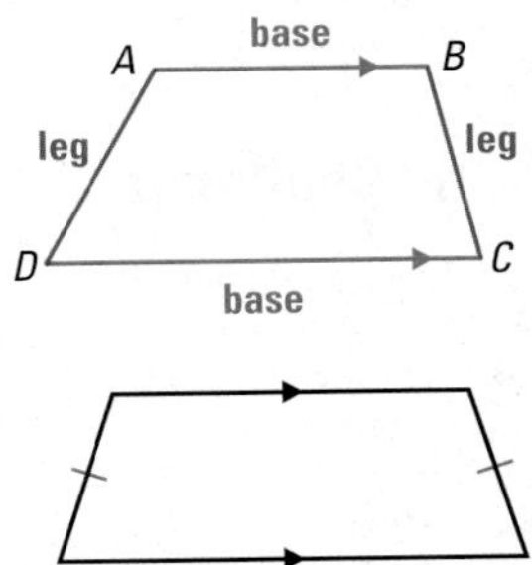

If the legs of a trapezoid are congruent, then the trapezoid is an **isosceles trapezoid.**

You are asked to prove the following theorems in the exercises.

THEOREMS

THEOREM 6.14
If a trapezoid is isosceles, then each pair of base angles is congruent.
$\angle A \cong \angle B$, $\angle C \cong \angle D$

THEOREM 6.15
If a trapezoid has a pair of congruent base angles, then it is an isosceles trapezoid.
$ABCD$ is an isosceles trapezoid.

THEOREM 6.16
A trapezoid is isosceles if and only if its diagonals are congruent.
$ABCD$ is isosceles if and only if $\overline{AC} \cong \overline{BD}$.

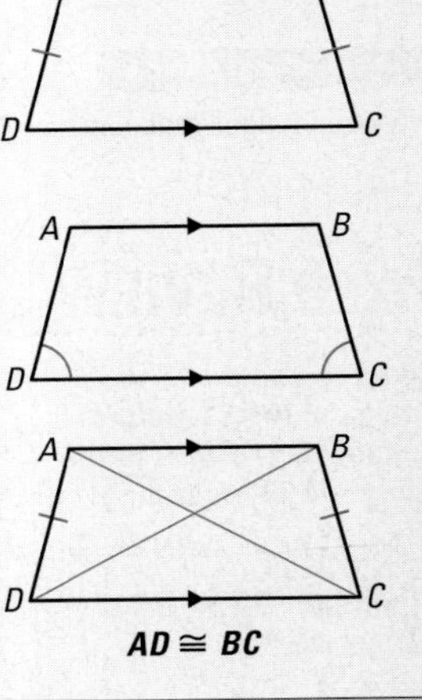

EXAMPLE 1 *Using Properties of Isosceles Trapezoids*

$PQRS$ is an isosceles trapezoid. Find $m\angle P$, $m\angle Q$, and $m\angle R$.

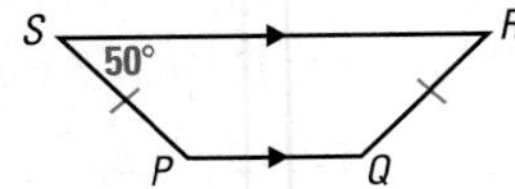

SOLUTION $PQRS$ is an isosceles trapezoid, so $m\angle R = m\angle S = 50°$. Because $\angle S$ and $\angle P$ are consecutive interior angles formed by parallel lines, they are supplementary. So, $m\angle P = 180° - 50° = 130°$, and $m\angle Q = m\angle P = 130°$.

HOMEWORK HELP
Visit our Web site www.mcdougallittell.com for extra examples.

EXAMPLE 2 *Using Properties of Trapezoids*

Show that *ABCD* is a trapezoid.

SOLUTION

Compare the slopes of opposite sides.

The slope of $\overline{AB} = \frac{5-0}{0-5} = \frac{5}{-5} = -1$.

The slope of $\overline{CD} = \frac{4-7}{7-4} = \frac{-3}{3} = -1$.

The slopes of $\overline{AB}$ and $\overline{CD}$ are equal, so $\overline{AB} \parallel \overline{CD}$.

The slope of $\overline{BC} = \frac{7-5}{4-0} = \frac{2}{4} = \frac{1}{2}$.

The slope of $\overline{AD} = \frac{4-0}{7-5} = \frac{4}{2} = 2$.

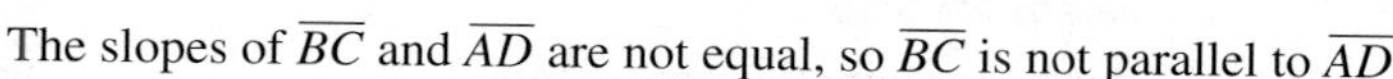

The slopes of $\overline{BC}$ and $\overline{AD}$ are not equal, so $\overline{BC}$ is not parallel to $\overline{AD}$.

▶ So, because $\overline{AB} \parallel \overline{CD}$ and $\overline{BC}$ is not parallel to $\overline{AD}$, *ABCD* is a trapezoid.

The **midsegment** of a trapezoid is the segment that connects the midpoints of its legs. Theorem 6.17 is similar to the Midsegment Theorem for triangles. You will justify part of this theorem in Exercise 42. A proof appears on page 839.

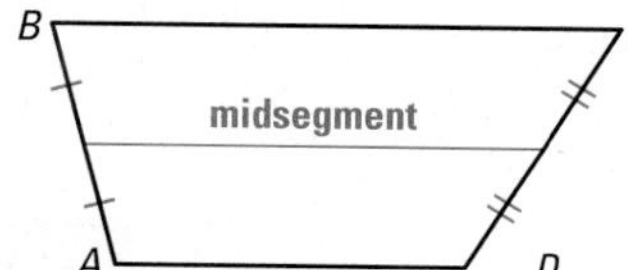

THEOREM

THEOREM 6.17 ***Midsegment Theorem for Trapezoids***

The midsegment of a trapezoid is parallel to each base and its length is one half the sum of the lengths of the bases.

$\overline{MN} \parallel \overline{AD}$, $\overline{MN} \parallel \overline{BC}$, $MN = \frac{1}{2}(AD + BC)$

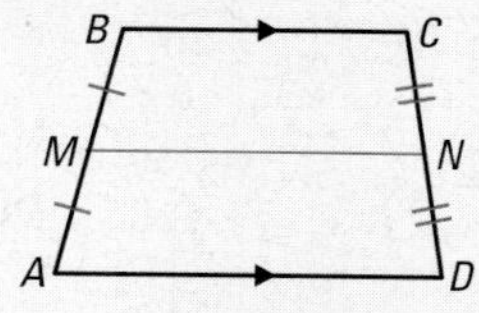

EXAMPLE 3 *Finding Midsegment Lengths of Trapezoids*

REAL LIFE **LAYER CAKE** A baker is making a cake like the one at the right. The top layer has a diameter of 8 inches and the bottom layer has a diameter of 20 inches. How big should the middle layer be?

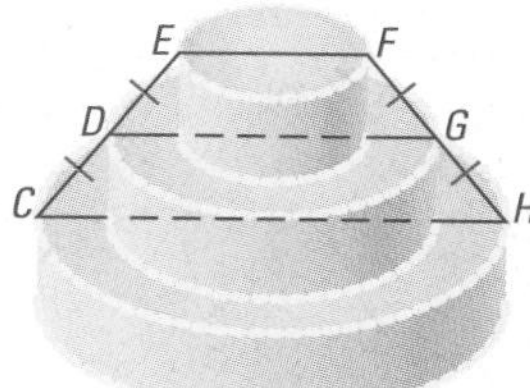

SOLUTION

Use the Midsegment Theorem for Trapezoids.

$$DG = \frac{1}{2}(EF + CH) = \frac{1}{2}(8 + 20) = 14 \text{ inches}$$

2 TEACH

MOTIVATING THE LESSON

Ask students who has heard of cataract surgery. An incision is made into the cornea, and the clouded lens is replaced with a new plastic lens. Some scalpels used for this have trapezoidal blades, a special quadrilateral shape that students will explore.

EXTRA EXAMPLE 1

CDEF is an isosceles trapezoid with $CE = 10$ and $m\angle E = 95°$. Find *DF*, $m\angle C$, $m\angle D$, and $m\angle F$. **$DF = 10$, $m\angle C = 85°$, $m\angle D = 95°$, $m\angle F = 85°$**

EXTRA EXAMPLE 2

The vertices of *WXYZ* are $W(-1, 2)$, $X(3, 0)$, $Y(4, -3)$, and $Z(-4, 1)$. Show that *WXYZ* is an isosceles trapezoid. **The slopes of $\overline{WX}$ and $\overline{YZ}$ are $-\frac{1}{2}$, so $\overline{WX} \parallel \overline{YZ}$; the slope of $\overline{WZ}$ differs from that of $\overline{XY}$, so $\overline{WZ}$ is not $\parallel$ to $\overline{XY}$, and *WXYZ* is a trapezoid. $WY = XZ = \sqrt{50}$, so the diagonals are $\cong$, and the trapezoid is isosceles.**

EXTRA EXAMPLE 3

A potter crafts a trapezoidal relish dish, placing a divider, shown by $\overline{AB}$, in the middle of the dish. How long must the divider be to ensure that it divides the legs in half? **9 in.**

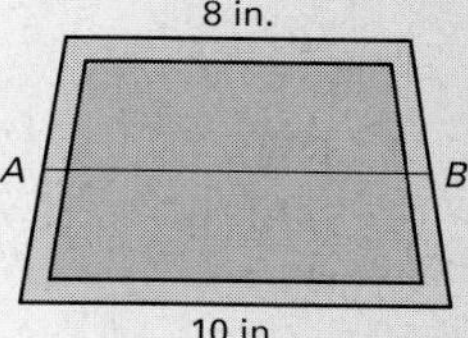

CHECKPOINT EXERCISES

For use after Examples 1–3:

1. The vertices of *KLMN* are $K(-3, 5)$, $L(0, 7)$, $M(2, 7)$, and $N(3, 5)$. Is *KLMN* a trapezoid? If it is, tell whether it is isosceles and find its midsegment length. **yes; no; 4**

EXTRA EXAMPLE 4

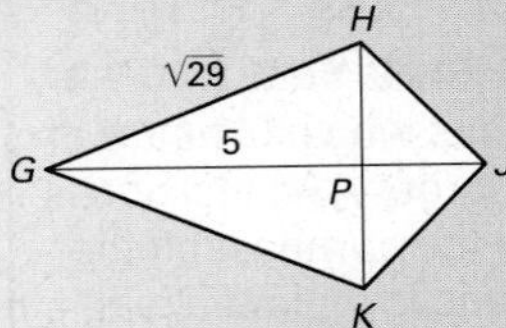

GHJK is a kite. Find *HP*. **2**

EXTRA EXAMPLE 5

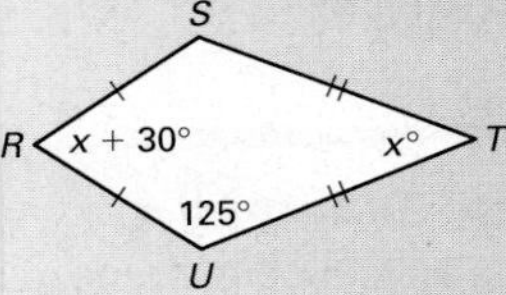

RSTU is a kite. Find $m\angle R$, $m\angle S$, and $m\angle T$. **70°; 125°; 40°**

CHECKPOINT EXERCISES

For use after Examples 4 and 5:

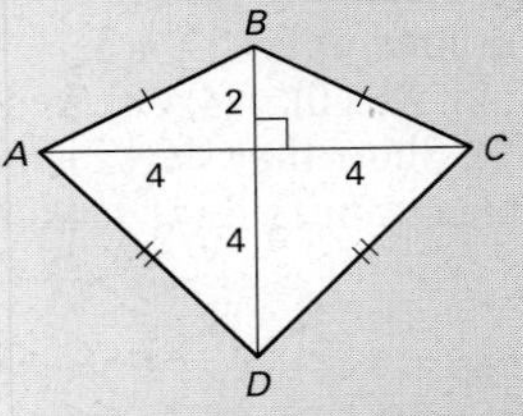

1. Find the length of each side of the kite shown. **$AB = BC \approx 4.47$; $AD = DC \approx 5.66$**
2. If $m\angle ADC = 92°$ and $m\angle ABC = 128°$, find $m\angle BAD$ and $m\angle BCD$. **70; 70°**

FOCUS ON VOCABULARY

What does the word *isosceles* tell you in the expression *isosceles trapezoid*?
that the legs are congruent

CLOSURE QUESTION

What is the difference between a trapezoid and a kite? **See below.**

DAILY PUZZLER

The figure shows a square and an isosceles trapezoid with its midsegment. What is the length of a diagonal of the trapezoid? **$\sqrt{97} \approx 9.85$**

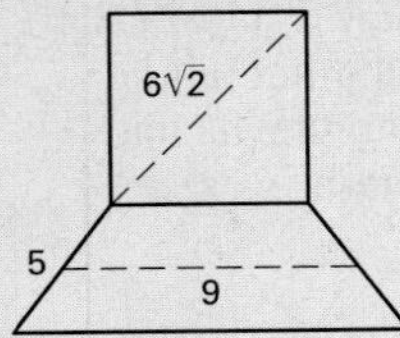

GOAL 2 USING PROPERTIES OF KITES

The simplest of flying kites often use the geometric kite shape.

A **kite** is a quadrilateral that has two pairs of consecutive congruent sides, but opposite sides are not congruent. You are asked to prove Theorem 6.18 and Theorem 6.19 in Exercises 46 and 47.

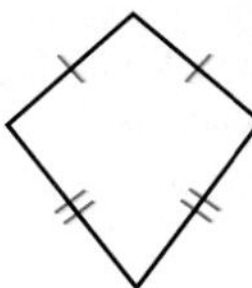

THEOREMS ABOUT KITES

THEOREM 6.18

If a quadrilateral is a kite, then its diagonals are perpendicular.

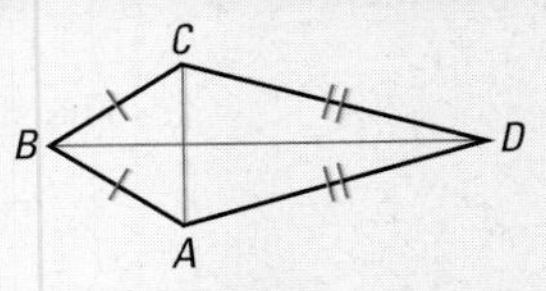

$\overline{AC} \perp \overline{BD}$

THEOREM 6.19

If a quadrilateral is a kite, then exactly one pair of opposite angles are congruent.

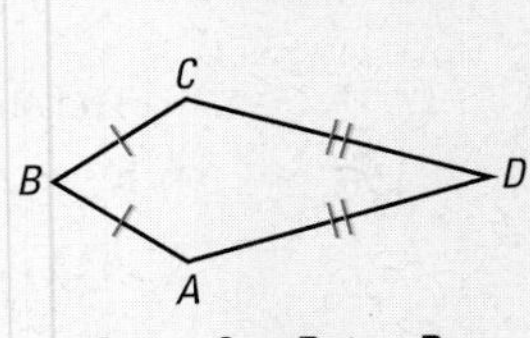

$\angle A \cong \angle C$, $\angle B \not\cong \angle D$

EXAMPLE 4 Using the Diagonals of a Kite

Using Algebra

WXYZ is a kite so the diagonals are perpendicular. You can use the Pythagorean Theorem to find the side lengths.

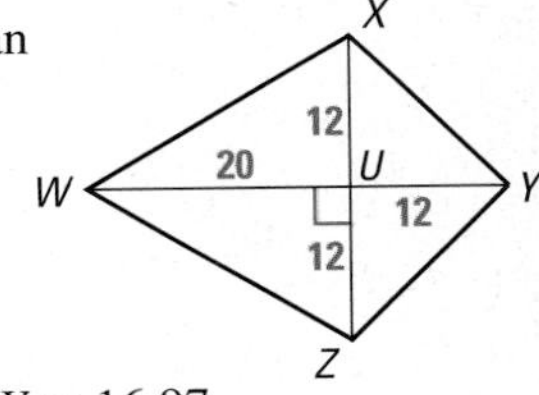

$$WX = \sqrt{20^2 + 12^2} \approx 23.32$$

$$XY = \sqrt{12^2 + 12^2} \approx 16.97$$

Because *WXYZ* is a kite, $WZ = WX \approx 23.32$ and $ZY = XY \approx 16.97$.

EXAMPLE 5 Angles of a Kite

Find $m\angle G$ and $m\angle J$ in the diagram at the right.

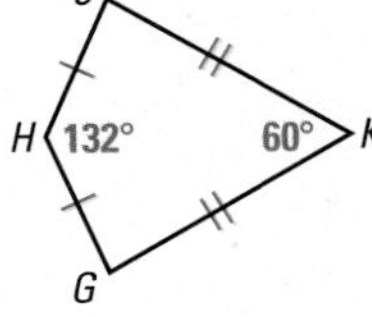

SOLUTION

GHJK is a kite, so $\angle G \cong \angle J$ and $m\angle G = m\angle J$.

$2(m\angle G) + 132° + 60° = 360°$ — **Sum of measures of int. ∡ of a quad. is 360°.**

$2(m\angle G) = 168°$ — **Simplify.**

$m\angle G = 84°$ — **Divide each side by 2.**

▶ So, $m\angle J = m\angle G = 84°$.

Closure Question ***Sample answer:***
A trapezoid is a quadrilateral with exactly one pair of parallel sides. A kite is a quadrilateral that has two pairs of consecutive congruent sides, but opposite sides are not congruent.

GUIDED PRACTICE

Vocabulary Check ✓ **1.** Name the bases of trapezoid $ABCD$. $\overline{AB}$ and $\overline{CD}$

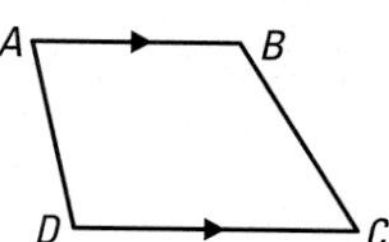

Concept Check ✓ **2.** Explain why a rhombus is not a kite. Use the definition of a kite.
Opp. sides of a kite are not ≅.

Skill Check ✓ **Decide whether the quadrilateral is a *trapezoid*, an *isosceles trapezoid*, a *kite*, or *none of these*.**

3. 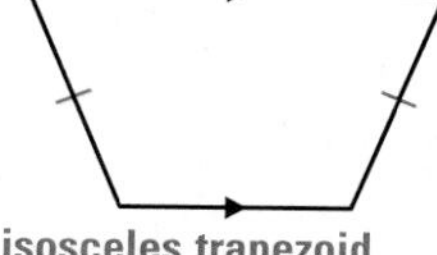 isosceles trapezoid

4. 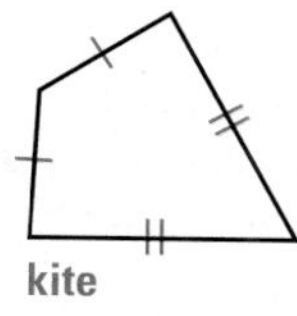 kite

5. 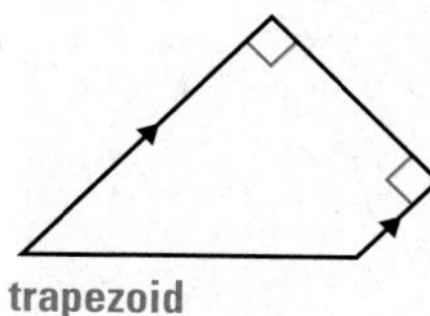 trapezoid

6. How can you prove that trapezoid $ABCD$ in Example 2 is isosceles?
Use coordinates to show that $\overline{AD} \cong \overline{BC}$ or that $\overline{AC} \cong \overline{BD}$.

Find the length of the midsegment.

7. 9 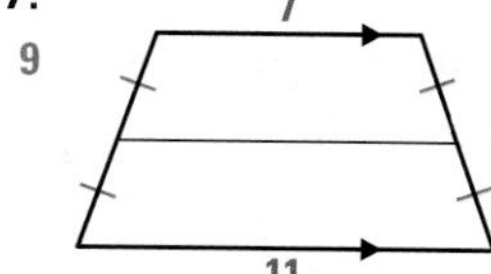

8. 5 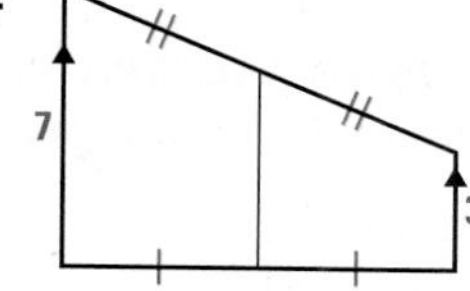

9. 9.5 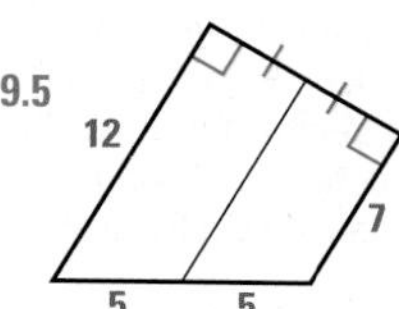

PRACTICE AND APPLICATIONS

STUDENT HELP
Extra Practice to help you master skills is on p. 814.

STUDYING A TRAPEZOID **Draw a trapezoid *PQRS* with $\overline{QR} \parallel \overline{PS}$. Identify the segments or angles of *PQRS* as *bases, consecutive sides, legs, diagonals, base angles,* or *opposite angles.***

10. $\overline{QR}$ and $\overline{PS}$ bases
11. $\overline{PQ}$ and $\overline{RS}$ legs
12. $\overline{PQ}$ and $\overline{QR}$ consec. sides
13. $\overline{QS}$ and $\overline{PR}$ diags.
14. $\angle Q$ and $\angle S$ opp. ∠s
15. $\angle S$ and $\angle P$ base ∠s

FINDING ANGLE MEASURES **Find the angle measures of *JKLM*.**

16. 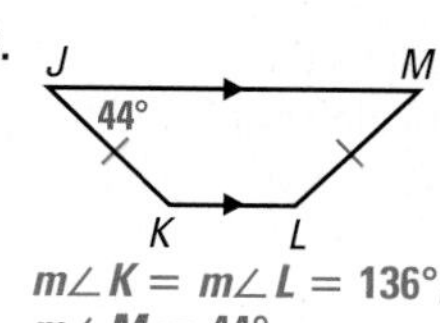
$m\angle K = m\angle L = 136°$, $m\angle M = 44°$

17. 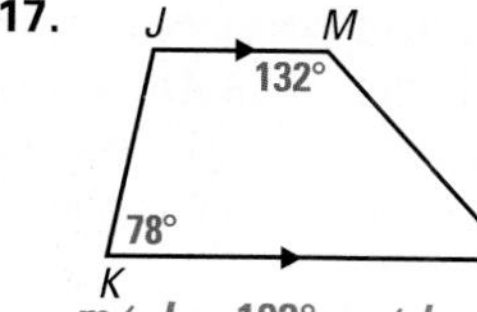
$m\angle J = 102°$, $m\angle L = 48°$

18. 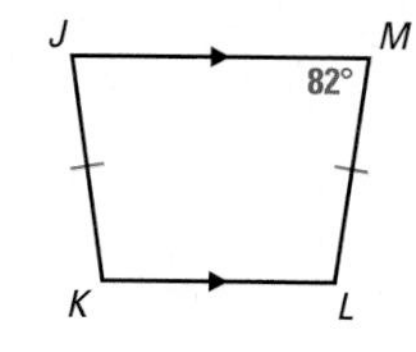
18. $m\angle J = 82°$, $m\angle K = m\angle L = 98°$

STUDENT HELP
HOMEWORK HELP
Example 1: Exs. 16–18
Example 2: Exs. 34, 37, 38, 48–50
Example 3: Exs. 19–24, 35, 39
Example 4: Exs. 28–30
Example 5: Exs. 31–33

FINDING MIDSEGMENTS **Find the length of the midsegment $\overline{MN}$.**

19. 8 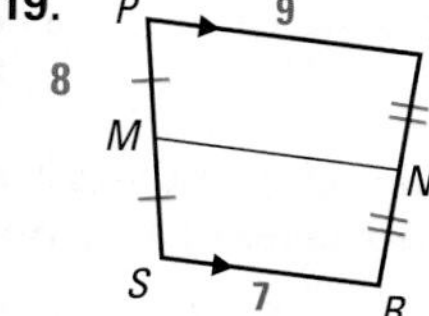

20. 15 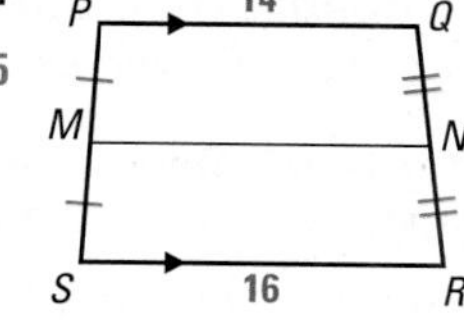

21. 12 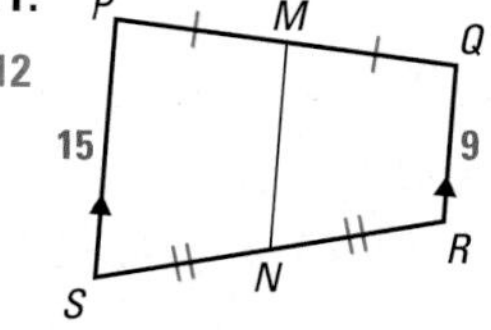

3 APPLY

ASSIGNMENT GUIDE

BASIC
Day 1: pp. 359–362 Exs. 10–24 even, 25–27, 28–40 even, 46, 48, 50–52
Day 2: pp. 359–363 Exs. 11–23 odd, 29–39 odd, 47, 49, 54–64 even, Quiz 2 Exs. 1–6

AVERAGE
Day 1: pp. 359–362 Exs. 10–24 even, 25–27, 28–40 even, 46, 48, 50–52
Day 2: pp. 359–363 Exs. 11–23 odd, 29–41 odd, 47, 49, 54–64 even, Quiz 2 Exs. 1–6

ADVANCED
Day 1: pp. 359–362 Exs. 10–24 even, 25–27, 28–40 even, 46, 48, 50–53
Day 2: pp. 359–363 Exs. 11–23 odd, 29–41 odd, 47, 49, 54–64 even, Quiz 2 Exs. 1–6

BLOCK SCHEDULE
pp. 359–362 Exs. 10–24 even, 25–27, 28–40 even, 46, 48, 50–52 (with 6.4)
pp. 359–363 Exs. 11–23 odd, 29–41 odd, 47, 49, 54–64 even, Quiz 2 Exs. 1–6 (with 6.6)

EXERCISE LEVELS
Level A: *Easier*
10–15, 54–62
Level B: *More Difficult*
16–40, 43–45, 48–52, 63, 64
Level C: *Most Difficult*
41, 42, 46, 47, 53

✓ HOMEWORK CHECK
To quickly check student understanding of key concepts, go over the following exercises: Exs. 12, 16, 20, 24, 28, 36, 38, 40, 46. See also the Daily Homework Quiz:
- Blackline Master (*Chapter 6 Resource Book,* p. 82)
- Transparency (p. 45)

APPLICATION NOTE

EXERCISE 25 Although the dodecagon provides a useful model for the web, an orb web is woven in a series of spirals. If points *A*–*M* were around a clockwise inward spiral, $\overline{XB}$ would be shorter than $\overline{XA}$, so you would lose the congruent base angles relationship that guarantees that *ABPQ* is isosceles.

! COMMON ERROR

EXERCISES 34 Some students may not understand that, though parallelograms and trapezoids are both subsets of the set of quadrilaterals, the set of parallelograms and the set of trapezoids are disjoint. It may help students to include trapezoids and kites in a Venn diagram or other diagram of the relationships among the quadrilaterals they have studied in this chapter.

34. A trapezoid has exactly one pair of parallel opposite sides. Because a ▱ has two pairs of parallel opposite sides, *ABCD* cannot be a trapezoid.

25. Yes; *X* is equidistant from the vertices of the dodecagon, so $\overline{XA} \cong \overline{XB}$ and $\angle XAB \cong \angle XBA$ by the Base Angles Theorem. Since trapezoid *ABPQ* has a pair of ≅ base ∠s, *ABPQ* is isosceles.

FOCUS ON APPLICATIONS

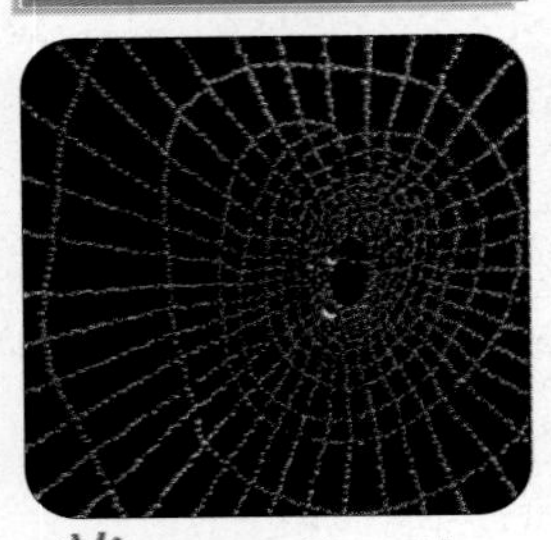

WEBS The spider web above is called an orb web. Although it looks like concentric polygons, the spider actually followed a spiral path to spin the web.

28. $AB = AD \approx 3.61$, $BC = DC = 5$

29. $EF = GF \approx 6.40$, $HE = HG \approx 8.60$

30. $JK = JM \approx 14.42$, $LK = LM \approx 9.43$

36. Yes; $AB = AD = \sqrt{53}$ and $CB = CD = \sqrt{265}$, so *ABCD* has two pairs of consec. ≅ sides, but opp. sides are not ≅.

37. *ABCD* is a trapezoid; slope of $\overline{BC}$ = slope of $\overline{AD} = 0$, so $\overline{BC} \parallel \overline{AD}$; slope of $\overline{AB} = 2$ and slope of $\overline{CD} = -\frac{4}{3}$, so $\overline{AB}$ is not ∥ to $\overline{CD}$. *ABCD* is not isosceles; $AB = 2\sqrt{5}$ and $CD = 5$.

38. *EFGH* is a trapezoid; slope of $\overline{EH}$ = slope of $\overline{FG} = 0$, so $\overline{EH} \parallel \overline{FG}$; slope of $\overline{EF} = -\frac{7}{3}$ and slope of $\overline{HG} = \frac{7}{3}$, so $\overline{EF}$ is not ∥ to $\overline{HG}$. *EFGH* is isosceles; $EF = HG = \sqrt{58}$.

USING ALGEBRA Find the value of *x*.

22. 5 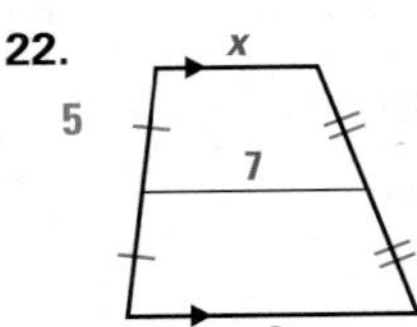

23. 10 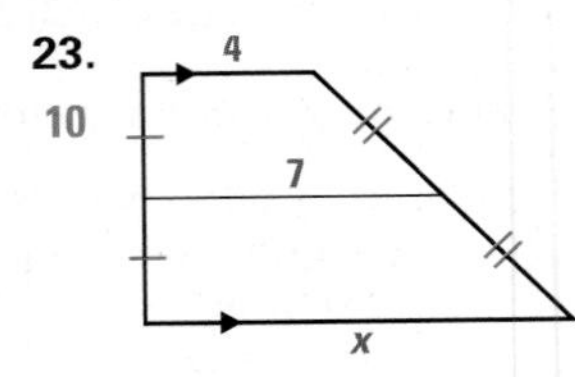

24. 5 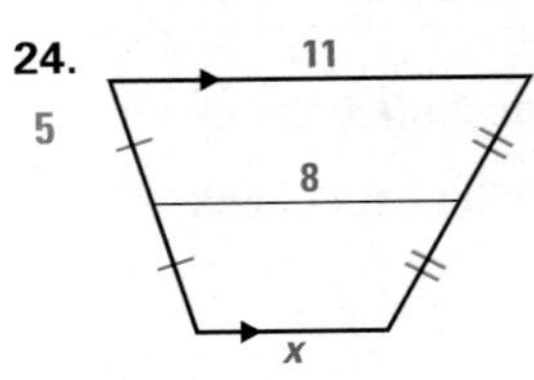

CONCENTRIC POLYGONS In the diagram, *ABCDEFGHJKLM* is a regular dodecagon, $\overline{AB} \parallel \overline{PQ}$, and *X* is equidistant from the vertices of the dodecagon.

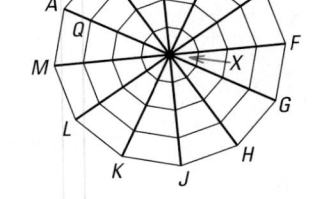

25. Are you given enough information to prove that *ABPQ* is isosceles? Explain your reasoning. See margin.

26. What is the measure of ∠*AXB*? 30°

27. What is the measure of each interior angle of *ABPQ*?
$m\angle A = m\angle B = 75°$, $m\angle P = m\angle Q = 105°$

USING ALGEBRA What are the lengths of the sides of the kite? Give your answer to the nearest hundredth. 28–30. See margin.

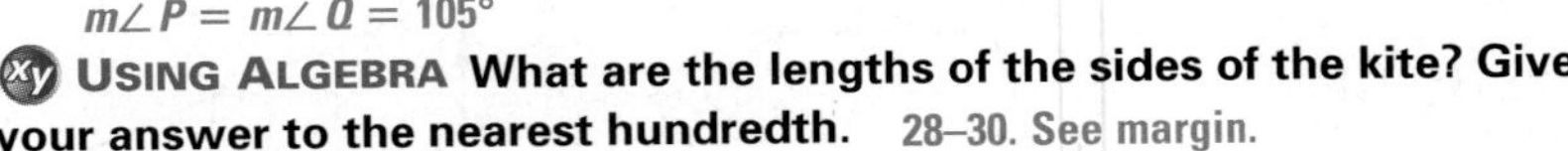

28. 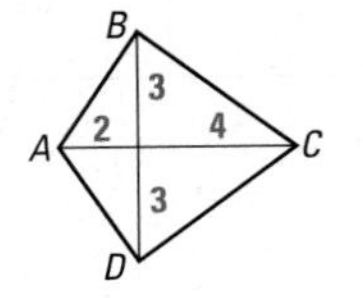

29. 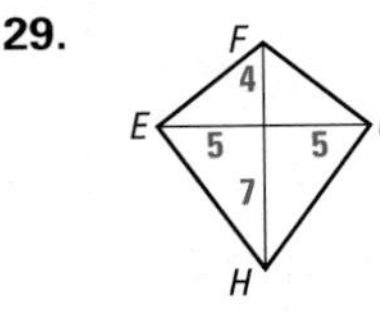

30. 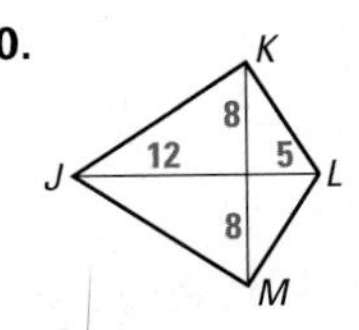

ANGLES OF KITES *EFGH* is a kite. What is $m\angle G$?

31. 95° 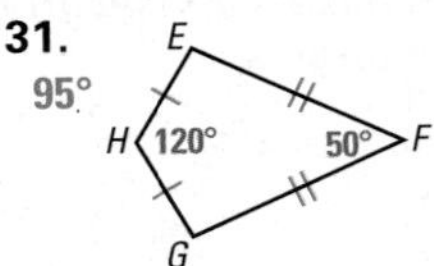

32. 70° 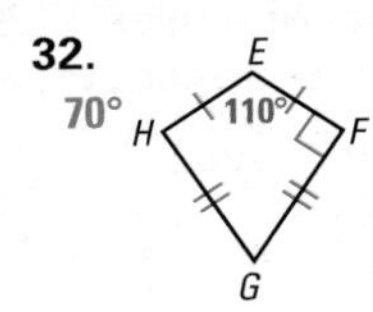

33. 90° 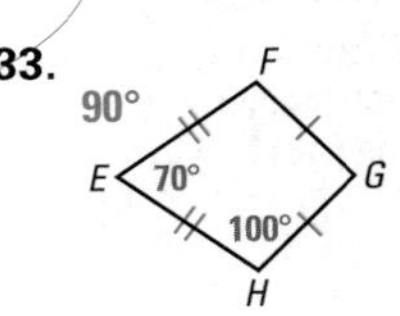

34. **ERROR ANALYSIS** A student says that parallelogram *ABCD* is an isosceles trapezoid because $\overline{AB} \parallel \overline{DC}$ and $\overline{AD} \cong \overline{BC}$. Explain what is wrong with this reasoning. See margin.

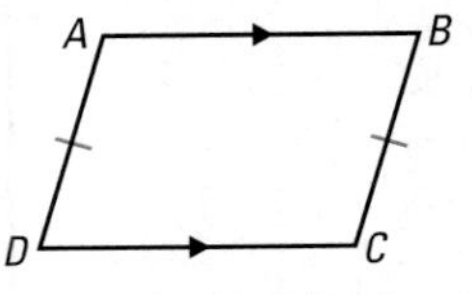

35. **CRITICAL THINKING** The midsegment of a trapezoid is 5 inches long. What are possible lengths of the bases?
any two positive numbers (except 5 and 5) whose sum is 10.

36. **COORDINATE GEOMETRY** Determine whether the points $A(4, 5)$, $B(-3, 3)$, $C(-6, -13)$, and $D(6, -2)$ are the vertices of a kite. Explain your answer. See margin.

TRAPEZOIDS Determine whether the given points represent the vertices of a trapezoid. If so, is the trapezoid isosceles? Explain your reasoning. 37, 38. See margin.

37. $A(-2, 0)$, $B(0, 4)$, $C(5, 4)$, $D(8, 0)$

38. $E(1, 9)$, $F(4, 2)$, $G(5, 2)$, $H(8, 9)$

FOCUS ON CAREERS

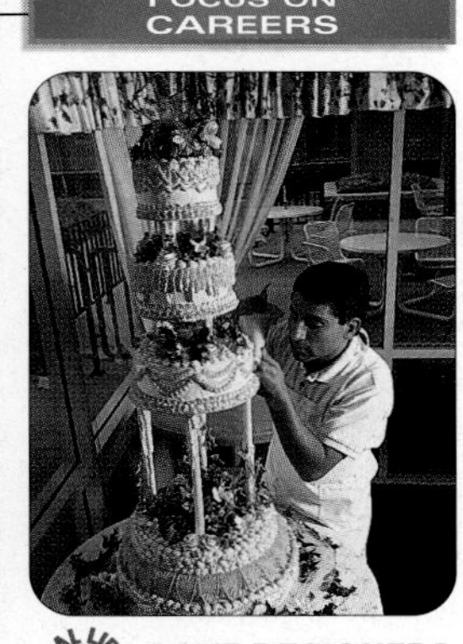

REAL LIFE **CAKE DESIGNERS** design cakes for many occasions, including weddings, birthdays, anniversaries, and graduations.

INTERNET CAREER LINK
www.mcdougallittell.com

40. Draw $\overline{AE} \parallel \overline{BC}$. (Parallel Postulate) Both pairs of opp. sides of $ABCE$ are $\parallel$, so $ABCE$ is a ▱. Opp. sides of a ▱ are ≅, so $\overline{AE} \cong \overline{BC}$. $\overline{AE} \cong \overline{AD}$ by the Transitive Prop. of Cong. Then $\angle D \cong \angle AED$ by the Base Angles Theorem and, since corresp. ∠s AED and C are ≅, $\angle D \cong \angle C$ by the Transitive Prop. of Cong. $\angle DAB$ and $\angle D$ are supplementary as are $\angle B$ and $\angle C$. (Consecutive Interior Angles Theorem) Then $m\angle DAB = 180° - m\angle D = 180° - m\angle C = m\angle B$ and $\angle DAB \cong \angle B$.

STUDENT HELP

INTERNET SOFTWARE HELP
Visit our Web site www.mcdougallittell.com to see instructions for several software applications.

43. If $AC \neq BC$, then $ACBD$ is a kite; $AC = AD$ and $BC = BD$, so the quad. has two pairs of ≅ sides, but opp. sides are not ≅. (If $AC = BC$, then $ACBD$ is a rhombus); $ACBD$ remains a kite in all 3 cases.

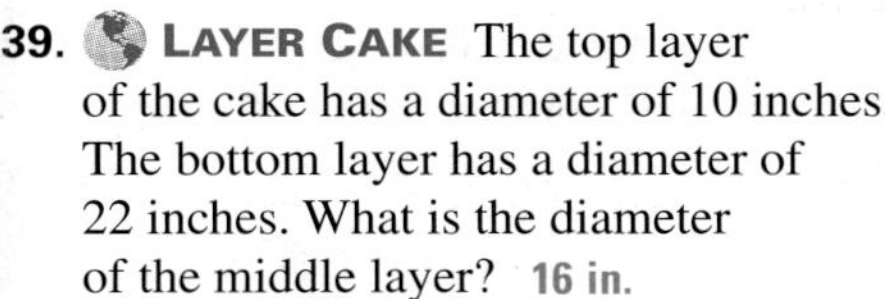

39. **LAYER CAKE** The top layer of the cake has a diameter of 10 inches. The bottom layer has a diameter of 22 inches. What is the diameter of the middle layer? 16 in.

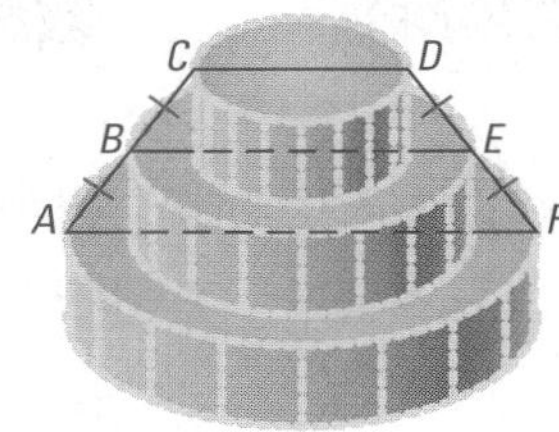

40. **PROVING THEOREM 6.14** Write a proof of Theorem 6.14. See margin.

GIVEN ▶ $ABCD$ is an isosceles trapezoid.
$\overline{AB} \parallel \overline{DC}$, $\overline{AD} \cong \overline{BC}$

PROVE ▶ $\angle D \cong \angle C$, $\angle DAB \cong \angle B$

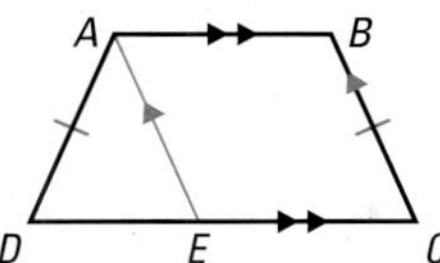

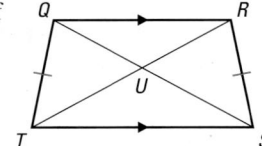

Plan for Proof To show $\angle D \cong \angle C$, first draw $\overline{AE}$ so $ABCE$ is a parallelogram. Then show $\overline{BC} \cong \overline{AE}$, so $\overline{AE} \cong \overline{AD}$ and $\angle D \cong \angle AED$. Finally, show $\angle D \cong \angle C$. To show $\angle DAB \cong \angle B$, use the consecutive interior angles theorem and substitution.

41. **PROVING THEOREM 6.16** Write a proof of one conditional statement of Theorem 6.16. See margin.

GIVEN ▶ $TQRS$ is an isosceles trapezoid.
$\overline{QR} \parallel \overline{TS}$ and $\overline{QT} \cong \overline{RS}$

PROVE ▶ $\overline{TR} \cong \overline{SQ}$

Q R U T S

42. **JUSTIFYING THEOREM 6.17** In the diagram below, $\overline{BG}$ is the midsegment of $\triangle ACD$ and $\overline{GE}$ is the midsegment of $\triangle ADF$. Explain why the midsegment of trapezoid $ACDF$ is parallel to each base and why its length is one half the sum of the lengths of the bases. See margin.

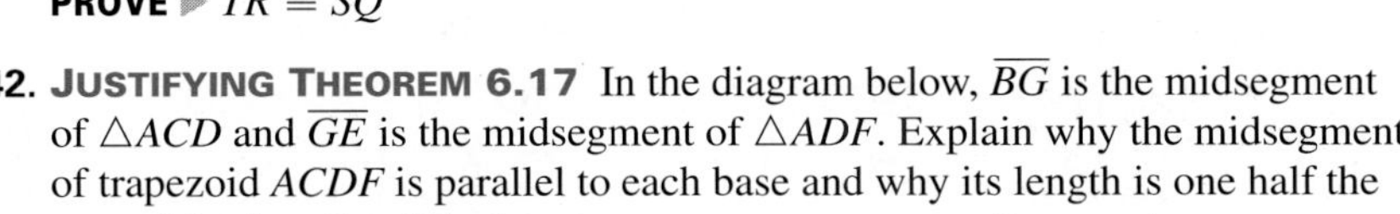

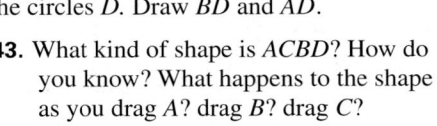

USING TECHNOLOGY In Exercises 43–45, use geometry software.
Draw points A, B, C and segments $\overline{AC}$ and $\overline{BC}$. Construct a circle with center A and radius AC. Construct a circle with center B and radius BC. Label the other intersection of the circles D. Draw $\overline{BD}$ and $\overline{AD}$.

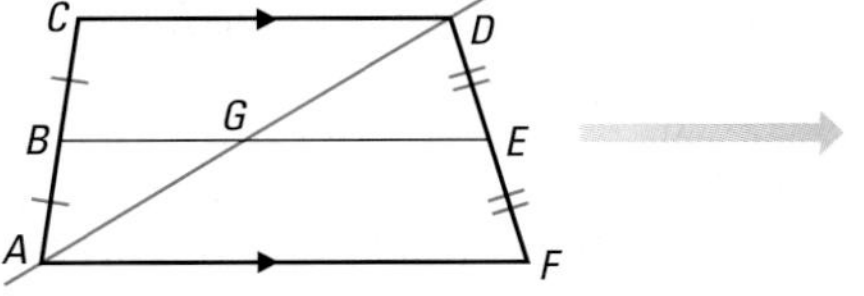

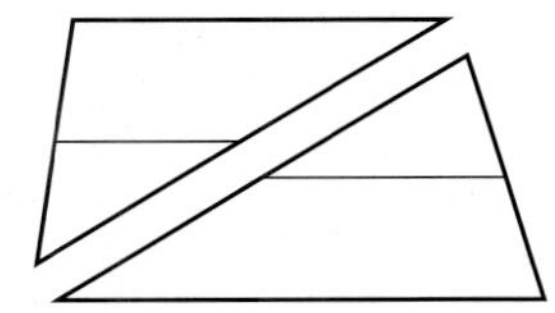

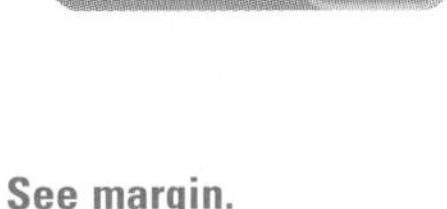

43. What kind of shape is $ACBD$? How do you know? What happens to the shape as you drag A? drag B? drag C?

44. Measure $\angle ACB$ and $\angle ADB$. What happens to the angle measures as you drag A, B, or C? See margin.

45. Which theorem does this construction illustrate? See margin.

CAREER NOTE
EXERCISE 39 Additional information about cake designers is available at **www.mcdougallittell.com.**

STUDENT HELP NOTES
Software Help Instructions for several software packages are available in **blackline** format in the *Chapter 6 Resource Book*, p. 70 and at **www.mcdougallittell.com.**

41. $TQRS$ is an isos. trap., so $\angle QTS \cong \angle RST$ because base ∠s of an isos. trap. are ≅. $\overline{TS} \cong \overline{TS}$ by the Reflexive Prop. of Cong., and $\overline{QT} \cong \overline{RS}$, so $\triangle QTS \cong \triangle RST$ by the SAS Cong. Post. Then $\overline{TR} \cong \overline{SQ}$ because corresp. parts of ≅ △s are ≅.

42. The diag. $\overline{AD}$ divides trap. $ACDF$ into two △s, which divides the midsegment into two segments. One is the midsegment of $\triangle ACD$ and, so, has length $\frac{1}{2}CD$. The other is the midsegment of $\triangle ADF$ and, so, has length $\frac{1}{2}AF$. Then the total length of the midsegment of the trap. is $\frac{1}{2}CD + \frac{1}{2}AF = \frac{1}{2}(CD + AF)$. $\overline{BE}$ is parallel to both $\overline{CD}$ and $\overline{AF}$ because $\overline{BG}$, $\overline{GE}$, and $\overline{BE}$ all lie on the same line.

44. The ∠s are ≅; the ∠ measures change, but the ∠s remain ≅.

45. If a quad. is a kite, then exactly 1 pair of opp. ∠s are ≅.

ENGLISH LEARNERS

EXERCISE 1 Explain that in Exercise 1 of Quiz 2 *Positioning Buttons* means "putting buttons in certain places," not "buttons used for placing things." Note that it can be difficult for English learners to sense whether an *-ing* form preceding a noun has the function of a transitive verb, as in running laps, or an adjective, as in running shoes.

46. **Statements (Reasons)**

1. $\overline{AB} \cong \overline{CB}$, $\overline{AD} \cong \overline{CD}$ (Given)
2. $\overline{BD} \cong \overline{BD}$ (Reflexive Prop. of $\cong$)
3. $\triangle BCD \cong \triangle BAD$ (SSS Cong. Post.)
4. $\angle CBX \cong \angle ABX$ (Corresp. parts of $\cong$ ▵ are $\cong$.)
5. $\overline{BX} \cong \overline{BX}$ (Reflexive Prop. of $\cong$)
6. $\triangle CBX \cong \triangle ABX$ (SAS Cong. Post.)
7. $\angle CXB \cong \angle AXB$ (Corresp. parts of $\cong$ ▵ are $\cong$.)
8. $\angle CXB$ and $\angle AXB$ are a linear pair. (Def. of linear pair)
9. $\overline{AC} \perp \overline{BD}$ (If 2 lines form a linear pair of $\cong$ ∠s, then the lines are $\perp$.)

53. Draw a $\perp$ segment from Q to $\overline{PS}$ intersecting $\overline{PS}$ at M and a $\perp$ segment from R to $\overline{PS}$ intersecting $\overline{PS}$ at N. (Perpendicular Post.) In a plane, 2 lines $\perp$ to the same line are $\parallel$, so $QRNM$ is a ▱ and $\overline{QM} \cong \overline{RN}$. Then $\triangle QMS \cong \triangle RNP$ by the HL Cong. Thm. and corresp. ∠s RPS and QSP are $\cong$. It follows that $\triangle QPS \cong \triangle RSP$ (SAS Cong. Post.) and that corresp. sides $\overline{QP}$ and $\overline{RS}$ are $\cong$.

ADDITIONAL PRACTICE AND RETEACHING

For Lesson 6.5:

- Practice Levels A, B, and C (*Chapter 6 Resource Book,* p. 71)
- Reteaching with Practice (*Chapter 6 Resource Book,* p. 74)
- See Lesson 6.5 of the *Personal Student Tutor*

For more Mixed Review:

- Search the *Test and Practice Generator* for key words or specific lessons.

47. Draw $\overline{BD}$. (Through any 2 points, there is exactly 1 line.) Since $\overline{AB} \cong \overline{CB}$ and $\overline{AD} \cong \overline{CD}$, $\triangle BCD \cong \triangle BAD$ by the SSS Cong. Postulate. Then corresp. ∠s A and C are $\cong$. Assume temporarily that $\angle B \cong \angle D$. Then both pairs of opp. ∠s of $ABCD$ are $\cong$, so $ABCD$ is a ▱ and opp. sides are $\cong$. This contradicts the definition of a kite. It follows that $\angle B \not\cong \angle D$.

48. No; the given information does not indicate that $\overline{AD}$ and $\overline{BC}$ are not $\parallel$.

49. Yes; $ABCD$ has one pair of $\parallel$ sides and the diagonals are $\cong$. $ABCD$ is not a ▱ because opp. ∠s are not $\cong$.

50. Yes; $\angle A \cong \angle B$ and $\angle D \cong \angle C$. Then $m\angle A = m\angle B$ and $m\angle D = m\angle C$. By the Interior ∠s of a Quad. Thm., $m\angle A + m\angle B + m\angle C + m\angle D = 360°$. By substitution and the props. of $=$, $m\angle A + m\angle D = 180°$. By the Consec. ∠s Converse, $\overline{AB} \parallel \overline{DC}$. $ABCD$ is not a ▱ because it is given that $\angle A \not\cong \angle C$ so opposite ∠s are not $\cong$. So $ABCD$ is a trapezoid and since it has a pair of congruent base angles, then it is an isosceles trapezoid.

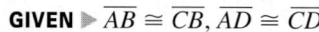

46. **PROVING THEOREM 6.18** Write a two-column proof of Theorem 6.18. **See margin.**

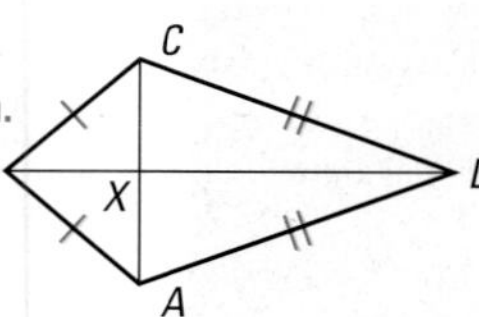

GIVEN ▶ $\overline{AB} \cong \overline{CB}$, $\overline{AD} \cong \overline{CD}$

PROVE ▶ $\overline{AC} \perp \overline{BD}$

47. **PROVING THEOREM 6.19** Write a paragraph proof of Theorem 6.19. **See margin.**

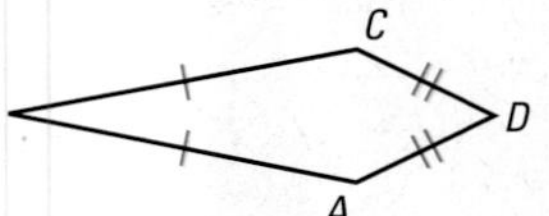

GIVEN ▶ $ABCD$ is a kite with $\overline{AB} \cong \overline{CB}$ and $\overline{AD} \cong \overline{CD}$.

PROVE ▶ $\angle A \cong \angle C$, $\angle B \not\cong \angle D$

Plan for Proof First show that $\angle A \cong \angle C$. Then use an indirect argument to show $\angle B \not\cong \angle D$: If $\angle B \cong \angle D$, then $ABCD$ is a parallelogram. But opposite sides of a parallelogram are congruent. This contradicts the definition of a kite.

TRAPEZOIDS Decide whether you are given enough information to conclude that *ABCD* is an isosceles trapezoid. Explain your reasoning. **48–50. See margin.**

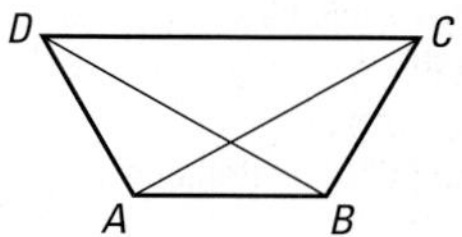

48. $\overline{AB} \parallel \overline{DC}$	**49.** $\overline{AB} \parallel \overline{DC}$	**50.** $\angle A \cong \angle B$
$\overline{AD} \cong \overline{BC}$	$\overline{AC} \cong \overline{BD}$	$\angle D \cong \angle C$
$\overline{AD} \cong \overline{AB}$	$\angle A \not\cong \angle C$	$\angle A \not\cong \angle C$

Test Preparation

51. **MULTIPLE CHOICE** In the trapezoid at the right, $NP = 15$. What is the value of x? **E**

Ⓐ 2 Ⓑ 3 Ⓒ 4 Ⓓ 5 Ⓔ 6

J, $2x - 2$, M, N, 15, P, K, $3x + 2$, L

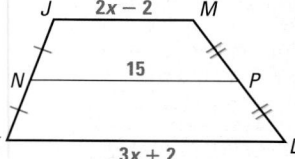

52. **MULTIPLE CHOICE** Which one of the following can a trapezoid have? **C**

Ⓐ congruent bases

Ⓑ diagonals that bisect each other

Ⓒ exactly two congruent sides

Ⓓ a pair of congruent opposite angles

Ⓔ exactly three congruent angles

★ Challenge

53. **PROOF** Prove one direction of Theorem 6.16: If the diagonals of a trapezoid are congruent, then the trapezoid is isosceles. **See margin.**

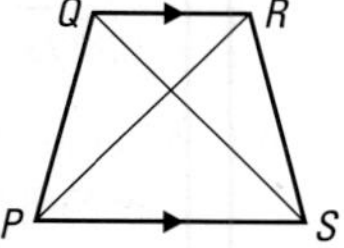

GIVEN ▶ $PQRS$ is a trapezoid. $\overline{QR} \parallel \overline{PS}$, $\overline{PR} \cong \overline{SQ}$

PROVE ▶ $\overline{QP} \cong \overline{RS}$

Plan for Proof Draw a perpendicular segment from Q to $\overline{PS}$ and label the intersection M. Draw a perpendicular segment from R to $\overline{PS}$ and label the intersection N. Prove that $\triangle QMS \cong \triangle RNP$. Then prove that $\triangle QPS \cong \triangle RSP$.

EXTRA CHALLENGE

www.mcdougallittell.com

MIXED REVIEW

CONDITIONAL STATEMENTS **Rewrite the statement in if-then form.** (Review 2.1)

54. A scalene triangle has no congruent sides.
If a △ is scalene, then it has no ≅ sides.

55. A kite has perpendicular diagonals.
If a quad. is a kite, then its diags. are ⊥.

56. A polygon is a pentagon if it has five sides.
If a polygon is a pentagon, then it has 5 sides.

FINDING MEASUREMENTS **Use the diagram to find the side length or angle measure.** (Review 6.2 for 6.6)

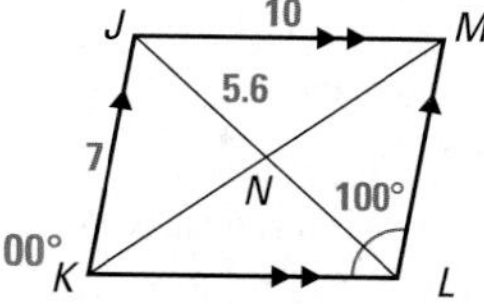

57. LN 5.6 **58.** KL 10 **59.** ML 7

60. JL 11.2 **61.** $m\angle JML$ 80° **62.** $m\angle MJK$ 100°

PARALLELOGRAMS **Determine whether the given points represent the vertices of a parallelogram. Explain your answer.** (Review 6.3 for 6.6)
63, 64. See margin.

63. $A(-2, 8)$, $B(5, 8)$, $C(2, 0)$, $D(-5, 0)$

64. $P(4, -3)$, $Q(9, -1)$, $R(8, -6)$, $S(3, -8)$

63. Yes; *Sample answer:* slope of $\overline{AB}$ = slope of $\overline{CD} = 0$, so $\overline{AB} \parallel \overline{CD}$ and $AB = CD = 7$. Then one pair of opp. sides are both ≅ and ∥, so $ABCD$ is a ▱.

64. Yes; *Sample answer:* $\left(6, -4\frac{1}{2}\right)$ is the midpoint of both $\overline{PR}$ and $\overline{QS}$. Since the diags. of $PQRS$ bisect each other, $PQRS$ is a ▱.

QUIZ 2

Self-Test for Lessons 6.4 and 6.5

1. **POSITIONING BUTTONS** The tool at the right is used to decide where to put buttons on a shirt. The tool is stretched to fit the length of the shirt, and the pointers show where to put the buttons. Why are the pointers always evenly spaced? (*Hint:* You can prove that $\overline{HJ} \cong \overline{JK}$ if you know that $\triangle JFK \cong \triangle HEJ$.) (Lesson 6.4)

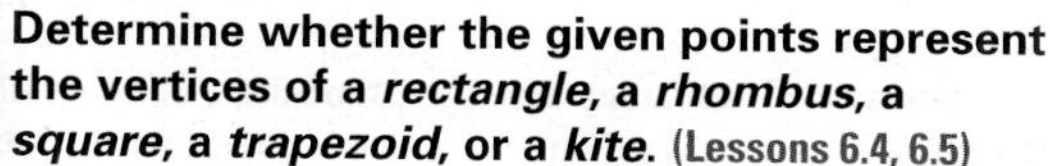

Determine whether the given points represent the vertices of a *rectangle*, a *rhombus*, a *square*, a *trapezoid*, or a *kite*. (Lessons 6.4, 6.5)

2. $P(2, 5)$, $Q(-4, 5)$, $R(2, -7)$, $S(-4, -7)$ rectangle

3. $A(-3, 6)$, $B(0, 9)$, $C(3, 6)$, $D(0, -10)$ kite

4. $J(-5, 6)$, $K(-4, -2)$, $L(4, -1)$, $M(3, 7)$ square

5. $P(-5, -3)$, $Q(1, -2)$, $R(6, 3)$, $S(7, 9)$ trapezoid

6. **PROVING THEOREM 6.15** Write a proof of Theorem 6.15. See margin.

GIVEN ▶ $ABCD$ is a trapezoid with $\overline{AB} \parallel \overline{DC}$. $\angle D \cong \angle C$

PROVE ▶ $\overline{AD} \cong \overline{BC}$

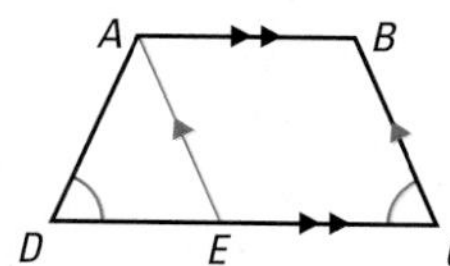

Plan for Proof Draw $\overline{AE}$ so $ABCE$ is a parallelogram. Use the Transitive Property of Congruence to show $\angle AED \cong \angle D$. Then $\overline{AD} \cong \overline{AE}$, so $\overline{AD} \cong \overline{BC}$. (Lesson 6.5)

1. *Sample answer:* Opposite sides of $EBFJ$ are congruent, so $EBFJ$ is a parallelogram. Opposite angles of a parallelogram are congruent, so $\angle BEJ \cong \angle BFJ$. By the Cong. Supplements Theorem, $\angle HEJ \cong \angle KFJ$. Since $\overline{HE} \cong \overline{JE} \cong \overline{JF} \cong \overline{KF}$, $\triangle HEJ \cong \triangle JFK$ by the SAS Cong. Postulate and, since corresp. sides of ≅ △s are ≅, $\overline{HJ} \cong \overline{JK}$.

Additional Test Preparation *Sample answer:*
1. Only the diagonals of a rhombus bisect each other. If the diagonals of a kite bisected each other, it would then be a parallelogram, specifically, a rhombus. A kite is not a parallelogram.

4 ASSESS

DAILY HOMEWORK QUIZ

Transparency Available

1. In isosceles trapezoid $EFGH$, $m\angle E = 106°$, and $\overline{EH}$ is a base. What are the measures of the other angles? $m\angle F = 74°$, $m\angle G = 74°$, $m\angle H = 106°$

2. A nonisosceles trapezoid has one base of length 37 and a midsegment of length 29. What is the length of the second base? 21

3. To the nearest hundredth, what are the lengths of the sides of the kite?

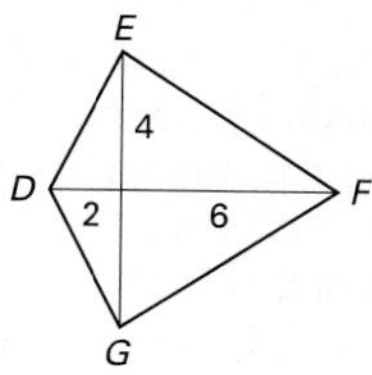

$ED = GD = 4.47$, $EF = FG = 7.21$

4. Determine whether the points $A(-3, 1)$, $B(-1, 5)$, $C(3, 7)$, and $D(5, -2)$ are the vertices of a kite. Explain. No; $AB = BC = 2\sqrt{5}$, but $CD = \sqrt{85} \neq \sqrt{73} = AD$, so only one pair of consec. sides is ≅.

EXTRA CHALLENGE NOTE

Challenge problems for Lesson 6.5 are available in **blackline** format in the *Chapter 6 Resource Book,* p. 78 and at **www.mcdougallittell.com.**

ADDITIONAL TEST PREPARATION

1. WRITING The diagonals of both kites and rhombuses are perpendicular. Do the diagonals of both bisect each other? Explain. See answer at left.

ADDITIONAL RESOURCES

An alternative Quiz for Lessons 6.4 and 6.5 is available in the *Chapter 6 Resource Book,* p. 79.

6. See Additional Answers beginning on page AA1.

1 PLAN

PACING
Basic: 1 day
Average: 1 day
Advanced: 1 day
Block Schedule: 0.5 block with 6.5

LESSON OPENER
VISUAL APPROACH
An alternative way to approach Lesson 6.6 is to use the Visual Approach Lesson Opener:

- Blackline Master (*Chapter 6 Resource Book,* p. 83)
- Transparency (p. 39)

MEETING INDIVIDUAL NEEDS

- ***Chapter 6 Resource Book***
  Prerequisite Skills Review (p. 5)
  Practice Level A (p. 84)
  Practice Level B (p. 85)
  Practice Level C (p. 86)
  Reteaching with Practice (p. 87)
  Absent Student Catch-Up (p. 89)
  Challenge (p. 92)
- ***Resources in Spanish***
- ***Personal Student Tutor***

NEW-TEACHER SUPPORT
See the Tips for New Teachers on pp. 1–2 of the *Chapter 6 Resource Book* for additional notes about Lesson 6.6.

WARM-UP EXERCISES

 ***Transparency Available***

Name the figure.

1. a quadrilateral with exactly one pair of opposite angles congruent and perpendicular diagonals **kite**
2. a quadrilateral that is both a rhombus and a rectangle **square**
3. a quadrilateral with exactly one pair of parallel sides **trapezoid**
4. any parallelogram with perpendicular diagonals **rhombus**

6.6 Special Quadrilaterals

What you should learn

GOAL 1 Identify special quadrilaterals based on limited information.

GOAL 2 Prove that a quadrilateral is a special type of quadrilateral, such as a rhombus or a trapezoid.

Why you should learn it

▼ To understand and describe **real-world** shapes such as gem facets in **Exs. 42 and 43.**

CALIFORNIA STANDARDS AND ASSESSMENT

CA Standards: 7, 12

GOAL 1 SUMMARIZING PROPERTIES OF QUADRILATERALS

In this chapter, you have studied the seven special types of quadrilaterals at the right. Notice that each shape has all the properties of the shapes linked above it. For instance, squares have the properties of rhombuses, rectangles, parallelograms, and quadrilaterals.

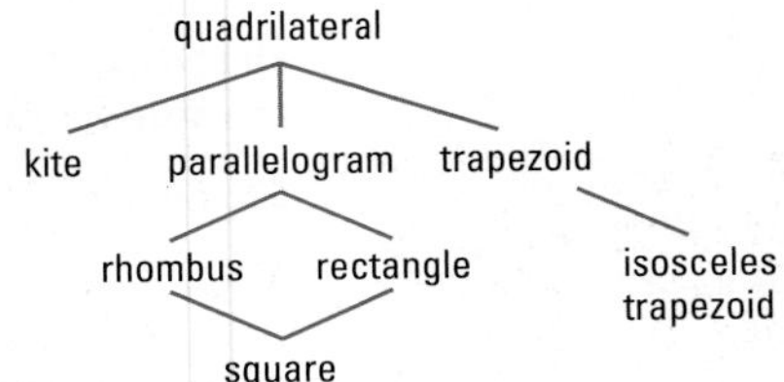

EXAMPLE 1 *Identifying Quadrilaterals*

Quadrilateral $ABCD$ has at least one pair of opposite sides congruent. What kinds of quadrilaterals meet this condition?

SOLUTION

There are many possibilities.

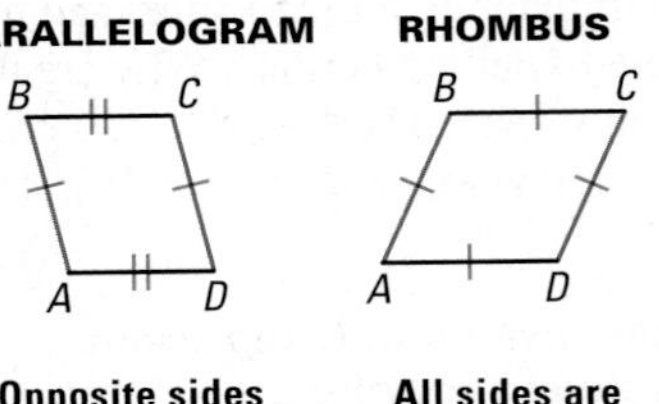

PARALLELOGRAM — **Opposite sides are congruent.**

RHOMBUS — **All sides are congruent.**

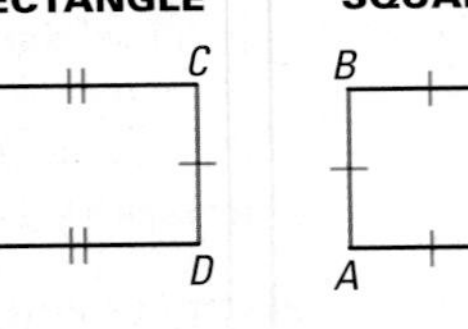

RECTANGLE — **Opposite sides are congruent.**

SQUARE — **All sides are congruent.**

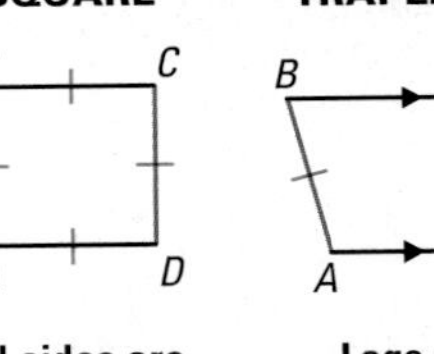

ISOSCELES TRAPEZOID — **Legs are congruent.**

EXAMPLE 2 *Connecting Midpoints of Sides*

When you join the midpoints of the sides of any quadrilateral, what special quadrilateral is formed? Why?

SOLUTION

Let E, F, G, and H be the midpoints of the sides of any quadrilateral, $ABCD$, as shown.

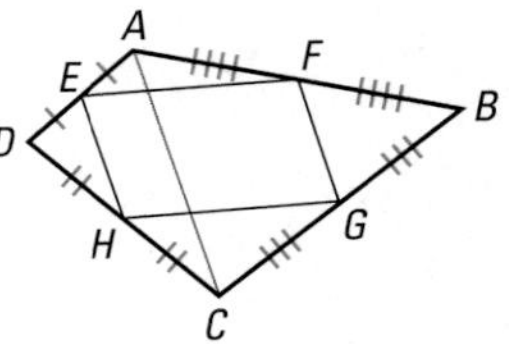

If you draw $\overline{AC}$, the Midsegment Theorem for triangles says $\overline{FG} \parallel \overline{AC}$ and $\overline{EH} \parallel \overline{AC}$, so $\overline{FG} \parallel \overline{EH}$. Similar reasoning shows that $\overline{EF} \parallel \overline{HG}$.

▶ So, by definition, $EFGH$ is a parallelogram.

GOAL 2 PROOF WITH SPECIAL QUADRILATERALS

When you want to prove that a quadrilateral has a specific shape, you can use either the definition of the shape as in Example 2, *or* you can use a theorem.

CONCEPT SUMMARY **PROVING QUADRILATERALS ARE RHOMBUSES**

You have learned three ways to prove that a quadrilateral is a rhombus.

1. You can use the definition and show that the quadrilateral is a *parallelogram* that has four congruent sides. It is easier, however, to use the Rhombus Corollary and simply show that all four sides of the quadrilateral are congruent.
2. Show that the quadrilateral is a parallelogram *and* that the diagonals are perpendicular. (*Theorem 6.11*)
3. Show that the quadrilateral is a parallelogram *and* that each diagonal bisects a pair of opposite angles. (*Theorem 6.12*)

STUDENT HELP

Look Back
For help with proving a quadrilateral is a parallelogram, see pp. 338–341.

EXAMPLE 3 ***Proving a Quadrilateral is a Rhombus***

Show that $KLMN$ is a rhombus.

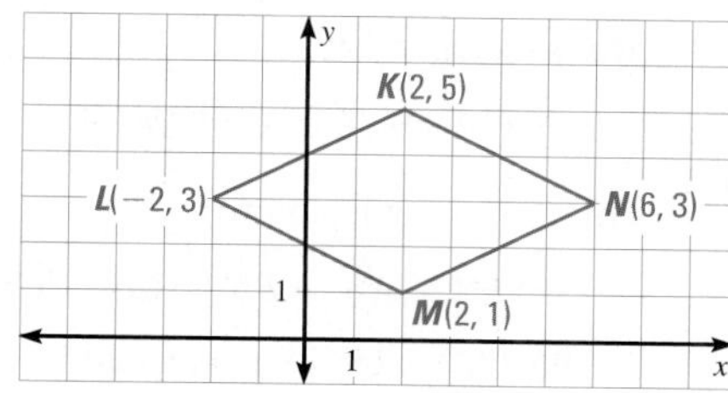

SOLUTION You can use any of the three ways described in the concept summary above. For instance, you could show that opposite sides have the same slope and that the diagonals are perpendicular. Another way, shown below, is to prove that all four sides have the same length.

$$LM = \sqrt{[2-(-2)]^2 + (1-3)^2} = \sqrt{4^2 + (-2)^2} = \sqrt{20}$$

$$NK = \sqrt{(2-6)^2 + (5-3)^2} = \sqrt{(-4)^2 + 2^2} = \sqrt{20}$$

$$MN = \sqrt{(6-2)^2 + (3-1)^2} = \sqrt{4^2 + 2^2} = \sqrt{20}$$

$$KL = \sqrt{(-2-2)^2 + (3-5)^2} = \sqrt{(-4)^2 + (-2)^2} = \sqrt{20}$$

▶ So, because $LM = NK = MN = KL$, $KLMN$ is a rhombus.

2 TEACH

MOTIVATING THE LESSON
Ask students who has tried *origami*, the ancient art of paper folding. Folding a square into thirds involves folds that create trapezoids and rectangles. The properties of the figures ensure that the final folds create three congruent rectangles that divide the square into thirds.

EXTRA EXAMPLE 1
ABCD has at least two congruent consecutive sides. What quadrilaterals meet this condition?
rhombus, square, kite

EXTRA EXAMPLE 2
When you join the midpoints of the sides of an isosceles trapezoid in order, what special quadrilateral is formed? Why?

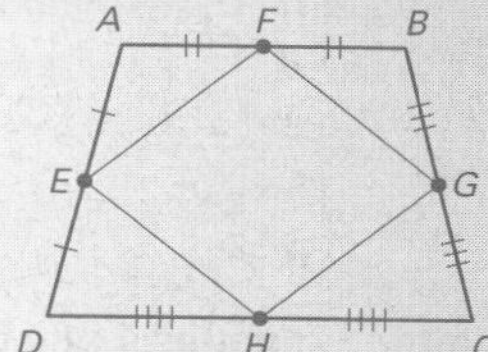

Let E, F, G, and H be the midpoints of the sides of any isosceles trapezoid $ABCD$, as shown. As in Example 2, $EFGH$ is a ▱. Because $ABCD$ is isosceles $\overline{AD} \cong \overline{BC}$, so $\overline{AE} \cong \overline{BG}$. Also, $\angle A \cong \angle B$. By the SAS Cong. Post., $\triangle AEF \cong \triangle BGF$. So $\overline{EF} \cong \overline{FG}$. Because opposite sides of a ▱ are ≅, and using the Transitive Prop. of Cong., all four sides of $EFGH$ are ≅, so it is a rhombus.

EXTRA EXAMPLE 3
The coordinates of $ABCD$ are $A(-2, 5)$, $B(1, 8)$, $C(4, 5)$, and $D(1, 2)$. Show that $ABCD$ is a rhombus.
$AB = BC = CD = AD = \sqrt{18}$

CHECKPOINT EXERCISES
For use after Examples 1–3:
1. The diagonals of $RSTQ$ are perpendicular. What quadrilaterals meet this condition?
square, rhombus, kite

EXTRA EXAMPLE 4
In quadrilateral $RSTV$, $m\angle R = 88°$, $m\angle S = 113°$, and $m\angle V = 113°$. What type of quadrilateral could $RSTV$ be? Must it be this type? Explain. **A kite; no; $m\angle T = 46°$, so $RSTV$ is not a ▱. No pair of consec. ∠s are supplementary, so $RSTV$ is not a trapezoid. $RSTV$ will be a kite only if two pairs of consec. sides are also ≅.**

EXTRA EXAMPLE 5
The diagonals of $ABCD$ intersect at point N to form four congruent isosceles triangles: $\triangle ANB \cong \triangle CNB \cong \triangle CND \cong \triangle AND$. What type of quadrilateral is $ABCD$? Prove that your answer is correct. **A square; because they are corresp. sides of ≅ △s, $\overline{AB} \cong \overline{BC} \cong \overline{CD} \cong \overline{AD}$, so $ABCD$ is a rhombus. Because the △s are isosceles, $\overline{AN} \cong \overline{BN} \cong \overline{CN} \cong \overline{DN}$. Then as shown in Example 5, the diagonals are ≅, so $ABCD$ is a rectangle as well as a rhombus. So, it is a square.**

CHECKPOINT EXERCISES

For use after Examples 4 and 5:

1. The diagonals of $ABCD$ are congruent. $m\angle A = m\angle B = 95°$ and $m\angle C = m\angle D = 85°$. What kind of figure is $ABCD$? **isosceles trapezoid**

CLOSURE QUESTION
At least two opposite angles of $EFGH$ are congruent. What kind of quadrilateral might it be? **parallelogram, rhombus, rectangle, square, kite**

DAILY PUZZLER
The sum of the measures of the interior angles of a regular polygon is 20 times the square of the number of sides. What kind(s) of polygon(s) could this be? **triangle or hexagon**

EXAMPLE 4 *Identifying a Quadrilateral*

What type of quadrilateral is $ABCD$? Explain your reasoning.

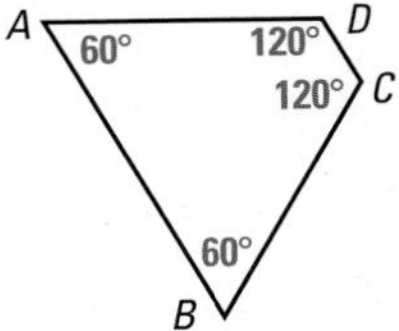

SOLUTION

$\angle A$ and $\angle D$ are supplementary, but $\angle A$ and $\angle B$ are not. So, $\overline{AB} \parallel \overline{DC}$ but $\overline{AD}$ is not parallel to $\overline{BC}$. By definition, $ABCD$ is a trapezoid. Because base angles are congruent, $ABCD$ is an isosceles trapezoid.

EXAMPLE 5 *Identifying a Quadrilateral*

The diagonals of quadrilateral $ABCD$ intersect at point N to produce four congruent segments: $\overline{AN} \cong \overline{BN} \cong \overline{CN} \cong \overline{DN}$. What type of quadrilateral is $ABCD$? Prove that your answer is correct.

SOLUTION

Draw a diagram:

Draw the diagonals as described. Then connect the endpoints to draw quadrilateral $ABCD$.

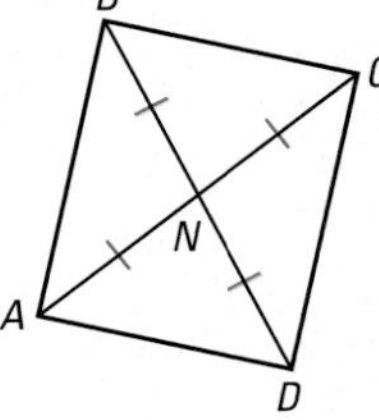

Make a conjecture:

Quadrilateral $ABCD$ looks like a rectangle.

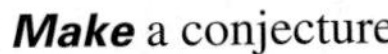

Prove your conjecture:

GIVEN ▶ $\overline{AN} \cong \overline{BN} \cong \overline{CN} \cong \overline{DN}$

PROVE ▶ $ABCD$ is a rectangle.

Paragraph Proof Because you are given information about the diagonals, show that $ABCD$ is a parallelogram with congruent diagonals.

First prove that $ABCD$ is a parallelogram.

Because $\overline{BN} \cong \overline{DN}$ and $\overline{AN} \cong \overline{CN}$, $\overline{BD}$ and $\overline{AC}$ bisect each other. Because the diagonals of $ABCD$ bisect each other, $ABCD$ is a parallelogram.

Then prove that the diagonals of $ABCD$ are congruent.

From the given you can write $BN = AN$ and $DN = CN$ so, by the Addition Property of Equality, $BN + DN = AN + CN$. By the Segment Addition Postulate, $BD = BN + DN$ and $AC = AN + CN$ so, by substitution, $BD = AC$.

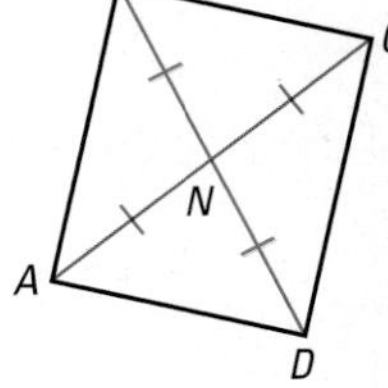

So, $\overline{BD} \cong \overline{AC}$.

▶ $ABCD$ is a parallelogram with congruent diagonals, so $ABCD$ is a rectangle.

GUIDED PRACTICE

Concept Check ✓

Skill Check ✓

1. In Example 2, explain how to prove that $\overline{EF} \parallel \overline{HG}$. **See margin.**

1. Draw $\overline{DB}$. According to the Midsegment Theorem for Triangles, $\overline{EF} \parallel \overline{DB}$ and $\overline{HG} \parallel \overline{DB}$. Two lines $\parallel$ to the same line are $\parallel$ to each other, so $\overline{EF} \parallel \overline{HG}$.

Copy the chart. Put an X in the box if the shape *always* has the given property.

	Property	▱	Rectangle	Rhombus	Square	Kite	Trapezoid
2.	Both pairs of opp. sides are $\parallel$.	? X	? X	? X	? X	?	?
3.	Exactly 1 pair of opp. sides are $\parallel$.	?	?	?	?	?	? X
4.	Diagonals are $\perp$.	?	?	? X	? X	? X	?
5.	Diagonals are $\cong$.	?	? X	?	? X	?	?
6.	Diagonals bisect each other.	? X	? X	? X	? X	?	?

7. Which quadrilaterals can you form with four sticks of the same length? You must attach the sticks at their ends and cannot bend or break any of them. **▱, rectangle, rhombus, square**

PRACTICE AND APPLICATIONS

STUDENT HELP

Extra Practice to help you master skills is on p. 814.

PROPERTIES OF QUADRILATERALS **Copy the chart. Put an X in the box if the shape *always* has the given property.**

	Property	▱	Rectangle	Rhombus	Square	Kite	Trapezoid
8.	Both pairs of opp. sides are $\cong$.	? X	? X	? X	? X	?	?
9.	Exactly 1 pair of opp. sides are $\cong$.	?	?	?	?	?	?
10.	All sides are $\cong$.	?	?	? X	? X	?	?
11.	Both pairs of opp. $\angle$s are $\cong$.	? X	? X	? X	? X	?	?
12.	Exactly 1 pair of opp. $\angle$s are $\cong$.	?	?	?	?	? X	?
13.	All $\angle$s are $\cong$.	?	? X	?	? X	?	?

FOCUS ON APPLICATIONS

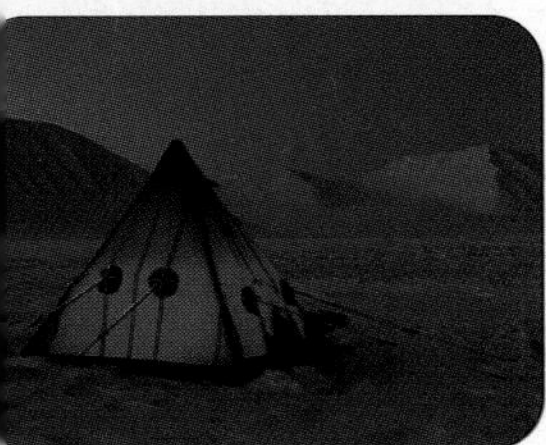

REAL LIFE Tents are designed differently for different climates. For example, winter tents are designed to shed snow. Desert tents can have flat roofs because they don't need to shed rain.

TENT SHAPES **What kind of special quadrilateral is the red shape?**

14.

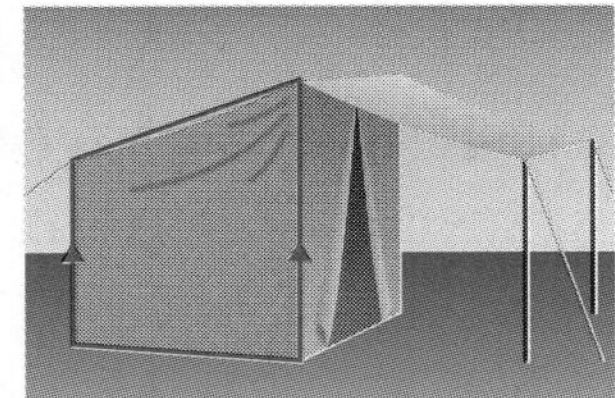

trapezoid

15.

isosceles trapezoid

3 APPLY

ASSIGNMENT GUIDE

BASIC
Day 1: pp. 367–370 Exs. 8–36, 38, 40, 45–47, 49, 53, 56–64 even

AVERAGE
Day 1: pp. 367–370 Exs. 8–36, 38, 40, 45–50, 53, 56–64 even

ADVANCED
Day 1: pp. 367–370 Exs. 8–40, 42–54, 56–64 even

BLOCK SCHEDULE WITH 6.5
pp. 367–370 Exs. 8–36, 38, 40, 45–50, 53, 56–64 even

EXERCISE LEVELS

Level A: ***Easier***
8–18, 55–60, 63–65

Level B: ***More Difficult***
19–50, 53, 61, 62

Level C: ***Most Difficult***
51, 52, 54

✓ HOMEWORK CHECK

To quickly check student understanding of key concepts, go over the following exercises: Exs. 12, 18, 22, 30, 38, 46, 49. See also the Daily Homework Quiz:

- Blackline Master (*Chapter 6 Resource Book,* p. 95)
- Transparency (p. 46)

! COMMON ERROR

EXERCISES 16–18 Refer students who have trouble with the expression *most specific* to the diagram on page 364. Tell them to identify their choice of quadrilateral in the diagram. Then have them look *down* the diagram to see if any other quadrilaterals satisfy the conditions given.

25. Show that the quad. has 2 pairs of consec. ≅ sides, but opp. sides are not ≅ (def. of a kite)
26. Show that the quad. is both a rhombus and a rectangle.
27. Show that the quad. has 4 right ∠s; show that the quad. is a ▱ and that its diags. are ≅.
28. Show that exactly 2 sides are ∥. (def. of trap.)
29. Show that exactly 2 sides are ∥ and that the nonparallel sides are ≅ (def. of trap.); show that the quad. is a trap. and that one pair of base ∠s are ≅; show that the quad. is a trap. and that its diags. are ≅.
38. Trapezoid; $\overline{PS} \parallel \overline{QR}$ and $\overline{PQ}$ is not ∥ to $\overline{RS}$.
39. ▱; *Sample answer:* $\overline{PQ} \parallel \overline{RS}$ and $\overline{PS} \parallel \overline{QR}$.
40. Rectangle; $\overline{PQ} \parallel \overline{RS}$, $\overline{PS} \parallel \overline{QR}$, and $\overline{PR} \cong \overline{QS}$.
41. Rhombus: *Sample answer:* $\overline{PQ} \cong \overline{QR} \cong \overline{RS} \cong \overline{PS}$.

STUDENT HELP

HOMEWORK HELP
Example 1: Exs. 8–24, 30–35
Example 2: Exs. 14–18, 42–44
Example 3: Exs. 25–29, 36–41
Example 4: Exs. 14–18, 42, 43
Example 5: Exs. 45–47

IDENTIFYING QUADRILATERALS Identify the special quadrilateral. Use the most specific name.

16. 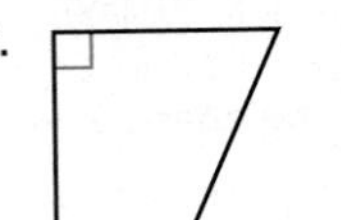
trapezoid

17. 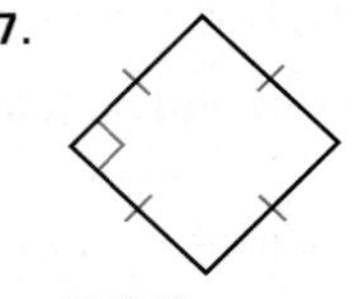
square

18. 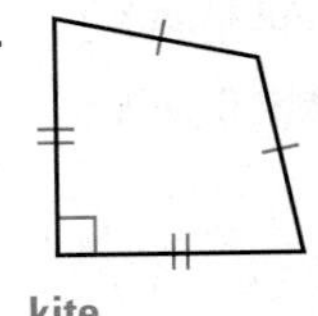
kite

IDENTIFYING QUADRILATERALS What kinds of quadrilaterals meet the conditions shown? *ABCD* is not drawn to scale.

19. ▱, rectangle, rhombus, square, kite
20. rectangle, square, isosceles trapezoid
21. rhombus, square
22. ▱, rectangle, rhombus, square, isosceles trapezoid
23. rectangle, square
24. square

19. 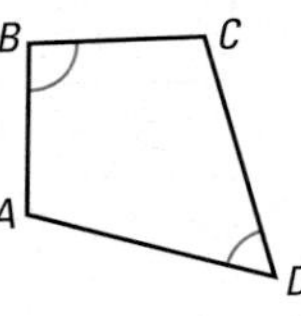

20. 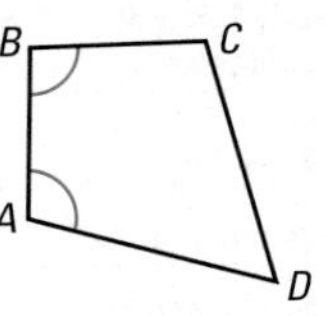

21. 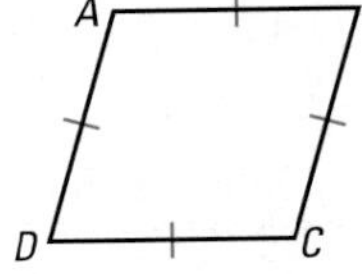

22. 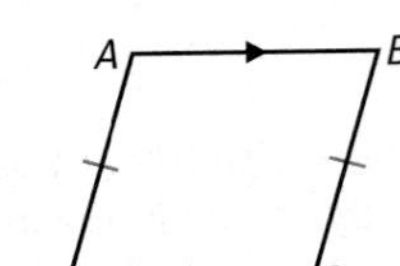

23. 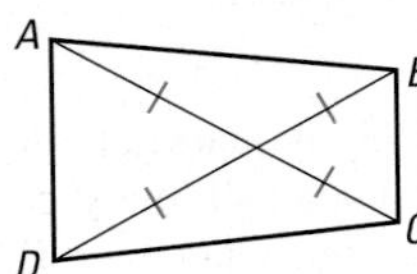

24. 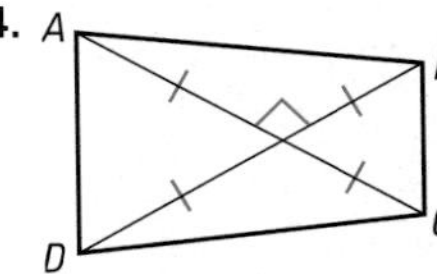

STUDENT HELP

Study Tip
See the summaries for parallelograms and rhombuses on pp. 340 and 365, and the list of postulates and theorems on pp. 828–837. You can refer to your summaries as you do the rest of the exercises.

DESCRIBING METHODS OF PROOF Summarize the ways you have learned to prove that a quadrilateral is the given special type of quadrilateral.

25–29. See margin.

25. kite
26. square
27. rectangle
28. trapezoid
29. isosceles trapezoid

DEVELOPING PROOF Which two segments or angles must be congruent to enable you to prove *ABCD* is the given quadrilateral? Explain your reasoning. There may be more than one right answer.

30. ∠*A* and ∠*D*, or ∠*B* and ∠*C*

30. isosceles trapezoid
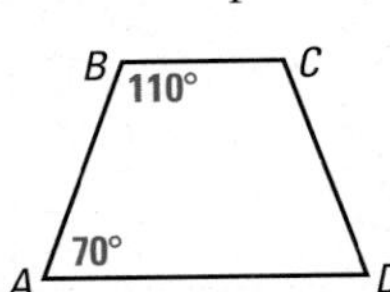

31. parallelogram
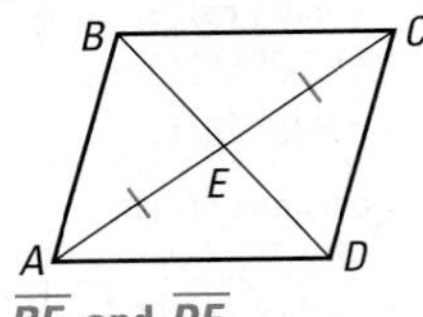

$\overline{BE}$ and $\overline{DE}$

32. rhombus
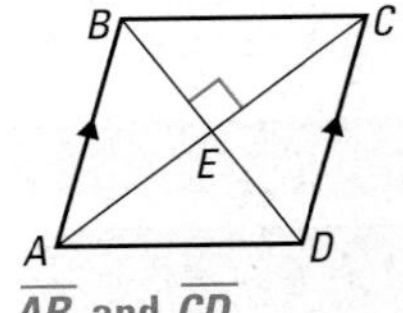

$\overline{AB}$ and $\overline{CD}$

33. $\overline{AE}$ and $\overline{BE}$ or $\overline{DE}$ (and so on), $\overline{AC}$ and $\overline{BD}$

33. rectangle
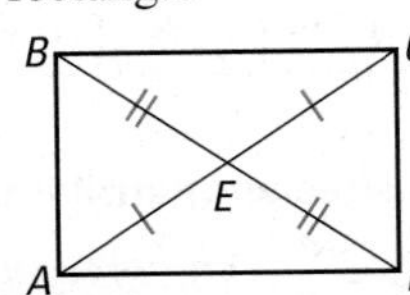

34. kite
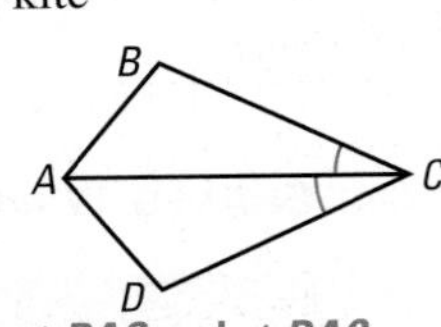

∠*BAC* and ∠*DAC*

35. square
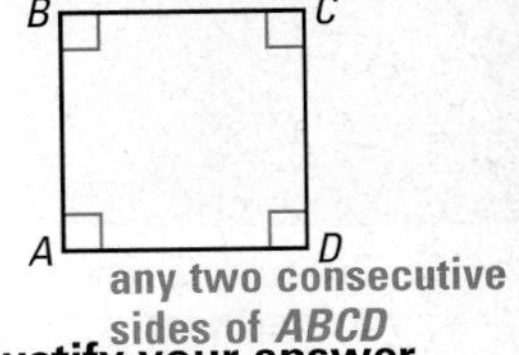

any two consecutive sides of *ABCD*

QUADRILATERALS What kind of quadrilateral is *PQRS*? Justify your answer.

36–41. See margin.

36. Kite; $\overline{PQ} \cong \overline{PS}$ and $\overline{RQ} \cong \overline{RS}$, but opp. sides are not ≅.
37. Isosceles trapezoid; $\overline{PQ} \parallel \overline{RS}$, and $\overline{PS}$ and $\overline{QR}$ are ≅ but not ∥.

36. $P(0, 0)$, $Q(0, 2)$, $R(5, 5)$, $S(2, 0)$
37. $P(1, 1)$, $Q(5, 1)$, $R(4, 8)$, $S(2, 8)$
38. $P(2, 1)$, $Q(7, 1)$, $R(7, 7)$, $S(2, 5)$
39. $P(0, 7)$, $Q(4, 8)$, $R(5, 2)$, $S(1, 1)$
40. $P(1, 7)$, $Q(5, 9)$, $R(8, 3)$, $S(4, 1)$
41. $P(5, 1)$, $Q(9, 6)$, $R(5, 11)$, $S(1, 6)$

FOCUS ON CAREERS

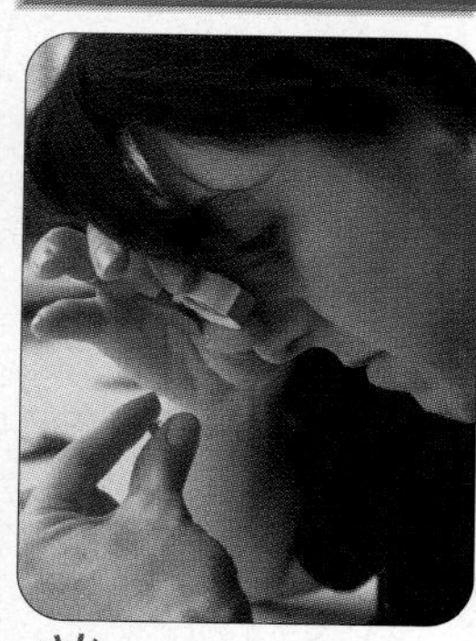

GEMOLOGISTS analyze the cut of a gem when determining its value.

CAREER LINK www.mcdougallittell.com

GEM CUTTING **In Exercises 42 and 43, use the following information.** There are different ways of cutting gems to enhance the beauty of the jewel. One of the earliest shapes used for diamonds is called the *table cut*, as shown at the right. Each face of a cut gem is called a *facet*.

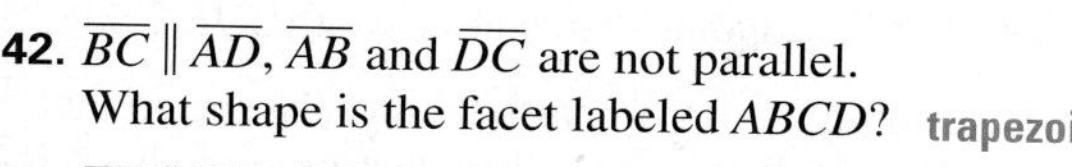

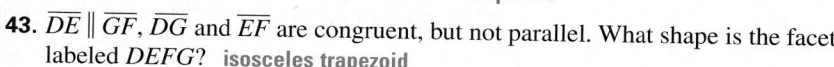

42. $\overline{BC} \parallel \overline{AD}$, $\overline{AB}$ and $\overline{DC}$ are not parallel. What shape is the facet labeled $ABCD$? trapezoid

43. $\overline{DE} \parallel \overline{GF}$, $\overline{DG}$ and $\overline{EF}$ are congruent, but not parallel. What shape is the facet labeled $DEFG$? isosceles trapezoid

44. JUSTIFYING A CONSTRUCTION Look back at the *Perpendicular to a Line* construction on page 130. Explain why this construction works. See margin.

DRAWING QUADRILATERALS **Draw $\overline{AC}$ and $\overline{BD}$ as described. What special type of quadrilateral is $ABCD$? Prove that your answer is correct.** 45–47. See margin.

45. $\overline{AC}$ and $\overline{BD}$ bisect each other, but they are not perpendicular or congruent.

46. $\overline{AC}$ and $\overline{BD}$ bisect each other. $\overline{AC} \perp \overline{BD}$, $\overline{AC} \not\cong \overline{BD}$

47. $\overline{AC} \perp \overline{BD}$, and $\overline{AC}$ bisects $\overline{BD}$. $\overline{BD}$ does not bisect $\overline{AC}$.

48. LOGICAL REASONING $EFGH$, $GHJK$, and $JKLM$ are all parallelograms. If $\overline{EF}$ and $\overline{LM}$ are not collinear, what kind of quadrilateral is $EFLM$? Prove that your answer is correct. See margin.

STUDENT HELP

HOMEWORK HELP Visit our Web site www.mcdougallittell.com for help with Exs. 45–47.

49. PROOF Prove that the median of a right triangle is one half the length of the hypotenuse. See margin.

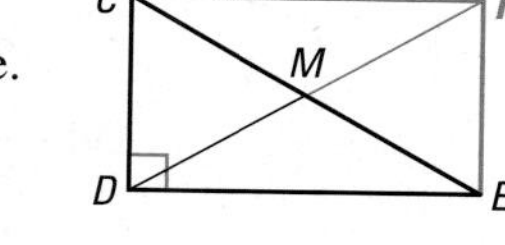

GIVEN ▶ $\angle CDE$ is a right angle. $\overline{CM} \cong \overline{EM}$

PROVE ▶ $\overline{DM} \cong \overline{CM}$

Plan for Proof First draw $\overline{CF}$ and $\overline{EF}$ so $CDEF$ is a rectangle. (How?)

50. PROOF Use facts about angles to prove that the quadrilateral in Example 5 is a rectangle. (*Hint:* Let $x°$ be the measure of $\angle ABN$. Find the measures of the other angles in terms of x.) See margin.

PROOF **What special type of quadrilateral is $EFGH$? Prove that your answer is correct.** 51, 52. See margin.

51. GIVEN ▶ $PQRS$ is a square. E, F, G, and H are midpoints of the sides of the square.

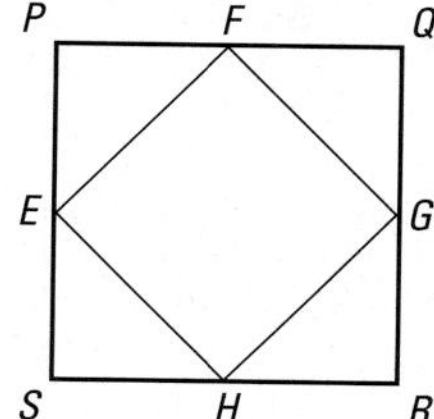

52. GIVEN ▶ $\overline{JK} \cong \overline{LM}$, E, F, G, and H are the midpoints of $\overline{JL}$, $\overline{KL}$, $\overline{KM}$, and $\overline{JM}$.

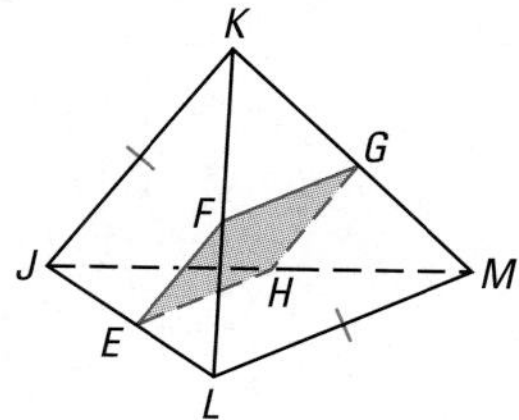

APPLICATION NOTE

EXERCISES 42 AND 43 In the table cut, or *brilliant* cut, the table is the top surface. The planes adjacent to the table, such as *ABCD*, make up the *crown* of the stone. *DEFG* lies below the widest part of the cut stone on the *pavilion* or *base*. The facets in the base slope inward to the bottom, where they intersect another plane parallel to the table. Normally, a modern table cut has 32 crown facets and 24 base facets, with the facet angles chosen to maximize the stone's brilliance.

CAREER NOTE

EXERCISES 42 AND 43 Additional information about gemologists is available at **www.mcdougallittell.com.**

STUDENT HELP NOTES

Homework Help Students can find help for Exs. 45–47 at **www.mcdougallittell.com.** The information can be printed out for students who don't have access to the Internet.

44. If you draw the figure whose vertices are the original point, the two points on the given line, and the point on the other side of the line, the figure is a kite. The given line and the constructed line are the diags. of the kite. They are, therefore, ⊥.

45–52. See Additional Answers beginning on page AA1.

ADDITIONAL PRACTICE AND RETEACHING

For Lesson 6.6:

- Practice Levels A, B, and C (*Chapter 6 Resource Book*, p. 84)
- Reteaching with Practice (*Chapter 6 Resource Book*, p. 87)
- See Lesson 6.6 of the *Personal Student Tutor*

For more Mixed Review:

- Search the *Test and Practice Generator* for key words or specific lessons.

4 ASSESS

DAILY HOMEWORK QUIZ

Transparency Available

1. For which special quadrilaterals is it *sometimes*, but *not always* true that the diagonals are congruent? **parallelogram, rhombus, trapezoid, kite**

2. What kinds of quadrilaterals meet the conditions shown? *RSTU* is not drawn to scale.

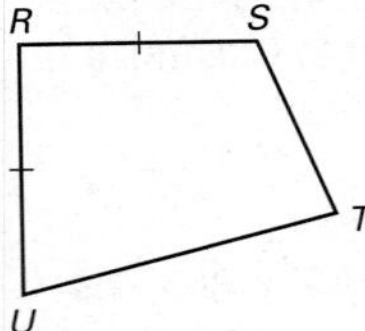

rhombus, square, kite

What kind of quadrilateral is *EFGH*? Justify your answer.

3. $E(-3, -2)$, $F(-1, 1)$, $G(2, 3)$, $H(3, -3)$ **Kite; $\overline{EF} \cong \overline{FG}$ and $\overline{GH} \cong \overline{EH}$, but opp. sides are not $\cong$.**

4. $E(1, 4)$, $F(4, 3)$, $G(-1, -2)$, $H(-2, 1)$ **Isosceles trapezoid; $\overline{EH} \parallel \overline{FG}$, and $\overline{EF}$ and $\overline{HG}$ are $\cong$ but not $\parallel$.**

EXTRA CHALLENGE NOTE

Challenge problems for Lesson 6.6 are available in **blackline** format in the *Chapter 6 Resource Book,* p. 92 and at **www.mcdougallittell.com.**

ADDITIONAL TEST PREPARATION

1. WRITING Explain why a parallelogram with one right angle must be a rectangle.
See sample answer at right.

2. OPEN ENDED Sketch a non-square quadrilateral with perpendicular, congruent diagonals.
Students can draw a kite, isosceles trapezoid, or certain irregular quadrilaterals.

53, 54. See Additional Answers beginning on page AA1.

Test Preparation

53. d. **Yes; *JLMN* and *JKMN* are isosceles trapezoids, so $\overline{JN} \cong \overline{MN}$. Since *JPMN* is a ▱, $\overline{PJ} \cong \overline{MN}$ and $\overline{PM} \cong \overline{JN}$. It follows from the Transitive Prop. of Cong. that all 4 sides of *JPMN* are $\cong$ and *JPMN* is a rhombus.**

53. MULTI-STEP PROBLEM Copy the diagram. *JKLMN* is a regular pentagon. You will identify *JPMN*.
53 a, b, d. See margin.

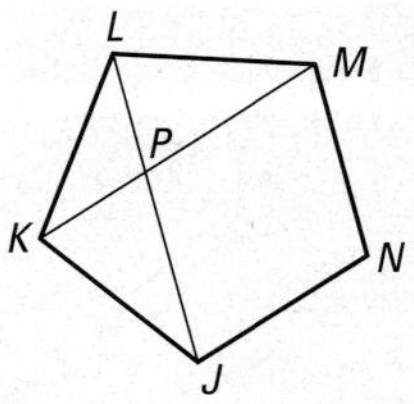

a. What kind of triangle is $\triangle JKL$? Use $\triangle JKL$ to prove that $\angle LJN \cong \angle JLM$.

b. List everything you know about the interior angles of *JLMN*. Use these facts to prove that $\overline{JL} \parallel \overline{NM}$.

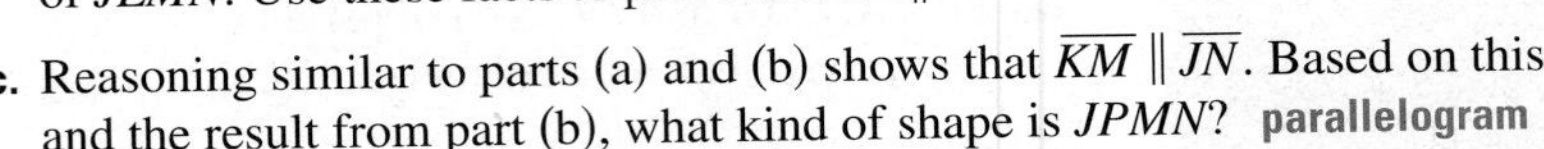

c. Reasoning similar to parts (a) and (b) shows that $\overline{KM} \parallel \overline{JN}$. Based on this and the result from part (b), what kind of shape is *JPMN*? **parallelogram**

d. *Writing* Is *JPMN* a rhombus? Justify your answer.

★ Challenge

54. PROOF $\overline{AC}$ and $\overline{BD}$ intersect each other at *N*. $\overline{AN} \cong \overline{BN}$ and $\overline{CN} \cong \overline{DN}$, but $\overline{AC}$ and $\overline{BD}$ do not bisect each other. Draw $\overline{AC}$ and $\overline{BD}$, and *ABCD*. What special type of quadrilateral is *ABCD*? Write a plan for a proof of your answer. **See margin.**

MIXED REVIEW

FINDING AREA **Find the area of the figure.** (Review 1.7 for 6.7)

55.

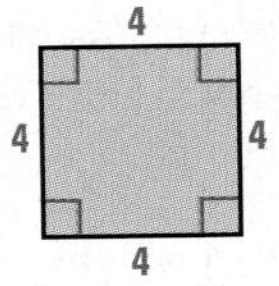

16 sq. units

56.

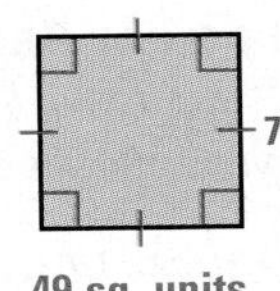

49 sq. units

57.

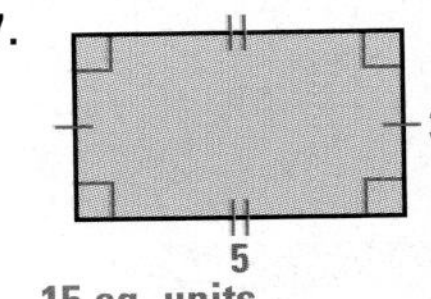

15 sq. units

58. (rectangle 9 by 6) **54 sq. units**

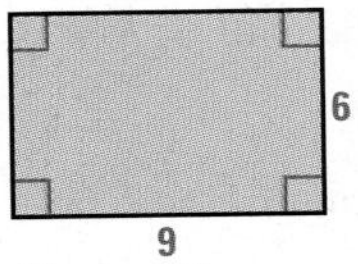

59. (right triangle 5, 12, 13) **30 sq. units**

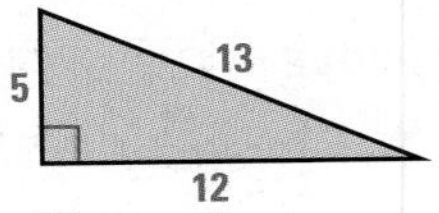

60.

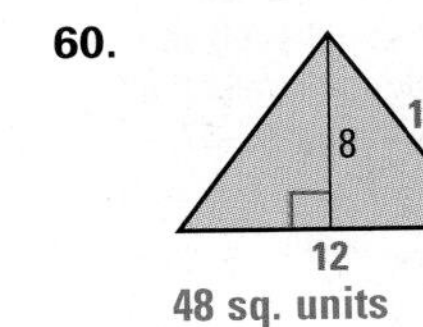

48 sq. units

USING ALGEBRA **In Exercises 61 and 62, use the diagram at the right.** (Review 6.1)

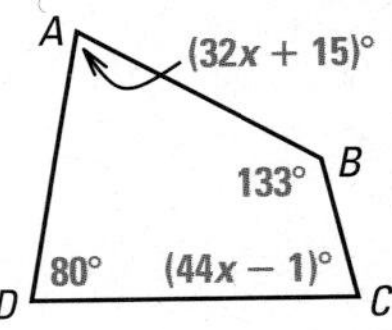

61. What is the value of *x*? **1.75**

62. What is $m\angle A$? Use your result from Exercise 61. **71°**

FINDING THE MIDSEGMENT **Find the length of the midsegment of the trapezoid.** (Review 6.5 for 6.7)

63. **7**

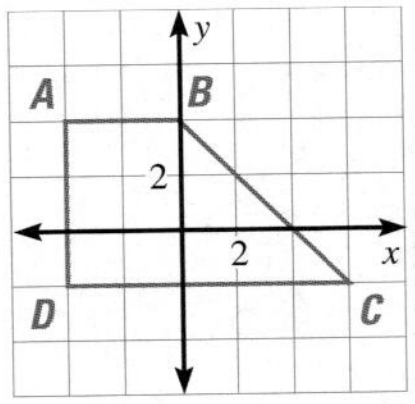

64. **6**

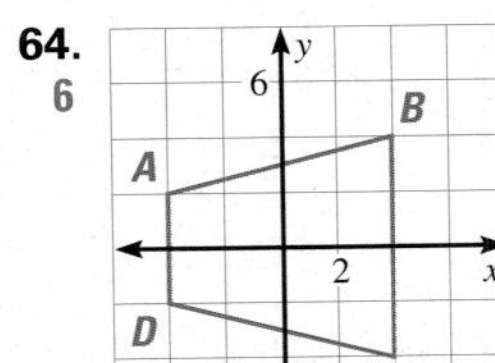

65. **5**

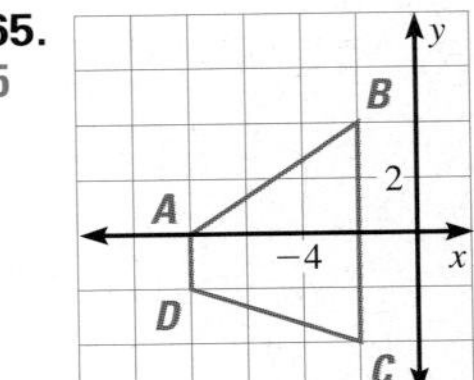

Additional Test Preparation ***Sample answer:***

1. Opposite angles of a parallelogram are congruent and consecutive angles are supplementary. It follows that each angle must be 90°. By definition, the parallelogram is a rectangle.

ACTIVITY 6.7

Developing Concepts

Areas of Quadrilaterals

GROUP ACTIVITY
Work with a partner.

MATERIALS
- ruler
- paper
- pencils
- index card
- straightedge
- scissors
- tape

QUESTION How are the areas of a rectangle, parallelogram, triangle, and trapezoid related to each other? Steps 1–6. Check figures.

EXPLORING AREA OF A PARALLELOGRAM

1. Use a straightedge to draw a line through one of the vertices of an index card, as shown at the right.
2. Cut off the triangle and tape it to the opposite side to form a parallelogram.

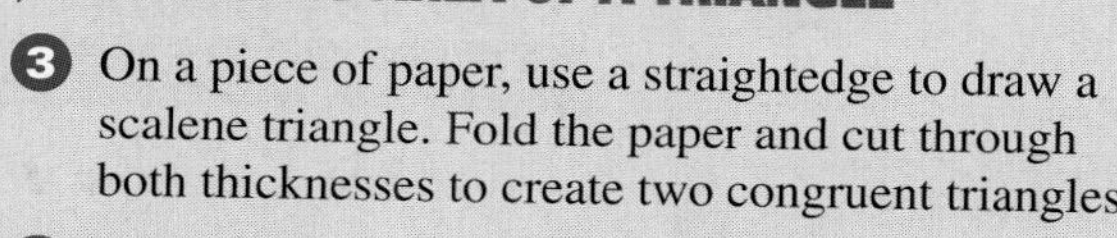

DRAWING CONCLUSIONS

1. How does the area of the parallelogram compare to the area of the rectangular index card? How do their bases compare? their heights?
They are the same; they are the same; they are the same.

EXPLORING AREA OF A TRIANGLE

3. On a piece of paper, use a straightedge to draw a scalene triangle. Fold the paper and cut through both thicknesses to create two congruent triangles.
4. Line up corresponding sides to form a parallelogram, as shown at the left.

DRAWING CONCLUSIONS

2. How does the area of each triangle compare to the area of the parallelogram? How do the bases and heights compare?
The area of each △ is half the area of the ▱; the bases and heights are the same.

EXPLORING AREA OF A TRAPEZOID

5. On a piece of paper, draw any trapezoid. Fold and cut the paper to create two congruent trapezoids.
6. Form a parallelogram, as shown at the right.

DRAWING CONCLUSIONS

3. How does the area of each trapezoid compare to the area of the parallelogram? How do the bases and heights compare? See margin.

3. The area of each trapezoid is half the area of the ▱; the heights are the same and the base of the ▱ is equal to the sum of the bases of each trapezoid.

EXTENSION

The area A of a rectangle with base b and height h is given by the formula $A = bh$. Write formulas for the areas of a parallelogram, a triangle, and a trapezoid.

Extension. In each case, A is the area. The area of a ▱ with base b and height h is given by $A = bh$. The area of a triangle with base b and height h is given by $A = \frac{1}{2}bh$. The area of a trapezoid with bases b_1 and b_2 and height h is given by $A = \frac{1}{2}h(b_1 + b_2)$.

1 Planning the Activity

PURPOSE
To investigate the relationship among the areas of rectangles, parallelograms, triangles, and trapezoids.

MATERIALS
- index card
- straightedge
- scissors
- tape
- Activity Support Master (*Chapter 6 Resource Book*, p. 96)

PACING
- Activity — 20 min

LINK TO LESSON
This activity uses the principle of the Area Addition Postulate in Lesson 6.7.

2 Managing the Activity

ALTERNATIVE APPROACH
Have students use geometry software to draw and compare the areas of figures with the base and height relationships in the activity.

3 Closing the Activity

KEY DISCOVERY
The area of a rectangle equals that of a parallelogram with the same base and height. The area of a triangle is half that of a parallelogram with the same base and height. The area of a trapezoid is its height multiplied by half the sum of its bases.

ACTIVITY ASSESSMENT
JOURNAL Draw a diagonal of a parallelogram of known base and height. Explain how you can use the parallelogram to find the area of each of the triangles formed.
Find bh, the area of the parallelogram, and divide the area in half.

1 PLAN

PACING
Basic: 2 days
Average: 2 days
Advanced: 2 days
Block Schedule: 1 block

LESSON OPENER
VISUAL APPROACH
An alternative way to approach Lesson 6.7 is to use the Visual Approach Lesson Opener:
- Blackline Master (*Chapter 6 Resource Book*, p. 98)
- Transparency (p. 40)

MEETING INDIVIDUAL NEEDS
- ***Chapter 6 Resource Book***
  Prerequisite Skills Review (p. 5)
  Practice Level A (p. 102)
  Practice Level B (p. 103)
  Practice Level C (p. 104)
  Reteaching with Practice (p. 105)
  Absent Student Catch-Up (p. 107)
  Challenge (p. 109)
- ***Resources in Spanish***
- ***Personal Student Tutor***

NEW-TEACHER SUPPORT
See the Tips for New Teachers on pp. 1–2 of the *Chapter 6 Resource Book* for additional notes about Lesson 6.7.

WARM-UP EXERCISES
Transparency Available
1. $P = 2L + 2W$; Find P when $L = 3$ and $W = 5$. 16
2. $A = \pi r^2$; Find A for $\pi = 3.14$ and $r = 3$. 28.26
3. $A = \pi d$; Find d for $\pi = 3.14$ and $A = 21.98$. 7
4. $P = 4s$; Find P when $s = 10$. 40
5. $P = 2b + a$; Find b when $a = 5$ and $P = 23$. 9

6.7 Areas of Triangles and Quadrilaterals

What you should learn

GOAL 1 Find the areas of squares, rectangles, parallelograms, and triangles.

GOAL 2 Find the areas of trapezoids, kites, and rhombuses, as applied in **Example 6**.

Why you should learn it

▼ To find areas of **real-life** surfaces, such as the roof of the covered bridge in **Exs. 48 and 49**.

CALIFORNIA STANDARDS AND ASSESSMENT
CA Standards: 7, 8, 10
SAT9 Task 1: Obj. 23
SAT9 Task 2: Obj. 29

GOAL 1 USING AREA FORMULAS

You can use the postulates below to prove several area theorems.

AREA POSTULATES

POSTULATE 22 ***Area of a Square Postulate***
The area of a square is the square of the length of its side, or $A = s^2$.

POSTULATE 23 ***Area Congruence Postulate***
If two polygons are congruent, then they have the same area.

POSTULATE 24 ***Area Addition Postulate***
The area of a region is the sum of the areas of its nonoverlapping parts.

AREA THEOREMS

THEOREM 6.20 ***Area of a Rectangle***
The area of a rectangle is the product of its base and height.
$A = bh$

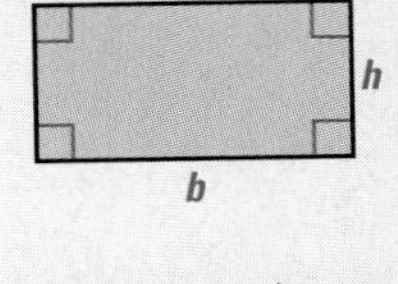

THEOREM 6.21 ***Area of a Parallelogram***
The area of a parallelogram is the product of a base and its corresponding height.
$A = bh$

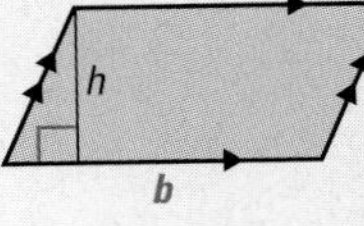

THEOREM 6.22 ***Area of a Triangle***
The area of a triangle is one half the product of a base and its corresponding height.
$A = \frac{1}{2}bh$

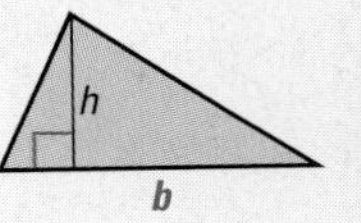

You can justify the area formulas for triangles and parallelograms as follows.

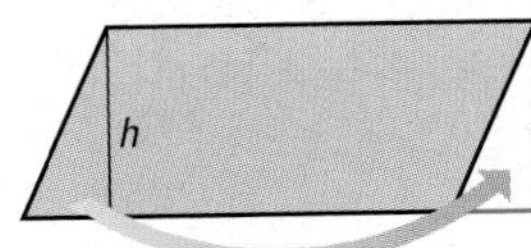

The area of a parallelogram is the area of a rectangle with the same base and height.

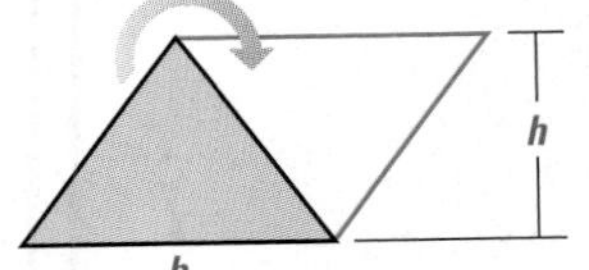

The area of a triangle is half the area of a parallelogram with the same base and height.

STUDENT HELP

Study Tip
To find the area of a parallelogram or triangle, you can use any side as the base. But be sure you measure the height of an altitude that is perpendicular to the base you have chosen.

EXAMPLE 1 *Using the Area Theorems*

Find the area of $\square ABCD$.

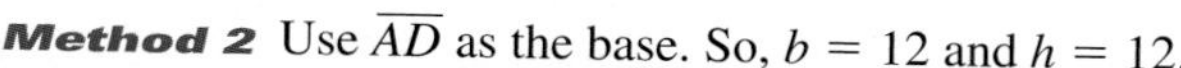

SOLUTION

Method 1 Use $\overline{AB}$ as the base. So, $b = 16$ and $h = 9$.

Area $= bh = 16(9) = 144$ square units.

Method 2 Use $\overline{AD}$ as the base. So, $b = 12$ and $h = 12$.

Area $= bh = 12(12) = 144$ square units.

Notice that you get the same area with either base.

EXAMPLE 2 *Finding the Height of a Triangle*

Rewrite the formula for the area of a triangle in terms of h. Then use your formula to find the height of a triangle that has an area of 12 and a base length of 6.

SOLUTION

Rewrite the area formula so h is alone on one side of the equation.

$A = \frac{1}{2}bh$ — Formula for the area of a triangle

$2A = bh$ — Multiply both sides by 2.

$\frac{2A}{b} = h$ — Divide both sides by b.

Substitute 12 for A and 6 for b to find the height of the triangle.

$$h = \frac{2A}{b} = \frac{2(12)}{6} = 4$$

▶ The height of the triangle is 4.

EXAMPLE 3 *Finding the Height of a Triangle*

A triangle has an area of 52 square feet and a base of 13 feet. Are all triangles with these dimensions congruent?

SOLUTION

Using the formula from Example 2, the height is $h = \frac{2(52)}{13} = 8$ feet.

There are many triangles with these dimensions. Some are shown below.

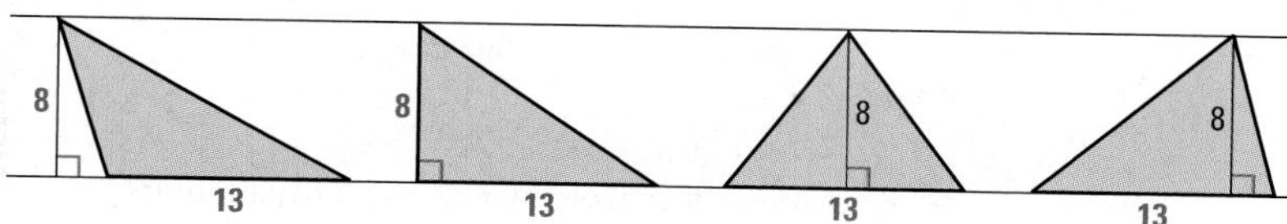

STUDENT HELP

Study Tip
Notice that the altitude of a triangle can be outside the triangle.

2 TEACH

MOTIVATING THE LESSON
Some cafeteria trays are designed to use the area on a table efficiently. One design has a rectangular base and a trapezoidal top. The area the tray takes is the sum of the areas of the rectangle and the trapezoid, whose area formulas students will now explore.

EXTRA EXAMPLE 1
Find the area of $\triangle RST$.

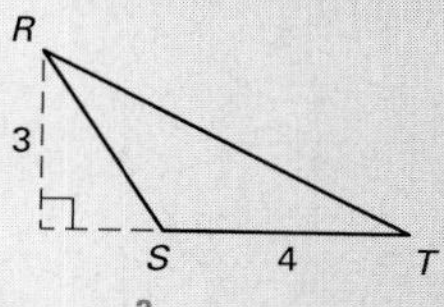

6 units^2

EXTRA EXAMPLE 2
Rewrite the formula for the area of a rectangle in terms of b. Then use your formula to find the base of a triangle that has an area of 48 and a height of 3. $b = \frac{A}{h}$; 16

EXTRA EXAMPLE 3
A rectangle has an area of 100 square meters and a height of 25 meters. Are all rectangles with these dimensions congruent? yes

CHECKPOINT EXERCISES

For use after Example 1:

1. Find the area of $\square RSTU$.

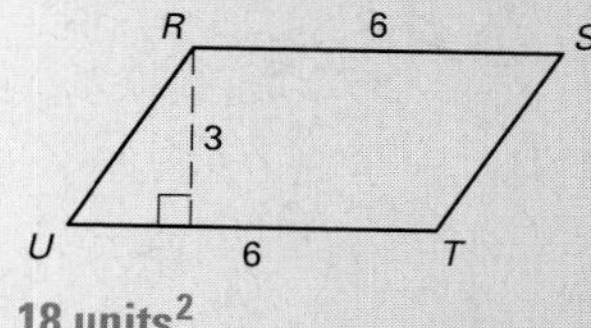

18 units^2

For use after Examples 2 and 3:

2. Rewrite the formula for the area of a parallelogram in terms of h. Then use your formula to find the height of a parallelogram that has an area of 96 square feet and a base length of 8 feet. $h = \frac{A}{b}$; 12 ft

EXTRA EXAMPLE 4

Find the area of trapezoid *EFGH*.

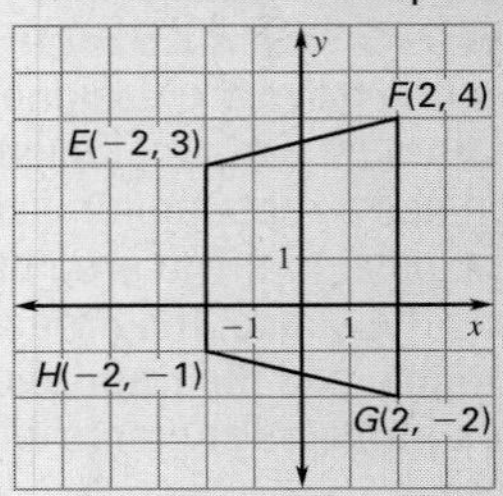

20 units^2

CHECKPOINT EXERCISES

For use after Example 4:

1. Find the area of kite *ABCD*.

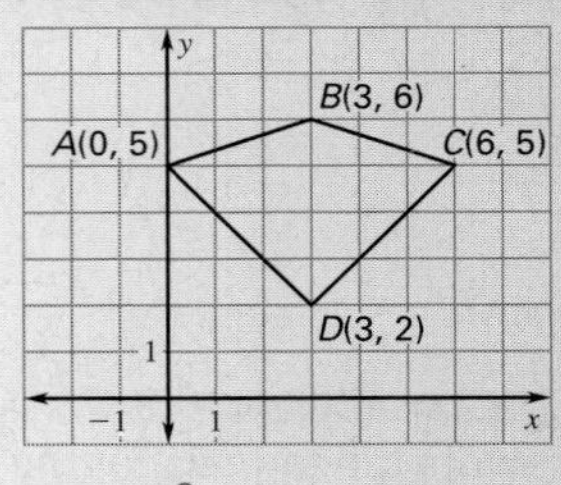

12 units^2

STUDENT HELP NOTES

Look Back As students review the formula for the length of a midsegment, remind them that both parallel segments of a trapezoid are called bases, regardless of their orientation.

GOAL 2 AREAS OF TRAPEZOIDS, KITES, AND RHOMBUSES

THEOREMS

THEOREM 6.23 ***Area of a Trapezoid***

The area of a trapezoid is one half the product of the height and the sum of the bases.

$$A = \frac{1}{2}h(b_1 + b_2)$$

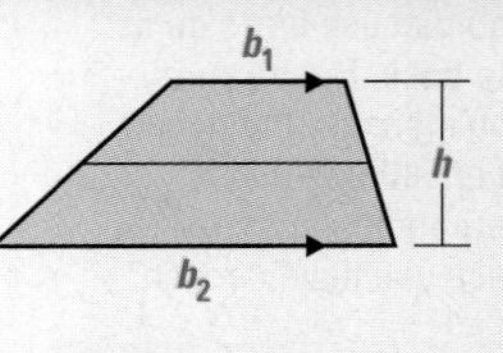

THEOREM 6.24 ***Area of a Kite***

The area of a kite is one half the product of the lengths of its diagonals.

$$A = \frac{1}{2}d_1 d_2$$

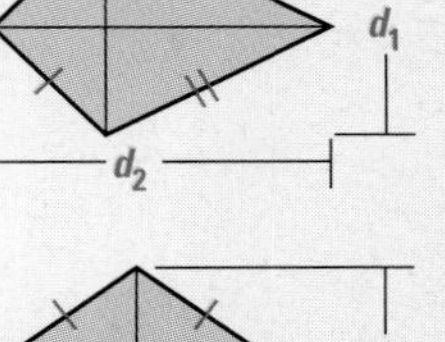

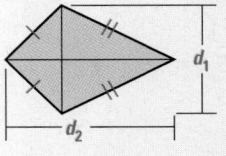

THEOREM 6.25 ***Area of a Rhombus***

The area of a rhombus is equal to one half the product of the lengths of the diagonals.

$$A = \frac{1}{2}d_1 d_2$$

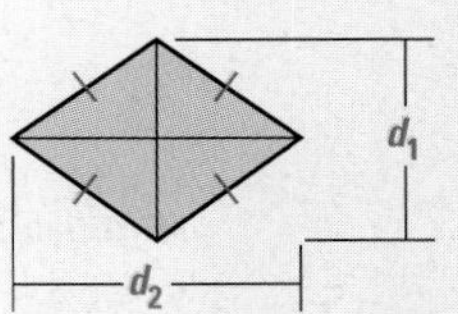

STUDENT HELP

Look Back
Remember that the length of the midsegment of a trapezoid is the average of the lengths of the bases. (p. 357)

You will justify Theorem 6.23 in Exercises 58 and 59. You may find it easier to remember the theorem this way.

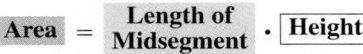

Area = **Length of Midsegment** • **Height**

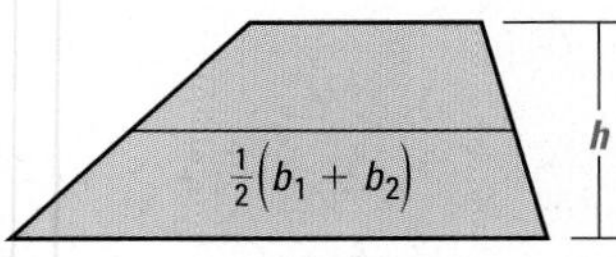

EXAMPLE 4 *Finding the Area of a Trapezoid*

Find the area of trapezoid *WXYZ*.

SOLUTION

The height of *WXYZ* is $h = 5 - 1 = 4$.

Find the lengths of the bases.

$b_1 = YZ = 5 - 2 = 3$

$b_2 = XW = 8 - 1 = 7$

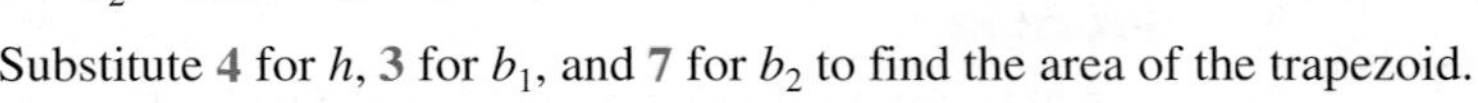

Substitute 4 for h, 3 for b_1, and 7 for b_2 to find the area of the trapezoid.

$A = \frac{1}{2}h(b_1 + b_2)$	**Formula for area of a trapezoid**
$= \frac{1}{2}(4)(3 + 7)$	**Substitute.**
$= 20$	**Simplify.**

▶ The area of trapezoid *WXYZ* is 20 square units.

The diagram at the right justifies the formulas for the areas of kites and rhombuses.

The diagram shows that the area of a kite is half the area of the rectangle whose length and width are the lengths of the diagonals of the kite. The same is true for a rhombus.

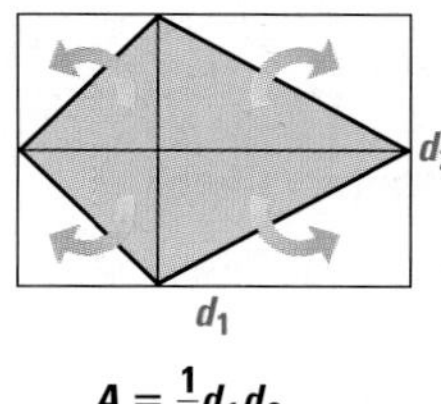

$A = \frac{1}{2}d_1d_2$

EXAMPLE 5 ***Finding the Area of a Rhombus***

Use the information given in the diagram to find the area of rhombus *ABCD*.

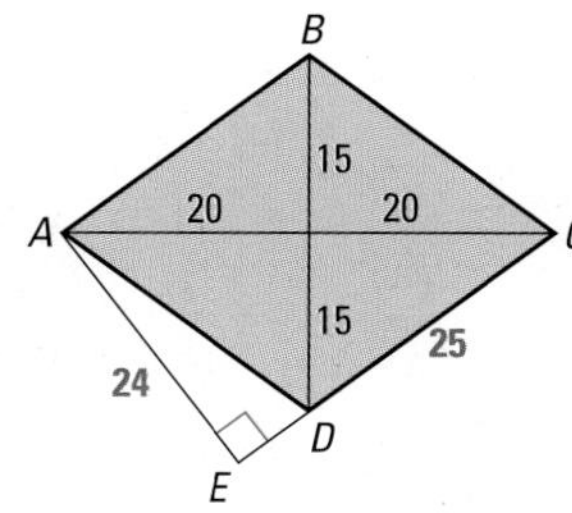

SOLUTION

Method 1 Use the formula for the area of a rhombus. $d_1 = BD = 30$ and $d_2 = AC = 40$.

$$A = \frac{1}{2}d_1d_2$$
$$= \frac{1}{2}(30)(40)$$
$$= 600 \text{ square units}$$

Method 2 Use the formula for the area of a parallelogram. $b = 25$ and $h = 24$.

$$A = bh = 25(24) = 600 \text{ square units}$$

EXAMPLE 6 ***Finding Areas***

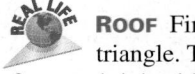

REAL LIFE **ROOF** Find the area of the roof. *G*, *H*, and *K* are trapezoids and *J* is a triangle. The hidden back and left sides of the roof are the same as the front and right sides.

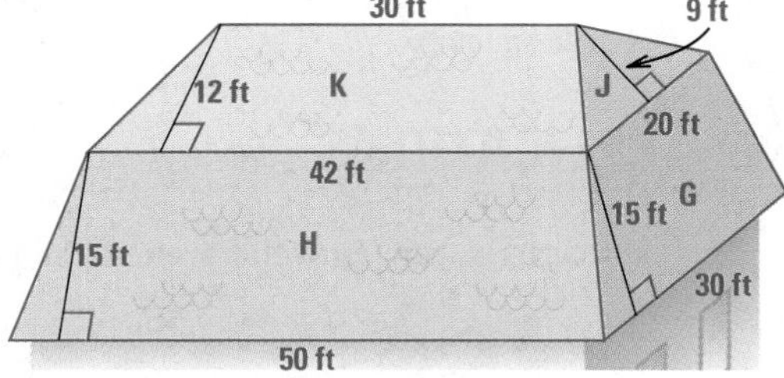

SOLUTION

Area of $J = \frac{1}{2}(20)(9) = 90 \text{ ft}^2$ Area of $H = \frac{1}{2}(15)(42 + 50) = 690 \text{ ft}^2$

Area of $G = \frac{1}{2}(15)(20 + 30) = 375 \text{ ft}^2$ Area of $K = \frac{1}{2}(12)(30 + 42) = 432 \text{ ft}^2$

The roof has two congruent faces of each type.

Total Area $= 2(90 + 375 + 690 + 432) = 3174$

▶ The total area of the roof is 3174 square feet.

STUDENT HELP

Study Tip
To check that the answer is reasonable, approximate each trapezoid by a rectangle. The area of *H* should be less than 50 • 15, but more than 40 • 15.

Closure Question ***Sample answer:***
Because a rhombus is a parallelogram, you can multiply the base by the height. Alternatively, you can take half the product of the lengths of the diagonals.

EXTRA EXAMPLE 5
Use the information given in the diagram to find the area of kite *ABCD*. **192 units²**

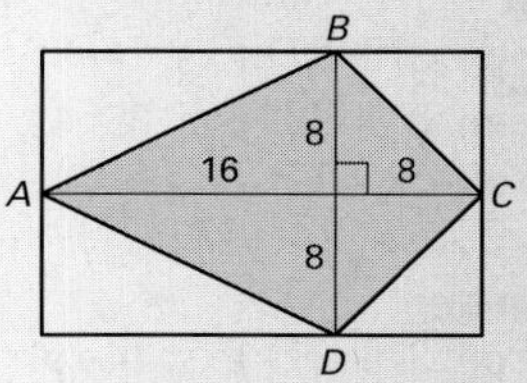

EXTRA EXAMPLE 6
The tray below is designed to save space on cafeteria tables. How much table area does the tray use? **167 in.²**

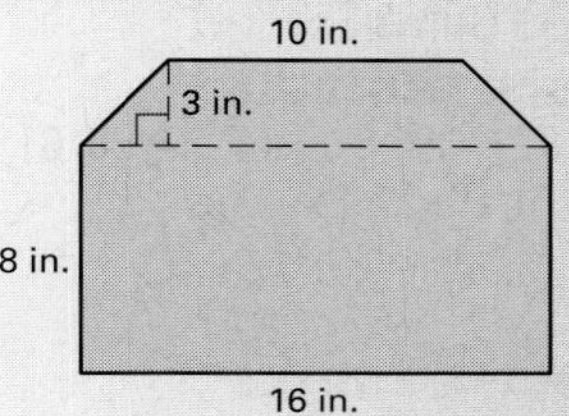

CHECKPOINT EXERCISES

For use after Example 5:

1. Find the area of rhombus *EFGH* if *EG* = 10 and *FH* = 15. **75 units²**

For use after Example 6:

2. Find the area of the figure shown. **30 units²**

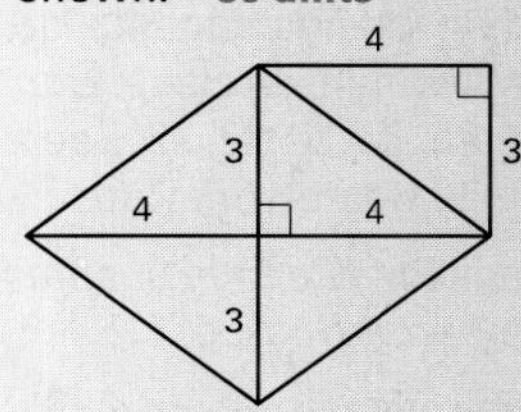

CLOSURE QUESTION
Describe two ways to find the area of a rhombus.
See sample answer at left.

DAILY PUZZLER

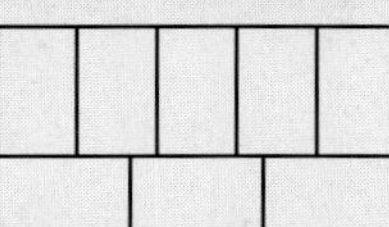

Eight congruent rectangles form the large rectangle, whose area is 120 square units. What is the perimeter of the large rectangle?
46 units

3 APPLY

ASSIGNMENT GUIDE

BASIC

Day 1: pp. 376–377 Exs. 14–34

Day 2: pp. 377–380 Exs. 35–43, 50–52, 60, 61, 63–70, Quiz 3 Exs. 1–7

AVERAGE

Day 1: pp. 376–377 Exs. 14–34

Day 2: pp. 377–380 Exs. 35–57, 60, 61, 63–70, Quiz 3 Exs. 1–7

ADVANCED

Day 1: pp. 376–377 Exs. 14–34

Day 2: pp. 377–380 Exs. 35–70, Quiz 3 Exs. 1–7

BLOCK SCHEDULE

pp. 377–380 Exs. 14–57, 60, 61, 63–70, Quiz 3 Exs. 1–7

EXERCISE LEVELS

Level A: *Easier*
14–25, 63–70

Level B: *More Difficult*
26–57, 60, 61

Level C: *Most Difficult*
58, 59, 62

✔ HOMEWORK CHECK

To quickly check student understanding of key concepts, go over the following exercises: Exs. 14, 18, 24, 28, 30, 36, 42, 52. See also the Daily Homework Quiz:

- Blackline Master (*Chapter 7 Resource Book,* p. 11)
- Transparency (p. 48)

GUIDED PRACTICE

Vocabulary Check ✓

1. What is the *midsegment* of a trapezoid?
the segment that connects the midpoints of the legs

Concept Check ✓

2. If you use AB as the base to find the area of $\square ABCD$ shown at the right, what should you use as the height?
DE

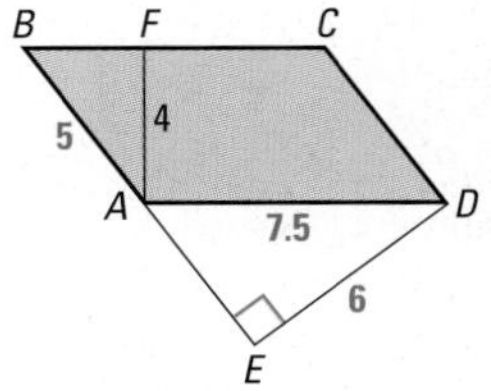

B F C 4 5 A 7.5 D 6 E

Skill Check ✓

Match the region with a formula for its area. Use each formula exactly once.

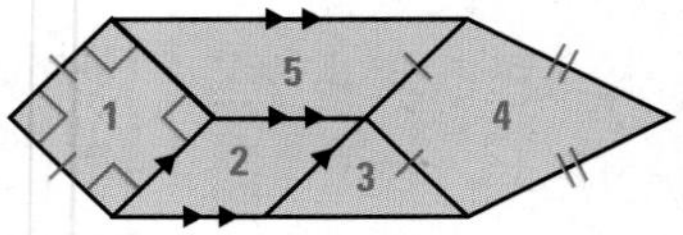

3. Region 1 A — (A) $A = s^2$
4. Region 2 E — (B) $A = \frac{1}{2}d_1d_2$
5. Region 3 C — (C) $A = \frac{1}{2}bh$
6. Region 4 B — (D) $A = \frac{1}{2}h(b_1 + b_2)$
7. Region 5 D — (E) $A = bh$

Find the area of the polygon.

8. 14 sq. units
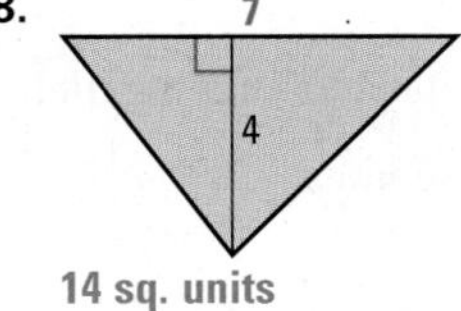

9. 25 sq. units

10. 36 sq. units

11. 40 sq. units

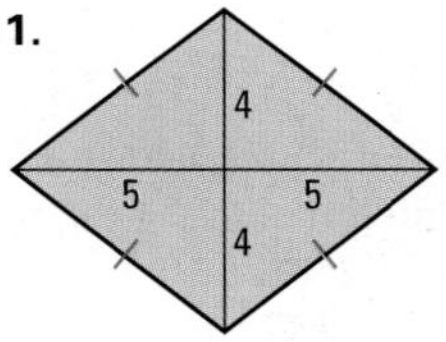

12. 72 sq. units
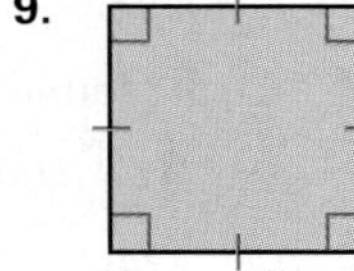
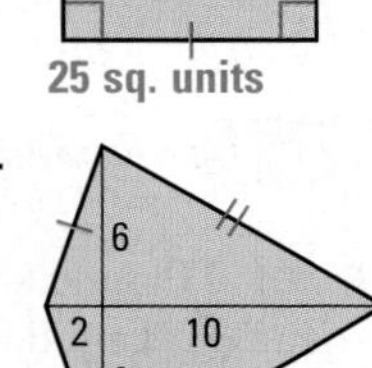

13. 36 sq. units

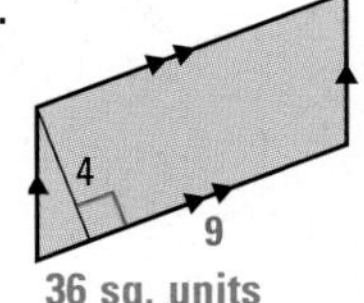
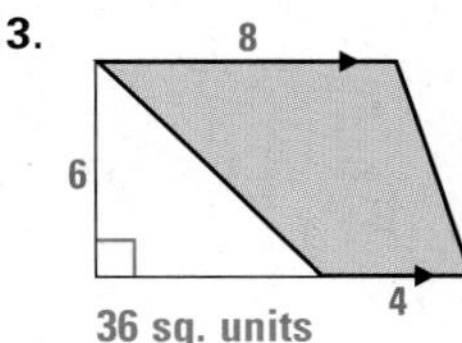

PRACTICE AND APPLICATIONS

STUDENT HELP

Extra Practice to help you master skills is on p. 814.

STUDENT HELP

HOMEWORK HELP

Example 1: Exs. 14–19, 41–47

Example 2: Exs. 26–31

continued on p. 377

FINDING AREA **Find the area of the polygon.**

14. 17.5 sq. units

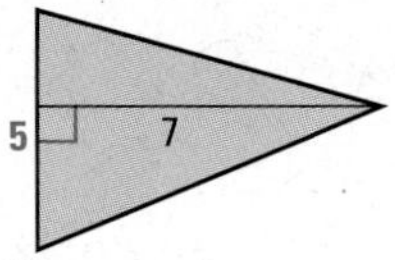

15. 49 sq. units

16. 45 sq. units
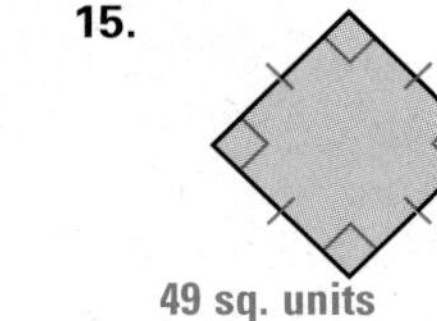
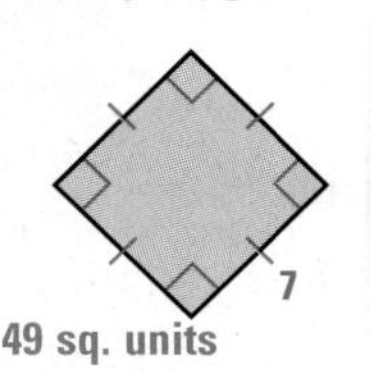
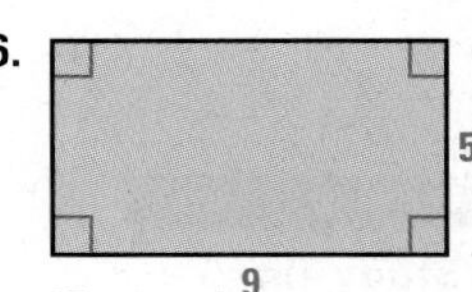

17. 120 sq. units

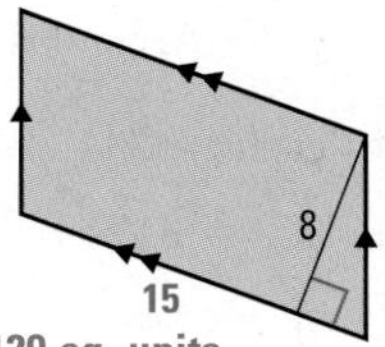

18. 462 sq. units

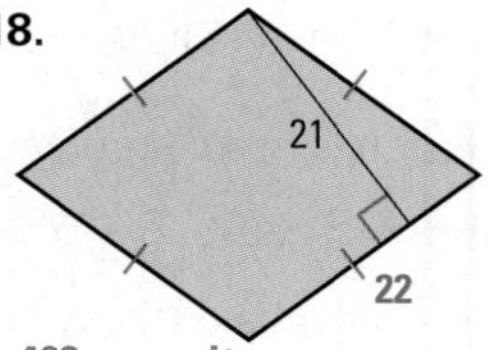

19. 10 sq. units
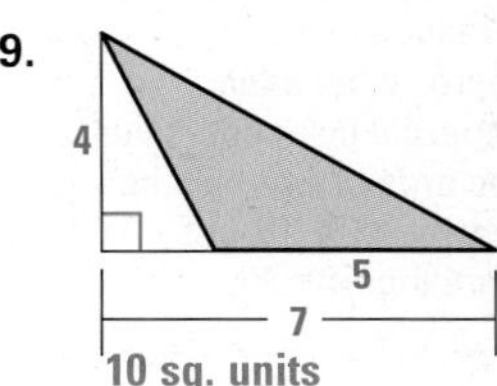

STUDENT HELP

HOMEWORK HELP
continued from p. 376
Example 3: Exs. 26–28, 39, 40
Example 4: Exs. 32–34
Example 5: Exs. 20–25, 44
Example 6: Exs. 35–38, 48–52

FINDING AREA **Find the area of the polygon.**

20.
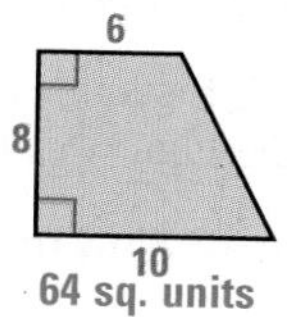

64 sq. units

21.
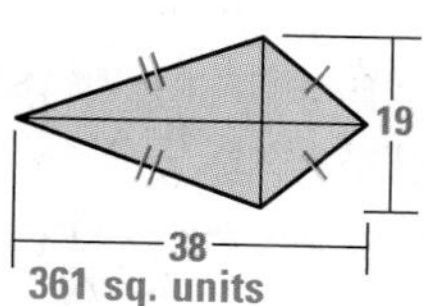

361 sq. units

22.
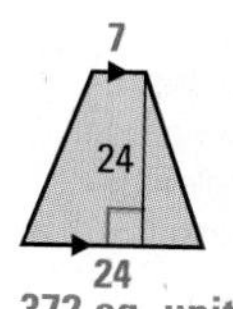

372 sq. units

23.
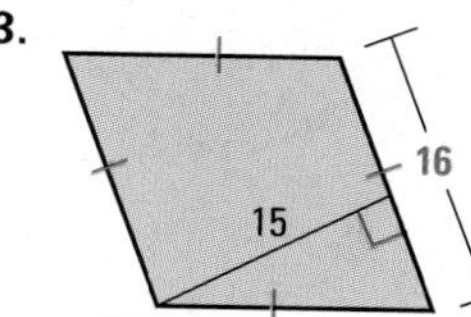

240 sq. units

24. 16, 8, 14

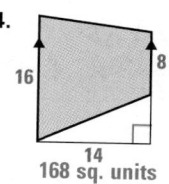

168 sq. units

25. 5, 7, 7, 5

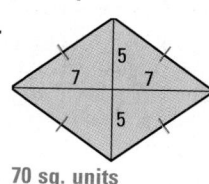

70 sq. units

USING ALGEBRA **Find the value of x.**

26. $A = 63\text{ cm}^2$

7 cm

9 cm

27. $A = 48\text{ ft}^2$
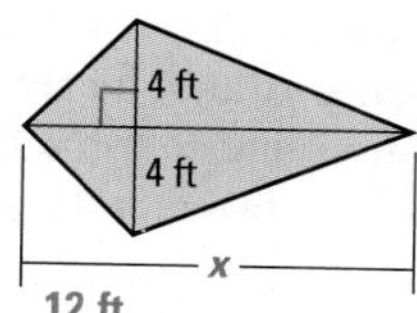

12 ft

28. $A = 48\text{ in.}^2$
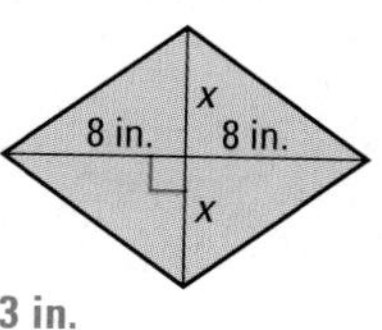

3 in.

REWRITING FORMULAS **Rewrite the formula for the area of the polygon in terms of the given variable. Use the formulas on pages 372 and 374.**

29. triangle, b $b = \frac{2A}{h}$

30. kite, d_1 $d_1 = \frac{2A}{d_2}$

31. trapezoid, b_1
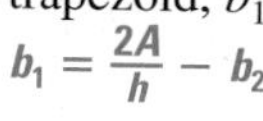
$b_1 = \frac{2A}{h} - b_2$

FINDING AREA **Find the area of quadrilateral *ABCD*.**

32.
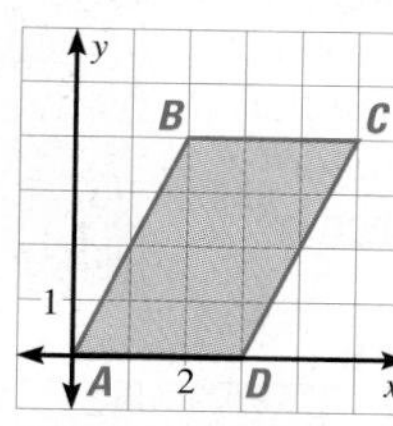

12 sq. units

33.
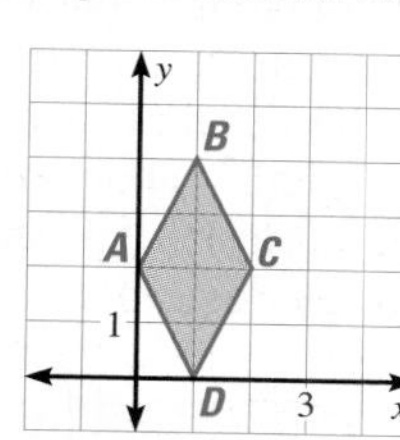

4 sq. units

34.
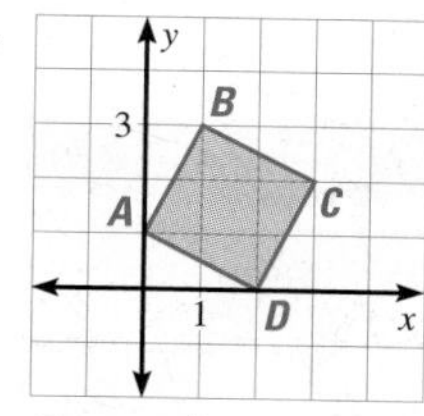

5 sq. units

ENERGY CONSERVATION **The total area of a building's windows affects the cost of heating or cooling the building. Find the area of the window.**

35.
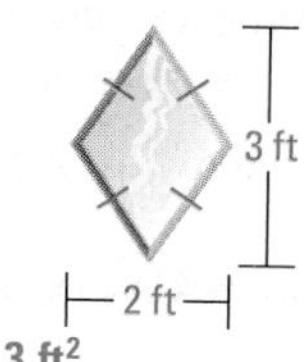

3 ft^2

36.
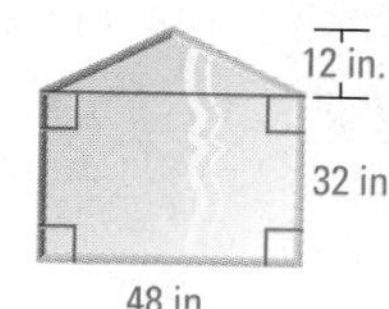

1824 in.^2

37.
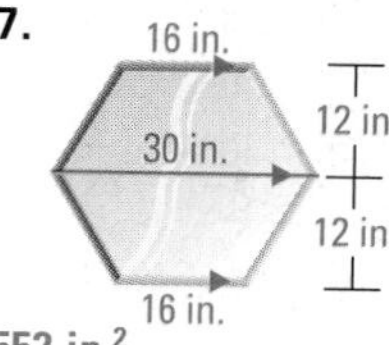

552 in.^2

38.
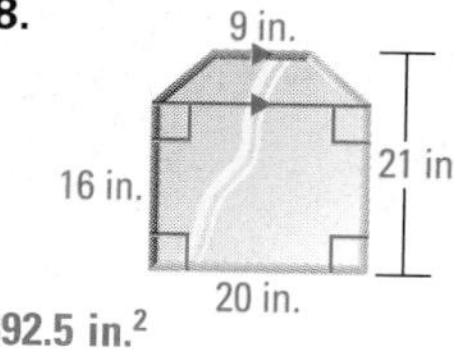

392.5 in.^2

FOCUS ON APPLICATIONS

REAL LIFE **INSULATION** Insulation makes a building more energy efficient. The ability of a material to insulate is called its *R*-value. Many windows have an *R*-value of 1. Adobe has an *R*-value of 11.9.

APPLICATION LINK
www.mcdougallittell.com

COMMON ERROR
EXERCISE 31 Some students may need to review the order in which inverse operations are performed when solving multi-step equations to avoid common errors such as first subtracting b_2 from both sides.

APPLICATION NOTE
EXERCISES 35–38
Additional information about insulation is available at **www.mcdougallittell.com.**

APPLICATION NOTE

EXERCISE 49 Remind students that the Area Addition Postulate states that the area of a region is the sum of the areas of its *nonoverlapping* parts. The way each row of shakes overlaps, most of each single shake is covered. So, the total number of shakes required to roof the bridge is much greater than the number of shakes required to cover the area with no overlapping.

STUDENT HELP

Study Tip
Remember that two polygons are congruent if their corresponding angles and sides are congruent.

39. No; such a ▱ has base 6 ft and height 4 ft; two such ▱ that have ∠s with different measures are not ≅.

40. Yes; any two rectangles with base 6 ft and height 4 ft are ≅ because all 4 ∠s of any such rectangles are ≅.

39. **LOGICAL REASONING** Are all parallelograms with an area of 24 square feet and a base of 6 feet congruent? Explain. **See margin.**

40. **LOGICAL REASONING** Are all rectangles with an area of 24 square feet and a base of 6 feet congruent? Explain. **See margin.**

USING THE PYTHAGOREAN THEOREM **Find the area of the polygon.**

41. 6, 10
24 sq. units

42.

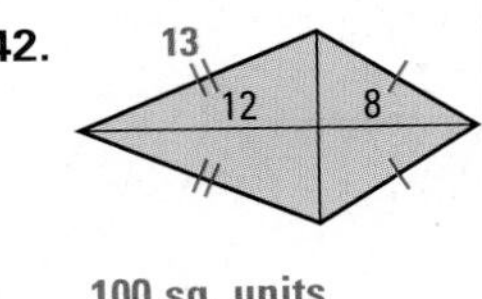

100 sq. units

43.

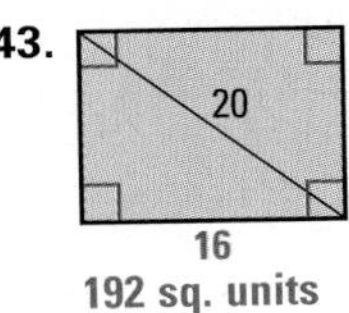

192 sq. units

44. **LOGICAL REASONING** What happens to the area of a kite if you double the length of one of the diagonals? if you double the length of both diagonals? **The area doubles; the area quadruples.**

PARADE FLOATS **You are decorating a float for a parade. You estimate that, on average, a carnation will cover 3 square inches, a daisy will cover 2 square inches, and a chrysanthemum will cover 4 square inches. About how many flowers do you need to cover the shape on the float?**

45. Carnations: 2 ft by 5 ft rectangle **about 480 carnations**

46. Daisies: trapezoid ($b_1 = 5$ ft, $b_2 = 3$ ft, $h = 2$ ft) **about 576 daisies**

47. Chrysanthemums: triangle ($b = 3$ ft, $h = 8$ ft) **about 432 chrysanthemums**

BRIDGES **In Exercises 48 and 49, use the following information.**

The town of Elizabethton, Tennessee, restored the roof of this covered bridge with cedar shakes, a kind of rough wooden shingle. The shakes vary in width, but the average width is about 10 inches. So, on average, each shake protects a 10 inch by 10 inch square of roof.

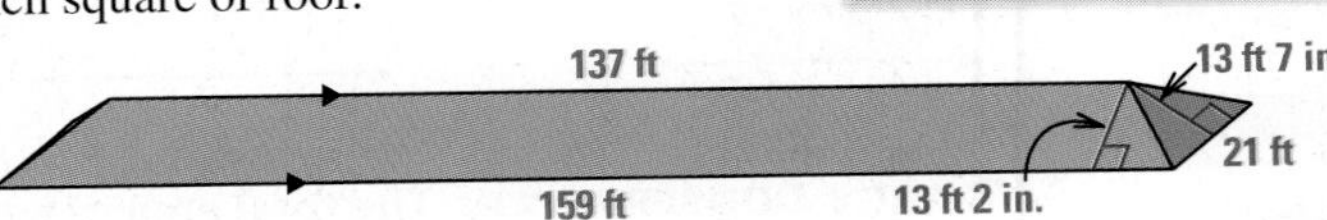

48. In the diagram of the roof, the hidden back and left sides are the same as the front and right sides. What is the total area of the roof? **about 4182.6 ft^2**

49. Estimate the number of shakes needed to cover the roof. **about 6023 shakes**

FOCUS ON PEOPLE

MARK CANDELARIA
When Mark Candelaria restored historic buildings in Scottsdale, Arizona, he calculated the areas of the walls and floors that needed to be replaced.

AREAS **Find the areas of the blue and yellow regions.**

50.

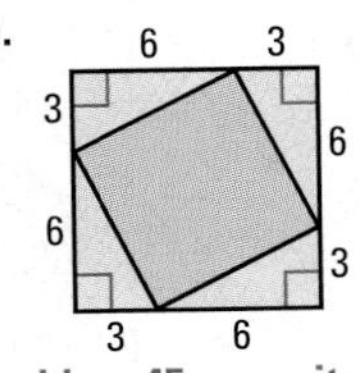

blue: 45 sq. units; yellow: 36 sq. units

51.

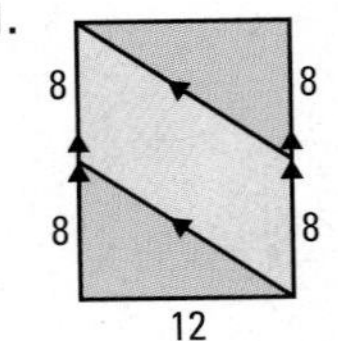

blue: 96 sq. units; yellow: 96 sq. units

52.

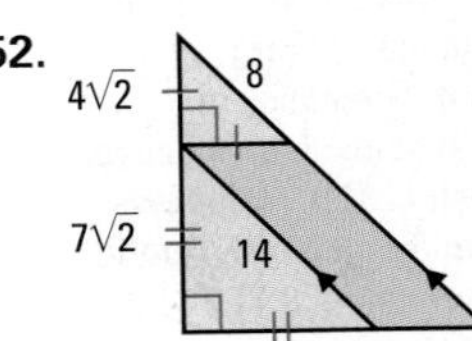

blue: 56 sq. units; yellow: 65 sq. units

JUSTIFYING THEOREM 6.20 **In Exercises 53–57, you will justify the formula for the area of a rectangle. In the diagram, *AEJH* and *JFCG* are congruent rectangles with base length *b* and height *h*.**

53, 54. See margin.

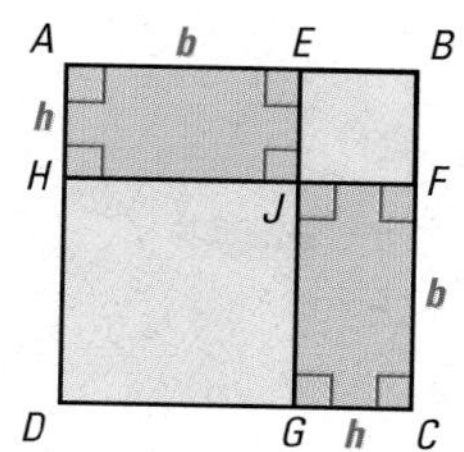

53. What kind of shape is *EBFJ*? *HJGD*? Explain.

54. What kind of shape is *ABCD*? How do you know?

55. Write an expression for the length of a side of *ABCD*. Then write an expression for the area of *ABCD*.
$b + h$; $(b + h)^2$

56. Write expressions for the areas of *EBFJ* and *HJGD*.
h^2, b^2

STUDENT HELP

Look Back
For help with squaring binomial expressions, see p. 798.

57. Substitute your answers from Exercises 55 and 56 into the following equation. Let A = the area of *AEJH*. Solve the equation to find an expression for A.
Area of $ABCD$ = Area of $HJGD$ + Area of $EBFJ$ + 2(Area of $AEJH$)
$(b + h)^2 = b^2 + h^2 + 2A$; $A = bh$

JUSTIFYING THEOREM 6.23 **Exercises 58 and 59 illustrate two ways to prove Theorem 6.23. Use the diagram to write a plan for a proof.**

58, 59. See margin.

58. GIVEN ▶ *LPQK* is a trapezoid as shown. $LPQK \cong PLMN$.

PROVE ▶ The area of *LPQK* is $\frac{1}{2}h(b_1 + b_2)$.

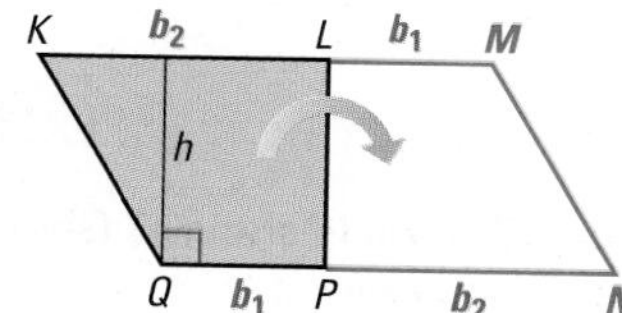

59. GIVEN ▶ *ABCD* is a trapezoid as shown. $EBCF \cong GHDF$.

PROVE ▶ The area of *ABCD* is $\frac{1}{2}h(b_1 + b_2)$.

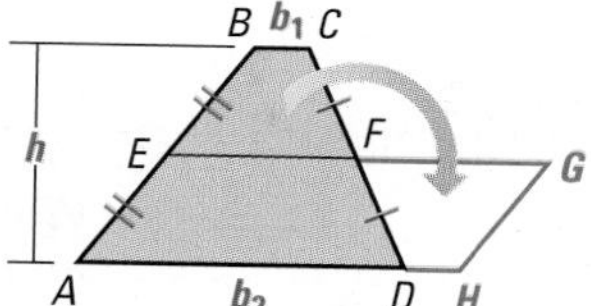

Test Preparation

60. MULTIPLE CHOICE What is the area of trapezoid *EFGH*? D

Ⓐ 25 in.^{2} Ⓑ 416 in.^{2}
Ⓒ 84 in.^{2} Ⓓ 42 in.^{2}
Ⓔ 68 in.^{2}

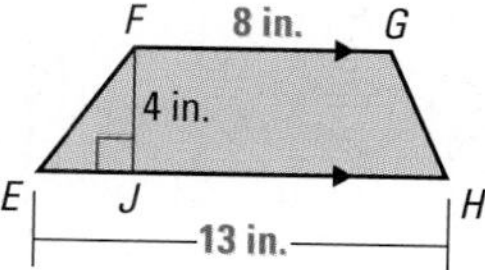

61. MULTIPLE CHOICE What is the area of parallelogram *JKLM*? B

Ⓐ 12 cm^2 Ⓑ 15 cm^2
Ⓒ 18 cm^2 Ⓓ 30 cm^2
Ⓔ 40 cm^2

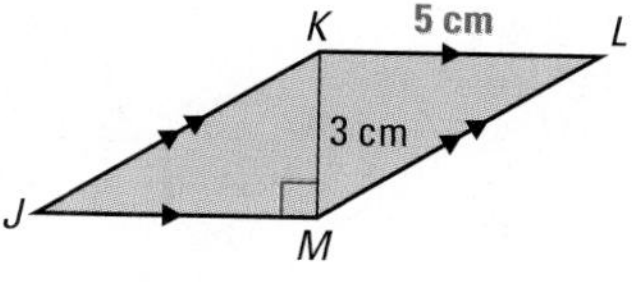

★ Challenge

62. *Writing* Explain why the area of *any* quadrilateral with perpendicular diagonals is $A = \frac{1}{2}d_1d_2$, where d_1 and d_2 are the lengths of the diagonals.
See margin.

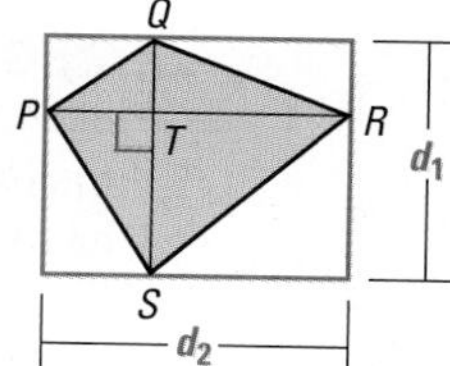

EXTRA CHALLENGE

www.mcdougallittell.com

STUDENT HELP NOTES

Look Back As students review squaring binomial expressions, point out that the diagram for Exercises 53–57 corresponds to an algebra tile model for squaring a binomial. They may also find it helpful to rewrite the equation for the area of *ABCD* so that the term for the areas of the rectangles is the middle term.

! COMMON ERROR

EXERCISE 58 Some students may find it difficult to visualize the congruent trapezoids. Before they begin the proof, ask them to state what transformation of the shaded trapezoid will coincide with the unshaded trapezoid.

53. Square; square; *Sample answer:* In quad. *EBFJ*, ∠*E*, ∠*J*, and ∠*F* are right ∠s by the Linear Pair Post., and ∠*B* is a right ∠ by the Int. Angles of a Quad. Thm. Then *EBFJ* is a rectangle by the Rectangle Corollary. $\overline{EJ} \cong \overline{FJ}$ because they are corresp. parts of ≅ ▱s. Then by the def. of a ▱ and the Transitive Prop. of Cong., *EBFJ* is a rhombus, and, therefore, a square. Similarly, *HJGD* is a square.

54, 58, 59, 62. See Additional Answers beginning on page AA1.

ADDITIONAL PRACTICE AND RETEACHING

For Lesson 6.7:

- Practice Levels A, B, and C (*Chapter 6 Resource Book*, p. 102)
- Reteaching with Practice (*Chapter 6 Resource Book*, p. 105)
- See Lesson 6.7 of the *Personal Student Tutor*

For more Mixed Review:

- Search the *Test and Practice Generator* for key words or specific lessons.

4 ASSESS

DAILY HOMEWORK QUIZ

Transparency Available

Find the area of the polygon.

1.

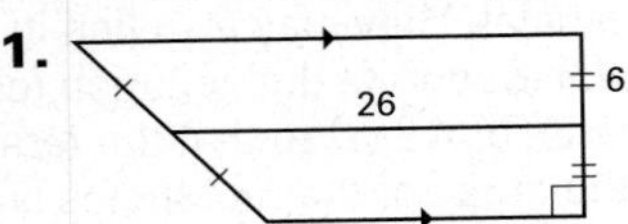

312 sq. units

2. 56 sq. units

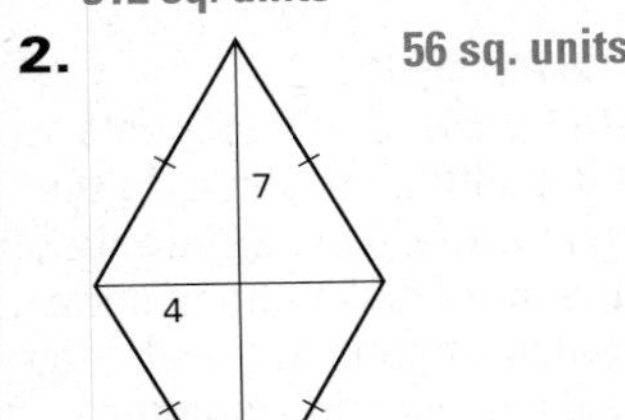

3.

17
9
15

192 sq. units

4.

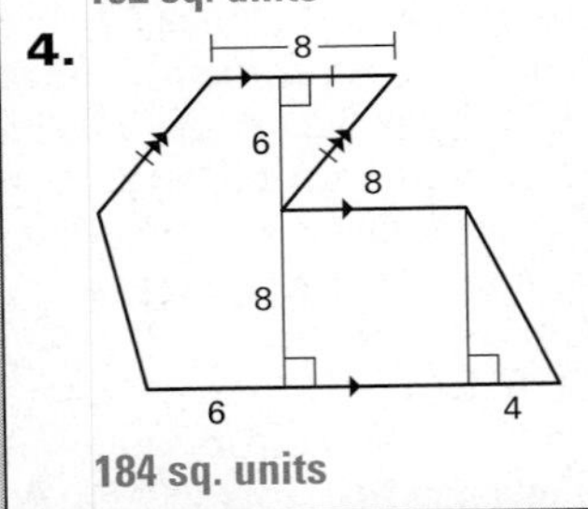

184 sq. units

EXTRA CHALLENGE NOTE

Challenge problems for Lesson 6.7 are available in **blackline** format in the *Chapter 6 Resource Book,* p. 109 and at **www.mcdougallittell.com.**

ADDITIONAL TEST PREPARATION

1. **OPEN ENDED** Choose dimensions for the base(s), height, and area of a parallelogram, a rectangle, a triangle, and a trapezoid that all have the same area and same height. See sample answer at right.

66, 67. See next page.

MIXED REVIEW

CLASSIFYING ANGLES **State whether the angle appears to be *acute, right,* or *obtuse.* Then estimate its measure.** (Review 1.4 for 7.1)

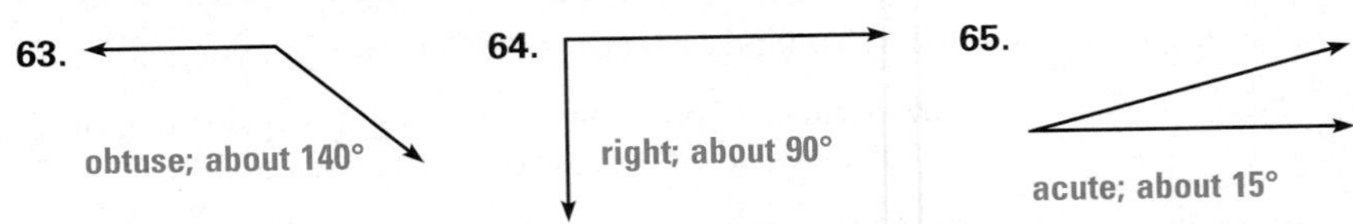

63. obtuse; about 140°

64. right; about 90°

65. acute; about 15°

PLACING FIGURES IN A COORDINATE PLANE **Place the triangle in a coordinate plane and label the coordinates of the vertices.** (Review 4.7 for 7.1)

66, 67. Sample answers are given; See margin.

66. A triangle has a base length of 3 units and a height of 4 units.

67. An isosceles triangle has a base length of 10 units and a height of 5 units.

USING ALGEBRA **In Exercises 68–70, $\overline{AE}$, $\overline{BF}$, and $\overline{CG}$ are medians. Find the value of x.** (Review 5.3)

68. 7

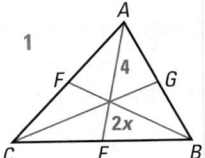

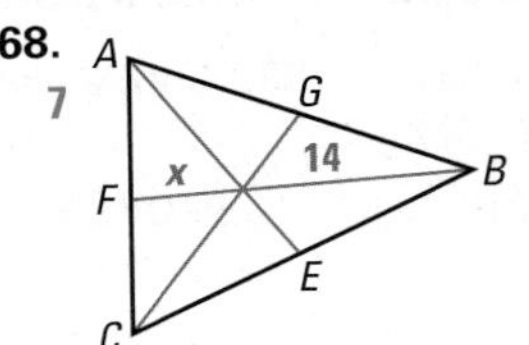

69. 1

A
4
F
G
2x
C
E
B

70. 6

x + 6
D
A
x
C
G
E
B

QUIZ 3

Self-Test for Lessons 6.6 and 6.7

What special type of quadrilateral is shown? Give the most specific name, and justify your answer. (Lesson 6.6)

1. Kite; $\overline{ON} \cong \overline{OP}$ and $\overline{MN} \cong \overline{MP}$ but opp. sides are not $\cong$.
2. Trapezoid; $\overline{QR} \parallel \overline{TS}$ but $\overline{QT}$ and $\overline{RS}$ are not $\parallel$.
3. ▱; *Sample answer:* $\overline{ZY} \cong \overline{WX}$ and $\overline{ZY} \parallel \overline{WX}$.

1.

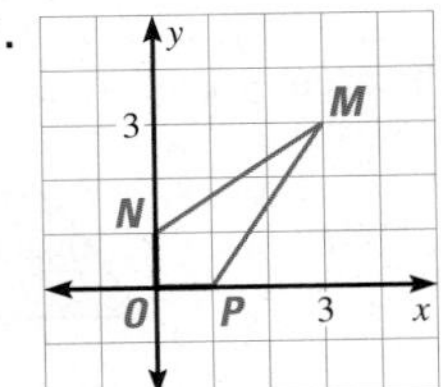

2.

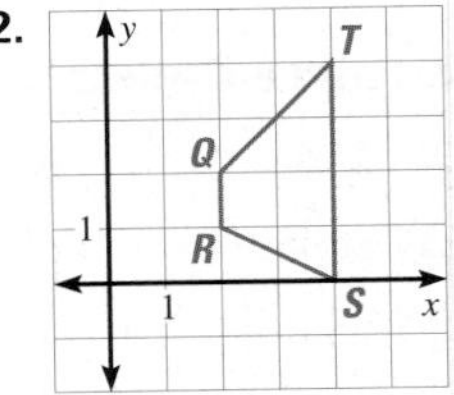

3.

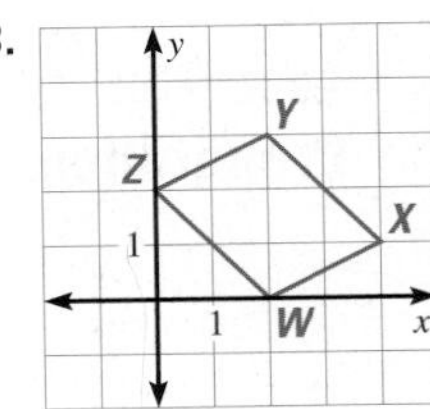

The shape has an area of 60 square inches. Find the value of x. (Lesson 6.7)

4.

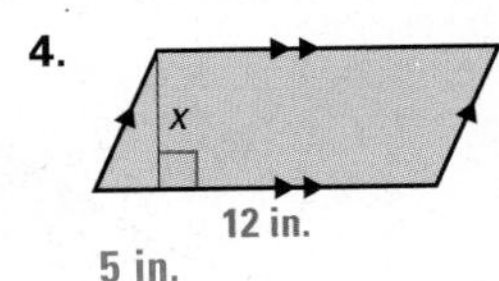

5 in.

5.

x
10 in.

12 in.

6.

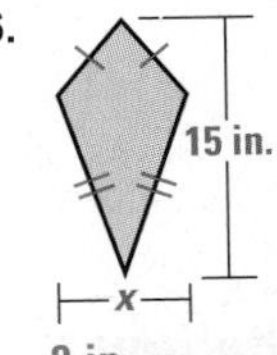

8 in.

7. **GOLD BULLION** Gold bullion is molded into blocks with cross sections that are isosceles trapezoids. A cross section of a 25 kilogram block has a height of 5.4 centimeters and bases of 8.3 centimeters and 11 centimeters. What is the area of the cross section? (Lesson 6.7) 52.11 cm²

Additional Test Preparation *Sample answer:*

1. Check students' work. If A is the area and h is the height, the bases of the rectangle and parallelogram will be $\frac{A}{h}$. The base of the triangle will be $\frac{2A}{h}$. The bases of the trapezoid will be $\frac{A}{h} - x$ and $\frac{A}{h} + x$ for some number x.

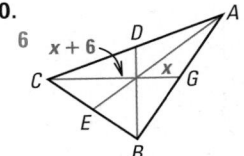

CHAPTER 6

Chapter Summary

WHAT did you learn?	*WHY did you learn it?*
Identify, name, and describe polygons. **(6.1)**	Lay the foundation for work with polygons.
Use the sum of the measures of the interior angles of a quadrilateral. **(6.1)**	Find an unknown measure of an angle of a quadrilateral. **(p. 324)**
Use properties of parallelograms. **(6.2)**	Solve problems in areas such as furniture design. **(p. 333)**
Prove that a quadrilateral is a parallelogram. **(6.3)**	Explore real-life tools, such as a bicycle derailleur. **(p. 343)**
Use coordinate geometry with parallelograms. **(6.3)**	Use coordinates to prove theorems. **(p. 344)**
Use properties of rhombuses, rectangles, and squares, including properties of diagonals. **(6.4)**	Simplify real-life tasks, such as building a rectangular frame. **(p. 350)**
Use properties of trapezoids and kites. **(6.5)**	Reach conclusions about geometric figures and real-life objects, such as a wedding cake. **(p. 357)**
Identify special types of quadrilaterals based on limited information. **(6.6)**	Describe real-world shapes, such as tents. **(p. 367)**
Prove that a quadrilateral is a special type of quadrilateral. **(6.6)**	Use alternate methods of proof. **(p. 365)**
Find the areas of rectangles, kites, parallelograms, squares, triangles, trapezoids, and rhombuses. **(6.7)**	Find areas of real-life surfaces, such as the roof of a covered bridge. **(p. 378)**

How does Chapter 6 fit into the BIGGER PICTURE of geometry?

In this chapter, you studied properties of polygons, focusing on properties of quadrilaterals. You learned in Chapter 4 that a triangle is a rigid structure. Polygons with more than three sides do not form rigid structures. For instance, on page 336, you learned that a scissors lift can be raised and lowered because its beams form parallelograms, which are nonrigid figures. Quadrilaterals occur in many natural and manufactured structures. Understanding properties of special quadrilaterals will help you analyze real-life problems in areas such as architecture, design, and construction.

STUDY STRATEGY

How did your study group help you learn?

The notes you made, following the **Study Strategy** on page 320, may resemble this one about order of operations.

Lesson 6.3

Parallelograms have the following properties. You can use them in proofs or to find missing measures in parallelograms.

- opposite sides are congruent
- opposite angles are congruent
- consecutive angles are supplementary
- diagonals bisect each other

66. 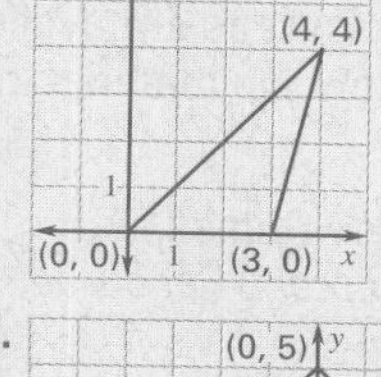

67. 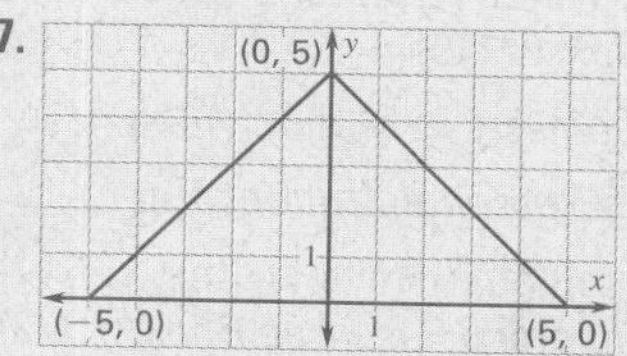

ADDITIONAL RESOURCES

The following resources are available to help review the material in this chapter.

- Chapter Review Games and Activities (*Chapter 6 Resource Book*, p. 110)
- *Geometry in Motion video*
- *Personal Student Tutor*
- Cumulative Review, Chs. 1–6 (*Chapter 6 Resource Book*, p. 122)

1.

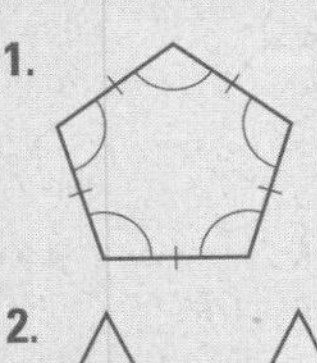

2.

CHAPTER 6 Chapter Review

- polygon, p. 322
- sides of a polygon, p. 322
- vertex, vertices, p. 322
- convex, p. 323
- nonconvex, concave, p. 323
- equilateral polygon, p. 323
- equiangular polygon, p. 323
- regular polygon, p. 323
- diagonal of a polygon, p. 324
- parallelogram, p. 330
- rhombus, p. 347
- rectangle, p. 347
- square, p. 347
- trapezoid, p. 356
- bases of a trapezoid, p. 356
- base angles of a trapezoid, p. 356
- legs of a trapezoid, p. 356
- isosceles trapezoid, p. 356
- midsegment of a trapezoid, p. 357
- kite, p. 358

6.1 POLYGONS

Examples on pp. 322–324

EXAMPLES Hexagon *ABCDEF* is convex and equilateral. It is not regular because it is not both equilateral and equiangular. $\overline{AD}$ is a diagonal of *ABCDEF*. The sum of the measures of the interior angles of quadrilateral *ABCD* is 360°.

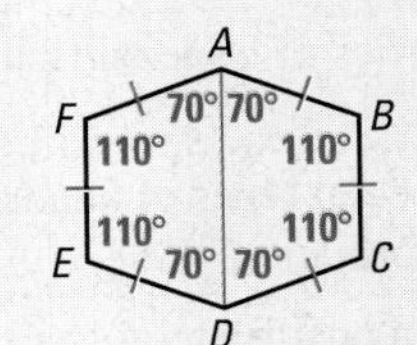

Draw a figure that fits the description. 1, 2. Sample answers are given. See margin.

1. a regular pentagon

2. a concave octagon

Find the value of *x*.

3.

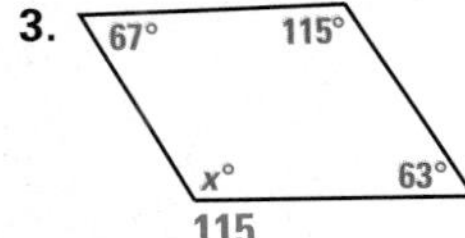

115

4.

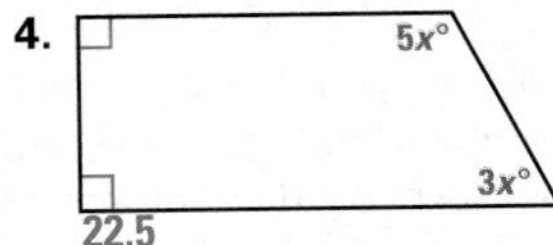

22.5

5.

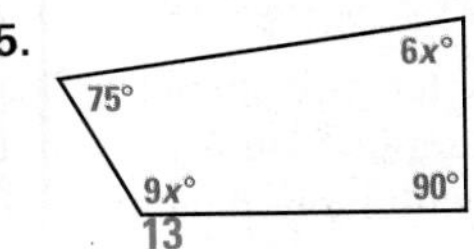

13

6.2 PROPERTIES OF PARALLELOGRAMS

Examples on pp. 330–333

EXAMPLES Quadrilateral *JKLM* is a parallelogram. Opposite sides are parallel and congruent. Opposite angles are congruent. Consecutive angles are supplementary. The diagonals bisect each other.

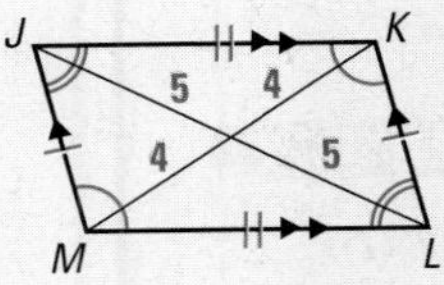

Use parallelogram *DEFG* at the right.

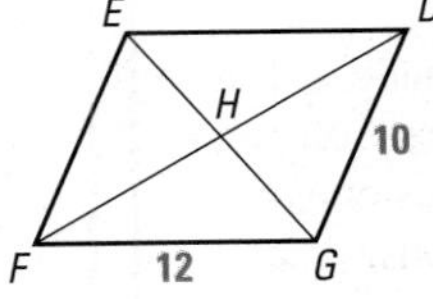

6. If $DH = 9.5$, find FH and DF. 9.5, 19

7. If $m\angle GDE = 65°$, find $m\angle EFG$ and $m\angle DEF$. 65°, 115°

8. Find the perimeter of $\square DEFG$. 44

6.3 PROVING QUADRILATERALS ARE PARALLELOGRAMS

Examples on pp. 338–341

EXAMPLES You are given that $\overline{PQ} \cong \overline{RS}$ and $\overline{PS} \cong \overline{RQ}$. Since both pairs of opposite sides are congruent, *PQRS* must be a parallelogram.

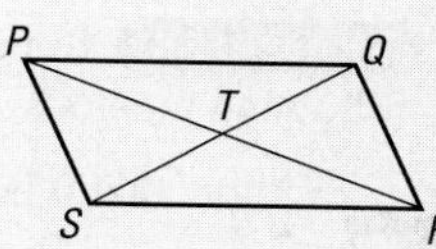

Is *PQRS* a parallelogram? Explain. 9, 11. See margin.

9. $PQ = QR$, $RS = SP$

10. $\angle SPQ \cong \angle QRS$, $\angle PQR \cong \angle RSP$
Yes; opposite angles are congruent.

11. $\overline{PS} \cong \overline{RQ}$, $\overline{PQ} \parallel \overline{RS}$

12. $m\angle PSR + m\angle SRQ = 180°$, $\angle PSR \cong \angle RQP$
Yes; consecutive angles are supplementary.

6.4 RHOMBUSES, RECTANGLES, AND SQUARES

Examples on pp. 347–350

EXAMPLES *ABCD* is a rhombus since it has 4 congruent sides. The diagonals of a rhombus are perpendicular and each one bisects a pair of opposite angles.

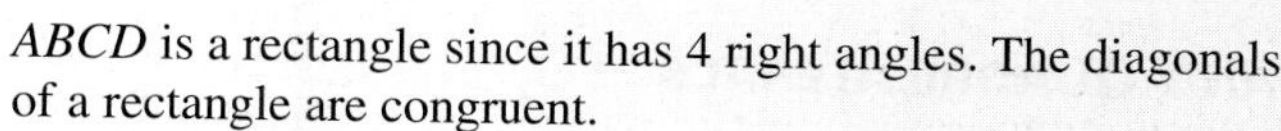

ABCD is a rectangle since it has 4 right angles. The diagonals of a rectangle are congruent.

ABCD is a square since it has 4 congruent sides and 4 right angles.

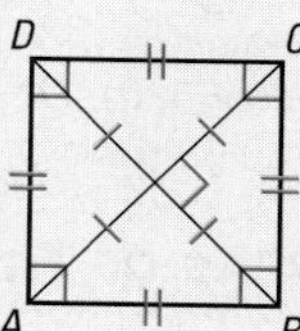

List each special quadrilateral for which the statement is always true. Consider parallelograms, rectangles, rhombuses, and squares.

13. Diagonals are perpendicular. rhombus, square

14. Opposite sides are parallel. ▱, rectangle, rhombus, square

15. It is equilateral. rhombus, square

6.5 TRAPEZOIDS AND KITES

Examples on pp. 356–358

EXAMPLES *EFGH* is a trapezoid. *ABCD* is an isosceles trapezoid. Its base angles and diagonals are congruent. *JKLM* is a kite. Its diagonals are perpendicular, and one pair of opposite angles are congruent.

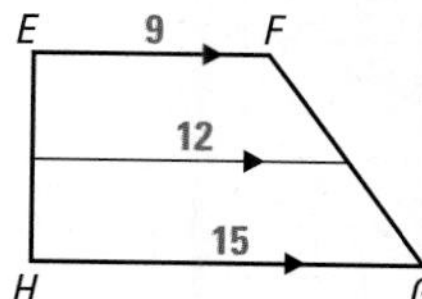

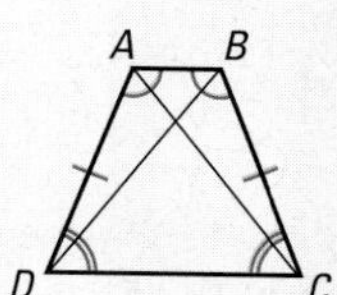

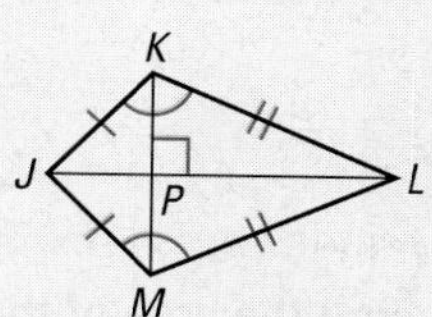

Use the diagram of isosceles trapezoid *ABCD*.

16. If $AB = 6$ and $CD = 16$, find the length of the midsegment. 11

17. If $m\angle DAB = 112°$, find the measures of the other angles of *ABCD*.
$m\angle ABC = 112°$, $m\angle ADC = m\angle BCD = 68°$

18. Explain how you could use congruent triangles to show that $\angle ACD \cong \angle BDC$. See margin.

9. No; you are not given information about opp. sides.

11. Yes; you can prove △ *PQT* and *SRT* are ≅ and opp. sides are ≅.

18. $\overline{AD} \cong \overline{BC}$ and $\overline{AC} \cong \overline{BD}$ because *ABCD* is an isos. trap.; $\overline{DC} \cong \overline{DC}$ by the Reflexive Prop. of Cong. Then $\triangle ADC \cong \triangle BCD$ by the SSS Cong.Post. and $\angle ACD \cong \angle BDC$ because corresp. parts of ≅ △ are ≅.

19. Square; *Sample answer:* $PQ = QR = RS = PS = \sqrt{34}$, so *PQRS* is a rhombus; $QS = PR = 2\sqrt{17}$, so the diags. of *PQRS* are ≅ and *PQRS* is a rectangle. A quad. that is both a rhombus and a rectangle is a square.

Examples on pp. 364–366

6.6 SPECIAL QUADRILATERALS

EXAMPLES To prove that a quadrilateral is a rhombus, you can use any one of the following methods.

- Show that it has four congruent sides.
- Show that it is a parallelogram whose diagonals are perpendicular.
- Show that each diagonal bisects a pair of opposite angles.

What special type of quadrilateral is *PQRS*? Give the most specific name, and justify your answer.

19. $P(0, 3), Q(5, 6), R(2, 11), S(-3, 8)$ See margin.

20. $P(0, 0), Q(6, 8), R(8, 5), S(4, -6)$
Trapezoid; $\overline{PS} \parallel \overline{QR}$ and $\overline{PQ}$ and $\overline{SR}$ are not ∥.

21. $P(2, -1), Q(4, -5), R(0, -3), S(-2, 1)$
Rhombus; $PQ = QR = RS = PS = 2\sqrt{5}$

22. $P(-5, 0), Q(-3, 6), R(1, 6), S(1, 2)$
Kite; $\overline{PQ} \cong \overline{PS}$ and $\overline{RQ} \cong \overline{RS}$ but opp. sides are not ≅.

Examples on pp. 372–375

6.7 AREAS OF TRIANGLES AND QUADRILATERALS

EXAMPLES

Area of $\square ABCD = bh = 5 \cdot 4 = 20$

Area of $\triangle ABD = \frac{1}{2}bh = \frac{1}{2} \cdot 5 \cdot 4 = 10$

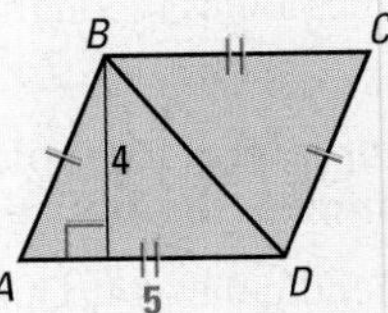

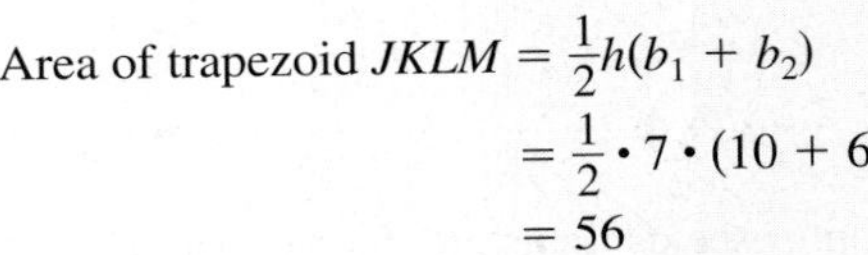

Area of trapezoid $JKLM = \frac{1}{2}h(b_1 + b_2)$

$= \frac{1}{2} \cdot 7 \cdot (10 + 6)$

$= 56$

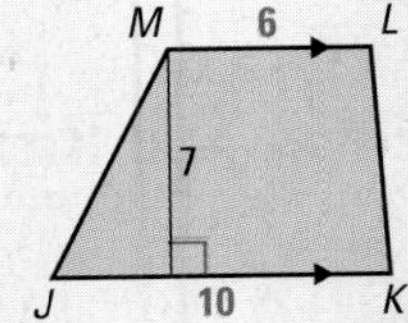

Area of rhombus $WXYZ = \frac{1}{2}d_1d_2$

$= \frac{1}{2} \cdot 10 \cdot 4$

$= 20$

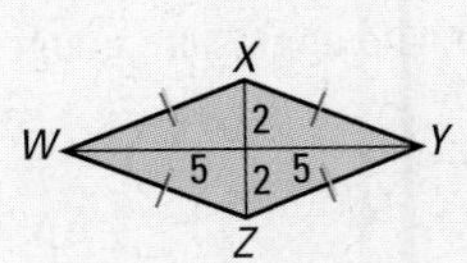

Find the area of the triangle or quadrilateral.

23. $29\frac{3}{4}$ in.^{2}

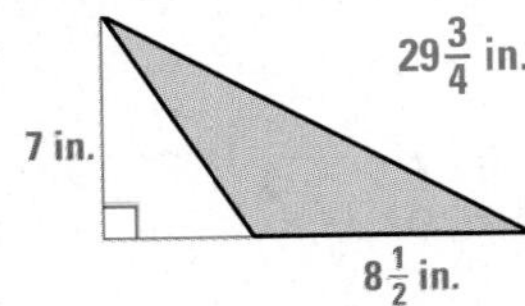

24. $13\frac{1}{2}$ ft^2

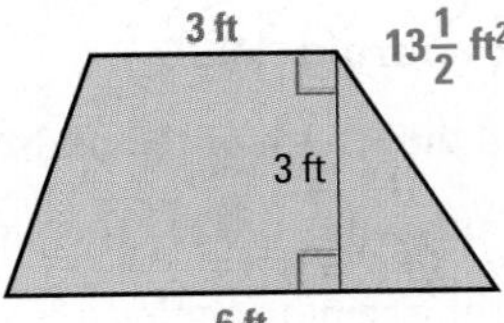

25. 12 sq. units

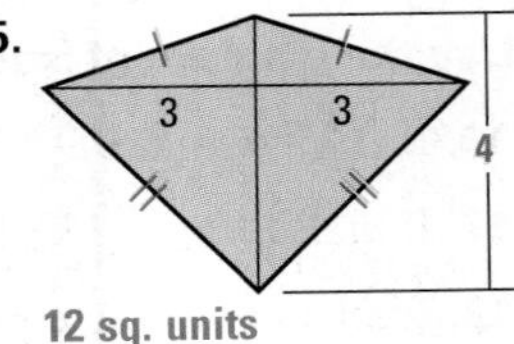

CHAPTER 6 Chapter Test

1. Sketch a concave pentagon. See margin.

Find the value of each variable.

2. 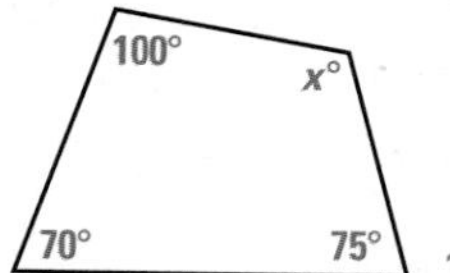

115

3. 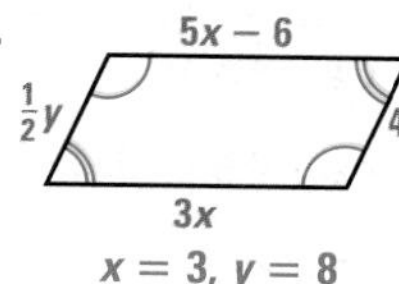

$x = 3$, $y = 8$

4. 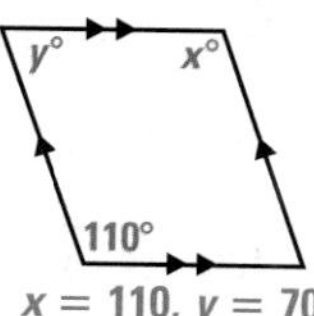

$x = 110$, $y = 70$

5. 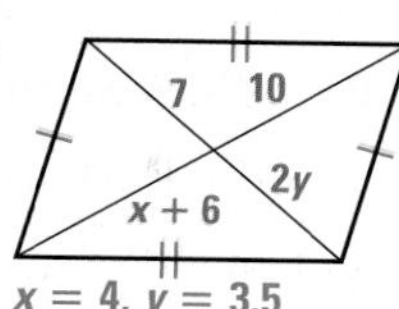

$x = 4$, $y = 3.5$

Decide if you are given enough information to prove that the quadrilateral is a parallelogram.

6. Diagonals are congruent. no

7. Consecutive angles are supplementary. yes

8. Two pairs of consecutive angles are congruent. no

9. The diagonals have the same midpoint. yes

Decide whether the statement is *always, sometimes,* or *never* true.

10. A rectangle is a square. sometimes

11. A parallelogram is a trapezoid. never

12. A rhombus is a parallelogram. always

What special type of quadrilateral is shown? Justify your answer. 13–16. See margin.

13. 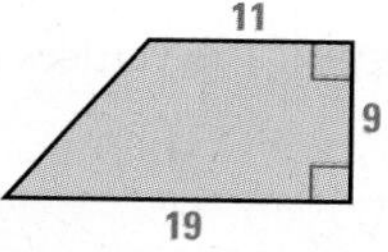

14. 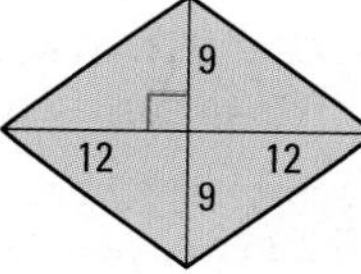

15. 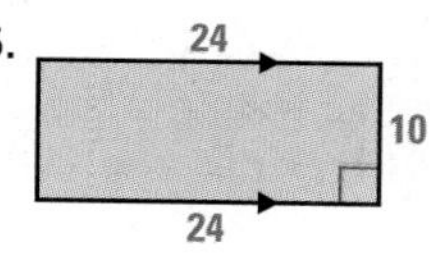

16. 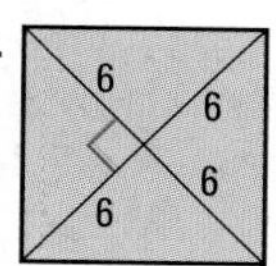

17. Refer to the coordinate diagram at the right. Use the Distance Formula to prove that $WXYZ$ is a rhombus. Then explain how the diagram can be used to show that the diagonals of a rhombus bisect each other and are perpendicular. See margin.

$X(0, b)$, $Y(-a, 0)$, $W(a, 0)$, $Z(0, -b)$

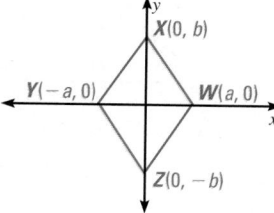

18. Sketch a kite and label it $ABCD$. Mark all congruent sides and angles of the kite. State what you know about the diagonals $\overline{AC}$ and $\overline{BD}$ and justify your answer. See margin.

19. **PLANT STAND** You want to build a plant stand with three equally spaced circular shelves. You want the top shelf to have a diameter of 6 inches and the bottom shelf to have a diameter of 15 inches. The diagram at the right shows a vertical cross section of the plant stand. What is the diameter of the middle shelf? 10.5 in.

20. **HIP ROOF** The sides of a *hip roof* form two trapezoids and two triangles, as shown. The two sides not shown are congruent to the corresponding sides that are shown. Find the total area of the sides of the roof. 1218 ft^2

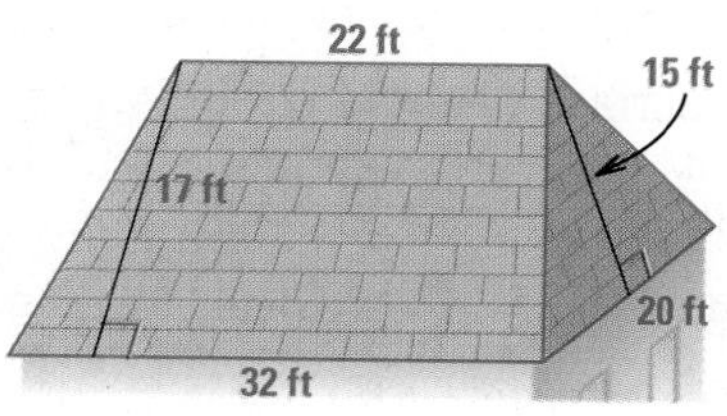

ADDITIONAL RESOURCES

- ***Chapter 6 Resource Book***
  Chapter Test (3 levels) (p. 111)
  SAT/ACT Chapter Test (p. 117)
  Alternative Assessment (p. 118)
- ***Test and Practice Generator***

1. *Sample answer:*

13. Trapezoid; exactly one pair of sides are ∥.

14. Rhombus; the diags. bisect each other and are ⊥.

15. Rectangle; one pair of opp. sides are both ≅ and ∥, and, since one ∠ is a right angle, the opp. ∠ and the two consec. ∠s are right ∠s.

16. Square; the diags. bisect each other, and are ≅ and ⊥, so the quad. is a ▱, a rectangle, and a rhombus. So, it is a square.

17. $WX = XY = YZ = WZ = \sqrt{a^2 + b^2}$; Let O be the origin (the intersection of the diags.); $OX = OZ = b$ and $OW = OY = a$, so the diags. bisect each other; one diag. is vertical and the other horizontal, so the diags. are ⊥.

18. *Sample answer:*

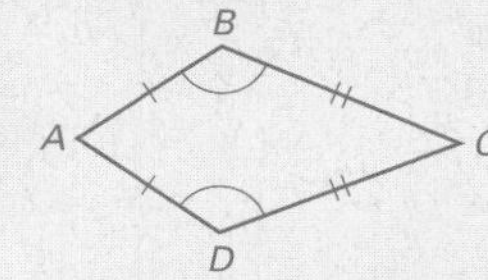

$\overline{AC} \perp \overline{BD}$; Draw $\overline{AC}$ and $\overline{BD}$ intersecting at P. $\overline{AC} \cong \overline{AC}$ by the Reflexive Prop. of Cong. so by the SSS Cong. Post., $\triangle ABC \cong \triangle ADC$. Then $\angle BAC \cong \angle DAC$. $\overline{AP} \cong \overline{AP}$ by the Reflexive Prop. of Cong. so $\triangle BAP \cong \triangle DAP$ by the SAS Cong. Post. Corresp. ∠s BPA and DPA are ≅. Since $\overline{AC}$ and $\overline{BD}$ form a linear pair of ≅ ∠s, $\overline{AC} \perp \overline{BD}$.

ADDITIONAL RESOURCES

- ***Chapter 6 Resource Book***
  Chapter Test (3 levels) (p. 111)
  SAT/ACT Chapter Test (p. 117)
  Alternative Assessment (p. 118)
- ***Test and Practice Generator***

20. *Sample answer: QRTU* is an isos. trap., so $\overline{QU} \cong \overline{RT}$. $\angle P$ and $\angle S$ are right △s, so $\triangle PQU$ and $\triangle SRT$ are right △s. $\overline{QP} \cong \overline{RS}$, so $\triangle PQU \cong \triangle SRT$ by the HL Cong. Thm.

21. Isosceles trapezoid;
(1) Show that $\overline{AB} \parallel \overline{CD}$, $\overline{AD} \cong \overline{BC}$, and $\overline{AD}$ and $\overline{BC}$ are not $\parallel$.
(2) Show that $\overline{AB} \parallel \overline{CD}$, $\overline{AD}$ and $\overline{BC}$ are not $\parallel$, and $\overline{AC} \cong \overline{BD}$.

CHAPTER 6

Chapter Standardized Test

TEST-TAKING STRATEGY Staying physically relaxed during the SAT is very important. If you find yourself tensing up, put your pencil down and take a couple of deep breaths. This will help you stay calm.

1. **MULTIPLE CHOICE** In $\triangle JKL$, $\overline{JK} \cong \overline{KL} \cong \overline{JL}$. Which statements are true? D

   I. $\triangle JKL$ is equilateral.
   II. $\triangle JKL$ is equiangular.
   III. $\triangle JKL$ is regular.

   (A) I only (B) II only (C) III only (D) I, II, and III (E) none of these

2. **MULTIPLE CHOICE** Find the value of x. C

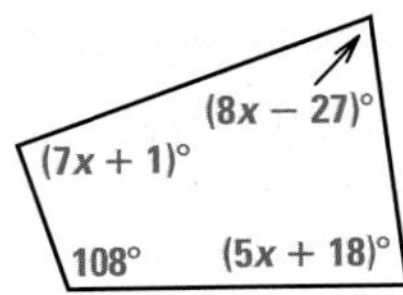

   (A) 7 (B) 11 (C) 13 (D) 15 (E) 23

3. **MULTIPLE CHOICE** What are the values of the variables in parallelogram $ABCD$? C

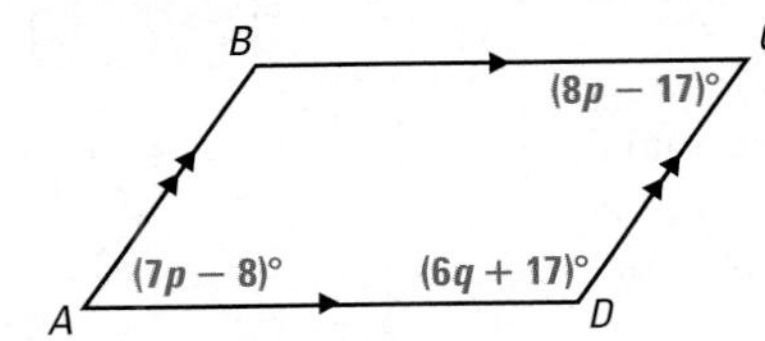

   (A) $p = 8, q = 20$ (B) $p = 11, q = 18$ (C) $p = 9, q = 18$ (D) $p = 10, q = 18$ (E) $p = 9, q = 20$

4. **MULTIPLE CHOICE** The diagonals of a parallelogram must D

   (A) be congruent. (B) be parallel. (C) be perpendicular. (D) bisect each other. (E) be longer than the sides.

5. **MULTIPLE CHOICE** What special type of quadrilateral has the vertices $M(3, 4)$, $N(1, -6)$, $P(6, -7)$, and $Q(8, 3)$? C

   (A) square (B) rhombus (C) rectangle (D) trapezoid (E) kite

6. **MULTIPLE CHOICE** $ABCD$ is a quadrilateral. Which information would *not* allow you to conclude that $ABCD$ is a parallelogram? A

   (A) $\overline{AB} \cong \overline{BC}$ and $\overline{CD} \cong \overline{AD}$
   (B) $\overline{AB} \parallel \overline{CD}$ and $\overline{BC} \parallel \overline{AD}$
   (C) $\angle A \cong \angle C$, $\angle B \cong \angle D$
   (D) $m\angle A = 25°$, $m\angle B = 155°$, $m\angle C = 25°$
   (E) $\overline{BC} \cong \overline{AD}$ and $\overline{BC} \parallel \overline{AD}$

7. **MULTIPLE CHOICE** What special type of quadrilateral has the vertices $R(-5, -7)$, $S(-3, -9)$, $T(-1, -7)$, and $U(-3, 11)$? B

   (A) parallelogram (B) kite (C) trapezoid (D) rectangle (E) rhombus

8. **QUANTITATIVE COMPARISON** The vertices of two quadrilaterals are given.

Column A	Column B
Area of $JKLM$ for $J(-5, 7)$, $K(7, 7)$, $L(6, -2)$, and $M(-2, -2)$	Area of $PQRS$ for $P(-10, 4)$, $Q(1, 4)$, $R(7, -5)$, and $S(-4, -5)$

   Choose the statement that is true. B

   (A) The quantity in column A is greater.
   (B) The quantity in column B is greater.
   (C) The two quantities are equal.
   (D) The relationship cannot be determined from the given information.

9. **MULTIPLE CHOICE** $ABCD$ is a trapezoid and $EF = 21$. Find the value of x. D

   (A) 18 (B) 23 (C) 25 (D) 30 (E) 33

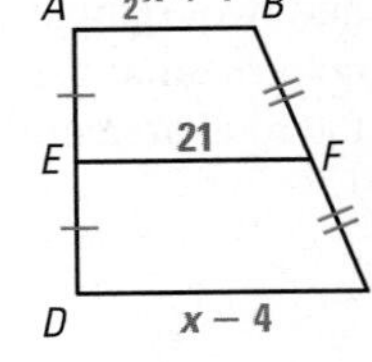

10. MULTIPLE CHOICE Find the area of a triangle with vertices $A(-3, 6)$, $B(-7, -4)$, and $C(6, -4)$. **D**

Ⓐ 39 square units Ⓑ 52 square units Ⓒ 60 square units

Ⓓ 65 square units Ⓔ 78 square units

MULTI-STEP PROBLEM In Exercises 11–14, use the following information.
The framework of a railroad bridge is shown below. In the diagram, $\overline{GB} \parallel \overline{HC}$, $\overline{AH} \parallel \overline{BJ}$, and $\angle FBA \cong \angle DBC$.

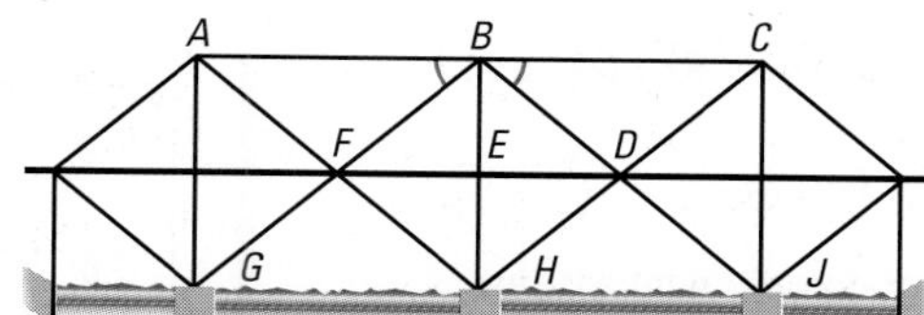

11. Are you given enough information to prove that $\overline{BE} \cong \overline{HE}$? If so, explain how.
Yes; since $\overline{GB} \parallel \overline{HC}$ and $\overline{AH} \parallel \overline{BJ}$, $FBDH$ is a ▱, and the diags. of a ▱ bisect each other. Therefore, $\overline{BE} \cong \overline{HE}$.

12. If $m\angle FBA = 40°$, what are the measures of $\angle BDH$ and $\angle DHF$?
80°, 100°

13. Are you given enough information to prove that $\triangle BEF \cong \triangle HED$? If so, write a plan for a proof. **Yes; *Sample answer:* as shown in Ex. 11, $FBDH$ is a ▱, so $\overline{BF} \cong \overline{HD}$, $\overline{BE} \cong \overline{HE}$, and $\overline{EF} \cong \overline{ED}$. Then $\triangle BEF \cong \triangle HED$ by the SSS Cong. Postulate.**

14. Suppose you were given the additional information that $\overline{BH}$ and $\overline{FD}$ are perpendicular. What could you conclude about a special quadrilateral? Explain.
Given that $\overline{BH}$ and $\overline{FD}$ are ⊥, it could be shown that $FBDH$ is a rhombus; if the diags. of a ▱ are ⊥, the ▱ is a rhombus.

MULTI-STEP PROBLEM In Exercises 15–20, use the given information and the diagram at the right.

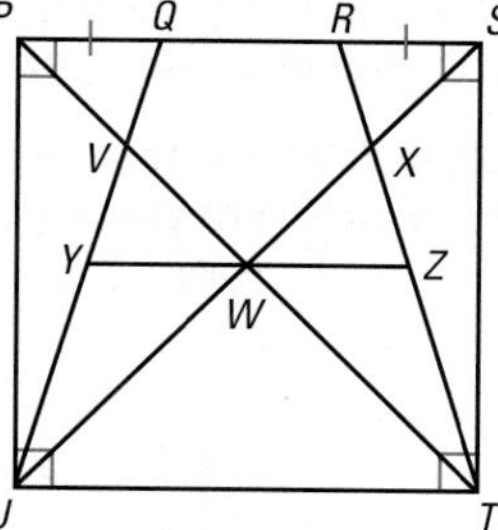

GIVEN ▶ $PSTU$ is a rectangle and $\overline{PQ} \cong \overline{SR}$. $\overline{YZ}$ is the midsegment of isosceles trapezoid $QRTU$.

15. $QR = 3x - 10$, $UT = 2x + 3$, and $YZ = 9$. Find the value of x. **5**

16. $PQ = 2y$, $UT = 6y + 1$, and $QR = 5$. Find the value of y. **2**

17. $PT = 3a - 2$ and $UW = 14 - a$. Find the value of a. **6**

18. $UY = 3b + 4$ and $TZ = 4b - 5$. Find the value of b. **9**

19. What kind of polygon is $QRXWV$? Is it convex or concave? **pentagon; convex**

20. Use the given information. Write a two-column proof that shows that $\triangle PQU \cong \triangle SRT$. **See margin.**

MULTI-STEP PROBLEM In Exercises 21 and 22, use the following information.

A *concrete slump test* is used to measure the water content and consistency of concrete mix. Concrete is placed in a mold for a period of time, and then the mold is removed. The distance from the top of the mold to the top of the "slumped" concrete is then evaluated. The shape of the cross section of the slump mold can be modeled by the points $A(4, 12)$, $B(8, 12)$, $C(10, 0)$, and $D(2, 0)$.

21. What special type of quadrilateral is $ABCD$? Describe two different ways that you could prove that your answer is correct. **See margin.**

22. What is the area of the cross section? **72 sq. units**

ADDITIONAL RESOURCES
A Cumulative Review covering Chapters 1–6 is available in the *Chapter 6 Resource Book*, p. 122.

4a. $\angle QPR$ and $\angle SPT$, or $\angle QPS$ and $\angle RPT$
b. *Sample answer:* $\angle 1$ and $\angle T$
c. *Sample answer:* $\angle QPR$ and $\angle RPT$
d. $\angle RQS$ and $\angle QST$

5. $\triangle QPR \cong \triangle QPS$ and $\triangle QPR \cong \triangle TPS$; $\angle 1 \cong \angle 2$, $\overline{QP} \cong \overline{QP}$, and $m\angle QPS = 90° = m\angle QPR$, so $\triangle QPR \cong \triangle QPS$ by the ASA Cong. Post. Therefore, since corresp. parts of $\cong$ ▲ are $\cong$, $\overline{PR} \cong \overline{PS}$. $\angle 2 \cong \angle T$ and $\angle QRP \cong \angle TSP$ by the Alt. Int. Angles Thm., so $\triangle QPR \cong \triangle TPS$ by the AAS Cong. Thm.

6. From Question 5, $PR = PS$. By the Segment Addition Post., $RS = PS + PR$. By the Substitution prop. of equality, $RS = PS + PS = 2 \cdot PS$.

7. P is equidistant from $\overrightarrow{QS}$ and $\overrightarrow{QR}$ by the Angle Bisector Thm.

18. the circumcenter, or the intersection of the three $\perp$ bisectors of $\triangle ABC$

CHAPTER 6

Cumulative Practice

for Chapters 1–6

1. Find the decimal forms for $\frac{4}{99}$, $\frac{18}{99}$, and $\frac{35}{99}$. Use your answers to make a conjecture about the decimal form for $\frac{89}{99}$. **(1.1)** 0.040404..., 0.181818..., 0.353535...; 0.898989...

2. Draw an obtuse angle. Then bisect it. **(1.4, 1.5)** Check drawings.

In Exercises 3–8, use the figure at the right, in which $\overline{QR} \parallel \overline{ST}$, $\overline{QT} \perp \overline{SU}$, $\overline{QS} \perp \overline{ST}$, and $\angle 1 \cong \angle 2$.

3. Find the measures of $\angle URQ$ and $\angle PTS$. **(3.3, 4.1)** 135°; 45°

4. Name a pair of (a) vertical angles, (b) nonadjacent complementary angles, (c) congruent supplementary angles, and (d) same-side interior angles. **(1.6, 3.3, 4.1)** See margin.

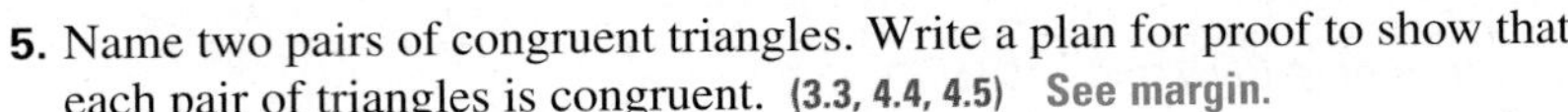

5. Name two pairs of congruent triangles. Write a plan for proof to show that each pair of triangles is congruent. **(3.3, 4.4, 4.5)** See margin.

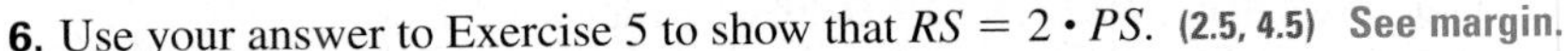

6. Use your answer to Exercise 5 to show that $RS = 2 \cdot PS$. **(2.5, 4.5)** See margin.

7. P lies on the bisector of $\angle SQR$. What can you conclude about P? Explain. **(5.1)** See margin.

8. What kind of polygon is $PRQST$? Is it *convex* or *concave*? **(6.1)** pentagon; concave

9. The measure of an exterior angle of a triangle is $(21x + 1)°$ and the measures of the two nonadjacent interior angles are $(5x + 18)°$ and $(14x - 3)°$. Find the measures of the three interior angles of the triangle. Then classify the triangle as *acute*, *obtuse*, or *right*. **(4.1)** 53°, 95°, 32°; obtuse

Is it possible to prove that the triangles are congruent? If so, name the postulate or theorem you would use. **(4.3, 4.4, 4.6)**

10.

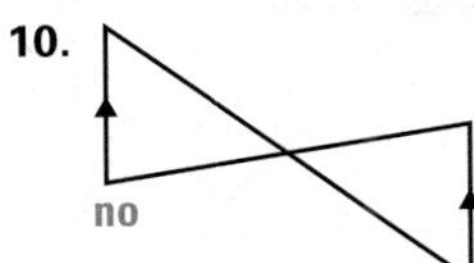

no

11.

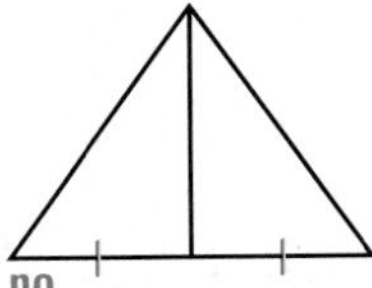

no

12.

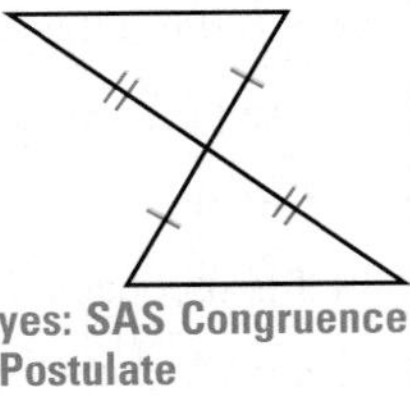

yes: SAS Congruence Postulate

13.

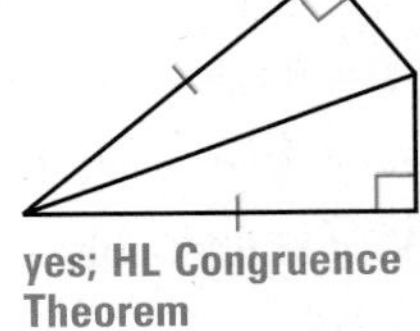

yes; HL Congruence Theorem

A triangle has vertices $A(11, 1)$, $B(3, 6)$, and $C(3, -4)$.

14. Find an equation of the line that is parallel to $\overleftrightarrow{AB}$ and contains point C. **(3.6)** $y = -\frac{5}{8}x - \frac{17}{8}$

15. Show that the triangle is isosceles. **(4.1, 4.7)** $AB = AC = \sqrt{89}$

16. Which two angles of $\triangle ABC$ are congruent? Which theorem justifies your answer? **(4.6)** $\angle B$ and $\angle C$; the Base Angles Theorem

17. Find an equation of the perpendicular bisector of $\overline{AC}$. **(3.7, 5.1)** $y = -\frac{8}{5}x + \frac{97}{10}$

18. Describe the point that is equidistant from A, B, and C. **(5.2)** See margin.

19. Find the coordinates of the centroid of $\triangle ABC$. **(5.3)** $\left(\frac{17}{3}, 1\right)$

20. Find the length of the midsegment that connects sides $\overline{AB}$ and $\overline{CB}$. **(5.4)** $\frac{\sqrt{89}}{2}$

21. State the converse of the Linear Pair Postulate in if-then form. Decide whether the converse is *true* or *false*. If false, provide a counterexample.
(2.1, 2.6) If two angles are supplementary, then they form a linear pair; false; *Sample answer:* two consecutive angles of a parallelogram are supplementary, but they do not form a linear pair.

In $\triangle XYZ$, $XY = 8$ and $YZ = 12$.

22. Describe the possible lengths for $\overline{XZ}$. **(5.5)** XZ must be greater than 4 and less than 20.

23. Complete with $<$, $>$, or $=$: $m\angle X$ _?_ $m\angle Z$. Explain your answer. **(5.5)**
$m\angle X > m\angle Z$; the angle opposite the longer side is larger than the angle opposite the shorter side.

In Exercises 24–26, the vertices A and C of square $ABCD$ are pinched together to form quadrilateral $WXYZ$.

24. Explain why $m\angle D > m\angle Z$. **(5.6)** See margin.

25. What special kind of parallelogram is quadrilateral $WXYZ$? **(6.4)**
rhombus

26. If $m\angle X = 25°$, find the measures of the other three angles of $WXYZ$.
(6.1, 6.2) $m\angle W = 155°$, $m\angle Z = 25°$, $m\angle Y = 155°$

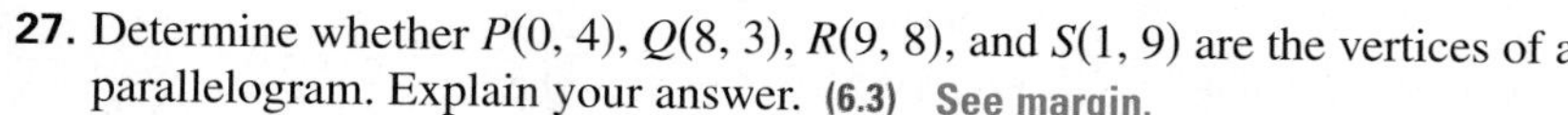

27. Determine whether $P(0, 4)$, $Q(8, 3)$, $R(9, 8)$, and $S(1, 9)$ are the vertices of a parallelogram. Explain your answer. **(6.3)** See margin.

28. In quadrilateral $EFGH$, $m\angle E = 90°$, $m\angle F = 90°$, and $m\angle G = 67°$. What special kind of quadrilateral must it be? Explain. **(6.1, 6.5)** See margin.

29. List all the types of special quadrilaterals whose diagonals are always (a) perpendicular and (b) congruent. **(6.4, 6.5, 6.6)** a. square, rhombus, kite, b. square, rectangle, isosceles trapezoid

30. A trapezoid has vertices $A(0, 0)$, $B(12, 0)$, $C(10, 6)$, and $D(5, 6)$. Find the length of its midsegment and its area. **(6.5, 6.7)**
8.5 units; 51 square units

BILLBOARD SUPPORTS **The two 10 ft posts that support a vertical billboard form an angle of 115° with level ground, as shown.** 31, 32. See margin.

31. How could you show that $\triangle ABC \cong \triangle DEF$? **(4.4)**

32. What special kind of quadrilateral must $ADEB$ be? Explain. **(6.6)**

BOOKSHELF **An A-frame bookshelf has two congruent supports that intersect to form an angle of 42°.**

33. Find the measure of the acute angle that each shelf forms with the supports. **(4.6)** 69°

34. The shelves divide each support into four congruent lengths. If the distance between the supports for the middle shelf is 30 inches, find the distance between the supports for the top shelf and at the floor. **(5.4, 6.5)** 15 in.; 60 in.

35. The distance between each pair of shelves is $19\frac{1}{2}$ inches. Find the area of the region enclosed by the top shelf, the middle shelf, and the two supports. **(6.7)** 438.75 in.^{2}

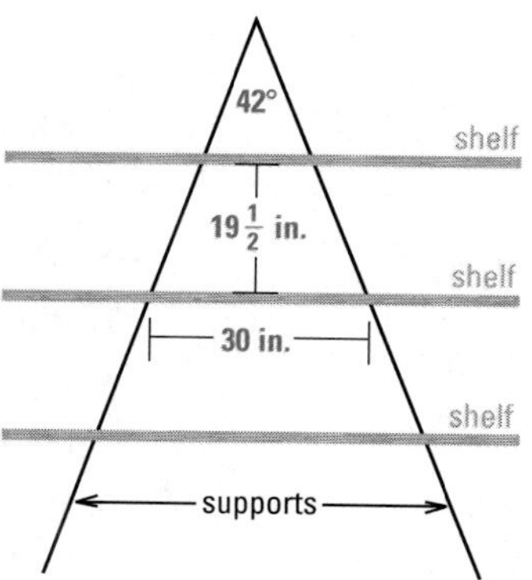

24. Use the converse of the Hinge Thm. in triangles ACD and WYZ. Since $AC > WY$, $m\angle D > m\angle Z$.

27. Yes; methods may vary. For example, the diags. both intersect at their midpoint (4.5, 6), so the diags. bisect each other. Thus, $PQRS$ is a ▱.

28. a trapezoid; $m\angle H = 113°$. Since $\angle E$ and $\angle F$ are supplementary, $\overline{EH} \parallel \overline{FG}$, but the other two sides are not $\parallel$.

31. $AC = DF$, $m\angle ACB = 65° = m\angle DFE$, and $m\angle ABC = 90° = m\angle DEF$, so $\triangle ABC \cong \triangle DEF$ by the AAS Cong. Thm.

32. a rectangle; since $\triangle ABC \cong \triangle DEF$, $\overline{AB} \cong \overline{DE}$. $\overline{AB}$ and $\overline{DE}$ are both $\perp$ to $\overline{BE}$, so $\overline{AB} \parallel \overline{DE}$ by the Prop. of Perpendicular Lines. One pair of opp. sides of quad. $ADEB$ are both $\cong$ and $\parallel$, so $ADEB$ is a ▱. $\angle ABE$ and $\angle DEB$ are both right $\angle$s, so all 4 angles are right $\angle$s, and quad. $ADEB$ must be a rectangle.

EXTRA EXAMPLE 1

a. You are making a cake. Recipe A calls for $2\frac{1}{4}$ cups of sugar and Recipe B calls for $1\frac{1}{2}$ cups of sugar. What is the ratio of cups of sugar for Recipe A to Recipe B? $\frac{3}{2}$

b. Hannah worked 35 hours last week. Josalyn worked 42 hours. What is the ratio of hours worked for Hannah to hours worked for Josalyn? $\frac{5}{6}$

CHECKPOINT EXERCISES

For use after Example 1:

1. You spend 1 hour 45 minutes each day commuting to and from work. Your friend spends 40 minutes commuting each day. What is the ratio of your commute time to that of your friend's? $\frac{21}{8}$

CHAPTER 6

Algebra Review

EXAMPLE 1 *Writing and Simplifying Ratios*

a. Train A takes 35 minutes to travel its route. Train B, traveling the same route but making more stops, takes 47 minutes. What is the ratio of the time of Train A to Train B?

b. Jennie's height is 4 feet, 7 inches. Her younger sister's height is 25 inches. Find the ratio of Jennie's height to her sister's.

SOLUTIONS

a. 35 minutes to 47 minutes $= \frac{35 \text{ minutes}}{47 \text{ minutes}} = \frac{35}{47}$

b. Convert 4 feet, 7 inches to inches: $4(12) + 7 = 55$ inches

55 inches to 25 inches $= \frac{55 \text{ inches}}{25 \text{ inches}} = \frac{55}{25} = \frac{11}{5}$

EXERCISES

Write the following ratios.

1. Basmati rice needs to cook for 20 minutes, while quinoa (another grain) cooks for 25 minutes. What is the ratio of cooking times for rice to quinoa? $\frac{4}{5}$
2. Jonathan caught 7 fish and Geogeanne caught 4. What is the ratio of fish caught of Jonathan to Geogeanne? $\frac{7}{4}$
3. Two sunflowers' growth was measured daily. At the end of the experiment, Sunflower A had grown from 2 inches to 2 feet, 3 inches. Sunflower B had grown from 3 inches to 2 feet, 6 inches. Find the ratio of the growth in height of Sunflower A to Sunflower B. $\frac{25}{27}$
4. A soccer team won 22 games and lost 8. What is their win-loss ratio? $\frac{11}{4}$
5. Charlotte's essay on pigs was 824 words in length. Wilbur's essay was only 360 words long. What is the ratio of the length of Charlotte's essay to Wilbur's essay? $\frac{103}{45}$
6. A gingham bed sheet has 220 threads per square inch while an embroidered white sheet has 180 threads per square inch. Find the ratio of threads per square inch of the gingham sheet to the white sheet. $\frac{11}{9}$

Use the diagram at the right.

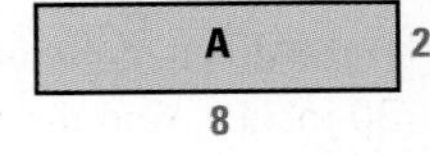

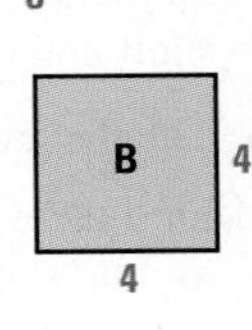

7. What is the ratio of length to width of rectangle A? $\frac{4}{1}$
8. What is the ratio of the perimeter of rectangle A to the perimeter of rectangle B? $\frac{5}{4}$
9. What is the ratio of the area of rectangle A to the area of rectangle B? $\frac{1}{1}$

EXAMPLE 2 Distributive Property

Solve.

a. $4(x + 3) = 36$
$4x + 12 = 36$
$4x = 24$
$x = 6$

b. $6(x + 4) + 12 = 5(x + 3) + 7$
$6x + 24 + 12 = 5x + 15 + 7$
$6x + 36 = 5x + 22$
$x = -14$

EXERCISES

Solve.

10. $2(x + 7) = 20$ **3**

11. $8(x + 6) = 24$ **−3**

12. $6(x - 2) = 24$ **6**

13. $-10(y + 8) = -40$ **−4**

14. $16(3 - d) = -4$ $\frac{13}{4}$

15. $7(2 - x) = 5x$ $\frac{7}{6}$

16. $-4(x - 6) = 28$ **−1**

17. $-9(5 - 3x) = 9$ **2**

18. $\frac{1}{2}(10 - 9x) = \frac{3}{2}$ $\frac{7}{9}$

19. $\frac{2}{3}(m + 4) - 8 = \frac{11}{3}$ $\frac{27}{2}$

20. $5(3a - 2) = 2(6a - 8)$ **−2**

21. $3(x - 1) + 3 = 4(x - 2)$ **8**

EXAMPLE 3 Solving Proportions

Solve.

a. $\frac{x}{8} = \frac{3}{4}$
$4x = 8 \cdot 3$
$4x = 24$
$x = 6$

b. $\frac{6}{x + 4} = \frac{1}{9}$
$6 \cdot 9 = x + 4$
$54 = x + 4$
$50 = x$

EXERCISES

Solve.

22. $\frac{x}{20} = \frac{1}{5}$ **4**

23. $\frac{2}{q} = \frac{4}{18}$ **9**

24. $\frac{7}{100} = \frac{14}{y}$ **200**

25. $\frac{t}{27} = \frac{4}{9}$ **12**

26. $\frac{5}{6} = \frac{4}{r}$ $\frac{24}{5}$

27. $\frac{w}{6} = \frac{7}{17}$ $\frac{42}{17}$

28. $\frac{27}{5} = \frac{3}{z}$ $\frac{5}{9}$

29. $\frac{y}{50} = \frac{3}{100}$ $\frac{3}{2}$

30. $\frac{6}{19} = \frac{m}{95}$ **30**

31. $\frac{3}{8} = \frac{3}{2d}$ **4**

32. $\frac{6}{5m} = \frac{6}{25}$ **5**

33. $\frac{19}{x} = \frac{9}{5}$ $\frac{95}{9}$

34. $\frac{3w + 6}{28} = \frac{3}{4}$ **5**

35. $\frac{6}{45} = \frac{2z + 10}{15}$ **−4**

36. $\frac{3a}{11} = \frac{54}{22}$ **9**

37. $\frac{-3}{8} = \frac{21}{2(y + 1)}$ **−29**

38. $\frac{1}{18} = \frac{5}{-4(x - 1)}$ $-\frac{43}{2}$

39. $\frac{3}{m + 4} = \frac{9}{14}$ $\frac{2}{3}$

40. $\frac{3}{p - 6} = \frac{1}{p}$ **−3**

41. $\frac{r}{3r + 1} = \frac{2}{3}$ $-\frac{2}{3}$

42. $\frac{w}{4} = \frac{9}{w}$ **±6**

EXTRA EXAMPLE 2

Solve.

a. $3(2x + 1) = -12$ $-\frac{5}{2}$

b. $\frac{1}{3}(x + 8) = 10 - 2(x - 1)$ 4

EXTRA EXAMPLE 3

Solve.

a. $\frac{5}{7} = \frac{20}{x}$ 28

b. $-\frac{4}{7} = \frac{x + 3}{14}$ −11

CHECKPOINT EXERCISES

For use after Example 2:

1. Solve $7(x + 9) = 4x$ −21

For use after Example 3:

2. Solve $\frac{4}{3x} = \frac{18}{27}$. 2

3. Solve $\frac{3}{x - 2} = \frac{9}{24}$. 10

CHAPTER 7

PLANNING THE CHAPTER

Transformations

GOALS

Lesson	Goals	NCTM	ITED	SAT9 (TASK 1)	Terra-Nova	Local
7.1 *pp. 395–402*	CONCEPT ACTIVITY: 7.1 *Investigate motion in the plane.* GOAL 1 Identify the three basic rigid transformations. GOAL 2 Use transformations in real-life situations.	1, 2, 3, 8, 9, 10	MIG, MIGE	34	11, 14, 16, 18, 49, 51	17, 22
7.2 *pp. 403–410*	CONCEPT ACTIVITY: 7.2 *Investigate the relationship between the line of reflection and the segment connecting a point and its image.* GOAL 1 Identify and use reflections in a plane. GOAL 2 Identify relationships between reflections and line symmetry.	1, 2, 3, 9, 10	MIG, MIGE	34	11, 14, 16, 49, 51	17, 22
7.3 *pp. 411–420*	TECHNOLOGY ACTIVITY: 7.3 *Discover what type of transformation results when a triangle is reflected twice in the plane using geometry software.* GOAL 1 Identify rotations in a plane. GOAL 2 Use rotational symmetry in real-life situations.	1, 2, 3, 9, 10	MIG, MIGE	34	11, 14, 16, 49, 51	16, 17, 22
7.4 *pp. 421–428*	GOAL 1 Identify and use translations in the plane. GOAL 2 Use vectors in real-life situations.	1, 2, 3, 8, 9, 10	MIG, MIGE	34	11, 14, 16, 18, 49, 51	17, 22
7.5 *pp. 429–436*	CONCEPT ACTIVITY: 7.5 *Investigate multiple transformations.* GOAL 1 Identify glide reflections in a plane. GOAL 2 Represent transformations as compositions of simpler transformations.	1, 2, 3, 8, 10	MIG, MIGE	34	11, 14, 16, 18, 49, 51	17, 22
7.6 *pp. 437–444*	GOAL 1 Use transformations to classify frieze patterns. GOAL 2 Use frieze patterns in real life.	1, 2, 3, 9, 10	MIG, MIGE	34	11, 14, 16, 49, 51	17, 22

RESOURCES

Chapter Resource Booklets

Chapter Support

Tips for New Teachers	p. 1	Prerequisite Skills Review	p. 5
Parent Guide for Student Success	p. 3	Strategies for Reading Mathematics	p. 7

Lesson Support

Lesson Support	7.1	7.2	7.3	7.4	7.5	7.6
Lesson Plans (regular and block)	p. 9	p. 21	p. 37	p. 53	p. 66	p. 82
Warm-Up Exercises and Daily Quiz	p. 11	p. 23	p. 39	p. 55	p. 68	p. 84
Activity Support Masters						
Lesson Openers	p. 12	p. 24	p. 40	p. 56	p. 69	p. 85
Technology Activities & Keystrokes		p. 25	p. 41		p. 70	
Practice (3 levels)	p. 13	p. 29	p. 43	p. 57	p. 74	p. 86
Reteaching with Practice	p. 16	p. 32	p. 46	p. 60	p. 77	p. 89
Quick Catch-Up for Absent Students	p. 18	p. 34	p. 48	p. 62	p. 79	p. 91
Cooperative Learning Activities				p. 63		
Interdisciplinary Applications		p. 35		p. 64		p. 92
Real-Life Applications	p. 19		p. 49		p. 80	
Math & History Applications			p. 50			
Challenge: Skills and Applications	p. 20	p. 36	p. 51	p. 65	p. 81	p. 93

Review and Assessment

Quizzes	pp. 52, 94	Alternative Assessment with Math Journal	p. 103
Chapter Review Games and Activities	p. 95	Project with Rubric	p. 105
Chapter Test (3 levels)	pp. 96–101	Cumulative Review	p. 107
SAT/ACT Chapter Test	p. 102	Resource Book Answers	p. A1

Transparencies

	7.1	7.2	7.3	7.4	7.5	7.6
Warm-Up Exercises and Daily Quiz	p. 48	p. 49	p. 50	p. 51	p. 52	p. 53
Alternative Lesson Opener Transparencies	p. 41	p. 42	p. 43	p. 44	p. 45	p. 46
Examples/Standardized Test Practice	✓	✓	✓	✓	✓	✓
Answer Transparencies	✓	✓	✓	✓	✓	✓

Technology

- Electronic Teaching Tools
- Online Lesson Planner
- Internet Support
- Personal Student Tutor
- Test and Practice Generator
- Geometry in Motion video
- Electronic Lesson Presentations (Lesson 7.4)

Additional Resources

- Basic Skills Workbook: Diagnosis and Remediation
- Worked-Out Solution Key
- Resources in Spanish
- Standardized Test Practice Workbook
- Practice Workbook with Examples

Correlations to the California Curriculum

Correlations to California Standards
See Teacher's Edition pp. CA9–CA11

Correlations to SAT9
Task 1: See Teacher's Edition pp. CA12–CA14
Task 2: See Teacher's Edition pp. CA15–CA17

CHAPTER 7

PACING THE CHAPTER

Resource Key
- STUDENT EDITION
- CHAPTER 7 RESOURCE BOOK
- TEACHER'S EDITION

REGULAR SCHEDULE

Day 1

7.1

STARTING OPTIONS
- Prereq. Skills Review
- Strategies for Reading
- Homework Check
- Warm-Up or Daily Quiz

TEACHING OPTIONS
- Motivating the Lesson
- Concept Activity
- Les. Opener (Software)
- Examples 1–5
- Guided Practice Exs.

APPLY/HOMEWORK
- See Assignment Guide.
- See the CRB: Practice, Reteach, Apply, Extend

ASSESSMENT OPTIONS
- Checkpoint Exercises

Day 2

7.1 *(cont.)*

STARTING OPTIONS
- Homework Check

TEACHING OPTIONS
- Examples 1–5
- Closure Question

APPLY/HOMEWORK
- See Assignment Guide.
- See the CRB: Practice, Reteach, Apply, Extend

ASSESSMENT OPTIONS
- Checkpoint Exercises
- Daily Quiz (7.1)
- Stand. Test Practice

Day 3

7.2

STARTING OPTIONS
- Homework Check
- Warm-Up or Daily Quiz

TEACHING OPTIONS
- Concept Activity
- Les. Opener (Activity)
- Technology Activity
- Examples 1–2, 4
- Guided Practice Exs. 1–11

APPLY/HOMEWORK
- See Assignment Guide.
- See the CRB: Practice, Reteach, Apply, Extend

ASSESSMENT OPTIONS
- Checkpoint Exercises, pp. 405–406

Day 4

7.2 *(cont.)*

STARTING OPTIONS
- Homework Check

TEACHING OPTIONS
- Examples 3, 5
- Closure Question
- Guided Practice Exs. 12–14

APPLY/HOMEWORK
- See Assignment Guide.
- See the CRB: Practice, Reteach, Apply, Extend

ASSESSMENT OPTIONS
- Checkpoint Exercises, pp. 405–406
- Daily Quiz (7.2)
- Stand. Test Practice

Day 5

7.3

STARTING OPTIONS
- Homework Check
- Warm-Up or Daily Quiz

TEACHING OPTIONS
- Motivating the Lesson
- Les. Opener (Activity)
- Examples 1–3
- Guided Practice Exs. 1–9

APPLY/HOMEWORK
- See Assignment Guide.
- See the CRB: Practice, Reteach, Apply, Extend

ASSESSMENT OPTIONS
- Checkpoint Exercises, pp. 413–414

Day 6

7.3 *(cont.)*

STARTING OPTIONS
- Homework Check

TEACHING OPTIONS
- Examples 4–5
- Technology Activity
- Closure Question
- Guided Practice Exs. 10–12

APPLY/HOMEWORK
- See Assignment Guide.
- See the CRB: Practice, Reteach, Apply, Extend

ASSESSMENT OPTIONS
- Checkpoint Exercises, p. 415
- Daily Quiz (7.3)
- Stand. Test Practice
- Quiz (7.1–7.3)

Day 9

7.5 *(cont.)*

STARTING OPTIONS
- Homework Check

TEACHING OPTIONS
- Examples 4–5
- Closure Question
- Guided Practice Ex. 8

APPLY/HOMEWORK
- See Assignment Guide.
- See the CRB: Practice, Reteach, Apply, Extend

ASSESSMENT OPTIONS
- Checkpoint Exercises, p. 432
- Daily Quiz (7.5)
- Stand. Test Practice

Day 10

7.6

STARTING OPTIONS
- Homework Check
- Warm-Up or Daily Quiz

TEACHING OPTIONS
- Motivating the Lesson
- Les. Opener (Visual)
- Examples 1–2
- Guided Practice Exs.

APPLY/HOMEWORK
- See Assignment Guide.
- See the CRB: Practice, Reteach, Apply, Extend

ASSESSMENT OPTIONS
- Checkpoint Exercises, p. 438

Day 11

7.6 *(cont.)*

STARTING OPTIONS
- Homework Check

TEACHING OPTIONS
- Examples 3–4
- Closure Question

APPLY/HOMEWORK
- See Assignment Guide.
- See the CRB: Practice, Reteach, Apply, Extend

ASSESSMENT OPTIONS
- Checkpoint Exercises, p. 439
- Daily Quiz (7.6)
- Stand. Test Practice
- Quiz (7.3–7.6)

Day 12

Review

DAY 12 START OPTIONS
- Homework Check

REVIEWING OPTIONS
- Chapter 7 Summary
- Chapter 7 Review
- Chapter Review Games and Activities

APPLY/HOMEWORK
- Chapter 7 Test (practice)
- Ch. Standardized Test (practice)

Day 13

Assess

DAY 13 START OPTIONS
- Homework Check

ASSESSMENT OPTIONS
- Chapter 7 Test
- SAT/ACT Ch. 7 Test
- Alternative Assessment

APPLY/HOMEWORK
- Skill Review, p. 456

Day 7

7.4

Starting Options
- Homework Check
- Warm-Up or Daily Quiz

Teaching Options
- Les. Opener (Application)
- Examples 1–6
- Closure Question
- Guided Practice Exs.

Apply/Homework
- See Assignment Guide.
- See the CRB: Practice, Reteach, Apply, Extend

Assessment Options
- Checkpoint Exercises
- Daily Quiz (7.4)
- Stand. Test Practice

Day 8

7.5

Starting Options
- Homework Check
- Warm-Up or Daily Quiz

Teaching Options
- Concept Activity
- Les. Opener (Application)
- Technology Activity
- Examples 1–3
- Guided Practice Exs. 1–7

Apply/Homework
- See Assignment Guide.
- See the CRB: Practice, Reteach, Apply, Extend

Assessment Options
- Checkpoint Exercises, p. 431

BLOCK SCHEDULE

Day 1

7.1

Day 1 Start Options
- Prereq. Skills Review
- Strategies for Reading
- Homework Check
- Warm-Up or Daily Quiz

Teaching 7.1 Options
- Motivating the Lesson
- Concept Activity
- Les. Opener (Software)
- Examples 1–5
- Closure Question
- Guided Practice Exs.

Apply/Homework
- See Assignment Guide.
- See the CRB: Practice, Reteach, Apply, Extend

Assessment Options
- Checkpoint Exercises
- Daily Quiz (Les. 7.1)
- Stand. Test Practice

Day 2

7.2

Day 2 Start Options
- Homework Check
- Warm-Up or Daily Quiz

Teaching 7.2 Options
- Concept Activity
- Les. Opener (Activity)
- Technology Activity
- Examples 1–5
- Closure Question
- Guided Practice Exs.

Apply/Homework
- See Assignment Guide.
- See the CRB: Practice, Reteach, Apply, Extend

Assessment Options
- Checkpoint Exercises
- Daily Quiz (Les. 7.2)
- Stand. Test Practice

Day 3

7.3

Day 3 Start Options
- Homework Check
- Warm-Up or Daily Quiz

Teaching 7.3 Options
- Motivating the Lesson
- Les. Opener (Activity)
- Examples 1–5
- Technology Activity
- Closure Question
- Guided Practice Exs.

Apply/Homework
- See Assignment Guide.
- See the CRB: Practice, Reteach, Apply, Extend

Assessment Options
- Checkpoint Exercises
- Daily Quiz (Les. 7.3)
- Stand. Test Practice
- Quiz (7.1–7.3)

Day 4

7.4 & 7.5

Day 4 Start Options
- Homework Check
- Warm-Up (Les. 7.4) or Daily Quiz (Les. 7.3)

Teaching 7.4 Options
- Les. Opener (Appl.)
- Examples 1–6
- Closure Question
- Guided Practice Exs.

Beginning 7.5 Options
- Warm-Up (Les. 7.5)
- Concept Activity
- Les. Opener (Appl.)
- Technology Activity
- Examples 1–3
- Guided Practice Exs. 1–7

Apply/Homework
- See Assignment Guide.
- See the CRB: Practice, Reteach, Apply, Extend

Assessment Options
- Checkpoint Exercises
- Daily Quiz (Les. 7.4)
- Stand. Test Prac. (7.4)

Day 5

7.5 & 7.6

Day 5 Start Options
- Homework Check
- Daily Quiz (Les. 7.4)

Finishing 7.5 Options
- Examples 4–5
- Closure Question
- Guided Practice Ex. 8

Beginning 7.6 Options
- Warm-Up (Les. 7.6)
- Motivating the Lesson
- Les. Opener (Visual)
- Examples 1–2
- Guided Practice Exs.

Apply/Homework
- See Assignment Guide.
- See the CRB: Practice, Reteach, Apply, Extend

Assessment Options
- Checkpoint Exercises
- Daily Quiz (Les. 7.5)
- Stand. Test Prac. (7.5)

Day 6

7.6 & Review

Day 6 Start Options
- Homework Check
- Daily Quiz (Les. 7.5)

Finishing 7.6 Options
- Examples 3–4
- Closure Question

Reviewing Options
- Chapter 7 Summary
- Chapter 7 Review
- Chapter Review Games and Activities

Apply/Homework
- See Assignment Guide.
- See the CRB: Practice, Reteach, Apply, Extend
- Chapter 7 Test (practice)
- Ch. Standardized Test (practice)

Assessment Options
- Checkpoint Exercises
- Daily Quiz (Les. 7.6)
- Stand. Test Practice
- Quiz (7.3–7.6)

Day 7

Assess & 8.1

(Day 7 = Ch. 8 Day 1)

Assessment Options
- Chapter 7 Test
- SAT/ACT Ch. 7 Test
- Alternative Assessment

Ch. 8 Start Options
- Skills Review, p. 456
- Prereq. Skills Review
- Strategies for Reading

Teaching 8.1 Options
- Warm-Up (Les. 8.1)
- Motivating the Lesson
- Les. Opener (Appl.)
- Examples 1–7
- Closure Question
- Guided Practice Exs.

Apply/Homework
- See Assignment Guide.
- See the CRB: Practice, Reteach, Apply, Extend

Assessment Options
- Checkpoint Exercises
- Daily Quiz (8.1)
- Stand. Test Practice

CHAPTER 7

MEETING INDIVIDUAL NEEDS

BEFORE THE CHAPTER

The *Chapter 7 Resource Book* has the following materials to distribute and use before the chapter:

- **Parent Guide for Student Success**
- **Prerequisite Skills Review (pictured below)**
- **Strategies for Reading Mathematics**

PREREQUISITE SKILLS *Pages 5–6*

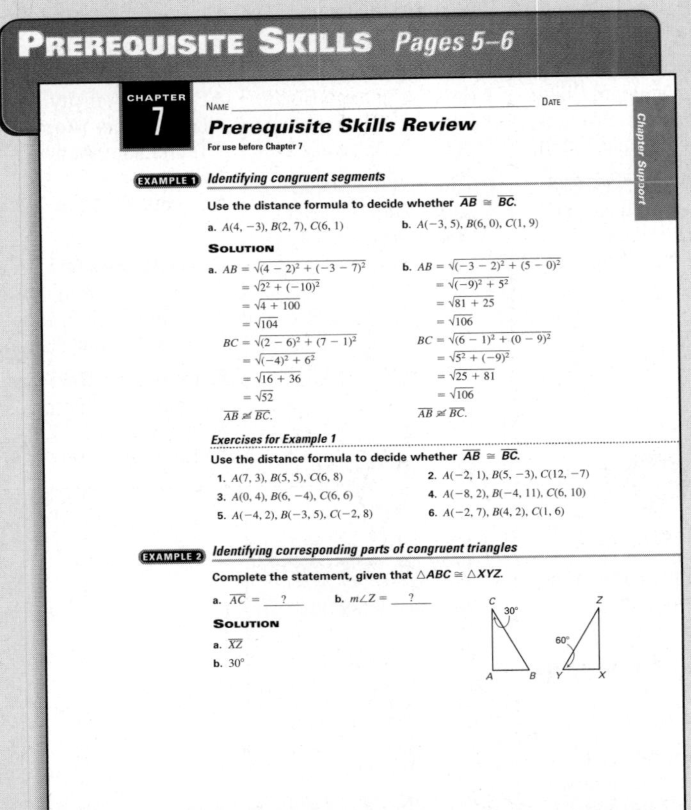

CHAPTER 7 NAME ______ DATE ______

Prerequisite Skills Review

For use before Chapter 7

Chapter Support

EXAMPLE 1 ***Identifying congruent segments***

Use the distance formula to decide whether $\overline{AB} \cong \overline{BC}$.

a. $A(4, -3), B(2, 7), C(6, 1)$ b. $A(-3, 5), B(6, 0), C(1, 9)$

SOLUTION

a. $AB = \sqrt{(4-2)^2 + (-3-7)^2} = \sqrt{2^2 + (-10)^2} = \sqrt{4 + 100} = \sqrt{104}$

$BC = \sqrt{(2-6)^2 + (7-1)^2} = \sqrt{(-4)^2 + 6^2} = \sqrt{16 + 36} = \sqrt{52}$

$\overline{AB} \not\cong \overline{BC}$.

b. $AB = \sqrt{(-3-2)^2 + (5-0)^2} = \sqrt{(-9)^2 + 5^2} = \sqrt{81 + 25} = \sqrt{106}$

$BC = \sqrt{(6-1)^2 + (0-9)^2} = \sqrt{5^2 + (-9)^2} = \sqrt{25 + 81} = \sqrt{106}$

$\overline{AB} \not\cong \overline{BC}$.

Exercises for Example 1

Use the distance formula to decide whether $\overline{AB} \cong \overline{BC}$.

1. $A(7, 3), B(5, 5), C(6, 8)$
2. $A(-2, 1), B(5, -3), C(12, -7)$
3. $A(0, 4), B(6, -4), C(6, 6)$
4. $A(-8, 2), B(-4, 11), C(6, 10)$
5. $A(-4, 2), B(-3, 5), C(-2, 8)$
6. $A(-2, 7), B(4, 2), C(1, 6)$

EXAMPLE 2 ***Identifying corresponding parts of congruent triangles***

Complete the statement, given that $\triangle ABC \cong \triangle XYZ$.

a. $\overline{AC}$ = __?__ b. $m\angle Z$ = __?__

SOLUTION

a. $\overline{XZ}$

b. $30°$

PREREQUISITE SKILLS REVIEW These two pages support the Study Guide on page 394. They help students prepare for Chapter 7 by providing worked-out examples and practice for the following skills needed in the chapter:

- **Identify congruent segments.**
- **Identify corresponding parts of congruent triangles.**
- **Identify congruent triangles and their measures.**

DURING EACH LESSON

The *Chapter 7 Resource Book* has the following alternatives for introducing the lesson:

- **Lesson Openers (pictured below)**
- **Technology Activities with Keystrokes**

LESSON OPENER *Page 12*

LESSON 7.1 NAME ______ DATE ______

Available as a transparency

Geometry Software Lesson Opener

For use with pages 396–402

Use geometry software to experiment with three basic transformations–translations, reflections, and rotations. Before you begin, select the option to keep the preimage displayed.

Lesson 7.1

1. Draw a square with a side length of 1 in. Translate the square three times: (1) 1 inch horizontally and 0 inches vertically; (2) 0 inches horizontally and 1 inch vertically; (3) -1 inch horizontally and 0 inches vertically. On paper, sketch your final figure and shade the original square.
2. Draw a square with a side length of 1 inch. Use *translations* to draw a rectangle as shown at the right. Explain your steps.
3. Draw a right triangle ABC with right angle at C. Reflect $\triangle ABC$ in $\overline{BC}$. Label the new vertex A'. Reflect $\triangle A'BC$ in $\overline{CA'}$. Label the new vertex B'. Reflect $\triangle A'B'C$ in $\overline{CB'}$. On paper, sketch your final figure and shade $\triangle ABC$. Name the shape of figure $ABA'B'$.
4. Draw a scalene obtuse triangle ABC. Mark A as the center of rotation and rotate $\triangle ABC$ 180°. Label the new vertices B' and C'. Construct segments $\overline{BC'}$ and $\overline{CB'}$. On paper, sketch your final figure and shade $\triangle ABC$. Name the shape of figure $BCB'C'$.

GEOMETRY SOFTWARE LESSON OPENER This Lesson Opener provides an alternative way to start Lesson 7.1 through the use of geometry software. Students manipulate a square and triangles to develop an understanding of transformations.

FOLLOWING EACH LESSON

The *Chapter 7 Resource Book* has a variety of materials to follow-up each lesson. They include the following:

- **Practice (3 levels)**
- **Reteaching with Practice**
- **Quick Catch-Up for Absent Students (pictured below)**
- **Interdisciplinary Applications**
- **Real-Life Applications**

QUICK CATCH-UP *Page 18*

LESSON 7.1

NAME ______ DATE ______

Quick Catch-Up for Absent Students

For use with pages 395–402

The items checked below were covered in class on (date missed) ______

Activity 7.1: Motion in the Plane (p. 395)

____ **Goal:** Determine which types of motion in a plane maintain the congruence of a figure.

Lesson 7.1: Rigid Motion in a Plane

____ **Goal 1:** Identify the three basic rigid transformations. (pp. 396–397)

Material Covered:

____ Student Help: Study Tip

____ Example 1: Naming Transformations

____ Example 2: Identifying Isometries

____ Example 3: Preserving Length and Angle Measure

Vocabulary:

image, p. 396 — preimage, p. 396

transformation, p. 396 — isometry, p. 397

____ **Goal 2:** Use transformations in real-life situations. (p. 398)

Material Covered:

____ Example 4: Identifying Transformations

____ Example 5: Using Transformations

____ Other (specify) ______

Homework and Additional Learning Support

____ Textbook (specify) pp. 399–402

____ *Reteaching with Practice* worksheet (specify exercises) ______

____ *Personal Student Tutor* for Lesson 7.1

Lesson 7.1

QUICK CATCH-UP FOR ABSENT STUDENTS You can use this form to let students know what they have missed when they've been absent from class. It allows you to quickly check off which Examples and other elements of Lesson 7.1 were covered on a given day and provides space for filling in the homework assignment.

TECHNOLOGY RESOURCE

Students who have missed class can find software help for the technology activity in Lesson 7.3 on the Internet at www.mcdougallittell.com.

ASSESSING THE CHAPTER

The *Chapter 7 Resource Book* has the following review and assessment materials:

- **Quizzes (pictured below)**
- **Chapter Review Games and Activities**
- **Chapter Test (3 levels)**
- **SAT/ACT Chapter Test**
- **Alternative Assessment with Rubric and Math Journal**
- **Project with Rubric**
- **Cumulative Review**

QUIZ *Page 52*

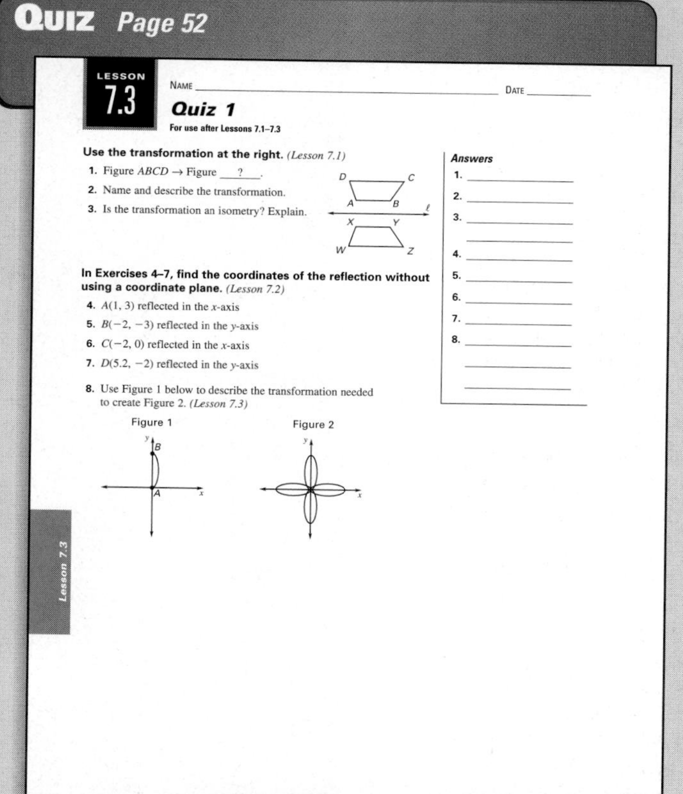

LESSON 7.3

NAME ______ DATE ______

Quiz 1

For use after Lessons 7.1–7.3

Use the transformation at the right. *(Lesson 7.1)*

1. Figure $ABCD \rightarrow$ Figure __?__.
2. Name and describe the transformation.
3. Is the transformation an isometry? Explain.

In Exercises 4–7, find the coordinates of the reflection without using a coordinate plane. *(Lesson 7.2)*

4. $A(1, 3)$ reflected in the x-axis
5. $B(-2, -3)$ reflected in the y-axis
6. $C(-2, 0)$ reflected in the x-axis
7. $D(5.2, -2)$ reflected in the y-axis
8. Use Figure 1 below to describe the transformation needed to create Figure 2. *(Lesson 7.3)*

Answers

1. ______
2. ______
3. ______
4. ______
5. ______
6. ______
7. ______
8. ______

Lesson 7.3

QUIZ Lessons 7.1–7.3 are covered on this quiz, which is an alternate form of the Quiz on page 420 of the textbook. You might want to assign the quiz in the textbook for homework and then use this version for assessment.

TECHNOLOGY RESOURCE

Teachers can use the Time-Saving Test and Practice Generator to create a customized quiz for Lessons 7.1–7.3, for Lessons 7.4–7.6, or for any other combination of lessons in Chapter 7.

CHAPTER OVERVIEW

CHAPTER GOALS

Students will identify reflections, rotations, translations, and the characteristics of an isometry. They will solve problems involving rigid transformations in the coordinate plane and will prove theorems about reflections, rotations, and translations. They will also use software to investigate double reflections in the coordinate plane. Students will describe translations using vectors and will identify vector components. Students will also learn how two or more translations produce a composition and they will identify glide reflections in a plane. In the final lesson, they will use transformations to classify, identify, and draw frieze patterns. Then they will examine how to use frieze patterns to create decorative borders for real-life objects. Throughout the chapter, students will apply what they learn to real-life applications such as stenciling designs, carpentry, surveying, molecular chemistry, log design, navigation, and architecture.

APPLICATION NOTE

The use of geometry to create repetitive designs creates a unity in the design. Geometric transformations are also apparent in the construction of buildings. Early classical construction used post-and-lintel construction, in which lintels or beams were laid horizontally across the tops of columns or posts to create ceilings and roofs. When a space between two vertical supports is too great for an available horizontal beam, an arch, each side of which is a reflection of the other side, can be constructed to bridge the span. And an arch, when rotated from its peak, forms a dome, which can be use to roof a large area.

Additional information about transformations and patterns in architecture is available at **www.mcdougallittell.com.**

TRANSFORMATIONS

How do architects use transformations?

CHAPTER
7

APPLICATION: Architecture

Architects often include decorative patterns and designs in their plans for a building. These adornments add interest and give a building character.

Some designs found on buildings are created by taking an image and transforming it. For instance, an image can be slid, flipped, or turned to create a pattern.

Think & Discuss

1. What motion is used to move box A onto box B? box C onto box D? **flip, turn**

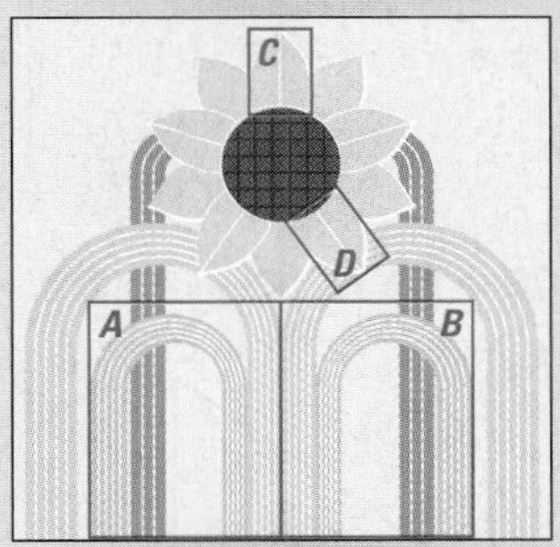

2. Describe any other uses of transformations in the design. **See margin.**

Learn More About It

You will identify transformations in architecture in Exercises 35–37 on p. 435.

APPLICATION LINK Visit www.mcdougallittell.com for more information about transformations and patterns in architecture.

PROJECTS

A project covering Chapters 6 and 7 appears on page 452 of the Student Edition. An additional project for Chapter 7 is available in the *Chapter 7 Resource Book,* p. 105.

TECHNOLOGY

Software

- *Electronic Teaching Tools*
- *Online Lesson Planner*
- *Personal Student Tutor*
- *Test and Practice Generator*
- *Electronic Lesson Presentations (Lesson 7.4)*

Video

- *Geometry in Motion*

Internet Connections
www.mcdougallittell.com

- **Application Links**
  393, 406, 418
- **Student Help**
  400, 408, 411, 414, 424, 426, 434, 443
- **Career Links**
  409, 415, 435
- **Extra Challenge**
  402, 410, 419, 428

2. ***Sample answer:*** **The blue arch shapes are enlarged versions of the purple arches. The light blue and purple arch unit is slid horizontally.**

PREPARE

DIAGNOSTIC TOOLS

The **Skill Review** exercises can help you diagnose whether students have the following skills needed in Chapter 7:

- Use the distance formula to determine whether two segments are congruent.
- Determine angle and side measures in congruent triangles.

The following resources are available for students who need additional help with these skills:

- Prerequisite Skills Review (*Chapter 7 Resource Book,* p. 5; *Warm-Up Transparencies,* p. 47)
- Reteaching with Practice (Chapter Resource Books for Lessons 1.3 and 4.2)
- *Personal Student Tutor*

ADDITIONAL RESOURCES

The following resources are provided to help you prepare for the upcoming chapter and customize review materials:

- ***Chapter 7 Resource Book***
  Tips for New Teachers (p. 1)
  Parent Guide (p. 3)
  Lesson Plans (every lesson)
  Lesson Plans for Block Scheduling (every lesson)
- ***Electronic Teaching Tools***
- ***Online Lesson Planner***
- ***Test and Practice Generator***

CHAPTER 7

Study Guide

PREVIEW

What's the chapter about?

Chapter 7 is about **transformations**. Transformations describe how geometric figures of the same shape are related to one another. In Chapter 7, you'll learn

- three ways to describe motion of geometric figures in the plane.
- how to use transformations in real-life situations, such as making a kaleidoscope or designing a border pattern.

KEY VOCABULARY

▶ **Review**
- **Distance Formula, p. 19**
- **parallel lines, p. 129**
- **congruent figures, p. 202**
- **corresponding sides, p. 202**
- **corresponding angles, p. 202**

▶ **New**
- **image, p. 396**
- **preimage, p. 396**
- **transformation, p. 396**
- **reflection, p. 404**
- **rotation, p. 412**
- **translation, p. 421**
- **vector, p. 423**
- **glide reflection, p. 430**
- **frieze pattern, p. 437**

PREPARE

Are you ready for the chapter?

SKILL REVIEW Do these exercises to review key skills that you'll apply in this chapter. See the given **reference page** if there is something you don't understand.

STUDENT HELP

▶ **Study Tip**
"Student Help" boxes throughout the chapter give you study tips and tell you where to look for extra help in this book and on the Internet.

Use the Distance Formula to decide whether $\overline{AB} \cong \overline{BC}$. (Review p. 19)

1. $A(-6, 4)$ congruent
$B(1, 3)$
$C(8, 4)$

2. $A(0, 3)$ not congruent
$B(3, 1)$
$C(7, 4)$

3. $A(1, 1)$ congruent
$B(4, 6)$
$C(7, 1)$

Complete the statement, given that $\triangle PQR \cong \triangle XYZ$. (Review p. 202)

4. $XZ =$? 10

5. $m\angle X =$? 35°

6. $m\angle Q =$? 55°

7. $m\angle Z =$? 90°

8. $\overline{YZ} \cong$? $\overline{QR}$

9. $QR =$? about 7

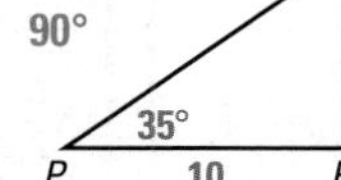

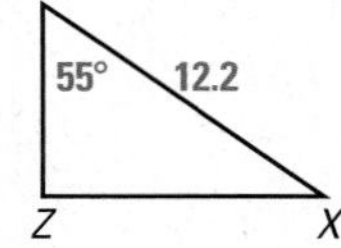

STUDY STRATEGY

Here's a study strategy!

Making Sample Exercises

Writing your own exercises can test what you have learned in this chapter. After each lesson, follow these steps:

- Write a summary of the lesson.
- Write at least three exercises that test the lesson's goals.

ACTIVITY 7.1

Developing Concepts

Motion in the Plane

GROUP ACTIVITY
Work with a partner.

MATERIALS
- tracing paper
- pencils

▶ **QUESTION** **Which types of motion in the plane maintain the congruence of a figure?**

▶ EXPLORING THE CONCEPT

1. In the pairs of figures below, the blue figure was transformed to produce the congruent red figure. For each pair, name the corresponding sides. (For example, in part (a) $\overline{FG}$ corresponds to $\overline{KJ}$.

a.

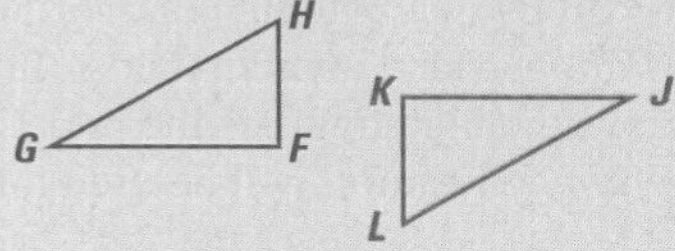

b.

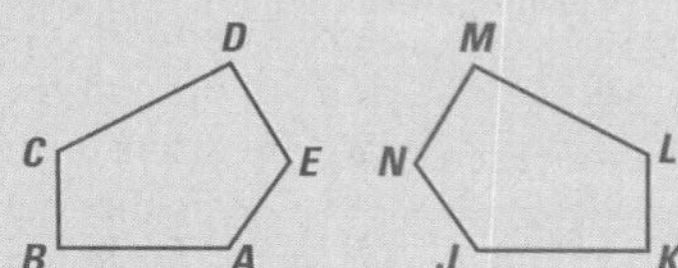

c.

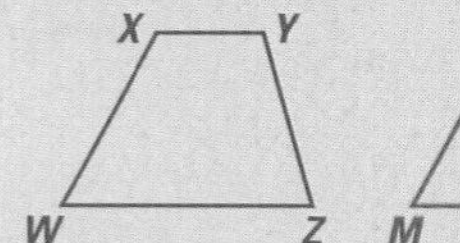

d.

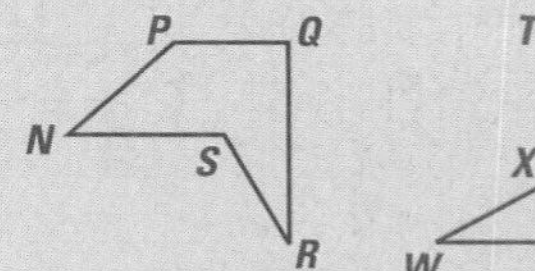

1. a. $\overline{FG}$ and $\overline{KJ}$, $\overline{FH}$ and $\overline{KL}$, $\overline{GH}$ and $\overline{JL}$
   b. $\overline{AB}$ and $\overline{JK}$, $\overline{BC}$ and $\overline{KL}$, $\overline{CD}$ and $\overline{LM}$, $\overline{DE}$ and $\overline{MN}$, $\overline{EA}$ and $\overline{NJ}$
   c. $\overline{XY}$ and $\overline{NP}$, $\overline{YZ}$ and $\overline{PQ}$, $\overline{ZW}$ and $\overline{QM}$, $\overline{WX}$ and $\overline{MN}$
   d. $\overline{NP}$ and $\overline{TU}$, $\overline{PQ}$ and $\overline{UV}$, $\overline{QR}$ and $\overline{VW}$, $\overline{RS}$ and $\overline{WX}$, $\overline{SN}$ and $\overline{XT}$

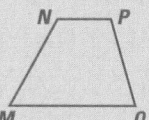

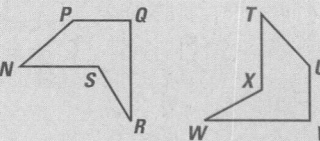

2. For each pair above, use words such as "flip," "slide," and "turn" to describe how to move from the blue figure to the red figure. Tracing paper can be used to help you.

2. a. turn
   b. flip
   c. slide
   d. turn

▶ MAKE A CONJECTURE

3. State the types of motion that preserve the congruence of a figure when it is moved in the plane. flip, slide, turn

▶ INVESTIGATE

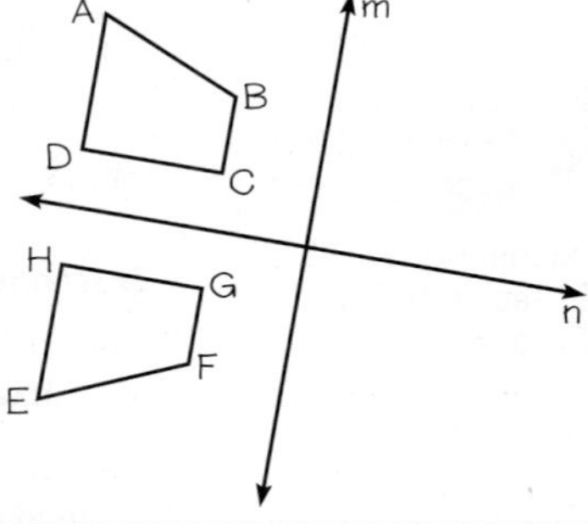

4. Describe the motion that moves *ABCD* onto *EFGH*. flip

5. Copy the figures at the right. Flip *EFGH* over line *m* and name the corresponding vertices of the new figure *JKLM*. Is *EFGH* congruent to *JKLM*? yes

6. Describe the motion that maps *ABCD* onto *JKLM*. Is *ABCD* congruent to *JKLM*? turn; yes

7. Can one "flip" be used to move *ABCD* onto *JKLM*? Explain why or why not. No; there is no line over which *ABCD* can be flipped to give *JKLM*.

1 Planning the Activity

PURPOSE
To identify the types of rigid motion in a plane that preserve the congruence of figures.

MATERIALS
- tracing paper
- pencils

PACING
- Exploring the Concept — 5 min
- Make a Conjecture — 15 min

▶ ***LINK TO LESSON***
Students should see the relationship between "flip," "slide," and "turn" and the vocabulary introduced on page 396.

2 Managing the Activity

ALTERNATIVE APPROACH
Make manipulatives of the figures, coloring them to match those in the text. Tape the figures to the board. Ask the class to decide on the congruence relation. Then ask students to demonstrate which moves make the figures coincide.

CLASSROOM MANAGEMENT
To verify their answers, ask students to write the congruence relationship between the figures in each exercise. Then tell them to check that the resulting corresponding angles in each pair appear congruent.

3 Closing the Activity

★ ***KEY DISCOVERY***
When a figure is reflected, rotated, or translated, the resulting figure is congruent to the original.

ACTIVITY ASSESSMENT
Draw a plane figure. Then rotate, reflect it, and translate it. State the congruence relation between each new figure and the original figure.

1 PLAN

PACING
Basic: 2 days
Average: 2 days
Advanced: 2 days
Block Schedule: 1 block

LESSON OPENER
GEOMETRY SOFTWARE
An alternative way to approach Lesson 7.1 is to use the Geometry Software Lesson Opener:
- Blackline Master (*Chapter 7 Resource Book*, p. 12)
- Transparency (p. 41)

MEETING INDIVIDUAL NEEDS
- ***Chapter 7 Resource Book***
  Prerequisite Skills Review (p. 5)
  Practice Level A (p. 13)
  Practice Level B (p. 14)
  Practice Level C (p. 15)
  Reteaching with Practice (p. 16)
  Absent Student Catch-Up (p. 18)
  Challenge (p. 20)
- ***Resources in Spanish***
- ***Personal Student Tutor***

NEW-TEACHER SUPPORT
See the Tips for New Teachers on pp. 1–2 of the *Chapter 7 Resource Book* for additional notes about Lesson 7.1.

WARM-UP EXERCISES
Transparency Available
1. $\triangle XYZ \cong \triangle MNO$. List the pairs of corresponding sides and angles. $\angle X \cong \angle M$, $\angle Y \cong \angle N$, $\angle Z \cong \angle O$, $\overline{XY} \cong \overline{MN}$, $\overline{YZ} \cong \overline{NO}$, and $\overline{XZ} \cong \overline{MO}$.
2. Quadrilateral $ABCD \cong$ quadrilateral $PQRS$. The measure of $\angle A = 62°$, $m\angle B = 128°$, $m\angle C = 97°$. Find $m\angle S$. 73°
3. Name 3 points the same distance from (0, 0) as (2, 5). (2, –5), (–2, –5), and (–2, 5)
4. If $B(-1, 4)$ is moved right 2 units and down 1 unit, where is its new location? (1, 3)

7.1 Rigid Motion in a Plane

What you should learn

GOAL 1 Identify the three basic rigid transformations.

GOAL 2 Use transformations in **real-life** situations, such as building a kayak in **Example 5**.

Why you should learn it

▼ Transformations help you when planning a stenciled design, such as on the wall below and the stencil in **Ex. 41**.

REAL LIFE

CALIFORNIA STANDARDS AND ASSESSMENT
CA Standards: 17, 22
SAT9 Task 1: Obj. 31
SAT9 Task 2: Obj. 34

GOAL 1 IDENTIFYING TRANSFORMATIONS

Figures in a plane can be reflected, rotated, or translated to produce new figures. The new figure is called the **image**, and the original figure is called the **preimage**. The operation that *maps*, or moves, the preimage onto the image is called a **transformation**.

In this chapter, you will learn about three basic transformations—*reflections*, *rotations*, and *translations*—and combinations of these. For each of the three transformations below, the blue figure is the preimage and the red figure is the image. This color convention will be used throughout this book.

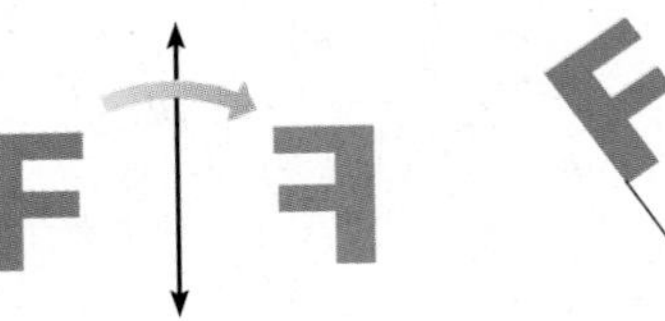

Reflection in a line

Rotation about a point

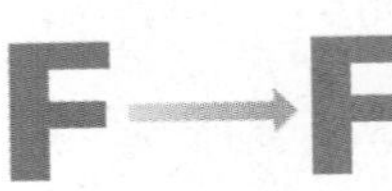

Translation

Some transformations involve labels. When you name an image, take the corresponding point of the preimage and add a prime symbol. For instance, if the preimage is A, then the image is A', read as "*A prime*."

EXAMPLE 1 *Naming Transformations*

Use the graph of the transformation at the right.

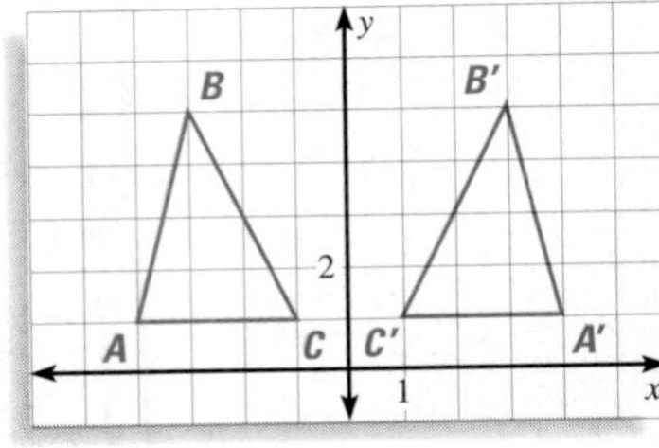

a. Name and describe the transformation.

b. Name the coordinates of the vertices of the image.

c. Is $\triangle ABC$ congruent to its image?

SOLUTION

a. The transformation is a reflection in the y-axis. You can imagine that the image was obtained by flipping $\triangle ABC$ over the y-axis.

b. The coordinates of the vertices of the image, $\triangle A'B'C'$, are $A'(4, 1)$, $B'(3, 5)$, and $C'(1, 1)$.

c. Yes, $\triangle ABC$ is congruent to its image $\triangle A'B'C'$. One way to show this would be to use the Distance Formula to find the lengths of the sides of both triangles. Then use the SSS Congruence Postulate.

STUDENT HELP

Study Tip
The term **isometry** comes from the Greek phrase *isos metrom*, meaning *equal measure.*

An **isometry** is a transformation that preserves lengths. Isometries also preserve angle measures, parallel lines, and distances between points. Transformations that are isometries are called *rigid transformations*.

EXAMPLE 2 *Identifying Isometries*

Which of the following transformations appear to be isometries?

a.

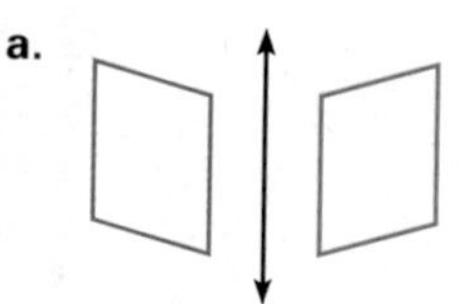

b.

c.

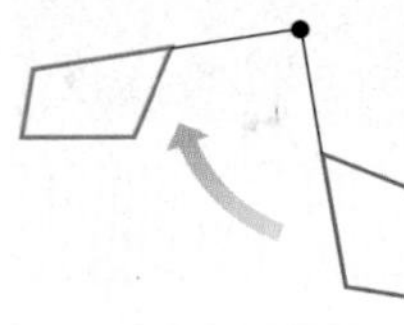

SOLUTION

a. This transformation appears to be an isometry. The blue parallelogram is reflected in a line to produce a congruent red parallelogram.

b. This transformation is not an isometry. The image is not congruent to the preimage.

c. This transformation appears to be an isometry. The blue parallelogram is rotated about a point to produce a congruent red parallelogram.

MAPPINGS You can describe the transformation in the diagram by writing "$\triangle ABC$ is *mapped onto* $\triangle DEF$." You can also use arrow notation as follows:

$\triangle ABC \to \triangle DEF$

The order in which the vertices are listed specifies the correspondence. Either of the descriptions implies that $A \to D$, $B \to E$, and $C \to F$.

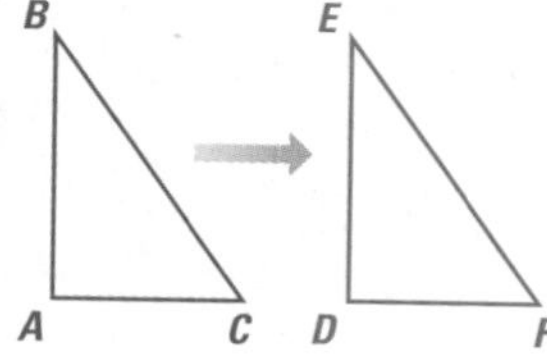

EXAMPLE 3 *Preserving Length and Angle Measure*

In the diagram, $\triangle PQR$ is mapped onto $\triangle XYZ$. The mapping is a rotation. Given that $\triangle PQR \to \triangle XYZ$ is an isometry, find the length of $\overline{XY}$ and the measure of $\angle Z$.

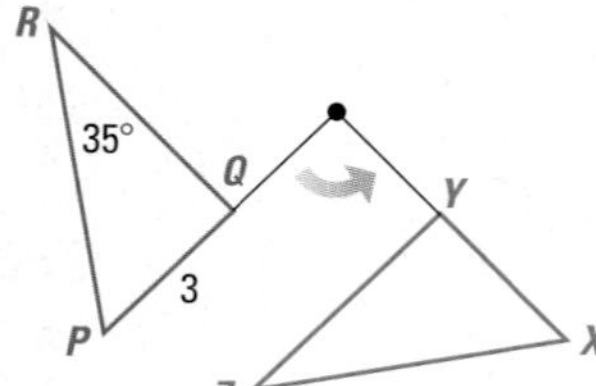

SOLUTION

The statement "$\triangle PQR$ is mapped onto $\triangle XYZ$" implies that $P \to X$, $Q \to Y$, and $R \to Z$. Because the transformation is an isometry, the two triangles are congruent.

▶ So, $XY = PQ = 3$ and $m\angle Z = m\angle R = 35°$.

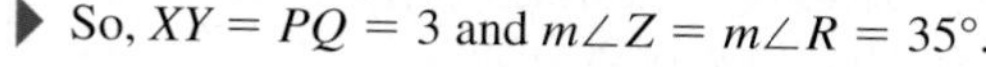

2 TEACH

MOTIVATING THE LESSON
Patchwork quilts may use transformations of geometric shapes. In this lesson you will see the results of manipulating geometric figures in a plane.

EXTRA EXAMPLE 1
Use the graph below.

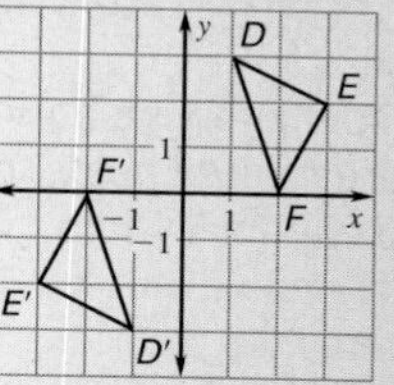

a. Name and describe the transformation. **The transformation is a 180° rotation about (0, 0).**

b. Name the coordinates of the vertices of the image. $D'(-1, -3)$, $E'(-3, -2)$, $F'(-2, 0)$

c. Is $\triangle DEF$ congruent to its image? **Yes**

EXTRA EXAMPLE 2
Which of the following transformations appear to be isometries? **a, b, and c**

a.

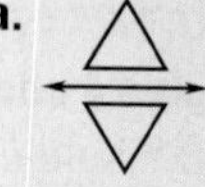

b.

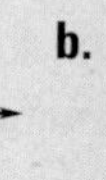

c.

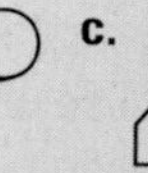

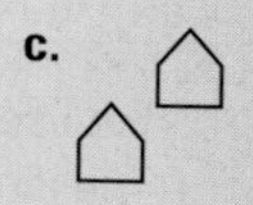

EXTRA EXAMPLE 3
$\triangle GHJ$ is mapped onto $\triangle UVW$. The mapping is a translation. Given $\triangle GHJ \to \triangle UVW$ is an isometry, $UV = 8$, and $m\angle H = 37°$, find the length of $\overline{GH}$ and $m\angle V$. $GH = 8$ **and** $m\angle V = 37°$

CHECKPOINT EXERCISES
For use after Examples 1–3:
The coordinates of $\triangle JKL$ are $J(1, 1)$, $K(-2, 4)$, and $L(-2, -1)$. The coordinates of $\triangle J'K'L'$ are $J'(2, -3)$, $K'(-1, 0)$, and $L'(-1, -5)$.

1. Name and describe the transformation. **$\triangle JKL$ is translated right 1 unit and down 4 units.**

2. Is this an isometry? **Yes**

3. If $m\angle K = 45°$, find $m\angle K'$. **45°**

EXTRA EXAMPLE 4

The blades on a windmill are tilted to catch wind, which then turns them.

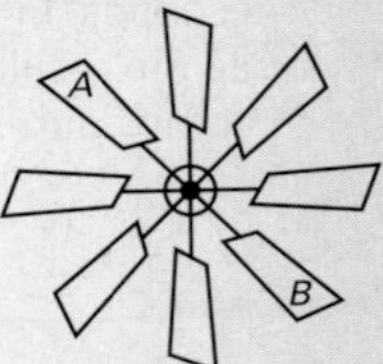

a. How are blades **A** and **B** related? **They are related by a rotation.**

b. Explain how knowing how the blades are related helps to build the windmill. **Knowing that each blade is rotated 45° to determine the position of the next blade allows you to place the blades in the correct position.**

EXTRA EXAMPLE 5

a. How much of the diagram of the windmill in Extra Example 4 is necessary to build all the blades? **two consecutive blades**

b. What is the measure of the angle between blade **A** and blade **B**? **180°**

CHECKPOINT EXERCISES

For use after Examples 4 and 5:

The digits on an LED display are constructed from a set of seven segments.

0 1 2 3 4 5 6 7 8 9

1. Which digits can be constructed using only half the digit and a reflection? **0, 1, 3, 8**

FOCUS ON VOCABULARY

Name three isometric transformations.
reflection, rotation, translation

CLOSURE QUESTION

$\triangle ABC$ is reflected over the x-axis. Its reflection is $\triangle A'B'C'$. If the coordinates of A are (3, 2) what are the coordinates of A'? **(3, −2)**

FOCUS ON APPLICATIONS

CARPENTER GOTHIC The woodwork of carpenter gothic houses contains decorative patterns. Notice the translations in the patterns of the carpenter gothic house above.

GOAL 2 USING TRANSFORMATIONS IN REAL LIFE

EXAMPLE 4 *Identifying Transformations*

CARPENTRY You are assembling pieces of wood to complete a railing for your porch. The finished railing should resemble the one below.

a. How are pieces 1 and 2 related? pieces 3 and 4?

b. In order to assemble the rail as shown, explain why you need to know how the pieces are related.

SOLUTION

a. Pieces 1 and 2 are related by a rotation. Pieces 3 and 4 are related by a reflection.

b. Knowing how the pieces are related helps you manipulate the pieces to create the desired pattern.

EXAMPLE 5 *Using Transformations*

BUILDING A KAYAK Many building plans for kayaks show the layout and dimensions for only half of the kayak. A plan of the top view of a kayak is shown below.

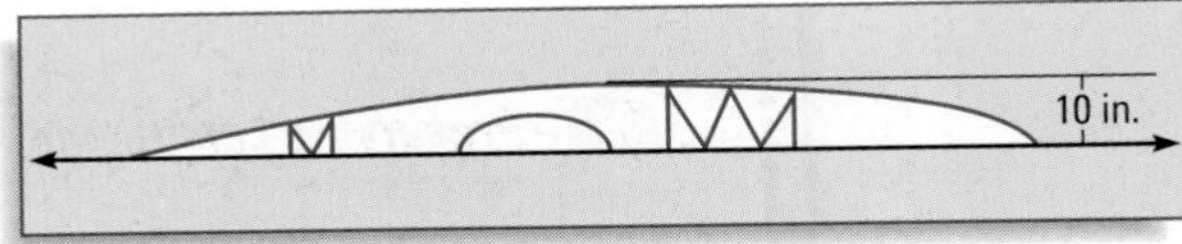

a. What type of transformation can a builder use to visualize plans for the entire body of the kayak?

b. Using the plan above, what is the maximum width of the entire kayak?

SOLUTION

a. The builder can use a reflection to visualize the entire kayak. For instance, when one half of the kayak is reflected in a line through its center, you obtain the other half of the kayak.

b. The two halves of the finished kayak are congruent, so the width of the entire kayak will be 2(10), or 20 inches.

GUIDED PRACTICE

Vocabulary Check ✓

1. An operation that maps a preimage onto an image is called a __?__. transformation

Concept Check ✓

Complete the statement with *always, sometimes,* or *never.*

2. The preimage and the image of a transformation are __?__ congruent. sometimes
3. A transformation that is an isometry __?__ preserves length. always
4. An isometry __?__ maps an acute triangle onto an obtuse triangle. never

Skill Check ✓

Name the transformation that maps the blue pickup truck (preimage) onto the red pickup (image).

5. translation

6. reflection

7. rotation

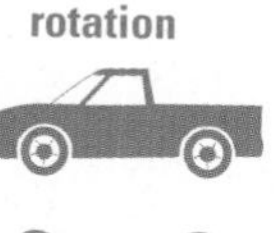

Use the figure shown, where figure *QRST* is mapped onto figure *VWXY*.

8. Name the preimage of $\overline{XY}$. $\overline{ST}$
9. Name the image of $\overline{QR}$. $\overline{VW}$
10. Name two angles that have the same measure.
11. Name a triangle that appears to be congruent to $\triangle RST$. $\triangle WXY$

10. $\angle Q$ and $\angle V$, $\angle QRS$ and $\angle VWX$, $\angle S$ and $\angle X$, or $\angle QTS$ and $\angle VYX$

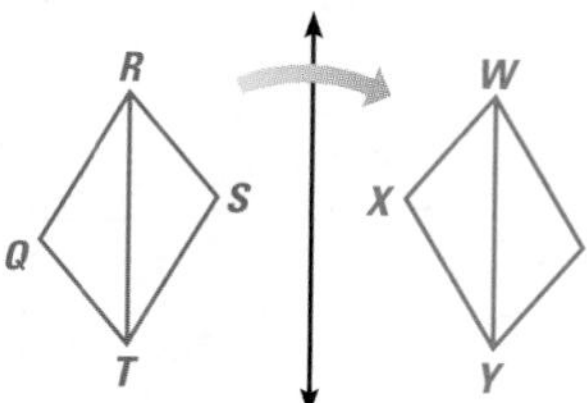

PRACTICE AND APPLICATIONS

STUDENT HELP

Extra Practice to help you master skills is on p. 815.

NAMING TRANSFORMATIONS **Use the graph of the transformation below.**

12. Figure $ABCDE \rightarrow$ Figure __?__ $JKLMN$
13. Name and describe the transformation. rotation about the origin; a turn about the origin
14. Name two sides with the same length.
15. Name two angles with the same measure.
16. Name the coordinates of the preimage of point L. (2, 4)
17. Show two corresponding sides have the same length, using the Distance Formula. *Sample answer:* $JK = \sqrt{(-3-(-1))^2 + (2-1)^2} = \sqrt{5}$; $AB = \sqrt{(2-1)^2 + (3-1)^2} = \sqrt{5}$

14. $\overline{AB}$ and $\overline{JK}$, $\overline{BC}$ and $\overline{KL}$, $\overline{CD}$ and $\overline{LM}$, $\overline{DE}$ and $\overline{MN}$, or $\overline{AE}$ and $\overline{JN}$

15. $\angle A$ and $\angle J$, $\angle B$ and $\angle K$, $\angle C$ and $\angle L$, $\angle D$ and $\angle M$, or $\angle E$ and $\angle N$

STUDENT HELP

HOMEWORK HELP
Example 1: Exs. 12–22
Example 2: Exs. 23–25
Example 3: Exs. 26–31
Example 4: Exs. 36–39
Example 5: Ex. 41

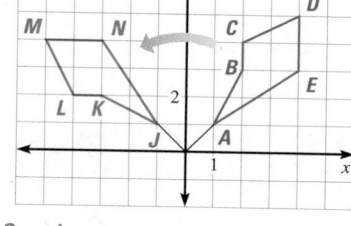

ANALYZING STATEMENTS **Is the statement *true* or *false*?**

18. Isometries preserve angle measures and parallel lines. true
19. Transformations that are *not* isometries are called rigid transformations. false
20. A reflection in a line is a type of transformation. true

3 APPLY

ASSIGNMENT GUIDE

BASIC
Day 1: pp. 399–401 Exs. 12–42 even
Day 2: pp. 399–402 Exs. 13–39 odd, 44, 45, 47–58

AVERAGE
Day 1: pp. 399–401 Exs. 12–42 even
Day 2: pp. 399–402 Exs. 13–39 odd, 44, 45, 47–58

ADVANCED
Day 1: pp. 399–401 Exs. 12–42 even
Day 2: pp. 399–402 Exs. 13–39 odd, 44–58

BLOCK SCHEDULE
pp. 399–402 Exs. 12–42, 44, 45, 47–58

EXERCISE LEVELS

Level A: *Easier*
18–20, 23–25

Level B: *More Difficult*
12–17, 21, 22, 26–45

Level C: *Most Difficult*
46

✓ HOMEWORK CHECK

To quickly check student understanding of key concepts, go over the following exercises: Exs. 16, 20, 24, 26, 32, 38, 42. See also the Daily Homework Quiz:

- Blackline Master (*Chapter 7 Resource Book*, p. 23)
- Transparency (p. 49)

TEACHING TIPS

EXERCISES 32 AND 33

Remind students that isometries preserve congruence. If the lengths of corresponding sides are congruent, then the triangles are congruent by SSS.

STUDENT HELP NOTES

Homework Help Students can find help for Exs. 32 and 33 at **www.mcdougallittell.com.** The information can be printed out for students who don't have access to the Internet.

21. reflection in the line $x = 1$; a flip over the line $x = 1$; $A'(6, 2)$, $B'(3, 4)$, $C'(3, -1)$, $D'(6, -1)$
22. translation; slide 6 units to the right; $L'(2, -2)$, $M'(3, 4)$, $N'(5, -2)$
23. Yes; the preimage and image appear to be ≅.
24. Yes; the preimage and image appear to be ≅.
25. No; the preimage and image are not ≅.

STUDENT HELP

HOMEWORK HELP
Visit our Web site www.mcdougallittell.com for help with Exs. 32 and 33.

32. $FG = RS = \sqrt{10}$, $GH = ST = \sqrt{13}$, $FH = RT = 3$
33. $AB = XY = 3\sqrt{2}$, $BC = YZ = \sqrt{10}$, $AC = XZ = 4$

DESCRIBING TRANSFORMATIONS Name and describe the transformation. Then name the coordinates of the vertices of the image.

21.

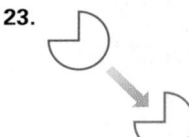

22.
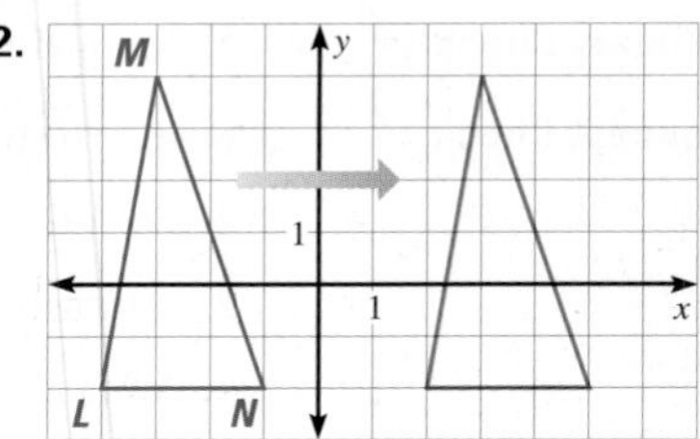

ISOMETRIES Does the transformation appear to be an isometry? Explain.

23.
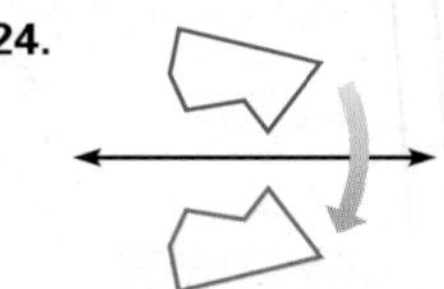

24.

25.
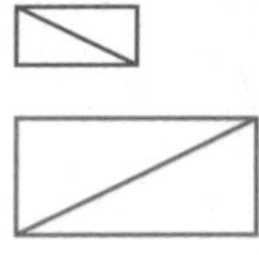

COMPLETING STATEMENTS Use the diagrams to complete the statement.

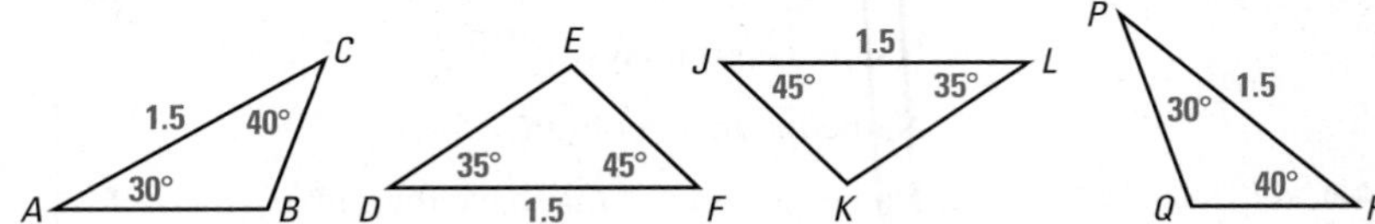

26. $\triangle ABC \rightarrow \triangle$ __?__ **PQR**
27. $\triangle DEF \rightarrow \triangle$ __?__ **LKJ**
28. $\triangle$ __?__ $\rightarrow \triangle EFD$ **KJL**
29. $\triangle$ __?__ $\rightarrow \triangle ACB$ **PRQ**
30. $\triangle LJK \rightarrow \triangle$ __?__ **DFE**
31. $\triangle$ __?__ $\rightarrow \triangle CBA$ **RQP**

SHOWING AN ISOMETRY Show that the transformation is an isometry by using the Distance Formula to compare the side lengths of the triangles.

32. $\triangle FGH \rightarrow \triangle RST$ **See margin.**

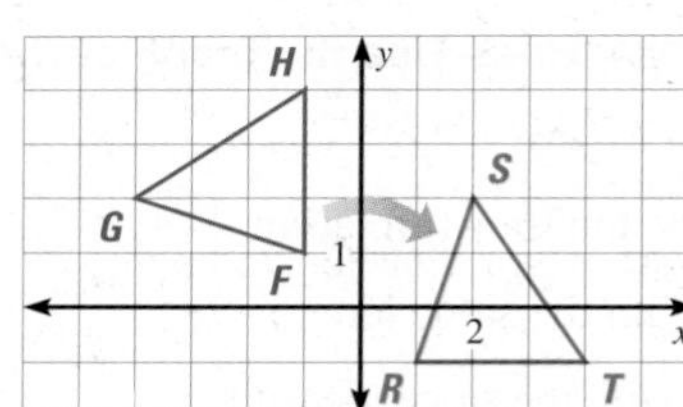

33. $\triangle ABC \rightarrow \triangle XYZ$ **See margin.**

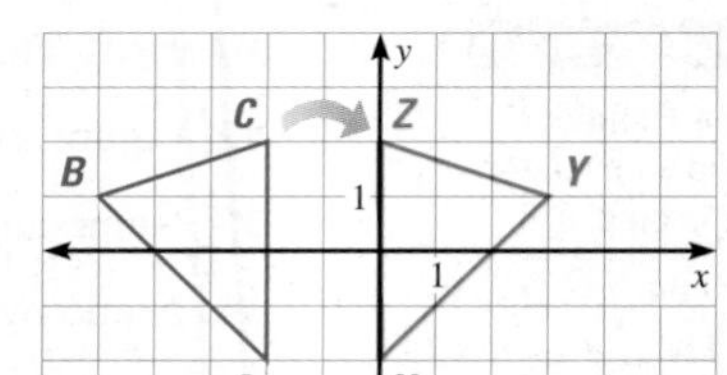

USING ALGEBRA Find the value of each variable, given that the transformation is an isometry.

34.

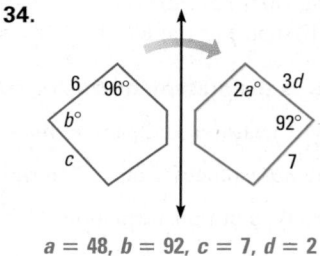

$a = 48$, $b = 92$, $c = 7$, $d = 2$

35.
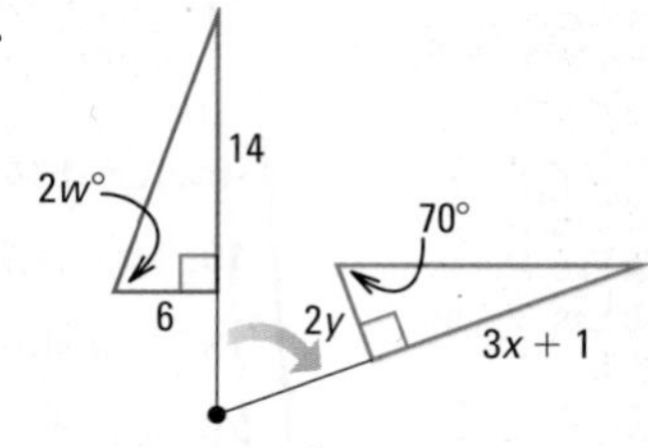

$w = 35$, $x = 4\frac{1}{3}$, $y = 3$

FOOTPRINTS In Exercises 36–39, name the transformation that will map footprint *A* onto the indicated footprint.

36. Footprint *B*
 translation
37. Footprint *C*
 translation
38. Footprint *D*
 reflection
39. Footprint *E*
 rotation

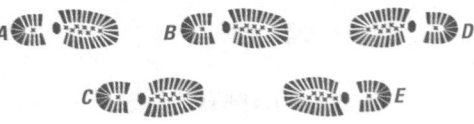

40. *Writing* Can a point or a line segment be its own preimage? Explain and illustrate your answer. See margin.

41. **STENCILING** You are stenciling the living room of your home. You want to use the stencil pattern below on the left to create the design shown. What type of transformation will you use to manipulate the stencil from *A* to *B*? from *A* to *C*? from *A* to *D*? reflection; reflection; rotation (or two reflections)

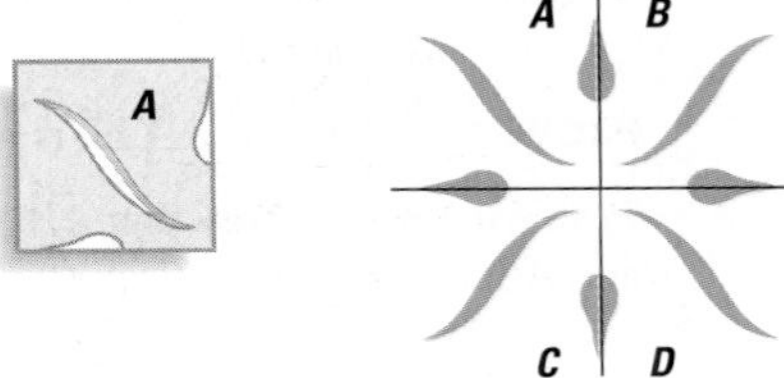

42. **MACHINE EMBROIDERY** Computerized embroidery machines are used to sew letters and designs on fabric. A computerized embroidery machine can use the same symbol to create several different letters. Which of the letters below are rigid transformations of other letters? Explain how a computerized embroidery machine can create these letters from one symbol. See margin.

abcdefghijklm
nopqrstuvwxyz

43. **TILING A FLOOR** You are tiling a kitchen floor using the design shown below. You use a plan to lay the tile for the upper right corner of the floor design. Describe how you can use the plan to complete the other three corners of the floor. See margin.

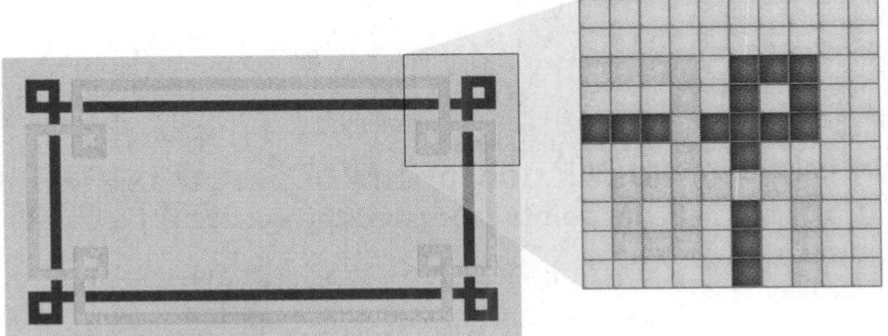

APPLICATION NOTE

EXERCISE 41 Each of the curved areas on the stencil is cut out. When paint is brushed over the surface of the stencil, the design is imprinted on the wall. Students may note that a translation of the stencil at *A* will produce a different design. Silk screen designs, which often appear on T-shirts, can also be created with stenciling.

EXERCISE 43 Many tilings such as those seen on floors, on walls and on decorative papers, which are made from a series of translations and rotations, are called tessellations. Tessellations combine both mathematics and art and have fascinated creative people for centuries.

40. Points or line segments can be their own preimages with respect to reflections or rotations, but not translations. Points or line segments on a line of reflection are their own preimages. A center of rotation is its own preimage. To picture one example of a rotated line segment that is its own image, imagine rotating a segment 180° about its midpoint.

ADDITIONAL PRACTICE AND RETEACHING

For Lesson 7.1:

- Practice Levels A, B, and C (*Chapter 7 Resource Book,* p. 13)
- Reteaching with Practice (*Chapter 7 Resource Book,* p. 16)
- See Lesson 7.1 of the *Personal Student Tutor*

For more Mixed Review:

- Search the *Test and Practice Generator* for key words or specific lessons.

42. The letters *b, d, p,* and *q* can be formed from each other by reflection or rotation; the letters *u* and *n* can be formed from each other by rotation or repeated reflection.

FOCUS ON APPLICATIONS

EMBROIDERY Before machines, all stitching was done by hand. Completing samplers, such as the one above, served as practice for those learning how to stitch.

43. *Sample answer:* Flip the plan vertically to lay the upper left corner, then horizontally to lay the lower left corner, then vertically again to lay the lower right corner.

4 ASSESS

DAILY HOMEWORK QUIZ

Transparency Available

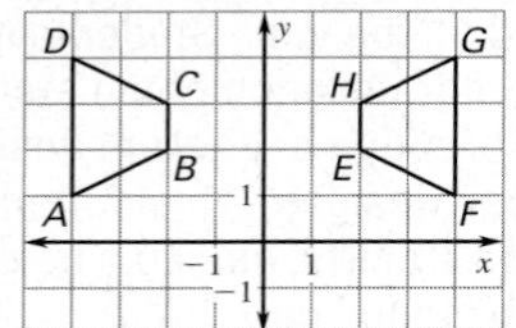

1. $ABCD \rightarrow$ ____. FEHG
2. Name the transformation. A reflection in the y-axis
3. Name the coordinates of the image of point D. (4, 4)
4. Is the transformation an isometry? Explain.

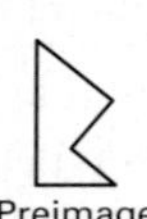
Preimage

Image

No; the image is not congruent to the preimage.

5. Find the value of each variable, given that the transformation is an isometry.

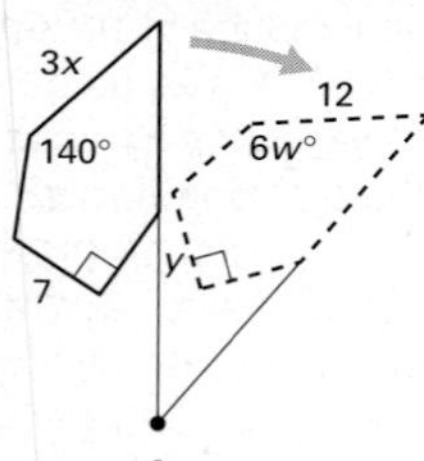

$w = 23\frac{1}{3}$, $x = 4$, $y = 7$

EXTRA CHALLENGE NOTE

Challenge problems for Lesson 7.1 are available in **blackline** format in the *Chapter 7 Resource Book,* p. 20 and at **www.mcdougallittell.com.**

ADDITIONAL TEST PREPARATION

1. **WRITING** Explain how a reflection and a rotation are different. How are they alike? See margin.

46. See Additional Answers beginning on page AA1.

Test Preparation

44. **MULTIPLE CHOICE** What type of transformation is shown? B

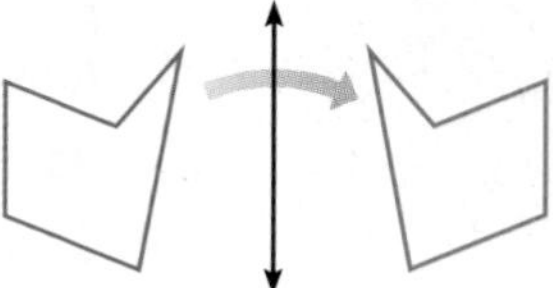

Ⓐ slide Ⓑ reflection
Ⓒ translation Ⓓ rotation

45. **MULTIPLE CHOICE** Which of the following is *not* a rotation of the figure at right? D

Ⓐ 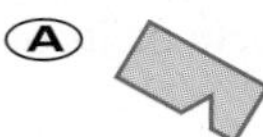 Ⓑ  Ⓒ 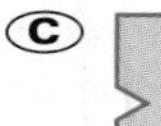 Ⓓ 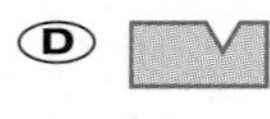

★ Challenge

46. **TWO-COLUMN PROOF** Write a two-column proof using the given information and the diagram.

GIVEN ▶ $\triangle ABC \rightarrow \triangle PQR$ and $\triangle PQR \rightarrow \triangle XYZ$ are isometries.

PROVE ▶ $\triangle ABC \rightarrow \triangle XYZ$ is an isometry.

Plan for Proof Show that $\overline{AB} \cong \overline{XY}$, $\overline{BC} \cong \overline{YZ}$, and $\overline{AC} \cong \overline{XZ}$. See margin.

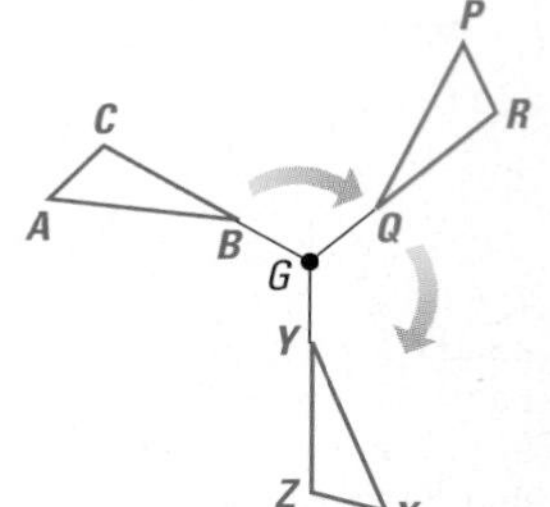

EXTRA CHALLENGE
www.mcdougallittell.com

MIXED REVIEW

USING THE DISTANCE FORMULA Find the distance between the two points. (Review 1.3 for 7.2)

47. $A(3, 10)$, $B(-2, -2)$ 13
48. $C(5, -7)$, $D(-11, 6)$ $5\sqrt{17}$
49. $E(0, 8)$, $F(-8, 3)$ $\sqrt{89}$
50. $G(0, -7)$, $H(6, 3)$ $2\sqrt{34}$

IDENTIFYING POLYGONS Determine whether the figure is a polygon. If it is not, explain why not. (Review 6.1 for 7.2)

51. 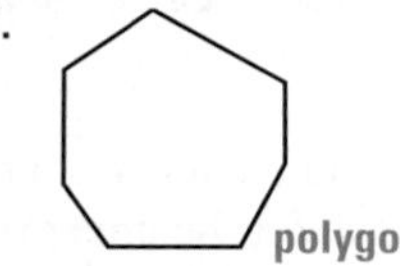 polygon

52.  polygon

53. 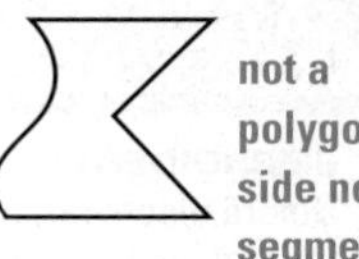 not a polygon; one side not a segment

54. 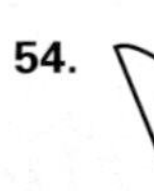 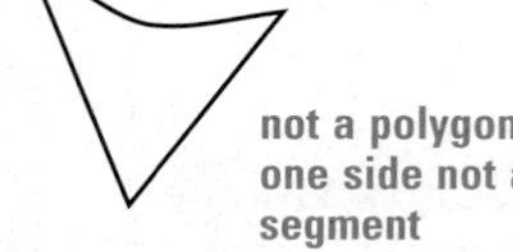 not a polygon; one side not a segment

55. 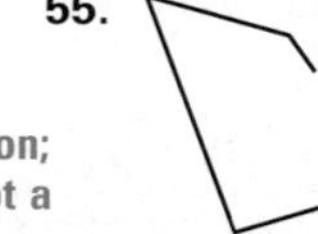 not a polygon; two of the sides intersect only one other side

56. 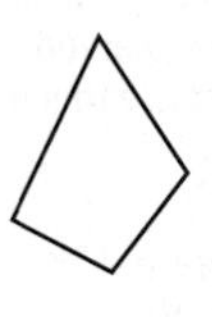 polygon

USING COORDINATE GEOMETRY Use two different methods to show that the points represent the vertices of a parallelogram. (Review 6.3) 57, 58. See margin.

57. $P(0, 4)$, $Q(7, 6)$, $R(8, -2)$, $S(1, -4)$
58. $W(1, 5)$, $X(9, 5)$, $Y(6, -1)$, $Z(-2, -1)$

57. (1) Since slope of $\overline{PQ}$ = slope of $\overline{SR} = \frac{2}{7}$ and slope of $\overline{PS}$ = slope of $\overline{QR} = -8$, both pairs of opposite sides are ∥ and $PQRS$ is a parallelogram.
(2) Since $PQ = SR = \sqrt{53}$ and $PS = QR = \sqrt{65}$, both pairs of opposite sides are ≅ and $PQRS$ is a parallelogram.

58. (1) Since slope of $\overline{WX}$ = slope of $\overline{ZY} = 0$, $\overline{WX}$ and $\overline{ZY}$ are ∥. But $WX = ZY = 8$, so one pair of opposite sides are both ≅ and ∥ so $WXYZ$ is a parallelogram.
(2) The midpoint of $\overline{WY}$ is $\left(\frac{7}{2}, 2\right)$, as is the midpoint of $\overline{XZ}$. Then the diagonals of $WXYZ$ bisect each other, so $WXYZ$ is a parallelogram.

Additional Test Preparation *Sample answer:*

1. In a reflection, each point has an image that is the same distance from the line of reflection of its preimage. In a rotation, every point moves along a circular path around a fixed point. Both reflections and rotations preserve congruence.

ACTIVITY 7.2

Developing Concepts

GROUP ACTIVITY
Work with a partner.

MATERIALS
- tracing paper
- pencils
- ruler
- protractor

Reflections in the Plane

QUESTION **What is the relationship between the line of reflection and the segment connecting a point and its image?**

EXPLORING THE CONCEPT Steps 1–3. Check drawings.

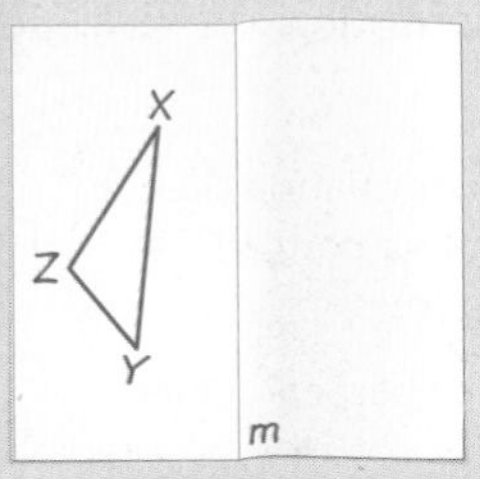

1. Fold a piece of tracing paper in half. Open the paper and label the fold line m. Draw a scalene triangle, $\triangle XYZ$, on one side of line m.

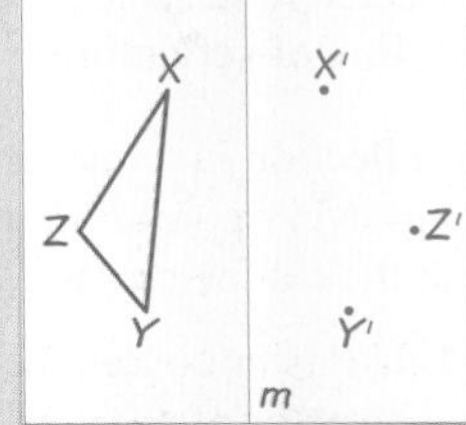

2. Fold the tracing paper on line m and trace points X, Y, and Z on the back of the paper. Open the paper and label the reflected points X', Y', and Z'.

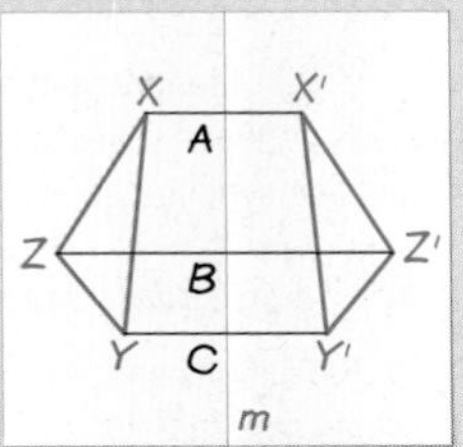

3. Draw $\triangle X'Y'Z'$. Then draw $\overline{XX'}$, $\overline{ZZ'}$, and $\overline{YY'}$. Label the points where these segments intersect line m as A, B, and C respectively.

INVESTIGATE

1. Measure and compare $\overline{XA}$ and $\overline{AX'}$, $\overline{ZB}$ and $\overline{BZ'}$, and $\overline{YC}$ and $\overline{CY'}$.

   1. $\overline{XA} \cong \overline{AX'}$, $\overline{ZB} \cong \overline{BZ'}$, $\overline{YC} \cong \overline{CY'}$

2. Measure and compare $\angle XAB$, $\angle ZBA$, and $\angle YCB$.
   The measure of each angle is 90°.
3. How does line m relate to $\overline{XX'}$, $\overline{ZZ'}$, and $\overline{YY'}$?
   Line m is the $\perp$ bisector of each segment.

EXPLORING THE CONCEPT Steps 4, 5. Check drawings.

4. Fold a piece of tracing paper in half and label the fold line m. Draw $\overline{AB}$ as shown. Then draw its reflection in line m.

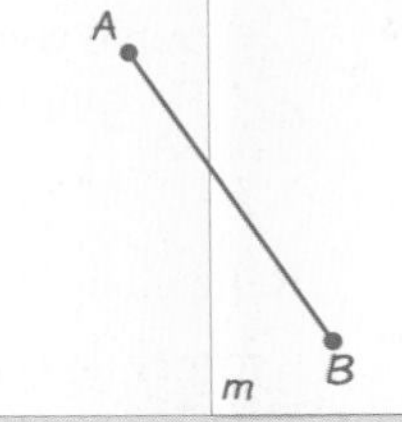

5. Draw $\overline{AA'}$ and $\overline{B'B}$. Label the points where these segments intersect line m as C and D as shown.

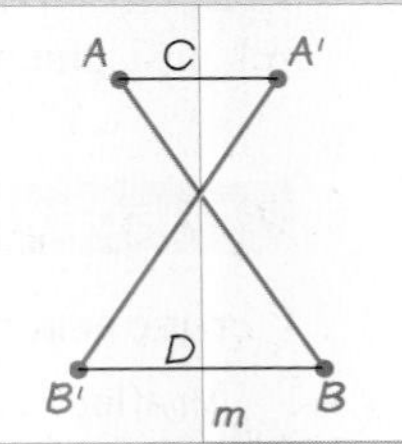

MAKE A CONJECTURE

4. How does line m relate to $\overline{AA'}$ and $\overline{BB'}$? Explain your answer.

   4. Line m is the $\perp$ bisector of each segment; *Sample answer:* As above, $\overline{AC} \cong \overline{A'C}$ and $\overline{AA'} \perp m$. Also, $\overline{BD} \cong \overline{B'D}$ and $\overline{BB'} \perp m$.

5. How does the line of reflection relate to the segment connecting a point and its image?

   5. The line of reflection is the $\perp$ bisector of the segment connecting a point and its image.

1 Planning the Activity

PURPOSE
To investigate the relationship between the line of reflection and the segment connecting a point and its image.

MATERIALS
- tracing paper
- pencils
- ruler
- protractor

PACING
- Exploring the Concept — 10 min
- Make a Conjecture — 10 min

LINK TO LESSON
As students read the properties on page 404, they should recognize that this activity models property 1.

2 Managing the Activity

ALTERNATIVE APPROACH
Draw a triangle and a line of reflection on the chalkboard or on an overhead. Ask students to make a conjecture about the relationship of the preimage and image to the line of reflection. Tell them to record their conjectures, then assess them after they have completed the explorations.

3 Closing the Activity

KEY DISCOVERY
If a point not on a line is reflected in the line, then the line is the perpendicular bisector of the segment joining the point and its image.

ACTIVITY ASSESSMENT
If $\triangle ABC$ is reflected in line q so that its image is $\triangle A'B'C'$, name three relationships of perpendicularity.
$\overline{AA'} \perp q$, $\overline{BB'} \perp q$, and $\overline{CC'} \perp q$

1 PLAN

PACING
Basic: 2 days
Average: 2 days
Advanced: 2 days
Block Schedule: 1 block

LESSON OPENER ACTIVITY

An alternative way to approach Lesson 7.2 is to use the Activity Lesson Opener:

- Blackline Master (*Chapter 7 Resource Book*, p. 24)
- Transparency (p. 42)

MEETING INDIVIDUAL NEEDS

- ***Chapter 7 Resource Book***
  Prerequisite Skills Review (p. 5)
  Practice Level A (p. 29)
  Practice Level B (p. 30)
  Practice Level C (p. 31)
  Reteaching with Practice (p. 32)
  Absent Student Catch-Up (p. 34)
  Challenge (p. 36)
- ***Resources in Spanish***
- ***Personal Student Tutor***

NEW-TEACHER SUPPORT

See the Tips for New Teachers on pp. 1–2 of the *Chapter 7 Resource Book* for additional notes about Lesson 7.2.

WARM-UP EXERCISES

Transparency Available

1. $P(5, 4)$ is reflected in the x-axis. In which quadrant is its image? **IV**
2. $Q(5, 4)$ is reflected in the y-axis. In which quadrant is its image? **II**
3. What is the hypothesis of the statement *If Q lies on m and $\overline{PQ} \perp m$, then $\overline{PQ} \cong \overline{P'Q'}$*? **$Q$ lies on m and $\overline{PQ} \perp m$**
4. If $\angle A \cong \angle A'$, $\angle B \cong \angle B'$, and $\overline{AB} \cong \overline{A'B'}$, by what congruence postulate is $\triangle ABC \cong \triangle A'B'C'$? **ASA**

7.2 Reflections

What you should learn

GOAL 1 Identify and use reflections in a plane.

GOAL 2 Identify relationships between reflections and line symmetry.

Why you should learn it

▼ Reflections and line symmetry can help you understand how mirrors in a kaleidoscope create interesting patterns, as in **Example 5**.

REAL LIFE

CALIFORNIA STANDARDS AND ASSESSMENT

CA Standards: 17, 22
SAT9 Task 1: Obj. 31
SAT9 Task 2: Obj. 34

GOAL 1 USING REFLECTIONS IN A PLANE

One type of transformation uses a line that acts like a mirror, with an image reflected in the line. This transformation is a **reflection** and the mirror line is the **line of reflection**.

A reflection in a line m is a transformation that maps every point P in the plane to a point P', so that the following properties are true:

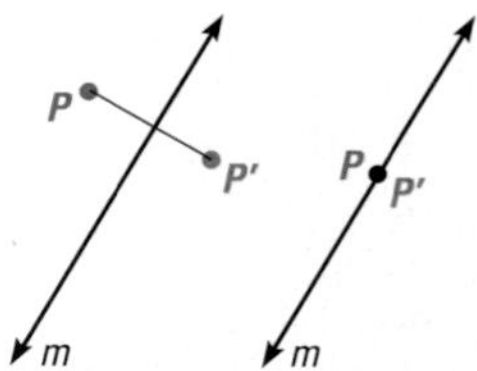

1. If P is not on m, then m is the perpendicular bisector of $\overline{PP'}$.
2. If P is on m, then $P = P'$.

EXAMPLE 1 *Reflections in a Coordinate Plane*

Graph the given reflection.

a. $H(2, 2)$ in the x-axis

b. $G(5, 4)$ in the line $y = 4$

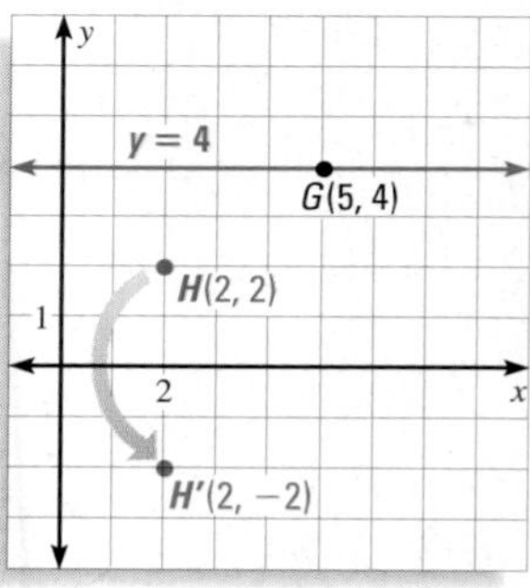

SOLUTION

a. Since H is two units above the x-axis, its reflection, H', is two units below the x-axis.

b. Start by graphing $y = 4$ and G. From the graph, you can see that G is on the line. This implies that $G = G'$.

Reflections in the coordinate axes have the following properties:

1. If (x, y) is reflected in the x-axis, its image is the point $(x, -y)$.
2. If (x, y) is reflected in the y-axis, its image is the point $(-x, y)$.

In Lesson 7.1, you learned that an isometry preserves lengths. Theorem 7.1 relates isometries and reflections.

THEOREM

THEOREM 7.1 ***Reflection Theorem***

A reflection is an isometry.

STUDENT HELP

Study Tip
Some theorems have more than one case, such as the Reflection Theorem. To fully prove this type of theorem, all of the cases must be proven.

To prove the Reflection Theorem, you need to show that a reflection preserves the length of a segment. Consider a segment $\overline{PQ}$ that is reflected in a line m to produce $\overline{P'Q'}$. The four cases to consider are shown below.

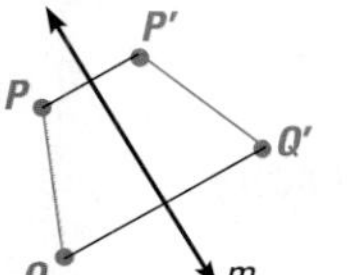

Case 1
P and Q are on the same side of m.

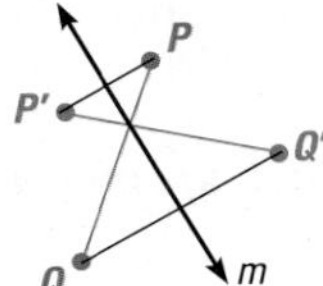

Case 2
P and Q are on opposite sides of m.

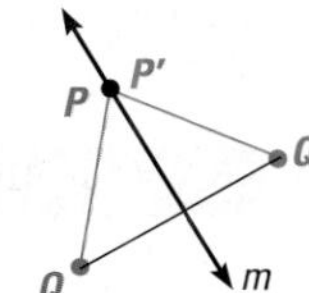

Case 3
One point lies on m and $\overline{PQ}$ is not perpendicular to m.

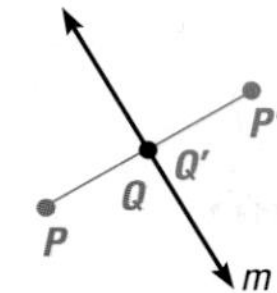

Case 4
Q lies on m and $\overline{PQ} \perp m$.

EXAMPLE 2 Proof of Case 1 of Theorem 7.1

Proof

GIVEN ▶ A reflection in m maps P onto P' and Q onto Q'.

PROVE ▶ $PQ = P'Q'$

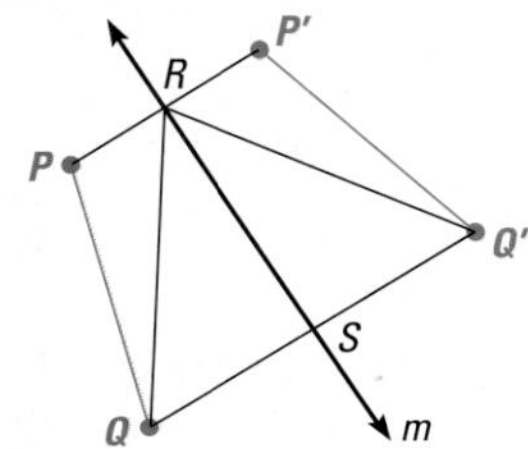

Paragraph Proof For this case, P and Q are on the same side of line m. Draw $\overline{PP'}$ and $\overline{QQ'}$, intersecting line m at R and S. Draw $\overline{RQ}$ and $\overline{RQ'}$.

By the definition of a reflection, $m \perp \overline{QQ'}$ and $\overline{QS} \cong \overline{Q'S}$. It follows that $\triangle RSQ \cong \triangle RSQ'$ using the SAS Congruence Postulate. This implies $\overline{RQ} \cong \overline{RQ'}$ and $\angle QRS \cong \angle Q'RS$. Because $\overleftrightarrow{RS}$ is a perpendicular bisector of $\overline{PP'}$, you have enough information to apply SAS to conclude that $\triangle RQP \cong \triangle RQ'P'$. Because corresponding parts of congruent triangles are congruent, $PQ = P'Q'$.

EXAMPLE 3 Finding a Minimum Distance

REAL LIFE

SURVEYING Two houses are located on a rural road m, as shown at the right. You want to place a telephone pole on the road at point C so that the length of the telephone cable, $AC + BC$, is a minimum. Where should you locate C?

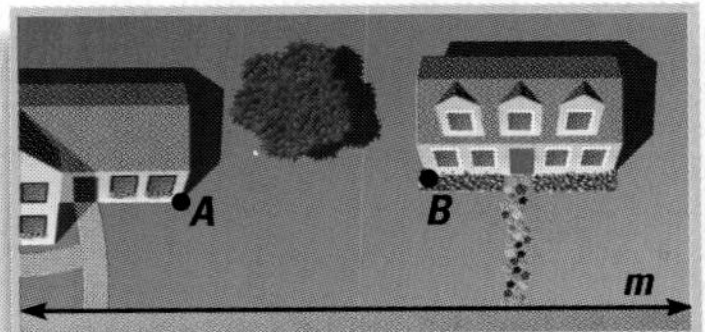

SOLUTION

Reflect A in line m to obtain A'. Then, draw $\overline{A'B}$. Label the point at which this segment intersects m as C. Because $\overline{A'B}$ represents the shortest distance between A' and B, and $AC = A'C$, you can conclude that at point C a minimum length of telephone cable is used.

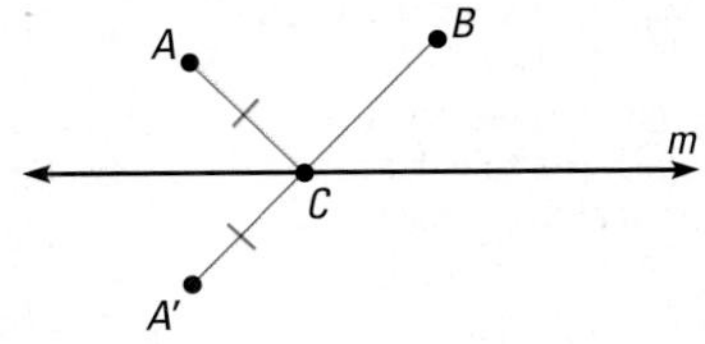

2 TEACH

EXTRA EXAMPLE 1
Graph the given reflection.
a. $W(-3, 3)$ in the y-axis.
b. $Z(1, 3)$ in the line $x = 1$.

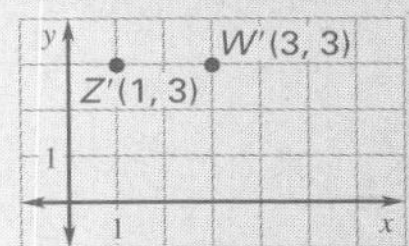

EXTRA EXAMPLE 2
Given: A reflection in m maps $\triangle PRQ$ onto $\triangle P'R'Q'$.
Prove: $\angle P \cong \angle P'$

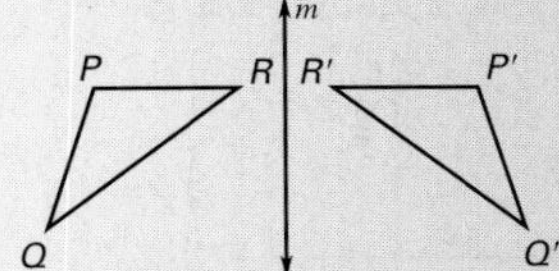

From the proof of Case 1 for Theorem 7.1 in Example 2, $PQ = P'Q'$, $PR = P'R'$, and $RQ = R'Q'$. From the SSS Congruence Postulate it follows that $\triangle PQR \cong \triangle P'Q'R'$. Because corresponding parts of congruent triangles are congruent, $\angle P \cong \angle P'$.

EXTRA EXAMPLE 3
Two identical house plots in a new development will be reached by the same road. How can you locate the road to ensure that all corresponding points on the two plots are equidistant from the road? **Connect two corresponding points such as Q and Q' on the plots. Construct the perpendicular bisector of this line. This is the line of reflection for the plots.**

CHECKPOINT EXERCISES
For use after Examples 1–3:
1. The coordinates of $\triangle ABC$ are $A(1, 3)$, $B(4, 2)$, and $C(3, 6)$. If the triangle is reflected on the x-axis, what is the length of $\overline{A'B'}$? **about 3.2 units**

APPLICATION NOTE
EXAMPLE 3 The same minimum distance can be found by first reflecting B in line m.

EXTRA EXAMPLE 4

Determine the number of lines of symmetry in the quadrilateral.

a. 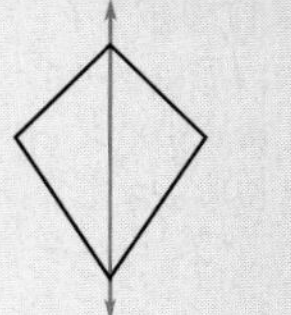 b. 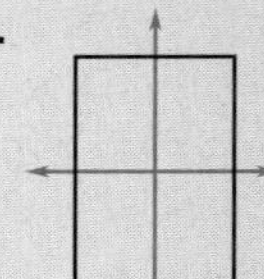

c. 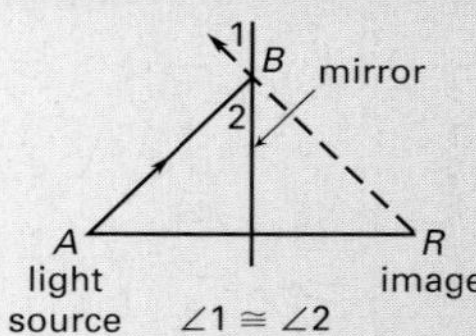

1; 2; 4

EXTRA EXAMPLE 5

1, B, mirror, 2, A light source, R image, $\angle 1 \cong \angle 2$

When light reflects off a flat mirror, the angle at which the light makes contact with the mirror is equal to the angle at which the light reflects off the mirror. Thus, when a light source at *A* bounces off a flat mirror at *B,* the mirror acts as a line of symmetry and creates an image that appears to come from a point *R* that is behind the mirror. If the light source at *A* is 1 ft from the mirror, how many feet behind the mirror does its image appear to be? 1 ft

CHECKPOINT EXERCISES

For use after Example 4:

1. What is the maximum number of lines of symmetry that an octagon can have? the minimum number? 8; 0

For use after Example 5:

2. If the image in a kaleidoscope has 5 lines of symmetry, at what angle are the mirrors placed? 36°

CLOSURE QUESTION

What are the coordinates of the image of (x, y) when it is reflected in the x-axis? In the y-axis? $(x, -y)$; $(-x, y)$

GOAL 2 REFLECTIONS AND LINE SYMMETRY

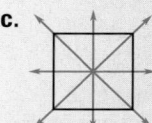

A figure in the plane has a **line of symmetry** if the figure can be mapped onto itself by a reflection in the line.

EXAMPLE 4 *Finding Lines of Symmetry*

Hexagons can have different lines of symmetry depending on their shape.

a. 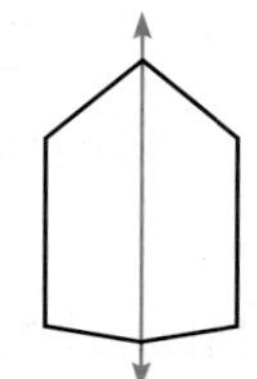

This hexagon has only one line of symmetry.

b.

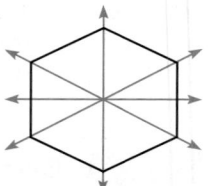

This hexagon has four lines of symmetry.

c. 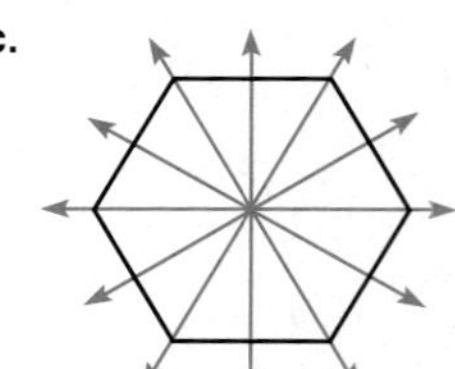

This hexagon has six lines of symmetry.

EXAMPLE 5 *Identifying Reflections*

KALEIDOSCOPES Inside a kaleidoscope, two mirrors are placed next to each other to form a V, as shown at the right. The angle between the mirrors determines the number of lines of symmetry in the image. The formula below can be used to calculate the angle between the mirrors, A, or the number of lines of symmetry in the image, n.

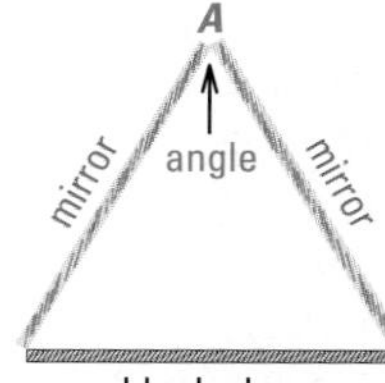

$n(m\angle A) = 180°$

Use the formula to find the angle that the mirrors must be placed for the image of a kaleidoscope to resemble the design.

a. 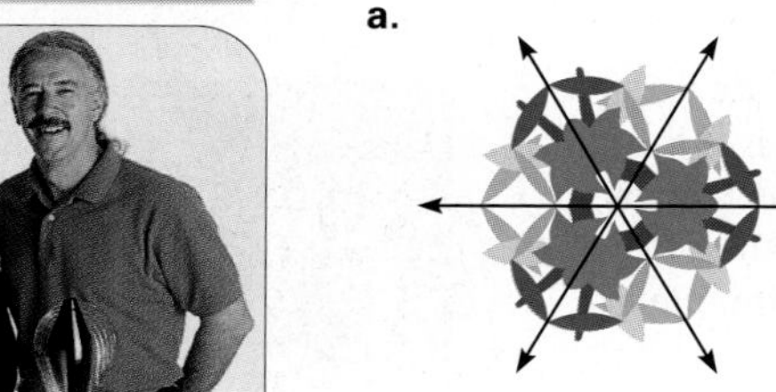 **b.** 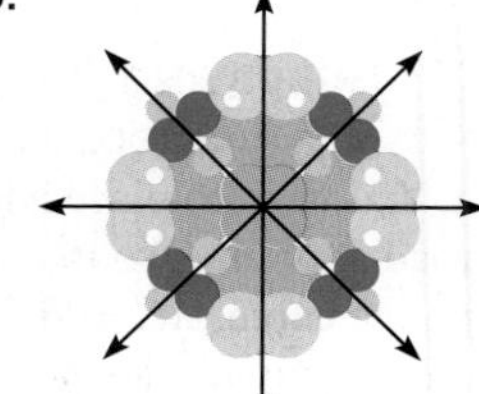 **c.** 

SOLUTION

a. There are 3 lines of symmetry. So, you can write $3(m\angle A) = 180°$. The solution is $m\angle A = 60°$.

b. There are 4 lines of symmetry. So, you can write $4(m\angle A) = 180°$. The solution is $m\angle A = 45°$.

c. There are 6 lines of symmetry. So, you can write $6(m\angle A) = 180°$. The solution is $m\angle A = 30°$.

FOCUS ON PEOPLE

REAL LIFE **KALEIDOSCOPES** Sue and Bob Rioux design and make kaleidoscopes. The kaleidoscope in front of Sue is called *Sea Angel.*

 APPLICATION LINK www.mcdougallittell.com

GUIDED PRACTICE

Vocabulary Check ✓

1. Describe what a *line of symmetry* is. See margin.

Concept Check ✓

2. When a point is reflected in the x-axis, how are the coordinates of the image related to the coordinates of the preimage? See margin.

Skill Check ✓

1. *Sample answer:* A line of symmetry for a plane figure is a line in which, when the figure is reflected, its image is itself.

2. The point and its image have the same x-coordinate and the y-coordinates are opposites.

18. True; N is 2 units above the line $y = 2$, so its image is 2 units below the line.

19. True; M is 3 units to the right of the line $x = 3$, so its image is 3 units to the left of the line.

20. False; W is 1 unit below the line $y = -2$, so its image is 1 unit above the line and the coordinates of the image are $(-6, -1)$.

Determine whether the blue figure maps onto the red figure by a reflection in line *m*.

3. 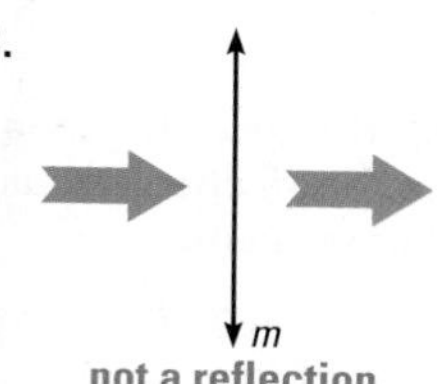

not a reflection

4. 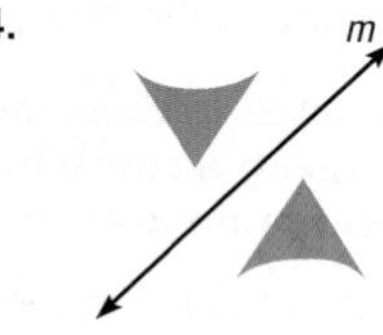

not a reflection

5. 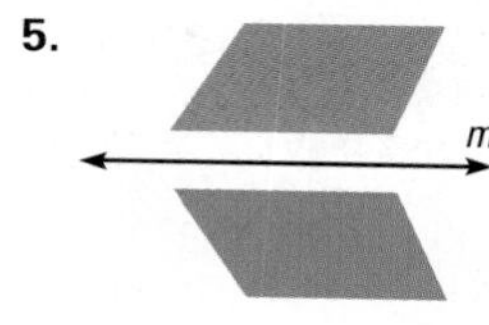

reflection

Use the diagram at the right to complete the statement.

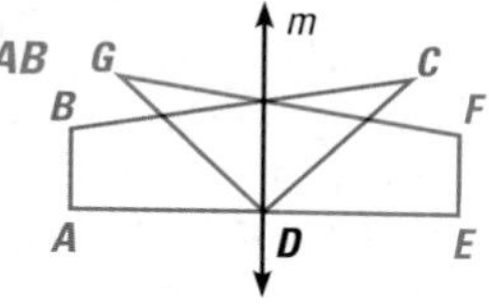

6. $\overline{AB} \rightarrow$ ___?___ $\overline{EF}$

7. ___?___ $\rightarrow \angle DEF$ $\angle DAB$

8. $C \rightarrow$ ___?___ G

9. $D \rightarrow$ ___?___ D

10. ___?___ $\rightarrow \angle GFE$ $\angle CBA$

11. ___?___ $\rightarrow \overline{DG}$ $\overline{DC}$

FLOWERS Determine the number of lines of symmetry in the flower.

12. 3 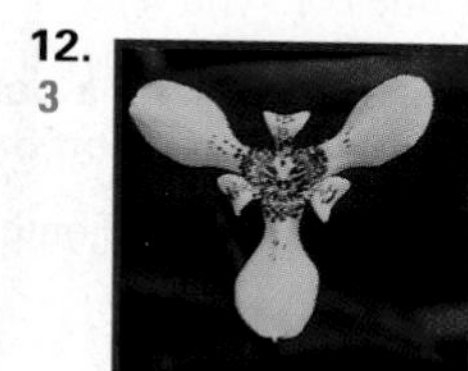

13. 4 

14. 5 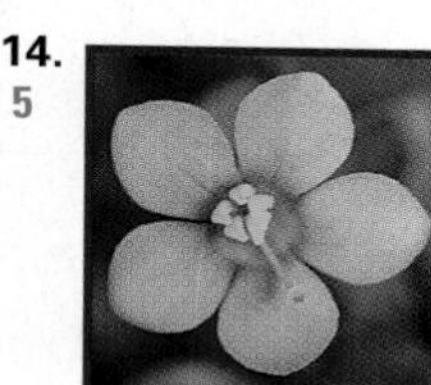

PRACTICE AND APPLICATIONS

STUDENT HELP

Extra Practice to help you master skills is on pp. 815 and 816.

STUDENT HELP

HOMEWORK HELP

Example 1: Exs. 15–30
Example 2: Exs. 33–35
Example 3: Exs. 36–40
Example 4: Exs. 31, 32
Example 5: Exs. 44–46

DRAWING REFLECTIONS Trace the figure and draw its reflection in line *k*. 15–17. See margin.

15. 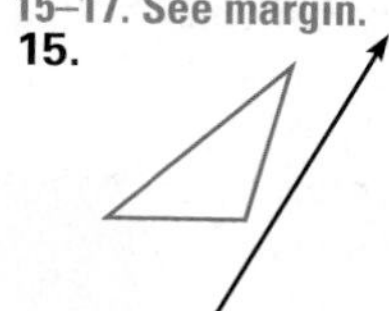

16. 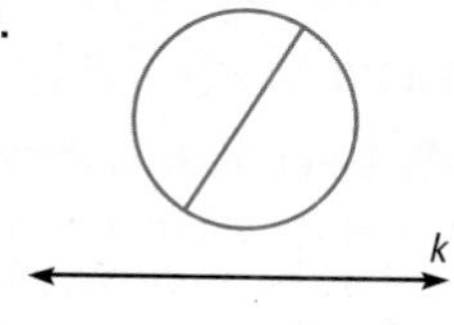

17. 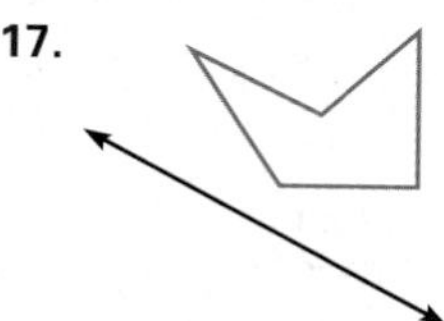

ANALYZING STATEMENTS Decide whether the conclusion is *true* or *false*. Explain your reasoning. 18–20. See margin.

18. If $N(2, 4)$ is reflected in the line $y = 2$, then N' is $(2, 0)$.

19. If $M(6, -2)$ is reflected in the line $x = 3$, then M' is $(0, -2)$.

20. If $W(-6, -3)$ is reflected in the line $y = -2$, then W' is $(-6, 1)$.

21. If $U(5, 3)$ is reflected in the line $x = 1$, then U' is $(-3, 3)$. True; U is 4 units to the right of the line $x = 1$, so its image is 4 units to the left of the line.

3 APPLY

ASSIGNMENT GUIDE

BASIC
Day 1: pp. 407–408 Exs. 15–35
Day 2: pp. 408–410 Exs. 36–46, 48–51, 57–71

AVERAGE
Day 1: pp. 407–408 Exs. 15–35
Day 2: pp. 408–410 Exs. 36–46, 48–51, 51–71

ADVANCED
Day 1: pp. 407–408 Exs. 15–35
Day 2: pp. 408–410 Exs. 36–46, 48–71

BLOCK SCHEDULE
pp. 407–410 Exs. 15–46, 48–51, 57–71

EXERCISE LEVELS

Level A: *Easier*
15–17

Level B: *More Difficult*
18–51

Level C: *Most Difficult*
52–56

✓ HOMEWORK CHECK

To quickly check student understanding of key concepts, go over the following exercises: Exs. 17, 20, 24, 28, 34, 38, 48. See also the Daily Homework Quiz:

- Blackline Master (*Chapter 7 Resource Book*, p. 39)
- Transparency (p. 50)

15–17. See Additional Answers beginning on page AA1.

MATHEMATICAL REASONING
EXERCISES 33–35 $\triangle ABC \cong \triangle A'B'C'$ and the midpoints of $\overline{AA'}$, $\overline{BB'}$, and $\overline{CC'}$ lie on line m. What kind of line is m?
a line of reflection

STUDENT HELP NOTES
Homework Help Students can find help for Exs. 37–40 at **www.mcdougallittell.com.** The information can be printed out for students who don't have access to the Internet.

31.

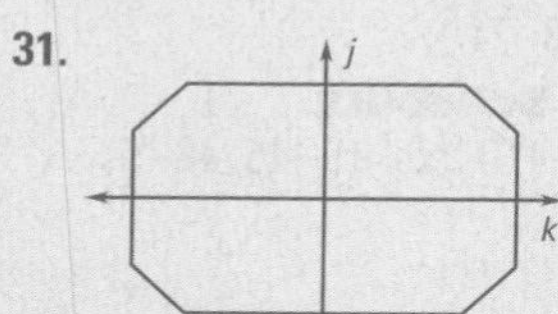

32.

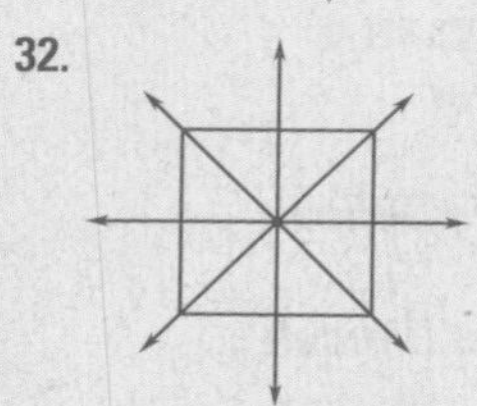

41. Each structure is a reflection of the other.
42. Triangle 2 is a reflection of triangle 1; triangle 3 is translation of triangle 1.
43. Triangles 2 and 3 are reflections of triangle 1; triangle 4 is rotation of triangle 1.

33. Draw $\overline{PP'}$ and $\overline{QQ'}$ intersecting line m at points S and T. By the def. of reflection, $\overline{P'S} \cong \overline{PS}$ and $\overline{RS} \perp \overline{PP'}$ and $\overline{Q'T} \cong \overline{QT}$ and $\overline{RT} \perp \overline{QQ'}$. It follows that $\triangle P'SR \cong \triangle PSR$ and $\triangle Q'TR \cong \triangle QTR$ by the SAS Congruence Postulate. Since corresp. parts of $\cong$ ▲ are $\cong$, $\overline{P'R} \cong \overline{PR}$ and $\overline{Q'R} \cong \overline{QR}$. So $P'R = PR$ and $Q'R = QR$. Since $P'Q' = P'R + Q'R$ and $PQ = PR + QR$ by the Segment Addition Postulate, we get by substitution $PQ = P'Q'$, or $\overline{PQ} \cong \overline{P'Q'}$.

34. P is on line m, so $P = P'$. Draw $\overline{QQ'}$ intersecting line m at point R. By the def. of reflection, $\overline{PR} \perp \overline{QQ'}$ and $\overline{RQ} \cong \overline{RQ'}$, so $\triangle PQR \cong \triangle PQ'R$ by the SAS Cong. Postulate. Then corresponding sides $\overline{PQ}$ and $\overline{PQ'}$ ($\overline{P'Q'}$) are cong.

35. Q is on line m, so $Q = Q'$. By the def. of reflection, $\overline{PQ} \cong \overline{P'Q}$ ($\overline{P'Q'}$).

36. Reflect H in line n to obtain its image, H'. Then draw $\overline{H'J}$. Let K be the point where $\overline{H'J}$ intersects line n.

STUDENT HELP

HOMEWORK HELP
Visit our Web site www.mcdougallittell.com for help with Exs. 37–40.

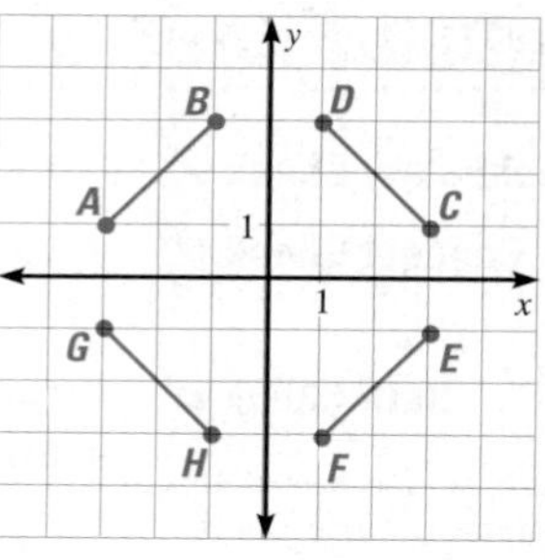

REFLECTIONS IN A COORDINATE PLANE **Use the diagram at the right to name the image of $\overline{AB}$ after the reflection.**

22. Reflection in the x-axis $\overline{GH}$

23. Reflection in the y-axis $\overline{CD}$

24. Reflection in the line $y = x$ $\overline{FE}$

25. Reflection in the y-axis, followed by a reflection in the x-axis. $\overline{EF}$

REFLECTIONS **In Exercises 26–29, find the coordinates of the reflection without using a coordinate plane. Then check your answer by plotting the image and preimage on a coordinate plane.**

26. $S(0, 2)$ reflected in the x-axis (0, −2)

27. $T(3, 8)$ reflected in the x-axis (3, −8)

28. $Q(-3, -3)$ reflected in the y-axis (3, −3)

29. $R(7, -2)$ reflected in the y-axis (−7, −2)

30. **CRITICAL THINKING** Draw a triangle on the coordinate plane and label its vertices. Then reflect the triangle in the line $y = x$. What do you notice about the coordinates of the vertices of the preimage and the image?
Check drawings; the coordinates of the image of (x, y) are (y, x).

LINES OF SYMMETRY **Sketch the figure, if possible.**

31. An octagon with exactly two lines of symmetry See margin.

32. A quadrilateral with exactly four lines of symmetry See margin.

PARAGRAPH PROOF **In Exercises 33–35, write a paragraph proof for each case of Theorem 7.1. (Refer to the diagrams on page 405.)**
33–35. See margin.

33. In Case 2, it is given that a reflection in m maps P onto P' and Q onto Q'. Also, $\overline{PQ}$ intersects m at point R.

PROVE ▶ $PQ = P'Q'$

34. In Case 3, it is given that a reflection in m maps P onto P' and Q onto Q'. Also, P lies on line m and $\overline{PQ}$ is not perpendicular to m.

PROVE ▶ $PQ = P'Q'$

35. In Case 4, it is given that a reflection in m maps P onto P' and Q onto Q'. Also, Q lies on line m and $\overline{PQ}$ is perpendicular to line m.

PROVE ▶ $PQ = P'Q'$

36. **DELIVERING PIZZA** You park your car at some point K on line n. You deliver a pizza to house H, go back to your car, and deliver a pizza to house J. Assuming that you cut across both lawns, explain how to estimate K so the distance that you travel is as small as possible.

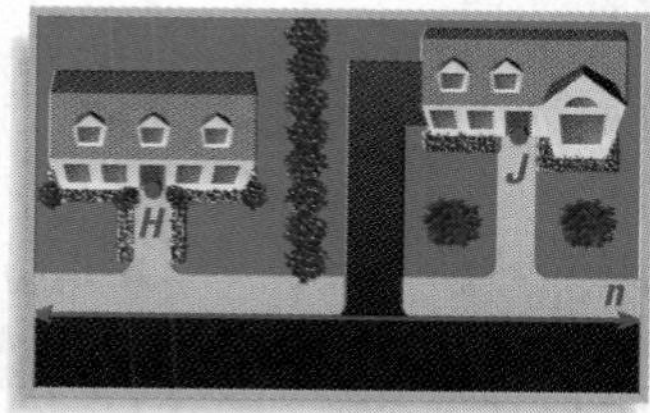

MINIMUM DISTANCE **Find point C on the x-axis so $AC + BC$ is a minimum.**

37. $A(1, 5)$, $B(7, 1)$ (6, 0)

38. $A(2, -2)$, $B(11, -4)$ (5, 0)

39. $A(-1, 4)$, $B(6, 3)$ (3, 0)

40. $A(-4, 6)$, $B(3.5, 9)$ (−1, 0)

FOCUS ON CAREERS

CHEMIST Some chemists study the molecular structure of living things. The research done by these chemists has led to important discoveries in the field of medicine.

CAREER LINK
www.mcdougallittell.com

41. CHEMISTRY CONNECTION The figures at the right show two versions of the carvone molecule. One version is oil of spearmint and the other is caraway. How are the structures of these two molecules related? **See margin.**

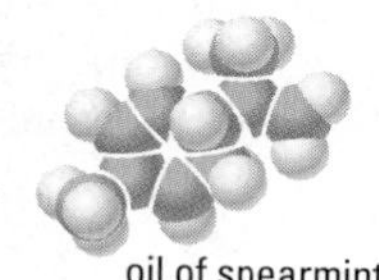
oil of spearmint

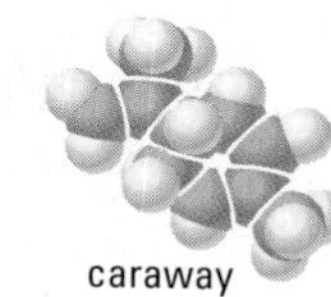
caraway

42. **PAPER FOLDING** Fold a piece of paper and label it as shown. Cut a scalene triangle out of the folded paper and unfold the paper. How are triangle 2 and triangle 3 related to triangle 1? **See margin.**

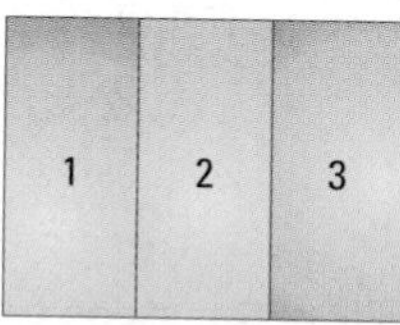

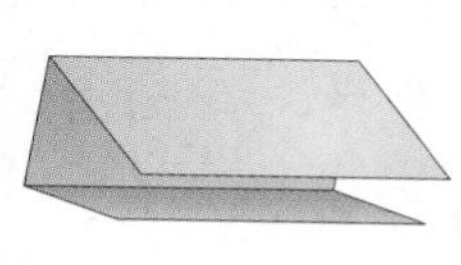

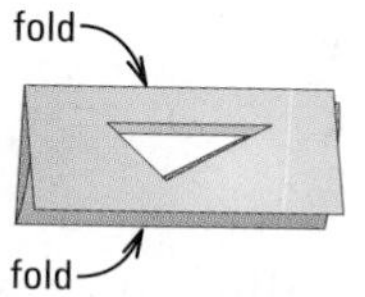

43. **PAPER FOLDING** Fold a piece of paper and label it as shown. Cut a scalene triangle out of the folded paper and unfold the paper. How are triangles 2, 3, and 4 related to triangle 1? **See margin.**

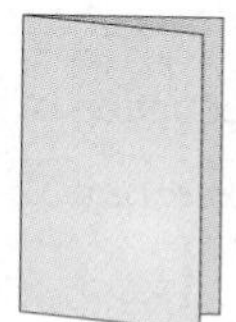

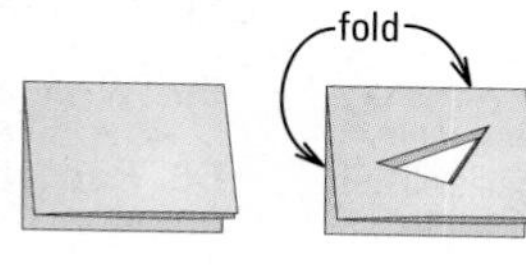

KALEIDOSCOPES In Exercises 44–46, calculate the angle at which the mirrors must be placed for the image of a kaleidoscope to resemble the given design. (Use the formula in Example 5 on page 406.)

44. 45°

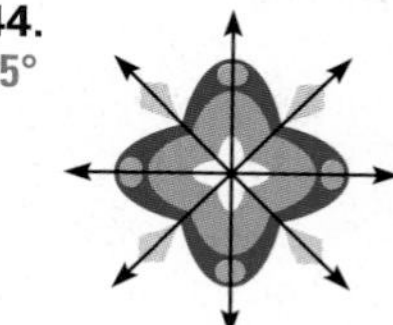

45. 90°

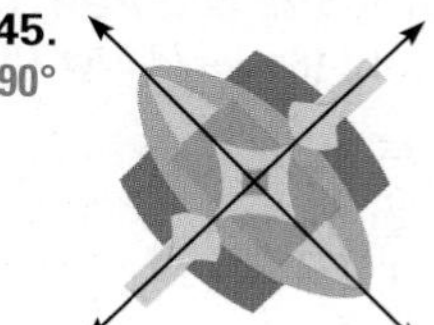

46. 60°

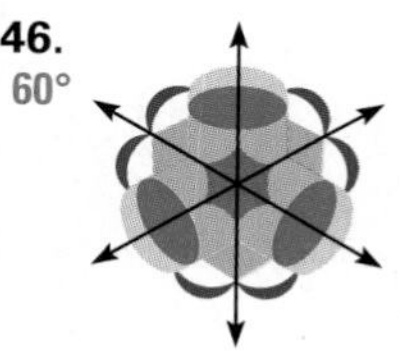

47. The distance between each vertex of the preimage and line m is equal to the distance between the corresponding vertex of the image and line m.

47. **TECHNOLOGY** Use geometry software to draw a polygon reflected in line m. Connect the corresponding vertices of the preimage and image. Measure the distance between each vertex and line m. What do you notice about these measures?

USING ALGEBRA Find the value of each variable, given that the diagram shows a reflection in a line.

48.

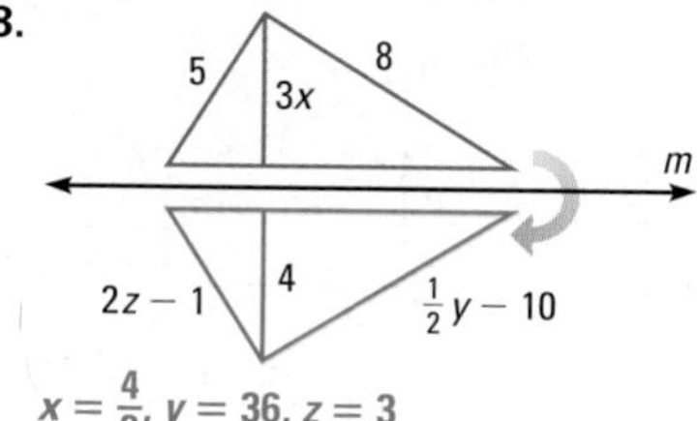

$x = \frac{4}{3}$, $y = 36$, $z = 3$

49.

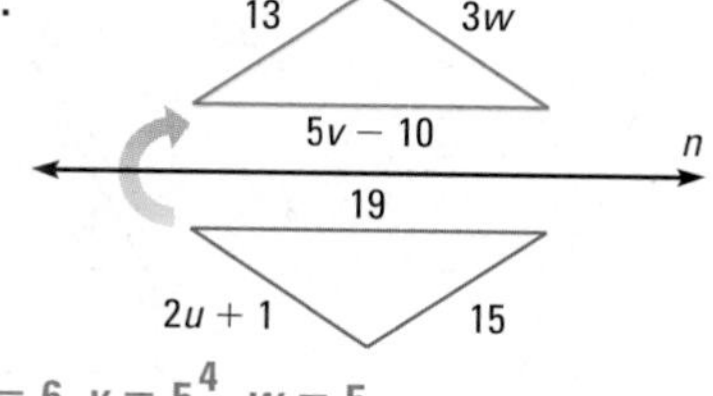

$u = 6$, $v = 5\frac{4}{5}$, $w = 5$

APPLICATION NOTE

EXERCISE 41 Electron pairs reside in the outer shell of a central atom. Because the pairs are oppositely charged, they are positioned as far as possible from each other. Thus the angles at which the central atom bonds with the surrounding atoms in the molecule depends upon the outer shell positions of the electron pairs.

CAREER NOTE

EXERCISE 41 Additional information about chemists is available at **www.mcdougallittell.com.**

APPLICATION NOTE

EXERCISES 44–46 In the kaleidoscopes described in these exercises, light enters the tube from the nonviewing end. As the light rays are incident on the mirrors, they bounce off at angles equal to the angle of incidence until they reach the eye. Colored glass, beads, plastic, or oil and water mixtures in the tube create changing patterns when the tube is rotated.

ADDITIONAL PRACTICE AND RETEACHING

For Lesson 7.2:

- Practice Levels A, B, and C (*Chapter 7 Resource Book,* p. 29)
- Reteaching with Practice (*Chapter 7 Resource Book,* p. 32)
- See Lesson 7.2 of the *Personal Student Tutor*

For more Mixed Review:

- Search the *Test and Practice Generator* for key words or specific lessons.

4 ASSESS

DAILY HOMEWORK QUIZ

Transparency Available

1. Find the coordinates of $A(3, 2)$ reflected in the line $y = 1$. **$A'(3, 0)$**
2. Find the coordinates of $B(-2, 4)$ reflected in the y-axis. **$B'(2, 4)$**
3. Sketch a hexagon with exactly two lines of symmetry. **Check drawings.**
4. Given $A(1, -2)$, $B(6, -3)$ find point C on the x-axis so that $AC + BC$ is a minimum. **(3, 0)**

EXTRA CHALLENGE NOTE

Challenge problems for Lesson 7.2 are available in **blackline** format in the *Chapter 7 Resource Book,* p. 36 and at **www.mcdougallittell.com.**

ADDITIONAL TEST PREPARATION

1. **OPEN ENDED** Find four capital letters that have vertical symmetry, four that have horizontal symmetry, and four that have both vertical and horizontal symmetry.
vertical: A, H, I, M, O, T, U, V, W, X, Y; horizontal: B, C, D, E, H, I, K, O, X; both: H, I, O, X
2. **WRITING** Explain what happens to the orientation of a polygon when it is reflected on a line.
***Sample answer:* The orientation changes. For example, if the vertices of $\triangle ABC$ are labeled in a counterclockwise direction, the vertices of its image, $\triangle A'B'C'$ will be labeled in a clockwise position.**

Test Preparation

50. **MULTIPLE CHOICE** A piece of paper is folded in half and some cuts are made, as shown. Which figure represents the piece of paper unfolded? **B**

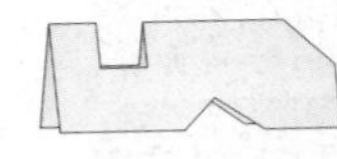

Ⓐ 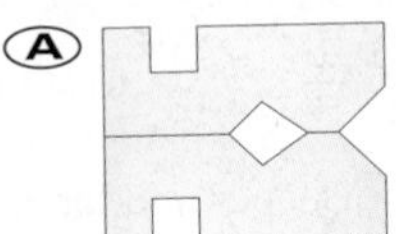 Ⓑ 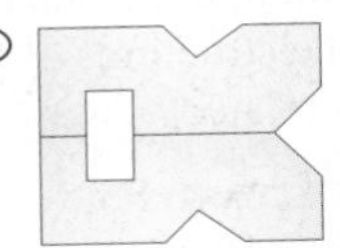 Ⓒ 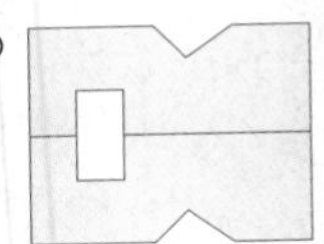 Ⓓ 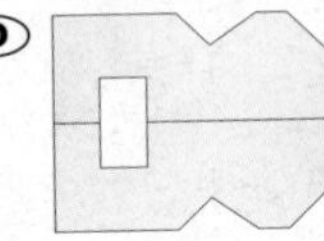

51. **MULTIPLE CHOICE** How many lines of symmetry does the figure at the right have? **B**

Ⓐ 0 Ⓑ 1 Ⓒ 2
Ⓓ 3 Ⓔ 6

★ Challenge

56. (52) **Check drawings.**
(53) $Q\left(\frac{1}{2}, \frac{1}{2}\right)$
(54) -1; 1
(55) $y = x$

EXTRA CHALLENGE
www.mcdougallittell.com

WRITING AN EQUATION Follow the steps to write an equation for the line of reflection.

52. Graph $R(2, 1)$ and $R'(-2, -1)$. Draw a segment connecting the two points. **Check drawings.**
53. Find the midpoint of $\overline{RR'}$ and name it Q. **$Q(0, 0)$**
54. Find the slope of $\overline{RR'}$. Then write the slope of a line perpendicular to $\overline{RR'}$. **$\frac{1}{2}$; -2**
55. Write an equation of the line that is perpendicular to $\overline{RR'}$ and passes through Q. **$y = -2x$**
56. Repeat Exercises 52–55 using $R(-2, 3)$ and $R'(3, -2)$. **See margin.**

MIXED REVIEW

CONGRUENT TRIANGLES Use the diagram, in which $\triangle ABC \cong \triangle PQR$, to complete the statement. (Review 4.2 for 7.3)

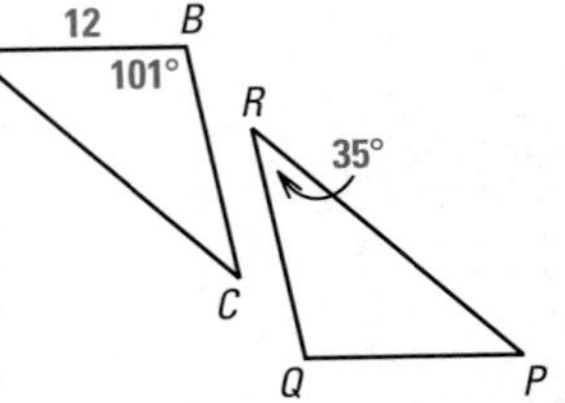

57. $\angle A \cong$ __?__ **$\angle P$**
58. $PQ =$ __?__ **12**
59. $\overline{QR} \cong$ __?__ **$\overline{BC}$**
60. $m\angle C =$ __?__ **35°**
61. $m\angle Q =$ __?__ **101°**
62. $\angle R \cong$ __?__ **$\angle C$**

FINDING SIDE LENGTHS OF A TRIANGLE Two side lengths of a triangle are given. Describe the length of the third side, c, with an inequality. (Review 5.5)

63. $a = 7, b = 17$ **$10 < c < 24$**
64. $a = 9, b = 21$ **$12 < c < 30$**
65. $a = 12, b = 33$ **$21 < c < 45$**
66. $a = 26, b = 6$ **$20 < c < 32$**
67. $a = 41.2, b = 15.5$ **$25.7 < c < 56.7$**
68. $a = 7.1, b = 11.9$ **$4.8 < c < 19$**

FINDING ANGLE MEASURES Find the angle measures of *ABCD*. (Review 6.5)

69. 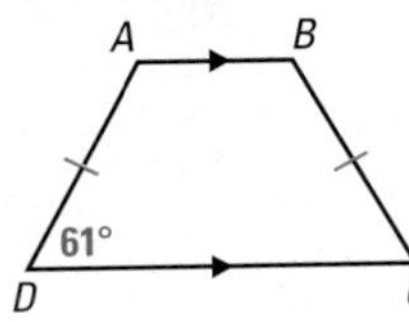

$m\angle A = m\angle B = 119°$, $m\angle C = 61°$

70. 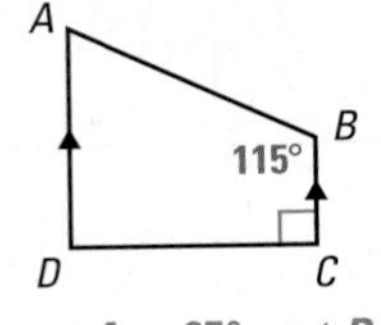

$m\angle A = 65°$, $m\angle D = 90°$

71. 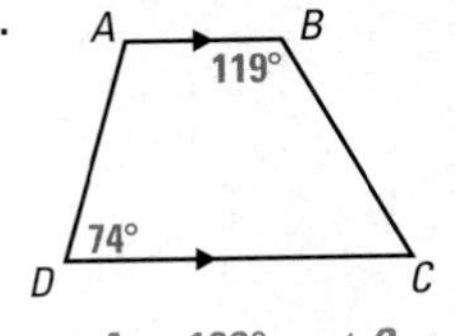

$m\angle A = 106°$, $m\angle C = 61°$

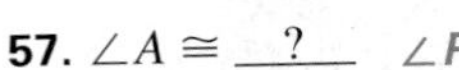

Investigating Double Reflections

You can use geometry software to discover the type of transformation that results when a triangle is reflected twice in the plane.

SOFTWARE HELP

Visit our Web site www.mcdougallittell.com to see instructions for several software applications.

▶ CONSTRUCT Steps 1–3. Check drawings.

1. Draw a scalene triangle similar to the one at the right. Label the vertices *A*, *B*, and *C*.
2. Draw two lines that intersect. Label the lines *k* and *m*. Make sure that the lines do not intersect the triangle.
3. Label the point of intersection of lines *k* and *m* as *P*.

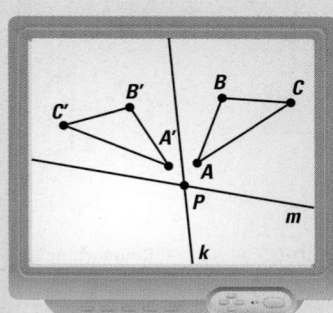

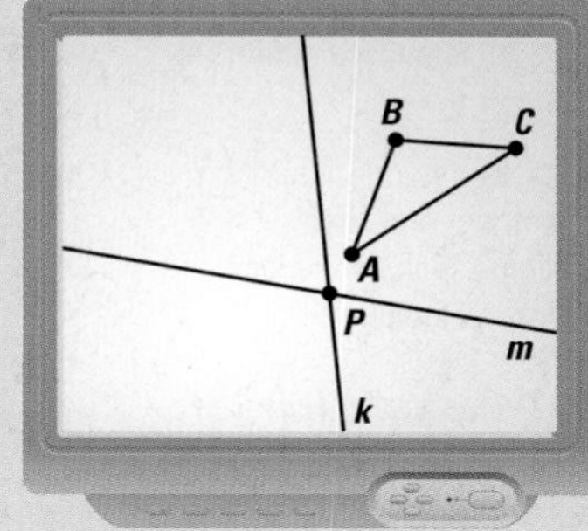

▶ INVESTIGATE

1. Reflect $\triangle ABC$ in line *k* to obtain $\triangle A'B'C'$. Reflect $\triangle A'B'C'$ in line *m* to obtain $\triangle A''B''C''$. How is $\triangle ABC$ related to $\triangle A''B''C''$? $\triangle ABC \cong \triangle A''B''C''$

▶ MAKE A CONJECTURE

2. What other transformation maps a figure onto the same image as a reflection in two intersecting lines? a rotation about the point of intersection of the lines

▶ INVESTIGATE

3. Draw segments connecting points *A* and *P* and points A'' and *P*. Measure $\angle APA''$. This angle is an example of an *angle of rotation*. Answers will vary.
4. Measure the acute angle formed by lines *k* and *m*. Compare this measure to the measure of $\angle APA''$. The measure of the angle is half the measure of $\angle APA''$.
5. Find the measures of $\angle BPB''$ and $\angle CPC''$. What do you notice? $m\angle BPB'' = m\angle CPC'' =$ twice the measure of the acute angle formed by lines *m* and *k*

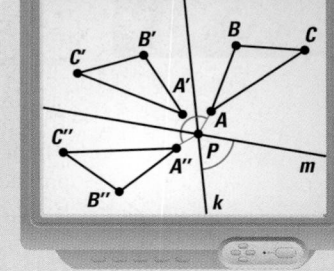

▶ MAKE A CONJECTURE

6. In the reflection of a figure in two intersecting lines, what is the relationship between the acute angle formed by the two lines and the angle of rotation? The measure of the angle of rotation is twice the measure of the acute angle formed by the two lines.

EXTENSION

Repeat **Steps 1–3** using a different scalene triangle. Is the conjecture that you made in Exercise 6 correct? Yes.

Activity Assessment *Sample answer:*
As the angle's measure increases, the angle of rotation also increases. As the angle's measure decreases, the angle of rotation also decreases.

1 Planning the Activity

PURPOSE
To use geometry software to investigate the resulting transformation when a triangle is reflected twice in the plane.

MATERIALS
- Geometry software
- Software Help (*Chapter 7 Resource Book,* p. 41)

PACING
- Exploring the Concept — 15 min
- Make a Conjecture — 15 min

LINK TO LESSON
Students should recall the results of this activity when studying Theorem 7.3 and Example 3 on page 414.

2 Managing the Activity

ALTERNATIVE APPROACH
Have students draw the triangles using graph paper with the coordinate axes as the reflection lines.

COOPERATIVE LEARNING
Have students work in groups of four. Two students should manipulate the software while the other two complete the reflections using graph paper. Ask them to compare their results before making the conjecture.

3 Closing the Activity

KEY DISCOVERY
The acute angle formed by the intersecting lines in a double reflection is half the angle of rotation.

ACTIVITY ASSESSMENT
JOURNAL Describe the effects of changing the measure of the angle formed by the intersection of lines *m* and *k*.
See sample answer at left.

1 PLAN

PACING
Basic: 2 days
Average: 2 days
Advanced: 2 days
Block Schedule: 1 block

LESSON OPENER ACTIVITY
An alternative way to approach Lesson 7.3 is to use the Activity Lesson Opener:
- Blackline Master (*Chapter 7 Resource Book*, p. 40)
- Transparency (p. 43)

MEETING INDIVIDUAL NEEDS
- ***Chapter 7 Resource Book***
  Prerequisite Skills Review (p. 5)
  Practice Level A (p. 43)
  Practice Level B (p. 44)
  Practice Level C (p. 45)
  Reteaching with Practice (p. 46)
  Absent Student Catch-Up (p. 48)
  Challenge (p. 51)
- ***Resources in Spanish***
- ***Personal Student Tutor***

NEW-TEACHER SUPPORT
See the Tips for New Teachers on pp. 1–2 of the *Chapter 7 Resource Book* for additional notes about Lesson 7.3.

WARM-UP EXERCISES

Transparency Available

State the definition, theorem, or postulate that justifies each statement.

1. If $\angle ABC \cong \angle A'B'C'$, $\overline{AB} \cong \overline{A'B'}$, and $\overline{BC} \cong \overline{B'C'}$, then $\triangle ABC \cong \triangle A'B'C'$. SAS
2. If $3x + 10 = 15$, then $3x = 5$. subtraction property of equality

Find the measure of a counterclockwise rotation that would equal each rotation.

3. 180° clockwise rotation 180°
4. 90° clockwise rotation 270°

7.3 Rotations

What you should learn

GOAL 1 Identify rotations in a plane.

GOAL 2 Use rotational symmetry in **real-life** situations, such as the logo designs in **Example 5**.

Why you should learn it

▼ Rotations and rotational symmetry can be used to create a design, as in the wheel hubs below and in **Exs. 36–38**.

GOAL 1 USING ROTATIONS

A **rotation** is a transformation in which a figure is turned about a fixed point. The fixed point is the **center of rotation**. Rays drawn from the center of rotation to a point and its image form an angle called the **angle of rotation**.

A rotation about a point P through x degrees ($x°$) is a transformation that maps every point Q in the plane to a point Q', so that the following properties are true:

1. If Q is not point P, then $QP = Q'P$ and $m\angle QPQ' = x°$.
2. If Q is point P, then $Q = Q'$.

Rotations can be clockwise or counterclockwise, as shown below.

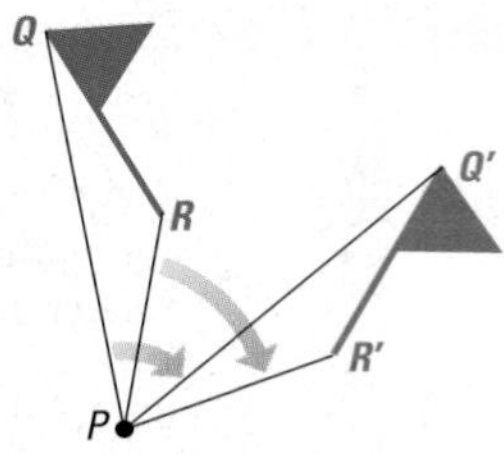

Clockwise rotation of 60°

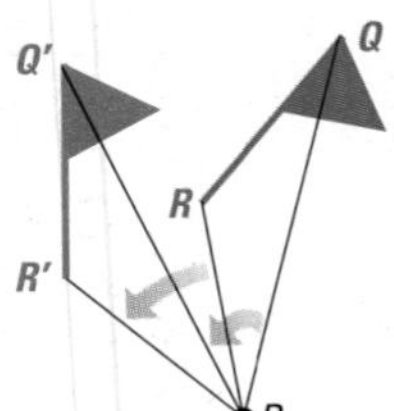

Counterclockwise rotation of 40°

THEOREM

THEOREM 7.2 ***Rotation Theorem***

A rotation is an isometry.

To prove the Rotation Theorem, you need to show that a rotation preserves the length of a segment. Consider a segment $\overline{QR}$ that is rotated about a point P to produce $\overline{Q'R'}$. The three cases are shown below. The first case is proved in Example 1.

CASE 1

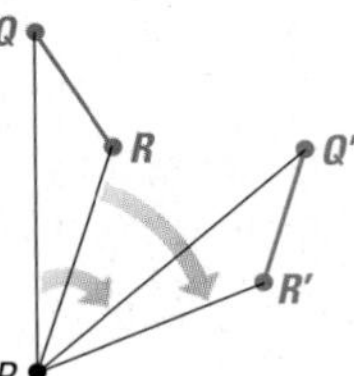

R, Q, and *P* are noncollinear.

CASE 2

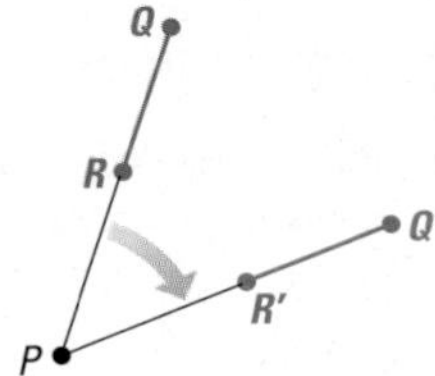

R, Q, and *P* are collinear.

CASE 3

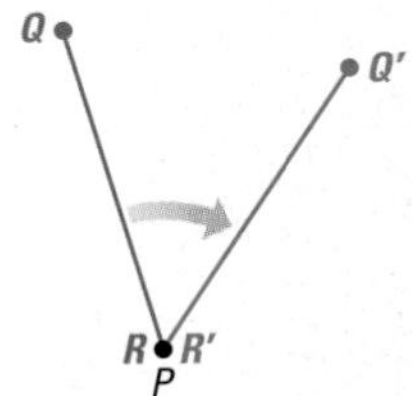

P and *R* are the same point.

CALIFORNIA STANDARDS AND ASSESSMENT

CA Standards: 16, 17, 22
SAT9 Task 1: Obj. 31
SAT9 Task 2: Obj. 34

EXAMPLE 1 Proof of Theorem 7.2

Write a paragraph proof for Case 1 of the Rotation Theorem.

GIVEN ▶ A rotation about P maps Q onto Q' and R onto R'.

PROVE ▶ $\overline{QR} \cong \overline{Q'R'}$

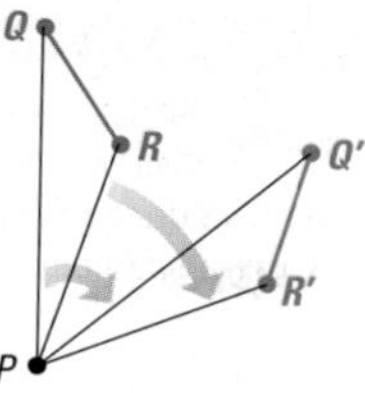

SOLUTION

Paragraph Proof By the definition of a rotation, $PQ = PQ'$ and $PR = PR'$. Also, by the definition of a rotation, $m\angle QPQ' = m\angle RPR'$.

You can use the Angle Addition Postulate and the subtraction property of equality to conclude that $m\angle QPR = m\angle Q'PR'$. This allows you to use the SAS Congruence Postulate to conclude that $\triangle QPR \cong \triangle Q'PR'$. Because corresponding parts of congruent triangles are congruent, $\overline{QR} \cong \overline{Q'R'}$.

STUDENT HELP

Look Back
For help with using a protractor, see p. 27.

You can use a compass and a protractor to help you find the images of a polygon after a rotation. The following construction shows you how.

ACTIVITY Construction

Rotating a Figure

Use the following steps to draw the image of $\triangle ABC$ after a 120° counterclockwise rotation about point P. Steps 1–4. Check drawings.

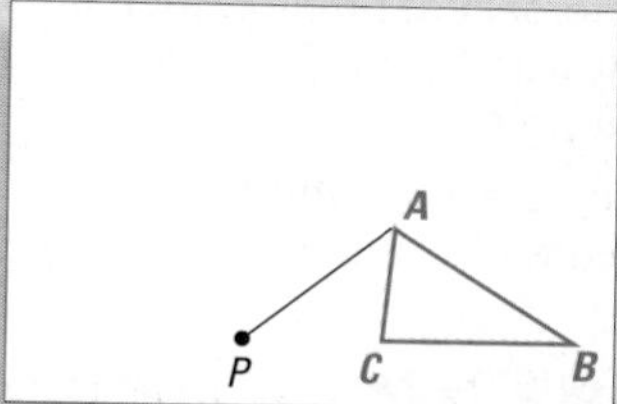

❶ Draw a segment connecting vertex A and the center of rotation point P.

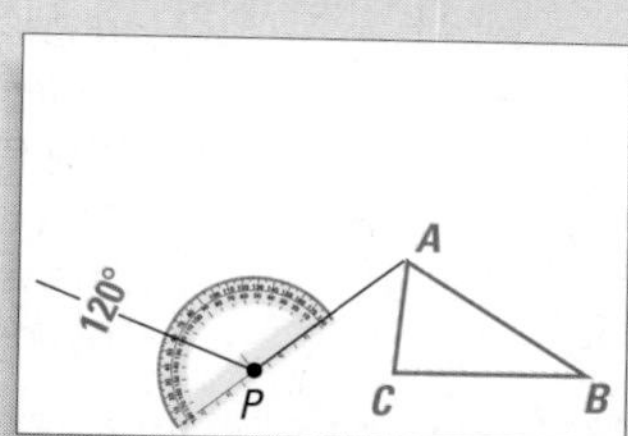

❷ Use a protractor to measure a 120° angle counterclockwise and draw a ray.

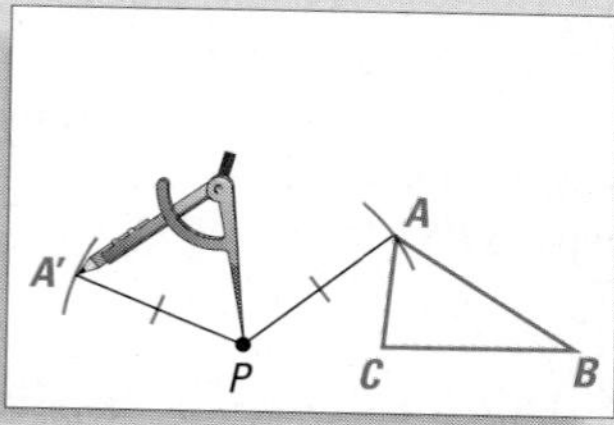

❸ Place the point of the compass at P and draw an arc from A to locate A'.

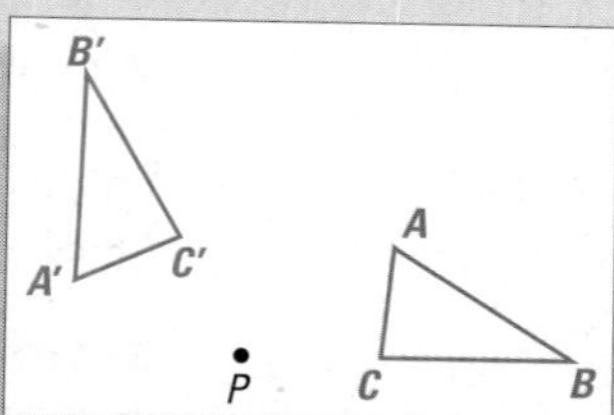

❹ Repeat **Steps 1–3** for each vertex. Connect the vertices to form the image.

2 TEACH

MOTIVATING THE LESSON
Suppose you have a multi-disc compact disk player which holds disks in a circular arrangement. The tray holding the disks is rotated each time a new disk is selected for play. This is an example of a rotation about a point in a plane.

ACTIVITY NOTE
Manipulatives Make sure that students understand that the center of the angle they draw in Step 2 is at P.

EXTRA EXAMPLE 1
Write a paragraph proof.

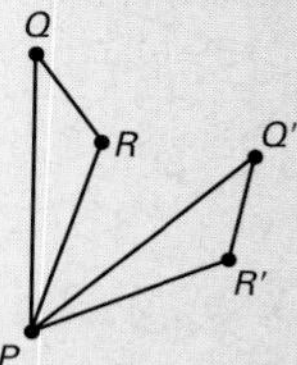

Given: A rotation about P maps Q onto Q' and R onto R'.
Prove: $\angle Q \cong \angle Q'$
See below.

CHECKPOINT EXERCISES
For use after Example 1:
1. Write a paragraph proof.

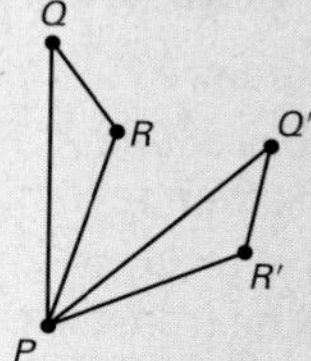

Given: A rotation about P maps Q onto Q' and R onto R'.
Prove: $m\angle PR'R = m\angle PRR'$
By the definition of rotation, $PR = PR'$. Therefore, by the Base Angles Theorem, $m\angle PR'R = m\angle PRR'$.

STUDENT HELP NOTES
Look Back As students look back to page 27, remind them that they can use a protractor to measure from either ray of an angle.

Extra Example 1 *Sample answer:*
By the definition of rotation, $PQ = PQ'$ and $PR = PR'$. From the definition of congruent segments, $QR = Q'R'$. Therefore, by the SSS Congruence Postulate and the Base Angles Theorem, $\triangle PQR \cong \triangle PQ'R'$. Since corresponding parts of congruent triangles are congruent, it follows that $\angle Q \cong \angle Q'$.

EXTRA EXAMPLE 2

A quadrilateral has vertices $P(3, -1)$, $Q(4, 0)$, $R(4, 3)$, and $S(2, 4)$. Rotate $PQRS$ 180° counterclockwise about (0, 0) and name the coordinates of the new vertices. $P'(-3, 1)$, $Q'(-4, 0)$, $R'(-4, -3)$, and $S'(-2, -4)$

EXTRA EXAMPLE 3

$\triangle JKL$ is reflected in line k to produce $\triangle J'K'L'$. This triangle is then reflected in the line m to produce $\triangle J''K''L''$. Describe the transformation that maps $\triangle JKL$ to $\triangle J''K''L''$.

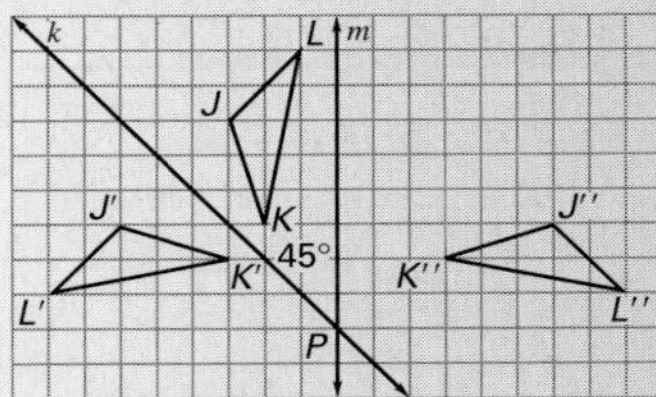

a clockwise rotation of 90°

CHECKPOINT EXERCISES

For use after Example 2:

1. $\triangle RST$ has coordinates $R(-2, 3)$, $S(0, 4)$, and $T(3, 1)$. If $\triangle RST$ is rotated 90° clockwise about the origin, what are the coordinates of the new vertices? $R'(3, 2)$, $S'(4, 0)$, $T'(1, -3)$

For use after Example 3:

2. In the diagram, $\overline{XY}$ is reflected in line p to produce $\overline{X'Y'}$. This segment is then reflected in the line q to produce $\overline{X''Y''}$. Describe the transformation that maps $\overline{XY}$ to $\overline{X''Y''}$.

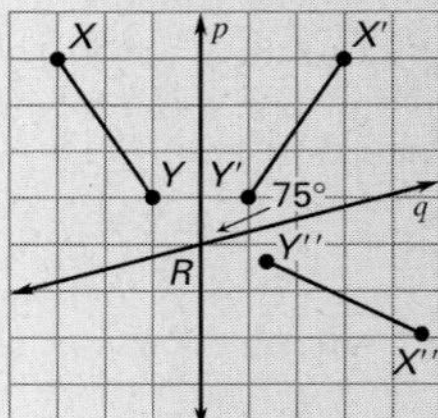

a clockwise rotation of 150°

STUDENT HELP

INTERNET HOMEWORK HELP
Visit our Web site www.mcdougallittell.com for extra examples.

EXAMPLE 2 Rotations in a Coordinate Plane

In a coordinate plane, sketch the quadrilateral whose vertices are $A(2, -2)$, $B(4, 1)$, $C(5, 1)$, and $D(5, -1)$. Then, rotate $ABCD$ 90° counterclockwise about the origin and name the coordinates of the new vertices. Describe any patterns you see in the coordinates.

SOLUTION

Plot the points, as shown in blue. Use a protractor, a compass, and a straightedge to find the rotated vertices. The coordinates of the preimage and image are listed below.

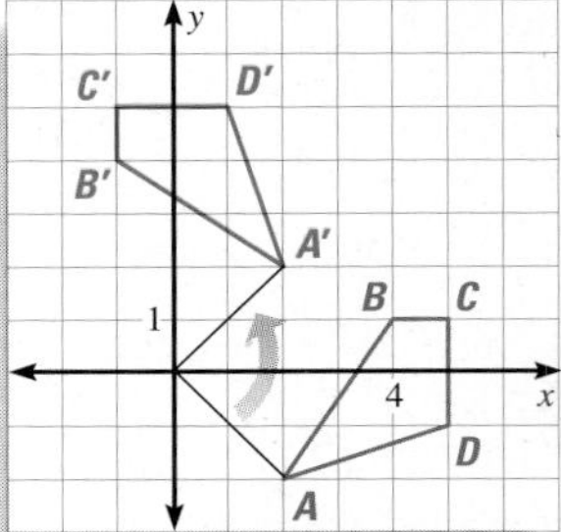

Figure $ABCD$	Figure $A'B'C'D'$
$A(2, -2)$	$A'(2, 2)$
$B(4, 1)$	$B'(-1, 4)$
$C(5, 1)$	$C'(-1, 5)$
$D(5, -1)$	$D'(1, 5)$

In the list above, the x-coordinate of the image is the opposite of the y-coordinate of the preimage. The y-coordinate of the image is the x-coordinate of the preimage.

▶ This transformation can be described as $(x, y) \rightarrow (-y, x)$.

THEOREM

THEOREM 7.3

If lines k and m intersect at point P, then a reflection in k followed by a reflection in m is a rotation about point P.

The angle of rotation is $2x°$, where $x°$ is the measure of the acute or right angle formed by k and m.

$$m\angle BPB'' = 2x°$$

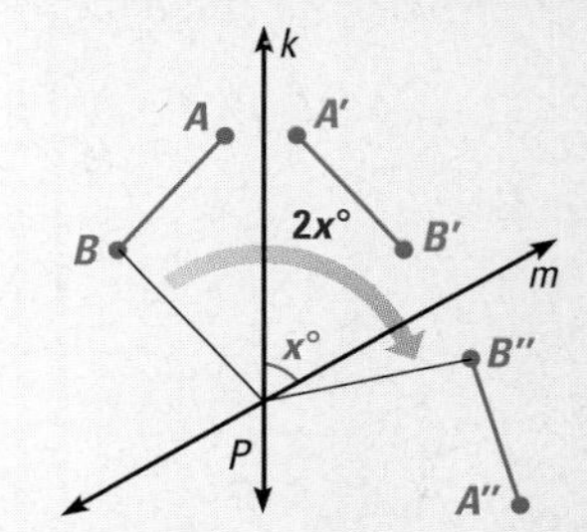

EXAMPLE 3 Using Theorem 7.3

In the diagram, $\triangle RST$ is reflected in line k to produce $\triangle R'S'T'$. This triangle is then reflected in line m to produce $\triangle R''S''T''$. Describe the transformation that maps $\triangle RST$ to $\triangle R''S''T''$.

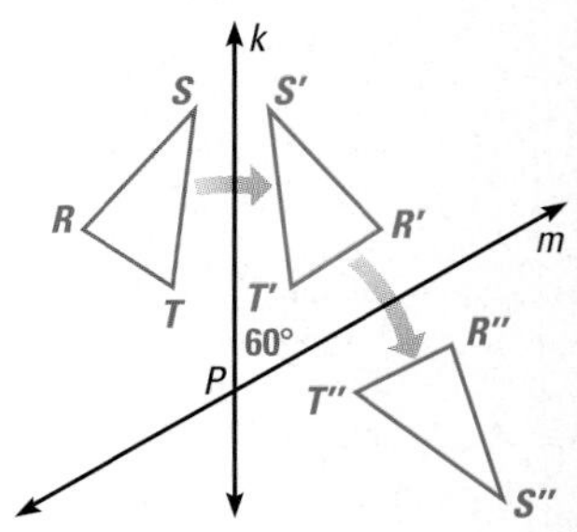

SOLUTION

The acute angle between lines k and m has a measure of 60°. Applying Theorem 7.3 you can conclude that the transformation that maps $\triangle RST$ to $\triangle R''S''T''$ is a clockwise rotation of 120° about point P.

GOAL 2 ROTATIONS AND ROTATIONAL SYMMETRY

A figure in the plane has **rotational symmetry** if the figure can be mapped onto itself by a rotation of 180° or less. For instance, a square has rotational symmetry because it maps onto itself by a rotation of 90°.

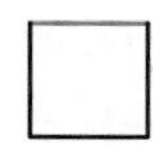
0° rotation

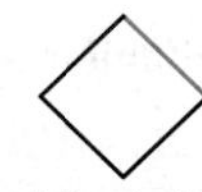
45° rotation

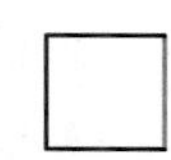
90° rotation

EXAMPLE 4 *Identifying Rotational Symmetry*

Which figures have rotational symmetry? For those that do, describe the rotations that map the figure onto itself.

a. Regular octagon

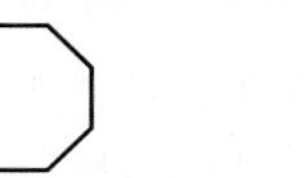

b. Parallelogram

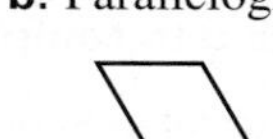
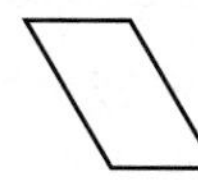

c. Trapezoid

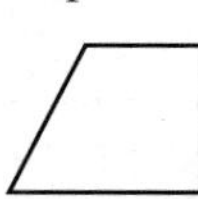

SOLUTION

a. This octagon has rotational symmetry. It can be mapped onto itself by a clockwise or counterclockwise rotation of 45°, 90°, 135°, or 180° about its center.

b. This parallelogram has rotational symmetry. It can be mapped onto itself by a clockwise or counterclockwise rotation of 180° about its center.

c. The trapezoid does not have rotational symmetry.

EXAMPLE 5 *Using Rotational Symmetry*

LOGO DESIGN A music store called Ozone is running a contest for a store logo. The winning logo will be displayed on signs throughout the store and in the store's advertisements. The only requirement is that the logo include the store's name. Two of the entries are shown below. What do you notice about them?

a. ozone

b. OZONE

SOLUTION

a. This design has rotational symmetry about its center. It can be mapped onto itself by a clockwise or counterclockwise rotation of 180°.

b. This design also has rotational symmetry about its center. It can be mapped onto itself by a clockwise or counterclockwise rotation of 90° or 180°.

FOCUS ON CAREERS

LOGO DESIGNERS create symbols that represent the name of a company or organization. The logos appear on packaging, letterheads, and Web sites.

CAREER LINK
www.mcdougallittell.com

EXTRA EXAMPLE 4

Which figures have rotational symmetry? For those that do, describe the rotations that map the figure onto itself.

a.

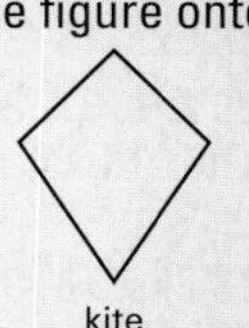
kite

b.

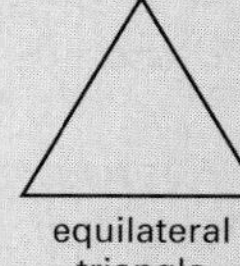
equilateral triangle

b; The equilateral triangle has rotational symmetry. It can be mapped onto itself by a clockwise or counterclockwise rotation of 60° or 120° about its center.

EXTRA EXAMPLE 5

Explain how the design can be mapped onto itself by a rotation.

a.

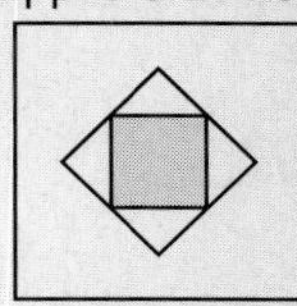

b.

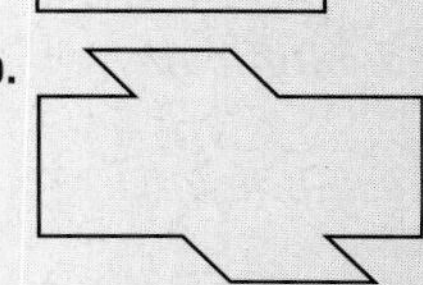

Design (a) can be mapped onto itself by a clockwise or counterclockwise rotation of 90° or 180° about its center. Design (b) can be mapped onto itself by a clockwise or counterclockwise rotation of 180° about its center.

CHECKPOINT EXERCISES

For use after Examples 4 and 5:

1. Do the initials **SHS** have rotation symmetry? If so, explain how the design can be mapped onto itself by a rotation. Yes; SHS can be mapped onto itself by a clockwise or counterclockwise rotation of 180°.

CLOSURE QUESTION

Lines m and n intersect at Q to form a 30° angle. If a pentagon is reflected in m, then in n about point Q, what is the angle of rotation of the pentagon? 60°

3 APPLY

ASSIGNMENT GUIDE

BASIC
Day 1: pp. 416–418 Exs. 13–30
Day 2: pp. 418–420 Exs. 31–38, 43, 45–54 Quiz 1 Exs. 1–8

AVERAGE
Day 1: pp. 416–418 Exs. 13–30
Day 2: pp. 418–420 Exs. 31–43, 45–54, Quiz 1 Exs. 1–8

ADVANCED
Day 1: pp. 416–418 Exs. 13–30
Day 2: pp. 418–420 Exs. 31–54, Quiz 1 Exs. 1–8

BLOCK SCHEDULE
pp. 416–420 Exs. 13–43, 45–54, Quiz 1 Exs. 1–8

EXERCISE LEVELS

Level A: ***Easier***
13–19

Level B: ***More Difficult***
20–43

Level C: ***Most Difficult***
44

✔ HOMEWORK CHECK

To quickly check student understanding of key concepts, go over the following exercises: Exs. 16, 20, 22, 26, 30, 32, 34. See also the Daily Homework Quiz:

- Blackline Master (*Chapter 7 Resource Book*, p. 55)
- Transparency (p. 51)

GUIDED PRACTICE

Vocabulary Check ✔

1. What is a *center of rotation*?
the fixed point about which a figure being rotated is turned

Concept Check ✔

Use the diagram, in which $\triangle ABC$ is mapped onto $\triangle A'B'C'$ by a rotation of 90° about the origin.

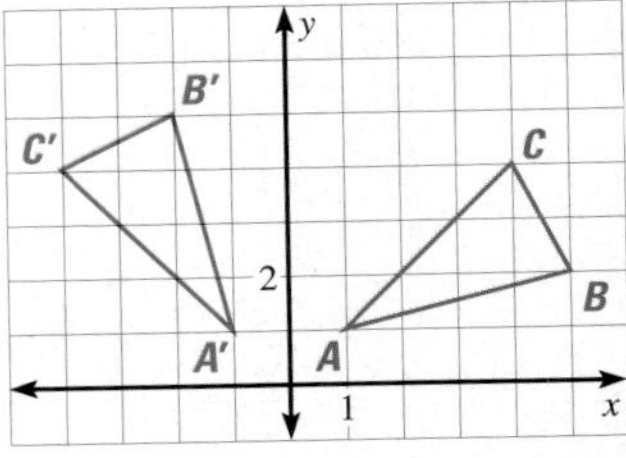

2. Is the rotation clockwise or counterclockwise?
counterclockwise

3. Does $AB = A'B'$? Explain.
Yes; a rotation is an isometry.

4. Does $AA' = BB'$? Explain.

4. No; the distance between any point and its image after a rotation is not fixed.

5. If the rotation of $\triangle ABC$ onto $\triangle A'B'C'$ was obtained by a reflection of $\triangle ABC$ in some line k followed by a reflection in some line m, what would be the measure of the acute angle between lines k and m? Explain. See margin.

5. 45°; *Sample answer:* $m\angle AOA' = 90°$, which is the measure of the angle of rotation. The measure of the acute or right angle formed by k and m is equal to one-half the measure of the angle of rotation.

Skill Check ✔

The diagonals of the regular hexagon below form six equilateral triangles. Use the diagram to complete the sentence.

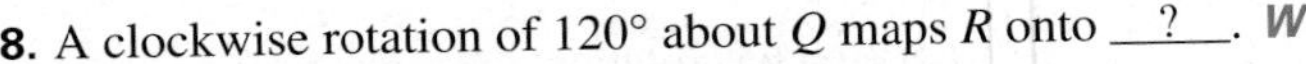

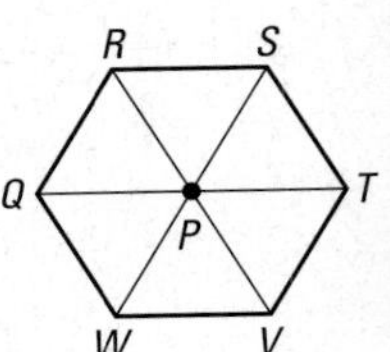

6. A clockwise rotation of 60° about P maps R onto ___?___. S

7. A counterclockwise rotation of 60° about ___?___ maps R onto Q. P

8. A clockwise rotation of 120° about Q maps R onto ___?___. W

9. A counterclockwise rotation of 180° about P maps V onto ___?___. R

Determine whether the figure has rotational symmetry. If so, describe the rotations that map the figure onto itself.

10.

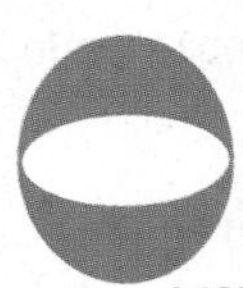

yes; a rotation of 180° clockwise or counterclockwise about its center

11.

yes; a rotation of 180° clockwise or counterclockwise about its center

12.

no

PRACTICE AND APPLICATIONS

STUDENT HELP

Extra Practice to help you master skills is on p. 816.

DESCRIBING AN IMAGE **State the segment or triangle that represents the image. You can use tracing paper to help you visualize the rotation.**

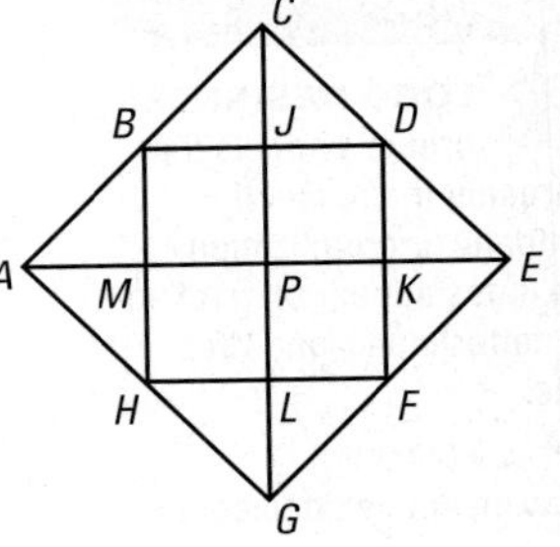

13. 90° clockwise rotation of $\overline{AB}$ about P $\overline{CD}$

14. 90° clockwise rotation of $\overline{KF}$ about P $\overline{LH}$

15. 90° counterclockwise rotation of $\overline{CE}$ about E $\overline{GE}$

16. 90° counterclockwise rotation of $\overline{FL}$ about H $\overline{BM}$

17. 180° rotation of $\triangle KEF$ about P $\triangle MAB$

18. 180° rotation of $\triangle BCJ$ about P $\triangle FGL$

19. 90° clockwise rotation of $\triangle APG$ about P $\triangle CPA$

STUDENT HELP

HOMEWORK HELP
Example 1: Exs. 13–21
Example 2: Exs. 22–29
Example 3: Exs. 30–33
Example 4: Exs. 36–38
Example 5: Exs. 39–42

20. By the def. of a rotation, $\overline{RP} \cong \overline{R'P}$ and $\overline{QP} \cong \overline{Q'P}$. By the definition of congruent segments, $RP = R'P$ and $QP = Q'P$. By the Segment Addition Postulate, $RP + QR = R'P + Q'R'$, so by the subtraction prop. of equality, $QR = Q'R'$ and $\overline{QR} \cong \overline{Q'R'}$.

21. By the def. of a rotation, $\overline{QP} \cong \overline{Q'P}$. Since P and R are the same point, as are R and R', $\overline{QR} \cong \overline{Q'R'}$.

PARAGRAPH PROOF Write a paragraph proof for the case of Theorem 7.2. 20, 21. See margin.

20. GIVEN ▶ A rotation about P maps Q onto Q' and R onto R'.

PROVE ▶ $\overline{QR} \cong \overline{Q'R'}$

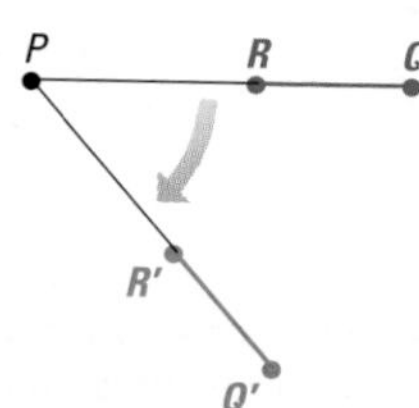

21. GIVEN ▶ A rotation about P maps Q onto Q' and R onto R'. P and R are the same point.

PROVE ▶ $\overline{QR} \cong \overline{Q'R'}$

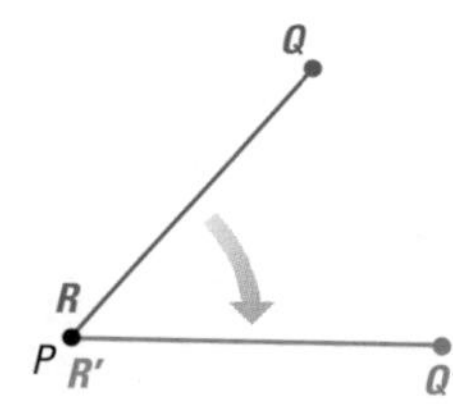

ROTATING A FIGURE Trace the polygon and point P on paper. Then, use a straightedge, compass, and protractor to rotate the polygon clockwise the given number of degrees about P. 22–24. See margin.

22. 60°

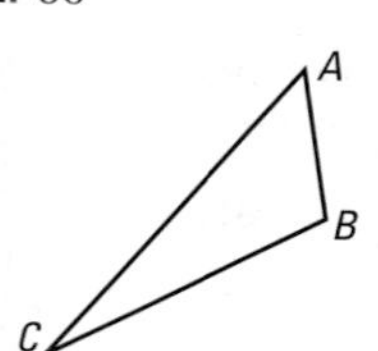

23. 135°

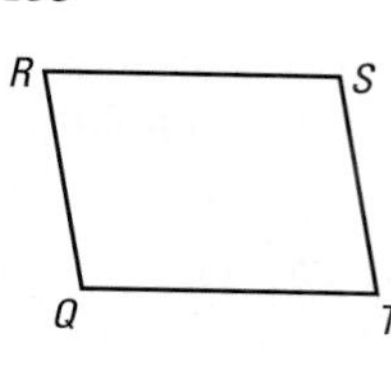

24. 150°

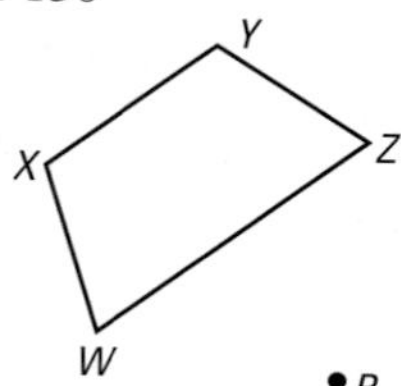

ROTATIONS IN A COORDINATE PLANE Name the coordinates of the vertices of the image after a clockwise rotation of the given number of degrees about the origin.

25. $J'(1, 2)$, $K'(4, 1)$, $L'(4, -3)$, $M'(1, -3)$

26. $P'(-1, -3)$, $Q'(-3, -5)$, $R'(-4, -2)$, $S'(-2, 0)$

27. $D'(4, 1)$, $E'(0, 2)$, $F'(2, 5)$

25. 90°

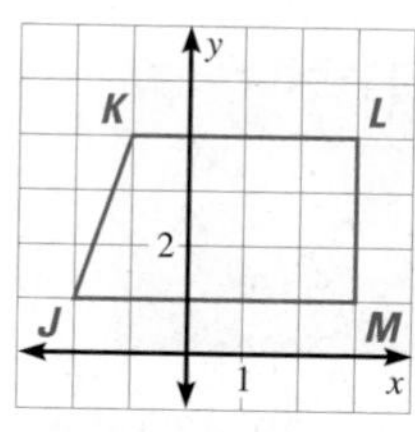

26. 180°

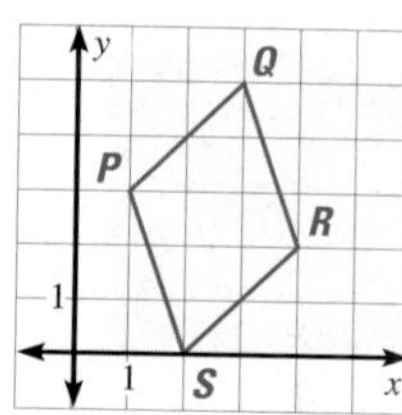

27. 270°

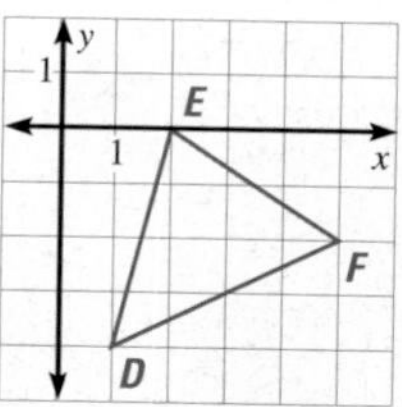

FINDING A PATTERN Use the given information to rotate the triangle. Name the vertices of the image and compare with the vertices of the preimage. Describe any patterns you see.

28. $A'(1, 1)$, $B'(4, -2)$, $C'(2, -5)$; the coordinates of the image of the point (x, y) after a 90° clockwise rotation about the origin are $(y, -x)$.

29. $X'(2, 3)$, $O'(0, 0)$, $Z'(-3, 4)$; the coordinates of the image of the point (x, y) after a 180° clockwise rotation about the origin are $(-x, -y)$.

28. 90° clockwise about origin

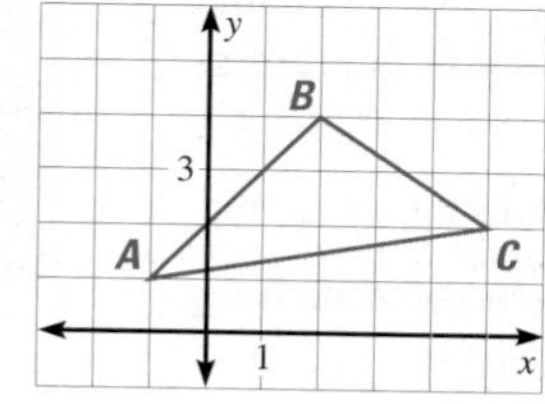

29. 180° clockwise about origin

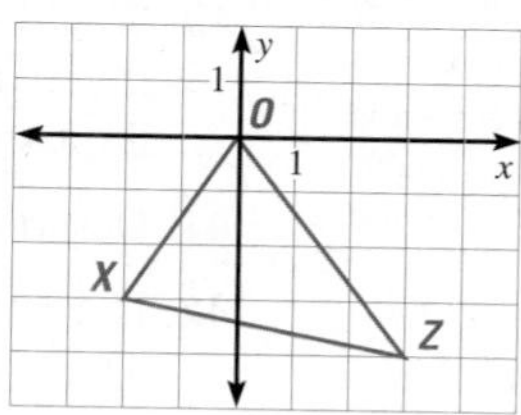

! COMMON ERROR
EXERCISE 15 Students may want to reflect $\overline{CE}$ over some imaginary line. Remind them that if E is the center of rotation, the segment is pivoted about E, which remains stationary.

CONCEPT QUESTION
EXERCISES 22–24 Name a counterclockwise rotation that would give the same results as the clockwise rotation in Exercise 22, Exercise 23, and Exercise 24.
300°; 225°; 210°

MATHEMATICAL REASONING
EXERCISES 28–29 A plane figure is rotated 180° and its center of rotation is the origin. Explain why the origin is the midpoint of the segment joining each point and its image. The distance from the origin to (x, y) is the same as the distance from the origin to $(-x, -y)$ and each point (x, y) is mapped to $(-x, -y)$. Thus, the origin is the midpoint of the segment joining at $P(x, y)$ and its image at $P'(-x, -y)$.

ENGLISH LEARNERS
EXERCISE 5 Although English learners may understand the concepts presented in this chapter, word problems with complex sentence structure may cause comprehension problems that prevent them from demonstrating their understanding. You may want to work through this exercise phrase by phrase with students to ensure that they understand what is being asked.

22.

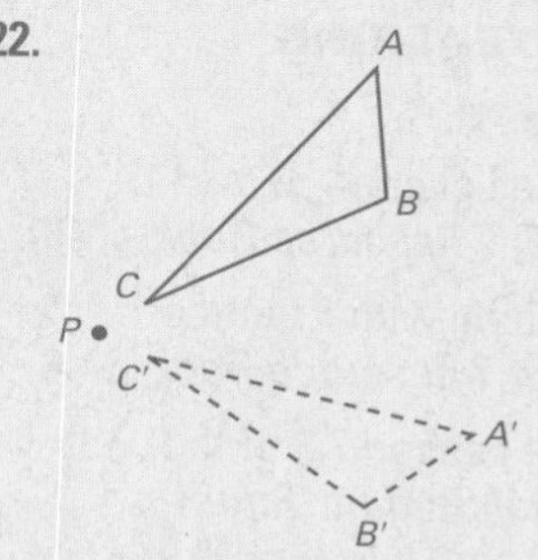

23–24. See Additional Answers beginning on page AA1.

APPLICATION NOTE

EXERCISE 37 The design of a wheel hub does not affect its functionality. It is important to those for whom the visual effect of the wheel matters. The rotational symmetry of this design will emphasize the increased number of rotations of the wheel as the vehicle increases its speed.

EXERCISES 39–42

M.C. Escher's art often involves tessellations. Tessellating figures can be created from rotations of parts of polygons that have congruent adjacent sides, such as squares, regular hexagons, or equilateral triangles. Additional information about M.C. Escher is available at **www.mcdougallittell.com.**

39. Yes. The image can be mapped onto itself by a clockwise or counterclockwise rotation of 180° about its center.
40. Yes, the answer would change to a clockwise or counterclockwise rotation of 90° or 180° about its center. This is because the white figures can be mapped onto the black figures.
42. Yes, it is possible because the image can be mapped onto itself by a clockwise or counterclockwise rotation of 180°.

ADDITIONAL PRACTICE AND RETEACHING

For Lesson 7.3:

- Practice Levels A, B, and C (*Chapter 7 Resource Book,* p. 43)
- Reteaching with Practice (*Chapter 7 Resource Book,* p. 46)
- See Lesson 7.3 of the *Personal Student Tutor*

For more Mixed Review:

- Search the *Test and Practice Generator* for key words or specific lessons.

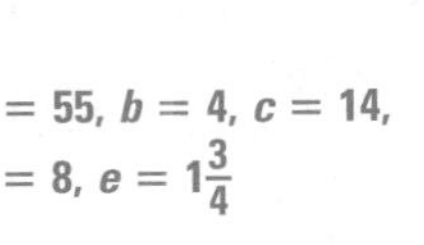

34. $a = 55$, $b = 4$, $c = 14$, $d = 8$, $e = 1\frac{3}{4}$

35. $q = 30$, $r = 5$, $s = 11$, $t = 1$, $u = 2$

36. The wheel hub can be mapped onto itself by a clockwise or counterclockwise rotation of 45°, 90°, 135°, or 180° about its center.

37. The wheel hub can be mapped onto itself by a clockwise or counterclockwise rotation of $51\frac{3}{7}°$, $102\frac{6}{7}°$, or $154\frac{2}{7}°$ about its center.

38. The wheel hub can be mapped onto itself by a clockwise or counterclockwise rotation of 72° or 144° about its center.

FOCUS ON PEOPLE

M.C. ESCHER is a Dutch graphic artist whose works include optical illusions and geometric patterns. (M.C. Escher's *"Hand with Reflecting Sphere"* © 1999 Cordon Art B.V. - Baarn - Holland. All rights reserved.)

APPLICATION LINK www.mcdougallittell.com

USING THEOREM 7.3 **Find the angle of rotation that maps $\triangle ABC$ onto $\triangle A''B''C''$.**

30. 70°

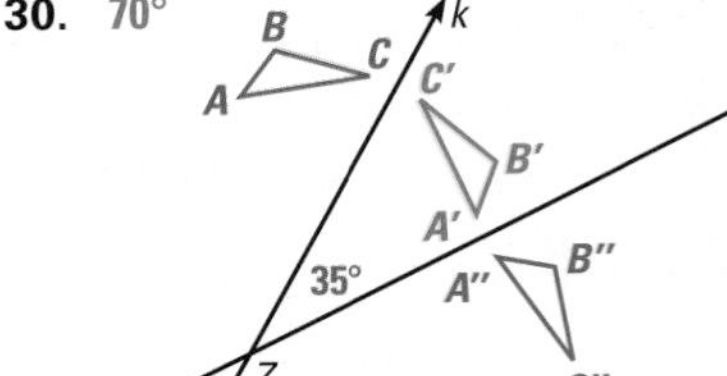

31. 30°

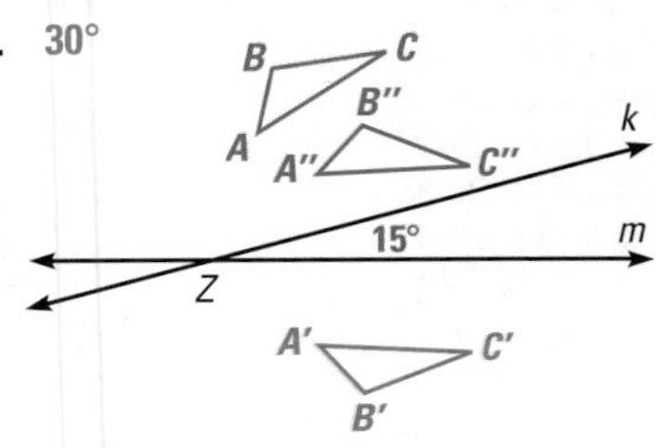

LOGICAL REASONING **Lines m and n intersect at point D. Consider a reflection of $\triangle ABC$ in line m followed by a reflection in line n.**

32. What is the angle of rotation about D, when the measure of the acute angle between lines m and n is 36°? 72°

33. What is the measure of the acute angle between lines m and n, when the angle of rotation about D is 162°? 81°

USING ALGEBRA **Find the value of each variable in the rotation of the polygon about point P.** 34, 35. See margin.

34.

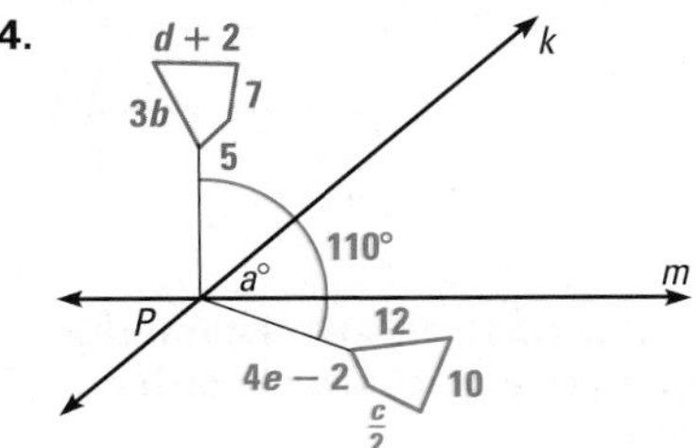

35.

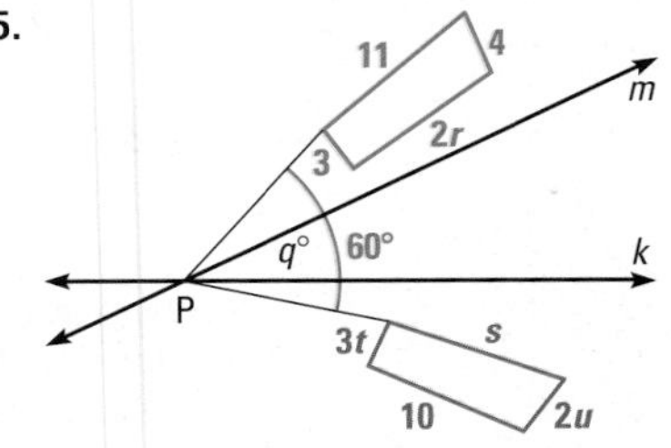

WHEEL HUBS **Describe the rotational symmetry of the wheel hub.** 36–38. See margin.

36. **37.** **38.**

ROTATIONS IN ART **In Exercises 39–42, refer to the image below by M.C. Escher. The piece is called *Development I* and was completed in 1937.**

39. Does the piece have rotational symmetry? If so, describe the rotations that map the image onto itself. See margin.

40. Would your answer to Exercise 39 change if you disregard the shading of the figures? Explain your reasoning. See margin.

41. Describe the center of rotation. the center of the square, that is, the intersection of the diagonals

42. Is it possible that this piece could be hung upside down? Explain. See margin.

M.C. Escher's *"Development I"* © 1999 Cordon Art B.V. - Baarn - Holland. All rights reserved.

Test Preparation

e. Reflect the figure either in the line $y = x$ or $y = -x$ and then in one of the axes. Then the measure of the acute angle between the two lines is 45° and the angle of rotation is 90°.

43. MULTI-STEP PROBLEM Follow the steps below.

a. Graph $\triangle RST$ whose vertices are $R(1, 1)$, $S(4, 3)$, and $T(5, 1)$. Check drawings.

b. Reflect $\triangle RST$ in the y-axis to obtain $\triangle R'S'T'$. Name the coordinates of the vertices of the reflection. $R'(-1, 1)$, $S'(-4, 3)$, $T'(-5, 1)$

c. Reflect $\triangle R'S'T'$ in the line $y = -x$ to obtain $\triangle R''S''T''$. Name the coordinates of the vertices of the reflection. $R''(-1, 1)$, $S''(-3, 4)$, $T''(-1, 5)$

d. Describe a single transformation that maps $\triangle RST$ onto $\triangle R''S''T''$. rotation of 90° counterclockwise about the origin

e. *Writing* Explain how to show a 90° counterclockwise rotation of any polygon about the origin using two reflections of the figure. See margin.

★ Challenge

44. PROOF Use the diagram and the given information to write a paragraph proof for Theorem 7.3. See margin.

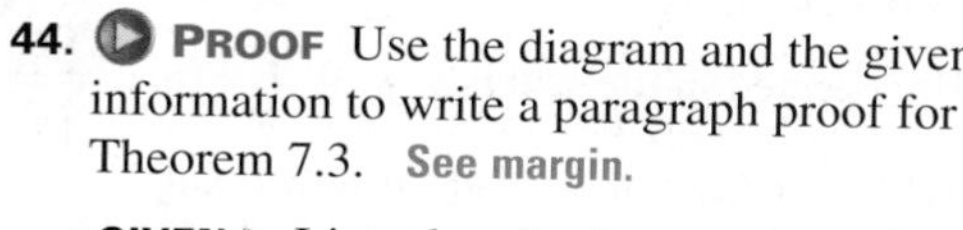

GIVEN ▶ Lines k and m intersect at point P, Q is any point not on k or m.

PROVE ▶ a. If you reflect point Q in k, and then reflect its image Q' in m, Q'' is the image of Q after a rotation about point P.

b. $m\angle QPQ'' = 2(m\angle APB)$.

Plan for Proof First show $k \perp \overline{QQ'}$ and $\overline{QA} \cong \overline{Q'A}$. Then show $\triangle QAP \cong \triangle Q'AP$. Use a similar argument to show $\triangle Q'BP \cong \triangle Q''BP$. Use the congruent triangles and substitution to show that $\overline{QP} \cong \overline{Q''P}$. That proves part (a) by the definition of a rotation. You can use the congruent triangles to prove part (b).

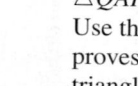

EXTRA CHALLENGE
www.mcdougallittell.com

MIXED REVIEW

PARALLEL LINES Find the measure of the angle using the diagram, in which $j \parallel k$ and $m\angle 1 = 82°$. (Review 3.3 for 7.4)

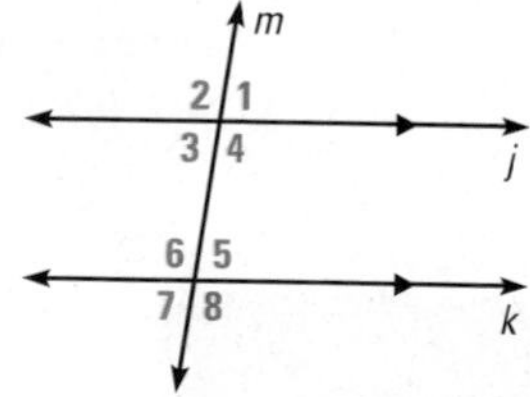

45. $m\angle 5$ 82°

46. $m\angle 7$ 82°

47. $m\angle 3$ 82°

48. $m\angle 6$ 98°

49. $m\angle 4$ 98°

50. $m\angle 8$ 98°

DRAWING TRIANGLES In Exercises 51–53, draw the triangle. (Review 5.2)

51. Draw a triangle whose circumcenter lies outside the triangle. any obtuse triangle

52. Draw a triangle whose circumcenter lies on the triangle. any right triangle

53. Draw a triangle whose circumcenter lies inside the triangle. any acute triangle

54. PARALLELOGRAMS Can it be proven that the figure at the right is a parallelogram? If not, explain why not. (Review 6.2)

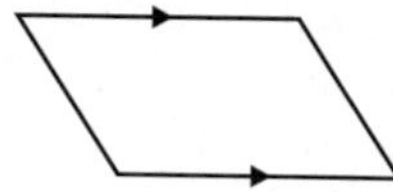

54. The figure indicates only that one pair of opposite sides of the figure are parallel, which is insufficient to show that the figure is a parallelogram.

4 ASSESS

DAILY HOMEWORK QUIZ

Transparency Available

1. Draw a square. Below the square draw a point P. Then use a straightedge, compass, and protractor to rotate the square clockwise 60° about P. Check drawings.
2. In a coordinate plane, sketch the triangle whose vertices are $A(2, -2)$, $B(4, 1)$, $C(5, 1)$. Then rotate $\triangle ABC$ 90° clockwise about (0, 0) and name the coordinates of the new vertices. $A'(-2, -2)$, $B'(1, -4)$, $C'(1, -5)$
3. Lines m and n intersect at D. If $\triangle ABC$ is reflected in line m followed by a reflection in line n, what is the angle of rotation about D, when the measure of the acute angle between m and n is 25°? 50°

EXTRA CHALLENGE NOTE

Challenge problems for Lesson 7.3 are available in **blackline** format in the *Chapter 7 Resource Book*, p. 51 and at **www.mcdougallittell.com.**

ADDITIONAL TEST PREPARATION

1. **OPEN ENDED** Write a word or acronym that has rotational symmetry. *Sample answer:* SIS
2. **WRITING** A pilot flying over a desert in an airplane sees **SOS** written in the sand. Explain why for any position from which the pilot views the distress signal, there is another position from which the signal will appear the same to the pilot. See answer at left.

44. See Additional Answers beginning on page AA1.

Additional Test Preparation *Sample answer:*

2. When the S's are congruent and the spacing between letters is equal, the signal has rotational symmetry about its center. Since it can be mapped onto itself by a rotation of 180°, the signal will appear the same to the pilot from any given compass direction and its polar opposite direction.

ADDITIONAL RESOURCES
An alternative Quiz for Lessons 7.1–7.3 is available in the *Chapter 7 Resource Book,* p. 52.

A **blackline** master with additional Math & History exercises is available in the *Chapter 7 Resource Book,* p. 50.

APPLICATION NOTE
Additional information about decorative patterns is available at **www.mcdougallittell.com.**

QUIZ 1

Self-Test for Lessons 7.1–7.3

Use the transformation at the right. (Lesson 7.1)

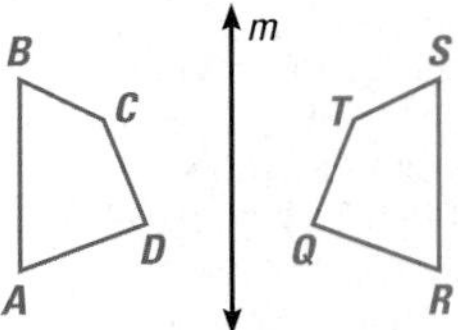

1. Figure $ABCD \rightarrow$ Figure __?__ RSTQ
2. Name and describe the transformation.
3. Is the transformation an isometry? Explain.
   Yes; the transformation preserves lengths.

2. Reflection in line *m*; the figure is flipped over line *m*.

In Exercises 4–7, find the coordinates of the reflection without using a coordinate plane. (Lesson 7.2)

4. $L(2, 3)$ reflected in the x-axis (2, −3)
5. $M(-2, -4)$ reflected in the y-axis (2, −4)
6. $N(-4, 0)$ reflected in the x-axis (−4, 0)
7. $P(8.2, -3)$ reflected in the y-axis (−8.2, −3)
8. **KNOTS** The knot at the right is a *wall knot*, which is generally used to prevent the end of a rope from running through a pulley. Describe the rotations that map the knot onto itself and describe the center of rotation. (Lesson 7.3)
   rotations by mutiples of 120° clockwise or counterclockwise about the center of the knot where the rope starts to unravel.

MATH & History — History of Decorative Patterns

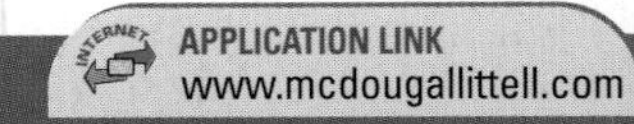

THEN — **FOR THOUSANDS OF YEARS,** people have adorned their buildings, pottery, clothing, and jewelry with decorative patterns. Simple patterns were created by using a transformation of a shape.

NOW — **TODAY,** you are likely to find computer generated patterns decorating your clothes, CD covers, sports equipment, computer desktop, and even textbooks.

1. The design at the right is based on a piece of pottery by Marsha Gomez. How many lines of symmetry does the design have? 2
2. Does the design have rotational symmetry? If so, describe the rotation that maps the pattern onto itself.
   yes; a rotation of 180° clockwise or counterclockwise about its center

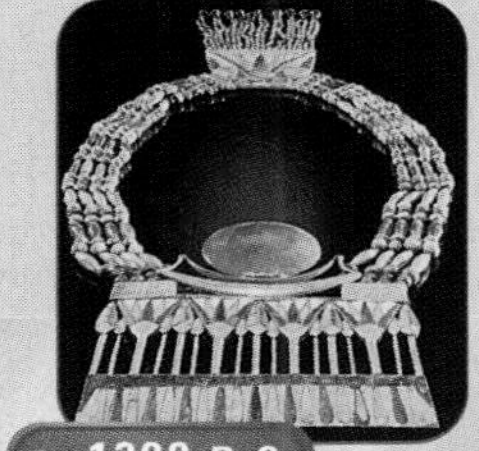
c. 1300 B.C.
Egyptian jewelry is decorated with patterns.

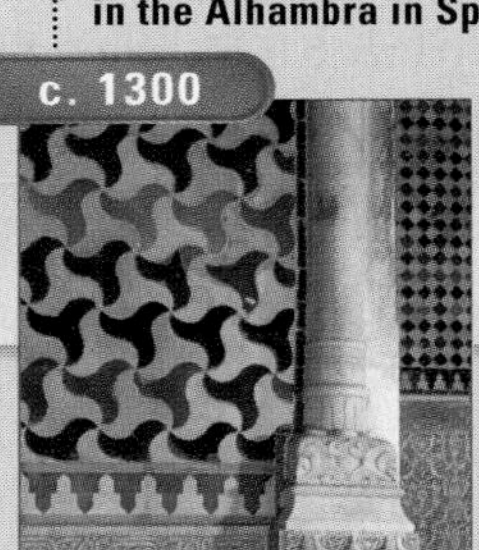
c. 1300
Tiles are arranged in symmetric patterns in the Alhambra in Spain.

1899
Painted textile pattern called 'Bulow Birds'

1990s
Marsha Gomez decorates pottery with symmetrical patterns.

7.4 Translations and Vectors

GOAL 1 USING PROPERTIES OF TRANSLATIONS

What you should learn

GOAL 1 Identify and use translations in the plane.

GOAL 2 Use vectors in **real-life** situations, such as navigating a sailboat in **Example 6**.

Why you should learn it

▼ You can use translations and vectors to describe the path of an aircraft, such as the hot-air balloon in **Exs. 53–55**.

REAL LIFE

A **translation** is a transformation that maps every two points P and Q in the plane to points P' and Q', so that the following properties are true:

1. $PP' = QQ'$
2. $\overline{PP'} \parallel \overline{QQ'}$, or $\overline{PP'}$ and $\overline{QQ'}$ are collinear.

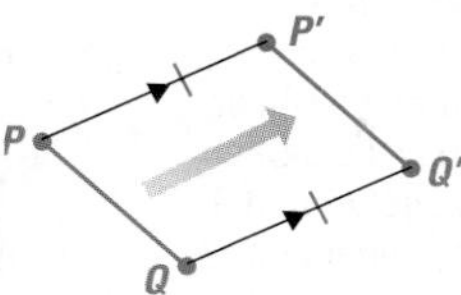

THEOREM

THEOREM 7.4 *Translation Theorem*

A translation is an isometry.

Theorem 7.4 can be proven as follows.

GIVEN ▶ $PP' = QQ'$, $\overline{PP'} \parallel \overline{QQ'}$

PROVE ▶ $PQ = P'Q'$

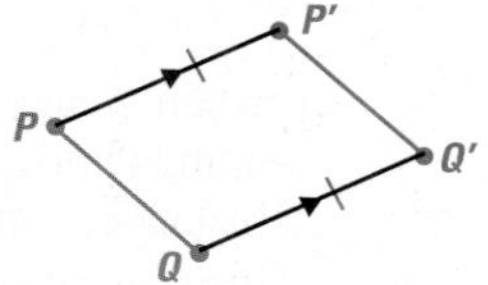

Paragraph Proof The quadrilateral $PP'Q'Q$ has a pair of opposite sides that are congruent and parallel, which implies $PP'Q'Q$ is a parallelogram. From this you can conclude $PQ = P'Q'$. (Exercise 43 asks for a coordinate proof of Theorem 7.4, which covers the case where $\overline{PQ}$ and $\overline{P'Q'}$ are collinear.)

You can find the image of a translation by gliding a figure in the plane. Another way to find the image of a translation is to complete one reflection after another in two parallel lines, as shown. The properties of this type of translation are stated below.

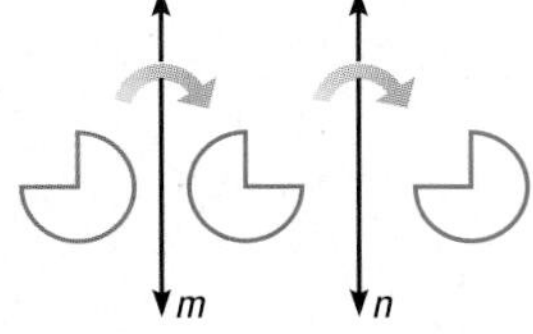

THEOREM

THEOREM 7.5

If lines k and m are parallel, then a reflection in line k followed by a reflection in line m is a translation. If P'' is the image of P, then the following is true:

1. $\overleftrightarrow{PP''}$ is perpendicular to k and m.
2. $PP'' = 2d$, where d is the distance between k and m.

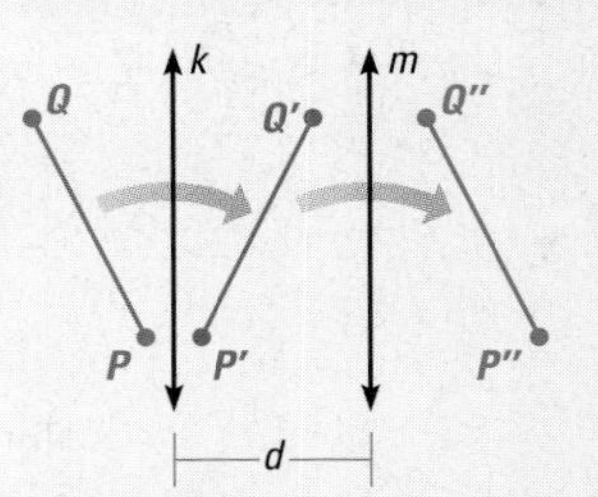

CALIFORNIA STANDARDS AND ASSESSMENT

CA Standards: 17, 22
SAT9 Task 1: Obj. 31
SAT9 Task 2: Obj. 34

1 PLAN

PACING

Basic: 1 day
Average: 1 day
Advanced: 1 day
Block Schedule: 0.5 block with 7.5

***LESSON OPENER* APPLICATION**

An alternative way to approach Lesson 7.4 is to use the Application Lesson Opener:

- Blackline Master (*Chapter 7 Resource Book,* p. 56)
- Transparency (p. 44)

MEETING INDIVIDUAL NEEDS

- ***Chapter 7 Resource Book***
  Prerequisite Skills Review (p. 5)
  Practice Level A (p. 57)
  Practice Level B (p. 58)
  Practice Level C (p. 59)
  Reteaching with Practice (p. 60)
  Absent Student Catch-Up (p. 62)
  Challenge (p. 65)
- ***Resources in Spanish***
- ***Personal Student Tutor***

NEW-TEACHER SUPPORT

See the Tips for New Teachers on pp. 1–2 of the *Chapter 7 Resource Book* for additional notes about Lesson 7.4.

WARM-UP EXERCISES

Transparency Available

The vertices of $\triangle KLM$ are $K(3, 3)$, $L(5, 4)$, and $M(0, 6)$. Find the new vertices after each slide.

1. left two units
   $K'(1, 3)$, $L'(3, 4)$, $M'(-2, 6)$
2. down five units
   $K'(3, -2)$, $L'(5, -1)$, $M'(0, 1)$

The coordinates of the endpoints of $\overline{PQ}$ are $P(1, 2)$ and $Q(4, 6)$.

3. What is the length of $\overline{PQ}$?
   5 units
4. If $\overline{PQ}$ is translated right five units, what is the length of its image? **5 units**

2 TEACH

EXTRA EXAMPLE 1
In the diagram, a reflection in line k maps $\triangle XYZ$ to $\triangle X'Y'Z'$, a reflection in line m maps $\triangle X'Y'Z'$ to $\triangle X''Y''Z''$, $k \parallel m$, $AZ' = 3$, and $Z'B = 2$.

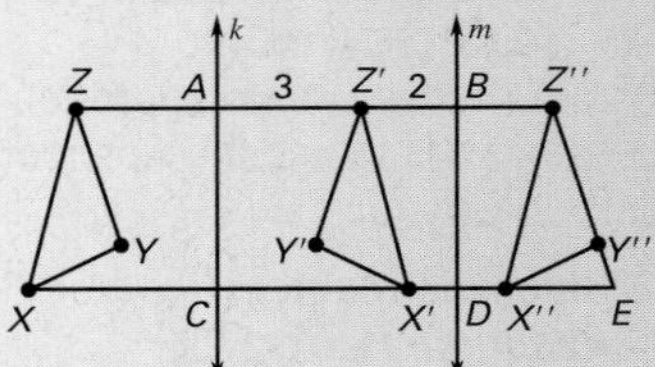

a. Name some congruent segments. ***Sample answer:*** $\overline{XY}$, $\overline{X'Y'}$, **and** $\overline{X''Y''}$; $\overline{AZ}$ **and** $\overline{AZ'}$; $\overline{AB}$ **and** $\overline{CD}$

b. What kind of figure is $ZZ''EX$? What is the length of $\overline{ZZ''}$? **trapezoid; 10**

c. Name a pair of perpendicular segments. ***Sample answer:*** $\overline{ZB}$ **and** $\overline{AC}$; $\overline{CD}$ **and** $\overline{BD}$

EXTRA EXAMPLE 2
Sketch a parallelogram with vertices $R(-4, -1)$, $S(-2, 0)$, $T(-1, 3)$, $U(-3, 2)$. Then sketch the image of the parallelogram after translation $(x, y) \to (x + 4, y - 2)$.

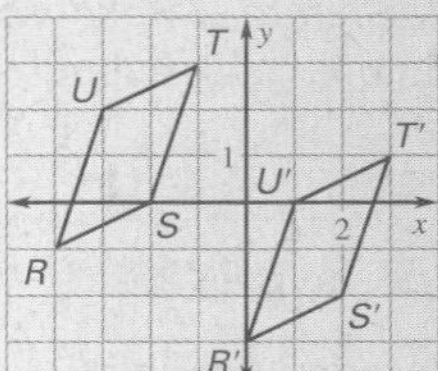

CHECKPOINT EXERCISES
For use after Examples 1 and 2:

1. $\triangle ABC \to \triangle A'B'C'$ by a translation defined by $(x, y) \to (x - 5, y)$. The coordinates of the vertices of $\triangle ABC$ are $A(7, 4)$, $B(-1, -1)$, and $C(3, -5)$. What are the coordinates of the vertices of $\triangle A'B'C'$?
$A'(2, 4)$, $B'(-6, -1)$, $C'(-2, -5)$

STUDENT HELP

Study Tip
In Lesson 7.2, you learned that the line of reflection is the perpendicular bisector of the segment connecting a point and its image. In Example 1, you can use this property to conclude that figure $ABDC$ is a rectangle.

EXAMPLE 1 Using Theorem 7.5

In the diagram, a reflection in line k maps $\overline{GH}$ to $\overline{G'H'}$, a reflection in line m maps $\overline{G'H'}$ to $\overline{G''H''}$, $k \parallel m$, $HB = 5$, and $DH'' = 2$.

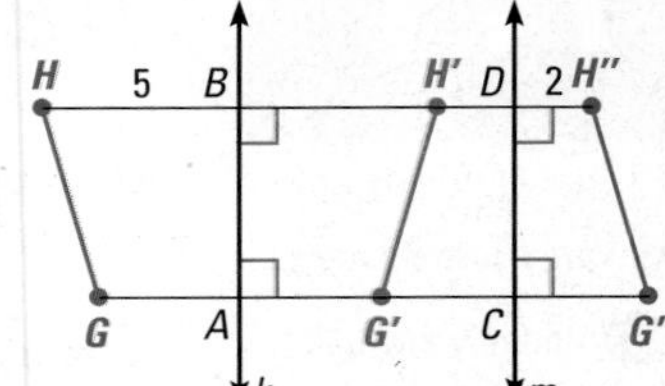

a. Name some congruent segments.

b. Does $AC = BD$? Explain.

c. What is the length of $\overline{GG''}$?

SOLUTION

a. Here are some sets of congruent segments: $\overline{GH}$, $\overline{G'H'}$, and $\overline{G''H''}$; $\overline{HB}$ and $\overline{H'B}$; $\overline{H'D}$ and $\overline{H''D}$.

b. Yes, $AC = BD$ because $\overline{AC}$ and $\overline{BD}$ are opposite sides of a rectangle.

c. Because $GG'' = HH''$, the length of $\overline{GG''}$ is $5 + 5 + 2 + 2$, or 14 units.

Translations in a coordinate plane can be described by the following coordinate notation:

$$(x, y) \to (x + a, y + b)$$

where a and b are constants. Each point shifts a units horizontally and b units vertically. For instance, in the coordinate plane at the right, the translation $(x, y) \to (x + 4, y - 2)$ shifts each point 4 units to the right and 2 units down.

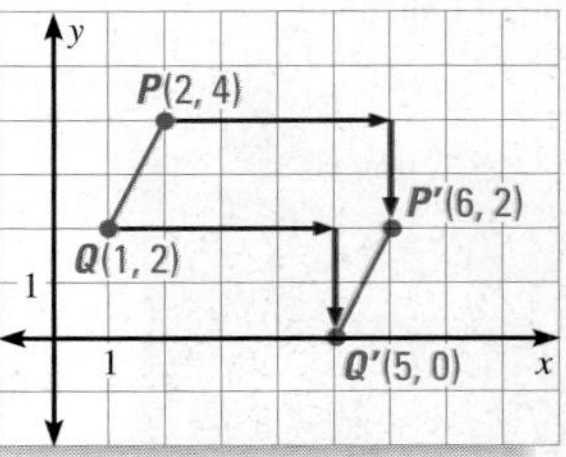

EXAMPLE 2 Translations in a Coordinate Plane

Sketch a triangle with vertices $A(-1, -3)$, $B(1, -1)$, and $C(-1, 0)$. Then sketch the image of the triangle after the translation $(x, y) \to (x - 3, y + 4)$.

SOLUTION

Plot the points as shown. Shift each point 3 units to the left and 4 units up to find the translated vertices. The coordinates of the vertices of the preimage and image are listed below.

$\triangle ABC$	$\triangle A'B'C'$
$A(-1, -3)$	$A'(-4, 1)$
$B(1, -1)$	$B'(-2, 3)$
$C(-1, 0)$	$C'(-4, 4)$

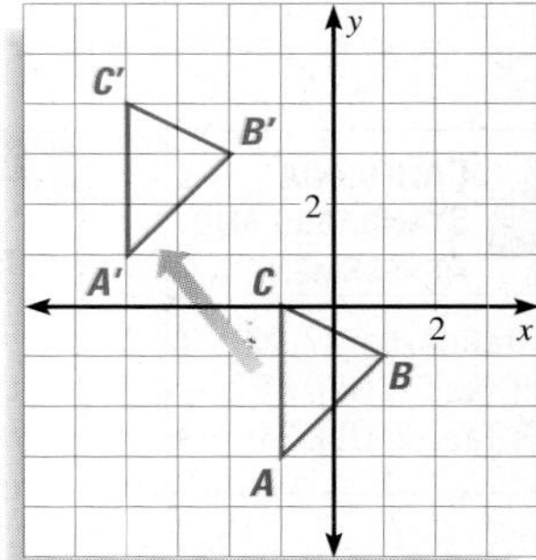

Notice that each x-coordinate of the image is 3 units less than the x-coordinate of the preimage and each y-coordinate of the image is 4 units more than the y-coordinate of the preimage.

STUDENT HELP

Study Tip
When writing a vector in component form, use the correct brackets. The brackets used to write the component form of a vector are different than the parentheses used to write an ordered pair.

GOAL 2 TRANSLATIONS USING VECTORS

Another way to describe a translation is by using a vector. A **vector** is a quantity that has both direction and *magnitude*, or size, and is represented by an arrow drawn between two points.

The diagram shows a vector. The **initial point**, or starting point, of the vector is P and the **terminal point**, or ending point, is Q. The vector is named $\overrightarrow{PQ}$, which is read as "vector PQ." The *horizontal component* of $\overrightarrow{PQ}$ is 5 and the *vertical component* is 3.

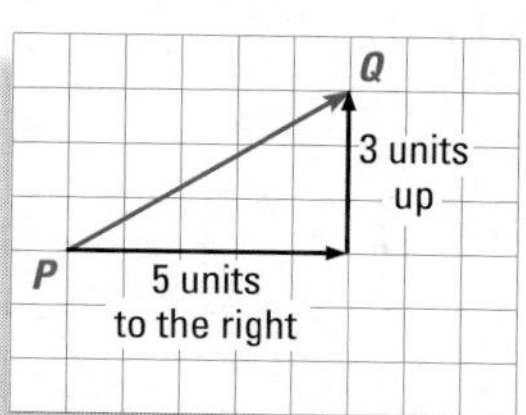

The **component form** of a vector combines the horizontal and vertical components. So, the component form of $\overrightarrow{PQ}$ is $\langle 5, 3\rangle$.

EXAMPLE 3 *Identifying Vector Components*

In the diagram, name each vector and write its component form.

a.

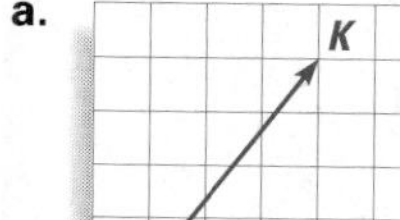

b.

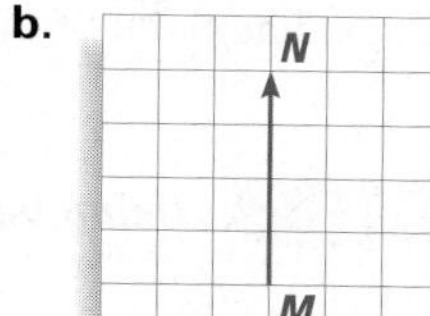

c.

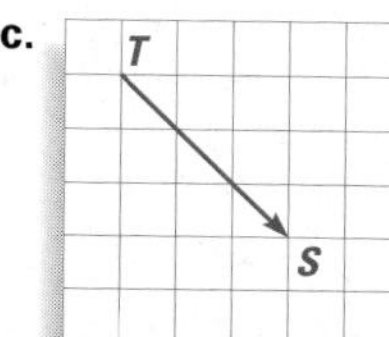

SOLUTION

a. The vector is $\overrightarrow{JK}$. To move from the initial point J to the terminal point K, you move 3 units to the right and 4 units up. So, the component form is $\langle 3, 4\rangle$.

b. The vector is $\overrightarrow{MN} = \langle 0, 4\rangle$.

c. The vector is $\overrightarrow{TS} = \langle 3, -3\rangle$.

EXAMPLE 4 *Translation Using Vectors*

The component form of $\overrightarrow{GH}$ is $\langle 4, 2\rangle$. Use $\overrightarrow{GH}$ to translate the triangle whose vertices are $A(3, -1)$, $B(1, 1)$, and $C(3, 5)$.

SOLUTION

First graph $\triangle ABC$. The component form of $\overrightarrow{GH}$ is $\langle 4, 2\rangle$, so the image vertices should all be 4 units to the right and 2 units up from the preimage vertices. Label the image vertices as $A'(7, 1)$, $B'(5, 3)$, and $C'(7, 7)$. Then, using a straightedge, draw $\triangle A'B'C'$. Notice that the vectors drawn from preimage to image vertices are parallel.

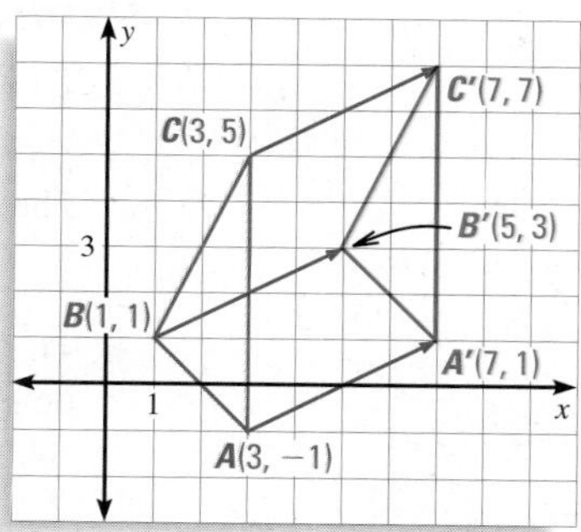

Extra Example 4 *Sample answer:*
The images of the vertices are $G'(-1, 2)$, $H'(2, 0)$, $J'(3, 0)$, and $K(5, -5)$.

EXTRA EXAMPLE 3
In the diagram, name each vector and write its component form.

a.

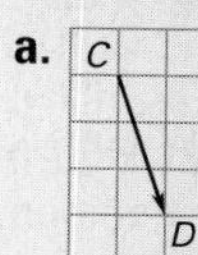

b.

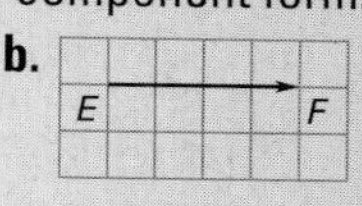

c.

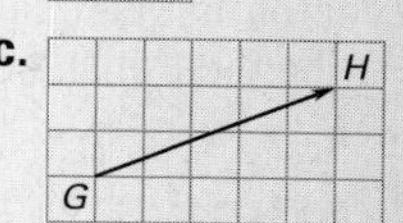

a. $\overrightarrow{CD} = \langle 1, -3\rangle$; b. $\overrightarrow{EF} = \langle 4, 0\rangle$;
c. $\overrightarrow{GH} = \langle 5, 2\rangle$.

EXTRA EXAMPLE 4
The component form of $\overrightarrow{RS}$ is $\langle 2, -3\rangle$. Use $\overrightarrow{RS}$ to translate the quadrilateral whose vertices are $G(-3, 5)$, $H(0, 3)$, $J(1, 3)$, and $K(3, -2)$. See margin.

CHECKPOINT EXERCISES

For use after Example 3:

1. The initial point of a vector is $V(-2, 3)$ and the terminal point is $W(-4, -7)$. Name the vector and write its component parts. $\overrightarrow{VW} = \langle -2, -10\rangle$
2. The initial point of a vector is $E(2, -6)$ and the terminal point is $F(2, -9)$. Name the vector and write its component parts. $\overrightarrow{EF} = \langle 0, -3\rangle$

For use after Example 4:

3. The component form of $\overrightarrow{MN}$ is $\langle 3, 1\rangle$. Use $\overrightarrow{MN}$ to translate the triangle whose vertices are $R(0, 4)$, $S(3, 1)$, and $T(4, -2)$. The images of the vertices are $R'(3, 5)$, $S'(6, 2)$, and $T(7, -1)$.

TEACHING TIPS

EXAMPLE 3 Explain to students that it is not necessary to reference the vectors to the coordinate axes. Although the initial point of each vector can be placed at the origin, an infinite number of vectors is equivalent to a given vector with initial point at the origin. Ask students to name the initial and terminal points of several vectors that could identify the vector in each sketch.

EXTRA EXAMPLE 5

$\triangle ABC \to \triangle A'B'C'$ using a translation. The vertices of $\triangle ABC$ are $A(-4, 5)$, $B(-1, -1)$, and $C(2, 3)$. The vertices of $\triangle A'B'C'$ are $A'(-3, 2)$, $B'(0, -4)$, and $C'(3, 0)$. Write the component form of the vector that can be used to describe the translation. $\langle 1, -3\rangle$

EXTRA EXAMPLE 6

The coordinates of a logging site are $S(5, 7)$. A logging truck traveling a straight line from the site to a mill at M encounters a road detour at D when it is 4 mi west and 2 mi south of the logging site. The truck must travel an alternate route to $A(4, 3)$.

a. Write the component forms of the vectors from S to D and from D to A. $\overrightarrow{SD} = \langle -4, -2\rangle$ and $\overrightarrow{DA} = \langle 3, -2\rangle$

b. The mill is 6 mi west and 3 mi south of the logging site. Write the component form of the vector that describes the route the logging truck can follow to arrive at the mill. $\overrightarrow{AM} = \langle -5, 1\rangle$

CHECKPOINT EXERCISES

For use after Examples 5 and 6:

1. $\overline{AB} \to \overline{A'B'}$ using a translation. The coordinates of the endpoints of $\overline{AB}$ are $A(-2, 1)$ and $B(3, -1)$. The coordinates of $\overline{A'B'}$ are $A'(1, -2)$ and $B'(6, -4)$. Write the component form of the vector that can be used to describe the translation. $\langle 3, -3\rangle$

FOCUS ON VOCABULARY

What is another name for a translation? a slide

CLOSURE QUESTION

Vertex $A(-3, 0)$ in $\triangle ABC \to A'(5, 3)$. Describe the translation. $(x, y) \to (x + 8, y + 3)$

STUDENT HELP

INTERNET **HOMEWORK HELP** Visit our Web site www.mcdougallittell.com for extra examples.

EXAMPLE 5 *Finding Vectors*

In the diagram, $QRST$ maps onto $Q'R'S'T'$ by a translation. Write the component form of the vector that can be used to describe the translation.

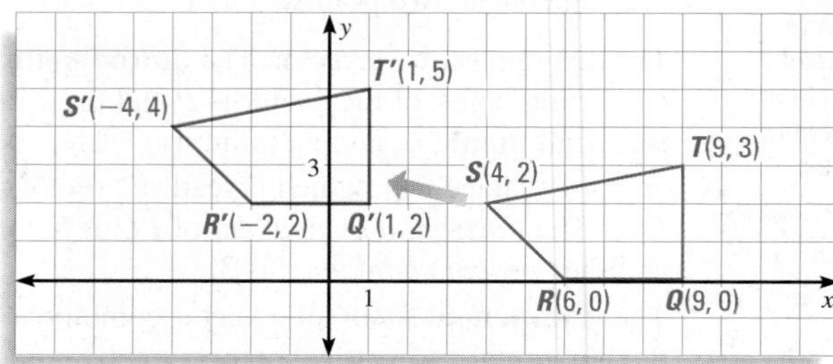

SOLUTION

Choose any vertex and its image, say R and R'. To move from R to R', you move 8 units to the left and 2 units up. The component form of the vector is $\langle -8, 2\rangle$.

✓**CHECK** To check the solution, you can start any where on the preimage and move 8 units to the left and 2 units up. You should end on the corresponding point of the image.

EXAMPLE 6 *Using Vectors*

REAL LIFE **NAVIGATION** A boat travels a straight path between two islands, A and D. When the boat is 3 miles east and 2 miles north of its starting point it encounters a storm at point B. The storm pushes the boat off course to point C, as shown.

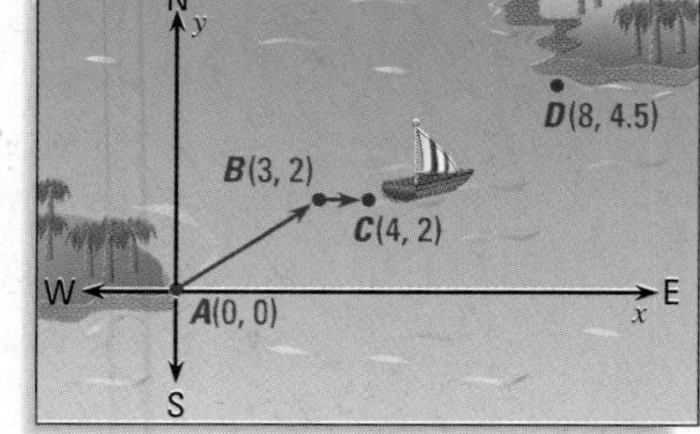

a. Write the component forms of the two vectors shown in the diagram.

b. The final destination is 8 miles east and 4.5 miles north of the starting point. Write the component form of the vector that describes the path the boat can follow to arrive at its destination.

SOLUTION

a. The component form of the vector from $A(0, 0)$ to $B(3, 2)$ is

$$\overrightarrow{AB} = \langle 3 - 0, 2 - 0\rangle = \langle 3, 2\rangle.$$

The component form of the vector from $B(3, 2)$ to $C(4, 2)$ is

$$\overrightarrow{BC} = \langle 4 - 3, 2 - 2\rangle = \langle 1, 0\rangle.$$

b. The boat needs to travel from its current position, point C, to the island, point D. To find the component form of the vector from $C(4, 2)$ to $D(8, 4.5)$, subtract the corresponding coordinates:

$$\overrightarrow{CD} = \langle 8 - 4, 4.5 - 2\rangle = \langle 4, 2.5\rangle.$$

GUIDED PRACTICE

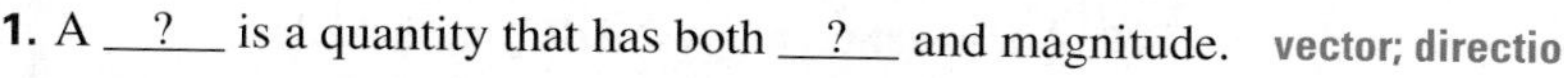

Vocabulary Check ✓
Concept Check ✓

1. A __?__ is a quantity that has both __?__ and magnitude. vector; direction

2. **ERROR ANALYSIS** Describe Jerome's error.

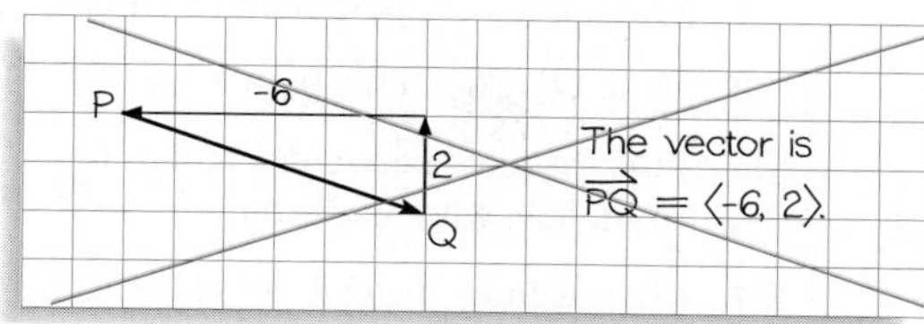

2. *Sample answer:* He confused the initial and terminal points of the vector; the vector is $\overrightarrow{PQ} = \langle 6, -2 \rangle$.

Skill Check ✓

Use coordinate notation to describe the translation.

3. 6 units to the right and 2 units down $(x, y) \rightarrow (x + 6, y - 2)$
4. 3 units up and 4 units to the right $(x, y) \rightarrow (x + 4, y + 3)$
5. 7 units to the left and 1 unit up $(x, y) \rightarrow (x - 7, y + 1)$
6. 8 units down and 5 units to the left $(x, y) \rightarrow (x - 5, y - 8)$

Complete the statement using the description of the translation. In the description, points (0, 2) and (8, 5) are two vertices of a pentagon.

7. If (0, 2) maps onto (0, 0), then (8, 5) maps onto (_?_, _?_). 8; 3
8. If (0, 2) maps onto (_?_, _?_), then (8, 5) maps onto (3, 7). −5; 4
9. If (0, 2) maps onto (−3, −5), then (8, 5) maps onto (_?_, _?_). 5; −2
10. If (0, 2) maps onto (_?_, _?_), then (8, 5) maps onto (0, 0). −8; −3

Draw three vectors that can be described by the given component form.
11–14. Sample figures are given; See margin.

11. $\langle 3, 5 \rangle$
12. $\langle 0, 4 \rangle$
13. $\langle -6, 0 \rangle$
14. $\langle -5, -1 \rangle$

PRACTICE AND APPLICATIONS

STUDENT HELP

► **Extra Practice** to help you master skills is on p. 816.

DESCRIBING TRANSLATIONS **Describe the translation using (a) coordinate notation and (b) a vector in component form.**

15.

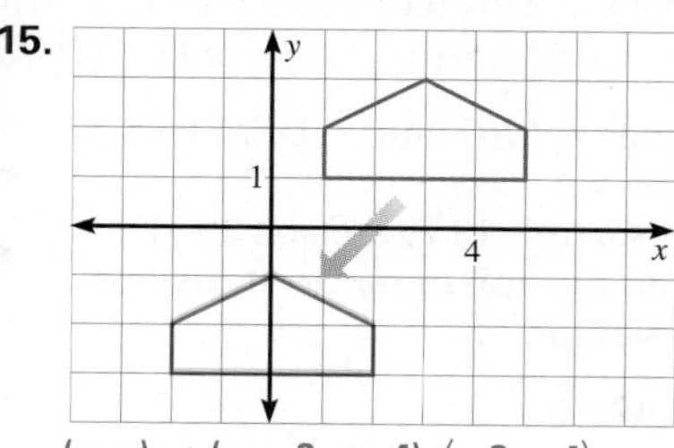

$(x, y) \rightarrow (x - 3, y - 4)$; $\langle -3, -4 \rangle$

16.

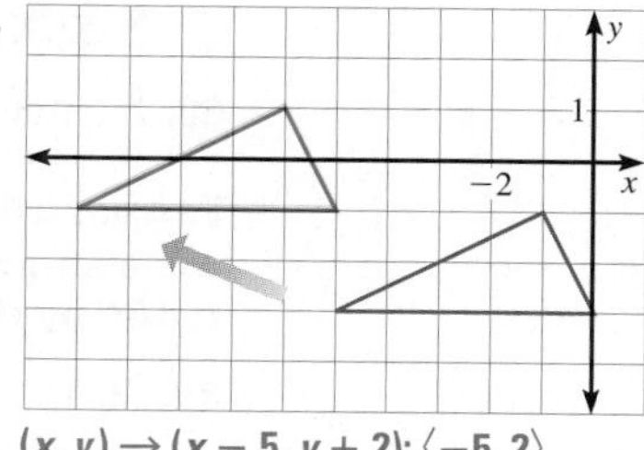

$(x, y) \rightarrow (x - 5, y + 2)$; $\langle -5, 2 \rangle$

STUDENT HELP

► HOMEWORK HELP
Example 1: Exs. 20–24
Example 2: Exs. 15, 16, 25–34
Example 3: Exs. 15–19
Example 4: Exs. 39–42
Example 5: Exs. 44–47
Example 6: Exs. 53–55

IDENTIFYING VECTORS **Name the vector and write its component form.**

17.

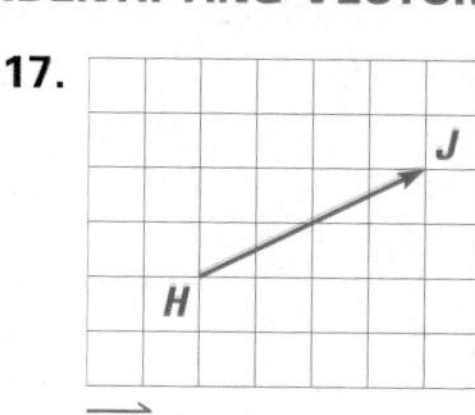

$\overrightarrow{HJ}$; $\langle 4, 2 \rangle$

18.

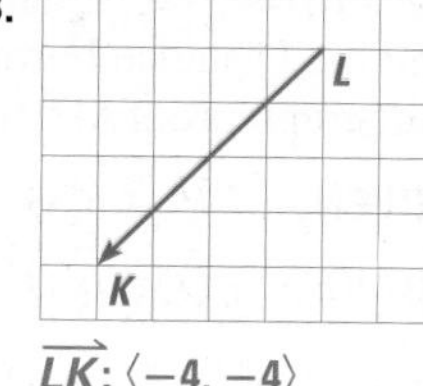

$\overrightarrow{LK}$; $\langle -4, -4 \rangle$

19.

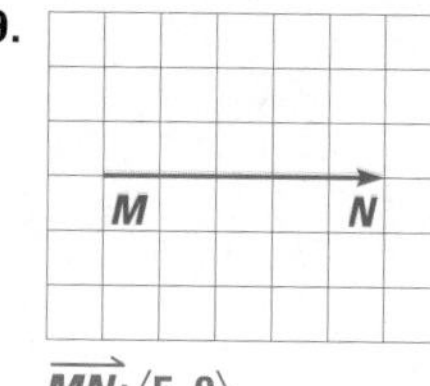

$\overrightarrow{MN}$; $\langle 5, 0 \rangle$

3 APPLY

ASSIGNMENT GUIDE

BASIC
Day 1: pp. 425–428 Exs. 16–46 even, 56–59, 62–72 even

AVERAGE
Day 1: pp. 425–428 Exs. 16–46 even, 43, 53–59, 62–72 even

ADVANCED
Day 1: pp. 425–428 Exs. 16–46 even, 43, 53–61, 62–72 even

BLOCK SCHEDULE WITH 7.5
pp. 425–428 Exs. 16–46 even, 43, 53–59, 62–72 even

EXERCISE LEVELS

Level A: *Easier*
16–19, 48–50

Level B: *More Difficult*
20–47, 51–59

Level C: *Most Difficult*
60, 61

✓ HOMEWORK CHECK

To quickly check student understanding of key concepts, go over the following exercises: Exs. 18, 24, 26, 32, 38, 42. See also the Daily Homework Quiz:

- Blackline Master (*Chapter 7 Resource Book*, p. 68)
- Transparency (p. 52)

11–14. See Additional Answers beginning on page AA1.

STUDENT HELP NOTES

Homework Help Students can find help for Exs. 35–38 at **www.mcdougallittell.com.** The information can be printed out for students who don't have access to the Internet.

! COMMON ERROR

EXERCISES 39–42 Some students may confuse the horizontal and vertical moves from a preimage vertex. Suggest that they draw the vector with initial point (0, 0) The vectors from each preimage to its image should be parallel to the given vector.

31. 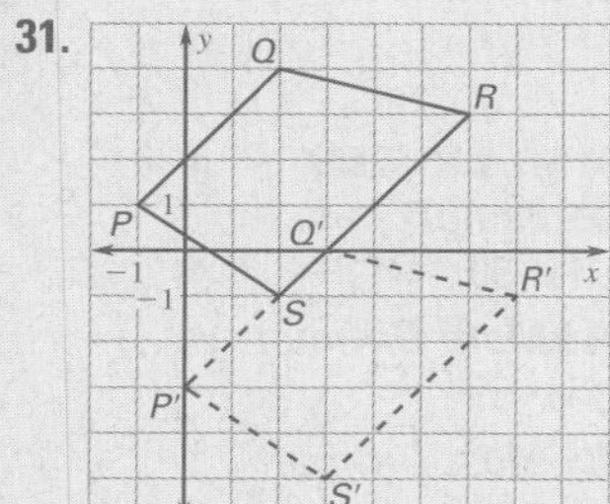

32. 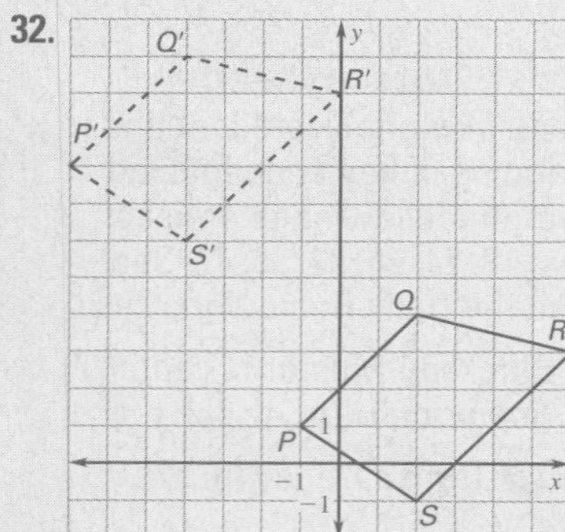

33. 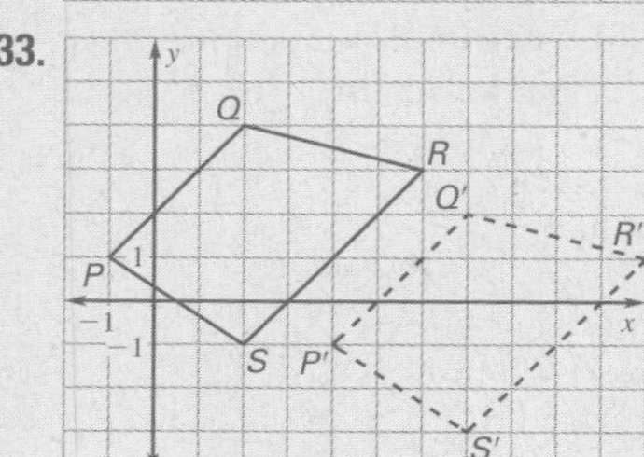

34. 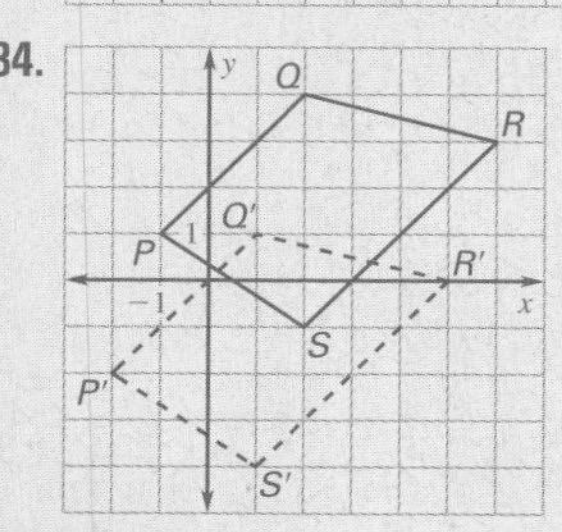

USING THEOREM 7.5 In the diagram, $k \parallel m$, $\triangle ABC$ is reflected in line k, and $\triangle A'B'C'$ is reflected in line m.

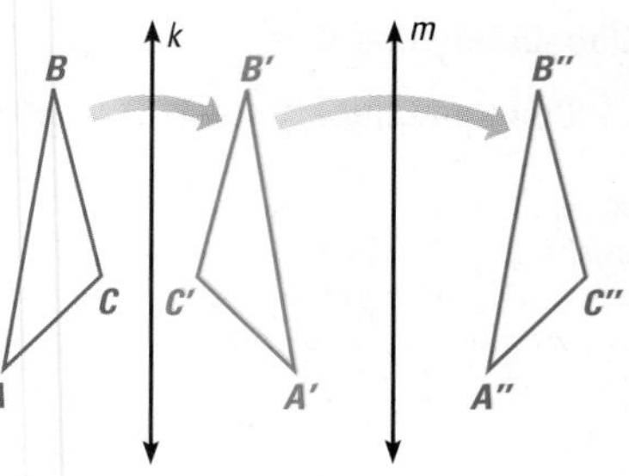

20. A translation maps $\triangle ABC$ onto which triangle? $\triangle A''B''C''$

21. Which lines are perpendicular to $\overleftrightarrow{AA''}$? *k* and *m*

22. Name two segments parallel to $\overline{BB''}$. *Sample answers:* $\overline{AA'}$, $\overline{CC'}$

23. If the distance between k and m is 1.4 inches, what is the length of $\overline{CC''}$? 2.8 in.

24. Is the distance from B' to m the same as the distance from B'' to m? Explain. yes; def. of reflection

IMAGE AND PREIMAGE Consider the translation that is defined by the coordinate notation $(x, y) \rightarrow (x + 12, y - 7)$.

25. What is the image of (5, 3)? (17, −4)

26. What is the image of (−1, −2)? (11, −9)

27. What is the preimage of (−2, 1)? (−14, 8)

28. What is the preimage of (0, −6)? (−12, 1)

29. What is the image of (0.5, 2.5)? (12.5, −4.5)

30. What is the preimage of (−5.5, −5.5)? (−17.5, 1.5)

DRAWING AN IMAGE Copy figure *PQRS* and draw its image after the translation. 31–34. See margin.

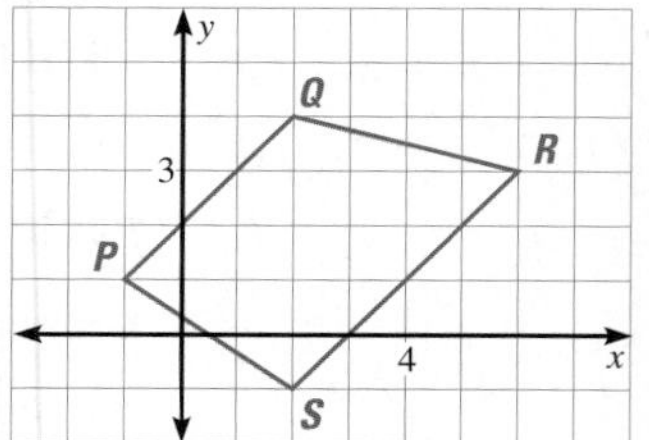

31. $(x, y) \rightarrow (x + 1, y - 4)$

32. $(x, y) \rightarrow (x - 6, y + 7)$

33. $(x, y) \rightarrow (x + 5, y - 2)$

34. $(x, y) \rightarrow (x - 1, y - 3)$

STUDENT HELP

HOMEWORK HELP
Visit our Web site www.mcdougallittell.com for help with Exs. 35–38.

LOGICAL REASONING Use a straightedge and graph paper to help determine whether the statement is true.

35. If line p is a translation of a different line q, then p is parallel to q. true

36. It is possible for a translation to map a line p onto a perpendicular line q. false

37. If a translation maps $\triangle ABC$ onto $\triangle DEF$ and a translation maps $\triangle DEF$ onto $\triangle GHK$, then a translation maps $\triangle ABC$ onto $\triangle GHK$. true

38. If a translation maps $\triangle ABC$ onto $\triangle DEF$, then $AD = BE = CF$. true

TRANSLATING A TRIANGLE In Exercises 39–42, use a straightedge and graph paper to translate $\triangle ABC$ by the given vector. 39–42. See margin.

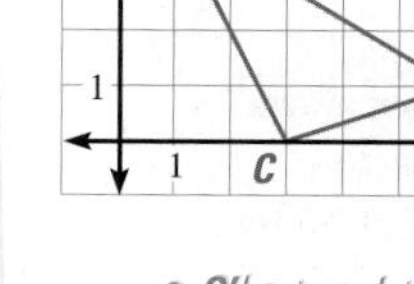

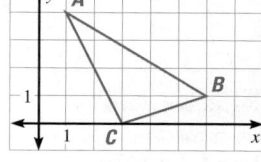

39. $\langle 2, 4\rangle$ **40.** $\langle 3, -2\rangle$

41. $\langle -1, -5\rangle$ **42.** $\langle -4, 1\rangle$

43. **PROOF** Use coordinate geometry and the Distance Formula to write a paragraph proof of Theorem 7.4.

GIVEN ▶ $PP' = QQ'$ and $\overline{PP'} \parallel \overline{QQ'}$

PROVE ▶ $PQ = P'Q'$ See margin.

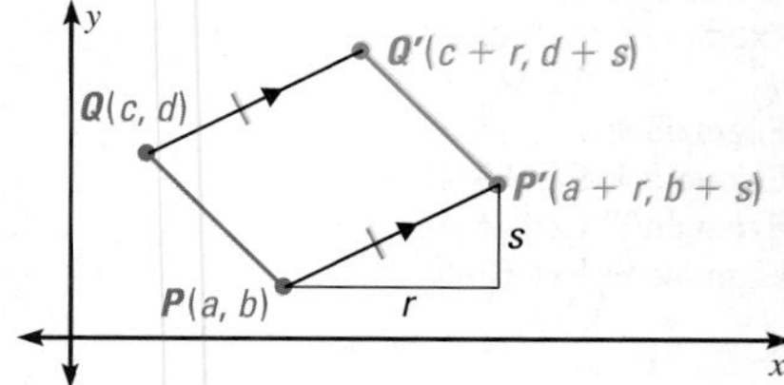

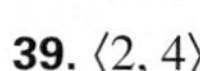

39–43. See Additional Answers beginning on page AA1.

VECTORS The vertices of the image of *GHJK* after a translation are given. Choose the vector that describes the translation.

A. $\overrightarrow{PQ} = \langle 1, -3 \rangle$ **B.** $\overrightarrow{PQ} = \langle 0, 1 \rangle$

C. $\overrightarrow{PQ} = \langle -1, -3 \rangle$ **D.** $\overrightarrow{PQ} = \langle 6, -1 \rangle$

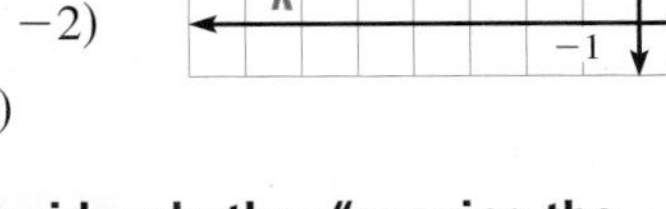

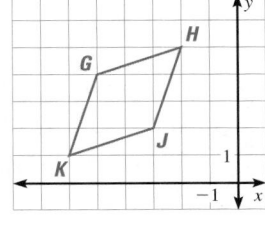

44. $G'(-6, 1), H'(-3, 2), J'(-4, -1), K'(-7, -2)$ C

45. $G'(1, 3), H'(4, 4), J'(3, 1), K'(0, 0)$ D

46. $G'(-4, 1), H'(-1, 2), J'(-2, -1), K'(-5, -2)$ A

47. $G'(-5, 5), H'(-2, 6), J'(-3, 3), K'(-6, 2)$ B

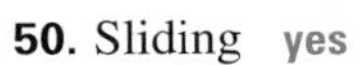

WINDOW FRAMES In Exercises 48–50, decide whether "opening the window" is a translation of the moving part.

48. Double hung yes **49.** Casement no **50.** Sliding yes

51. DATA COLLECTION Look through some newspapers and magazines to find patterns containing translations.
Samples might include photographs of floor tiles or of fabric patterns.

52. $C: (x, y) \rightarrow (x + 12, y)$, $D: (x, y) \rightarrow (x, y - 6)$, $E: (x, y) \rightarrow (x + 6, y - 6)$, $F: (x, y) \rightarrow (x + 12, y - 6)$

52. COMPUTER-AIDED DESIGN Mosaic floors can be designed on a computer. An example is shown at the right. On the computer, the design in square *A* is copied to cover an entire floor. The translation $(x, y) \rightarrow (x + 6, y)$ maps square *A* onto square *B*. Use coordinate notation to describe the translations that map square *A* onto squares *C*, *D*, *E*, and *F*.

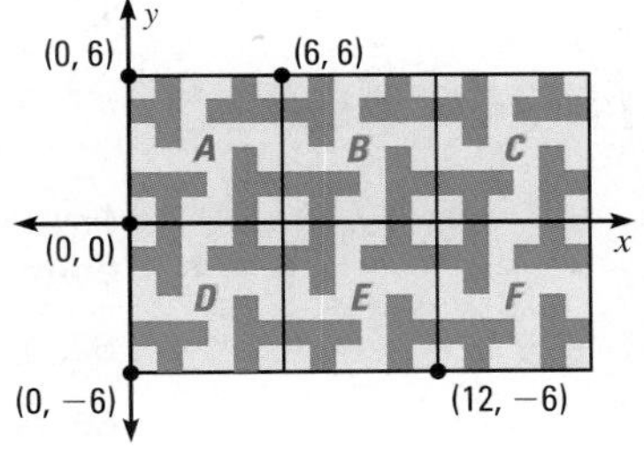

FOCUS ON APPLICATIONS

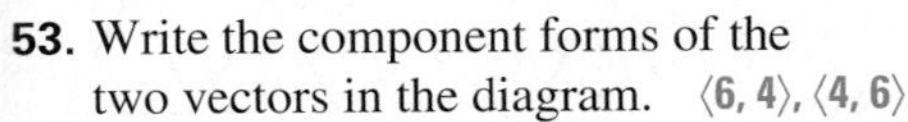

HOT-AIR BALLOONS
Bertrand Piccard and Brian Jones journeyed around the world in their hot-air balloon in 19 days.

NAVIGATION A hot-air balloon is flying from town *A* to town *D*. After the balloon leaves town *A* and travels 6 miles east and 4 miles north, it runs into some heavy winds at point *B*. The balloon is blown off course as shown in the diagram.

53. Write the component forms of the two vectors in the diagram. $\langle 6, 4 \rangle, \langle 4, 6 \rangle$

54. Write the component form of the vector that describes the path the balloon can take to arrive in town *D*. $\langle 8, 2 \rangle$

55. Suppose the balloon was not blown off course. Write the component form of the vector that describes this journey from town *A* to town *D*. $\langle 18, 12 \rangle$

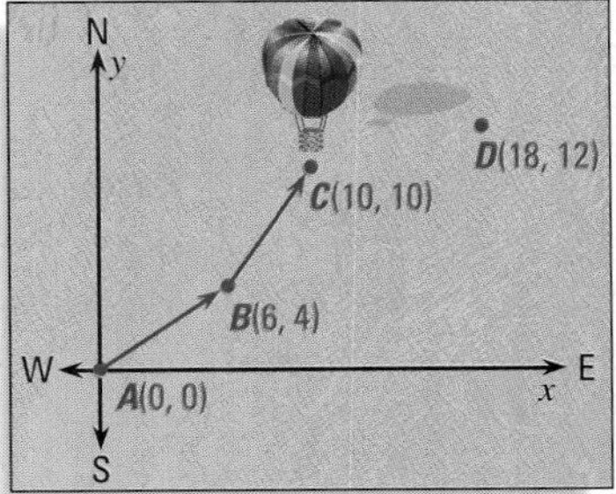

APPLICATION NOTE

EXERCISES 48–50 Students should recognize that double hung windows model a translation in only a vertical direction and a sliding window models a translation in only a horizontal direction. These translations provide ventilation from only one-half the window area. A casement window, however, provides ventilation from the entire window area.

EXERCISE 51 Students should look for graphs as well as logos and other designs. Bar charts, where two or more bars are the same height and pie charts with exploded sectors can also model translations.

EXERCISE 52 A translation of the rectangle of squares *A, B,* and *C* can also produce the rectangle of squares *D, E,* and *F.*

ADDITIONAL PRACTICE AND RETEACHING

For Lesson 7.4:

- Practice Levels A, B, and C (*Chapter 7 Resource Book,* p. 57)
- Reteaching with Practice (*Chapter 7 Resource Book,* p. 60)
-  See Lesson 7.4 of the *Personal Student Tutor*

For more Mixed Review:

- Search the *Test and Practice Generator* for key words or specific lessons.

4 ASSESS

DAILY HOMEWORK QUIZ

Transparency Available

1. Describe the translation using (**a**) coordinate notation and (**b**) a vector in component form.

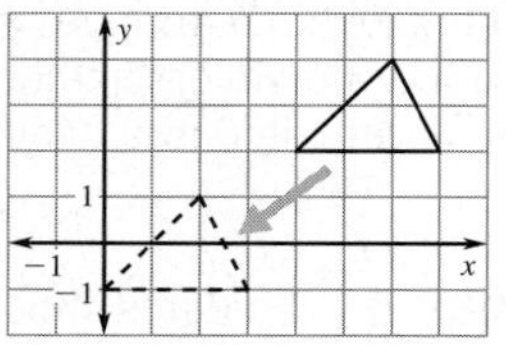

$(x, y) \rightarrow (x - 4, y - 3)$; $\langle -4, -3 \rangle$

2. Name the vector and write its component form.

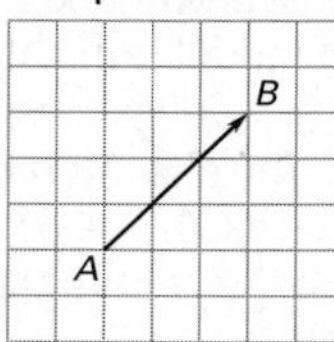

$\overrightarrow{AB} = \langle 3, 3 \rangle$

3. Consider the translation that is defined by the coordinate notation $(x, y) \rightarrow (x + 4, y - 1)$.

a. What is the image of (2, 5)? (6, 4)

b. What is the preimage of (−1, 3)? (−5, 4)

4. The vertices of $\triangle ABC$ are $A(-5, 3)$, $B(4, 2)$, and $C(-1, -1)$. Name the vector that describes a translation such that $A'(-2, -1)$, $B'(7, -2)$, and $C'(2, -5)$. $\langle 3, -4 \rangle$

EXTRA CHALLENGE NOTE

Challenge problems for Lesson 7.4 are available in **blackline** format in the *Chapter 7 Resource Book,* p. 65 and at **www.mcdougallittell.com.**

ADDITIONAL TEST PREPARATION

1. OPEN ENDED Give an example of a translation of a plane figure in the coordinate plane that maps a first quadrant figure to a third quadrant figure. See margin.

Test Preparation

QUANTITATIVE COMPARISON In Exercises 56–59, choose the statement that is true about the given quantities.

Ⓐ The quantity in column A is greater.

Ⓑ The quantity in column B is greater.

Ⓒ The two quantities are equal.

Ⓓ The relationship cannot be determined from the given information.

The translation $(x, y) \rightarrow (x + 5, y - 3)$ maps $\overline{AB}$ to $\overline{A'B'}$, and the translation $(x, y) \rightarrow (x + 5, y)$ maps $\overline{A'B'}$ to $\overline{A''B''}$.

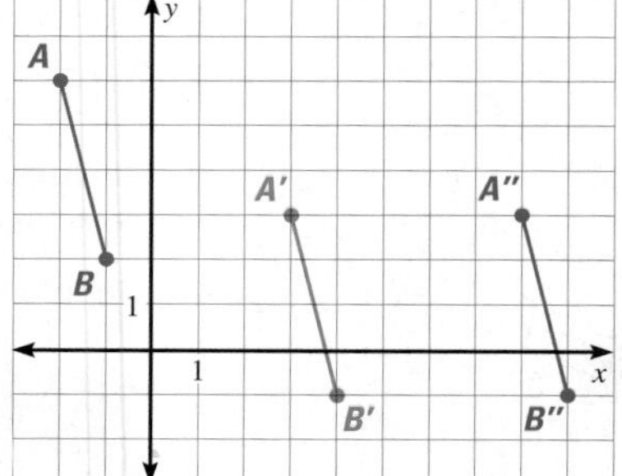

	Column A	Column B	
56.	AB	$A'B'$	C
57.	AB	AA'	B
58.	BB'	$A'A''$	A
59.	$A'B''$	$A''B'$	A

★ Challenge

USING ALGEBRA A translation of $\overline{AB}$ is described by $\overrightarrow{PQ}$. Find the value of each variable.

60. $\overrightarrow{PQ} = \langle 4, 1 \rangle$

$A(-1, w)$, $A'(2x + 1, 4)$

$B(8y - 1, 1)$, $B'(3, 3z)$

$w = 3, x = 1, y = 0, z = \frac{2}{3}$

61. $\overrightarrow{PQ} = \langle 3, -6 \rangle$

$A(r - 1, 8)$, $A'(3, s + 1)$

$B(2t - 2, u)$, $B'(5, -2u)$

$r = 1, s = 1, t = 2, u = 2$

EXTRA CHALLENGE

www.mcdougallittell.com

MIXED REVIEW

FINDING SLOPE Find the slope of the line that passes through the given points. (Review 3.6)

62. $A(0, -2)$, $B(-7, -8)$ **63.** $C(2, 3)$, $D(-1, 18)$ **64.** $E(-10, 1)$, $F(-1, 1)$

65. $G(-2, 12)$, $H(-1, 6)$ **66.** $J(-6, 0)$, $K(0, 10)$ **67.** $M(-3, -3)$, $N(9, 6)$

62. $\frac{6}{7}$
63. −5
64. 0
65. −6
66. $\frac{5}{3}$
67. $\frac{3}{4}$

COMPLETING THE STATEMENT In $\triangle JKL$, points Q, R, and S are midpoints of the sides. (Review 5.4)

68. If $JK = 12$, then $SR =$ __?__. 6

69. If $QR = 6$, then $JL =$ __?__. 12

70. If $RL = 6$, then $QS =$ __?__. 6

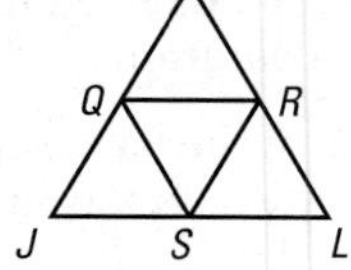

REFLECTIONS IN A COORDINATE PLANE Decide whether the statement is *true* or *false*. (Review 7.2 for 7.5)

71. If $N(3, 4)$ is reflected in the line $y = -1$, then N' is $(3, -6)$. true

72. If $M(-5, 3)$ is reflected in the line $x = -2$, then M' is $(3, 1)$. false

73. If $W(4, 3)$ is reflected in the line $y = 2$, then W' is $(1, 4)$. false

Additional Test Preparation *Sample answer:*

1. The transformation $(x, y) \rightarrow (x - 5, y - 6)$ maps $\triangle ABC$ with vertices $A(2, 1)$, $B(4, 3)$, and $C(4, 5)$ to $\triangle A'B'C'$, whose vertices are $A'(-3, -5)$, $B'(-1, -3)$, and $C'(-1, -1)$.

Multiple Transformations

GROUP ACTIVITY
Work with a partner.

MATERIALS
- graph paper
- ruler
- protractor
- compass

QUESTION **Does the order in which two transformations are performed affect the final image?**

EXPLORING THE CONCEPT Steps 1, 2. Check drawings.

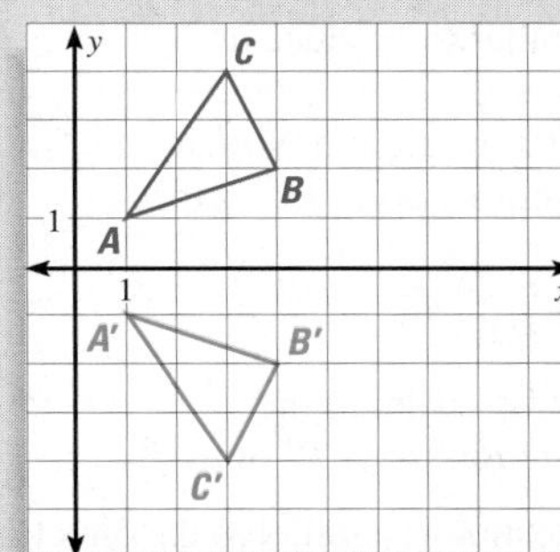

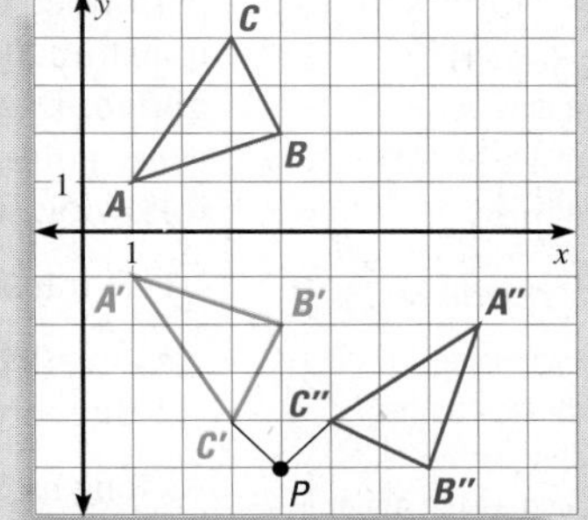

1. Draw △*ABC* with vertices *A*(1, 1), *B*(4, 2), and *C*(3, 4). Reflect △*ABC* in the *x*-axis to obtain △*A′B′C′*.

2. Rotate △*A′B′C′* 90° clockwise about *P*(4, −5) to obtain △*A″B″C″*.

INVESTIGATE

1. Name the coordinates of △*A″B″C″*. *A″*(8, −2), *B″*(7, −5), *C″*(5, −4)

2. Repeat **Steps 1** and **2**, but switch the order of the transformations by performing the rotation first and the reflection second. Name the coordinates of △*A″B″C″*. *A″*(10, 2), *B″*(11, 5), *C″*(13, 4)

MAKE A CONJECTURE

3. Does the order in which transformations are completed affect the final image? conjecture: yes

INVESTIGATE

4. *H″*(11, −3), *J″*(8, −7), *K″*(11, −8)

4. Copy △*HJK*. Reflect △*HJK* in the line $x = 6$ to obtain △*H′J′K′*. Then translate △*H′J′K′* using $(x, y) \rightarrow (x, y - 6)$ to obtain △*H″J″K″*. Name the coordinates of △*H″J″K″*.

5. *H″*(11, −3), *J″*(8, −7), *K″*(11, −8); the coordinates are the same; in this case, the order did not affect the final image.

5. Repeat Exercise 4, but switch the order of the transformations. Name the coordinates of △*H″J″K″* and compare them with the coordinates of △*H″J″K″* from Exercise 4. What do you notice?

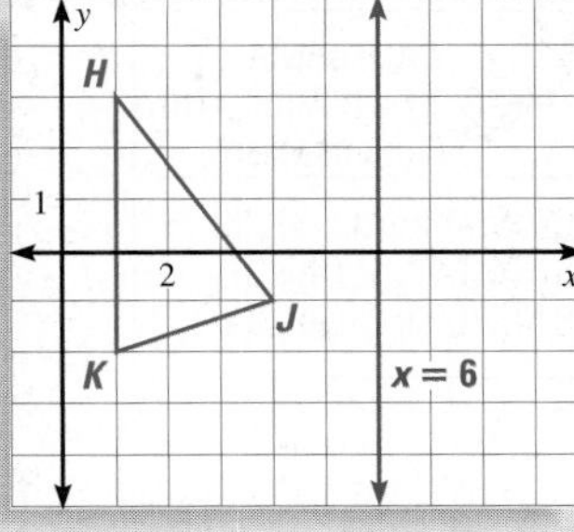

By the Distance Formula, $A''B'' = AB = \sqrt{10}$, $B''C'' = BC = \sqrt{5}$, and $A''C'' = AC = \sqrt{13}$, so by definition, the transformation is an isometry.

EXTENSION

CRITICAL THINKING Use the Distance Formula to show that the transformation that maps △*ABC* onto △*A″B″C″* in **Step 2** is an isometry.

1 Planning the Activity

PURPOSE
To investigate the results of multiple transformations.

MATERIALS
- graph paper
- ruler
- protractor
- compass

PACING
- Exploring the Concept — 10 min
- Investigate — 15 min

LINK TO LESSON
Students should recall the results of this activity as they study glide reflections in Lesson 7.5.

2 Managing the Activity

ALTERNATIVE APPROACH
If you have access to computers and software, have students complete the activity using geometry software.

3 Closing the Activity

KEY DISCOVERY
When a translation and a reflection are performed to produce a transformation, the order in which the translation and the reflection are performed may or may not affect the image.

ACTIVITY ASSESSMENT
△*ABC* with vertices *A*(1, 2), *B*(3, 1), and *C*(4, 2) is reflected in the *y*-axis to produce △*A′B′C′*. Then △*A′B′C′* is translated using $(x, y) \rightarrow (x + 1, y - 4)$ to produce △*A″B″C″*. What are the coordinates of the vertices of △*A″B″C″*? What are the coordinates if the translation is performed first?
A″(0, −2), *B″*(−2, −3), *C″*(−3, −2);
A″(−2, −2), *B″*(−4, −3), *C″*(−5, −2)

1 PLAN

PACING
Basic: 2 days
Average: 2 days
Advanced: 2 days
Block Schedule: 0.5 block with 7.4
0.5 block with 7.6

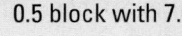

LESSON OPENER
APPLICATION
An alternative way to approach Lesson 7.5 is to use the Application Lesson Opener:

- Blackline Master (*Chapter 7 Resource Book*, p. 69)
- Transparency (p. 45)

MEETING INDIVIDUAL NEEDS

- ***Chapter 7 Resource Book***
  Prerequisite Skills Review (p. 5)
  Practice Level A (p. 74)
  Practice Level B (p. 75)
  Practice Level C (p. 76)
  Reteaching with Practice (p. 77)
  Absent Student Catch-Up (p. 79)
  Challenge (p. 81)
- ***Resources in Spanish***
- 

NEW-TEACHER SUPPORT
See the Tips for New Teachers on pp. 1–2 of the *Chapter 7 Resource Book* for additional notes about Lesson 7.5.

WARM-UP EXERCISES

Transparency Available

$\overline{PQ}$ has endpoints $P(-4, -4)$ and $Q(-1, -3)$. Find the coordinates of P' and Q' after each translation.

1. $(x, y) \rightarrow (x, y + 3)$
   $P'(-4, -1)$, $Q'(-1, 0)$
2. $(x, y) \rightarrow (x + 1, y - 1)$
   $P'(-3, -5)$, $Q'(0, -4)$
3. Find the coordinates of the endpoints of $\overline{P'Q'}$ after $\overline{PQ}$ is rotated 180° about the origin.
   $P'(4, 4)$, $Q'(1, 3)$
4. Find the coordinates of $\overline{P'Q'}$ after $\overline{PQ}$ is reflected in the x-axis. $P'(-4, 4)$, $Q'(-1, 3)$

7.5 Glide Reflections and Compositions

What you should learn

GOAL 1 Identify glide reflections in a plane.

GOAL 2 Represent transformations as compositions of simpler transformations.

Why you should learn it

▼ Compositions of transformations can help when creating patterns in **real life**, such as the decorative pattern below and in **Exs. 35–37**.

CA Standards: 17, 22
SAT9 Task 1: Obj. 31
SAT9 Task 2: Obj. 34

GOAL 1 USING GLIDE REFLECTIONS

A translation, or glide, and a reflection can be performed one after the other to produce a transformation known as a *glide reflection*. A **glide reflection** is a transformation in which every point P is mapped onto a point P'' by the following steps:

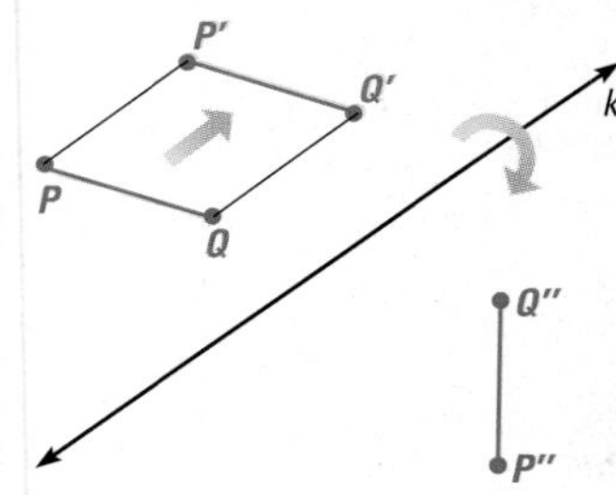

1. A translation maps P onto P'.
2. A reflection in a line k parallel to the direction of the translation maps P' onto P''.

As long as the line of reflection is parallel to the direction of the translation, it does not matter whether you glide first and then reflect, or reflect first and then glide.

EXAMPLE 1 *Finding the Image of a Glide Reflection*

Use the information below to sketch the image of $\triangle ABC$ after a glide reflection.

$A(-1, -3)$, $B(-4, -1)$, $C(-6, -4)$

Translation: $(x, y) \rightarrow (x + 10, y)$

Reflection: in the x-axis

SOLUTION

Begin by graphing $\triangle ABC$. Then, shift the triangle 10 units to the right to produce $\triangle A'B'C'$. Finally, reflect the triangle in the x-axis to produce $\triangle A''B''C''$.

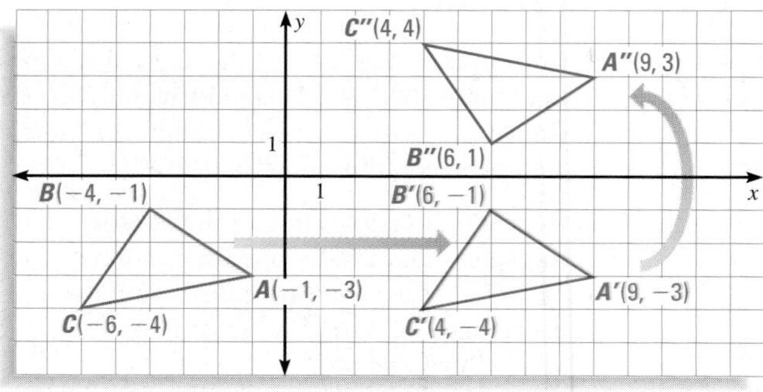

....

In Example 1, try reversing the order of the transformations. Notice that the resulting image will have the same coordinates as $\triangle A''B''C''$ above. This is true because the line of reflection is parallel to the direction of the translation.

GOAL 2 USING COMPOSITIONS

When two or more transformations are combined to produce a single transformation, the result is called a **composition** of the transformations.

THEOREM

THEOREM 7.6 *Composition Theorem*

The composition of two (or more) isometries is an isometry.

Because a glide reflection is a composition of a translation and a reflection, this theorem implies that glide reflections are isometries. In a glide reflection, the order in which the transformations are performed does not affect the final image. For other compositions of transformations, the order may affect the final image.

EXAMPLE 2 *Finding the Image of a Composition*

Sketch the image of $\overline{PQ}$ after a composition of the given rotation and reflection.

$P(2, -2)$, $Q(3, -4)$

Rotation: 90° counterclockwise about the origin

Reflection: in the y-axis

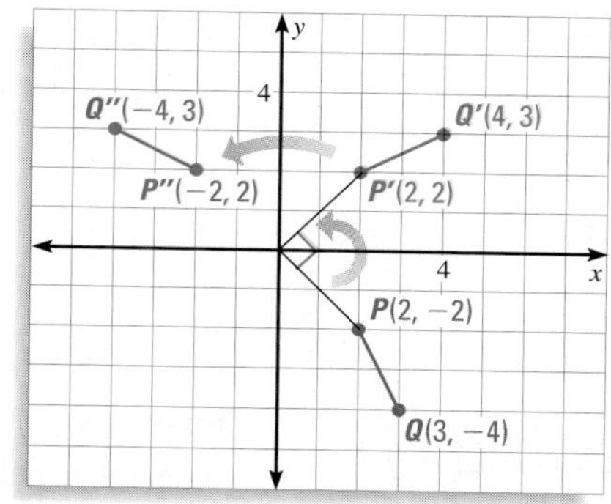

SOLUTION

Begin by graphing $\overline{PQ}$. Then rotate the segment 90° counterclockwise about the origin to produce $\overline{P'Q'}$. Finally, reflect the segment in the y-axis to produce $\overline{P''Q''}$.

EXAMPLE 3 *Comparing Orders of Compositions*

Repeat Example 2, but switch the order of the composition by performing the reflection first and the rotation second. What do you notice?

SOLUTION

Graph $\overline{PQ}$. Then reflect the segment in the y-axis to obtain $\overline{P'Q'}$. Rotate $\overline{P'Q'}$ 90° counterclockwise about the origin to obtain $\overline{P''Q''}$. Instead of being in Quadrant II, as in Example 2, the image is in Quadrant IV.

▶ The order which the transformations are performed affects the final image.

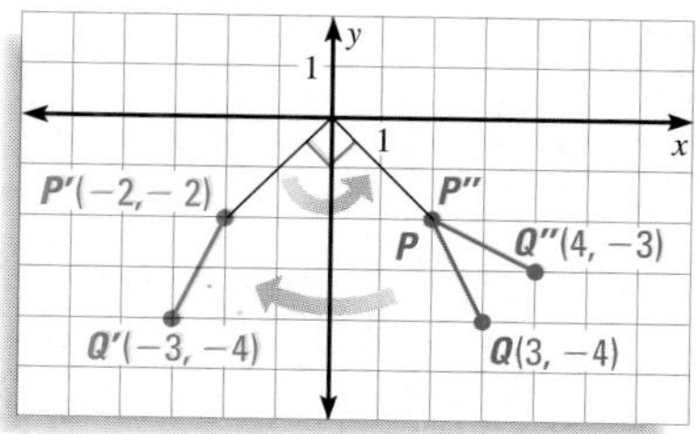

STUDENT HELP

Study Tip

Unlike the addition or multiplication of real numbers, the composition of transformations is not generally commutative.

2 TEACH

EXTRA EXAMPLE 1

Use the information below to sketch the image of $\triangle QRS$ after a glide reflection.

$Q(2, -3)$, $R(4, -4)$ and $S(5, -1)$

translation: $(x, y) \rightarrow (x, y + 5)$

reflection: in the y-axis.

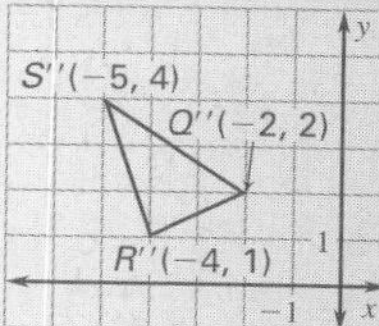

EXTRA EXAMPLE 2

Sketch the image of $\overline{CD}$ after a composition of the given rotation and reflection. $C(2, 0)$, $D(3, 3)$

reflection: in the x-axis

rotation: 270° counterclockwise about the origin

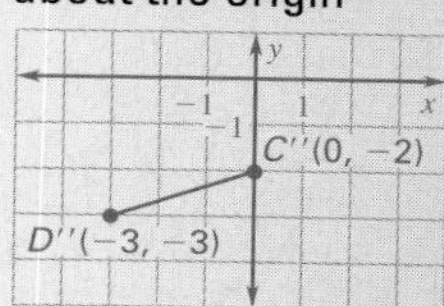

EXTRA EXAMPLE 3

Repeat Extra Example 2, but switch the order of the composition by performing the rotation first and the reflection second. What do you notice?

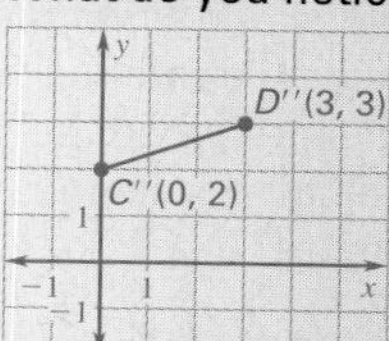

The order in which the transformations are performed affects the final image.

CHECKPOINT EXERCISES

For use after Examples 1–3:

1. State the coordinates of the image of $\overline{EF}$ after a composition of the given rotation and translation. $E(-3, 5)$, $F(2, 7)$

rotation: 270° clockwise about the origin

translation: $(x, y) \rightarrow (x - 3, y + 1)$

$E''(-8, -2)$, $F''(-10, 3)$

Extra Example 4

Describe the composition of transformations in the diagram.

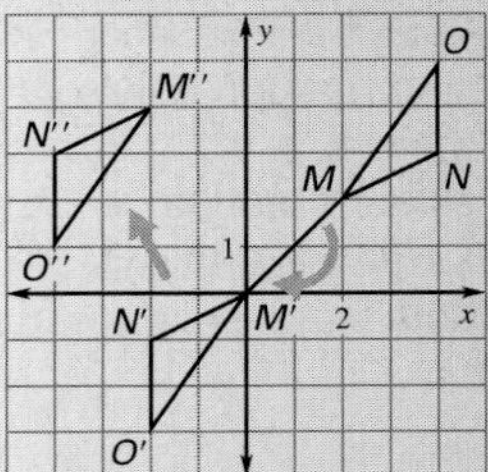

$\triangle MNO$ is first rotated 180° about the point (1, 1) to produce $\triangle M'N'O'$. Then $\triangle M'N'O'$ is translated by $(x, y) \rightarrow (x - 2, y + 4)$ to produce $\triangle M''N''O''$.

Extra Example 5

Describe the composition of transformations in the diagram.

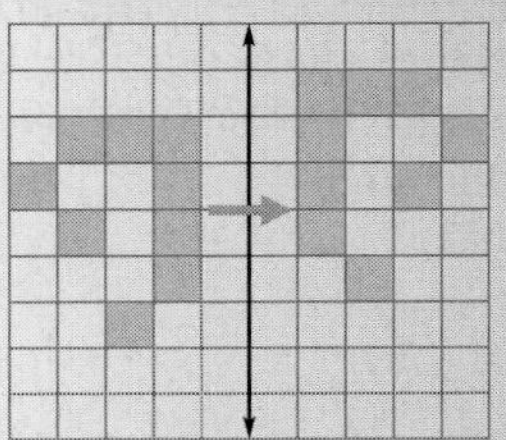

The figure on the left is translated up one unit and reflected over the vertical line shown. The order of transformations does not matter.

Checkpoint Exercises

For use after Examples 4 and 5:

1. Which series of transformations including a rotation and a reflection produced the unshaded figure from the shaded figure?

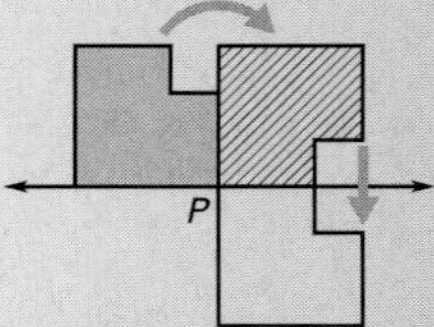

a 90° clockwise rotation and then a reflection over a horizontal line

Closure Question

Since reflections, rotations, and translations are all isometries, what can you say about a glide reflection? **It is an isometry.**

EXAMPLE 4 Describing a Composition

Describe the composition of transformations in the diagram.

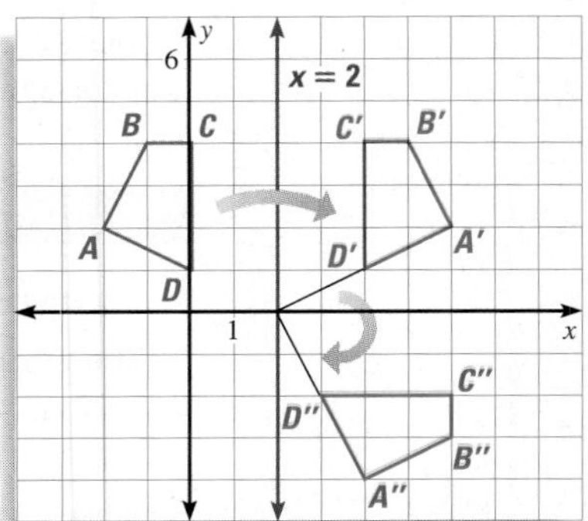

Solution

Two transformations are shown. First, figure $ABCD$ is reflected in the line $x = 2$ to produce figure $A'B'C'D'$. Then, figure $A'B'C'D'$ is rotated 90° clockwise about the point (2, 0) to produce figure $A''B''C''D''$.

EXAMPLE 5 Describing a Composition

REAL LIFE **PUZZLES** The mathematical game pentominoes is a tiling game that uses twelve different types of tiles, each composed of five squares. The tiles are referred to by the letters they resemble. The object of the game is to pick up and arrange the tiles to create a given shape. Use compositions of transformations to describe how the tiles below will complete the 6 × 5 rectangle.

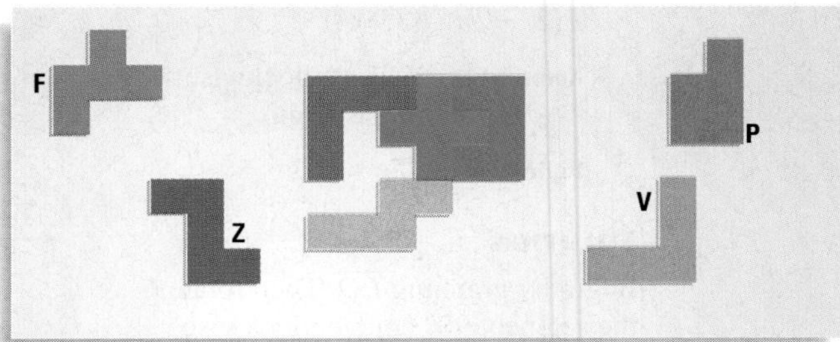

STUDENT HELP

Study Tip
You can make your own pentomino tiles by cutting the shapes out of graph paper.

Solution

To complete part of the rectangle, rotate the F tile 90° clockwise, reflect the tile over a horizontal line, and translate it into place.

To complete the rest of the rectangle, rotate the P tile 90° clockwise, reflect the tile over a vertical line, and translate it into place.

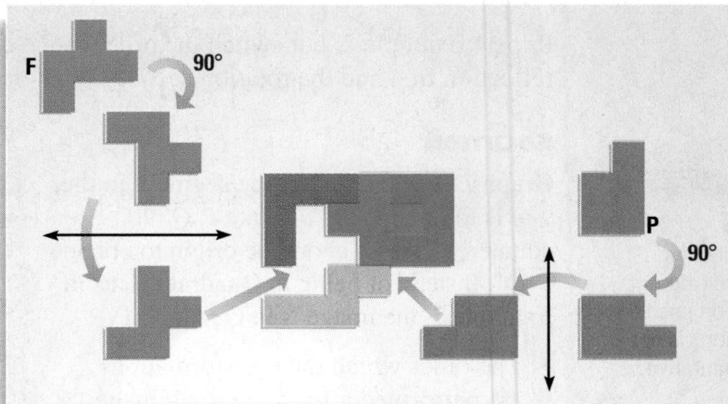

GUIDED PRACTICE

Vocabulary Check ✓

1. In a glide reflection, the direction of the __?__ must be parallel to the line of __?__. **translation; reflection**

Concept Check ✓

Complete the statement with *always, sometimes,* or *never*.

2. The order in which two transformations are performed __?__ affects the resulting image. **sometimes**

3. In a glide reflection, the order in which the two transformations are performed __?__ matters. **never**

4. A composition of isometries is __?__ an isometry. **always**

Skill Check ✓

In the diagram, $\overline{AB}$ is the preimage of a glide reflection.

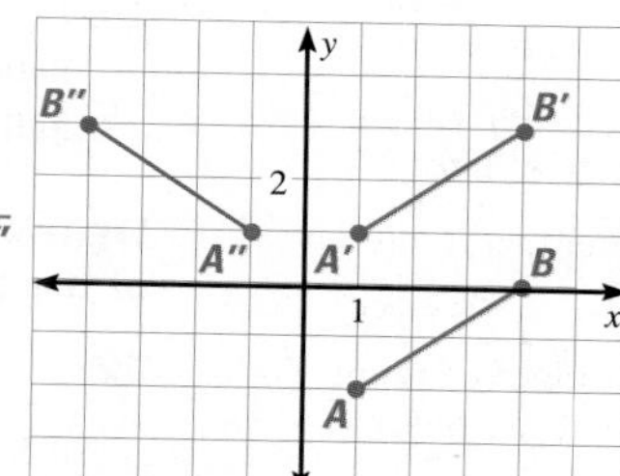

5. Which segment is a translation of $\overline{AB}$? $\overline{A'B'}$

6. Which segment is a reflection of $\overline{A'B'}$? $\overline{A''B''}$

7. Name the line of reflection. **the *y*-axis**

8. Use coordinate notation to describe the translation. $(x, y) \rightarrow (x, y + 3)$

PRACTICE AND APPLICATIONS

STUDENT HELP
Extra Practice to help you master skills is on p. 816.

LOGICAL REASONING **Match the composition with the diagram, in which the blue figure is the preimage of the red figure and the red figure is the preimage of the green figure.**

A.

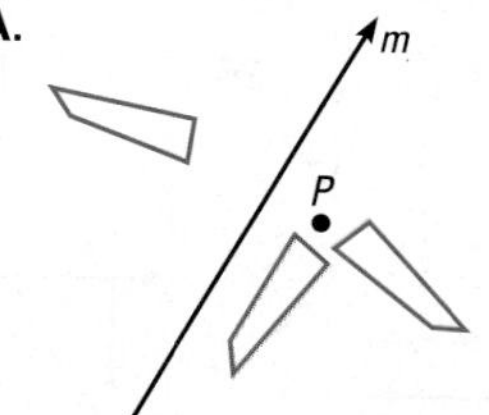

B.

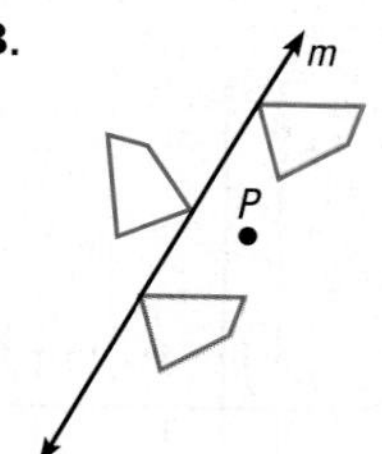

C.

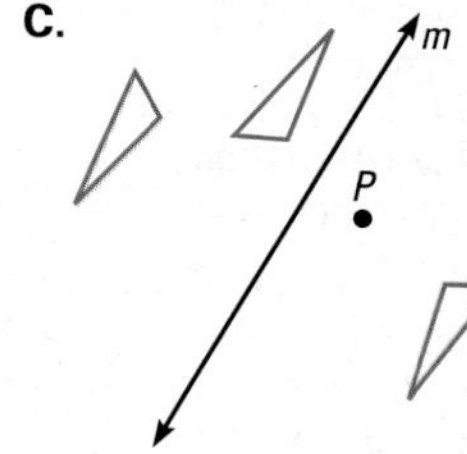

9. Rotate about point P, then reflect in line m. **A**

10. Reflect in line m, then rotate about point P. **C**

11. Translate parallel to line m, then rotate about point P. **B**

STUDENT HELP
HOMEWORK HELP
Example 1: Exs. 9–15
Example 2: Exs. 16–19
Example 3: Exs. 20, 21
Example 4: Exs. 22–25
Example 5: Ex. 38

FINDING AN IMAGE **Sketch the image of $A(-3, 5)$ after the described glide reflection.**

12. **Translation:** $(x, y) \rightarrow (x, y - 4)$
Reflection: in the y-axis **(3, 1)**

13. **Translation:** $(x, y) \rightarrow (x + 4, y + 1)$
Reflection: in $y = -2$ **(1, −10)**

14. **Translation:** $(x, y) \rightarrow (x - 6, y - 1)$
Reflection: in $x = -1$ **(7, 4)**

15. **Translation:** $(x, y) \rightarrow (x - 3, y - 3)$
Reflection: in $y = x$ **(2, −6)**

3 APPLY

ASSIGNMENT GUIDE

BASIC
Day 1: pp. 433–434 Exs. 9–21
Day 2: pp. 434–436 Exs. 22–27, 29, 30, 32–34, 39, 41–45, 46–54 even

AVERAGE
Day 1: pp. 433–434 Exs. 9–21
Day 2: pp. 434–436 Exs. 22–27, 29, 30, 32–39, 41–45, 46–54 even

ADVANCED
Day 1: pp. 433–434 Exs. 9–21
Day 2: pp. 434–436 Exs. 22–27, 29, 30, 32–45, 46–54 even

BLOCK SCHEDULE
pp. 433–434 Exs. 9–21 (with 7.4)
pp. 434–436 Exs. 22–27, 29, 30, 32–39, 41–45, 46–54 even (with 7.6)

EXERCISE LEVELS

Level A: ***Easier***
9–11
Level B: ***More Difficult***
12–39
Level C: ***Most Difficult***
40

✓ HOMEWORK CHECK

To quickly check student understanding of key concepts, go over the following exercises: Exs. 10, 14, 18, 20, 22, 30, 34. See also the Daily Homework Quiz:

- Blackline Master (*Chapter 7 Resource Book,* p. 84)
- Transparency (p. 53)

STUDENT HELP NOTES

Homework Help Students can find help for Exs. 16–19 at **www.mcdougallittell.com.** The information can be printed out for students who don't have access to the Internet.

MATHEMATICAL REASONING EXERCISES 22–24 Point out to students that more than one composition of transformations may describe a transformation. For example, in Exercise 24, a rotation about P followed by a slide or a rotation about (0, 1) can produce $\overline{P'Q'}$.

16.

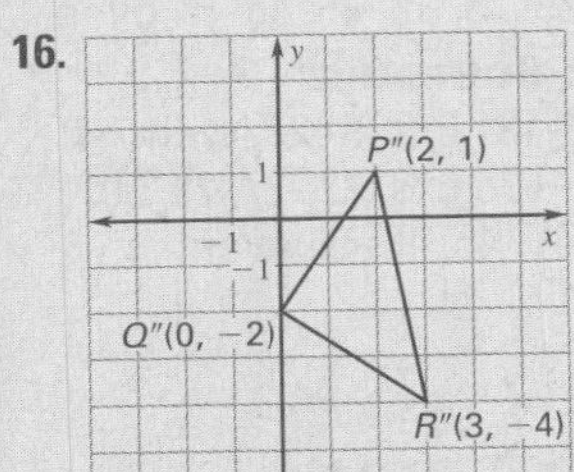

17.

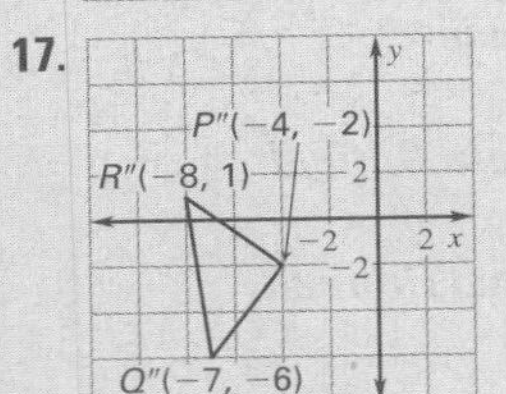

18.

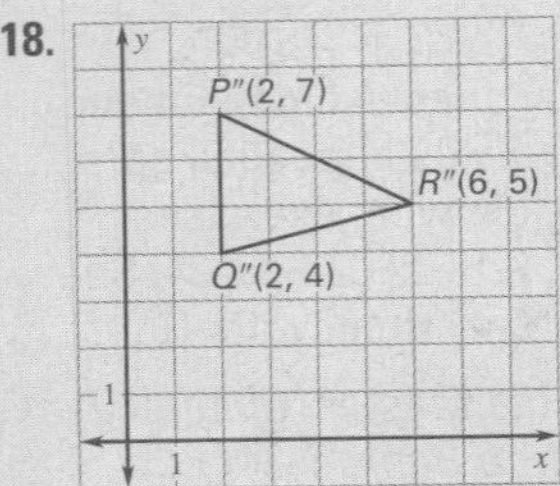

19.

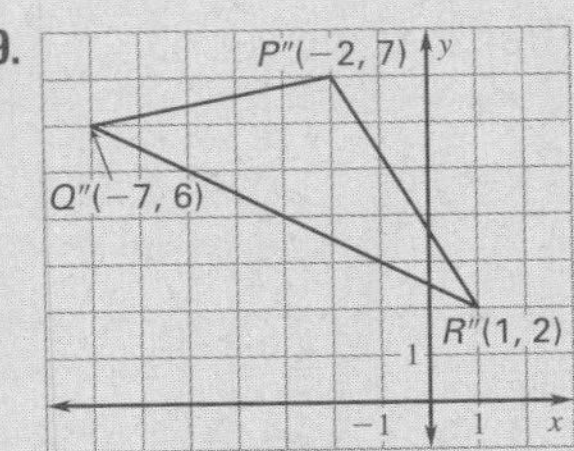

20–21. See Additional Answers beginning on page AA1.

STUDENT HELP

HOMEWORK HELP Visit our Web site www.mcdougallittell.com for help with Exs. 16–19.

SKETCHING COMPOSITIONS Sketch the image of $\triangle PQR$ after a composition using the given transformations in the order they appear. 16–19. See margin.

16. $P(4, 2)$, $Q(7, 0)$, $R(9, 3)$
Translation: $(x, y) \to (x - 2, y + 3)$
Rotation: 90° clockwise about $T(0, 3)$

17. $P(4, 5)$, $Q(7, 1)$, $R(8, 8)$
Translation: $(x, y) \to (x, y - 7)$
Reflection: in the y-axis

18. $P(-9, -2)$, $Q(-9, -5)$, $R(-5, -4)$
Translation: $(x, y) \to (x + 14, y + 1)$
Translation: $(x, y) \to (x - 3, y + 8)$

19. $P(-7, 2)$, $Q(-6, 7)$, $R(-2, -1)$
Reflection: in the x-axis
Rotation: 90° clockwise about origin

REVERSING ORDERS Sketch the image of $\overline{FG}$ after a composition using the given transformations in the order they appear. Then, perform the transformations in reverse order. Does the order affect the final image?

20, 21. See margin for sketches.

20. The order does affect the final image.

21. The order does affect the final image.

20. $F(4, -4)$, $G(1, -2)$
Rotation: 90° clockwise about origin
Reflection: in the y-axis

21. $F(-1, -3)$, $G(-4, -2)$
Reflection: in the line $x = 1$
Translation: $(x, y) \to (x + 2, y + 10)$

DESCRIBING COMPOSITIONS In Exercises 22–25, describe the composition of the transformations.

22. reflection in the line $y = -\frac{1}{2}$, followed by 90° clockwise rotation about the origin

23. reflection in the line $y = 2$, followed by reflection in the line $x = -2$

24. 90° clockwise rotation about the origin, followed by the translation $(x, y) \to (x, y - 3)$

25. 90° counterclockwise rotation about the point (0, 1), followed by the translation $(x, y) \to (x + 2, y + 3)$

26. A glide reflection is a composition of a translation and a reflection, both of which are isometries. The composition of two isometries is an isometry.

22.

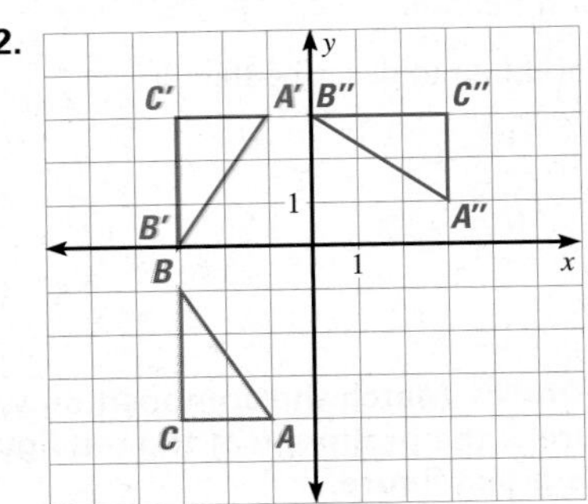

23.

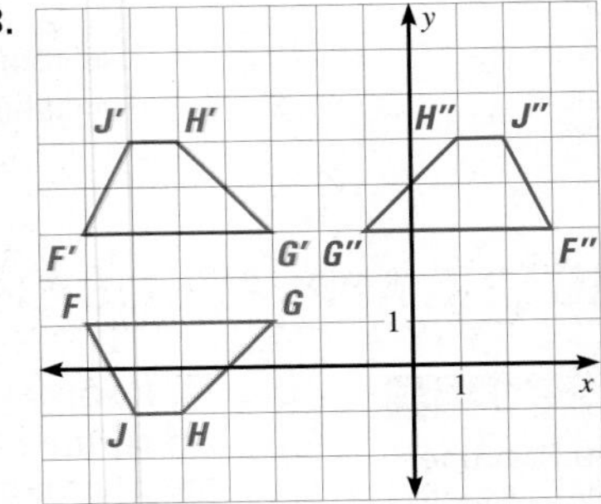

24.

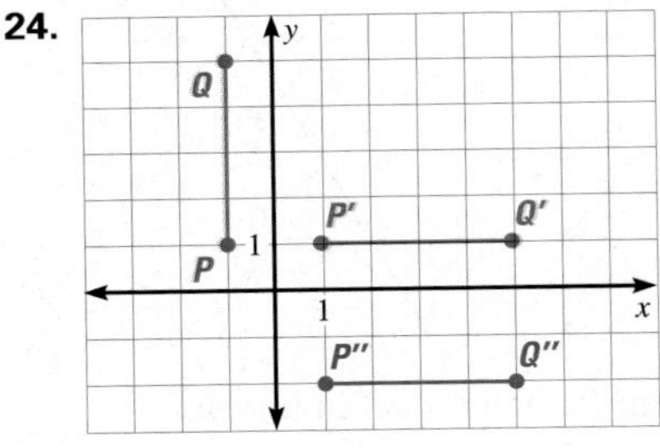

25.

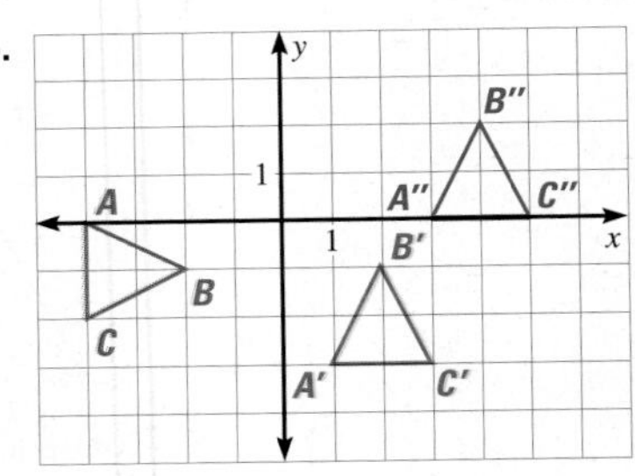

26. *Writing* Explain why a glide reflection is an isometry. See margin.

27. **LOGICAL REASONING** Which are preserved by a glide reflection? A, B, C

A. distance **B.** angle measure **C.** parallel lines

28. **TECHNOLOGY** Use geometry software to draw a polygon. Show that if you reflect the polygon and then translate it in a direction that is *not* parallel to the line of reflection, then the final image is *different* from the final image if you perform the translation first and the reflection second. Check drawings.

CRITICAL THINKING In Exercises 29 and 30, the first translation maps J to J' and the second maps J' to J''. Find the translation that maps J to J''.

29. Translation 1: $(x, y) \rightarrow (x + 7, y - 2)$
Translation 2: $(x, y) \rightarrow (x - 1, y + 3)$
Translation: $(x, y) \rightarrow (\underline{?}, \underline{?})$
$(x, y) \rightarrow (x + 6, y + 1)$

30. Translation 1: $(x, y) \rightarrow (x + 9, y + 4)$
Translation 2: $(x, y) \rightarrow (x + 6, y - 4)$
Translation: $(x, y) \rightarrow (\underline{?}, \underline{?})$
$(x, y) \rightarrow (x + 15, y)$

31. **STENCILING A BORDER** The border pattern below was made with a stencil. Describe how the border was created using one stencil four times.

31. After each part was painted, the stencil was moved through a glide reflection (reflection in a horizontal line through its center and translation to the right) to paint the next part.

CLOTHING PATTERNS The diagram shows the pattern pieces for a jacket arranged on some blue fabric.

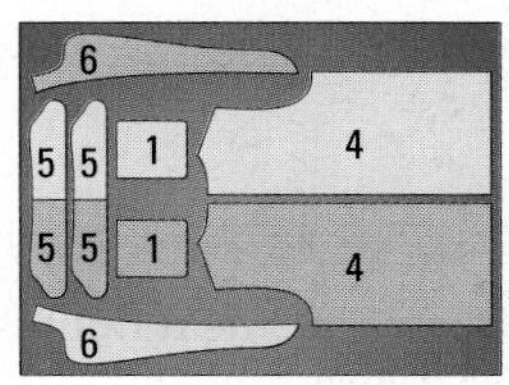

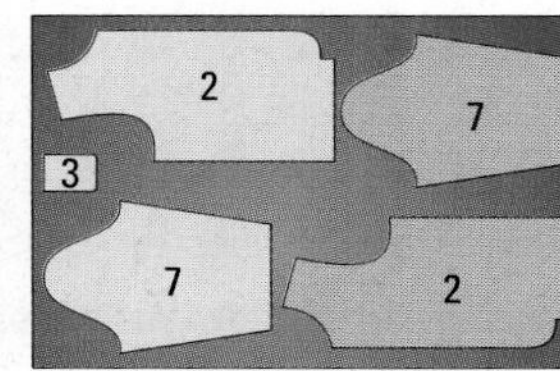

Pattern right side up
Pattern right side down
Fabric

32. Which pattern pieces are translated? 5
33. Which pattern pieces are reflected? 1, 4, 5, 6
34. Which pattern pieces are glide reflected? 2, 7

ARCHITECTURE In Exercises 35–37, describe the transformations that are combined to create the pattern in the architectural element.
35–37. See margin.

35. 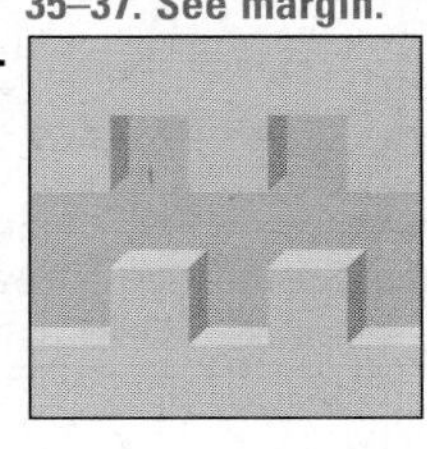

36. 

37. 

38. **PENTOMINOES** Use compositions of transformations to describe how to pick up and arrange the tiles to complete the 6×10 rectangle.

Sample answer: Rotate the X tile 90° clockwise, then reflect it in a horizontal line. Rotate the Y tile 90° counterclockwise, then reflect it in a horizontal line.

FOCUS ON CAREERS

ARCHITECTURAL HISTORIANS play an important role in the renovation of an old building. Their expertise is used to help restore a building to its original splendor.

CAREER LINK
www.mcdougallittell.com

APPLICATION NOTE

EXERCISE 33 When a component of a clothing piece, such as the back of a jacket, has a line of symmetry, one-half of the shape can be used for the pattern piece. Then the pattern is placed on the fold of the fabric. The fold acts as a line of reflection. After the pattern is cut from the fabric, the fabric is then unfolded to reveal the entire piece.

EXERCISE 38 Students can sketch all 12 playing pieces on graph paper by first sketching a 1×5 rectangle. Then they can sketch a 1×4 rectangle and place the fifth square in all possible positions without duplicating any shapes. Continue the procedure for a 1×3 rectangle, a 1×2 rectangle, and a 1×1 rectangle.

CAREER NOTE

Additional information about architectural historians is available at **www.mcdougallittell.com.**

35. The pattern can be created by horizontal translation, 180° rotation, vertical line reflection, or horizontal glide reflection.
36. The pattern can be created by vertical translation.
37. The pattern can be created by translation or 180° rotation.

ADDITIONAL PRACTICE AND RETEACHING

For Lesson 7.5:

- Practice Levels A, B, and C (*Chapter 7 Resource Book,* p. 74)
- Reteaching with Practice (*Chapter 7 Resource Book,* p. 77)
- See Lesson 7.5 of the *Personal Student Tutor*

For more Mixed Review:

- Search the *Test and Practice Generator* for key words or specific lessons.

4 ASSESS

DAILY HOMEWORK QUIZ

Transparency Available

1. Name the coordinates of the image of $A(-3, 2)$ after a glide reflection. **$A''(1, -2)$**

Translation: $(x, y) \rightarrow (x + 4, y)$
Reflection: in the x-axis

2. Name the coordinates of the image of $A(-3, 2)$ after a composition of the given rotation and reflection. **$A''(2, 3)$**

Rotation: 90° counterclockwise about the origin
Reflection: in the y-axis

3. Describe the composition of the transformations.

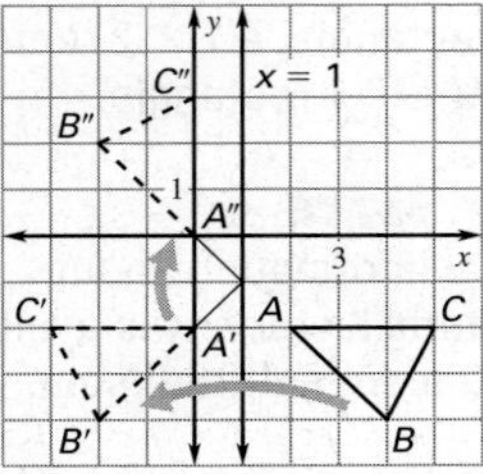

$\triangle ABC$ is reflected in line $x = 1$ to produce $\triangle A'B'C'$. Then $\triangle A'B'C'$ is rotated 90° clockwise about the point $(1, -1)$ to produce $\triangle A''B''C''$.

EXTRA CHALLENGE NOTE

Challenge problems for Lesson 7.5 are available in **blackline** format in the *Chapter 7 Resource Book,* p. 81 and at **www.mcdougallittell.com.**

ADDITIONAL TEST PREPARATION

1. OPEN ENDED Describe an example of a glide transformation. **See margin.**

2. WRITING Explain why a glide transformation reverses orientation. **A glide transformation involves a reflection, which reverses orientation.**

39, 41–44, 49–54. **See Additional Answers beginning on page AA1.**

Test Preparation 

39. MULTI-STEP PROBLEM Follow the steps below. **See margin.**

a. On a coordinate plane, draw a point and its image after a glide reflection that uses the x-axis as the line of reflection.

b. Connect the point and its image. Make a conjecture about the midpoint of the segment.

c. Use the coordinates from part (a) to prove your conjecture.

d. CRITICAL THINKING Can you extend your conjecture to include glide reflections that do not use the x-axis as the line of reflection?

★ Challenge

40. **USING ALGEBRA** Solve for the variables in the glide reflection of $\triangle JKL$ described below. **$a = 2, b = 5, c = 0, d = 2, e = \frac{3}{2}, f = -1, g = -3, h = -2$**

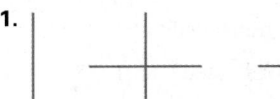

EXTRA CHALLENGE
www.mcdougallittell.com

$J(-2, -1)$
$K(-4, 2a)$
$L(b - 6, 6)$

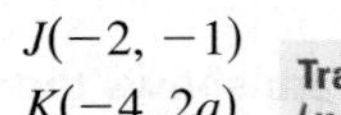

$J'(c + 1, -1)$
$K'(5d - 11, 4)$
$L'(2, 4e)$

Reflect in x-axis

$J''(1, -f)$
$K''(-1, 3g + 5)$
$L''(h + 4, -6)$

MIXED REVIEW

ANALYZING PATTERNS **Sketch the next figure in the pattern.** **(Review 1.1 for 7.6)** **41–44. See margin.**

41.

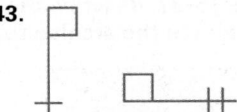

42. 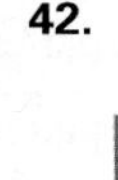 

43. 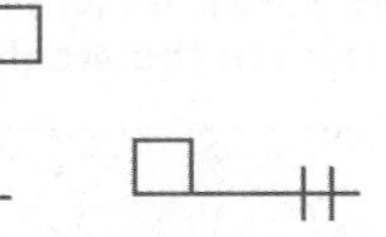 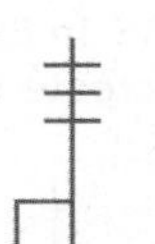

44. 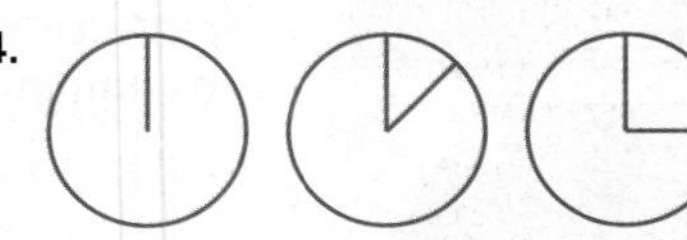

COORDINATE GEOMETRY **In Exercises 45–47, decide whether $\square PQRS$ is a *rhombus,* a *rectangle,* or a *square.* Explain your reasoning.** **(Review 6.4)** **45–47. Sample explanations are given. See margin.**

45. $P(1, -2), Q(5, -1), R(6, -5), S(2, -6)$

46. $P(10, 7), Q(15, 7), R(15, 1), S(10, 1)$

47. $P(8, -4), Q(10, -7), R(8, -10), S(6, -7)$

48. ROTATIONS A segment has endpoints $(3, -8)$ and $(7, -1)$. If the segment is rotated 90° counterclockwise about the origin, what are the endpoints of its image? **(Review 7.3)** **(8, 3) and (1, 7)**

STUDYING TRANSLATIONS **Sketch $\triangle ABC$ with vertices $A(-9, 7)$, $B(-9, 1)$, and $C(-5, 6)$. Then translate the triangle by the given vector and name the vertices of the image.** **(Review 7.4)** **49–54. Check sketches. See margin for coordinates.**

49. $\langle 3, 2 \rangle$ **50.** $\langle -1, -5 \rangle$ **51.** $\langle 6, 0 \rangle$

52. $\langle -4, -4 \rangle$ **53.** $\langle 0, 2.5 \rangle$ **54.** $\langle 1.5, -4.5 \rangle$

---

45. Square; $PQ = QR = RS = PS = \sqrt{17}$, so $PQRS$ is a rhombus. Also, since $PR = QS = \sqrt{34}$, the diagonals of $PQRS$ are $\cong$, so $PQRS$ is a rectangle. Then by the Square Corollary, $PQRS$ is a square.

46. Rectangle; $PQ = RS = 5$ and $PS = QR = 6$, so $PQRS$ is a parallelogram. Also, since $PR = QS = \sqrt{61}$, the diagonals of $PQRS$ are $\cong$, so $PQRS$ is a rectangle.

47. Rhombus; $PQ = QR = RS = PS = \sqrt{13}$, so $PQRS$ is a rhombus. Since $PR = 6$ and $SQ = 4$, the diagonals are not congruent, so $PQRS$ is not a rectangle or a square.

Additional Test Preparation *Sample answer:*

1. $\triangle ABC$ has vertices $A(0, 0)$, $B(1, 3)$, and $C(4, 4)$. A translation described by $(x, y) \rightarrow (x, y - 4)$ maps $\triangle ABC$ to $\triangle A'B'C'$ with vertices $A'(0, -4)$, $B'(1, -1)$, and $C'(4, 0)$. A reflection of $\triangle A'B'C'$ in the y-axis then produces $\triangle A''B''C''$ with vertices $A''(0, -4)$, $B''(-1, -1)$, and $C''(-4, 0)$.

7.6 Frieze Patterns

What you should learn

GOAL 1 Use transformations to classify frieze patterns.

GOAL 2 Use frieze patterns to design border patterns in **real life**, such as the tiling pattern in **Example 4**.

Why you should learn it

▼ You can use frieze patterns to create decorative borders for **real-life** objects, such as the pottery below and the pottery in **Exs. 35–37**.

REAL LIFE

CALIFORNIA STANDARDS AND ASSESSMENT

CA Standards: 17, 22
SAT9 Task 1: Obj. 31
SAT9 Task 2: Obj. 34

GOAL 1 CLASSIFYING FRIEZE PATTERNS

A **frieze pattern** or **border pattern** is a pattern that extends to the left and right in such a way that the pattern can be mapped onto itself by a horizontal translation. In addition to being mapped onto itself by a horizontal translation, some frieze patterns can be mapped onto themselves by other transformations.

1. Translation T
2. 180° rotation R
3. Reflection in a horizontal line H
4. Reflection in a vertical line V
5. Horizontal glide reflection G

EXAMPLE 1 *Describing Frieze Patterns*

Describe the transformations that will map each frieze pattern onto itself.

a. 

b. 

c. 

d. 

SOLUTION

a. This frieze pattern can be mapped onto itself by a horizontal translation (T).

b. This frieze pattern can be mapped onto itself by a horizontal translation (T) or by a 180° rotation (R).

c. This frieze pattern can be mapped onto itself by a horizontal translation (T) or by a horizontal glide reflection (G).

d. This frieze pattern can be mapped onto itself by a horizontal translation (T) or by a reflection in a vertical line (V).

1 PLAN

PACING
Basic: 2 days
Average: 2 days
Advanced: 2 days
Block Schedule: 0.5 block with 7.5
0.5 block with Ch. Rev.

LESSON OPENER
VISUAL APPROACH
An alternative way to approach Lesson 7.6 is to use the Visual Approach Lesson Opener:
- Blackline Master (*Chapter 7 Resource Book,* p. 85)
- Transparency (p. 46)

MEETING INDIVIDUAL NEEDS
- ***Chapter 7 Resource Book***
  Prerequisite Skills Review (p. 5)
  Practice Level A (p. 86)
  Practice Level B (p. 87)
  Practice Level C (p. 88)
  Reteaching with Practice (p. 89)
  Absent Student Catch-Up (p. 91)
  Challenge (p. 93)
- ***Resources in Spanish***
- ***Personal Student Tutor***

NEW-TEACHER SUPPORT
See the Tips for New Teachers on pp. 1–2 of the *Chapter 7 Resource Book* for additional notes about Lesson 7.6.

WARM-UP EXERCISES
Transparency Available
Match the transformation of the preimage with its image.

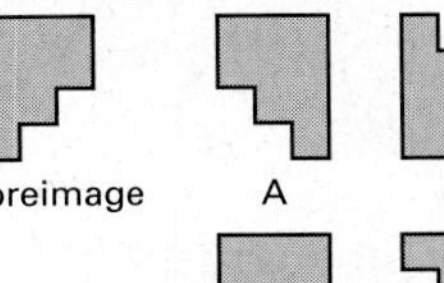

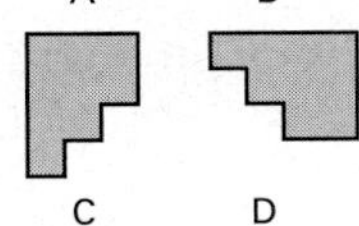

1. translation C
2. rotation D
3. reflection A
4. glide reflection B

2 TEACH

MOTIVATING THE LESSON

Many wallpaper borders contain repeated patterns that are created using several transformations. Some of these patterns are called frieze patterns. You will learn how to create frieze patterns in this lesson.

EXTRA EXAMPLE 1

Describe the transformations that will map each frieze pattern onto itself.

a. 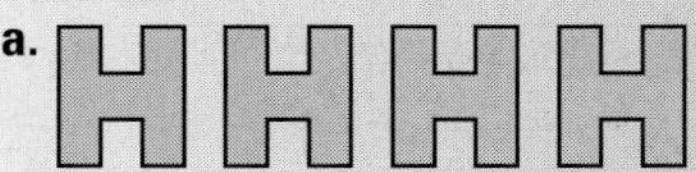

horizontal translation or a reflection in a vertical line

b. 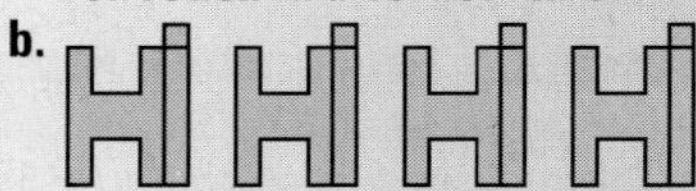

horizontal translation

c. 

horizontal translation or horizontal glide reflection

EXTRA EXAMPLE 2

Categorize the pattern of the design.

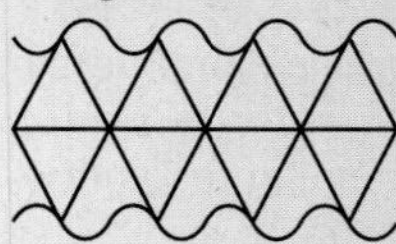

TRHVG

CHECKPOINT EXERCISES

For use after Examples 1 and 2:

1. Categorize the pattern of the design.

TG

438

CONCEPT SUMMARY — CLASSIFICATIONS OF FRIEZE PATTERNS

T	**Translation**
TR	**Translation and 180° rotation**
TG	**Translation and horizontal glide reflection**
TV	**Translation and vertical line reflection**
THG	**Translation, horizontal line reflection, and horizontal glide reflection**
TRVG	**Translation, 180° rotation, vertical line reflection, and horizontal glide reflection**
TRHVG	**Translation, 180° rotation, horizontal line reflection, vertical line reflection, and horizontal glide reflection**

STUDENT HELP

Study Tip

To help classify a frieze pattern, you can use a process of elimination. This process is described at the right and in the tree diagram in **Ex. 53**.

To classify a frieze pattern into one of the seven categories, you first decide whether the pattern has 180° rotation. If it does, then there are three possible classifications: TR, TRVG, and TRHVG.

If the frieze pattern does not have 180° rotation, then there are four possible classifications: T, TV, TG, and THG. Decide whether the pattern has a line of reflection. By a process of elimination, you will reach the correct classification.

EXAMPLE 2 *Classifying a Frieze Pattern*

SNAKES Categorize the snakeskin pattern of the mountain adder.

SOLUTION

This pattern is a TRHVG. The pattern can be mapped onto itself by a translation, a 180° rotation, a reflection in a horizontal line, a reflection in a vertical line, and a horizontal glide reflection.

FOCUS ON APPLICATIONS

ARCHITECTURE Features of classical architecture from Greece and Rome are seen in "neo-classical" buildings today, such as the Supreme Court building shown.

GOAL 2 USING FRIEZE PATTERNS IN REAL LIFE

EXAMPLE 3 *Identifying Frieze Patterns*

ARCHITECTURE The frieze patterns of ancient Doric buildings are located between the cornice and the architrave, as shown at the right. The frieze patterns consist of alternating sections. Some sections contain a person or a symmetric design. Other sections have simple patterns of three or four vertical lines.

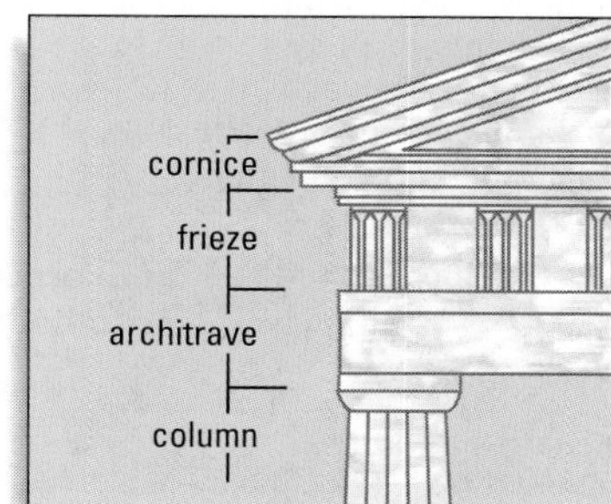

Portions of two frieze patterns are shown below. Classify the patterns.

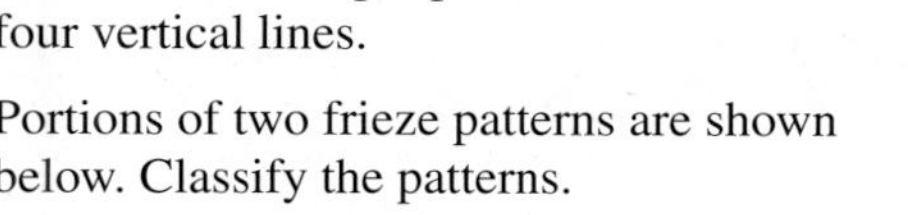

a. 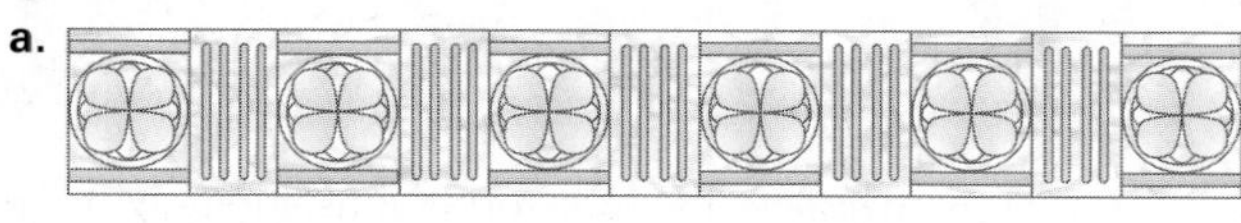

b. 

SOLUTION

a. Following the diagrams on the previous page, you can see that this frieze pattern has rotational symmetry, line symmetry about a horizontal line and a vertical line, and that the pattern can be mapped onto itself by a glide reflection. So, the pattern can be classified as TRHVG.

b. The only transformation that maps this pattern onto itself is a translation. So, the pattern can be classified as T.

EXAMPLE 4 *Drawing a Frieze Pattern*

TILING A border on a bathroom wall is created using the decorative tile at the right. The border pattern is classified as TR. Draw one such pattern.

SOLUTION

Begin by rotating the given tile 180°. Use this tile and the original tile to create a pattern that has rotational symmetry. Then translate the pattern several times to create the frieze pattern.

EXTRA EXAMPLE 3
Classify the patterns found in each frieze.

a.

T

b. 

THG

EXTRA EXAMPLE 4
Use the tile to create a border pattern classified as TV.

Sample answer:

CHECKPOINT EXERCISES
For use after Examples 3 and 4:

1. Classify the pattern found in the frieze pattern.

TV

APPLICATION NOTE
EXAMPLE 3 The use of the frieze contributed to the overall order and harmony for which Doric architects strove.

FOCUS ON VOCABULARY
Which transformations compose a frieze pattern if its classification is THG? **translation, horizontal line reflection, and horizontal glide reflection**

CLOSURE QUESTION
Classify the pattern found in the frieze pattern.

TRHVG

DAILY PUZZLER
How many rectangles are in this frieze pattern? **18**

3 APPLY

ASSIGNMENT GUIDE

BASIC

Day 1: pp. 440–441 Exs. 8–26

Day 2: pp. 441–444 Exs. 29–45, 49–52, 54–64, Quiz 2 Exs. 1–7

AVERAGE

Day 1: pp. 440–441 Exs. 8–26

Day 2: pp. 441–444 Exs. 29–52, 54–64, Quiz 2 Exs. 1–7

ADVANCED

Day 1: pp. 440–441 Exs. 8–26

Day 2: pp. 441–444 Exs. 29–64, Quiz 2 Exs. 1–7

BLOCK SCHEDULE

pp. 440–441 Exs. 8–26 (with 7.5)
pp. 441–444 Exs. 29–48, 50–55, 57–64, Quiz 2 Exs. 1–7
(with Ch. Rev.)

EXERCISE LEVELS

Level A: ***Easier***
8–11

Level B: ***More Difficult***
12–52

Level C: ***Most Difficult***
53

✓ HOMEWORK CHECK

To quickly check student understanding of key concepts, go over the following exercises: Exs. 12, 16, 20, 22, 24, 30, 36, 42, 44. See also the Daily Homework Quiz:

- Blackline Master (*Chapter 8 Resource Book,* p. 11)
- Transparency (p. 55)

GUIDED PRACTICE

Vocabulary Check ✓

1. Describe the term *frieze pattern* in your own words. *Sample answer*: a pattern that continues to the left and right and can be mapped onto itself by a horizontal translation

Concept Check ✓

2. ERROR ANALYSIS Describe Lucy's error below.

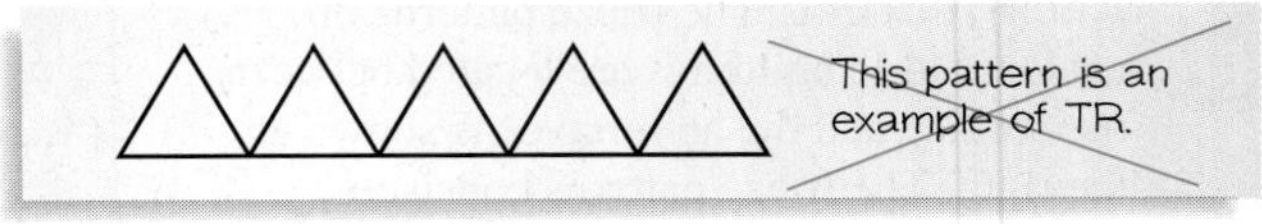

2. The pattern cannot be mapped onto itself by a 180° rotation. However, it can be mapped onto itself by a vertical line reflection. It is a TV pattern.

Skill Check ✓

In Exercises 3–6, describe the transformations that map the frieze pattern onto itself.

3. 

4. 

5. 

6. 

3. translation, vertical line reflection

4. translation, rotation, horizontal line reflection, vertical line reflection, horizontal glide reflection

5. translation, rotation, vertical line reflection, horizontal glide reflection

6. translation, rotation, vertical line reflection, horizontal glide reflection

7. List the five possible transformations, along with their letter abbreviations, that can be found in a frieze pattern.
translation (T), 180° rotation (R), horizontal glide reflection (G), vertical line reflection (V), horizontal line reflection (H)

PRACTICE AND APPLICATIONS

STUDENT HELP

Extra Practice to help you master skills is on p. 816.

SWEATER PATTERN **Each row of the sweater is a frieze pattern. Match the row with its classification.**

A. TRHVG **B.** TR **C.** TRVG **D.** THG

8.  C

9.  D

10. 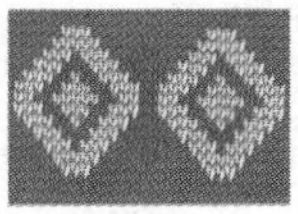 A

11.  B

CLASSIFYING PATTERNS **Name the isometries that map the frieze pattern onto itself.** 12–15. See margin.

12. 

13. 

14. 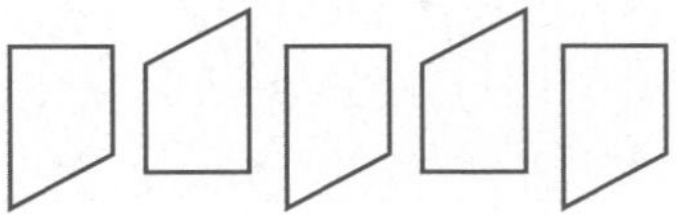

15. 

12. translation, horizontal line reflection, horizontal glide reflection

13. translation, 180° rotation

14. translation, 180° rotation

15. translation, 180° rotation, horizontal line reflection, vertical line reflection, horizontal glide reflection

STUDENT HELP

HOMEWORK HELP
Example 1: Exs. 8–15
Example 2: Exs. 16–23
Example 3: Exs. 32–39
Example 4: Exs. 40–43

DESCRIBING TRANSFORMATIONS **Use the diagram of the frieze pattern.**

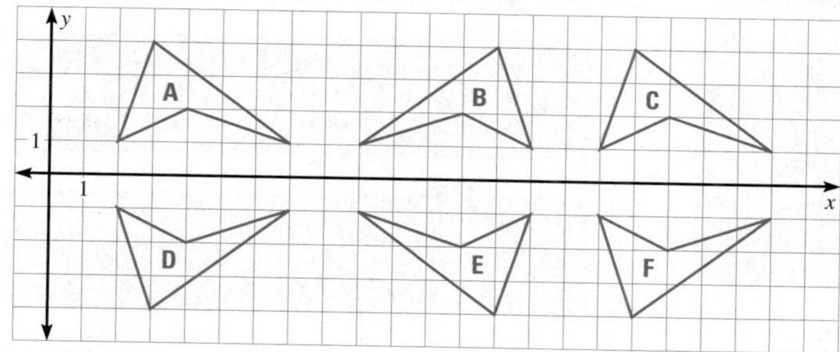

16. Is there a reflection in a vertical line? If so, describe the reflection(s). yes; reflection in any vertical line that lies midway between two figures

17. Is there a reflection in a horizontal line? If so, describe the reflection(s). yes; reflection in the x-axis

18. Name and describe the transformation that maps A onto F. the glide reflection consisting of reflection in the x-axis and the translation $(x, y) \rightarrow (x + 14, y)$

19. Name and describe the transformation that maps D onto B. 180° rotation about the point (8, 0)

20. Classify the frieze pattern. TRHVG

PET COLLARS **In Exercises 21–23, use the chart on page 438 to classify the frieze pattern on the pet collars.**

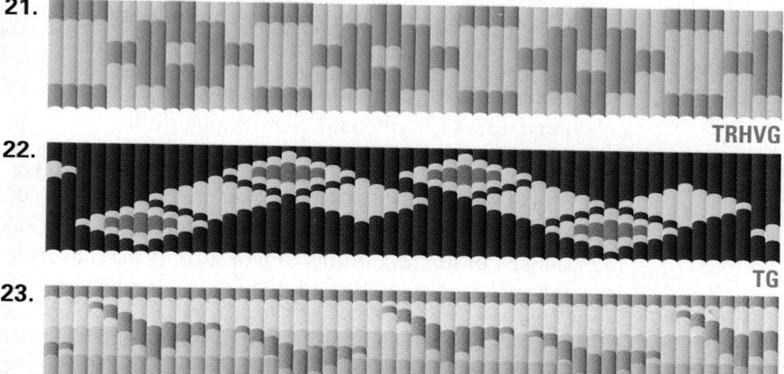

21. TRHVG

22. TG

23. T

24. **TECHNOLOGY** Pick one of the seven classifications of patterns and use geometry software to create a frieze pattern of that classification. Print and color your frieze pattern. Check patterns.

25. **DATA COLLECTION** Use a library, magazines, or some other reference source to find examples of frieze patterns. How many of the seven classifications of patterns can you find? Answers will vary.

CREATING A FRIEZE PATTERN **Use the design below to create a frieze pattern with the given classification.** 26–31. Sample patterns are given. See margin.

26. TR **27.** TV

28. TG **29.** THG

30. TRVG **31.** TRHVG

31.

! COMMON ERROR

EXERCISES 8–18 Because students have worked in previous lessons with rotations that are less than 180°, they may need reminding that only 180° rotations are considered in a frieze.

APPLICATION NOTE

EXERCISE 25 Architectural magazines are an obvious choice for finding frieze patterns. Any textile references with examples of quilts, including Internet sites, will also be a good source for frieze patterns.

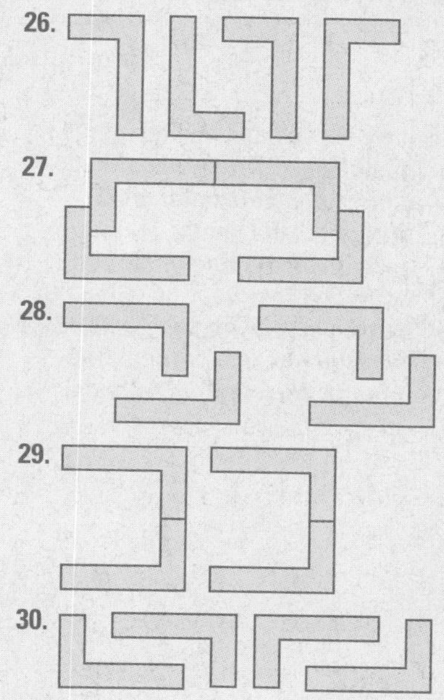

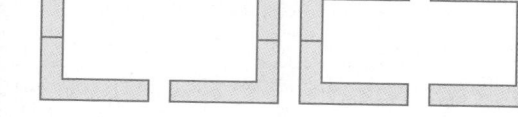

APPLICATION NOTE

EXERCISES 32–34 The Nazca culture also incorporated transformations in their woven textiles. To make the fringes on cloths that they had woven, the Nazca employed a form of knitting which rotates the stitches 180°.

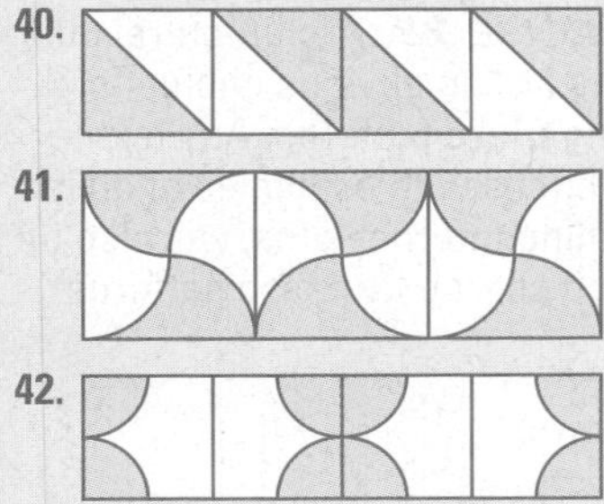

46. If a pattern can be mapped onto itself by a 180° rotation about a point and a horizontal glide reflection, the center of rotation must be on the line of reflection for the glide reflection. Then the pattern can be mapped onto itself by reflection in a vertical line through the center of rotation.

FOCUS ON APPLICATIONS

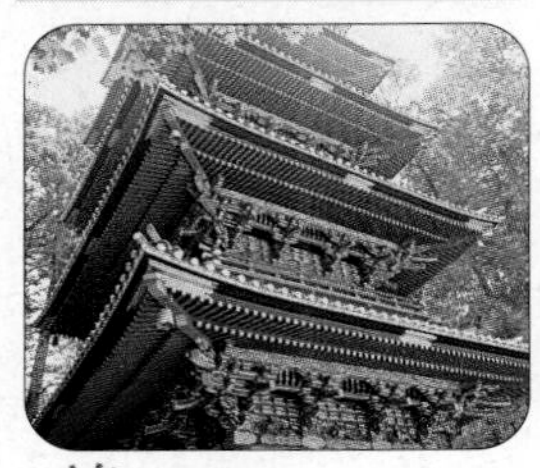

NIKKO MEMORIAL
The building shown is a memorial to Tokugawa Ieyasu (1543–1616), the founder of the Tokugawa Shogunate.

43. *Sample answer:* In order for a pattern to have, for example, horizontal symmetry, the tile must be able to be positioned in such a way that it has horizontal symmetry. The tile in Ex. 40 cannot be positioned in such a way that it has horizontal symmetry, so it cannot be used to create a row of tiles classified as THG.

44. If a pattern can be mapped onto itself by a horizontal glide reflection and by a vertical line reflection, it can be mapped onto itself by a 180° rotation about the point where the lines of reflection intersect.

45. If a pattern can be mapped onto itself by a horizontal line reflection and by a vertical line reflection, it can be mapped onto itself by a 180° rotation about the point where the lines intersect. It can also be mapped onto itself by a horizontal glide reflection involving the given horizontal line reflection and any translation.

JAPANESE PATTERNS **The patterns shown were used in Japan during the Tokugawa Shogunate. Classify the frieze patterns.**

POTTERY **In Exercises 35–37, use the pottery shown below. This pottery was created by the Acoma Indians. The Acoma pueblo is America's oldest continually inhabited city.**

35. Identify any frieze patterns on the pottery. There are three bands of frieze patterns visible.

36. Classify the frieze pattern(s) you found in Exercise 35. upper band: T; middle band: TR; lower band: T

37. Create your own frieze pattern similar to the patterns shown on the pottery. Check patterns.

38. Look back to the southwestern pottery on page 437. Describe and classify one of the frieze patterns on the pottery. *Sample answer*: The pattern consisting of reddish triangular shapes on the white stripe can be classified THG.

39. **LOGICAL REASONING** You are decorating a large circular vase and decide to place a frieze pattern around its base. You want the pattern to consist of ten repetitions of a design. If the diameter of the base is about 9.5 inches, how wide should each design be? just under 3 in.

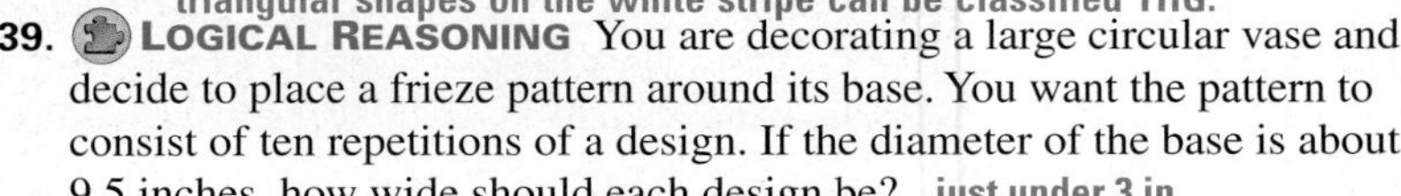

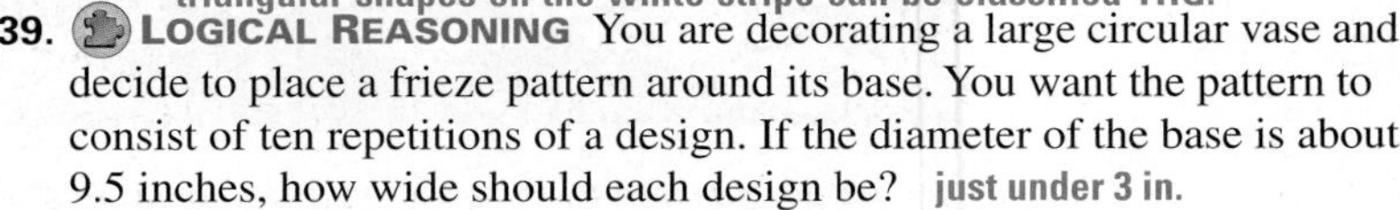

TILING **In Exercises 40–42, use the tile to create a border pattern with the given classification. Your border should consist of one row of tiles.** 40–42. See margin.

40. TR

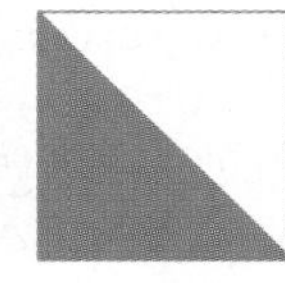

41. TRVG

42. TRHVG

43. *Writing* Explain how the design of the tiles in Exercises 40–42 is a factor in the classification of the patterns. For instance, could the tile in Exercise 40 be used to create a single row of tiles classified as THG? See margin.

CRITICAL THINKING **Explain why the combination is not a category for frieze pattern classification.** 44–46. See margin.

44. TVG **45.** THV **46.** TRG

STUDENT HELP

HOMEWORK HELP Visit our Web site www.mcdougallittell.com for help with Exs. 47 and 48.

USING THE COORDINATE PLANE **The figure shown in the coordinate plane is part of a frieze pattern with the given classification. Copy the graph and draw the figures needed to complete the pattern.** 47, 48. See margin.

47. TR

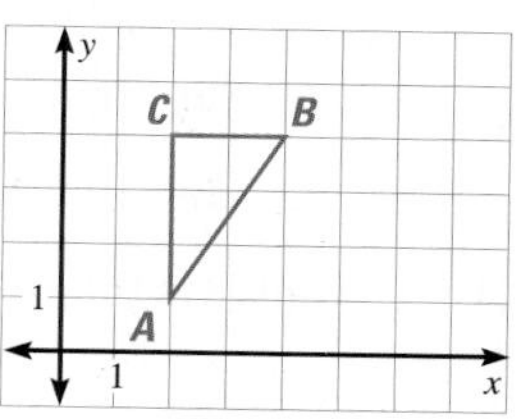

48. TRVG

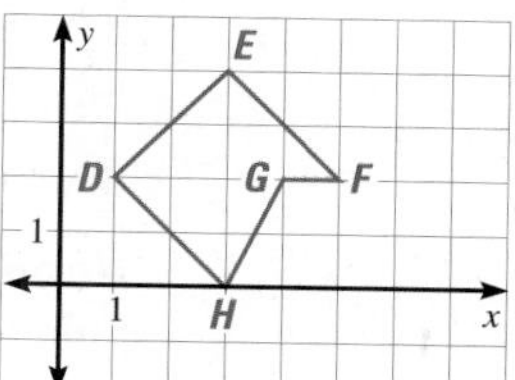

Test Preparation

MULTI-STEP PROBLEM **In Exercises 49–52, use the following information.**

In Celtic art and design, border patterns are used quite frequently, especially in jewelry. Three different designs are shown.

A.

B.

C.

49. Use translations to create a frieze pattern of each design. Sample patterns are given. See margin.

50. Classify each frieze pattern that you created. A: T; B: TVG; C: TRVG

51. Which design does not have rotational symmetry? Use rotations to create a new frieze pattern of this design. A; See margin.

52. *Writing* If a design has 180° rotational symmetry, it cannot be used to create a frieze pattern with classification *T*. Explain why not. See margin.

52. *Sample answer:* If a design has 180° rotational symmetry and its frieze pattern is created by a translation, its frieze pattern could also be created by a 180° rotation. Thus the frieze pattern could not have classification T, but rather must be TR, TRVG, or TRHVG.

★ Challenge

53. TREE DIAGRAM The following tree diagram can help classify frieze patterns. Copy the tree diagram and fill in the missing parts.

53. Line 2: Is there a line of reflection?

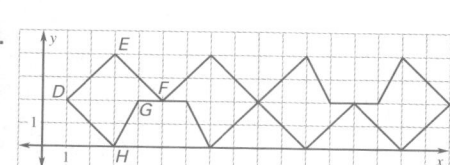

Line 4: Is the reflection in a horizontal line?

Line 6: TRVG; THG; TV

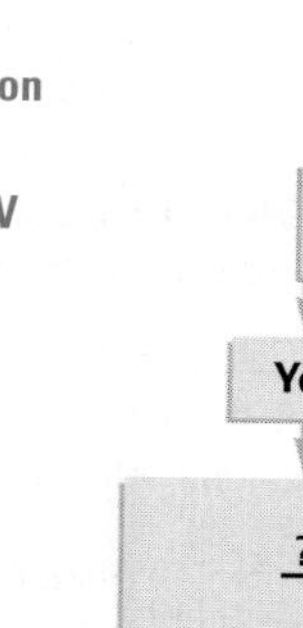

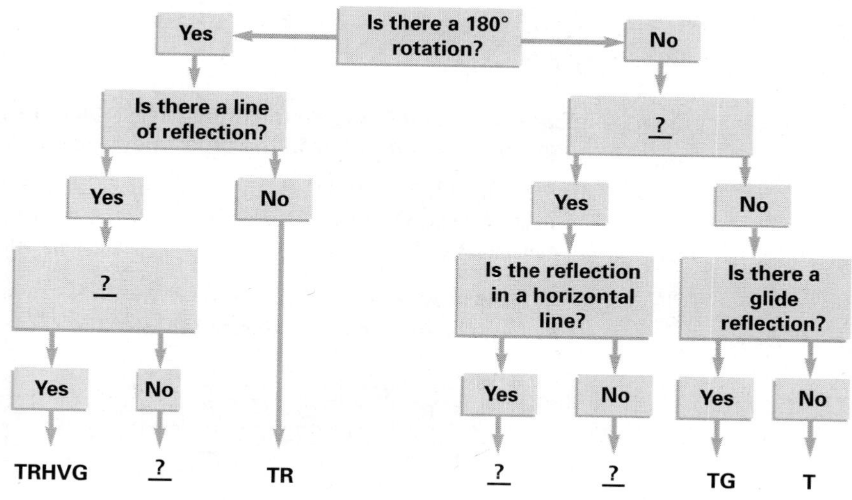

48. (sample pattern graph) y E D F G 1 1 H x

STUDENT HELP NOTES

Homework Help Students can find help for Exs. 47 and 48 at **www.mcdougallittell.com.** The information can be printed out for students who don't have access to the Internet.

47–48. Sample patterns are given.

47. y C B 1 A 1 x

49.

51. *Sample answer:*

ADDITIONAL PRACTICE AND RETEACHING

For Lesson 7.6:

- Practice Levels A, B, and C (*Chapter 7 Resource Book*, p. 86)
- Reteaching with Practice (*Chapter 7 Resource Book*, p. 89)
- See Lesson 7.6 of the *Personal Student Tutor*

For more Mixed Review:

- Search the *Test and Practice Generator* for key words or specific lessons.

4 ASSESS

DAILY HOMEWORK QUIZ

Transparency Available

Describe the transformations that will map the frieze pattern onto itself.

1. ∝/∝/∝/∝/∝/∝/∝/∝
   T
2. ⊃⊂⊃⊂⊃⊂⊃⊂⊃⊂⊃⊂
   TV
3. Use the design below to create a frieze pattern with the classification THG.

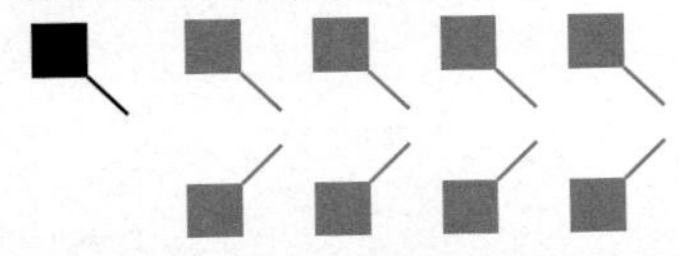

EXTRA CHALLENGE NOTE

Challenge problems for Lesson 7.6 are available in **blackline** format in the *Chapter 7 Resource Book,* p. 93 and at **www.mcdougallittell.com.**

ADDITIONAL TEST PREPARATION

1. **WRITING** How are a frieze pattern classified as TG and one classified as TV alike? How are they different? See below.
2. **OPEN ENDED** Use the tile to create a border frieze pattern that can be classified as TRHVG.

Sample answer:

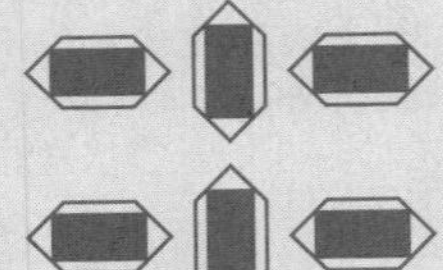

ADDITIONAL RESOURCES

An alternative Quiz for Lessons 7.4–7.6 is available in the *Chapter 7 Resource Book,* p. 94.

MIXED REVIEW

RATIOS Find the ratio of girls to boys in a class, given the number of boys and the total number of students. (Skills Review for 8.1)

54. 12 boys, 23 students $\frac{11}{12}$

55. 8 boys, 21 students $\frac{13}{8}$

56. 3 boys, 13 students $\frac{10}{3}$

57. 19 boys, 35 students $\frac{16}{19}$

58. 11 boys, 18 students $\frac{7}{11}$

59. 10 boys, 20 students 1

PROPERTIES OF MEDIANS Given that *D* is the centroid of $\triangle ABC$, find the value of each variable. (Review 5.3)

60.

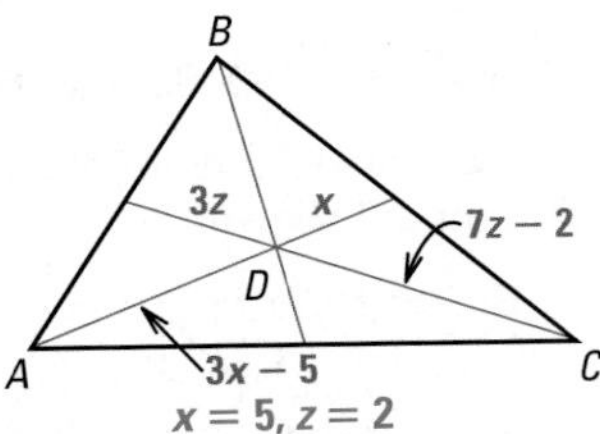

$x = 5, z = 2$

61.

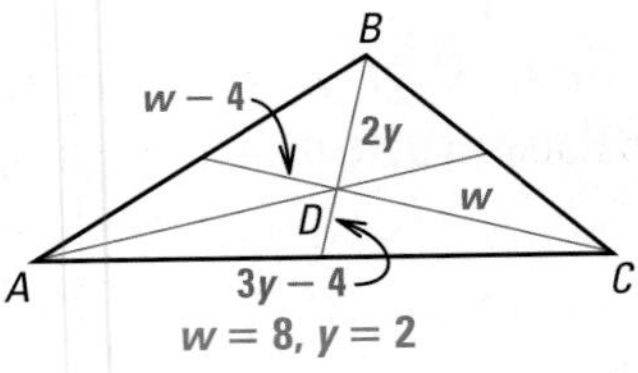

$w = 8, y = 2$

FINDING AREA Find the area of the quadrilateral. (Review 6.7)

62.

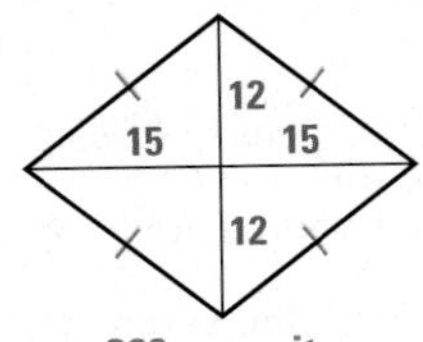

360 sq. units

63.

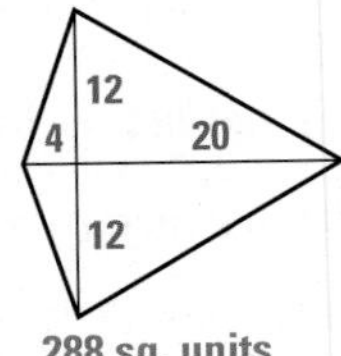

288 sq. units

64.

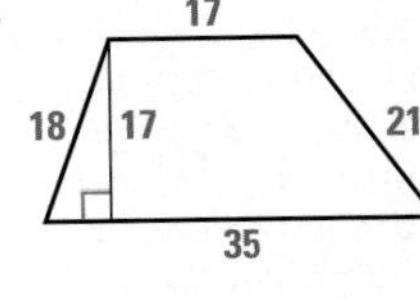

442 sq. units

QUIZ 2

Self-Test for Lessons 7.4–7.6

1. A' (0, 5), B' (5, 6), C' (2, 4)
2. A' (−4, 6), B' (1, 7), C' (−2, 5)
3. A' (−3, −2), B' (2, −1), C' (−1, −3)
4. A' (4, 4), B' (9, 5), C' (6, 3)

Write the coordinates of the vertices A', B', and C' after $\triangle ABC$ is translated by the given vector. (Lesson 7.4)

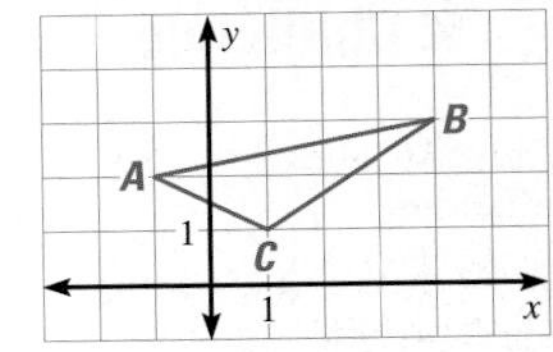

1. $\langle 1, 3\rangle$

2. $\langle -3, 4\rangle$

3. $\langle -2, -4\rangle$

4. $\langle 5, 2\rangle$

In Exercises 5 and 6, sketch the image of $\triangle PQR$ after a composition using the given transformations in the order they appear. (Lesson 7.5) 5, 6. See margin.

5. $P(5, 1)$, $Q(3, 4)$, $R(0, 1)$
Translation: $(x, y) \rightarrow (x - 2, y - 4)$
Reflection: in the y-axis

6. $P(7, 2)$, $Q(3, 1)$, $R(6, -1)$
Translation: $(x, y) \rightarrow (x - 4, y + 3)$
Rotation: 90° clockwise about origin

7. **MUSICAL NOTES** Do the notes shown form a frieze pattern? If so, classify the frieze pattern. (Lesson 7.6) yes; TR

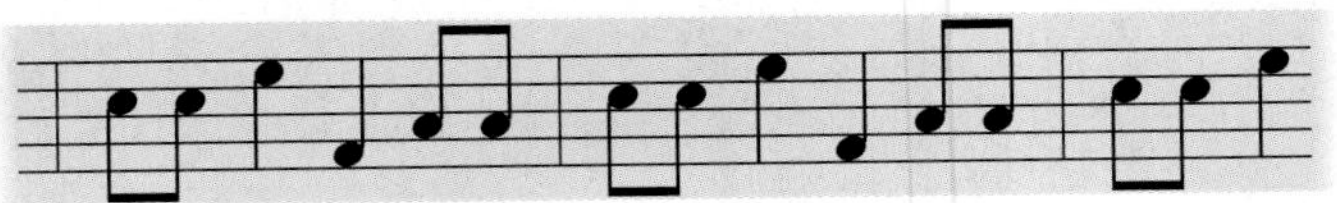

Additional Test Preparation *Sample answer:*

1. Both patterns can be created using a translation. A pattern classified as TG can be created using a horizontal glide reflection. A pattern classified as TV can be created using a vertical line reflection.

Chapter Summary

WHAT did you learn?	*WHY did you learn it?*
Identify types of rigid transformations. **(7.1)**	Plan a stencil pattern, using one design repeated many times. **(p. 401)**
Use properties of reflections. **(7.2)**	Choose the location of a telephone pole so that the length of the cable is a minimum. **(p. 405)**
Relate reflections and line symmetry. **(7.2)**	Understand the construction of the mirrors in a kaleidoscope. **(p. 406)**
Relate rotations and rotational symmetry. **(7.3)**	Use rotational symmetry to design a logo. **(p. 415)**
Use properties of translations. **(7.4)**	Use vectors to describe the path of a hot-air balloon. **(p. 427)**
Use properties of glide reflections. **(7.5)**	Describe the transformations in patterns in architecture. **(p. 435)**
Classify frieze patterns. **(7.6)**	Identify the frieze patterns in pottery. **(p. 442)**

How does Chapter 7 fit into the BIGGER PICTURE of geometry?

In this chapter, you learned that the basic rigid transformations in the plane are reflections, rotations, translations, and glide reflections. Rigid transformations are closely connected to the concept of congruence. That is, two plane figures are congruent if and only if one can be mapped onto the other by exactly one rigid transformation or by a composition of rigid transformations. In the next chapter, you will study transformations that are not rigid. You will learn that some nonrigid transformations are closely connected to the concept of similarity.

STUDY STRATEGY

How did making sample exercises help you?

Some sample exercises you made, following the **Study Strategy** on p. 394, may resemble these.

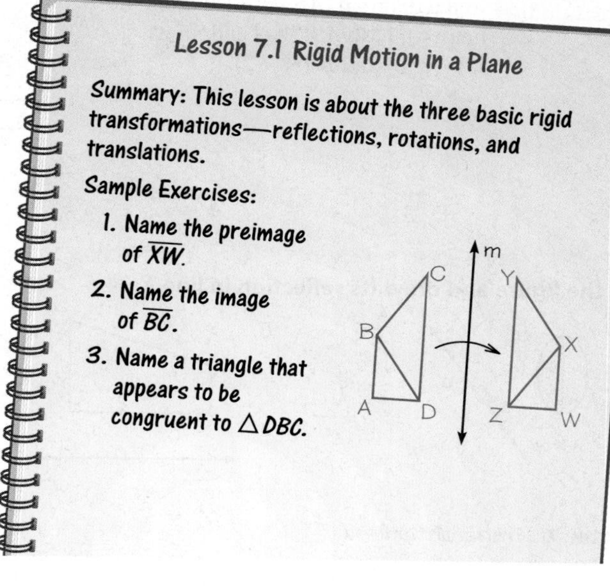

Lesson 7.1 Rigid Motion in a Plane
Summary: This lesson is about the three basic rigid transformations—reflections, rotations, and translations.
Sample Exercises:
1. Name the preimage of $\overline{XW}$.
2. Name the image of $\overline{BC}$.
3. Name a triangle that appears to be congruent to $\triangle DBC$.
m
C
B
A
D
Y
X
Z
W

5.
$Q''(-1, 0)$
$P''(-3, -3)$
$R''(2, -3)$

6.
$Q''(4, 1)$
$R''(2, -2)$
$P''(5, -3)$

445

ADDITIONAL RESOURCES

The following resources are available to help review the material in this chapter.

- Chapter Review Games and Activities (*Chapter 7 Resource Book*, p. 95)
- *Geometry in Motion video*
- *Personal Student Tutor*
- Cumulative Review, Chs. 1–7 (*Chapter 7 Resource Book*, p. 107)

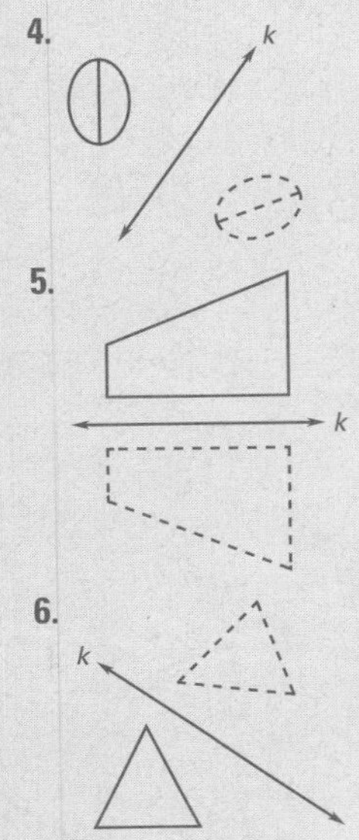

CHAPTER 7

Chapter Review

- image, p. 396
- preimage, p. 396
- transformation, p. 396
- isometry, p. 397
- reflection, p. 404
- line of reflection, p. 404
- line of symmetry, p. 406
- rotation, p. 412
- center of rotation, p. 412
- angle of rotation, p. 412
- rotational symmetry, p. 415
- translation, p. 421
- vector, p. 423
- initial point, p. 423
- terminal point, p. 423
- component form, p. 423
- glide reflection, p. 430
- composition, p. 431
- frieze pattern, or border pattern, p. 437

7.1 RIGID MOTION IN A PLANE

Examples on pp. 396–398

EXAMPLE The blue triangle is reflected to produce the congruent red triangle, so the transformation is an isometry.

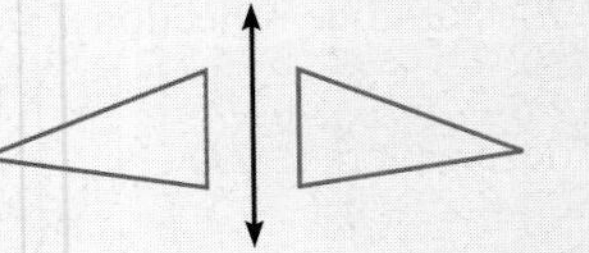

Does the transformation appear to be an isometry? Explain.

1.

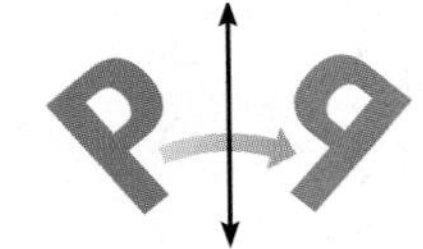

Yes; the figure and its image appear to be congruent.

2.

No; the figure and its image are not congruent.

3.

Yes; the figure and its image appear to be congruent.

7.2 REFLECTIONS

Examples on pp. 404–406

EXAMPLE In the diagram, $\overline{AB}$ is reflected in the line $y = 1$, so $\overline{A'B'}$ has endpoints $A'(-2, 0)$ and $B'(3, -2)$.

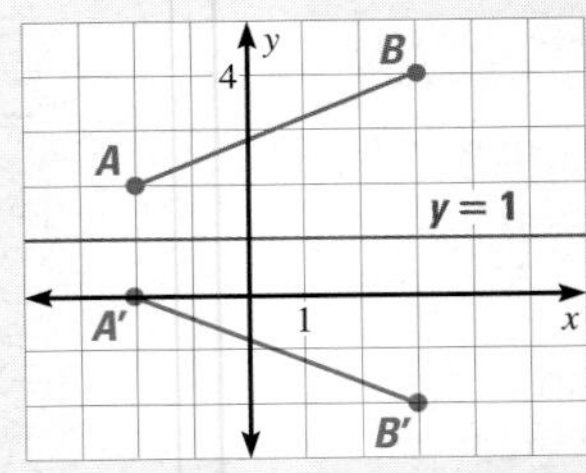

Copy the figure and draw its reflection in line *k*. 4–6. See margin.

4.

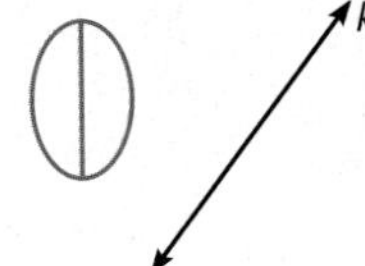

5.

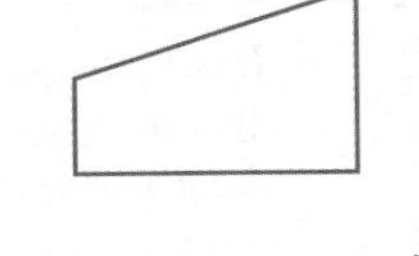

6.

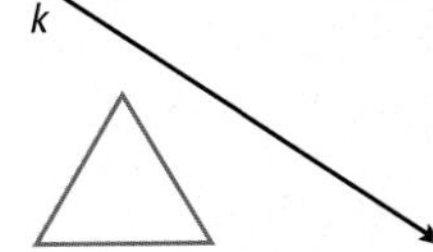

7.3 ROTATIONS

Examples on pp. 412–415

EXAMPLE In the diagram, $\triangle FGH$ is rotated 90° clockwise about the origin.

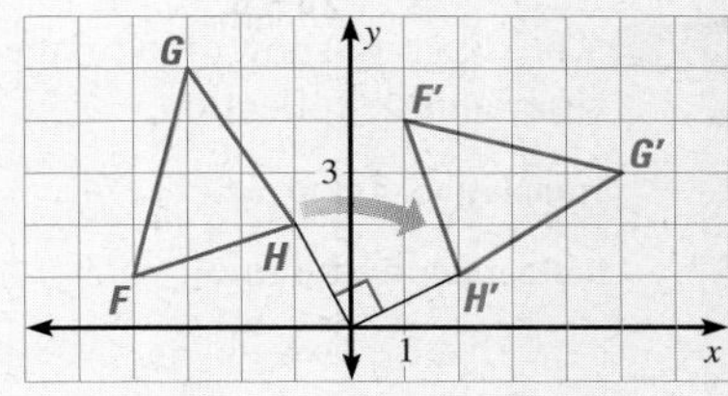

Copy the figure and point *P*. Then, use a straightedge, a compass, and a protractor to rotate the figure 60° counterclockwise about *P*. 7–9. See margin.

7. 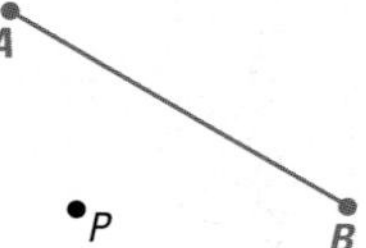

8. 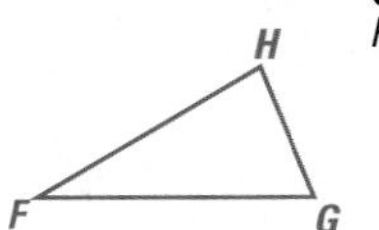

9. 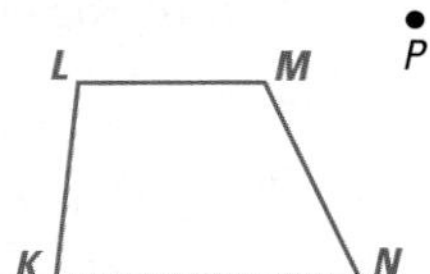

7.4 TRANSLATIONS AND VECTORS

Examples on pp. 421–424

EXAMPLE Using the vector $\langle -3, -4 \rangle$, $\triangle ABC$ can be translated to $\triangle A'B'C'$.

$A(2, 4)$	$A'(-1, 0)$
$B(1, 2)$	$B'(-2, -2)$
$C(5, 2)$	$C'(2, -2)$

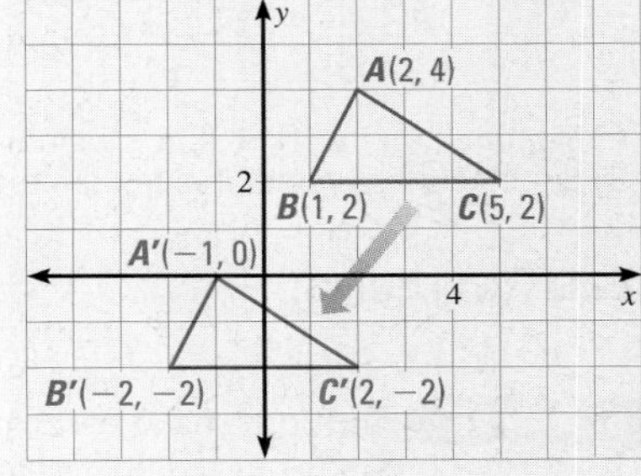

The vertices of the image of $\triangle LMN$ after a translation are given. Choose the vector that describes the translation.

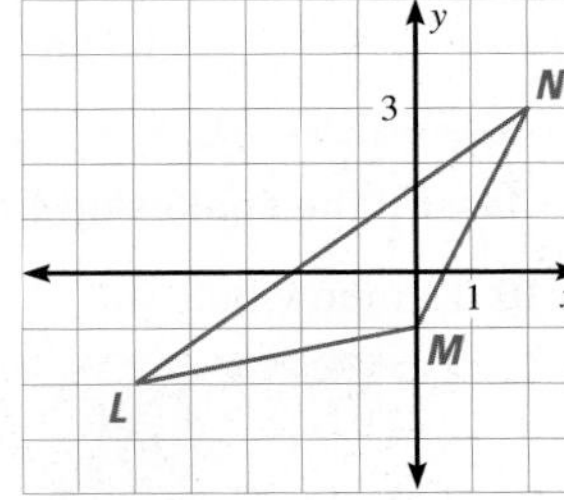

10. $L'(-1, -3), M'(4, -2), N'(6, 2)$ C

11. $L'(-5, 1), M'(0, 2), N'(2, 6)$ A

12. $L'(-3, 2), M'(2, 3), N'(4, 7)$ D

13. $L'(-7, 3), M'(-2, 4), N'(0, 8)$ B

A. $\overrightarrow{PQ} = \langle 0, 3 \rangle$

B. $\overrightarrow{PQ} = \langle -2, 5 \rangle$

C. $\overrightarrow{PQ} = \langle 4, -1 \rangle$

D. $\overrightarrow{PQ} = \langle 2, 4 \rangle$

7.
8.
9.

5. *Sample answer:*

6. *Sample answer:*

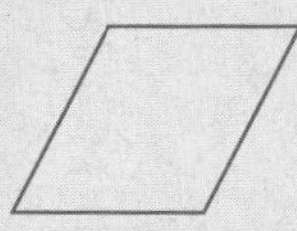

14. *Sample answer:*

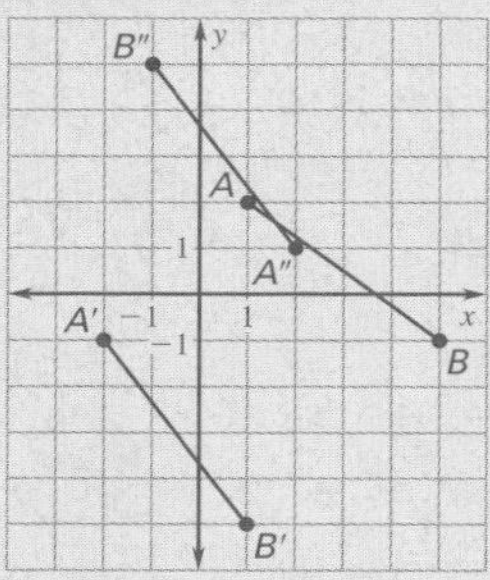

$\overline{A'B'}$ is the final image when $\overline{AB}$ is rotated 90° clockwise about the origin, then reflected in the y-axis. $\overline{A''B''}$ is the final image when $\overline{AB}$ is reflected in the y-axis, then rotated 90° clockwise about the origin.

15. *Sample answer:*

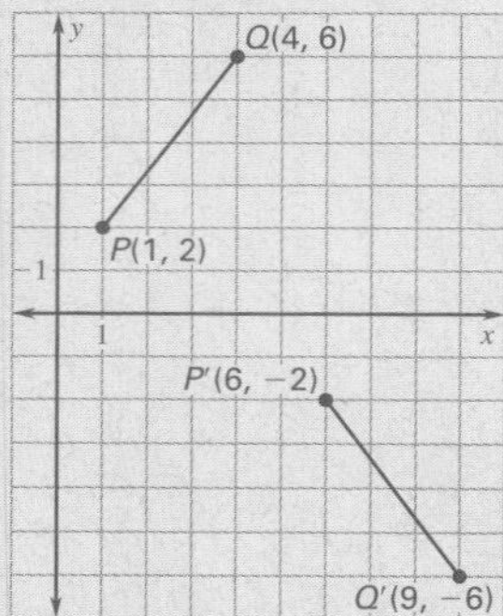

$\overline{PQ}$ is reflected in the x-axis, then translated $(x, y) \rightarrow (x + 5, y)$. The same image results if the transformations are performed in reverse order.

7.5 Glide Reflections and Compositions

Examples on pp. 430–432

EXAMPLE The diagram shows the image of $\triangle XYZ$ after a glide reflection.

Translation: $(x, y) \rightarrow (x + 4, y)$

Reflection: in the line $y = 3$

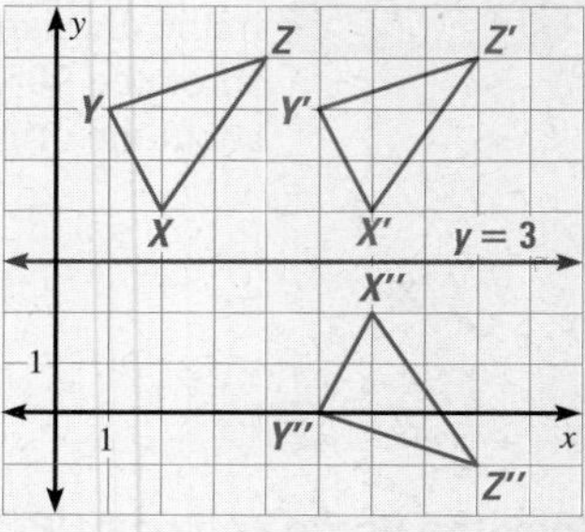

Describe the composition of the transformations.

14.

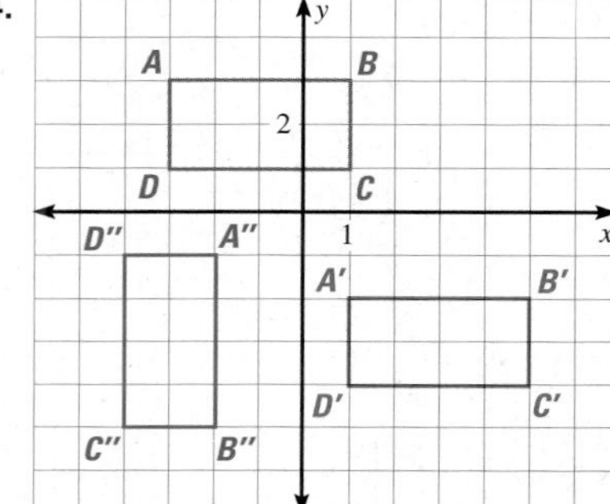

translation $(x, y) \rightarrow (x + 4, y - 5)$, followed by 90° clockwise rotation about the origin

15.

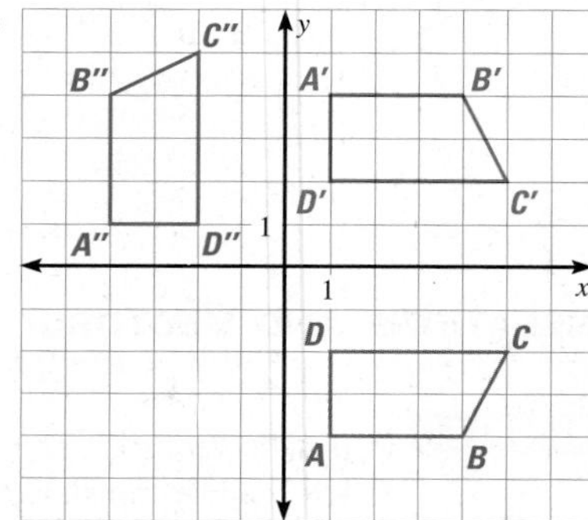

reflection in the x-axis followed by 90° counterclockwise rotation about the origin

7.6 Frieze Patterns

Examples on pp. 437–439

EXAMPLE The corn snake frieze pattern at the right can be classified as TRHVG because the pattern can be mapped onto itself by a translation, 180° rotation, horizontal line reflection, vertical line reflection, and glide reflection.

Classify the snakeskin frieze pattern.

16. Rainbow boa **TR**

17. Gray-banded kingsnake **TRHVG**

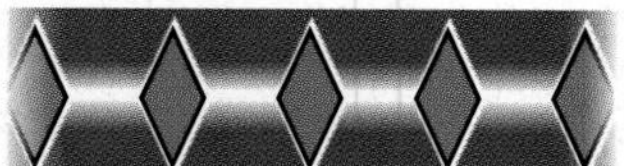

CHAPTER 7

Chapter Test

In Exercises 1–4, use the diagram.

1. Identify the transformation $\triangle RST \to \triangle XYZ$. **reflection in the *y*-axis**
2. Is $\overline{RT}$ congruent to $\overline{XZ}$? **yes**
3. What is the image of T? **Z**
4. What is the preimage of Y? **S**
5. Sketch a polygon that has line symmetry, but not rotational symmetry. ***Sample answer:* See margin.**
6. Sketch a polygon that has rotational symmetry, but not line symmetry. ***Sample answer:* See margin.**

Use the diagram, in which lines *m* and *n* are lines of reflection.

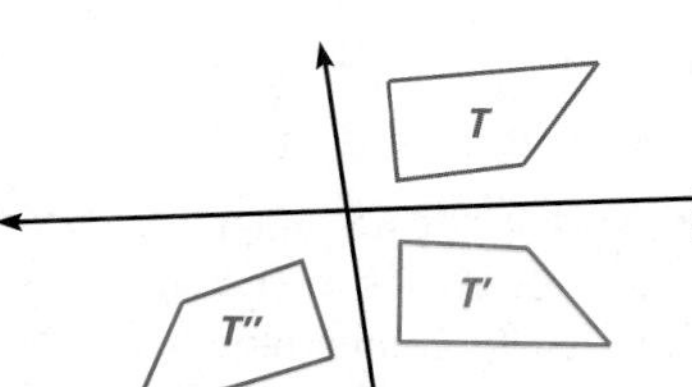

7. Identify the transformation that maps figure T onto figure T'. **reflection in line *m***
8. Identify the transformation that maps figure T onto figure T''. **rotation about the intersection of lines *m* and *n***
9. If the measure of the acute angle between m and n is 85°, what is the angle of rotation from figure T to figure T''? **170°**

In Exercises 10–12, use the diagram, in which $k \parallel m$.

10. Identify the transformation that maps figure R onto figure R'. **reflection in line *k***
11. Identify the transformation that maps figure R onto figure R''. **translation**
12. If the distance between k and m is 5 units, what is the distance between corresponding parts of figure R and figure R''? **10 units**
13. What type of transformation is a composition of a translation followed by a reflection in a line parallel to the translation vector? **glide reflection**

Give an example of the described composition of transformations. **14, 15. See margin.**

14. The order in which two transformations are performed affects the final image.
15. The order in which two transformations are performed does not affect the final image.

FLAGS Identify any symmetry in the flag. **16–21. See margin.**

16. Switzerland

17. Jamaica

18. United Kingdom

Name all of the isometries that map the frieze pattern onto itself.

19.

20.

21.

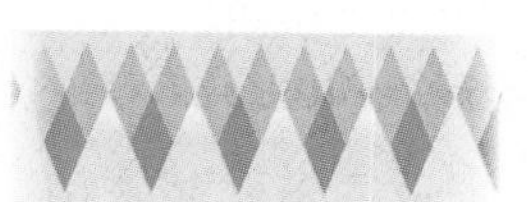

ADDITIONAL RESOURCES

- ***Chapter 7 Resource Book***
  Chapter Test (3 levels) (p. 96)
  SAT/ACT Chapter Test (p. 102)
  Alternative Assessment (p. 103)
- ***Test and Practice Generator***

16. four lines of symmetry (one vertical, one horizontal, two diagonal); 180° rotational symmetry clockwise or counterclockwise about its center
17. two lines of symmetry (one vertical, one horizontal); 180° rotational symmetry clockwise or counterclockwise about its center
18. two lines of symmetry (one vertical, one horizontal); 180° rotational symmetry clockwise or counterclockwise about its center
19. translation, 180° rotation, horizontal line reflection, vertical line reflection, glide reflection
20. translation, 180° rotation, horizontal line reflection, vertical line reflection, glide reflection
21. translation, vertical line reflection

ADDITIONAL RESOURCES

- ***Chapter 7 Resource Book***
  Chapter Test (3 levels) (p. 96)
  SAT/ACT Chapter Test (p. 102)
  Alternative Assessment (p. 103)
- ***Test and Practice Generator***

CHAPTER 7

Chapter Standardized Test

TEST-TAKING STRATEGY Sketch graphs or figures in your test booklet to help you solve the problems. Even though you must keep your answer sheet neat, you can make any kind of mark you want in your test booklet.

1. MULTIPLE CHOICE How many lines of symmetry does the polygon at the right have? B

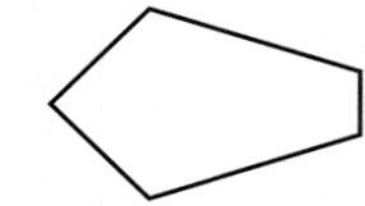

Ⓐ 0 Ⓑ 1 Ⓒ 2
Ⓓ 3 Ⓔ More than 3

2. MULTIPLE CHOICE The point $P(-2, -11)$ is reflected in the line $y = -1$. What are the coordinates of P'? D

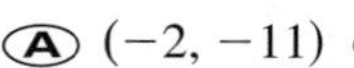

Ⓐ $(-2, -11)$ Ⓑ $(-2, -9)$ Ⓒ $(-2, 10)$
Ⓓ $(-2, 9)$ Ⓔ $(-2, 11)$

3. MULTIPLE CHOICE Suppose $\triangle ABC$ has vertices $A(-8, -2)$, $B(-5, -2)$, and $C(-8, -7)$. If $\triangle ABC$ is rotated 90° counterclockwise about the origin, what are the coordinates of the vertices of $\triangle A'B'C'$? E

Ⓐ $A'(2, -5)$, $B'(2, -8)$, $C'(7, -8)$
Ⓑ $A'(2, -8)$, $B'(2, -5)$, $C'(8, -7)$
Ⓒ $A'(7, -8)$, $B'(2, -8)$, $C'(2, -5)$
Ⓓ $A'(-8, 2)$, $B'(-5, 2)$, $C'(-8, 7)$
Ⓔ $A'(2, -8)$, $B'(2, -5)$, $C'(7, -8)$

4. MULTIPLE CHOICE The transformation below is an isometry. What are the values of the variables? A

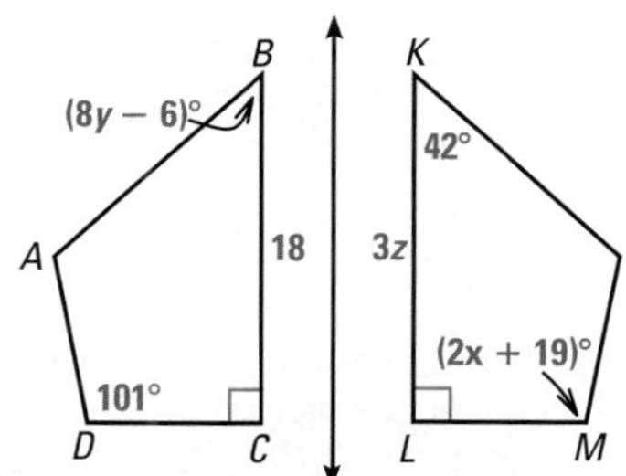

Ⓐ $x = 41, y = 6, z = 6$
Ⓑ $x = 40, y = 6, z = 9$
Ⓒ $x = 50, y = 6, z = 6$
Ⓓ $x = 6, y = 40, z = 6$
Ⓔ $x = 41, y = 8, z = 6$

5. MULTIPLE CHOICE $\triangle WXY$ has vertices $W(3, 8)$, $X(7, 6)$, and $Y(5, 2)$. What are the coordinates of the vertices of $\triangle W'X'Y'$ after the translation $(x, y) \to (x - 8, y - 10)$? B

Ⓐ $W'(-5, 18)$, $X'(-3, 12)$, $Y'(-1, 16)$
Ⓑ $W'(-5, -2)$, $X'(-1, -4)$, $Y'(-3, -8)$
Ⓒ $W'(11, -2)$, $X'(15, -4)$, $Y'(13, -8)$
Ⓓ $W'(-2, -5)$, $X'(-1, 4)$, $Y'(-3, -8)$
Ⓔ $W'(11, 18)$, $X'(15, 16)$, $Y'(13, 12)$

6. MULTIPLE CHOICE Name the vector that describes the translation in the diagram. D

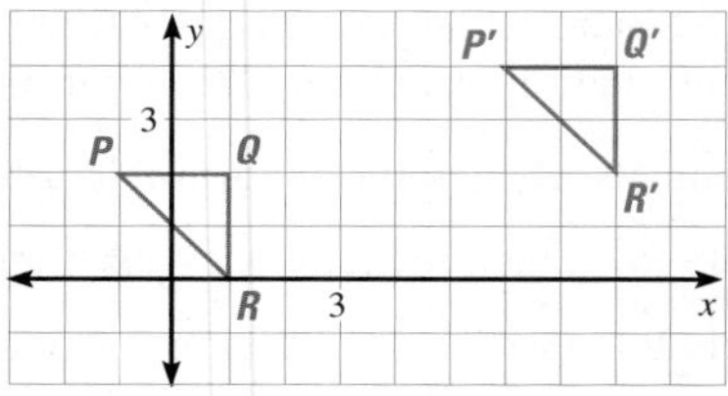

Ⓐ $\langle -7, 2\rangle$ Ⓑ $\langle 7, 1\rangle$ Ⓒ $\langle 6, 2\rangle$
Ⓓ $\langle 7, 2\rangle$ Ⓔ $\langle 6, 3\rangle$

7. MULTIPLE CHOICE What two transformations were performed to obtain $\overline{A''B''}$ in the diagram?

D

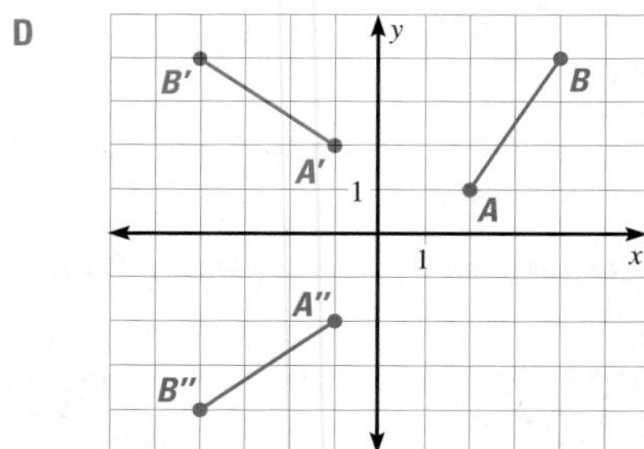

Ⓐ A rotation and a translation
Ⓑ A reflection and a translation
Ⓒ A translation and a translation
Ⓓ A rotation and a reflection
Ⓔ A rotation and a rotation

8. **MULTIPLE CHOICE** What are the isometries that map the Seminole Indian frieze pattern onto itself? **C**

Ⓐ translation, horizontal line reflection

Ⓑ translation, horizontal glide reflection

Ⓒ translation, vertical line reflection

Ⓓ translation, 180° rotation, vertical line reflection

Ⓔ translation, 180° rotation, horizontal glide reflection

9. **MULTIPLE CHOICE** Using the composition shown, what are the coordinates of the endpoints of $\overline{S''T''}$? **E**

$S(-6, -2), T(-3, -5)$

Reflection: in $y = 1$

Rotation: 90° clockwise about the point $(-3, 2)$

Ⓐ $S''(2, 2), T''(-1, 5)$ Ⓑ $S''(-1, 4), T''(2, 2)$ Ⓒ $S''(-3, 5), T''(2, 0)$

Ⓓ $S''(-6, 4), T''(-3, 7)$ Ⓔ $S''(-1, 5), T''(2, 2)$

MULTI-STEP PROBLEM Use the alphabet displayed in the typeface below.

10. Which letters have a vertical line of symmetry? **A, H, I, M, O, T, W, X, Y**

11. Which letters have a horizontal line of symmetry? **C, E, H, K, O, X**

12. Which letters have rotational symmetry? **H, N, O, S, X, Z**

MULTI-STEP PROBLEM Use the diagram at the right.

13. Describe the translation using (a) coordinate notation and (b) a vector in component form. **See margin.**

14. A translation that maps figure $J'K'L'M'$ onto figure $WXYZ$ can be described as follows: $(x, y) \rightarrow (x + 7, y - 2)$. What are the coordinates of the vertices of figure $WXYZ$?
$W(9, 4)$, $X(11, 4)$, $Y(12, 1)$, $Z(7, 1)$

15. A transformation that maps figure $J'K'L'M'$ onto figure $PQRS$, so that figure $PQRS$ has the following vertices: $P(6, -2)$, $Q(6, -4)$, $R(3, -5)$, and $S(3, 0)$. Describe the transformation.
90° clockwise rotation about the origin

16. Give an example of a transformation that maps figure $J'K'L'M'$ onto figure $J''K''L''M''$, so that figure $JKLM$ maps onto figure $J''K''L''M''$ by a glide reflection. **See margin.**

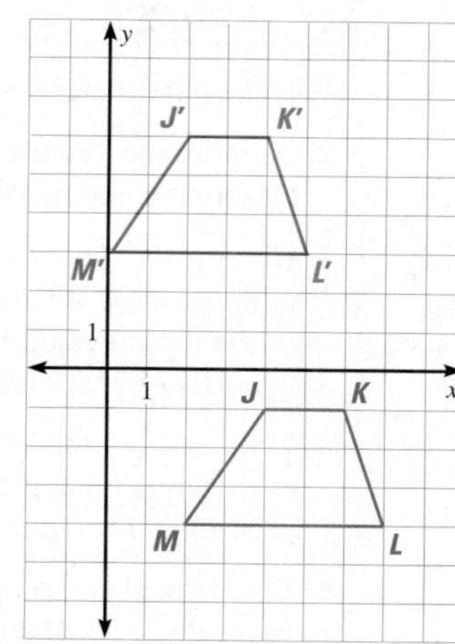

13a. $(x, y) \rightarrow (x - 2, y + 7)$

b. $\langle -2, 7 \rangle$

16 ***Sample answer:*** **reflection in $y = 2\frac{1}{2}$**

PROJECT OVERVIEW

PROJECT GOALS

- Identify tessellations, including regular and semi-regular tessellations.
- Determine whether a given polygon can be used to create a tessellation.
- Use transformations to map a tessellation onto itself.

MANAGING THE PROJECT

CLASSROOM MANAGEMENT

The Chapter 7 Project may be completed by individual students or by students working with partners. If students work with a partner, they should discuss and agree upon the answers to Exercises 1–8. The partners might take turns sketching the tessellations.

GUIDING STUDENT'S WORK

It may be helpful to have tracing paper available for students to use when determining which transformations map the tessellation onto itself. Then students can trace a portion of the tessellation and physically translate, reflect, or rotate it. You might also suggest that students use cardboard to make some of the polygons from Exercises 6–8 and use the shapes to find the tessellation.

CONCLUDING THE PROJECT

Have students color the tessellations they made and use them to create a bulletin board display.

Invite an art teacher, local artist, or art museum representative to speak about the works of M.C. Escher.

4. Squares and equilateral triangles can be used because $4 \times 90° = 360°$ and $6 \times 60° = 360°$. By placing four squares together at a point or six equilateral triangles, you can form a regular tessellation.
5. Check tessellations. A horizontal translation, vertical translation, or a combination of these can map the tessellation onto itself.

PROJECT for Chapters 6 and 7

Investigating Tessellations

OBJECTIVE **Create tessellations using polygons.**

Materials: cardboard, scissors, protractor, colored pencils, file folder

A *tessellation*, or tiling, of a plane is a collection of tiles that fill the plane with no gaps or overlaps. The tiles in a *regular tessellation* are congruent regular polygons. The tessellation at the right is regular because it is made of congruent regular hexagons.

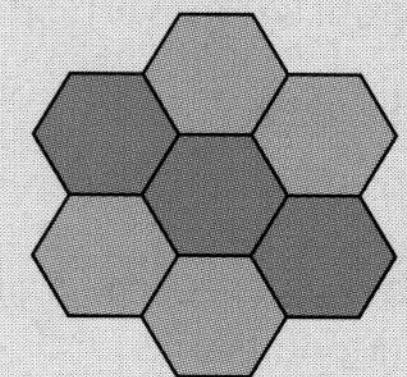

TESSELLATIONS USING ONE POLYGON

Follow these steps to make a tessellation of a quadrilateral.

1. Cut a quadrilateral that is not a rectangle from a piece of cardboard. Trace the shape on a piece of paper.
2. Rotate the quadrilateral 180° so an edge of the cardboard matches an edge of the shape on the paper. Trace the new position of the quadrilateral.
3. Continue rotating and tracing the quadrilateral to make a tessellation. Color your tessellation.

INVESTIGATION

1. Is the quadrilateral tessellation a regular tessellation? Explain.
2. Suppose the quadrilateral tessellation extends forever in all directions. Describe some transformations that map the pattern onto itself.
3. Choose any vertex on your quadrilateral tessellation and measure the angles at that vertex. What is the sum of the measures of the angles? Find the sum of the measures of the angles at a different vertex. Explain why *any* quadrilateral will tessellate.
4. There are only three possible regular tessellations. The hexagonal tessellation is shown at the top of the page. Decide what other regular polygons can be used to create regular tessellations. Explain your reasoning. See margin.
5. Draw a scalene triangle on a piece of cardboard and cut it out. Use the shape to create a tessellation. Describe any transformations that can map the tessellation onto itself. See margin.

1. No; the quadrilateral is not a regular polygon.
2. Sample answer: Rotate the pattern 180° about any vertex. Translate the pattern horizontally, vertically, or in a combination of these. Reflect the pattern twice with two horizontal or vertical lines of reflection.
3. 360°; 360°; the sum of the measures of the angles of any quadrilateral is 360°, so by placing the four angles so they are adjacent, you cover the full rotation of 360°.

TESSELLATIONS USING MORE THAN ONE POLYGON

In a *semiregular tessellation*, more than one kind of regular polygon is used and the same arrangement of polygons meets at any vertex of the tessellation. You can also make nonregular tessellations with more than one kind of nonregular polygon. As with any tessellation, the sum of the measures of the angles of the polygons at any vertex should be 360°. Here are some examples.

Semiregular: squares and equilateral triangles

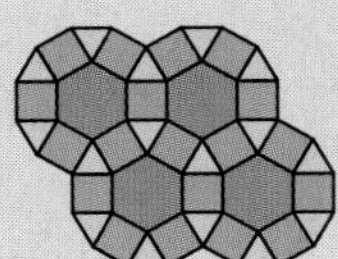

Semiregular: regular hexagons, squares, and equilateral triangles

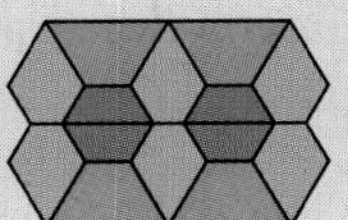

Nonregular: pentagons and isosceles trapezoids

INVESTIGATION

Determine whether the shapes can be used to create a tessellation. If so, sketch the tessellation, and classify it as *semiregular* or *nonregular*.

6. Regular octagon and square **See margin.**

7. Regular pentagon and rectangle **No**

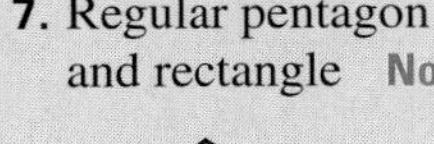

8. Isosceles triangle and parallelogram **See margin.**

135°

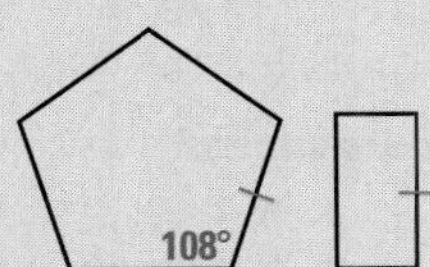

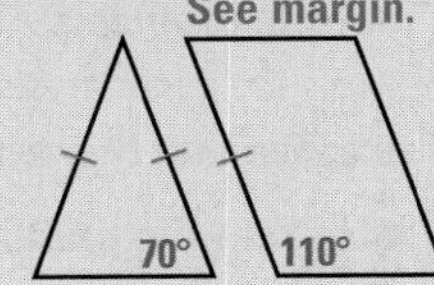

PRESENT YOUR RESULTS

Gather your drawings of tessellations and present them in a file folder.

- Include your quadrilateral tessellation.
- Include your answers to Exercises 1–8.
- Summarize what you have learned about tessellations.
- Describe how transformations can be used to map a tessellation onto itself.

EXTENSIONS

- Create your own tessellation using polygons. The sum of the measures of the angles of the polygon at any vertex should be 360°. Color your tessellation.
- Research the Dutch graphic artist M. C. Escher and find examples of tessellations in his work.

GRADING THE PROJECT
RUBRIC FOR CHAPTER PROJECT

4 Students' answers to the Investigation Exercises are correct and complete. The sketches of the tessellations are included and carefully done. The written report demonstrates an understanding of the project and the mathematics involved.

3 Students' answers to the Investigation Exercises are included but may be lacking in some details. The sketches are included but may not be carefully done. The written report contains all the required elements but may not explain each part well.

2 The Investigation Exercise answers or the sketches contain serious errors or are incomplete. Not all of the questions are answered in the report.

1 The answers to the Investigation Exercises show that the students do not have an understanding of the material presented. The sketches are missing or are incorrectly marked. The report is incomplete or not understandable. The project should be returned with a new deadline for completion. The students should speak with the teacher as soon as possible so that they understand the purpose and format of the project.

6. yes; semi-regular; *sample answer:*

8. yes; non-regular; *sample answer:*

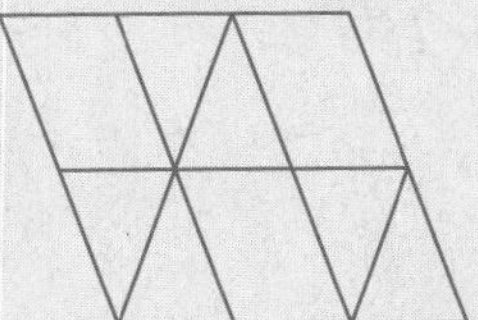

CHAPTER 8

PLANNING THE CHAPTER

Similarity

LESSON	GOALS	NCTM	ITED	SAT9 (TASK 1)	Terra-Nova	Local
8.1 *pp. 457–464*	GOAL 1 Find and simplify the ratio of two numbers. GOAL 2 Use proportions to solve real-life problems.	1, 2, 3, 6, 9, 10	MIRA, APRA, RQRA	1	11, 14, 16, 17, 48, 49, 51, 52	5
8.2 *pp. 465–471*	GOAL 1 Use properties of proportions. GOAL 2 Use proportions to solve real-life problems.	1, 2, 3, 6, 9, 10	MIRA, APRA, RQRA	1	11, 14, 16, 17, 48, 49, 51, 52	5
8.3 *pp. 472–479*	CONCEPT ACTIVITY: 8.3 *Investigate making conjectures about similarity.* GOAL 1 Identify similar polygons. GOAL 2 Use similar polygons to solve real-life problems.	1, 2, 3, 4, 6, 7, 8, 9, 10	MIGE, RQGE	1, 24	11, 13, 14, 16, 17, 18, 49, 51, 52	11
8.4 *pp. 480–487*	GOAL 1 Identify similar triangles. GOAL 2 Use similar triangles in real-life problems.	1, 2, 3, 4, 6, 9, 10	MIGE, RQGE	1, 24	11, 13, 14, 16, 17, 49, 51, 52	5, 17
8.5 *pp. 488–496*	GOAL 1 Use similarity theorems to prove that two triangles are similar. GOAL 2 Use similar triangles to solve real-life problems.	1, 2, 3, 4, 6, 7, 8, 9, 10	MIGE, RQGE	1, 24	11, 13, 14, 16, 17, 18, 49, 51, 52	5, 16
8.6 *pp. 497–505*	TECHNOLOGY ACTIVITY: 8.6 *Compare segment lengths in triangles using geometry software.* GOAL 1 Use proportionality theorems to calculate segment lengths. GOAL 2 Use proportionality theorems to solve real-life problems.	1, 2, 3, 4, 6, 7, 9, 10	MIM, MIGE, MIRA, APRA, RQGE, RQRA	1, 24	11, 13, 14, 16, 17, 49, 51, 52	7, 16
8.7 *pp. 506–514*	GOAL 1 Identify dilations. GOAL 2 Use properties of dilations to create a real-life perspective drawing. TECHNOLOGY ACTIVITY: 8.7 *Explore properties of dilations using geometry software.*	3, 9, 10	MIG, MIGE	34	14, 52	11, 16

RESOURCES

Chapter Resource Booklets

Chapter Support

Tips for New Teachers	p. 1	Prerequisite Skills Review	p. 5
Parent Guide for Student Success	p. 3	Strategies for Reading Mathematics	p. 7

Lesson Support

Lesson Support	8.1	8.2	8.3	8.4	8.5	8.6	8.7
Lesson Plans (regular and block)	p. 9	p. 21	p. 33	p. 47	p. 63	p. 81	p. 95
Warm-Up Exercises and Daily Quiz	p. 11	p. 23	p. 35	p. 49	p. 65	p. 83	p. 97
Activity Support Masters			p. 36				
Lesson Openers	p. 12	p. 24	p. 37	p. 50	p. 66	p. 84	p. 98
Technology Activities & Keystrokes				p. 51	p. 67	p. 85	p. 99
Practice (3 levels)	p. 13	p. 25	p. 38	p. 55	p. 70	p. 87	p. 101
Reteaching with Practice	p. 16	p. 28	p. 41	p. 58	p. 73	p. 90	p. 104
Quick Catch-Up for Absent Students	p. 18	p. 30	p. 43	p. 60	p. 75	p. 92	p. 106
Cooperative Learning Activities					p. 76		
Interdisciplinary Applications		p. 31		p. 61		p. 93	
Real-Life Applications	p. 19		p. 44		p. 77		p. 107
Math & History Applications					p. 78		
Challenge: Skills and Applications	p. 20	p. 32	p. 45	p. 62	p. 79	p. 94	p. 108

Review and Assessment

Quizzes	pp. 46, 80	Alternative Assessment with Math Journal	p. 117
Chapter Review Games and Activities	p. 109	Project with Rubric	p. 119
Chapter Test (3 levels)	pp. 110–115	Cumulative Review	p. 121
SAT/ACT Chapter Test	p. 116	Resource Book Answers	p. A1

Transparencies

	8.1	8.2	8.3	8.4	8.5	8.6	8.7
Warm-Up Exercises and Daily Quiz	p. 55	p. 56	p. 57	p. 58	p. 59	p. 60	p. 61
Alternative Lesson Opener Transparencies	p. 47	p. 48	p. 49	p. 50	p. 51	p. 52	p. 53
Examples/Standardized Test Practice	✓	✓	✓	✓	✓	✓	✓
Answer Transparencies	✓	✓	✓	✓	✓	✓	✓

Technology

- Electronic Teaching Tools
- Online Lesson Planner
- Internet Support
- Personal Student Tutor
- Test and Practice Generator
- Geometry in Motion video
- Electronic Lesson Presentations (Lesson 8.5)

Additional Resources

- Basic Skills Workbook: Diagnosis and Remediation
- Worked-Out Solution Key
- Resources in Spanish
- Standardized Test Practice Workbook
- Practice Workbook with Examples

Correlations to the California Curriculum

Correlations to California Standards
See Teacher's Edition pp. CA9–CA11

Correlations to SAT9
Task 1: See Teacher's Edition pp. CA12–CA14
Task 2: See Teacher's Edition pp. CA15–CA17

CHAPTER 8

PACING THE CHAPTER

Resource Key
- STUDENT EDITION
- CHAPTER 8 RESOURCE BOOK
- TEACHER'S EDITION

REGULAR SCHEDULE

Day 1

8.1

STARTING OPTIONS
- Prereq. Skills Review
- Strategies for Reading
- Homework Check
- Warm-Up or Daily Quiz

TEACHING OPTIONS
- Motivating the Lesson
- Les. Opener (Appl.)
- Examples 1–7
- Closure Question
- Guided Practice Exs.

APPLY/HOMEWORK
- See Assignment Guide.
- See the CRB: Practice, Reteach, Apply, Extend

ASSESSMENT OPTIONS
- Checkpoint Exercises
- Daily Quiz (8.1)
- Stand. Test Practice

Day 2

8.2

STARTING OPTIONS
- Homework Check
- Warm-Up or Daily Quiz

TEACHING OPTIONS
- Motivating the Lesson
- Les. Opener (Technology)
- Examples 1–4
- Closure Question
- Guided Practice Exs.

APPLY/HOMEWORK
- See Assignment Guide.
- See the CRB: Practice, Reteach, Apply, Extend

ASSESSMENT OPTIONS
- Checkpoint Exercises
- Daily Quiz (8.2)
- Stand. Test Practice

Day 3

8.3

STARTING OPTIONS
- Homework Check
- Warm-Up or Daily Quiz

TEACHING OPTIONS
- Concept Act. & Wksht.
- Les. Opener (Visual)
- Examples 1–4
- Guided Practice Exs.

APPLY/HOMEWORK
- See Assignment Guide.
- See the CRB: Practice, Reteach, Apply, Extend

ASSESSMENT OPTIONS
- Checkpoint Exercises, p. 475

Day 4

8.3 *(cont.)*

STARTING OPTIONS
- Homework Check

TEACHING OPTIONS
- Example 5
- Closure Question

APPLY/HOMEWORK
- See Assignment Guide.
- See the CRB: Practice, Reteach, Apply, Extend

ASSESSMENT OPTIONS
- Checkpoint Exercises, p. 475
- Daily Quiz (8.3)
- Stand. Test Practice
- Quiz (8.1–8.3)

Day 5

8.4

STARTING OPTIONS
- Homework Check
- Warm-Up or Daily Quiz

TEACHING OPTIONS
- Les. Opener (Application)
- Technology Activity
- Examples 1–3
- Guided Practice Exs.

APPLY/HOMEWORK
- See Assignment Guide.
- See the CRB: Practice, Reteach, Apply, Extend

ASSESSMENT OPTIONS
- Checkpoint Exercises, p. 481

Day 6

8.4 *(cont.)*

STARTING OPTIONS
- Homework Check

TEACHING OPTIONS
- Examples 4–5
- Closure Question

APPLY/HOMEWORK
- See Assignment Guide.
- See the CRB: Practice, Reteach, Apply, Extend

ASSESSMENT OPTIONS
- Checkpoint Exercises, p. 482
- Daily Quiz (8.4)
- Stand. Test Practice

Day 9

8.6

STARTING OPTIONS
- Homework Check
- Warm-Up or Daily Quiz

TEACHING OPTIONS
- Motivating the Lesson
- Les. Opener (Activity)
- Examples 1–4
- Guided Practice Exs.

APPLY/HOMEWORK
- See Assignment Guide.
- See the CRB: Practice, Reteach, Apply, Extend

ASSESSMENT OPTIONS
- Checkpoint Exercises, p. 500

Day 10

8.6 *(cont.)*

STARTING OPTIONS
- Homework Check

TEACHING OPTIONS
- Examples 5–6
- Closure Question

APPLY/HOMEWORK
- See Assignment Guide.
- See the CRB: Practice, Reteach, Apply, Extend

ASSESSMENT OPTIONS
- Checkpoint Exercises, p. 501
- Daily Quiz (8.6)
- Stand. Test Practice

Day 11

8.7

STARTING OPTIONS
- Homework Check
- Warm-Up or Daily Quiz

TEACHING OPTIONS
- Motivating the Lesson
- Les. Opener (Software)
- Examples 1–3
- Guided Practice Exs.

APPLY/HOMEWORK
- See Assignment Guide.
- See the CRB: Practice, Reteach, Apply, Extend

ASSESSMENT OPTIONS
- Checkpoint Exercises

Day 12

8.7 *(cont.)*

STARTING OPTIONS
- Homework Check

TEACHING OPTIONS
- Examples 1–3
- Technology Activity
- Closure Question

APPLY/HOMEWORK
- See Assignment Guide.
- See the CRB: Practice, Reteach, Apply, Extend

ASSESSMENT OPTIONS
- Checkpoint Exercises
- Daily Quiz (8.7)
- Stand. Test Practice
- Quiz (8.6–8.7)

Day 13

Review

DAY 13 START OPTIONS
- Homework Check

REVIEWING OPTIONS
- Chapter 8 Summary
- Chapter 8 Review
- Chapter Review Games and Activities

APPLY/HOMEWORK
- Chapter 8 Test (practice)
- Ch. Standardized Test (practice)

Day 14

Assess

DAY 14 START OPTIONS
- Homework Check

ASSESSMENT OPTIONS
- Chapter 8 Test
- SAT/ACT Ch. 8 Test
- Alternative Assessment

APPLY/HOMEWORK
- Skill Review, p. 526

Day 7

8.5

Starting Options
- Homework Check
- Warm-Up or Daily Quiz

Teaching Options
- Les. Opener (Activity)
- Technology Activity
- Examples 1–4
- Guided Practice Exs.

Apply/Homework
- See Assignment Guide.
- See the CRB: Practice, Reteach, Apply, Extend

Assessment Options
- Checkpoint Exercises, pp. 489–490

Day 8

8.5 *(cont.)*

Starting Options
- Homework Check

Teaching Options
- Examples 5–6
- Closure Question

Apply/Homework
- See Assignment Guide.
- See the CRB: Practice, Reteach, Apply, Extend

Assessment Options
- Checkpoint Exercises, p. 491
- Daily Quiz (8.5)
- Stand. Test Practice
- Quiz (8.4–8.5)

BLOCK SCHEDULE

Day 1

Assess & 8.1

(Day 1 = Ch. 7 Day 7)

Assessment Options
- Chapter 7 Test
- SAT/ACT Ch. 7 Test
- Alternative Assessment

Ch. 8 Start Options
- Skills Review, p. 456
- Prereq. Skills Review
- Strategies for Reading

Teaching 8.1 Options
- Warm-Up (Les. 8.1)
- Motivating the Lesson
- Les. Opener (Appl.)
- Examples 1–7
- Closure Question
- Guided Practice Exs.

Apply/Homework
- See Assignment Guide.
- See the CRB: Practice, Reteach, Apply, Extend

Assessment Options
- Checkpoint Exercises
- Daily Quiz (Les. 8.1)
- Stand. Test Practice

Day 2

8.2 & 8.3

Day 2 Start Options
- Homework Check
- Warm-Up (Les. 8.2) or Daily Quiz (Les. 8.1)

Teaching 8.2 Options
- Motivating the Lesson
- Les. Opener (Tech.)
- Examples 1–4
- Closure Question
- Guided Practice Exs.

Beginning 8.3 Options
- Warm-Up (Les. 8.3)
- Concept Act. & Wksht.
- Les. Opener (Visual)
- Examples 1–4
- Guided Practice Exs.

Apply/Homework
- See Assignment Guide.
- See the CRB: Practice, Reteach, Apply, Extend

Assessment Options
- Checkpoint Exercises
- Daily Quiz (Les. 8.2)
- Stand. Test Prac. (8.2)

Day 3

8.3 & 8.4

Day 3 Start Options
- Homework Check
- Daily Quiz (Les. 8.2)

Finishing 8.3 Options
- Example 5
- Closure Question

Beginning 8.4 Options
- Warm-Up (Les. 8.4)
- Les. Opener (Appl.)
- Technology Activity
- Examples 1–3
- Guided Practice Exs.

Apply/Homework
- See Assignment Guide.
- See the CRB: Practice, Reteach, Apply, Extend

Assessment Options
- Checkpoint Exercises
- Daily Quiz (Les. 8.3)
- Stand. Test Prac. (8.3)
- Quiz (8.1–8.3)

Day 4

8.4 & 8.5

Day 4 Start Options
- Homework Check
- Daily Quiz (Les. 8.3)

Finishing 8.4 Options
- Examples 4–5
- Closure Question

Beginning 8.5 Options
- Warm-Up (Les. 8.5)
- Les. Opener (Activity)
- Technology Activity
- Examples 1–4
- Guided Practice Exs.

Apply/Homework
- See Assignment Guide.
- See the CRB: Practice, Reteach, Apply, Extend

Assessment Options
- Checkpoint Exercises
- Daily Quiz (Les. 8.4)
- Stand. Test Prac. (8.4)

Day 5

8.5 & 8.6

Day 5 Start Options
- Homework Check
- Daily Quiz (Les. 8.4)

Finishing 8.5 Options
- Examples 5–6
- Closure Question

Beginning 8.6 Options
- Warm-Up (Les. 8.6)
- Motivating the Lesson
- Les. Opener (Activity)
- Examples 1–4
- Guided Practice Exs.

Apply/Homework
- See Assignment Guide.
- See the CRB: Practice, Reteach, Apply, Extend

Assessment Options
- Checkpoint Exercises
- Daily Quiz (Les. 8.5)
- Stand. Test Prac. (8.5)
- Quiz (8.4–8.5)

Day 6

8.6 & 8.7

Day 6 Start Options
- Homework Check
- Daily Quiz (Les. 8.5)

Finishing 8.6 Options
- Examples 5–6
- Closure Question

Beginning 8.7 Options
- Warm-Up (Les. 8.7)
- Motivating the Lesson
- Les. Opener (Software)
- Examples 1–3
- Guided Practice Exs.

Apply/Homework
- See Assignment Guide.
- See the CRB: Practice, Reteach, Apply, Extend

Assessment Options
- Checkpoint Exercises
- Daily Quiz (Les. 8.6)
- Stand. Test Prac. (8.6)

Day 7

8.7 & Review

Day 7 Start Options
- Homework Check
- Daily Quiz (Les. 8.6)

Finishing 8.7 Options
- Examples 1–3
- Technology Activity
- Closure Question

Reviewing Options
- Chapter 8 Summary
- Chapter 8 Review
- Chapter Review Games and Activities

Apply/Homework
- See Assignment Guide.
- See the CRB: Practice, Reteach, Apply, Extend
- Chapter 8 Test (practice)
- Ch. Standardized Test (practice)

Assessment Options
- Checkpoint Exercises
- Daily Quiz (Les. 8.7)
- Stand. Test Practice
- Quiz (8.6–8.7)

Day 8

Assess & 9.1

(Day 8 = Ch. 9 Day 1)

Assessment Options
- Chapter 8 Test
- SAT/ACT Ch. 8 Test
- Alternative Assessment

Ch. 9 Start Options
- Skills Review, p. 526
- Prereq. Skills Review
- Strategies for Reading

Teaching 9.1 Options
- Warm-Up (Les. 9.1)
- Motivating the Lesson
- Les. Opener (Software)
- Examples 1–3
- Closure Question
- Guided Practice Exs.

Apply/Homework
- See Assignment Guide.
- See the CRB: Practice, Reteach, Apply, Extend

Assessment Options
- Checkpoint Exercises
- Daily Quiz (Les. 9.1)
- Stand. Test Practice

CHAPTER 8 MEETING INDIVIDUAL NEEDS

BEFORE THE CHAPTER

The *Chapter 8 Resource Book* has the following materials to distribute and use before the chapter:

- **Parent Guide for Student Success**
- **Prerequisite Skills Review**
- **Strategies for Reading Mathematics (pictured below)**

STRATEGIES FOR READING *Pages 7–8*

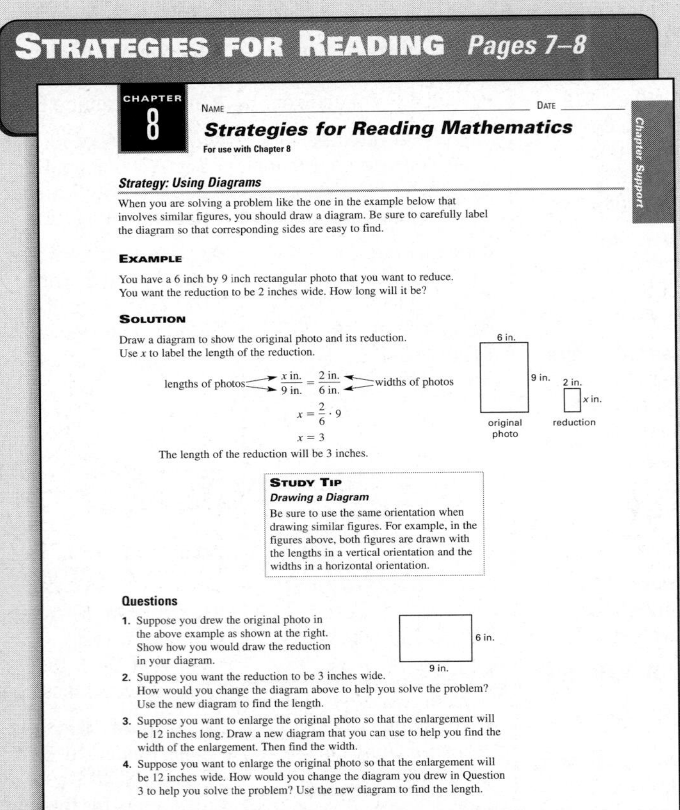

CHAPTER 8 NAME ______ DATE ______

Strategies for Reading Mathematics

For use with Chapter 8

Chapter Support

Strategy: Using Diagrams

When you are solving a problem like the one in the example below that involves similar figures, you should draw a diagram. Be sure to carefully label the diagram so that corresponding sides are easy to find.

EXAMPLE

You have a 6 inch by 9 inch rectangular photo that you want to reduce. You want the reduction to be 2 inches wide. How long will it be?

SOLUTION

Draw a diagram to show the original photo and its reduction. Use x to label the length of the reduction.

lengths of photos → $\frac{x \text{ in.}}{9 \text{ in.}} = \frac{2 \text{ in.}}{6 \text{ in.}}$ ← widths of photos

$x = \frac{2}{6} \cdot 9$

$x = 3$

The length of the reduction will be 3 inches.

STUDY TIP
Drawing a Diagram
Be sure to use the same orientation when drawing similar figures. For example, in the figures above, both figures are drawn with the lengths in a vertical orientation and the widths in a horizontal orientation.

Questions

1. Suppose you drew the original photo in the above example as shown at the right. Show how you would draw the reduction in your diagram.
2. Suppose you want the reduction to be 3 inches wide. How would you change the diagram above to help you solve the problem? Use the new diagram to find the length.
3. Suppose you want to enlarge the original photo so that the enlargement will be 12 inches long. Draw a new diagram that you can use to help you find the width of the enlargement. Then find the width.
4. Suppose you want to enlarge the original photo so that the enlargement will be 12 inches wide. How would you change the diagram you drew in Question 3 to help you solve the problem? Use the new diagram to find the length.

STRATEGIES FOR READING MATHEMATICS These two pages give students tips about using and drawing diagrams as they prepare for Chapter 8 and provide a visual glossary of key vocabulary words in the chapter, such as proportion and similar polygons.

DURING EACH LESSON

The *Chapter 8 Resource Book* has the following alternatives for introducing the lesson:

- **Lesson Openers (pictured below)**
- **Technology Activities with Keystrokes**

LESSON OPENER *Page 50*

LESSON 8.4 NAME ______ DATE ______

Available as a transparency

Application Lesson Opener

For use with pages 480–487

You can use similar triangles when playing miniature golf. In the diagram below, a golf ball putted from point *B* hits a wall at *D* and travels into the hole at *H*. By physics, the angles that the path of the ball makes with the wall are always congruent. The challenge for the golfer is in putting the ball so that it hits the wall at the correct point.

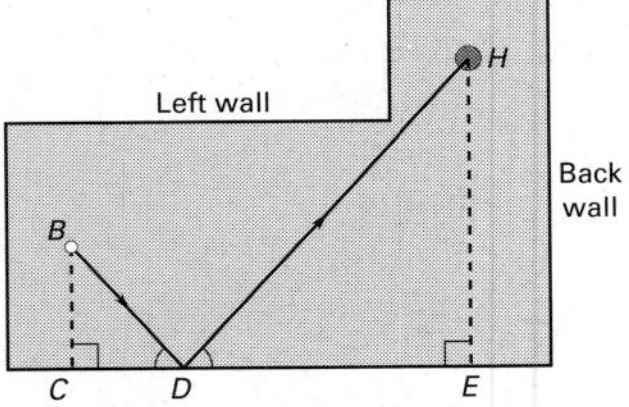

1. Two similar right triangles are shown in the diagram. Name the triangles and any pairs of congruent angles. Write the statement of proportionality for the triangles.
2. Trace the diagram except for the path. Draw a path for the ball to reach the hole in one putt by hitting the back wall instead of the right wall. Use a protractor to verify congruent angles.
3. Trace the diagram except for the path. Draw a path for the ball to reach the hole in one putt by hitting two walls. (*Hint:* Hit the left wall first.) Use a protractor to verify congruent angles.
4. Design your own miniature golf hole that requires the ball to hit one or two walls. Draw at least one possible path to the hole.

Lesson 8.4

APPLICATION LESSON OPENER This Lesson Opener provides an alternative way to start Lesson 8.4 in the form of a real-life application. Students see how similar triangles relate to miniature golf.

TECHNOLOGY RESOURCE

Students and teachers can look to the Application Links and the Career Links at www.mcdougallittell.com for more information about selected applications in Chapter 8.

FOLLOWING EACH LESSON

The *Chapter 8 Resource Book* has a variety of materials to follow-up each lesson. They include the following:

- **Practice (3 levels)**
- **Reteaching with Practice**
- **Quick Catch-Up for Absent Students**
- **Interdisciplinary Applications**
- **Real-Life Applications (pictured below)**

APPLICATION *Page 44*

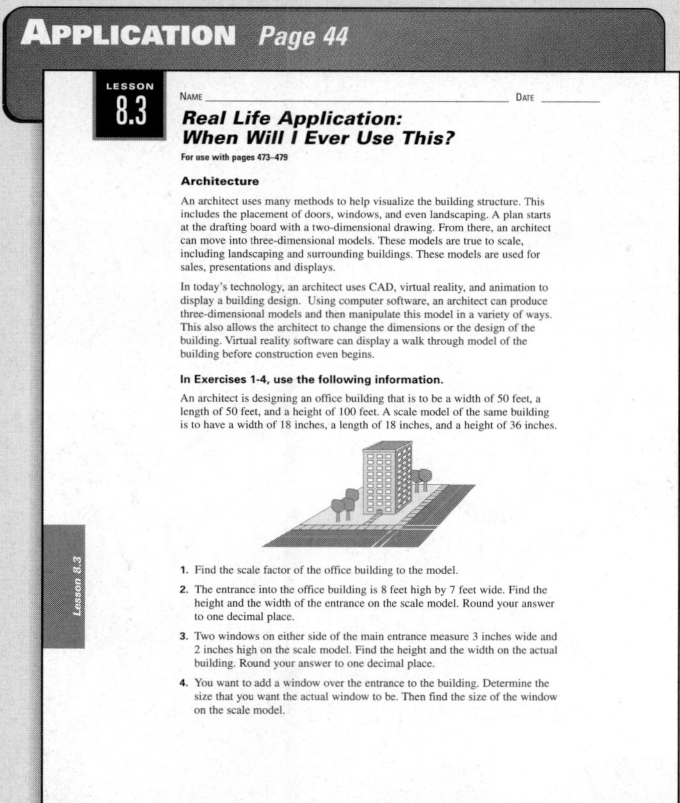

LESSON 8.3

NAME ______________________ DATE __________

Real Life Application: When Will I Ever Use This?

For use with pages 473–479

Architecture

An architect uses many methods to help visualize the building structure. This includes the placement of doors, windows, and even landscaping. A plan starts at the drafting board with a two-dimensional drawing. From there, an architect can move into three-dimensional models. These models are true to scale, including landscaping and surrounding buildings. These models are used for sales, presentations and displays.

In today's technology, an architect uses CAD, virtual reality, and animation to display a building design. Using computer software, an architect can produce three-dimensional models and then manipulate this model in a variety of ways. This also allows the architect to change the dimensions or the design of the building. Virtual reality software can display a walk through model of the building before construction even begins.

In Exercises 1-4, use the following information.

An architect is designing an office building that is to be a width of 50 feet, a length of 50 feet, and a height of 100 feet. A scale model of the same building is to have a width of 18 inches, a length of 18 inches, and a height of 36 inches.

1. Find the scale factor of the office building to the model.
2. The entrance into the office building is 8 feet high by 7 feet wide. Find the height and the width of the entrance on the scale model. Round your answer to one decimal place.
3. Two windows on either side of the main entrance measure 3 inches wide and 2 inches high on the scale model. Find the height and the width on the actual building. Round your answer to one decimal place.
4. You want to add a window over the entrance to the building. Determine the size that you want the actual window to be. Then find the size of the window on the scale model.

Lesson 8.3

REAL-LIFE APPLICATION When students ask "When will I ever use scale factors?," you can have them work through this Real-Life Application in which they apply the content of Lesson 8.3 to architecture.

ASSESSING THE CHAPTER

The *Chapter 8 Resource Book* has the following review and assessment materials:

- **Quizzes**
- **Chapter Review Games and Activities**
- **Chapter Test (3 levels)**
- **SAT/ACT Chapter Test**
- **Alternative Assessment with Rubric and Math Journal**
- **Project with Rubric (pictured below)**
- **Cumulative Review**

PROJECT WITH RUBRIC *Pages 119–120*

CHAPTER 8

NAME ______________________ DATE __________

Project: Self-Similarity

For use with Chapter 8

OBJECTIVE Create fractal designs.

MATERIALS plain white and colored paper, ruler, scissors, and glue

INVESTIGATION In this project, you will investigate fractals. Two characteristics of fractals are *self-similarity* and *iteration*. Think of *self-similarity* as meaning that part of the whole looks like or closely resembles the whole. Think of *iteration* as a repetitive process that allows a fractal pattern to grow.

Exploring Self-Similarity and Iteration Draw and analyze a fractal pattern.

1. Begin by drawing a 9-inch line segment and label it I(0).
2. For the next iteration draw a line segment below the previous segment but with the middle third of the segment missing. Label this row I(1).
3. Continue the iteration process four more times, leaving out the middle third of *each* segment, and label each row of segments appropriately.
4. Assume the beginning segment, I(0), is one unit long. Make a table up to I(5) like the one shown. Then include a row for the general pattern, I(*n*).

Iteration	*Length of each segment*	*No. of segments in row*	*Total length shown in row*
0	1	1	1

5. How is self-similarity evident in this fractal pattern, known as *Cantor dust*?

Creating a Fractal Card

Step 1 Fold a sheet of paper in half, vertically.

Step 2 Mark two points along the folded edge, each about one-fourth the distance from one end to the other. Make a cut from each point, perpendicular to the fold, that extends half way across the paper.

Step 3 Fold that middle section over and crease it. Open the paper and push that middle section to the inside as shown at the right.

Step 4 Repeat the process of Steps 2 and 3 several times, each time cutting into the remaining middle portion of the folded paper.

Step 5 Once the folding and cutting is complete, open the paper, push out the cut shape from the backside of the paper and crease firmly.

Step 6 Complete your card by gluing a piece of folded paper to the back of your fractal paper. You will have created a fractal pop-up card.

Create a fractal pop-up card of your own design that demonstrates self-similarity and iteration. Write the rule for it.

PRESENT YOUR RESULTS Your report should contain the sketch and the completed table of iterations for *Cantor dust*, two fractal pop-up cards, and the rule for the card with your design. Explain how your card demonstrates self-similarity and iteration.

Review and Assess

PROJECT WITH RUBRIC The Project for Chapter 8 provides students with the opportunity to apply the concepts they have learned in the chapter in a new way. In this project, students use what they have learned about similarity to investigate fractals. Teacher's notes and a scoring rubric are provided on a separate sheet.

CHAPTER OVERVIEW

CHAPTER GOALS

Throughout Chapter 8 students will explore the concept of similarity. Students will first simplify ratios, solve proportions using the cross product property, and use properties of proportions to solve real-life problems. Similar polygons are then introduced and their properties are used to solve real-life problems. Next, similar triangles are explored in greater depth. Students will learn to prove that two triangles are similar using the AA Similarity Postulate, the SSS Similarity Theorem, and the SAS Similarity Theorem. Similar triangles are used to solve indirect measurement problems. Proportionality theorems involving parallel lines, angle bisectors, and transversals are examined and used to calculate segment lengths. Finally students identify dilations and use properties of dilations in real-life applications.

APPLICATION NOTE

When a large mural is created from a drawing, it is common to overlay the drawing with a grid. The outline of the drawing in each section of the grid can be traced and then enlarged using a photocopier. The enlarged pieces can then be used to create the mural. Most copiers have settings that allow you to enlarge the drawing by a percentage. You can use repeated enlarging to enlarge by a greater percentage.

Additional information about scale drawings is available at **www.mcdougallittell.com.**

SIMILARITY

How can you use proportions to turn a drawing into a mural?

CHAPTER

8

APPLICATION: Scale Drawing

Murals are often created by enlarging an original drawing. Different methods are used to make sure that all parts of the enlargement are in proportion to the original drawing.

One common method used in mural making is to enlarge each piece of art by the same percentage. If a drawing is enlarged to 300% of its original size, then the length and width of the enlargement will each be three times the size of the original.

Think & Discuss

1. Describe some other common methods used to enlarge a drawing. *Sample answer:* photocopier, computer software, pantograph
2. Estimate how much larger Figure 2 is than Figure 1. Can you discover a way to check your estimate? about twice as large; compare length and width

Figure 1

Figure 2

Learn More About It

You will learn another way to enlarge a drawing in Example 4 on p. 490.

APPLICATION LINK Visit www.mcdougallittell.com for more information about scale drawings.

PROJECTS

A project covering Chapters 8 and 9 appears on pages 590–591 of the Student Edition. An additional project for Chapter 8 is available in the *Chapter 8 Resource Book,* p. 119.

TECHNOLOGY

Software

- *Electronic Teaching Tools*
- *Online Lesson Planner*
- *Personal Student Tutor*
- *Test and Practice Generator*
- *Electronic Lesson Presentations (Lesson 8.5)*

Video

- *Geometry in Motion*

Internet Connections
www.mcdougallittell.com

- **Application Links**
  455, 462, 469, 496
- **Student Help**
  463, 466, 477, 482, 485, 486, 491, 497, 504, 511, 514
- **Career Links**
  482, 503, 512
- **Extra Challenge**
  471, 478, 487, 495

PREPARE

DIAGNOSTIC TOOLS

The **Skill Review** exercises can help you diagnose whether students have the following skills needed in Chapter 8:

- Find the perimeter of a figure.
- Find the slope of a line that passes though two points.

The following resources are available for students who need additional help with these skills:

- Prerequisite Skills Review (*Chapter 8 Resource Book,* p. 5; *Warm-Up Transparencies,* p. 54)
- Reteaching with Practice (Chapter Resource Books for Lessons 1.7 and 3.6)
- *Personal Student Tutor*

ADDITIONAL RESOURCES

The following resources are provided to help you prepare for the upcoming chapter and customize review materials:

- ***Chapter 8 Resource Book***
  Tips for New Teachers (p. 1)
  Parent Guide (p. 3)
  Lesson Plans (every lesson)
  Lesson Plans for Block Scheduling (every lesson)
- ***Electronic Teaching Tools***
- ***Online Lesson Planner***
- ***Test and Practice Generator***

CHAPTER 8 Study Guide

PREVIEW

What's the chapter about?

Chapter 8 is about **similar polygons**. Two polygons are similar if their corresponding angles are congruent and the lengths of corresponding sides are proportional. In Chapter 8, you'll learn

- four ways to prove triangles are similar given information about their sides and angles.
- how to use similar polygons to solve real-life problems.

KEY VOCABULARY

▶ **Review**
- angle bisector, p. 36
- slope, p. 165
- transformation, p. 396
- image, p. 396
- preimage, p. 396

▶ **New**
- ratio, p. 457
- proportion, p. 459
- means, p. 459
- extremes, p. 459
- geometric mean, p. 466
- similar polygons, p. 473
- scale factor, p. 474
- dilation, p. 506
- reduction, p. 506
- enlargement, p. 506

PREPARE

Are you ready for the chapter?

SKILL REVIEW Do these exercises to review key skills that you'll apply in this chapter. See the given **reference page** if there is something you don't understand.

> **STUDENT HELP**
> **Study Tip**
> "Student Help" boxes throughout the chapter give you study tips and tell you where to look for extra help in this book and on the Internet.

Find the perimeter of the figure. **(Review pp. 51–54)**

1. 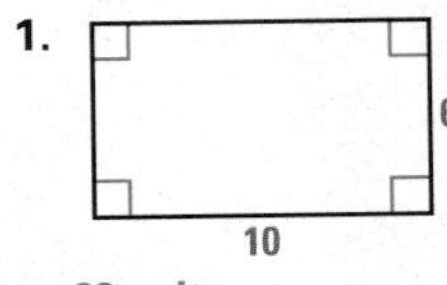

32 units

2. 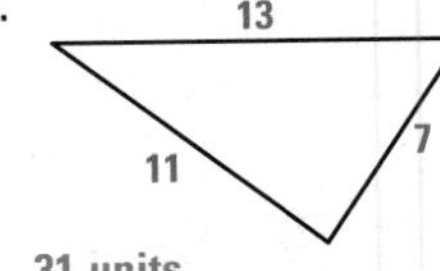

31 units

3. 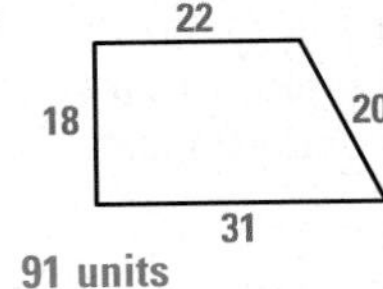

91 units

Find the slope of the line that passes through the points. **(Review Example 2, p. 165)**

4. $A(0, 0)$ and $B(4, 2)$ $\frac{1}{2}$

5. $C(-1, 2)$ and $D(6, 5)$ $\frac{3}{7}$

6. $E(0, 3)$ and $F(-4, -8)$ $\frac{11}{4}$

Here's a study strategy!

Connect to the Real World

Make a list of the main topics of the chapter. Give a real-world example for each.

8.1 Ratio and Proportion

What you should learn

GOAL 1 Find and simplify the ratio of two numbers.

GOAL 2 Use proportions to solve **real-life** problems, such as computing the width of a painting in **Example 6**.

Why you should learn it

▼ To solve **real-life** problems, such as using a scale model to determine the dimensions of a sculpture like the baseball glove below and the baseball bat in **Exs. 51–53**.

REAL LIFE

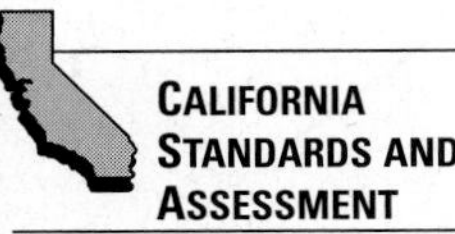

CALIFORNIA STANDARDS AND ASSESSMENT

CA Standards: 5
SAT9 Task 1: Obj. 1
SAT9 Task 2: Obj. 1

GOAL 1 COMPUTING RATIOS

If a and b are two quantities that are measured in the *same* units, then the **ratio of a to b** is $\frac{a}{b}$. The ratio of a to b can also be written as $a:b$. Because a ratio is a quotient, its denominator cannot be zero.

Ratios are usually expressed in simplified form. For instance, the ratio of 6:8 is usually simplified as 3:4.

EXAMPLE 1 *Simplifying Ratios*

Simplify the ratios.

a. $\frac{12 \text{ cm}}{4 \text{ m}}$ **b.** $\frac{6 \text{ ft}}{18 \text{ in.}}$

SOLUTION

To simplify ratios with unlike units, convert to like units so that the units divide out. Then simplify the fraction, if possible.

a. $\frac{12 \text{ cm}}{4 \text{ m}} = \frac{12 \text{ cm}}{4 \cdot 100 \text{ cm}} = \frac{12}{400} = \frac{3}{100}$ **b.** $\frac{6 \text{ ft}}{18 \text{ in.}} = \frac{6 \cdot 12 \text{ in.}}{18 \text{ in.}} = \frac{72}{18} = \frac{4}{1}$

ACTIVITY Developing Concepts

Investigating Ratios

Steps 1–4. Answers may vary.

1. Use a tape measure to measure the circumference of the base of your thumb, the circumference of your wrist, and the circumference of your neck. Record the results in a table.
2. Compute the ratio of your wrist measurement to your thumb measurement. Then, compute the ratio of your neck measurement to your wrist measurement.
3. Compare the two ratios.

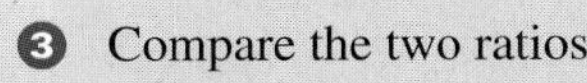

4. Compare your ratios to those of others in the class.
5. Does it matter whether you record your measurements all in inches or all in centimeters? Explain.
No; if all the units of measure are the same, they do not affect the ratio.

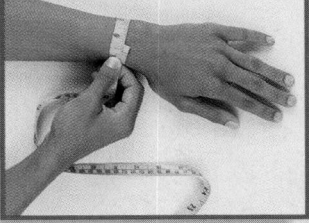

1 PLAN

PACING
Basic: 1 day
Average: 1 day
Advanced: 1 day
Block Schedule: 0.5 block with Ch. 7 Assess.

LESSON OPENER APPLICATION
An alternative way to approach Lesson 8.1 is to use the Application Lesson Opener:
- Blackline Master (*Chapter 8 Resource Book,* p. 12)
- Transparency (p. 47)

MEETING INDIVIDUAL NEEDS
- ***Chapter 8 Resource Book***
  Prerequisite Skills Review (p. 5)
  Practice Level A (p. 13)
  Practice Level B (p. 14)
  Practice Level C (p. 15)
  Reteaching with Practice (p. 16)
  Absent Student Catch-Up (p. 18)
  Challenge (p. 20)
- ***Resources in Spanish***
- ***Personal Student Tutor***

NEW-TEACHER SUPPORT
See the Tips for New Teachers on pp. 1–2 of the *Chapter 8 Resource Book* for additional notes about Lesson 8.1.

WARM-UP EXERCISES

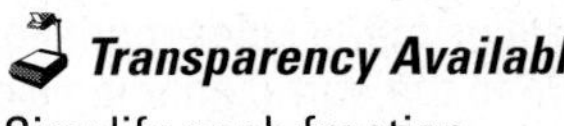

Transparency Available

Simplify each fraction.

1. $\frac{12}{15}$ $\frac{4}{5}$
2. $\frac{14}{56}$ $\frac{1}{4}$
3. $\frac{21}{6}$ $\frac{7}{2}$
4. $\frac{90}{450}$ $\frac{1}{5}$

2 TEACH

MOTIVATING THE LESSON

Ask students for examples of ratios used in real-life, such as win-to-loss ratios and percents. Explain that in this lesson, they will learn about ratios in geometry and techniques they can use to solve geometric and real-life problems with ratios.

ACTIVITY NOTE

This activity gives students experience using ratios in a real-life situation.

EXTRA EXAMPLE 1

Simplify the ratios.

a. $\frac{1\text{ m}}{2\text{ km}}$ $\frac{1}{2000}$ b. $\frac{3\text{ yd}}{6\text{ ft}}$ $\frac{3}{2}$

EXTRA EXAMPLE 2

The perimeter of the isosceles triangle shown is 56 in. The ratio of $LM : MN$ is 5:4. Find the lengths of the sides and the base of the triangle. 20 in., 20 in., 16 in.

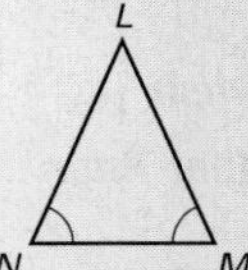

EXTRA EXAMPLE 3

The measures of the angles in a triangle are in the extended ratio 3:4:8. Find the measures of the angles. 36°, 48°, 96°

EXTRA EXAMPLE 4

The ratios of the side lengths of $\triangle QRS$ to the corresponding side lengths of $\triangle VTU$ are 3:2. Find the unknown lengths.
$TU = 12$ cm, $TV = 2\sqrt{37}$ cm,
$QS = 3$ cm, $QR = 3\sqrt{37}$ cm

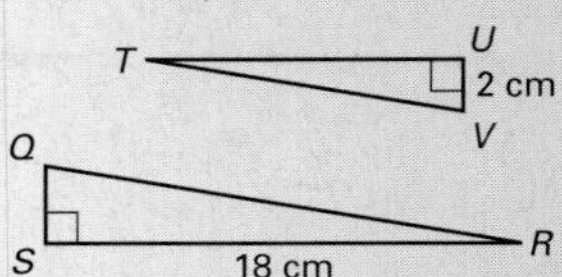

Checkpoint Exercises for Examples 1–4 on next page.

STUDENT HELP

Look Back
For help with perimeter, see p. 51.

EXAMPLE 2 Using Ratios

The perimeter of rectangle $ABCD$ is 60 centimeters. The ratio of $AB:BC$ is 3:2. Find the length and width of the rectangle.

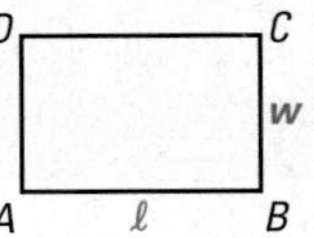

SOLUTION

Because the ratio of $AB:BC$ is 3:2, you can represent the length AB as $3x$ and the width BC as $2x$.

$2\ell + 2w = P$	**Formula for perimeter of rectangle**
$2(3x) + 2(2x) = 60$	**Substitute for ℓ, w, and P.**
$6x + 4x = 60$	**Multiply.**
$10x = 60$	**Combine like terms.**
$x = 6$	**Divide each side by 10.**

▶ So, $ABCD$ has a length of 18 centimeters and a width of 12 centimeters.

Using Algebra

EXAMPLE 3 Using Extended Ratios

The measure of the angles in $\triangle JKL$ are in the *extended ratio* of 1:2:3. Find the measures of the angles.

SOLUTION

Begin by sketching a triangle. Then use the extended ratio of 1:2:3 to label the measures of the angles as $x°$, $2x°$, and $3x°$.

$x° + 2x° + 3x° = 180°$	**Triangle Sum Theorem**
$6x = 180$	**Combine like terms.**
$x = 30$	**Divide each side by 6.**

▶ So, the angle measures are 30°, $2(30°) = 60°$, and $3(30°) = 90°$.

Logical Reasoning

EXAMPLE 4 Using Ratios

The ratios of the side lengths of $\triangle DEF$ to the corresponding side lengths of $\triangle ABC$ are 2:1. Find the unknown lengths.

SOLUTION

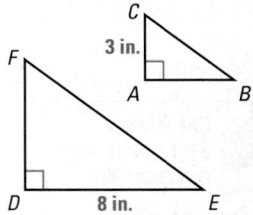

- DE is twice AB and $DE = 8$, so $AB = \frac{1}{2}(8) = 4$.
- Using the Pythagorean Theorem, you can determine that $BC = 5$.
- DF is twice AC and $AC = 3$, so $DF = 2(3) = 6$.
- EF is twice BC and $BC = 5$, so $EF = 2(5) = 10$.

STUDENT HELP

Look Back
For help with the Pythagorean Theorem, see p. 20.

GOAL 2 USING PROPORTIONS

An equation that equates two ratios is a **proportion**. For instance, if the ratio $\frac{a}{b}$ is equal to the ratio $\frac{c}{d}$, then the following proportion can be written:

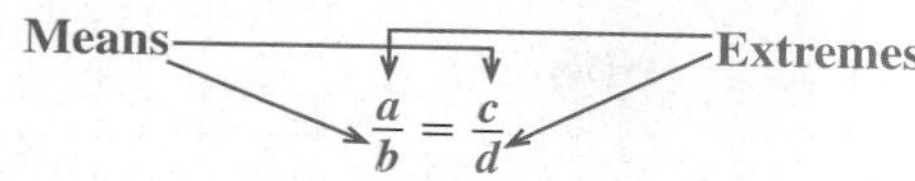

$$\frac{a}{b} = \frac{c}{d}$$

The numbers a and d are the **extremes** of the proportion. The numbers b and c are the **means** of the proportion.

PROPERTIES OF PROPORTIONS

1. **CROSS PRODUCT PROPERTY** The product of the extremes equals the product of the means.

   If $\frac{a}{b} = \frac{c}{d}$, then $ad = bc$.

2. **RECIPROCAL PROPERTY** If two ratios are equal, then their reciprocals are also equal.

   If $\frac{a}{b} = \frac{c}{d}$, then $\frac{b}{a} = \frac{d}{c}$.

STUDENT HELP

Skills Review
For help with reciprocals, see p. 788.

To *solve the proportion* you find the value of the variable.

EXAMPLE 5 ***Solving Proportions***

Solve the proportions.

a. $\frac{4}{x} = \frac{5}{7}$ **b.** $\frac{3}{y+2} = \frac{2}{y}$

SOLUTION

a. $\frac{4}{x} = \frac{5}{7}$ Write original proportion.

$\frac{x}{4} = \frac{7}{5}$ Reciprocal property

$x = 4\left(\frac{7}{5}\right)$ Multiply each side by 4.

$x = \frac{28}{5}$ Simplify.

b. $\frac{3}{y+2} = \frac{2}{y}$ Write original proportion.

$3y = 2(y + 2)$ Cross product property

$3y = 2y + 4$ Distributive property

$y = 4$ Subtract $2y$ from each side.

▶ The solution is 4. Check this by substituting in the original proportion.

CHECKPOINT EXERCISES

For use after Example 1:

1. Simplify the ratio.

a. $\frac{10 \text{ ft}}{2 \text{ in.}}$ $\frac{60}{1}$ **b.** $\frac{9 \text{ in.}}{2 \text{ yd}}$ $\frac{1}{8}$

For use after Examples 2–4:

2. The ratios of side lengths of $\triangle DEF$ to the corresponding side lengths of $\triangle GHI$ are 1:3. If the base and height of $\triangle DEF$ are 8 and 4 respectively, find the area of $\triangle GHI$. 144 square units

EXTRA EXAMPLE 5

Solve the proportions.

a. $\frac{9}{14} = \frac{6}{x}$ $\frac{28}{3}$ **b.** $\frac{s-5}{4} = \frac{s}{10}$ $\frac{25}{3}$

CHECKPOINT EXERCISES

For use after Example 5:

Solve the proportions.

1. $\frac{8}{b} = \frac{14}{5}$ $\frac{20}{7}$ **2.** $\frac{3-x}{6} = \frac{x}{2}$ $\frac{3}{4}$

STUDENT HELP NOTES

Skills Review As students review reciprocals on page 788, remind them that the product of a number and its reciprocal is 1.

MATHEMATICAL REASONING

EXAMPLE 5 Ask students if they could use the cross product property to solve part (**a**). yes Have them use the cross product property to solve this proportion. Then have students investigate whether the reciprocal property can be used for part (**b**). yes Ask them why they think the author chose the particular method used for each part.

EXTRA EXAMPLE 6

A photo of a building has the measurements given in the sketch below. The actual building is $26\frac{1}{4}$ ft wide. How tall is it? $38\frac{1}{2}$ ft

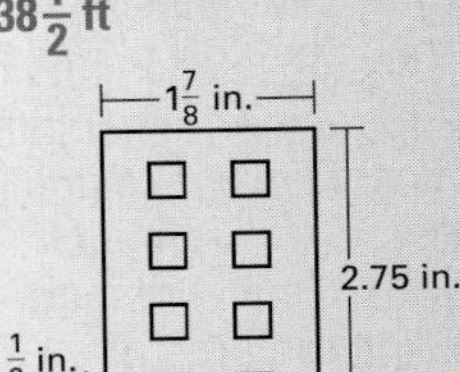

EXTRA EXAMPLE 7

What is the height of the door in the actual building described in Extra Example 6? 7 ft

CHECKPOINT EXERCISES

For use after Examples 6 and 7:

1. In a photograph taken from an airplane, a section of a city street is 3.5 inches long and $\frac{1}{8}$ of an inch wide. If the actual street is 30 feet wide, how long is it? 840 ft

FOCUS ON VOCABULARY

What distinguishes a *ratio* from other quotients? The numerator and denominator of a ratio must be measured in the same units.

CLOSURE QUESTION

Describe two ways to solve a proportion. You can use the cross product property or the reciprocal property.

DAILY PUZZLER

In one town, the ratio of cats to dogs is 3:2 and the ratio of cats to rabbits it 18:1. What is the ratio of dogs to rabbits? 12:1

EXAMPLE 6 *Solving a Proportion*

PAINTING The photo shows Bev Dolittle's painting *Music in the Wind.* Her actual painting is 12 inches high. How wide is it?

SOLUTION

You can reason that in the photograph all measurements of the artist's painting have been reduced by the same ratio. That is, the ratio of the actual width to the reduced width is equal to the ratio of the actual height to the reduced height. The photograph is $1\frac{1}{4}$ inches by $4\frac{3}{8}$ inches.

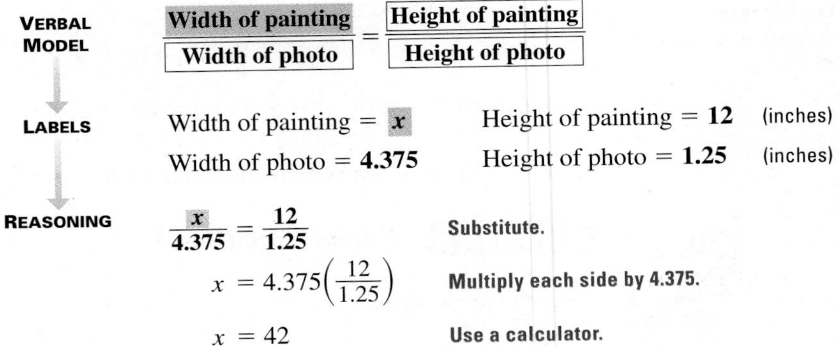

VERBAL MODEL $\frac{\text{Width of painting}}{\text{Width of photo}} = \frac{\text{Height of painting}}{\text{Height of photo}}$

LABELS

Width of painting $= x$ Height of painting $= \mathbf{12}$ (inches)

Width of photo $= \mathbf{4.375}$ Height of photo $= \mathbf{1.25}$ (inches)

REASONING

$\frac{x}{4.375} = \frac{12}{1.25}$ **Substitute.**

$x = 4.375\left(\frac{12}{1.25}\right)$ **Multiply each side by 4.375.**

$x = 42$ **Use a calculator.**

▶ So, the actual painting is 42 inches wide.

EXAMPLE 7 *Solving a Proportion*

Estimate the length of the hidden flute in Bev Doolittle's actual painting.

SOLUTION

In the photo, the flute is about $1\frac{7}{8}$ inches long. Using the reasoning from above you can say that:

$$\frac{\text{Length of flute in painting}}{\text{Length of flute in photo}} = \frac{\text{Height of painting}}{\text{Height of photo}}.$$

$\frac{f}{1.875} = \frac{12}{1.25}$ **Substitute.**

$f = 18$ **Multiply each side by 1.875 and simplify.**

▶ So, the flute is about 18 inches long in the painting.

GUIDED PRACTICE

Vocabulary Check ✓

1. In the proportion $\frac{r}{s} = \frac{p}{q}$, the variables s and p are the __?__ of the proportion and r and q are the __?__ of the proportion. means; extremes

Concept Check ✓

ERROR ANALYSIS In Exercises 2 and 3, find and correct the errors.

2. The ratio is $\frac{3 \cdot 12 \text{ in.}}{18 \text{ in.}} = 2{:}1$.
3. The Distributive Property was not used correctly; $10x = 4(x + 6) = 4x + 24$, and $x = 4$.

2.

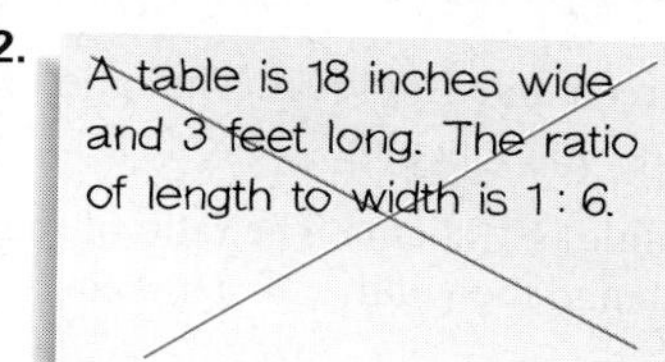

A table is 18 inches wide and 3 feet long. The ratio of length to width is 1 : 6.

3.

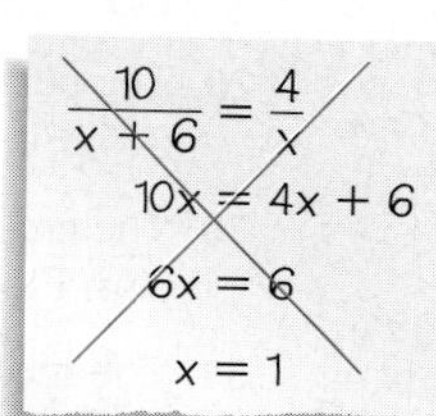

Skill Check ✓

Given that the track team won 8 meets and lost 2, find the ratios.

4. What is the ratio of wins to losses? What is the ratio of losses to wins? 4:1; 1:4
5. What is the ratio of wins to the total number of track meets? 4:5

In Exercises 6–8, solve the proportion.

6. $\frac{2}{x} = \frac{3}{9}$ 6
7. $\frac{5}{8} = \frac{6}{z}$ $\frac{48}{5}$
8. $\frac{2}{b + 3} = \frac{4}{b}$ −6

9. The ratio $BC{:}DC$ is 2:9. Find the value of x. 6

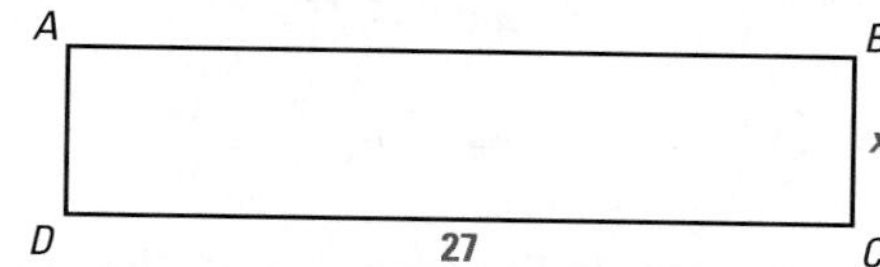

PRACTICE AND APPLICATIONS

STUDENT HELP

Extra Practice to help you master skills is on p. 817.

SIMPLIFYING RATIOS Simplify the ratio.

10. $\frac{16 \text{ students}}{24 \text{ students}}$ $\frac{2}{3}$
11. $\frac{48 \text{ marbles}}{8 \text{ marbles}}$ $\frac{6}{1}$
12. $\frac{22 \text{ feet}}{52 \text{ feet}}$ $\frac{11}{26}$
13. $\frac{6 \text{ meters}}{9 \text{ meters}}$ $\frac{2}{3}$

WRITING RATIOS Find the width to length ratio of each rectangle. Then simplify the ratio.

14. (rectangle: 16 mm, 20 mm) $\frac{16 \text{ mm}}{20 \text{ mm}}$; $\frac{4}{5}$
15. (rectangle: 10 cm, 7.5 cm) $\frac{7.5 \text{ cm}}{10 \text{ cm}}$; $\frac{3}{4}$
16. (rectangle: 12 in., 2 ft) $\frac{12 \text{ in.}}{24 \text{ in.}}$; $\frac{1}{2}$

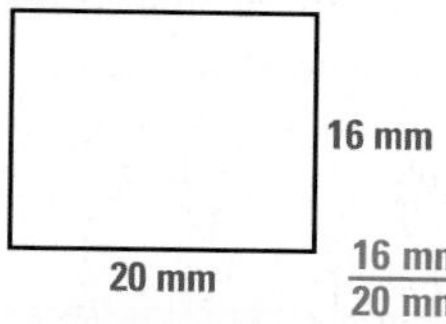

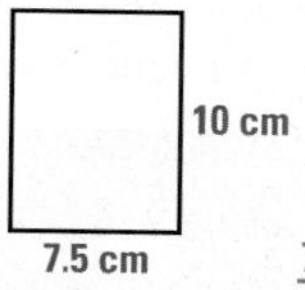

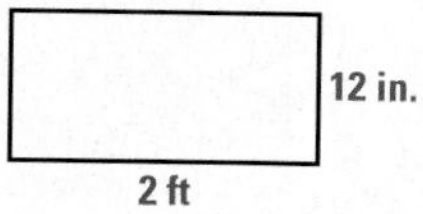

17. $\frac{36 \text{ in.}}{12 \text{ in.}}$ or $\frac{3 \text{ ft}}{1 \text{ ft}}$; $\frac{3}{1}$

STUDENT HELP

HOMEWORK HELP
Example 1: Exs. 10–24
Example 2: Exs. 29, 30
Example 3: Exs. 31, 32
Example 4: Exs. 57, 58

continued on p. 462

CONVERTING UNITS Rewrite the fraction so that the numerator and denominator have the same units. Then simplify.

17. $\frac{3 \text{ ft}}{12 \text{ in.}}$ See margin.
18. $\frac{60 \text{ cm}}{1 \text{ m}}$ $\frac{60 \text{ cm}}{100 \text{ cm}}$; $\frac{3}{5}$
19. $\frac{350 \text{ g}}{1 \text{ kg}}$ $\frac{350 \text{ g}}{1000 \text{ g}}$; $\frac{7}{20}$
20. $\frac{2 \text{ mi}}{3000 \text{ ft}}$ $\frac{10{,}560 \text{ ft}}{3000 \text{ ft}}$; $\frac{88}{25}$
21. $\frac{6 \text{ yd}}{10 \text{ ft}}$ $\frac{18 \text{ ft}}{10 \text{ ft}}$; $\frac{9}{5}$
22. $\frac{2 \text{ lb}}{20 \text{ oz}}$ $\frac{32 \text{ oz}}{20 \text{ oz}}$; $\frac{8}{5}$
23. $\frac{400 \text{ m}}{0.5 \text{ km}}$ $\frac{400 \text{ m}}{500 \text{ m}}$; $\frac{4}{5}$
24. $\frac{20 \text{ oz}}{4 \text{ lb}}$ $\frac{20 \text{ oz}}{64 \text{ oz}}$; $\frac{5}{16}$

3 APPLY

ASSIGNMENT GUIDE

BASIC
Day 1: pp. 461–464 Exs. 12, 16, 20, 24, 28, 32, 36, 40, 44, 45–47, 54–58, 62–66, 68–76 even

AVERAGE
Day 1: pp. 461–464 Exs. 12, 16, 20, 24, 28, 32, 36, 40, 44, 45–47, 51–58, 62–66, 68–76 even

ADVANCED
Day 1: pp. 461–464 Exs. 12, 16, 20, 24, 28, 32, 36, 40, 44, 45–47, 51–58, 62–76 even

BLOCK SCHEDULE
pp. 461–464 Exs. 12, 16, 20, 24, 28, 32, 36, 44, 45–47, 51–58, 62–66, 68–76 even (with Ch. 7 Assess.)

EXERCISE LEVELS

Level A: ***Easier***
10–16

Level B: ***More Difficult***
17–66

Level C: ***Most Difficult***
67

✓ HOMEWORK CHECK

To quickly check student understanding of key concepts, go over the following exercises: Exs. 16, 24, 28, 40, 46, 56, 62. See also the Daily Homework Quiz:

- Blackline Master (*Chapter 8 Resource Book,* p. 23)
- Transparency (p. 56)

! COMMON ERROR
EXERCISES 39–44 Students often use the distributive property incorrectly when the numerator or denominator of one of the ratios has more than one term. Encourage students to write an intermediate step using parentheses before applying the distributive property. Also, students should check their work by substituting the value of the variable into the original equation.

APPLICATION NOTE
EXERCISES 48–50 Additional information about gravity is available at **www.mcdougallittell.com.**

STUDENT HELP

HOMEWORK HELP
continued from p. 461
Example 5: Exs. 33–44
Example 6: Exs. 48–53, 59–61
Example 7: Exs. 48–53, 59–61

FINDING RATIOS **Use the number line to find the ratio of the distances.**

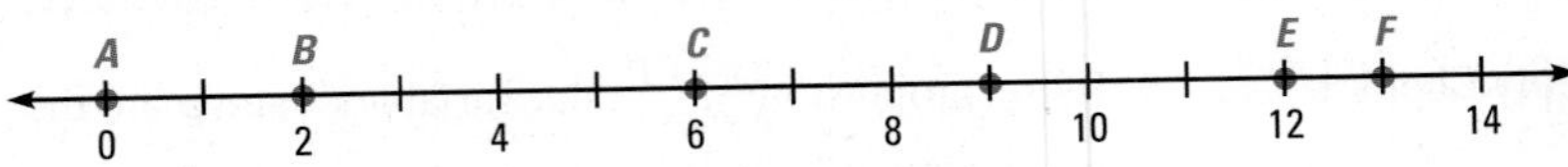

25. $\frac{AB}{CD} = \underline{\ ?\ }$ $\frac{2}{3}$
26. $\frac{BD}{CF} = \underline{\ ?\ }$ $\frac{7}{7} = 1$
27. $\frac{BF}{AD} = \underline{\ ?\ }$ $\frac{11}{9}$
28. $\frac{CF}{AB} = \underline{\ ?\ }$ $\frac{7}{2}$

29. The perimeter of a rectangle is 84 feet. The ratio of the width to the length is 2:5. Find the length and the width. **30 ft, 12 ft**

30. The area of a rectangle is 108 cm^2. The ratio of the width to the length is 3:4. Find the length and the width. **12 cm, 9 cm**

31. The measures of the angles in a triangle are in the extended ratio of 1:4:7. Find the measures of the angles. **15°, 60°, 105°**

32. The measures of the angles in a triangle are in the extended ratio of 2:15:19. Find the measures of the angles. **10°, 75°, 95°**

SOLVING PROPORTIONS **Solve the proportion.**

33. $\frac{x}{4} = \frac{5}{7}$ $\frac{20}{7}$
34. $\frac{y}{8} = \frac{9}{10}$ $\frac{36}{5}$
35. $\frac{7}{z} = \frac{10}{25}$ $\frac{35}{2}$
36. $\frac{4}{b} = \frac{10}{3}$ $\frac{6}{5}$
37. $\frac{30}{5} = \frac{14}{c}$ $\frac{7}{3}$
38. $\frac{16}{3} = \frac{d}{6}$ 32
39. $\frac{5}{x+3} = \frac{4}{x}$ 12
40. $\frac{4}{y-3} = \frac{8}{y}$ 6
41. $\frac{7}{2z+5} = \frac{3}{z}$ 15
42. $\frac{3x-8}{6} = \frac{2x}{10}$ $\frac{40}{9}$
43. $\frac{5y-8}{7} = \frac{5y}{6}$ $-\frac{48}{5}$
44. $\frac{4}{2z+6} = \frac{10}{7z-2}$ $\frac{17}{2}$

USING PROPORTIONS **In Exercises 45–47, the ratio of the width to the length for each rectangle is given. Solve for the variable.**

45. $AB:BC$ is 3:8. **16**

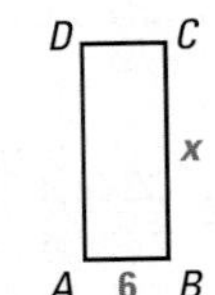

46. $EF:FG$ is 4:5. **25**

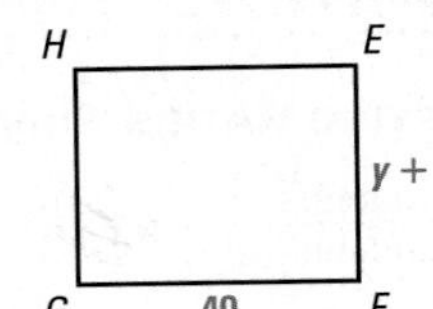

47. $JK:KL$ is 2:3. **21**

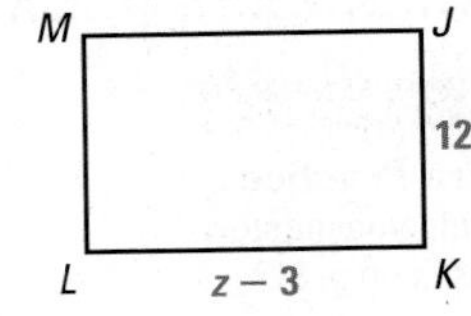

FOCUS ON APPLICATIONS

MOON'S GRAVITY Neil Armstrong's space suit weighed about 185 pounds on Earth and just over 30 pounds on the moon, due to the weaker force of gravity.

APPLICATION LINK
www.mcdougallittell.com

SCIENCE CONNECTION **Use the following information.**
The table gives the ratios of the gravity of four different planets to the gravity of Earth. Round your answers to the nearest whole number.

Planet	Venus	Mars	Jupiter	Pluto
Ratio of gravity	$\frac{9}{10}$	$\frac{38}{100}$	$\frac{236}{100}$	$\frac{7}{100}$

48. Which of the planets listed above has a gravity closest to the gravity of Earth? **Venus**

49. Estimate how much a person who weighs 140 pounds on Earth would weigh on Venus, Mars, Jupiter, and Pluto. **Venus: 126 lb; Mars: 53 lb; Jupiter: 330 lb; Pluto 10 lb**

50. If a person weighed 46 pounds on Mars, estimate how much he or she would weigh on Earth. **about 121 lb**

BASEBALL BAT SCULPTURE **A huge, free-standing baseball bat sculpture stands outside a sports museum in Louisville, Kentucky. It was patterned after Babe Ruth's 35 inch bat. The sculpture is 120 feet long. Round your answers to the nearest tenth of an inch.**

51. How long is the sculpture in inches? **1440 in.**

52. The diameter of the sculpture near the base is 9 feet. Estimate the corresponding diameter of Babe Ruth's bat. **about 2.6 in.**

53. The diameter of the handle of the sculpture is 3.5 feet. Estimate the diameter of the handle of Babe Ruth's bat. **about 1.0 in.**

USING PROPORTIONS **In Exercises 54–56, the ratio of two side lengths of the triangle is given. Solve for the variable.**

54. $PQ:QR$ is 3:4. **18**

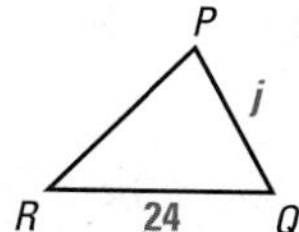

55. $SU:ST$ is 4:1. **6**

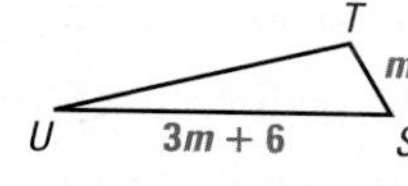

56. $WX:XV$ is 5:7. **$4\frac{2}{3}$**

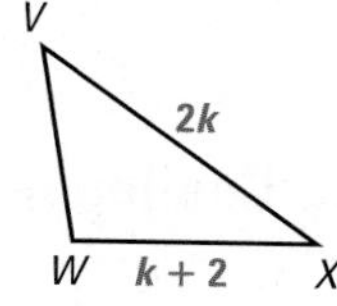

STUDENT HELP

HOMEWORK HELP Visit our Web site www.mcdougallittell.com for help with problem solving in Exs. 57 and 58.

PYTHAGOREAN THEOREM **The ratios of the side lengths of $\triangle PQR$ to the corresponding side lengths of $\triangle STU$ are 1:3. Find the unknown lengths.**

57.

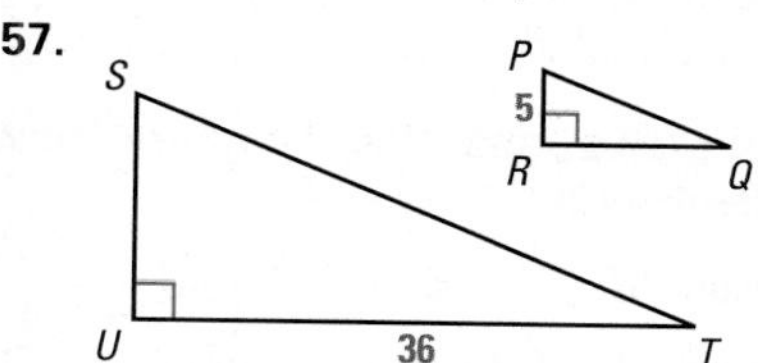

$RQ = 12$, $PQ = 13$, $SU = 15$, $ST = 39$

58.

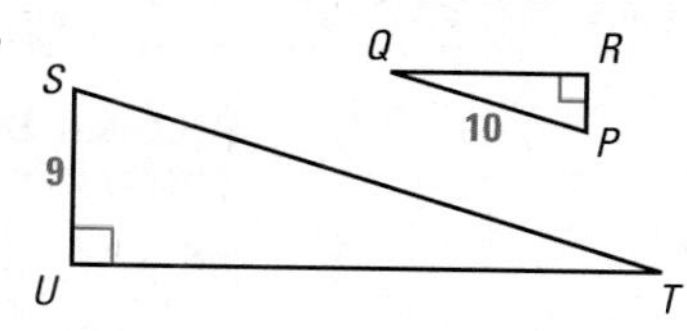

$PR = 3$, $RQ = \sqrt{91}$, $ST = 30$, $UT = 3\sqrt{91}$

GULLIVER'S TRAVELS **In Exercises 59–61, use the following information.**

Gulliver's Travels was written by Jonathan Swift in 1726. In the story, Gulliver is shipwrecked and wanders ashore to the island of Lilliput. The average height of the people in Lilliput is 6 inches.

59. Gulliver is 6 feet tall. What is the ratio of his height to the average height of a Lilliputian? **12:1**

60. After leaving Lilliput, Gulliver visits the island of Brobdingnag. The ratio of the average height of these natives to Gulliver's height is proportional to the ratio of Gulliver's height to the average height of a Lilliputian. What is the average height of a Brobdingnagian? **72 ft**

61. What is the ratio of the average height of a Brobdingnagian to the average height of a Lilliputian? **144:1**

STUDENT HELP NOTES

Homework Help Students can find help for Exs. 57 and 58 at **www.mcdougallittell.com.** The information can be printed out for students who don't have access to the Internet.

ENGLISH LEARNERS

EXERCISES 59–61 Being uncertain of the correct pronunciation of a number of terms in a problem can distract students and cause them to lose focus. Before students begin working on Exercises 59–61, you may want to model the pronunciation of *Gulliver, Lilliput, Lilliputian, Brobdingnag,* and *Brobdingnagian* for the class.

ADDITIONAL PRACTICE AND RETEACHING

For Lesson 8.1:

- Practice Levels A, B, and C (*Chapter 8 Resource Book,* p. 13)
- Reteaching with Practice (*Chapter 8 Resource Book,* p. 16)
- See Lesson 8.1 of the *Personal Student Tutor*

For more Mixed Review:

- Search the *Test and Practice Generator* for key words or specific lessons.

4 ASSESS

DAILY HOMEWORK QUIZ

Transparency Available

1. The perimeter of a living room is 64 ft. The ratio of width to length is 3:5. What are the dimensions of the living room? **12 ft by 20 ft**
2. The measures of the angles of a triangle are in the extended ratio of 1:3:5. Find the measures of the angles. **20°, 60°, 100°**

Solve the proportion.

3. $\frac{a}{8} = \frac{6}{20}$ $\frac{12}{5}$ 4. $\frac{10}{x+6} = \frac{2}{x}$ $\frac{3}{2}$

EXTRA CHALLENGE NOTE

Challenge problems for Lesson 8.1 are available in **blackline** format in the *Chapter 8 Resource Book,* p. 20 and at **www.mcdougallittell.com.**

ADDITIONAL TEST PREPARATION

1. **WRITING** Show how to solve the proportion $\frac{10}{3y-1} = \frac{5}{y}$. Explain each step of the process.
Sample answer: Use the cross product property to rewrite the equation as $10y = 5(3y-1)$. Use the distributive property to rewrite the equation as $10y = 15y - 5$. Subtract $15y$ from both sides of the equation to get $-5y = -5$, and finally divide by -5 to get $y = 1$.

76.

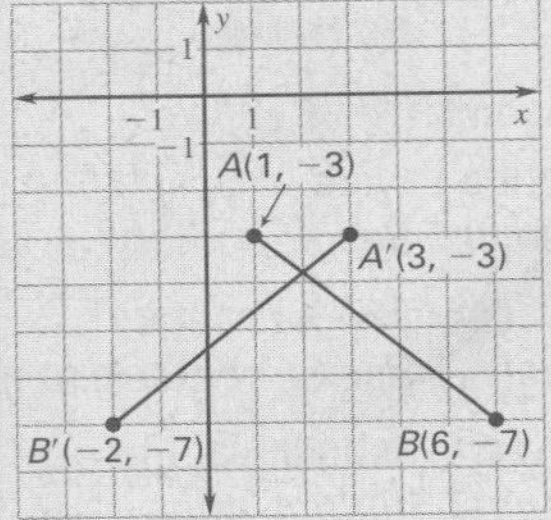

USING ALGEBRA You are given an extended ratio that compares the lengths of the sides of the triangle. Find the lengths of all unknown sides.

62. $BC:AC:AB$ is 3:4:5.

(Triangle ABC with AB = $x + 2$, BC = 6, AC = x)

$AC = 8,\ AB = 10$

63. $DE:EF:DF$ is 4:5:6.

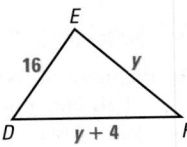

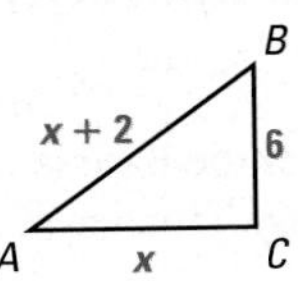

$EF = 20,\ DF = 24$

64. $GH:HR:GR$ is 5:5:6.

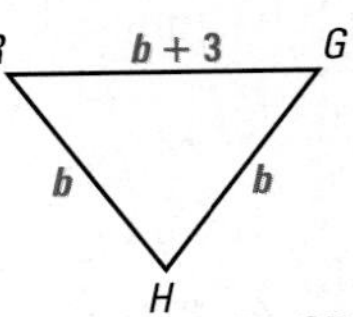

$GH = HR = 15,\ GR = 18$

Test Preparation

65. MULTIPLE CHOICE For planting roses, a gardener uses a special mixture of soil that contains sand, peat moss, and compost in the ratio 2:5:3. How many pounds of compost does she need to add if she uses three 10 pound bags of peat moss? D

Ⓐ 12 Ⓑ 14 Ⓒ 15 Ⓓ 18 Ⓔ 20

66. MULTIPLE CHOICE If the measures of the angles of a triangle have the ratio 2:3:7, the triangle is D

Ⓐ acute. Ⓑ right. Ⓒ isosceles.
Ⓓ obtuse. Ⓔ equilateral.

★ Challenge

67. FINDING SEGMENT LENGTHS Suppose the points B and C lie on $\overline{AD}$. What is the length of $\overline{AC}$ if $\frac{AB}{BD} = \frac{2}{3}$, $\frac{CD}{AC} = \frac{1}{9}$, and $BD = 24$? 36

MIXED REVIEW

FINDING UNKNOWN MEASURES Use the figure shown, in which $\triangle STU \cong \triangle XWV$. (Review 4.2)

68. What is the measure of $\angle X$? 20°

69. What is the measure of $\angle V$? 95°

70. What is the measure of $\angle T$? 65°

71. What is the measure of $\angle U$? 95°

72. Which side is congruent to $\overline{TU}$? $\overline{WV}$

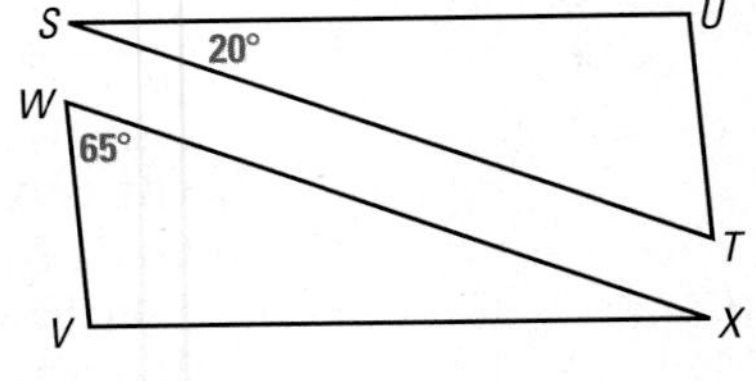

FINDING COORDINATES Find the coordinates of the endpoints of each midsegment shown in red. (Review 5.4 for 8.2)

73 $\left(-1\frac{1}{2}, 3\right)$ and (1, 3)

74. (1, −2) and $\left(3\frac{1}{2}, -1\frac{1}{2}\right)$

75. $\left(-\frac{1}{2}, 3\frac{1}{2}\right)$ and $\left(1\frac{1}{2}, 1\right)$

73.

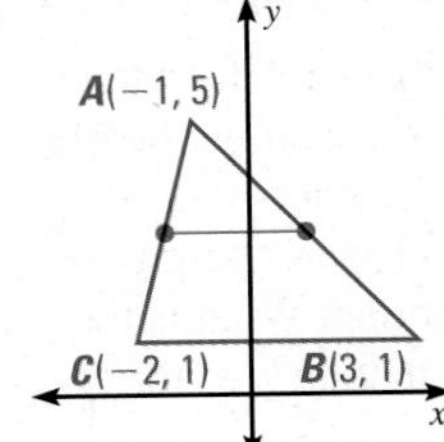

74.

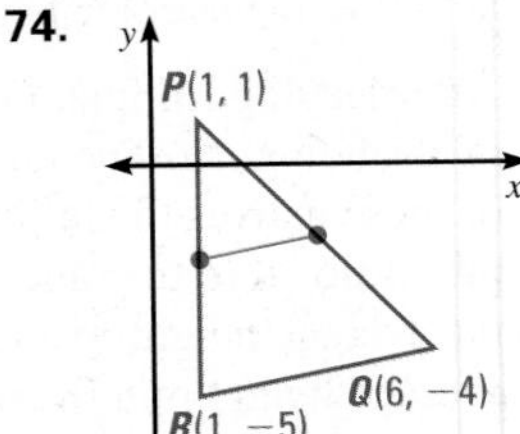

75.

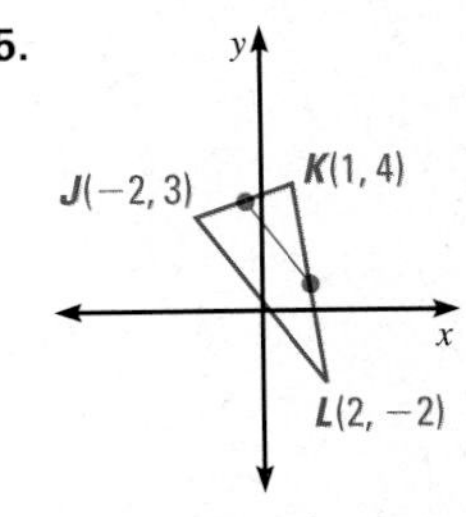

76. A line segment has endpoints $A(1, -3)$ and $B(6, -7)$. Graph $\overline{AB}$ and its image $\overline{A'B'}$ if $\overline{AB}$ is reflected in the line $x = 2$. (Review 7.2) See margin.

8.2 Problem Solving in Geometry with Proportions

What you should learn

GOAL 1 Use properties of proportions.

GOAL 2 Use proportions to solve **real-life** problems, such as using the scale of a map in **Exs. 41 and 42**.

Why you should learn it

▼ To solve **real-life** problems, such as using a scale model to calculate the dimensions of the Titanic in **Example 4**.

CALIFORNIA STANDARDS AND ASSESSMENT

CA Standards: 5
SAT9 Task 1: Obj. 1
SAT9 Task 2: Obj. 1

GOAL 1 USING PROPERTIES OF PROPORTIONS

In Lesson 8.1, you studied the reciprocal property and the cross product property. Two more properties of proportions, which are especially useful in geometry, are given below.

You can use the cross product property and the reciprocal property to help prove these properties in Exercises 36 and 37.

ADDITIONAL PROPERTIES OF PROPORTIONS

3. If $\frac{a}{b} = \frac{c}{d}$, then $\frac{a}{c} = \frac{b}{d}$.

4. If $\frac{a}{b} = \frac{c}{d}$, then $\frac{a+b}{b} = \frac{c+d}{d}$.

EXAMPLE 1 *Using Properties of Proportions*

Tell whether the statement is true.

a. If $\frac{p}{6} = \frac{r}{10}$, then $\frac{p}{r} = \frac{3}{5}$.

b. If $\frac{a}{3} = \frac{c}{4}$, then $\frac{a+3}{3} = \frac{c+3}{4}$.

SOLUTION

a. $\frac{p}{6} = \frac{r}{10}$ — **Given**

$\frac{p}{r} = \frac{6}{10}$ — **If $\frac{a}{b} = \frac{c}{d}$, then $\frac{a}{c} = \frac{b}{d}$.**

$\frac{p}{r} = \frac{3}{5}$ — **Simplify.**

▶ The statement is true.

b. $\frac{a}{3} = \frac{c}{4}$ — **Given**

$\frac{a+3}{3} = \frac{c+4}{4}$ — **If $\frac{a}{b} = \frac{c}{d}$, then $\frac{a+b}{b} = \frac{c+d}{d}$.**

Because $\frac{c+4}{4} \neq \frac{c+3}{4}$, the conclusions are not equivalent.

▶ The statement is false.

1 PLAN

PACING
Basic: 1 day
Average: 1 day
Advanced: 1 day
Block Schedule: 0.5 block with 8.3

LESSON OPENER
CALCULATOR
An alternative way to approach Lesson 8.2 is to use the Calculator Lesson Opener:

- Blackline Master (*Chapter 8 Resource Book,* p. 24)
- Transparency (p. 57)

MEETING INDIVIDUAL NEEDS

- ***Chapter 8 Resource Book***
  Prerequisite Skills Review (p. 5)
  Practice Level A (p. 25)
  Practice Level B (p. 26)
  Practice Level C (p. 27)
  Reteaching with Practice (p. 28)
  Absent Student Catch-Up (p. 30)
  Challenge (p. 32)
- ***Resources in Spanish***
- ***Personal Student Tutor***

NEW-TEACHER SUPPORT
See the Tips for New Teachers on pp. 1–2 of the *Chapter 8 Resource Book* for additional notes about Lesson 8.2.

WARM-UP EXERCISES

 ***Transparency Available***

Solve each proportion.

1. $\frac{x}{4} = \frac{5}{8}$ $\frac{5}{2}$

2. $\frac{10}{9} = \frac{25}{x}$ $\frac{45}{2}$

3. $\frac{2}{y+1} = \frac{6}{y}$ $-\frac{3}{2}$

4. $\frac{x-2}{5} = \frac{x+4}{35}$ 3

2 TEACH

MOTIVATING THE LESSON
Tell students to imagine that they are making a scale model. Ask how they might determine the dimensions of the model so that the model looks the same as the object. In this lesson, students will see how proportions can be used to make scale models.

EXTRA EXAMPLE 1
Tell whether the statement is true.
a. If $\frac{s}{10} = \frac{15}{t}$, then $\frac{s}{t} = \frac{3}{2}$. false
b. If $\frac{3}{x} = \frac{5}{y}$, then $\frac{3+x}{x} = \frac{5+y}{y}$. true

EXTRA EXAMPLE 2
In the diagram $\frac{MQ}{MN} = \frac{LQ}{LP}$. Find the length of LQ. 17.5

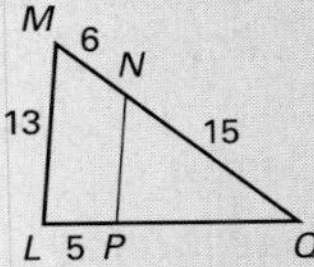

EXTRA EXAMPLE 3
Find the geometric mean between 35 and 175. $35\sqrt{5}$

CHECKPOINT EXERCISES
For use after Example 1:
1. Tell whether the statement is true. If $\frac{3}{b} = \frac{d}{7}$, then $\frac{3+b}{d} = \frac{d+7}{b}$. false

For use after Example 2:
2. In the diagram from Extra Example 2 above, $\frac{LM}{PN} = \frac{MQ}{NQ}$. Find PN. $\frac{65}{7}$

For use after Example 3:
3. Find the geometric mean between 36 and 128. $48\sqrt{2}$

EXAMPLE 2 Using Properties of Proportions

In the diagram $\frac{AB}{BD} = \frac{AC}{CE}$. Find the length of $\overline{BD}$.

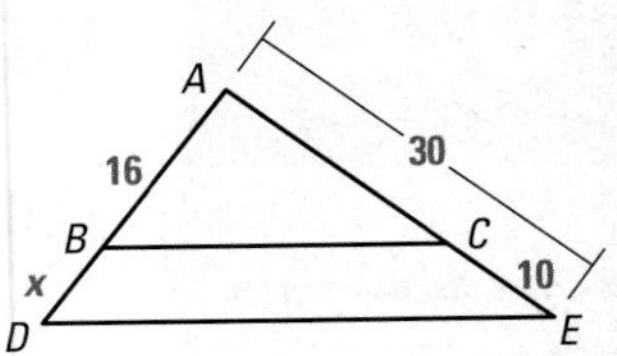

SOLUTION

$\frac{AB}{BD} = \frac{AC}{CE}$ Given

$\frac{16}{x} = \frac{30-10}{10}$ Substitute.

$\frac{16}{x} = \frac{20}{10}$ Simplify.

$20x = 160$ Cross product property

$x = 8$ Divide each side by 20.

▶ So, the length of $\overline{BD}$ is 8.

STUDENT HELP
HOMEWORK HELP
Visit our Web site www.mcdougallittell.com for extra examples.

The **geometric mean** of two positive numbers a and b is the positive number x such that $\frac{a}{x} = \frac{x}{b}$. If you solve this proportion for x, you find that $x = \sqrt{a \cdot b}$, which is a positive number.

For example, the geometric mean of 8 and 18 is 12, because $\frac{8}{12} = \frac{12}{18}$, and also because $\sqrt{8 \cdot 18} = \sqrt{144} = 12$.

EXAMPLE 3 Using a Geometric Mean

REAL LIFE **PAPER SIZES** International standard paper sizes are commonly used all over the world. The various sizes all have the same width-to-length ratios. Two sizes of paper are shown, called A4 and A3. The distance labeled x is the geometric mean of 210 mm and 420 mm. Find the value of x.

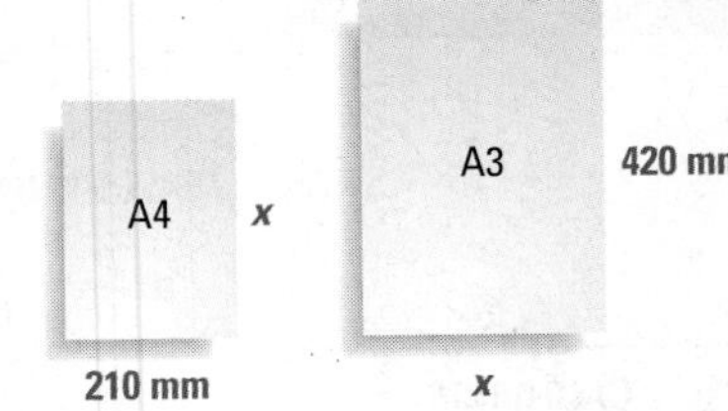

SOLUTION

$\frac{210}{x} = \frac{x}{420}$ Write proportion.

$x^2 = 210 \cdot 420$ Cross product property

$x = \sqrt{210 \cdot 420}$ Simplify.

$x = \sqrt{210 \cdot 210 \cdot 2}$ Factor.

$x = 210\sqrt{2}$ Simplify.

▶ The geometric mean of 210 and 420 is $210\sqrt{2}$, or about 297. So, the distance labeled x in the diagram is about 297 mm.

STUDENT HELP
Skills Review
For help with simplifying square roots, see p. 799.

GOAL 2 USING PROPORTIONS IN REAL LIFE

In general, when solving word problems that involve proportions, there is more than one correct way to set up the proportion.

EXAMPLE 4 *Solving a Proportion*

MODEL BUILDING A scale model of the Titanic is 107.5 inches long and 11.25 inches wide. The Titanic itself was 882.75 feet long. How wide was it?

SOLUTION

One way to solve this problem is to set up a proportion that compares the measurements of the Titanic to the measurements of the scale model.

PROBLEM SOLVING STRATEGY

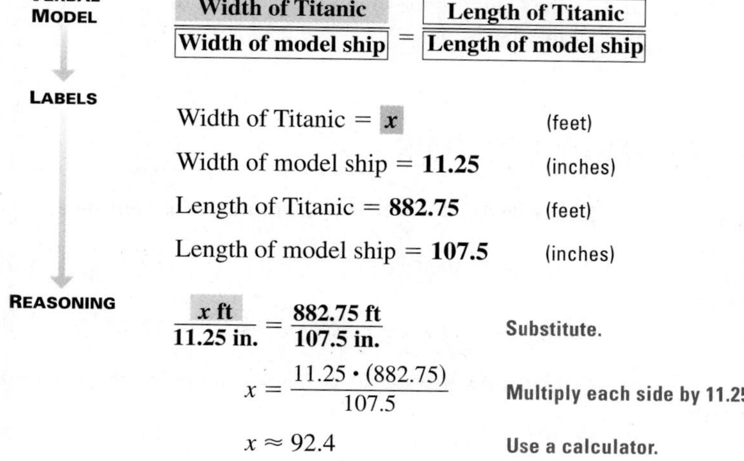

VERBAL MODEL

$$\frac{\text{Width of Titanic}}{\text{Width of model ship}} = \frac{\text{Length of Titanic}}{\text{Length of model ship}}$$

LABELS

Width of Titanic = x (feet)

Width of model ship = **11.25** (inches)

Length of Titanic = **882.75** (feet)

Length of model ship = **107.5** (inches)

REASONING

$$\frac{x \text{ ft}}{11.25 \text{ in.}} = \frac{882.75 \text{ ft}}{107.5 \text{ in.}}$$ Substitute.

$$x = \frac{11.25 \cdot (882.75)}{107.5}$$ Multiply each side by 11.25.

$$x \approx 92.4$$ Use a calculator.

▶ So, the Titanic was about 92.4 feet wide.

Notice that the proportion in Example 4 contains measurements that are not in the same units. When writing a proportion with unlike units, the numerators should have the same units and the denominators should have the same units.

STUDENT HELP NOTES

→ **Homework Help** Students can find extra examples at **www.mcdougallittell.com** that parallel the examples in the student edition.

→ **Skills Review** As students review square roots on page 799, remind them to look for the largest perfect square factor.

EXTRA EXAMPLE 4

You are building a scale model of your uncle's fishing boat. The boat is 62 ft long and 23 ft wide. The model will be 14 in. long. How wide should it be? about 5.2 in.

CHECKPOINT EXERCISES

For use after Example 4:

1. The mast of your uncle's fishing boat from Extra Example 4 is 30 feet tall. How tall should the mast be in the model? about 6.8 in.

FOCUS ON VOCABULARY

Ask students to explain the difference between the geometric mean and the arithmetic mean of two numbers.

CLOSURE QUESTION

Give an example illustrating each of the two properties of proportions given in this lesson. Check students' work.

DAILY PUZZLER

The geometric mean of 12 and another number is 30. What is the other number? 75

3 APPLY

ASSIGNMENT GUIDE

BASIC
Day 1: pp. 468–471 Exs. 10–28 even, 29, 30, 33, 34, 38–40, 44, 45, 47–57

AVERAGE
Day 1: pp. 468–471 Exs. 10–28 even, 29–31, 33, 34, 38–40, 44, 45, 47–57

ADVANCED
Day 1: pp. 468–471 Exs. 10–28 even, 29–31, 33, 34, 36–40, 44, 45, 47–57

BLOCK SCHEDULE
pp. 468–471 Exs. 10–28 even, 29–31, 33, 34, 36–40, 44, 45, 47–57 (with 8.3)

EXERCISE LEVELS

Level A: *Easier*
9–12, 17–19

Level B: *More Difficult*
13–16, 20–45

Level C: *Most Difficult*
46

✔ HOMEWORK CHECK

To quickly check student understanding of key concepts, go over the following exercises: Exs. 10, 16, 22, 24, 30, 34, 40. See also the Daily Homework Quiz:

- Blackline Master (*Chapter 8 Resource Book,* p. 35)
- Transparency (p. 57)

! COMMON ERROR

EXERCISES 9–16 Students may forget the properties of proportions or memorize them incorrectly. To help students avoid these errors, encourage them to use the cross product property as a check. If the original statement is true, the resulting equations will be equivalent.

GUIDED PRACTICE

Vocabulary Check ✔

1. If x is the *geometric mean* of two positive numbers a and b, write a proportion that relates a, b, and x. $\frac{a}{x} = \frac{x}{b}$

Concept Check ✔

2. If $\frac{x}{4} = \frac{y}{5}$, then $\frac{x+4}{4} = \frac{?}{5}$. $y + 5$

3. If $\frac{b}{6} = \frac{c}{2}$, then $\frac{b}{c} = \frac{?}{?}$. $\frac{6}{2}$; or 3

Skill Check ✔

4. Decide whether the statement is *true* or *false*. true

If $\frac{r}{s} = \frac{6}{15}$, then $\frac{15}{s} = \frac{6}{r}$.

5. Find the geometric mean of 3 and 12. 6

6. In the diagram $\frac{AB}{BC} = \frac{AD}{DE}$. Substitute the known values into the proportion and solve for DE. 9

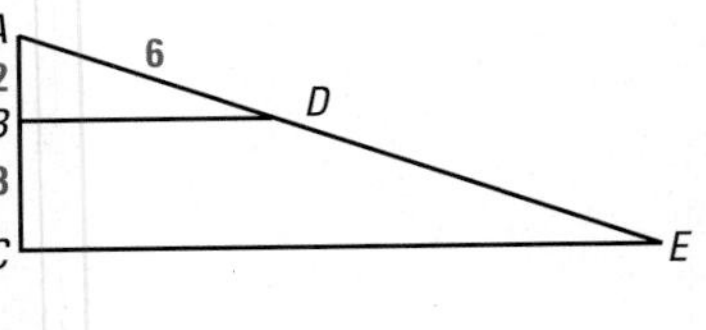

7. **UNITED STATES FLAG** The official height-to-width ratio of the United States flag is 1 : 1.9. If a United States flag is 6 feet high, how wide is it? 11.4 ft

8. **UNITED STATES FLAG** The blue portion of the United States flag is called the union. What is the ratio of the height of the union to the height of the flag? $\frac{7}{13}$

PRACTICE AND APPLICATIONS

STUDENT HELP
Extra Practice to help you master skills is on p. 817.

STUDENT HELP
HOMEWORK HELP
Example 1: Exs. 9–16
Example 2: Exs. 23–28
Example 3: Exs. 17–22, 43
Example 4: Exs. 29–32, 38–42

LOGICAL REASONING **Complete the sentence.**

9. If $\frac{2}{x} = \frac{7}{y}$, then $\frac{2}{7} = \frac{?}{?}$. $\frac{x}{y}$

10. If $\frac{x}{6} = \frac{y}{34}$, then $\frac{x}{y} = \frac{?}{?}$. $\frac{6}{34}$ or $\frac{3}{17}$

11. If $\frac{x}{5} = \frac{y}{12}$, then $\frac{x+5}{5} = \frac{?}{?}$. $\frac{y+12}{12}$

12. If $\frac{13}{7} = \frac{x}{y}$, then $\frac{20}{7} = \frac{?}{?}$. $\frac{x+y}{y}$

LOGICAL REASONING **Decide whether the statement is *true* or *false*.**

13. If $\frac{7}{a} = \frac{b}{2}$, then $\frac{7+a}{a} = \frac{b+2}{2}$. true

14. If $\frac{3}{4} = \frac{p}{r}$, then $\frac{4}{3} = \frac{p}{r}$. false

15. If $\frac{c}{6} = \frac{d+2}{10}$, then $\frac{c}{d+2} = \frac{6}{10}$. true

16. If $\frac{12+m}{12} = \frac{3+n}{n}$, then $\frac{m}{12} = \frac{3}{n}$. true

GEOMETRIC MEAN **Find the geometric mean of the two numbers.**

17. 3 and 27 9

18. 4 and 16 8

19. 7 and 28 14

20. 2 and 40 $4\sqrt{5}$

21. 8 and 20 $4\sqrt{10}$

22. 5 and 15 $5\sqrt{3}$

PROPERTIES OF PROPORTIONS **Use the diagram and the given information to find the unknown length.**

23. GIVEN ▶ $\frac{AB}{BD} = \frac{AC}{CE}$, find BD. 11.25

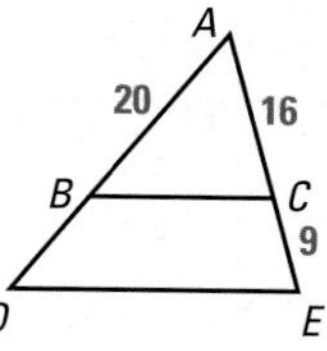

24. GIVEN ▶ $\frac{VW}{WY} = \frac{VX}{XZ}$, find VX. 9

24
V
W
6
X
3
Y
Z

25. GIVEN ▶ $\frac{BT}{TR} = \frac{ES}{SL}$, find TR. $6\frac{2}{3}$

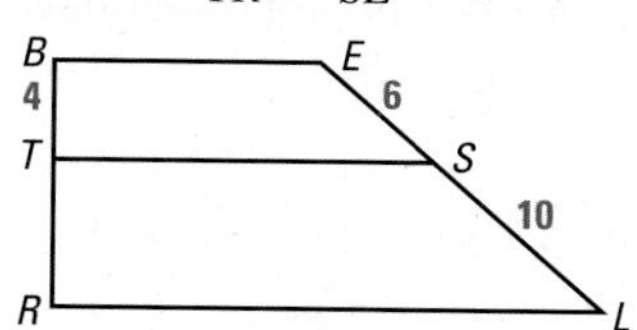

26. GIVEN ▶ $\frac{SP}{SK} = \frac{SQ}{SJ}$, find SQ. $17\frac{1}{2}$

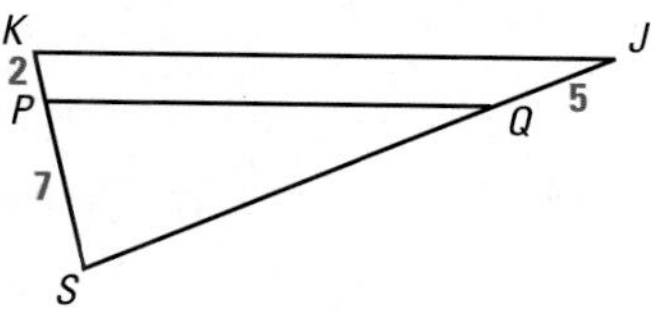

27. GIVEN ▶ $\frac{LJ}{JN} = \frac{MK}{KP}$, find JN. $6\frac{6}{7}$

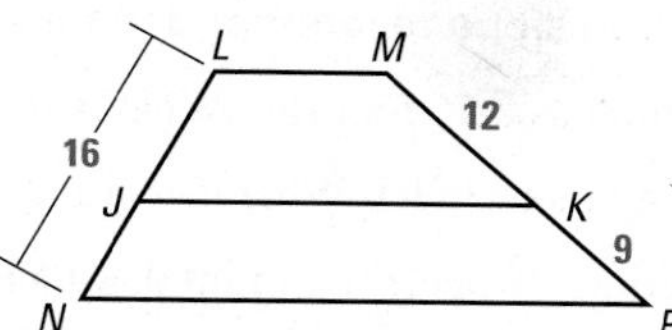

28. GIVEN ▶ $\frac{QU}{QS} = \frac{RV}{RT}$, find SU. 9

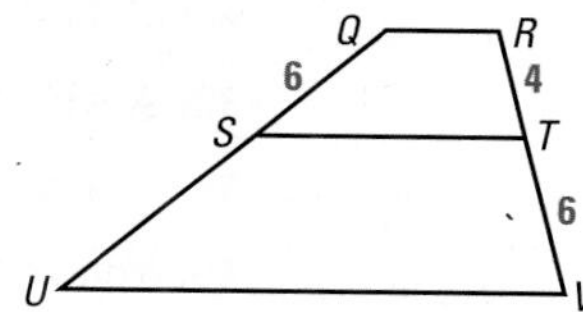

BLUEPRINTS **In Exercises 29 and 30, use the blueprint of the house in which $\frac{1}{16}$ inch = 1 foot. Use a ruler to approximate the dimension.**

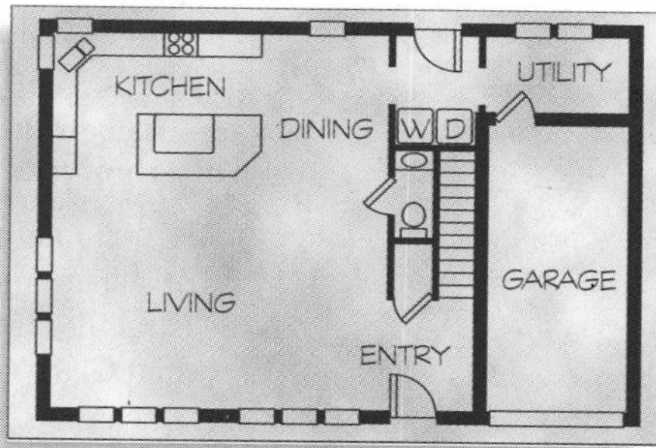

29. Find the approximate width of the house to the nearest 5 feet.
about 25 ft

30. Find the approximate length of the house to the nearest 5 feet.
about 40 ft

31. **BATTING AVERAGE** The batting average of a baseball player is the ratio of the number of hits to the number of official at-bats. In 1998, Sammy Sosa of the Chicago Cubs had 643 official at-bats and a batting average of .308. Use the following verbal model to find the number of hits Sammy Sosa got.
198 hits

$$\frac{\textit{Number of hits}}{\textit{Number of at-bats}} = \frac{\textit{Batting average}}{1.000}$$

32. **CURRENCY EXCHANGE** Natalie has relatives in Russia. She decides to take a trip to Russia to visit them. She took 500 U.S. dollars to the bank to exchange for Russian rubles. The exchange rate on that day was 22.76 rubles per U.S. dollar. How many rubles did she get in exchange for the 500 U.S. dollars? ▶ Source: Russia Today 11,380 rubles

FOCUS ON PEOPLE

REAL LIFE **SAMMY SOSA** was the National League Most Valuable Player in 1998. He hit 66 home runs to finish second to Mark McGwire who hit 70, a new record.

INTERNET APPLICATION LINK
www.mcdougallittell.com

TEACHING TIPS

EXERCISES 23 AND 24 Problems such as these will be revisited in Section 8.6 when the Triangle Proportionality Theorem and its converse are introduced.

! COMMON ERROR

EXERCISES 29–32 Remind students that when setting up proportions with different units, the numerators should have the same units and the denominators should have the same units.

APPLICATION NOTE

EXERCISE 31 Additional information about baseball statistics can be found at **www.mcdougallittell.com.**

MATHEMATICAL REASONING EXERCISES 36 AND 37 Students can choose the method of proof for these exercises. You may then want to have them compare their proof with the proof of a student who chose a different method.

ENGLISH LEARNERS EXERCISES 38–40 Remembering English language mathematical terms can be especially challenging for English learners. Before students begin these exercises, you may want to review the meanings of *rise* and *run* by setting a ruler against a pile of books and explaining that the *rise* is the height of the pile of books and the *run* is the distance from the end of the ruler on the desk top to the bottom of the pile of books.

36. Statements and (Reasons)
1. $\frac{a}{b} = \frac{c}{d}$ (Given)
2. $ad = bc$ (Cross product prop.)
3. $\frac{ad}{cd} = \frac{bc}{cd}$ (Division prop. of equality)
4. $\frac{a}{c} \cdot \frac{d}{d} = \frac{b}{d} \cdot \frac{c}{c}$ (Multiplication of fractions)
5. $\frac{a}{c} \cdot 1 = \frac{b}{d} \cdot 1$ (Inverse prop. of multiplication)
6. $\frac{a}{c} = \frac{b}{d}$ (Identity prop. of multiplication)

37. See Additional Answers beginning on page AA1.

ADDITIONAL PRACTICE AND RETEACHING

For Lesson 8.2:
- Practice Levels A, B, and C (*Chapter 8 Resource Book,* p. 25)
- Reteaching with Practice (*Chapter 8 Resource Book,* p. 28)
- See Lesson 8.2 of the *Personal Student Tutor*

For more Mixed Review:
- Search the *Test and Practice Generator* for key words or specific lessons.

35. Each side of the equation represents the slope of the line through two of the points; if the points are collinear, the slopes are the same.

40. *Sample answer:* Construct a ramp consisting of two ramps in opposite directions, each 18 ft long. The first should be 3 ft high at its beginning and $1\frac{1}{2}$ ft high at its end, for a rise:run ratio of $\frac{1}{12}$. The second would be $1\frac{1}{2}$ ft high at its beginning and ground level at its end. The second ramp also has a rise:run ratio of $\frac{1}{12}$.

43. If the two sizes share a dimension, the shorter dimension of A5 paper must be the longer dimension of A6 paper. That is, the length of A6 paper must be 148 mm. Let x be the width of A6 paper; 148 is the geometric mean of x and 210. Then $\frac{x}{148} = \frac{148}{210}$ and $x \approx 104$ mm.

FOCUS ON PEOPLE

SACAGAWEA Representing liberty on the new dollar coin is Sacagawea, who played a crucial role in the Lewis and Clark expedition. She acted as an interpreter and guide, and is now given credit for much of the mission's success.

33. COORDINATE GEOMETRY The points $(-4, -1)$, $(1, 1)$, and $(x, 5)$ are collinear. Find the value of x by solving the proportion below. **11**

$$\frac{1-(-1)}{1-(-4)} = \frac{5-1}{x-1}$$

34. COORDINATE GEOMETRY The points $(2, 8)$, $(6, 18)$, and $(8, y)$ are collinear. Find the value of y by solving the proportion below. **23**

$$\frac{18-8}{6-2} = \frac{y-18}{8-6}$$

35. CRITICAL THINKING Explain why the method used in Exercises 33 and 34 is a correct way to express that three given points are collinear. **See margin.**

36. PROOF Prove property 3 of proportions (see page 465). **See margin.**

If $\frac{a}{b} = \frac{c}{d}$, then $\frac{a}{c} = \frac{b}{d}$.

37. PROOF Prove property 4 of proportions (see page 465). **See margin.**

If $\frac{a}{b} = \frac{c}{d}$, then $\frac{a+b}{b} = \frac{c+d}{d}$.

RAMP DESIGN Assume that a wheelchair ramp has a slope of $\frac{1}{12}$, which is the maximum slope recommended for a wheelchair ramp.

38. A wheelchair ramp has a 15 foot run. What is its rise? **$1\frac{1}{4}$ ft**

39. A wheelchair ramp rises 2 feet. What is its run? **24 ft**

40. You are constructing a wheelchair ramp that must rise 3 feet. Because of space limitations, you cannot build a continuous ramp with a length greater than 21 feet. Design a ramp that solves this problem. **See margin.**

HISTORY CONNECTION Part of the Lewis and Clark Trail on which Sacagawea acted as guide is now known as the Lolo Trail. The map, which shows a portion of the trail, has a scale of 1 inch = 6.7 miles.

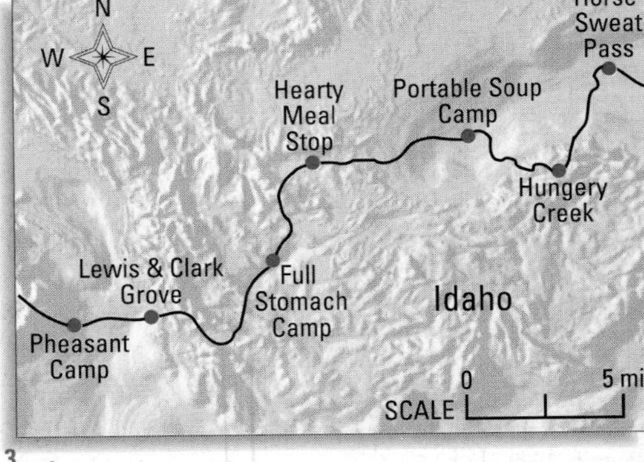

41. Use a ruler to estimate the distance (measured in a straight line) between Lewis and Clark Grove and Pheasant Camp. Then calculate the actual distance in miles. **about $\frac{3}{8}$ in.; about $2\frac{1}{2}$ mi**

42. Estimate the distance along the trail between Portable Soup Camp and Full Stomach Camp. Then calculate the actual distance in miles. **about $1\frac{1}{4}$ in.; about $8\frac{3}{8}$ mi**

43. *Writing* Size A5 paper has a width of 148 mm and a length of 210 mm. Size A6, which is the next smaller size, shares a dimension with size A5. Use the proportional relationship stated in Example 3 and geometric mean to explain how to determine the length and width of size A6 paper. **See margin.**

Test Preparation

44. MULTIPLE CHOICE There are 24 fish in an aquarium. If $\frac{1}{8}$ of the fish are tetras, and $\frac{2}{3}$ of the remaining fish are guppies, how many guppies are in the aquarium? **D**

Ⓐ 2 Ⓑ 3 Ⓒ 10 Ⓓ 14 Ⓔ 16

45. MULTIPLE CHOICE A basketball team had a ratio of wins to losses of 3 : 1. After winning 6 games in a row, the team's ratio of wins to losses was 5 : 1. How many games had the team won before it won the 6 games in a row? **C**

Ⓐ 3 Ⓑ 6 Ⓒ 9 Ⓓ 15 Ⓔ 24

★ Challenge

46. GOLDEN RECTANGLE A golden rectangle has its length and width in the golden ratio $\frac{1+\sqrt{5}}{2}$. If you cut a square away from a golden rectangle, the shape that remains is also a golden rectangle.

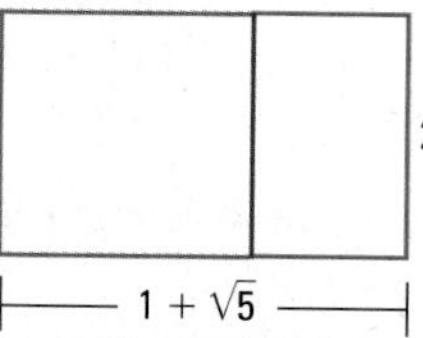

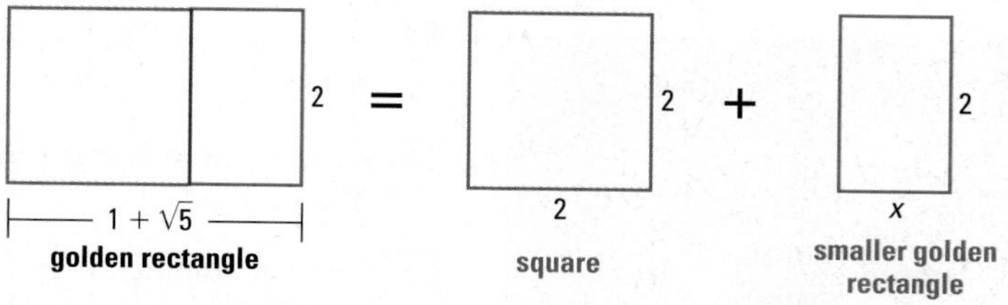

= (square: 2, 2) square +

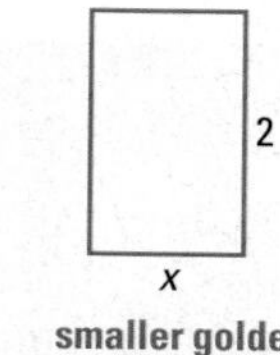

a. The diagram indicates that $1 + \sqrt{5} = 2 + x$. Find x. $-1 + \sqrt{5}$

b. To prove that the large and small rectangles are both golden rectangles, show that $\frac{1+\sqrt{5}}{2} = \frac{2}{x}$.

c. Give a decimal approximation for the golden ratio to six decimal places. **1.618034**

46. b. $\frac{1+\sqrt{5}}{2} = \frac{2}{x}$ if 2 is the geometric mean of $1 + \sqrt{5}$ and x. The geometric mean of $1 + \sqrt{5}$ and $-1 + \sqrt{5}$ is $\sqrt{(1+\sqrt{5})(-1+\sqrt{5})} = \sqrt{4} = 2$.

EXTRA CHALLENGE
www.mcdougallittell.com

MIXED REVIEW

FINDING AREA **Find the area of the figure described.** (Review 1.7)

47. Rectangle: width = 3 m, length = 4 m **12 m²**

48. Square: side = 3 cm **9 cm²**

49. Triangle: base = 13 cm, height = 4 cm **26 cm²**

50. Circle: diameter = 11 ft **about 95 ft²**

FINDING ANGLE MEASURES **Find the angle measures.** (Review 6.5 for 8.3)

51.

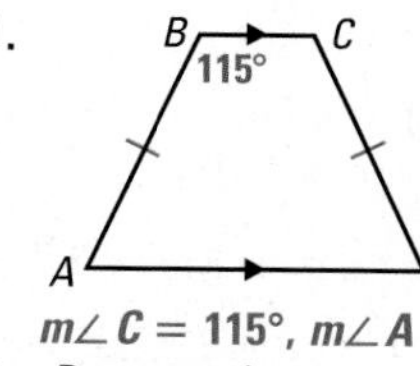

$m\angle C = 115°$, $m\angle A = m\angle D = 65°$

52.

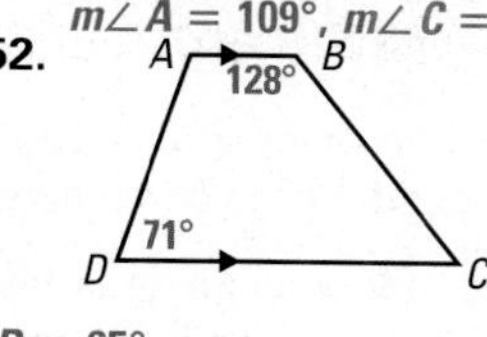

$m\angle A = 109°$, $m\angle C = 52°$

53.

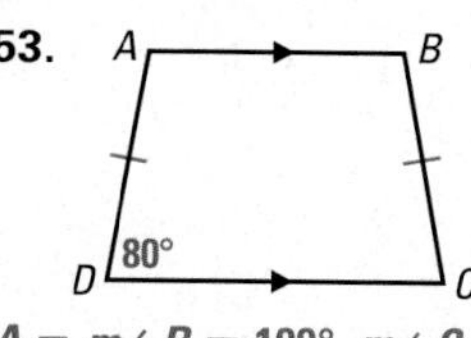

$m\angle A = m\angle B = 100°$, $m\angle C = 80°$

54.

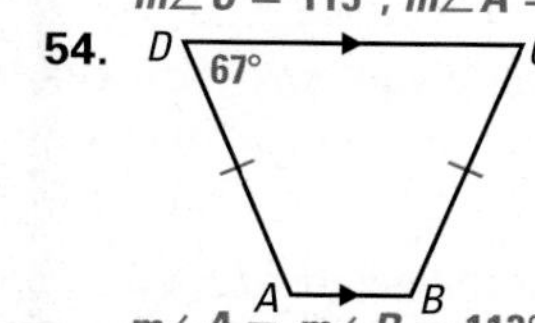

$m\angle A = m\angle B = 113°$, $m\angle C = 67°$

55.

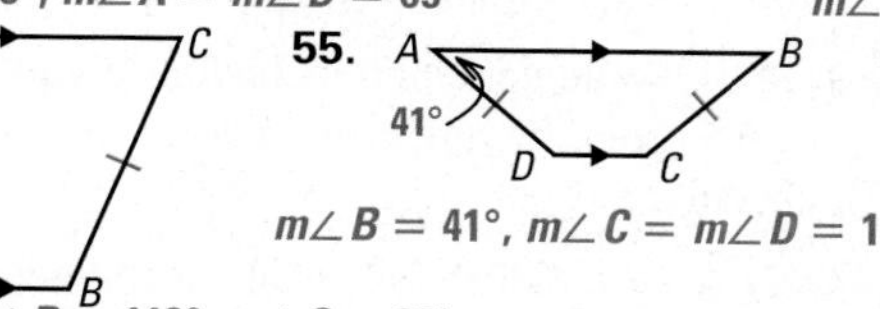

$m\angle B = 41°$, $m\angle C = m\angle D = 139°$

56.

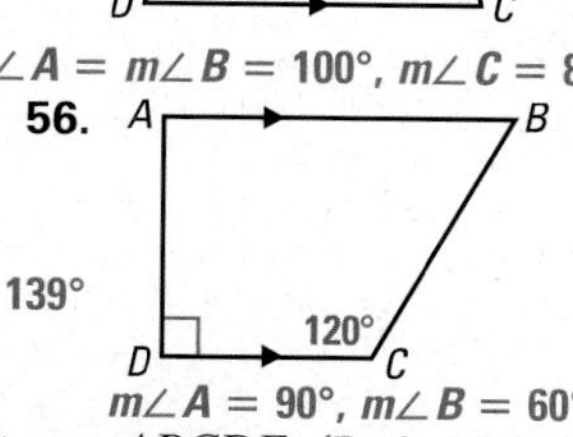

$m\angle A = 90°$, $m\angle B = 60°$

57. PENTAGON Describe any symmetry in a regular pentagon $ABCDE$. (Review 7.2, 7.3)

57. A regular pentagon has 5 lines of symmetry (one from each vertex to the midpoint of the opposite side) and rotational symmetries of 72° and 144°, clockwise and counterclockwise, about the center of the pentagon.

4 ASSESS

DAILY HOMEWORK QUIZ

Transparency Available

Decide whether the statement is *true* or *false*.

1. If $\frac{a}{6} = \frac{b-1}{8}$, then $\frac{a+6}{6} = \frac{b+8}{8}$. **false**

2. If $\frac{x}{y} = \frac{x+5}{y-3}$, then $\frac{x}{x+5} = \frac{y}{y-3}$. **true**

3. Find the geometric mean of 9 and 25. **15**

4. Given: $\frac{PT}{PR} = \frac{QU}{QS}$, find SU. **12.5**

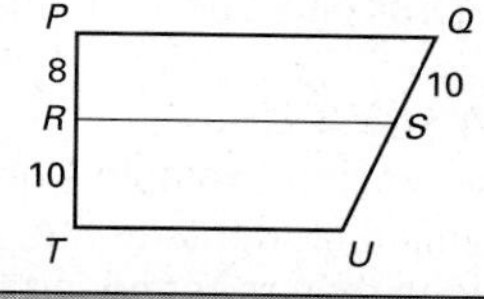

EXTRA CHALLENGE NOTE

Challenge problems for Lesson 8.2 are available in **blackline** format in the *Chapter 8 Resource Book*, p. 32 and at **www.mcdougallittell.com.**

ADDITIONAL TEST PREPARATION

1. OPEN ENDED Make up a problem involving a scale model. Show how proportion can be used to find an unknown dimension. **Answers will vary.**

2. WRITING Is the geometric mean the same as the mean or average of two numbers? Explain your answer with examples. **No; you find the mean by adding the numbers and dividing by 2, whereas you find the geometric mean by multiplying the two numbers and taking the square root; examples will vary.**

1 Planning the Activity

PURPOSE
To investigate the effect of a scale change on the dimensions, angles, and perimeter of a figure.

MATERIALS
- ruler
- protractor
- calculator
- Activity Support Master (*Chapter 8 Resource Book,* p. 36)

PACING
- Exploring the Concept — 15 min
- Drawing Conclusions — 10 min

LINK TO LESSON
When discussing Example 1 on p. 473, remind students of the conclusions they reached in this activity.

2 Managing the Activity

ALTERNATIVE APPROACH
This activity can be done as a class. Divide the class into four sections and have one section measure the angles and one section measure the lengths for each photo. The table can be completed at the chalkboard or on an overhead projector.

3 Closing the Activity

★ ***KEY DISCOVERY***
When a figure is enlarged, the angle measures of corresponding angles are equal and the lengths of corresponding sides have a constant ratio.

ACTIVITY ASSESSMENT
A polygon with one side 4 in. long is enlarged so that the corresponding side in the new polygon is 8 in. long. How do the other sides and angles of the enlarged figure compare to the corresponding sides and angles in the original figure. **The angle measures are the same and the sides in the new figure are twice as long as the sides in the original.**

ACTIVITY 8.3
Developing Concepts

Group Activity for use with Lesson 8.3

Making Conjectures about Similarity

GROUP ACTIVITY
Work with a partner.

MATERIALS
- paper
- pencil
- ruler
- protractor
- calculator

▶ **QUESTION** **When a figure is enlarged, what appears to be true about corresponding lengths? corresponding angles? corresponding perimeters?**

▶ **EXPLORING THE CONCEPT**

1. Photo 1 is an enlargement of Photo 2. Use a ruler to find the length of $\overline{AB}$ in each photo. **photo 1: 4.2 cm, photo 2: 3.0 cm**

2. Write the ratio of the length of $\overline{AB}$ in Photo 1 to the length of $\overline{AB}$ in Photo 2. **1.4**

Photo 1

Photo 2

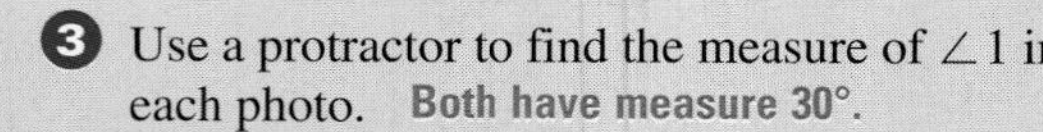

3. Use a protractor to find the measure of $\angle 1$ in each photo. **Both have measure 30°.**

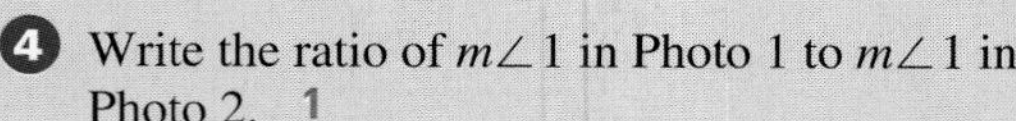

4. Write the ratio of $m\angle 1$ in Photo 1 to $m\angle 1$ in Photo 2. **1**

5. Continue finding the measurements in the photos. Find the ratios of the measurements in Photo 1 to the measurements in Photo 2. Use the same units throughout the activity. Record your results in a table similar to the one shown. **See margin.**

Measurement	Photo 1	Photo 2	Ratio
AB	4.2 cm	3.0 cm	$\frac{4.2}{3} = 1.4$
AF	?	?	?
CD	?	?	?
$m\angle 1$	?	?	?
$m\angle 2$	?	?	?
Perimeter of photo	?	?	?

▶ **DRAWING CONCLUSIONS**

1. Suppose a segment in Photo 2 has a length of 5 centimeters. Estimate the length of the corresponding segment in Photo 1. **7 cm**
2. Suppose an angle in Photo 1 has a measure of 35°. Estimate the measure of the corresponding angle in Photo 2. **35°**
3. Make some general conclusions about how corresponding lengths, corresponding angles, and corresponding perimeters are related when a figure is enlarged. **Any two corresponding lengths or corresponding perimeters have the same ratio; corresponding ∠s are ≅.**
4. **CRITICAL THINKING** Make a conjecture about how corresponding areas are related when a figure is enlarged. **The ratio of two corresponding areas is the square of the ratio of corresponding lengths.**

Step 5. See Additional Answers beginning on page AA1.

8.3 Similar Polygons

What you should learn

GOAL 1 Identify similar polygons.

GOAL 2 Use similar polygons to solve **real-life** problems, such as making an enlargement similar to an original photo in **Example 3**.

Why you should learn it

▼ To solve **real-life** problems, such as comparing television screen sizes in **Exs. 43 and 44**.

REAL LIFE

GOAL 1 IDENTIFYING SIMILAR POLYGONS

When there is a correspondence between two polygons such that their corresponding angles are congruent and the lengths of corresponding sides are proportional the two polygons are called **similar polygons**.

In the diagram, *ABCD* is similar to *EFGH*. The symbol ~ is used to indicate similarity. So, $ABCD \sim EFGH$.

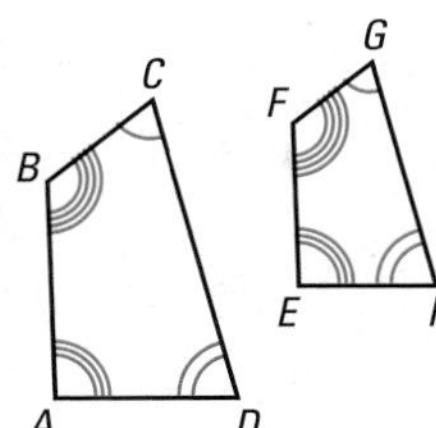

$$\frac{AB}{EF} = \frac{BC}{FG} = \frac{CD}{GH} = \frac{DA}{HE}$$

EXAMPLE 1 *Writing Similarity Statements*

Pentagons *JKLMN* and *STUVW* are similar. List all the pairs of congruent angles. Write the ratios of the corresponding sides in a statement of proportionality.

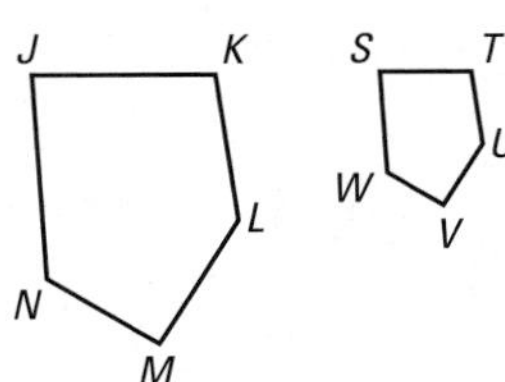

SOLUTION

Because $JKLMN \sim STUVW$, you can write $\angle J \cong \angle S$, $\angle K \cong \angle T$, $\angle L \cong \angle U$, $\angle M \cong \angle V$, and $\angle N \cong \angle W$.

You can write the statement of proportionality as follows:

$$\frac{JK}{ST} = \frac{KL}{TU} = \frac{LM}{UV} = \frac{MN}{VW} = \frac{NJ}{WS}.$$

EXAMPLE 2 *Comparing Similar Polygons*

Decide whether the figures are similar. If they are similar, write a similarity statement.

SOLUTION

As shown, the corresponding angles of *WXYZ* and *PQRS* are congruent. Also, the corresponding side lengths are proportional.

$$\frac{WX}{PQ} = \frac{15}{10} = \frac{3}{2} \qquad \frac{XY}{QR} = \frac{6}{4} = \frac{3}{2}$$

$$\frac{YZ}{RS} = \frac{9}{6} = \frac{3}{2} \qquad \frac{ZW}{SP} = \frac{12}{8} = \frac{3}{2}$$

▶ So, the two figures are similar and you can write $WXYZ \sim PQRS$.

STUDENT HELP

Study Tip
When you refer to similar polygons, their corresponding vertices must be listed in the same order.

CALIFORNIA STANDARDS AND ASSESSMENT

CA Standards: 11
SAT9 Task 1: Objs. 1, 22
SAT9 Task 2: Objs. 1, 24

1 PLAN

PACING
Basic: 2 days
Average: 2 days
Advanced: 2 days
Block Schedule: 0.5 block with 8.2
0.5 block with 8.4

LESSON OPENER
VISUAL APPROACH
An alternative way to approach Lesson 8.3 is to use the Visual Approach Lesson Opener:

- Blackline Master (*Chapter 8 Resource Book,* p. 37)
- Transparency (p. 49)

MEETING INDIVIDUAL NEEDS

- ***Chapter 8 Resource Book***
  Prerequisite Skills Review (p. 5)
  Practice Level A (p. 38)
  Practice Level B (p. 39)
  Practice Level C (p. 40)
  Reteaching with Practice (p. 41)
  Absent Student Catch-Up (p. 43)
  Challenge (p. 45)
- ***Resources in Spanish***
- ***Personal Student Tutor***

NEW-TEACHER SUPPORT
See the Tips for New Teachers on pp. 1–2 of the *Chapter 8 Resource Book* for additional notes about Lesson 8.3.

WARM-UP EXERCISES

Transparency Available

Find the measure of the angles in the figure below.

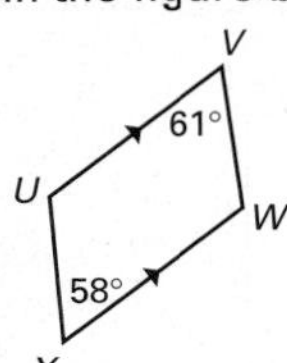

1. $\angle U$ 122° **2.** $\angle W$ 119°

Solve each proportion.

3. $\frac{2}{x} = \frac{5}{20}$ 8 **4.** $\frac{18}{5} = \frac{12}{t}$ $\frac{10}{3}$

2 TEACH

EXTRA EXAMPLE 1

Trapezoid *ABCD* is similar to trapezoid *PQRS*. List all the pairs of congruent angles, and write the ratios of the corresponding sides in a statement of proportionality.

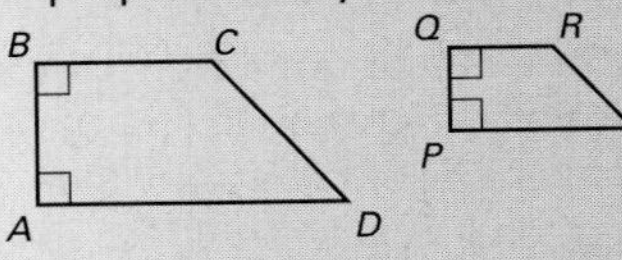

$\angle A \cong \angle P$, $\angle B \cong \angle Q$, $\angle C \cong \angle R$, $\angle D \cong \angle S$; $\frac{AB}{PQ} = \frac{BC}{QR} = \frac{CD}{RS} = \frac{AD}{PS}$

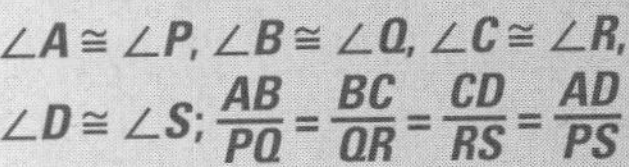

EXTRA EXAMPLE 2

Decide whether the figures are similar. If they are, write the similarity statement.

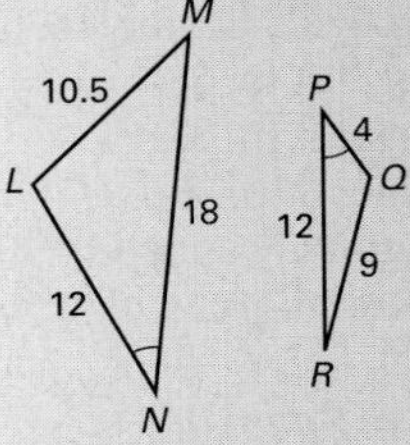

The triangles are not similar.

EXTRA EXAMPLE 3

You have a photo 4 in. wide by 6 in. long that you want to reduce to fit in a frame that is 1.5 in. wide. How long will the reduced photo be? 2.25 in.

EXTRA EXAMPLE 4

A painting is similar to the wall on which it is hanging. Calculate the scale factor of the wall to the paining and find the ratio of their perimeters. $\frac{5}{2}, \frac{5}{2}$

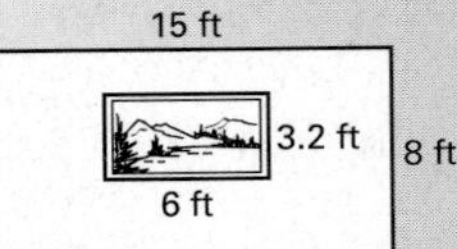

Checkpoint Exercises for Examples 1–4 on next page.

GOAL 2 USING SIMILAR POLYGONS IN REAL LIFE

EXAMPLE 3 *Comparing Photographic Enlargements*

REAL LIFE **POSTER DESIGN** You have been asked to create a poster to advertise a field trip to see the Liberty Bell. You have a 3.5 inch by 5 inch photo that you want to enlarge. You want the enlargement to be 16 inches wide. How long will it be?

SOLUTION

To find the length of the enlargement, you can compare the enlargement to the original measurements of the photo.

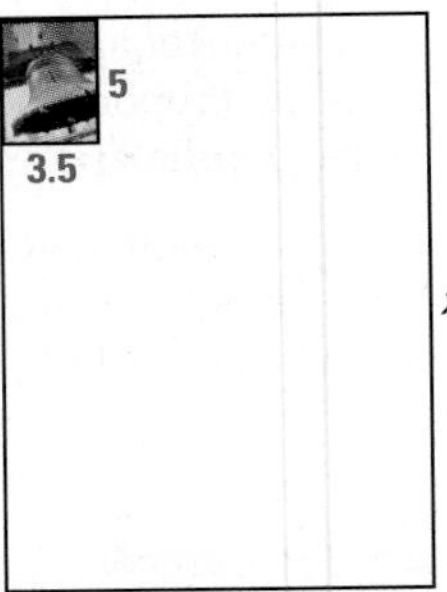

$$\frac{16 \text{ in.}}{3.5 \text{ in.}} = \frac{x \text{ in.}}{5 \text{ in.}}$$

$$x = \frac{16}{3.5} \cdot 5$$

$$x \approx 22.9 \text{ inches}$$

▶ The length of the enlargement will be about 23 inches.

....

If two polygons are similar, then the ratio of the lengths of two corresponding sides is called the **scale factor**. In Example 2 on the previous page, the common ratio of $\frac{3}{2}$ is the scale factor of *WXYZ* to *PQRS*.

EXAMPLE 4 *Using Similar Polygons*

The rectangular patio around a pool is similar to the pool as shown. Calculate the scale factor of the patio to the pool, and find the ratio of their perimeters.

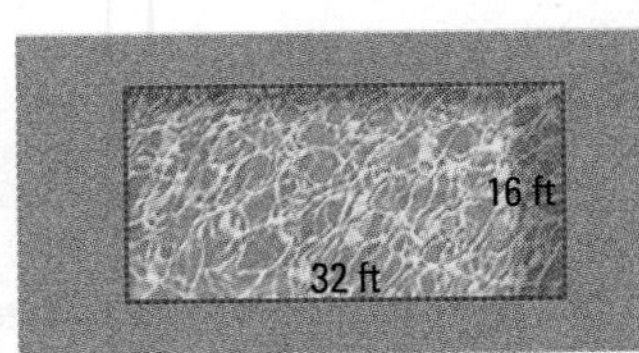

SOLUTION

Because the rectangles are similar, the scale factor of the patio to the pool is 48 ft : 32 ft, which is 3 : 2 in simplified form.

The perimeter of the patio is $2(24) + 2(48) = 144$ feet and the perimeter of the pool is $2(16) + 2(32) = 96$ feet. The ratio of the perimeters is $\frac{144}{96}$, or $\frac{3}{2}$.

....

Notice in Example 4 that the ratio of the perimeters is the same as the scale factor of the rectangles. This observation is generalized in the following theorem. You are asked to prove Theorem 8.1 for two similar rectangles in Exercise 45.

THEOREM

THEOREM 8.1

If two polygons are similar, then the ratio of their perimeters is equal to the ratios of their corresponding side lengths.

If $KLMN \sim PQRS$, then

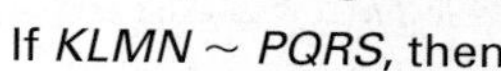

$$\frac{KL + LM + MN + NK}{PQ + QR + RS + SP} = \frac{KL}{PQ} = \frac{LM}{QR} = \frac{MN}{RS} = \frac{NK}{SP}.$$

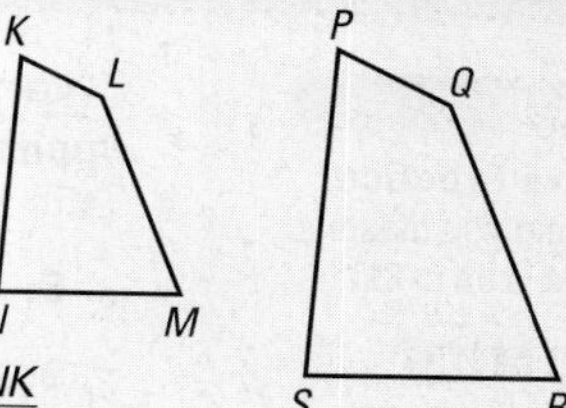

EXAMPLE 5 *Using Similar Polygons*

Quadrilateral $JKLM$ is similar to quadrilateral $PQRS$.

Find the value of z.

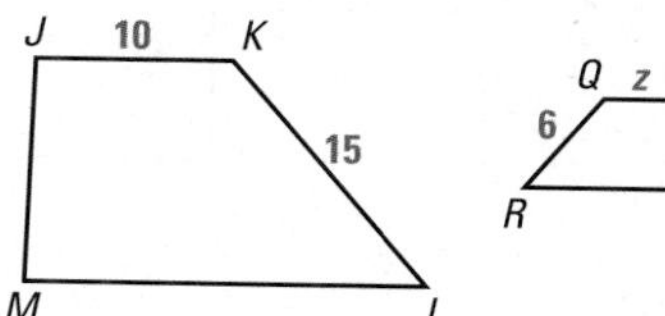

SOLUTION

Set up a proportion that contains PQ.

$\frac{KL}{QR} = \frac{JK}{PQ}$ **Write proportion.**

$\frac{15}{6} = \frac{10}{z}$ **Substitute.**

$z = 4$ **Cross multiply and divide by 15.**

GUIDED PRACTICE

Vocabulary Check ✓

Concept Check ✓

1. If two polygons are similar, must they also be congruent? Explain. **No; the figures are ≅ only if the scale factor is 1.**

Decide whether the figures are similar. Explain your reasoning. **2–3. See margin.**

2.

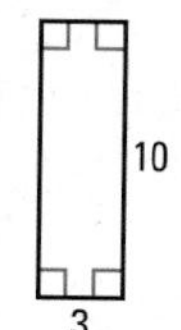

3.

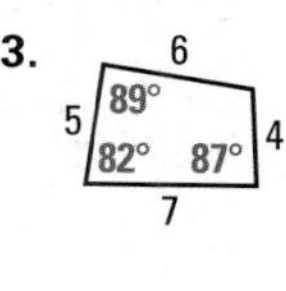

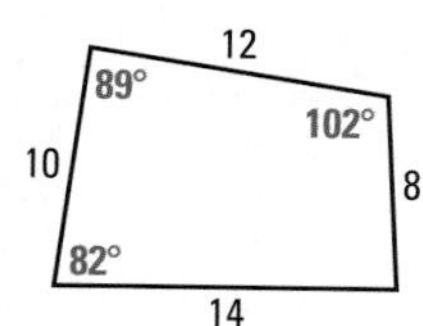

2. No; lengths of corresponding sides are not proportional; $\frac{15}{10} \neq \frac{8}{3}$.

Skill Check ✓

3. Yes; corresp. ∠s can be shown to be ≅ by the Interior Angles of a Quad. Thm. and lengths of corresp. sides are proportional (The scale factor is 2:1).

In the diagram, $TUVW \sim ABCD$.

4. List all pairs of congruent angles and write the statement of proportionality for the polygons. **See margin.**

5. Find the scale factor of $TUVW$ to $ABCD$. **5:3**

6. Find the length of $\overline{TW}$. **10**

7. Find the measure of $\angle TUV$. **110°**

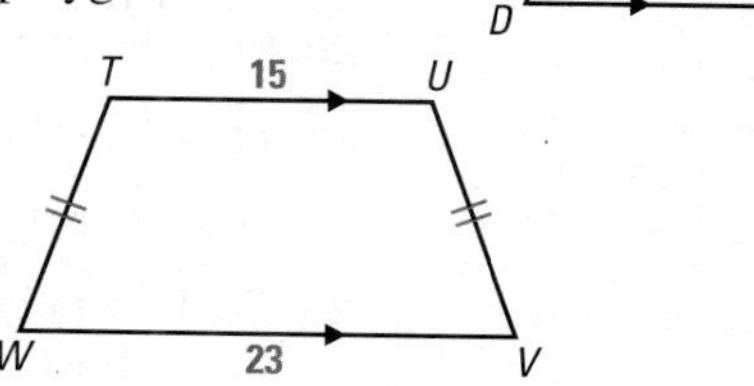

4. $\angle A \cong \angle T$, $\angle B \cong \angle U$, $\angle C \cong \angle V$, $\angle D \cong \angle W$; $\frac{AB}{TU} = \frac{BC}{UV} = \frac{CD}{VW} = \frac{AD}{TW}$

CHECKPOINT EXERCISES

For use after Examples 1–4:

1. Verify that these two pentagons are similar. Then find the ratio of their perimeters.

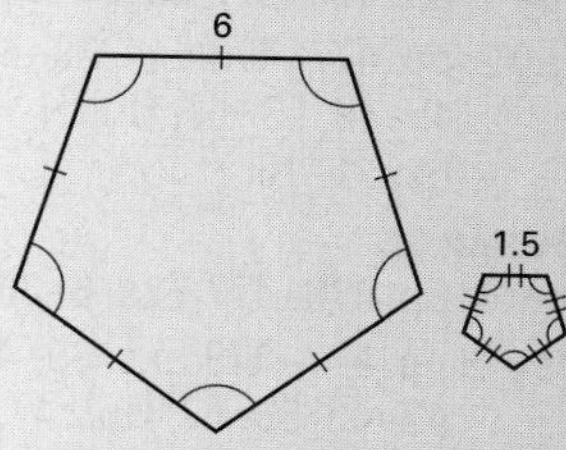

These pentagons are similar because all the angles are congruent and all the corresponding sides are in the ratio 4:1; 4:1.

EXTRA EXAMPLE 5

Parallelogram $ABCD$ is similar to parallelogram $GBEF$. Find the value of y. **19.2**

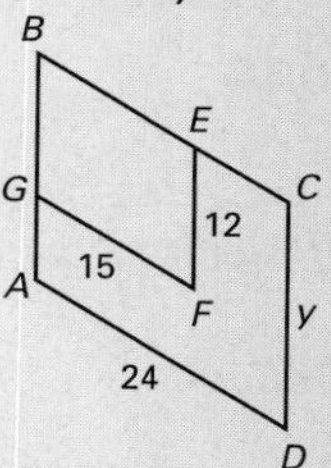

CHECKPOINT EXERCISES

For use after Example 5:

1. $\triangle UVW$ is similar to $\triangle YXW$. Find the value of a. **9.375**

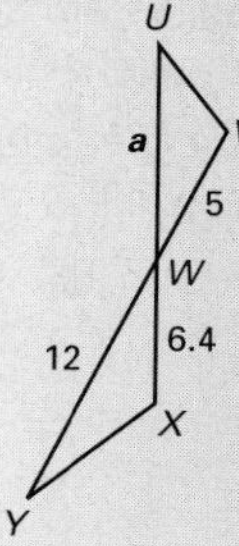

CLOSURE QUESTION

How are the perimeters of similar polygons related?

The ratio of perimeters of the two polygons is the same as the ratio of their corresponding sides.

3 APPLY

ASSIGNMENT GUIDE

BASIC
Day 1: pp. 476–477 Exs. 8–38
Day 2: pp. 477–479 Exs. 39–42, 45–49, 53–67, Quiz 1 Exs. 1–10

AVERAGE
Day 1: pp. 476–477 Exs. 8–38
Day 2: pp. 477–479 Exs. 39–42, 45–49, 53–67, Quiz 1 Exs. 1–10

ADVANCED
Day 1: pp. 476–477 Exs. 8–38
Day 2: pp. 477–479 Exs. 39–42, 45–49, 50–67, Quiz 1 Exs. 1–10

BLOCK SCHEDULE
pp. 476–477 Exs. 8–38 (with 8.2)
pp. 477–479 Exs. 39–42, 45–49, 53–67, Quiz 1 Exs. 1–10 (with 8.4)

EXERCISE LEVELS

Level A: *Easier*
8–10

Level B: *More Difficult*
11–49

Level C: *Most Difficult*
50–52

✔ HOMEWORK CHECK

To quickly check student understanding of key concepts, go over the following exercises: Exs. 10, 12, 18, 20, 28, 30, 38, 42, 46. See also the Daily Homework Quiz:

- Blackline Master (*Chapter 8 Resource Book,* p. 49)
- Transparency (p. 58)

PRACTICE AND APPLICATIONS

STUDENT HELP

Extra Practice to help you master skills is on p. 817.

WRITING SIMILARITY STATEMENTS Use the information given to list all pairs of congruent angles and write the statement of proportionality for the figures.

8. $\triangle DEF \sim \triangle PQR$ $\angle D \cong \angle P, \angle E \cong \angle Q, \angle F \cong \angle R; \frac{DE}{PQ} = \frac{EF}{QR} = \frac{DF}{PR}$

9. $\square JKLM \sim \square WXYZ$ $\angle J \cong \angle W, \angle K \cong \angle X, \angle L \cong \angle Y, \angle M \cong \angle Z; \frac{JK}{WX} = \frac{KL}{XY} = \frac{LM}{YZ} = \frac{JM}{WZ}$

10. $QRSTU \sim ABCDE$

DETERMINING SIMILARITY Decide whether the quadrilaterals are similar. Explain your reasoning. 11–14. See margin.

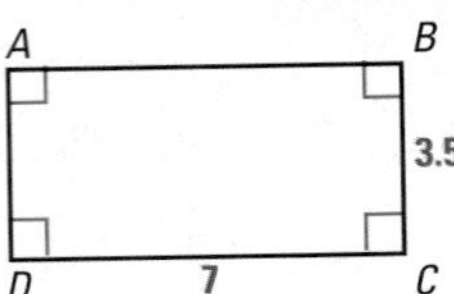

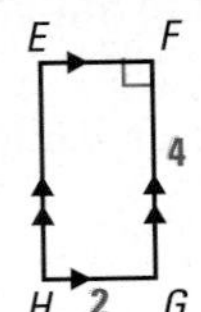

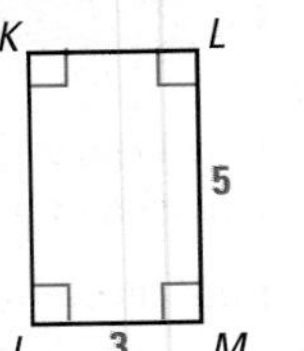

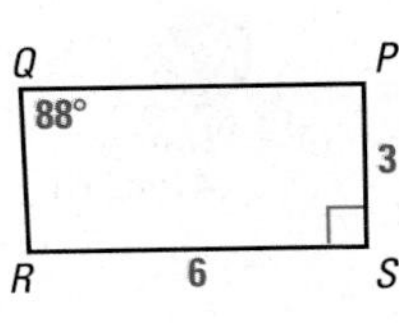

11. *ABCD* and *FGHE*

12. *ABCD* and *JKLM*

13. *ABCD* and *PQRS*

14. *JKLM* and *PQRS*

DETERMINING SIMILARITY Decide whether the polygons are similar. If so, write a similarity statement.

15. A, B, C, D (4, 4); E, F, G, H (5, 5)

16. no T, U, V, W (4, 6)

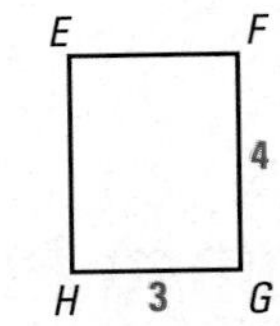

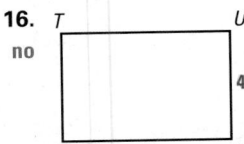

17.

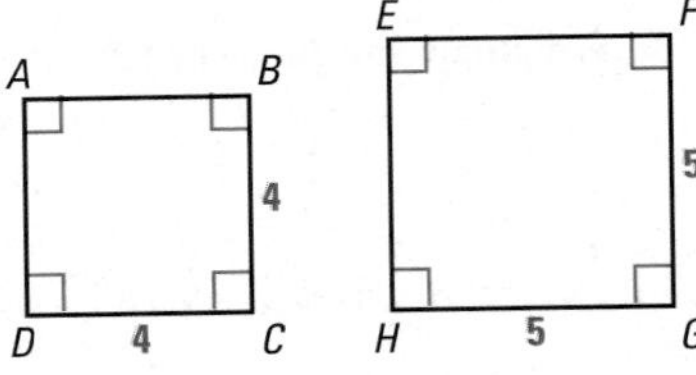

yes; $\triangle XYZ \sim \triangle CAB$

18. no

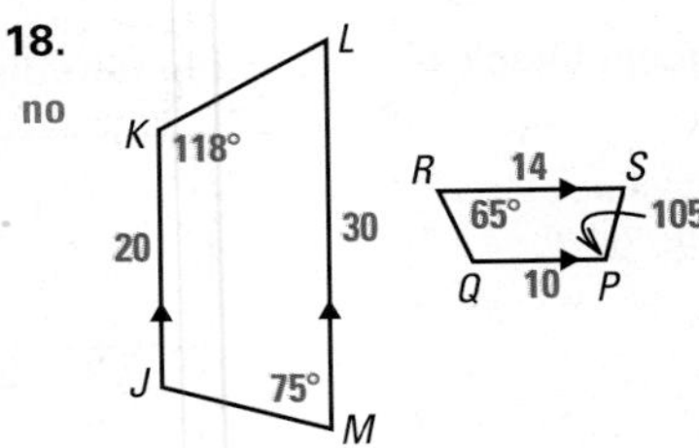

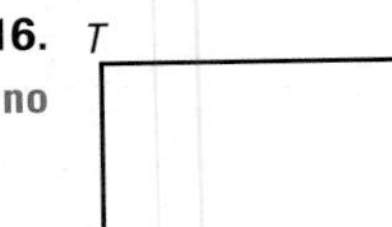

USING SIMILAR POLYGONS $PQRS \sim JKLM$.

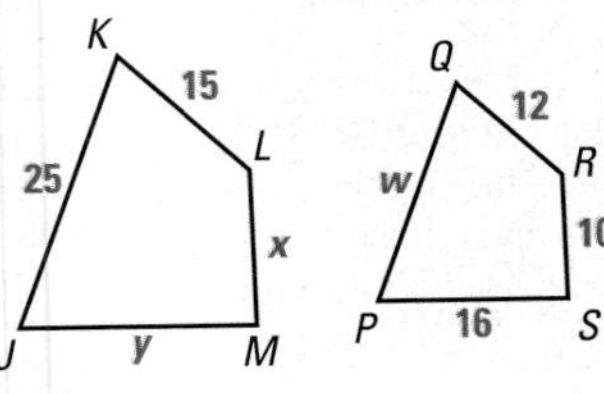

19. Find the scale factor of *PQRS* to *JKLM*. 4:5

20. Find the scale factor of *JKLM* to *PQRS*. 5:4

21. Find the values of *w*, *x*, and *y*. 20, 12.5, 20

22. Find the perimeter of each polygon. *JKLM*: 72.5; *PQRS*: 58

23. Find the ratio of the perimeter of *PQRS* to the perimeter of *JKLM*. $\frac{4}{5}$

10. $\angle Q \cong \angle A, \angle R \cong \angle B, \angle S \cong \angle C, \angle T \cong \angle D, \angle U \cong \angle E; \frac{QR}{AB} = \frac{RS}{BC} = \frac{ST}{CD} = \frac{TU}{DE} = \frac{QU}{AE}$

11. Yes; both figures are rectangles, so all 4 ∠s are ≅ and $\frac{AB}{FG} = \frac{BC}{GH} = \frac{CD}{HE} = \frac{AD}{FE} = \frac{7}{4}$.

12. No; lengths of corresp. sides are not proportional; $\frac{7}{5} \neq \frac{3.5}{3}$.

13. No; $m\angle B = 90°$ and $m\angle Q = 88°$, so corresp. ∠s are not ≅.

14. No; $m\angle K = 90°$ and $m\angle Q = 88°$, so corresp. ∠s are not ≅ and $\frac{6}{5} \neq \frac{3}{3}$, so lengths of corresp. sides are not proportional.

15. yes; *Sample answers:* $ABCD \sim EFGH$, $ABCD \sim FEHG$

STUDENT HELP

HOMEWORK HELP
Example 1: Exs. 8–10
Example 2: Exs. 11–18
Example 3: Exs. 19–30, 43, 44
Example 4: Exs. 19–30, 46–48
Example 5: Exs. 39–42

USING SIMILAR POLYGONS $\square ABCD \sim \square EFGH$.

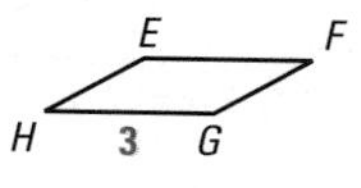

24. Find the scale factor of $\square ABCD$ to $\square EFGH$. 2:1

25. Find the length of $\overline{EH}$. 2

26. Find the measure of $\angle G$. 150°

27. Find the perimeter of $\square EFGH$. 10

28. Find the ratio of the perimeter of $\square EFGH$ to the perimeter of $\square ABCD$. $\frac{1}{2}$

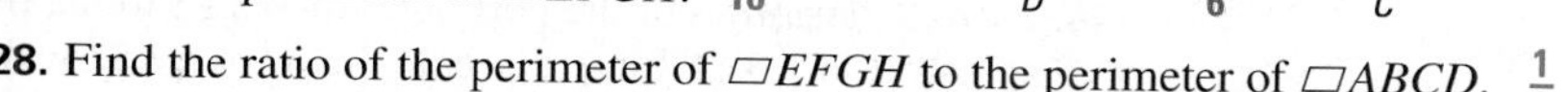

DETERMINING SIMILARITY **Decide whether the polygons are similar. If so, find the scale factor of Figure A to Figure B.**

29. no

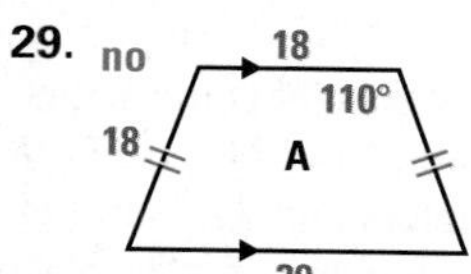

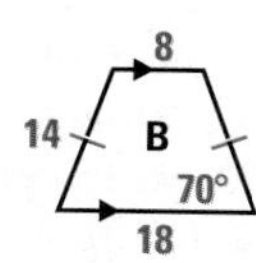

30. yes; 3:2

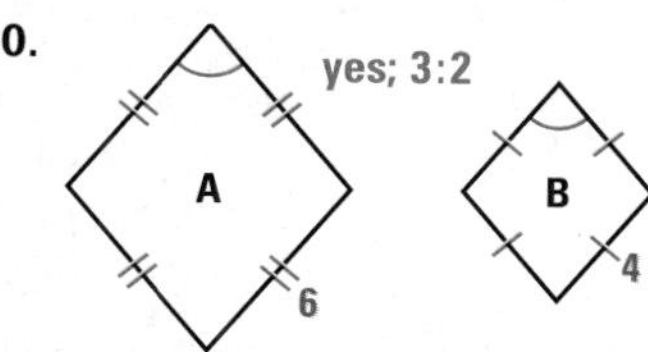

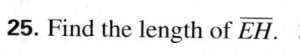

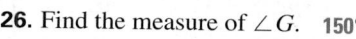

HOMEWORK HELP Visit our Web site www.mcdougallittell.com for help with problem solving in Exs. 31–38.

44. No; the ratio of length to width $= \frac{4}{3}$ for a standard screen and $\frac{16}{9}$ for a digital screen. Then $\frac{\text{length}}{\text{length}} = \frac{4}{16}$ and $\frac{\text{width}}{\text{width}} = \frac{3}{9}$, and $\frac{4}{16} \neq \frac{3}{9}$.

LOGICAL REASONING **Tell whether the polygons are *always*, *sometimes*, or *never* similar.**

31. Two isosceles triangles sometimes

32. Two regular polygons sometimes

33. Two isosceles trapezoids sometimes

34. Two rhombuses sometimes

35. Two squares always

36. An isosceles and a scalene triangle never

37. Two equilateral triangles always

38. A right and an isosceles triangle sometimes

USING ALGEBRA **The two polygons are similar. Find the values of x and y.**

39.

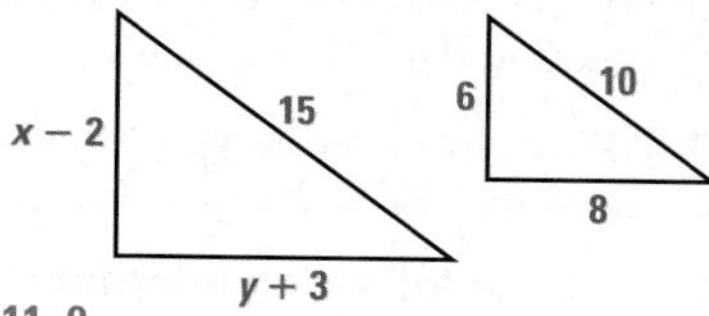

11, 9

40.

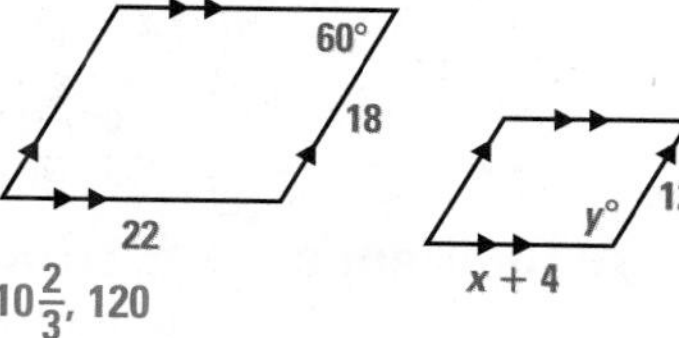

$10\frac{2}{3}$, 120

41.

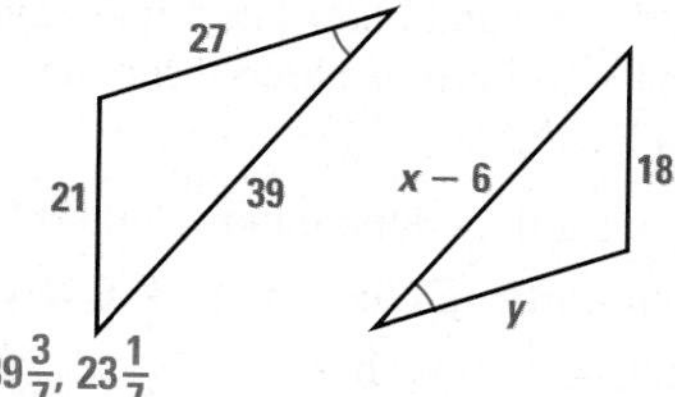

$39\frac{3}{7}$, $23\frac{1}{7}$

42.

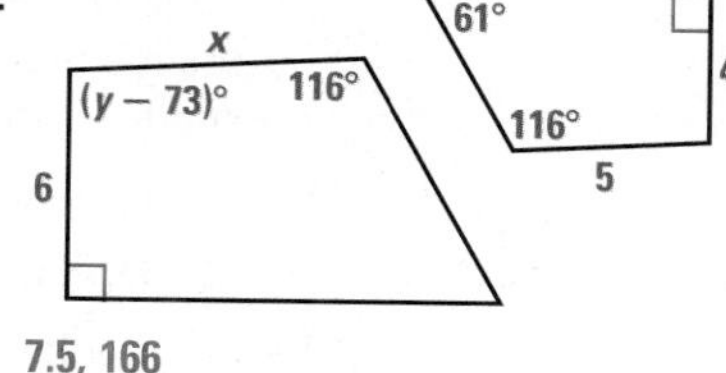

7.5, 166

FOCUS ON APPLICATIONS

DIGITAL TELEVISION screens contain over 6 times as many pixels (the tiny dots that make up the picture) as standard analog screens.

TV SCREENS **In Exercises 43 and 44, use the following information.**
Television screen sizes are based on the length of the diagonal of the screen. The *aspect ratio* refers to the length to width ratio of the screen. A standard 27 inch analog television screen has an aspect ratio of 4:3. A 27 inch digital television screen has an aspect ratio of 16:9.

43. Make a scale drawing of each television screen. Use proportions and the Pythagorean Theorem to calculate the lengths and widths of the screens in inches. Check scale drawings; analog tv: 21.6 in by 16.2 in.; digital tv: about 23.5 in. by 13.2 in.

44. Are the television screens similar? Explain. See margin.

COMMON ERROR

EXERCISES 16–18 Students often have difficulty determining the corresponding sides of similar figures when one figure is rotated. To avoid this problem, students can trace one of the figures and rotate the tracing to make the two similar figures easier to compare.

STUDENT HELP NOTES

Homework Help Students can find help for Exs. 31–38 at **www.mcdougallittell.com.** The information can be printed out for students who don't have access to the Internet.

45. $ABCD \sim EFGH$ with scale factor $1:k$, so $\frac{AB}{EF} = \frac{BC}{FG} = \frac{CD}{GH} = \frac{AD}{EH} = \frac{1}{k}$. Then $EF = k \cdot AB$, $FG = k \cdot BC$, $GH = k \cdot CD$, and $EH = k \cdot AD$, so $\frac{\text{perimeter of } ABCD}{\text{perimeter of } EFGH} = \frac{AB + BC + CD + AD}{EF + FG + GH + EH} = \frac{AB + BC + CD + AD}{k \cdot AB + k \cdot BC + k \cdot CD + k \cdot AD} = \frac{AB + BC + CD + AD}{k(AB + BC + CD + AD)} = \frac{1}{k} = \frac{AB}{EF}$.

49a. 4.2; 2.1; 3.5; 1.4; 2.8

49b.

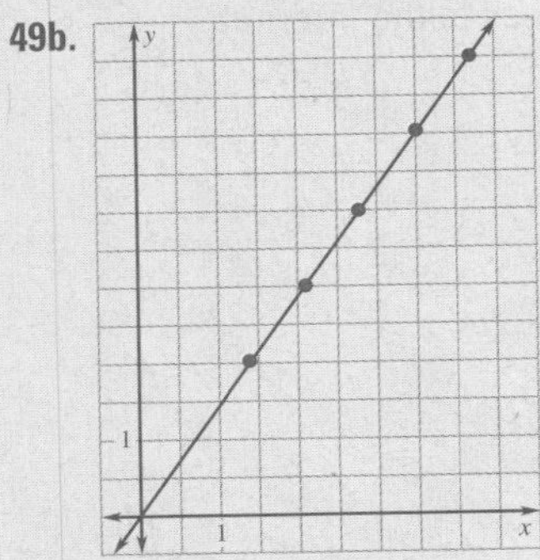

50–52. See Additional Answers beginning on page AA1.

ADDITIONAL PRACTICE AND RETEACHING

For Lesson 8.3:

- Practice Levels A, B, and C (*Chapter 8 Resource Book,* p. 38)
- Reteaching with Practice (*Chapter 8 Resource Book,* p. 41)
- See Lesson 8.3 of the *Personal Student Tutor*

For more Mixed Review:

- Search the *Test and Practice Generator* for key words or specific lessons.

49. a. Figure 1: $AB = 4.2$, $BC = 2.1$, $CD = 3.5$, $DE = 1.4$, $EA = 2.8$
b. See margin for graph; $y = \frac{10}{7}x$
c. $\frac{10}{7}$; it is the reciprocal of the scale factor.

45. **PROOF** Prove Theorem 8.1 for two similar rectangles. See margin.

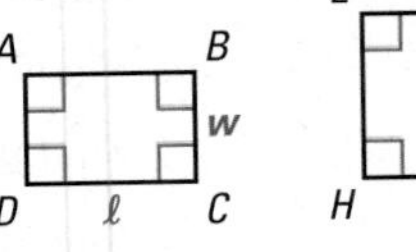

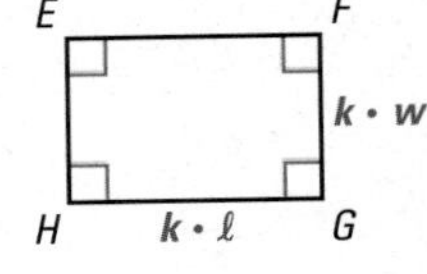

GIVEN ▶ $ABCD \sim EFGH$

PROVE ▶ $\frac{\text{perimeter of } ABCD}{\text{perimeter of } EFGH} = \frac{AB}{EF}$

46. **SCALE** The ratio of the perimeter of $WXYZ$ to the perimeter of $QRST$ is 7.5 : 2. Find the scale factor of $QRST$ to $WXYZ$. 2:7.5 or 4:15

47. **SCALE** The ratio of one side of $\triangle CDE$ to the corresponding side of similar $\triangle FGH$ is 2 : 5. The perimeter of $\triangle FGH$ is 28 inches. Find the perimeter of $\triangle CDE$. 11.2 in.

48. **SCALE** The perimeter of ▱$PQRS$ is 94 centimeters. The perimeter of ▱$JKLM$ is 18.8 centimeters, and ▱$JKLM \sim$ ▱$PQRS$. The lengths of the sides of ▱$PQRS$ are 15 centimeters and 32 centimeters. Find the scale factor of ▱$PQRS$ to ▱$JKLM$, and the lengths of the sides of ▱$JKLM$. 94:18.8 or 5:1; 3 cm and 6.4 cm

Test Preparation

49. **MULTI-STEP PROBLEM** Use the similar figures shown. The scale factor of Figure 1 to Figure 2 is 7 : 10. See margin.

a. Copy and complete the table.

	AB	BC	CD	DE	EA
Figure 1	?	?	?	?	?
Figure 2	6.0	3.0	5.0	2.0	4.0

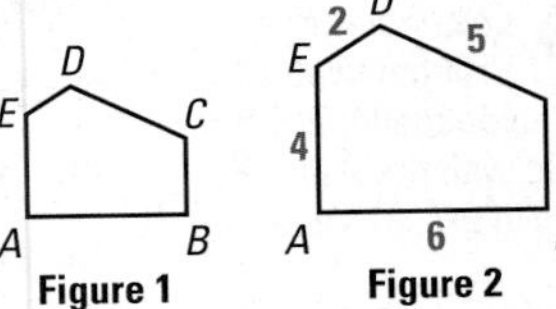

b. Graph the data in the table. Let x represent the length of a side in Figure 1 and let y represent the length of the corresponding side in Figure 2. Determine an equation that relates x and y.

c. **ANALYZING DATA** The equation you obtained in part (b) should be linear. What is its slope? How does its slope compare to the scale factor?

★ Challenge

TOTAL ECLIPSE Use the following information in Exercises 50–52. From your perspective on Earth during a total eclipse of the sun, the moon is directly in line with the sun and blocks the sun's rays. The ratio of the radius of the moon to its distance to Earth is about the same as the ratio of the radius of the sun to its distance to Earth. 50–52. See margin.

Distance between Earth and the moon: 240,000 miles

Distance between Earth and the sun: 93,000,000 miles

Radius of the sun: 432,500 miles

50. Make a sketch of Earth, the moon, and the sun during a total eclipse of the sun. Include the given distances in your sketch.

51. Your sketch should contain some similar triangles. Use the similar triangles in your sketch to explain a total eclipse of the sun.

52. Write a statement of proportionality for the similar triangles. Then use the given distances to estimate the radius of the moon.

EXTRA CHALLENGE
www.mcdougallittell.com

MIXED REVIEW

FINDING SLOPE **Find the slope of the line that passes through the given points.** (Review 3.6 for 8.4)

53. $A(-1, 4), B(3, 8)$ 1 **54.** $P(0, -7), Q(-6, -3)$ $-\frac{2}{3}$ **55.** $J(9, 4), K(2, 5)$ $-\frac{1}{7}$

56. $L(-2, -3), M(1, 10)$ $\frac{13}{3}$ **57.** $S(-4, 5), T(2, -2)$ $-\frac{7}{6}$ **58.** $Y(-1, 6), Z(5, -5)$ $-\frac{11}{6}$

FINDING ANGLE MEASURES **Find the value of *x*.** (Review 4.1 for 8.4)

59. 49

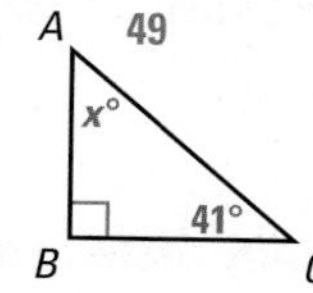

60. 7

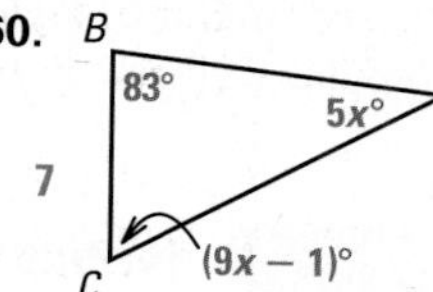

61. 9

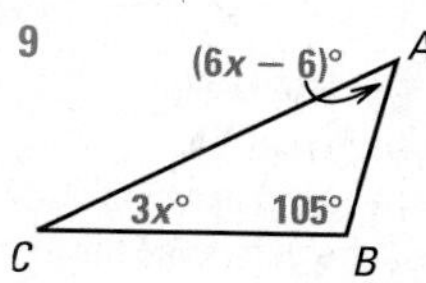

SOLVING PROPORTIONS **Solve the proportion.** (Review 8.1)

62. $\frac{x}{9} = \frac{6}{27}$ 2 **63.** $\frac{4}{y} = \frac{2}{19}$ 38 **64.** $\frac{5}{24} = \frac{25}{z}$ 120

65. $\frac{4}{13} = \frac{b}{8}$ $\frac{32}{13}$ **66.** $\frac{11}{x+2} = \frac{9}{x}$ 9 **67.** $\frac{3x+7}{5} = \frac{4x}{6}$ 21

QUIZ 1

Self-Test for Lessons 8.1–8.3

Solve the proportions. (Lesson 8.1)

1. $\frac{p}{15} = \frac{2}{3}$ 10 **2.** $\frac{5}{7} = \frac{20}{d}$ 28 **3.** $\frac{4}{2x-6} = \frac{16}{x}$ $\frac{24}{7}$

Find the geometric mean of the two numbers. (Lesson 8.2)

4. 7 and 63 21 **5.** 5 and 11 $\sqrt{55} \approx 7.42$ **6.** 10 and 7 $\sqrt{70} \approx 8.37$

In Exercises 7 and 8, the two polygons are similar. Find the value of *x*. Then find the scale factor and the ratio of the perimeters. (Lesson 8.3)

7. 3; 1:2; $\frac{1}{2}$

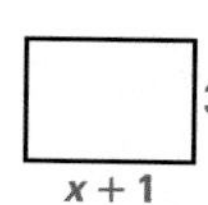

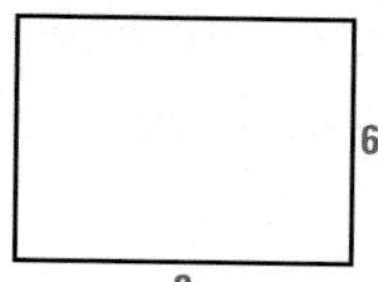

8. 30; 3:2; $\frac{3}{2}$

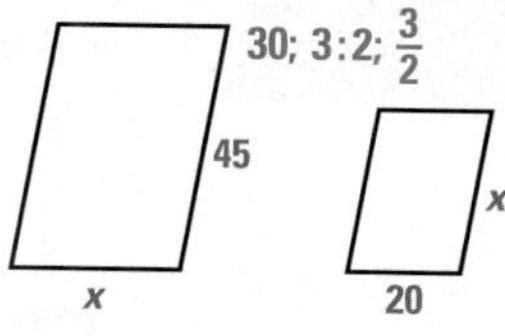

COMPARING PHOTO SIZES **Use the following information.** (Lesson 8.3)
You are ordering your school pictures. You decide to order one 8 × 10 (8 inches by 10 inches), two 5 × 7's (5 inches by 7 inches), and 24 wallets $\left(2\frac{1}{4}\text{ inches by } 3\frac{1}{4}\text{ inches}\right)$.

9. Are any of these sizes similar to each other?

10. Suppose you want the wallet photos to be similar to the 8 × 10 photo. If the wallet photo were $2\frac{1}{2}$ inches wide, how tall would it be? $3\frac{1}{8}$ in.

9. None are exactly similar, but the 5 × 7 and wallet sizes are very nearly similar. $\left(\frac{5}{2.25} \approx 2.22, \frac{7}{3.25} \approx 2.15\right)$

4 ASSESS

DAILY HOMEWORK QUIZ

Transparency Available

Are the polygons similar? If so, write a similarity statement.

1.

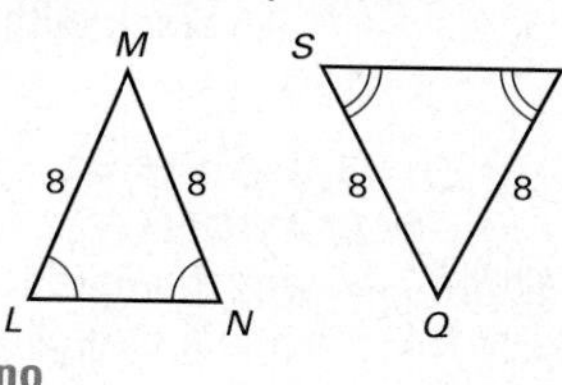

no

2.

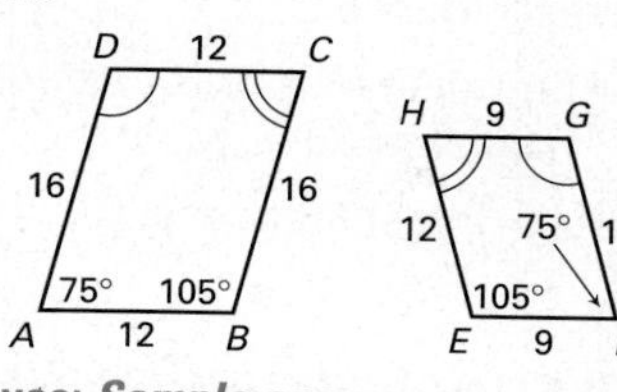

yes; *Sample answer:* *ABCD* ~ *FEHG*

In Exs. 3–5, $\triangle KLM \sim \triangle PQR$.

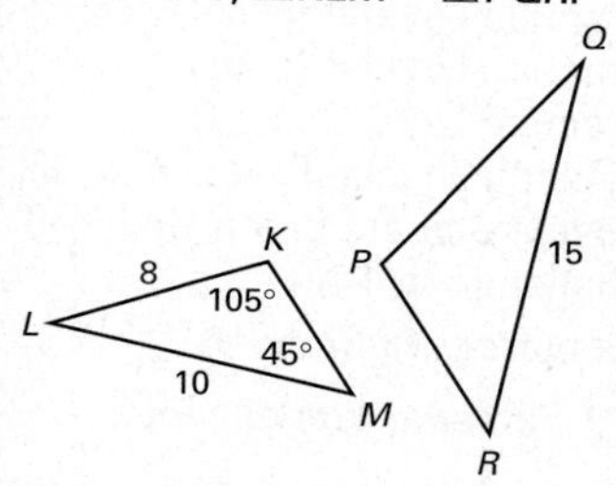

3. Find the scale factor. 2:3

4. Find the length of $\overline{PQ}$. 12

5. Find the measure of $\angle Q$. 30°

EXTRA CHALLENGE NOTE

Challenge problems for Lesson 8.3 are available in **blackline** format in the *Chapter 8 Resource Book*, p. 45 and at **www.mcdougallittell.com.**

ADDITIONAL TEST PREPARATION

1. OPEN ENDED Draw two similar figures. Explain why they are similar and write the similarity statement. Check students' work.

ADDITIONAL RESOURCES

An alternative Quiz for Lessons 8.1–8.3 is available in the *Chapter 8 Resource Book*, p. 46.

1 PLAN

PACING
Basic: 2 days
Average: 2 days
Advanced: 2 days
Block Schedule: 0.5 block with 8.3
0.5 block with 8.5

LESSON OPENER
APPLICATION
An alternative way to approach Lesson 8.4 is to use the Application Lesson Opener:
- Blackline Master (*Chapter 8 Resource Book*, p. 50)
- Transparency (p. 50)

MEETING INDIVIDUAL NEEDS
- ***Chapter 8 Resource Book***
  Prerequisite Skills Review (p. 5)
  Practice Level A (p. 55)
  Practice Level B (p. 56)
  Practice Level C (p. 57)
  Reteaching with Practice (p. 58)
  Absent Student Catch-Up (p. 60)
  Challenge (p. 62)
- ***Resources in Spanish***
- ***Personal Student Tutor***

NEW-TEACHER SUPPORT
See the Tips for New Teachers on pp. 1–2 of the *Chapter 8 Resource Book* for additional notes about Lesson 8.4.

WARM-UP EXERCISES
Transparency Available
In the diagram, $\triangle ABC \sim \triangle DEF$. Find the measure.

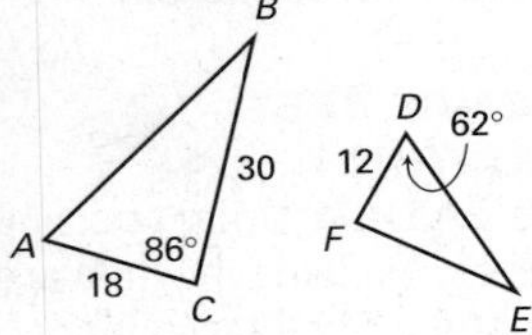

1. $m\angle F$ 86° **2.** $m\angle A$ 62°
3. $m\angle B$ 32° **4.** FE 20

8.4 Similar Triangles

What you should learn

GOAL 1 Identify similar triangles.

GOAL 2 Use similar triangles in **real-life** problems, such as using shadows to determine the height of the Great Pyramid in **Ex. 55**.

Why you should learn it

▼ To solve **real-life** problems, such as using similar triangles to understand aerial photography in **Example 4**.

REAL LIFE

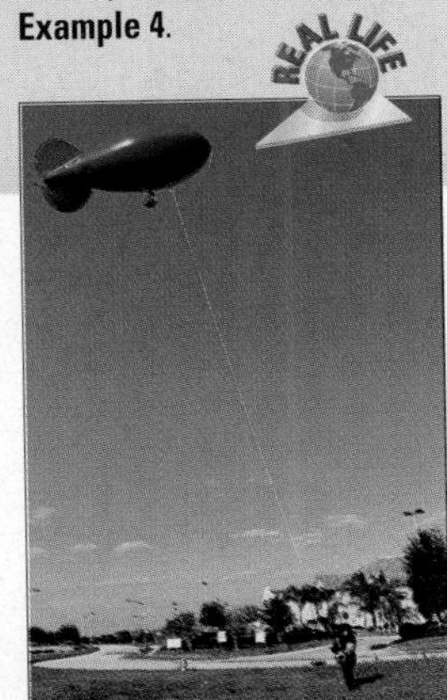

CALIFORNIA STANDARDS AND ASSESSMENT
CA Standards: 5, 17
SAT9 Task 1: Objs. 1, 22
SAT9 Task 2: Objs. 1, 24

GOAL 1 IDENTIFYING SIMILAR TRIANGLES

In this lesson, you will continue the study of similar polygons by looking at properties of similar triangles. The activity that follows Example 1 allows you to explore one of these properties.

EXAMPLE 1 *Writing Proportionality Statements*

In the diagram, $\triangle BTW \sim \triangle ETC$.

a. Write the statement of proportionality.

b. Find $m\angle TEC$.

c. Find ET and BE.

T 34°
E C
3
20
79°
B 12 W

SOLUTION

a. $\dfrac{ET}{BT} = \dfrac{TC}{TW} = \dfrac{CE}{WB}$

b. $\angle B \cong \angle TEC$, so $m\angle TEC = 79°$.

c. $\dfrac{CE}{WB} = \dfrac{ET}{BT}$ **Write proportion.**

$\dfrac{3}{12} = \dfrac{ET}{20}$ **Substitute.**

$\dfrac{3(20)}{12} = ET$ **Multiply each side by 20.**

$5 = ET$ **Simplify.**

Because $BE = BT - ET$, $BE = 20 - 5 = 15$.

▶ So, ET is 5 units and BE is 15 units.

ACTIVITY
Developing Concepts

Investigating Similar Triangles

Use a protractor and a ruler to draw two noncongruent triangles so that each triangle has a 40° angle and a 60° angle. Check your drawing by measuring the third angle of each triangle—it should be 80°. Why? Measure the lengths of the sides of the triangles and compute the ratios of the lengths of corresponding sides. Are the triangles similar?

Triangle Sum Thm.; yes

POSTULATE

POSTULATE 25 ***Angle-Angle (AA) Similarity Postulate***

If two angles of one triangle are congruent to two angles of another triangle, then the two triangles are similar.

If $\angle JKL \cong \angle XYZ$ and $\angle KJL \cong \angle YXZ$, then $\triangle JKL \sim \triangle XYZ$.

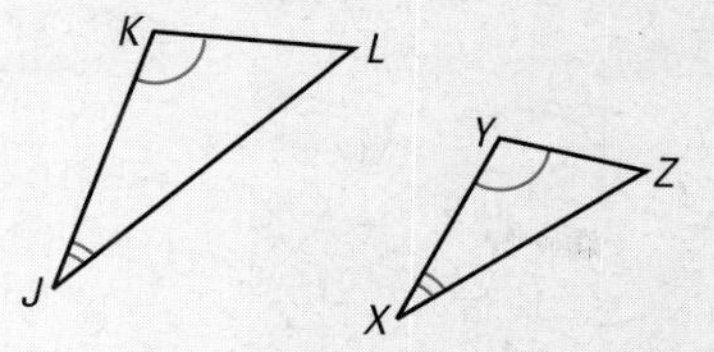

EXAMPLE 2 *Proving that Two Triangles are Similar*

Color variations in the tourmaline crystal shown lie along the sides of isosceles triangles. In the triangles each vertex angle measures 52°. Explain why the triangles are similar.

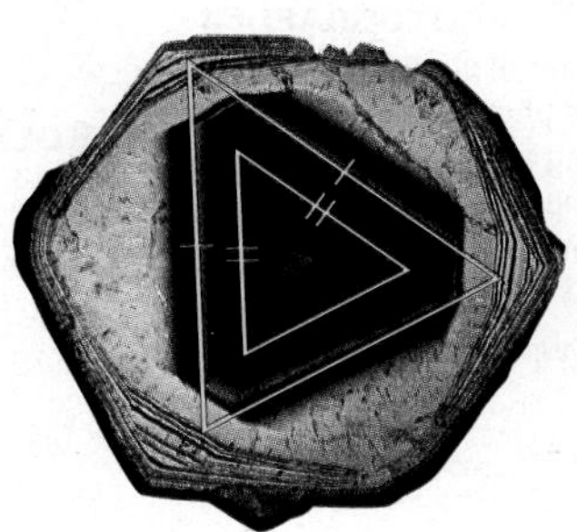

SOLUTION

Because the triangles are isosceles, you can determine that each base angle is 64°. Using the AA Similarity Postulate, you can conclude that the triangles are similar.

EXAMPLE 3 *Why a Line Has Only One Slope*

Using Algebra

Use properties of similar triangles to explain why any two points on a line can be used to calculate the slope. Find the slope of the line using both pairs of points shown.

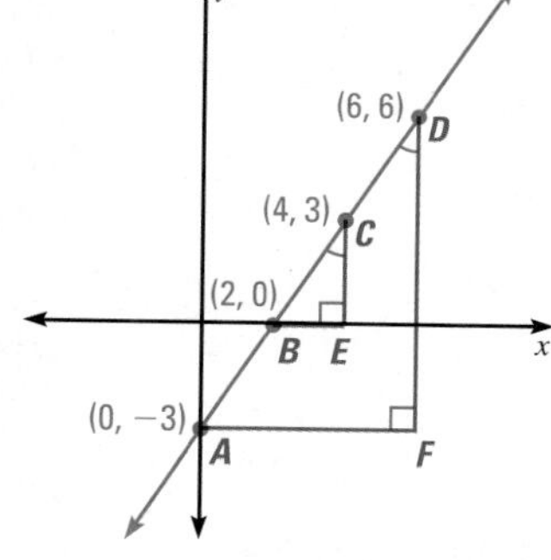

SOLUTION

By the AA Similarity Postulate $\triangle BEC \sim \triangle AFD$, so the ratios of corresponding sides are the same. In particular, $\frac{CE}{DF} = \frac{BE}{AF}$.

By a property of proportions, $\frac{CE}{BE} = \frac{DF}{AF}$.

STUDENT HELP

Look Back
For help with finding slope, see p. 165.

The slope of a line is the ratio of the change in y to the corresponding change in x. The ratios $\frac{CE}{BE}$ and $\frac{DF}{AF}$ represent the slopes of $\overline{BC}$ and $\overline{AD}$, respectively.

Because the two slopes are equal, any two points on a line can be used to calculate its slope. You can verify this with specific values from the diagram.

$$\text{slope of } \overline{BC} = \frac{3-0}{4-2} = \frac{3}{2}$$

$$\text{slope of } \overline{AD} = \frac{6-(-3)}{6-0} = \frac{9}{6} = \frac{3}{2}$$

2 TEACH

EXTRA EXAMPLE 1

In the diagram, $\triangle LMN \sim \triangle PQN$.

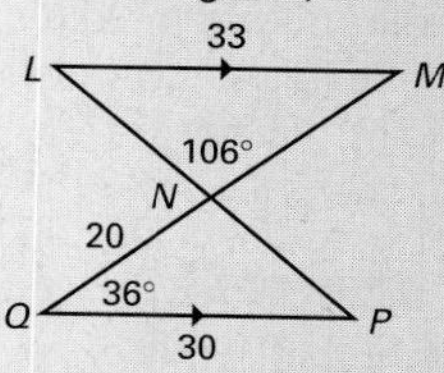

a. Write the statement of proportionality. $\frac{PQ}{LM} = \frac{QN}{MN} = \frac{NP}{NL}$

b. Find $m\angle M$ and $m\angle P$. **36°, 38°**

c. Find MN and QM. **22, 42**

EXTRA EXAMPLE 2

Explain why $\triangle WVX \sim \triangle WZY$.

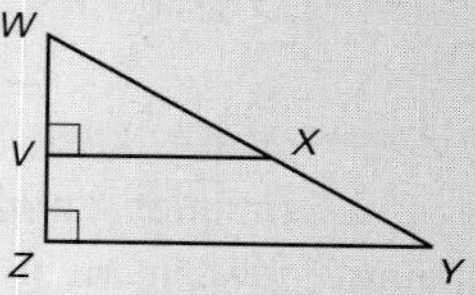

Both triangles share $\angle W$ and both have a right angle. By AA, the triangles are similar.

EXTRA EXAMPLE 3

Use points G and J in the diagram below to find the slope of the line containing $\overline{GJ}$. Name five other segments whose endpoints could be used to find the slope of the line.

−2; $\overline{GH}$; $\overline{GI}$; $\overline{HI}$; $\overline{HJ}$; $\overline{IJ}$

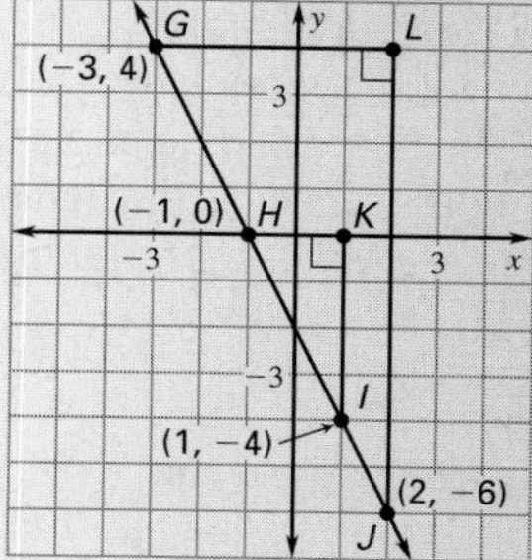

CHECKPOINT EXERCISES

For use after Examples 1–3:

1. Refer to the diagram for Extra Example 1. Explain why the two triangles are similar.
Since $\overline{LM}$ and $\overline{QP}$ are parallel, the alternate interior angles are congruent. The triangles are then similar by AA.

Extra Example 4

In another camera, $f = 10$ cm and $n = 6$ cm. Use the proportion $\frac{f}{h} = \frac{n}{g}$ to estimate the altitude h in meters required to take a photo that covers a ground distance g of 100 meters. **about 167 meters**

Extra Example 5

Find the length of $\overline{EH}$. **15**

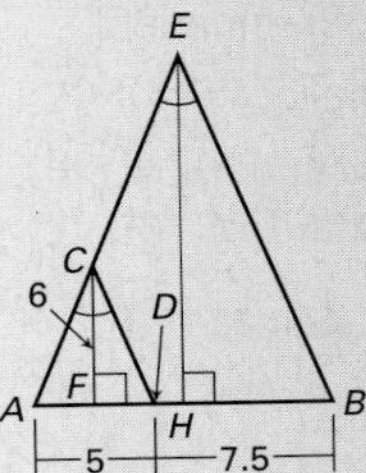

Checkpoint Exercises

For use after Examples 4 and 5:

The company logo shown below uses equilateral triangles and inscribed and circumscribed circles.

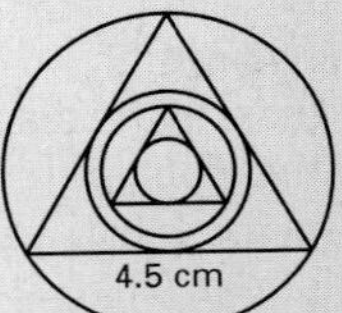

1. If the scale factor between the two triangles is 5:2, how long is a side of the smaller equilateral triangle? **1.8 cm**
2. In a larger version of the logo, the smaller triangle has a side length of 4.5 cm. How long is a side of the larger triangle? **11.25 cm**

Closure Question

Explain how the AA Similarity Postulate can save time when proving that two triangles are similar. **Using the AA Similarity Postulate, you need only show that two pairs of corresponding angles are congruent; you do not need to show that the ratios of corresponding side lengths are equal.**

AERIAL PHOTOGRAPHER

An aerial photographer can take photos from a plane or using a remote-controlled blimp as discussed in Example 4.

CAREER LINK www.mcdougallittell.com

GOAL 2 Using Similar Triangles in Real Life

EXAMPLE 4 *Using Similar Triangles*

Aerial Photography Low-level aerial photos can be taken using a remote-controlled camera suspended from a blimp. You want to take an aerial photo that covers a ground distance g of 50 meters. Use the proportion $\frac{f}{h} = \frac{n}{g}$ to estimate the altitude h that the blimp should fly at to take the photo. In the proportion, use $f = 8$ cm and $n = 3$ cm. These two variables are determined by the type of camera used.

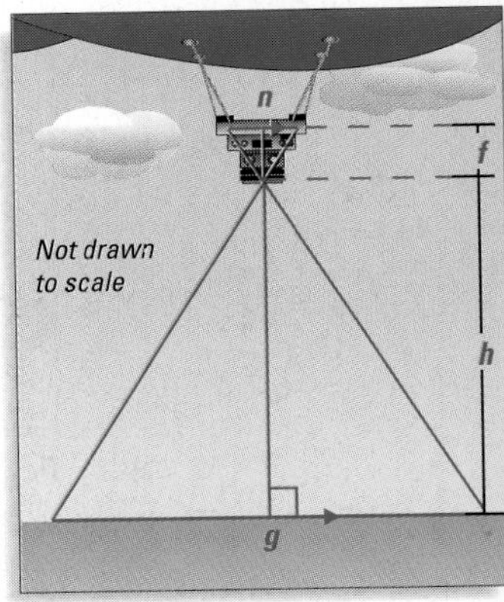

Solution

$\frac{f}{h} = \frac{n}{g}$ **Write proportion.**

$\frac{8 \text{ cm}}{h} = \frac{3 \text{ cm}}{50 \text{ m}}$ **Substitute.**

$3h = 400$ **Cross product property**

$h \approx 133$ **Divide each side by 3.**

▶ The blimp should fly at an altitude of about 133 meters to take a photo that covers a ground distance of 50 meters.

. . . .

In Lesson 8.3, you learned that the perimeters of similar polygons are in the same ratio as the lengths of the corresponding sides. This concept can be generalized as follows. If two polygons are similar, then the ratio of *any two corresponding lengths* (such as altitudes, medians, angle bisector segments, and diagonals) is equal to the scale factor of the similar polygons.

EXAMPLE 5 *Using Scale Factors*

Find the length of the altitude $\overline{QS}$.

Solution

Find the scale factor of $\triangle NQP$ to $\triangle TQR$.

$$\frac{NP}{TR} = \frac{12 + 12}{8 + 8} = \frac{24}{16} = \frac{3}{2}$$

Now, because the ratio of the lengths of the altitudes is equal to the scale factor, you can write the following equation.

$$\frac{QM}{QS} = \frac{3}{2}$$

▶ Substitute 6 for QM and solve for QS to show that $QS = 4$.

STUDENT HELP

HOMEWORK HELP Visit our Web site www.mcdougallittell.com for extra examples.

Guided Practice

Vocabulary Check ✓

1. If $\triangle ABC \sim \triangle XYZ$, $AB = 6$, and $XY = 4$, what is the *scale factor* of the triangles? 3:2

Concept Check ✓

2. The points $A(2, 3)$, $B(-1, 6)$, $C(4, 1)$, and $D(0, 5)$ lie on a line. Which two points could be used to calculate the slope of the line? Explain. See margin.

3. Can you assume that corresponding sides and corresponding angles of any two similar triangles are congruent? No; corresp. sides of ~ △ are not ≅ unless the scale factor of the △ is 1:1. Corresp. ∠s are ≅, however.

Skill Check ✓

Determine whether $\triangle CDE \sim \triangle FGH$.

4. no

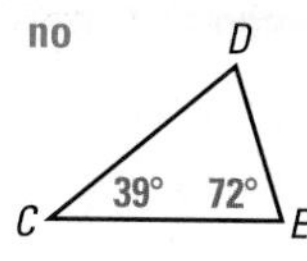

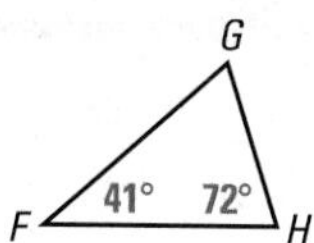

5. yes

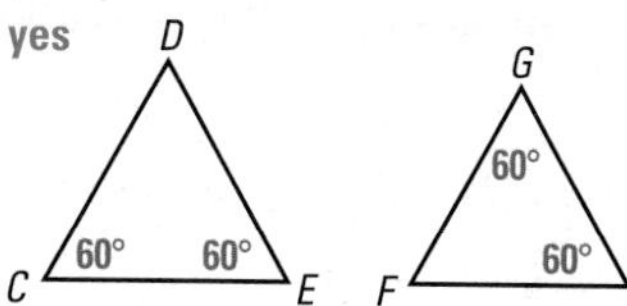

In the diagram shown $\triangle JKL \sim \triangle MNP$.

N, 8, M, 37°, P; J, 4, K, 3, 5, 53°, L

6. Find $m\angle J$, $m\angle N$, and $m\angle P$. 37°, 90°, 53°

7. Find MP and PN. 10, 6

8. Given that $\angle CAB \cong \angle CBD$, how do you know that $\triangle ABC \sim \triangle BDC$? Explain your answer.
By the Reflexive Prop. of Cong., $\angle C \cong \angle C$, so $\triangle ABC \sim \triangle BDC$ by the AA Similarity Post.

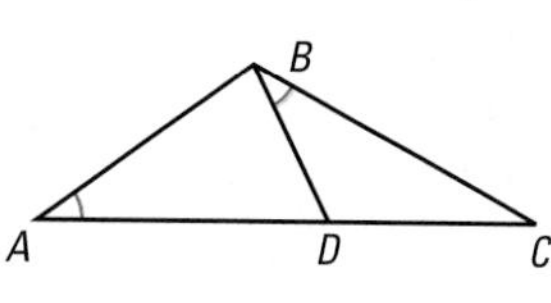

2. Any two of the points; as shown in Example 3 on p. 481, any two points on a line can be used to calculate the slope of the line.

9. $\angle J$ and $\angle F$, $\angle K$ and $\angle G$, $\angle L$ and $\angle H$, $\frac{JK}{FG} = \frac{KL}{GH} = \frac{JL}{FH}$

10. $\angle V$ and $\angle S$, $\angle T$ and $\angle T$, $\angle W$ and $\angle U$, $\frac{VT}{ST} = \frac{TW}{TU} = \frac{VW}{SU}$

11. $\angle L$ and $\angle Q$, $\angle M$ and $\angle P$, $\angle N$ and $\angle N$, $\frac{LM}{QP} = \frac{MN}{PN} = \frac{LN}{QN}$

Practice and Applications

Student Help

Extra Practice to help you master skills is on p. 818.

Using Similarity Statements The triangles shown are similar. List all the pairs of congruent angles and write the statement of proportionality. 9–11. See margin.

9.

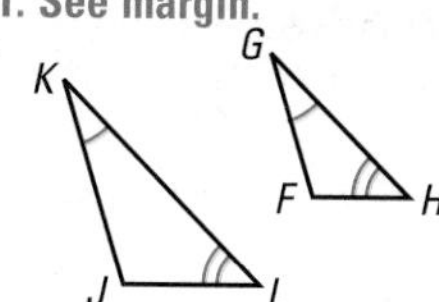

10.

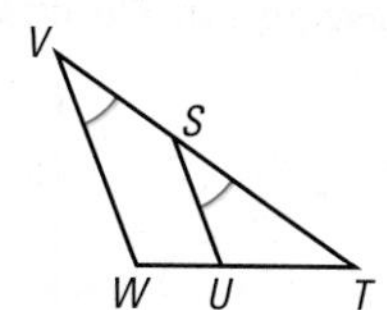

11.

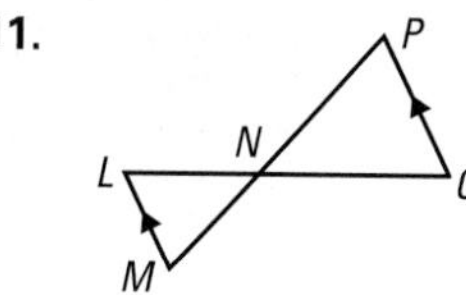

Student Help

Homework Help
Example 1: Exs. 9–17, 33–38
Example 2: Exs. 18–26
Example 3: Exs. 27–32
Example 4: Exs. 39–44, 53, 55, 56
Example 5: Exs. 45–47

Logical Reasoning Use the diagram to complete the following.

12. $\triangle PQR \sim$ __?__ $\triangle LMN$

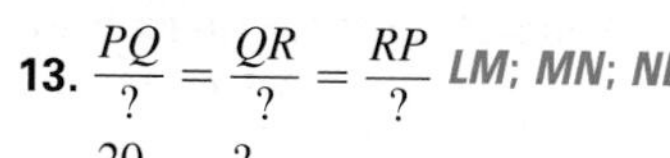

13. $\frac{PQ}{?} = \frac{QR}{?} = \frac{RP}{?}$ LM; MN; NL

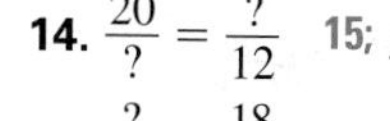

14. $\frac{20}{?} = \frac{?}{12}$ 15; y

15. $\frac{?}{20} = \frac{18}{?}$ 15; x

16. $y =$ __?__ 16

17. $x =$ __?__ 24

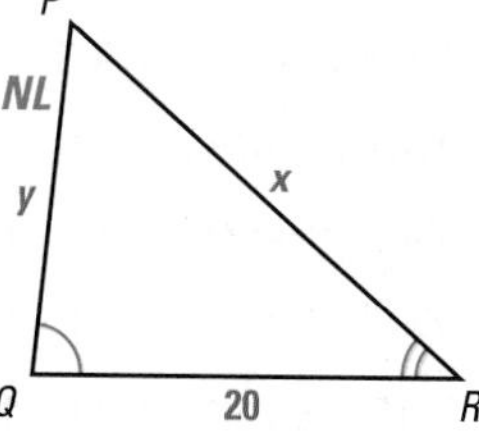

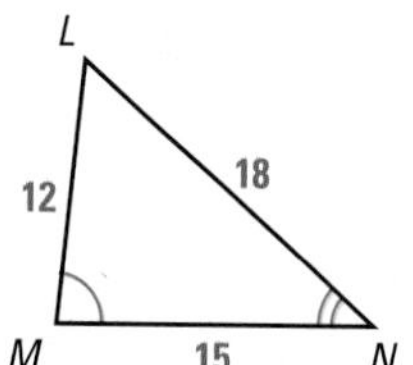

3 Apply

Assignment Guide

Basic
Day 1: pp. 483–485 Exs. 9–38
Day 2: pp. 485–487 Exs. 39–52, 57, 61–71

Average
Day 1: pp. 483–485 Exs. 9–38
Day 2: pp. 485–487 Exs. 39–53, 55–57, 61–71

Advanced
Day 1: pp. 483–485 Exs. 9–38
Day 2: pp. 485–487 Exs. 39–53, 55–71

Block Schedule
pp. 483–487 Exs. 9–38 (with 8.3)
pp. 485–487 Exs. 39–53, 55–57, 61–71 (with 8.5)

Exercise Levels

Level A: *Easier*
9–17

Level B: *More Difficult*
18–47, 50–54, 56, 57

Level C: *Most Difficult*
48, 49, 55, 58–60

✓ Homework Check

To quickly check student understanding of key concepts, go over the following exercises: Exs. 10, 14, 20, 28, 30, 36, 42, 46, 48. See also the Daily Homework Quiz:

- Blackline Master (*Chapter 8 Resource Book*, p. 65)
- Transparency (p. 59)

! COMMON ERROR
EXERCISES 23 AND 24 In problems such as these, where the triangles do not have the corresponding parts aligned, it is common for students to have trouble identifying the corresponding parts. To help students avoid this difficulty, have them copy the diagram and mark the corresponding angles in the triangles. Some students may also need to trace one of the triangles and rotate it so that the corresponding parts are more evident.

! COMMON ERROR
EXERCISE 26 In problems such as this, where the triangles are nested and/or rotated, it is common for student to have trouble identifying corresponding parts. To help students avoid this difficulty, have them trace both triangles on separate sheets of paper. They can then rotate one of the triangles until the corresponding parts of both triangles align and mark congruent any angles that are shared by both triangles in the original figure.

18. No; $m\angle C = 31°$ and $m\angle D = 47°$; the corresponding ∠s are not ≅.

22. No; $m\angle E = 94°$, $m\angle B = 94°$, and $m\angle A = 54°$; the corresponding ∠s are not ≅.

DETERMINING SIMILARITY Determine whether the triangles can be proved similar. If they are similar, write a similarity statement. If they are not similar, explain why.

18.

19.

yes; $\triangle PQR \sim \triangle WPV$

20.

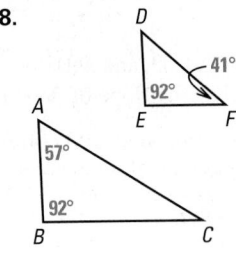

no; $\frac{RS}{MP} \neq \frac{ST}{PQ}$, so the lengths of corresponding sides are not proportional.

21.

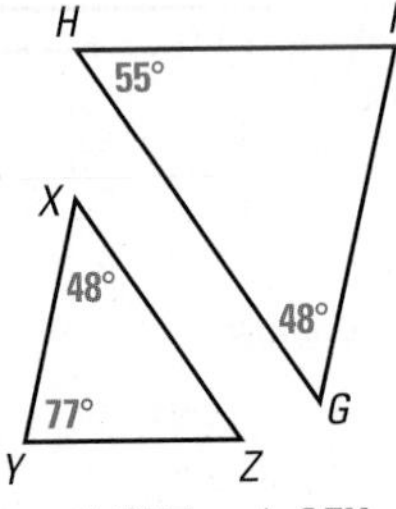

yes; $\triangle XYZ \sim \triangle GFH$

22.

See margin.

23.

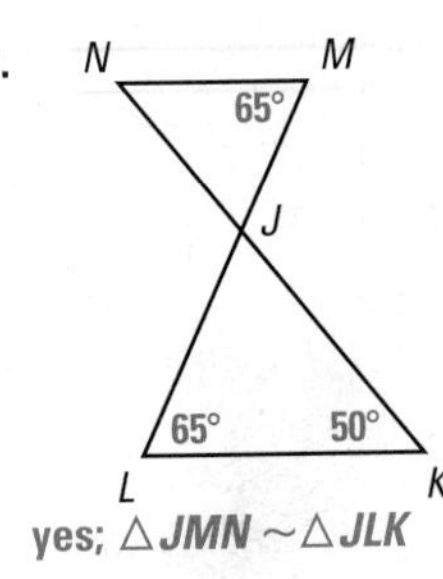

yes; $\triangle JMN \sim \triangle JLK$

24.

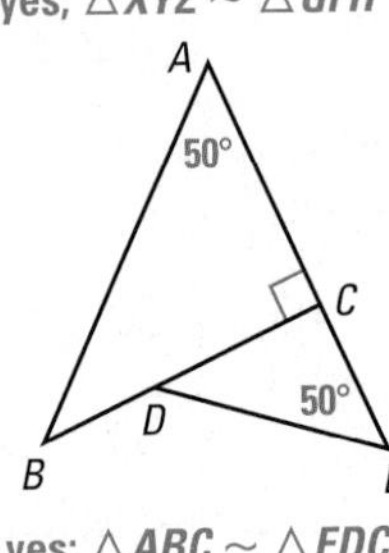

yes; $\triangle ABC \sim \triangle EDC$

25.

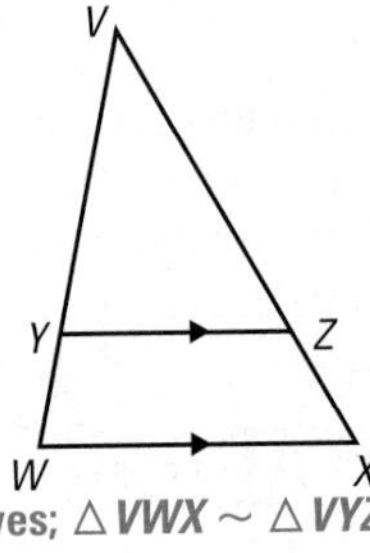

yes; $\triangle VWX \sim \triangle VYZ$

26.

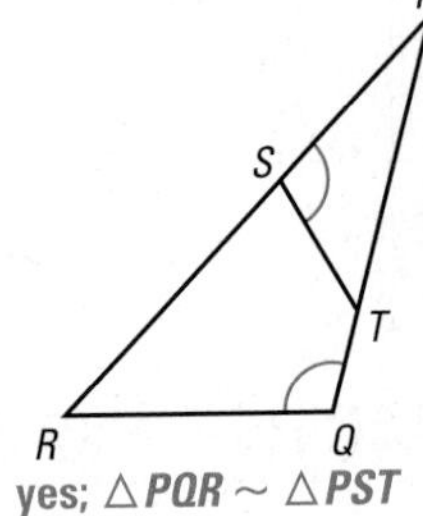

yes; $\triangle PQR \sim \triangle PST$

USING ALGEBRA Using the labeled points, find the slope of the line. To verify your answer, choose another pair of points and find the slope using the new points. Compare the results.

27. $-\frac{2}{5}$

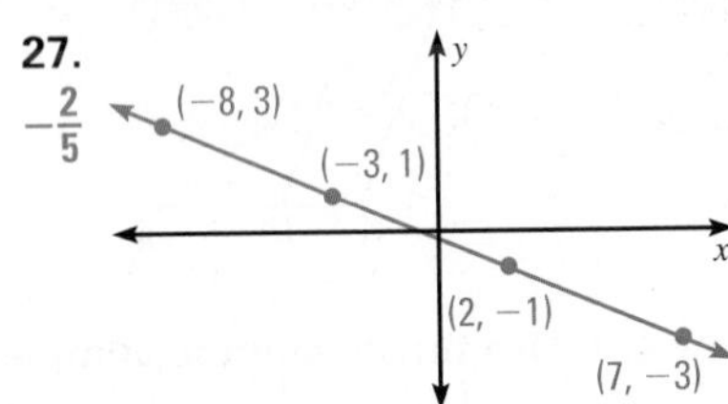

28. $\frac{1}{3}$

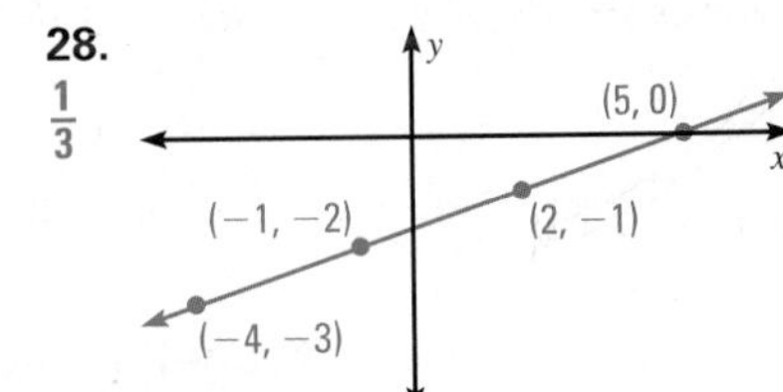

USING ALGEBRA Find coordinates for point E so that $\triangle OBC \sim \triangle ODE$.

29. $O(0, 0)$, $B(0, 3)$, $C(6, 0)$, $D(0, 5)$ (10, 0)

30. $O(0, 0)$, $B(0, 4)$, $C(3, 0)$, $D(0, 7)$ $\left(5\frac{1}{4}, 0\right)$

31. $O(0, 0)$, $B(0, 1)$, $C(5, 0)$, $D(0, 6)$ (30, 0)

32. $O(0, 0)$, $B(0, 8)$, $C(4, 0)$, $D(0, 9)$ $\left(4\frac{1}{2}, 0\right)$

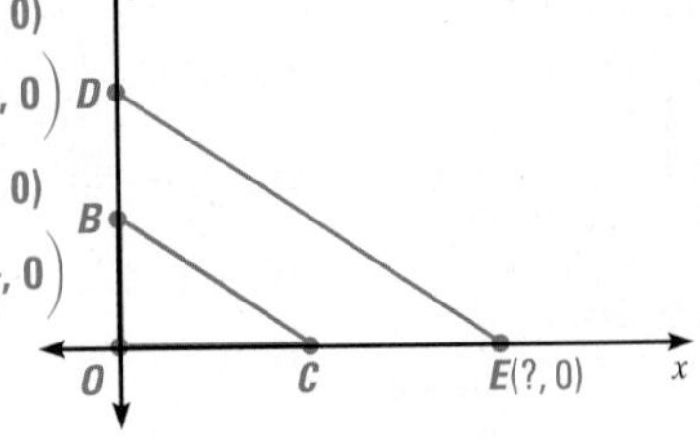

USING ALGEBRA You are given that *ABCD* is a trapezoid, *AB* = 8, *AE* = 6, *EC* = 15, and *DE* = 10.

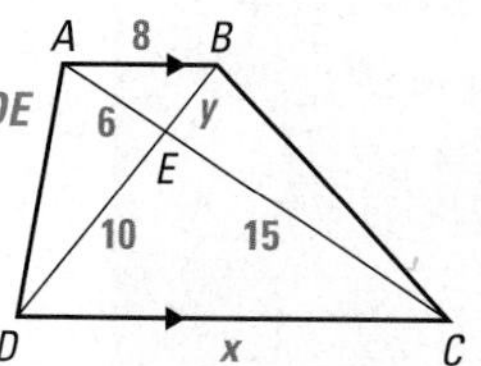

33. $\triangle ABE \sim \triangle$? CDE

34. $\frac{AB}{?} = \frac{AE}{?} = \frac{BE}{?}$ CD; CE; DE

35. $\frac{6}{?} = \frac{8}{?}$ $\frac{6}{15} = \frac{8}{x}$

36. $\frac{15}{?} = \frac{10}{?}$ $\frac{15}{6} = \frac{10}{y}$

37. $x =$? 20

38. $y =$? 4

STUDENT HELP

HOMEWORK HELP Visit our Web site www.mcdougallittell.com for help with problem solving in Exs. 39–44.

SIMILAR TRIANGLES The triangles are similar. Find the value of the variable.

39. 14

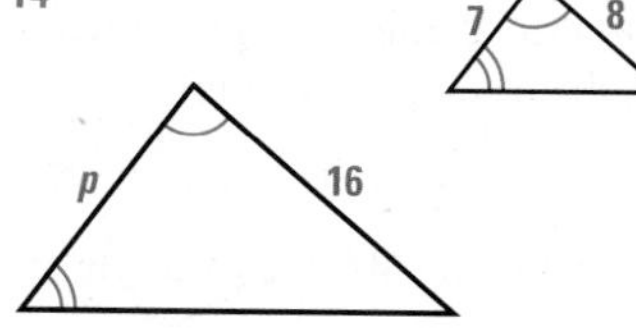

40. $2\frac{6}{11}$

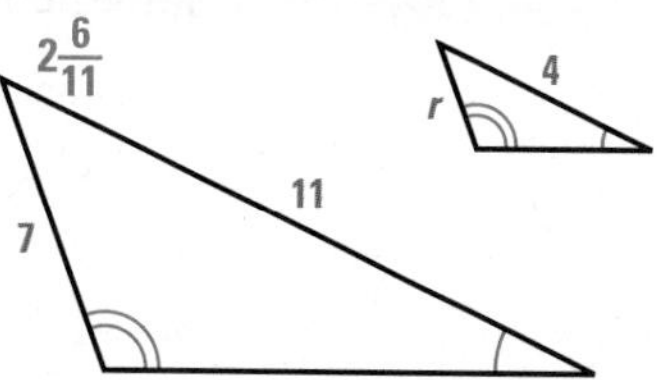

41. 27

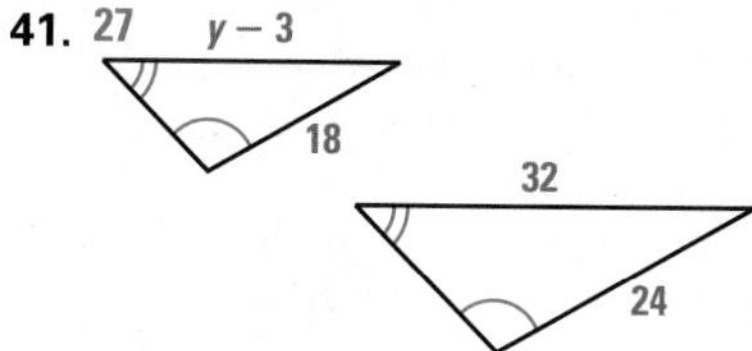

42. 36

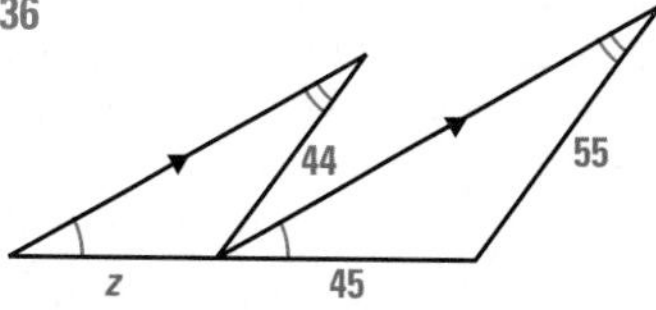

43. 100

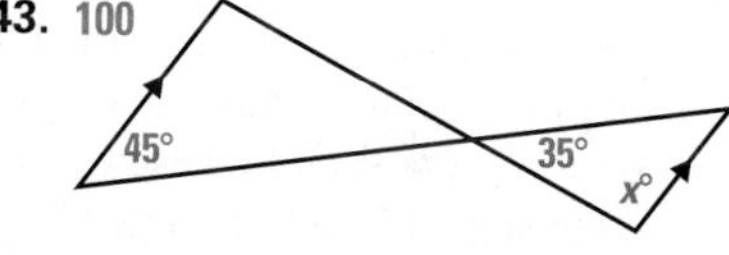

44. $13\frac{1}{2}$

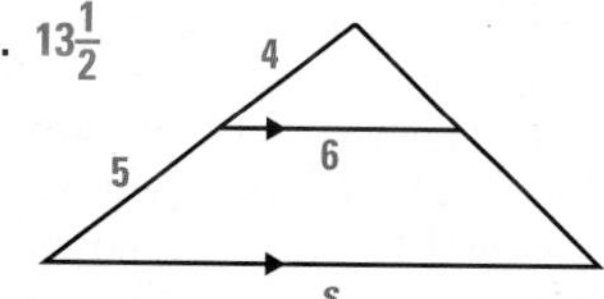

SIMILAR TRIANGLES The segments in blue are special segments in the similar triangles. Find the value of the variable.

45. 12

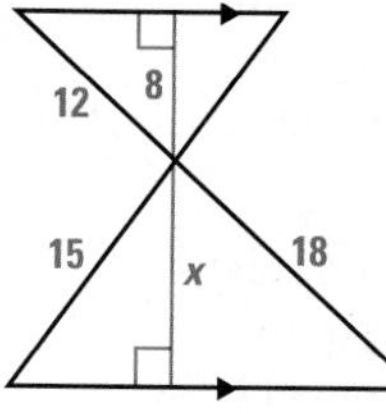

46. 80

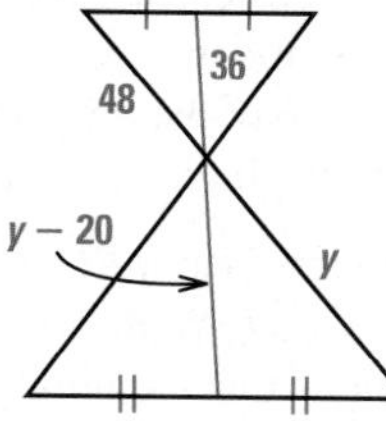

47. 25

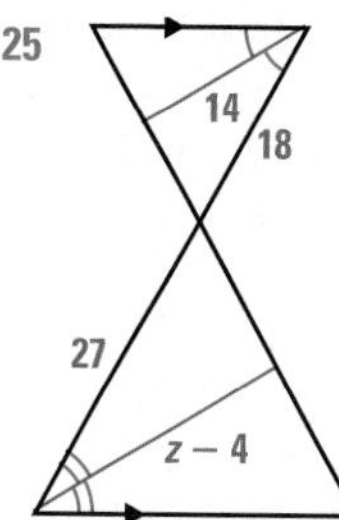

48. **PROOF** Write a paragraph or two-column proof.

GIVEN ▶ $\overline{KM} \perp \overline{JL}, \overline{JK} \perp \overline{KL}$

PROVE ▶ $\triangle JKL \sim \triangle JMK$

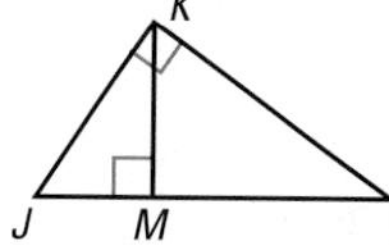

48. Since $\overline{KM} \perp \overline{JL}$ and $\overline{JK} \perp \overline{KL}$, $\angle JMK$ and $\angle JKL$ are right ∠s. Since all right ∠s are ≅, $\angle JMK \cong \angle JKL$. By the Reflexive Prop. of Cong., $\angle J \cong \angle J$, so $\triangle JKL \sim \triangle JMK$ by the AA Similarity Post.

STUDENT HELP NOTES

Homework Help Students can find help for Exs. 39–44 at **www.mcdougallittell.com.** The information can be printed out for students who don't have access to the Internet.

CONCEPT QUESTION

EXERCISES 45–47 Ask students to identify each type of special segment shown in these exercises. Ex. 45: altitude; Ex. 46: median; Ex. 47: angle bisector

MATHEMATICAL REASONING

EXERCISE 51 Ask students what they can conclude by showing that this statement is false. All equilateral triangles are similar. Explain that this statement is the *negation* of the statement given in the exercise.

STUDENT HELP NOTES

Software Help Instructions for several software packages are available in blackline format in the *Chapter 8 Resource Book*, p. 54 and at **www.mcdougallittell.com.**

TEACHING TIPS

EXERCISE 56 Students will need some time at school to do this exercise. You might turn this exercise into a class activity. Divide the class into small groups and give each group a pole of different length. They can then compare their results to see that the height of the building is independent of the length of the pole.

49, 55. See Additional Answers beginning on page AA1.

ADDITIONAL PRACTICE AND RETEACHING

For Lesson 8.4:

- Practice Levels A, B, and C (*Chapter 8 Resource Book*, p. 55)
- Reteaching with Practice (*Chapter 8 Resource Book*, p. 58)
- See Lesson 8.4 of the *Personal Student Tutor*

For more Mixed Review:

- Search the *Test and Practice Generator* for key words or specific lessons.

49. **PROOF** Write a paragraph proof or a two-column proof. The National Humanities Center is located in Research Triangle Park in North Carolina. Some of its windows consist of nested right triangles, as shown in the diagram. Prove that $\triangle ABE \sim \triangle CDE$. See margin.

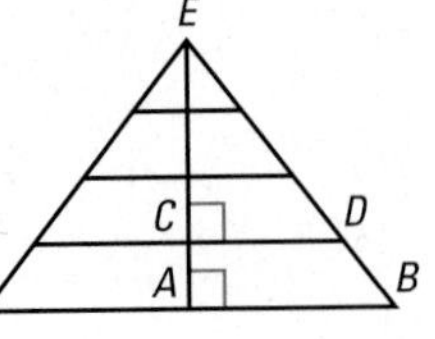

GIVEN ▶ $\angle ECD$ is a right angle, $\angle EAB$ is a right angle.

PROVE ▶ $\triangle ABE \sim \triangle CDE$

51. False; all △ of any 2 equilateral △ are ≅, so the △ are ~ by the AA Similarity Post. (Note also, that if one △ has sides of length x and the other has sides of length y, then the ratio of any two side lengths is $\frac{x}{y}$. Then all corresp. side lengths are in proportion, so the def. of ~ △ can also be used to show that any 2 equilateral △ are ~.)

LOGICAL REASONING In Exercises 50–52, decide whether the statement is *true* or *false*. Explain your reasoning.

50. If an acute angle of a right triangle is congruent to an acute angle of another right triangle, then the triangles are similar. True; all right △ are ≅, so the △ are ~ by the AA Similarity Post.

51. Some equilateral triangles are not similar.

52. All isosceles triangles with a 40° vertex angle are similar. See margin.

53. **ICE HOCKEY** A hockey player passes the puck to a teammate by bouncing the puck off the wall of the rink as shown. From physics, the angles that the path of the puck makes with the wall are congruent. How far from the wall will the pass be picked up by his teammate? 1.5 m

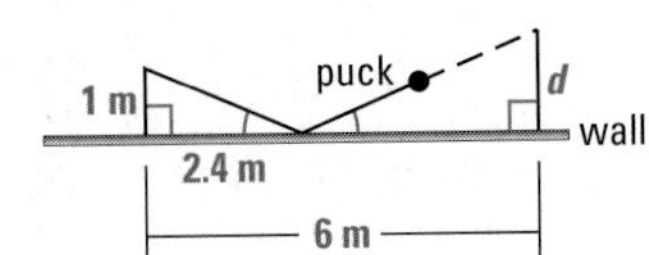

STUDENT HELP

INTERNET

SOFTWARE HELP
Visit our Web site www.mcdougallittell.com to see instructions for several software applications.

54. **TECHNOLOGY** Use geometry software to verify that any two points on a line can be used to calculate the slope of the line. Draw a line k with a negative slope in a coordinate plane. Draw two right triangles of different size whose hypotenuses lie along line k and whose other sides are parallel to the x- and y-axes. Calculate the slope of each triangle by finding the ratio of the vertical side length to the horizontal side length. Are the slopes equal? yes

52. True; since the vertex ∠ of each isosceles △ has measure 40°, the measure of each base ∠ is $\frac{1}{2}(180° - 40°) = 70°$. Then the △ are ~ by the AA Similarity Post.

55. **THE GREAT PYRAMID** The Greek mathematician Thales (640–546 B.C.) calculated the height of the Great Pyramid in Egypt by placing a rod at the tip of the pyramid's shadow and using similar triangles.

P
Not drawn to scale
S
4 ft
Q
R
T
780 ft
6.5 ft

In the figure, $\overline{PQ} \perp \overline{QT}$, $\overline{SR} \perp \overline{QT}$, and $\overline{PR} \parallel \overline{ST}$. Write a paragraph proof to show that the height of the pyramid is 480 feet. See margin.

56. **ESTIMATING HEIGHT** On a sunny day, use a rod or pole to estimate the height of your school building. Use the method that Thales used to estimate the height of the Great Pyramid in Exercise 55. Answers will vary.

Test Preparation

57. a. Right △s ABX and DCX are ≅ and vertical △s AXB and DXC are ≅. Then $\triangle ABX \sim \triangle DCX$ by the AA Similarity Post.

57. MULTI-STEP PROBLEM Use the following information. Going from his own house to Raul's house, Mark drives due south one mile, due east three miles, and due south again three miles. What is the distance between the two houses as the crow flies?

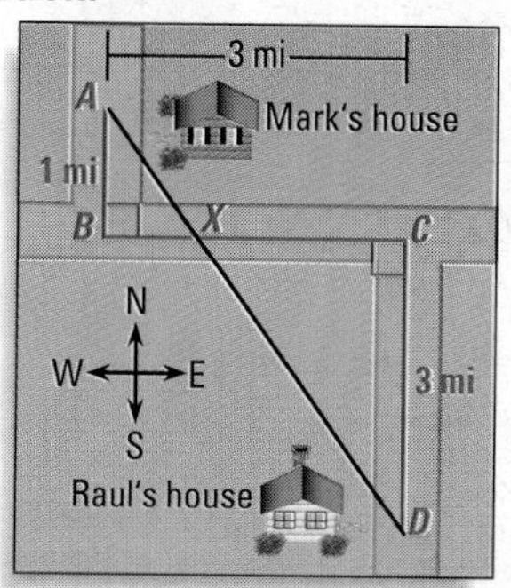

a. Explain how to prove that $\triangle ABX \sim \triangle DCX$.

b. Use corresponding side lengths of the triangles to calculate BX. $\frac{3}{4}$ mi

c. Use the Pythagorean Theorem to calculate AX, and then DX. Then find AD. 1.25 mi; 3.75 mi; 5 mi

d. *Writing* Using the properties of rectangles, explain a way that a point E could be added to the diagram so that $\overline{AD}$ would be the hypotenuse of $\triangle AED$, and $\overline{AE}$ and $\overline{ED}$ would be its legs of known length. See margin.

★ Challenge

HUMAN VISION In Exercises 58–60, use the following information. The diagram shows how similar triangles relate to human vision. An image similar to a viewed object appears on the retina. The actual height of the object h is proportional to the size of the image as it appears on the retina r. In the same manner, the distances from the object to the lens of the eye d and from the lens to the retina, 25 mm in the diagram, are also proportional.

58. Write a proportion that relates r, d, h, and 25 mm. *Sample answer:* $\frac{d}{25} = \frac{h}{r}$

59. An object that is 10 meters away appears on the retina as 1 mm tall. Find the height of the object. 400 mm

60. An object that is 1 meter tall appears on the retina as 1 mm tall. How far away is the object? 25 m

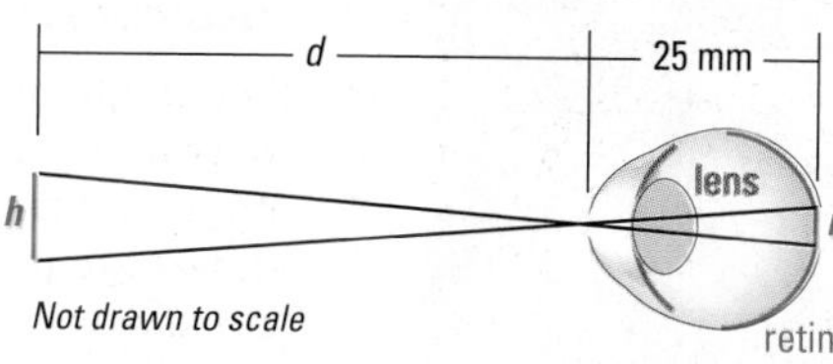

Not drawn to scale

EXTRA CHALLENGE

www.mcdougallittell.com

MIXED REVIEW

57. d. *Sample answer:* Construct a line ∥ to $\overline{BC}$ through A and extend $\overline{DC}$ up to this line to intersect it at E. Since $\overline{AE} \parallel \overline{BC}$, $\overline{CE} \parallel \overline{AB}$, and $\angle B$ is a right ∠, $ABCE$ is a rectangle. Thus $AB = CE = 1$ mi and $BC = AE = 3$ mi. Since $\angle E$ is a right ∠, $\triangle AED$ is a right triangle with hypotenuse $\overline{AD}$ and legs of 1 mi and 3 mi.

61. **USING THE DISTANCE FORMULA** Find the distance between the points $A(-17, 12)$ and $B(14, -21)$. (Review 1.3) $5\sqrt{82}$

TRIANGLE MIDSEGMENTS M, N, and P are the midpoints of the sides of $\triangle JKL$. Complete the statement. (Review 5.4 for 8.5)

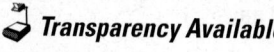

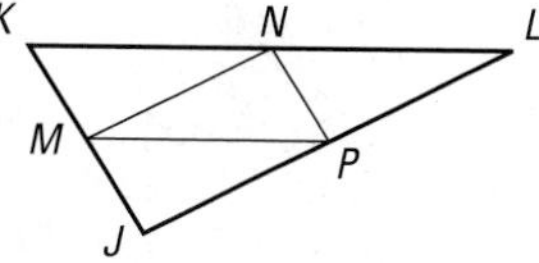

62. $\overline{NP} \parallel$ __?__ $\overline{KJ}$

63. If $NP = 23$, then $KJ =$ __?__. 46

64. If $KN = 16$, then $MP =$ __?__. 16

65. If $JL = 24$, then $MN =$ __?__. 12

PROPORTIONS Solve the proportion. (Review 8.1)

66. $\frac{x}{12} = \frac{3}{8}$ $\frac{9}{2}$

67. $\frac{3}{y} = \frac{12}{32}$ 8

68. $\frac{17}{x} = \frac{11}{33}$ 51

69. $\frac{34}{11} = \frac{x+6}{3}$ $\frac{36}{11}$

70. $\frac{23}{24} = \frac{x}{72}$ 69

71. $\frac{8}{x} = \frac{x}{32}$ −16, 16

4 ASSESS

DAILY HOMEWORK QUIZ

Transparency Available

Use the diagram for Exercises 1–5.

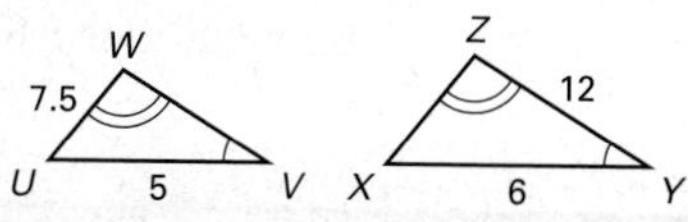

1. $\triangle UVW \sim \triangle$ ____ XYZ
2. What is the scale factor of $\triangle UVW$ to $\triangle XYZ$? $\frac{5}{6}$
3. What is VW? 10
4. What is XZ? 9
5. If $m\angle U = 50°$ and $m\angle Y = 30°$, what is $m\angle Z$? 100°

EXTRA CHALLENGE NOTE

Challenge problems for Lesson 8.4 are available in **blackline** format in the *Chapter 8 Resource Book*, p. 62 and at **www.mcdougallittell.com**.

ADDITIONAL TEST PREPARATION

1. **WRITING** Explain how to use shadows to indirectly measure the height of a tall object. Illustrate your explanation with a sketch. *Sample answer:* Erect a pole perpendicular to the ground. Measure the height of the pole and the length of its shadow. Then measure the length of the shadow of the tall object. Use similar triangles to find the height of the tall object. Check students' sketches.

1 PLAN

PACING
Basic: 2 days
Average: 2 days
Advanced: 2 days
Block Schedule: 0.5 block with 8.4
0.5 block with 8.6

LESSON OPENER ACTIVITY
An alternative way to approach Lesson 8.5 is to use the Activity Lesson Opener:

- Blackline Master (*Chapter 8 Resource Book*, p. 66)
- Transparency (p. 51)

MEETING INDIVIDUAL NEEDS
- ***Chapter 8 Resource Book***
  Prerequisite Skills Review (p. 5)
  Practice Level A (p. 70)
  Practice Level B (p. 71)
  Practice Level C (p. 72)
  Reteaching with Practice (p. 73)
  Absent Student Catch-Up (p. 75)
  Challenge (p. 79)
- ***Resources in Spanish***
- ***Personal Student Tutor***

NEW-TEACHER SUPPORT
See the Tips for New Teachers on pp. 1–2 of the *Chapter 8 Resource Book* for additional notes about Lesson 8.5.

WARM-UP EXERCISES
Transparency Available
In the figure below, find a pair of similar triangles and use them to complete Exercises 1–3.

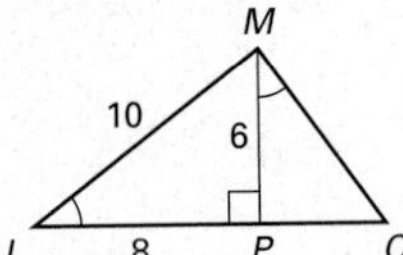

1. Write the statement of similarity for the two triangles. **$\triangle LMP \sim \triangle MQP$**
2. Explain why the two triangles are similar. **by the AA Similarity Postulate**
3. Find MQ. **7.5**

8.5 Proving Triangles are Similar

What you should learn

GOAL 1 Use similarity theorems to prove that two triangles are similar.

GOAL 2 Use similar triangles to solve **real-life** problems, such as finding the height of a climbing wall in **Example 5**.

Why you should learn it

▼ To solve **real-life** problems, such as estimating the height of the Unisphere in **Ex. 29**.

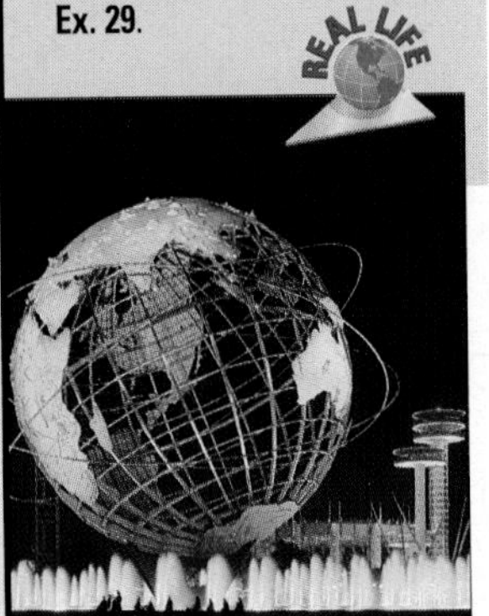

GOAL 1 USING SIMILARITY THEOREMS

In this lesson, you will study two additional ways to prove that two triangles are similar: the Side-Side-Side (SSS) Similarity Theorem and the Side-Angle-Side (SAS) Similarity Theorem. The first theorem is proved in Example 1 and you are asked to prove the second theorem in Exercise 31.

THEOREMS

THEOREM 8.2 ***Side-Side-Side (SSS) Similarity Theorem***

If the corresponding sides of two triangles are proportional, then the triangles are similar.

If $\frac{AB}{PQ} = \frac{BC}{QR} = \frac{CA}{RP}$,

then $\triangle ABC \sim \triangle PQR$.

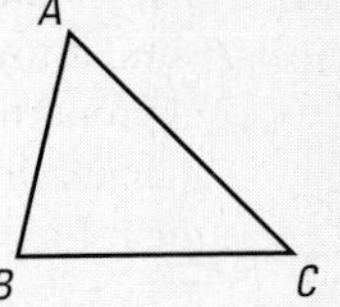

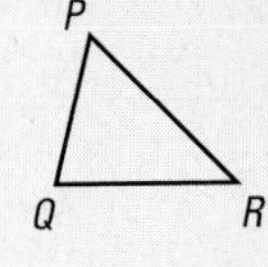

THEOREM 8.3 ***Side-Angle-Side (SAS) Similarity Theorem***

If an angle of one triangle is congruent to an angle of a second triangle and the lengths of the sides including these angles are proportional, then the triangles are similar.

If $\angle X \cong \angle M$ and $\frac{ZX}{PM} = \frac{XY}{MN}$,

then $\triangle XYZ \sim \triangle MNP$.

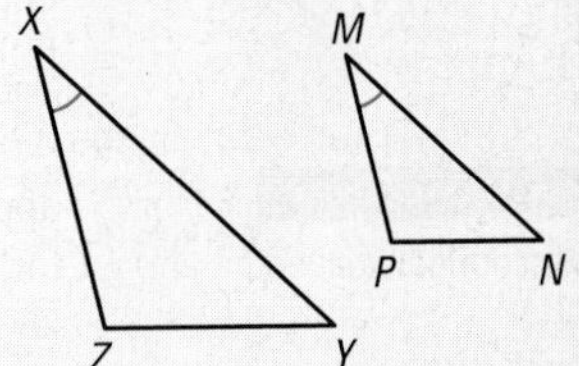

EXAMPLE 1 ***Proof of Theorem 8.2***

GIVEN ▶ $\frac{RS}{LM} = \frac{ST}{MN} = \frac{TR}{NL}$

PROVE ▶ $\triangle RST \sim \triangle LMN$

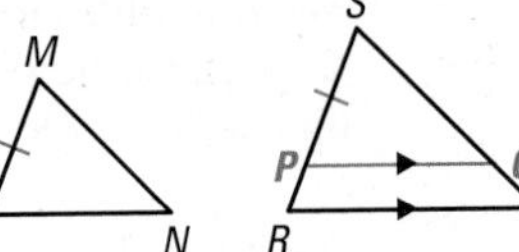

SOLUTION

Paragraph Proof Locate P on $\overline{RS}$ so that $PS = LM$. Draw $\overline{PQ}$ so that $\overline{PQ} \parallel \overline{RT}$. Then $\triangle RST \sim \triangle PSQ$, by the AA Similarity Postulate, and $\frac{RS}{PS} = \frac{ST}{SQ} = \frac{TR}{QP}$. Because $PS = LM$, you can substitute in the given proportion and find that $SQ = MN$ and $QP = NL$. By the SSS Congruence Theorem, it follows that $\triangle PSQ \cong \triangle LMN$. Finally, use the definition of congruent triangles and the AA Similarity Postulate to conclude that $\triangle RST \sim \triangle LMN$.

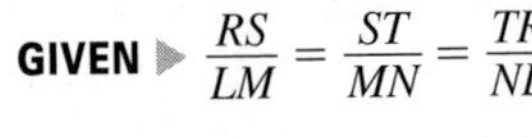

CALIFORNIA STANDARDS AND ASSESSMENT
CA Standards: 5, 16
SAT9 Task 1: Objs. 1, 22
SAT9 Task 2: Objs. 1, 24

EXAMPLE 2 Using the SSS Similarity Theorem

Which of the following three triangles are similar?

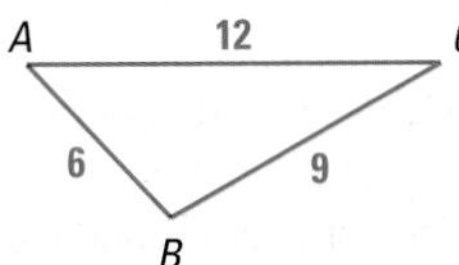

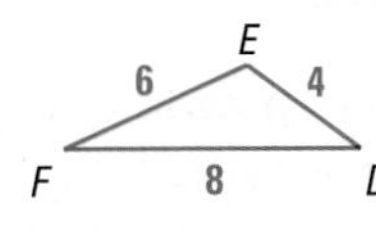

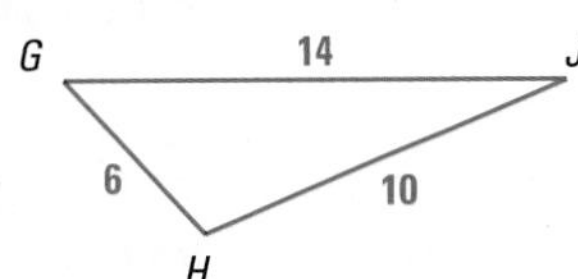

STUDENT HELP

Study Tip
Note that when using the SSS Similarity Theorem it is useful to compare the shortest sides, the longest sides, and then the remaining sides.

SOLUTION

To decide which, if any, of the triangles are similar, you need to consider the ratios of the lengths of corresponding sides.

Ratios of Side Lengths of $\triangle ABC$ and $\triangle DEF$

$\frac{AB}{DE} = \frac{6}{4} = \frac{3}{2}$, Shortest sides

$\frac{CA}{FD} = \frac{12}{8} = \frac{3}{2}$, Longest sides

$\frac{BC}{EF} = \frac{9}{6} = \frac{3}{2}$ Remaining sides

▶ Because all of the ratios are equal, $\triangle ABC \sim \triangle DEF$.

Ratios of Side Lengths of $\triangle ABC$ and $\triangle GHJ$

$\frac{AB}{GH} = \frac{6}{6} = 1$, Shortest sides

$\frac{CA}{JG} = \frac{12}{14} = \frac{6}{7}$, Longest sides

$\frac{BC}{HJ} = \frac{9}{10}$ Remaining sides

▶ Because the ratios are not equal, $\triangle ABC$ and $\triangle GHJ$ are not similar.

Since $\triangle ABC$ is similar to $\triangle DEF$ and $\triangle ABC$ is not similar to $\triangle GHJ$, $\triangle DEF$ is not similar to $\triangle GHJ$.

EXAMPLE 3 Using the SAS Similarity Theorem

Use the given lengths to prove that $\triangle RST \sim \triangle PSQ$.

SOLUTION

GIVEN ▶ $SP = 4$, $PR = 12$, $SQ = 5$, $QT = 15$

PROVE ▶ $\triangle RST \sim \triangle PSQ$

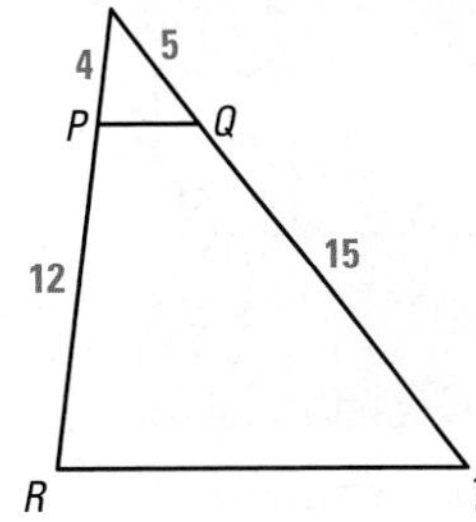

Paragraph Proof Use the SAS Similarity Theorem. Begin by finding the ratios of the lengths of the corresponding sides.

$$\frac{SR}{SP} = \frac{SP + PR}{SP} = \frac{4 + 12}{4} = \frac{16}{4} = 4$$

$$\frac{ST}{SQ} = \frac{SQ + QT}{SQ} = \frac{5 + 15}{5} = \frac{20}{5} = 4$$

So, the side lengths $\overline{SR}$ and $\overline{ST}$ are proportional to the corresponding side lengths of $\triangle PSQ$. Because $\angle S$ is the included angle in both triangles, use the SAS Similarity Theorem to conclude that $\triangle RST \sim \triangle PSQ$.

2 TEACH

EXTRA EXAMPLE 1
Write a paragraph proof.
Given: $\triangle AEC \sim \triangle GFH$; $DC = FH$
Prove: $\triangle BCD \cong \triangle GHF$

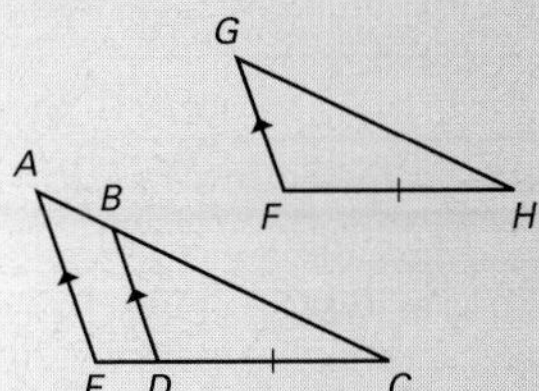

Since $\triangle AEC \sim \triangle GFH$, $\angle C \cong \angle H$ and $\angle E \cong \angle F$. Also, since $\overline{BD} \parallel \overline{AE}$, $\angle BDC \cong \angle E$ by the Corresponding Angles Postulate. By the Trans. Prop. of Cong., $\angle BDC \cong \angle F$. It is given that $DC = FH$; therefore, $\triangle BCD \cong \triangle GHF$ by the ASA Congruence Post.

EXTRA EXAMPLE 2
Which of the following three triangles are similar?
$\triangle KML$ and $\triangle QSR$

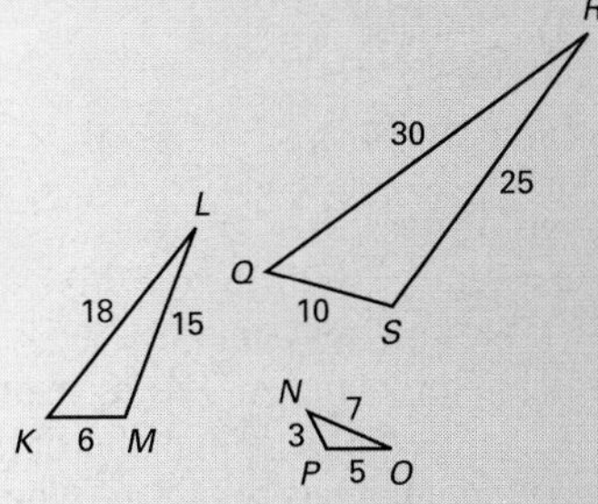

EXTRA EXAMPLE 3
In the figure $AC = 6$, $AD = 10$, $BC = 9$, and $BE = 15$.

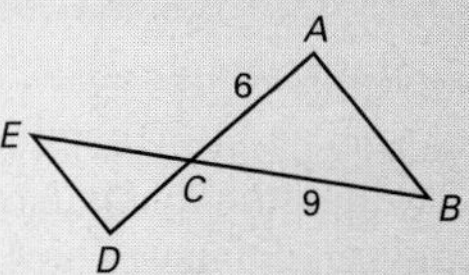

Describe how to prove that $\triangle ACB$ is similar to $\triangle DCE$.
Find CD and EC and show that corresponding sides are proportional. Then use the SAS Similarity Theorem with vertical angles $\angle ACB$ and $\angle DCE$.

Checkpoint Exercises for Examples 1–3 on next page.

CHECKPOINT EXERCISES

For use after Examples 1–3:

In Exercises 1–3, draw the given triangles roughly to scale. If possible, name theorems that can be used to prove the triangles are similar. **Check students' drawings.**

1. In $\triangle ABC$, $AC = 5$, $BC = 20$, and $m\angle C = 90°$. In $\triangle DEF$, $DF = 3$, $EF = 12$, and $m\angle F = 90°$. **SAS Similarity Theorem**
2. In $\triangle XYZ$, $XY = 5$, $YZ = 4$, and $m\angle Z = 50°$. In $\triangle UVW$, $UV = 10$, $VW = 8$, and $m\angle W = 50°$. **not possible**
3. In $\triangle PQR$, $PQ = 22.5$, $QR = 12$, and $PR = 13.5$. In $\triangle STU$, $ST = 30$, $TU = 16$, and $SU = 18$. **SSS Similarity Theorem**

EXTRA EXAMPLE 4

A pantograph is used to draw an enlargement of a daisy. In the diagram, $\frac{PB}{PD} = \frac{PA}{PC}$.

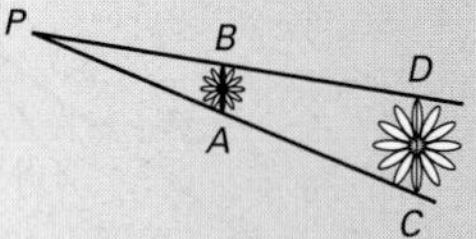

a. Why is $\triangle PBA \sim \triangle PDC$? **by the SAS Similarity Thm.**

b. In the diagram, $PA = 8$ in. and $AC = 8$ in. The diameter of the original daisy is 1.8 in. What is the diameter of the daisy in the enlargement? **3.6 in.**

CHECKPOINT EXERCISES

For use after Example 4:

1. In Extra Example 4, suppose you wanted the diameter of the enlarged daisy to be 4 in. What would the ratio $\frac{PA}{PC}$ have to be? $\frac{9}{20}$

GOAL 2 USING SIMILAR TRIANGLES IN REAL LIFE

EXAMPLE 4 *Using a Pantograph*

SCALE DRAWING As you move the tracing pin of a *pantograph* along a figure, the pencil attached to the far end draws an enlargement. As the pantograph expands and contracts, the three brads and the tracing pin always form the vertices of a parallelogram. The ratio of PR to PT is always equal to the ratio of PQ to PS. Also, the suction cup, the tracing pin, and the pencil remain collinear.

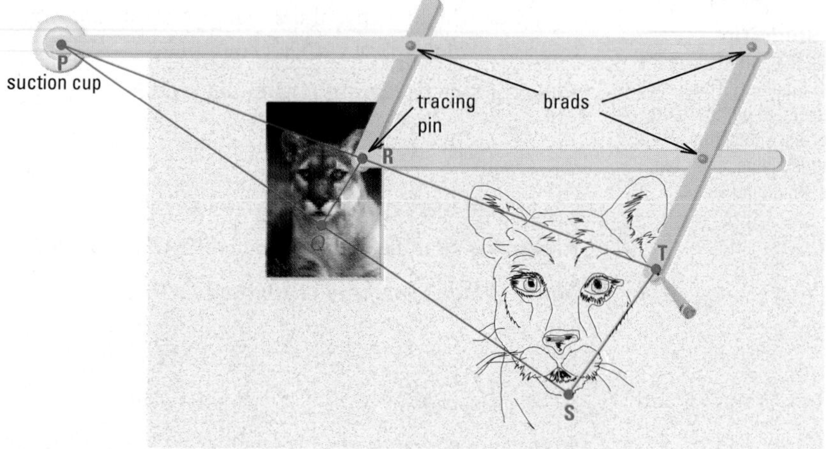

a. How can you show that $\triangle PRQ \sim \triangle PTS$?

b. In the diagram, PR is 10 inches and RT is 10 inches. The length of the cat, RQ, in the original print is 2.4 inches. Find the length TS in the enlargement.

SOLUTION

a. You know that $\frac{PR}{PT} = \frac{PQ}{PS}$. Because $\angle P \cong \angle P$, you can apply the SAS Similarity Theorem to conclude that $\triangle PRQ \sim \triangle PTS$.

b. Because the triangles are similar, you can set up a proportion to find the length of the cat in the enlarged drawing.

$\frac{PR}{PT} = \frac{RQ}{TS}$ **Write proportion.**

$\frac{10}{20} = \frac{2.4}{TS}$ **Substitute.**

$TS = 4.8$ **Solve for *TS*.**

▶ So, the length of the cat in the enlarged drawing is 4.8 inches.

FOCUS ON APPLICATIONS

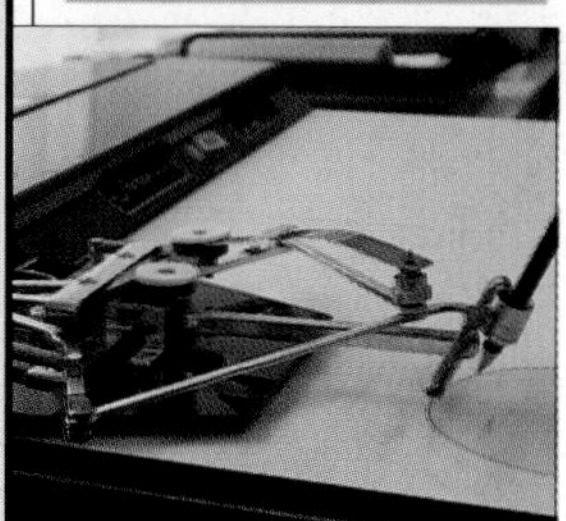

PANTOGRAPH Before photocopiers, people used pantographs to make enlargements. As the tracing pin is guided over the figure, the pencil draws an enlargement.

Similar triangles can be used to find distances that are difficult to measure directly. One technique is called *Thales' shadow method* (page 486), named after the Greek geometer Thales who used it to calculate the height of the Great Pyramid.

FOCUS ON APPLICATIONS

ROCK CLIMBING Interest in rock climbing appears to be growing. From 1988 to 1998, over 700 indoor rock climbing gyms opened in the United States.

STUDENT HELP

HOMEWORK HELP Visit our Web site www.mcdougallittell.com for extra examples.

EXAMPLE 5 *Finding Distance Indirectly*

ROCK CLIMBING You are at an indoor climbing wall. To estimate the height of the wall, you place a mirror on the floor 85 feet from the base of the wall. Then you walk backward until you can see the top of the wall centered in the mirror. You are 6.5 feet from the mirror and your eyes are 5 feet above the ground. Use similar triangles to estimate the height of the wall.

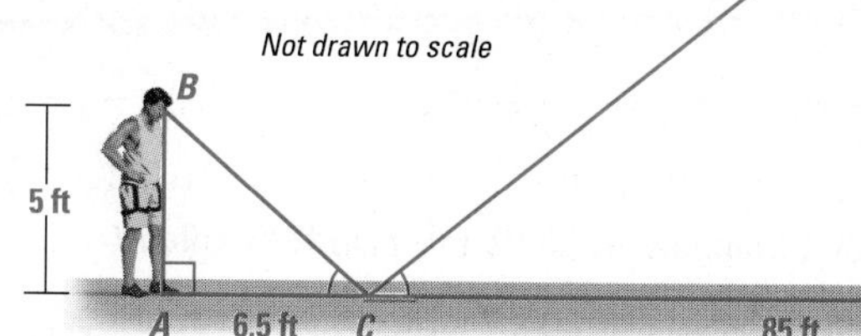

SOLUTION

Due to the reflective property of mirrors, you can reason that $\angle ACB \cong \angle ECD$. Using the fact that $\triangle ABC$ and $\triangle EDC$ are right triangles, you can apply the AA Similarity Postulate to conclude that these two triangles are similar.

$\frac{DE}{BA} = \frac{EC}{AC}$ **Ratios of lengths of corresponding sides are equal.**

$\frac{DE}{5} = \frac{85}{6.5}$ **Substitute.**

$65.38 \approx DE$ **Multiply each side by 5 and simplify.**

▶ So, the height of the wall is about 65 feet.

EXAMPLE 6 *Finding Distance Indirectly*

INDIRECT MEASUREMENT To measure the width of a river, you use a surveying technique, as shown in the diagram. Use the given lengths (measured in feet) to find RQ.

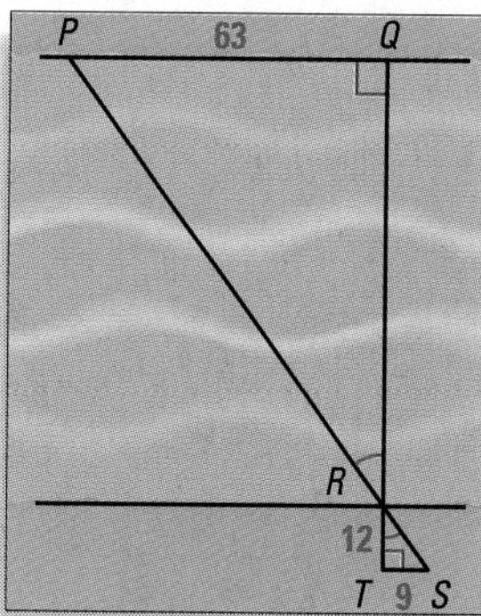

SOLUTION

By the AA Similarity Postulate, $\triangle PQR \sim \triangle STR$.

$\frac{RQ}{RT} = \frac{PQ}{ST}$ **Write proportion.**

$\frac{RQ}{12} = \frac{63}{9}$ **Substitute.**

$RQ = 12 \cdot 7$ **Multiply each side by 12.**

$RQ = 84$ **Simplify.**

▶ So, the river is 84 feet wide.

EXTRA EXAMPLE 5

At another indoor climbing wall, a person whose eyes are 6 ft from the floor places a mirror on the floor 60 ft from the base of the wall. They then walk backwards 5 ft before seeing the top of the wall in the center of the mirror. Use similar triangles to estimate the height of this wall. **72 ft**

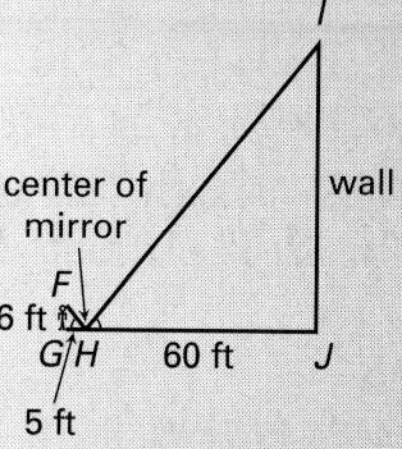

EXTRA EXAMPLE 6

Use the given lengths to find the width LM of the river below. **26.25 ft**

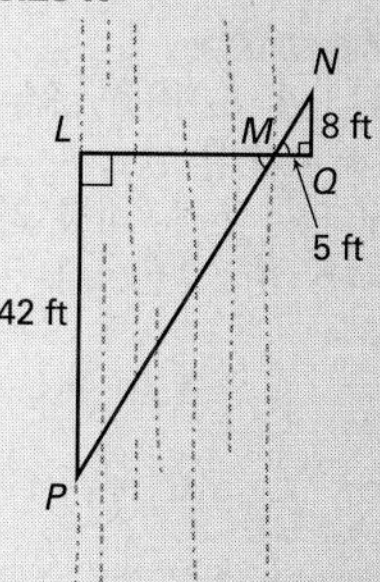

CHECKPOINT EXERCISES

For use after Examples 5 and 6:

1. Refer to Example 5. Suppose another person whose eyes are 5.5 ft from the floor places the mirror 50 ft from the base of this wall. If the wall is 65 ft high, how far from the mirror will the person need to stand to see the top of the wall centered in the mirror? **about 4.2 ft**

CLOSURE QUESTION

State the two similarity theorems presented in this lesson.

Sample answer: **The SSS Similarity Theorem states that two triangles are similar if their corresponding sides are proportional. The SAS Similarity Theorem states that two triangles are similar if one angle is congruent, and the sides including these angles are proportional.**

ASSIGNMENT GUIDE

BASIC
Day 1: pp. 492–494 Exs. 6–18 even, 19–28, 30
Day 2: pp. 492–496 Exs. 7–17 odd, 31–37, 39–47, Quiz 2 Exs. 1–7

AVERAGE
Day 1: pp. 492–494 Exs. 6–18 even, 19–28, 30
Day 2: pp. 492–496 Exs. 7–17 odd, 29, 31–37, 39–47, Quiz 2 Exs. 1–7

ADVANCED
Day 1: pp. 492–494 Exs. 6–18 even, 19–28, 30
Day 2: pp. 492–496 Exs. 7–17 odd, 29, 31–38, 39–47, Quiz 2 Exs. 1–7

BLOCK SCHEDULE
pp. 492–494 Exs. 6–18 even, 19–28, 30 (with 8.4)
pp. 492–496 Exs. 7–17 odd, 29, 31–37, 39–47, Quiz 2 Exs. 1–7 (with 8.6)

EXERCISE LEVELS

Level A: ***Easier***
6–8
Level B: ***More Difficult***
9–29, 32–37
Level C: ***Most Difficult***
30, 31, 38

✔ HOMEWORK CHECK

To quickly check student understanding of key concepts, go over the following exercises: Exs. 6, 12, 16, 20, 24, 28, 30, 32. See also the Daily Homework Quiz:

- Blackline Master (*Chapter 8 Resource Book*, p. 83)
- Transparency (p. 60)

GUIDED PRACTICE

Vocabulary Check ✔

1. You want to prove that $\triangle FHG$ is similar to $\triangle RXS$ by the SSS Similarity Theorem. Complete the proportion that is needed to use this theorem.

$$\frac{FH}{?} = \frac{?}{XS} = \frac{FG}{?}$$ ***RX; HG; RS***

Concept Check ✔

Name a postulate or theorem that can be used to prove that the two triangles are similar. Then, write a similarity statement.

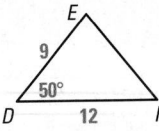

2.

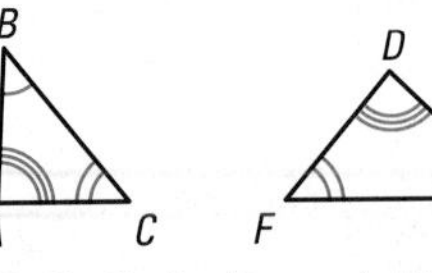

D
F
E

AA Similarity Post.; $\triangle ABC \sim \triangle DEF$

3.

C
6
50°
A 8 B

E
9
50°
D 12 F

SAS Similarity Thm.; $\triangle ABC \sim \triangle DFE$

Skill Check ✔

4. Which triangles are similar to $\triangle ABC$? Explain.

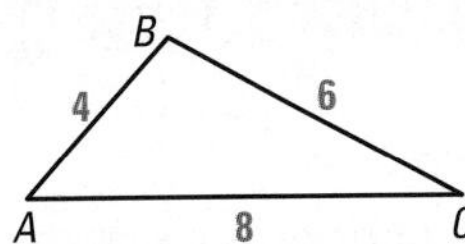

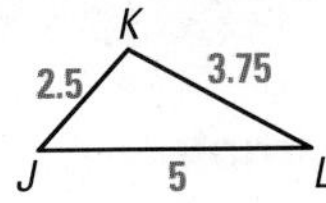

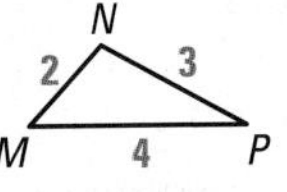

4. $\triangle JKL$ and $\triangle MNP$ are both $\sim$ to $\triangle ABC$; $\frac{AB}{JK} = \frac{BC}{KL} = \frac{AC}{JL} = \frac{8}{5}$ and $\frac{AB}{MN} = \frac{BC}{NP} = \frac{AC}{MP} = 2$; the $\triangle$s are $\sim$ by the SSS Similarity Thm.

5. The side lengths of $\triangle ABC$ are 2, 5, and 6, and $\triangle DEF$ has side lengths of 12, 30, and 36. Find the ratios of the lengths of the corresponding sides of $\triangle ABC$ to $\triangle DEF$. Are the two triangles similar? Explain. **$\frac{1}{6}$; yes; SSS Similarity Thm.**

PRACTICE AND APPLICATIONS

STUDENT HELP
Extra Practice to help you master skills is on p. 818.

DETERMINING SIMILARITY **In Exercises 6–8, determine which two of the three given triangles are similar. Find the scale factor for the pair.**

6.

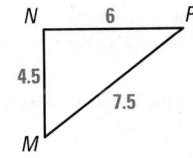

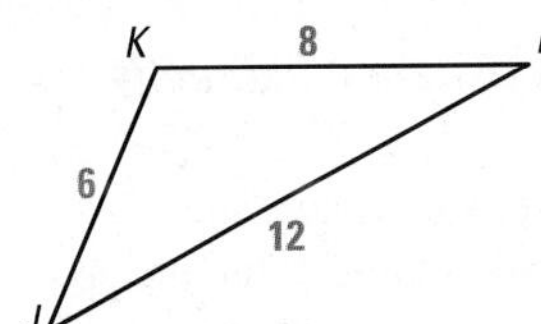

N 6 P
4.5
7.5
M

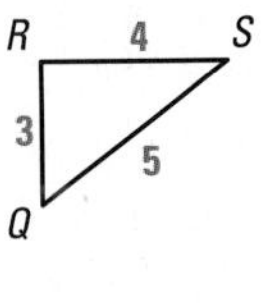

$\triangle MNP \sim \triangle QRS$; 3:2

7.

E
8
4
D 10 F

B
10
6
A 12 C

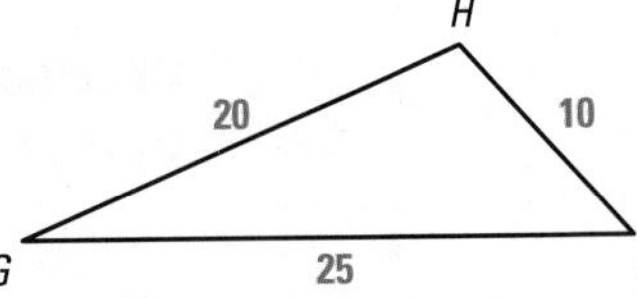

$\triangle DEF \sim \triangle GHJ$; 2:5

STUDENT HELP
HOMEWORK HELP
Example 1: Exs. 30, 31
Example 2: Exs. 6–18

8.

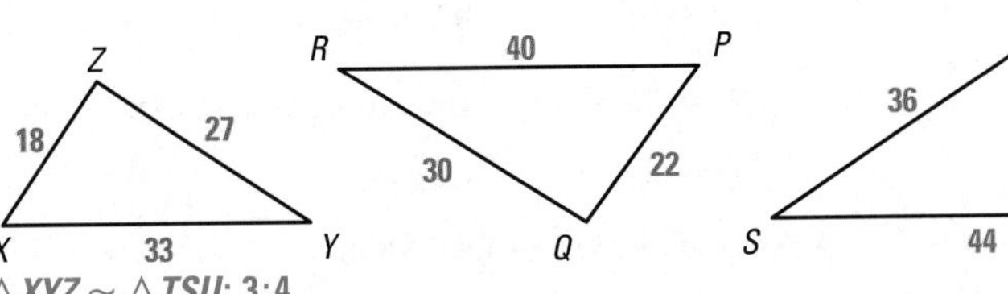

$\triangle XYZ \sim \triangle TSU$; 3:4

STUDENT HELP

HOMEWORK HELP
Example 3: Exs. 6–18, 30, 31
Example 4: Exs. 19–26, 29, 32–35
Example 5: Exs. 29, 32–35
Example 6: Exs. 29, 32–35

DETERMINING SIMILARITY Are the triangles similar? If so, state the similarity and the postulate or theorem that justifies your answer.

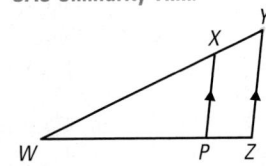

9.

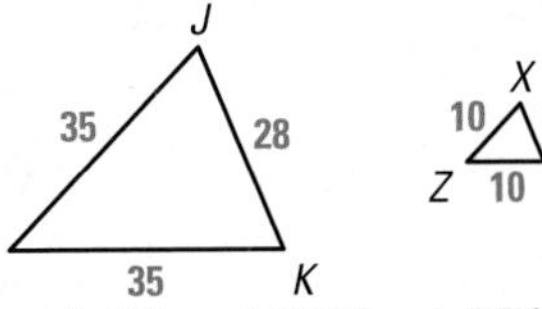

yes; $\triangle JKL \sim \triangle XYZ$ (or $\triangle XZY$); SSS Similarity Thm.

10.

yes; $\triangle PMS \sim \triangle RMN$; SAS Similarity Thm.

11.

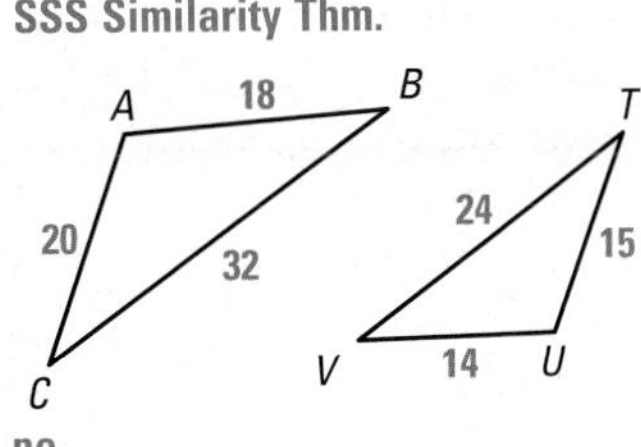

no

12.

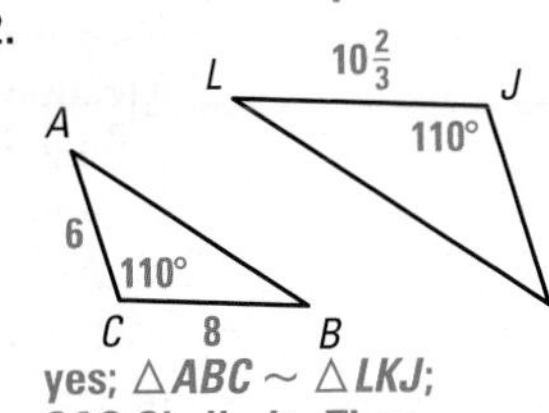

yes; $\triangle ABC \sim \triangle LKJ$; SAS Similarity Thm.

13.

yes; $\triangle PQR \sim \triangle DEF$; SSS or SAS Similarity Thm.

14.

14. yes; $\triangle WXP \sim \triangle WYZ$; AA Similarity Post.

LOGICAL REASONING Draw the given triangles roughly to scale. Then, name a postulate or theorem that can be used to prove that the triangles are similar. 15–18. Check drawings.

15. The side lengths of $\triangle PQR$ are 16, 8, and 18, and the side lengths of $\triangle XYZ$ are 9, 8, and 4. SSS Similarity Thm.

16. In $\triangle ABC$, $m\angle A = 28°$ and $m\angle B = 62°$. In $\triangle DEF$, $m\angle D = 28°$ and $m\angle F = 90°$. AA Similarity Post.

17. In $\triangle STU$, the length of $\overline{ST}$ is 18, the length of $\overline{SU}$ is 24, and $m\angle S = 65°$. The length of $\overline{JK}$ is 6, $m\angle J = 65°$, and the length of $\overline{JL}$ is 8 in $\triangle JKL$. SAS Similarity Thm.

18. The ratio of VW to MN is 6 to 1. In $\triangle VWX$, $m\angle W = 30°$, and in $\triangle MNP$, $m\angle N = 30°$. The ratio of WX to NP is 6 to 1. SAS Similarity Thm.

FINDING MEASURES AND LENGTHS Use the diagram shown to complete the statements.

19. $m\angle CED =$ __?__. 53°

20. $m\angle EDC =$ __?__. 45°

21. $m\angle DCE =$ __?__. 82°

22. $FC =$ __?__. 12

23. $EC =$ __?__. 15

24. $DE =$ __?__. 21

25. $CB =$ __?__. $4\sqrt{2}$

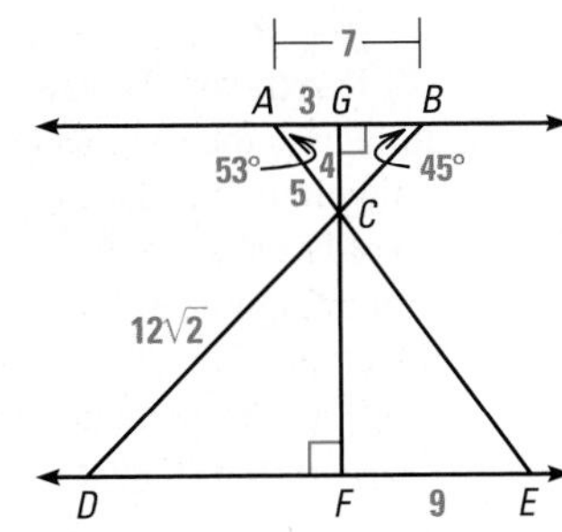

26. Name the three pairs of triangles that are similar in the figure.
$\triangle AGC$ and $\triangle EFC$, $\triangle BGC$ and $\triangle DFC$, $\triangle ABC$ and $\triangle EDC$

! COMMON ERROR
EXERCISE 8 Students may not identify the corresponding sides prior to finding the ratios. Encourage them to start with the shortest sides and then work through to the longest sides. Also, point out that all three pairs of the corresponding sides must be proportional.

! COMMON ERROR
EXERCISES 10–13 As mentioned in Section 8.4, students may have trouble identifying corresponding parts when the orientation of the triangles is different. Remind them that they can trace the triangles on separate sheets of paper and then rotate them so that their orientation is the same.

TEACHING TIPS
EXERCISES 19–26 You may want to ask students to justify their answers by using postulates, theorems, or definitions.

TEACHING TIPS

EXERCISES 32–34 Students should make sure that they know which two triangles in the figure are similar and why they are similar prior to using any proportions when solving these problems. They might find it helpful to label the vertices of the triangles.

30.

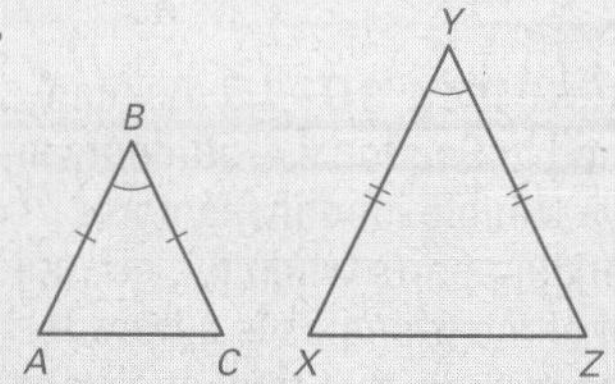

ADDITIONAL PRACTICE AND RETEACHING

For Lesson 8.5:

- Practice Levels A, B, and C (*Chapter 8 Resource Book*, p. 70)
- Reteaching with Practice (*Chapter 8 Resource Book*, p. 73)
- See Lesson 8.5 of the *Personal Student Tutor*

For more Mixed Review:

- Search the *Test and Practice Generator* for key words or specific lessons.

DETERMINING SIMILARITY **Determine whether the triangles are similar. If they are, write a similarity statement and solve for the variable.**

27. $\triangle ABC \sim \triangle BDC$; 18

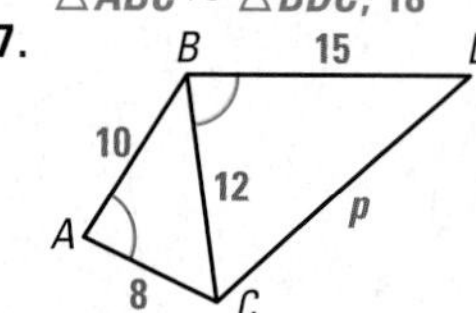

28. $\triangle EFG \sim \triangle EJH$; 10

29. **UNISPHERE** You are visiting the Unisphere at Flushing Meadow Park in New York. To estimate the height of the stainless steel model of Earth, you place a mirror on the ground and stand where you can see the top of the model in the mirror. Use the diagram shown to estimate the height of the model. **140 ft**

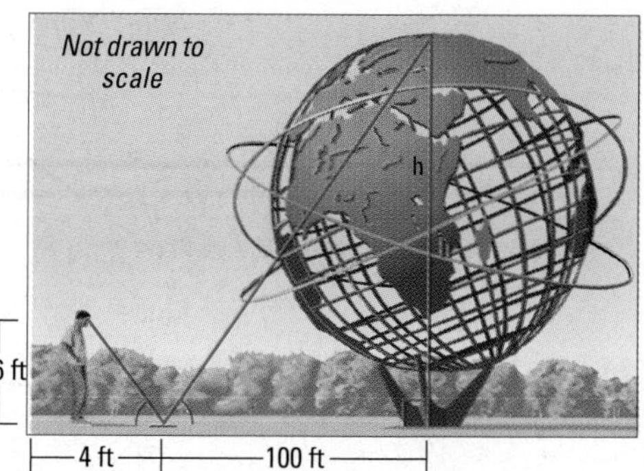

30. See margin for figure. Given: $\angle B \cong \angle Y$, $\overline{BA} \cong \overline{BC}$ and $\overline{YX} \cong \overline{YZ}$

Prove: $\triangle ABC \sim \triangle XYZ$

Sample answer: Since $\overline{BA} \cong \overline{BC}$ and $\overline{YX} \cong \overline{YZ}$, $BA = BC$ and $YX = YZ$. Then $\frac{BA}{YX} = \frac{BC}{YZ}$ and, since $\angle B \cong \angle Y$, $\triangle ABC \sim \triangle XYZ$ by the SAS Similarity Thm.

30. **PARAGRAPH PROOF** Two isosceles triangles are similar if the vertex angle of one triangle is congruent to the vertex angle of the other triangle. Write a paragraph proof of this statement and include a labeled figure.

31. Locate G on $\overline{AB}$ so that $GB = DE$ and draw $\overline{GH}$ through $G \parallel$ to $\overline{AC}$. Corresp. ∠s A and BGH are ≅ as are corresp. ∠s C and BHG, so $\triangle ABC \sim \triangle GBH$. Then $\frac{AB}{GB} = \frac{AC}{GH}$. But $\frac{AB}{DE} = \frac{AC}{DF}$ and $GB = DE$, so $\frac{AC}{GH} = \frac{AC}{DF}$ and $GH = DF$. By the SAS Cong. Post., $\triangle BGH \cong \triangle EDF$. Corresp. ∠s F and BHG are ≅, so $\angle F \cong \angle C$ by the Transitive Prop. of Cong. $\triangle ABC \sim \triangle DEF$ by the AA Similarity Post.

31. **PARAGRAPH PROOF** Write a paragraph proof of Theorem 8.3.

GIVEN ▶ $\angle A \cong \angle D$, $\frac{AB}{DE} = \frac{AC}{DF}$

PROVE ▶ $\triangle ABC \sim \triangle DEF$

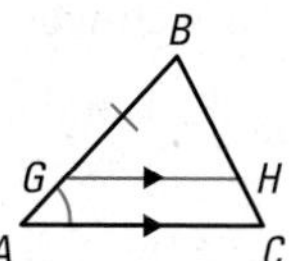

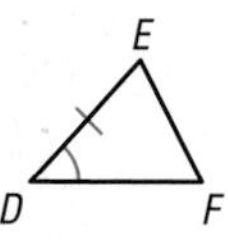

FINDING DISTANCES INDIRECTLY **Find the distance labeled x.**

32.

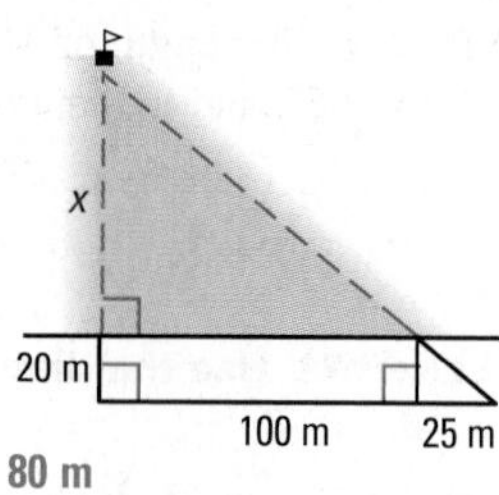

80 m

33.

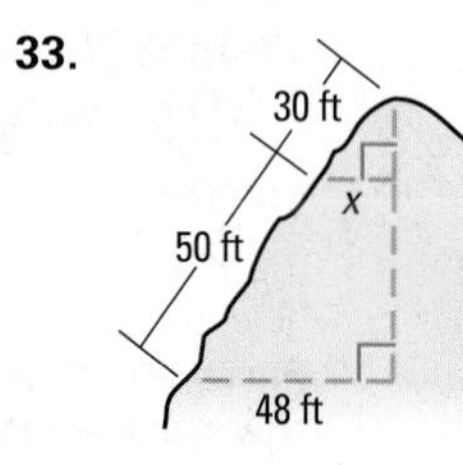

18 ft

FLAGPOLE HEIGHT **In Exercises 34 and 35, use the following information.**

Julia uses the shadow of the flagpole to estimate its height. She stands so that the tip of her shadow coincides with the tip of the flagpole's shadow as shown. Julia is 5 feet tall. The distance from the flagpole to Julia is 28 feet and the distance between the tip of the shadows and Julia is 7 feet.

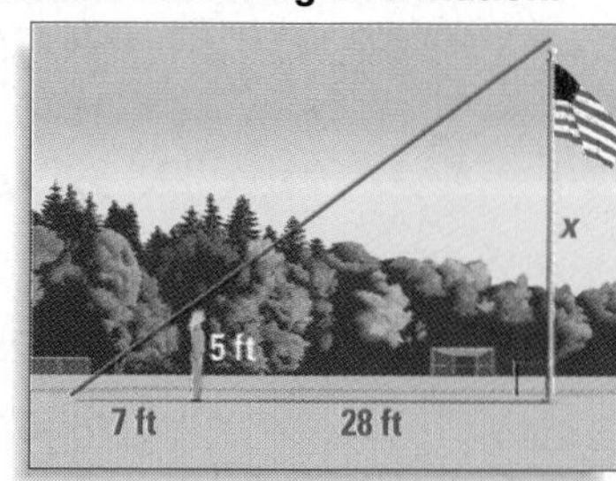

34. Calculate the height of the flagpole. **25 ft**

35. Explain why Julia's shadow method works. **See margin.**

35. Julia and the flagpole are both perpendicular to the ground and the two △s formed (one by Julia's head, feet, and the tip of the shadow, and the other by the top and bottom of the flag pole and the tip of the shadow) have a shared angle. Then the △s are ~ by the AA Similarity Post.

Test Preparation

QUANTITATIVE COMPARISON In Exercises 36 and 37, use the diagram, in which $\triangle ABC \sim \triangle XYZ$, and the ratio $AB:XY$ is 2:5. Choose the statement that is true about the given quantities.

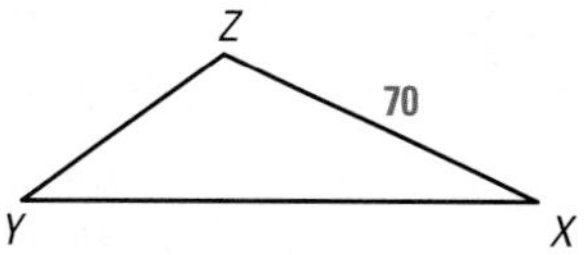

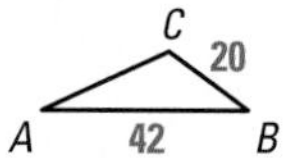

Ⓐ The quantity in column A is greater.

Ⓑ The quantity in column B is greater.

Ⓒ The two quantities are equal.

Ⓓ The relationship cannot be determined from the given information.

	Column A	Column B	
36.	The perimeter of $\triangle ABC$	The length XY	B
37.	The distance $XY + BC$	The distance $XZ + YZ$	A

★ Challenge

38. **DESIGNING THE LOOP** A portion of an amusement park ride called the Loop is shown. Find the length of $\overline{EF}$. (*Hint:* Use similar triangles.)

$17\frac{1}{7}$ ft

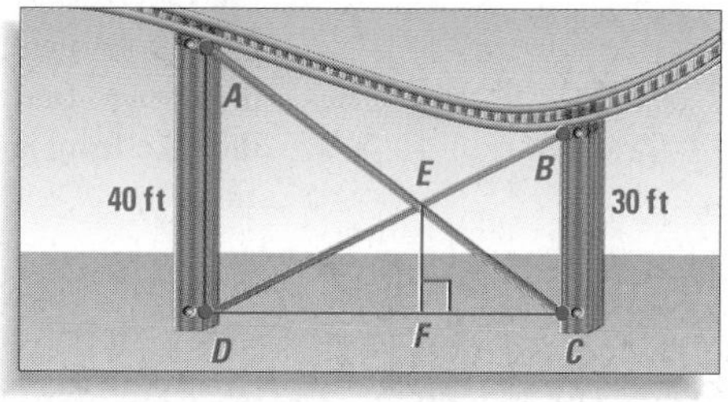

EXTRA CHALLENGE

www.mcdougallittell.com

MIXED REVIEW

ANALYZING ANGLE BISECTORS $\overrightarrow{BD}$ is the angle bisector of $\angle ABC$. Find any angle measures not given in the diagram. (Review 1.5 for 8.6)

39.

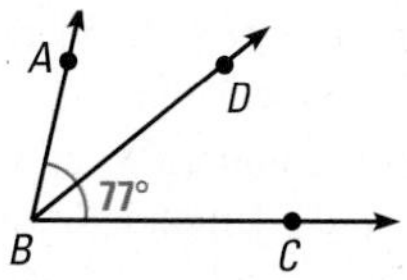

$m\angle ABD = m\angle DBC = 38.5°$

40.

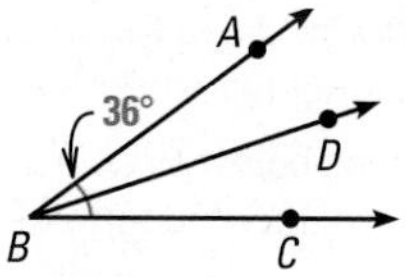

$m\angle ABD = m\angle DBC = 18°$

41.

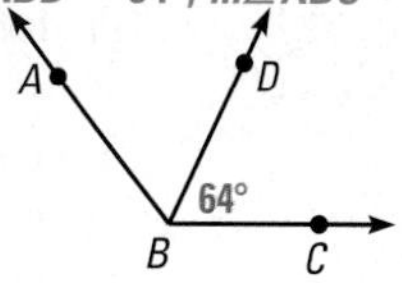

$m\angle ABD = 64°$, $m\angle ABC = 128°$

RECOGNIZING ANGLES Use the diagram shown to complete the statement. (Review 3.1 for 8.6)

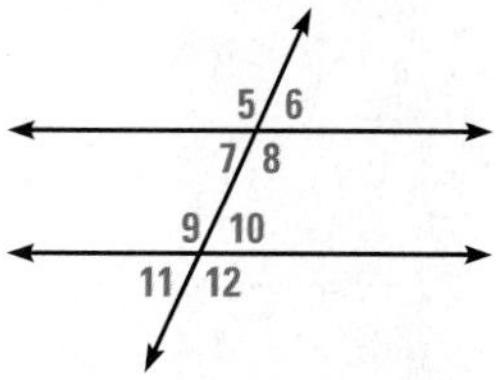

42. $\angle 5$ and __?__ are alternate exterior angles. $\angle 12$

43. $\angle 8$ and __?__ are consecutive interior angles. $\angle 10$

44. $\angle 10$ and __?__ are alternate interior angles. $\angle 7$

45. $\angle 9$ and __?__ are corresponding angles. $\angle 5$

FINDING COORDINATES Find the coordinates of the image after the reflection without using a coordinate plane. (Review 7.2)

46. $T(0, 5)$ reflected in the x-axis
(0, −5)

47. $P(-2, 7)$ reflected in the y-axis
(2, 7)

48. $B(-3, -10)$ reflected in the y-axis
(3, −10)

49. $C(-5, -1)$ reflected in the x-axis
(−5, 1)

Additional Test Preparation *Sample answer:*

1. You can use the AA Similarity Postulate if you know that two pairs of corresponding angles are congruent. If you know that the three pairs of corresponding sides are proportional, you can use the SSS Similarity Theorem. If you know that one pair of angles are congruent and that the sides including these angles are proportional, you can use the SAS Similarity Theorem.

4 ASSESS

DAILY HOMEWORK QUIZ

Transparency Available

Are the triangles similar? If so, state the similarity and the postulate or theorem that justifies it.

1.

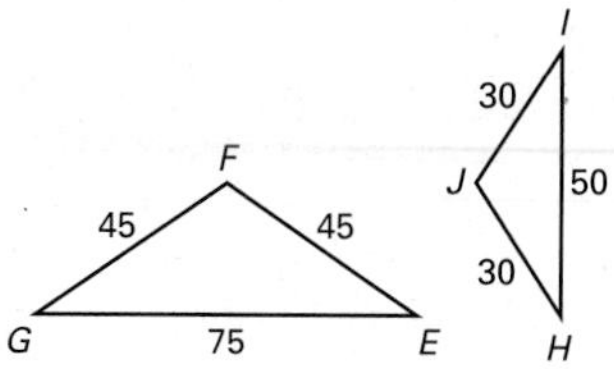

yes; $\triangle FGE \sim \triangle JHI$; SSS Similarity Thm.

2.

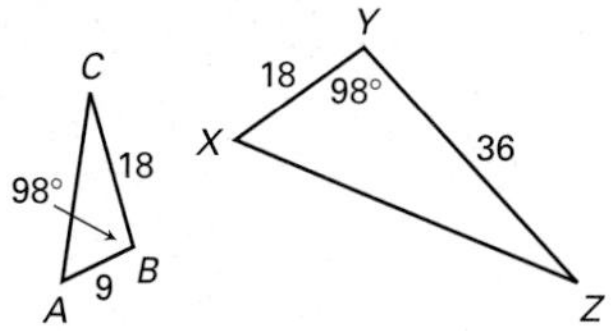

yes; $\triangle ABC \sim \triangle XYZ$; SAS Similarity Thm.

3. Find the distance across the lake shown if $CD = 120$ ft, $DX = 90$ ft, $AX = 180$ ft, and $\overline{AB} \parallel \overline{CD}$. 240 ft

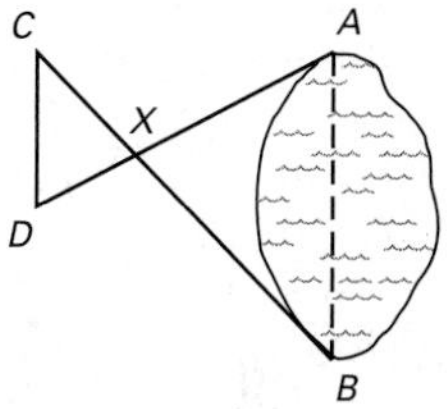

EXTRA CHALLENGE NOTE

Challenge problems for Lesson 8.5 are available in **blackline** format in the *Chapter 8 Resource Book*, p. 79 and at **www.mcdougallittell.com.**

ADDITIONAL TEST PREPARATION

1. WRITING You have two triangles that you want to prove are similar. Describe the postulates or theorems you could use.
See left.

ADDITIONAL RESOURCES

An alternative Quiz for Lessons 8.4 and 8.5 is available in the *Chapter 8 Resource Book*, p. 80.

A **blackline** master with additional Math & History exercises is available in the *Chapter 8 Resource Book*, p. 78.

1. yes; $m\angle B = m\angle E = 81°$, $m\angle ANB = 46°$, $m\angle A = 53°$
2. yes; $m\angle VSU = m\angle P = 47°$, $m\angle U = 101°$, $m\angle V = 32°$
3. no; $m\angle J = m\angle H = 42°$, $m\angle A = 43°$, $m\angle P = 94°$

QUIZ 2

Self-Test for Lessons 8.4 and 8.5

Determine whether you can show that the triangles are similar. State any angle measures that are not given. (Lesson 8.4)

1.

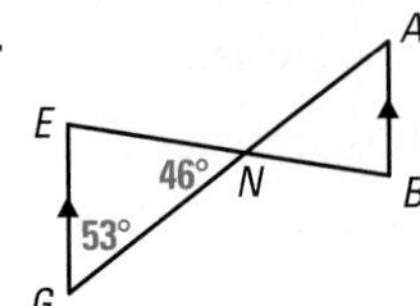

2.

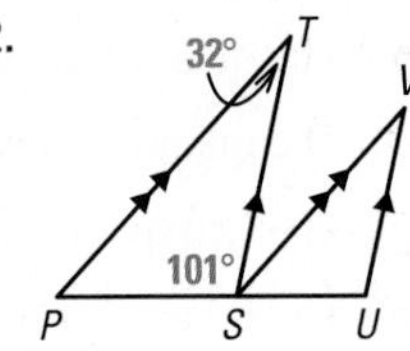

3.

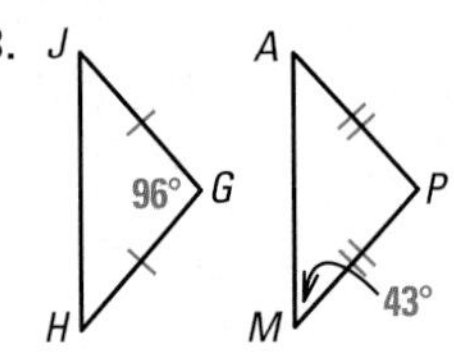

In Exercises 4–6, you are given the ratios of the lengths of the sides of △*DEF*. If △*ABC* has sides of lengths 3, 6, and 7 units, are the triangles similar? (Lesson 8.5)

4. 4 : 7 : 8 no

5. 6 : 12 : 14 yes

6. $1:2:\frac{7}{3}$ yes

7. **DISTANCE ACROSS WATER** Use the known distances in the diagram to find the distance across the lake from A to B. (Lesson 8.5) 10 mi

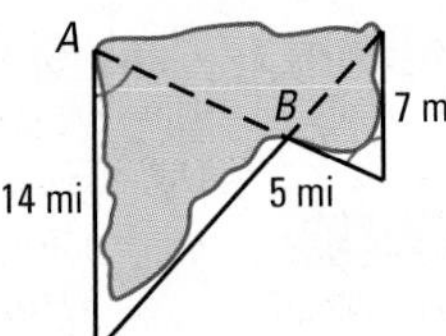

MATH & History — The Golden Rectangle

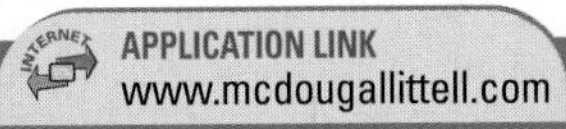

THEN **THOUSANDS OF YEARS AGO,** Greek mathematicians became interested in the *golden ratio*, a ratio of about 1 : 1.618. A rectangle whose side lengths are in the golden ratio is called a *golden rectangle*. Such rectangles are believed to be especially pleasing to look at.

NOW **THE GOLDEN RATIO** has been found in the proportions of many works of art and architecture, including the works shown in the timeline below.

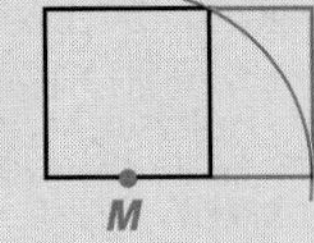

1. Follow the steps below to construct a golden rectangle. When you are done, check to see whether the ratio of the width to the length is 1 : 1.618.
   - Construct a square. Mark the midpoint M of the bottom side. Check constructions.
   - Place the compass point at M and draw an arc through the upper right corner of the square.
   - Extend the bottom side of the square to intersect with the arc. The intersection point is the corner of a golden rectangle. Complete the rectangle.

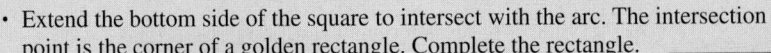

c. 1300 B.C.

The Osirion (underground Egyptian temple)

c. 440 B.C.

The Parthenon, Athens, Greece

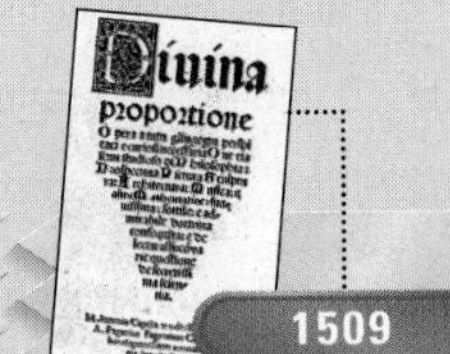

1509

Leonardo da Vinci illustrates Luca Pacioli's book on the golden ratio.

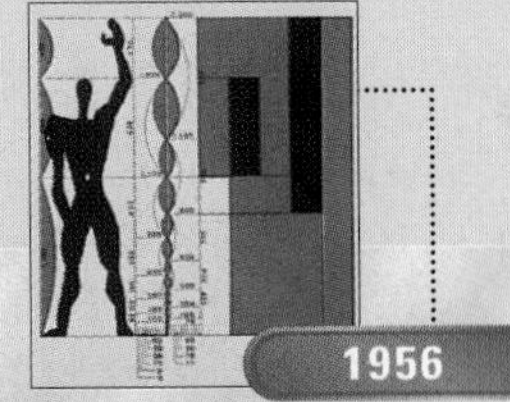

1956

Le Corbusier uses golden ratios based on this human figure in his architecture.

ACTIVITY 8.6

Using Technology

Geometry Software Activity for use with Lesson 8.6

Investigating Proportional Segments

You can use geometry software to compare segment lengths in triangles.

STUDENT HELP

SOFTWARE HELP

Visit our Web site www.mcdougallittell.com to see instructions for several software applications.

CONSTRUCT Construct a line parallel to a triangle's third side.

1. Draw a triangle. Label the vertices A, B, and C.
2. Draw a point on $\overline{AB}$. Label the point D.
3. Draw a line through D that is parallel to $\overline{AC}$. Label the intersection of the line and $\overline{BC}$ as point E.

INVESTIGATE

1. Measure $\overline{BD}$, $\overline{DA}$, $\overline{BE}$, and $\overline{EC}$. Calculate the ratios $\frac{BD}{DA}$ and $\frac{BE}{EC}$. $\frac{BD}{DA} = \frac{BE}{EC}$
2. Drag $\overline{DE}$ to different locations and compare the ratios from Exercise 1. The ratios remain the same.
3. Drag one or more of the triangle's vertices to change its shape. Continue to compare the ratios as the shape changes. The ratios remain the same.

MAKE A CONJECTURE

4. Make a conjecture about the ratios of segment lengths of a triangle's sides when the triangle is cut by a line parallel to the triangle's third side.

4. When a line ∥ to one side of a △ intersects the other two sides, it divides them proportionally.

CONSTRUCT Construct an angle bisector of a triangle.

4. Draw a triangle. Label the vertices P, Q, and R.
5. Draw the angle bisector of $\angle QPR$. Label the intersection of the angle bisector and $\overline{QR}$ as point B.

INVESTIGATE

5. Measure $\overline{BR}$, $\overline{RP}$, $\overline{BQ}$, and $\overline{QP}$. Calculate the ratios $\frac{BR}{BQ}$ and $\frac{RP}{QP}$. $\frac{BR}{BQ} = \frac{RP}{QP}$
6. Drag one or more of the triangle's vertices to change its shape. Continue to compare the ratios as the shape changes. The ratios remain the same.

MAKE A CONJECTURE

7. Make a conjecture about how the ratio of two side lengths of a triangle relates to the ratio of the segment lengths of the third side formed by an angle bisector. See margin.

7. The bisector of an ∠ of a △ divides the opp. side into 2 segments which are in the same ratio as the lengths of the other 2 sides of the △.

Extension: The △s are ~ if and only if the original △ is isosceles. (If so, the resulting △s are not only ~, they are ≅.)

EXTENSION

CRITICAL THINKING Are the two triangles formed by the angle bisector similar? Explain your reasoning.

1 Planning the Activity

PURPOSE

To investigate the relationship between segments formed by drawing a line parallel to one side of a triangle or by drawing an angle bisector of one of the angles.

MATERIALS

- a computer with geometry software
- Software Help (*Chapter 8 Resource Book*, p. 85)

PACING

- Exploring the Concept — 15 min
- Drawing Conclusions — 10 min

LINK TO LESSON

Remind students of the first investigation when discussing Theorem 8.4. When discussing Theorem 8.7, students should recall the second investigation.

2 Managing the Activity

ALTERNATIVE APPROACH

This activity can be done as a classroom demonstration using a computer with an overhead display.

3 Closing the Activity

KEY DISCOVERY

If a line parallel to one side of a triangle intersects the other two sides, then it divides the two sides proportionally. Also, if a ray bisects an angle of a triangle, then it divides the opposite side into segments whose lengths are proportional to the lengths of the other two sides.

ACTIVITY ASSESSMENT

A line parallel to one side of a triangle divides one of the other sides into segments of lengths 15 and 9 and divides the third side so that the longest portion is 36. How long is the shorter portion of the third side? 21.6

1 PLAN

PACING
Basic: 2 days
Average: 2 days
Advanced: 2 days
Block Schedule: 0.5 block with 8.5
0.5 block with 8.7

LESSON OPENER ACTIVITY
An alternative way to approach Lesson 8.6 is to use the Activity Lesson Opener:
- Blackline Master (*Chapter 8 Resource Book*, p. 84)
- Transparency (p. 52)

MEETING INDIVIDUAL NEEDS
- ***Chapter 8 Resource Book***
  Prerequisite Skills Review (p. 5)
  Practice Level A (p. 87)
  Practice Level B (p. 88)
  Practice Level C (p. 89)
  Reteaching with Practice (p. 90)
  Absent Student Catch-Up (p. 92)
  Challenge (p. 94)
- ***Resources in Spanish***
- 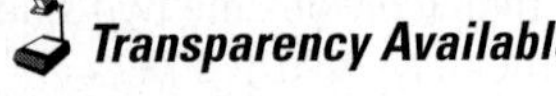

NEW-TEACHER SUPPORT
See the Tips for New Teachers on pp. 1–2 of the *Chapter 8 Resource Book* for additional notes about Lesson 8.6.

WARM-UP EXERCISES
Transparency Available
Solve each proportion.

1. $\frac{4}{x} = \frac{21}{7}$ $\frac{4}{3}$
2. $\frac{4}{11} = \frac{18}{z}$ 49.5
3. $\frac{x+1}{4} = \frac{6}{10}$ 1.4
4. $\frac{3-y}{y} = \frac{1}{5}$ 2.5

8.6 Proportions and Similar Triangles

What you should learn

GOAL 1 Use proportionality theorems to calculate segment lengths.

GOAL 2 To solve **real-life** problems, such as determining the dimensions of a piece of land in **Exs. 29 and 30**.

Why you should learn it

▼ Model **real-life** situations using proportionality theorems, as in the construction problem in **Example 5**.

CALIFORNIA STANDARDS AND ASSESSMENT
CA Standards: 7, 16
SAT9 Task 1: Objs. 1, 22
SAT9 Task 2: Objs. 1, 24

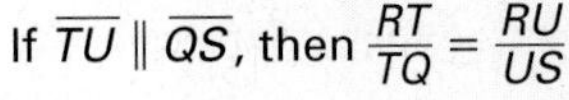

GOAL 1 USING PROPORTIONALITY THEOREMS

In this lesson, you will study four proportionality theorems. Similar triangles are used to prove each theorem. You are asked to prove the theorems in Exercises 31–33 and 38.

THEOREMS

THEOREM 8.4 ***Triangle Proportionality Theorem***

If a line parallel to one side of a triangle intersects the other two sides, then it divides the two sides proportionally.

If $\overline{TU} \parallel \overline{QS}$, then $\frac{RT}{TQ} = \frac{RU}{US}$.

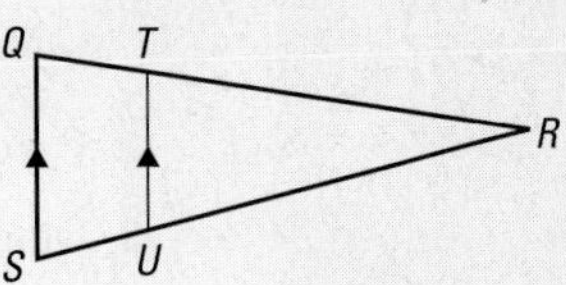

THEOREM 8.5 ***Converse of the Triangle Proportionality Theorem***

If a line divides two sides of a triangle proportionally, then it is parallel to the third side.

If $\frac{RT}{TQ} = \frac{RU}{US}$, then $\overline{TU} \parallel \overline{QS}$.

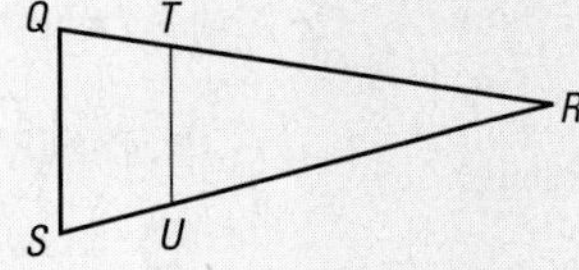

EXAMPLE 1 ***Finding the Length of a Segment***

In the diagram $\overline{AB} \parallel \overline{ED}$, $BD = 8$, $DC = 4$, and $AE = 12$. What is the length of $\overline{EC}$?

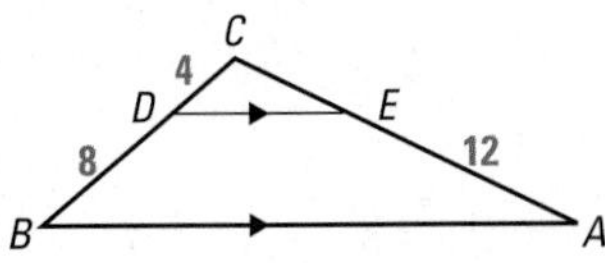

SOLUTION

$\frac{DC}{BD} = \frac{EC}{AE}$ **Triangle Proportionality Theorem**

$\frac{4}{8} = \frac{EC}{12}$ **Substitute.**

$\frac{4(12)}{8} = EC$ **Multiply each side by 12.**

$6 = EC$ **Simplify.**

▶ So, the length of $\overline{EC}$ is 6.

EXAMPLE 2 Determining Parallels

Given the diagram, determine whether $\overline{MN} \parallel \overline{GH}$.

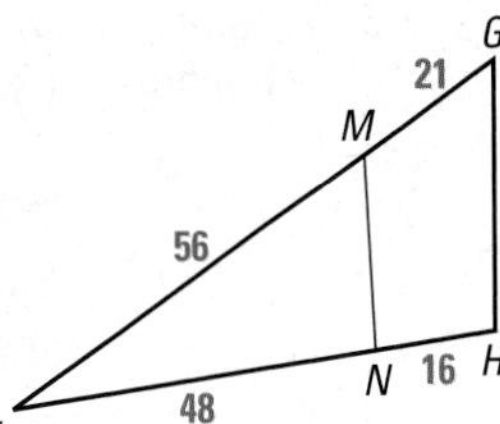

SOLUTION

Begin by finding and simplifying the ratios of the two sides divided by $\overline{MN}$.

$$\frac{LM}{MG} = \frac{56}{21} = \frac{8}{3} \qquad \frac{LN}{NH} = \frac{48}{16} = \frac{3}{1}$$

Because $\frac{8}{3} \neq \frac{3}{1}$, $\overline{MN}$ is not parallel to $\overline{GH}$.

THEOREMS

THEOREM 8.6

If three parallel lines intersect two transversals, then they divide the transversals proportionally.

If $r \parallel s$ and $s \parallel t$, and ℓ and m intersect r, s, and t, then $\frac{UW}{WY} = \frac{VX}{XZ}$.

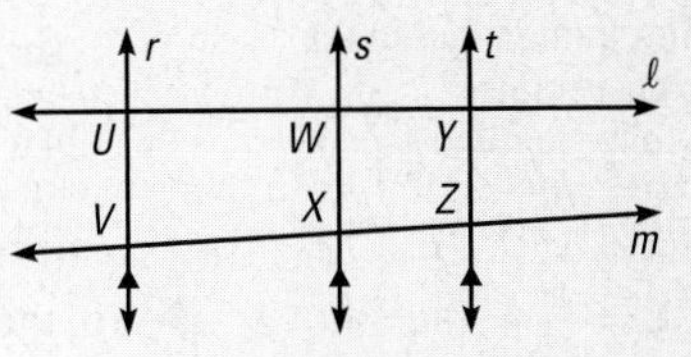

THEOREM 8.7

If a ray bisects an angle of a triangle, then it divides the opposite side into segments whose lengths are proportional to the lengths of the other two sides.

If $\overrightarrow{CD}$ bisects $\angle ACB$, then $\frac{AD}{DB} = \frac{CA}{CB}$.

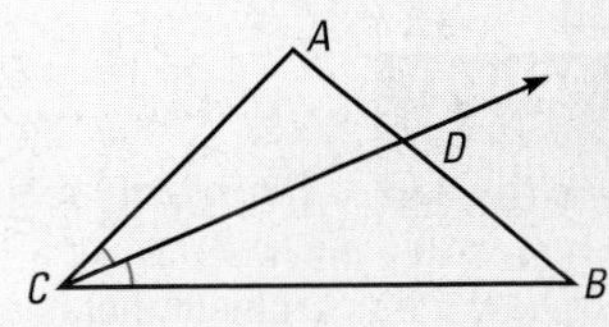

EXAMPLE 3 Using Proportionality Theorems

In the diagram, $\angle 1 \cong \angle 2 \cong \angle 3$, and $PQ = 9$, $QR = 15$, and $ST = 11$. What is the length of $\overline{TU}$?

SOLUTION

Because corresponding angles are congruent the lines are parallel and you can use Theorem 8.6.

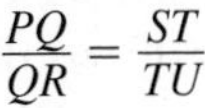

$\frac{PQ}{QR} = \frac{ST}{TU}$ **Parallel lines divide transversals proportionally.**

$\frac{9}{15} = \frac{11}{TU}$ **Substitute.**

$9 \cdot TU = 15 \cdot 11$ **Cross product property**

$TU = \frac{15(11)}{9} = \frac{55}{3}$ **Divide each side by 9 and simplify.**

▶ So, the length of $\overline{TU}$ is $\frac{55}{3}$, or $18\frac{1}{3}$.

2 TEACH

MOTIVATING THE LESSON

Show students a map of city streets that includes parallel streets with several diagonal streets. Discuss the fact that the lengths of blocks varies where the diagonal streets cut across the parallel ones. In this lesson, students will learn some proportionality theorems that will allow them to find the lengths of blocks in such situations.

EXTRA EXAMPLE 1

In the diagram $\overline{UY}$ is parallel to $\overline{VX}$, $UV = 3$, $UW = 18$, and $XW = 16$. What is the length of $\overline{YX}$? 3.2

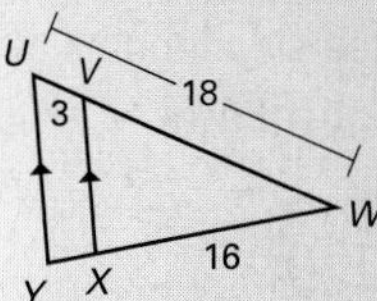

EXTRA EXAMPLE 2

Given the diagram, determine whether $\overline{PQ}$ is parallel to $\overline{TR}$. yes

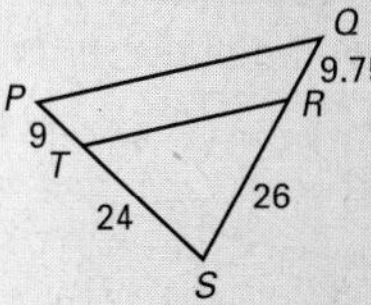

EXTRA EXAMPLE 3

In the diagram, $\angle 1 \cong \angle 2 \cong \angle 3$, $AB = 6$, $BC = 9$, $EF = 8$. What is x? $5\frac{1}{3}$

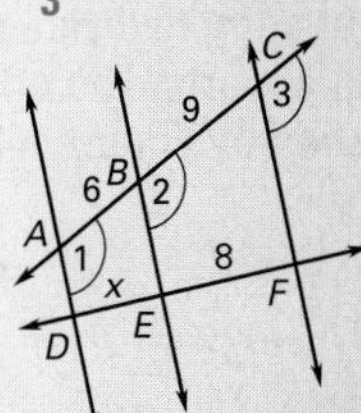

Checkpoint Exercises for Examples 1–3 on next page.

CHECKPOINT EXERCISES

For use after Examples 1–3:

In the diagram, $\overline{PK} \parallel \overline{QL} \parallel \overline{NM}$. Complete the statements.

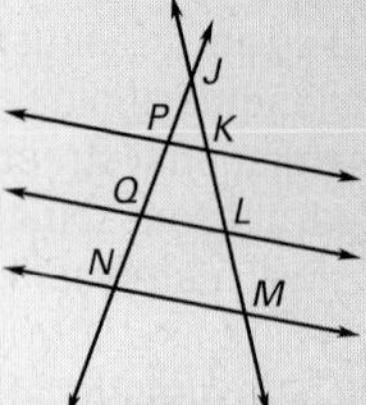

1. $\frac{KL}{LM} =$ ______ $\frac{PQ}{QN}$
2. $\frac{JP}{PQ} =$ ______ $\frac{JK}{KL}$

EXTRA EXAMPLE 4

In the diagram, $\angle LKM \cong \angle MKN$. Use the given side lengths to find the length of $\overline{MN}$. 12.75

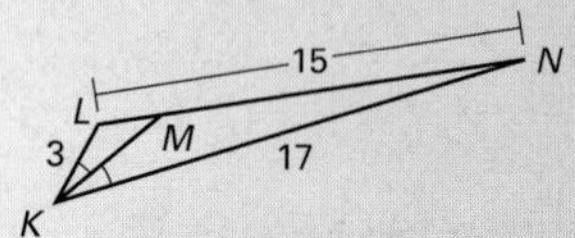

CHECKPOINT EXERCISES

For use after Example 4:

1. Find the value of the variable. about 7.27

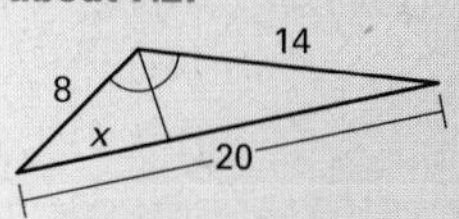

ACTIVITY NOTE

In the Activity, students use a compass and straight edge to divide a segment into equal parts. The construction is justified by Theorem 8.6.

4. The $\parallel$ lines divide the transversals proportionally. Since $\frac{AD}{DE} = \frac{DE}{EF} = \frac{EF}{FG} = 1$, then $\frac{AJ}{JK} = \frac{JK}{KL} = \frac{KL}{LB} = 1$ and $AJ = JK = KL = LB$.

EXAMPLE 4 ***Using Proportionality Theorems***

In the diagram, $\angle CAD \cong \angle DAB$. Use the given side lengths to find the length of $\overline{DC}$.

SOLUTION

Since $\overline{AD}$ is an angle bisector of $\angle CAB$, you can apply Theorem 8.7.

Let $x = DC$. Then, $BD = 14 - x$.

$\frac{AB}{AC} = \frac{BD}{DC}$	Apply Theorem 8.7.
$\frac{9}{15} = \frac{14 - x}{x}$	Substitute.
$9 \cdot x = 15(14 - x)$	Cross product property
$9x = 210 - 15x$	Distributive property
$24x = 210$	Add $15x$ to each side.
$x = 8.75$	Divide each side by 24.

▶ So, the length of $\overline{DC}$ is 8.75 units.

4. The $\parallel$ lines divide the transversals proportionally. Since $\frac{AD}{DE} = \frac{DE}{EF} = \frac{EF}{FG} = 1$, $\frac{AJ}{JK} = \frac{JK}{KL} = \frac{KL}{LB} = 1$, and $AJ = JK = KL = LB$.

ACTIVITY
Construction

Dividing a Segment into Equal Parts (4 shown)

1–3. Check drawings.

❶ Draw a line segment that is about 3 inches long. Label the endpoints A and B. Choose any point C not on $\overleftrightarrow{AB}$. Draw $\overrightarrow{AC}$.

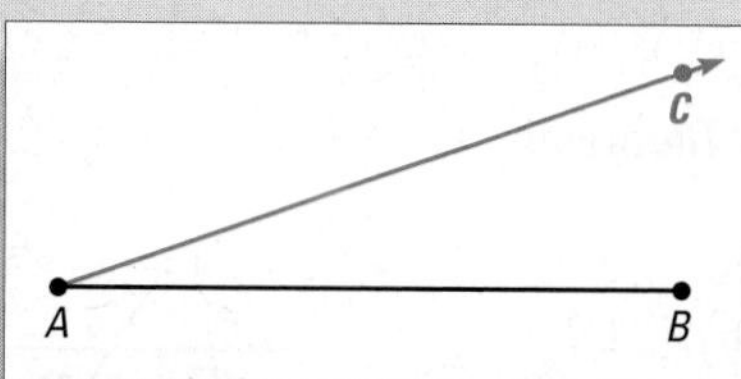

❷ Using any length, place the compass point at A and make an arc intersecting $\overrightarrow{AC}$ at D.

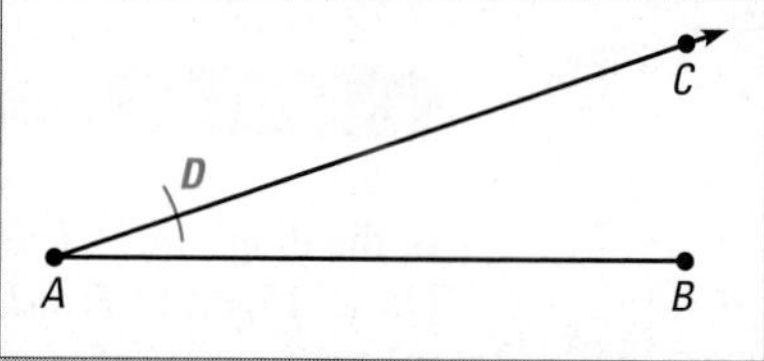

❸ Using the same compass setting, make additional arcs on $\overrightarrow{AC}$. Label the points E, F, and G so that $AD = DE = EF = FG$.

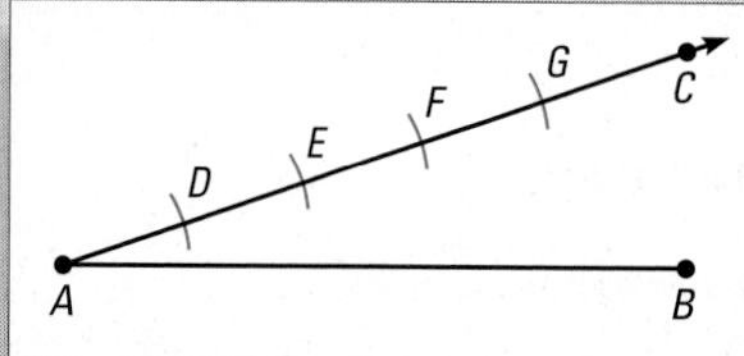

❹ Draw $\overline{GB}$. Construct a line parallel to $\overline{GB}$ through D. Continue constructing parallel lines and label the points as shown. Explain why $AJ = JK = KL = LB$. See margin.

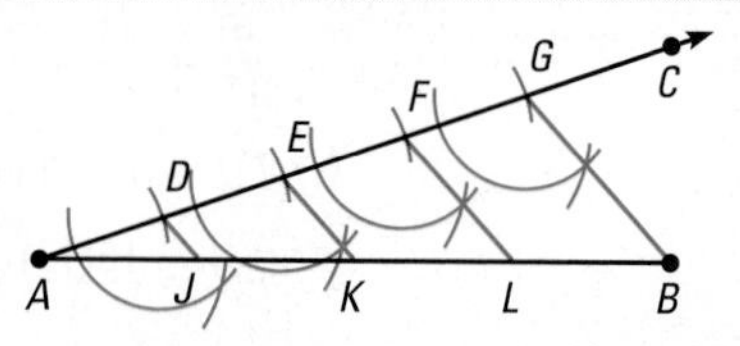

GOAL 2 USING PROPORTIONALITY THEOREMS IN REAL LIFE

EXAMPLE 5 *Finding the Length of a Segment*

REAL LIFE

BUILDING CONSTRUCTION You are insulating your attic, as shown. The vertical 2×4 studs are evenly spaced. Explain why the diagonal cuts at the tops of the strips of insulation should have the same lengths.

SOLUTION

Because the studs $\overline{AD}$, $\overline{BE}$, and $\overline{CF}$ are each vertical, you know that they are parallel to each other. Using Theorem 8.6, you can conclude that $\frac{DE}{EF} = \frac{AB}{BC}$. Because the studs are evenly spaced, you know that $DE = EF$. So, you can conclude that $AB = BC$, which means that the diagonal cuts at the tops of the strips have the same lengths.

EXAMPLE 6 *Finding Segment Lengths*

In the diagram $\overline{KL} \parallel \overline{MN}$. Find the values of the variables.

SOLUTION

To find the value of x, you can set up a proportion.

$\frac{9}{13.5} = \frac{37.5 - x}{x}$	**Write proportion.**
$13.5(37.5 - x) = 9x$	**Cross product property**
$506.25 - 13.5x = 9x$	**Distributive property**
$506.25 = 22.5x$	**Add 13.5*x* to each side.**
$22.5 = x$	**Divide each side by 22.5.**

Since $\overline{KL} \parallel \overline{MN}$, $\triangle JKL \sim \triangle JMN$ and $\frac{JK}{JM} = \frac{KL}{MN}$.

$\frac{9}{13.5 + 9} = \frac{7.5}{y}$	**Write proportion.**
$9y = 7.5(22.5)$	**Cross product property**
$y = 18.75$	**Divide each side by 9.**

EXTRA EXAMPLE 5

You are installing vinyl siding below the peak of a roof. All the pieces of siding are the same width and are installed horizontally. Are $\overline{AB}$ and $\overline{CD}$ the same length? Explain.

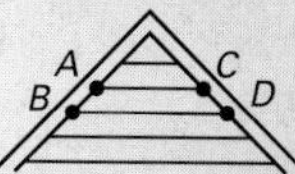

Not necessarily. You know that each diagonal cut on the right-hand side of the house is the same length and each diagonal cut on the left-hand side of the house is the same length, but you do not know the two sides have equal length cuts.

EXTRA EXAMPLE 6

$\overline{FJ} \parallel \overline{GI}$. Find the values of the variables. **$x = 9.6$, $y = 7.2$**

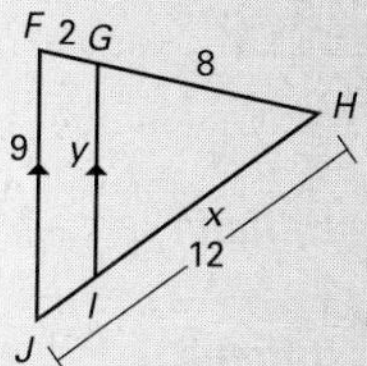

CHECKPOINT EXERCISES

For use after Examples 5 and 6:

1. l, m, n, k are parallel. Find the values of the variables.
$x = 13.5$, $y = 16.2$

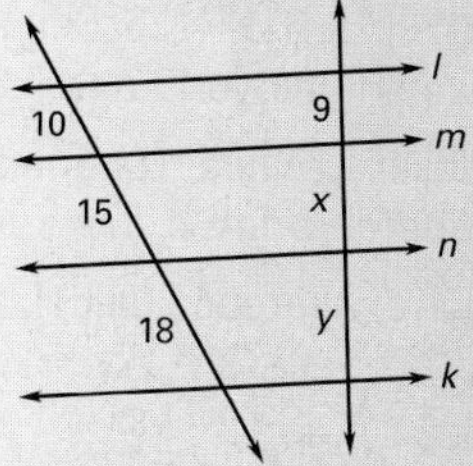

FOCUS ON VOCABULARY

Discuss the difference between dividing segments proportionally and dividing segments equally.

CLOSURE QUESTION

Explain what you know about a triangle that has a ray bisecting one of the angles. **The ray cuts the third side of the triangle into segments whose lengths are proportional to the lengths of the other two sides.**

3 APPLY

ASSIGNMENT GUIDE

BASIC
Day 1: pp. 502–503 Exs. 11–28
Day 2: pp. 503–505 Exs. 29–39, 41–53

AVERAGE
Day 1: pp. 502–503 Exs. 11–28
Day 2: pp. 503–505 Exs. 29–39, 41–53

ADVANCED
Day 1: pp. 502–503 Exs. 11–28
Day 2: pp. 503–505 Exs. 29–39, 40–53

BLOCK SCHEDULE
pp. 502–503 Exs. 11–28 (with 8.5)
pp. 502–505 Exs. 29–39, 41–53 (with 8.7)

EXERCISE LEVELS

Level A: ***Easier***
11–14
Level B: ***More Difficult***
15–39
Level C: ***Most Difficult***
40

✓ HOMEWORK CHECK

To quickly check student understanding of key concepts, go over the following exercises: Exs. 12, 16, 22, 26, 28, 32, 34, 36. See also the Daily Homework Quiz:

- Blackline Master (*Chapter 8 Resource Book*, p. 97)
- Transparency (p. 61)

GUIDED PRACTICE

Vocabulary Check ✓

1. Complete the following: If a line divides two sides of a triangle proportionally, then it is __?__ to the third side. This theorem is known as the __?__. parallel; △ Proportionality Converse

Concept Check ✓

2. In $\triangle ABC$, $\overrightarrow{AR}$ bisects $\angle CAB$. Write the proportionality statement for the triangle that is based on Theorem 8.7. $\frac{AB}{AC} = \frac{BR}{CR}$

Determine whether the statement is *true* or *false*. Explain your reasoning. 3–6. See margin.

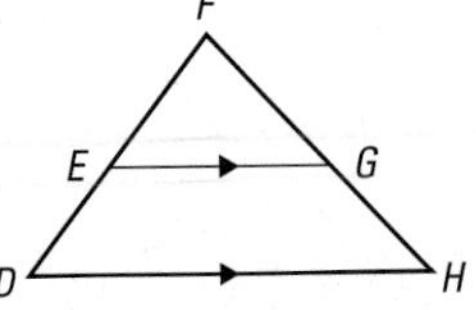

3. $\frac{FE}{ED} = \frac{FG}{GH}$
4. $\frac{FE}{FD} = \frac{FG}{FH}$
5. $\frac{EG}{DH} = \frac{EF}{DF}$
6. $\frac{ED}{FE} = \frac{EG}{DH}$

3. true; △ Proportionality Thm.

4. true; Corresponding Angles Post., AA Similarity Post., def. of ~ △s

5. true; Corresponding Angles Post., AA Similarity Post., def. of ~ △s

6. False; the statement does not follow from similarity.

Skill Check ✓

Use the figure to complete the proportion.

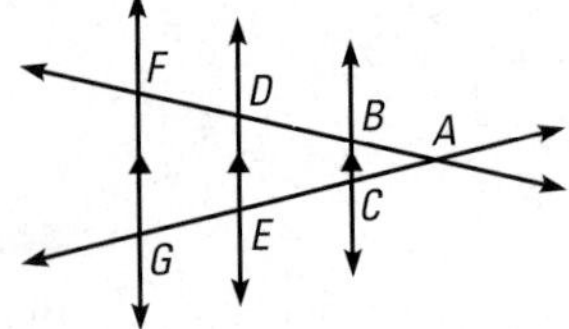

7. $\frac{BD}{BF} = \frac{?}{CG}$ CE
8. $\frac{AE}{CE} = \frac{?}{BD}$ AD
9. $\frac{?}{GA} = \frac{FD}{FA}$ GE
10. $\frac{GA}{?} = \frac{FA}{DA}$ EA

PRACTICE AND APPLICATIONS

STUDENT HELP
Extra Practice to help you master skills is on p. 818.

LOGICAL REASONING Determine whether the given information implies that $\overline{QS} \parallel \overline{PT}$. Explain.

11.

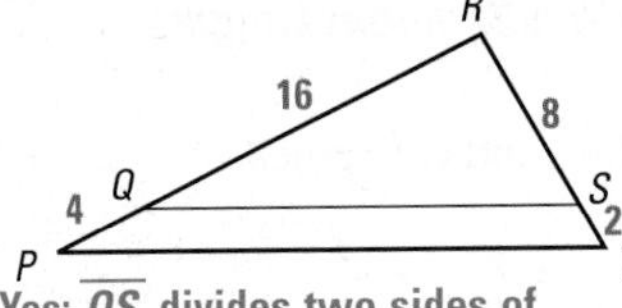

Yes; $\overline{QS}$ divides two sides of $\triangle PRT$ proportionally.

12. Yes; $\overline{QS}$ divides two sides of $\triangle PRT$ proportionally.

13.

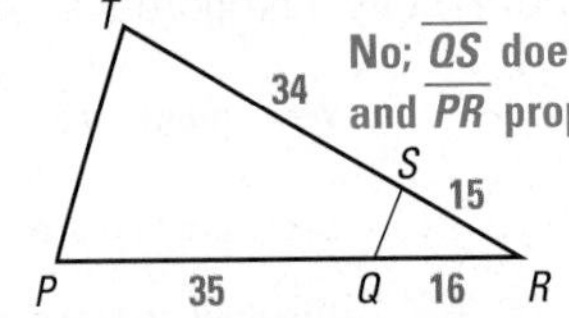

No; $\overline{QS}$ does not divide $\overline{TR}$ and $\overline{PR}$ proportionally.

14.

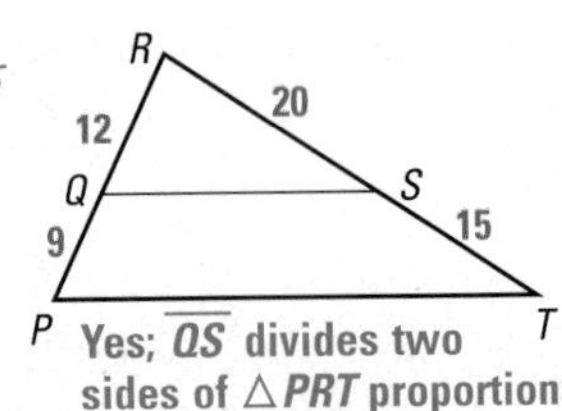

Yes; $\overline{QS}$ divides two sides of $\triangle PRT$ proportionally.

LOGICAL REASONING Use the diagram shown to decide if you are given enough information to conclude that $\overline{LP} \parallel \overline{MQ}$. If so, state the reason.

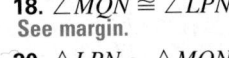

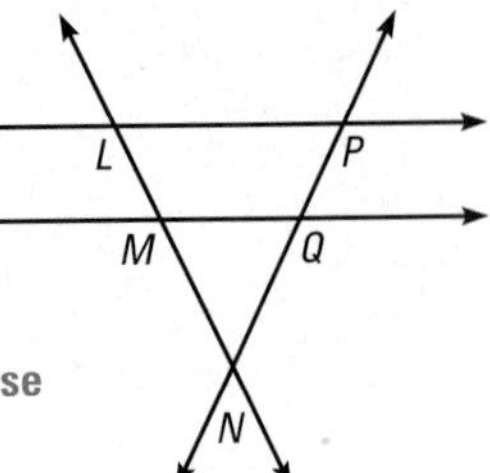

15. $\frac{NM}{ML} = \frac{NQ}{QP}$ See margin.
16. $\angle MNQ \cong \angle LNP$ no
17. $\angle NLP \cong \angle NMQ$ See margin.
18. $\angle MQN \cong \angle LPN$ See margin.
19. $\frac{LM}{MN} = \frac{LP}{MQ}$ no
20. $\triangle LPN \sim \triangle MQN$ yes; def. of ~ △s and Corresponding Angles Converse

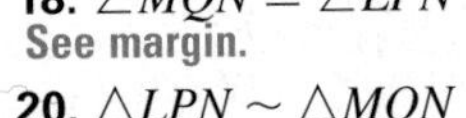

15. yes; △ Proportionality Converse.

17. yes; Corresponding Angles Converse

18. yes; Corresponding. Angles Converse

STUDENT HELP
HOMEWORK HELP
Example 1: Exs. 21–28
Example 2: Exs. 11–20
Example 3: Exs. 21–28
Example 4: Exs. 21–28
Example 5: Exs. 29, 30, 36, 37
Example 6: Exs. 34–37

USING PROPORTIONALITY THEOREMS **Find the value of the variable.**

21. 3

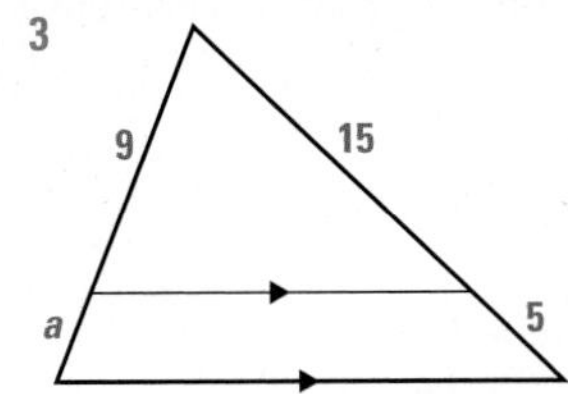

22. 9

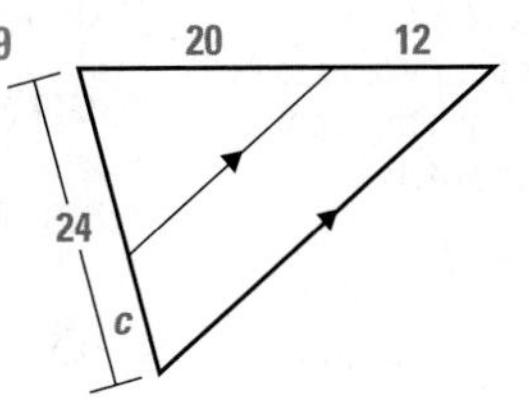

23. 6

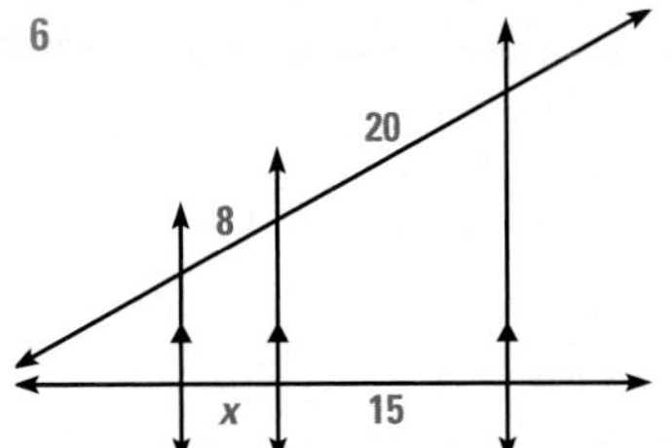

24. 15

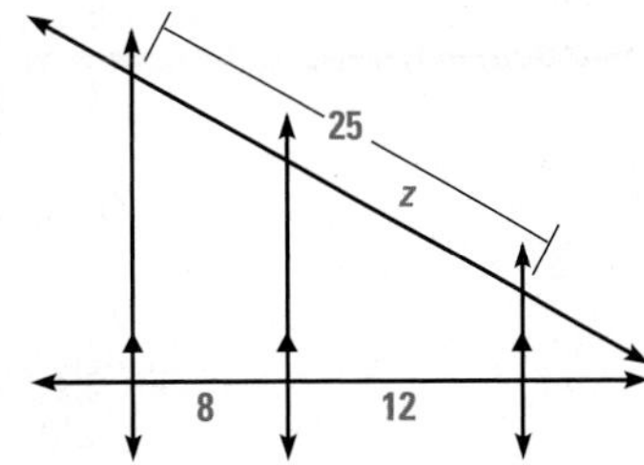

USING ALGEBRA **Find the value of the variable.**

25. 14

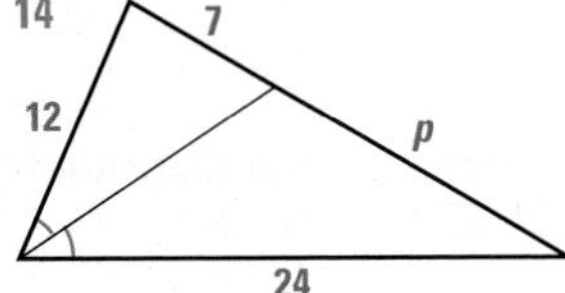

26. 27.5

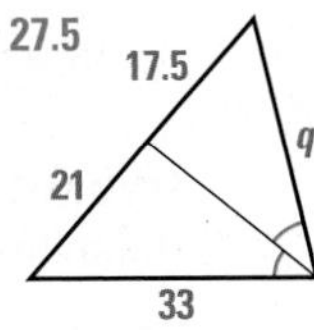

27. 29.4

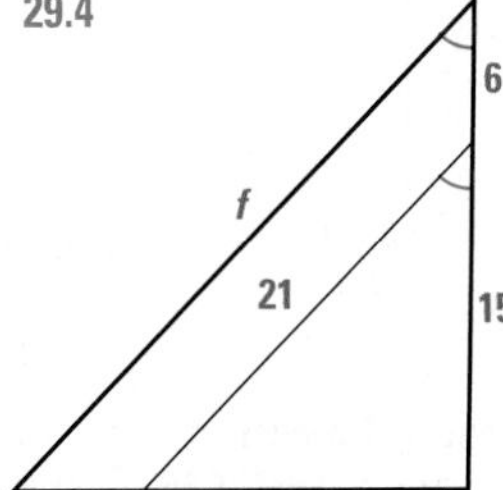

28. 12

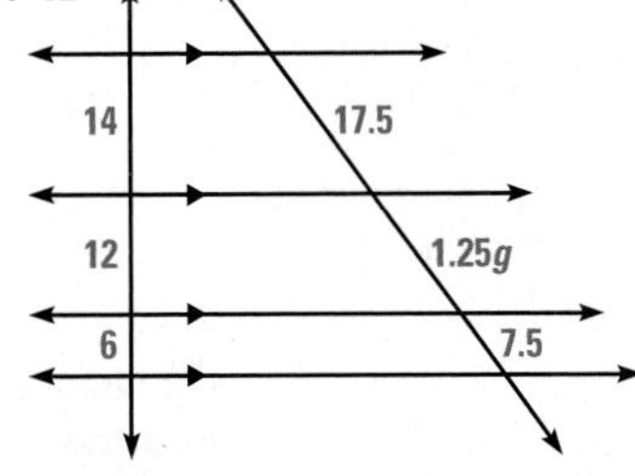

LOT PRICES **The real estate term for the distance along the edge of a piece of property that touches the ocean is "ocean frontage."**

29. Find the ocean frontage (to the nearest tenth of a meter) for each lot shown. A: 47.8 m, B: 40.2 m, C: 34.0 m

30. **CRITICAL THINKING** In general, the more ocean frontage a lot has, the higher its selling price. Which of the lots should be listed for the highest price? Lot A

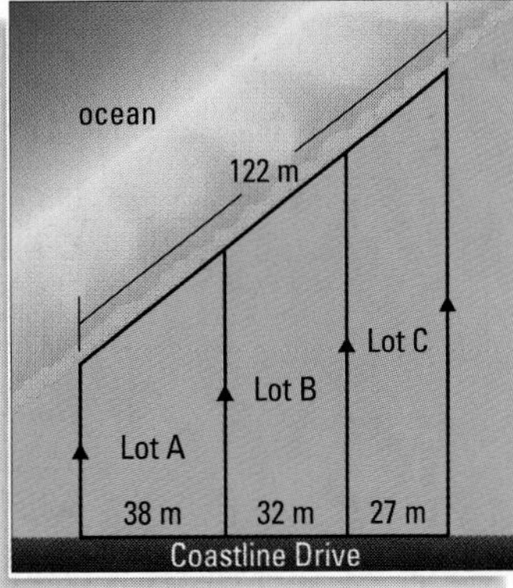

FOCUS ON CAREERS

REAL ESTATE SALESPERSON

A real estate salesperson can help a seller establish a price for their property as discussed in Exercise 30.

CAREER LINK
www.mcdougallittell.com

! COMMON ERROR

EXERCISE 24 Students may have trouble setting up the proportion for this exercise. Encourage them to follow Example 6 on page 501. They must also remember to use the distributive property when solving for the variable.

CAREER NOTE

EXERCISES 29 AND 30
Additional information about careers in real estate is available at **www.mcdougallittell.com.**

STUDENT HELP NOTES

Homework Help Students can find help for Exs. 31–33 at **www.mcdougallittell.com.** The information can be printed out for students who don't have access to the Internet.

31. Statements (Reasons)

1. $\overline{DE} \parallel \overline{AC}$ (Given)
2. $\angle BDE \cong \angle A$, $\angle BED \cong \angle C$ (If 2 $\parallel$ lines are cut by a transversal, corresp. $\angle$s are $\cong$.)
3. $\triangle DBE \sim \triangle ABC$ (AA Similarity Post.)
4. $\frac{BA}{BD} = \frac{BC}{BE}$ (Def. of $\sim$ $\triangle$s)
5. $\frac{BD + DA}{BD} = \frac{BE + EC}{BE}$ (Segment Addition Post.)
6. $\frac{BD}{BD} + \frac{DA}{BD} = \frac{BE}{BE} + \frac{EC}{BE}$ (Addition of fractions)
7. $1 + \frac{DA}{BD} = 1 + \frac{EC}{BE}$ (Substitution prop. of equality)
8. $\frac{DA}{BD} = \frac{EC}{BE}$ (Subtraction prop. of equality)

ADDITIONAL PRACTICE AND RETEACHING

For Lesson 8.6:

- Practice Levels A, B, and C (*Chapter 8 Resource Book*, p. 87)
- Reteaching with Practice (*Chapter 8 Resource Book*, p. 90)
- See Lesson 8.6 of the *Personal Student Tutor*

For more Mixed Review:

- Search the *Test and Practice Generator* for key words or specific lessons.

STUDENT HELP

HOMEWORK HELP Visit our Web site www.mcdougallittell.com for help with proofs in Exs. 31–33.

32. Draw $\overline{AD}$ intersecting $\overline{BE}$ at X. (Through any 2 points, there is exactly 1 line.) By the $\triangle$ Proportionality Thm., since $k_1 \parallel k_2$ and $k_2 \parallel k_3$, $\frac{CB}{BA} = \frac{DX}{XA}$ and $\frac{DX}{XA} = \frac{DE}{EF}$. Then $\frac{CB}{BA} = \frac{DE}{EF}$ by the transitive prop. of equality.

33. Draw a $\parallel$ to $\overline{XW}$ through Z ($\parallel$ Post.) and extend $\overline{XY}$ to intersect the $\parallel$ at A. ($\overline{XY}$ is not $\parallel$ to $\overline{AZ}$ because it would also have to be $\parallel$ to $\overline{XW}$.) Then $\frac{YW}{WZ} = \frac{XY}{XA}$. Also, corresp. $\angle$s YXW and A are $\cong$, as are alternate interior $\angle$s WXZ and AZX. Since $\angle YXW \cong \angle WXZ$, $\angle A \cong \angle AZX$ by the Transitive Prop. of Cong. By the Converse of the Base Angles Thm., $\overline{XA} \cong \overline{XZ}$ or $XA = XZ$. Then by the substitution prop. of equality, $\frac{YW}{WZ} = \frac{XY}{XZ}$.

34. $AB = 7$, $DF = 5.25$, $GJ = 4$, $BC = 4$, $FG = 13.8$, $HJ = 15.8$

35. $MT = 8.4$, $LN = 8$, $SN = 8$, $PR = 27$, $UR = 21$

31. **TWO-COLUMN PROOF** Use the diagram shown to write a two-column proof of Theorem 8.4.

B, D, E, A, C

GIVEN ▶ $\overline{DE} \parallel \overline{AC}$

PROVE ▶ $\frac{DA}{BD} = \frac{EC}{BE}$ **See margin.**

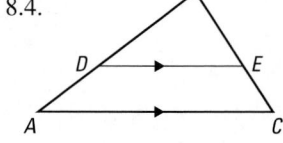

32. **PARAGRAPH PROOF** Use the diagram with the auxiliary line drawn to write a paragraph proof of Theorem 8.6.

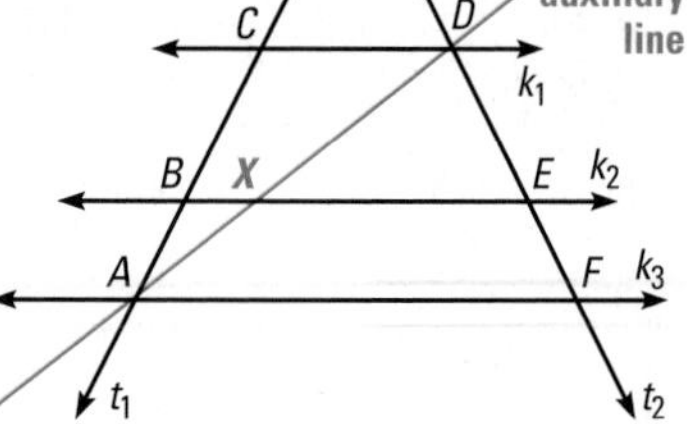

GIVEN ▶ $k_1 \parallel k_2$, $k_2 \parallel k_3$

PROVE ▶ $\frac{CB}{BA} = \frac{DE}{EF}$

33. **PARAGRAPH PROOF** Use the diagram with the auxiliary lines drawn to write a paragraph proof of Theorem 8.7.

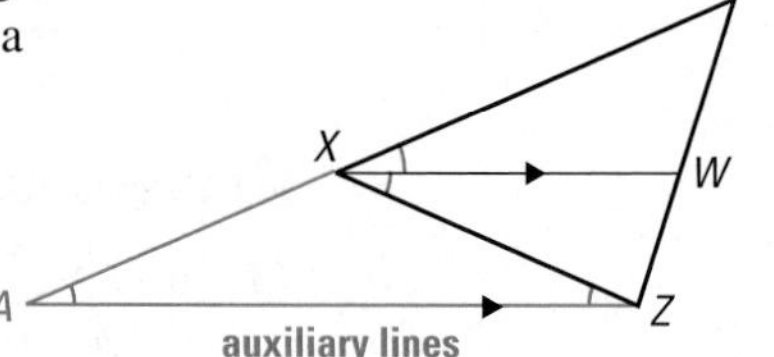

GIVEN ▶ $\angle YXW \cong \angle WXZ$

PROVE ▶ $\frac{YW}{WZ} = \frac{XY}{XZ}$

FINDING SEGMENT LENGTHS **Use the diagram to determine the lengths of the missing segments.** **34–35. See margin.**

34.

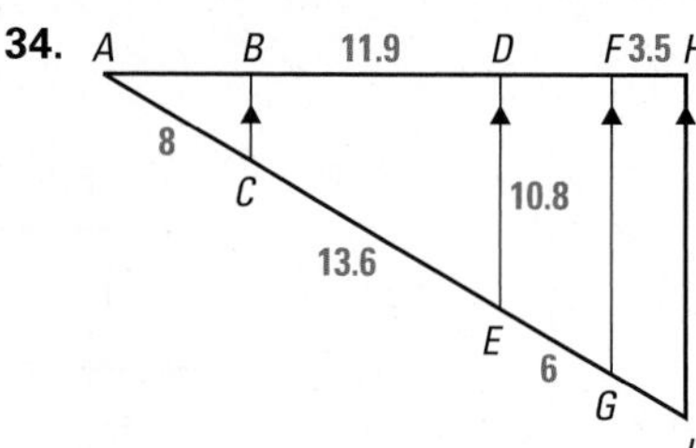

35.

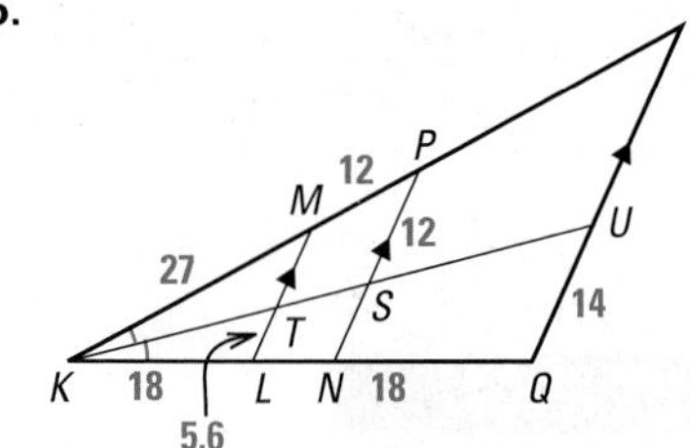

NEW YORK CITY **Use the following information and the map of New York City.** On Fifth Avenue, the distance between E 33rd Street and E 24th Street is about 2600 feet. The distance between those same streets on Broadway is about 2800 feet. All numbered streets are parallel.

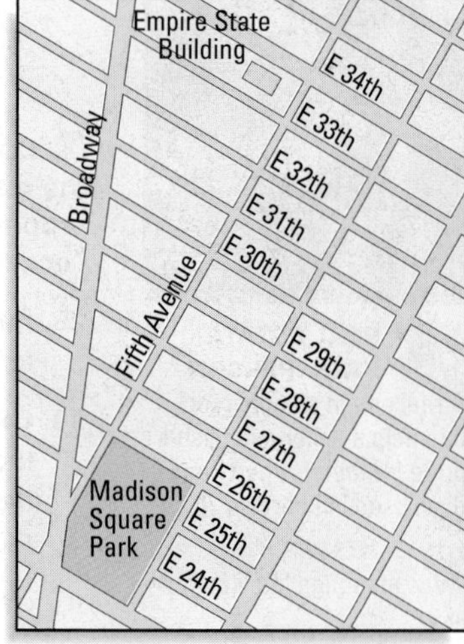

36. On Fifth Avenue, the distance between E 24th Street and E 29th Street is about 1300 feet. What is the distance between these two streets on Broadway? **about 1400 ft**

37. On Broadway, the distance between E 33rd Street and E 30th Street is about 1120 feet. What is the distance between these two streets on Fifth Avenue? **about 1040 ft**

38. *Writing* Use the diagram given for the proof of Theorem 8.4 from Exercise 31 to explain how you can prove the Triangle Proportionality Converse, Theorem 8.5. See margin.

Test Preparation

39. b. *Sample answers:* $\frac{BD}{BA} = \frac{BE}{BC}$, $\frac{BD}{DA} = \frac{BE}{EC}$, $\frac{BA}{BD} = \frac{AC}{DE}$

39. MULTI-STEP PROBLEM Use the diagram shown.

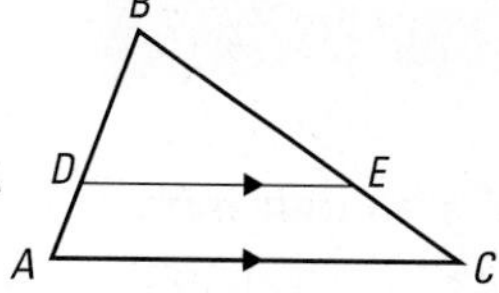

a. If $DB = 6$, $AD = 2$, and $CB = 20$, find EB. 15

b. Use the diagram to state three correct proportions. See margin.

c. If $DB = 4$, $AB = 10$, and $CB = 20$, find CE. 12

d. *Writing* Explain how you know that $\triangle ABC$ is similar to $\triangle DBE$. See margin.

★ Challenge

39. d. *Sample answer:* If 2 ∥ lines are cut by a trans., corresp. ∠s are ≅, so $\angle BDE \cong \angle A$ and $\angle BED \cong \angle C$, so $\triangle ABC \sim \triangle DBE$ by the AA Similarity Post.

40. **CONSTRUCTION** Perform the following construction.

GIVEN ▶ Segments with lengths x, y, and z

CONSTRUCT ▶ A segment of length p, such that $\frac{x}{y} = \frac{z}{p}$.

(*Hint:* This construction is like the construction on page 500.)

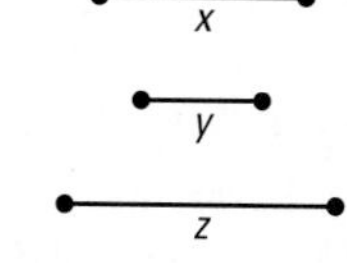

Sample construction: Construct $\overline{AB}$ with $AB = x$ and $\overline{BC}$ with $BC = z$ and A, B, and C not collinear. On $\overline{BA}$ construct $\overline{AD}$ with $AD = y$. Construct a line ∥ to $\overline{AC}$ through D and extend it to intersect $\overline{BC}$ at E. Let $p = CE$. Since $\overline{AC} \parallel \overline{DE}$, $\frac{x}{y} = \frac{z}{p}$.

MIXED REVIEW

USING THE DISTANCE FORMULA Find the distance between the two points. (Review 1.3)

41. $A(10, 5)$, $B(-6, -4)$ $\sqrt{337}$

42. $A(7, -3)$, $B(-9, 4)$ $\sqrt{305}$

43. $A(-1, -9)$, $B(6, -2)$ $7\sqrt{2}$

44. $A(0, 11)$, $B(-5, 2)$ $\sqrt{106}$

45. $A(0, -10)$, $B(4, 7)$ $\sqrt{305}$

46. $A(8, -5)$, $B(0, 4)$ $\sqrt{145}$

USING THE DISTANCE FORMULA Place the figure in a coordinate plane and find the requested information. (Review 4.7)

47–49. Positions of figures may vary. Check drawings.

47. Draw a right triangle with legs of 12 units and 9 units. Find the length of the hypotenuse. 15 units

48. Draw a rectangle with length 16 units and width 12 units. Find the length of a diagonal. 20 units

49. Draw an isosceles right triangle with legs of 6 units. Find the length of the hypotenuse. $6\sqrt{2}$ units

50. Draw an isosceles triangle with base of 16 units and height of 6 units. Find the length of the legs. 10 units

TRANSFORMATIONS Name the type of transformation. (Review 7.1–7.3, 7.5 for 8.7)

51. reflection

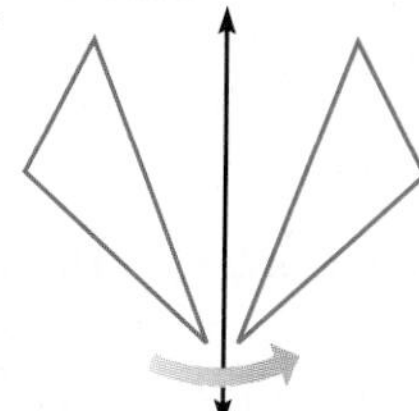

52. glide reflection

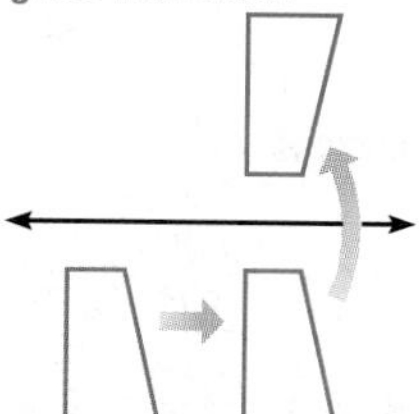

53. rotation

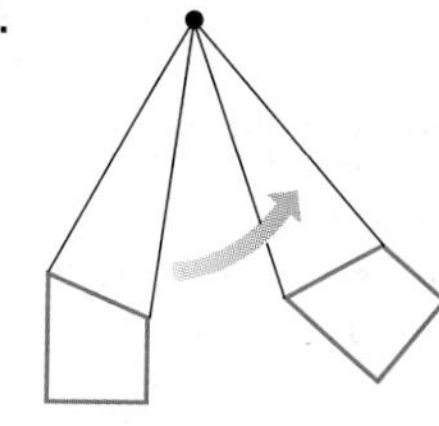

4 ASSESS

DAILY HOMEWORK QUIZ

Transparency Available

Find the value of the variable.

1. 8

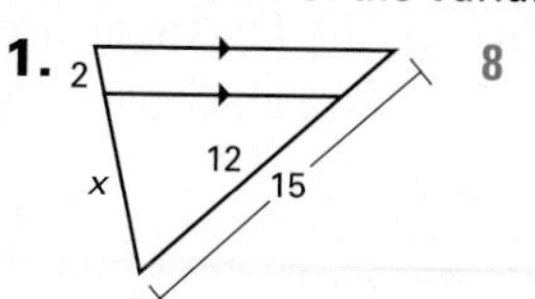

2. 6.3

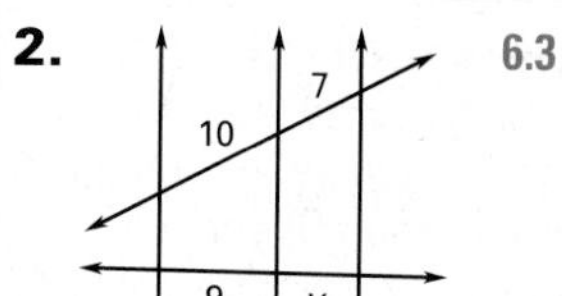

3. Is $\overline{GH} \parallel \overline{FE}$? no

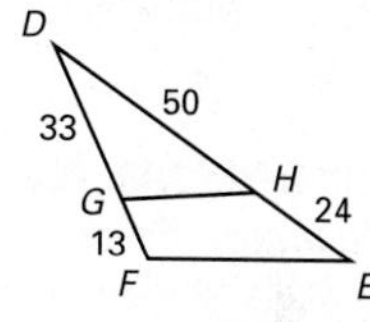

4. In $\triangle RST$, $\overrightarrow{RV}$ bisects $\angle TRS$. Write a proportionality statement for $\triangle RST$ based on Theorem 8.7. $\frac{TV}{VS} = \frac{RT}{RS}$

EXTRA CHALLENGE NOTE

Challenge problems for Lesson 8.6 are available in **blackline** format in the *Chapter 8 Resource Book*, p. 94 and at **www.mcdougallittell.com.**

ADDITIONAL TEST PREPARATION

1. OPEN ENDED Write and illustrate each of the four theorems from this lesson. For one of the theorems, write a problem you can solve using the theorem and show how to solve it. Check students' work.

38. See Additional Answers beginning on page AA1.

1 PLAN

PACING
Basic: 2 days
Average: 2 days
Advanced: 2 days
Block Schedule: 0.5 block with 8.6
0.5 block with Ch. Rev.

LESSON OPENER
GEOMETRY SOFTWARE
An alternative way to approach Lesson 8.7 is to use the Geometry Software Lesson Opener:

- Blackline Master (*Chapter 8 Resource Book*, p. 98)
- Transparency (p. 53)

MEETING INDIVIDUAL NEEDS

- ***Chapter 8 Resource Book***
  Prerequisite Skills Review (p. 5)
  Practice Level A (p. 101)
  Practice Level B (p. 102)
  Practice Level C (p. 103)
  Reteaching with Practice (p. 104)
  Absent Student Catch-Up (p. 106)
  Challenge (p. 108)
- ***Resources in Spanish***
-  ***Personal Student Tutor***

NEW-TEACHER SUPPORT
See the Tips for New Teachers on pp. 1–2 of the *Chapter 8 Resource Book* for additional notes about Lesson 8.7.

WARM-UP EXERCISES
Transparency Available
Find the distance between the two points.

1. $A(3, 1)$, $B(5, -2)$ $\sqrt{13}$
2. $G(7, -5)$, $H(8, 0)$ $\sqrt{26}$

Describe each type of transformation.

3. a rotation **A figure is rotated around a fixed point.**
4. a reflection **A figure is reflected over a line.**
5. a translation **A figure is shifted up or down and/or right or left.**

8.7 Dilations

What you should learn

GOAL 1 Identify dilations.

GOAL 2 Use properties of dilations to create a **real-life** perspective drawing in **Ex. 34**.

Why you should learn it

▼ To solve **real-life** problems, such as estimating the height of the shadow of a shadow puppet in **Example 3**.

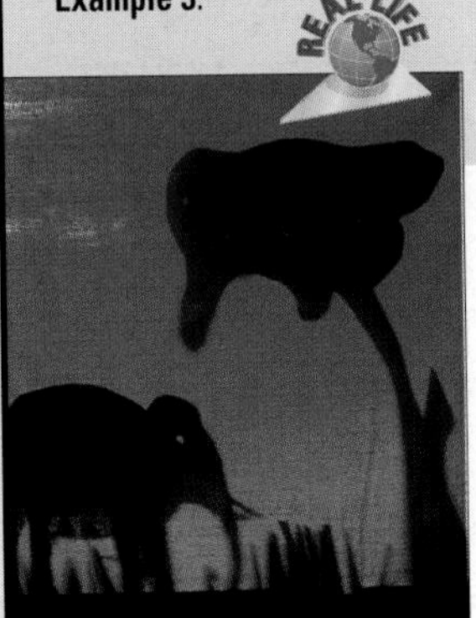

CALIFORNIA STANDARDS AND ASSESSMENT
CA Standards: 11, 16
SAT9 Task 1: Obj. 31
SAT9 Task 2: Obj. 34

GOAL 1 IDENTIFYING DILATIONS

In Chapter 7, you studied rigid transformations, in which the image and preimage of a figure are *congruent*. In this lesson, you will study a type of nonrigid transformation called a *dilation*, in which the image and preimage of a figure are *similar*.

A **dilation** with center C and scale factor k is a transformation that maps every point P in the plane to a point P' so that the following properties are true.

1. If P is not the center point C, then the image point P' lies on $\overrightarrow{CP}$. The scale factor k is a positive number such that $k = \frac{CP'}{CP}$, and $k \neq 1$.
2. If P is the center point C, then $P = P'$.

The dilation is a **reduction** if $0 < k < 1$ and it is an **enlargement** if $k > 1$.

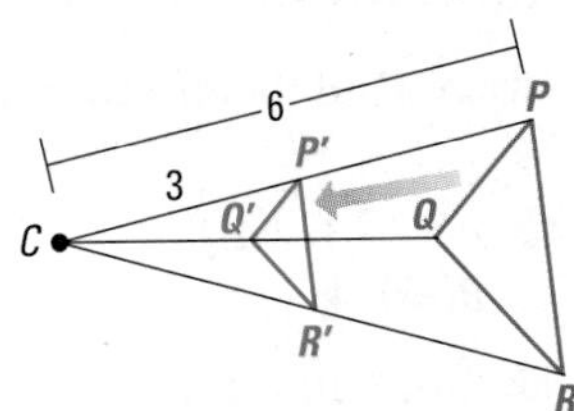

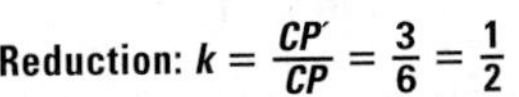
Reduction: $k = \frac{CP'}{CP} = \frac{3}{6} = \frac{1}{2}$

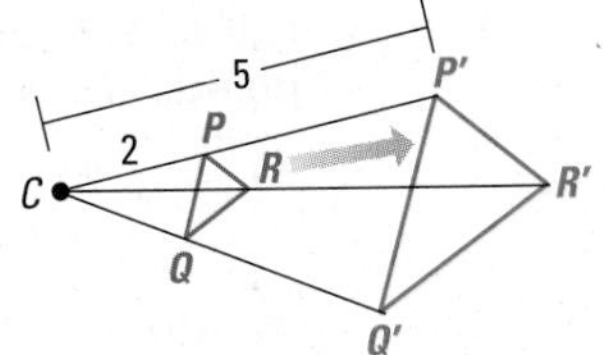

Enlargement: $k = \frac{CP'}{CP} = \frac{5}{2}$

Because $\triangle PQR \sim \triangle P'Q'R'$, $\frac{P'Q'}{PQ}$ is equal to the scale factor of the dilation.

EXAMPLE 1 *Identifying Dilations*

Identify the dilation and find its scale factor.

a.

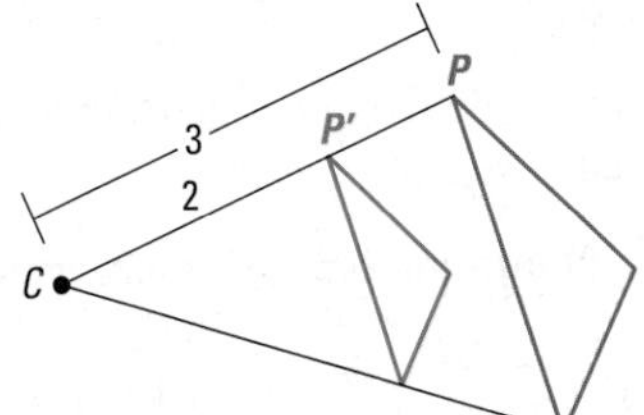

b.

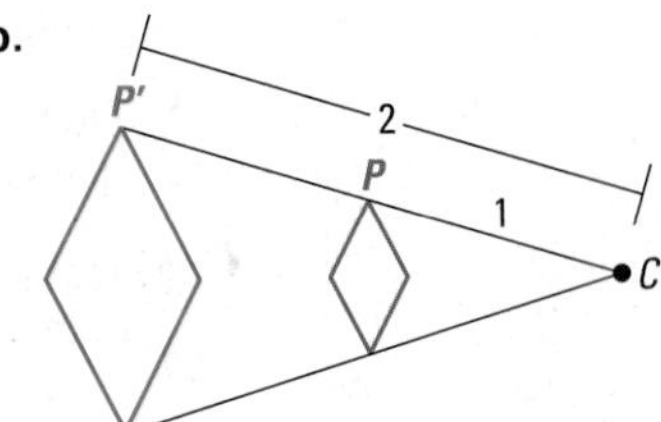

SOLUTION

a. Because $\frac{CP'}{CP} = \frac{2}{3}$, the scale factor is $k = \frac{2}{3}$. This is a reduction.

b. Because $\frac{CP'}{CP} = \frac{2}{1}$, the scale factor is $k = 2$. This is an enlargement.

STUDENT HELP
Look Back
For help with the blue to red color scheme used in transformations, see p. 396.

In a coordinate plane, dilations whose centers are the origin have the property that the image of $P(x, y)$ is $P'(kx, ky)$.

EXAMPLE 2 Dilation in a Coordinate Plane

Draw a dilation of rectangle $ABCD$ with $A(2, 2)$, $B(6, 2)$, $C(6, 4)$, and $D(2, 4)$. Use the origin as the center and use a scale factor of $\frac{1}{2}$. How does the perimeter of the preimage compare to the perimeter of the image?

SOLUTION

Because the center of the dilation is the origin, you can find the image of each vertex by multiplying its coordinates by the scale factor.

$A(2, 2) \rightarrow A'(1, 1)$

$B(6, 2) \rightarrow B'(3, 1)$

$C(6, 4) \rightarrow C'(3, 2)$

$D(2, 4) \rightarrow D'(1, 2)$

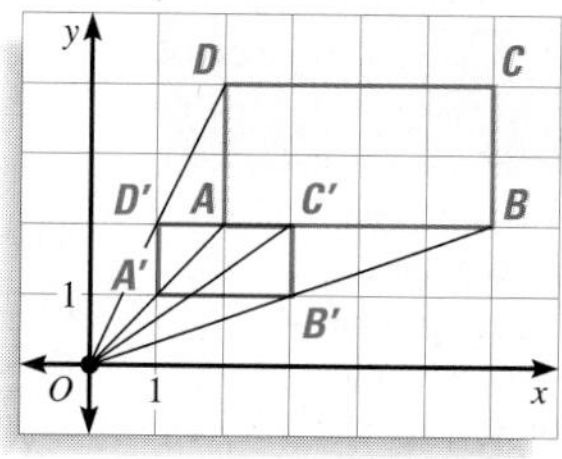

From the graph, you can see that the preimage has a perimeter of 12 and the image has a perimeter of 6. A preimage and its image after a dilation are similar figures. Therefore, the ratio of the perimeters of a preimage and its image is equal to the scale factor of the dilation.

ACTIVITY Construction

Drawing a Dilation

Use the following steps to construct a dilation ($k = 2$) of a triangle using a straightedge and a compass. **1–3. Check drawings.**

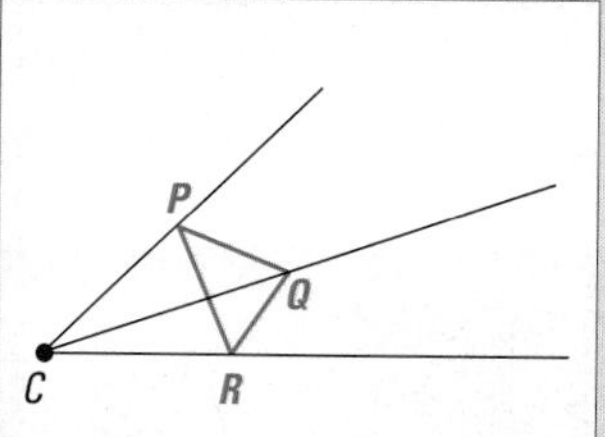

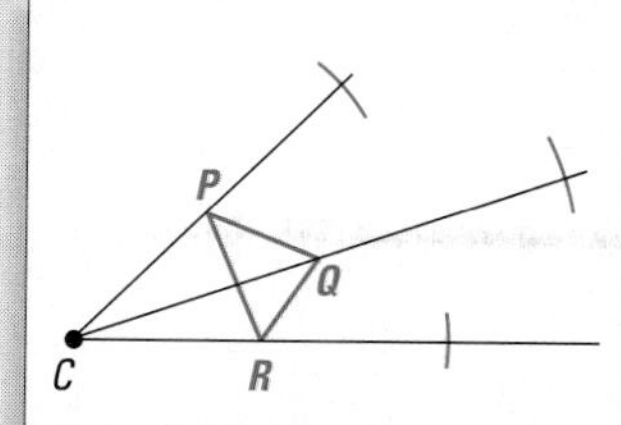

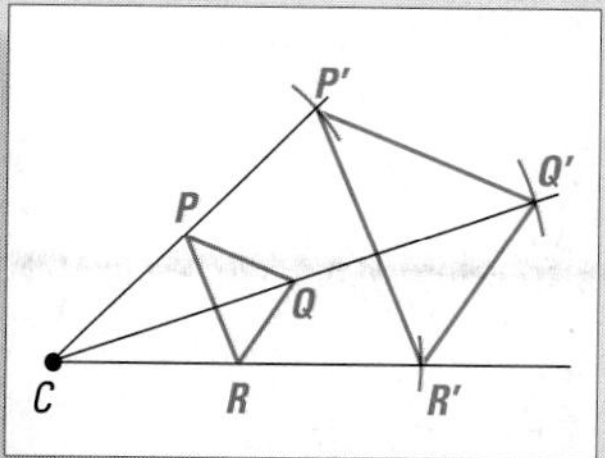

1. Draw $\triangle PQR$ and choose the center of the dilation C. Use a straightedge to draw lines from C through the vertices of the triangle.
2. Use the compass to locate P' on $\overrightarrow{CP}$ so that $CP' = 2(CP)$. Locate Q' and R' in the same way.
3. Connect the points P', Q', and R'.

In the construction above, notice that $\triangle PQR \sim \triangle P'Q'R'$. You can prove this by using the SAS and SSS Similarity Theorems.

2 TEACH

EXTRA EXAMPLE 1

Identify the dilation and find its scale factor.

a. an enlargement, $k = \frac{7}{3}$

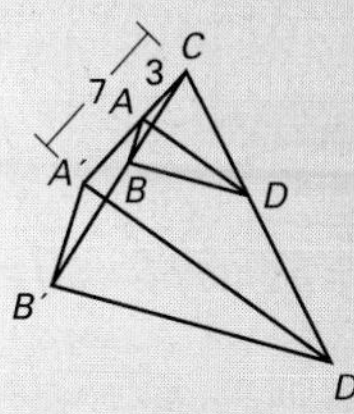

b. a reduction, $k = \frac{3}{4}$

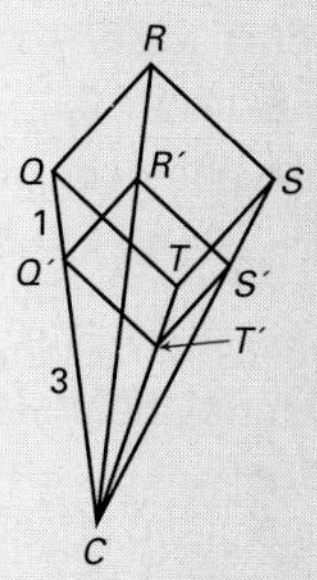

EXTRA EXAMPLE 2

Draw a dilation of $\triangle ABC$ with $A(-2, 1)$, $B(-6, 0)$ and $C(-1, -1)$. Use the origin as the center and use a scale factor of $\frac{3}{2}$. How does the perimeter of the preimage compare to the perimeter of the image? **Check student graphs. The perimeter of the image is 1.5 times the perimeter of the preimage.**

CHECKPOINT EXERCISES

For use after Examples 1 and 2:

1. Is the dilation shown a reduction or an enlargement? **enlargement**

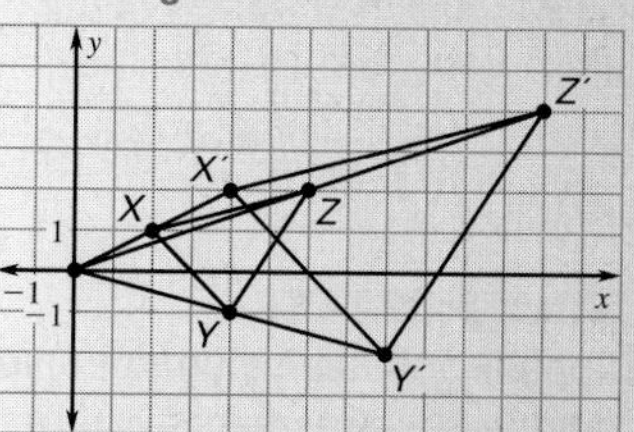

2. What is the scale factor? **2**
3. What are the coordinates of the vertices of the image triangle? ***X'*(4, 2), *Y'*(8, –2), *Z'*(12,4)**

Extra Example 3

In the diagram, the puppet is 10 in. tall. In each case, by what percent is the shadow larger than the puppet?

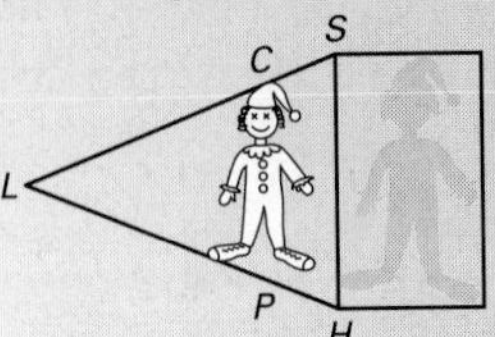

a. $LC = LP = 53$ in.; $LS = LH = 60$ in. 13%

b. $LC = LP = 50$ in.; $LS = LH = 60$ in. 20%

Checkpoint Exercises

For use after Example 3:

1. A circle in a photocopier enlargement has a 6 in. diameter. If the enlargement percentage is 125%, what is the diameter of the preimage circle? 4.8 in.

2. A reduction of the preimage circle in Exercise 1 has a 3.6 in. diameter. What percentage was used for the reduction? 75%

Focus on Vocabulary

What is a reduction? **A reduction is a dilation in which the scale factor is between 0 and 1. The image in a reduction is smaller than the preimage.**

Closure Question

How are the coordinates of the vertex of a figure related to the coordinates of the vertex of the image after a dilation with center at the origin? **The coordinates of the image vertex are equal to the coordinates of the preimage vertex multiplied by the scale factor.**

Daily Puzzler

Suppose you have a photocopier that does enlargements where the image is 50% larger than the original. Explain how you can use repeated copying to make an enlargement where the image is 125% larger than the original. See right.

GOAL 2 Using Dilations in Real Life

EXAMPLE 3 *Finding the Scale Factor*

Focus on Applications

Real Life — SHADOW PUPPETS Some experienced shadowmaster puppeteers can manipulate over 20 carved leather puppets at the same time.

Shadow Puppets Shadow puppets have been used in many countries for hundreds of years. A flat figure is held between a light and a screen. The audience on the other side of the screen sees the puppet's shadow. The shadow is a dilation, or enlargement, of the shadow puppet. When looking at a cross sectional view, $\triangle LCP \sim \triangle LSH$.

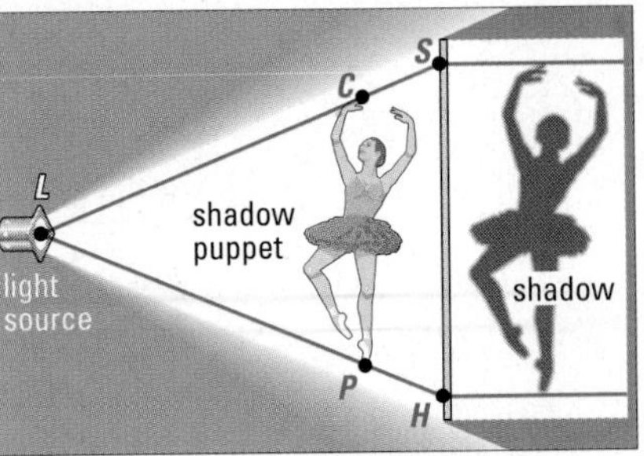

The shadow puppet shown is 12 inches tall (CP in the diagram). Find the height of the shadow, SH, for each distance from the screen. In each case, by what percent is the shadow larger than the puppet?

a. $LC = LP = 59$ in.; $LS = LH = 74$ in.

b. $LC = LP = 66$ in.; $LS = LH = 74$ in.

Solution

a. $\frac{59}{74} = \frac{12}{SH}$ $\quad\quad \frac{LC}{LS} = \frac{CP}{SH}$

$59(SH) = 888$

$SH \approx 15$ inches

To find the percent of size increase, use the scale factor of the dilation.

$\text{scale factor} = \frac{SH}{CP}$

$\frac{15}{12} = 1.25$

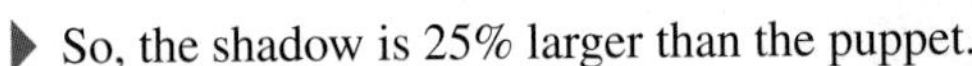

▶ So, the shadow is 25% larger than the puppet.

b. $\frac{66}{74} = \frac{12}{SH}$

$66(SH) = 888$

$SH \approx 13.45$ inches

Use the scale factor again to find the percent of size increase.

$\text{scale factor} = \frac{SH}{CP}$

$\frac{13.45}{12} \approx 1.12$

▶ So, the shadow is about 12% larger than the puppet.

Notice that as the puppet moves closer to the screen, the shadow height decreases.

Daily Puzzler *Sample answer:*
Copy the image one time to get a scale factor of 1.5.
Then copy it again to get a scale factor of 1.5 • 1.5 = 2.25.
This image is 125% larger than the original.

GUIDED PRACTICE

Vocabulary Check ✓

1. In a *dilation* every image is __?__ to its preimage. similar

Concept Check ✓

2. She found $\frac{CP}{CP'}$ rather than $\frac{CP'}{CP}$.

2. **ERROR ANALYSIS** Katie found the scale factor of the dilation shown to be $\frac{1}{2}$. What did Katie do wrong?

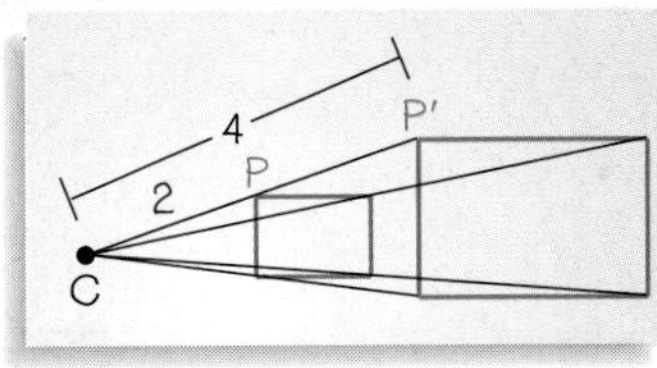

3. Is the dilation shown a reduction or an enlargement? How do you know? See margin.

Skill Check ✓

3. Enlargement; the scale factor is greater than 1. (Also, it is apparent that the image is larger than the preimage.)

$\triangle PQR$ is mapped onto $\triangle P'Q'R'$ by a dilation with center C. Complete the statement.

4. $\triangle PQR$ is (similar, congruent) to $\triangle P'Q'R'$. similar

5. If $\frac{CP'}{CP} = \frac{4}{3}$, then $\triangle P'Q'R'$ is (larger, smaller) than $\triangle PQR$, and the dilation is (a reduction, an enlargement). larger; enlargement

Use the following information to draw a dilation of rectangle *ABCD*.

6. Draw a dilation of rectangle *ABCD* on a coordinate plane, with $A(3, 1)$, $B(3, 2.5)$, $C(5, 2.5)$, and $D(5, 1)$. Use the origin as the center and use a scale factor of 2. See margin.

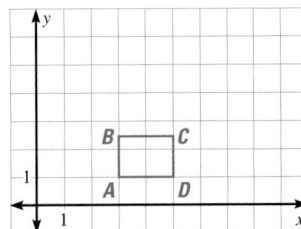

7. Is $ABCD \sim A'B'C'D'$? Explain your answer.
Yes; *Sample answer:* a preimage and its image after a dilation are $\sim$.

PRACTICE AND APPLICATIONS

STUDENT HELP

Extra Practice to help you master skills is on p. 818.

IDENTIFYING DILATIONS **Identify the dilation and find its scale factor.**

8.

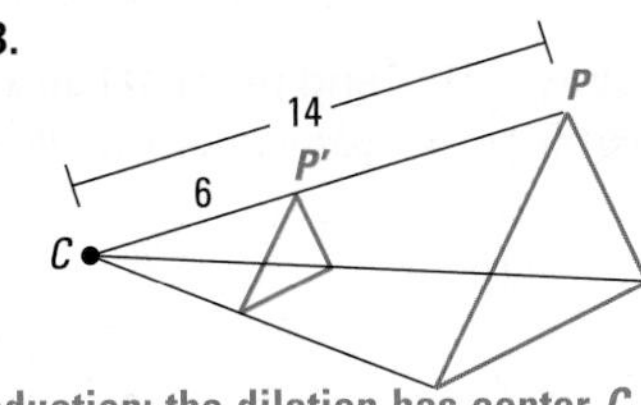

Reduction; the dilation has center C and scale factor $\frac{3}{7}$.

9.

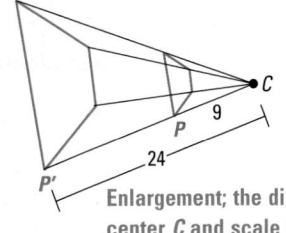

Enlargement; the dilation has center C and scale factor $\frac{8}{3}$.

FINDING SCALE FACTORS **Identify the dilation, and find its scale factor. Then, find the values of the variables.**

10.

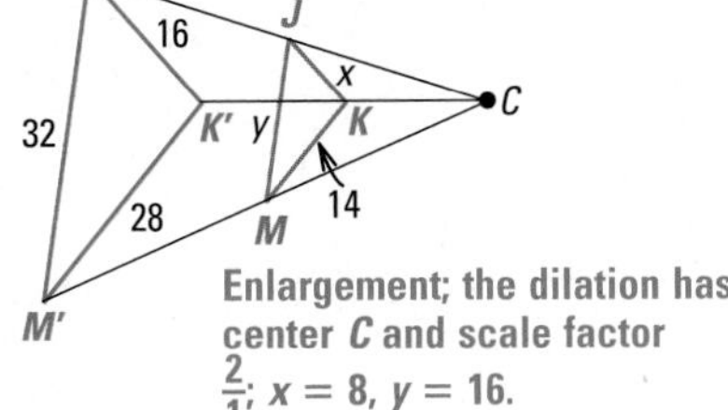

Enlargement; the dilation has center C and scale factor $\frac{2}{1}$; $x = 8$, $y = 16$.

11.

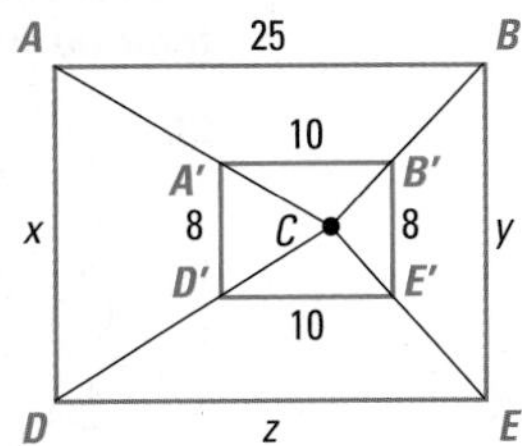

Reduction; the dilation has center C and scale factor $\frac{2}{5}$; $x = y = 20$, $z = 25$.

STUDENT HELP

HOMEWORK HELP
Example 1: Exs. 8–11, 20–23
Example 2: Exs. 12–15
Example 3: Exs. 24–26, 33

3 APPLY

ASSIGNMENT GUIDE

BASIC
Day 1: pp. 509–512 Exs. 8–22 even, 35, 36
Day 2: pp. 509–513 Exs. 9–23 odd, 32, 34, 38–44, Quiz 3 Exs. 1–8

AVERAGE
Day 1: pp. 509–512 Exs. 8–22 even, 35, 36
Day 2: pp. 509–513 Exs. 9–23 odd, 27–32, 34, 38–44, Quiz 3 Exs. 1–8

ADVANCED
Day 1: pp. 509–512 Exs. 8–22 even, 35, 36
Day 2: pp. 509–513 Exs. 9–23 odd, 27–32, 34, 37–44, Quiz 3 Exs. 1–8

BLOCK SCHEDULE
pp. 509–512 Exs. 8–22 even, 35, 36 (with 8.6)
pp. 509–513 Exs. 9–23 odd, 27–32, 34, 38–44, Quiz 3 Exs. 1–8 (with Ch. Rev.)

EXERCISE LEVELS

Level A: *Easier*
8, 9
Level B: *More Difficult*
10–36
Level C: *Most Difficult*
37

✓ HOMEWORK CHECK

To quickly check student understanding of key concepts, go over the following exercises: Exs. 8, 10, 14, 18, 20, 22, 32. See also the Daily Homework Quiz:

- Blackline Master (*Chapter 9 Resource Book,* p. 11)
- Transparency (p. 63)

6. See Additional Answers beginning on page AA1.

TEACHING TIPS

EXERCISE 16 Students should use the Pythagorean Theorem and the fact that $EG = 2PG$ and $GF = 2GQ$ when finding the ratio of EF to PQ. The result should not be surprising, since the preimage and image of a dilation are similar figures.

12. $J'\left(-2\frac{1}{2}, 1\frac{1}{2}\right)$, $K'\left(1, 1\frac{1}{2}\right)$, $L'\left(1, -1\frac{1}{2}\right)$, $M'\left(-2\frac{1}{2}, -1\frac{1}{2}\right)$

14. $D'\left(-1\frac{2}{3}, 1\frac{1}{3}\right)$, $E'\left(1, \frac{2}{3}\right)$, $F'\left(1\frac{2}{3}, -1\right)$, $G'\left(-1, -1\frac{1}{3}\right)$

DILATIONS IN A COORDINATE PLANE **Use the origin as the center of the dilation and the given scale factor to find the coordinates of the vertices of the image of the polygon.**

12. $k = \frac{1}{2}$

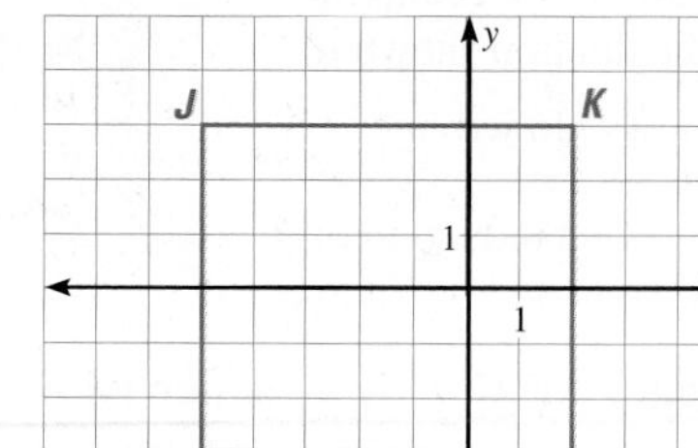

13. $k = 2$ $P'(6, 10)$, $Q'(8, 0)$, $R'(2, 2)$

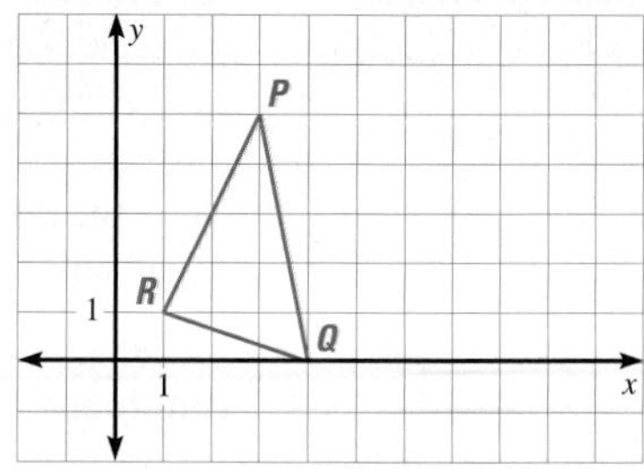

14. $k = \frac{1}{3}$ See margin.

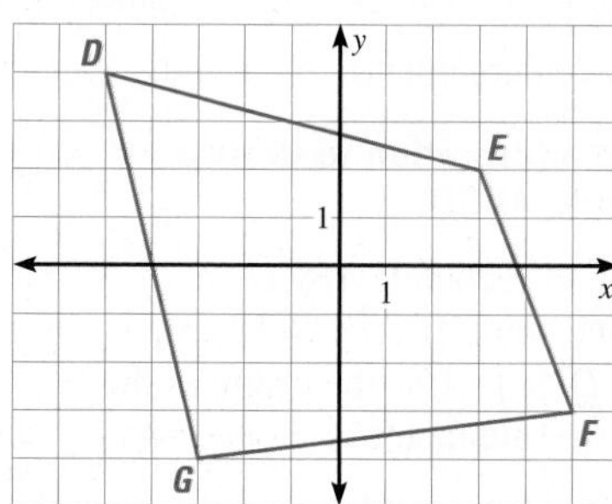

15. $k = 4$ $S'(-20, 8)$, $T'(-12, 16)$, $U'(-4, 4)$, $V'(-12, -4)$

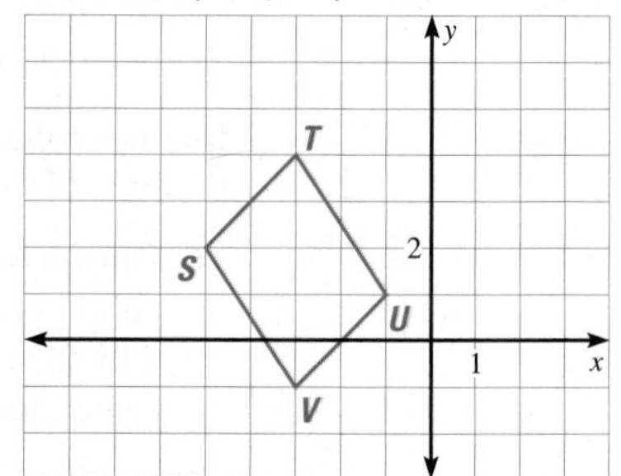

16. COMPARING RATIOS Use the triangle shown. Let P and Q be the midpoints of the sides $\overline{EG}$ and $\overline{FG}$, respectively. Find the scale factor and the center of the dilation that enlarges $\triangle PQG$ to $\triangle EFG$. Find the ratio of EF to PQ. How does this ratio compare to the scale factor? 2, G; 2:1; same as the scale factor

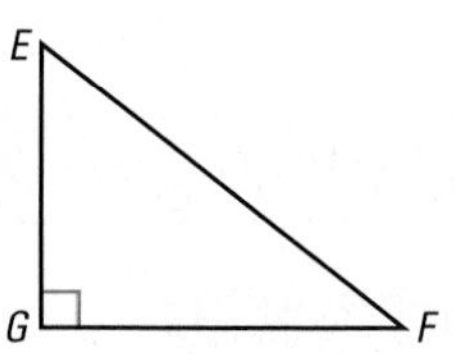

CONSTRUCTION **Copy $\triangle DEF$ and points G and H as shown. Then, use a straightedge and a compass to construct the dilation.** 17–19. Check drawings.

17. $k = 3$; Center: G

18. $k = \frac{1}{2}$; Center: H

19. $k = 2$; Center: E

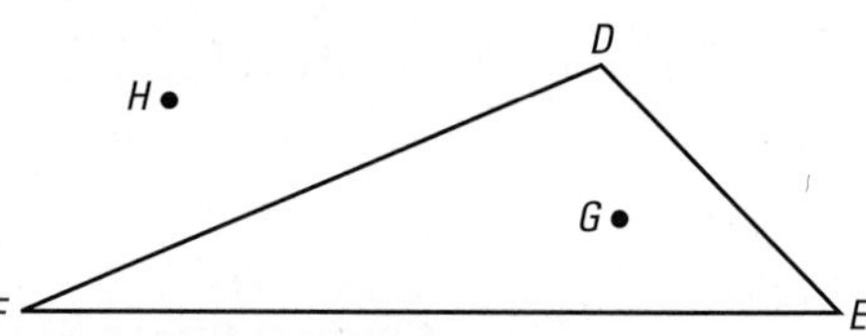

SIMILAR TRIANGLES **The red triangle is the image of the blue triangle after a dilation. Find the values of the variables. Then find the ratio of their perimeters.**

20.

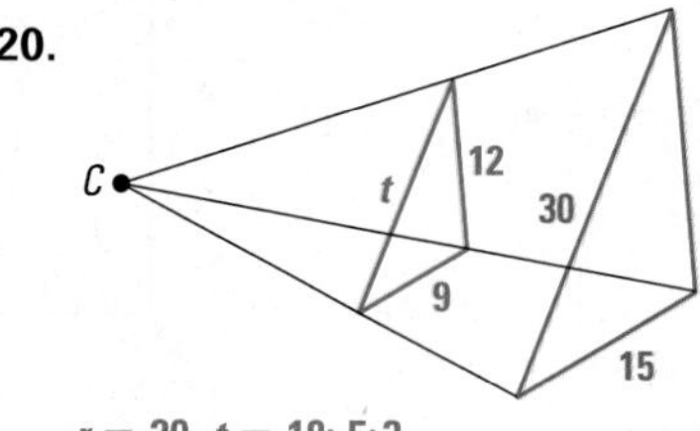

$r = 20$, $t = 18$; 5:3

21.

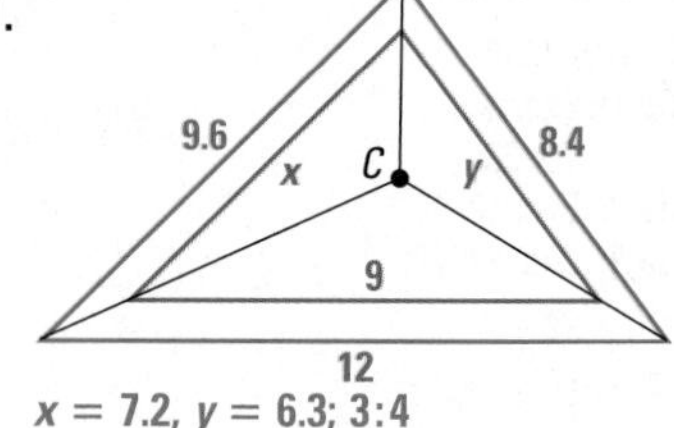

$x = 7.2$, $y = 6.3$; 3:4

STUDENT HELP

HOMEWORK HELP
Visit our Web site www.mcdougallittell.com for help with problem solving in Exs. 22 and 23.

IDENTIFYING DILATIONS $\triangle ABC$ is mapped onto $\triangle A'B'C'$ by a dilation. Use the given information to sketch the dilation, identify it as a reduction or an enlargement, and find the scale factor. Then find the missing lengths.

22. In $\triangle ABC$, $AB = 6$, $BC = 9$, and $AC = 12$. In $\triangle A'B'C'$, $A'B' = 2$. Find the lengths of $\overline{B'C'}$ and $\overline{A'C'}$. Check drawings; reduction; $k = \frac{1}{3}$; 3, 4

23. In $\triangle ABC$, $AB = 5$ and $BC = 7$. In $\triangle A'B'C'$, $A'B' = 20$ and $A'C' = 36$. Find the lengths of $\overline{AC}$ and $\overline{B'C'}$. Check drawings; enlargement; $k = 4$; 9, 28

FLASHLIGHT IMAGE In Exercises 24–26, use the following information. You are projecting images onto a wall with a flashlight. The lamp of the flashlight is 8.3 centimeters away from the wall. The preimage is imprinted onto a clear cap that fits over the end of the flashlight. This cap has a diameter of 3 centimeters. The preimage has a height of 2 centimeters, and the lamp of the flashlight is located 2.7 centimeters from the preimage.

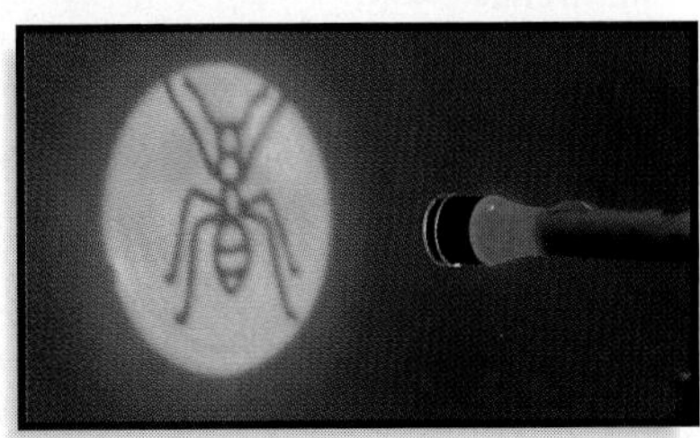

24. Sketch a diagram of the dilation. See margin.

25. Find the diameter of the circle of light projected onto the wall from the flashlight. about 9.2 cm

26. Find the height of the image projected onto the wall. about 6.1 cm

ENLARGEMENTS In Exercises 27 and 28, use the following information. By adjusting the distance between the negative and the enlarged print in the photographic enlarger shown, you can make prints of different sizes. In the diagram shown, you want the enlarged print to be 7 inches wide ($A'B'$). The negative is 1 inch wide (AB), and the distance between the light source and the negative is 1.25 inches (CD).

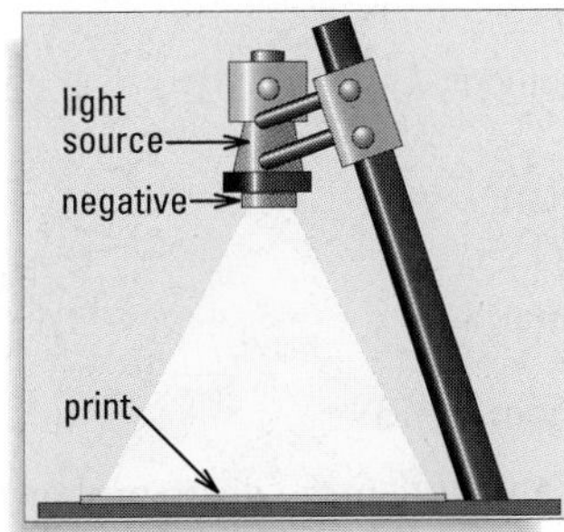

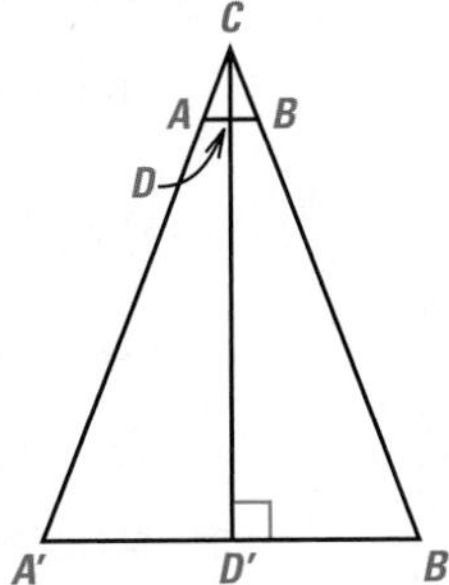

27. What is the scale factor of the enlargement? 7:1

28. What is the distance between the light source and the enlarged print? 8.75 in.

DIMENSIONS OF PHOTOS Use the diagram from Exercise 27 to determine the missing information.

	CD	CD'	AB	$A'B'$	
29.	1.2 in.	7.2 in.	0.8 in.	?	4.8 in.
30.	?	14 cm	2 cm	12 cm	about 2.33 cm
31.	2 in.	10 in.	?	8.5 in.	1.7 in.

STUDENT HELP NOTES

Homework Help Students can find help for Exs. 22 and 23 at **www.mcdougallittell.com.** The information can be printed out for students who don't have access to the Internet.

24. See Additional Answers beginning on page AA1.

CAREER NOTE

EXERCISE 34 Additional information about architectural rendering is available at **www.mcdougallittell.com.**

33. *Sample answer:*

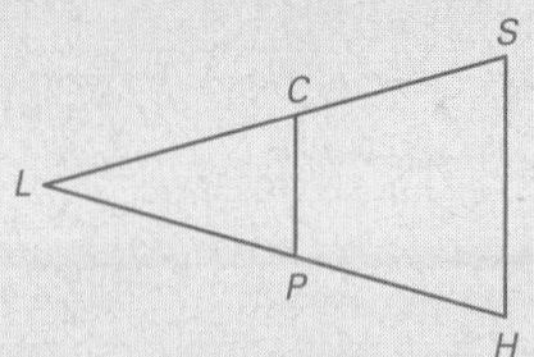

I would show the student this figure and explain that *L* represents the light source, *CP* the height of the puppet, and *SH* the height of the image. I would tell the student that a dilation transforms a figure in such a way that the original figure (or *preimage*) and the figure after the dilation (the *image*) are similar. In the figure, the center of the dilation is *L* and the scale factor is the ratio of *LS* to *LC*.

ADDITIONAL PRACTICE AND RETEACHING

For Lesson 8.7:

- Practice Levels A, B, and C (*Chapter 8 Resource Book*, p. 101)
- Reteaching with Practice (*Chapter 8 Resource Book*, p. 104)
- See Lesson 8.7 of the *Personal Student Tutor*

For more Mixed Review:

- Search the *Test and Practice Generator* for key words or specific lessons.

FOCUS ON CAREERS

ARCHITECTURAL RENDERING An architectural renderer uses techniques like the one shown in Exercise 34 to create three dimensional drawings of buildings and other structures.

CAREER LINK www.mcdougallittell.com

32. **LOGICAL REASONING** Draw any triangle, and label it $\triangle PQR$. Using a scale factor of 2, draw the image of $\triangle PQR$ after a dilation with a center outside the triangle, with a center inside the triangle, and with a center on the triangle. Explain the relationship between the three images created. See margin.

33. *Writing* Use the information about shadow puppet theaters from Example 3, page 508. Explain how you could use a shadow puppet theater to help another student understand the terms *image*, *preimage*, *center of dilation*, and *dilation*. Draw a diagram and label the terms on the diagram. See margin.

34. **PERSPECTIVE DRAWING** Create a perspective drawing by following the given steps. Check drawings.

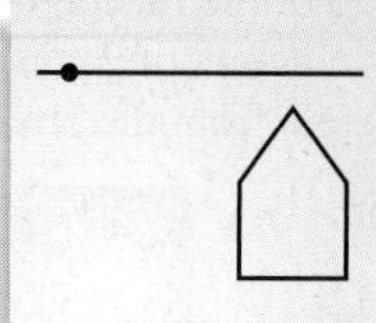

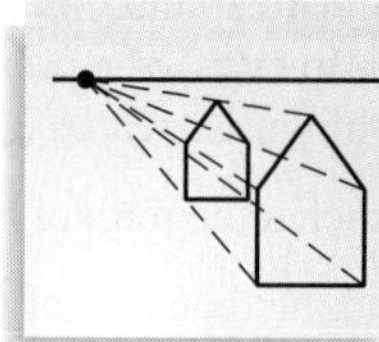

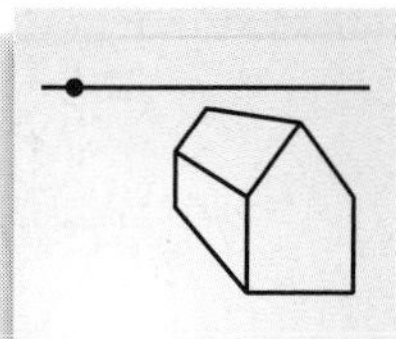

1. Draw a horizontal line across the paper, and choose a point on this line to be the center of the dilation, also called the *vanishing point*. Next, draw a polygon.
2. Draw rays from the vanishing point to all vertices of the polygon. Draw a reduction of the polygon by locating image points on the rays.
3. Connect the preimage to the image by darkening the segments between them. Erase all hidden lines.

Test Preparation

32. The △s are ≅. All 3 △s are ~ to $\triangle PQR$, so all the corresp. ∠s are ≅. The scale factor of each dilation is 2, so each side of every image △ is twice as long as the corresp. side of $\triangle PQR$. Then the corresp. sides of the 3 △s are ≅ and the 3 △s are ≅ by the def. of ≅ △s.

35. **MULTIPLE CHOICE** Identify the dilation shown as an enlargement or reduction and find its scale factor. C

Ⓐ enlargement; $k = 2$

Ⓑ enlargement; $k = \frac{1}{3}$

Ⓒ reduction; $k = \frac{1}{3}$

Ⓓ reduction; $k = \frac{1}{2}$

Ⓔ reduction; $k = 3$

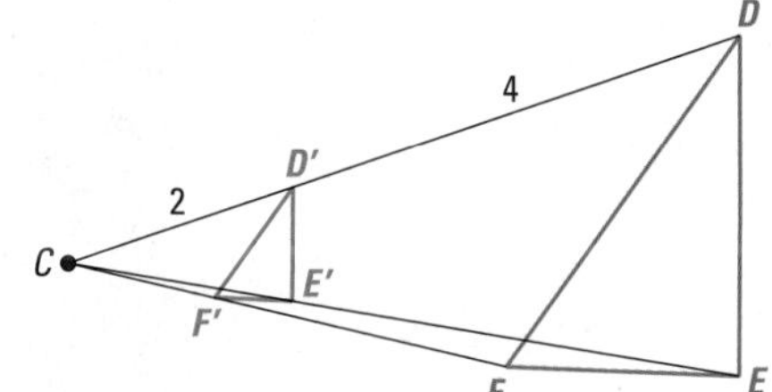

36. **MULTIPLE CHOICE** In the diagram shown, the center of the dilation of $\square JKLM$ is point C. The length of a side of $\square J'K'L'M'$ is what percent of the length of the corresponding side of $\square JKLM$? D

Ⓐ 3%　Ⓑ 12%　Ⓒ 20%

Ⓓ $33\frac{1}{3}\%$　Ⓔ 300%

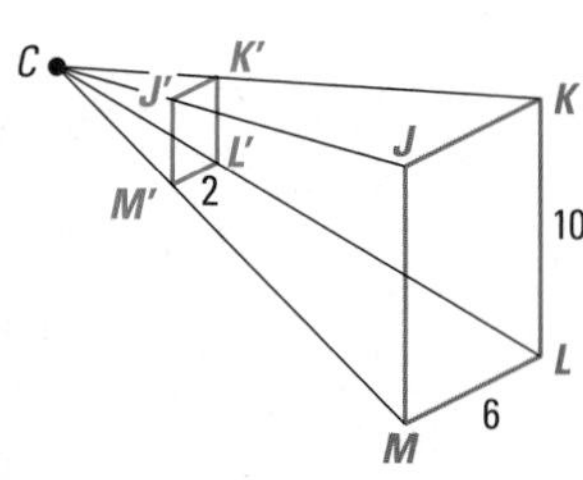

★ **Challenge**

37. **CREATING NEW IMAGES** A polygon is reduced by a dilation with center C and scale factor $\frac{1}{k}$. The image is then enlarged by a dilation with center C and scale factor k. Describe the size and shape of this new image.
The new image is the original figure.

MIXED REVIEW

USING THE PYTHAGOREAN THEOREM Refer to the triangle shown to find the length of the missing side by using the Pythagorean Theorem. (Review 1.3 for 9.1)

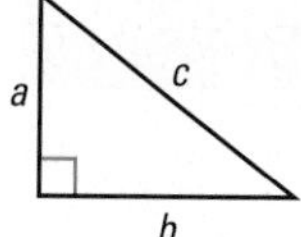

38. $a = 5, b = 12$ $c = 13$
39. $a = 8, c = 2\sqrt{65}$ $b = 14$
40. $b = 2, c = 5\sqrt{5}$ $a = 11$
41. $b = 1, c = \sqrt{50}$ $a = 7$
42. Find the geometric mean of 11 and 44. (Review 8.2 for 9.1) 22

DETERMINING SIMILARITY Determine whether the triangles can be proved similar or not. Explain your reasoning. (Review 8.4 and 8.5)

43.

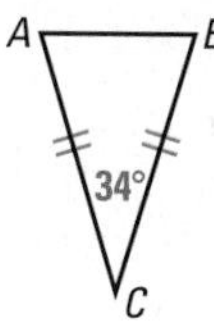

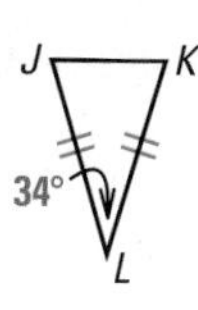

Yes; *Sample answer:* $\angle C \cong \angle L$ and $\frac{CA}{LJ} = \frac{CB}{LK}$, so the △s are ~ by the SAS Similarity Thm.

44.

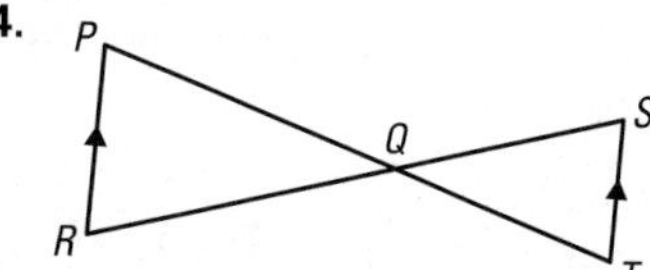

Yes; $\angle P \cong \angle T$ and $\angle R \cong \angle S$ by the Alternate Interior Angles Thm. (Vertical △s PQR and TQS are also ≅.) Then $\triangle PQR \sim \triangle TQS$ by the AA Similarity Post.

QUIZ 3

Self-Test for Lessons 8.6 and 8.7

Use the figure to complete the proportion. (Lesson 8.6)

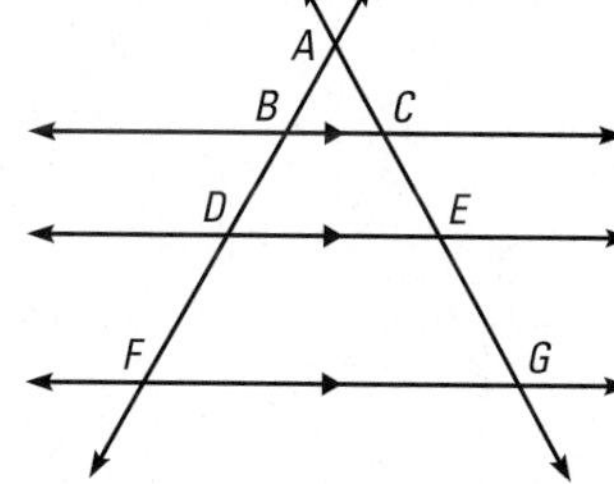

1. $\frac{AC}{CE} = \frac{AB}{?}$ BD
2. $\frac{BD}{BF} = \frac{?}{CG}$ CE
3. $\frac{EG}{AG} = \frac{DF}{?}$ AF
4. $\frac{GA}{EA} = \frac{?}{DA}$ FA

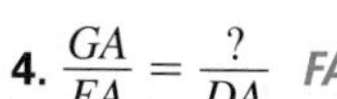

In Exercises 5 and 6, identify the dilation and find its scale factor. (Lesson 8.7)

5.

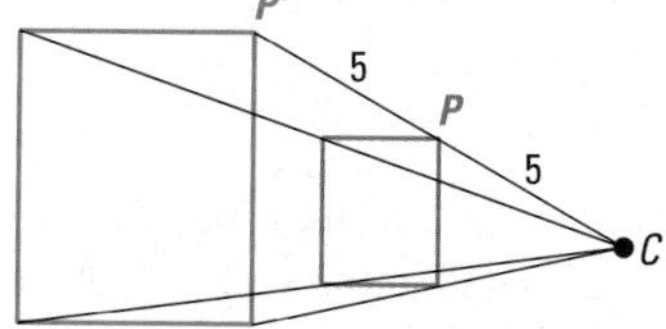

The dilation is an enlargement with center C and scale factor 2.

6.

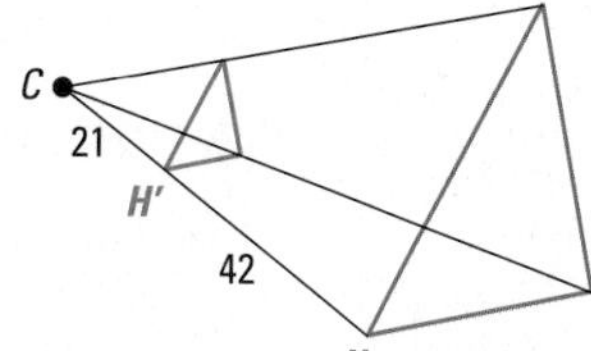

The dilation is a reduction with center C and scale factor $\frac{1}{3}$.

7. $\triangle JKL$ is mapped onto $\triangle J'K'L'$ by a dilation, with center C. If $\frac{CJ'}{CJ} = \frac{5}{6}$, then the dilation is (a reduction, an enlargement) and $\triangle JKL$ is (larger, smaller) than $\triangle J'K'L'$. (Lesson 8.7) reduction, larger

8. **ENLARGING PHOTOS** An 8 inch by 10 inch photo is enlarged to produce an 18 inch by $22\frac{1}{2}$ inch photo. What is the scale factor? (Lesson 8.7) $\frac{9}{4}$

4 ASSESS

DAILY HOMEWORK QUIZ

Transparency Available

1. Identify the dilation and find its scale factor. Then find the values of the variables.

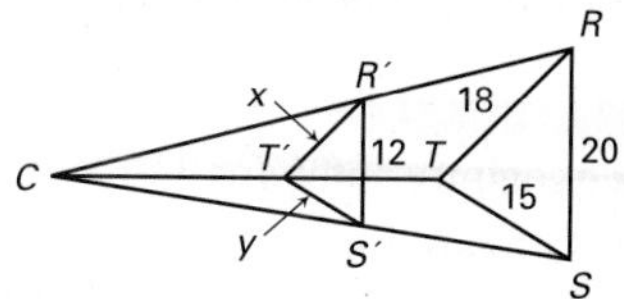

The dilation has center C and scale factor $\frac{3}{5}$; $x = 10.8$, $y = 9$

Use the origin as the center of the dilation, the given scale factor, and the given coordinates of the vertices of the preimage polygon to find the coordinates of the vertices of the image polygon.

2. $\triangle XYZ$, with scale factor 5 and vertices $X(3, 1)$, $Y(6, 4)$, and $Z(8, -1)$ $X'(15, 5)$, $Y'(30, 20)$, $Z'(40, -5)$
3. ▱$PQRS$ with scale factor $\frac{2}{3}$ and vertices $P(-6, 3)$, $Q(3, 3)$, $R(3, -6)$, and $S(-6, -6)$ $P'(-4, 2)$, $Q'(2, 2)$, $R'(2, -4)$, $S'(-4, -4)$

EXTRA CHALLENGE NOTE

Challenge problems for Lesson 8.7 are available in **blackline** format in the *Chapter 8 Resource Book*, p. 108 and at **www.mcdougallittell.com.**

ADDITIONAL TEST PREPARATION

1. **WRITING** Draw a triangle and a point C, outside the triangle. Describe how to draw the image of the triangle after a dilation with scale factor 3. See left.

Additional Test Preparation *Sample answer:*

1. Check students' drawings. After drawing the triangle, draw a line through C and each vertex of the triangle. Use a compass to mark a point three times as far from C as each original vertex and on the line between C and the vertex. Join these three points to form the image.

1 Planning the Activity

PURPOSE
To investigate the effect the location of the center of dilation has on the dilation and to determine how the area of a polygon and the area of its image after a dilation are related to the scale factor.

MATERIALS
- geometry software
- Software Help (*Chapter 8 Resource Book*, p. 99)

PACING
- Exploring the Concept — 10 min
- Drawing Conclusions — 15 min

LINK TO LESSON
You can refer back to Exercise 32 on page 512 when completing this activity. Students can check their conclusions from this exercise using the graphing software.

2 Managing the Activity

COOPERATIVE LEARNING
Have students work in pairs at one computer. They should take turns using the software and should discuss Question 6 prior to writing a response.

ALTERNATIVE APPROACH
This activity can be done as a class demonstration using a computer with an overhead display. You might have volunteers come up to draw the pentagon and drag point *P*.

3 Closing the Activity

KEY DISCOVERY
To find the area of the image of a polygon after a dilation, multiply the area of the preimage by the square of the scale factor.

ACTIVITY ASSESSMENT
A triangle that has an area of 4 cm^2 is dilated with a scale factor of $\frac{3}{2}$. What is the area of the image?
9 cm^2

ACTIVITY 8.7
Using Technology

Exploring Dilations

You can use geometry software to explore properties of dilations.

STUDENT HELP

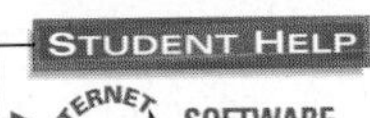

SOFTWARE HELP
Visit our Web site www.mcdougallittell.com to see instructions for several software applications.

CONSTRUCT

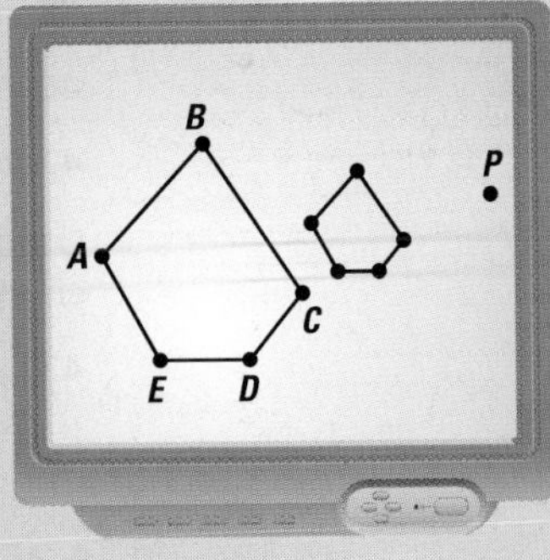
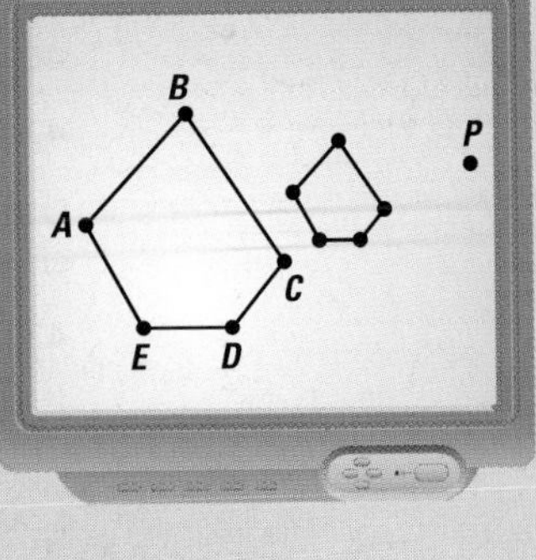

1. Draw a pentagon and label it *ABCDE*.
2. Draw a point outside the polygon. Label it *P*.
3. Dilate the polygon using a scale factor of $\frac{1}{2}$ and center *P*. Label the image $A'B'C'D'E'$.

INVESTIGATE

1. Measure AP and $A'P$ and calculate the ratio $\frac{AP}{A'P}$. What do you notice? $\frac{2}{1}$; the ratio is the reciprocal of the scale factor of the dilation.
2. Measure AB and $A'B'$ and calculate the ratio $\frac{AB}{A'B'}$. What do you notice? $\frac{2}{1}$; the ratio is the reciprocal of the scale factor of the dilation.
3. Drag point *P* to several locations outside *ABCDE*. Do the ratios you found in Exercises 1 and 2 change? no
4. Drag point *P* to several locations inside *ABCDE*. What do you notice about the position of $A'B'C'D'E'$? $A'B'C'D'E'$ is inside *ABCDE*.
5. Determine the areas of *ABCDE* and $A'B'C'D'E'$. Calculate the ratio of the area of *ABCDE* to the area of $A'B'C'D'E'$. $\frac{4}{1}$

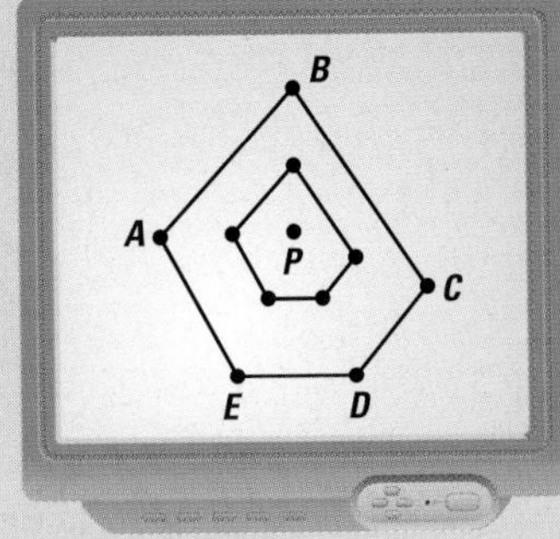

CONJECTURE

6. Make a conjecture about how the area of a polygon and the area of its image after a dilation are related to the scale factor of the dilation. Test your conjecture using a different polygon and scale factor. See margin.

EXTENSION

CRITICAL THINKING Suppose a polygon is dilated with scale factor *x* and then the image is dilated with scale factor *y*. What scale factor could you use to dilate the original polygon to the final polygon? Explain. See margin.

6. If the scale factor of a dilation is $a:b$, then the ratio of the area of a polygon to the area of its image after a dilation is $a^2:b^2$.

Extension *yx* (or *xy*); *Sample answer:* Let $\overline{AB}$ be a side of a polygon, $\overline{A'B'}$ its image after the first dilation, and $\overline{A''B''}$ its image after the second. Since the first image is ~ to the preimage and the second is ~ to the first, the transitive properties of congruence and equality can be used to show that the second image is ~ to the preimage. As shown above, $\frac{AB}{A'B'} = \frac{1}{x}$, so $A'B' = x \cdot AB$. Similarly, $A''B'' = y \cdot A'B' = y \cdot x \cdot AB$. Then the scale factor of the dilation that maps the original polygon to the final one is *yx*.

CHAPTER 8

Chapter Summary

WHAT did you learn?	*WHY did you learn it?*
Write and simplify the ratio of two numbers. **(8.1)**	Find the ratio of the track team's wins to losses. **(p. 461)**
Use proportions to solve problems. **(8.1)**	Use measurements of a baseball bat sculpture to find the dimensions of Babe Ruth's bat. **(p. 463)**
Understand properties of proportions. **(8.2)**	Determine the width of the actual Titanic ship from the dimensions of a scale model. **(p. 467)**
Identify similar polygons and use properties of similar polygons. **(8.3)**	Determine whether two television screens are similar. **(p. 477)**
Prove that two triangles are similar using the definition of similar triangles and the AA Similarity Postulate. **(8.4)**	Use similar triangles to determine the altitude of an aerial photography blimp. **(p. 482)**
Prove that two triangles are similar using the SSS Similarity Theorem and the SAS Similarity Theorem. **(8.5)**	Use similar triangles to estimate the height of the Unisphere. **(p. 494)**
Use proportionality theorems to solve problems. **(8.6)**	Explain why the diagonal cuts on insulation strips have the same length. **(p. 501)**
Identify and draw dilations and use properties of dilations. **(8.7)**	Understand how the shadows in a shadow puppet show change size. **(p. 508)**

How does Chapter 8 fit into the BIGGER PICTURE of geometry?

In this chapter, you learned that if two polygons are similar, then the lengths of their corresponding sides are proportional. You also studied several connections among real-life situations, geometry, and algebra. For instance, solving a problem that involves similar polygons (geometry) often requires the use of a proportion (algebra). In later chapters, remember that the measures of corresponding angles of similar polygons are equal, but the lengths of corresponding sides of similar polygons are proportional.

STUDY STRATEGY

How did you use your list of real-world examples?

The list of the main topics of the chapter with corresponding real-world examples that you made following the **Study Strategy** on page 456, may resemble this one.

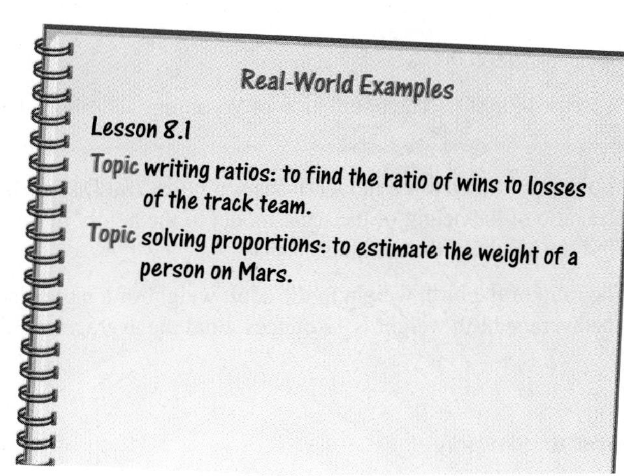

Real-World Examples
Lesson 8.1
Topic writing ratios: to find the ratio of wins to losses of the track team.
Topic solving proportions: to estimate the weight of a person on Mars.

515

ADDITIONAL RESOURCES

The following resources are available to help review the material in this chapter.

- Chapter Review Games and Activities (*Chapter 8 Resource Book,* p. 109)
- *Geometry in Motion video*
- *Personal Student Tutor*
- Cumulative Review, Chs. 1–8 (*Chapter 8 Resource Book,* p. 121)

CHAPTER 8

Chapter Review

VOCABULARY

- **ratio, p. 457**
- **proportion, p. 459**
- **extremes, p. 459**
- **means, p. 459**
- **geometric mean, p. 466**
- **similar polygons, p. 473**
- **scale factor, p. 474**
- **dilation, p. 506**
- **reduction, p. 506**
- **enlargement, p. 506**

8.1 RATIO AND PROPORTION

Examples on pp. 457–460

EXAMPLE You can solve a proportion by finding the value of the variable.

$$\frac{x}{12} = \frac{x+6}{30}$$ **Write original proportion.**

$$30x = 12(x+6)$$ **Cross product property**

$$30x = 12x + 72$$ **Distributive property**

$$18x = 72$$ **Subtract 12*x* from each side.**

$$x = 4$$ **Divide each side by 18.**

Solve the proportion.

1. $\frac{3}{x} = \frac{2}{7}$ $\frac{21}{2}$

2. $\frac{a+1}{5} = \frac{2a}{9}$ 9

3. $\frac{2}{x+1} = \frac{4}{x+6}$ 4

4. $\frac{d-4}{d} = \frac{3}{7}$ 7

8.2 PROBLEM SOLVING IN GEOMETRY WITH PROPORTIONS

Examples on pp. 465–467

EXAMPLE In 1997, the ratio of the population of South Carolina to the population of Wyoming was 47 : 6. The population of South Carolina was about 3,760,000. You can find the population of Wyoming by solving a proportion.

$$\frac{47}{6} = \frac{3{,}760{,}000}{x}$$

$$47x = 22{,}560{,}000$$

$x = 480{,}000$ The population of Wyoming was about 480,000.

5. You buy a 13 inch scale model of the sculpture *The Dancer* by Edgar Degas. The ratio of the height of the scale model to the height of the sculpture is 1 : 3. Find the height of the sculpture. 39 in.

6. The ratio of the birth weight to the adult weight of a male black bear is 3 : 1000. The average birth weight is 12 ounces. Find the average adult weight in pounds. 250 lb

8.3 SIMILAR POLYGONS

Examples on pp. 473–475

EXAMPLE The two parallelograms shown are similar because their corresponding angles are congruent and the lengths of their corresponding sides are proportional.

$$\frac{WX}{PQ} = \frac{ZY}{SR} = \frac{XY}{QR} = \frac{WZ}{PS} = \frac{3}{4}$$

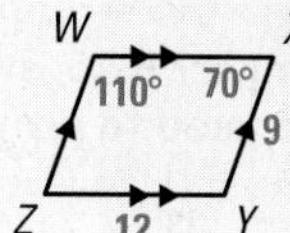

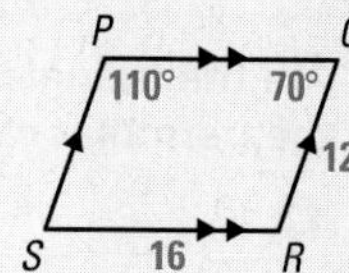

$m\angle P = m\angle R = m\angle W = m\angle Y = 110°$

$m\angle Q = m\angle S = m\angle X = m\angle Z = 70°$

The scale factor of $\square WXYZ$ to $\square PQRS$ is $\frac{3}{4}$.

In Exercises 7–9, $\square DEFG \sim \square HJKL$.

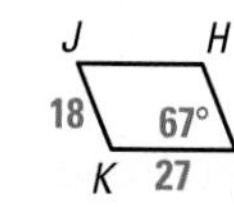

7. Find the scale factor of $\square DEFG$ to $\square HJKL$. $\frac{5}{3}$

8. Find the length of $\overline{DE}$ and the measure of $\angle F$. 45 ; 113°

9. Find the ratio of the perimeter of $\square HJKL$ to the perimeter of $\square DEFG$. $\frac{3}{5}$

8.4 SIMILAR TRIANGLES

Examples on pp. 480–482

EXAMPLE Because two angles of $\triangle ABC$ are congruent to two angles of $\triangle DEF$, $\triangle ABC \sim \triangle DEF$ by the Angle-Angle (AA) Similarity Postulate.

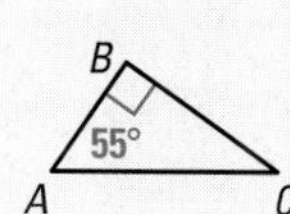

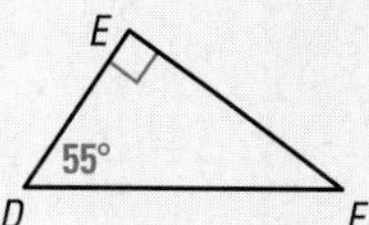

Determine whether the triangles can be proved similar or not. Explain why or why not. If they are similar, write a similarity statement.

10.

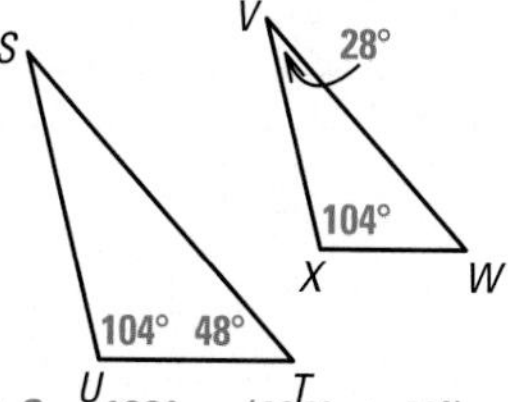

Yes; $m\angle S = 180° - (104° + 48°) = 28°$, so $\angle S \cong \angle V$ and the △ are ~ by the AA Similarity Post; $\triangle STU \sim \triangle VWX$.

11. no

12.

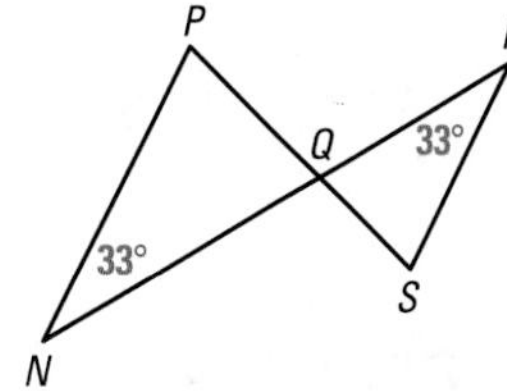

Yes; vertical △ PQN and SQR are ≅, so the △ are ~ by the AA Similarity Post; $\triangle PQN \sim \triangle SQR$.

8.5 PROVING TRIANGLES ARE SIMILAR

Examples on pp. 488–491

EXAMPLES Three sides of $\triangle JKL$ are proportional to three sides of $\triangle MNP$, so $\triangle JKL \sim \triangle MNP$ by the Side-Side-Side (SSS) Similarity Theorem.

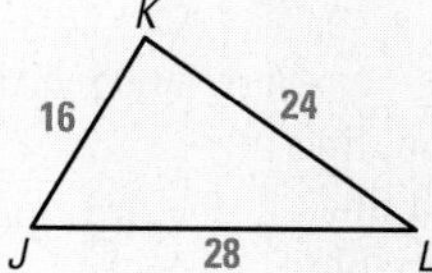

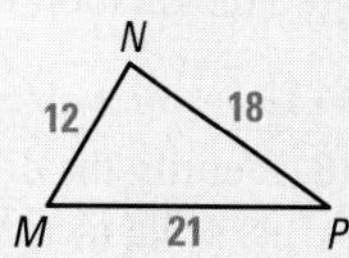

8.5 continued

Two sides of $\triangle XYZ$ are proportional to two sides of $\triangle WXY$, and the included angles are congruent. By the Side-Angle-Side (SAS) Similarity Theorem, $\triangle XYZ \sim \triangle WXY$.

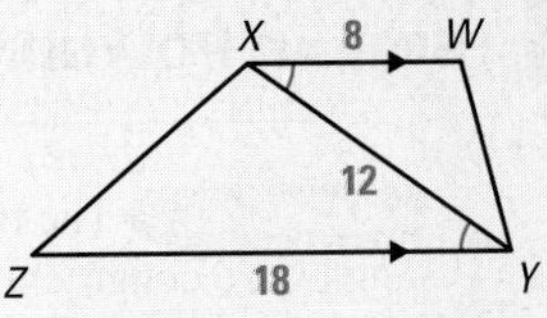

Are the triangles similar? If so, state the similarity and a postulate or theorem that can be used to prove that the triangles are similar.

13. no

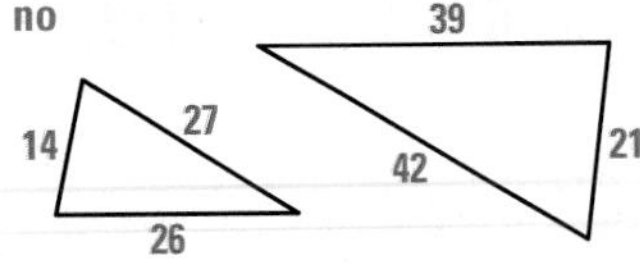

14.

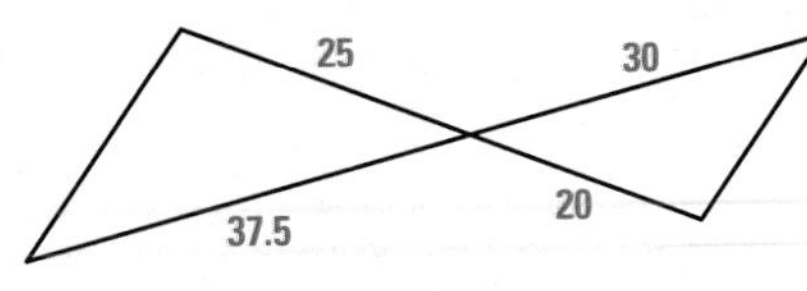

yes; SAS Similarity Thm.

8.6 PROPORTIONS AND SIMILAR TRIANGLES

Examples on pp. 498–501

EXAMPLES You can use proportionality theorems to compare proportional lengths.

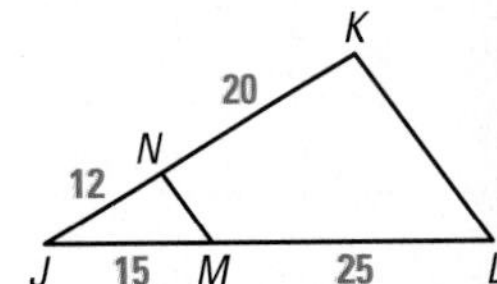

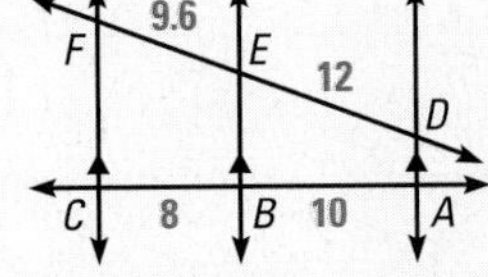

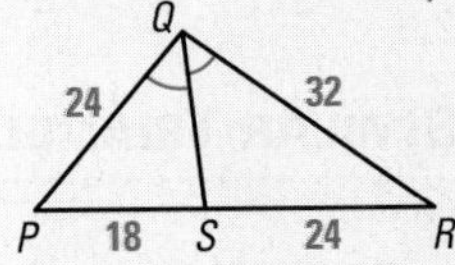

$\frac{JN}{NK} = \frac{12}{20} = \frac{3}{5}$ $\frac{JM}{ML} = \frac{15}{25} = \frac{3}{5}$ $\frac{AB}{BC} = \frac{10}{8} = \frac{5}{4}$ $\frac{DE}{EF} = \frac{12}{9.6} = \frac{5}{4}$ $\frac{QP}{QR} = \frac{24}{32} = \frac{3}{4}$ $\frac{SP}{SR} = \frac{18}{24} = \frac{3}{4}$

Find the value of the variable.

15. 22

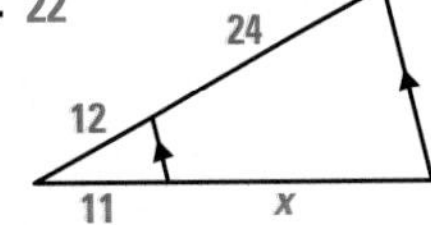

16.

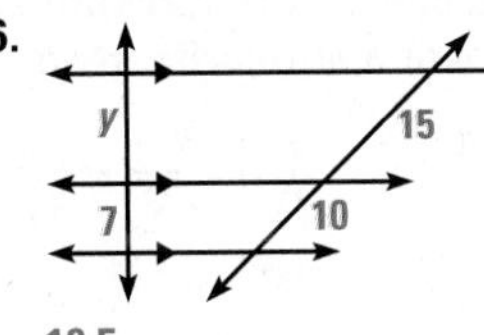

10.5

17.

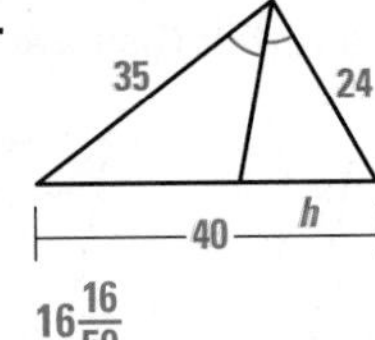

$16\frac{16}{59}$

8.7 DILATIONS

Examples on pp. 506–508

EXAMPLE The blue triangle is mapped onto the red triangle by a dilation with center C. The scale factor is $\frac{1}{5}$, so the dilation is a reduction.

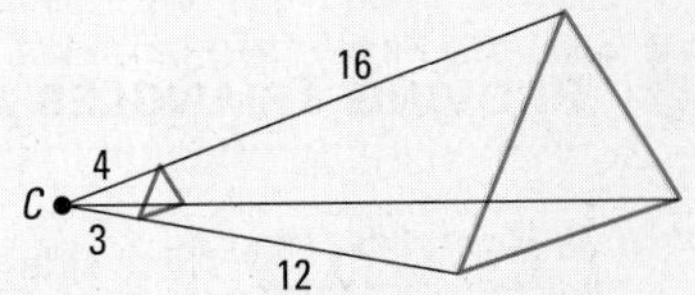

18. Identify the dilation, find its scale factor, and find the value of the variable.
reduction; $\frac{4}{7}$; 17.5

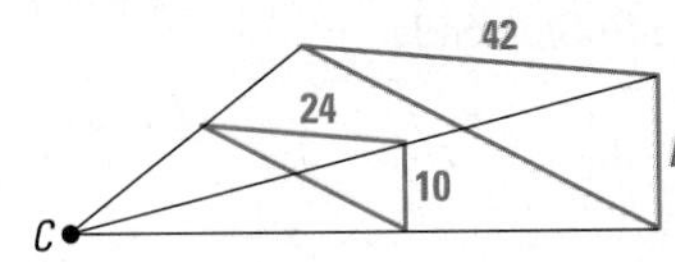

CHAPTER 8

Chapter Test

In Exercises 1–3, solve the proportion.

1. $\frac{x}{3} = \frac{12}{9}$ 4

2. $\frac{18}{y} = \frac{15}{20}$ 24

3. $\frac{11}{110} = \frac{z}{10}$ 1

Complete the sentence.

4. If $\frac{5}{2} = \frac{a}{b}$, then $\frac{5}{a} = \frac{?}{b}$. 2

5. If $\frac{8}{x} = \frac{3}{y}$, then $\frac{8+x}{x} = \frac{?}{y}$. 3 + y

In Exercises 6–8, use the figure shown.

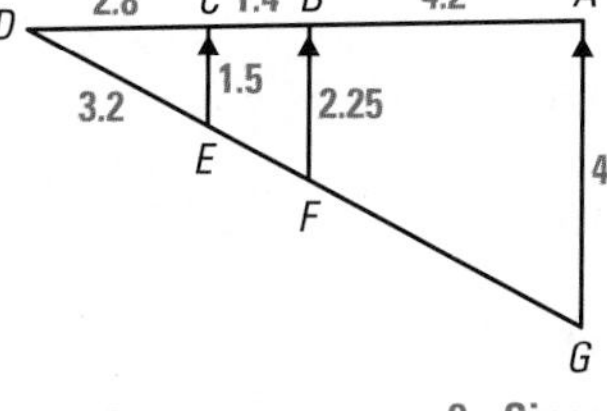

6. Find the length of $\overline{EF}$. 1.6

7. Find the length of $\overline{FG}$. 4.8

8. Is quadrilateral $FECB$ similar to quadrilateral $GFBA$? If so, what is the scale factor? no

In Exercises 9–12, use the figure shown.

9. Prove that $\triangle RSQ \sim \triangle RQT$. See margin.

10. What is the scale factor of $\triangle RSQ$ to $\triangle RQT$? $\frac{3}{5}$

11. Is $\triangle RSQ$ similar to $\triangle QST$? Explain. See margin.

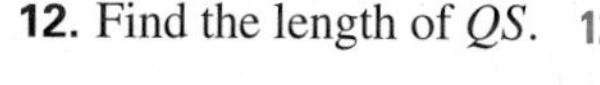

12. Find the length of $\overline{QS}$. 12

In Exercises 13–15, use the figure shown to decide if you are given enough information to conclude that $\overline{JK} \parallel \overline{LM}$. If so, state the reason.

13. $\frac{LJ}{JH} = \frac{MK}{KH}$ yes; △ Proportionality Converse

14. $\angle HJK \cong \angle HLM$ yes; Corresponding Angles Converse

15. $\frac{LH}{JH} = \frac{MH}{KH}$ yes; *Sample answer: SAS Similarity Theorem*

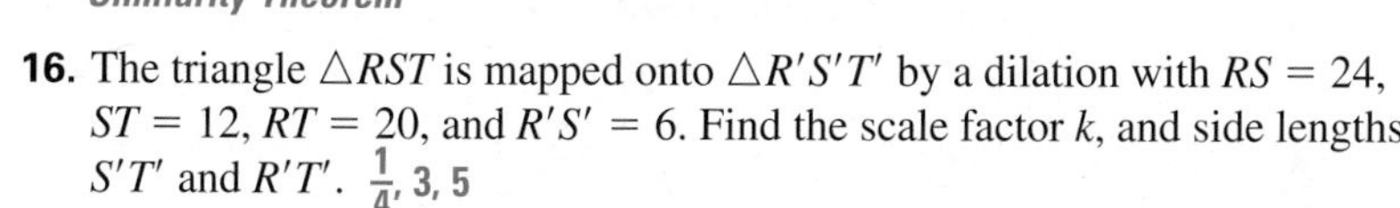

16. The triangle $\triangle RST$ is mapped onto $\triangle R'S'T'$ by a dilation with $RS = 24$, $ST = 12$, $RT = 20$, and $R'S' = 6$. Find the scale factor k, and side lengths $S'T'$ and $R'T'$. $\frac{1}{4}$, 3, 5

17. Two sides of a triangle have lengths of 14 inches and 18 inches. The measure of the angle included by the sides is 45°. Two sides of a second triangle have lengths of 7 inches and 8 inches. The measure of the angle included by the sides is 45°. Are the two triangles similar? Explain. See margin.

18. You shine a flashlight on a book that is 9 inches tall and 6 inches wide. It makes a shadow on the wall that is 3 feet tall and 2 feet wide. What is the scale factor of the book to its shadow? $\frac{1}{4}$

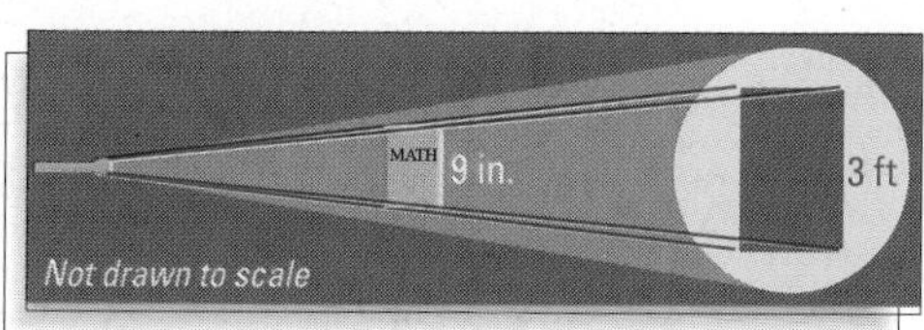

9. Since $\angle R \cong \angle R$ by the Reflexive Prop. of Cong. and $\angle RSQ \cong \angle RQT$. (All right ∠s are ≅.), $\triangle RSQ \sim \triangle RQT$ by the AA Similarity Post.

11. Yes; Sample answer: since $\angle RSQ$ is a right ∠, $\angle QST$ is also a right ∠. Also, since $\triangle RSQ \sim \triangle RQT$, corresp. ∠s RQS and T are ≅. Then $\triangle RSQ \sim \triangle QST$ by the AA Similarity Postulate.

17. no; $\frac{7}{8} \neq \frac{14}{18}$ (Note that it is not possible that the triangle contains a second 45° ∠ for which the ratio of the included sides is $\frac{7}{9}$. If there were another 45° ∠, the △ would be an isosceles right △. Such an isosceles right △ is impossible.)

Additional Resources

- ***Chapter 8 Resource Book***
  Chapter Test (3 levels) (p. 110)
  SAT/ACT Chapter Test (p. 116)
  Alternative Assessment (p. 117)
- ***Test and Practice Generator***

ADDITIONAL RESOURCES

- ***Chapter 8 Resource Book***
  Chapter Test (3 levels) (p. 110)
  SAT/ACT Chapter Test (p. 116)
  Alternative Assessment (p. 117)
- ***Test and Practice Generator***

CHAPTER 8

Chapter Standardized Test

TEST-TAKING STRATEGY When checking your work, try to use a method other than the one you originally used to get your answer. If you use the same method, you may make the same mistake twice.

1. **MULTIPLE CHOICE** If $\frac{a}{b} = \frac{m}{n}$, then which of the following is not necessarily true? B

   Ⓐ $\frac{a}{m} = \frac{b}{n}$ Ⓑ $\frac{a}{n} = \frac{b}{m}$

   Ⓒ $an = bm$ Ⓓ $\frac{b}{a} = \frac{n}{m}$

   Ⓔ $\frac{a+b}{b} = \frac{m+n}{n}$

2. **MULTIPLE CHOICE** Simplify $\frac{20\text{ft}}{5\text{ yd}}$. D

   Ⓐ $\frac{1}{4}$ Ⓑ $\frac{3}{4}$ Ⓒ $\frac{5}{4}$

   Ⓓ $\frac{4}{3}$ Ⓔ $\frac{4}{1}$

3. **MULTIPLE CHOICE** The perimeter of a parallelogram is 54. The ratio of the lengths of the sides is 2:7. What are the lengths of the sides? C

   Ⓐ 4 and 14 Ⓑ 8 and 28

   Ⓒ 6 and 21 Ⓓ 24 and 30

   Ⓔ 12 and 42

4. **MULTIPLE CHOICE** Which of the following pairs of numbers has a geometric mean of 64? B

   Ⓐ 4 and 6 Ⓑ 16 and 256

   Ⓒ 32 and 96 Ⓓ 2 and 32

   Ⓔ 2 and 1024

5. **MULTIPLE CHOICE** The two polygons shown are similar. What are the values of x and y? E

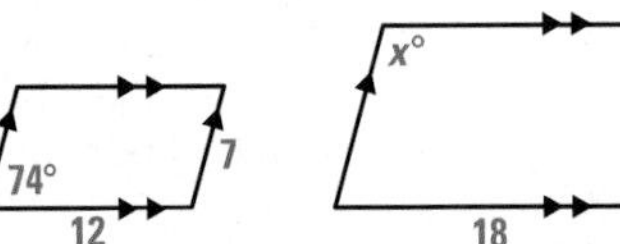

   Ⓐ $x = 74°, y = \frac{15}{2}$ Ⓑ $x = 106°, y = 10.5$

   Ⓒ $x = 74°, y = 10.5$ Ⓓ $x = 106°, y = 10$

   Ⓔ $x = 106°, y = \frac{15}{2}$

6. **MULTIPLE CHOICE** The triangles shown are similar. Which of the following is *not* a correct statement? B

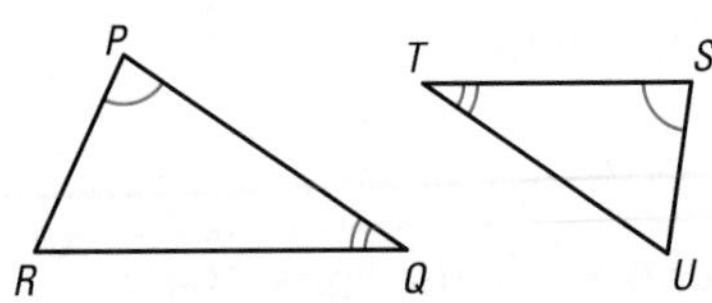

   Ⓐ $\triangle PQR \sim \triangle STU$ Ⓑ $\frac{PR}{TU} = \frac{PQ}{ST}$

   Ⓒ $\frac{TU}{QR} = \frac{TS}{QP}$ Ⓓ $\frac{RQ}{UT} = \frac{RP}{US}$

   Ⓔ $\triangle QPR \sim \triangle TSU$

7. **MULTIPLE CHOICE** You use a pantograph to enlarge a drawing of a car that is 4 inches long. You want your enlargement to be 12 inches long. What is the scale factor of the enlargement to the drawing? A

   Ⓐ 3 to 1 Ⓑ 4 to 1 Ⓒ 1 to 3

   Ⓓ 1 to 4 Ⓔ 1 to 2

8. **MULTIPLE CHOICE** What is the perimeter of $\triangle ABC$? E

   Ⓐ 90 Ⓑ 97

   Ⓒ 98 Ⓓ 100

   Ⓔ 105

9. **MULTIPLE CHOICE** What is JN? B

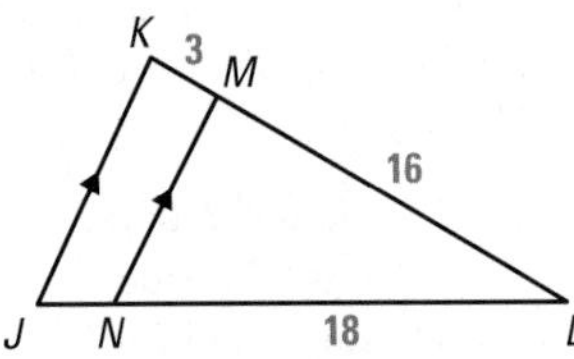

   Ⓐ 3 Ⓑ $\frac{27}{8}$

   Ⓒ 3.5 Ⓓ 4

   Ⓔ 5

10. MULTIPLE CHOICE What is CD? C

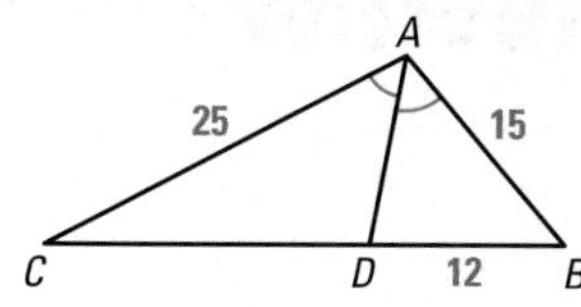

Ⓐ 7.2 Ⓑ 15 Ⓒ 20 Ⓓ 24 Ⓔ 31.25

QUANTITATIVE COMPARISON In Exercises 11 and 12, use the dilation shown to choose the statement that is true about the given quantities.

Ⓐ The quantity in column A is greater.

Ⓑ The quantity in column B is greater

Ⓒ The two quantities are equal.

Ⓓ The relationship cannot be determined from the given information.

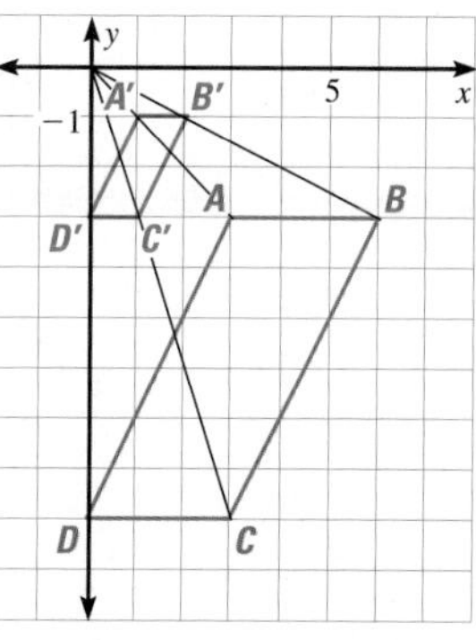

	Column A	Column B	
11.	The perimeter of the preimage	The perimeter of the image	A
12.	The scale factor of the dilation	$\frac{1}{3}$	C

MULTI-STEP PROBLEM In Exercises 13–17, use the table, which shows the color popularity survey results for sport/compact cars manufactured during the 1997 model year in North America.

Color	Percent
white	14%
black	13%
bright red	9%
silver	6%
purple	3%
medium red	8%
dark green	20%
light brown	13%
bright blue	3%
dark blue	5%
other	6%

13. Find the ratio of the number of medium red cars to the number of dark green cars. $\frac{2}{5}$

14. Find the ratio of the number of purple cars to the number of bright red cars. $\frac{1}{3}$

15. Suppose that in 1997 a manufacturer produced cars in colors that approximate the percents given in the table. If the manufacturer produced 12,560 sport/compact cars in 1997, how many would be dark blue? about 628 cars

16. Suppose a car dealer is ordering 800 sport/compact cars. How many light brown cars should he order? about 104 cars

17. *Writing* Explain why you do not need to know the total number of cars manufactured to find the ratios in Exercises 13 and 14. See margin.

MULTI-STEP PROBLEM In Exercises 18–21, use the diagram shown, where *ABCD* ~ *EFGD*.

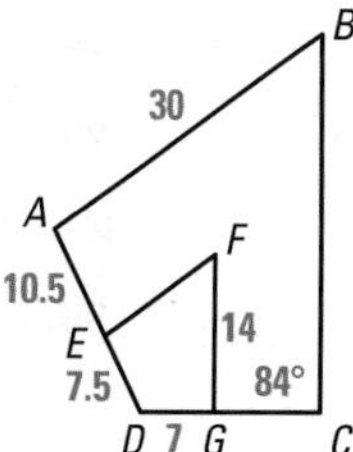

18. a. $ED =$ __?__ 7.5 **b.** $BC =$ __?__ 33.6

c. $EF =$ __?__ 12.5 **d.** $m\angle DGF =$ __?__ 84°

19. Find the scale factor of $ABCD$ to $EFGD$. $\frac{12}{5}$

20. What is the perimeter of $ABCD$? and $EFGD$? 98.4; 41

21. Find the ratio of the perimeter of $ABCD$ to the perimeter of $EFGD$. $\frac{12}{5}$

17. Consider, say, red and blue cars; $\frac{\text{percent of cars that are red}}{\text{percent of cars that are blue}} = \frac{\frac{\text{number of red cars}}{\text{100 cars}}}{\frac{\text{number of blue cars}}{\text{100 cars}}} = \frac{\text{number of red cars}}{\text{number of blue cars}}$.

EXTRA EXAMPLE 1

Simplify the expression $\sqrt{75}$.

$5\sqrt{3}$

EXTRA EXAMPLE 2

Simplify the radical expression.

a. $\sqrt{5}+\sqrt{20}$ $3\sqrt{5}$

b. $(\sqrt{3})(\sqrt{27})$ 9

c. $(4\sqrt{13})^2$ 208

CHECKPOINT EXERCISES

For use after Example 1:

1. Simplify the expression $\sqrt{500}$.
$10\sqrt{5}$

For use after Example 2:

2. a. $\sqrt{12}-\sqrt{27}$ $-\sqrt{3}$

b. $(\sqrt{48}\sqrt{6})$ $12\sqrt{2}$

c. $(5\sqrt{11})^2$ 275

CHAPTER 8

Algebra Review

EXAMPLE 1 Simplifying Radicals

Simplify the expression $\sqrt{20}$.

$\sqrt{20} = \sqrt{4}\cdot\sqrt{5}$ **Use product property.**

$= 2\sqrt{5}$ **Simplify.**

EXERCISES

Simplify the expression.

1. $\sqrt{121}$ 11 **2.** $\sqrt{52}$ $2\sqrt{13}$ **3.** $\sqrt{45}$ $3\sqrt{5}$

4. $\sqrt{72}$ $6\sqrt{2}$ **5.** $\sqrt{40}$ $2\sqrt{10}$ **6.** $\sqrt{27}$ $3\sqrt{3}$

7. $\sqrt{80}$ $4\sqrt{5}$ **8.** $\sqrt{50}$ $5\sqrt{2}$ **9.** $\sqrt{243}$ $9\sqrt{3}$

10. $\sqrt{288}$ $12\sqrt{2}$ **11.** $\sqrt{320}$ $8\sqrt{5}$ **12.** $\sqrt{225}$ 15

EXAMPLE 2 Simplifying Radical Expressions

Simplify the radical expression.

a. $5\sqrt{3}-\sqrt{3}-\sqrt{2}$
$= 4\sqrt{3}-\sqrt{2}$

b. $(2\sqrt{2})(5\sqrt{3})$
$= 2\cdot 5\cdot\sqrt{2}\cdot\sqrt{3}$
$= 10\sqrt{6}$

c. $(5\sqrt{7})^2$
$= 5^2\sqrt{7^2}$
$= 25\cdot 7$
$= 175$

EXERCISES

Simplify the radical expression.

13. $\sqrt{75}+\sqrt{3}$ $6\sqrt{3}$ **14.** $\sqrt{50}-\sqrt{18}$ $2\sqrt{2}$ **15.** $\sqrt{64}-\sqrt{28}$ $8-2\sqrt{7}$

16. $\sqrt{44}+2\sqrt{11}$ $4\sqrt{11}$ **17.** $\sqrt{125}-\sqrt{80}$ $\sqrt{5}$ **18.** $\sqrt{242}+\sqrt{200}$ $21\sqrt{2}$

19. $-\sqrt{147}-\sqrt{243}$ $-16\sqrt{3}$ **20.** $\sqrt{28}+\sqrt{63}$ $5\sqrt{7}$ **21.** $\sqrt{20}+\sqrt{45}-\sqrt{5}$ $4\sqrt{5}$

22. $(\sqrt{13})(\sqrt{26})$ $13\sqrt{2}$ **23.** $(3\sqrt{14})(\sqrt{35})$ $21\sqrt{10}$ **24.** $(\sqrt{363})(\sqrt{300})$ 330

25. $(6\sqrt{2})(2\sqrt{2})$ 24 **26.** $(\sqrt{18})(\sqrt{72})$ 36 **27.** $(\sqrt{21})(\sqrt{24})$ $6\sqrt{14}$

28. $(\sqrt{32})(\sqrt{2})$ 8 **29.** $(\sqrt{98})(\sqrt{128})$ 112 **30.** $(5\sqrt{4})(2\sqrt{4})$ 40

31. $(6\sqrt{5})^2$ 180 **32.** $(4\sqrt{2})^2$ 32 **33.** $(8\sqrt{3})^2$ 192

34. $(2\sqrt{3})^2$ 12 **35.** $(5\sqrt{5})^2$ 125 **36.** $(10\sqrt{11})^2$ 1100

EXAMPLE 3 *Simplifying Quotients with Radicals*

Simplify the quotient $\frac{6}{\sqrt{5}}$.

$\frac{6}{\sqrt{5}} = \frac{6}{\sqrt{5}} \cdot \frac{\sqrt{5}}{\sqrt{5}}$ **Multiply numerator and denominator by $\sqrt{5}$, to eliminate a radical in the denominator.**

$= \frac{6\sqrt{5}}{\sqrt{5}\sqrt{5}}$

$= \frac{6\sqrt{5}}{5}$

EXERCISES

Simplify the quotient.

37. $\frac{4}{\sqrt{3}}$ $\frac{4\sqrt{3}}{3}$ **38.** $\frac{5}{\sqrt{7}}$ $\frac{5\sqrt{7}}{7}$ **39.** $\frac{2\sqrt{3}}{\sqrt{6}}$ $\sqrt{2}$ **40.** $\frac{2\sqrt{3}}{\sqrt{5}}$ $\frac{2\sqrt{15}}{5}$

41. $\frac{\sqrt{18}}{3\sqrt{2}}$ 1 **42.** $\frac{4}{\sqrt{8}}$ $\sqrt{2}$ **43.** $\frac{16}{\sqrt{24}}$ $\frac{4\sqrt{6}}{3}$ **44.** $\frac{\sqrt{5}}{\sqrt{10}}$ $\frac{\sqrt{2}}{2}$

45. $\frac{4}{\sqrt{12}}$ $\frac{2\sqrt{3}}{3}$ **46.** $\frac{3\sqrt{5}}{\sqrt{20}}$ $\frac{3}{2}$ **47.** $\frac{9}{\sqrt{52}}$ $\frac{9\sqrt{13}}{26}$ **48.** $\frac{\sqrt{12}}{\sqrt{24}}$ $\frac{\sqrt{2}}{2}$

49. $\frac{\sqrt{18}}{\sqrt{10}}$ $\frac{3\sqrt{5}}{5}$ **50.** $\frac{\sqrt{32}}{\sqrt{5}}$ $\frac{4\sqrt{10}}{5}$ **51.** $\frac{\sqrt{27}}{\sqrt{45}}$ $\frac{\sqrt{15}}{5}$ **52.** $\frac{\sqrt{50}}{\sqrt{75}}$ $\frac{\sqrt{6}}{3}$

EXAMPLE 4 *Solving Quadratic Equations*

Solve.

$x^2 - 5 = 16$

$x^2 = 21$ **Add 5 to each side.**

$x = \pm\sqrt{21}$ **Find square roots.**

EXERCISES

Solve.

53. $x^2 = 9$ ± 3 **54.** $x^2 = 625$ ± 25 **55.** $x^2 = 289$ ± 17

56. $x^2 + 3 = 13$ $\pm\sqrt{10}$ **57.** $x^2 - 4 = 12$ ± 4 **58.** $x^2 - 7 = 6$ $\pm\sqrt{13}$

59. $7x^2 = 252$ ± 6 **60.** $3x^2 = 192$ ± 8 **61.** $6x^2 = 294$ ± 7

62. $4x^2 + 5 = 45$ $\pm\sqrt{10}$ **63.** $2x^2 + 5 = 23$ ± 3 **64.** $9x^2 + 7 = 52$ $\pm\sqrt{5}$

65. $11x^2 + 4 = 48$ ± 2 **66.** $6x^2 - 3 = 9$ $\pm\sqrt{2}$ **67.** $10x^2 - 16 = -6$ ± 1

68. $5x^2 - 6 = 29$ $\pm\sqrt{7}$ **69.** $8x^2 - 12 = 36$ $\pm\sqrt{6}$ **70.** $5x^2 - 61 = 64$ ± 5

71. $x^2 + 3^2 = 5^2$ ± 4 **72.** $7^2 + x^2 = 25^2$ ± 24 **73.** $5^2 + 12^2 = x^2$ ± 13

EXTRA EXAMPLE 3

Simplify the quotient $\frac{10}{\sqrt{5}}$. $2\sqrt{5}$

EXTRA EXAMPLE 4

Solve $3x^2 + 2 = 20$ $\pm\sqrt{6}$

CHECKPOINT EXERCISES

For use after Example 3:

1. Simplify the quotient $\frac{7}{\sqrt{8}}$.

$\frac{7\sqrt{2}}{4}$

For use after Extra Example 4:

2. Solve $x^2 - 11 = 21$. $\pm 4\sqrt{2}$

CHAPTER 9

PLANNING THE CHAPTER

Right Triangles and Trigonometry

GOALS

Lesson	Goals	NCTM	ITED	SAT9	Terra-Nova	Local
9.1 pp. 527–534	GOAL 1 Solve problems involving similar right triangles formed by the altitude drawn to the hypotenuse of a right triangle. GOAL 2 Use a geometric mean to solve problems.	1, 2, 3, 4, 5, 6, 9, 10	MCWN, MIM, MIGE, RQGE	1, 24	11, 13, 14, 16, 17, 49, 51, 52	5
9.2 pp. 535–541	GOAL 1 Prove the Pythagorean Theorem. GOAL 2 Use the Pythagorean Theorem to solve real-life problems.	1, 2, 3, 4, 6, 7, 8, 9, 10	MCE, MIM, MIGE, RQGE	1, 7, 25	10, 11, 13, 14, 16, 17, 18, 49, 51, 52	8, 10, 14, 15
9.3 pp. 542–549	TECHNOLOGY ACTIVITY: 9.3 *Explore how the angle measures of a triangle are related to its side lengths using geometry software.* GOAL 1 Use the Converse of the Pythogorean Theorem to solve problems. GOAL 2 Use side lengths to classify triangles by their angle measures.	1, 2, 3, 4, 6, 7, 8, 9, 10	MCE, SAPE, MCWN, MIM, MIGE, RQGE	1, 7, 25	10, 11, 13, 14, 16, 17, 18, 49, 51, 52	15
9.4 pp. 550–557	CONCEPT ACTIVITY: 9.4 *Investigate special right triangles.* GOAL 1 Find the side lengths of special right triangles. GOAL 2 Uses special right triangles to solve real-life problems.	1, 2, 3, 4, 6, 9, 10	MCE, SAPE, MCWN, MIM, MIGE, RQGE	1, 25	10, 11, 13, 14, 16, 17, 49, 51, 52	14, 20
9.5 pp. 558–566	GOAL 1 Find the sine, the cosine, and the tangent of an acute angle. GOAL 2 Use trigonometric ratios to solve real-life problems.	1, 2, 3, 4, 6, 9, 10	MIGE, MIRA, APRA, RQRA, RQGE	1, 35	11, 13, 14, 16, 17, 48, 49, 51, 52	18, 19
9.6 pp. 567–572	GOAL 1 Solve a right triangle. GOAL 2 Use right triangles to solve real-life problems.	1, 2, 3, 4, 6, 9, 10	MIGE, MCE, SAPE, RQGE	1, 25, 36	10, 11, 13, 14, 16, 17, 49, 51, 52	19
9.7 pp. 573–580	GOAL 1 Find the magnitude and the direction of a vector. GOAL 2 Add vectors.	1, 2, 3, 4	MIGE		11, 13, 14, 16, 49, 51	17

RESOURCES

Chapter Resource Booklets

Chapter Support

Tips for New Teachers	p. 1	Prerequisite Skills Review	p. 5
Parent Guide for Student Success	p. 3	Strategies for Reading Mathematics	p. 7

Lesson Support

Lesson Support	9.1	9.2	9.3	9.4	9.5	9.6	9.7
Lesson Plans (regular and block)	p. 9	p. 22	p. 37	p. 53	p. 66	p. 82	p. 96
Warm-Up Exercises and Daily Quiz	p. 11	p. 24	p. 39	p. 55	p. 68	p. 84	p. 98
Activity Support Masters							
Lesson Openers	p. 12	p. 25	p. 40	p. 56	p. 69	p. 85	p. 99
Technology Activities & Keystrokes	p. 13	p. 26	p. 41		p. 70	p. 86	p. 100
Practice (3 levels)	p. 14	p. 29	p. 44	p. 57	p. 72	p. 88	p. 103
Reteaching with Practice	p. 17	p. 32	p. 47	p. 60	p. 75	p. 91	p. 106
Quick Catch-Up for Absent Students	p. 19	p. 34	p. 49	p. 62	p. 77	p. 93	p. 108
Cooperative Learning Activities					p. 78		
Interdisciplinary Applications	p. 20		p. 50		p. 79		p. 109
Real-Life Applications		p. 35		p. 63		p. 94	
Math & History Applications				p. 64			
Challenge: Skills and Applications	p. 21	p. 36	p. 51	p. 65	p. 80	p. 95	p. 110

Review and Assessment

Quizzes	pp. 52, 81	Alternative Assessment with Math Journal	p. 119
Chapter Review Games and Activities	p. 111	Project with Rubric	p. 121
Chapter Test (3 levels)	pp. 112–117	Cumulative Review	p. 123
SAT/ACT Chapter Test	p. 118	Resource Book Answers	p. A1

Transparencies

	9.1	9.2	9.3	9.4	9.5	9.6	9.7
Warm-Up Exercises and Daily Quiz	p. 63	p. 64	p. 65	p. 66	p. 67	p. 68	p. 69
Alternative Lesson Opener Transparencies	p. 54	p. 55	p. 56	p. 57	p. 58	p. 59	p. 60
Examples/Standardized Test Practice	✓	✓	✓	✓	✓	✓	✓
Answer Transparencies	✓	✓	✓	✓	✓	✓	✓

Technology

- Electronic Teaching Tools
- Online Lesson Planner
- Internet Support
- Personal Student Tutor
- Test and Practice Generator
- Geometry in Motion video
- Electronic Lesson Presentations (Lesson 9.2)

Additional Resources

- Basic Skills Workbook: Diagnosis and Remediation
- Worked-Out Solution Key
- Resources in Spanish
- Standardized Test Practice Workbook
- Practice Workbook with Examples

Correlations to the California Curriculum

Correlations to California Standards
See Teacher's Edition pp. CA9–CA11

Correlations to SAT9
Task 1: See Teacher's Edition pp. CA12–CA14
Task 2: See Teacher's Edition pp. CA15–CA17

CHAPTER 9

PACING THE CHAPTER

Resource Key
- STUDENT EDITION
- CHAPTER 9 RESOURCE BOOK
- TEACHER'S EDITION

REGULAR SCHEDULE

Day 1

9.1

STARTING OPTIONS
- Prereq. Skills Review
- Strategies for Reading
- Homework Check
- Warm-Up or Daily Quiz

TEACHING OPTIONS
- Motivating the Lesson
- Les. Opener (Software)
- Examples 1–3
- Closure Question
- Guided Practice Exs.

APPLY/HOMEWORK
- See Assignment Guide.
- See the CRB: Practice, Reteach, Apply, Extend

ASSESSMENT OPTIONS
- Checkpoint Exercises
- Daily Quiz (9.1)
- Stand. Test Practice

Day 2

9.2

STARTING OPTIONS
- Homework Check
- Warm-Up or Daily Quiz

TEACHING OPTIONS
- Motivating the Lesson
- Les. Opener (Activity)
- Technology Activity
- Examples 1–4
- Closure Question
- Guided Practice Exs.

APPLY/HOMEWORK
- See Assignment Guide.
- See the CRB: Practice, Reteach, Apply, Extend

ASSESSMENT OPTIONS
- Checkpoint Exercises
- Daily Quiz (9.2)
- Stand. Test Practice

Day 3

9.3

STARTING OPTIONS
- Homework Check
- Warm-Up or Daily Quiz

TEACHING OPTIONS
- Motivating the Lesson
- Les. Opener (Application)
- Examples 1–3
- Guided Practice Exs.

APPLY/HOMEWORK
- See Assignment Guide.
- See the CRB: Practice, Reteach, Apply, Extend

ASSESSMENT OPTIONS
- Checkpoint Exercises

Day 4

9.3 *(cont.)*

STARTING OPTIONS
- Homework Check

TEACHING OPTIONS
- Examples 1–3
- Technology Activity
- Closure Question

APPLY/HOMEWORK
- See Assignment Guide.
- See the CRB: Practice, Reteach, Apply, Extend

ASSESSMENT OPTIONS
- Checkpoint Exercises
- Daily Quiz (9.3)
- Stand. Test Practice
- Quiz (9.1–9.3)

Day 5

9.4

STARTING OPTIONS
- Homework Check
- Warm-Up or Daily Quiz

TEACHING OPTIONS
- Motivating the Lesson
- Concept Activity
- Les. Opener (Visual)
- Examples 1–5
- Guided Practice Exs.

APPLY/HOMEWORK
- See Assignment Guide.
- See the CRB: Practice, Reteach, Apply, Extend

ASSESSMENT OPTIONS
- Checkpoint Exercises

Day 6

9.4 *(cont.)*

STARTING OPTIONS
- Homework Check

TEACHING OPTIONS
- Examples 1–5
- Closure Question

APPLY/HOMEWORK
- See Assignment Guide.
- See the CRB: Practice, Reteach, Apply, Extend

ASSESSMENT OPTIONS
- Checkpoint Exercises
- Daily Quiz (9.4)
- Stand. Test Practice

Day 9

9.6

STARTING OPTIONS
- Homework Check
- Warm-Up or Daily Quiz

TEACHING OPTIONS
- Motivating the Lesson
- Les. Opener (Application)
- Technology Activity
- Examples 1–3
- Closure Question
- Guided Practice Exs.

APPLY/HOMEWORK
- See Assignment Guide.
- See the CRB: Practice, Reteach, Apply, Extend

ASSESSMENT OPTIONS
- Checkpoint Exercises
- Daily Quiz (9.6)
- Stand. Test Practice

Day 10

9.7

STARTING OPTIONS
- Homework Check
- Warm-Up or Daily Quiz

TEACHING OPTIONS
- Les. Opener (Application)
- Technology Activity
- Examples 1–3
- Guided Practice Exs. 1–8

APPLY/HOMEWORK
- See Assignment Guide.
- See the CRB: Practice, Reteach, Apply, Extend

ASSESSMENT OPTIONS
- Checkpoint Exercises, p. 574

Day 11

9.7 *(cont.)*

STARTING OPTIONS
- Homework Check

TEACHING OPTIONS
- Examples 4–5
- Closure Question
- Guided Practice Ex. 9

APPLY/HOMEWORK
- See Assignment Guide.
- See the CRB: Practice, Reteach, Apply, Extend

ASSESSMENT OPTIONS
- Checkpoint Exercises, p. 575
- Daily Quiz (9.7)
- Stand. Test Practice
- Quiz (9.6–9.7)

Day 12

Review

DAY 12 START OPTIONS
- Homework Check

REVIEWING OPTIONS
- Chapter 9 Summary
- Chapter 9 Review
- Chapter Review Games and Activities

APPLY/HOMEWORK
- Chapter 9 Test (practice)
- Ch. Standardized Test (practice)

Day 13

Assess

DAY 13 START OPTIONS
- Homework Check

ASSESSMENT OPTIONS
- Chapter 9 Test
- SAT/ACT Ch. 9 Test
- Alternative Assessment

APPLY/HOMEWORK
- Skill Review, p. 594

Day 7

9.5

Starting Options
- Homework Check
- Warm-Up or Daily Quiz

Teaching Options
- Les. Opener (Activity)
- Examples 1–7
- Guided Practice Exs.

Apply/Homework
- See Assignment Guide.
- See the CRB: Practice, Reteach, Apply, Extend

Assessment Options
- Checkpoint Exercises

Day 8

9.5 *(cont.)*

Starting Options
- Homework Check

Teaching Options
- Examples 1–7
- Closure Question

Apply/Homework
- See Assignment Guide.
- See the CRB: Practice, Reteach, Apply, Extend

Assessment Options
- Checkpoint Exercises
- Daily Quiz (9.5)
- Stand. Test Practice
- Quiz (9.4–9.5)

BLOCK SCHEDULE

Day 1

Assess & 9.1

(Day 1 = Ch. 8 Day 8)

Assessment Options
- Chapter 8 Test
- SAT/ACT Ch. 8 Test
- Alternative Assessment

Ch. 9 Start Options
- Skills Review, p. 526
- Prereq. Skills Review
- Strategies for Reading

Teaching 9.1 Options
- Warm-Up (Les. 9.1)
- Motivating the Lesson
- Les. Opener (Software)
- Examples 1–3
- Closure Question
- Guided Practice Exs.

Apply/Homework
- See Assignment Guide.
- See the CRB: Practice, Reteach, Apply, Extend

Assessment Options
- Checkpoint Exercises
- Daily Quiz (Les. 9.1)
- Stand. Test Practice

Day 2

9.2 & 9.3

Day 2 Start Options
- Homework Check
- Warm-Up (Les. 9.2) or Daily Quiz (Les. 9.1)

Teaching 9.2 Options
- Motivating the Lesson
- Les. Opener (Activity)
- Technology Activity
- Examples 1–4
- Closure Question
- Guided Practice Exs.

Beginning 9.3 Options
- Warm-Up (Les. 9.3)
- Motivating the Lesson
- Les. Opener (Appl.)
- Examples 1–3
- Guided Practice Exs.

Apply/Homework
- See Assignment Guide.
- See the CRB: Practice, Reteach, Apply, Extend

Assessment Options
- Checkpoint Exercises
- Daily Quiz (Les. 9.2)
- Stand. Test Prac. (9.2)

Day 3

9.3 & 9.4

Day 3 Start Options
- Homework Check
- Daily Quiz (Les. 9.2)

Finishing 9.3 Options
- Examples 1–3
- Technology Activity
- Closure Question

Beginning 9.4 Options
- Warm-Up (Les. 9.4)
- Motivating the Lesson
- Concept Activity
- Les. Opener (Visual)
- Examples 1–5
- Guided Practice Exs.

Apply/Homework
- See Assignment Guide.
- See the CRB: Practice, Reteach, Apply, Extend

Assessment Options
- Checkpoint Exercises
- Daily Quiz (Les. 9.3)
- Stand. Test Prac. (9.3)
- Quiz (9.1–9.3)

Day 4

9.4 & 9.5

Day 4 Start Options
- Homework Check
- Daily Quiz (Les. 9.3)

Finishing 9.4 Options
- Examples 1–5
- Closure Question

Beginning 9.5 Options
- Warm-Up (Les. 9.5)
- Les. Opener (Activity)
- Examples 1–7
- Guided Practice Exs.

Apply/Homework
- See Assignment Guide.
- See the CRB: Practice, Reteach, Apply, Extend

Assessment Options
- Checkpoint Exercises
- Daily Quiz (Les. 9.4)
- Stand. Test Prac. (9.4)

Day 5

9.5 & 9.6

Day 5 Start Options
- Homework Check
- Daily Quiz (Les. 9.4)

Finishing 9.5 Options
- Examples 1–7
- Closure Question

Teaching 9.6 Options
- Warm-Up (Les. 9.6)
- Motivating the Lesson
- Les. Opener (Appl.)
- Technology Activity
- Examples 1–3
- Closure Question
- Guided Practice Exs.

Apply/Homework
- See Assignment Guide.
- See the CRB: Practice, Reteach, Apply, Extend

Assessment Options
- Checkpoint Exercises
- Daily Quiz (Les. 9.5, 9.6)
- Stand. Test Practice
- Quiz (9.4–9.5)

Day 6

9.7

Day 6 Start Options
- Homework Check
- Warm-Up or Daily Quiz

Teaching 9.7 Options
- Les. Opener (Appl.)
- Technology Activity
- Examples 1–5
- Closure Question
- Guided Practice Exs.

Apply/Homework
- See Assignment Guide.
- See the CRB: Practice, Reteach, Apply, Extend

Assessment Options
- Checkpoint Exercises
- Daily Quiz (Les. 9.7)
- Stand. Test Practice
- Quiz (9.6–9.7)

Day 7

Review/Assess

Day 7 Start Options
- Homework Check

Reviewing Options
- Chapter 9 Summary
- Chapter 9 Review
- Chapter Review Games and Activities
- Chapter 9 Test (practice)
- Ch. Standardized Test (practice)

Assessment Options
- Chapter 9 Test
- SAT/ACT Ch. 9 Test
- Alternative Assessment

Apply/Homework
- Skill Review, p. 594

CHAPTER 9 MEETING INDIVIDUAL NEEDS

BEFORE THE CHAPTER

The *Chapter 9 Resource Book* has the following materials to distribute and use before the chapter:

- **Parent Guide for Student Success (pictured below)**
- **Prerequisite Skills Review**
- **Strategies for Reading Mathematics**

PARENT GUIDE *Pages 3–4*

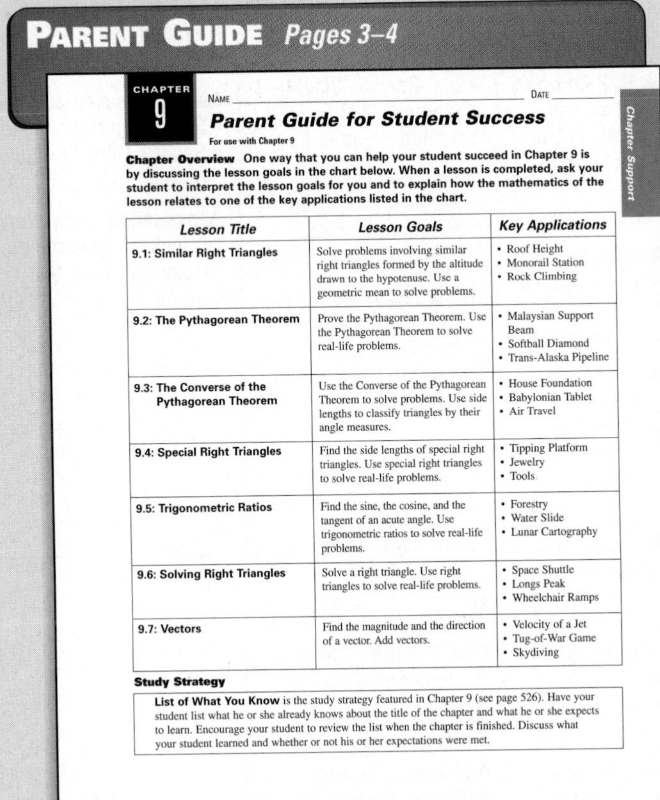

CHAPTER 9 NAME ______ DATE ______

Parent Guide for Student Success

For use with Chapter 9

Chapter Support

Chapter Overview One way that you can help your student succeed in Chapter 9 is by discussing the lesson goals in the chart below. When a lesson is completed, ask your student to interpret the lesson goals for you and to explain how the mathematics of the lesson relates to one of the key applications listed in the chart.

Lesson Title	Lesson Goals	Key Applications
9.1: Similar Right Triangles	Solve problems involving similar right triangles formed by the altitude drawn to the hypotenuse. Use a geometric mean to solve problems.	• Roof Height • Monorail Station • Rock Climbing
9.2: The Pythagorean Theorem	Prove the Pythagorean Theorem. Use the Pythagorean Theorem to solve real-life problems.	• Malaysian Support Beam • Softball Diamond • Trans-Alaska Pipeline
9.3: The Converse of the Pythagorean Theorem	Use the Converse of the Pythagorean Theorem to solve problems. Use side lengths to classify triangles by their angle measures.	• House Foundation • Babylonian Tablet • Air Travel
9.4: Special Right Triangles	Find the side lengths of special right triangles. Use special right triangles to solve real-life problems.	• Tipping Platform • Jewelry • Tools
9.5: Trigonometric Ratios	Find the sine, the cosine, and the tangent of an acute angle. Use trigonometric ratios to solve real-life problems.	• Forestry • Water Slide • Lunar Cartography
9.6: Solving Right Triangles	Solve a right triangle. Use right triangles to solve real-life problems.	• Space Shuttle • Longs Peak • Wheelchair Ramps
9.7: Vectors	Find the magnitude and the direction of a vector. Add vectors.	• Velocity of a Jet • Tug-of-War Game • Skydiving

Study Strategy

List of What You Know is the study strategy featured in Chapter 9 (see page 526). Have your student list what he or she already knows about the title of the chapter and what he or she expects to learn. Encourage your student to review the list when the chapter is finished. Discuss what your student learned and whether or not his or her expectations were met.

PARENT GUIDE FOR STUDENT SUCCESS The first page summarizes the content of Chapter 9. Parents are encouraged to have their students explain how the material relates to key applications in the chapter, such as rock climbing. The second page (not shown) provides exercises and an activity that parents can do with their students. In the activity, parents and students construct a right triangle using a piece of rope.

DURING EACH LESSON

The *Chapter 9 Resource Book* has the following alternatives for introducing the lesson:

- **Lesson Openers (pictured below)**
- **Technology Activities with Keystrokes**

LESSON OPENER *Page 12*

LESSON 9.1 NAME ______ DATE ______

Available as a transparency

Geometry Software Lesson Opener

For use with pages 527–534

Lesson 9.1

Use geometry software to construct, separate, and nest the three similar right triangles that result when the altitude is drawn to the hypotenuse of a right triangle. Before you begin, select the option to keep the preimage displayed.

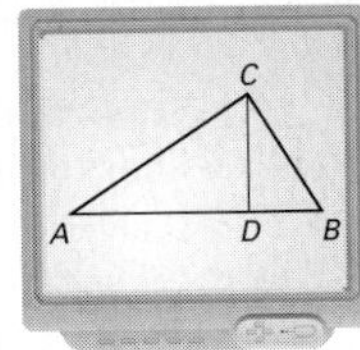

1. Draw a right triangle ABC with side $\overline{AB}$ horizontal and right angle at C. Measure all the angles of $\triangle ABC$. Construct a perpendicular to $\overline{AB}$ from C. Construct D, the point of intersection. Hide the perpendicular line and construct $\overline{CD}$. Sketch your result and identify the three similar right triangles: $\triangle CDB$, $\triangle ADC$, and $\triangle ACB$.
2. Now you will separate the three similar triangles, positioning them so that corresponding parts are easy to identify. $\triangle CDB$ will stay in place. To separate $\triangle ADC$, mark A as a center of rotation and rotate $\triangle ADC - 90°$ about A. To separate $\triangle ABC$, mark $\overline{BC}$ as a mirror line and reflect $\triangle ABC$ in $\overline{BC}$. Then mark C as a center of rotation and rotate the image of $\triangle ABC$ the same measure as $\angle CBA$. Sketch and label each of the three similar right triangles. Write a statement of similarity.
3. Repeat Exercise 1. Now you will nest the three similar triangles, positioning them on top of each other. $\triangle CDB$ will stay in place. Mark D as a center of rotation and rotate $\triangle ADC - 90°$ about D. Mark $\overline{BC}$ as a mirror line and reflect $\triangle ABC$ in $\overline{BC}$. Mark C as a center of rotation and rotate the image of $\triangle ABC$ the same measure as $\angle CBA$. Translate this image down the length of $\overline{CD}$. Sketch the three nested triangles. Do they appear to be similar?

GEOMETRY SOFTWARE LESSON OPENER This Lesson Opener provides an alternative way to start Lesson 9.1 through the use of geometry software. Students construct and manipulate three right triangles to develop an understanding of similar right triangles.

TECHNOLOGY RESOURCE

The Geometry in Motion video can be used to give dynamic presentations of selected material in Chapter 9.

Following Each Lesson

The *Chapter 9 Resource Book* has a variety of materials to follow-up each lesson. They include the following:

- **Practice (3 levels) (pictured below)**
- **Reteaching with Practice**
- **Quick Catch-Up for Absent Students**
- **Interdisciplinary Applications**
- **Real-Life Applications**

Practice *Page 30*

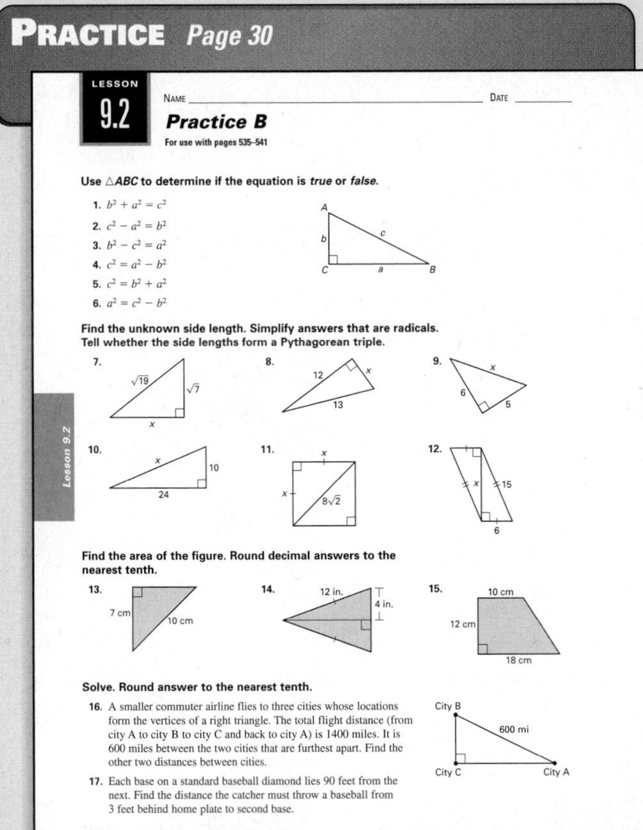

LESSON 9.2

NAME ______________________ DATE ________

Practice B

For use with pages 535–541

Use △*ABC* to determine if the equation is *true* or *false*.

1. $b^2 + a^2 = c^2$
2. $c^2 - a^2 = b^2$
3. $b^2 - c^2 = a^2$
4. $c^2 = a^2 - b^2$
5. $c^2 = b^2 + a^2$
6. $a^2 = c^2 - b^2$

Find the unknown side length. Simplify answers that are radicals. Tell whether the side lengths form a Pythagorean triple.

7. 8. 9. 10. 11. 12.

Find the area of the figure. Round decimal answers to the nearest tenth.

13. 14. 15.

Solve. Round answer to the nearest tenth.

16. A smaller commuter airline flies to three cities whose locations form the vertices of a right triangle. The total flight distance (from city A to city B to city C and back to city A) is 1400 miles. It is 600 miles between the two cities that are furthest apart. Find the other two distances between cities.
17. Each base on a standard baseball diamond lies 90 feet from the next. Find the distance the catcher must throw a baseball from 3 feet behind home plate to second base.

Practice Each lesson has three levels of practice: basic (A), average (B), and advanced (C). This Practice B involves more advanced work with application problems than Practice A but does not have as much work with finding missing side lengths as Practice C.

Technology Resource

Teachers can use the Time-Saving Test and Practice Generator to create additional practice worksheets for Lesson 9.2 and for the other lessons in Chapter 9.

Assessing the Chapter

The *Chapter 9 Resource Book* has the following review and assessment materials:

- **Quizzes**
- **Chapter Review Games and Activities (pictured below)**
- **Chapter Test (3 levels)**
- **SAT/ACT Chapter Test**
- **Alternative Assessment with Rubric and Math Journal**
- **Project with Rubric**
- **Cumulative Review**

Chapter Review Games *Page 111*

CHAPTER 9

NAME ______________________ DATE ________

Chapter Review Games and Activities

For use after Chapter 9

The answer to each question below is a positive integer. Put the answers to the first six questions in the circles on the first triangle in such a way that the sum of the numbers along any side is 14. Do the same for the last six questions and the second triangle.

Triangle 1 Triangle 2

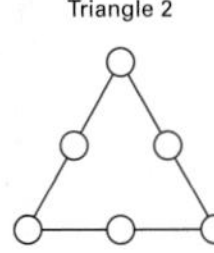

1. The length of the shorter leg of a 30°-60°-90° triangle is 3. What is the length of the hypotenuse?
2. The length of one leg of a right triangle is 1 and the length of the hypotenuse is $\sqrt{50}$. What is the length of the other leg?
3. The length of one leg of 45°-45°-90° triangle is $\sqrt{2}$. What is the length of the hypotenuse?
4. The length of one leg of a right triangle is $\sqrt{17}$ and the length of the other leg is $\sqrt{8}$. What is the length of the hypotenuse?
5. The length of the longer leg of a 30°-60°-90° triangle is $\sqrt{108}$. What is the length of the shorter leg?
6. The length of the hypotenuse of a right triangle is 18 and the sine of $\angle A$ is $\frac{1}{6}$. What is the length of the side opposite $\angle A$?
7. The length of one leg of a right triangle is equal to the length of the other leg. What is the tangent of the angle between the hypotenuse and one of the other sides?
8. A vector has an initial point of (2, 4) and a terminal point of (5, 8). What is the magnitude of this vector?
9. What is the largest number the sine of an angle could be?
10. What is the first component of the sum of $\langle -1, -2 \rangle$ and $\langle 5, -3 \rangle$?
11. A vector has an initial point of (1, −5) and a terminal point of (2, 3). What is the second component of this vector?
12. In a right triangle, the altitude from the right angle to the hypotenuse divides the hypotenuse into two segments, one of length 10 and the other of length $\frac{5}{2}$. What is the length of the altitude?

Review and Assess

Chapter Review Games and Activities On this worksheet, students answer questions about triangles as a motivating means of reviewing the material in Chapter 9.

CHAPTER OVERVIEW

CHAPTER GOALS

The goals of this chapter include solving problems involving similar right triangles using the geometric mean and indirect measurement. Students prove the Pythagorean Theorem and use it and its converse to solve problems. Students find the lengths of sides of special right triangles and use them to solve real-life problems. They find the sine, cosine, and tangent ratios and use them to solve real-life problems. Finally, students find the magnitude and direction of vectors and add vectors.

APPLICATION NOTE

Mathematics is often used to measure indirectly lengths that are otherwise too difficult to measure. The skywalk in the opening photo connects the Petronas Twin Towers in Kuala Lumpur, Malaysia. It can be measured indirectly to be 58.4 meters long with 42.6 meter long supports. The skywalk is located at levels 41 and 42, and the structural support points for the skywalk are located at level 29. The supports form two congruent triangles with the skywalk. There are spherical bearings at the support points so that the skywalk doesn't twist, and the skywalk structure is designed so that it will not collapse if it loses its arch support. At 451.9 meters, Petronas Twin Towers is 8.9 meters taller than the Sears Tower in Chicago.

Additional information about skyscrapers is available at **www.mcdougallittell.com.**

RIGHT TRIANGLES AND TRIGONOMETRY

▶ *How do builders find the dimensions of a skywalk support beam?*

APPLICATION: Support Beam

When constructing a skywalk for a skyscraper, builders often use mathematics to measure some lengths indirectly.

One method for indirect measurement involves using relationships in a right triangle.

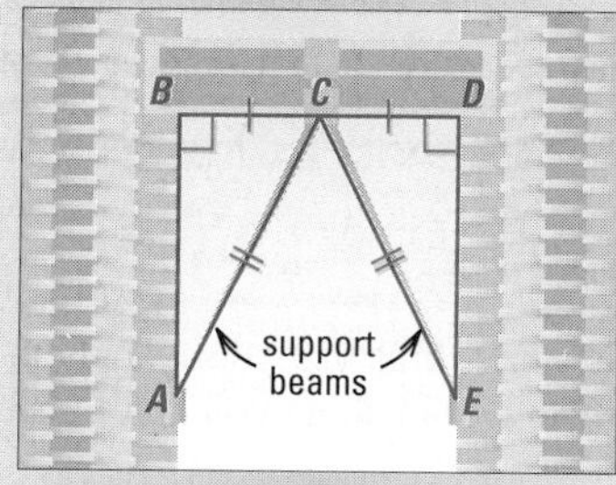

Think & Discuss

Use the diagram of a skywalk connecting two buildings for Exercises 1 and 2.

1. Given the information in the diagram, how do you know that the skyscrapers are parallel to each other? $\overleftrightarrow{AB} \perp \overleftrightarrow{BD}$, $\overleftrightarrow{DE} \perp \overleftrightarrow{BD}$, and, in a plane, 2 lines $\perp$ to the same line are parallel.
2. How do you know that the two right triangles created by the skywalk, beams, and buildings are congruent? by the HL Congruence Theorem

Learn More About It

You will see how the Pythagorean Theorem is used to find the length of a skywalk support beam in Example 4 on p. 537.

APPLICATION LINK Visit www.mcdougallittell.com for more information about skyscrapers.

PROJECTS

A project covering Chapters 8–9 appears on pages 590–591 of the Student Edition. An additional project for Chapter 9 is available in the *Chapter 9 Resource Book*, p. 121.

TECHNOLOGY

Software

- *Electronic Teaching Tools*
- *Online Lesson Planner*
- *Personal Student Tutor*
- *Test and Practice Generator*
- *Electronic Lesson Presentations (Lesson 9.2)*

Video

- *Geometry in Motion*

Internet Connections
www.mcdougallittell.com

- **Application Links** 525, 557
- **Student Help** 532, 540, 542, 547, 552, 559, 569
- **Career Links** 540, 569
- **Extra Challenge** 534, 541, 548, 556, 565, 572, 579

PREPARE

DIAGNOSTIC TOOLS

The **Skill Review** exercises can help you diagnose whether students have the following skills needed in Chapter 9:

- Classify triangles as acute, right, or obtuse.
- Sketch triangles and similar triangles.
- Draw vectors.
- Solve proportions containing a variable.

The following resources are available for students who need additional help with these skills:

- Prerequisite Skills Review (*Chapter 9 Resource Book,* p. 5; *Warm-Up Transparencies,* p. 62)
- Reteaching with Practice (Chapter Resource Books for Lessons 4.1, 5.3, 7.4, 8.1 and 8.4)
- *Personal Student Tutor*

ADDITIONAL RESOURCES

The following resources are provided to help you prepare for the upcoming chapter and customize review materials:

- ***Chapter 9 Resource Book***
  Tips for New Teachers (p. 1)
  Parent Guide (p. 3)
  Lesson Plans (every lesson)
  Lesson Plans for Block Scheduling (every lesson)
- ***Electronic Teaching Tools***
- ***Online Lesson Planner***
- ***Test and Practice Generator***

2. ***Sample answer:***

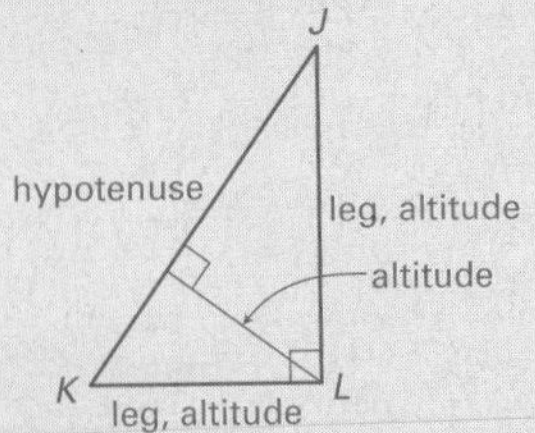

3, 5. See Additional Answers beginning on page AA1.

CHAPTER 9

Study Guide

PREVIEW

What's the chapter about?

Chapter 9 is about **right triangles** and a related branch of mathematics called **trigonometry**. In Chapter 9, you'll learn

- about properties related to general right triangles, similar right triangles, and special right triangles.
- about some applications of right triangles, including *trigonometry*, or triangle measurement, and vectors.

KEY VOCABULARY

▶ **Review**
- converse, p. 72
- right triangle, p. 194
- altitude, p. 281
- proportion, p. 459
- geometric mean, p. 466
- similar polygons, p. 473

▶ **New**
- Pythagorean triple, p. 536
- special right triangles, p. 551
- trigonometric ratio, p. 558
- angle of elevation, p. 561
- solve a right triangle, p. 567
- magnitude of a vector, p. 573
- direction of a vector, p. 574
- sum of two vectors, p. 575

PREPARE

Are you ready for the chapter?

SKILL REVIEW Do these exercises to review key skills that you'll apply in this chapter. See the given **reference page** if there is something you don't understand.

Exercises 1 and 2 refer to $\triangle JKL$ with $m\angle J = 30°$ and $m\angle K = 60°$.

1. Find $m\angle L$. Classify $\triangle JKL$ as *acute*, *right*, or *obtuse*. **(Review pp. 194–197)** **90°; right**
2. Sketch $\triangle JKL$. Label its legs, hypotenuse, and altitudes. **(Review pp. 195, 281)** **See margin.**
3. Draw a vector in a coordinate plane whose component form is $\langle 5, -2\rangle$. **(Review p. 423)** **See margin.**
4. Solve the proportion: $\frac{x+3}{5} = \frac{x}{3}$. **(Review p. 459)** **4.5**
5. Refer to $\triangle JKL$ in Exercises 1 and 2 above. Sketch a triangle, $\triangle ABC$, that is similar to $\triangle JKL$. Explain how you know the triangles are similar. **(Review p. 481)** **See margin.**

Here's a study strategy!

What Do You Know?

Make a list of what you already know about right triangles and trigonometry. Make another list of what you expect to learn about these topics. After studying Chapter 9, review these lists as you review the chapter to see what you have learned.

9.1

Similar Right Triangles

What you should learn

GOAL 1 Solve problems involving similar right triangles formed by the altitude drawn to the hypotenuse of a right triangle.

GOAL 2 Use a geometric mean to solve problems, such as estimating a climbing distance in **Ex. 32**.

Why you should learn it

▼ You can use right triangles and a geometric mean to help you estimate distances, such as finding the approximate height of a monorail track in **Example 3**.

CALIFORNIA STANDARDS AND ASSESSMENT

CA Standards: 5
SAT9 Task 1: Objs. 1, 22
SAT9 Task 2: Objs. 1, 24

GOAL 1 PROPORTIONS IN RIGHT TRIANGLES

In Lesson 8.4, you learned that two triangles are similar if two of their corresponding angles are congruent. For example, $\triangle PQR \sim \triangle STU$. Recall that the corresponding side lengths of similar triangles are in proportion.

In the activity, you will see how a right triangle can be divided into two similar right triangles.

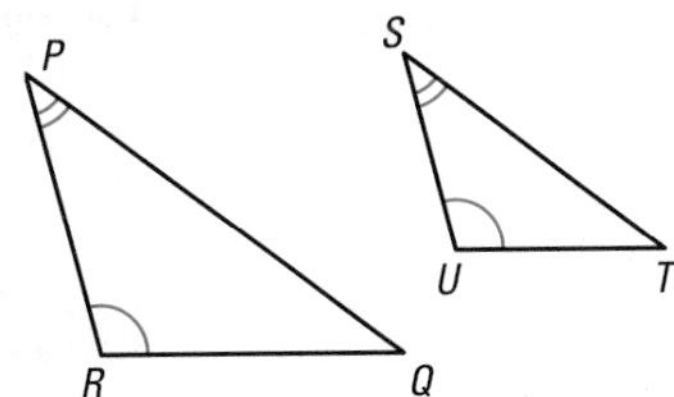

ACTIVITY Developing Concepts — Investigating Similar Right Triangles

1. Cut an index card along one of its diagonals.
2. On one of the right triangles, draw an altitude from the right angle to the hypotenuse. Cut along the altitude to form two right triangles.
3. You should now have three right triangles. Compare the triangles. What special property do they share? Explain. The triangles are all similar to each other.

In the activity, you may have discovered the following theorem. A plan for proving the theorem appears on page 528, and you are asked to prove it in Exercise 34 on page 533.

THEOREM

THEOREM 9.1

If the altitude is drawn to the hypotenuse of a right triangle, then the two triangles formed are similar to the original triangle and to each other.

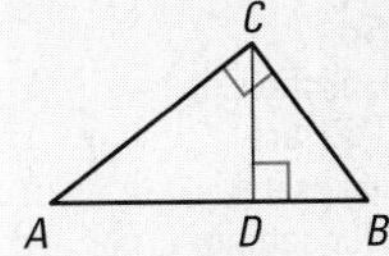

$\triangle CBD \sim \triangle ABC$, $\triangle ACD \sim \triangle ABC$, and $\triangle CBD \sim \triangle ACD$

1 PLAN

PACING

Basic: 1 day
Average: 1 day
Advanced: 1 day
Block Schedule: 0.5 block with Ch. 8 Assess.

LESSON OPENER
GEOMETRY SOFTWARE

An alternative way to approach Lesson 9.1 is to use the Geometry Software Lesson Opener:

- Blackline Master (*Chapter 9 Resource Book*, p. 12)
- Transparency (p. 54)

MEETING INDIVIDUAL NEEDS

- ***Chapter 9 Resource Book***
  Prerequisite Skills Review (p. 5)
  Practice Level A (p. 14)
  Practice Level B (p. 15)
  Practice Level C (p. 16)
  Reteaching with Practice (p. 17)
  Absent Student Catch-Up (p. 19)
  Challenge (p. 21)
- ***Resources in Spanish***
-  ***Personal Student Tutor***

NEW-TEACHER SUPPORT

See the Tips for New Teachers on pp. 1–2 of the *Chapter 9 Resource Book* for additional notes about Lesson 9.1.

WARM-UP EXERCISES

Transparency Available

Solve the proportion.

1. $\frac{x}{4} = \frac{12}{16}$ 3
2. $\frac{4}{y} = \frac{y}{9}$ 6; −6
3. $\frac{12}{6} = \frac{6}{r}$ 3
4. $\frac{4}{x} = \frac{x}{12}$ $4\sqrt{3}$; $-4\sqrt{3}$
5. $\frac{y-2}{6} = \frac{6}{2}$ 20

2 TEACH

Motivating the Lesson

Ask students if they can cut a right triangle in such a way that the new triangles will be similar to the original. Some experimentation may lead to cutting the triangle along the altitude to the hypotenuse. This produces similar right triangles, the focus of the lesson.

Activity Note

To verify that the triangles are similar, have students label and measure the angles.

Extra Example 1

A roof has a cross section that is a right triangle. The diagram shows the approximate dimensions of this cross section.

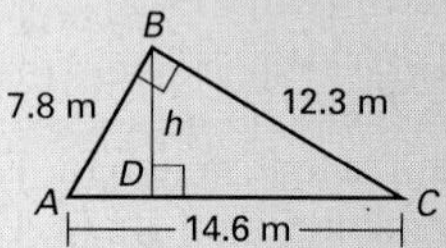

a. Identify the similar triangles in the diagram. $\triangle ABD \sim \triangle BCD \sim \triangle ACB$

b. Find the height h of the roof. 6.6 m

Checkpoint Exercises

For use after Example 1:

1. The diagram shows the approximate dimensions of a right triangle.

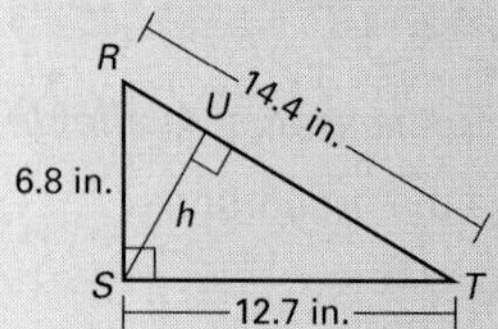

a. Identify the similar triangles in the diagram. $\triangle RSU \sim \triangle STU \sim \triangle RTS$

b. Find the height h of the triangle. 6.0 in.

A plan for proving Theorem 9.1 is shown below.

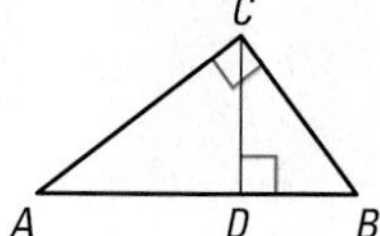

GIVEN ▶ $\triangle ABC$ is a right triangle; altitude $\overline{CD}$ is drawn to hypotenuse $\overline{AB}$.

PROVE ▶ $\triangle CBD \sim \triangle ABC$, $\triangle ACD \sim \triangle ABC$, and $\triangle CBD \sim \triangle ACD$.

Plan for Proof First prove that $\triangle CBD \sim \triangle ABC$. Each triangle has a right angle, and each includes $\angle B$. The triangles are similar by the AA Similarity Postulate. You can use similar reasoning to show that $\triangle ACD \sim \triangle ABC$. To show that $\triangle CBD \sim \triangle ACD$, begin by showing that $\angle ACD \cong \angle B$ because they are both complementary to $\angle DCB$. Then you can use the AA Similarity Postulate.

EXAMPLE 1 *Finding the Height of a Roof*

ROOF HEIGHT A roof has a cross section that is a right triangle. The diagram shows the approximate dimensions of this cross section.

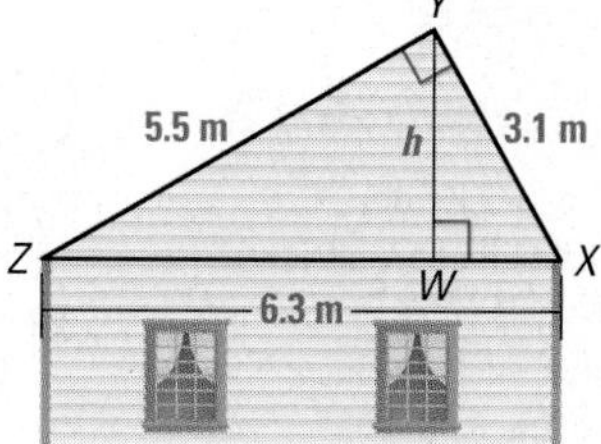

a. Identify the similar triangles.

b. Find the height h of the roof.

Solution

a. You may find it helpful to sketch the three similar right triangles so that the corresponding angles and sides have the same orientation. Mark the congruent angles. Notice that some sides appear in more than one triangle. For instance, $\overline{XY}$ is the hypotenuse in $\triangle XYW$ and the shorter leg in $\triangle XZY$.

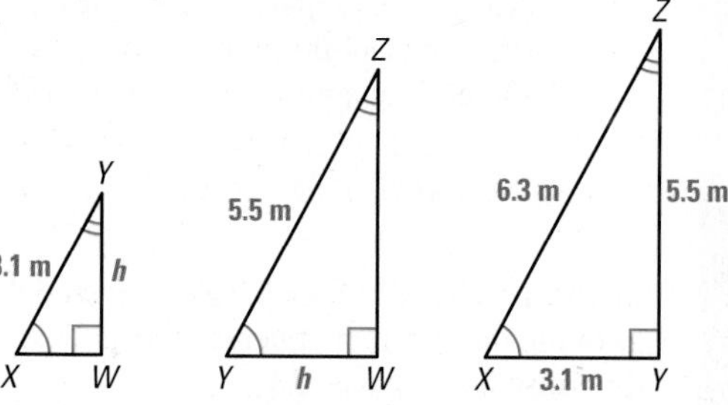

▶ $\triangle XYW \sim \triangle YZW \sim \triangle XZY$

b. Use the fact that $\triangle XYW \sim \triangle XZY$ to write a proportion.

$\frac{YW}{ZY} = \frac{XY}{XZ}$ **Corresponding side lengths are in proportion.**

$\frac{h}{5.5} = \frac{3.1}{6.3}$ **Substitute.**

$6.3h = 5.5(3.1)$ **Cross product property**

$h \approx 2.7$ **Solve for *h*.**

▶ The height of the roof is about 2.7 meters.

STUDENT HELP

Study Tip
In Example 1, all the side lengths of $\triangle XZY$ are given. This makes it a good choice for setting up a proportion to find an unknown side length of $\triangle XYW$.

GOAL 2 USING A GEOMETRIC MEAN TO SOLVE PROBLEMS

In right $\triangle ABC$, altitude $\overline{CD}$ is drawn to the hypotenuse, forming two smaller right triangles that are similar to $\triangle ABC$. From Theorem 9.1, you know that $\triangle CBD \sim \triangle ACD \sim \triangle ABC$.

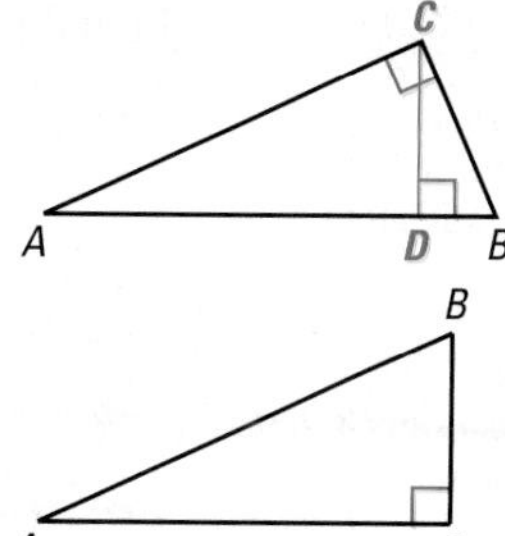

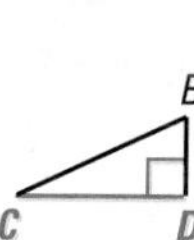

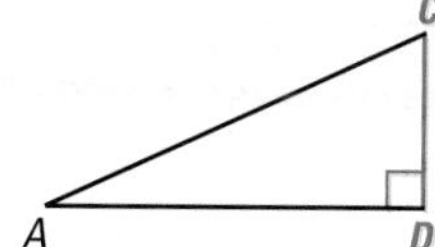

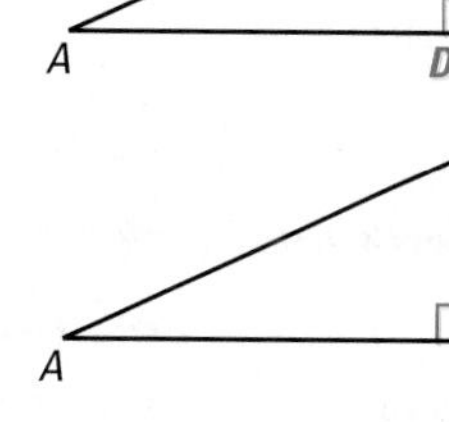

STUDENT HELP

Look Back
The geometric mean of two numbers a and b is the positive number x such that $\frac{a}{x} = \frac{x}{b}$. For more help with finding a geometric mean, see p. 466.

Notice that $\overline{CD}$ is the longer leg of $\triangle CBD$ and the shorter leg of $\triangle ACD$. When you write a proportion comparing the leg lengths of $\triangle CBD$ and $\triangle ACD$, you can see that CD is the *geometric mean* of BD and AD.

$$\frac{\text{shorter leg of } \triangle CBD}{\text{shorter leg of } \triangle ACD} \quad \frac{BD}{CD} = \frac{CD}{AD} \quad \frac{\text{longer leg of } \triangle CBD}{\text{longer leg of } \triangle ACD}$$

Sides $\overline{CB}$ and $\overline{AC}$ also appear in more than one triangle. Their side lengths are also geometric means, as shown by the proportions below:

$$\frac{\text{hypotenuse of } \triangle ABC}{\text{hypotenuse of } \triangle CBD} \quad \frac{AB}{CB} = \frac{CB}{DB} \quad \frac{\text{shorter leg of } \triangle ABC}{\text{shorter leg of } \triangle CBD}$$

$$\frac{\text{hypotenuse of } \triangle ABC}{\text{hypotenuse of } \triangle ACD} \quad \frac{AB}{AC} = \frac{AC}{AD} \quad \frac{\text{longer leg of } \triangle ABC}{\text{longer leg of } \triangle ACD}$$

These results are expressed in the theorems below. You are asked to prove the theorems in Exercises 35 and 36.

GEOMETRIC MEAN THEOREMS

THEOREM 9.2

In a right triangle, the altitude from the right angle to the hypotenuse divides the hypotenuse into two segments.

The length of the altitude is the geometric mean of the lengths of the two segments.

$$\frac{BD}{CD} = \frac{CD}{AD}$$

THEOREM 9.3

In a right triangle, the altitude from the right angle to the hypotenuse divides the hypotenuse into two segments.

The length of each leg of the right triangle is the geometric mean of the lengths of the hypotenuse and the segment of the hypotenuse that is adjacent to the leg.

$$\frac{AB}{CB} = \frac{CB}{DB}$$

$$\frac{AB}{AC} = \frac{AC}{AD}$$

CONCEPT QUESTION EXAMPLE 1 Explain why $\triangle XYZ \sim \triangle XWY$.
Since $\angle X \cong \angle X$ and $\angle XYZ \cong \angle XWY$, the AA Similarity Postulate applies.

STUDENT HELP NOTES

Look Back As students look back to p. 466, remind them the product of the means equals the product of the extremes in a proportion. Although there are two algebraic solutions, only the positive solution can represent the length of a segment.

MULTIPLE REPRESENTATIONS
Diagrams that involve overlapping or embedded triangles may best be viewed by breaking the original diagram into the separate triangles as demonstrated at the top of this page. Make certain that students understand how this is done as they will find it useful not only for this lesson, but for others as well.

EXTRA EXAMPLE 2

Find the value of each variable.

a. $2\sqrt{15}$

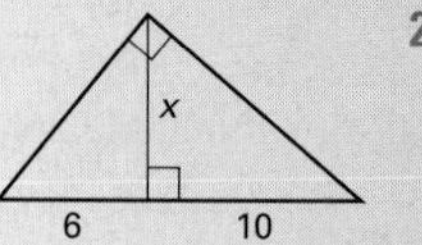

b. $\sqrt{65}$

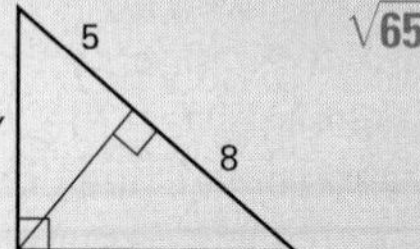

EXTRA EXAMPLE 3

To estimate the height of a statue, your friend holds a cardboard square at eye level. She lines up the top edge of the square with the top of the statue and the bottom edge with the bottom of the statue. You measure the distance from the ground to your friend's eye and the distance from your friend to the statue.

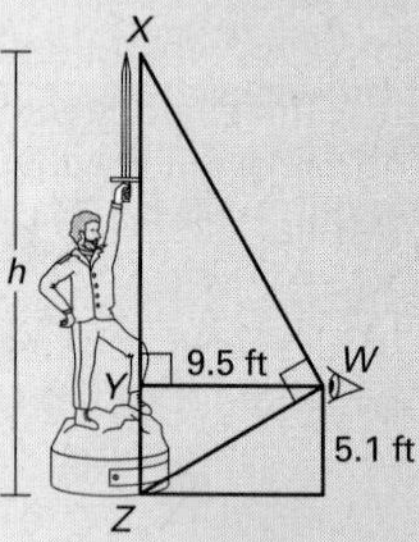

In the diagram, $XY = h - 5.1$ is the difference between the statue height h and your friend's eye level. Solve for h. about 22.8 ft

CHECKPOINT EXERCISES

For use after Examples 2 and 3:

1. Find the value of each variable.

a. $4\sqrt{21}$

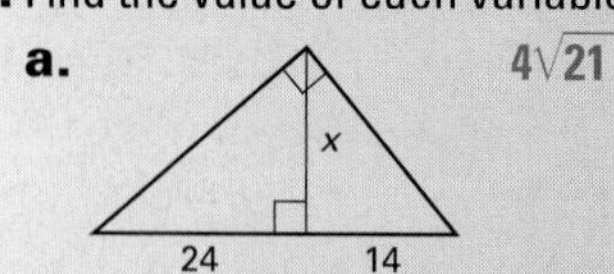

b. $3\sqrt{46}$

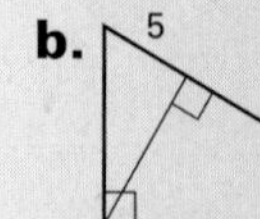

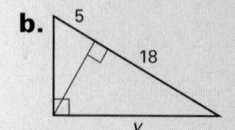

CLOSURE QUESTION

$\overline{CD}$ is the altitude to the hypotenuse of $\triangle ABC$ with right angle C. Find three pairs of similar triangles.

Sample answer: $\triangle ACD \sim \triangle CBD \sim \triangle ABC$

STUDENT HELP

Skills Review
For help with simplifying radicals, see p. 799.

Study Tip
In part (a) of Example 2, the equation $18 = x^2$ has two solutions, $+\sqrt{18}$ and $-\sqrt{18}$. Because you are finding a length, you use the *positive* square root.

EXAMPLE 2 *Using a Geometric Mean*

Find the value of each variable.

a.

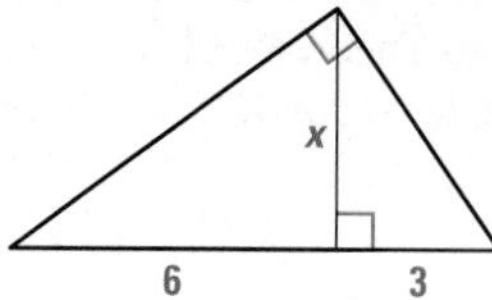

b.

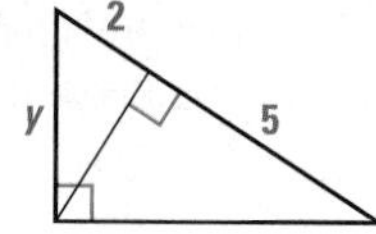

SOLUTION

a. Apply Theorem 9.2.

$$\frac{6}{x} = \frac{x}{3}$$
$$18 = x^2$$
$$\sqrt{18} = x$$
$$\sqrt{9} \cdot \sqrt{2} = x$$
$$3\sqrt{2} = x$$

b. Apply Theorem 9.3.

$$\frac{5+2}{y} = \frac{y}{2}$$
$$\frac{7}{y} = \frac{y}{2}$$
$$14 = y^2$$
$$\sqrt{14} = y$$

EXAMPLE 3 *Using Indirect Measurement*

FOCUS ON APPLICATIONS

MONORAILS are railways that have only one rail. The Jacksonville monorail, shown in the photo above, can travel up to 35 miles per hour and can carry about 56 passengers per car.

MONORAIL TRACK To estimate the height of a monorail track, your friend holds a cardboard square at eye level. Your friend lines up the top edge of the square with the track and the bottom edge with the ground. You measure the distance from the ground to your friend's eye and the distance from your friend to the track.

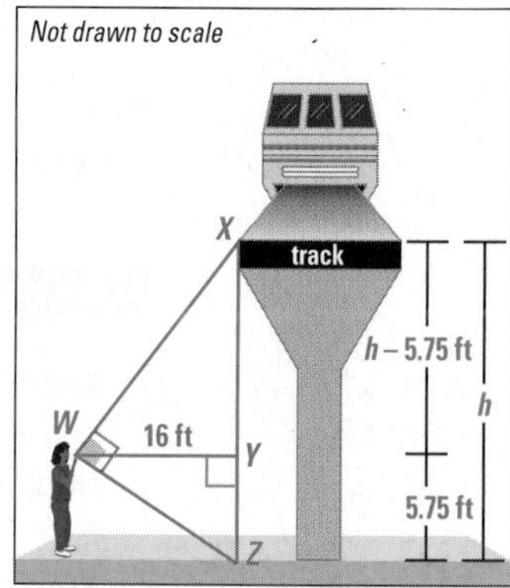

In the diagram, $XY = h - 5.75$ is the difference between the track height h and your friend's eye level. Use Theorem 9.2 to write a proportion involving XY. Then you can solve for h.

$$\frac{XY}{WY} = \frac{WY}{ZY} \quad \textbf{Geometric Mean Theorem 9.2}$$
$$\frac{h - 5.75}{16} = \frac{16}{5.75} \quad \textbf{Substitute.}$$
$$5.75(h - 5.75) = 16^2 \quad \textbf{Cross product property}$$
$$5.75h - 33.0625 = 256 \quad \textbf{Distributive property}$$
$$5.75h = 289.0625 \quad \textbf{Add 33.0625 to each side.}$$
$$h \approx 50 \quad \textbf{Divide each side by 5.75.}$$

▶ The height of the track is about 50 feet.

GUIDED PRACTICE

Vocabulary Check ✓ In Exercises 1–3, use the diagram at the right.

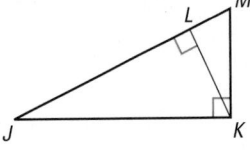

1. In the diagram, KL is the ___?___ of ML and JL. geometric mean

Concept Check ✓

2. Complete the following statement: $\triangle JKL \sim \triangle$ ___?___ $\sim \triangle$ ___?___. *KML, JMK*
3. Which segment's length is the geometric mean of ML and MJ? $\overline{MK}$

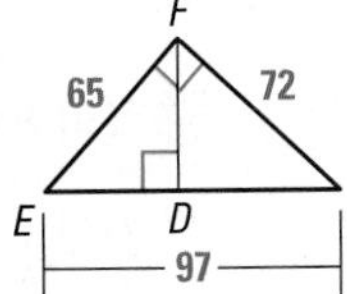

Skill Check ✓ In Exercises 4–9, use the diagram above. Complete the proportion.

4. $\frac{KM}{KL} = \frac{?}{JK}$ *JM*
5. $\frac{JM}{?} = \frac{JK}{JL}$ *JK*
6. $\frac{?}{LK} = \frac{LK}{LM}$ *JL*
7. $\frac{JM}{?} = \frac{KM}{LM}$ *KM*
8. $\frac{LK}{LM} = \frac{JK}{?}$ *KM*
9. $\frac{?}{JK} = \frac{MK}{MJ}$ *LK*
10. Use the diagram at the right. Find DC. Then find DF. Round decimals to the nearest tenth. 53.4; 48.3

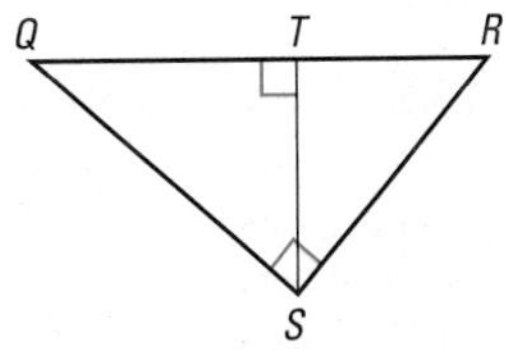

PRACTICE AND APPLICATIONS

STUDENT HELP
Extra Practice to help you master skills is on p. 819.

SIMILAR TRIANGLES Use the diagram.

11. Sketch the three similar triangles in the diagram. Label the vertices. See margin.
12. Write similarity statements for the three triangles. $\triangle QRS \sim \triangle QST \sim \triangle SRT$

USING PROPORTIONS Complete and solve the proportion.

13. $\frac{x}{20} = \frac{?}{12}$ 20; $33\frac{1}{3}$
14. $\frac{4}{x} = \frac{x}{?}$ 9; 6
15. $\frac{5}{x} = \frac{x}{?}$ 3; $\sqrt{15}$

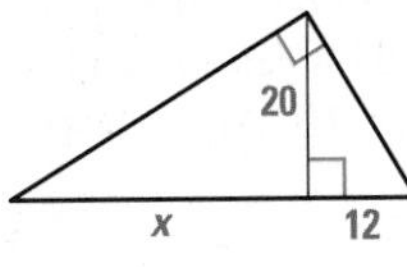

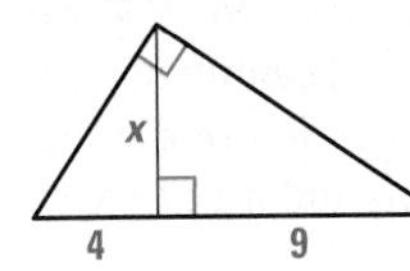

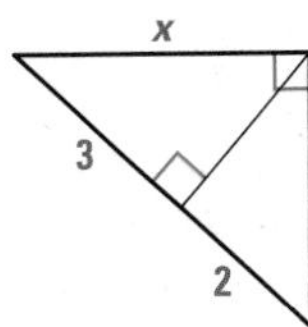

16. $\triangle XYZ \sim \triangle XZW \sim \triangle ZYW$; ZW

17. $\triangle QRS \sim \triangle QST \sim \triangle SRT$; RQ

18. $\triangle EFG \sim \triangle EGH \sim \triangle GFH$; EH

COMPLETING PROPORTIONS Write similarity statements for the three similar triangles in the diagram. Then complete the proportion.

16. $\frac{XW}{ZW} = \frac{?}{YW}$
17. $\frac{QT}{SQ} = \frac{SQ}{?}$
18. $\frac{?}{EG} = \frac{EG}{EF}$

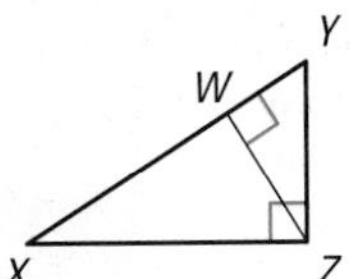

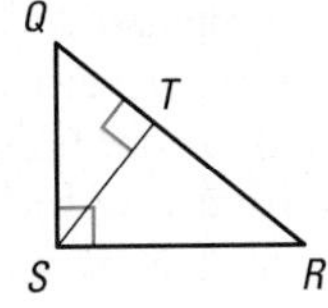

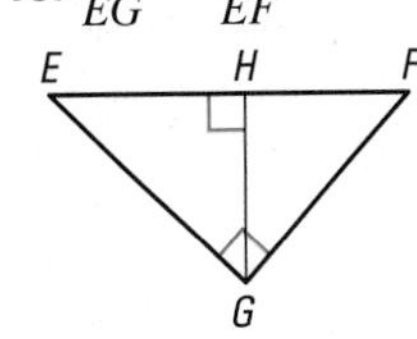

STUDENT HELP
HOMEWORK HELP
Example 1: Exs. 11–31
Example 2: Exs. 11–31
Example 3: Ex. 32

3 APPLY

ASSIGNMENT GUIDE

BASIC
Day 1: pp. 531–534 Exs. 11–30, 33, 34, 41, 42, 44–50 even

AVERAGE
Day 1: pp. 531–534 Exs. 11–30, 33–36, 41, 42, 44–50 even

ADVANCED
Day 1: pp. 531–534 Exs. 11–30, 32–36, 41–43, 44–50 even

BLOCK SCHEDULE (WITH CH. 8 ASSESS.)
pp. 531–534 Exs. 11–30, 33–36, 41, 42, 44–50 even

EXERCISE LEVELS

Level A: *Easier*
11–15

Level B: *More Difficult*
16–33, 37–42

Level C: *Most Difficult*
34–36, 43

✓ HOMEWORK CHECK

To quickly check student understanding of key concepts, go over the following exercises: Exs. 12, 14, 18, 20, 22, 28, 30, 34. See also the Daily Homework Quiz:

- Blackline Master (*Chapter 9 Resource Book*, p. 24)
- Transparency (p. 64)

11.
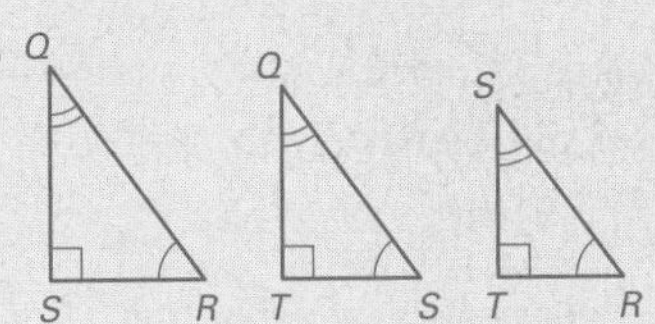

MATHEMATICAL REASONING

EXERCISE 19 The altitude to the hypotenuse of a right triangle is the geometric mean between each segment of the hypotenuse. This property can be used without first identifying the similar triangles. Ask students to solve the proportion $\frac{16}{12} = \frac{12}{DB}$ to find DB in this triangle.

STUDENT HELP NOTES

Homework Help Students can find help for Exs. 28–30 at **www.mcdougallittell.com.** The information can be printed out for students who don't have access to the Internet.

TEACHING TIPS

EXERCISE 31 Remind students that they can prove that the diagonals of a kite are perpendicular and that $\overline{AC}$ bisects $\overline{BD}$.

40. A good answer should include these steps:
- Use the right triangle ABC from Ex. 38. Measure $AD, BD, AB, BC,$ and AC.
- Use the calculate feature to calculate the values of the ratios $\frac{AB}{BC}, \frac{BC}{BD}, \frac{AB}{AC},$ and $\frac{AC}{AD}$. Notice that $\frac{AB}{BC} = \frac{BC}{BD}$ and $\frac{AB}{AC} = \frac{AC}{AD}$.
- Drag point C so that $m\angle C \neq 90°$. Calculate the ratios $\frac{AB}{BC}, \frac{BC}{BD}, \frac{AB}{AC},$ and $\frac{AC}{AD}$. Notice that $\frac{AB}{BC} \neq \frac{BC}{BD}$ and $\frac{AB}{AC} \neq \frac{AC}{AD}$.
- Conclude that Theorem 9.3 is true only for a right triangle.

FINDING LENGTHS **Write similarity statements for three triangles in the diagram. Then find the given length. Round decimals to the nearest tenth.**

19. Find DB.

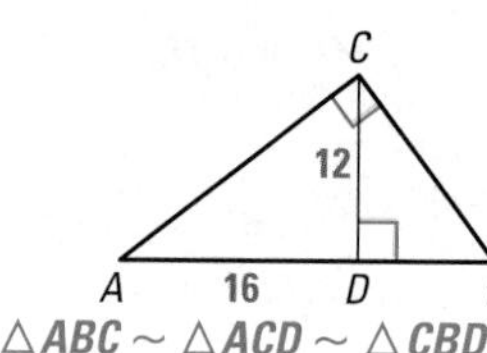

$\triangle ABC \sim \triangle ACD \sim \triangle CBD$; 9

20. Find HF.

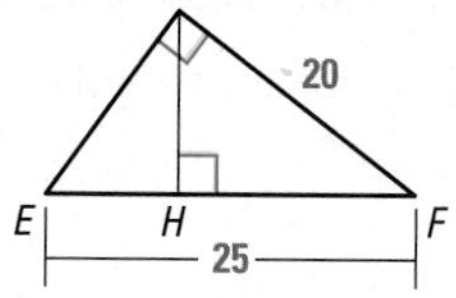

G
20
E
H
F
25

$\triangle EFG \sim \triangle EGH \sim \triangle GFH$; 16

21. Find JK.

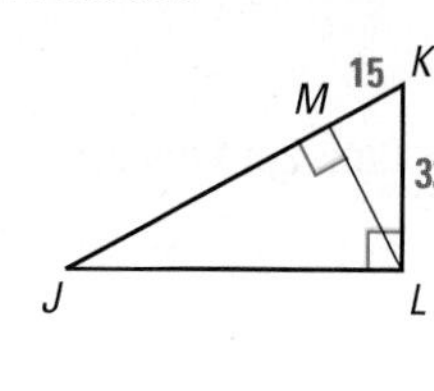

21. $\triangle JKL \sim \triangle JLM \sim \triangle LKM$; $\frac{1024}{15} \approx 68.3$

22. Find QS.

Q 40 R
32
T
S

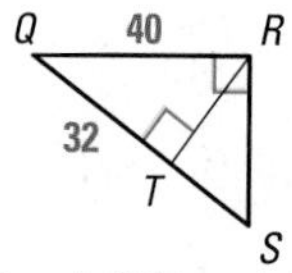

$\triangle QRS \sim \triangle QTR \sim \triangle RTS$; 50

23. Find CD.

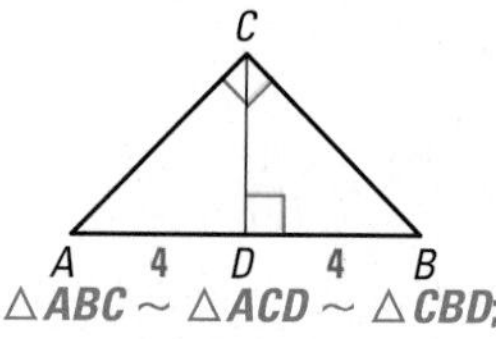

$\triangle ABC \sim \triangle ACD \sim \triangle CBD$; 4

24. Find FH.

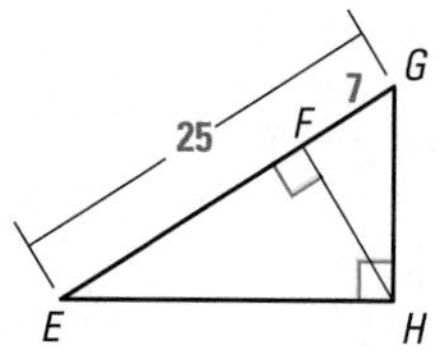

G
7
25
F
E
H

24. $\triangle EGH \sim \triangle EHF \sim \triangle HGF$; $3\sqrt{14} \approx 11.2$

USING ALGEBRA **Find the value of each variable.**

25.

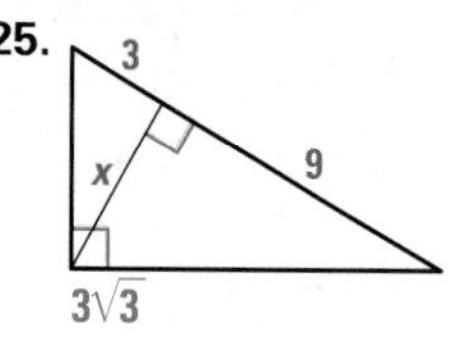

26.

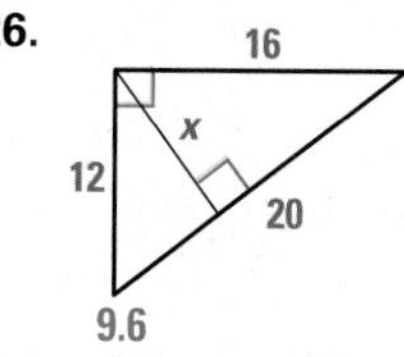

27.

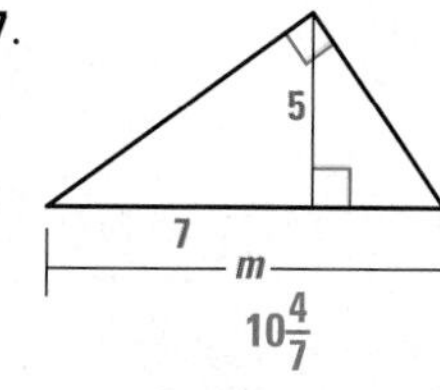

STUDENT HELP

HOMEWORK HELP Visit our Web site www.mcdougallittell.com for help with Exs. 28–30.

28.

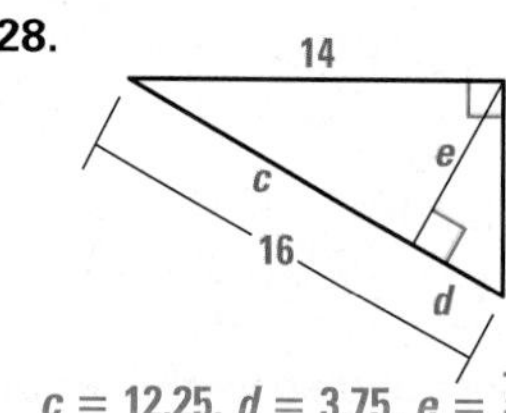

$c = 12.25,\ d = 3.75,\ e = \frac{7\sqrt{15}}{4}$

29.

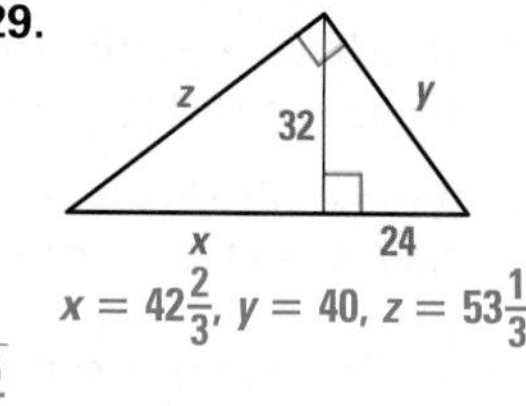

$x = 42\frac{2}{3},\ y = 40,\ z = 53\frac{1}{3}$

30.

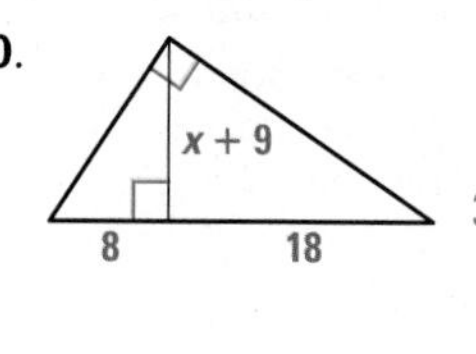

3

31. **KITE DESIGN** You are designing a diamond-shaped kite. You know that $AD = 44.8$ centimeters, $DC = 72$ centimeters, and $AC = 84.8$ centimeters. You want to use a straight crossbar $\overline{BD}$. About how long should it be? Explain.

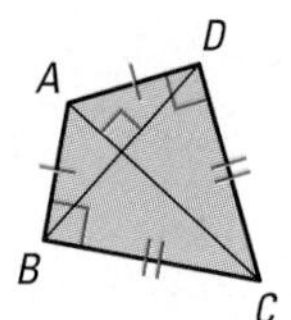

31. about 76 cm; $\triangle ABC$ and $\triangle ADC$ are congruent right triangles by the SSS Congruence Post., so $\overline{AC}$ is a perpendicular bisector of $\overline{BD}$. By Geometric Mean Theorem 9.3, the altitude from D to hypotenuse $\overline{AC}$ divides $\overline{AC}$ into segments of lengths 23.67 cm and 61.13 cm. By Geometric Mean Theorem 9.2, the length of the altitude to the hypotenuse of each right triangle is about 38 cm long, so the crossbar $\overline{BD}$ should be about 2 • 38, or 76 cm long.

32. **ROCK CLIMBING** You and a friend want to know how much rope you need to climb a large rock. To estimate the height of the rock, you use the method from Example 3 on page 530. As shown at the right, your friend uses a square to line up the top and the bottom of the rock. You measure the vertical distance from the ground to your friend's eye and the distance from your friend to the rock. Estimate the height of the rock.

about 64.4 ft

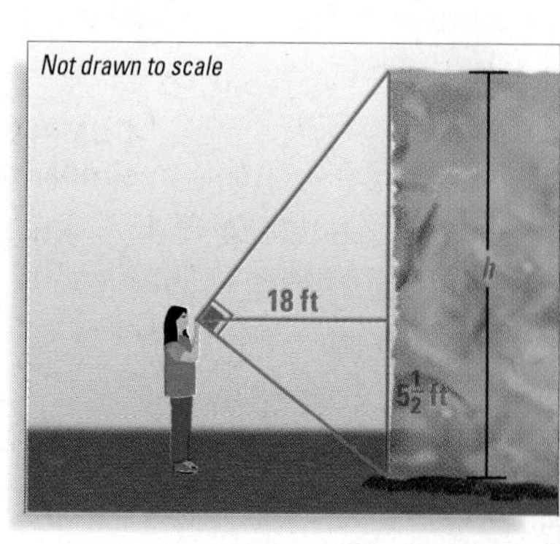

STUDENT HELP

Look Back
For help with finding the area of a triangle, see p. 51.

33. FINDING AREA Write similarity statements for the three similar right triangles in the diagram. Then find the area of each triangle. Explain how you got your answers.

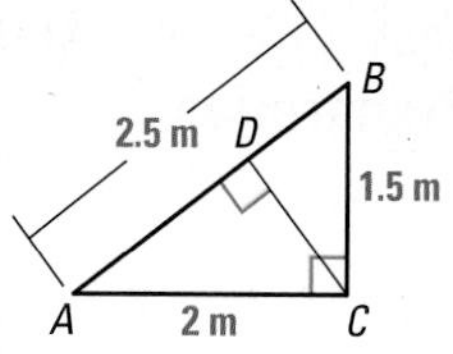

33. $\triangle ABC \sim \triangle ACD \sim \triangle CBD$; area of $\triangle ABC = \frac{1}{2}(2)(1.5) = 1.5\text{ m}^2$; $AD = 1.6$ and $DC = 1.2$, so the area of $\triangle ACD = \frac{1}{2}(1.6) \times (1.2) = 0.96\text{ m}^2$, and the area of $\triangle CBD = 1.5 - 0.96 = 0.54\text{ m}^2$.

PROVING THEOREMS 9.1, 9.2, AND 9.3 In Exercises 34–36, use the diagram at the right.

34. Use the diagram to prove Theorem 9.1 on page 527. (*Hint:* Look back at the plan for proof on page 528.)

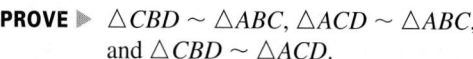

GIVEN ▶ $\triangle ABC$ is a right triangle; altitude $\overline{CD}$ is drawn to hypotenuse $\overline{AB}$.

PROVE ▶ $\triangle CBD \sim \triangle ABC$, $\triangle ACD \sim \triangle ABC$, and $\triangle CBD \sim \triangle ACD$.

34. Proof that $\triangle CBD \sim \triangle ABC$: All rt. $\angle$s are $\cong$, so $\angle BDC \cong \angle BCA$. $\angle B \cong \angle B$, so $\triangle CBD \sim \triangle ABC$ by the AA Similarity Post. Proof that $\triangle ACD \sim \triangle ABC$: All rt. $\angle$s are $\cong$, so $\angle CDA \cong \angle BCA$. $\angle A \cong \angle A$, so $\triangle ACD \sim \triangle ABC$ by the AA Similarity Post. Proof that $\triangle CBD \sim \triangle ACD$: Since $\triangle ACD \sim \triangle ABC$, $\angle ACD \cong \angle B$. All rt. $\angle$s are $\cong$, so $\angle BDC \cong \angle CDA$. Thus, $\triangle CBD \sim \triangle ACD$ by the AA Similarity Post.

35. Use the diagram to prove Theorem 9.2 on page 529.

GIVEN ▶ $\triangle ABC$ is a right triangle; altitude $\overline{CD}$ is drawn to hypotenuse $\overline{AB}$.

PROVE ▶ $\frac{BD}{CD} = \frac{CD}{AD}$

From Ex. 34, $\triangle CBD \sim \triangle ACD$. Corresponding side lengths are in proportion, so $\frac{BD}{CD} = \frac{CD}{AD}$.

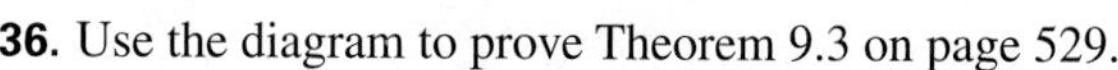

36. Use the diagram to prove Theorem 9.3 on page 529.

GIVEN ▶ $\triangle ABC$ is a right triangle; altitude $\overline{CD}$ is drawn to hypotenuse $\overline{AB}$.

PROVE ▶ $\frac{AB}{BC} = \frac{BC}{BD}$ and $\frac{AB}{AC} = \frac{AC}{AD}$

36. From Ex. 34, $\triangle CBD \sim \triangle ABC$. Corresponding side lengths are in proportion, so $\frac{AB}{BC} = \frac{BC}{BD}$. Also, from Ex. 34, $\triangle ACD \sim \triangle ABC$. Corresponding side lengths are in proportion, so $\frac{AB}{AC} = \frac{AC}{AD}$.

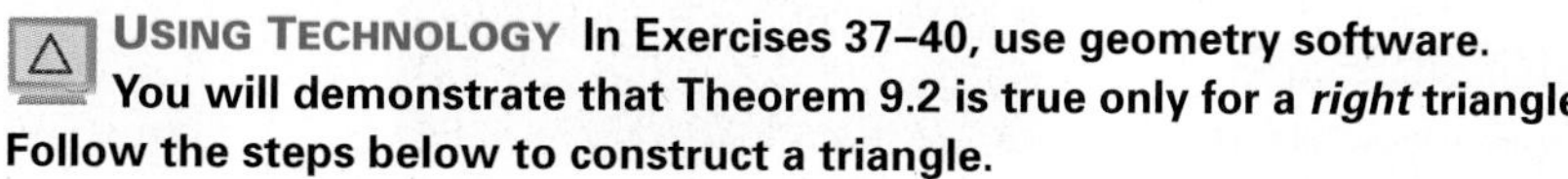

USING TECHNOLOGY In Exercises 37–40, use geometry software. You will demonstrate that Theorem 9.2 is true only for a *right* triangle. Follow the steps below to construct a triangle.

1. Draw a triangle and label its vertices A, B, and C. The triangle should *not* be a right triangle.
2. Draw altitude $\overline{CD}$ from point C to side $\overline{AB}$.
3. Measure $\angle C$. Then measure $\overline{AD}$, $\overline{CD}$, and $\overline{BD}$.

37. Calculate the values of the ratios $\frac{BD}{CD}$ and $\frac{CD}{AD}$. What does Theorem 9.2 say about the values of these ratios? **The values of the ratios will vary, but will not be equal. The theorem says that these ratios are equal.**

38. Drag point C until $m\angle C = 90°$. What happens to the values of the ratios $\frac{BD}{CD}$ and $\frac{CD}{AD}$? **The ratios are equal.**

39. Explain how your answers to Exercises 37 and 38 support the conclusion that Theorem 9.2 is true only for a right triangle.

39. The ratios are equal when the triangle is a right triangle, but are not equal when the triangle is not a right triangle.

40. Use the triangle you constructed to show that Theorem 9.3 is true only for a right triangle. Describe your procedure. **See margin.**

STUDENT HELP NOTES

Look Back As students look back to p. 51, remind them that either leg of a right triangle can be used as the altitude in the area formula.

TEACHING TIPS

EXERCISE 38 Dragging point C until the angle measures 90° uses the dynamic feature of the geometry drawing software. It is important that students first calculate the ratios in Ex. 37 and leave them visible on the screen so that they can see the changes as $\angle C$ changes.

ENGLISH LEARNERS

EXERCISES 37–40
Understanding English language directions for programming a graphing calculator can be difficult for English learners. You may want to have English learners work with an English fluent partner to follow the steps for constructing a triangle and solving Exercises 37–40.

ADDITIONAL PRACTICE AND RETEACHING

For Lesson 9.1:

- Practice Levels A, B, and C (*Chapter 9 Resource Book,* p. 14)
- Reteaching with Practice (*Chapter 9 Resource Book,* p. 17)
- See Lesson 9.1 of the *Personal Student Tutor*

For more Mixed Review:

- Search the *Test and Practice Generator* for key words or specific lessons.

4 ASSESS

DAILY HOMEWORK QUIZ

Transparency Available

Use the diagram.

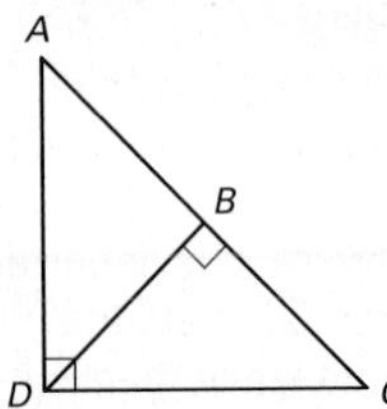

1. Write similarity statements for the three triangles.
   $\triangle ADC \sim \triangle ABD \sim \triangle DBC$
2. Complete the proportion.
   $\frac{AD}{DC} = \frac{CB}{?}$ BD

Find the value of the variable.

3. 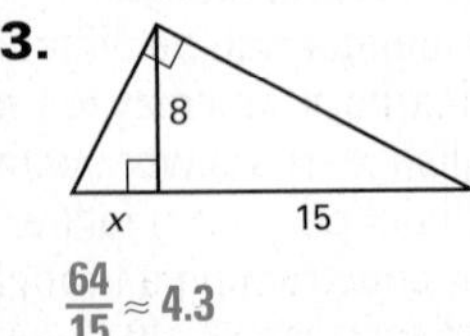

$\frac{64}{15} \approx 4.3$

EXTRA CHALLENGE NOTE

Challenge problems for Lesson 9.1 are available in **blackline** format in the *Chapter 9 Resource Book,* p. 21 and at **www.mcdougallittell.com.**

ADDITIONAL TEST PREPARATION

1. **OPEN ENDED** Draw and label a right triangle and the altitude to the hypotenuse. Identify three similar triangles in the diagram.
   Sample answer:

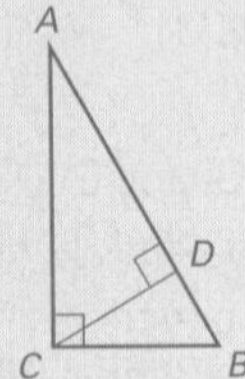

$\triangle ACD \sim \triangle CBD \sim \triangle ABC$

43. See Additional Answers beginning on page AA1.

Test Preparation

41. **MULTIPLE CHOICE** Use the diagram at the right. Decide which proportions are true. D

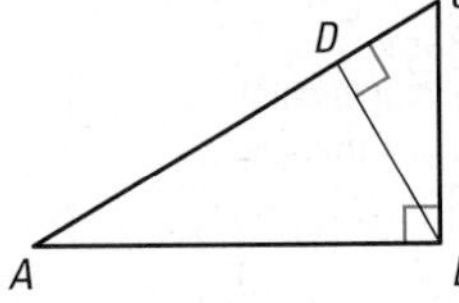

I. $\frac{DB}{DC} = \frac{DA}{DB}$ II. $\frac{BA}{CB} = \frac{CB}{BD}$

III. $\frac{CA}{BA} = \frac{BA}{CA}$ IV. $\frac{DB}{BC} = \frac{DA}{BA}$

Ⓐ I only Ⓑ II only Ⓒ I and II only Ⓓ I and IV only

42. **MULTIPLE CHOICE** In the diagram above, $AC = 24$ and $BC = 12$. Find AD. If necessary, round to the nearest hundredth. C

Ⓐ 6 Ⓑ 16.97 Ⓒ 18 Ⓓ 20.78

★ Challenge

43. *Writing* Two methods for indirectly measuring the height of a building are shown below. For each method, describe what distances need to be measured directly. Explain how to find the height of the building using these measurements. Describe one advantage and one disadvantage of each method. Copy and label the diagrams as part of your explanations. See margin.

Method 1 Use the method described in Example 3 on page 530.

Method 2 Use the method described in Exercises 55 and 56 on page 486.

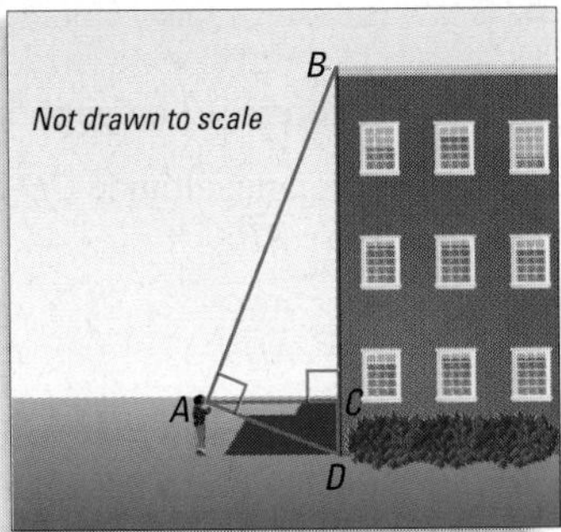

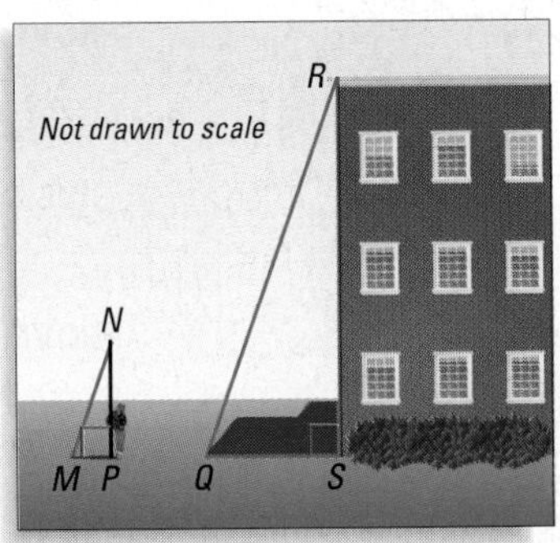

EXTRA CHALLENGE

www.mcdougallittell.com

MIXED REVIEW

SOLVING EQUATIONS Solve the equation. (Skills Review, p. 800, for 9.2)

44. $n^2 = 169$ 13, −13
45. $14 + x^2 = 78$ 8, −8
46. $d^2 + 18 = 99$ 9, −9

LOGICAL REASONING Write the converse of the statement. Decide whether the converse is *true* or *false*. (Review 2.1)

47. If a triangle is obtuse, then one of its angles is greater than 90°.
48. If two triangles are congruent, then their corresponding angles are congruent.

47. If the measure of one of the angles of a triangle is greater that 90°, then the triangle is obtuse; true.

48. If the corresponding angles of two triangles are congruent, then the triangles are congruent; false.

FINDING AREA Find the area of the figure. (Review 1.7, 6.7 for 9.2)

49. 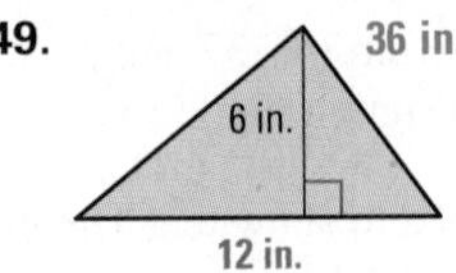

36 in.^{2}

50. 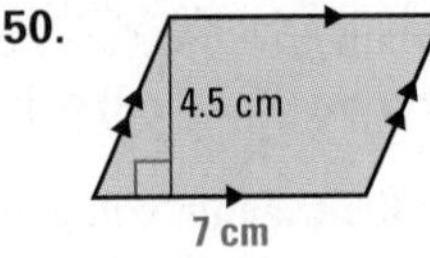

31.5 cm^2

51.  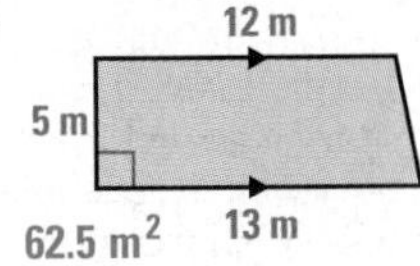

62.5 m^2

9.2 The Pythagorean Theorem

What you should learn

GOAL 1 Prove the Pythagorean Theorem.

GOAL 2 Use the Pythagorean Theorem to solve **real-life** problems, such as determining how far a ladder will reach in **Ex. 32**.

Why you should learn it

▼ To measure **real-life** lengths indirectly, such as the length of the support beam of a skywalk in **Example 4**.

GOAL 1 PROVING THE PYTHAGOREAN THEOREM

In this lesson, you will study one of the most famous theorems in mathematics—the *Pythagorean Theorem*. The relationship it describes has been known for thousands of years.

THEOREM

THEOREM 9.4 ***Pythagorean Theorem***

In a right triangle, the square of the length of the hypotenuse is equal to the sum of the squares of the lengths of the legs.

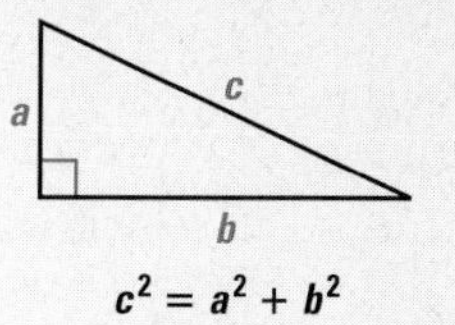

$c^2 = a^2 + b^2$

PROVING THE PYTHAGOREAN THEOREM There are many different proofs of the Pythagorean Theorem. One is shown below. Other proofs are found in Exercises 37 and 38 on page 540, and in the *Math and History* feature on page 557.

GIVEN ▶ In $\triangle ABC$, $\angle BCA$ is a right angle.

PROVE ▶ $a^2 + b^2 = c^2$

Plan for Proof Draw altitude $\overline{CD}$ to the hypotenuse. Then apply Geometric Mean Theorem 9.3, which states that when the altitude is drawn to the hypotenuse of a right triangle, each leg of the right triangle is the geometric mean of the hypotenuse and the segment of the hypotenuse that is adjacent to that leg.

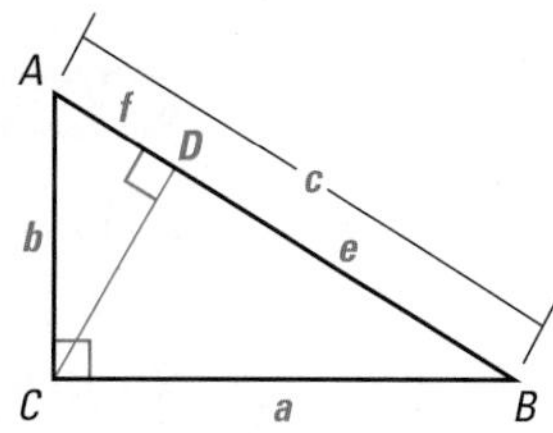

Proof

Statements	Reasons
1. Draw a perpendicular from C to $\overline{AB}$.	**1.** Perpendicular Postulate
2. $\frac{c}{a} = \frac{a}{e}$ and $\frac{c}{b} = \frac{b}{f}$	**2.** Geometric Mean Theorem 9.3
3. $ce = a^2$ and $cf = b^2$	**3.** Cross product property
4. $ce + cf = a^2 + b^2$	**4.** Addition property of equality
5. $c(e + f) = a^2 + b^2$	**5.** Distributive property
6. $e + f = c$	**6.** Segment Addition Postulate
7. $c^2 = a^2 + b^2$	**7.** Substitution property of equality

CALIFORNIA STANDARDS AND ASSESSMENT

CA Standards: 8, 10, 14, 15
SAT9 Task 1: Objs. 1, 5
SAT9 Task 2: Objs. 1, 7, 25

1 PLAN

PACING
Basic: 1 day
Average: 1 day
Advanced: 1 day
Block Schedule: 0.5 block with 9.3

LESSON OPENER ACTIVITY

An alternative way to approach Lesson 9.2 is to use the Activity Lesson Opener:

- Blackline Master (*Chapter 9 Resource Book*, p. 25)
- Transparency (p. 55)

MEETING INDIVIDUAL NEEDS

- ***Chapter 9 Resource Book***
  Prerequisite Skills Review (p. 5)
  Practice Level A (p. 29)
  Practice Level B (p. 30)
  Practice Level C (p. 31)
  Reteaching with Practice (p. 32)
  Absent Student Catch-Up (p. 34)
  Challenge (p. 36)
- ***Resources in Spanish***
-  ***Personal Student Tutor***

NEW-TEACHER SUPPORT

See the Tips for New Teachers on pp. 1–2 of the *Chapter 9 Resource Book* for additional notes about Lesson 9.2.

WARM-UP EXERCISES

Transparency Available

Solve the equation. Express the answer to the nearest tenth.

1. $\frac{8}{c} = \frac{c}{9}$ 8.5; –8.5
2. $c^2 = 36$ 6; –6
3. $c^2 = 84.2$ 9.2; –9.2
4. $c^2 = 28.2 + 42.1$ 8.4, –8.4
5. $c^2 - 81 = 144$ 15; –15

2 TEACH

MOTIVATING THE LESSON

Ask students to make a right triangle by equally spacing 12 knots in a string and then bending it to form a 3-4-5 triangle. Finding lengths that form right triangles is the focus of this lesson.

EXTRA EXAMPLE 1

Find the length of the hypotenuse of the right triangle. Tell whether the side lengths form a Pythagorean triple. 25; yes

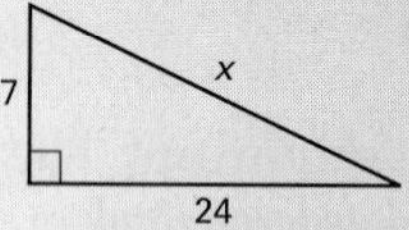

EXTRA EXAMPLE 2

Find the length of the leg of the right triangle. 6

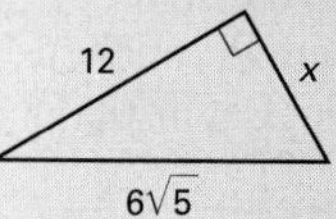

CHECKPOINT EXERCISES

For use after Example 1:

1. Find the length of the hypotenuse of the right triangle. Tell whether the lengths form a Pythagorean triple. $\frac{5}{2}$; no

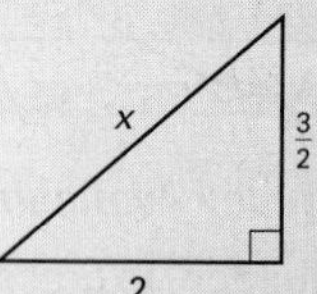

For use after Example 2:

2. Find the length of the leg of the right triangle. $6\sqrt{10}$

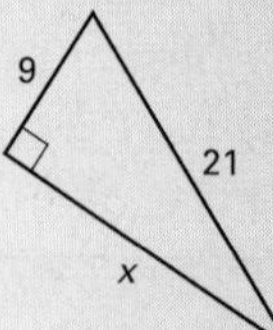

GOAL 2 USING THE PYTHAGOREAN THEOREM

A **Pythagorean triple** is a set of three positive integers a, b, and c that satisfy the equation $c^2 = a^2 + b^2$. For example, the integers 3, 4, and 5 form a Pythagorean triple because $5^2 = 3^2 + 4^2$.

EXAMPLE 1 *Finding the Length of a Hypotenuse*

Find the length of the hypotenuse of the right triangle. Tell whether the side lengths form a Pythagorean triple.

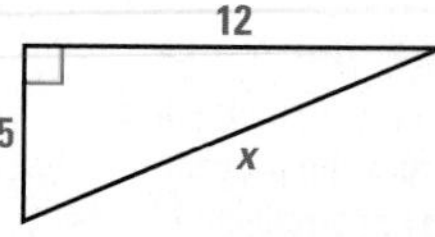

SOLUTION

$(\text{hypotenuse})^2 = (\text{leg})^2 + (\text{leg})^2$	Pythagorean Theorem
$x^2 = 5^2 + 12^2$	Substitute.
$x^2 = 25 + 144$	Multiply.
$x^2 = 169$	Add.
$x = 13$	Find the positive square root.

▶ Because the side lengths 5, 12, and 13 are integers, they form a Pythagorean triple.

Many right triangles have side lengths that do not form a Pythagorean triple, as shown in Example 2.

EXAMPLE 2 *Finding the Length of a Leg*

Find the length of the leg of the right triangle.

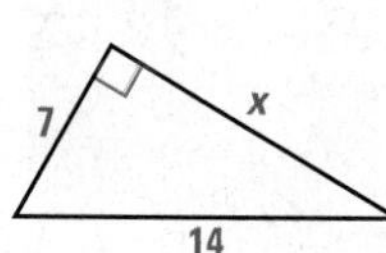

SOLUTION

$(\text{hypotenuse})^2 = (\text{leg})^2 + (\text{leg})^2$	Pythagorean Theorem
$14^2 = 7^2 + x^2$	Substitute.
$196 = 49 + x^2$	Multiply.
$147 = x^2$	Subtract 49 from each side.
$\sqrt{147} = x$	Find the positive square root.
$\sqrt{49} \cdot \sqrt{3} = x$	Use product property.
$7\sqrt{3} = x$	Simplify the radical.

STUDENT HELP

Skills Review

For help with simplifying radicals, see p. 799.

In Example 2, the side length was written as a radical in simplest form. In real-life problems, it is often more convenient to use a calculator to write a decimal approximation of the side length. For instance, in Example 2, $x = 7 \cdot \sqrt{3} \approx 12.1$.

EXAMPLE 3 *Finding the Area of a Triangle*

STUDENT HELP

Look Back
For help with finding the area of a triangle, see p. 51.

Find the area of the triangle to the nearest tenth of a meter.

SOLUTION

You are given that the base of the triangle is 10 meters, but you do not know the height h.

Because the triangle is isosceles, it can be divided into two congruent right triangles with the given dimensions. Use the Pythagorean Theorem to find the value of h.

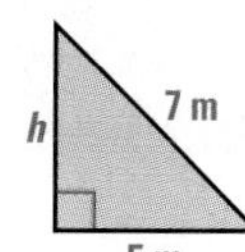

$7^2 = 5^2 + h^2$	**Pythagorean Theorem**
$49 = 25 + h^2$	**Multiply.**
$24 = h^2$	**Subtract 25 from both sides.**
$\sqrt{24} = h$	**Find the positive square root.**

Now find the area of the original triangle.

$$\text{Area} = \frac{1}{2}bh$$
$$= \frac{1}{2}(10)(\sqrt{24})$$
$$\approx 24.5 \text{ m}^2$$

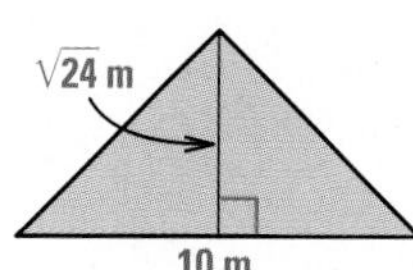

▶ The area of the triangle is about 24.5 m^2.

EXAMPLE 4 *Indirect Measurement*

SUPPORT BEAM The skyscrapers shown on page 535 are connected by a skywalk with support beams. You can use the Pythagorean Theorem to find the approximate length of each support beam.

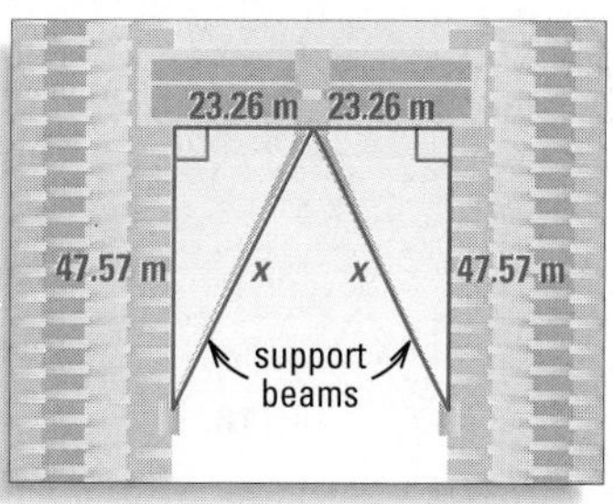

Each support beam forms the hypotenuse of a right triangle. The right triangles are congruent, so the support beams are the same length.

$x^2 = (23.26)^2 + (47.57)^2$	**Pythagorean Theorem**
$x = \sqrt{(23.26)^2 + (47.57)^2}$	**Find the positive square root.**
$x \approx 52.95$	**Use a calculator to approximate.**

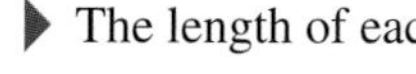

▶ The length of each support beam is about 52.95 meters.

FOCUS ON PEOPLE

CESAR PELLI is an architect who designed the twin skyscrapers shown on page 535. These 1483 foot buildings tower over the city of Kuala Lumpur, Malaysia.

EXTRA EXAMPLE 3

Find the area of the triangle to the nearest tenth of a meter. about 31.2 m^2

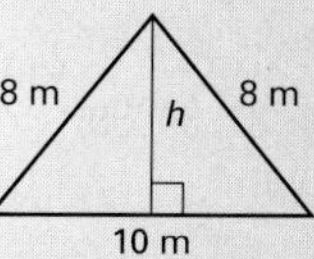

EXTRA EXAMPLE 4

The two antennas shown in the diagram are supported by cables 100 feet in length. If the cables are attached to the antennas 50 feet from the ground, how far apart are the antennas? about 173.2 ft

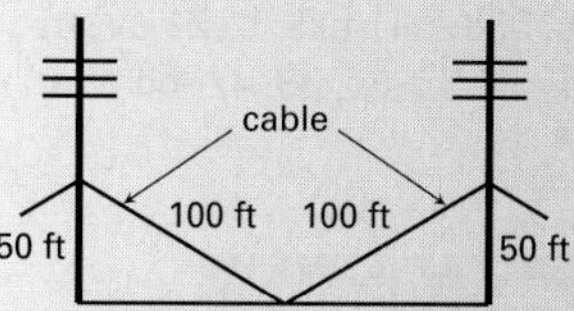

CHECKPOINT EXERCISES

For use after Examples 3 and 4:

1. Find the missing side of the triangle. Then find the area to the nearest tenth of a meter. 10.46 m; about 56.5 m^2

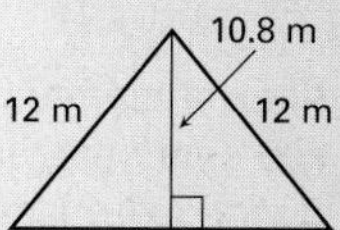

FOCUS ON VOCABULARY

Define Pythagorean triple and give an example. *Sample answer:* A set of three positive integers that satisfy the Pythagorean Theorem; 5, 12, 13

CLOSURE QUESTION

Find the length of the second leg of a right triangle with hypotenuse 18 and leg 12. Express your answer to the nearest tenth. 13.4

DAILY PUZZLER

Do the sides of every right triangle form a Pythagorean triple? Explain. No, because a Pythagorean triple is a triple of integers. The sides of a right triangle do not need to be integers.

3 APPLY

ASSIGNMENT GUIDE

BASIC
Day 1: pp. 538–541 Exs. 8–24 even, 24–31, 34, 39, 42–56 even

AVERAGE
Day 1: pp. 538–541 Exs. 8–24 even, 24–31, 33–36, 39, 42–56 even

ADVANCED
Day 1: pp. 538–541 Exs. 8–24 even, 24–31, 33–41, 42–56 even

BLOCK SCHEDULE WITH 9.3
pp. 538–541 Exs. 8–24 even, 24–31, 33–36, 39, 42–56 even

EXERCISE LEVELS

Level A: *Easier*
7–15

Level B: *More Difficult*
16–35, 39

Level C: *Most Difficult*
36–38, 40, 41

✓ HOMEWORK CHECK

To quickly check student understanding of key concepts, go over the following exercises: Exs. 8, 12, 18, 22, 28, 30, 34. See also the Daily Homework Quiz:

- Blackline Master (*Chapter 9 Resource Book,* p. 39)
- Transparency (p. 65)

GUIDED PRACTICE

Vocabulary Check ✓

Concept Check ✓

1. If you square the length of each leg of a right triangle and add the results, the sum is equal to the square of the length of the hypotenuse.

1. State the Pythagorean Theorem in your own words.

2. Which equations are true for $\triangle PQR$? **A and C**

A. $r^2 = p^2 + q^2$

B. $q^2 = p^2 + r^2$

C. $p^2 = r^2 - q^2$

D. $r^2 = (p + q)^2$

E. $p^2 = q^2 + r^2$

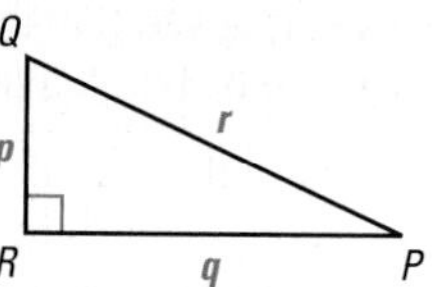

Skill Check ✓

Find the unknown side length. Tell whether the side lengths form a Pythagorean triple.

3.
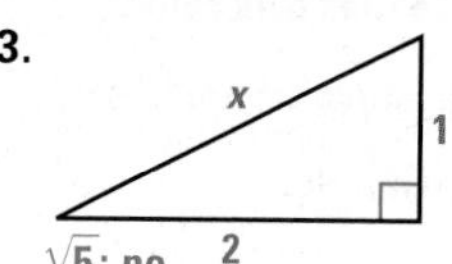

$\sqrt{5}$; no

4.
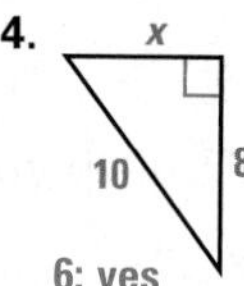

6; yes

5.
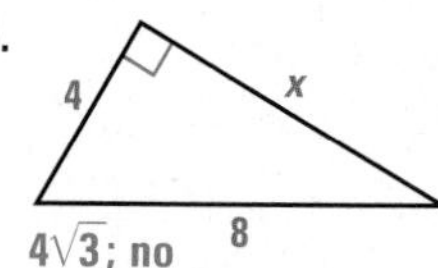

$4\sqrt{3}$; no

6. **ANEMOMETER** An anemometer (an uh MAHM ih tur) is a device used to measure windspeed. The anemometer shown is attached to the top of a pole. Support wires are attached to the pole 5 feet above the ground. Each support wire is 6 feet long. How far from the base of the pole is each wire attached to the ground? **about 3.3 ft**

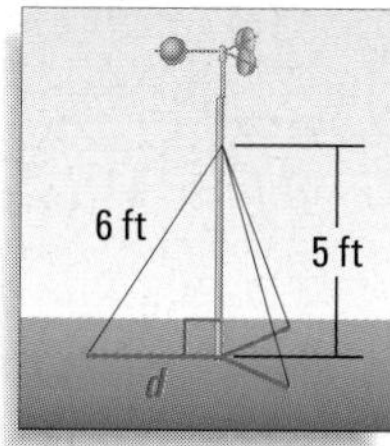

PRACTICE AND APPLICATIONS

STUDENT HELP

Extra Practice to help you master skills is on p. 819.

FINDING SIDE LENGTHS **Find the unknown side length. Simplify answers that are radicals. Tell whether the side lengths form a Pythagorean triple.**

7.
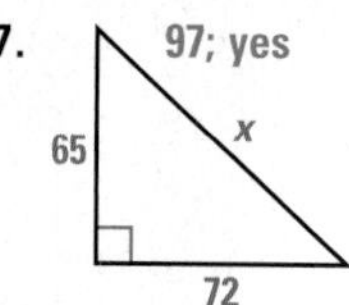

97; yes

8.
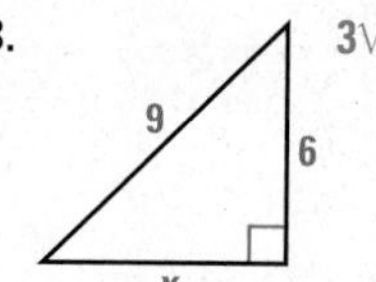

$3\sqrt{5}$; no

9.
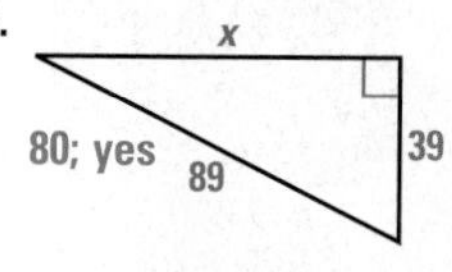

80; yes

10.
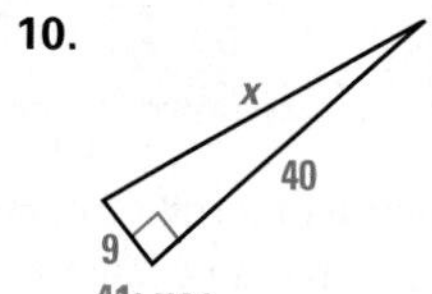

41; yes

11. 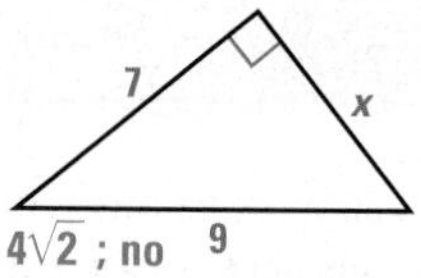
7, x, 9
$4\sqrt{2}$; no

12.
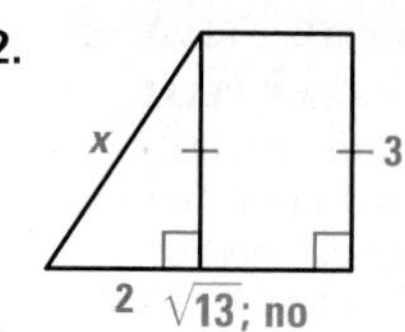

$\sqrt{13}$; no

13. 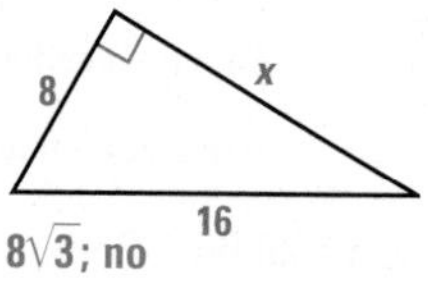
8, x, 16
$8\sqrt{3}$; no

14.
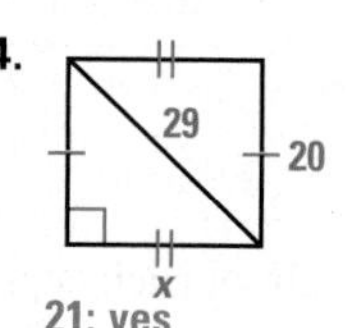

21; yes

15.
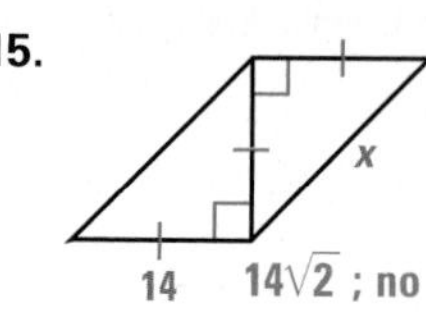

$14\sqrt{2}$; no

STUDENT HELP

HOMEWORK HELP
Example 1: Exs. 7–24
Example 2: Exs. 7–24
Example 3: Exs. 25–30
Example 4: Exs. 31–36

FINDING LENGTHS Find the value of x. Simplify answers that are radicals.

16. $8\sqrt{3}$

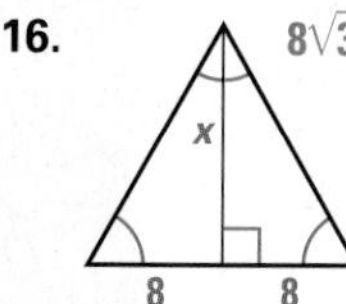

17. $2\sqrt{13}$

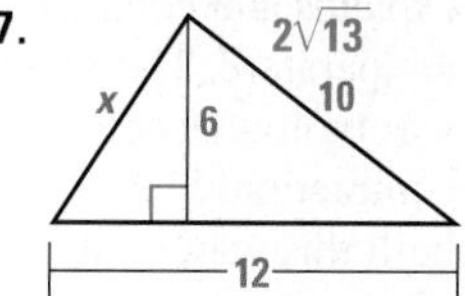

18. $\sqrt{58}$

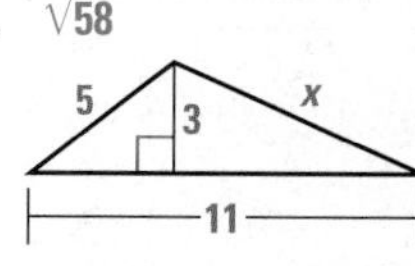

PYTHAGOREAN TRIPLES The variables r and s represent the lengths of the legs of a right triangle, and t represents the length of the hypotenuse. The values of r, s, and t form a Pythagorean triple. Find the unknown value.

19. $r = 12, s = 16$ $t = 20$ **20.** $r = 9, s = 12$ $t = 15$ **21.** $r = 18, t = 30$ $s = 24$

22. $s = 20, t = 101$ $r = 99$ **23.** $r = 35, t = 37$ $s = 12$ **24.** $t = 757, s = 595$ $r = 468$

STUDENT HELP

Look Back
For help with finding areas of quadrilaterals, see pp. 372–375.

FINDING AREA Find the area of the figure. Round decimal answers to the nearest tenth.

25. 35.7 cm²

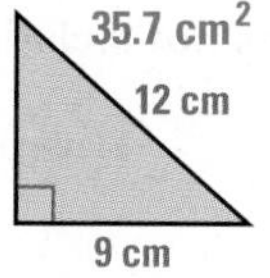

26.

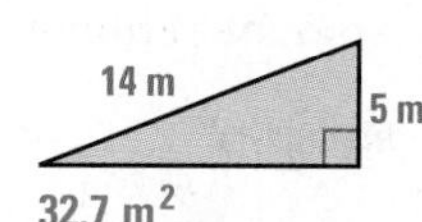

32.7 m²

27. 25.2 cm²

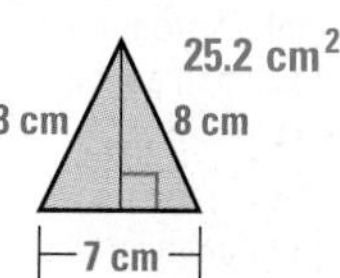

28.

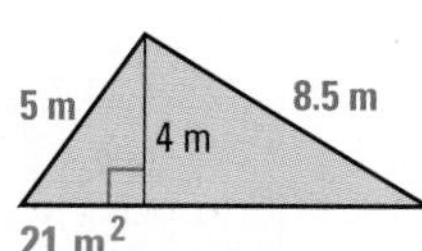

21 m²

29.

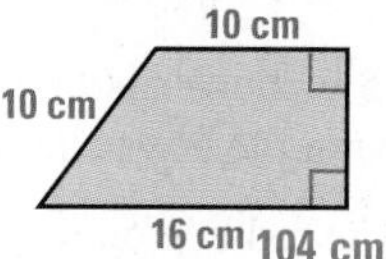

104 cm²

30.

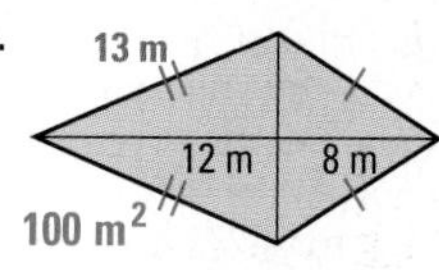

100 m²

31. about 41.9 ft; the distance from home plate to second base is about 91.9 ft, so the distance from the pitcher's plate to second base is about 91.9 – 50, or about 41.9 ft.

31. **SOFTBALL DIAMOND** In slow-pitch softball, the distance between consecutive bases is 65 feet. The pitcher's plate is located on a line between second base and home plate, 50 feet from home plate. How far is the pitcher's plate from second base? Justify your answer.

second
65 ft
third
pitcher's plate
first
50 ft
65 ft
home

32. 2.5 ft; about 9.7 ft; the base of the ladder should be at least $\frac{1}{4} \cdot 10 = 2.5$ ft from the wall, and the ladder will reach a height of $\sqrt{10^2 - 2.5^2} \approx 9.7$ ft up the wall. Check sketches.

32. **SAFETY** The distance of the base of a ladder from the wall it leans against should be at least $\frac{1}{4}$ of the ladder's total length. Suppose a 10 foot ladder is placed according to these guidelines. Give the minimum distance of the base of the ladder from the wall. How far up the wall will the ladder reach? Explain. Include a sketch with your explanation.

33. **ART GALLERY** You want to hang a painting 3 feet from a hook near the ceiling of an art gallery, as shown. In addition to the length of wire needed for hanging, you need 16 inches of wire to secure the wire to the back of the painting. Find the total length of wire needed to hang the painting. 94 in., or 7 ft 10 in.

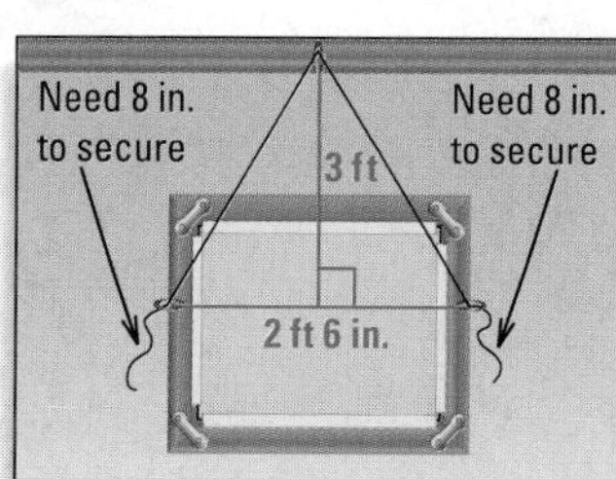

! COMMON ERROR
EXERCISES 19–24 Watch for students who do not read the question carefully and who assume the values given are the lengths of the two legs.

STUDENT HELP NOTES
Look Back As students look back to pp. 372–375, remind them that the area of a quadrilateral depends on the shape of the quadrilateral unless it is divided into two triangles.

APPLICATION NOTE
EXERCISE 32 Ladder safety is important because there are as many as 65,000 injuries each year that result in hospital treatment.

CAREER LINK
Additional information about mechanical engineers is available at **www.mcdougallittell.com.**

STUDENT HELP NOTES

Homework Help Students can find help for Exs. 37–38 at **www.mcdougallittell.com.** The information can be printed out for students who don't have access to the Internet.

MATHEMATICAL REASONING

EXERCISE 38 Even if the area of the same geometric shape is calculated differently, the answers must be the same. The area of this trapezoid can be found by adding up the area of the 3 triangles $\left(\frac{1}{2}ab + \frac{1}{2}ab + \frac{1}{2}c^2\right)$ or by applying the area of a trapezoid formula to get $\frac{1}{2}(a + b)(a + b)$. Setting these equal to each other and simplifying results in the Pythagorean Theorem.

ENGLISH LEARNERS

EXERCISE 34 Word problems are excellent for showing students how geometry can be applied to real life, but unfamiliar concepts can prevent English learners from fully understanding the situation. For instance, some students may not be aware of the extreme temperatures that occur in the region across which the Alaska pipeline extends.

ADDITIONAL PRACTICE AND RETEACHING

For Lesson 9.2:

- Practice Levels A, B, and C (*Chapter 9 Resource Book,* p. 29)
- Reteaching with Practice (*Chapter 9 Resource Book,* p. 32)
- See Lesson 9.2 of the *Personal Student Tutor*

For more Mixed Review:

- Search the *Test and Practice Generator* for key words or specific lessons.

FOCUS ON CAREERS

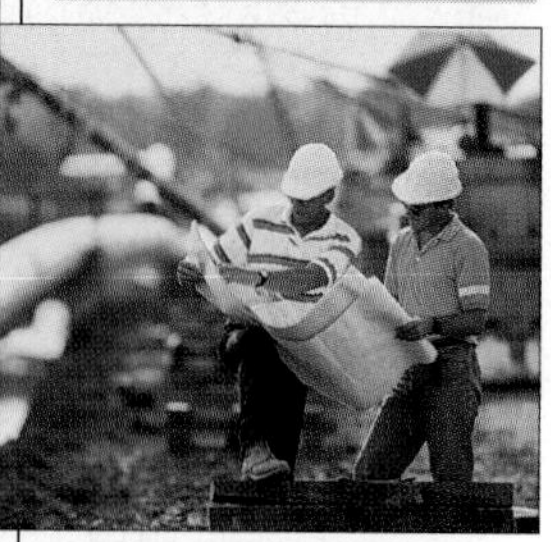

MECHANICAL ENGINEERS use science, mathematics, and engineering principles in their work. They evaluate, install, operate, and maintain mechanical products and systems, such as the Trans-Alaska pipeline.

CAREER LINK
www.mcdougallittell.com

37. The area of the large square is $(a + b)^2$. Also, the area of the large square is the sum of the areas of the four congruent right triangles plus the area of the small square, or $4(\frac{1}{2} \cdot a \cdot b) + c^2$. Thus, $(a + b)^2 = 4(\frac{1}{2} \cdot a \cdot b) + c^2$, and so $a^2 + 2ab + b^2 = 2ab + c^2$. Subtracting $2ab$ from each side gives $a^2 + b^2 = c^2$.

STUDENT HELP

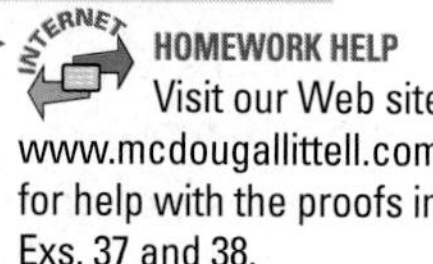

HOMEWORK HELP
Visit our Web site www.mcdougallittell.com for help with the proofs in Exs. 37 and 38.

34. TRANS-ALASKA PIPELINE Metal expands and contracts with changes in temperature. The Trans-Alaska pipeline was built to accommodate expansion and contraction. Suppose that it had not been built this way. Consider a 600 foot section of pipe that expands 2 inches and buckles, as shown below. Estimate the height h of the buckle. **about 85 in., or more than 7 ft**

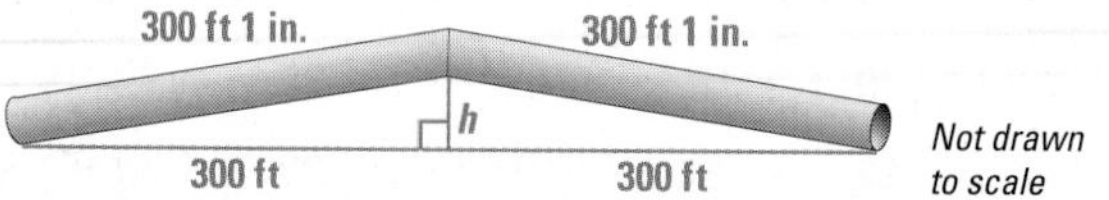

WRAPPING A BOX In Exercises 35 and 36, two methods are used to wrap ribbon around a rectangular box with the dimensions shown below. The amount of ribbon needed does not include a knot or bow.

Method 1

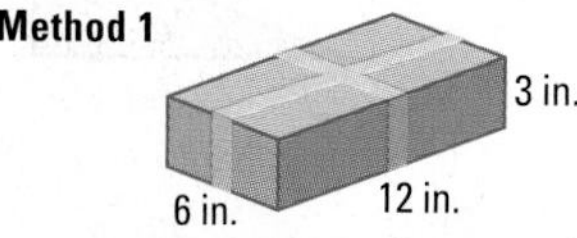

Method 2

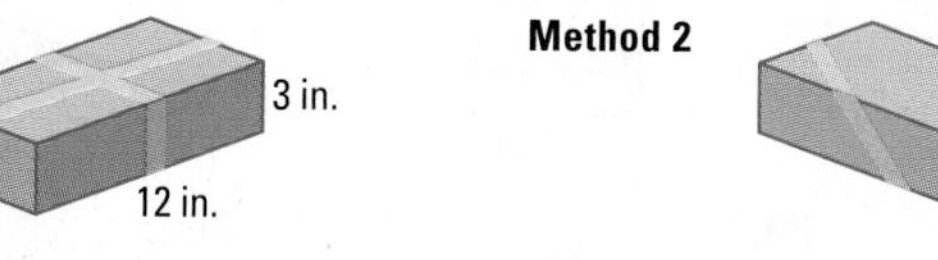

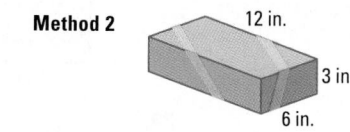

35. How much ribbon is needed to wrap the box using Method 1? **48 in.**

36. The red line on the diagram at the right shows the path the ribbon follows around the box when Method 2 is used. Does Method 2 use more or less ribbon than Method 1? Explain your thinking.
less; Method 2 uses $\sqrt{30^2 + 18^2} \approx 35.0$ in.

top
back
bottom
top
front
bottom
left side
right side

37. PROVING THE PYTHAGOREAN THEOREM Explain how the diagram at the right can be used to prove the Pythagorean Theorem algebraically. (*Hint:* Write two different expressions that represent the area of the large square. Then set them equal to each other.)

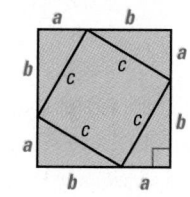

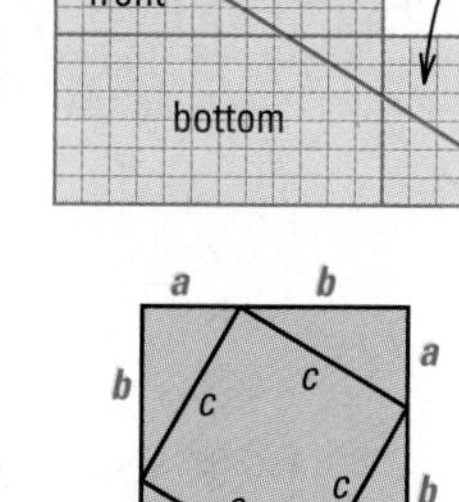

38. GARFIELD'S PROOF James Abram Garfield, the twentieth president of the United States, discovered a proof of the Pythagorean Theorem in 1876. His proof involved the fact that a trapezoid can be formed from two congruent right triangles and an isosceles right triangle.

Use the diagram to write a paragraph proof showing that $a^2 + b^2 = c^2$. (*Hint:* Write two different expressions that represent the area of the trapezoid. Then set them equal to each other.) **See margin.**

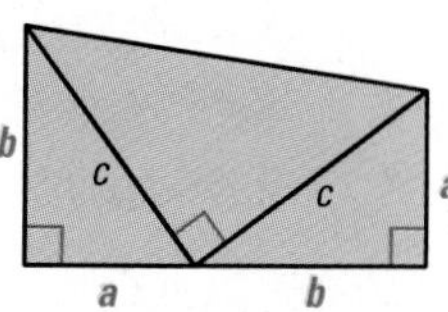

38. See Additional Answers beginning on page AA1.

Test Preparation

39. a. yes

b. No; the diagonal of the room is about 17.5 ft long.

c. $d = \sqrt{\ell^2 + w^2 + h^2}$; the diagonal of the base has length $\sqrt{\ell^2 + w^2}$ and the diagonal of the box has length $\sqrt{(\sqrt{\ell^2 + w^2})^2 + h^2} = \sqrt{\ell^2 + w^2 + h^2}$.

39. MULTI-STEP PROBLEM To find the length of a diagonal of a rectangular box, you can use the Pythagorean Theorem twice. Use the theorem once with right $\triangle ABC$ to find the length of the diagonal of the base.

$$AB = \sqrt{(AC)^2 + (BC)^2}$$

Then use the theorem with right $\triangle ABD$ to find the length of the diagonal of the box.

$$BD = \sqrt{(AB)^2 + (AD)^2}$$

a. Is it possible to carry a 9 foot piece of lumber in an enclosed rectangular trailer that is 4 feet by 8 feet by 4 feet?

b. Is it possible to store a 20 foot long pipe in a rectangular room that is 10 feet by 12 feet by 8 feet? Explain.

c. *Writing* Write a formula for finding the diagonal d of a rectangular box with length ℓ, width w, and height h. Explain your reasoning.

★ Challenge

PERIMETER OF A RHOMBUS The diagonals of a rhombus have lengths *a* and *b*. Use this information in Exercises 40 and 41.

40. Prove that the perimeter of the rhombus is $2\sqrt{a^2 + b^2}$. See margin.

41. The perimeter of a rhombus is 80 centimeters. The lengths of its diagonals are in the ratio 3:4. Find the length of each diagonal. 24 cm and 32 cm

EXTRA CHALLENGE
www.mcdougallittell.com

MIXED REVIEW

USING RADICALS Evaluate the expression. (Algebra Review, p. 522, for 9.3)

42. $(\sqrt{6})^2$ 6 **43.** $(\sqrt{9})^2$ 9 **44.** $(\sqrt{14})^2$ 14 **45.** $(2\sqrt{2})^2$ 8

46. $(4\sqrt{13})^2$ 208 **47.** $-(5\sqrt{49})^2$ −1225 **48.** $4(\sqrt{9})^2$ 36 **49.** $(-7\sqrt{3})^2$ 147

LOGICAL REASONING Determine whether the true statement can be combined with its converse to form a true biconditional statement. (Review 2.2)

50. If a quadrilateral is a square, then it has four congruent sides. no

51. If a quadrilateral is a kite, then it has two pairs of congruent sides. no

52. For all real numbers x, if $x \geq 1$, then $x^2 \geq 1$. no

53. For all real numbers x, if $x > 1$, then $\frac{1}{x} < 1$. no

54. If one interior angle of a triangle is obtuse, then the sum of the other two interior angles is less than 90°. yes

USING ALGEBRA Prove that the points represent the vertices of a parallelogram. (Review 6.3)

55. $P(4, 3)$, $Q(6, -8)$, $R(10, -3)$, $S(8, 8)$

56. $P(5, 0)$, $Q(2, 9)$, $R(-6, 6)$, $S(-3, -3)$

55. *Sample answer:* slope of $\overline{PQ} = -\frac{11}{2}$ = slope of $\overline{RS}$; slope of $\overline{QR} = \frac{5}{4}$ = slope of $\overline{PS}$. Both pairs of opposite sides are parallel, so $PQRS$ is a ▱ by the definition of a ▱.

56. *Sample answer:* The midpoint of $\overline{PR}$ is $\left(-\frac{1}{2}, 3\right)$, which is also the midpoint of $\overline{QS}$. Therefore, the diagonals bisect each other. If the diagonals of a quad. bisect each other, then it is a ▱.

4 ASSESS

DAILY HOMEWORK QUIZ

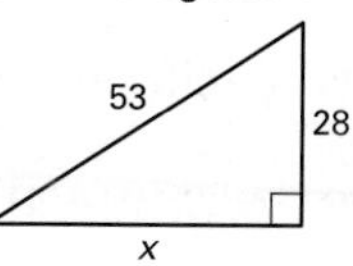
Transparency Available

Use the figure.

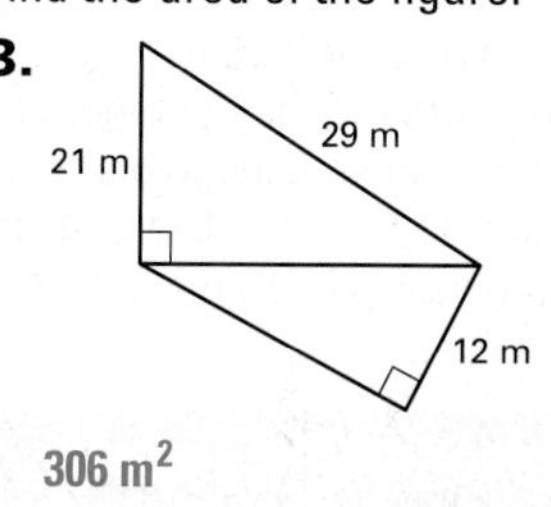

1. Find the unknown side length. 45

2. Tell whether the side lengths form a Pythagorean triple. yes

Find the area of the figure.

3.

306 m²

EXTRA CHALLENGE NOTE

Challenge problems for Lesson 9.2 are available in **blackline** format in the *Chapter 9 Resource Book*, p. 36 and at **www.mcdougallittell.com.**

ADDITIONAL TEST PREPARATION

1. WRITING Describe how to find the diagonal of rectangle with known sides 8 inches and 12 inches. Since the diagonal of a rectangle forms a right triangle, use the Pythagorean Theorem to find the diagonal. The diagonal has length $\sqrt{8^2 + 12^2}$, or about 14.4 inches.

40. The diagonals of a rhombus bisect each other and are perpendicular. The length of each side of the rhombus is $\sqrt{\left(\frac{a}{2}\right)^2 + \left(\frac{b}{2}\right)^2} = \sqrt{\frac{1}{4}(a^2 + b^2)} = \frac{1}{2}\sqrt{a^2 + b^2}$. All four sides are congruent, so the perimeter of the rhombus is $4 \cdot \frac{1}{2}\sqrt{a^2 + b^2} = 2\sqrt{a^2 + b^2}$.

1 Planning the Activity

PURPOSE
To explore how angle and side measures of triangles are related.

MATERIALS
- Geometry drawing software
- Software Help (*Chapter 9 Resource Book*, p. 41)

PACING
- Construct — 10 min
- Investigate — 10 min
- Conjecture — 5 min

LINK TO LESSON
The converse of the Pythagorean Theorem can be used to classify triangles. In Example 1 of Lesson 9.3, students will use this converse.

2 Managing the Activity

COOPERATIVE LEARNING
Ask students to do the activity with a partner. One student can draw a triangle while the other records the data.

ALTERNATIVE APPROACH
To save time, do this activity as a demonstration. Show the triangles with an overhead projection system. Ask students to record the data.

3 Closing the Activity

KEY DISCOVERY
If the square of the longest side is larger than the sum of the other two squares, then the triangle is obtuse. If it is less, then the triangle is acute. If it is equal, then the triangle is right.

ACTIVITY ASSESSMENT
JOURNAL In $\triangle ABC$, $AB^2 + BC^2 > AC^2$. Explain how you know that $m\angle B > 90°$. *Sample answer:* If $m\angle B = 90°$, then $AB^2 + BC^2 = AC^2$. The only way $AB^2 + BC^2$ can be greater than AC^2 is if $m\angle B > 90°$.

ACTIVITY 9.3
Using Technology

Investigating Sides and Angles of Triangles

You can use geometry software to explore how the angle measures of a triangle are related to its side lengths.

STUDENT HELP
SOFTWARE HELP
Visit our Web site www.mcdougallittell.com to see instructions for several different software applications.

CONSTRUCT

1. Construct a triangle. Label the vertices A, B, and C.
2. Measure $\overline{AC}$, $\overline{BC}$, and $\overline{AB}$.
3. Calculate the value of $(AC)^2 + (BC)^2$. Calculate the value of $(AB)^2$.
4. Measure $\angle C$.

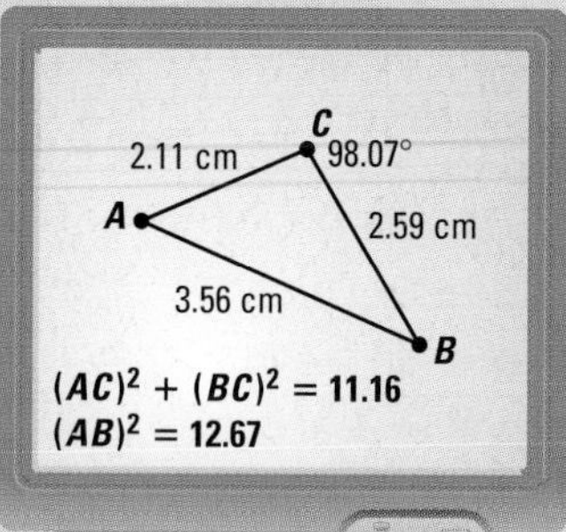

INVESTIGATE

1. Make a table like the one shown. Record the side lengths, the value of $(AC)^2 + (BC)^2$, the value of $(AB)^2$, and the measure of $\angle C$. Round decimals to the nearest hundredth. Answers will vary.

	AC	BC	AB	$(AC)^2 + (BC)^2$	$(AB)^2$	$m\angle C$
Triangle 1	2.11 cm	2.59 cm	3.56 cm	11.16 cm	12.67 cm	98.07°
Triangle 2	?	?	?	?	?	?
Triangle 3	?	?	?	?	?	?
Triangle 4	?	?	?	?	?	?
Triangle 5	?	?	?	?	?	?
Triangle 6	?	?	?	?	?	?

2. Drag point C to change the measure of $\angle C$ and the shape of $\triangle ABC$. Find and record the values in the table. Answers will vary.
3. Repeat Step 2 for several more triangles. In your table, be sure to include some triangles for which $\angle C$ is an acute angle, some for which $\angle C$ is a right angle, and some for which $\angle C$ is an obtuse angle. Answers will vary.

CONJECTURE

4. Use the data in the table to look for a pattern. Make a conjecture about how the value of $(AC)^2 + (BC)^2$ compares with the value of $(AB)^2$ when the measure of $\angle C$ is less than 90°, equal to 90°, and greater than 90°.
When $m\angle C < 90°$, $(AC)^2 + (BC)^2 > (AB)^2$. When $m\angle C = 90°$, $(AC)^2 + (BC)^2 = (AB)^2$. When $m\angle C > 90°$, $(AC)^2 + (BC)^2 < (AB)^2$.

9.3 The Converse of the Pythagorean Theorem

What you should learn

GOAL 1 Use the Converse of the Pythagorean Theorem to solve problems.

GOAL 2 Use side lengths to classify triangles by their angle measures.

Why you should learn it

▼ To determine whether **real-life** angles are right angles, such as the four angles formed by the foundation of a building in **Example 3**.

CALIFORNIA STANDARDS AND ASSESSMENT

CA Standards: 15
SAT9 Task 1: Objs. 1, 5
SAT9 Task 2: Objs. 1, 7, 25

GOAL 1 USING THE CONVERSE

In Lesson 9.2, you learned that if a triangle is a right triangle, then the square of the length of the hypotenuse is equal to the sum of the squares of the lengths of the legs. The Converse of the Pythagorean Theorem is also true, as stated below. Exercise 43 asks you to prove the Converse of the Pythagorean Theorem.

THEOREM

THEOREM 9.5 ***Converse of the Pythagorean Theorem***

If the square of the length of the longest side of a triangle is equal to the sum of the squares of the lengths of the other two sides, then the triangle is a right triangle.

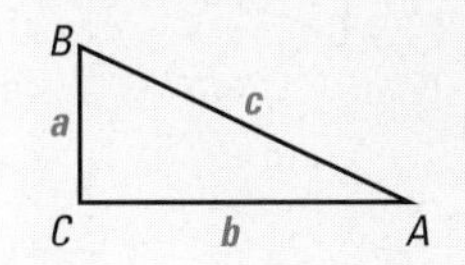

If $c^2 = a^2 + b^2$, then $\triangle ABC$ is a right triangle.

You can use the Converse of the Pythagorean Theorem to verify that a given triangle is a right triangle, as shown in Example 1.

EXAMPLE 1 *Verifying Right Triangles*

The triangles below appear to be right triangles. Tell whether they are right triangles.

a. 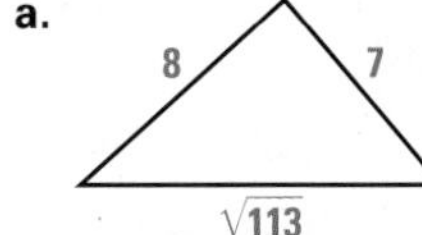

b. 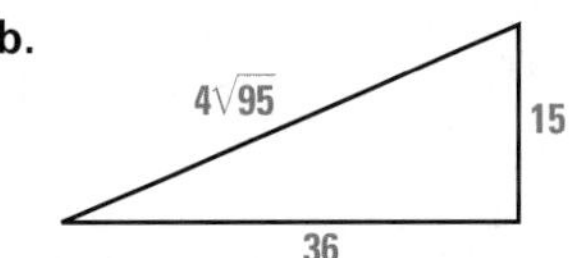

SOLUTION

Let c represent the length of the longest side of the triangle. Check to see whether the side lengths satisfy the equation $c^2 = a^2 + b^2$.

a. $(\sqrt{113})^2 \stackrel{?}{=} 7^2 + 8^2$

$113 \stackrel{?}{=} 49 + 64$

$113 = 113$ ✓

The triangle is a right triangle.

b. $(4\sqrt{95})^2 \stackrel{?}{=} 15^2 + 36^2$

$4^2 \cdot (\sqrt{95})^2 \stackrel{?}{=} 15^2 + 36^2$

$16 \cdot 95 \stackrel{?}{=} 225 + 1296$

$1520 \neq 1521$

The triangle is not a right triangle.

1 PLAN

PACING

Basic: 2 days
Average: 2 days
Advanced: 2 days
Block Schedule: 0.5 block with 9.2
0.5 block with 9.4

LESSON OPENER APPLICATION

An alternative way to approach Lesson 9.3 is to use the Application Lesson Opener:

- Blackline Master (*Chapter 9 Resource Book,* p. 40)
- Transparency (p. 56)

MEETING INDIVIDUAL NEEDS

- ***Chapter 9 Resource Book***
  Prerequisite Skills Review (p. 5)
  Practice Level A (p. 44)
  Practice Level B (p. 45)
  Practice Level C (p. 46)
  Reteaching with Practice (p. 47)
  Absent Student Catch-Up (p. 49)
  Challenge (p. 51)
- ***Resources in Spanish***
-  ***Personal Student Tutor***

NEW-TEACHER SUPPORT

See the Tips for New Teachers on pp. 1–2 of the *Chapter 9 Resource Book* for additional notes about Lesson 9.3.

WARM-UP EXERCISES

Transparency Available

Solve the equation for the missing variable. Assume all variables are positive. Express the answer to the nearest tenth.

1. $c^2 = 6^2 + 8^2$ 10
2. $c^2 - 4^2 = 3^2$ 5
3. $c^2 - 10^2 = 16^2$ 18.9
4. $a^2 + 6^2 = 14^2$ 12.6
5. $(14\sqrt{2})^2 = 14^2 + b^2$ 14

2 TEACH

Motivating the Lesson

Ask students why it would be important to make sure a foundation for a house is constructed with perfect 90° angles. Determining if a triangle is a right triangle, given its sides, is a topic in this lesson.

Extra Example 1

The triangles below appear to be right triangles. Tell whether they are right triangles.

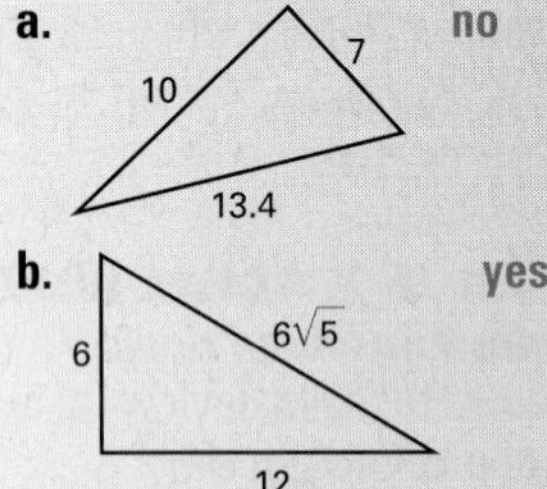

a. no

b. yes

Extra Example 2

Decide whether the set of numbers can represent the side lengths of a triangle. If they can, classify the triangle as right, acute, or obtuse.

a. 8, 18, 24 yes; obtuse

b. 3.2, 4.8, 5.1 yes; acute

Checkpoint Exercises

For use after Examples 1 and 2:

1. Decide whether the set of numbers can represent the side lengths of a triangle. If they can, classify the triangle as *right, acute,* or *obtuse.*

a. 12.3, 16.4, 20.5 yes; right

b. 8, 40, 41 yes; obtuse

Student Help Notes

Look Back As students look back to p. 297, remind them that the sum of each pair of sides in a triangle is greater than the third side.

Classifying Triangles

Sometimes it is hard to tell from looking whether a triangle is obtuse or acute. The theorems below can help you tell.

THEOREMS

THEOREM 9.6

If the square of the length of the longest side of a triangle is less than the sum of the squares of the lengths of the other two sides, then the triangle is acute.

If $c^2 < a^2 + b^2$, then $\triangle ABC$ is acute.

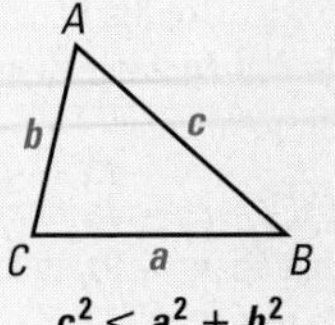

$c^2 < a^2 + b^2$

THEOREM 9.7

If the square of the length of the longest side of a triangle is greater than the sum of the squares of the lengths of the other two sides, then the triangle is obtuse.

If $c^2 > a^2 + b^2$, then $\triangle ABC$ is obtuse.

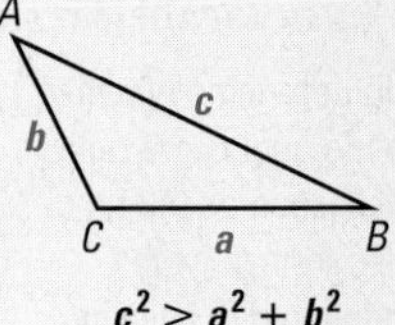

$c^2 > a^2 + b^2$

EXAMPLE 2 *Classifying Triangles*

Decide whether the set of numbers can represent the side lengths of a triangle. If they can, classify the triangle as *right*, *acute*, or *obtuse*.

a. 38, 77, 86 **b.** 10.5, 36.5, 37.5

Solution

Student Help

Look Back
For help with the Triangle Inequality, see p. 297.

You can use the Triangle Inequality to confirm that each set of numbers can represent the side lengths of a triangle.

Compare the square of the length of the longest side with the sum of the squares of the lengths of the two shorter sides.

a.

$c^2 \ \underline{?}\ a^2 + b^2$	**Compare c^2 with $a^2 + b^2$.**
$86^2 \ \underline{?}\ 38^2 + 77^2$	**Substitute.**
$7396 \ \underline{?}\ 1444 + 5929$	**Multiply.**
$7396 > 7373$	**c^2 is greater than $a^2 + b^2$.**

▶ Because $c^2 > a^2 + b^2$, the triangle is obtuse.

b.

$c^2 \ \underline{?}\ a^2 + b^2$	**Compare c^2 with $a^2 + b^2$.**
$37.5^2 \ \underline{?}\ 10.5^2 + 36.5^2$	**Substitute.**
$1406.25 \ \underline{?}\ 110.25 + 1332.25$	**Multiply.**
$1406.25 < 1442.5$	**c^2 is less than $a^2 + b^2$.**

▶ Because $c^2 < a^2 + b^2$, the triangle is acute.

EXAMPLE 3 *Building a Foundation*

CONSTRUCTION You use four stakes and string to mark the foundation of a house. You want to make sure the foundation is rectangular.

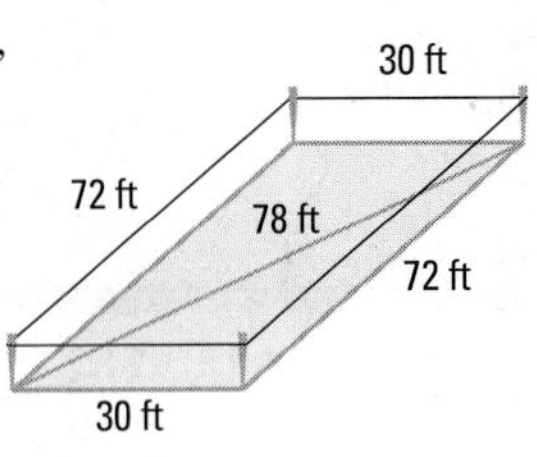

a. A friend measures the four sides to be 30 feet, 30 feet, 72 feet, and 72 feet. He says these measurements prove the foundation is rectangular. Is he correct?

b. You measure one of the diagonals to be 78 feet. Explain how you can use this measurement to tell whether the foundation will be rectangular.

SOLUTION

STUDENT HELP

Look Back
For help with classifying quadrilaterals, see Chapter 6.

a. Your friend is not correct. The foundation could be a nonrectangular parallelogram, as shown at the right.

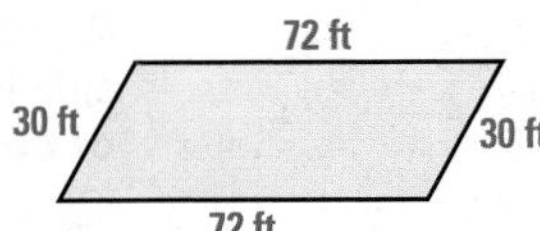

b. The diagonal divides the foundation into two triangles. Compare the square of the length of the longest side with the sum of the squares of the shorter sides of one of these triangles. Because $30^2 + 72^2 = 78^2$, you can conclude that both the triangles are right triangles.

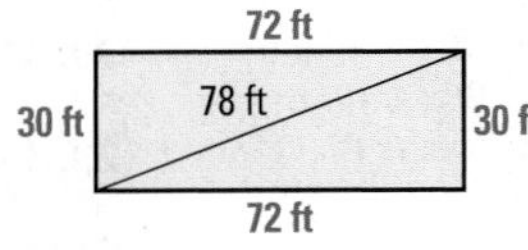

▶ The foundation is a parallelogram with two right angles, which implies that it is rectangular.

GUIDED PRACTICE

Vocabulary Check ✓

1. State the Converse of the Pythagorean Theorem in your own words. See margin.

Concept Check ✓

2. Use the triangle shown at the right. Find values for c so that the triangle is acute, right, and obtuse. See margin.

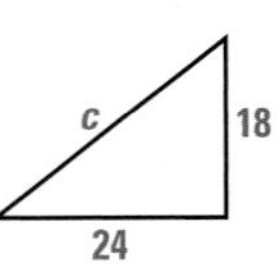

Skill Check ✓

In Exercises 3–6, match the side lengths with the appropriate description.

3. 2, 10, 11 C | **A.** right triangle

4. 13, 5, 7 D | **B.** acute triangle

5. 5, 11, 6 D | **C.** obtuse triangle

6. 6, 8, 10 A | **D.** not a triangle

7.  **KITE DESIGN** You are making the diamond-shaped kite shown at the right. You measure the crossbars to determine whether they are perpendicular. Are they? Explain. See margin.

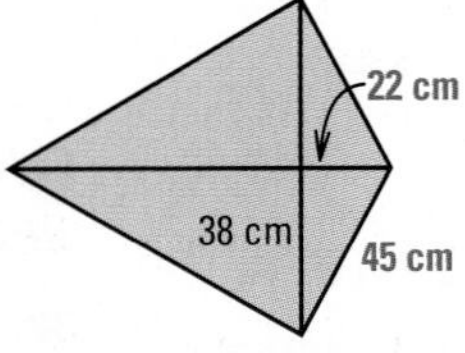

1. *Sample answer:* If you square the lengths of the two shorter sides of a triangle and add the results, and the sum is equal to the square of the length of the longest side of the triangle, then the triangle is a right triangle.

EXTRA EXAMPLE 3
You want to make sure a wall of a room is rectangular.

a. A friend measures the four sides to be 9 feet, 9 feet, 40 feet, and 40 feet. He says these measurements prove the wall is rectangular. Is he correct? no

b. You measure one of the diagonals to be 41 feet. Explain how you can use this measurement to tell whether the wall is rectangular. The diagonal divides the wall into two triangles. Compare the square of the longest side with the sum of the squares of the shorter sides of one of these triangles. Because $9^2 + 40^2 = 41^2$, you can conclude that both triangles are right triangles and that the wall is rectangular.

CHECKPOINT EXERCISES
For use after Example 3:

1. Decide whether a parallelogram with side lengths 18 feet, 18 feet, 24 feet, 24 feet and diagonal length 30 feet is a rectangle. yes

FOCUS ON VOCABULARY
Describe how to use the Converse of the Pythagorean Theorem. Find the squares of each side of a triangle. If the square of the largest side is equal to the sum of the squares of the other two sides, then the triangle is a right triangle.

CLOSURE QUESTION
Describe how to classify a triangle with side lengths 6, 9, and 10. Take the squares of all three sides. Since $10^2 < 6^2 + 9^2$, the triangle is acute.

DAILY PUZZLER
Find the value of k so that x, $2x$, and kx are the sides of a right triangle. $\sqrt{5}$ or $\sqrt{3}$

2, 7. See Additional Answers beginning on page AA1.

3 APPLY

ASSIGNMENT GUIDE

BASIC

Day 1: pp. 546–549 Exs. 8–28 even, 32–36 even

Day 2: pp. 546–549 Exs. 9–27 odd, 29, 30, 31–37 odd, 41, 44, 45, 47–57 odd, Quiz 1 Exs. 1–8

AVERAGE

Day 1: pp. 546–549 Exs. 8–28 even, 32–36 even

Day 2: pp. 546–549 Exs. 9–27 odd, 29, 30, 31–37 odd, 40, 41, 44, 45, 47–57 odd, Quiz 1 Exs. 1–8

ADVANCED

Day 1: pp. 546–549 Exs. 8–28 even, 32–36 even

Day 2: pp. 546–549 Exs. 9–27 odd, 29, 30, 31–37 odd, 40–46, 47–57 odd, Quiz 1 Exs. 1–8

BLOCK SCHEDULE

pp. 546–549 Exs. 8–28 even, 32–36 even (with 9.2)
pp. 546–549 Exs. 9–27 odd, 29, 30, 31–37 odd, 40, 41, 44, 45, 47–57 odd, Quiz 1 Exs. 1–8 (with 9.4)

EXERCISE LEVELS

Level A: *Easier*
8–13

Level B: *More Difficult*
14–41, 44, 45

Level C: *Most Difficult*
42, 43, 46

✔ HOMEWORK CHECK

To quickly check student understanding of key concepts, go over the following exercises: Exs. 10, 12, 18, 24, 26, 30, 32, 34, 36. See also the Daily Homework Quiz:

- Blackline Master (*Chapter 9 Resource Book*, p. 55)
- Transparency (p. 66)

PRACTICE AND APPLICATIONS

STUDENT HELP

Extra Practice to help you master skills is on pp. 819 and 820.

26. Rectangle. Both pairs of opp. sides are ≅, so the quad. is a ▱; $14^2 + 8^2 = (2\sqrt{65})^2$, so one pair of opposite angles are rt. ∠s; it follows that the ▱ is a rectangle.

27. Square. The diagonals bisect each other, so the quad. is a ▱; the diagonals are ≅, so the ▱ is a rectangle. $1^2 + 1^2 = (\sqrt{2})^2$, so the diagonals intersect at rt. ∠s to form ⊥ lines; thus, the ▱ is also a rhombus. A quad. that is both a rectangle and a rhombus must be a square.

28. Rhombus. The diagonals bisect each other, so the quad. is a ▱; $3^2 + 4^2 = 5^2$, so the diagonals intersect at rt. ∠s to form ⊥ lines; thus, the ▱ must be a rhombus.

29. $\frac{3}{4}$; $-\frac{4}{3}$; since $\left(\frac{3}{4}\right)\left(-\frac{4}{3}\right) = -1$, $\overline{AC} \perp \overline{BC}$, so ∠ACB is a rt. ∠. Therefore, △ABC is a rt. △ by the definition of a rt. △.

30. $(AC)^2 + (BC)^2 = 25 + 25 = 50 = (AB)^2$, so by the Converse of the Pythagorean Thm., △ABC is a rt. △.

STUDENT HELP

HOMEWORK HELP
Example 1: Exs. 8–13, 30
Example 2: Exs. 14–28, 31–35
Example 3: Exs. 39, 40

VERIFYING RIGHT TRIANGLES Tell whether the triangle is a right triangle.

8. 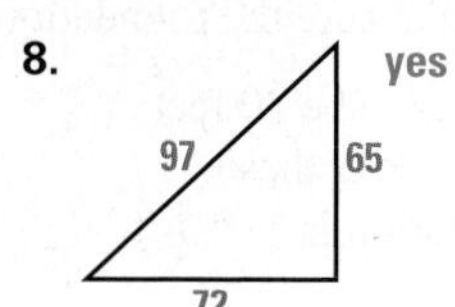

yes

9. 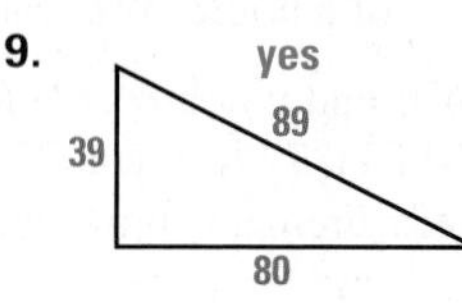

yes

10. 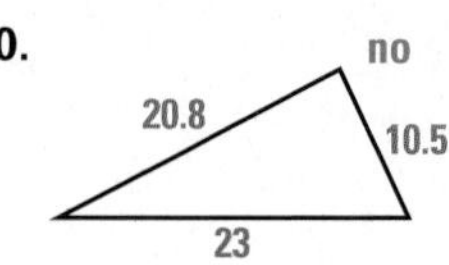

no

11. 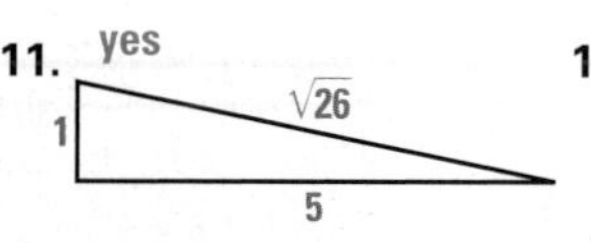

yes

12. 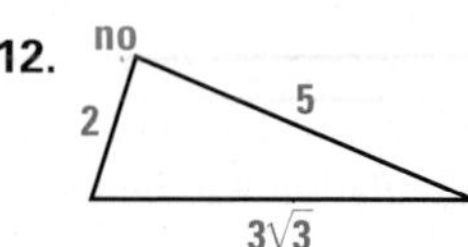

no

13. 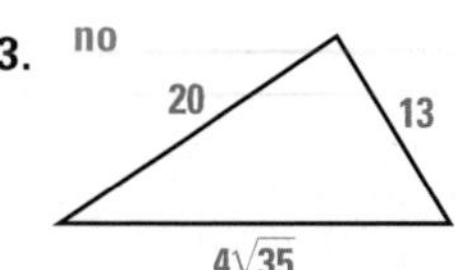

no

CLASSIFYING TRIANGLES Decide whether the numbers can represent the side lengths of a triangle. If they can, classify the triangle as *right, acute,* or *obtuse.*

14. 20, 99, 101 yes; right
15. 21, 28, 35 yes; right
16. 26, 10, 17 yes; obtuse
17. 2, 10, 12 no
18. 4, $\sqrt{67}$, 9 yes; acute
19. $\sqrt{13}$, 6, 7 yes; right
20. 16, 30, 34 yes; right
21. 10, 11, 14 yes; acute
22. 4, 5, 5 yes; acute
23. 17, 144, 145 yes; right
24. 10, 49, 50 yes; acute
25. $\sqrt{5}$, 5, 5.5 yes; obtuse

CLASSIFYING QUADRILATERALS Classify the quadrilateral. Explain how you can prove that the quadrilateral is that type. 26–28. See margin.

26. 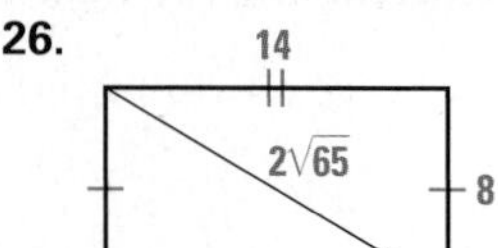

27. 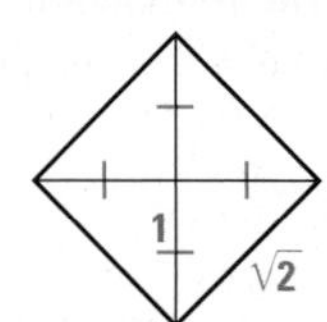

28. 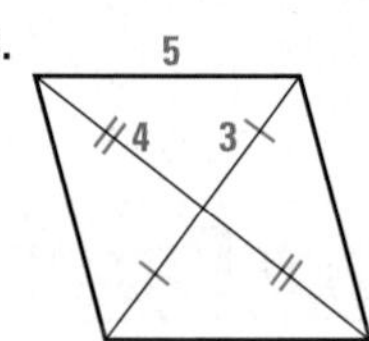

CHOOSING A METHOD In Exercises 29–31, you will use two different methods for determining whether △ABC is a right triangle.

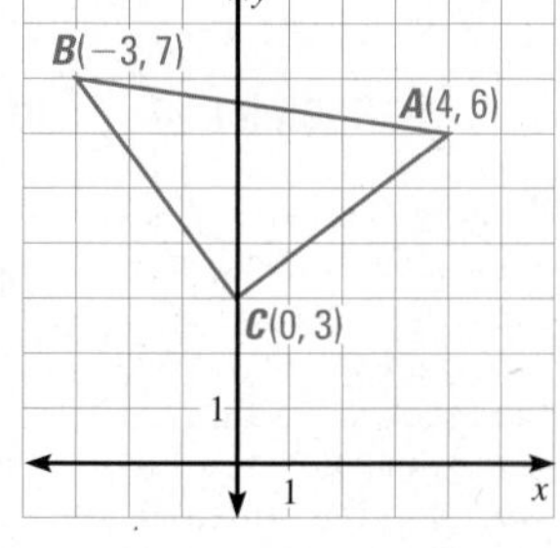

29. ***Method 1*** Find the slope of $\overline{AC}$ and the slope of $\overline{BC}$. What do the slopes tell you about ∠ACB? Is △ABC a right triangle? How do you know?

30. ***Method 2*** Use the Distance Formula and the Converse of the Pythagorean Theorem to determine whether △ABC is a right triangle.

31. Which method would you use to determine whether a given triangle is right, acute, or obtuse? Explain. See margin.

USING ALGEBRA Graph points *P, Q,* and *R.* Connect the points to form △PQR. Decide whether △PQR is *right, acute,* or *obtuse.*

32. P(−3, 4), Q(5, 0), R(−6, −2) right
33. P(−1, 2), Q(4, 1), R(0, −1) acute

34. Since $2^2 + 3^2 < 4^2$, $\triangle ABC$ is obtuse and $\angle ABC$ is obtuse. Since $\angle ABC$ and $\angle 1$ are a linear pair, $m\angle ABC + m\angle 1 = 180°$ by the Linear Pair Post. $\angle ABC$ is obtuse, so $m\angle ABC > 90°$. It follows that $m\angle 1 < 90°$, and by the def. of an acute $\angle$, $\angle 1$ is acute.

PROOF **Write a proof.**

34. GIVEN ▶ $AB = 3$, $BC = 2$, $AC = 4$

PROVE ▶ $\angle 1$ is acute.

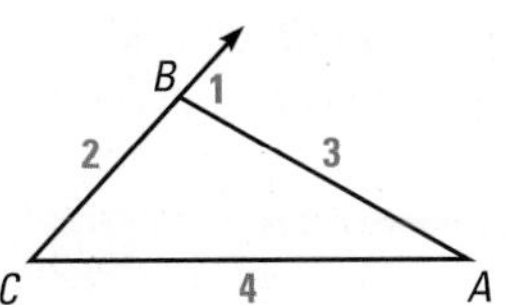

35. GIVEN ▶ $AB = 4$, $BC = 2$, $AC = \sqrt{10}$

PROVE ▶ $\angle 1$ is acute.
See margin.

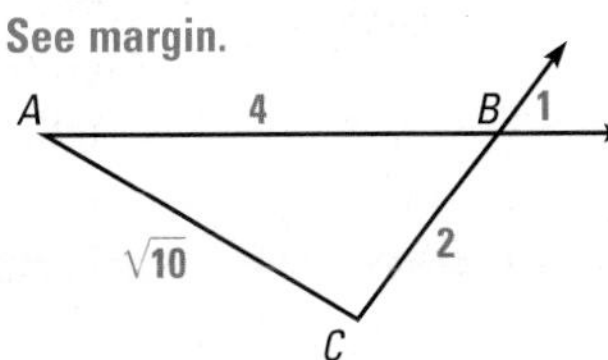

STUDENT HELP

HOMEWORK HELP Visit our Web site www.mcdougallittell.com for help with Ex. 36.

36. **PROOF** Prove that if a, b, and c are a Pythagorean triple, then ka, kb, and kc (where $k > 0$) represent the side lengths of a right triangle. See margin.

37. PYTHAGOREAN TRIPLES Use the results of Exercise 36 and the Pythagorean triple 5, 12, 13. Which sets of numbers can represent the side lengths of a right triangle? A, C, and D

A. 50, 120, 130 **B.** 20, 48, 56 **C.** $1\frac{1}{4}$, 3, $3\frac{1}{4}$ **D.** 1, 2.4, 2.6

35. Since $(\sqrt{10})^2 + 2^2 < 4^2$, $\triangle ABC$ is obtuse and $\angle C$ is obtuse. By the Triangle Sum Thm., $m\angle A + m\angle ABC + m\angle C = 180°$. $\angle C$ is obtuse, so $m\angle C > 90°$. It follows that $m\angle ABC < 90°$. Vertical angles are $\cong$, so $m\angle ABC = m\angle 1$. By substitution, $m\angle 1 < 90°$. By the definition of an acute $\angle$, $\angle 1$ is acute.

38. TECHNOLOGY Use geometry software to construct each of the following figures: a nonspecial quadrilateral, a parallelogram, a rhombus, a square, and a rectangle. Label the sides of each figure a, b, c, and d. Measure each side. Then draw the diagonals of each figure and label them e and f. Measure each diagonal. For which figures does the following statement appear to be true?

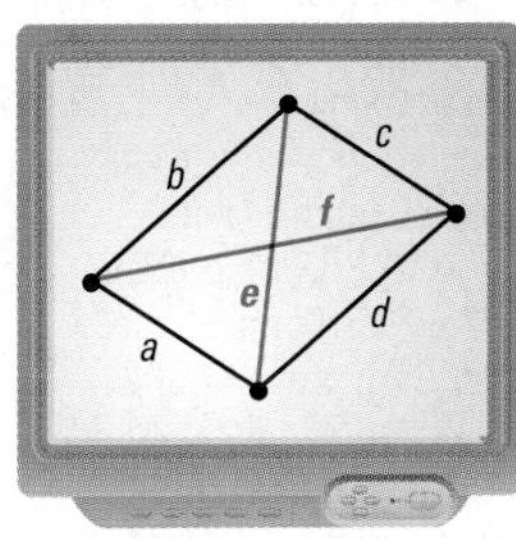

$a^2 + b^2 + c^2 + d^2 = e^2 + f^2$ parallelogram, rectangle, rhombus, square

FOCUS ON APPLICATIONS

BABYLONIAN TABLET
This photograph shows part of a Babylonian clay tablet made around 350 B.C. The tablet contains a table of numbers written in cuneiform characters.

39. HISTORY CONNECTION The Babylonian tablet shown at the left contains several sets of triangle side lengths, suggesting that the Babylonians may have been aware of the relationships among the side lengths of right triangles. The side lengths in the table at the right show several sets of numbers from the tablet. Verify that each set of side lengths forms a Pythagorean triple. See margin.

a	b	c
120	119	169
4,800	4,601	6,649
13,500	12,709	18,541

40. AIR TRAVEL You take off in a jet from Cincinnati, Ohio, and fly 403 miles due east to Washington, D.C. You then fly 714 miles to Tallahassee, Florida. Finally, you fly 599 miles back to Cincinnati. Is Cincinnati directly north of Tallahassee? If not, how would you describe its location relative to Tallahassee?
No; $714^2 < 403^2 + 599^2$, so Cincinnati is northwest of Tallahassee.

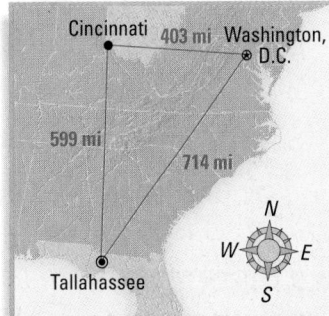

Cincinnati 403 mi Washington, D.C.
599 mi
714 mi
Tallahassee
N W E S

MATHEMATICAL REASONING

EXERCISE 29 If the slopes of two nonvertical intersecting lines are opposite reciprocals, the lines are perpendicular. Ask students to describe how to use this statement to determine if a triangle graphed in the coordinate plane is a right triangle. Find the slopes of each pair of intersecting sides. If any pair of slopes are opposite reciprocals, then those sides are perpendicular and the triangle is a right triangle.

STUDENT HELP NOTES

Homework Help Students can find help for Ex. 36 at **www.mcdougallittell.com.** The information can be printed out for students who don't have access to the Internet.

APPLICATION NOTE

EXERCISE 40 An air mile distance is a direct line drawn from one destination to another. Air distance is less than ground distance because ground travel on roads is never entirely straight.

31. *Sample answer:* I prefer to use slopes, because I have two computations rather than three, and computing slopes doesn't involve square roots.

36. Given: a, b, and c are a Pythagorean triple.
Prove: ka, kb, and kc (where $k > 0$) represent the side lengths of a right triangle.
Proof: By the definition of a Pythagorean triple, $a^2 + b^2 = c^2$. By the multiplication prop. of equality, $k^2(a^2 + b^2) = k^2c^2$. By the distributive prop., $k^2a^2 + k^2b^2 = k^2c^2$. Therefore, $(ka)^2 + (kb)^2 = (kc)^2$. Since $k > 0$, ka, kb, and kc represent the side lengths of a right triangle by the Converse of the Pythagorean Thm.

39. See Additional Answers beginning on page AA1.

! COMMON ERROR

EXERCISES 44–45 Watch for students who assume both triangles are right triangles. If they answer C to both exercises, they have not checked whether the triangles are right.

42. Given: In $\triangle ABC$, $c^2 > a^2 + b^2$ and $\angle C$ is the largest angle of $\triangle ABC$. Prove: $\triangle ABC$ is an obtuse triangle. Proof: Draw rt. $\triangle PQR$ with side lengths a, b, and hypotenuse x. $x^2 = a^2 + b^2$ by the Pythagorean Thm. It is given that $c^2 > a^2 + b^2$, so by the substitution prop. of equality, $c^2 > x^2$. By a prop. of square roots, $c > x$. By the Converse of the Hinge Thm., $m\angle C > m\angle R$. $\angle R$ is a right angle, so $m\angle R = 90°$. By the substitution prop. of equality, $m\angle C > 90°$. By the def. of an obtuse $\angle$, $\angle C$ is obtuse. By the def. of an obtuse $\triangle$, $\triangle ABC$ is an obtuse triangle.

46. Since $\overline{NP} \perp \overline{MQ}$, $\angle MPN$ and $\angle QPN$ are rt. $\angle$s. By the Pythagorean Thm., $(MN)^2 = s^2 + t^2$ and $(NQ)^2 = r^2 + t^2$. $(MN)^2 + (NQ)^2 = s^2 + t^2 + r^2 + t^2 = r^2 + 2t^2 + s^2$. Since t is the geometric mean of r and s, $\frac{r}{t} = \frac{t}{s}$. By the cross product prop., $t^2 = rs$. By the substitution prop. of equality, $(MN)^2 + (NQ)^2 = r^2 + 2rs + s^2 = (r + s)^2 = (MQ)^2$. Then, by the Converse of the Pythagorean Thm., $\triangle MQN$ is a rt. $\triangle$.

ADDITIONAL PRACTICE AND RETEACHING

For Lesson 9.3:

- Practice Levels A, B, and C (*Chapter 9 Resource Book*, p. 44)
- Reteaching with Practice (*Chapter 9 Resource Book*, p. 47)
- See Lesson 9.3 of the *Personal Student Tutor*

For more Mixed Review:

- Search the *Test and Practice Generator* for key words or specific lessons.

41. (1) Pythagorean Thm.
(2) Given
(3) Substitution prop. of equality
(5) Converse of the Hinge Thm.
(6) Given, def. of right angle, def. of acute angle, and substitution prop. of equality
(7) Def. of acute triangle ($\angle C$ is the largest angle of $\triangle ABC$.)

43. Draw rt. $\triangle PQR$ with side lengths a, b, and hypotenuse x. $x^2 = a^2 + b^2$ by the Pythagorean Thm. It is given that $c^2 = a^2 + b^2$, so by the substitution prop. of equality, $x^2 = c^2$. By a prop. of square roots, $x = c$. $\triangle PQR \cong \triangle LMN$ by the SSS Congruence Post. Corr. parts of $\cong$ $\triangle$s are $\cong$, so $m\angle R = 90° = m\angle N$. By def., $\angle N$ is a rt. $\angle$, and so $\triangle LNM$ is a right triangle.

41. **DEVELOPING PROOF** Complete the proof of Theorem 9.6 on page 544.

GIVEN ▶ In $\triangle ABC$, $c^2 < a^2 + b^2$.

PROVE ▶ $\triangle ABC$ is an acute triangle.

Plan for Proof Draw right $\triangle PQR$ with side lengths a, b, and x. Compare lengths c and x.

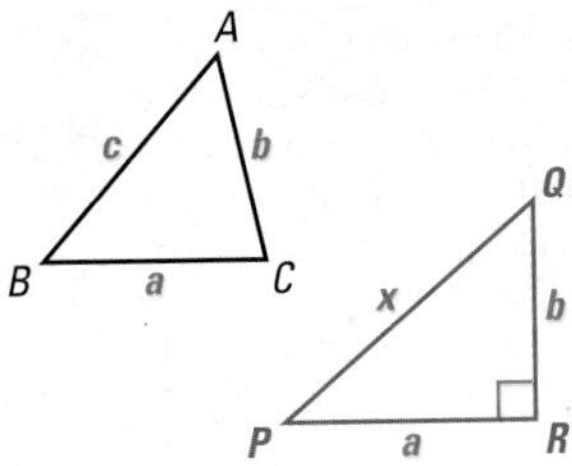

Statements	Reasons
1. $x^2 = a^2 + b^2$	1. ___?___
2. $c^2 < a^2 + b^2$	2. ___?___
3. $c^2 < x^2$	3. ___?___
4. $c < x$	4. A property of square roots
5. $m\angle C < m\angle R$	5. ___?___
6. $\angle C$ is an acute angle.	6. ___?___
7. $\triangle ABC$ is an acute triangle.	7. ___?___

42. **PROOF** Prove Theorem 9.7 on page 544. Include a diagram and *Given* and *Prove* statements. (*Hint:* Look back at Exercise 41.) See margin.

43. **PROOF** Prove the Converse of the Pythagorean Theorem.

GIVEN ▶ In $\triangle LNM$, $\overline{LM}$ is the longest side; $c^2 = a^2 + b^2$.

PROVE ▶ $\triangle LNM$ is a right triangle.

Plan for Proof Draw right $\triangle PQR$ with side lengths a, b, and x. Compare lengths c and x.

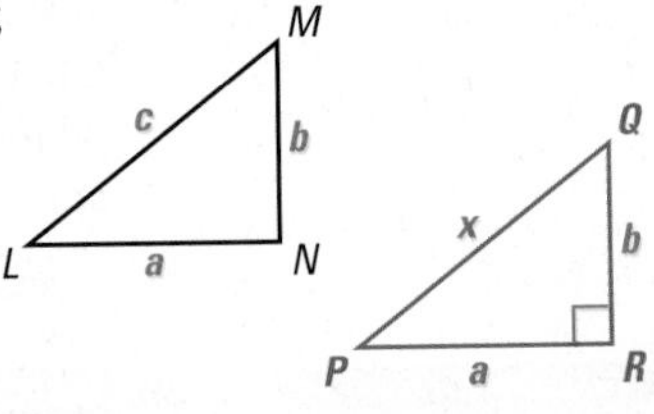

Test Preparation

QUANTITATIVE COMPARISON **Choose the statement that is true about the given quantities.**

Ⓐ The quantity in column A is greater.
Ⓑ The quantity in column B is greater.
Ⓒ The two quantities are equal.
Ⓓ The relationship cannot be determined from the given information.

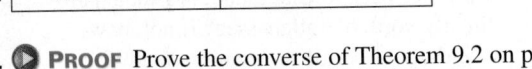

	Column A	Column B	
44.	$m\angle A$	$m\angle D$	A
45.	$m\angle B + m\angle C$	$m\angle E + m\angle F$	B

B, A, C: 77, 85, 36; E, D, F: 82, 91, 40

★ Challenge

46. **PROOF** Prove the converse of Theorem 9.2 on page 529.

GIVEN ▶ In $\triangle MQN$, altitude $\overline{NP}$ is drawn to $\overline{MQ}$; t is the geometric mean of r and s.

PROVE ▶ $\triangle MQN$ is a right triangle. See margin.

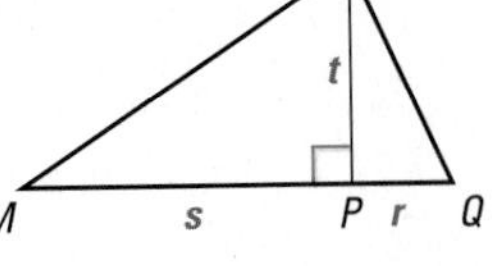

EXTRA CHALLENGE
www.mcdougallittell.com

MIXED REVIEW

SIMPLIFYING RADICALS Simplify the expression. (Skills Review, p. 799, for 9.4)

47. $\sqrt{22} \cdot \sqrt{2}$ $2\sqrt{11}$ **48.** $\sqrt{6} \cdot \sqrt{8}$ $4\sqrt{3}$ **49.** $\sqrt{14} \cdot \sqrt{6}$ $2\sqrt{21}$ **50.** $\sqrt{15} \cdot \sqrt{6}$ $3\sqrt{10}$

51. $\frac{3}{\sqrt{11}}$ $\frac{3\sqrt{11}}{11}$ **52.** $\frac{4}{\sqrt{5}}$ $\frac{4\sqrt{5}}{5}$ **53.** $\frac{12}{\sqrt{18}}$ $2\sqrt{2}$ **54.** $\frac{8}{\sqrt{24}}$ $\frac{2\sqrt{6}}{3}$

DILATIONS Identify the dilation and find its scale factor. (Review 8.7)

55. an enlargement with center C and scale factor $\frac{7}{4}$

56. a reduction with center C and scale factor $\frac{3}{5}$

55.

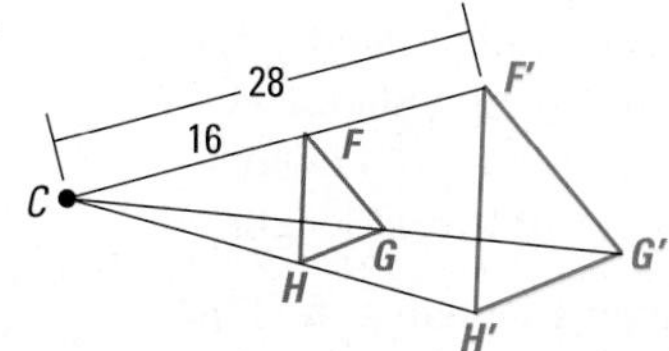

56.

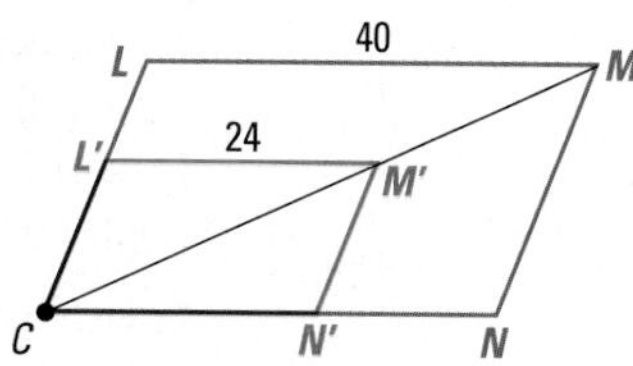

57. USING ALGEBRA In the diagram, $\overrightarrow{PS}$ bisects $\angle RPT$, and $\overline{PS}$ is the perpendicular bisector of $\overline{RT}$. Find the values of x and y. (Review 5.1) $x = 9$, $y = 11$

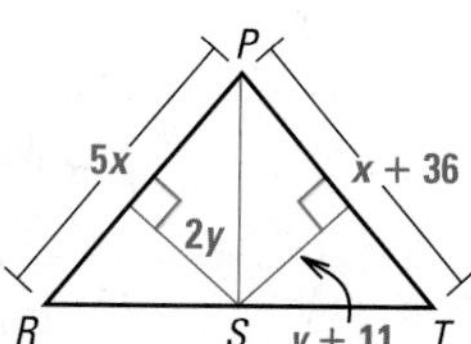

QUIZ 1

Self-Test for Lessons 9.1–9.3

In Exercises 1–4, use the diagram. (Lesson 9.1)

1. Write a similarity statement about the three triangles in the diagram. $\triangle ABC \sim \triangle ADB \sim \triangle BDC$

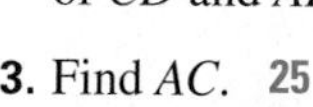

2. Which segment's length is the geometric mean of CD and AD? $\overline{BD}$

3. Find AC. 25

4. Find BD. 12

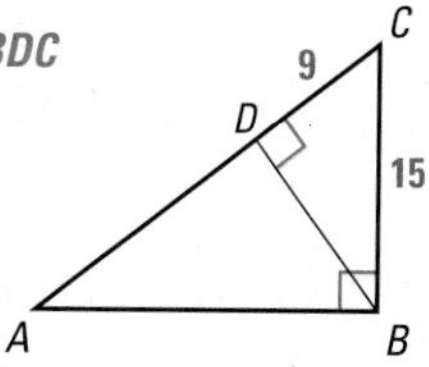

Find the unknown side length. Simplify answers that are radicals. (Lesson 9.2)

5.

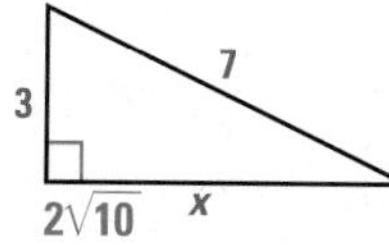

6.

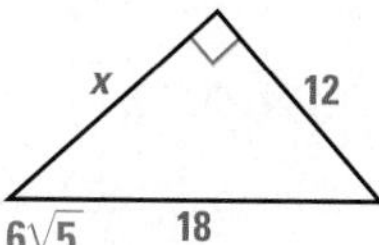

7.

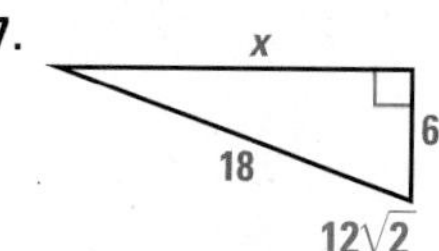

8. CITY PARK The diagram shown at the right shows the dimensions of a triangular city park. Does this city park have a right angle? Explain. (Lesson 9.3) no; $219^2 \neq 168^2 + 140^2$

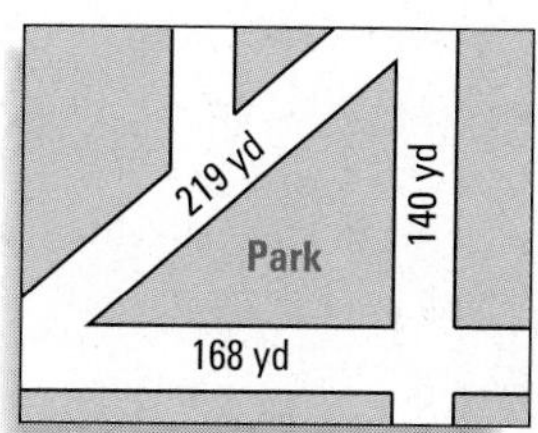

4 ASSESS

DAILY HOMEWORK QUIZ

Transparency Available

Decide whether the numbers can represent the side lengths of a triangle. If they can, classify the triangle as *right, acute,* or *obtuse.*

1. 12, 35, 37 yes; right
2. 22, 25, 40 yes; obtuse
3. 15, 17, 34 no

Graph points P, Q, and R. Connect the points to form $\triangle PQR$. Decide whether $\triangle PQR$ is *right, acute,* or *obtuse.*

4. $P(-3, 2)$, $Q(-2, -2)$, $R(1, 1)$ acute
5. $P(1, 2)$, $Q(5, -2)$, $R(3, -4)$ right

EXTRA CHALLENGE NOTE

Challenge problems for Lesson 9.3 are available in **blackline** format in the *Chapter 9 Resource Book,* p. 51 and at **www.mcdougallittell.com.**

ADDITIONAL TEST PREPARATION

1. **OPEN ENDED** Give an example of side lengths of a triangle that is an acute triangle. *Sample answer:* 8, 10, 12

ADDITIONAL RESOURCES

An alternative Quiz for Lessons 9.1–9.3 is available in the *Chapter 9 Resource Book,* p. 52.

1 Planning the Activity

PURPOSE

To find how the side lengths of 45°-45°-90° triangles or 30°-60°-90° triangles are related.

MATERIALS

- ruler
- compass

PACING

- Exploring the Concept: 45°-45°-90° — 15 min
- Conjecture — 15 min
- Exploring the Concept: 30°-60°-90° — 15 min
- Conjecture — 15 min

LINK TO LESSON

Students will use the 45°-45°-90° and 30°-60°-90° relationships in Examples 1–3 of Lesson 9.4.

2 Managing the Activity

CLASSROOM MANAGEMENT

If students have difficulty generalizing the relationships, ask each student to do more constructions.

ALTERNATIVE APPROACH

To save time, do this activity as a demonstration. Use a protractor to verify the size of the angles.

3 Closing the Activity

KEY DISCOVERY

The side lengths of a 45°-45°-90° or of a 30°-60°-90° have predictable ratios.

ACTIVITY ASSESSMENT

A 45°-45°-90° has a leg with length 8 inches. Find the length of the hypotenuse. $8\sqrt{2}$ The shortest side of a 30°-60°-90° triangle has length 4. Find the lengths of the other two sides. $4\sqrt{3}$; 8

ACTIVITY 9.4

Developing Concepts

Investigating Special Right Triangles

GROUP ACTIVITY

Work in a group of three students.

MATERIALS

- paper
- pencil
- ruler
- compass

QUESTION A triangle with angle measures of 45°, 45°, and 90°, or 30°, 60°, and 90° is called a *special right triangle*. How are the side lengths of a 45°-45°-90° triangle or a 30°-60°-90° triangle related?

EXPLORING THE CONCEPT: 45°-45°-90° TRIANGLE

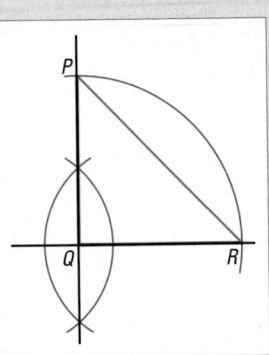

1. Construct an isosceles right triangle. The length of a leg of the triangle should be 3, 4, or 5 centimeters. Each person in your group should choose a different length.

   Check constructions, which should look like the one shown.

2. Use the Pythagorean Theorem to find the length of the hypotenuse. Write the length in simplest radical form.

   $3\sqrt{2}$ cm, $4\sqrt{2}$ cm, or $5\sqrt{2}$ cm, depending on the length of a leg

CONJECTURE

3. Compare your results with those of the other students in your group. What pattern do you observe? Make a conjecture about the relationships among the side lengths of an isosceles right triangle.

3. The pattern is that when a leg has length *x*, the hypotenuse has length $x \cdot \sqrt{2}$. Conjecture: The hypotenuse of an isosceles triangle is $\sqrt{2}$ times as long as each leg.

EXPLORING THE CONCEPT: 30°-60°-90° TRIANGLE

4. Construct an equilateral triangle with side lengths of 4, 6, or 8 centimeters. Each person in your group should choose a different length.

5. Next construct the altitude from one of the vertices. The equilateral triangle is now divided into two congruent right triangles whose angle measures are 30°-60°-90°.

4, 5. Check constructions, which should look like the one shown.

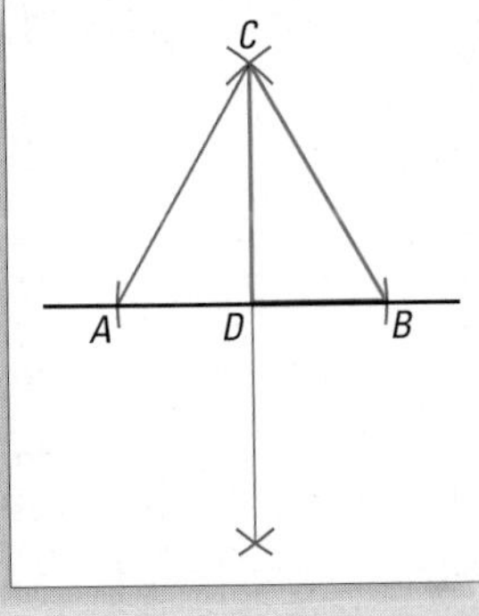

6. Find the side lengths of one of the right triangles. Write each length in simplest radical form.

6. 4 cm, 2 cm, $2\sqrt{3}$ cm, or 6 cm, 3 cm, $3\sqrt{3}$ cm, or 8 cm, 4 cm, $4\sqrt{3}$ cm

CONJECTURE

7. Find each of the following ratios:
   - the length of the hypotenuse to the length of the shorter leg
   - the length of the longer leg to the length of the shorter leg

   Compare your ratios with those of the other students in your group. What patterns do you observe? Make a conjecture about the ratios of the side lengths of a 30°-60°-90° triangle.

7. $\frac{2}{1}$; $\frac{\sqrt{3}}{1}$; these two ratios are the same for every right triangle examined. Conjecture: In a 30°–60°–90° triangle, the ratio of the length of the hypotenuse to the length of the shorter leg is $\frac{2}{1}$, and the ratio of the length of the longer leg to the length of the shorter leg is $\frac{\sqrt{3}}{1}$.

9.4 Special Right Triangles

What you should learn

GOAL 1 Find the side lengths of special right triangles.

GOAL 2 Use special right triangles to solve **real-life** problems, such as finding the side lengths of the triangles in the spiral quilt design in **Exs. 31–34**.

Why you should learn it

▼ To use special right triangles to solve **real-life** problems, such as finding the height of a tipping platform in **Example 4**.

REAL LIFE

CALIFORNIA STANDARDS AND ASSESSMENT

CA Standards: 14, 20
SAT9 Task 1: Obj. 1
SAT9 Task 2: Objs. 1, 25

GOAL 1 SIDE LENGTHS OF SPECIAL RIGHT TRIANGLES

Right triangles whose angle measures are 45°-45°-90° or 30°-60°-90° are called **special right triangles**. In the Activity on page 550, you may have noticed certain relationships among the side lengths of each of these special right triangles. The theorems below describe these relationships. Exercises 35 and 36 ask you to prove the theorems.

THEOREMS ABOUT SPECIAL RIGHT TRIANGLES

THEOREM 9.8 *45°-45°-90° Triangle Theorem*

In a 45°-45°-90° triangle, the hypotenuse is $\sqrt{2}$ times as long as each leg.

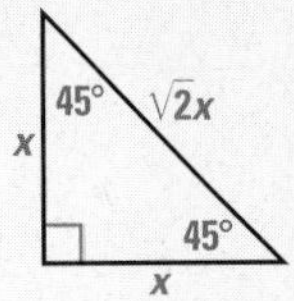

Hypotenuse = $\sqrt{2}$ · leg

THEOREM 9.9 *30°-60°-90° Triangle Theorem*

In a 30°-60°-90° triangle, the hypotenuse is twice as long as the shorter leg, and the longer leg is $\sqrt{3}$ times as long as the shorter leg.

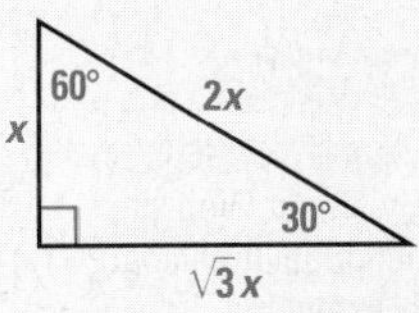

Hypotenuse = 2 · shorter leg
Longer leg = $\sqrt{3}$ · shorter leg

EXAMPLE 1 *Finding the Hypotenuse in a 45°-45°-90° Triangle*

Find the value of x.

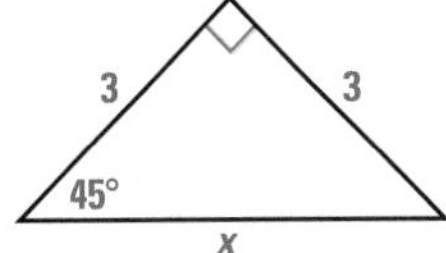

SOLUTION

By the Triangle Sum Theorem, the measure of the third angle is 45°. The triangle is a 45°-45°-90° right triangle, so the length x of the hypotenuse is $\sqrt{2}$ times the length of a leg.

Hypotenuse = $\sqrt{2}$ · leg — **45°-45°-90° Triangle Theorem**

$x = \sqrt{2} \cdot 3$ — **Substitute.**

$x = 3\sqrt{2}$ — **Simplify.**

1 PLAN

PACING
Basic: 2 days
Average: 2 days
Advanced: 2 days
Block Schedule: 0.5 block with 9.3; 0.5 block with 9.5

LESSON OPENER
VISUAL APPROACH
An alternative way to approach Lesson 9.4 is to use the Visual Approach Lesson Opener:
- Blackline Master (*Chapter 9 Resource Book*, p. 56)
- Transparency (p. 57)

MEETING INDIVIDUAL NEEDS
- ***Chapter 9 Resource Book***
  Prerequisite Skills Review (p. 5)
  Practice Level A (p. 57)
  Practice Level B (p. 58)
  Practice Level C (p. 59)
  Reteaching with Practice (p. 60)
  Absent Student Catch-Up (p. 62)
  Challenge (p. 65)
- ***Resources in Spanish***
- ***Personal Student Tutor***

NEW-TEACHER SUPPORT
See the Tips for New Teachers on pp. 1–2 of the *Chapter 9 Resource Book* for additional notes about Lesson 9.4.

WARM-UP EXERCISES

Transparency Available

Solve the equation for the missing variable. Assume all variables are positive. Express the answer in simplified radical form.

1. $c^2 = 6^2 + 6^2$ $6\sqrt{2}$
2. $c^2 - 4^2 = 4^2$ $4\sqrt{2}$
3. $c^2 - 100 = (10\sqrt{3})^2$ 20
4. $a^2 + 8^2 = 256$ $8\sqrt{3}$
5. $(18\sqrt{3})^2 + b^2 = 1296$ 18

2 TEACH

MOTIVATING THE LESSON

The diagonal of a baseball diamond forms two special triangles with angles of 45°, 45°, and 90°. The focus of this lesson is to find the lengths of special right triangles knowing only one side of the triangle.

EXTRA EXAMPLE 1

Find the value of x. $5\sqrt{2}$

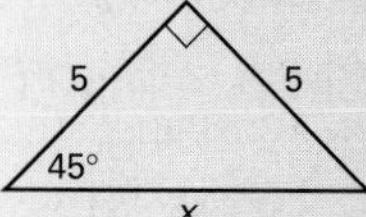

EXTRA EXAMPLE 2

Find the value of x. $6\sqrt{2}$

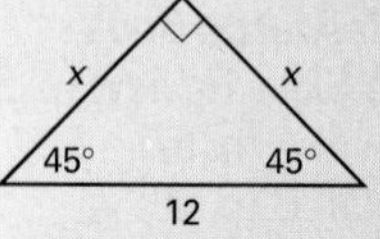

EXTRA EXAMPLE 3

Find the value of f and g.
$f = 6\sqrt{3}$; $g = 12\sqrt{3}$

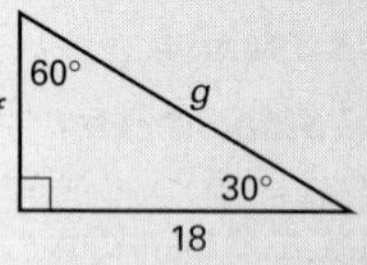

CHECKPOINT EXERCISES

For use after Examples 1–3:

Find the value of each variable. Express the answer in simplest radical form.

1. $8\sqrt{2}$

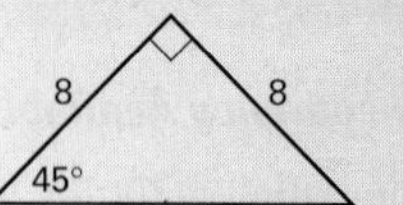

2. $\frac{21\sqrt{2}}{2}$

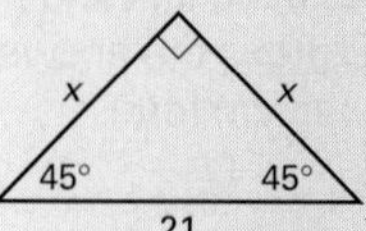

3.

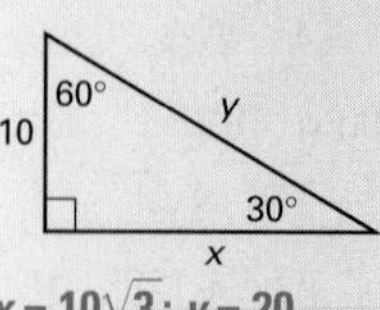

$x = 10\sqrt{3}$; $y = 20$

EXAMPLE 2 *Finding a Leg in a 45°-45°-90° Triangle*

Find the value of x.

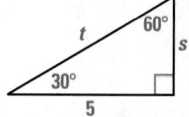

SOLUTION

Because the triangle is an isosceles right triangle, its base angles are congruent. The triangle is a 45°-45°-90° right triangle, so the length of the hypotenuse is $\sqrt{2}$ times the length x of a leg.

$\text{Hypotenuse} = \sqrt{2} \cdot \text{leg}$	**45°-45°-90° Triangle Theorem**
$5 = \sqrt{2} \cdot x$	**Substitute.**
$\frac{5}{\sqrt{2}} = \frac{\sqrt{2}x}{\sqrt{2}}$	**Divide each side by $\sqrt{2}$.**
$\frac{5}{\sqrt{2}} = x$	**Simplify.**
$\frac{\sqrt{2}}{\sqrt{2}} \cdot \frac{5}{\sqrt{2}} = x$	**Multiply numerator and denominator by $\sqrt{2}$.**
$\frac{5\sqrt{2}}{2} = x$	**Simplify.**

EXAMPLE 3 *Side Lengths in a 30°-60°-90° Triangle*

Find the values of s and t.

SOLUTION

Because the triangle is a 30°-60°-90° triangle, the longer leg is $\sqrt{3}$ times the length s of the shorter leg.

$\text{Longer leg} = \sqrt{3} \cdot \text{shorter leg}$	**30°-60°-90° Triangle Theorem**
$5 = \sqrt{3} \cdot s$	**Substitute.**
$\frac{5}{\sqrt{3}} = \frac{\sqrt{3} \cdot s}{\sqrt{3}}$	**Divide each side by $\sqrt{3}$.**
$\frac{5}{\sqrt{3}} = s$	**Simplify.**
$\frac{\sqrt{3}}{\sqrt{3}} \cdot \frac{5}{\sqrt{3}} = s$	**Multiply numerator and denominator by $\sqrt{3}$.**
$\frac{5\sqrt{3}}{3} = s$	**Simplify.**

The length t of the hypotenuse is twice the length s of the shorter leg.

$\text{Hypotenuse} = 2 \cdot \text{shorter leg}$	**30°-60°-90° Triangle Theorem**
$t = 2 \cdot \frac{5\sqrt{3}}{3}$	**Substitute.**
$t = \frac{10\sqrt{3}}{3}$	**Simplify.**

STUDENT HELP

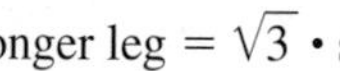

HOMEWORK HELP
Visit our Web site www.mcdougallittell.com for extra examples.

GOAL 2 USING SPECIAL RIGHT TRIANGLES IN REAL LIFE

EXAMPLE 4 *Finding the Height of a Ramp*

TIPPING PLATFORM A tipping platform is a ramp used to unload trucks, as shown on page 551. How high is the end of an 80 foot ramp when it is tipped by a 30° angle? by a 45° angle?

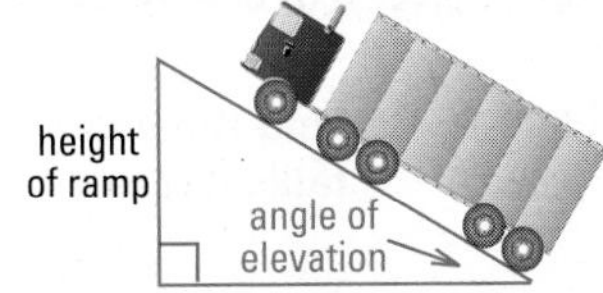

SOLUTION

When the angle of elevation is 30°, the height h of the ramp is the length of the shorter leg of a 30°-60°-90° triangle. The length of the hypotenuse is 80 feet.

$80 = 2h$ — **30°-60°-90° Triangle Theorem**

$40 = h$ — **Divide each side by 2.**

When the angle of elevation is 45°, the height of the ramp is the length of a leg of a 45°-45°-90° triangle. The length of the hypotenuse is 80 feet.

$80 = \sqrt{2} \cdot h$ — **45°-45°-90° Triangle Theorem**

$\frac{80}{\sqrt{2}} = h$ — **Divide each side by $\sqrt{2}$.**

$56.6 \approx h$ — **Use a calculator to approximate.**

▶ When the angle of elevation is 30°, the ramp height is 40 feet. When the angle of elevation is 45°, the ramp height is about 56 feet 7 inches.

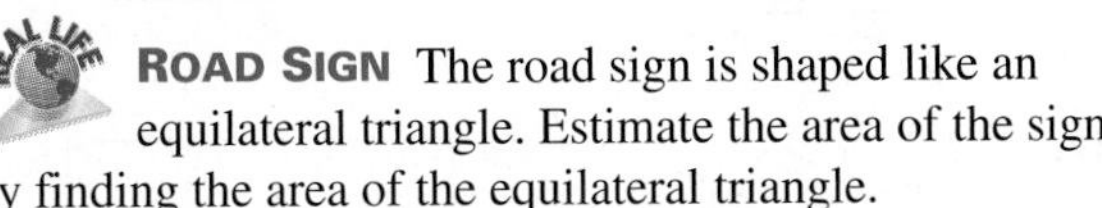

EXAMPLE 5 *Finding the Area of a Sign*

ROAD SIGN The road sign is shaped like an equilateral triangle. Estimate the area of the sign by finding the area of the equilateral triangle.

SOLUTION

First find the height h of the triangle by dividing it into two 30°-60°-90° triangles. The length of the longer leg of one of these triangles is h. The length of the shorter leg is 18 inches.

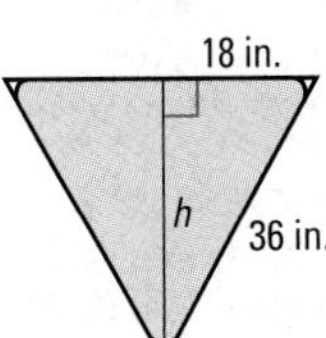

$h = \sqrt{3} \cdot 18 = 18\sqrt{3}$ — **30°-60°-90° Triangle Theorem**

Use $h = 18\sqrt{3}$ to find the area of the equilateral triangle.

$$\text{Area} = \frac{1}{2}bh = \frac{1}{2}(36)\left(18\sqrt{3}\right) \approx 561.18$$

▶ The area of the sign is about 561 square inches.

EXTRA EXAMPLE 4

A ramp is used to unload trucks. How high is the end of a 50 foot ramp when it is tipped by a 30° angle? **25 ft** by a 45° angle? **about 35.4 ft**

EXTRA EXAMPLE 5

The roof on a doghouse is shaped like an equilateral triangle with height 3 feet. Estimate the area of the cross-section of the roof. **about 5.2 ft^2**

CHECKPOINT EXERCISES

For use after Examples 4 and 5:

1. A ramp is used to unload trucks. How high is the end of a 36 foot ramp when it is tipped by a 30° angle? **18 ft** by a 45° angle? **about 25.5 ft**
2. An equilateral triangle has side length 8 feet. Estimate the area. **about 27.7 ft^2**

FOCUS ON VOCABULARY

Name the angle measures of special right triangles. **30°-60°-90° and 45°-45°-90°**

CLOSURE QUESTION

Find the ratio of the lengths of the sides of a 30°-60°-90° triangle and of a 45°-45°-90° triangle.
$1:\sqrt{3}:2$; $1:1:\sqrt{2}$

DAILY PUZZLER

Can the side lengths of a 45°-45°-90° triangle form a Pythagorean triple? ***Sample answer:*** **No; the hypotenuse is $\sqrt{2}$ times the length of the leg. Therefore no triple of three integers can be formed.**

3 APPLY

ASSIGNMENT GUIDE

BASIC

Day 1: pp. 554–555 Exs. 12–26

Day 2: pp. 555–557 Exs. 27–38, 42–49

AVERAGE

Day 1: pp. 554–555 Exs. 12–26

Day 2: pp. 555–557 Exs. 27–38, 42–49

ADVANCED

Day 1: pp. 554–555 Exs. 12–26

Day 2: pp. 555–557 Exs. 27–49

BLOCK SCHEDULE

pp. 554–555 Exs. 12–26 (with 9.3)
pp. 555–557 Exs. 27–38, 42–49 (with 9.5)

EXERCISE LEVELS

Level A: *Easier*
12–20

Level B: *More Difficult*
21–38

Level C: *Most Difficult*
39–41

✓ HOMEWORK CHECK

To quickly check student understanding of key concepts, go over the following exercises: Exs. 12, 18, 22, 24, 26, 30, 32, 34. See also the Daily Homework Quiz:

- Blackline Master (*Chapter 9 Resource Book*, p. 68)
- Transparency (p. 67)

GUIDED PRACTICE

Vocabulary Check ✓

1. What is meant by the term *special right triangles*?
a 45°–45°–90° triangle or a 30°–60°–90° triangle

Concept Check ✓

2. **CRITICAL THINKING** Explain why any two 30°-60°-90° triangles are similar.
They are similar by the AA Similarity Postulate.

Use the diagram to tell whether the equation is *true* or *false*.

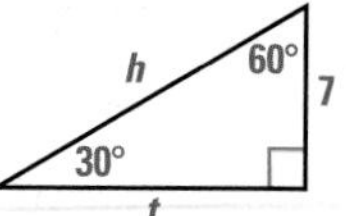

3. $t = 7\sqrt{3}$ true
4. $t = \sqrt{3h}$ false
5. $h = 2t$ false
6. $h = 14$ true
7. $7 = \frac{h}{2}$ true
8. $7 = \frac{t}{\sqrt{3}}$ true

Skill Check ✓

Find the value of each variable. Write answers in simplest radical form.

9.
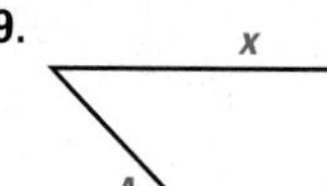

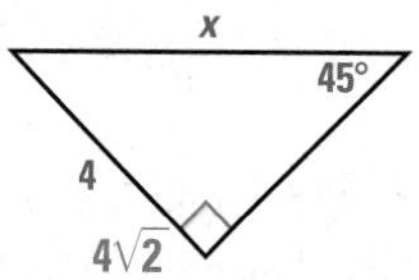

$4\sqrt{2}$

10.

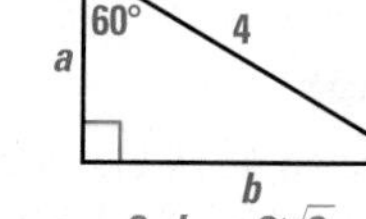

$a = 2$, $b = 2\sqrt{3}$

11.
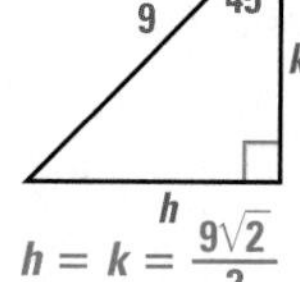

$h = k = \frac{9\sqrt{2}}{2}$

PRACTICE AND APPLICATIONS

STUDENT HELP

Extra Practice to help you master skills is on p. 820.

USING ALGEBRA **Find the value of each variable. Write answers in simplest radical form.**

12.

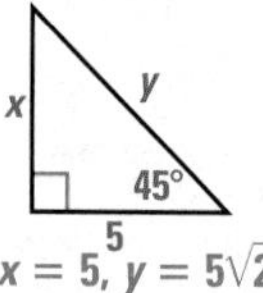

$x = 5$, $y = 5\sqrt{2}$

13.
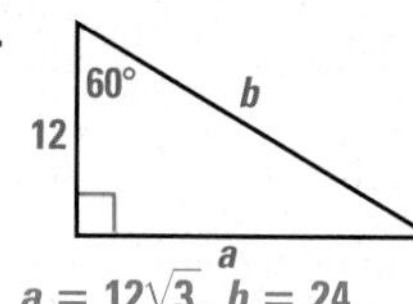

$a = 12\sqrt{3}$, $b = 24$

14.
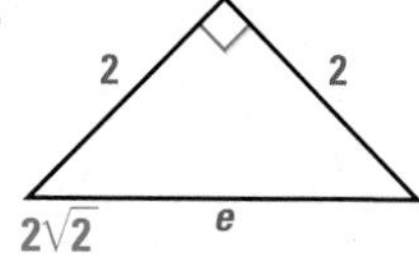

$2\sqrt{2}$

15.
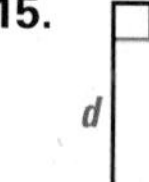
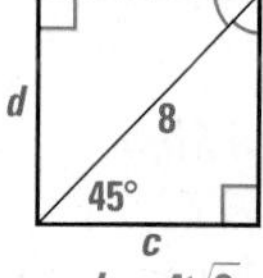

$c = d = 4\sqrt{2}$

16.
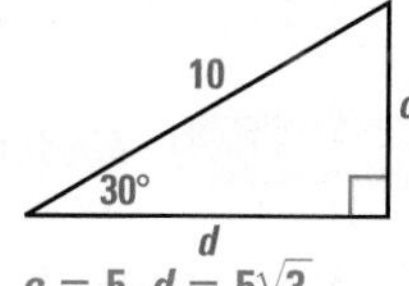

$c = 5$, $d = 5\sqrt{3}$

17.
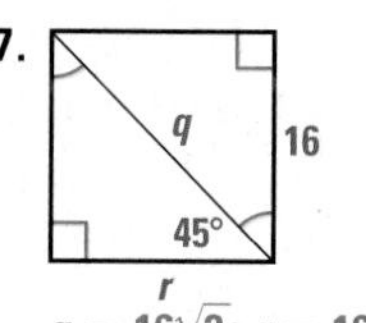

$q = 16\sqrt{2}$; $r = 16$

18.
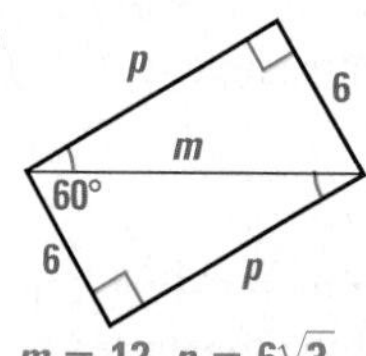

$m = 12$, $p = 6\sqrt{3}$

19.
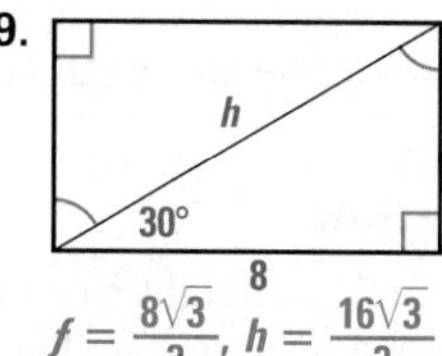

$f = \frac{8\sqrt{3}}{3}$, $h = \frac{16\sqrt{3}}{3}$

20.
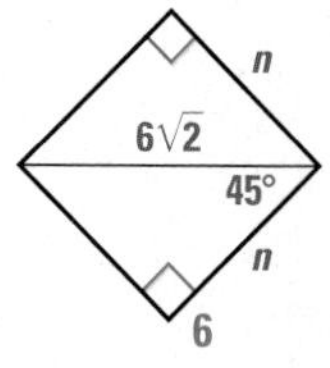

STUDENT HELP

HOMEWORK HELP
Example 1: Exs. 12–23
Example 2: Exs. 12–23
Example 3: Exs. 12–23
Example 4: Exs. 28–29, 34
Example 5: Exs. 24–27

FINDING LENGTHS **Sketch the figure that is described. Find the requested length. Round decimals to the nearest tenth.**

21. The side length of an equilateral triangle is 5 centimeters. Find the length of an altitude of the triangle. 4.3 cm

22. The perimeter of a square is 36 inches. Find the length of a diagonal. 12.7 in.

23. The diagonal of a square is 26 inches. Find the length of a side. 18.4 in.

FINDING AREA Find the area of the figure. Round decimal answers to the nearest tenth.

24.

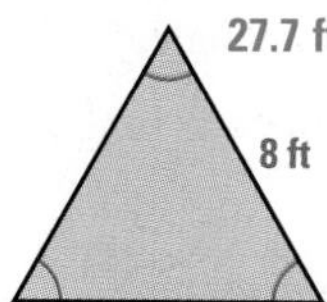

25.

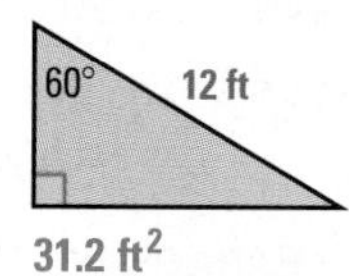

26.

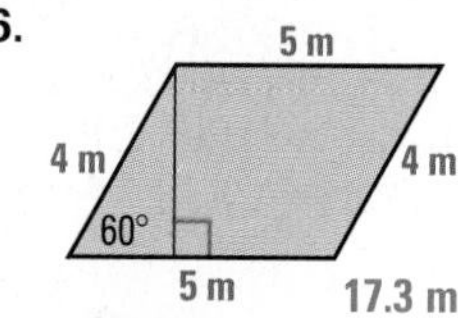

27. **AREA OF A WINDOW** A hexagonal window consists of six congruent panes of glass. Each pane is an equilateral triangle. Find the area of the entire window. $24\sqrt{3} \approx 41.6$ ft^2

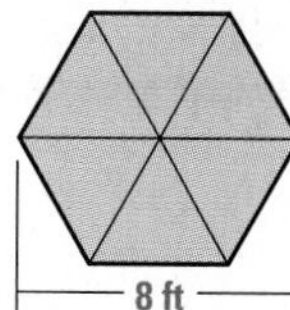

JEWELRY Estimate the length *x* of each earring.

28.

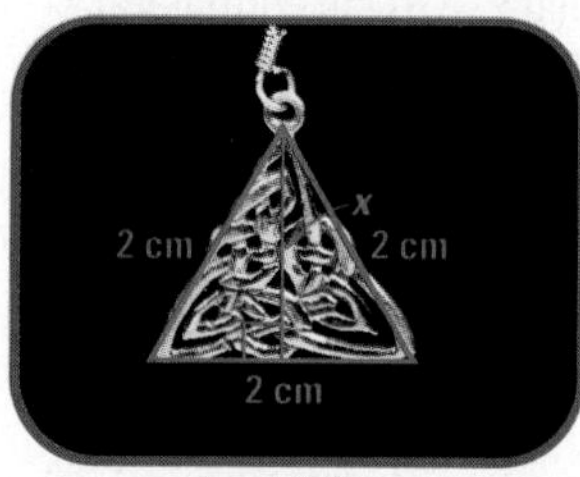

about 1.7 cm

29.

about 2 cm

30. **TOOLS** Find the values of x and y for the hexagonal nut shown at the right when $s = 2$ centimeters. (*Hint:* In Exercise 27 above, you saw that a regular hexagon can be divided into six equilateral triangles.)
$x = 4$, $y = 2\sqrt{3}$

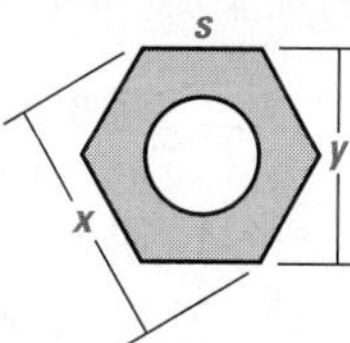

LOGICAL REASONING The quilt design in the photo is based on the pattern in the diagram below. Use the diagram in Exercises 31–34.

Wheel of Theodorus

31. $r = \sqrt{2}$; $s = \sqrt{3}$; $t = 2$; $u = \sqrt{5}$; $v = \sqrt{6}$; $w = \sqrt{7}$; I used the Pythagorean Theorem in each right triangle in turn, working from left to right.

32. the right triangle with legs of length 1 and hypotenuse $r = \sqrt{2}$

33. the right triangle with legs of lengths 1 and $s = \sqrt{3}$, and hypotenuse $t = 2$

31. Find the values of r, s, t, u, v, and w. Explain the procedure you used to find the values.

32. Which of the triangles, if any, is a 45°-45°-90° triangle?

33. Which of the triangles, if any, is a 30°-60°-90° triangle?

34. **USING ALGEBRA** Suppose there are n triangles in the spiral. Write an expression for the hypotenuse of the nth triangle. $\sqrt{n+1}$

! COMMON ERROR

EXERCISES 13, 16, 18, 19

Watch for students who think the hypotenuse is a multiple of $\sqrt{3}$ in a 30°-60°-90° triangle. Students may mistakenly think that $\sqrt{3} > 2$ and so corresponds to the hypotenuse. Have students find the value of $\sqrt{3}$ and compare it to 2.

36. Construct $\overrightarrow{CD}$ on $\overrightarrow{BC}$ so that $CD = BC = a$. Then $\triangle ABC \cong \triangle ADC$ by the SAS Congruence Post. $\angle B \cong \angle D$, so $m\angle D = 60°$. By the Triangle Sum Thm., $\triangle ABD$ is equiangular, and so it is also equilateral. Thus, $AB = a + a = 2a$. By the Pythagorean Thm., $(AC)^2 + (BC)^2 = (AB)^2$, or $(AC)^2 + a^2 = (2a)^2$; $(AC)^2 = 4a^2 - a^2 = 3a^2$; $AC = \sqrt{3a^2} = \sqrt{3} \cdot a$. Thus, the hypotenuse is twice as long as the shorter leg, and the longer leg is $\sqrt{3}$ times as long as the shorter leg.

Additional Practice and Reteaching

For Lesson 9.4:

- Practice Levels A, B, and C (*Chapter 9 Resource Book*, p. 57)
- Reteaching with Practice (*Chapter 9 Resource Book*, p. 60)
- See Lesson 9.4 of the *Personal Student Tutor*

For more Mixed Review:

- Search the *Test and Practice Generator* for key words or specific lessons.

35. Let $DF = x$. Then $EF = x$. By the Pythagorean Theorem, $x^2 + x^2 = (DE)^2$; $2x^2 = (DE)^2$; $DE = \sqrt{2x^2} = \sqrt{2} \cdot x$ by a property of square roots. Thus, the hypotenuse is $\sqrt{2}$ times as long as a leg.

35. **PARAGRAPH PROOF** Write a paragraph proof of Theorem 9.8 on page 551.

GIVEN ▶ $\triangle DEF$ is a 45°-45°-90° triangle.

PROVE ▶ The hypotenuse is $\sqrt{2}$ times as long as each leg.

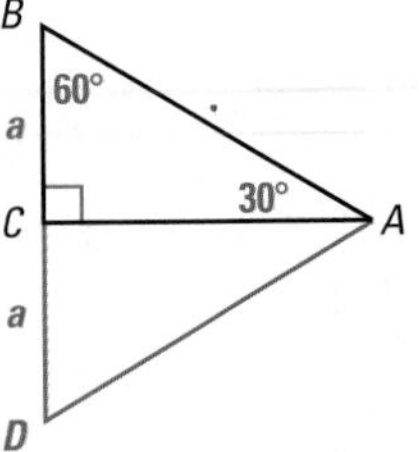

36. **PARAGRAPH PROOF** Write a paragraph proof of Theorem 9.9 on page 551. **See margin.**

GIVEN ▶ $\triangle ABC$ is a 30°-60°-90° triangle.

PROVE ▶ The hypotenuse is twice as long as the shorter leg and the longer leg is $\sqrt{3}$ times as long as the shorter leg.

Plan for Proof Construct $\triangle ADC$ congruent to $\triangle ABC$. Then prove that $\triangle ABD$ is equilateral. Express the lengths AB and AC in terms of a.

Test Preparation

37. **MULTIPLE CHOICE** Which of the statements below is true about the diagram at the right? **C**

Ⓐ $x < 45$ Ⓑ $x = 45$

Ⓒ $x > 45$ Ⓓ $x \leq 45$

Ⓔ Not enough information is given to determine the value of x.

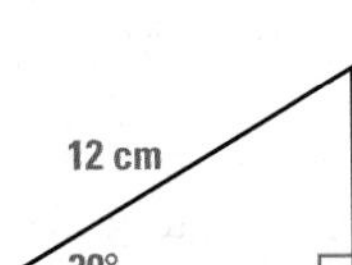

38. **MULTIPLE CHOICE** Find the perimeter of the triangle shown at the right to the nearest tenth of a centimeter. **A**

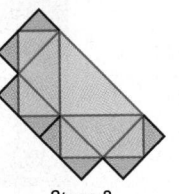

Ⓐ 28.4 cm Ⓑ 30 cm

Ⓒ 31.2 cm Ⓓ 41.6 cm

12 cm
30°

★ Challenge

39. Stage 1: $\frac{1}{\sqrt{2}}$; Stage 2: $\frac{1}{2}$; Stage 3: $\frac{1}{2\sqrt{2}}$; Stage 4: $\frac{1}{4}$

40. The length of the legs at each stage is $\frac{1}{\sqrt{2}}$ times the length at the previous stage. Also, the length of the legs at Stage n is $\left(\frac{1}{\sqrt{2}}\right)^n$ when $n = 1, 2, 3, \ldots$.

VISUAL THINKING In Exercises 39–41, use the diagram below. Each triangle in the diagram is a 45°-45°-90° triangle. At Stage 0, the legs of the triangle are each 1 unit long.

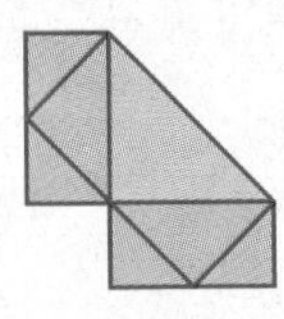

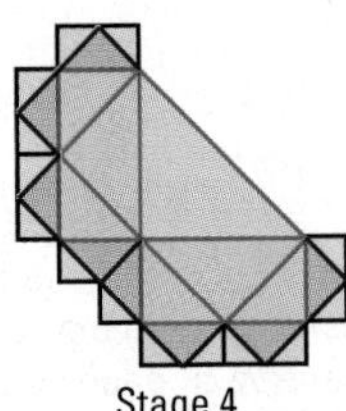

39. Find the exact lengths of the legs of the triangles that are added at each stage. Leave radicals in the denominators of fractions.

40. Describe the pattern of the lengths in Exercise 39.

41. Find the length of a leg of a triangle added in Stage 8. Explain how you found your answer. $\frac{1}{16}$; **I used the pattern I described in Ex. 40.**

www.mcdougallittell.com

MIXED REVIEW

42. **FINDING A SIDE LENGTH** A triangle has one side of 9 inches and another of 14 inches. Describe the possible lengths of the third side. **(Review 5.5)**
greater than 5 in. and less than 23 in.

FINDING REFLECTIONS Find the coordinates of the reflection without using a coordinate plane. (Review 7.2)

43. $Q(-1, -2)$ reflected in the x-axis
$Q'(-1, 2)$

44. $P(8, 3)$ reflected in the y-axis
$P'(-8, 3)$

45. $A(4, -5)$ reflected in the y-axis
$A'(-4, -5)$

46. $B(0, 10)$ reflected in the x-axis
$B'(0, -10)$

DEVELOPING PROOF Name a postulate or theorem that can be used to prove that the two triangles are similar. (Review 8.5 for 9.5)

2. The combined area of the blue triangles plus the area of the small red square equals the area of the whole square: $2ab + a^2 - 2ab + b^2 = c^2$. Thus, $a^2 + b^2 = c^2$.

47.
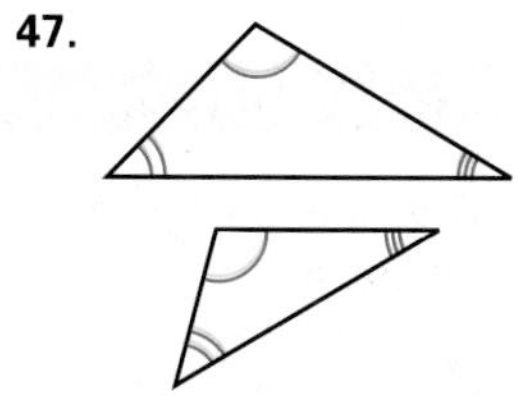
AA Similarity Post.

48.
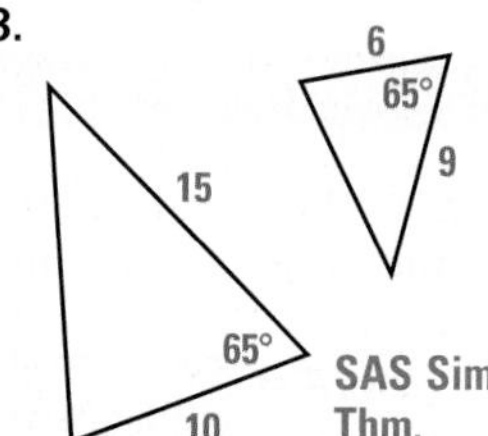

SAS Similarity Thm.

49.
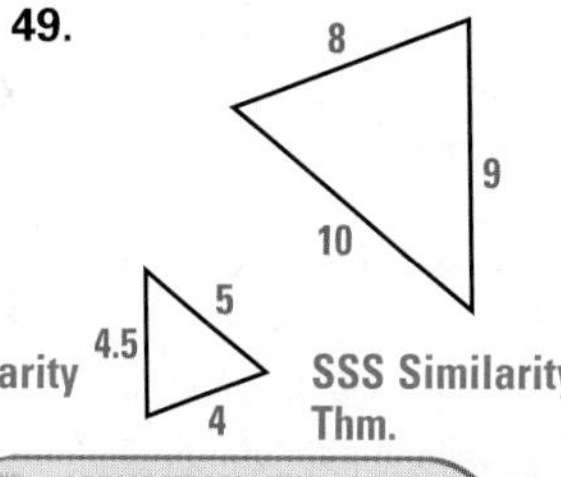

SSS Similarity Thm.

MATH & History — Pythagorean Theorem Proofs

THEN **AROUND THE SIXTH CENTURY B.C.,** the Greek mathematician Pythagoras founded a school for the study of philosophy, mathematics, and science. Many people believe that an early proof of the Pythagorean Theorem came from this school.

NOW **TODAY,** the Pythagorean theorem is one of the most famous theorems in geometry. More than 100 different proofs now exist.

The diagram is based on one drawn by the Hindu mathematician Bhāskara (1114–1185). The four blue right triangles are congruent.

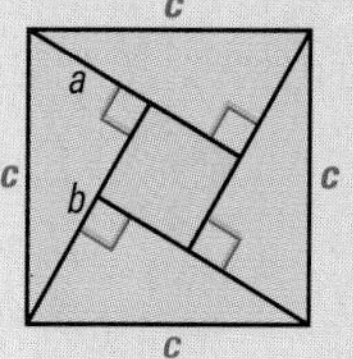

1. $4(\frac{1}{2} \cdot a \cdot b) = 2ab$; $(b - a)^2 = a^2 - 2ab + b^2$

1. Write an expression in terms of a and b for the combined areas of the blue triangles. Then write an expression in terms of a and b for the area of the small red square.
2. Use the diagram to show that $a^2 + b^2 = c^2$. (*Hint:* This proof of the Pythagorean Theorem is similar to the one in Exercise 37 on page 540.) **See margin.**

c. 529 B.C.
School of Pythagoras is founded.

Chinese manuscript includes a diagram that can be used to prove the theorem.
c. A.D. 275

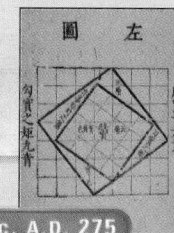

1876
Future U.S. President Garfield discovers a proof of the theorem.

Nicaraguan stamp commemorates the Pythagorean Theorem.
1971

4 ASSESS

DAILY HOMEWORK QUIZ

Transparency Available

Find the value of each variable. Write answers in simplest radical form.

1.
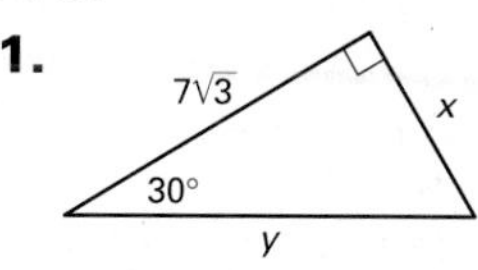

$x = 7$, $y = 14$

Sketch the figure that is described. Find the requested measure. Round decimals to the nearest tenth.
Check students' sketches.

2. The perimeter of a square is 48 meters. Find the length of a diagonal. $12\sqrt{2}$
3. An equilateral triangle has a side length of 10 inches. Find the area of the triangle. **43.3 square inches**

EXTRA CHALLENGE NOTE

Challenge problems for Lesson 9.4 are available in **blackline** format in the *Chapter 9 Resource Book,* p. 65 and at **www.mcdougallittell.com.**

ADDITIONAL TEST PREPARATION

1. **OPEN ENDED** Give an example of each type of special right triangle. ***Sample answer:*** $30°\text{-}60°\text{-}90°$: 10, $10\sqrt{3}$, 20, and $45°\text{-}45°\text{-}90°$: 10, 10, $10\sqrt{2}$

MATH & HISTORY NOTE

A **blackline** master with additional Math & History exercises is available in the *Chapter 9 Resource Book,* p. 64.

1 PLAN

PACING
Basic: 2 days
Average: 2 days
Advanced: 2 days
Block Schedule: 0.5 block with 9.4
0.5 block with 9.6

LESSON OPENER ACTIVITY
An alternative way to approach Lesson 9.5 is to use the Activity Lesson Opener:
- Blackline Master (*Chapter 9 Resource Book*, p. 69)
- Transparency (p. 58)

MEETING INDIVIDUAL NEEDS
- ***Chapter 9 Resource Book***
  Prerequisite Skills Review (p. 5)
  Practice Level A (p. 72)
  Practice Level B (p. 73)
  Practice Level C (p. 74)
  Reteaching with Practice (p. 75)
  Absent Student Catch-Up (p. 77)
  Challenge (p. 80)
- ***Resources in Spanish***
-  ***Personal Student Tutor***

NEW-TEACHER SUPPORT
See the Tips for New Teachers on pp. 1–2 of the *Chapter 9 Resource Book* for additional notes about Lesson 9.5.

WARM-UP EXERCISES
Transparency Available
Solve each equation.
1. $0.875 = \frac{x}{18}$ 15.75
2. $\frac{24}{y} = 0.5$ 48
3. $\frac{y}{25} = 0.96$ 24
4. $0.866x = 12$ 13.9
5. $0.5x = 18$ 36

9.5 Trigonometric Ratios

What you should learn

GOAL 1 Find the sine, the cosine, and the tangent of an acute angle.

GOAL 2 Use trigonometric ratios to solve **real-life** problems, such as estimating the height of a tree in **Example 6**.

Why you should learn it

▼ To solve **real-life** problems, such as in finding the height of a water slide in **Ex. 37**.

CALIFORNIA STANDARDS AND ASSESSMENT
CA Standards: 18, 19
SAT9 Task 1: Objs. 1, 25
SAT9 Task 2: Objs. 1, 35

GOAL 1 FINDING TRIGONOMETRIC RATIOS

A **trigonometric ratio** is a ratio of the lengths of two sides of a right triangle. The word *trigonometry* is derived from the ancient Greek language and means measurement of triangles. The three basic trigonometric ratios are **sine**, **cosine**, and **tangent**, which are abbreviated as *sin*, *cos*, and *tan*, respectively.

TRIGONOMETRIC RATIOS

Let $\triangle ABC$ be a right triangle. The sine, the cosine, and the tangent of the acute angle $\angle A$ are defined as follows.

$$\sin A = \frac{\text{side opposite } \angle A}{\text{hypotenuse}} = \frac{a}{c}$$

$$\cos A = \frac{\text{side adjacent to } \angle A}{\text{hypotenuse}} = \frac{b}{c}$$

$$\tan A = \frac{\text{side opposite } \angle A}{\text{side adjacent to } \angle A} = \frac{a}{b}$$

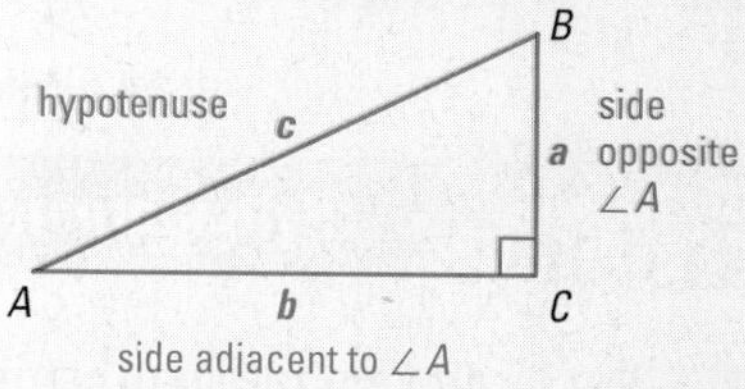

(Figure: right triangle ABC with hypotenuse c, side opposite ∠A labeled a, side adjacent to ∠A labeled b, right angle at C.)

The value of a trigonometric ratio depends only on the measure of the acute angle, not on the particular right triangle that is used to compute the value.

EXAMPLE 1 *Finding Trigonometric Ratios*

Compare the sine, the cosine, and the tangent ratios for $\angle A$ in each triangle below.

SOLUTION

By the SSS Similarity Theorem, the triangles are similar. Their corresponding sides are in proportion, which implies that the trigonometric ratios for $\angle A$ in each triangle are the same.

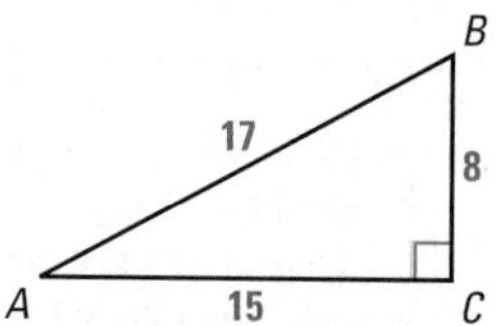

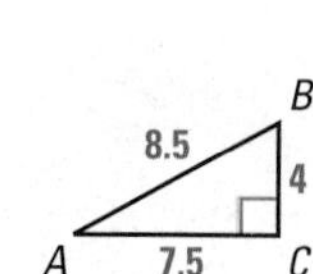

	Large triangle	Small triangle
$\sin A = \frac{\text{opposite}}{\text{hypotenuse}}$	$\frac{8}{17} \approx 0.4706$	$\frac{4}{8.5} \approx 0.4706$
$\cos A = \frac{\text{adjacent}}{\text{hypotenuse}}$	$\frac{15}{17} \approx 0.8824$	$\frac{7.5}{8.5} \approx 0.8824$
$\tan A = \frac{\text{opposite}}{\text{adjacent}}$	$\frac{8}{15} \approx 0.5333$	$\frac{4}{7.5} \approx 0.5333$

Trigonometric ratios are frequently expressed as decimal approximations.

EXAMPLE 2 *Finding Trigonometric Ratios*

STUDENT HELP

HOMEWORK HELP
Visit our Web site www.mcdougallittell.com for extra examples.

Find the sine, the cosine, and the tangent of the indicated angle.

a. $\angle S$ **b.** $\angle R$

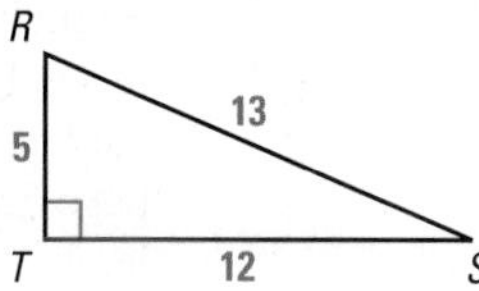

SOLUTION

a. The length of the hypotenuse is 13. For $\angle S$, the length of the opposite side is 5, and the length of the adjacent side is 12.

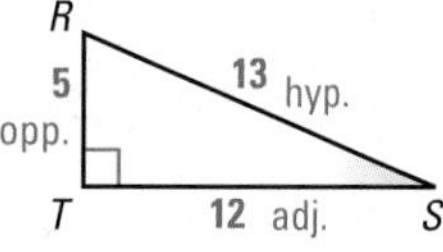

$$\sin S = \frac{\text{opp.}}{\text{hyp.}} = \frac{5}{13} \approx 0.3846$$

$$\cos S = \frac{\text{adj.}}{\text{hyp.}} = \frac{12}{13} \approx 0.9231$$

$$\tan S = \frac{\text{opp.}}{\text{adj.}} = \frac{5}{12} \approx 0.4167$$

b. The length of the hypotenuse is 13. For $\angle R$, the length of the opposite side is 12, and the length of the adjacent side is 5.

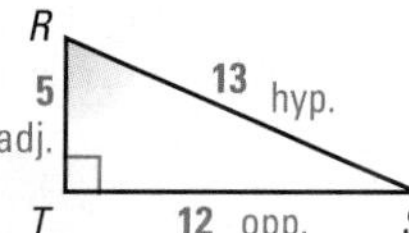

$$\sin R = \frac{\text{opp.}}{\text{hyp.}} = \frac{12}{13} \approx 0.9231$$

$$\cos R = \frac{\text{adj.}}{\text{hyp.}} = \frac{5}{13} \approx 0.3846$$

$$\tan R = \frac{\text{opp.}}{\text{adj.}} = \frac{12}{5} = 2.4$$

....

You can find trigonometric ratios for 30°, 45°, and 60° by applying what you know about special right triangles.

EXAMPLE 3 *Trigonometric Ratios for 45°*

Find the sine, the cosine, and the tangent of 45°.

SOLUTION

Begin by sketching a 45°-45°-90° triangle. Because all such triangles are similar, you can make calculations simple by choosing 1 as the length of each leg. From Theorem 9.8 on page 551, it follows that the length of the hypotenuse is $\sqrt{2}$.

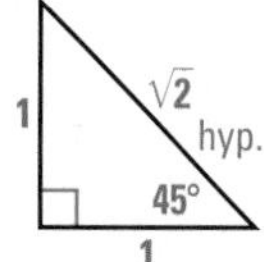

STUDENT HELP

Study Tip
The expression sin 45° means the sine of an angle whose measure is 45°.

$$\sin 45° = \frac{\text{opp.}}{\text{hyp.}} = \frac{1}{\sqrt{2}} = \frac{\sqrt{2}}{2} \approx 0.7071$$

$$\cos 45° = \frac{\text{adj.}}{\text{hyp.}} = \frac{1}{\sqrt{2}} = \frac{\sqrt{2}}{2} \approx 0.7071$$

$$\tan 45° = \frac{\text{opp.}}{\text{adj.}} = \frac{1}{1} = 1$$

Extra Example 3 *Sample answer:*

$\sin A = \frac{1}{\sqrt{2}} \approx 0.7071$; $\cos A = \frac{1}{\sqrt{2}} \approx 0.7071$; $\tan A = 1$

2 TEACH

EXTRA EXAMPLE 1

Compare the sine, the cosine, and the tangent ratios for $\angle A$ in each triangle below.

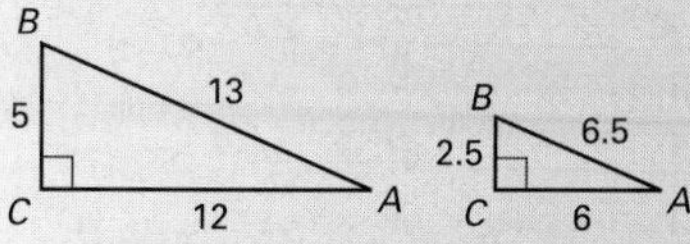

$\sin A \approx 0.3846$; $\cos A \approx 0.9231$; $\tan A \approx 0.4167$; The triangles are similar by SSS, so the trigonometric ratios for $\angle A$ in each triangle are the same.

EXTRA EXAMPLE 2

Find the sine, the cosine, and the tangent of the indicated angle.

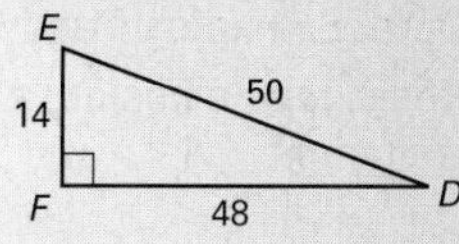

a. $\angle D$ $\sin D = \frac{7}{25} = 0.28$; $\cos D = \frac{24}{25} = 0.96$; $\tan D = \frac{7}{24} \approx 0.2917$

b. $\angle E$ $\sin E = \frac{24}{25} = 0.96$; $\cos E = \frac{7}{25} = 0.28$; $\tan E = \frac{24}{7} \approx 3.4286$

EXTRA EXAMPLE 3

Find the sine, the cosine, and the tangent of $\angle A$.

See below.

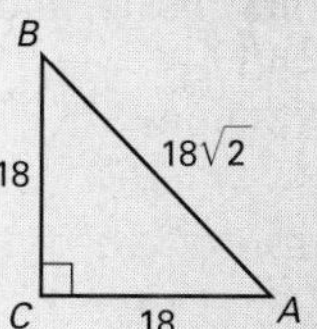

CHECKPOINT EXERCISES

For use after Examples 1–3:

1. Find the sine, the cosine, and the tangent of the angle.

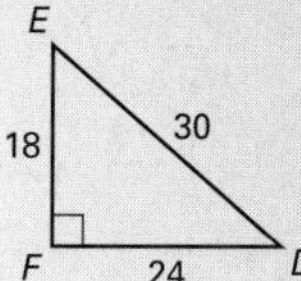

a. $\angle D$ $\sin D = \frac{3}{5} = 0.6$; $\cos D = \frac{4}{5} = 0.8$; $\tan D = \frac{3}{4} = 0.75$

b. $\angle E$ $\sin E = \frac{4}{5} = 0.8$; $\cos E = \frac{3}{5} = 0.6$; $\tan E = \frac{4}{3} \approx 1.3333$

Extra Example 4

Find the sine, the cosine, and the tangent of $\angle A$.

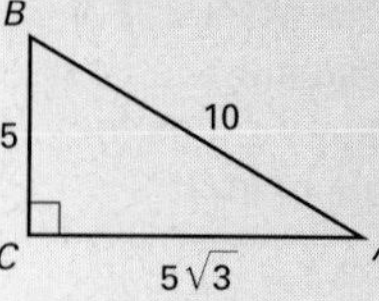

$\sin A = \frac{1}{2} = 0.5$; $\cos A = \frac{\sqrt{3}}{2} \approx 0.8660$; $\tan A = \frac{1}{\sqrt{3}} \approx 0.5774$

Extra Example 5

Use a calculator to approximate the sine, cosine, and tangent of 82°. $\sin 82° \approx 0.9903$; $\cos 82° \approx 0.1392$; $\tan 82° \approx 7.1154$

Checkpoint Exercises

For use after Examples 4 and 5:

1. Find the sine, the cosine, and the tangent of $\angle A$.

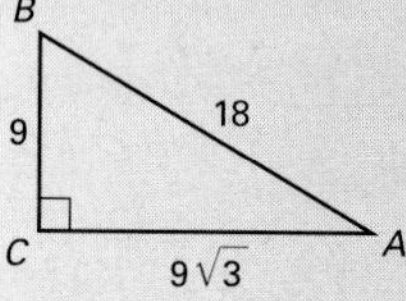

$\sin A = \frac{1}{2} = 0.5$; $\cos A = \frac{\sqrt{3}}{2} \approx 0.8660$; $\tan A = \frac{1}{\sqrt{3}} \approx 0.5774$

2. Use a calculator to approximate the sine, cosine, and tangent of 54°. $\sin 54° \approx 0.8090$; $\cos 54° \approx 0.5878$; $\tan 54° \approx 1.3764$

EXAMPLE 4 Trigonometric Ratios for 30°

Find the sine, the cosine, and the tangent of 30°.

SOLUTION

Begin by sketching a 30°-60°-90° triangle. To make the calculations simple, you can choose 1 as the length of the shorter leg. From Theorem 9.9 on page 551, it follows that the length of the longer leg is $\sqrt{3}$ and the length of the hypotenuse is 2.

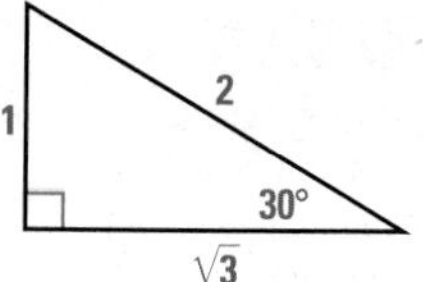

$$\sin 30° = \frac{\text{opp.}}{\text{hyp.}} = \frac{1}{2} = 0.5$$

$$\cos 30° = \frac{\text{adj.}}{\text{hyp.}} = \frac{\sqrt{3}}{2} \approx 0.8660$$

$$\tan 30° = \frac{\text{opp.}}{\text{adj.}} = \frac{1}{\sqrt{3}} = \frac{\sqrt{3}}{3} \approx 0.5774$$

EXAMPLE 5 Using a Calculator

You can use a calculator to approximate the sine, the cosine, and the tangent of 74°. Make sure your calculator is in *degree mode.* The table shows some sample keystroke sequences accepted by most calculators.

Sample keystroke sequences	Sample calculator display	Rounded approximation
74 SIN or SIN 74 ENTER	0.961261695	0.9613
74 COS or COS 74 ENTER	0.275637355	0.2756
74 TAN or TAN 74 ENTER	3.487414444	3.4874

STUDENT HELP

Trig Table
For a table of trigonometric ratios, see p. 845.

If you look back at Examples 1–5, you will notice that the sine or the cosine of an acute angle is always less than 1. The reason is that these trigonometric ratios involve the ratio of a leg of a right triangle to the hypotenuse. The length of a leg of a right triangle is always less than the length of its hypotenuse, so the ratio of these lengths is always less than one.

Because the tangent of an acute angle involves the ratio of one leg to another leg, the tangent of an angle can be less than 1, equal to 1, or greater than 1.

TRIGONOMETRIC IDENTITIES A trigonometric identity is an equation involving trigonometric ratios that is true for all acute angles. You are asked to prove the following identities in Exercises 47 and 52:

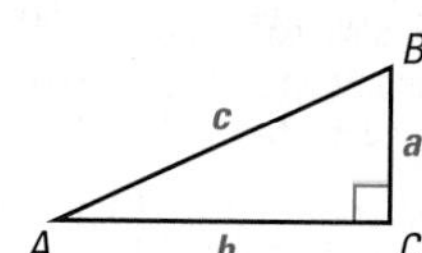

$$(\sin A)^2 + (\cos A)^2 = 1$$

$$\tan A = \frac{\sin A}{\cos A}$$

GOAL 2 USING TRIGONOMETRIC RATIOS IN REAL LIFE

Suppose you stand and look up at a point in the distance, such as the top of the tree in Example 6. The angle that your line of sight makes with a line drawn horizontally is called the **angle of elevation**.

EXAMPLE 6 *Indirect Measurement*

FORESTRY You are measuring the height of a Sitka spruce tree in Alaska. You stand 45 feet from the base of the tree. You measure the angle of elevation from a point on the ground to the top of the tree to be 59°. To estimate the height of the tree, you can write a trigonometric ratio that involves the height h and the known length of 45 feet.

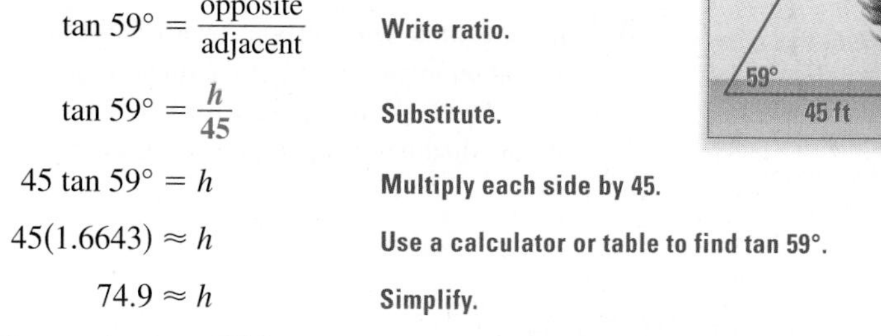

$\tan 59° = \frac{\text{opposite}}{\text{adjacent}}$ — **Write ratio.**

$\tan 59° = \frac{h}{45}$ — **Substitute.**

$45 \tan 59° = h$ — **Multiply each side by 45.**

$45(1.6643) \approx h$ — **Use a calculator or table to find tan 59°.**

$74.9 \approx h$ — **Simplify.**

▶ The tree is about 75 feet tall.

FOCUS ON CAREERS

FORESTRY Foresters manage and protect forests. Their work can involve measuring tree heights. Foresters can use an instrument called a *clinometer* to measure the angle of elevation from a point on the ground to the top of a tree.

CAREER LINK www.mcdougallittell.com

EXAMPLE 7 *Estimating a Distance*

ESCALATORS The escalator at the Wilshire/Vermont Metro Rail Station in Los Angeles rises 76 feet at a 30° angle. To find the distance d a person travels on the escalator stairs, you can write a trigonometric ratio that involves the hypotenuse and the known leg length of 76 feet.

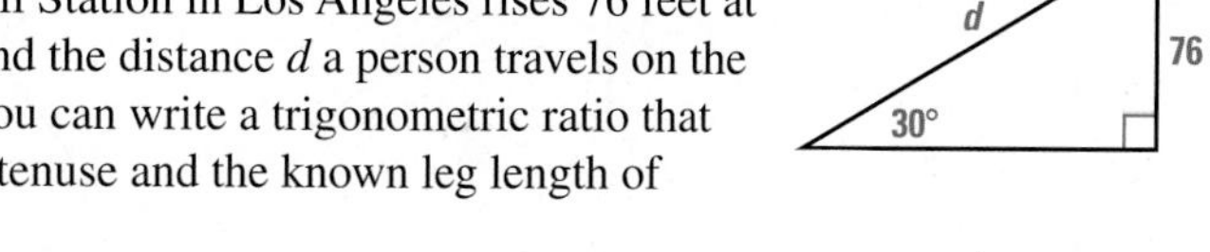

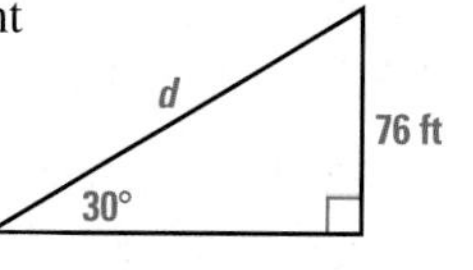

$\sin 30° = \frac{\text{opposite}}{\text{hypotenuse}}$ — **Write ratio for sine of 30°.**

$\sin 30° = \frac{76}{d}$ — **Substitute.**

$d \sin 30° = 76$ — **Multiply each side by d.**

$d = \frac{76}{\sin 30°}$ — **Divide each side by sin 30°.**

$d = \frac{76}{0.5}$ — **Substitute 0.5 for sin 30°.**

$d = 152$ — **Simplify.**

▶ A person travels 152 feet on the escalator stairs.

EXTRA EXAMPLE 6
You are measuring the height of a building. You stand 100 feet from the base of the building. You measure the angle of elevation from a point on the ground to the top of the building to be 48°. Estimate the height of the building. **about 111 ft**

EXTRA EXAMPLE 7
A driveway rises 12 feet over a distance d at an angle of 3.5°. Estimate the length of the driveway. **197 ft**

CHECKPOINT EXERCISES
For use after Examples 6 and 7:
1. You are measuring the height of a tower. You stand 154 feet from the base of the tower. You measure the angle of elevation from a point on the ground to the top of the tower to be 38°. Estimate the height of the tower. **about 120 ft**

FOCUS ON VOCABULARY
Give the definition of the sine, the cosine, and the tangent ratios.
For a right triangle, the sine of an angle is the ratio of the opposite side to the hypotenuse, the cosine is the ratio of the adjacent side to the hypotenuse, and the tangent is the ratio of the opposite side to the adjacent side.

CLOSURE QUESTION
Find the sine, the cosine, and the tangent of $\angle A$.

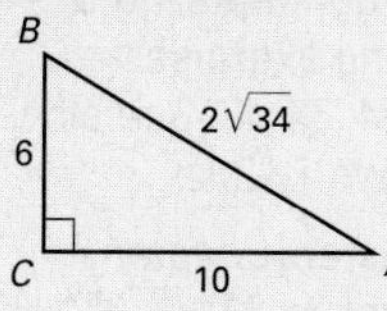

$\sin A = \frac{3}{\sqrt{34}} \approx 0.5145$; $\cos A = \frac{5}{\sqrt{34}} \approx 0.8575$; $\tan A = 0.6$

DAILY PUZZLER
Find tan A and the ratio $\frac{\sin A}{\cos A}$ for any right triangle. What do you notice? **$\tan A = \frac{\sin A}{\cos A}$**

3 APPLY

ASSIGNMENT GUIDE

BASIC

Day 1: pp. 562–565 Exs. 10–38 even

Day 2: pp. 562–566 Exs. 11–39 odd, 47–51, 53, 54, 56–60, Quiz 2 Exs. 1–7

AVERAGE

Day 1: pp. 562–565 Exs. 10–38 even, 40, 42, 46

Day 2: pp. 562–566 Exs. 11–39 odd, 43, 44, 47–51, 53, 54, 56–60, Quiz 2 Exs. 1–7

ADVANCED

Day 1: pp. 562–565 Exs. 10–38 even, 40–42, 46

Day 2: pp. 562–566 Exs. 11–39 odd, 43, 44, 47–60, Quiz 2 Exs. 1–7

BLOCK SCHEDULE

pp. 562–565 Exs. 10–38 even (with 9.4)

pp. 562–566 Exs. 11–39 odd, 43, 44, 47–51, 53, 54, 56–60, Quiz 2 Exs. 1–7 (with 9.6)

EXERCISE LEVELS

Level A: *Easier*
10–27

Level B: *More Difficult*
28–54

Level C: *Most Difficult*
55

✔ HOMEWORK CHECK

To quickly check student understanding of key concepts, go over the following exercises: Exs. 12, 24, 30, 34, 38, 48. See also the Daily Homework Quiz:

- Blackline Master (*Chapter 9 Resource Book*, p. 84)
- Transparency (p. 68)

GUIDED PRACTICE

Vocabulary Check ✔

Concept Check ✔

Skill Check ✔

In Exercises 1 and 2, use the diagram at the right.

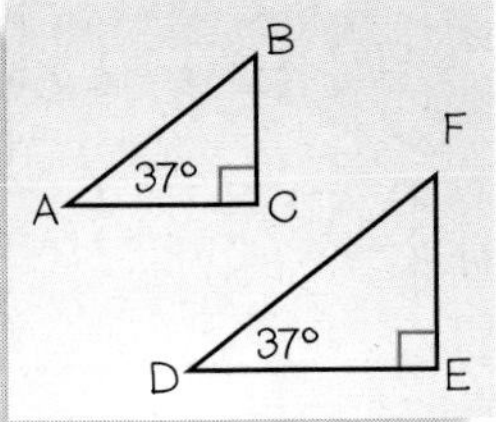

1. Use the diagram to explain what is meant by the *sine*, the *cosine*, and the *tangent* of $\angle A$. See margin.

2. ERROR ANALYSIS A student says that $\sin D > \sin A$ because the side lengths of $\triangle DEF$ are greater than the side lengths of $\triangle ABC$. Explain why the student is incorrect. See margin.

In Exercises 3–8, use the diagram shown at the right to find the trigonometric ratio.

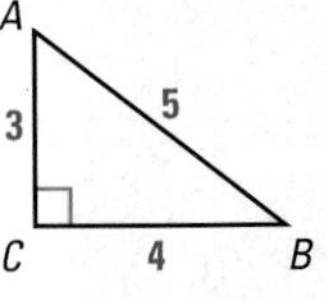

3. $\sin A$ $\frac{4}{5} = 0.8$ **4.** $\cos A$ $\frac{3}{5} = 0.6$

5. $\tan A$ $\frac{4}{3} \approx 1.3333$ **6.** $\sin B$ $\frac{3}{5} = 0.6$

7. $\cos B$ $\frac{4}{5} = 0.8$ **8.** $\tan B$ $\frac{3}{4} = 0.75$

9. ESCALATORS One early escalator built in 1896 rose at an angle of 25°. As shown in the diagram at the right, the vertical lift was 7 feet. Estimate the distance d a person traveled on this escalator. about 17 ft

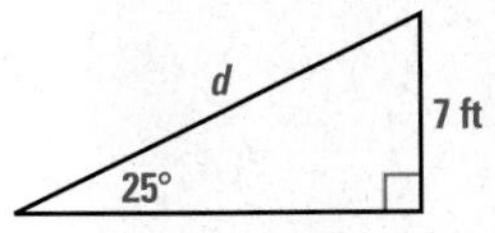

1. The sine of $\angle A$ is the ratio of the length of the leg opposite $\angle A$ to the length of the hypotenuse. The cosine of $\angle A$ is the ratio of the length of the leg adjacent to $\angle A$ to the hypotenuse. The tangent of $\angle A$ is the ratio of the length of the leg opposite $\angle A$ to the length of the leg adjacent to $\angle A$.

PRACTICE AND APPLICATIONS

STUDENT HELP

Extra Practice to help you master skills is on p. 820.

10. $\sin R \approx 0.8491$; $\cos R \approx 0.5283$; $\tan R \approx 1.6071$; $\sin S \approx 0.5283$; $\cos S \approx 0.8491$; $\tan S \approx 0.6222$

11. $\sin A = 0.8$; $\cos A = 0.6$; $\tan A \approx 1.3333$; $\sin B = 0.6$; $\cos B = 0.8$; $\tan B = 0.75$

STUDENT HELP

HOMEWORK HELP

Example 1: Exs. 10–15, 28–36
Example 2: Exs. 10–15, 28–36
Example 3: Exs. 34–36
Example 4: Exs. 34–36
Example 5: Exs. 16–27
Example 6: Exs. 37–42
Example 7: Exs. 37–42

FINDING TRIGONOMETRIC RATIOS Find the sine, the cosine, and the tangent of the acute angles of the triangle. Express each value as a decimal rounded to four places.

10.

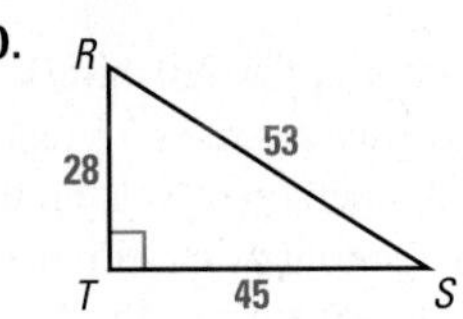

11.

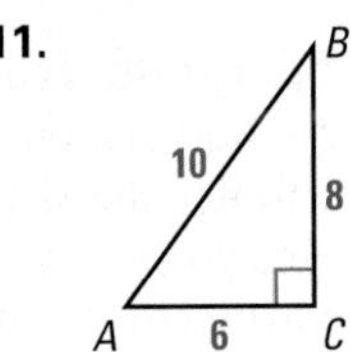

12.

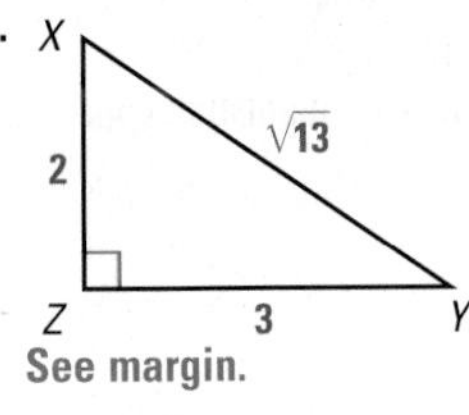

See margin.

13.

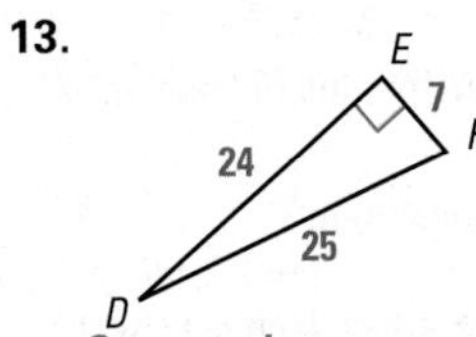

See margin.

14.

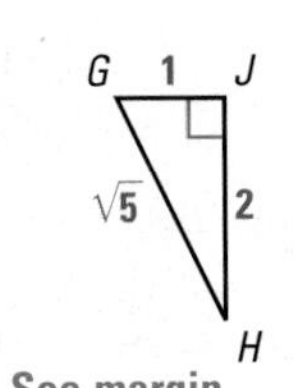

See margin.

15.

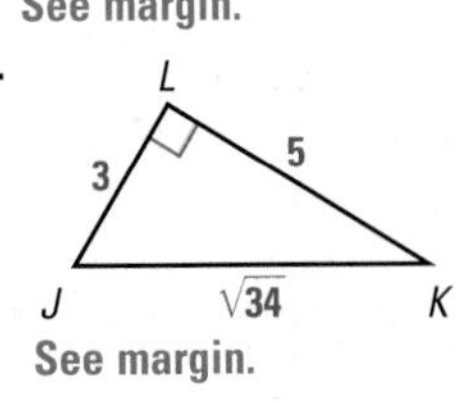

See margin.

CALCULATOR Use a calculator to approximate the given value to four decimal places.

16. sin 48° 0.7431 **17.** cos 13° 0.9744 **18.** tan 81° 6.3138 **19.** sin 27° 0.4540

20. cos 70° 0.3420 **21.** tan 2° 0.0349 **22.** sin 78° 0.9781 **23.** cos 36° 0.8090

24. tan 23° 0.4245 **25.** cos 63° 0.4540 **26.** sin 56° 0.8290 **27.** tan 66° 2.2460

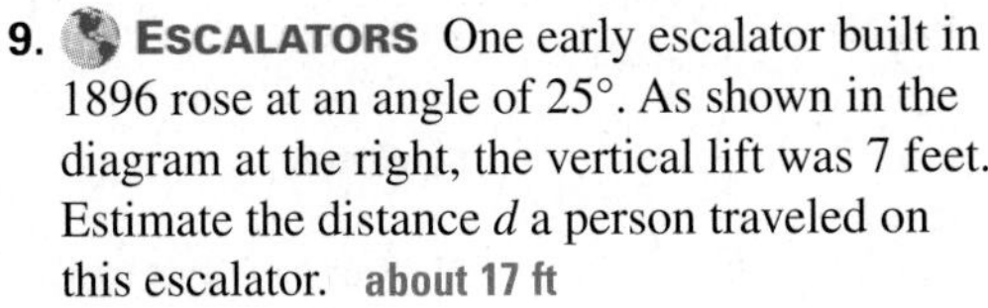

USING TRIGONOMETRIC RATIOS Find the value of each variable. Round decimals to the nearest tenth.

28.

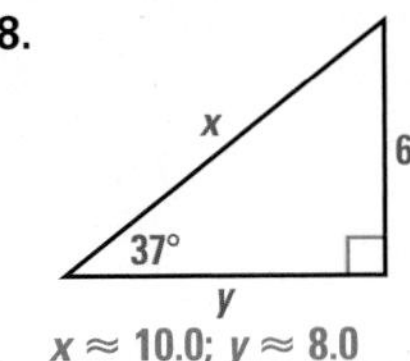

$x \approx 10.0$; $y \approx 8.0$

29.

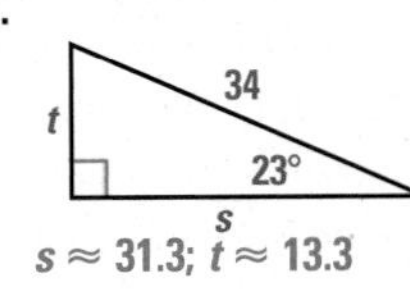

$s \approx 31.3$; $t \approx 13.3$

30.

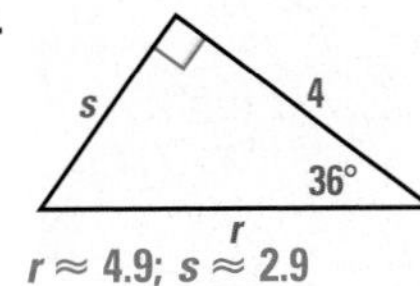

$r \approx 4.9$; $s \approx 2.9$

31.

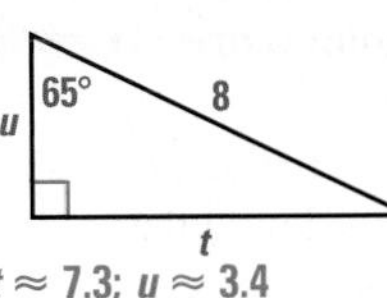

$t \approx 7.3$; $u \approx 3.4$

32.

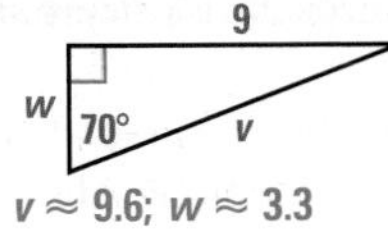

$v \approx 9.6$; $w \approx 3.3$

33.

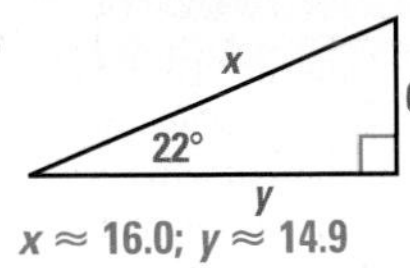

$x \approx 16.0$; $y \approx 14.9$

FINDING AREA Find the area of the triangle. Round decimals to the nearest tenth.

34. 4 cm^2

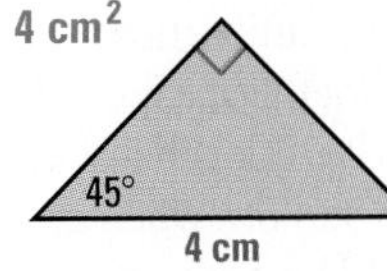

35. 41.6 m^2

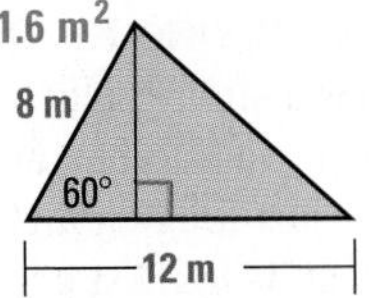

36. 34.9 m^2

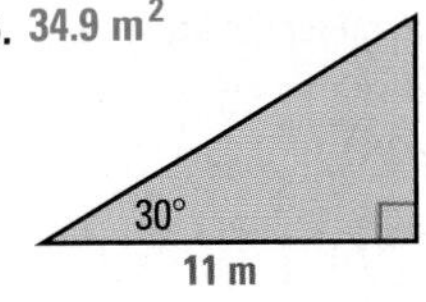

FOCUS ON APPLICATIONS

WATER SLIDE Even though riders on a water slide may travel at only 20 miles per hour, the curves on the slide can make riders feel as though they are traveling much faster.

37. **WATER SLIDE** The angle of elevation from the base to the top of a waterslide is about 13°. The slide extends horizontally about 58.2 meters. Estimate the height h of the slide. about 13.4 m

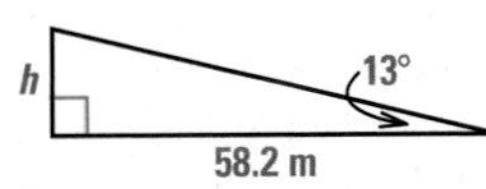

38. **SURVEYING** To find the distance d from a house on shore to a house on an island, a surveyor measures from the house on shore to point B, as shown in the diagram. An instrument called a *transit* is used to find the measure of $\angle B$. Estimate the distance d. about 36 m

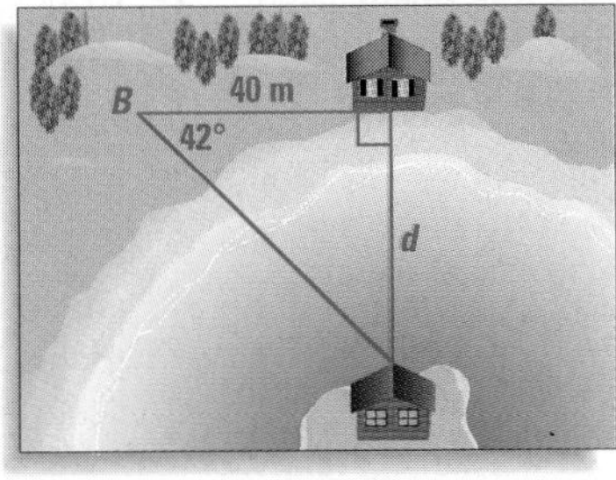

39. **SKI SLOPE** Suppose you stand at the top of a ski slope and look down at the bottom. The angle that your line of sight makes with a line drawn horizontally is called the *angle of depression*, as shown below. The *vertical drop* is the difference in the elevations of the top and the bottom of the slope. Find the vertical drop x of the slope in the diagram. Then estimate the distance d a person skiing would travel on this slope. 482 ft; about 1409 ft

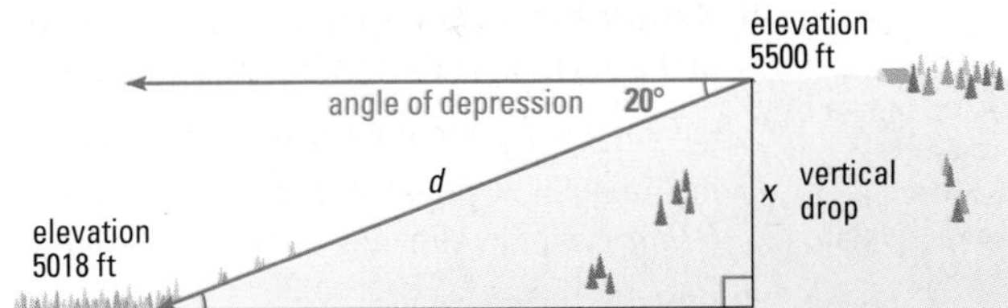

APPLICATION NOTE

EXERCISE 38 Trigonometry is applied extensively in surveying applications. For example, the Great Trigonometric Survey of India was done in the 19th century to map out the country and to measure the height of Mount Everest, the tallest mountain in the world. In 1852, the survey measured Mount Everest to be 29,002 feet, which is very close to the height of 29,035 feet measured in 1999.

2. The value of a trigonometric ratio depends only on the measure of the acute angle, not on the particular right triangle used to compute the value.
12. $\sin X \approx 0.8321$; $\cos X \approx 0.5547$; $\tan X = 1.5$; $\sin Y \approx 0.5547$; $\cos Y \approx 0.8321$; $\tan Y \approx 0.6667$
13. $\sin D = 0.28$; $\cos D = 0.96$; $\tan D \approx 0.2917$; $\sin F = 0.96$; $\cos F = 0.28$; $\tan F \approx 3.4286$
14. $\sin G \approx 0.8944$; $\cos G \approx 0.4472$; $\tan G = 2$; $\sin H \approx 0.4472$; $\cos H \approx 0.8944$; $\tan H = 0.5$
15. $\sin J \approx 0.8575$; $\cos J \approx 0.5145$; $\tan J \approx 1.6667$; $\sin K \approx 0.5145$; $\cos K \approx 0.8575$; $\tan K = 0.6$

! COMMON ERROR

EXERCISE 40 Students may have difficulty applying the correct ratio when solving this problem. Remind them that the sine or cosine ratios cannot be used unless the hypotenuse of the triangle is known.

EXERCISE 46 Students may want to apply the right triangle ratios to any triangle or to the right angle of the triangle. Remind students to check that a triangle is right before using the ratios and that the ratios apply only to the acute angles.

46. $m\angle B = 95°$, so $\triangle ABC$ is not a right triangle, as required by the definition of the tangent ratio. To find BC, draw an altitude, $\overline{BD}$, from B to $\overline{AC}$. $\triangle ABD$ is a 30°-60°-90° triangle with hypotenuse 18, so the shorter leg, $\overline{BD}$, has length 9. Then use right $\triangle BCD$ and the equation $\sin 55° = \frac{BD}{BC}$ to find BC.

52. Given: $\sin A = \frac{a}{c}$, $\cos A = \frac{b}{c}$, $\tan A = \frac{a}{b}$

Prove: $\tan A = \frac{\sin A}{\cos A}$

Statements (Reasons)

1. $\sin A = \frac{a}{c}$, $\cos A = \frac{b}{c}$, $\tan A = \frac{a}{b}$ (Given)
2. $\frac{\sin A}{\cos A} = \frac{a}{c} \div \frac{b}{c}$ (Substitution prop. of equality)
3. $\frac{a}{c} \div \frac{b}{c} = \frac{a}{b}$ (Dividing and simplifying fractions)
4. $\tan A = \frac{\sin A}{\cos A}$ (Substitution prop. of equality)

FOCUS ON APPLICATIONS

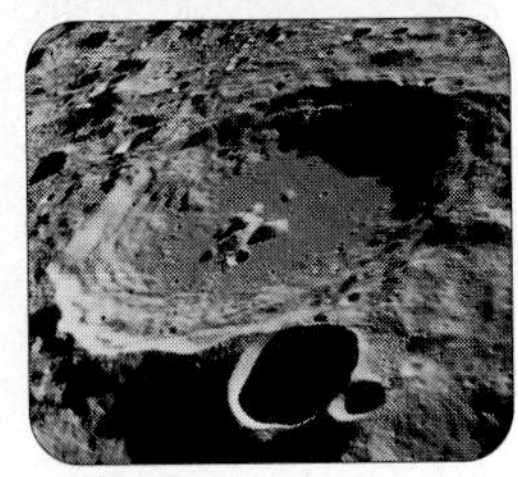

LUNAR CRATERS Because the moon has no atmosphere to protect it from being hit by meteorites, its surface is pitted with craters. There is no wind, so a crater can remain undisturbed for millions of years—unless another meteorite crashes into it.

43. $\sin A = \frac{a}{c}$; $\cos A = \frac{b}{c}$; $\tan A = \frac{a}{b}$; $\sin B = \frac{b}{c}$; $\cos B = \frac{a}{c}$; $\tan B = \frac{b}{a}$

44. The tangent of one acute angle of a right triangle is the reciprocal of the tangent of the other acute angle. The sine of one acute angle of a right triangle is equal to the cosine of the other acute angle, and the cosine of one acute angle is equal to the sine of the other acute angle.

45. Procedures may vary. One method is to reason that since the tangent ratio is equal to the ratio of the lengths of the legs, the tangent is equal to 1 when the legs are equal in length, that is, when the triangle is a 45°–45°–90° triangle. Tan $A > 1$ when $m\angle A > 45°$, and $\tan A < 1$ when $m\angle A < 45°$, since increasing the measure of $\angle A$ increases the length of the opposite leg and decreasing the measure of $\angle A$ decreases the length of the opposite leg.

40. SCIENCE CONNECTION Scientists can measure the depths of craters on the moon by looking at photos of shadows. The length of the shadow cast by the edge of a crater is about 500 meters. The sun's angle of elevation is 55°. Estimate the depth d of the crater. **about 714 m**

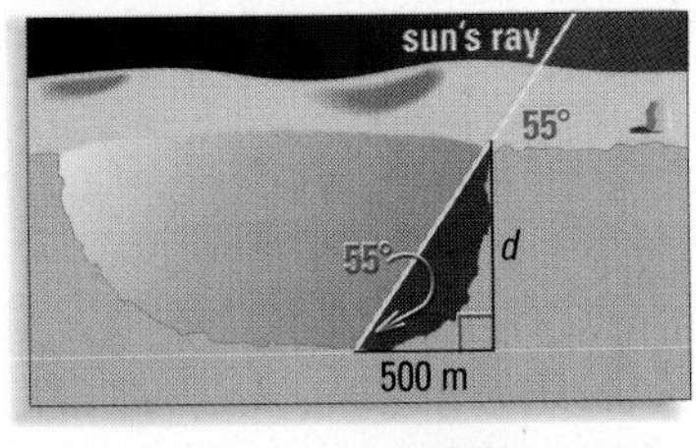

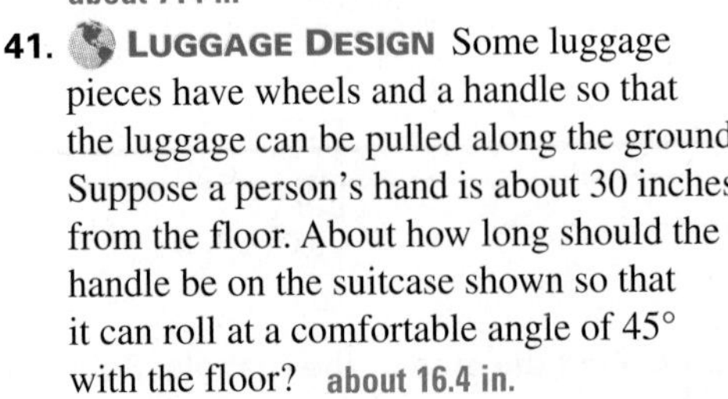

41. **LUGGAGE DESIGN** Some luggage pieces have wheels and a handle so that the luggage can be pulled along the ground. Suppose a person's hand is about 30 inches from the floor. About how long should the handle be on the suitcase shown so that it can roll at a comfortable angle of 45° with the floor? **about 16.4 in.**

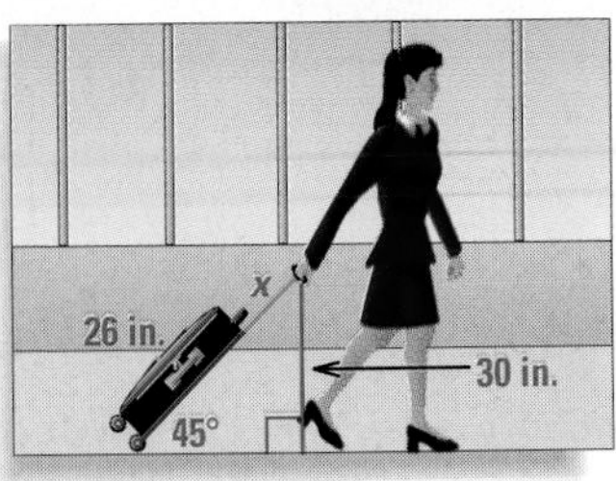

42. **BUYING AN AWNING** Your family room has a sliding-glass door with a southern exposure. You want to buy an awning for the door that will be just long enough to keep the sun out when it is at its highest point in the sky. The angle of elevation of the sun at this point is 70°, and the height of the door is 8 feet. About how far should the overhang extend? **about 2.9 ft**

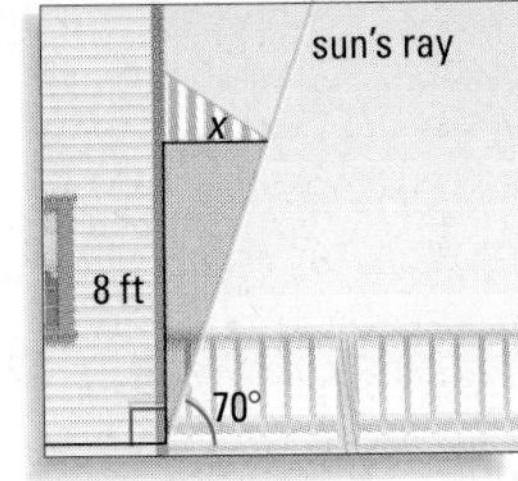

CRITICAL THINKING In Exercises 43 and 44, use the diagram.

43. Write expressions for the sine, the cosine, and the tangent of each acute angle in the triangle.

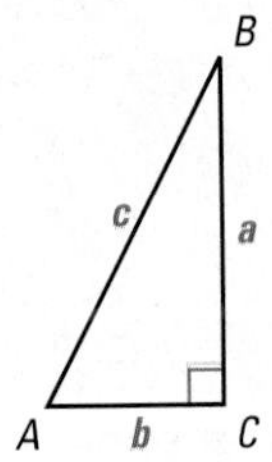

44. *Writing* Use your results from Exercise 43 to explain how the tangent of one acute angle of a right triangle is related to the tangent of the other acute angle. How are the sine and the cosine of one acute angle of a right triangle related to the sine and the cosine of the other acute angle?

45. **TECHNOLOGY** Use geometry software to construct a right triangle. Use your triangle to explore and answer the questions below. Explain your procedure.

- For what angle measure is the tangent of an acute angle equal to 1?
- For what angle measures is the tangent of an acute angle greater than 1?
- For what angle measures is the tangent of an acute angle less than 1?

46. **ERROR ANALYSIS** To find the length of $\overline{BC}$ in the diagram at the right, a student writes $\tan 55° = \frac{18}{BC}$. What mistake is the student making? Show how the student can find BC. (*Hint:* Begin by drawing an altitude from B to $\overline{AC}$.) **See margin.**

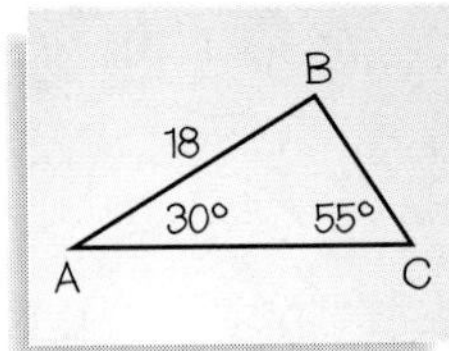

47. **PROOF** Use the diagram of $\triangle ABC$. Complete the proof of the trigonometric identity below.

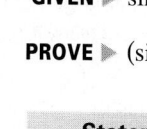

$$(\sin A)^2 + (\cos A)^2 = 1$$

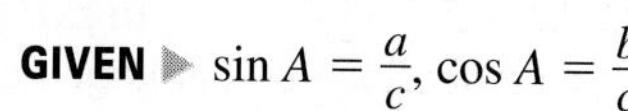

GIVEN ▶ $\sin A = \frac{a}{c}$, $\cos A = \frac{b}{c}$

PROVE ▶ $(\sin A)^2 + (\cos A)^2 = 1$

Statements	Reasons
1. $\sin A = \frac{a}{c}$, $\cos A = \frac{b}{c}$	1. ___?___ Given
2. $a^2 + b^2 = c^2$	2. ___?___ Pythagorean Thm.
3. $\frac{a^2}{c^2} + \frac{b^2}{c^2} = 1$	3. ___?___ Division prop. of equality
4. $\left(\frac{a}{c}\right)^2 + \left(\frac{b}{c}\right)^2 = 1$	4. A property of exponents
5. $(\sin A)^2 + (\cos A)^2 = 1$	5. ___?___ Substitution prop. of equality

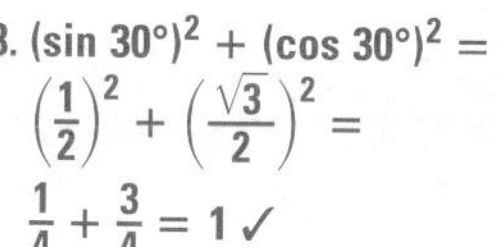

48. $(\sin 30°)^2 + (\cos 30°)^2 = \left(\frac{1}{2}\right)^2 + \left(\frac{\sqrt{3}}{2}\right)^2 = \frac{1}{4} + \frac{3}{4} = 1$ ✓

49. $(\sin 45°)^2 + (\cos 45°)^2 = \left(\frac{\sqrt{2}}{2}\right)^2 + \left(\frac{\sqrt{2}}{2}\right)^2 = \frac{2}{4} + \frac{2}{4} = 1$ ✓

50. $(\sin 60°)^2 + (\cos 60°)^2 = \left(\frac{\sqrt{3}}{2}\right)^2 + \left(\frac{1}{2}\right)^2 = \frac{3}{4} + \frac{1}{4} = 1$ ✓

51. $(\sin 13°)^2 + (\cos 13°)^2 \approx (0.2250)^2 + (0.9744)^2 \approx 1$ ✓

DEMONSTRATING A FORMULA Show that $(\sin A)^2 + (\cos A)^2 = 1$ for the given angle measure.

48. $m\angle A = 30°$ 49. $m\angle A = 45°$ 50. $m\angle A = 60°$ 51. $m\angle A = 13°$

52. **PROOF** Use the diagram in Exercise 47. Write a two-column proof of the following trigonometric identity: $\tan A = \frac{\sin A}{\cos A}$. See margin.

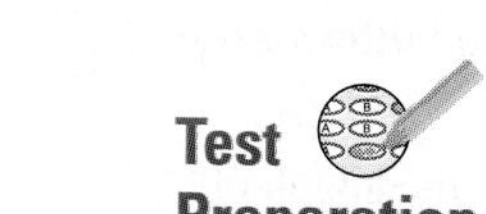

Test Preparation

53. **MULTIPLE CHOICE** Use the diagram at the right. Find CD. D

Ⓐ $8 \cos 25°$ Ⓑ $8 \sin 25°$ Ⓒ $8 \tan 25°$ Ⓓ $\frac{8}{\sin 25°}$ Ⓔ $\frac{8}{\cos 25°}$

54. **MULTIPLE CHOICE** Use the diagram at the right. Which expression is *not* equivalent to AC? C

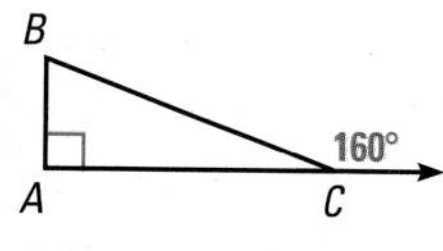

Ⓐ $BC \sin 70°$ Ⓑ $BC \cos 20°$ Ⓒ $\frac{BC}{\tan 20°}$ Ⓓ $\frac{BA}{\tan 20°}$ Ⓔ $BA \tan 70°$

★ Challenge

55. **PARADE** You are at a parade looking up at a large balloon floating directly above the street. You are 60 feet from a point on the street directly beneath the balloon. To see the top of the balloon, you look up at an angle of 53°. To see the bottom of the balloon, you look up at an angle of 29°.

Estimate the height h of the balloon to the nearest foot. 46 ft

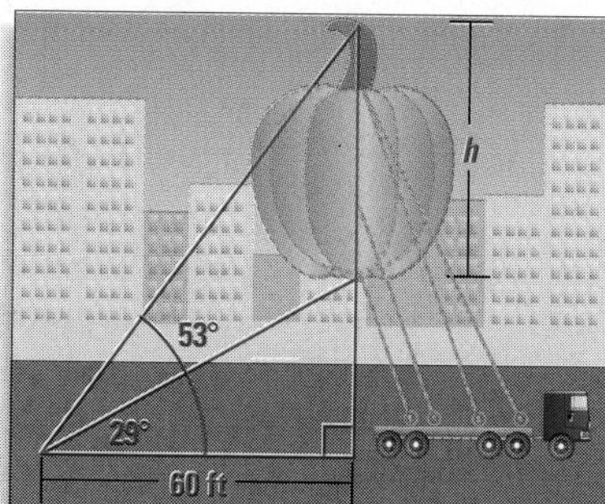

EXTRA CHALLENGE
www.mcdougallittell.com

56.

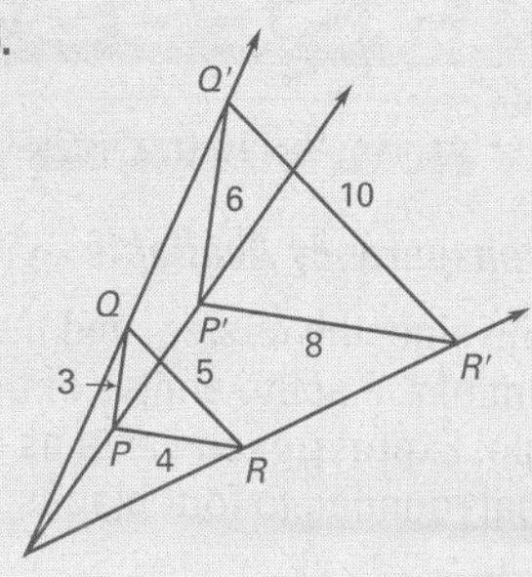

ADDITIONAL PRACTICE AND RETEACHING

For Lesson 9.5:

- Practice Levels A, B, and C (*Chapter 9 Resource Book*, p. 72)
- Reteaching with Practice (*Chapter 9 Resource Book*, p. 75)
- See Lesson 9.5 of the *Personal Student Tutor*

For more Mixed Review:

- Search the *Test and Practice Generator* for key words or specific lessons.

4 ASSESS

DAILY HOMEWORK QUIZ

Transparency Available

Find the sine, the cosine, and the tangent of the acute angles of the triangle. Express each value as a decimal rounded to four places.

1.

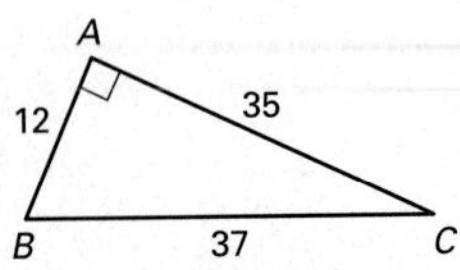

sin $B \approx 0.9459$, cos $B \approx 0.3243$, tan $B \approx 2.9167$, sin $C \approx 0.3243$, cos $C \approx 0.9459$, tan $C \approx 0.3429$

Use the diagram. Round decimals to the nearest tenth.

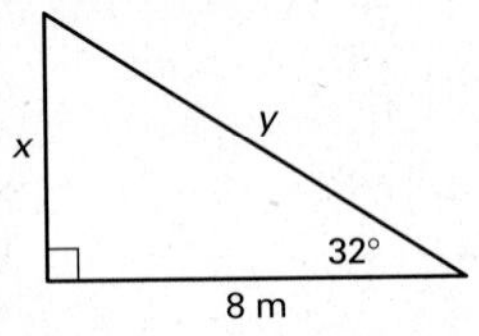

2. Find the value of each variable. $x \approx 5$ m, $y \approx 9.4$ m

3. Find the area of the triangle. 20 m^2

EXTRA CHALLENGE NOTE

Challenge problems for Lesson 9.5 are available in **blackline** format in the *Chapter 9 Resource Book,* p. 80 and at **www.mcdougallittell.com.**

ADDITIONAL TEST PREPARATION

1. WRITING Describe how to find the height of a tree if you know the angle of elevation and your distance from the tree. Find the tangent of the angle of elevation and multiply it by your distance from the tree.

ADDITIONAL RESOURCES

An alternative Quiz for Lessons 9.4–9.5 is available in the *Chapter 9 Resource Book,* p. 81.

MIXED REVIEW

56. An enlargement; 2; $Q'R' = 10$ and $P'R' = 8$

56. SKETCHING A DILATION $\triangle PQR$ is mapped onto $\triangle P'Q'R'$ by a dilation. In $\triangle PQR$, $PQ = 3$, $QR = 5$, and $PR = 4$. In $\triangle P'Q'R'$, $P'Q' = 6$. Sketch the dilation, identify it as a reduction or an enlargement, and find the scale factor. Then find the length of $Q'R'$ and $P'R'$. **(Review 8.7)**

57. FINDING LENGTHS Write similarity statements for the three similar triangles in the diagram. Then find QP and NP. Round decimals to the nearest tenth. **(Review 9.1)** $\triangle MNP \sim \triangle MQN \sim \triangle NQP$; $QP \approx 3.3$; $NP \approx 7.8$

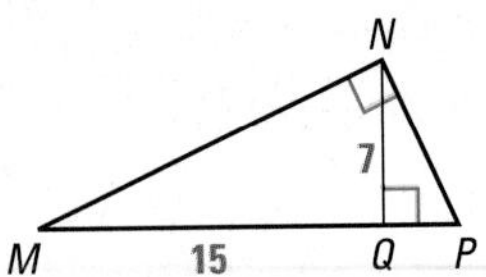

PYTHAGOREAN THEOREM Find the unknown side length. Simplify answers that are radicals. Tell whether the side lengths form a Pythagorean triple. **(Review 9.2 for 9.6)**

58.

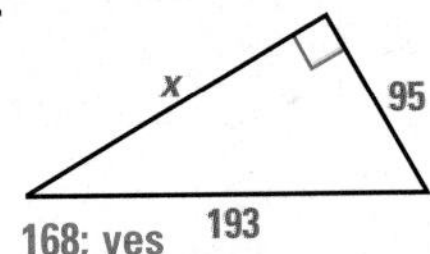

168; yes

59.

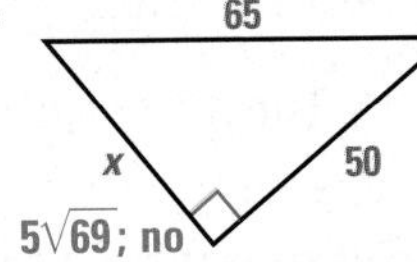

$5\sqrt{69}$; no

60.

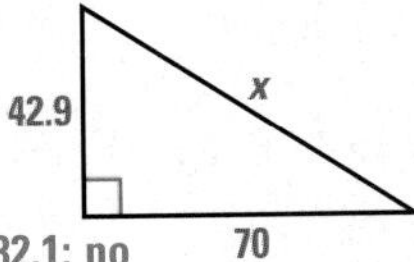

82.1; no

QUIZ 2

Self-Test for Lessons 9.4 and 9.5

Sketch the figure that is described. Then find the requested information. Round decimals to the nearest tenth. **(Lesson 9.4)**

1. The side length of an equilateral triangle is 4 meters. Find the length of an altitude of the triangle. 3.5 m
2. The perimeter of a square is 16 inches. Find the length of a diagonal. 5.7 in.
3. The side length of an equilateral triangle is 3 inches. Find the area of the triangle. 3.9 $in.^2$

Find the value of each variable. Round decimals to the nearest tenth. **(Lesson 9.5)**

4.

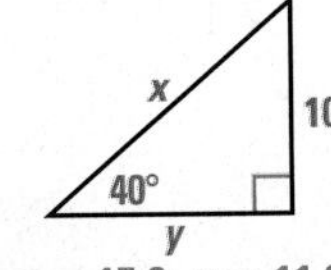

$x \approx 15.6$; $y \approx 11.9$

5.

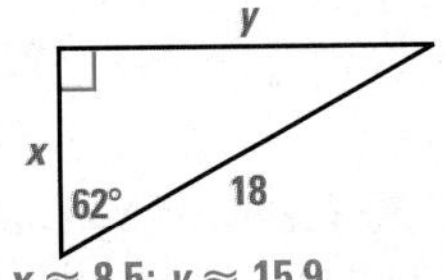

$x \approx 8.5$; $y \approx 15.9$

6.

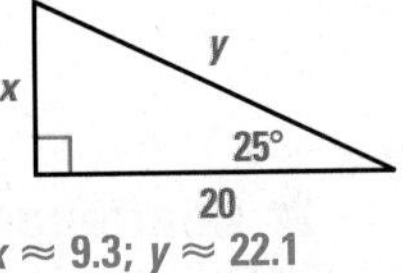

$x \approx 9.3$; $y \approx 22.1$

7. HOT-AIR BALLOON The ground crew for a hot-air balloon can see the balloon in the sky at an angle of elevation of 11°. The pilot radios to the crew that the hot-air balloon is 950 feet above the ground. Estimate the horizontal distance d of the hot-air balloon from the ground crew. **(Lesson 9.5)** about 4887 ft

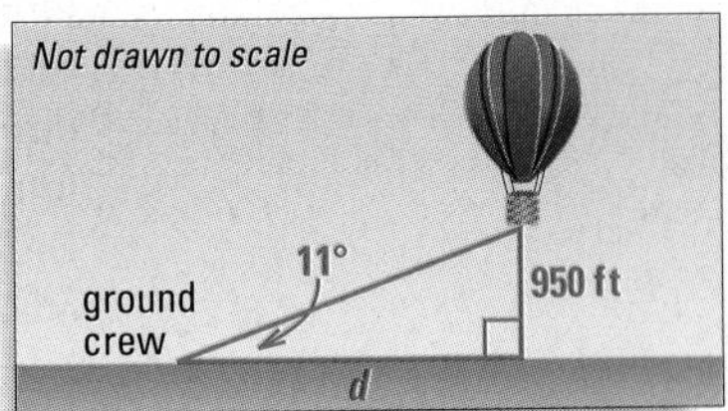

9.6 Solving Right Triangles

What you should learn

GOAL 1 Solve a right triangle.

GOAL 2 Use right triangles to solve **real-life** problems, such as finding the glide angle and altitude of a space shuttle in **Example 3**.

Why you should learn it

▼ To solve **real-life** problems such as determining the correct dimensions of a wheel-chair ramp in **Exs. 39–41**.

GOAL 1 SOLVING A RIGHT TRIANGLE

Every right triangle has one right angle, two acute angles, one hypotenuse, and two legs. To **solve a right triangle** means to determine the measures of all six parts. You can solve a right triangle if you know either of the following:

- Two side lengths
- One side length and one acute angle measure

As you learned in Lesson 9.5, you can use the side lengths of a right triangle to find trigonometric ratios for the acute angles of the triangle. As you will see in this lesson, once you know the sine, the cosine, or the tangent of an acute angle, you can use a calculator to find the measure of the angle.

In general, for an acute angle A:

if $\sin A = x$, then $\sin^{-1} x = m\angle A$. ⟵ **The expression $\sin^{-1} x$ is read as "the inverse sine of x."**

if $\cos A = y$, then $\cos^{-1} y = m\angle A$.

if $\tan A = z$, then $\tan^{-1} z = m\angle A$.

ACTIVITY — Developing Concepts: Finding Angles in Right Triangles

1. Carefully draw right $\triangle ABC$ with side lengths of 3 centimeters, 4 centimeters, and 5 centimeters, as shown. **Check sketches.**

2. Use trigonometric ratios to find the sine, the cosine, and the tangent of $\angle A$. Express the ratios in decimal form. **$\sin A = 0.6$; $\cos A = 0.8$; $\tan A = 0.75$**

3. In Step 2, you found that $\sin A = \frac{3}{5} = 0.6$. You can use a calculator to find $\sin^{-1} 0.6$. Most calculators use one of the keystroke sequences below. **Each trigonometric ratio gives $m\angle A \approx 36.9°$.**

Make sure your calculator is in degree mode. Then use each of the trigonometric ratios you found in Step 2 to approximate the measure of $\angle A$ to the nearest tenth of a degree.

4. Use a protractor to measure $\angle A$. How does the measured value compare with your calculated values? **The values are approximately equal.**

CALIFORNIA STANDARDS AND ASSESSMENT

CA Standards: 19
SAT9 Task 1: Objs. 1, 32
SAT9 Task 2: Objs. 1, 25, 36

1 PLAN

PACING
Basic: 1 day
Average: 1 day
Advanced: 1 day
Block Schedule: 0.5 block with 9.5

LESSON OPENER — APPLICATION

An alternative way to approach Lesson 9.6 is to use the Application Lesson Opener:

- Blackline Master (*Chapter 9 Resource Book*, p. 85)
- Transparency (p. 59)

MEETING INDIVIDUAL NEEDS

- ***Chapter 9 Resource Book***
  Prerequisite Skills Review (p. 5)
  Practice Level A (p. 88)
  Practice Level B (p. 89)
  Practice Level C (p. 90)
  Reteaching with Practice (p. 91)
  Absent Student Catch-Up (p. 93)
  Challenge (p. 95)
- ***Resources in Spanish***
- ***Personal Student Tutor***

NEW-TEACHER SUPPORT

See the Tips for New Teachers on pp. 1–2 of the *Chapter 9 Resource Book* for additional notes about Lesson 9.6.

WARM-UP EXERCISES

Transparency Available

Find each indicated ratio. Express the answer to the nearest ten-thousandth.

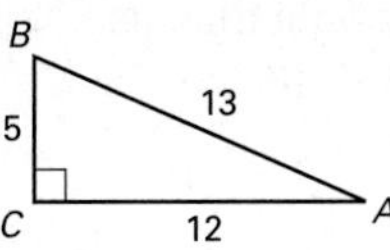

1. $\sin A$ ≈ 0.3846
2. $\cos A$ ≈ 0.9231
3. $\tan A$ ≈ 0.4167
4. $\sin B$ ≈ 0.9231
5. $\cos B$ ≈ 0.3846
6. $\tan B$ = 2.4

2 TEACH

MOTIVATING THE LESSON

Have students think of ramps that are steeper than others. Ask students how they could apply what they know about right triangles to describe the steepness of a ramp. *Sample answer:* the slope could be modeled by the angle between the hypotenuse and base of a right triangle.

ACTIVITY NOTE

The protractor measurement should be very close to the calculated measurement. However, these values may differ slightly because accuracy in tenths of a degree is difficult with a hand-drawn sketch.

EXTRA EXAMPLE 1

Solve the right triangle. Round decimals to the nearest tenth.

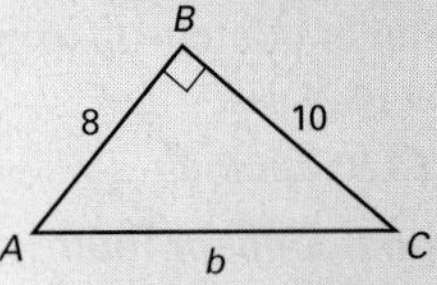

$b = 12.8$; $m\angle A = 51.3°$; $m\angle C = 38.7°$

EXTRA EXAMPLE 2

Solve the right triangle. Round decimals to the nearest tenth.

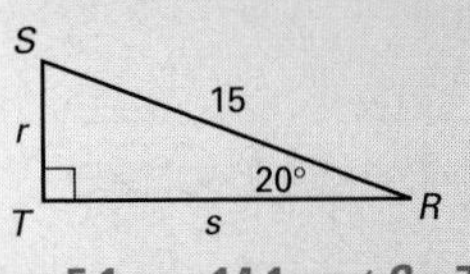

$r \approx 5.1$; $s \approx 14.1$; $m\angle S = 70°$

CHECKPOINT EXERCISES

For use after Examples 1 and 2:

1. Solve the right triangle. Round decimals to the nearest tenth.

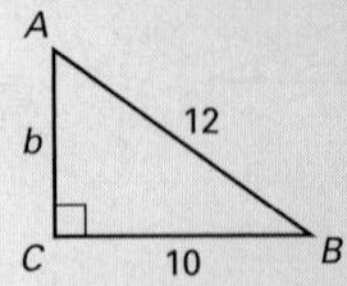

$b = 6.6$; $m\angle A = 56.4°$; $m\angle B = 33.6°$

EXAMPLE 1 *Solving a Right Triangle*

Solve the right triangle. Round decimals to the nearest tenth.

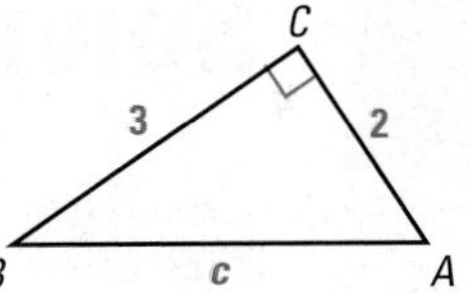

SOLUTION

Begin by using the Pythagorean Theorem to find the length of the hypotenuse.

$(\text{hypotenuse})^2 = (\text{leg})^2 + (\text{leg})^2$ **Pythagorean Theorem**

$c^2 = 3^2 + 2^2$ **Substitute.**

$c^2 = 13$ **Simplify.**

$c = \sqrt{13}$ **Find the positive square root.**

$c \approx 3.6$ **Use a calculator to approximate.**

Then use a calculator to find the measure of $\angle B$:

$\approx 33.7°$

Finally, because $\angle A$ and $\angle B$ are complements, you can write

$m\angle A = 90° - m\angle B \approx 90° - 33.7° = 56.3°.$

▶ The side lengths of the triangle are 2, 3, and $\sqrt{13}$, or about 3.6. The triangle has one right angle and two acute angles whose measures are about 33.7° and 56.3°.

EXAMPLE 2 *Solving a Right Triangle*

Solve the right triangle. Round decimals to the nearest tenth.

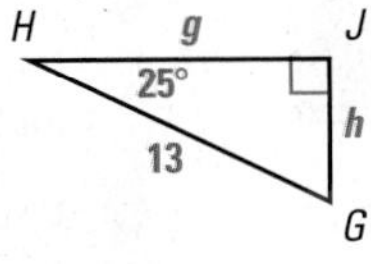

SOLUTION

Use trigonometric ratios to find the values of g and h.

$\sin H = \frac{\text{opp.}}{\text{hyp.}}$	$\cos H = \frac{\text{adj.}}{\text{hyp.}}$
$\sin 25° = \frac{h}{13}$	$\cos 25° = \frac{g}{13}$
$13 \sin 25° = h$	$13 \cos 25° = g$
$13(0.4226) \approx h$	$13(0.9063) \approx g$
$5.5 \approx h$	$11.8 \approx g$

Because $\angle H$ and $\angle G$ are complements, you can write

$m\angle G = 90° - m\angle H = 90° - 25° = 65°.$

▶ The side lengths of the triangle are about 5.5, 11.8, and 13. The triangle has one right angle and two acute angles whose measures are 65° and 25°.

STUDENT HELP

Study Tip
There are other ways to find the side lengths in Examples 1 and 2. For instance, in Example 2, you can use a trigonometric ratio to find one side length, and then use the Pythagorean Theorem to find the other side length.

GOAL 2 Using Right Triangles in Real Life

EXAMPLE 3 *Solving a Right Triangle*

FOCUS ON CAREERS

ASTRONAUT Some astronauts are pilots who are qualified to fly the space shuttle. Some shuttle astronauts are mission specialists whose responsibilities include conducting scientific experiments in space. All astronauts need to have a strong background in science and mathematics.

CAREER LINK www.mcdougallittell.com

SPACE SHUTTLE During its approach to Earth, the space shuttle's glide angle changes.

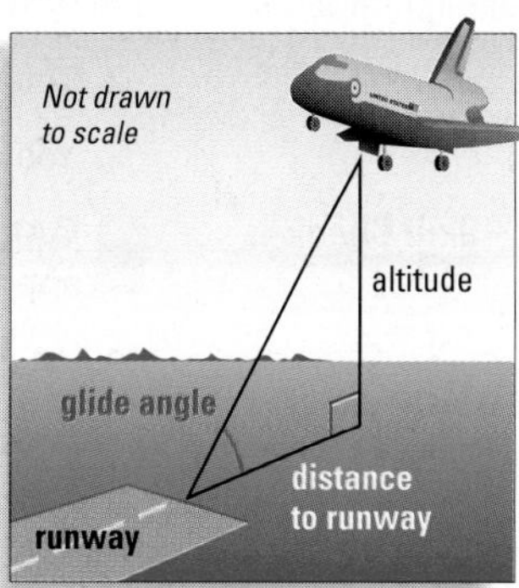

a. When the shuttle's altitude is about 15.7 miles, its horizontal distance to the runway is about 59 miles. What is its glide angle? Round your answer to the nearest tenth.

b. When the space shuttle is 5 miles from the runway, its glide angle is about 19°. Find the shuttle's altitude at this point in its descent. Round your answer to the nearest tenth.

SOLUTION

a. Sketch a right triangle to model the situation. Let $x° =$ the measure of the shuttle's glide angle. You can use the tangent ratio and a calculator to find the approximate value of x.

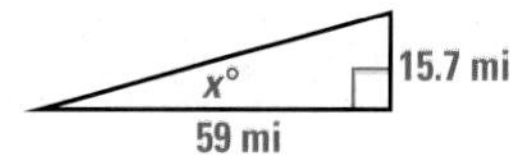

$\tan x° = \frac{\text{opp.}}{\text{adj.}}$

$\tan x° = \frac{15.7}{59}$ **Substitute.**

$x =$  [( ] 15.7 [÷] 59 [ )] [2nd] [TAN] **Use a calculator to find** $\tan^{-1}\left(\frac{15.7}{59}\right)$.

$x \approx 14.9$

▶ When the space shuttle's altitude is about 15.7 miles, the glide angle is about 14.9°.

b. Sketch a right triangle to model the situation. Let $h =$ the altitude of the shuttle. You can use the tangent ratio and a calculator to find the approximate value of h.

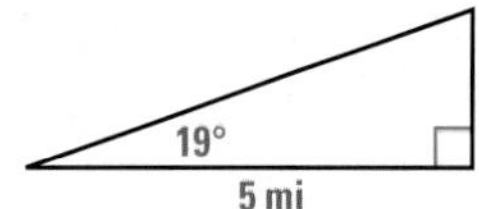

$\tan 19° = \frac{\text{opp.}}{\text{adj.}}$

$\tan 19° = \frac{h}{5}$ **Substitute.**

$0.3443 \approx \frac{h}{5}$ **Use a calculator.**

$1.7 \approx h$ **Multiply each side by 5.**

▶ The shuttle's altitude is about 1.7 miles.

STUDENT HELP

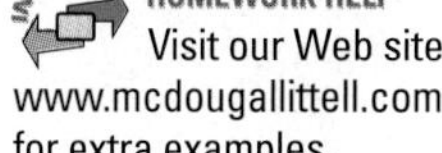

HOMEWORK HELP Visit our Web site www.mcdougallittell.com for extra examples.

EXTRA EXAMPLE 3

During a flight, a hot air balloon is observed by two persons standing at points A and B as illustrated in the diagram. The angle of elevation of point A is 28°. Point A is 1.8 miles from the balloon as measured along the ground.

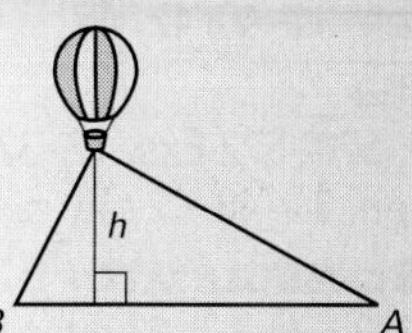

a. What is the height h of the balloon? **0.96 mi**

b. Point B is 2.8 miles from point A. Find the angle of elevation of point B. **43.8°**

CHECKPOINT EXERCISES

For use after Example 3:

1. The angle of elevation of an antenna is 43° as shown in the diagram.

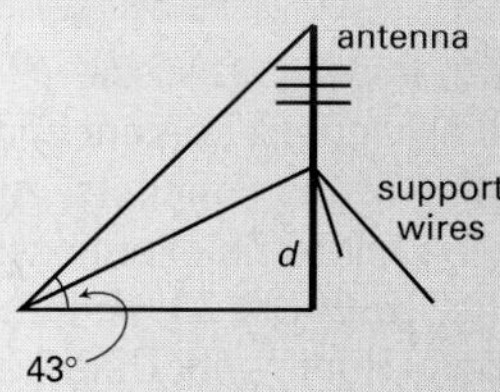

a. If the distance along the ground is 36 feet, find the height of the antenna. **about 33.6 ft**

b. Support wires are attached to the antenna as shown with an angle of elevation of 29°. Find the distance d from the bottom of the antenna to the point where the wires are attached. **about 20 ft**

CLOSURE QUESTION

What is the minimum amount of information you need to solve a right triangle? **2 side lengths or 1 side length and 1 acute angle measure**

3 APPLY

ASSIGNMENT GUIDE

BASIC
Day 1: pp. 570–572 Exs. 12–32 even, 34–40, 42–45

AVERAGE
Day 1: pp. 570–572 Exs. 12–32 even, 34–40, 42–45

ADVANCED
Day 1: pp. 570–572 Exs. 12–32 even, 34–40, 42–46

BLOCK SCHEDULE WITH 9.5
pp. 570–572 Exs. 12–32 even, 34–40, 42–45

EXERCISE LEVELS

Level A: *Easier*
11–21

Level B: *More Difficult*
22–45

Level C: *Most Difficult*
46

✓ HOMEWORK CHECK

To quickly check student understanding of key concepts, go over the following exercises: Exs. 12, 16, 24, 30, 38, 40. See also the Daily Homework Quiz:

- Blackline Master (*Chapter 9 Resource Book,* p. 98)
- Transparency (p. 69)

GUIDED PRACTICE

Vocabulary Check ✓

1. Explain what is meant by *solving* a right triangle.
finding the lengths of the sides and the measures of the angles

Concept Check ✓

Tell whether the statement is *true* or *false*.

2. You can solve a right triangle if you are given the lengths of any two sides. true

3. You can solve a right triangle if you know only the measure of one acute angle. false

Skill Check ✓

CALCULATOR In Exercises 4–7, $\angle A$ is an acute angle. Use a calculator to approximate the measure of $\angle A$ to the nearest tenth of a degree.

4. $\tan A = 0.7$ 35.0° **5.** $\tan A = 5.4$ 79.5° **6.** $\sin A = 0.9$ 64.2° **7.** $\cos A = 0.1$ 84.3°

Solve the right triangle. Round decimals to the nearest tenth.

8. A, C, B; 33, 56, c
$c = 65$, $m\angle A = 59.5°$, $m\angle B = 30.5°$

9. D, E, F; 109, 91, d
$d = 60$, $m\angle D = 33.4°$, $m\angle E = 56.6°$

10.

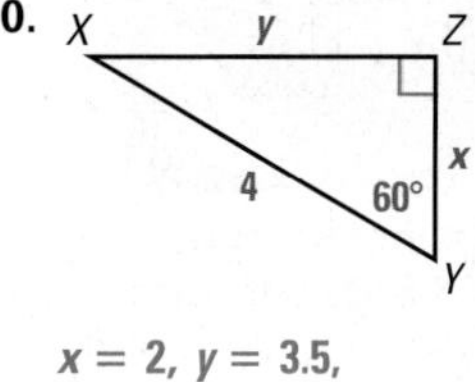

$x = 2$, $y = 3.5$, $m\angle X = 30°$

PRACTICE AND APPLICATIONS

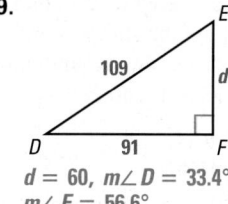

STUDENT HELP
Extra Practice to help you master skills is on p. 820.

FINDING MEASUREMENTS **Use the diagram to find the indicated measurement. Round your answer to the nearest tenth.**

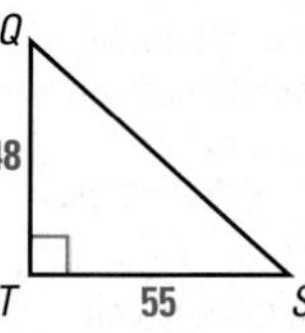

11. QS 73 **12.** $m\angle Q$ 48.9° **13.** $m\angle S$ 41.1°

CALCULATOR In Exercises 14–21, $\angle A$ is an acute angle. Use a calculator to approximate the measure of $\angle A$ to the nearest tenth of a degree.

14. $\tan A = 0.5$ 26.6° **15.** $\tan A = 1.0$ 45° **16.** $\sin A = 0.5$ 30° **17.** $\sin A = 0.35$ 20.5°

18. $\cos A = 0.15$ 81.4° **19.** $\cos A = 0.64$ 50.2° **20.** $\tan A = 2.2$ 65.6° **21.** $\sin A = 0.11$ 6.3°

SOLVING RIGHT TRIANGLES **Solve the right triangle. Round decimals to the nearest tenth.** 22–27. See margin.

22.

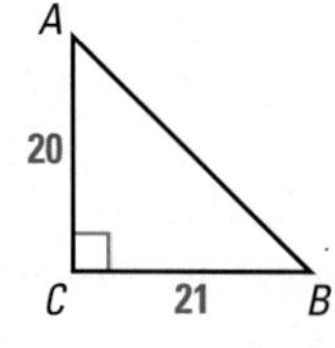

23.

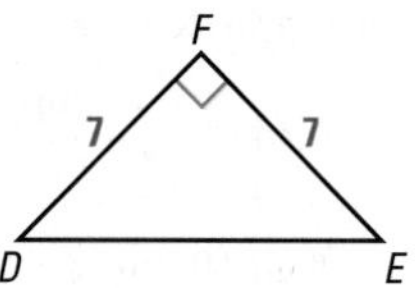

24.

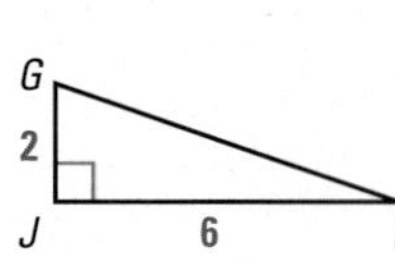

25. M, K, L; 8, 9.2

26.

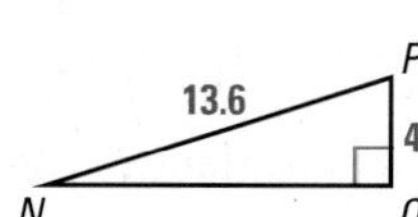

27.

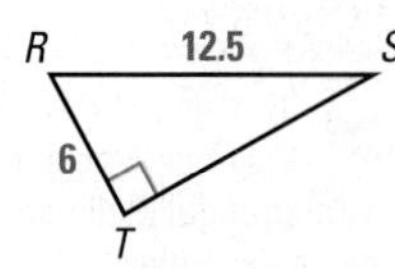

STUDENT HELP
HOMEWORK HELP
Example 1: Exs. 11–27, 34–37
Example 2: Exs. 28–33
Example 3: Exs. 38–41

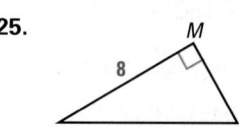

22. side lengths: 20, 21, and 29; angle measures: 90°, 43.6°, and 46.4°

23. side lengths: 7, 7, and 9.9; angle measures: 90°, 45°, and 45°

24. side lengths: 2, 6, and 6.3; angle measures: 90°, 71.6°, and 18.4°

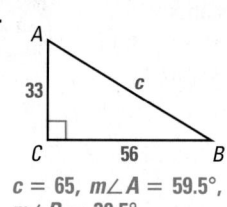

25. side lengths: 4.5, 8, and 9.2; angle measures: 90°, 29.6°, and 60.4°

26. side lengths: 4, 13.0, and 13.6; angle measures: 90°, 17.1°, and 72.9°

27. side lengths: 6, 11.0, and 12.5; angle measures: 90°, 28.7°, and 61.3°

SOLVING RIGHT TRIANGLES Solve the right triangle. Round decimals to the nearest tenth. 28–33. See margin.

28.

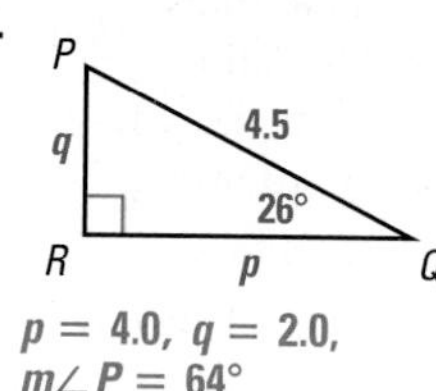

$p = 4.0,\ q = 2.0,\ m\angle P = 64°$

29. $s = 4.1,\ t = 11.3,\ m\angle T = 70°$

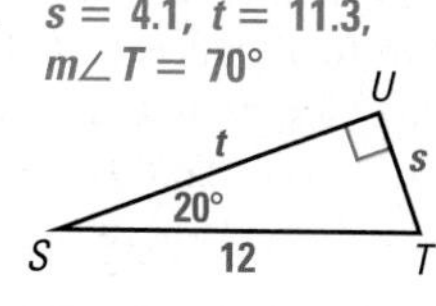

30. $x = 10.9,\ z = 13.8,\ m\angle Y = 38°$

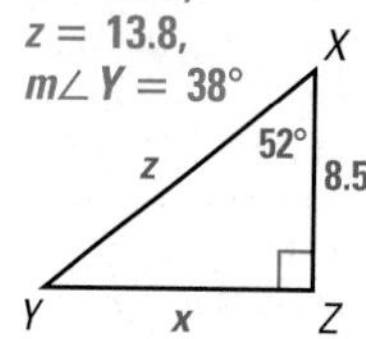

31.

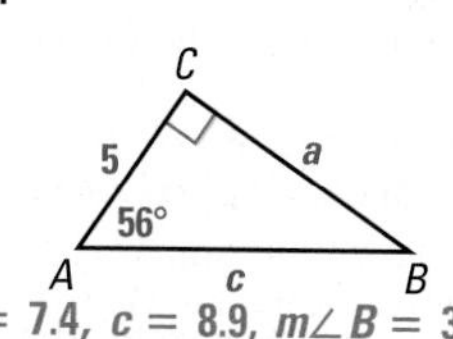

$a = 7.4,\ c = 8.9,\ m\angle B = 34°$

32. $d = 3.7,\ e = 4.8,\ m\angle F = 39°$

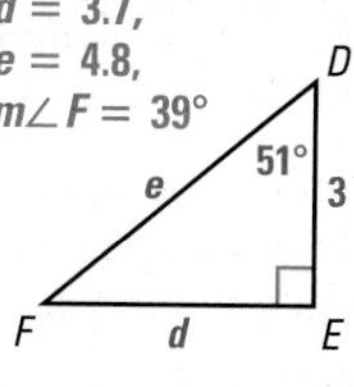

33.

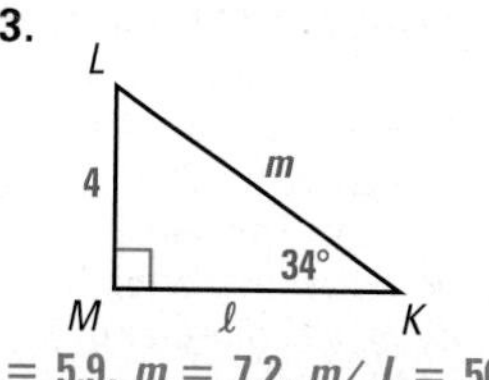

$\ell = 5.9,\ m = 7.2,\ m\angle L = 56°$

NATIONAL AQUARIUM Use the diagram of one of the triangular windowpanes at the National Aquarium in Baltimore, Maryland, to find the indicated value.

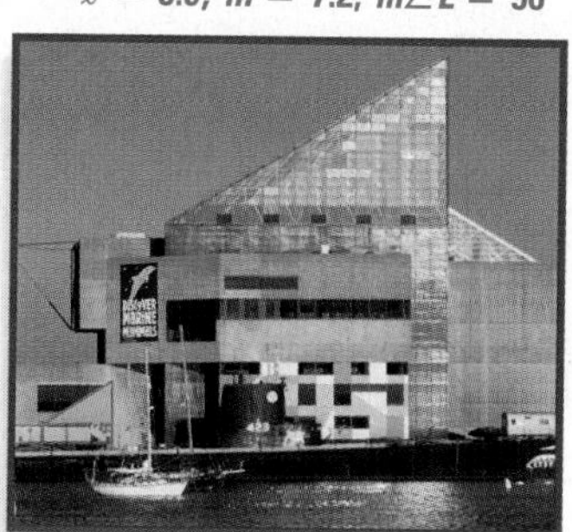

34. $\tan B \approx$ ___?___ 1.9167

35. $m\angle B \approx$ ___?___ 62.4°

36. $AB \approx$ ___?___ 77.8 in.

37. $\sin A \approx$ ___?___ 0.4626

38. **HIKING** You are hiking up a mountain peak. You begin hiking at a trailhead whose elevation is about 9400 feet. The trail ends near the summit at 14,255 feet. The horizontal distance between these two points is about 17,625 feet. Estimate the angle of elevation from the trailhead to the summit. about 15.4°

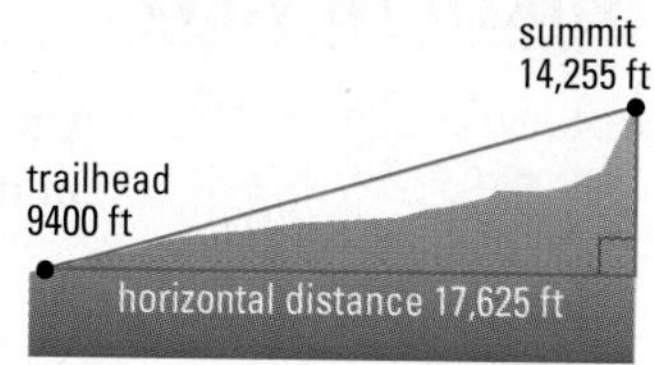

FOCUS ON APPLICATIONS

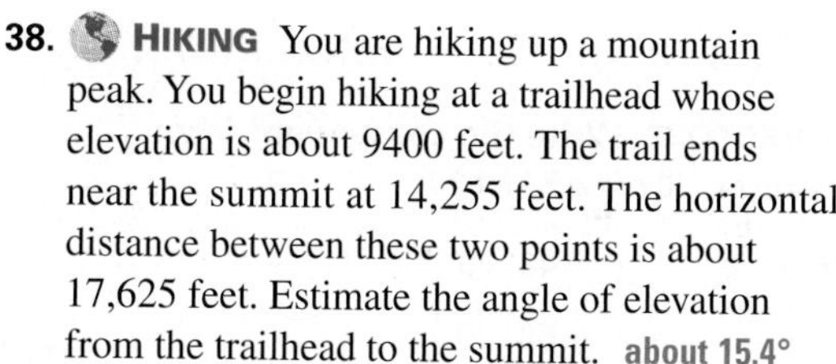

BENCHMARKS If you hike to the top of a mountain you may find a brass plate called a *benchmark.* A benchmark gives an official elevation for the point that can be used by surveyors as a reference for surveying elevations of other landmarks.

RAMPS In Exercises 39–41, use the information about wheelchair ramps.
The Uniform Federal Accessibility Standards specify that the ramp angle used for a wheelchair ramp must be less than or equal to 8.33°.

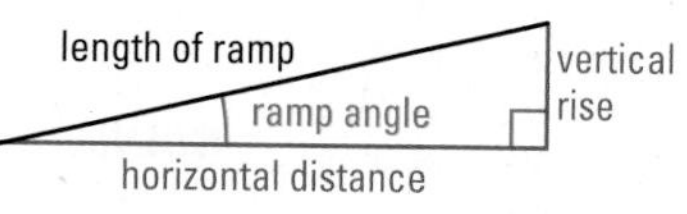

39. The length of one ramp is 20 feet. The vertical rise is 17 inches. Estimate the ramp's horizontal distance and its ramp angle.
about 239.4 in., or about 19 ft 11 in.; about 4.1°

40. You want to build a ramp with a vertical rise of 8 inches. You want to minimize the horizontal distance taken up by the ramp. Draw a sketch showing the approximate dimensions of your ramp. See margin.

41. *Writing* Measure the horizontal distance and the vertical rise of a ramp near your home or school. Find the ramp angle. Does the ramp meet the specifications described above? Explain. Answers will vary.

! COMMON ERROR
EXERCISE 22 Students may want to use the sine ratio for this problem. Caution them that they cannot find sin *A* unless they know the hypotenuse. Suggest that they use the Pythagorean Theorem to find the hypotenuse.

APPLICATION NOTE
EXERCISE 38 Elevation as referred to in this exercise is the vertical height from the ground. Long's Peak is in the Rocky Mountain National Park.

40.

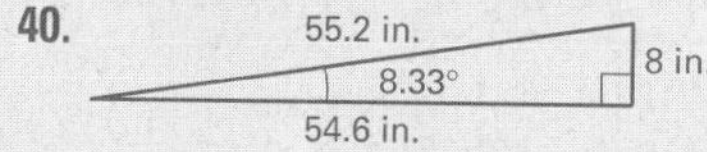

ADDITIONAL PRACTICE AND RETEACHING

For Lesson 9.6:

- Practice Levels A, B, and C (*Chapter 9 Resource Book,* p. 88)
- Reteaching with Practice (*Chapter 9 Resource Book,* p. 91)
- See Lesson 9.6 of the *Personal Student Tutor*

For more Mixed Review:

- Search the *Test and Practice Generator* for key words or specific lessons.

4 ASSESS

DAILY HOMEWORK QUIZ

Transparency Available

Use a calculator to approximate the measure of acute $\angle A$ to the nearest tenth of a degree.

1. $\sin A = 0.25$ 14.5°

2. $\cos A = 0.38$ 67.7°

Solve the right triangle. Round decimals to the nearest tenth.

3.

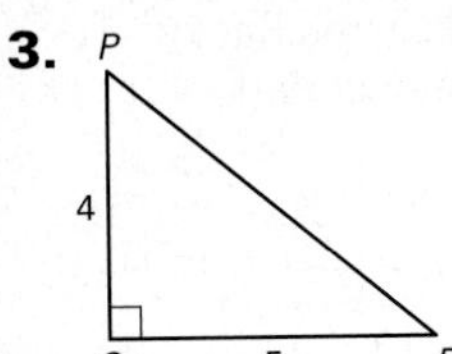

side lengths: 4, 5, 6.4; angle measures: 90°, 38.7°, 51.3°

4.

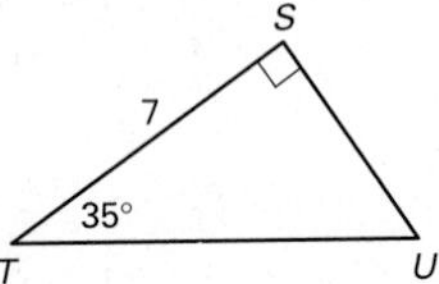

side lengths: 7, 4.9, 8.5; angle measures: 90°, 35°, 55°

EXTRA CHALLENGE NOTE

Challenge problems for Lesson 9.6 are available in **blackline** format in the *Chapter 9 Resource Book,* p. 95 and at **www.mcdougallittell.com.**

ADDITIONAL TEST PREPARATION

1. WRITING Summarize how to find the measures of the acute angles of a right triangle for which the sides are known. *Sample answer:* For one acute angle, find the inverse sine of the ratio of the side opposite the angle to the hypotenuse. Then subtract that angle from 90° to get the other acute angle.

Test Preparation

45. *Sample answer:* The riser-to-tread ratio affects the safety of the stairway in several ways. First, the deeper the tread the more of a person's foot can fit on the step. This makes a person less likely to fall. Also, the smaller the angle of inclination the less steep the stairway. This makes the stairs less tiring to climb, and therefore, safer.

MULTI-STEP PROBLEM In Exercises 42–45, use the diagram and the information below.

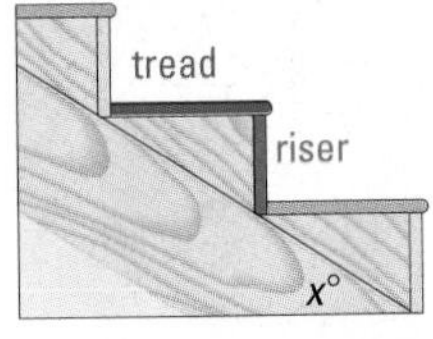

The horizontal part of a step is called the *tread.* The vertical part is called the *riser.* The ratio of the riser length to the tread length affects the safety of a staircase. Traditionally, builders have used a riser-to-tread ratio of about $8\frac{1}{4}$ inches : 9 inches. A newly recommended ratio is 7 inches : 11 inches.

42. Find the value of x for stairs built using the new riser-to-tread ratio. about 32.5

43. Find the value of x for stairs built using the old riser-to-tread ratio. about 42.5

44. Suppose you want to build a stairway that is less steep than either of the ones in Exercises 42 and 43. Give an example of a riser-to-tread ratio that you could use. Find the value of x for your stairway. *Sample answer:* 6 in.: 12 in.; about 26.6

45. *Writing* Explain how the riser-to-tread ratio that is used for a stairway could affect the safety of the stairway. See margin.

★ Challenge

46. **PROOF** Write a proof. See margin.

GIVEN ▶ $\angle A$ and $\angle B$ are acute angles.

PROVE ▶ $\frac{a}{\sin A} = \frac{b}{\sin B}$

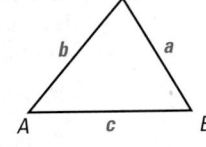

(*Hint:* Draw an altitude from C to $\overline{AB}$. Label it h.)

C
b a
A c B

EXTRA CHALLENGE

www.mcdougallittell.com

MIXED REVIEW

46. Draw an altitude, $\overline{CD}$, from C to $\overline{AB}$, and let $CD = h$. In rt. $\triangle ACD$, $\sin A = \frac{h}{b}$. In rt. $\triangle BCD$, $\sin B = \frac{h}{a}$. Thus, $h = b \cdot \sin A$ and $h = a \cdot \sin B$. By the substitution prop. of equality, $b \cdot \sin A = a \cdot \sin B$. Dividing both sides by $\sin A \cdot \sin B$ gives $\frac{b}{\sin B} = \frac{a}{\sin A}$, or $\frac{a}{\sin A} = \frac{b}{\sin B}$.

USING VECTORS Write the component form of the vector. (Review 7.4 for 9.7)

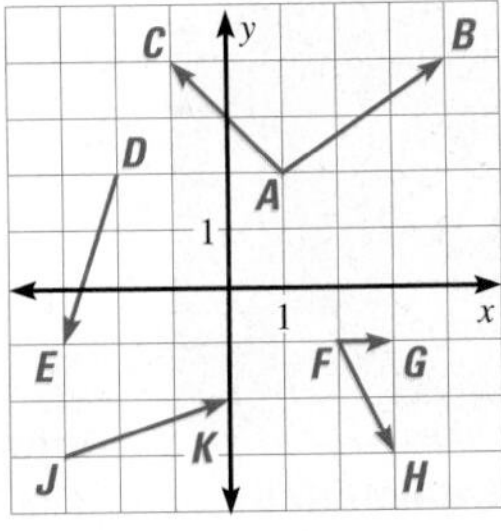

47. $\overrightarrow{AB}$ $\langle 3, 2\rangle$

48. $\overrightarrow{AC}$ $\langle -2, 2\rangle$

49. $\overrightarrow{DE}$ $\langle -1, -3\rangle$

50. $\overrightarrow{FG}$ $\langle 1, 0\rangle$

51. $\overrightarrow{FH}$ $\langle 1, -2\rangle$

52. $\overrightarrow{JK}$ $\langle 3, 1\rangle$

SOLVING PROPORTIONS Solve the proportion. (Review 8.1)

53. $\frac{x}{30} = \frac{5}{6}$ 25

54. $\frac{7}{16} = \frac{49}{y}$ 112

55. $\frac{3}{10} = \frac{g}{42}$ 12.6

56. $\frac{7}{18} = \frac{84}{k}$ 216

57. $\frac{m}{2} = \frac{7}{1}$ 14

58. $\frac{8}{t} = \frac{4}{11}$ 22

CLASSIFYING TRIANGLES Decide whether the numbers can represent the side lengths of a triangle. If they can, classify the triangle as *right, acute,* or *obtuse.* (Review 9.3)

59. 18, 14, 2 no

60. 60, 228, 220 yes; acute

61. 8.5, 7.7, 3.6 yes; right

62. 250, 263, 80 yes; obtuse

63. 113, 15, 112 yes; right

64. 15, 75, 59 no

9.7 Vectors

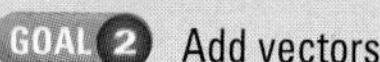

What you should learn

GOAL 1 Find the magnitude and the direction of a vector.

GOAL 2 Add vectors.

Why you should learn it

▼ To solve **real-life** problems, such as describing the velocity of a skydiver in **Exs. 41–45.**

GOAL 1 FINDING THE MAGNITUDE OF A VECTOR

As defined in Lesson 7.4, a *vector* is a quantity that has both magnitude and direction. In this lesson, you will learn how to find the *magnitude of a vector* and the *direction of a vector*. You will also learn how to add vectors.

The **magnitude of a vector** $\overrightarrow{AB}$ is the distance from the initial point A to the terminal point B, and is written $|\overrightarrow{AB}|$. If a vector is drawn in a coordinate plane, you can use the Distance Formula to find its magnitude.

$$|\overrightarrow{AB}| = \sqrt{(x_2 - x_1)^2 + (y_2 - y_1)^2}$$

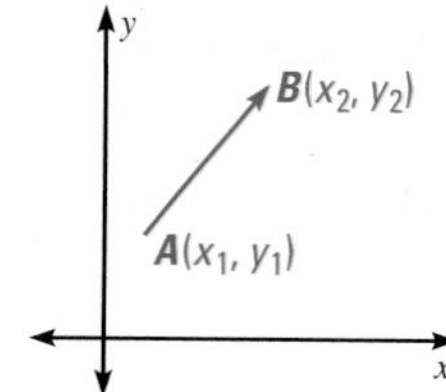

EXAMPLE 1 Finding the Magnitude of a Vector

Points P and Q are the initial and terminal points of the vector $\overrightarrow{PQ}$. Draw $\overrightarrow{PQ}$ in a coordinate plane. Write the component form of the vector and find its magnitude.

a. $P(0, 0), Q(-6, 3)$ **b.** $P(0, 2), Q(5, 4)$ **c.** $P(3, 4), Q(-2, -1)$

SOLUTION

a. Component form $= \langle x_2 - x_1, y_2 - y_1 \rangle$

$\overrightarrow{PQ} = \langle -6 - 0, 3 - 0 \rangle$

$= \langle -6, 3 \rangle$

Use the Distance Formula to find the magnitude.

$|\overrightarrow{PQ}| = \sqrt{(-6 - 0)^2 + (3 - 0)^2} = \sqrt{45} \approx 6.7$

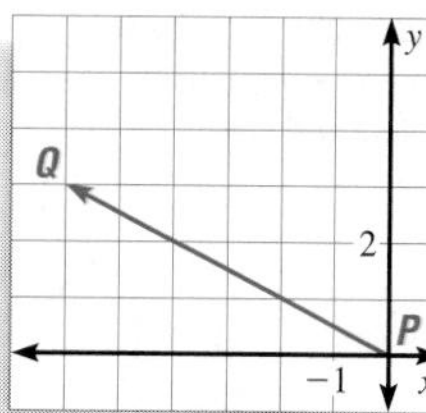

b. Component form $= \langle x_2 - x_1, y_2 - y_1 \rangle$

$\overrightarrow{PQ} = \langle 5 - 0, 4 - 2 \rangle$

$= \langle 5, 2 \rangle$

Use the Distance Formula to find the magnitude.

$|\overrightarrow{PQ}| = \sqrt{(5 - 0)^2 + (4 - 2)^2} = \sqrt{29} \approx 5.4$

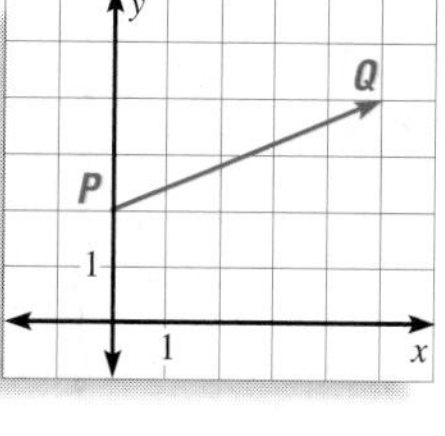

c. Component form $= \langle x_2 - x_1, y_2 - y_1 \rangle$

$\overrightarrow{PQ} = \langle -2 - 3, -1 - 4 \rangle$

$= \langle -5, -5 \rangle$

Use the Distance Formula to find the magnitude.

$|\overrightarrow{PQ}| = \sqrt{(-2 - 3)^2 + (-1 - 4)^2} = \sqrt{50} \approx 7.1$

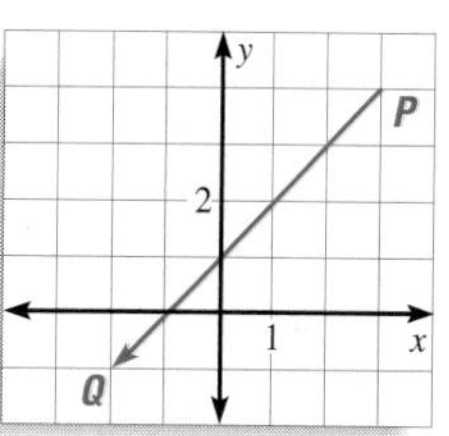

STUDENT HELP

Look Back
For help with the component form of a vector, see p. 423.

CALIFORNIA STANDARDS AND ASSESSMENT

CA Standards: 17
SAT9 Task 1: Obj. 25

1 PLAN

PACING
Basic: 2 days
Average: 2 days
Advanced: 2 days
Block Schedule: 1 block

LESSON OPENER
APPLICATION
An alternative way to approach Lesson 9.7 is to use the Application Lesson Opener:

- Blackline Master (*Chapter 9 Resource Book*, p. 99)
- Transparency (p. 60)

MEETING INDIVIDUAL NEEDS

- ***Chapter 9 Resource Book***
  Prerequisite Skills Review (p. 5)
  Practice Level A (p. 103)
  Practice Level B (p. 104)
  Practice Level C (p. 105)
  Reteaching with Practice (p. 106)
  Absent Student Catch-Up (p. 108)
  Challenge (p. 110)
- ***Resources in Spanish***
- ***Personal Student Tutor***

NEW-TEACHER SUPPORT
See the Tips for New Teachers on pp. 1–2 of the *Chapter 9 Resource Book* for additional notes about Lesson 9.7.

WARM-UP EXERCISES

Transparency Available

Find the distance between each pair of points. Leave answers in simplest radical form.

1. (0, 0), (3, 4) 5
2. (1, –4), (5, –1) 5
3. (–1, 3), (4, 2) $\sqrt{26}$
4. (0, 0), (4, 4) $4\sqrt{2}$
5. (7, 2), (2, 0) $\sqrt{29}$

2 TEACH

EXTRA EXAMPLE 1
P and Q are the initial and terminal points of $\overrightarrow{PQ}$. Write the component form and magnitude.
a. $P(0, 1)$, $Q(-3, 5)$ $\langle -3, 4\rangle$; 5
b. $P(-2, -1)$, $Q(1, 5)$ $\langle 3, 6\rangle$; 6.7

EXTRA EXAMPLE 2
$\overrightarrow{AB}$ describes the velocity of a plane. The scale is mi/h.

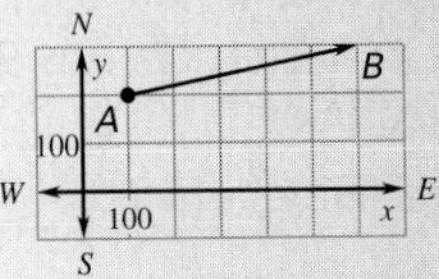

a. Find the speed. about 510 mi/h
b. Find the direction it is traveling relative to east.
11.3° north of east

EXTRA EXAMPLE 3

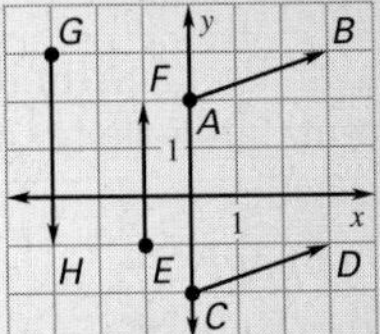

Which vectors have the same direction? $\overrightarrow{AB}$ and $\overrightarrow{CD}$
Which are equal? $\overrightarrow{AB}$ and $\overrightarrow{CD}$
Which are parallel?
$\overrightarrow{AB}$ and $\overrightarrow{CD}$; $\overrightarrow{EF}$ and $\overrightarrow{GH}$

CHECKPOINT EXERCISES
For use after Examples 1–3:
1. $P(3, 4)$and $Q(-2, 2)$ are initial and terminal points. Write the component form and magnitude. $\langle -5, -2\rangle$; 5.4
2. $\overrightarrow{AB}$ describes the velocity of a ship. The scale is mi/h.

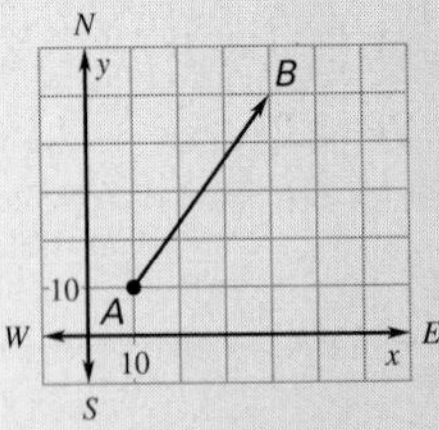

a. Find the speed. 50 mi/h
b. Find the direction it is traveling relative to east.
53.1° north of east

FOCUS ON APPLICATIONS

NAVIGATION One of the most common vector quantities in real life is the velocity of a moving object. A velocity vector is used in navigation to describe both the speed and the direction of a moving object.

STUDENT HELP
Look Back
For help with using trigonometric ratios to find angle measures, see pp. 567 and 568.

The **direction of a vector** is determined by the angle it makes with a horizontal line. In real-life applications, the direction angle is described relative to the directions north, east, south, and west. In a coordinate plane, the x-axis represents an east-west line. The y-axis represents a north-south line.

EXAMPLE 2 *Describing the Direction of a Vector*

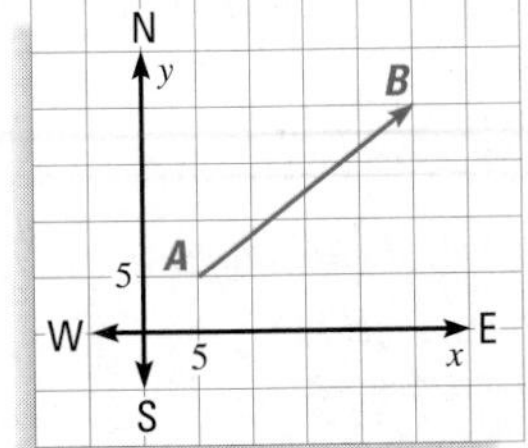

The vector $\overrightarrow{AB}$ describes the velocity of a moving ship. The scale on each axis is in miles per hour.

a. Find the speed of the ship.

b. Find the direction it is traveling relative to east.

SOLUTION

a. The magnitude of the vector $\overrightarrow{AB}$ represents the ship's speed. Use the Distance Formula.

$$|\overrightarrow{AB}| = \sqrt{(25-5)^2 + (20-5)^2}$$
$$= \sqrt{20^2 + 15^2}$$
$$= 25$$

▶ The speed of the ship is 25 miles per hour.

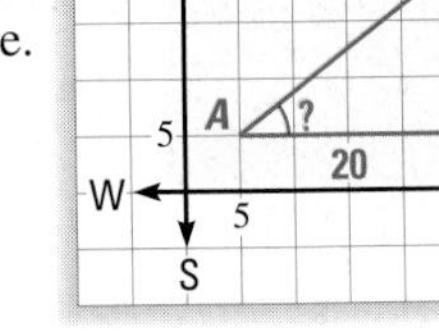

b. The tangent of the angle formed by the vector and a line drawn parallel to the x-axis is $\frac{15}{20}$, or 0.75. Use a calculator to find the angle measure.

0.75 [2nd] [TAN] $\approx 36.9°$

▶ The ship is traveling in a direction about 37° north of east.

Two vectors are **equal** if they have the same magnitude and direction. They do *not* have to have the same initial and terminal points. Two vectors are **parallel** if they have the same or opposite directions.

EXAMPLE 3 *Identifying Equal and Parallel Vectors*

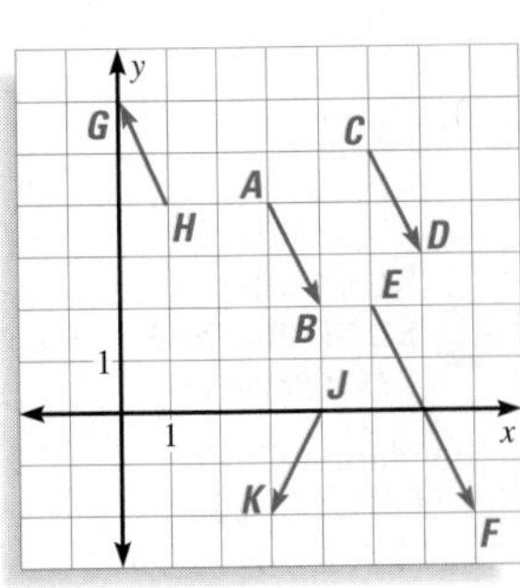

In the diagram, these vectors have the same direction: $\overrightarrow{AB}$, $\overrightarrow{CD}$, $\overrightarrow{EF}$.

These vectors are equal: $\overrightarrow{AB}$, $\overrightarrow{CD}$.

These vectors are parallel: $\overrightarrow{AB}$, $\overrightarrow{CD}$, $\overrightarrow{EF}$, $\overrightarrow{HG}$.

Checkpoint Exercises continued on next page.

GOAL 2 ADDING VECTORS

STUDENT HELP

Study Tip
A single letter with an arrow over it, such as $\vec{u}$, can be used to denote a vector.

Two vectors can be added to form a new vector. To add $\vec{u}$ and $\vec{v}$ geometrically, place the initial point of $\vec{v}$ on the terminal point of $\vec{u}$, (or place the initial point of $\vec{u}$ on the terminal point of $\vec{v}$). The sum is the vector that joins the initial point of the first vector and the terminal point of the second vector.

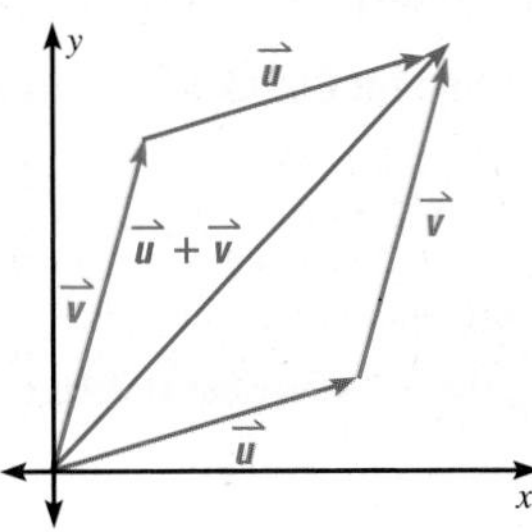

This method of adding vectors is often called the *parallelogram rule* because the sum vector is the diagonal of a parallelogram. You can also add vectors algebraically.

ADDING VECTORS

SUM OF TWO VECTORS

The **sum** of $\vec{u} = \langle a_1, b_1 \rangle$ and $\vec{v} = \langle a_2, b_2 \rangle$ is $\vec{u} + \vec{v} = \langle a_1 + a_2, b_1 + b_2 \rangle$.

EXAMPLE 4 *Finding the Sum of Two Vectors*

Let $\vec{u} = \langle 3, 5 \rangle$ and $\vec{v} = \langle -6, -1 \rangle$. To find the sum vector $\vec{u} + \vec{v}$, add the horizontal components and add the vertical components of $\vec{u}$ and $\vec{v}$.

$$\vec{u} + \vec{v} = \langle 3 + (-6), 5 + (-1) \rangle$$
$$= \langle -3, 4 \rangle$$

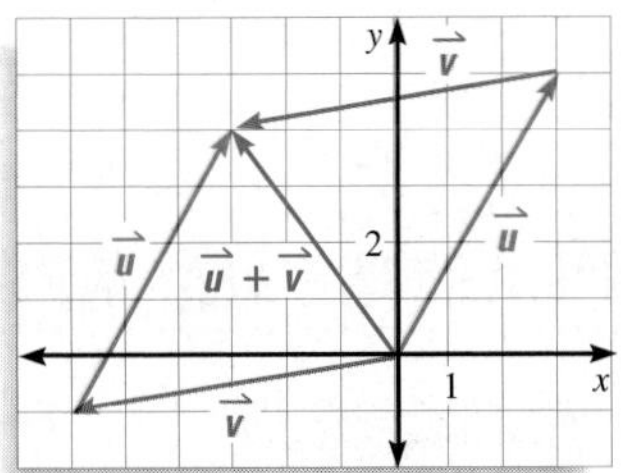

EXAMPLE 5 *Velocity of a Jet*

REAL LIFE

AVIATION A jet is flying northeast at about 707 miles per hour. Its velocity is represented by the vector $\vec{v} = \langle 500, 500 \rangle$.

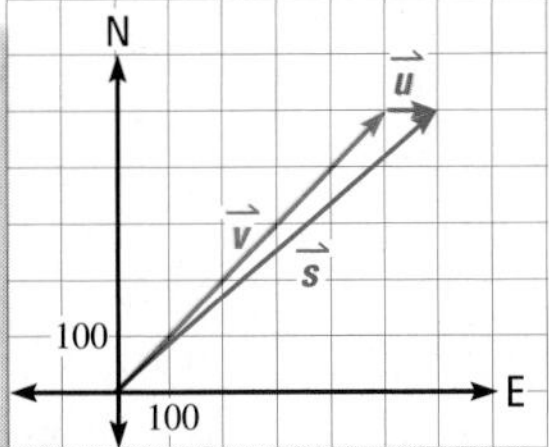

The jet encounters a wind blowing from the west at 100 miles per hour. The wind velocity is represented by $\vec{u} = \langle 100, 0 \rangle$. The jet's new velocity vector $\vec{s}$ is the sum of its original velocity vector and the wind's velocity vector.

$$\vec{s} = \vec{v} + \vec{u}$$
$$= \langle 500 + 100, 500 + 0 \rangle$$
$$= \langle 600, 500 \rangle$$

The magnitude of the sum vector $\vec{s}$ represents the new speed of the jet.

$$\text{New speed} = |\vec{s}| = \sqrt{(600 - 0)^2 + (500 - 0)^2} \approx 781 \text{ mi/h}$$

CHECKPOINT EXERCISES

For use after Examples 1–3:

3. 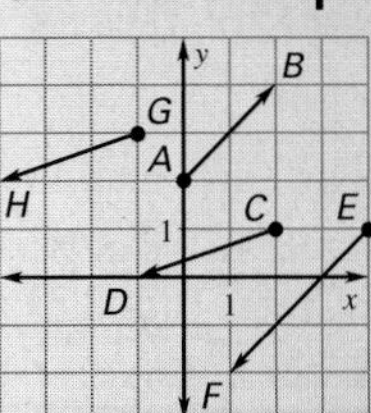

In the diagram, which vectors have the same direction? $\overrightarrow{CD}$; $\overrightarrow{GH}$

Which vectors are equal? $\overrightarrow{CD}$; $\overrightarrow{GH}$

Which vectors are parallel? $\overrightarrow{AB}$ and $\overrightarrow{EF}$; $\overrightarrow{CD}$ and $\overrightarrow{GH}$

EXTRA EXAMPLE 4

Let $\vec{u} = \langle 5, -1 \rangle$ and $\vec{v} = \langle 3, 4 \rangle$. Find $\vec{u} + \vec{v}$. $\langle 8, 3 \rangle$

EXTRA EXAMPLE 5

A jet is flying northeast at about 550 miles per hour. Its velocity is represented by the vector $\vec{v} = \langle 389, 389 \rangle$. The jet encounters a wind blowing from the west at 50 miles per hour. The wind velocity is represented by $\vec{u} = \langle 50, 0 \rangle$. Find the jet's new velocity vector $\vec{s}$ and the magnitude of $\vec{s}$. $\langle 439, 389 \rangle$; about 587 mi/h

CHECKPOINT EXERCISES

For use after Examples 4 and 5:

1. Let $\vec{u} = \langle 2, -3 \rangle$ and $\vec{v} = \langle 1, 6 \rangle$. Find $\vec{u} + \vec{v}$. $\langle 3, 3 \rangle$

2. A jet is flying northeast at about 670 miles per hour. Its velocity is represented by the vector $\vec{v} = \langle 474, 474 \rangle$. The jet encounters a wind blowing from the east at 80 miles per hour. The wind velocity is represented by $\vec{u} = \langle -80, 0 \rangle$. Find the jet's new velocity vector $\vec{s}$ and the magnitude of $\vec{s}$. $\langle 394, 474 \rangle$; about 616 mi/h

CLOSURE QUESTION

Let $\vec{u} = \langle 6, -3 \rangle$ and $\vec{v} = \langle 3, 4 \rangle$. Find the sum $\vec{u} + \vec{v}$. $\langle 9, 1 \rangle$

3 APPLY

ASSIGNMENT GUIDE

BASIC
Day 1: pp. 576–577 Exs. 10–30
Day 2: pp. 578–580 Exs. 31–45, 48, 53–60, Quiz 3 Exs. 1–17

AVERAGE
Day 1: pp. 576–577 Exs. 10–30
Day 2: pp. 578–580 Exs. 31–48, 53–60, Quiz 3 Exs. 1–17

ADVANCED
Day 1: pp. 576–577 Exs. 10–30
Day 2: pp. 578–580 Exs. 31–60

BLOCK SCHEDULE
pp. 576–580 Exs. 10–48, 53–60, Quiz 3 Exs. 1–17

EXERCISE LEVELS

Level A: *Easier*
10–12

Level B: *More Difficult*
13–48

Level C: *Most Difficult*
49–52

✓ HOMEWORK CHECK

To quickly check student understanding of key concepts, go over the following exercises: Exs. 10, 16, 22, 28, 30, 32, 36, 44. See also the Daily Homework Quiz:

- Blackline Master (*Chapter 10 Resource Book*, p. 11)
- Transparency (p. 71)

GUIDED PRACTICE

Vocabulary Check ✓

1. What is meant by the *magnitude of a vector* and the *direction of a vector*?

1. The magnitude of a vector is the distance from its initial point to its terminal point, and the direction is the angle the vector makes with a horizontal line.

Concept Check ✓

In Exercises 2–4, use the diagram.

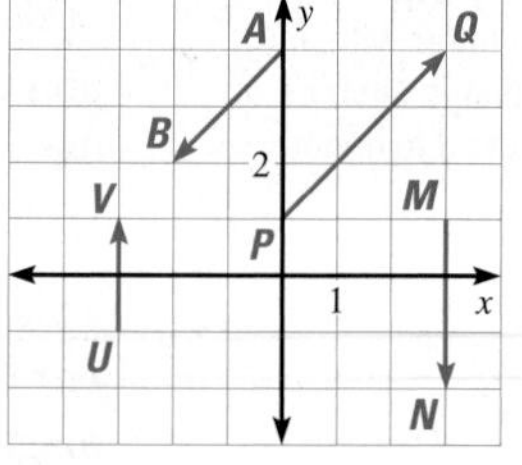

2. Write the component form of each vector. See margin.
3. Identify any parallel vectors. $\overrightarrow{AB}$, $\overrightarrow{PQ}$; $\overrightarrow{MN}$, $\overrightarrow{UV}$
4. Vectors $\overrightarrow{PQ}$ and $\overrightarrow{ST}$ are equal vectors. Although $\overrightarrow{ST}$ is not shown, the coordinates of its initial point are $(-1, -1)$. Give the coordinates of its terminal point. (2, 2)

2. $\overrightarrow{AB} = \langle -2, -2\rangle$; $\overrightarrow{MN} = \langle 0, -3\rangle$; $\overrightarrow{PQ} = \langle 3, 3\rangle$; $\overrightarrow{UV} = \langle 0, 2\rangle$

Skill Check ✓

Write the vector in component form. Find the magnitude of the vector. Round your answer to the nearest tenth.

5.
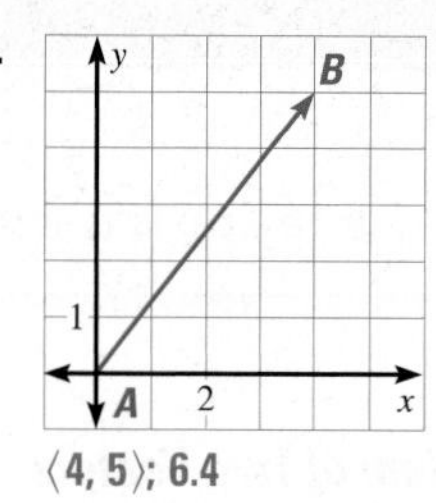

$\langle 4, 5\rangle$; 6.4

6.
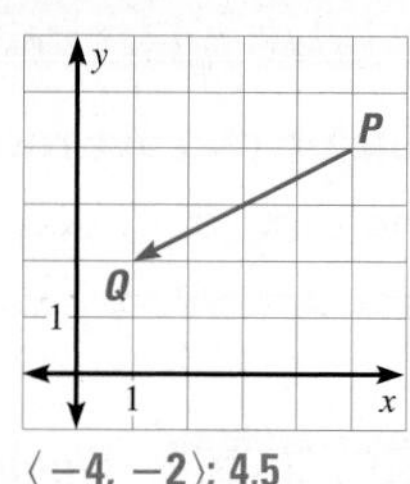

$\langle -4, -2\rangle$; 4.5

7.
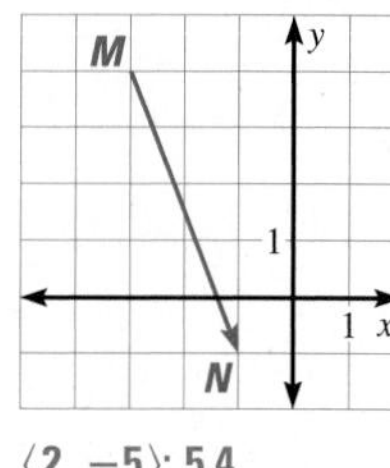

$\langle 2, -5\rangle$; 5.4

8. Use the vector in Exercise 5. Find the direction of the vector relative to east. about 51° north of east
9. Find the sum of the vectors in Exercises 5 and 6. $\langle 0, 3\rangle$

PRACTICE AND APPLICATIONS

STUDENT HELP

Extra Practice to help you master skills is on p. 820.

FINDING MAGNITUDE **Write the vector in component form. Find the magnitude of the vector. Round your answer to the nearest tenth.**

10.
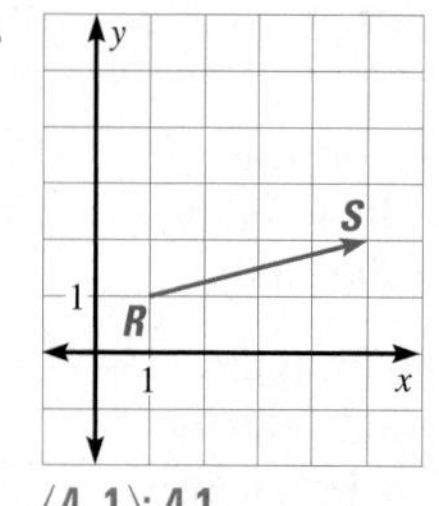

$\langle 4, 1\rangle$; 4.1

11.
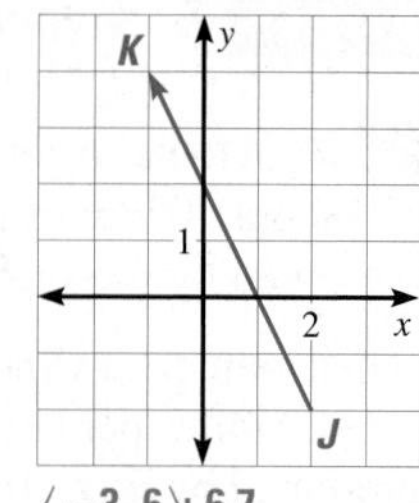

$\langle -3, 6\rangle$; 6.7

12.
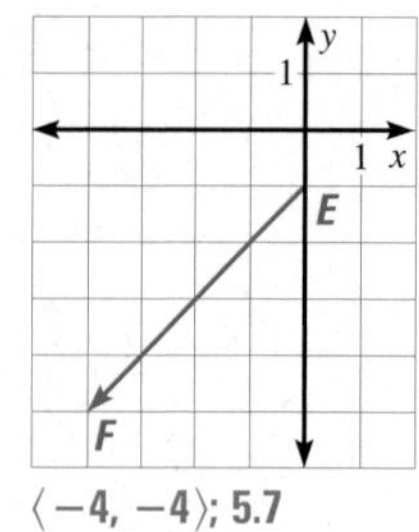

$\langle -4, -4\rangle$; 5.7

STUDENT HELP

HOMEWORK HELP
Example 1: Exs. 10–20
Example 2: Exs. 21–24
Example 3: Exs. 25–29
Example 4: Exs. 31–40
Example 5: Exs. 41–45

FINDING MAGNITUDE **Draw vector $\overrightarrow{PQ}$ in a coordinate plane. Write the component form of the vector and find its magnitude. Round your answer to the nearest tenth.**

13. $P(0, 0)$, $Q(2, 7)$ $\langle 2, 7\rangle$; 7.3
14. $P(5, 1)$, $Q(2, 6)$ $\langle -3, 5\rangle$; 5.8
15. $P(-3, 2)$, $Q(7, 6)$ $\langle 10, 4\rangle$; 10.8
16. $P(-4, -3)$, $Q(2, -7)$ $\langle 6, -4\rangle$; 7.2
17. $P(5, 0)$, $Q(-1, -4)$ $\langle -6, -4\rangle$; 7.2
18. $P(6, 3)$, $Q(-2, 1)$ $\langle -8, -2\rangle$; 8.2
19. $P(-6, 0)$, $Q(-5, -4)$ $\langle 1, -4\rangle$; 4.1
20. $P(0, 5)$, $Q(3, 5)$ $\langle 3, 0\rangle$; 3

NAVIGATION **The given vector represents the velocity of a ship at sea. Find the ship's speed, rounded to the nearest mile per hour. Then find the direction the ship is traveling relative to the given direction.**

21. Find direction relative to east.
about 61 mi/h; about 9° north of east

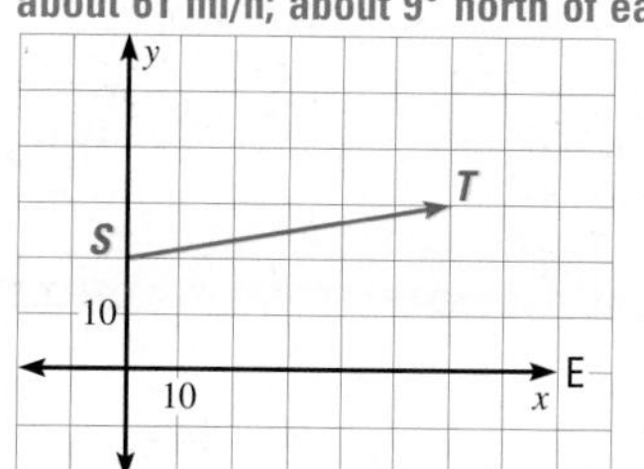

22. Find direction relative to east.
about 64 mi/h; about 51° south of east

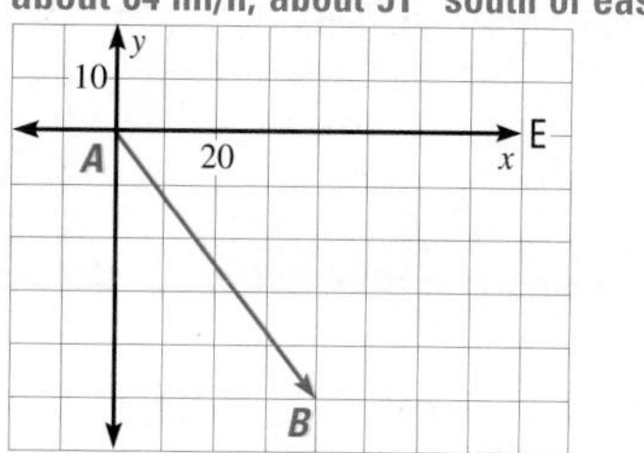

23. Find direction relative to west.
about 57 mi/h; 45° north of west

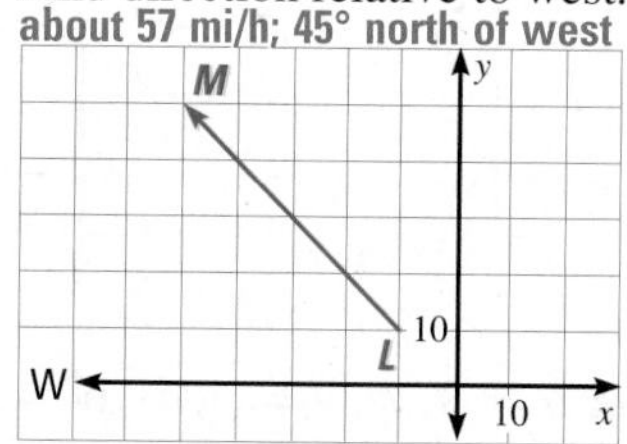

24. Find direction relative to west.
about 64 mi/h; about 39° south of west

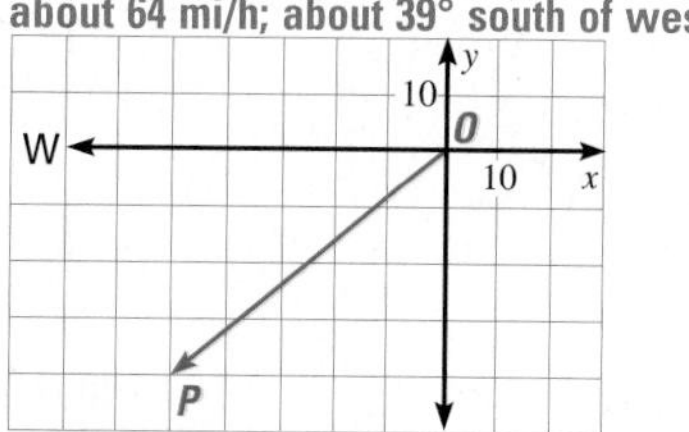

PARALLEL AND EQUAL VECTORS
In Exercises 25–28, use the diagram shown at the right.

25. Which vectors are parallel?
$\overrightarrow{EF}$, $\overrightarrow{CD}$, and $\overrightarrow{AB}$

26. Which vectors have the same direction?
$\overrightarrow{EF}$ and $\overrightarrow{CD}$

27. Which vectors are equal?
$\overrightarrow{EF}$ and $\overrightarrow{CD}$

28. Name two vectors that have the same magnitude but different directions.
$\overrightarrow{GH}$ and $\overrightarrow{JK}$

TUG-OF-WAR GAME **In Exercises 29 and 30, use the information below.**
The forces applied in a game of *tug-of-war* can be represented by vectors. The magnitude of the vector represents the amount of force with which the rope is pulled. The direction of the vector represents the direction of the pull. The diagrams below show the forces applied in two different rounds of tug-of-war.

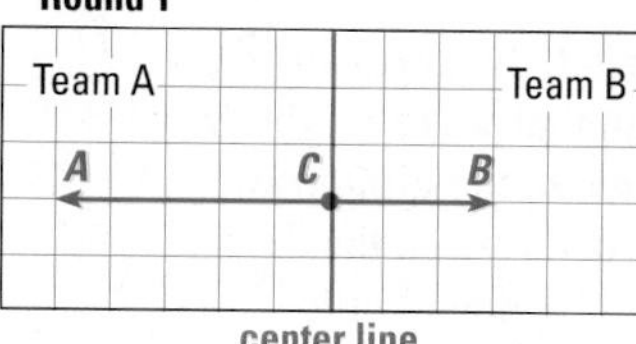

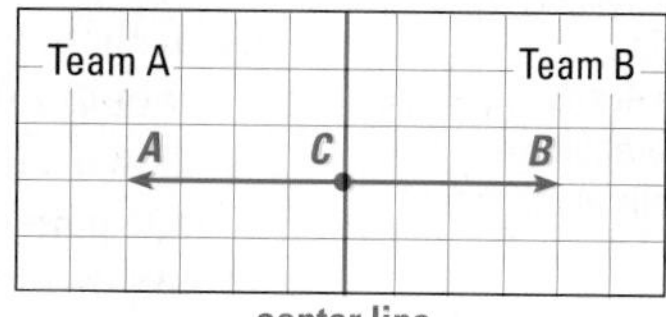

29. In Round 2, are $\overrightarrow{CA}$ and $\overrightarrow{CB}$ parallel vectors? Are they equal vectors? yes; no

30. In which round was the outcome a tie? How do you know? Describe the outcome in the other round. Explain your reasoning. See margin.

30. In Round 2, since the vectors have the same magnitude and opposite directions, the rope was pulled in opposite directions with equal force, and the match was a tie. In Round 1, Team A won since the magnitude of their force vector is greater than the magnitude of the force vector for Team B.

FOCUS ON APPLICATIONS

TUG-OF-WAR In the game *tug-of-war*, two teams pull on opposite ends of a rope. The team that succeeds in pulling a member of the other team across a center line wins.

TEACHING TIPS
EXERCISE 16 While direction is not important in finding magnitude, the component form depends on the direction. Make sure the terminal point is Q in this diagram.

! COMMON ERROR

EXERCISES 31–34 Students may make mistakes adding vectors if they do not pay attention to the location of the initial point and the terminal point. Remind them to pay attention to the direction of the vector when representing it with components.

APPLICATION NOTE

EXERCISES 41–45 The forces acting on a skydiver are gravity and air resistance. The amount of air resistance depends on the speed of the skydiver and the cross-sectional area of the skydiver. That is the reason some skydivers position themselves with their bodies parallel to Earth. It increases their cross-sectional area, which in turn increases the air resistance. This slows their descent.

42.

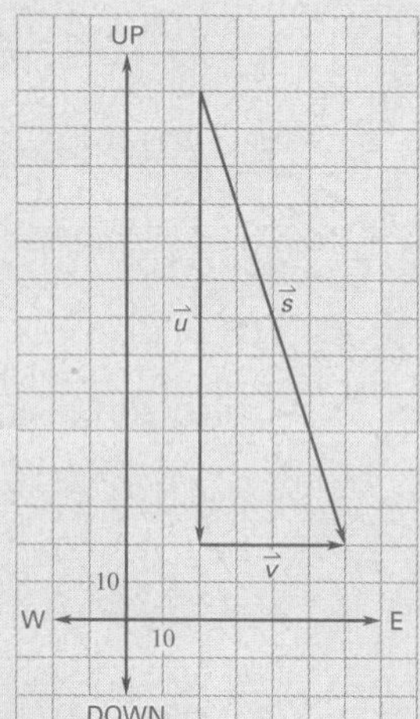

45.

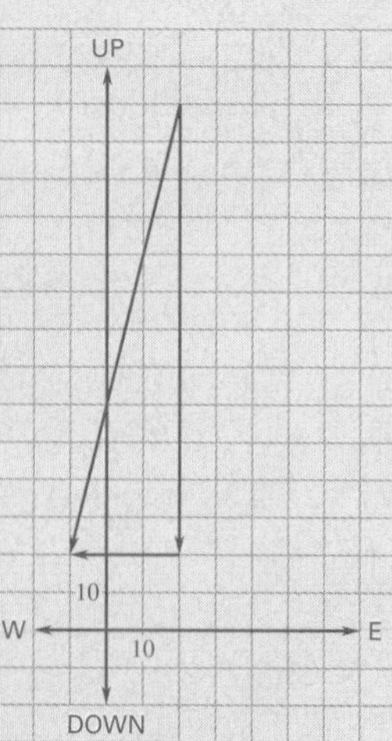

Ex. 31–34, check students' drawings.

31. $\vec{u} = \langle 4, 1 \rangle$; $\vec{v} = \langle 2, 4 \rangle$; $\vec{u} + \vec{v} = \langle 6, 5 \rangle$

32. $\vec{u} = \langle -6, 2 \rangle$; $\vec{v} = \langle 5, 3 \rangle$; $\vec{u} + \vec{v} = \langle -1, 5 \rangle$

33. $\vec{u} = \langle 2, -4 \rangle$; $\vec{v} = \langle 3, 6 \rangle$; $\vec{u} + \vec{v} = \langle 5, 2 \rangle$

34. $\vec{u} = \langle 2, 3 \rangle$; $\vec{v} = \langle 1, -6 \rangle$; $\vec{u} + \vec{v} = \langle 3, -3 \rangle$

43. about 126 mi/h; the speed at which the skydiver is falling, taking into account the breeze

PARALLELOGRAM RULE Copy the vectors $\vec{u}$ and $\vec{v}$. Write the component form of each vector. Then find the sum $\vec{u} + \vec{v}$ and draw the vector $\vec{u} + \vec{v}$.

31.

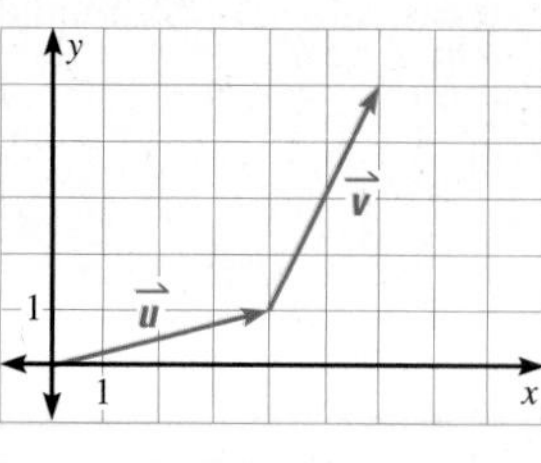

32.

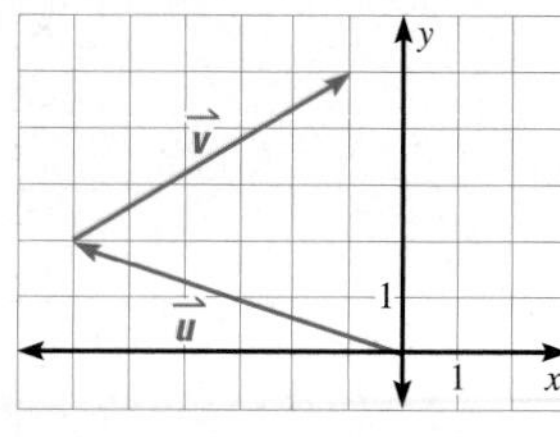

33.

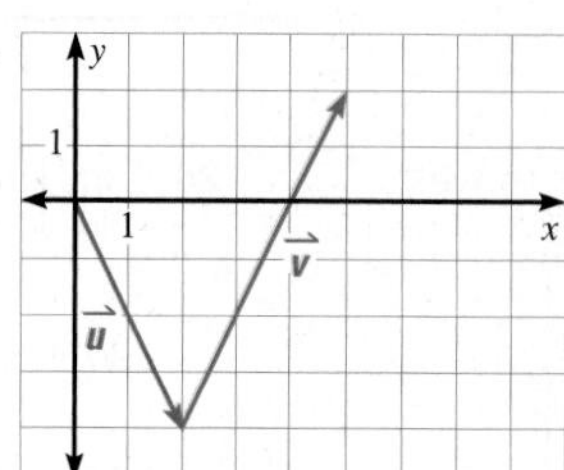

34.

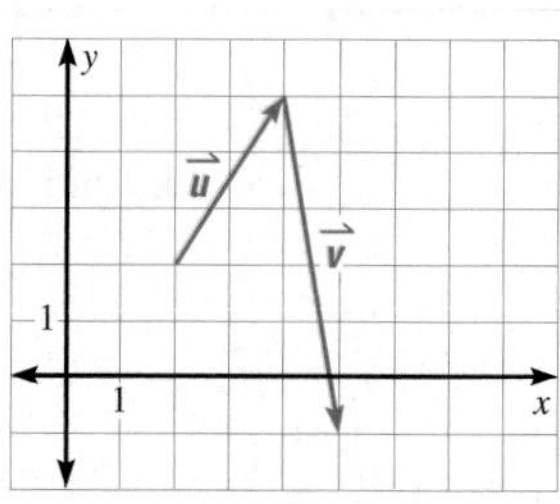

ADDING VECTORS Let $\vec{u} = \langle 7, 3 \rangle$, $\vec{v} = \langle 1, 4 \rangle$, $\vec{w} = \langle 3, 7 \rangle$, and $\vec{z} = \langle -3, -7 \rangle$. Find the given sum.

35. $\vec{v} + \vec{w}$ $\langle 4, 11 \rangle$

36. $\vec{u} + \vec{v}$ $\langle 8, 7 \rangle$

37. $\vec{u} + \vec{w}$ $\langle 10, 10 \rangle$

38. $\vec{v} + \vec{z}$ $\langle -2, -3 \rangle$

39. $\vec{u} + \vec{z}$ $\langle 4, -4 \rangle$

40. $\vec{w} + \vec{z}$ $\langle 0, 0 \rangle$

FOCUS ON APPLICATIONS

SKYDIVING A skydiver who has not yet opened his or her parachute is in *free fall*. During free fall, the skydiver accelerates at first. Air resistance eventually stops this acceleration, and the skydiver falls at *terminal velocity*.

SKYDIVING In Exercises 41–45, use the information and diagram below.

A skydiver is falling at a constant downward velocity of 120 miles per hour. In the diagram, vector $\vec{u}$ represents the skydiver's velocity. A steady breeze pushes the skydiver to the east at 40 miles per hour. Vector $\vec{v}$ represents the wind velocity. The scales on the axes of the graph are in miles per hour.

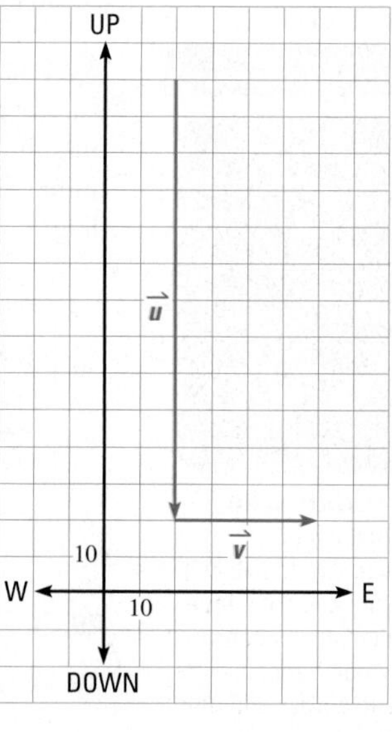

41. Write the vectors $\vec{u}$ and $\vec{v}$ in component form. $\vec{u} = \langle 0, -120 \rangle$; $\vec{v} = \langle 40, 0 \rangle$

42. Let $\vec{s} = \vec{u} + \vec{v}$. Copy the diagram and draw vector $\vec{s}$. See margin.

43. Find the magnitude of $\vec{s}$. What information does the magnitude give you about the skydiver's fall? See margin.

44. If there were no wind, the skydiver would fall in a path that was straight down. At what angle to the ground is the path of the skydiver when the skydiver is affected by the 40 mile per hour wind from the west? about 71.6°

45. Suppose the skydiver was blown to the west at 30 miles per hour. Sketch a new diagram and find the skydiver's new velocity.

See margin for graph. The new velocity is $s = \langle -30, -120 \rangle$.

46. *Writing* Write the component form of a vector with the same magnitude as $\overrightarrow{JK} = \langle 1, 3 \rangle$ but a different direction. Explain how you found the vector. *Sample answer:* $\langle -3, 1 \rangle$; methods may vary.

47. **LOGICAL REASONING** Let vector $\vec{u} = \langle r, s \rangle$. Suppose the horizontal and the vertical components of $\vec{u}$ are multiplied by a constant k. The resulting vector is $\vec{v} = \langle kr, ks \rangle$. How are the magnitudes and the directions of $\vec{u}$ and $\vec{v}$ related when k is positive? when k is negative? Justify your answers. See margin.

Test Preparation

47. When $k > 0$, the magnitude of $\vec{v}$ is k times the magnitude of $\vec{u}$ and the directions are the same. When $k < 0$, the magnitude of $\vec{v}$ is $|k|$ times the magnitude of $\vec{u}$ and the direction of $\vec{v}$ is opposite the direction of $\vec{u}$. Justifications may vary.

48. b. about 10.2 mi/h at a direction of about 11.3° north of east

48. **MULTI-STEP PROBLEM** A motorboat heads due east across a river at a speed of 10 miles per hour. Vector $\vec{u} = \langle 10, 0 \rangle$ represents the velocity of the motorboat. The current of the river is flowing due north at a speed of 2 miles per hour. Vector $\vec{v} = \langle 0, 2 \rangle$ represents the velocity of the current.

a. Let $\vec{s} = \vec{u} + \vec{v}$. Draw the vectors $\vec{u}$, $\vec{v}$, and $\vec{s}$ in a coordinate plane. See margin for graph.

b. Find the speed and the direction of the motorboat as it is affected by the current.

c. Suppose the speed of the motorboat is greater than 10 miles per hour, and the speed of the current is less than 2 miles per hour. Describe one possible set of vectors $\vec{u}$ and $\vec{v}$ that could represent the velocity of the motorboat and the velocity of the current. Write and solve a word problem that can be solved by finding the sum of the two vectors. *Sample answer:* $\vec{u} = \langle 12, 0 \rangle$ and $\vec{v} = \langle 0, 1.75 \rangle$; See margin for word problem.

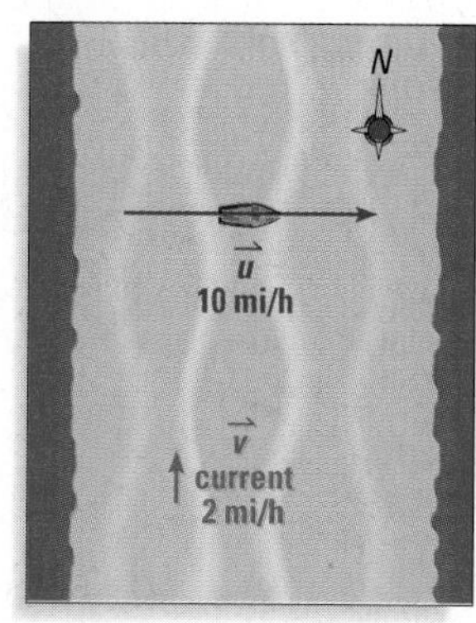

★ Challenge

48. c. A motorboat heads due east across a river at a speed of 12 mi/h. The current of the river is flowing due north at a speed of 1.75 mi/h. Find the speed and the velocity of the motorboat as it is affected by the current of the river. Answer: The speed is about 12.1 mi/h, and the velocity is given by the vector $\vec{u} + \vec{v} = \langle 12, 1.75 \rangle$.

52. The answer to Ex. 50 is a vector which gives the final position of the bumper car, while the answer to Ex. 51 is a number which gives the total distance traveled by the bumper car.

BUMPER CARS In Exercises 49–52, use the information below.

As shown in the diagram below, a bumper car moves from point A to point B to point C and back to point A. The car follows the path shown by the vectors. The magnitude of each vector represents the distance traveled by the car from the initial point to the terminal point.

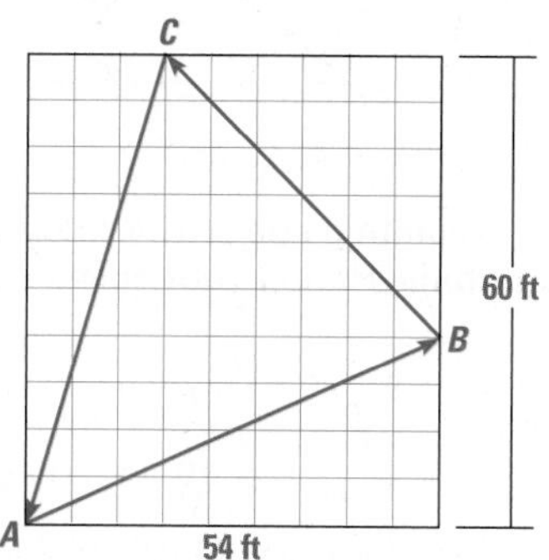

49. Find the sum of $\overrightarrow{AB}$ and $\overrightarrow{BC}$. Write the sum vector in component form. $\langle 18, 60 \rangle$

50. Add vector $\overrightarrow{CA}$ to the sum vector from Exercise 49. $\langle 0, 0 \rangle$

51. Find the total distance traveled by the car. about 173 ft

52. Compare your answers to Exercises 50 and 51. Why are they different? See margin.

EXTRA CHALLENGE
www.mcdougallittell.com

ENGLISH LEARNERS

EXERCISE 47 The structure of the language in Exercise 47 may cause difficulties for some English learners. You may want to read the three informational sentences aloud, offering explanations as necessary, and then have students carry out the reasoning task independently.

48a.

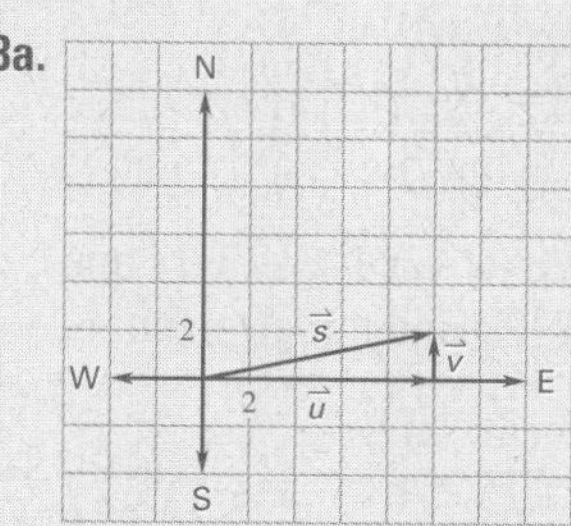

ADDITIONAL PRACTICE AND RETEACHING

For Lesson 9.7:

- Practice Levels A, B, and C (*Chapter 9 Resource Book*, p. 103)
- Reteaching with Practice (*Chapter 9 Resource Book*, p. 106)
- See Lesson 9.7 of the *Personal Student Tutor*

For more Mixed Review:

- Search the *Test and Practice Generator* for key words or specific lessons.

4 ASSESS

DAILY HOMEWORK QUIZ

Transparency Available

Draw vector $\overrightarrow{PQ}$ in a coordinate plane. Write the component form of the vector and find its magnitude. Round your answer to the nearest tenth. **Check students' drawings.**

1. $P(-2, -3)$, $Q(1, 4)$ $\langle 3, 7 \rangle$; 7.6

2. $P(-4, 5)$, $Q(3, -1)$ $\langle 7, -6 \rangle$; 9.2

Let $\vec{a} = \langle 4, -2 \rangle$, $\vec{b} = \langle -3, 1 \rangle$, and $\vec{c} = \langle 7, 2 \rangle$. Find the given sum.

3. $\vec{b} + \vec{c}$ $\langle 4, 3 \rangle$

4. $\vec{a} + \vec{c}$ $\langle 11, 0 \rangle$

EXTRA CHALLENGE NOTE

Challenge problems for Lesson 9.7 are available in **blackline** format in the *Chapter 9 Resource Book*, p. 110 and at **www.mcdougallittell.com.**

ADDITIONAL TEST PREPARATION

1. WRITING Summarize how to identify equal vectors and parallel vectors. *Sample answer:* Two vectors are equal if they have the same magnitude and direction. Two vectors are parallel if they have the same or opposite directions.

11.

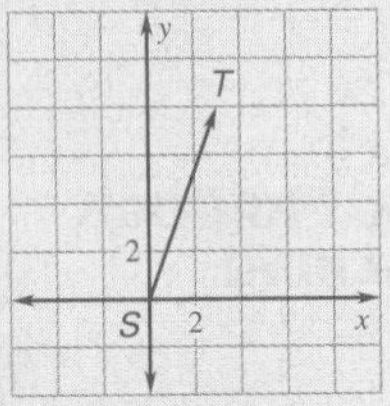

MIXED REVIEW

53. Since $\angle D$ and $\angle E$ are rt. △s and all rt. △s are ≅, $\angle D \cong \angle E$. Since $\triangle ABC$ is equilateral, $AB \cong BC$. $\overline{DE} \parallel \overline{AC}$, so $\angle DBA \cong \angle BAC$ and $\angle EBC \cong \angle BCA$ by the Alternate Interior Angles Thm. An equilateral triangle is also equiangular, so $m\angle BAC = m\angle BCA = 60°$. By the def. of ≅ △s and the substitution prop. of equality, $\angle DBA \cong \angle EBC$. $\triangle ADB \cong \triangle CEB$ by the AAS Congruence Thm. Corresponding parts of ≅ △s are ≅, so $\overline{DB} \cong \overline{EB}$. By the def. of midpoint, B is the midpoint of $\overline{DE}$.

53. PROOF Use the information and the diagram to write a proof. **(Review 4.5)**

GIVEN ▶ $\angle D$ and $\angle E$ are right angles; $\triangle ABC$ is equilateral; $\overline{DE} \parallel \overline{AC}$

PROVE ▶ B is the midpoint of $\overline{DE}$.

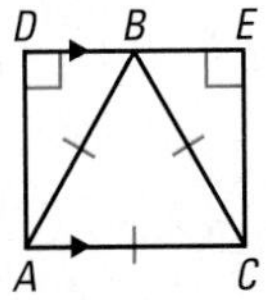

USING ALGEBRA Find the values of x and y. **(Review 4.6)**

54.

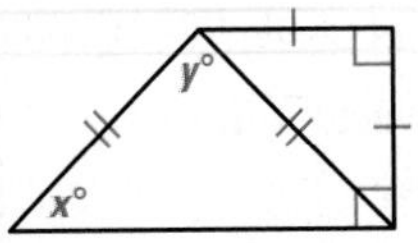

$x = 45$, $y = 90$

55.

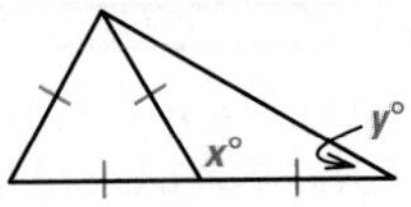

$x = 120$, $y = 30$

56.

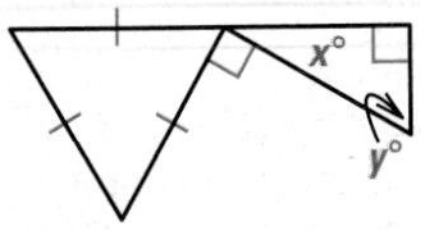

$x = 30$, $y = 60$

USING ALGEBRA Find the product. **(Skills Review, p. 798, for 10.1)**

57. $(x + 1)^2$ $x^2 + 2x + 1$

58. $(x + 7)^2$ $x^2 + 14x + 49$

59. $(x + 11)^2$ $x^2 + 22x + 121$

60. $(7 + x)^2$ $49 + 14x + x^2$

QUIZ 3

Self-Test for Lessons 9.6 and 9.7

1. $a = 41.7$, $b = 19.4$, $m\angle A = 65°$
2. $y = 12$, $z = 17.0$, $m\angle Y = 45°$
3. $m = 13.4$, $q = 20.9$, $m\angle N = 50°$
4. $p = 7.7$, $q = 2.1$, $m\angle Q = 15°$
5. $f = 4.7$, $m\angle F = 37.9°$, $m\angle G = 52.1°$
6. $\ell = 12.0$, $m\angle K = 14.0°$, $m\angle L = 76.0°$

Solve the right triangle. Round decimals to the nearest tenth. **(Lesson 9.6)**

1.

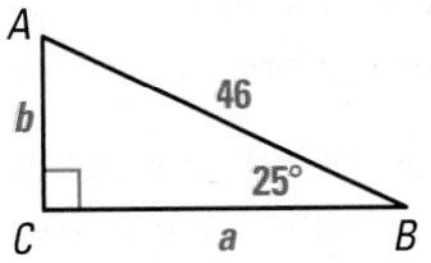

2.

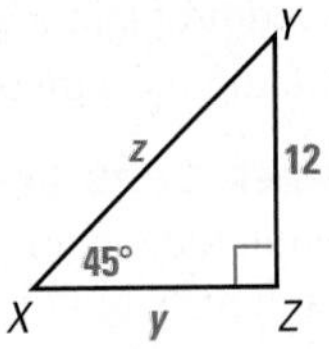

3.

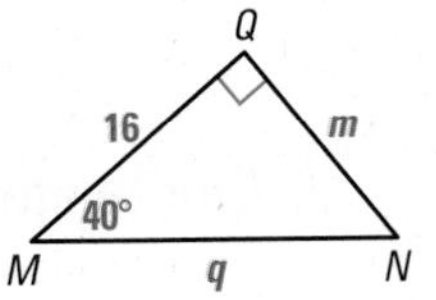

4.

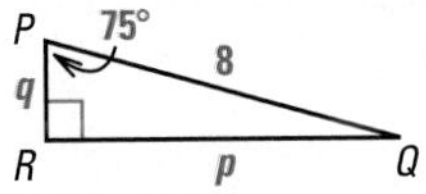

5.

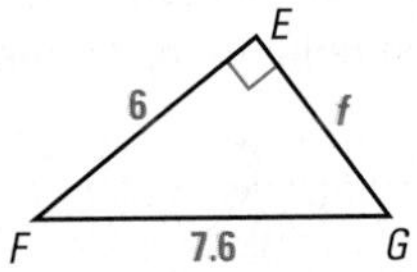

6.

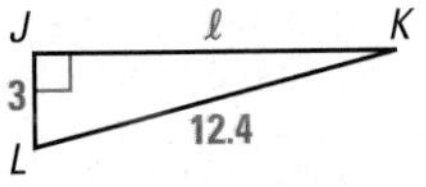

Draw vector $\overrightarrow{PQ}$ in a coordinate plane. Write the component form of the vector and find its magnitude. Round your answer to the nearest tenth. **(Lesson 9.7)**

7. $P(3, 4)$, $Q(-2, 3)$ $\langle -5, -1 \rangle$; 5.1

8. $P(-2, 2)$, $Q(4, -3)$ $\langle 6, -5 \rangle$; 7.8

9. $P(0, -1)$, $Q(3, 4)$ $\langle 3, 5 \rangle$; 5.8

10. $P(2, 6)$, $Q(-5, -5)$ $\langle -7, -11 \rangle$; 13.0

11. Vector $\overrightarrow{ST} = \langle 3, 8 \rangle$. Draw $\overrightarrow{ST}$ in a coordinate plane and find its direction relative to east. **(Lesson 9.7)** **See margin. about 69° north of east**

Let $\vec{u} = \langle 0, -5 \rangle$, $\vec{v} = \langle 4, 7 \rangle$, $\vec{w} = \langle -2, -3 \rangle$, and $\vec{z} = \langle 2, 6 \rangle$. Find the given sum. **(Lesson 9.7)**

12. $\vec{u} + \vec{v}$ $\langle 4, 2 \rangle$

13. $\vec{v} + \vec{w}$ $\langle 2, 4 \rangle$

14. $\vec{u} + \vec{w}$ $\langle -2, -8 \rangle$

15. $\vec{u} + \vec{z}$ $\langle 2, 1 \rangle$

16. $\vec{v} + \vec{z}$ $\langle 6, 13 \rangle$

17. $\vec{w} + \vec{z}$ $\langle 0, 3 \rangle$

CHAPTER 9

Chapter Summary

WHAT did you learn?	*WHY did you learn it?*
Solve problems involving similar right triangles formed by the altitude drawn to the hypotenuse of a right triangle. **(9.1)**	Find a height in a real-life structure, such as the height of a triangular roof. **(p. 528)**
Use the Pythagorean Theorem. **(9.2)**	Solve real-life problems, such as finding the length of a skywalk support beam. **(p. 537)**
Use the Converse of the Pythagorean Theorem. **(9.3)**	Use in construction methods, such as verifying whether a foundation is rectangular. **(p. 545)**
Use side lengths to classify triangles by their angle measures. **(9.3)**	Write proofs about triangles. **(p. 547)**
Find side lengths of special right triangles. **(9.4)**	Solve real-life problems, such as finding the height of a loading platform. **(p. 553)**
Find trigonometric ratios of an acute angle. **(9.5)**	Measure distances indirectly, such as the depth of a crater on the moon. **(p. 564)**
Solve a right triangle. **(9.6)**	Solve real-life problems, such as finding the glide angle and altitude of the space shuttle. **(p. 569)**
Find the magnitude and the direction of a vector. **(9.7)**	Describe physical quantities, such as the speed and direction of a ship. **(p. 574)**
Find the sum of two vectors. **(9.7)**	Model real-life motion, such as the path of a skydiver. **(p. 578)**

How does Chapter 9 fit into the BIGGER PICTURE of geometry?

In this chapter, you studied two of the most important theorems in mathematics—the Pythagorean Theorem and its converse. You were also introduced to a branch of mathematics called *trigonometry*. Properties of right triangles allow you to estimate distances and angle measures that cannot be measured directly. These properties are important tools in areas such as surveying, construction, and navigation.

STUDY STRATEGY

What did you learn about right triangles?

Your lists about what you knew and what you expected to learn about right triangles, following the study strategy on page 526, may resemble this one.

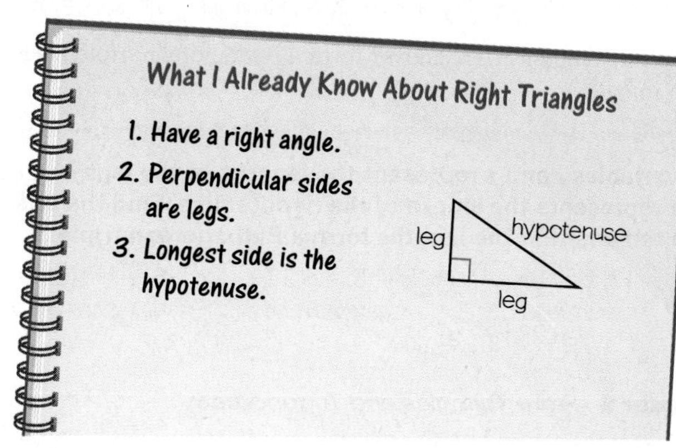

What I Already Know About Right Triangles
1. Have a right angle.
2. Perpendicular sides are legs.
3. Longest side is the hypotenuse.
leg
hypotenuse
leg
581

ADDITIONAL RESOURCES

The following resources are available to help review the material in this chapter.

- Chapter Review Games and Activities (*Chapter 9 Resource Book*, p. 111)
- *Geometry in Motion video*
- *Personal Student Tutor*
- Cumulative Review, Chs. 1–9 (*Chapter 9 Resource Book*, p. 123)

CHAPTER 9

Chapter Review

- Pythagorean triple, p. 536
- special right triangles, p. 551
- trigonometric ratio, p. 558
- sine, p. 558
- cosine, p. 558
- tangent, p. 558
- angle of elevation, p. 561
- solve a right triangle, p. 567
- magnitude of a vector, p. 573
- direction of a vector, p. 574
- equal vectors, p. 574
- parallel vectors, p. 574
- sum of two vectors, p. 575

9.1 SIMILAR RIGHT TRIANGLES

Examples on pp. 528–530

EXAMPLES

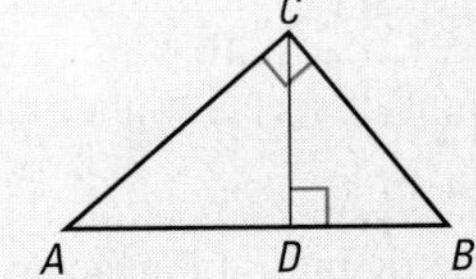

$\triangle ACB \sim \triangle CDB$, so $\frac{DB}{CB} = \frac{CB}{AB}$. CB is the geometric mean of DB and AB.

$\triangle ADC \sim \triangle ACB$, so $\frac{AD}{AC} = \frac{AC}{AB}$. AC is the geometric mean of AD and AB.

$\triangle CDB \sim \triangle ADC$, so $\frac{DA}{DC} = \frac{DC}{DB}$. DC is the geometric mean of DA and DB.

Find the value of each variable.

1.

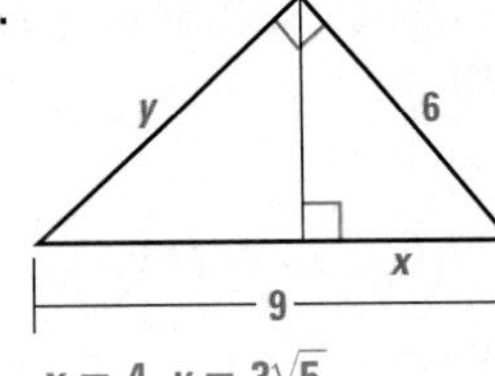

$x = 4$, $y = 3\sqrt{5}$

2.

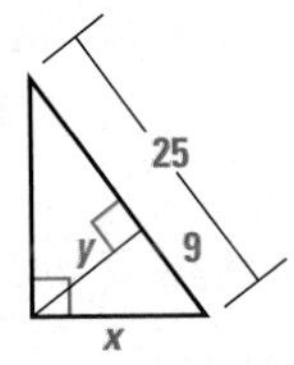

$x = 15$, $y = 12$

3.

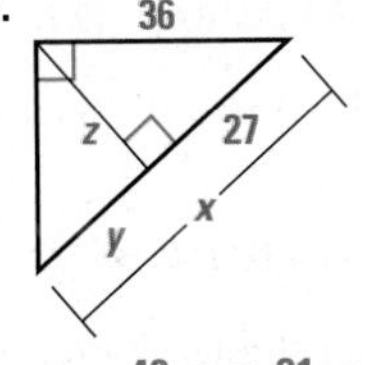

$x = 48$, $y = 21$, $z = 9\sqrt{7}$

9.2 THE PYTHAGOREAN THEOREM

Examples on pp. 536–537

EXAMPLE You can use the Pythagorean Theorem to find the value of r.

$17^2 = r^2 + 15^2$, or $289 = r^2 + 225$. Then $64 = r^2$, so $r = 8$.

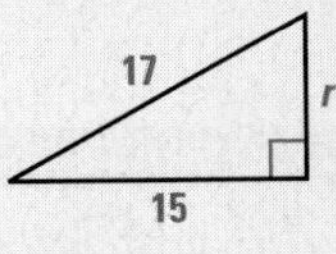

The side lengths 8, 15, and 17 form a Pythagorean triple because they are integers.

The variables *r* and *s* represent the lengths of the legs of a right triangle, and *t* represents the length of the hypotenuse. Find the unknown value. Then tell whether the lengths form a Pythagorean triple.

4. $r = 12$, $s = 16$ $t = 20$; yes

5. $r = 8$, $t = 12$ $s = 4\sqrt{5}$; no

6. $s = 16$, $t = 34$ $r = 30$; yes

7. $r = 4$, $s = 6$ $t = 2\sqrt{13}$; no

9.3 THE CONVERSE OF THE PYTHAGOREAN THEOREM

Examples on pp. 543–545

EXAMPLES You can use side lengths to classify a triangle by its angle measures. Let a, b, and c represent the side lengths of a triangle, with c as the length of the longest side.

If $c^2 = a^2 + b^2$, the triangle is a right triangle: $8^2 = (2\sqrt{7})^2 + 6^2$, so $2\sqrt{7}$, 6, and 8 are the side lengths of a right triangle.

If $c^2 < a^2 + b^2$, the triangle is an acute triangle: $12^2 < 8^2 + 9^2$, so 8, 9, and 12 are the side lengths of an acute triangle.

If $c^2 > a^2 + b^2$, the triangle is an obtuse triangle: $8^2 > 5^2 + 6^2$, so 5, 6, and 8 are the side lengths of an obtuse triangle.

Decide whether the numbers can represent the side lengths of a triangle. If they can, classify the triangle as *acute, right,* or *obtuse*.

8. 6, 7, 10 yes; obtuse **9.** 9, 40, 41 yes; right **10.** 8, 12, 20 no **11.** 3, $4\sqrt{5}$, 9 yes; acute

9.4 SPECIAL RIGHT TRIANGLES

Examples on pp. 551–553

EXAMPLES Triangles whose angle measures are 45°-45°-90° or 30°-60°-90° are called *special right triangles*.

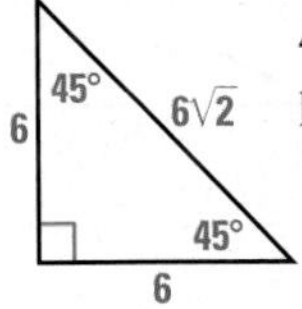

45°-45°-90° triangle
hypotenuse = $\sqrt{2}$ • leg

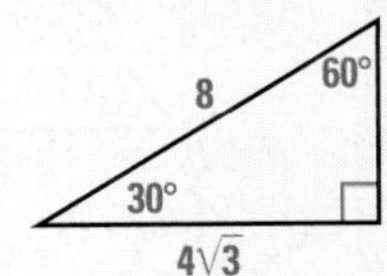

30°-60°-90° triangle
hypotenuse = 2 • shorter leg
longer leg = $\sqrt{3}$ • shorter leg

12. An isosceles right triangle has legs of length $3\sqrt{2}$. Find the length of the hypotenuse. 6

13. A diagonal of a square is 6 inches long. Find its perimeter and its area. $12\sqrt{2} \approx 17.0$ in.; 18 in.^{2}

14. A 30°-60°-90° triangle has a hypotenuse of length 12 inches. What are the lengths of the legs? 6 in. and $6\sqrt{3} \approx 10.4$ in.

15. An equilateral triangle has sides of length 18 centimeters. Find the length of an altitude of the triangle. Then find the area of the triangle. $9\sqrt{3}$ cm; $81\sqrt{3} \approx 140.3$ cm^2

9.5 TRIGONOMETRIC RATIOS

Examples on pp. 558–561

EXAMPLE A trigonometric ratio is a ratio of the lengths of two sides of a right triangle.

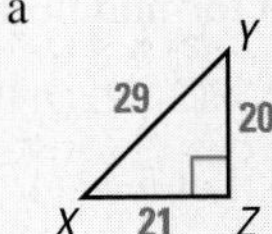

$\sin X = \frac{\text{opp.}}{\text{hyp.}} = \frac{20}{29}$ $\cos X = \frac{\text{adj.}}{\text{hyp.}} = \frac{21}{29}$ $\tan X = \frac{\text{opp.}}{\text{adj.}} = \frac{20}{21}$

9.5 continued

Find the sine, the cosine, and the tangent of the acute angles of the triangle. Express each value as a decimal rounded to four places.

16.

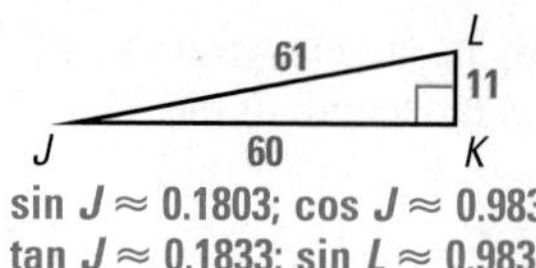

$\sin J \approx 0.1803$; $\cos J \approx 0.9836$; $\tan J \approx 0.1833$; $\sin L \approx 0.9836$; $\cos L \approx 0.1803$; $\tan L \approx 5.4545$

17.

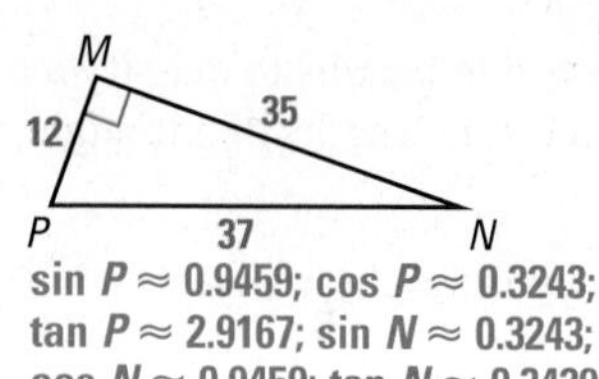

$\sin P \approx 0.9459$; $\cos P \approx 0.3243$; $\tan P \approx 2.9167$; $\sin N \approx 0.3243$; $\cos N \approx 0.9459$; $\tan N \approx 0.3429$

18.

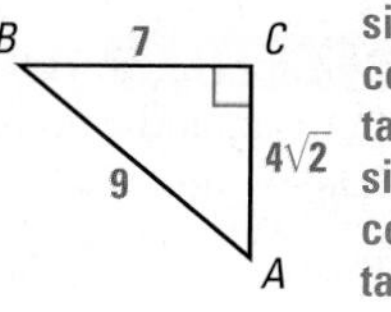

$\sin A \approx 0.7778$; $\cos A \approx 0.6285$; $\tan A \approx 1.2374$; $\sin B \approx 0.6285$; $\cos B \approx 0.7778$; $\tan B \approx 0.8081$

9.6 SOLVING RIGHT TRIANGLES

Examples on pp. 568–569

EXAMPLE To solve $\triangle ABC$, begin by using the Pythagorean Theorem to find the length of the hypotenuse.

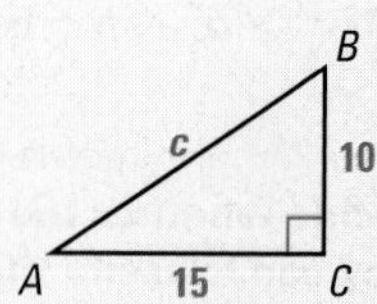

$$c^2 = 10^2 + 15^2 = 325. \text{ So, } c = \sqrt{325} = 5\sqrt{13}.$$

Then find $m\angle A$ and $m\angle B$.

$$\tan A = \frac{10}{15} = \frac{2}{3}. \text{ Use a calculator to find that } m\angle A \approx 33.7°.$$

Then $m\angle B = 90° - m\angle A \approx 90° - 33.7° = 56.3°$.

Solve the right triangle. Round decimals to the nearest tenth.

19.

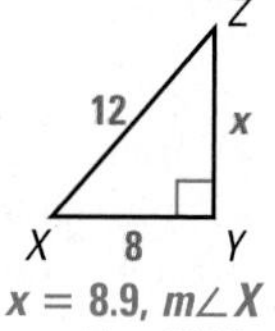

$x = 8.9$, $m\angle X = 48.2°$, $m\angle Z = 41.8°$

20.

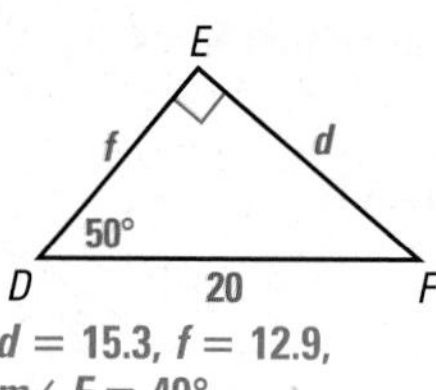

$d = 15.3$, $f = 12.9$, $m\angle F = 40°$

21.

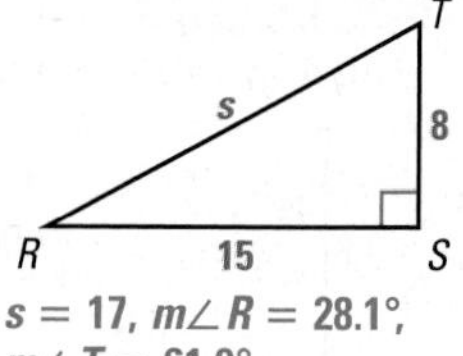

$s = 17$, $m\angle R = 28.1°$, $m\angle T = 61.9°$

9.7 VECTORS

Examples on pp. 573–575

EXAMPLES You can use the Distance Formula to find the magnitude of $\overrightarrow{PQ}$.

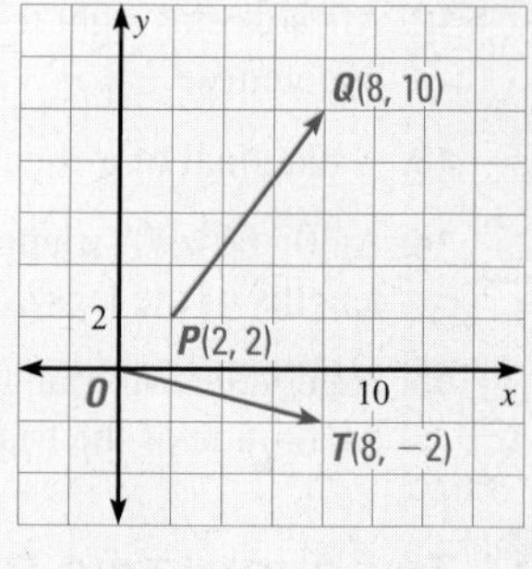

$$|\overrightarrow{PQ}| = \sqrt{(8-2)^2 + (10-2)^2} = \sqrt{6^2 + 8^2} = \sqrt{100} = 10$$

To add vectors, find the sum of their horizontal components and the sum of their vertical components.

$$\overrightarrow{PQ} + \overrightarrow{OT} = \langle 6, 8 \rangle + \langle 8, -2 \rangle = \langle 6 + 8, 8 + (-2) \rangle = \langle 14, 6 \rangle$$

Draw vector $\overrightarrow{PQ}$ in a coordinate plane. Write the component form of the vector and find its magnitude. Round decimals to the nearest tenth.

22. $P(2, 3)$, $Q(1, -1)$ $\langle -1, -4 \rangle$; 4.1

23. $P(-6, 3)$, $Q(6, -2)$ $\langle 12, -5 \rangle$; 13

24. $P(-2, 0)$, $Q(1, 2)$ $\langle 3, 2 \rangle$; 3.6

25. Let $\vec{u} = \langle 1, 2 \rangle$ and $\vec{v} = \langle 13, 7 \rangle$. Find $\vec{u} + \vec{v}$. Find the magnitude of the sum vector and its direction relative to east. $\langle 14, 9 \rangle$; about 16.6; about 32.7° north of east

CHAPTER 9

Chapter Test

Use the diagram at the right to match the angle or segment with its measure. (Some measures are rounded to two decimal places.)

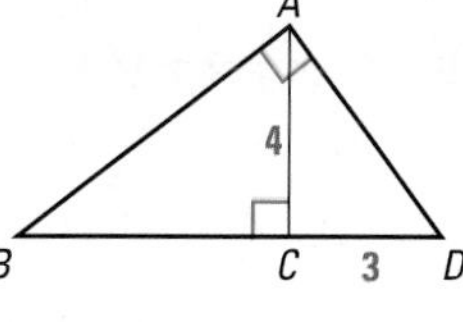

1. $\overline{AB}$ E	**A.** 5.33
2. $\overline{BC}$ A	**B.** 36.87°
3. $\overline{AD}$ C	**C.** 5
4. $\angle BAC$ D	**D.** 53.13°
5. $\angle CAD$ B	**E.** 6.67

6. Refer to the diagram above. Complete the following statement:

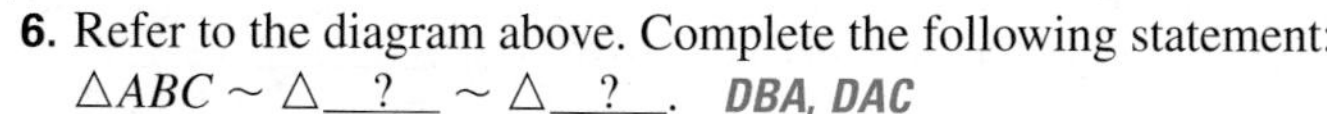

$\triangle ABC \sim \triangle$ __?__ $\sim \triangle$ __?__. ***DBA, DAC***

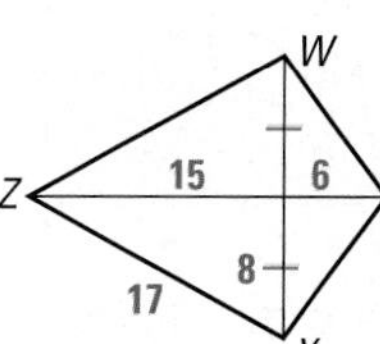

7. Classify quadrilateral *WXYZ* in the diagram at the right. Explain your reasoning.

7. A kite; since $8^2 + 15^2 = 17^2$, the diagonals intersect at right angles. *WXYZ* can be divided into two pairs of ≅ ⚠ by the SAS Congruence Post. Then, since $6^2 + 8^2 = 10^2$, *WXYZ* contains two pairs of consecutive ≅ sides, but opposite sides are not ≅. By the definition of a kite, *WXYZ* is a kite.

8. The vertices of $\triangle PQR$ are $P(-2, 3)$, $Q(3, 1)$, and $R(0, -3)$. Decide whether $\triangle PQR$ is *right*, *acute*, or *obtuse*. **acute**

9. Complete the following statement: 15, _?_, and 113 form a Pythagorean triple. **112**

10. The measure of one angle of a rhombus is 60°. The perimeter of the rhombus is 24 inches. Sketch the rhombus and give its side lengths. Then find its area.
See margin for graph. Each side has length 6 in.; $18\sqrt{3} \approx 31.2$ in.^{2}

Solve the right triangle. Round decimals to the nearest tenth.

11. **side lengths: 4.5, 7.8, and 9; angle measures: 90°, 30°, and 60°**

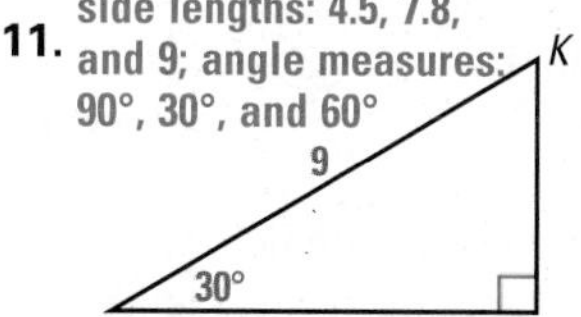

12.

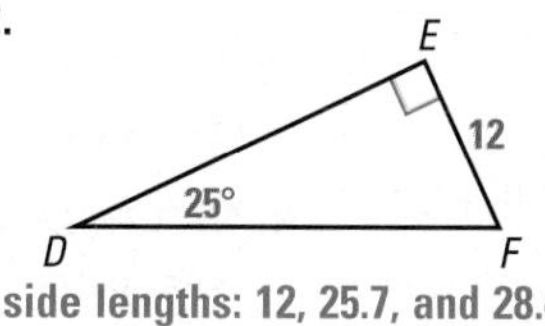

side lengths: 12, 25.7, and 28.4; angle measures: 90°, 25°, and 65°

13.

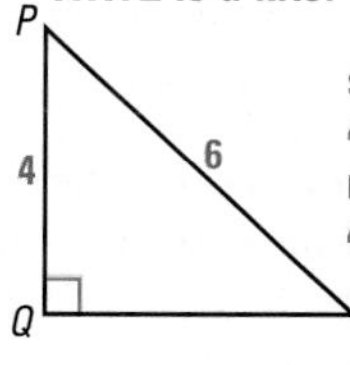

side lengths: 4.5, 4, and 6; angle measures: 90°, 41.8°, and 48.2°

14. $L = (3, 7)$ and $M = (7, 4)$ are the initial and the terminal points of $\overrightarrow{LM}$. Draw $\overrightarrow{LM}$ in a coordinate plane. Write the component form of the vector. Then find its magnitude and direction relative to east. **Check drawings. $\langle 4, -3 \rangle$; 5; about 37° south of east**

15. Find the lengths of $\overline{CD}$ and $\overline{AB}$. **about 6.4; about 13.1**

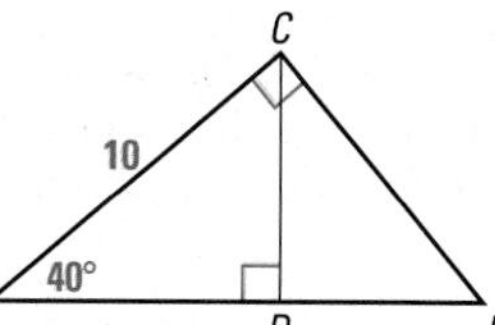

16. Find the measure of $\angle BCA$ and the length of $\overline{DE}$. **55°; about 32.8**

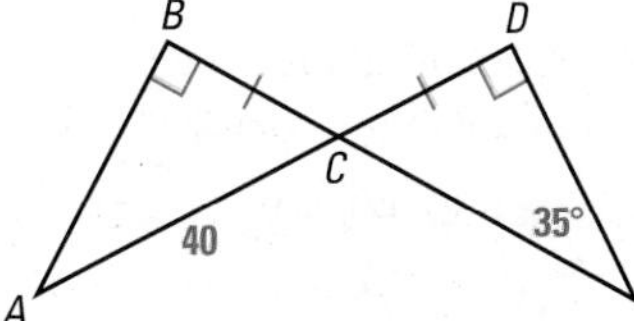

Let $\vec{u} = \langle 0, -5 \rangle$, $\vec{v} = \langle -2, -3 \rangle$, and $\vec{w} = \langle 4, 6 \rangle$. Find the given sum.

17. $\vec{u} + \vec{v}$ **$\langle -2, -8 \rangle$**

18. $\vec{u} + \vec{w}$ **$\langle 4, 1 \rangle$**

19. $\vec{v} + \vec{w}$ **$\langle 2, 3 \rangle$**

ADDITIONAL RESOURCES

- ***Chapter 9 Resource Book***
  Chapter Test (3 levels) (p. 112)
  SAT/ACT Chapter Test (p. 118)
  Alternative Assessment (p. 119)
- ***Test and Practice Generator***

10.

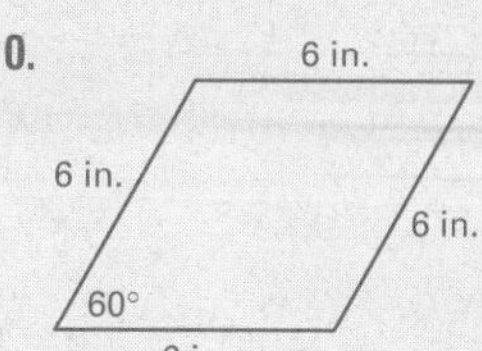

ADDITIONAL RESOURCES

- *Chapter 9 Resource Book*
  Chapter Test (3 levels) (p. 112)
  SAT/ACT Chapter Test (p. 118)
  Alternative Assessment (p. 119)
- *Test and Practice Generator*

CHAPTER 9

Chapter Standardized Test

TEST-TAKING STRATEGY When checking your work, try to use a method other than the one you originally used to get your answer. If you use the same method, you may make the same mistake twice.

1. **MULTIPLE CHOICE** Use the diagram to find the value of x. C

   (A) 6 (B) 7 (C) 9 (D) 10 (E) 11

In Questions 2 and 3, use the diagram below.

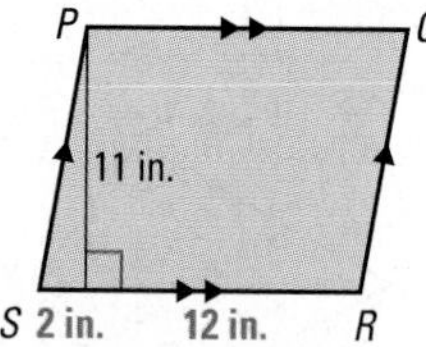

2. **MULTIPLE CHOICE** Find the area of $\square PQRS$. C

   (A) 132 in.^{2} (B) 143 in.^{2} (C) 154 in.^{2} (D) 156 in.^{2} (E) 166 in.^{2}

3. **MULTIPLE CHOICE** Find the perimeter of $\square PQRS$ rounded to the nearest tenth. D

   (A) 44.4 in. (B) 46.4 in. (C) 50 in. (D) 50.4 in. (E) 52.4 in.

4. **MULTIPLE CHOICE** Let the numbers represent the lengths of the sides of a triangle. Which of the triangles are right triangles? B

   I. 11, 14, $\sqrt{317}$ **II.** 7, 26, $5\sqrt{30}$
   III. 18, $2\sqrt{19}$, 20 **IV.** 9, 25, 27

   (A) I, II, and III only (B) I and III only (C) III only (D) IV only (E) none

5. **MULTIPLE CHOICE** Which set of numbers can represent the side lengths of an obtuse triangle? D

   (A) 71, 70, 68 (B) 30, 40, 50 (C) 41, 39, 2 (D) 25, 25, 40 (E) 17, 17, $17\sqrt{2}$

6. **MULTIPLE CHOICE** The length of a diagonal of a square is 16 inches. What is its perimeter? D

   (A) $8\sqrt{2}$ in. (B) $16\sqrt{2}$ in. (C) $30\sqrt{2}$ in. (D) $32\sqrt{2}$ in. (E) $48\sqrt{2}$ in.

7. **MULTIPLE CHOICE** Use the diagram below to find the values of x and y. The values are rounded to the nearest tenth. E

   (A) $x = 8.7, y = 18.8$
   (B) $x = 18.8, y = 20.1$
   (C) $x = 14.4, y = 19.2$
   (D) $x = 12.6, y = 18.5$
   (E) $x = 18.8, y = 20.5$

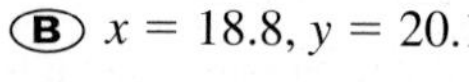

8. **MULTIPLE CHOICE** The base of an isosceles triangle is 18 centimeters long. The altitude to the base is 12 centimeters long. What is the approximate measure of a base angle of the triangle? A

   (A) 53.1° (B) 36.9° (C) 38.7° (D) 33.7° (E) 56.3°

9. **MULTIPLE CHOICE** In the diagram below, what is the measure of $\angle A$ to the nearest tenth of a degree? B

   (A) 31.6° (B) 38.0° (C) 38.7° (D) 51.3° (E) 52.0°

10. **MULTIPLE CHOICE** Let $\vec{v} = \langle -2, y\rangle$ and $\vec{w} = \langle x, 4\rangle$. If $\vec{v} + \vec{w} = \langle 6, 11\rangle$, what are the values of x and y? B

   (A) $x = 8, y = 8$ (B) $x = 8, y = 7$ (C) $x = 7, y = 8$ (D) $x = -8, y = 7$ (E) $x = 4, y = 7$

11. MULTIPLE CHOICE Points $A(-8, 3)$ and $B(1, -9)$ are the initial and the terminal points of $\overrightarrow{AB}$. Find the magnitude of $\overrightarrow{AB}$. D

(A) $\langle 9, -12 \rangle$ (B) $\langle -9, 12 \rangle$ (C) 225 (D) 15 (E) $\langle -7, -6 \rangle$

MULTI-STEP PROBLEM In Exercises 12–14, use the diagram at the right.

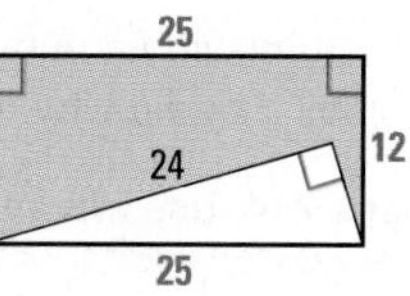

12. Find the perimeter of the right triangle. 56

13. Find the measures of the acute angles of the right triangle. about 73.7° and 16.3°

14. Find the area of the shaded region. 216 square units

MULTI-STEP PROBLEM In Exercises 15–18, use the diagram at the right. Round decimals to the nearest tenth.

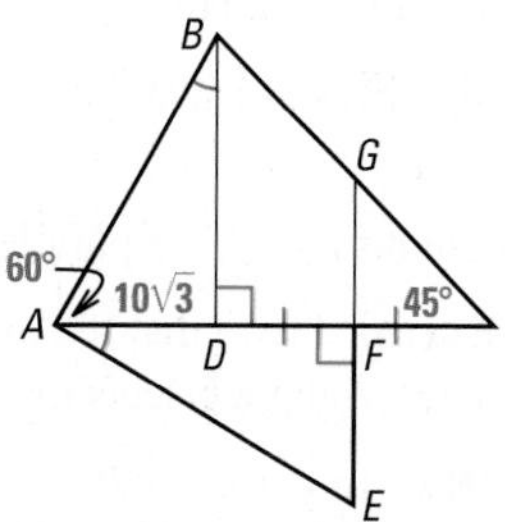

15. Find each of the following segment lengths: BD, BC, FG, GC, DC, and AF. 30; 42.4; 15; 21.2; 30; 32.3

16. Find $m\angle ABC$, $m\angle FEA$, and $m\angle BGF$. 75° ; 60° ; 135°

17. Find the approximate lengths of $\overline{FE}$ and $\overline{AE}$. 18.7; 37.3

18. Find the area of $\triangle ABC$. about 709.8 square units

MULTI-STEP PROBLEM In Exercises 19–22, use the information and the diagram.

You can use a device like the one shown to measure the sun's angle of elevation, $\angle A$, above the horizon. The variable b represents the length of the shadow cast by a vertical marker on a ruler.

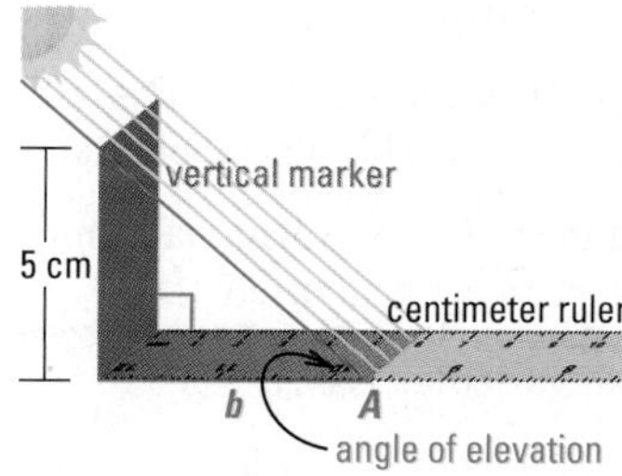

19. Find the shadow length b for each of the angle measures below.

a. $m\angle A = 30°$ 8.7 cm

b. $m\angle A = 40°$ 6.0 cm

c. $m\angle A = 50°$ 4.2 cm

d. $m\angle A = 60°$ 2.9 cm

e. $m\angle A = 70°$ 1.8 cm

20. Based on your answers to Exercise 19, what happens to the value of b as the sun rises in the sky? The value of b decreases.

21. At a certain hour, the shadow length b is 5.25 centimeters. Estimate the sun's angle of elevation. about 43.6°

22. The amount of Earth's atmosphere that sunlight passes through depends on the position of the sun in the sky. This amount is measured in "air masses." When the sun is not directly overhead, the number of air masses its rays pass through is approximately $\frac{1}{\sin A}$. What happens to the value of this expression as the sun approaches the horizon? This value gets larger and larger.

CHAPTER 9

Cumulative Practice

for Chapters 1–9

1. If three points all lie in two different planes, can the points be the vertices of a triangle? Explain why or why not. **(2.1)** See margin.

In Exercises 2–4, use *always, sometimes,* or *never* to complete the statement.

2. Lines m, n, and t are three different coplanar lines. If $m \perp t$ and $n \perp t$, then line m and line n are __?__ parallel. **(3.1, 3.5)** always

3. The numbers 8, 14, and 23 can __?__ represent the lengths of the sides of a triangle. **(5.5)** never

4. A rhombus is __?__ a parallelogram. **(6.6)** always

5. **PROOF** Prove that the median to the base of an isosceles triangle bisects the vertex angle. **(4.6, 5.3)** See margin.

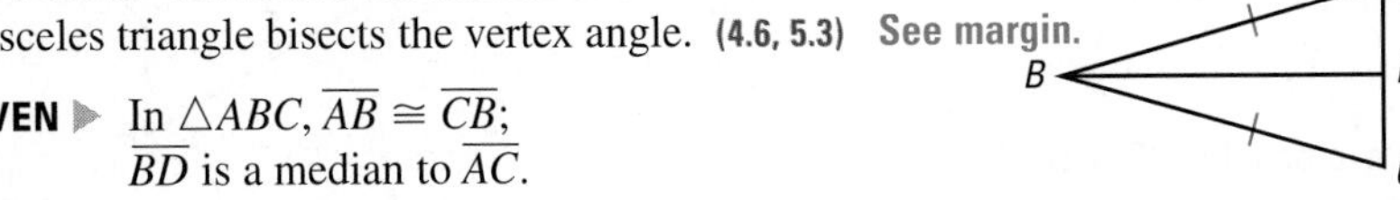

GIVEN ▶ In $\triangle ABC$, $\overline{AB} \cong \overline{CB}$; $\overline{BD}$ is a median to $\overline{AC}$.

PROVE ▶ $\overline{BD}$ bisects $\angle ABC$.

6. In quadrilateral $ABCD$, $m\angle A = 37°$, $m\angle B = 143°$, and $m\angle C = 37°$. Prove that quadrilateral $ABCD$ is a parallelogram. **(6.1, 6.3)** See margin.

7. Does the design at the right have rotational symmetry? If so, describe the rotations that map the image onto itself. **(7.3)**
yes; clockwise and counterclockwise rotational symmetry of 120°

Find the value of each variable. **(3.2, 3.3, 6.5)**

8.

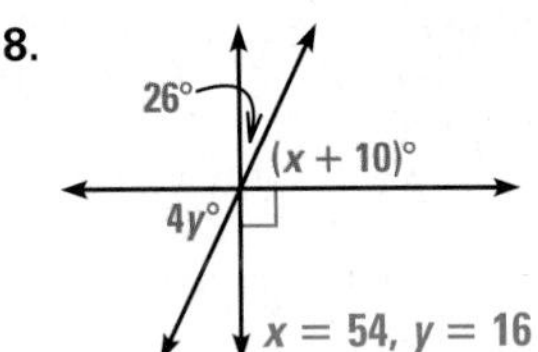

$x = 54$, $y = 16$

9.

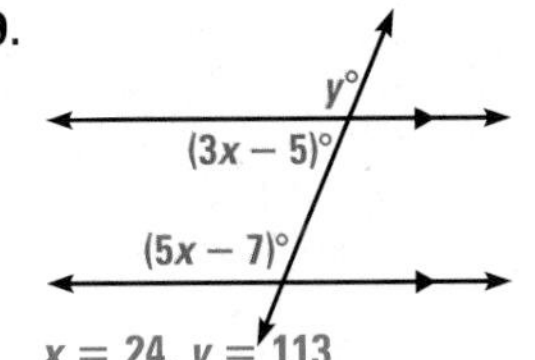

$x = 24$, $y = 113$

10.

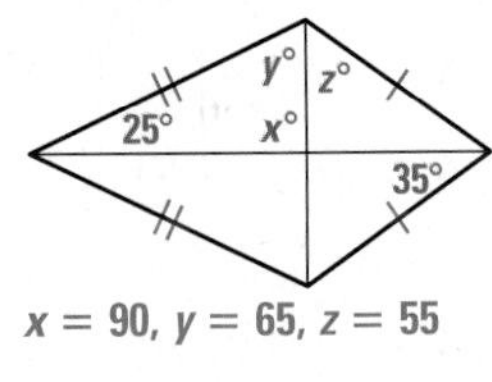

$x = 90$, $y = 65$, $z = 55$

In Exercises 11–15, use $\triangle ABC$ with vertices $A(1, -2)$, $B(-3, -5)$, and $C(-5, 6)$.

11. Find an equation of the perpendicular bisector of $\overline{AC}$. **(5.1)** $y = \frac{3}{4}x + \frac{7}{2}$

12. Classify $\triangle ABC$ by its sides and by its angles. **(4.1, 9.3)** right scalene triangle

13. Find the coordinates of the vertices of the image of $\triangle ABC$ after a reflection in the y-axis. **(7.2)** $A'(-1, -2)$, $B'(3, -5)$, $C'(5, 6)$

14. Find the coordinates of the vertices of the image of $\triangle ABC$ after a rotation of 90° counterclockwise about the origin. **(7.3)** $A'(2, 1)$, $B'(5, -3)$, $C'(-6, -5)$

15. Find the coordinates of the image of $\triangle ABC$ after the translation $(x, y) \rightarrow (x - 4, y - 4)$ and then a reflection in the x-axis. **(7.5)** $A'(-3, 6)$, $B'(-7, 9)$, $C'(-9, -2)$

Solve the proportion. **(8.1)**

16. $\frac{12}{x} = \frac{5}{2}$ 4.8

17. $\frac{3}{7} = \frac{x}{8}$ $3\frac{3}{7}$

18. $\frac{7}{9} = \frac{y}{y + 3}$ 10.5

ADDITIONAL RESOURCES

A Cumulative Review covering Chapters 1–9 is available in the *Chapter 9 Resource Book,* p. 123.

1. No; if two planes intersect, then their intersection is a line. The three points must be collinear, so they cannot be the vertices of a triangle.
5. Paragraph proof: $\overline{BD}$ is the median from point B, $\overline{AD} \cong \overline{CD}$, $\overline{BD} \cong \overline{BD}$, and it is given that $\overline{AB} \cong \overline{CB}$. Thus $\triangle ABD \cong \triangle CBD$ by the SSS Congruence Post. Also, $\angle ABD \cong \angle CBD$ since corresponding parts of $\cong$ ▲ are $\cong$. By the def. of an angle bisector, $\overline{BD}$ bisects $\angle ABC$.
6. Paragraph proof: $ABCD$ is a parallelogram because one of its angles ($\angle B$) is supplementary to both of its consecutive angles ($\angle A$ and $\angle C$).
19. No. In $ABCD$, the ratio of the length to width is 8:6, or 4:3. In $APQD$, the ratio of the length to width is 6:4, or 3:2. Since these ratios are not equal, the rectangles are not similar.
20. *Sample answer:* The midsegment of a triangle is parallel to the third side, and the parallel lines form 2 pairs of corresponding angles that are congruent. So the two triangles are similar by the AA Similarity Postulate.
21. Yes; the ratios $\frac{6}{9}$, $\frac{8}{12}$, and $\frac{12}{18}$ all equal $\frac{2}{3}$, so the triangles are similar by the SSS Similarity Theorem.
23. The image with scale factor $\frac{1}{3}$ has endpoints $\left(2, -\frac{4}{3}\right)$ and $(4, 3)$; its slope is $\frac{13/3}{2} = \frac{13}{6}$. The image with scale factor $\frac{1}{2}$ has endpoints $(3, -2)$ and $(6, 4.5)$; its slope is $\frac{13}{6}$. The two image segments are parallel.

19. Rectangle $ABCD$ has coordinates $A(0, 4)$, $B(8, 4)$, $C(8, -2)$, and $D(0, -2)$. Points P and Q are the midpoints of $\overline{AB}$ and $\overline{DC}$, respectively. Is rectangle $ABCD$ similar to rectangle $APQD$? Explain your answer. **(8.3)** **See margin.**

20. Show that the midsegment of a triangle forms one side of a triangle that is similar to the original triangle. **(5.4, 8.4)** **See margin.**

21. Is a triangle with sides of lengths 6, 8, and 12 similar to a triangle with sides of lengths 9, 12, and 18? Explain your answer. **(8.5)** **See margin.**

22. The side lengths of a triangle are 7 centimeters, 8 centimeters, and 9 centimeters. A ray bisects the largest angle, dividing the side opposite the angle into two segments. Find the lengths of these segments. **(8.6)** **4.2 cm and 4.8 cm**

23. A segment has endpoints at $A(6, -4)$ and $B(12, 9)$. Find the images of the segment under two dilations, one with scale factor $\frac{1}{3}$ and center $(0, 0)$, and the other with scale factor $\frac{1}{2}$ and center $(0, 0)$. Then tell whether the two image segments are parallel. **(8.7)** **See margin.**

In Exercises 24–26, use the diagram at the right.

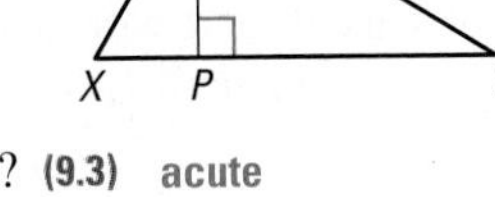

24. If $XP = 2$ and $PY = 6$, find ZP and XZ. **(9.1)** **$2\sqrt{3}$; 4**

25. Find XY if $ZY = 2\sqrt{3}$ and $PY = 3$. **(9.1)** **4**

26. Find XY if $XZ = 10$ and $ZY = 24$. **(9.2)** **26**

27. Is a triangle with side lengths 12, 15, and 19 *acute*, *right*, or *obtuse*? **(9.3)** **acute**

28. A square and an equilateral triangle have sides that are 8 feet long. Find the ratio of the length of a diagonal of the square to the height of the triangle. **(9.4)** **$\frac{2\sqrt{2}}{\sqrt{3}}$, or $\frac{2\sqrt{6}}{3}$**

29. The lengths of the legs of a right triangle are 8 and 15. Find the sine, the cosine, and the tangent of the smaller acute angle of the triangle. Express each value as a fraction. **(9.5)** **Let $\angle A$ be the smaller acute angle. $\sin A = \frac{8}{17}$, $\cos A = \frac{15}{17}$, and $\tan A = \frac{8}{15}$**

30. In right $\triangle RST$, $m\angle R = 57°$. The length of the hypotenuse, $\overline{RS}$, is 20 inches. Solve the right triangle. Round decimals to the nearest tenth. **(9.6)** **side lengths: 10.9, 16.8, and 20; angle measures: 90°, 33°, 57°**

31. Add the vectors $\vec{u} = \langle 5, 7 \rangle$ and $\vec{v} = \langle -3, 9 \rangle$. Draw the sum vector $\vec{u} + \vec{v}$ in a coordinate plane. Find its magnitude and its direction relative to east. **(9.7)** **$\langle 2, 16 \rangle$; about 16.1; about 83° north of east**

32. **JEWELRY DESIGN** A jewelry designer has a triangular piece of flat silver. The designer wants to cut out the largest possible circle from the piece of silver. Explain how to find the center and the radius of that circle. **(5.2)** **See margin.**

33. **CAR TRIP** On the first four days of an automobile trip, a family drove 376 miles on 16 gallons of gasoline. At that rate, how many gallons of gas will they need for the next 470 miles of their trip? **(8.1)** **20 gal**

34. **PHOTOGRAPHY** A 3 inch by 5 inch photograph is enlarged so its perimeter is 36 inches. What are the dimensions of the enlargement? **(8.3)** **$6\frac{3}{4}$ in. by $11\frac{1}{4}$ in.**

35. **AIRPLANES** Two jets leave an airport at the same time. One jet flies west, averaging 510 miles per hour. The other jet flies north, averaging 560 miles per hour. To the nearest tenth of a mile, how far apart are the jets after 15 minutes? **(9.2)** **189.4 mi**

32. **The designer needs to determine the inscribed circle. The designer can find the center of the inscribed circle by finding the intersection point P of two angle bisectors. The designer can find the radius by finding the perpendicular distance from point P to any of the three sides of the triangle.**

PROJECT OVERVIEW

PROJECT GOALS

- Use iteration to produce a simple fractal.
- Find patterns in fractals.
- Use formulas to describe the characteristics such as length or perimeter of a fractal at stage n.

MANAGING THE PROJECT

CLASSROOM MANAGEMENT

The Chapter 9 Project may be completed by individual students or by students working with partners. If students work with a partner they should discuss and agree upon the answers to Exercises 1–7. The partners should make their own sketches of the Koch snowflake and compare their sketches at each stage.

ALTERNATIVE APPROACH

This project can be completed as a class demonstration. Use an overhead projector to display the different stages of the fractal. Exercises 1–4 can be completed as a class. Then have students sketch their own Koch snowflake in Exercise 5 and answer Exercises 6 and 7.

CONCLUDING THE PROJECT

Have each student share part of his or her report with the class. Ask that each student report about something that has not been shared previously by another student.

You might find a book that contains pictures of fractals such as *Turbulent Mirror* by John Briggs & F. David Peat. Share these pictures with the class and have them discuss the self-similarity of the pattern and identify some of the stages.

PROJECT for Chapters 8 and 9

Investigating Fractals

OBJECTIVE **Learn how fractals are formed and explore the properties of fractals.**

Materials: ruler, protractor, graphing calculator, graph paper

A *fractal* is a mathematical object that has the property of *self-similarity*: a part of the shape resembles the whole shape.

Many fractals are formed by a repetitive process called *iteration*. The stages that lead to a simple fractal called a *Koch curve* are shown below.

STAGES OF A KOCH CURVE

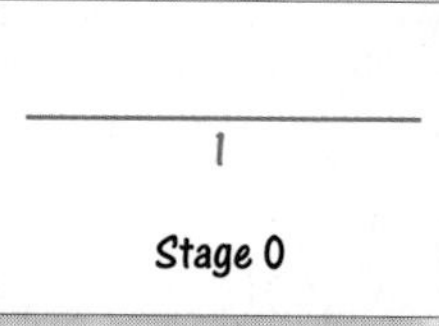

For stage 0, start with a segment of length 1.

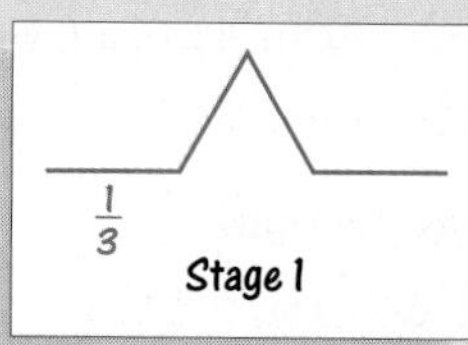

For stage 1, replace the middle third of the segment in stage 0 with two congruent segments of length $\frac{1}{3}$.

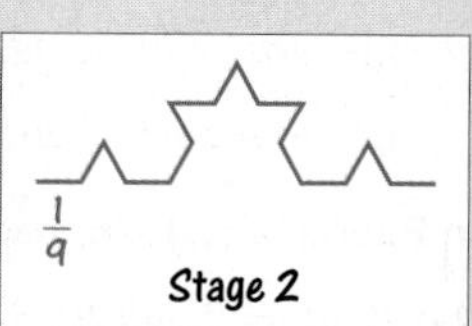

For stage 2, replace the middle third of every segment of stage 1 with two congruent segments of length $\frac{1}{9}$.

For later stages, replace the middle third of every segment of the previous stage with two congruent segments of the appropriate length. The fractal is the shape that would result if you could continue this process infinitely many times.

INVESTIGATION

Copy the table below. Then answer the exercises.

Stage, n	0	1	2	3	4
Length, L	1	?	?	?	?

1. Use the diagrams above to fill in the lengths for stages 1 and 2. $\frac{4}{3}$; $\frac{16}{9}$

2. Look for a pattern in the lengths at stages 0, 1, and 2. Use the pattern to predict the lengths of the Koch curve at stages 3 and 4. See margin.

3. Predict what happens to the length if you repeat this iteration many times. Explain your reasoning. See margin.

4. The length L of the fractal can be written as a function of stage n using this formula: $L = \left(\frac{4}{3}\right)^n$. Use a graphing calculator to sketch a graph of this function. Does the graph support your answer to Exercise 3? Explain.
Yes; the graph is a curve that increases sharply as n, the number of stages, increases.

2. The length at stage 1 is $\frac{4}{3}$ times the length at stage 0, and similarly, the length at stage 2 is $\frac{4}{3}$ the length at stage 1. So, the lengths at stages 3 and 4 are $\frac{64}{27}$ and $\frac{256}{81}$.

3. At each stage the length would be $\frac{4}{3}$ times the previous stage, so the length gets increasingly large.

STAGES OF A KOCH SNOWFLAKE

If you join three Koch curves, you can create a closed shape known as a *Koch snowflake*.

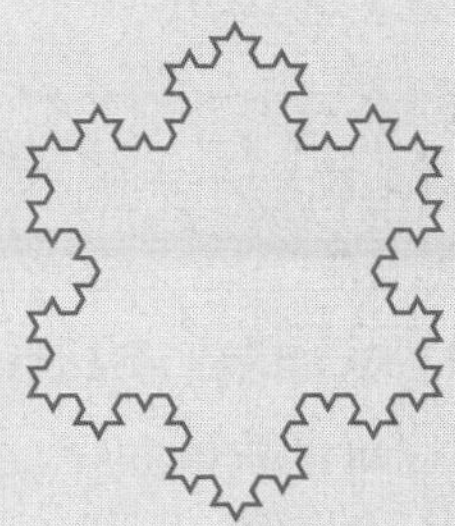

5. Sketch stage 0, stage 1, and stage 2 of the Koch snowflake. **See margin.**

6. Make a table like the one on the previous page to find the perimeter of the Koch snowflake at stage 3 and stage 4. **See margin.**

7. Write a formula for the perimeter P of the Koch snowflake at stage n. $P = 3\left(\frac{4}{3}\right)^n$

PRESENT YOUR RESULTS

Write a report or make a poster of your results.

- Include your drawing of the stages of the Koch snowflake fractal.
- Include the tables you made and the answers to Exercises 1–7.
- Describe what you learned about fractals.

EXTENSIONS

- Research the Sierpinski Triangle or the Cantor Set. Sketch the first four stages of these fractals.
- Create a fractal of your own. Start with a geometric shape and perform some alteration or transformation. Show the first three stages of your fractal.
- Suppose a Koch snowflake has an area of 1 at stage 0. Find the area of the snowflake at stage 1 and stage 2.
- Research the Mandelbrot Set and find some images of it. Many Web sites on the Internet feature images of this fractal.

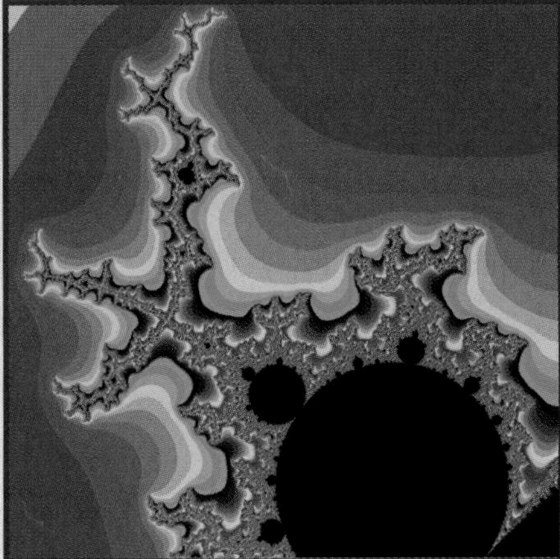

The Mandelbrot Set reveals dramatic images as you zoom in to see details.

GRADING THE PROJECT
RUBRIC FOR CHAPTER PROJECT

4 Students' answers to the Investigation Exercises are correct and complete. The sketches of the Koch snowflake are included and carefully done. The written report demonstrates an understanding of the project and the mathematics involved.

3 Students' answers to the Investigation Exercises are included but may be lacking in some details. The sketches are included but may not be carefully done. The written report contains all the required elements but may not explain each part well.

2 The Investigation Exercise answers or the sketches contain serious errors or are incomplete. Not all of the questions are answered in the report.

1 The answers to the Investigation Exercises show that the students do not understand the material. The sketches are missing or are incorrect. The report is incomplete or not understandable. The project should be returned with a new deadline for completion. The students should speak with the teacher as soon as possible so that they understand the purpose and format of the project.

5.

6.

Stage, n	0	1	2	3	4
Perimeter, P	3	4	$\frac{16}{3}$	$\frac{64}{9}$	$\frac{256}{27}$

CHAPTER 10

PLANNING THE CHAPTER

Circles

Lesson	GOALS	NCTM	ITED	SAT9 (TASK 1)	Terra-Nova	Local
10.1 *pp. 595–602*	GOAL 1 Identify segments and lines related to circles. GOAL 2 Use properties of a tangent to a circle.	3, 8, 10	MIGE, MIRA		14, 18	7, 21
10.2 *pp. 603–611*	GOAL 1 Use properties of arcs of circles. GOAL 2 Use properties of chords of circles.	3, 9, 10	MIGE		14	4, 7, 16, 21
10.3 *pp. 612–620*	CONCEPT ACTIVITY: 10.3 *Investigate inscribed angles.* GOAL 1 Use inscribed angles to solve problems. GOAL 2 Use properties of inscribed polygons.	3, 4, 6, 9, 10	MIGE, RQGE	1	13, 14	4, 7, 16, 21
10.4 *pp. 621–627*	GOAL 1 Use angles formed by tangents and chords to solve problems in geometry. GOAL 2 Use angles formed by lines that intersect a circle to solve problems.	1, 2, 3, 4, 6, 9, 10	MIGE, RQGE, MIRA	1	11, 13, 14, 16, 17, 49, 51	7, 21
10.5 *pp. 628–635*	TECHNOLOGY ACTIVITY: 10.5 *Explore lengths of segments in a circle using geometry software.* GOAL 1 Find the lengths of segments of chords. GOAL 2 Find the lengths of segments of tangents and secants.	1, 2, 3, 4	MIM, MIGE, MIRA	26	11, 13, 14, 16, 49, 51	4, 7, 21
10.6 *pp. 636–640*	GOAL 1 Write the equation of a circle. GOAL 2 Use the equation of a circle and its graph to solve problems.	1, 2, 3, 6, 8, 9, 10	MCE, SAPE, MIGE, MIG, RQGE	1	10, 11, 14, 16, 17, 18, 49, 51, 52	17
10.7 *pp. 641–648*	TECHNOLOGY ACTIVITY: 10.7 *Investigate points equidistant from a point and a line using geometry software.* GOAL 1 Draw the locus of points that satisfy a given condition. GOAL 2 Draw the locus of points that satisfy two or more conditions.	1, 2, 3, 4, 9, 10	MIM, MIG, MIGE		11, 13, 14, 16, 49, 51	7

RESOURCES

Chapter Resource Booklets

Chapter Support

Tips for New Teachers	p. 1	Prerequisite Skills Review	p. 5
Parent Guide for Student Success	p. 3	Strategies for Reading Mathematics	p. 7

Lesson Support

Lesson Support	10.1	10.2	10.3	10.4	10.5	10.6	10.7
Lesson Plans (regular and block)	p. 9	p. 24	p. 37	p. 51	p. 64	p. 79	p. 95
Warm-Up Exercises and Daily Quiz	p. 11	p. 26	p. 39	p. 53	p. 66	p. 81	p. 97
Activity Support Masters							
Lesson Openers	p. 12	p. 27	p. 40	p. 54	p. 67	p. 82	p. 98
Technology Activities & Keystrokes	p. 13		p. 41	p. 55	p. 68	p. 83	p. 99
Practice (3 levels)	p. 16	p. 28	p. 42	p. 56	p. 70	p. 86	p. 102
Reteaching with Practice	p. 19	p. 31	p. 45	p. 59	p. 73	p. 89	p. 105
Quick Catch-Up for Absent Students	p. 21	p. 33	p. 47	p. 61	p. 75	p. 91	p. 107
Cooperative Learning Activities		p. 34				p. 92	
Interdisciplinary Applications		p. 35		p. 62		p. 93	
Real-Life Applications	p. 22		p. 48		p. 76		p. 108
Math & History Applications							p. 109
Challenge: Skills and Applications	p. 23	p. 36	p. 49	p. 63	p. 77	p. 94	p. 110

Review and Assessment

Quizzes	pp. 50, 78	Alternative Assessment with Math Journal	p. 119
Chapter Review Games and Activities	p. 111	Project with Rubric	p. 121
Chapter Test (3 levels)	pp. 112–117	Cumulative Review	p. 123
SAT/ACT Chapter Test	p. 118	Resource Book Answers	p. A1

Transparencies

	10.1	10.2	10.3	10.4	10.5	10.6	10.7
Warm-Up Exercises and Daily Quiz	p. 71	p. 72	p. 73	p. 74	p. 75	p. 76	p. 77
Alternative Lesson Opener Transparencies	p. 61	p. 62	p. 63	p. 64	p. 65	p. 66	p. 67
Examples/Standardized Test Practice	✓	✓	✓	✓	✓	✓	✓
Answer Transparencies	✓	✓	✓	✓	✓	✓	✓

Technology

- Electronic Teaching Tools
- Online Lesson Planner
- Internet Support
- Personal Student Tutor
- Test and Practice Generator
- Geometry in Motion video
- Electronic Lesson Presentations (Lesson 10.3)

Additional Resources

- Basic Skills Workbook: Diagnosis and Remediation
- Worked-Out Solution Key
- Resources in Spanish
- Standardized Test Practice Workbook
- Practice Workbook with Examples

Correlations to the California Curriculum

Correlations to California Standards
See Teacher's Edition pp. CA9–CA11

Correlations to SAT9
Task 1: See Teacher's Edition pp. CA12–CA14
Task 2: See Teacher's Edition pp. CA15–CA17

CHAPTER 10

PACING THE CHAPTER

Resource Key
- STUDENT EDITION
- CHAPTER 10 RESOURCE BOOK
- TEACHER'S EDITION

REGULAR SCHEDULE

Day 1

10.1

STARTING OPTIONS
- Prereq. Skills Review
- Strategies for Reading
- Homework Check
- Warm-Up or Daily Quiz

TEACHING OPTIONS
- Les. Opener (Application)
- Technology Activity
- Examples 1–3
- Guided Practice Exs. 1–2, 4

APPLY/HOMEWORK
- See Assignment Guide.
- See the CRB: Practice, Reteach, Apply, Extend

ASSESSMENT OPTIONS
- Checkpoint Exercises, pp. 596–597

Day 2

10.1 *(cont.)*

STARTING OPTIONS
- Homework Check

TEACHING OPTIONS
- Examples 4–7
- Closure Question
- Guided Practice Exs. 3, 5–8

APPLY/HOMEWORK
- See Assignment Guide.
- See the CRB: Practice, Reteach, Apply, Extend

ASSESSMENT OPTIONS
- Checkpoint Exercises, pp. 597–598
- Daily Quiz (10.1)
- Stand. Test Practice

Day 3

10.2

STARTING OPTIONS
- Homework Check
- Warm-Up or Daily Quiz

TEACHING OPTIONS
- Motivating the Lesson
- Les. Opener (Application)
- Examples 1–4
- Guided Practice Exs. 1–8

APPLY/HOMEWORK
- See Assignment Guide.
- See the CRB: Practice, Reteach, Apply, Extend

ASSESSMENT OPTIONS
- Checkpoint Exercises, p. 605

Day 4

10.2 *(cont.)*

STARTING OPTIONS
- Homework Check

TEACHING OPTIONS
- Examples 5–7
- Closure Question
- Guided Practice Exs. 9–11

APPLY/HOMEWORK
- See Assignment Guide.
- See the CRB: Practice, Reteach, Apply, Extend

ASSESSMENT OPTIONS
- Checkpoint Exercises, pp. 605–606
- Daily Quiz (10.2)
- Stand. Test Practice

Day 5

10.3

STARTING OPTIONS
- Homework Check
- Warm-Up or Daily Quiz

TEACHING OPTIONS
- Motivating the Lesson
- Concept Activity
- Les. Opener (Software)
- Examples 1–6
- Guided Practice Exs.

APPLY/HOMEWORK
- See Assignment Guide.
- See the CRB: Practice, Reteach, Apply, Extend

ASSESSMENT OPTIONS
- Checkpoint Exercises

Day 6

10.3 *(cont.)*

STARTING OPTIONS
- Homework Check

TEACHING OPTIONS
- Examples 1–6
- Technology Activity
- Closure Question

APPLY/HOMEWORK
- See Assignment Guide.
- See the CRB: Practice, Reteach, Apply, Extend

ASSESSMENT OPTIONS
- Checkpoint Exercises
- Daily Quiz (10.3)
- Stand. Test Practice
- Quiz (10.1–10.3)

Day 9

10.5 *(cont.)*

STARTING OPTIONS
- Homework Check

TEACHING OPTIONS
- Examples 1–4
- Technology Activity
- Closure Question

APPLY/HOMEWORK
- See Assignment Guide.
- See the CRB: Practice, Reteach, Apply, Extend

ASSESSMENT OPTIONS
- Checkpoint Exercises
- Daily Quiz (10.5)
- Stand. Test Practice
- Quiz (10.4–10.5)

Day 10

10.6

STARTING OPTIONS
- Homework Check
- Warm-Up or Daily Quiz

TEACHING OPTIONS
- Les. Opener (Visual)
- Technology Activity
- Examples 1–4
- Closure Question
- Guided Practice Exs.

APPLY/HOMEWORK
- See Assignment Guide.
- See the CRB: Practice, Reteach, Apply, Extend

ASSESSMENT OPTIONS
- Checkpoint Exercises
- Daily Quiz (10.6)
- Stand. Test Practice

Day 11

10.7

STARTING OPTIONS
- Homework Check
- Warm-Up or Daily Quiz

TEACHING OPTIONS
- Motivating the Lesson
- Les. Opener (Activity)
- Examples 1–4
- Guided Practice Exs.

APPLY/HOMEWORK
- See Assignment Guide.
- See the CRB: Practice, Reteach, Apply, Extend

ASSESSMENT OPTIONS
- Checkpoint Exercises

Day 12

10.7 *(cont.)*

STARTING OPTIONS
- Homework Check

TEACHING OPTIONS
- Examples 1–4
- Technology Activity
- Closure Question

APPLY/HOMEWORK
- See Assignment Guide.
- See the CRB: Practice, Reteach, Apply, Extend

ASSESSMENT OPTIONS
- Checkpoint Exercises
- Daily Quiz (10.7)
- Stand. Test Practice
- Quiz (10.6–10.7)

Day 13

Review

DAY 13 START OPTIONS
- Homework Check

REVIEWING OPTIONS
- Chapter 10 Summary
- Chapter 10 Review
- Chapter Review Games and Activities

APPLY/HOMEWORK
- Chapter 10 Test (practice)
- Ch. Standardized Test (practice)

Day 14

Assess

DAY 14 START OPTIONS
- Homework Check

ASSESSMENT OPTIONS
- Chapter 10 Test
- SAT/ACT Ch. 10 Test
- Alternative Assessment

APPLY/HOMEWORK
- Skill Review, p. 660

Day 7

10.4

Starting Options
- Homework Check
- Warm-Up or Daily Quiz

Teaching Options
- Les. Opener (Visual)
- Examples 1–5
- Closure Question
- Guided Practice Exs.

Apply/Homework
- See Assignment Guide.
- See the CRB: Practice, Reteach, Apply, Extend

Assessment Options
- Checkpoint Exercises
- Daily Quiz (10.4)
- Stand. Test Practice

Day 8

10.5

Starting Options
- Homework Check
- Warm-Up or Daily Quiz

Teaching Options
- Motivating the Lesson
- Les. Opener (Activity)
- Examples 1–4
- Guided Practice Exs.

Apply/Homework
- See Assignment Guide.
- See the CRB: Practice, Reteach, Apply, Extend

Assessment Options
- Checkpoint Exercises

BLOCK SCHEDULE

Day 1

10.1

Day 1 Start Options
- Prereq. Skills Review
- Strategies for Reading
- Homework Check
- Warm-Up or Daily Quiz

Teaching 10.1 Options
- Les. Opener (Appl.)
- Technology Activity
- Examples 1–7
- Closure Question
- Guided Practice Exs.

Apply/Homework
- See Assignment Guide.
- See the CRB: Practice, Reteach, Apply, Extend

Assessment Options
- Checkpoint Exercises
- Daily Quiz (Les. 10.1)
- Stand. Test Practice

Day 2

10.2

Day 2 Start Options
- Homework Check
- Warm-Up or Daily Quiz

Teaching 10.2 Options
- Motivating the Lesson
- Les. Opener (Appl.)
- Examples 1–7
- Closure Question
- Guided Practice Exs.

Apply/Homework
- See Assignment Guide.
- See the CRB: Practice, Reteach, Apply, Extend

Assessment Options
- Checkpoint Exercises
- Daily Quiz (Les. 10.2)
- Stand. Test Practice

Day 3

10.3

Day 3 Start Options
- Homework Check
- Warm-Up or Daily Quiz

Teaching 10.3 Options
- Motivating the Lesson
- Concept Activity
- Les. Opener (Software)
- Examples 1–6
- Technology Activity
- Closure Question
- Guided Practice Exs.

Apply/Homework
- See Assignment Guide.
- See the CRB: Practice, Reteach, Apply, Extend

Assessment Options
- Checkpoint Exercises
- Daily Quiz (Les. 10.3)
- Stand. Test Practice
- Quiz (10.1–10.3)

Day 4

10.4 & 10.5

Day 4 Start Options
- Homework Check
- Warm-Up (Les. 10.4) or Daily Quiz (Les. 10.3)

Teaching 10.4 Options
- Les. Opener (Visual)
- Examples 1–5
- Closure Question
- Guided Practice Exs.

Beginning 10.5 Options
- Warm-Up (Les. 10.5)
- Motivating the Lesson
- Les. Opener (Activity)
- Examples 1–4
- Guided Practice Exs.

Apply/Homework
- See Assignment Guide.
- See the CRB: Practice, Reteach, Apply, Extend

Assessment Options
- Checkpoint Exercises
- Daily Quiz (Les. 10.4)
- Stand. Test Prac. (10.4)

Day 5

10.5 & 10.6

Day 5 Start Options
- Homework Check
- Daily Quiz (Les. 10.4)

Finishing 10.5 Options
- Examples 1–4
- Technology Activity
- Closure Question

Teaching 10.6 Options
- Warm-Up (Les. 10.6)
- Les. Opener (Visual)
- Technology Activity
- Examples 1–4
- Closure Question
- Guided Practice Exs.

Apply/Homework
- See Assignment Guide.
- See the CRB: Practice, Reteach, Apply, Extend

Assessment Options
- Checkpoint Exercises
- Daily Quiz (Les. 10.5, 10.6)
- Stand. Test Practice
- Quiz (10.4–10.5)

Day 6

10.7

Day 6 Start Options
- Homework Check
- Warm-Up or Daily Quiz

Teaching 10.7 Options
- Motivating the Lesson
- Les. Opener (Activity)
- Examples 1–4
- Technology Activity
- Closure Question
- Guided Practice Exs.

Apply/Homework
- See Assignment Guide.
- See the CRB: Practice, Reteach, Apply, Extend

Assessment Options
- Checkpoint Exercises
- Daily Quiz (Les. 10.7)
- Stand. Test Practice
- Quiz (10.6–10.7)

Day 7

Review/Assess

Day 7 Start Options
- Homework Check

Reviewing Options
- Chapter 10 Summary
- Chapter 10 Review
- Chapter Review Games and Activities
- Chapter 10 Test (practice)
- Ch. Standardized Test (practice)

Assessment Options
- Chapter 10 Test
- SAT/ACT Ch. 10 Test
- Alternative Assessment

Apply/Homework
- Skill Review, p. 660

CHAPTER 10 MEETING INDIVIDUAL NEEDS

BEFORE THE CHAPTER

The *Chapter 10 Resource Book* has the following materials to distribute and use before the chapter:

- **Parent Guide for Student Success**
- **Prerequisite Skills Review (pictured below)**
- **Strategies for Reading Mathematics**

PREREQUISITE SKILLS *Pages 5–6*

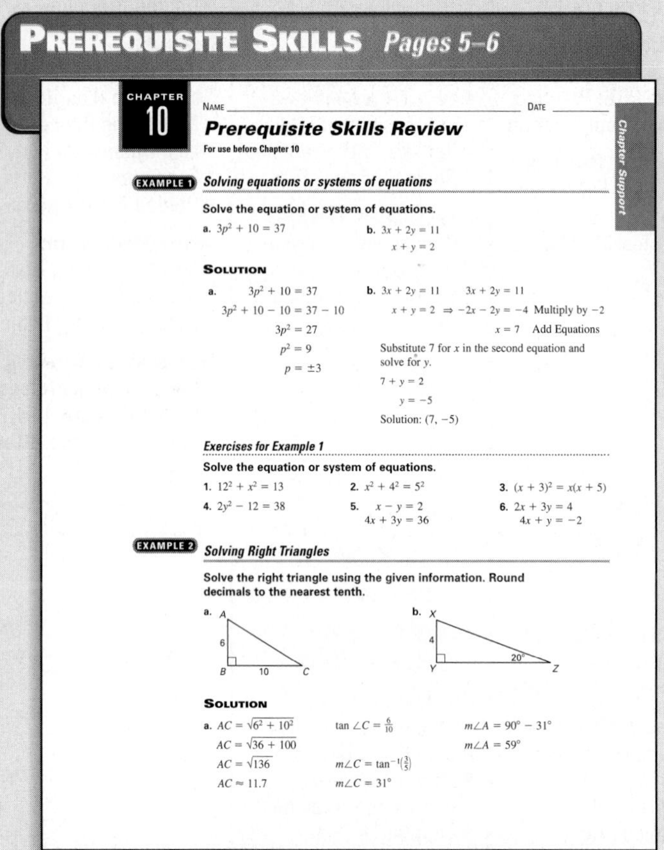

CHAPTER 10

NAME ____________ DATE ________

Prerequisite Skills Review

For use before Chapter 10

Chapter Support

EXAMPLE 1 *Solving equations or systems of equations*

Solve the equation or system of equations.

a. $3p^2 + 10 = 37$

b. $3x + 2y = 11$
$x + y = 2$

SOLUTION

a. $3p^2 + 10 = 37$
$3p^2 + 10 - 10 = 37 - 10$
$3p^2 = 27$
$p^2 = 9$
$p = \pm 3$

b. $3x + 2y = 11 \qquad 3x + 2y = 11$
$x + y = 2 \Rightarrow -2x - 2y = -4$ Multiply by -2
$x = 7$ Add Equations

Substitute 7 for x in the second equation and solve for y.

$7 + y = 2$
$y = -5$

Solution: $(7, -5)$

Exercises for Example 1

Solve the equation or system of equations.

1. $12^2 + x^2 = 13$
2. $x^2 + 4^2 = 5^2$
3. $(x + 3)^2 = x(x + 5)$
4. $2y^2 - 12 = 38$
5. $x - y = 2$; $4x + 3y = 36$
6. $2x + 3y = 4$; $4x + y = -2$

EXAMPLE 2 *Solving Right Triangles*

Solve the right triangle using the given information. Round decimals to the nearest tenth.

a.

b.

SOLUTION

a. $AC = \sqrt{6^2 + 10^2}$
$AC = \sqrt{36 + 100}$
$AC = \sqrt{136}$
$AC \approx 11.7$

$\tan \angle C = \frac{6}{10}$
$m\angle C = \tan^{-1}\left(\frac{3}{5}\right)$
$m\angle C = 31^\circ$

$m\angle A = 90^\circ - 31^\circ$
$m\angle A = 59^\circ$

PREREQUISITE SKILLS REVIEW These two pages support the Study Guide on page 594. They help students prepare for Chapter 10 by providing worked-out examples and practice for the following skills needed in the chapter:

- **Solve equations or systems of equations.**
- **Solve right triangles.**
- **Find the length and midpoint of a segment.**

TECHNOLOGY RESOURCE

Students can use the Personal Student Tutor to find additional reteaching and practice for skills from earlier chapters that are used in Chapter 10.

DURING EACH LESSON

The *Chapter 10 Resource Book* has the following alternatives for introducing the lesson:

- **Lesson Openers (pictured below)**
- **Technology Activities with Keystrokes**

LESSON OPENER *Page 98*

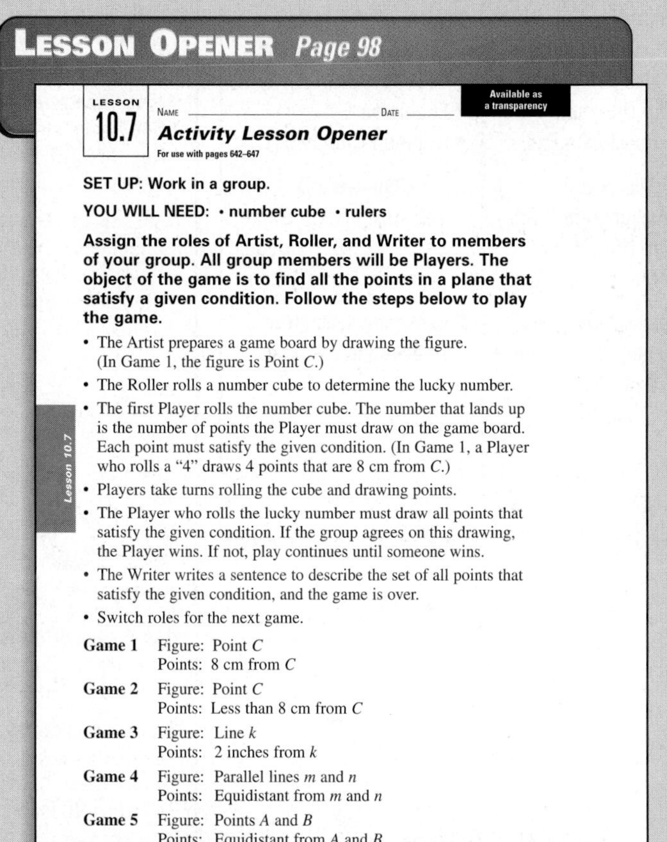

LESSON 10.7

NAME ____________ DATE ________

Available as a transparency

Activity Lesson Opener

For use with pages 642–647

Lesson 10.7

SET UP: Work in a group.

YOU WILL NEED: • number cube • rulers

Assign the roles of Artist, Roller, and Writer to members of your group. All group members will be Players. The object of the game is to find all the points in a plane that satisfy a given condition. Follow the steps below to play the game.

- The Artist prepares a game board by drawing the figure. (In Game 1, the figure is Point *C*.)
- The Roller rolls a number cube to determine the lucky number.
- The first Player rolls the number cube. The number that lands up is the number of points the Player must draw on the game board. Each point must satisfy the given condition. (In Game 1, a Player who rolls a "4" draws 4 points that are 8 cm from *C*.)
- Players take turns rolling the cube and drawing points.
- The Player who rolls the lucky number must draw all points that satisfy the given condition. If the group agrees on this drawing, the Player wins. If not, play continues until someone wins.
- The Writer writes a sentence to describe the set of all points that satisfy the given condition, and the game is over.
- Switch roles for the next game.

Game 1 Figure: Point *C*
Points: 8 cm from *C*

Game 2 Figure: Point *C*
Points: Less than 8 cm from *C*

Game 3 Figure: Line *k*
Points: 2 inches from *k*

Game 4 Figure: Parallel lines *m* and *n*
Points: Equidistant from *m* and *n*

Game 5 Figure: Points *A* and *B*
Points: Equidistant from *A* and *B*

ACTIVITY LESSON OPENER This Lesson Opener provides an alternative way to start Lesson 10.7 in the form of an activity. In this activity, students play a game using a number cube as they learn about drawing circles and lines.

Following Each Lesson

The *Chapter 10 Resource Book* has a variety of materials to follow-up each lesson. They include the following:

- **Practice (3 levels)**
- **Reteaching with Practice**
- **Quick Catch-Up for Absent Students**
- **Interdisciplinary Applications**
- **Real-Life Applications (pictured below)**

Application Page 76

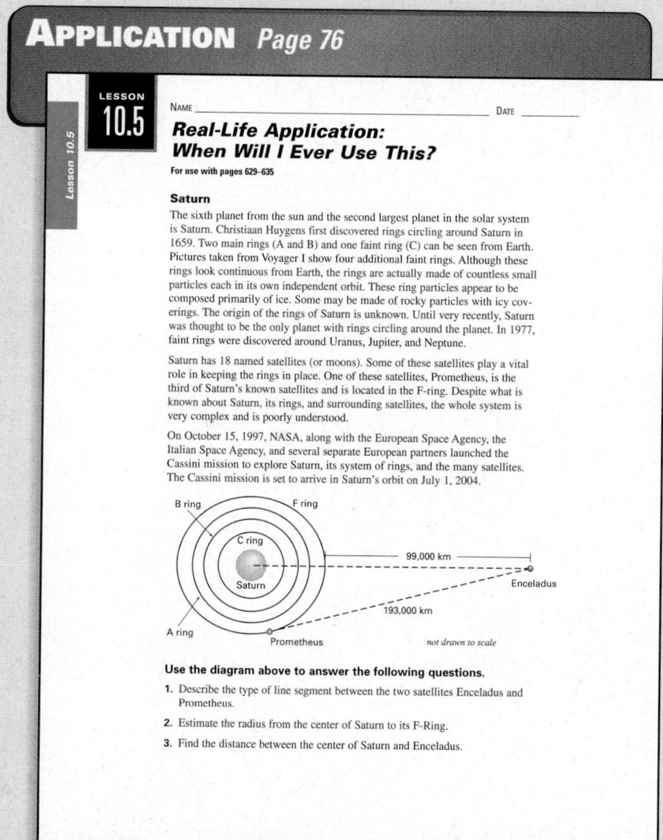

LESSON 10.5

Lesson 10.5

NAME ______________ DATE ________

Real-Life Application: When Will I Ever Use This?

For use with pages 629–635

Saturn

The sixth planet from the sun and the second largest planet in the solar system is Saturn. Christiaan Huygens first discovered rings circling around Saturn in 1659. Two main rings (A and B) and one faint ring (C) can be seen from Earth. Pictures taken from Voyager I show four additional faint rings. Although these rings look continuous from Earth, the rings are actually made of countless small particles each in its own independent orbit. These ring particles appear to be composed primarily of ice. Some may be made of rocky particles with icy coverings. The origin of the rings of Saturn is unknown. Until very recently, Saturn was thought to be the only planet with rings circling around the planet. In 1977, faint rings were discovered around Uranus, Jupiter, and Neptune.

Saturn has 18 named satellites (or moons). Some of these satellites play a vital role in keeping the rings in place. One of these satellites, Prometheus, is the third of Saturn's known satellites and is located in the F-ring. Despite what is known about Saturn, its rings, and surrounding satellites, the whole system is very complex and is poorly understood.

On October 15, 1997, NASA, along with the European Space Agency, the Italian Space Agency, and several separate European partners launched the Cassini mission to explore Saturn, its system of rings, and the many satellites. The Cassini mission is set to arrive in Saturn's orbit on July 1, 2004.

Use the diagram above to answer the following questions.

1. Describe the type of line segment between the two satellites Enceladus and Prometheus.
2. Estimate the radius from the center of Saturn to its F-Ring.
3. Find the distance between the center of Saturn and Enceladus.

Real-Life Application This application makes a connection between astronomy and segment lengths in circles, the topic of Lesson 10.5.

Assessing the Chapter

The *Chapter 10 Resource Book* has the following review and assessment materials:

- **Quizzes**
- **Chapter Review Games and Activities**
- **Chapter Test (3 levels)**
- **SAT/ACT Chapter Test (pictured below)**
- **Alternative Assessment with Rubric and Math Journal**
- **Project with Rubric**
- **Cumulative Review**

SAT/ACT Chapter Test Page 118

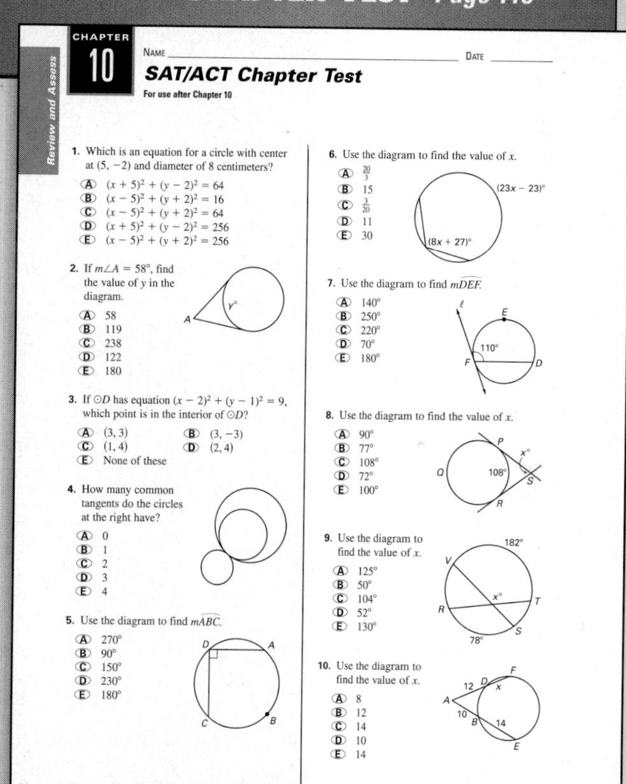

CHAPTER 10

Review and Assess

NAME ______________ DATE ________

SAT/ACT Chapter Test

For use after Chapter 10

1. Which is an equation for a circle with center at $(5, -2)$ and diameter of 8 centimeters?
   (A) $(x + 5)^2 + (y - 2)^2 = 64$
   (B) $(x - 5)^2 + (y + 2)^2 = 16$
   (C) $(x - 5)^2 + (y + 2)^2 = 64$
   (D) $(x + 5)^2 + (y - 2)^2 = 256$
   (E) $(x - 5)^2 + (y + 2)^2 = 256$

2. If $m\angle A = 58°$, find the value of y in the diagram.
   (A) 58 (B) 119 (C) 238 (D) 122 (E) 180

3. If $\odot D$ has equation $(x - 2)^2 + (y - 1)^2 = 9$, which point is in the interior of $\odot D$?
   (A) (3, 3) (B) (3, −3) (C) (1, 4) (D) (2, 4) (E) None of these

4. How many common tangents do the circles at the right have?
   (A) 0 (B) 1 (C) 2 (D) 3 (E) 4

5. Use the diagram to find $m\widehat{ABC}$.
   (A) 270° (B) 90° (C) 150° (D) 230° (E) 180°

6. Use the diagram to find the value of x.
   (A) $\frac{20}{3}$ (B) 15 (C) $\frac{3}{20}$ (D) 11 (E) 30

7. Use the diagram to find $m\widehat{DEF}$.
   (A) 140° (B) 250° (C) 220° (D) 70° (E) 180°

8. Use the diagram to find the value of x.
   (A) 90° (B) 77° (C) 108° (D) 72° (E) 100°

9. Use the diagram to find the value of x.
   (A) 125° (B) 50° (C) 104° (D) 52° (E) 130°

10. Use the diagram to find the value of x.
    (A) 8 (B) 12 (C) 14 (D) 10 (E) 14

SAT/ACT Chapter Test This test covers the material in Chapter 10 in a standardized test format. Students taking this form of the test should be reminded to read all of the answer choices before deciding which is the correct one.

CHAPTER OVERVIEW

CHAPTER GOALS

The goals of this chapter include identifying segments and lines related to circles, using properties of a tangent to a circle, using properties of arcs and chords of circles, using inscribed angles and properties of inscribed polygons to solve problems related to circles, and finding angles and arc measures related to circles. Students find the lengths of the segments of chords, tangents, and secants. They find the equation of a circle and use it to graph and solve problems. Finally, students draw loci that satisfy given conditions.

APPLICATION NOTE

Fireworks displays are associated with various celebrations throughout the year. Some fireworks can be seen from a distance because they reach a height of 1000 to 1300 feet before they explode and can remain visible for several seconds after they burst. Explosives include ingredients such as potassium nitrate, charcoal, and sulfur. A fuse is also attached that determines how high the firework travels.

Additional information about fireworks is available at **www.mcdougallittell.com.**

CIRCLES

▶ *From how far away can you see fireworks?*

592

CHAPTER 10

APPLICATION: Fireworks

If you watch fireworks as you sail out to sea on a clear night, the fireworks will gradually disappear over the horizon.

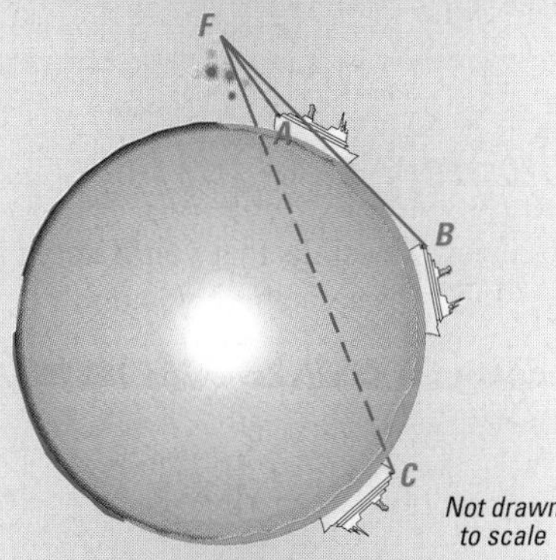

Think & Discuss

1. As you sail away, at which point do the fireworks disappear over the horizon? B
2. Imagine that the surface of the water is perfectly smooth. How many points of intersection do $\overline{FB}$ and the circle have when the fireworks disappear? 1
3. The diagram is not drawn to scale. How would the diagram be different if it were to scale? The fireworks would be closer to Earth and the ships would be smaller and closer together.

Learn More About It

You will learn more about fireworks in Exercise 35 on p. 625.

APPLICATION LINK Visit www.mcdougallittell.com for more information about fireworks.

PROJECTS

A project covering Chapters 10–11 appears on pages 714–715 of the Student Edition. An additional project for Chapter 10 is available in the *Chapter 10 Resource Book,* p. 121.

TECHNOLOGY

Software

- *Electronic Teaching Tools*
- *Online Lesson Planner*
- *Personal Student Tutor*
- *Test and Practice Generator*
- *Electronic Lesson Presentations (Lesson 10.3)*

Video

- *Geometry in Motion*

Internet Connections
www.mcdougallittell.com

- **Application Links**
  593, 625, 631, 634, 639, 648
- **Student Help**
  596, 610, 618, 622, 626, 628, 633, 641
- **Career Links**
  609
- **Extra Challenge**
  602, 611, 619, 627, 634

PREPARE

DIAGNOSTIC TOOLS

The **Skill Review** exercises can help you diagnose whether students have the following skills needed in Chapter 10:

- Solve equations.
- Solve systems of equations.
- Solve right triangles.
- Given the endpoints of a segment, find the midpoint, equation of a line containing the segment, and a translation image.

The following resources are available for students who need additional help with these skills:

- Prerequisite Skills Review (*Chapter 10 Resource Book*, p. 5; *Warm-Up Transparencies*, p. 70)
- *Personal Student Tutor*

ADDITIONAL RESOURCES

The following resources are provided to help you prepare for the upcoming chapter and customize review materials:

- ***Chapter 10 Resource Book***
  Tips for New Teachers (p. 1)
  Parent Guide (p. 3)
  Lesson Plans (every lesson)
  Lesson Plans for Block Scheduling (every lesson)
- ***Electronic Teaching Tools***
- ***Online Lesson Planner***
- ***Test and Practice Generator***

CHAPTER 10

Study Guide

PREVIEW

What's the chapter about?

Chapter 10 is about **circles** and their properties. In Chapter 10, you'll learn

- how to use arcs, angles, and segments in circles to solve real-life problems.
- how to use the graph of an equation of a circle to model real-life situations.

KEY VOCABULARY

- circle, p. 595
- secant, p. 595
- tangent, p. 595
- point of tangency, p. 597
- central angle, p. 603
- arc, p. 603
- measure of an arc, p. 603
- inscribed angle, p. 613
- intercepted arc, p. 613
- inscribed polygon, p. 615
- circumscribed circle, p. 615
- standard equation of a circle, p. 636
- locus, p. 642

PREPARE

Are you ready for the chapter?

SKILL REVIEW Do these exercises to review key skills that you'll apply in this chapter. See the given **reference page** if there is something you don't understand.

Solve the equation or system of equations. **(Skills Review pp. 789, 790, 796, 798, 800, 801)**

1. $(x + 4)^2 = x^2 + 6^2$ $2\frac{1}{2}$

2. $132 = \frac{1}{2}[(360 - x) - x]$ 48

3. $15(y + 15) = 24^2$ 23.4

4. $2z^2 + 7 = 19$ $-\sqrt{6}, \sqrt{6}$

5. $8^2 = x(x + 12)$ $-16, 4$

6. $x + y = 18$
$3x + 4y = 64$ (8, 10)

7. In $\triangle JKL$, $JK = 8$, $KL = 9$, and $\angle K$ is a right angle. Solve the right triangle. Round decimals to the nearest tenth. **(Review Example 1, p. 568)** See margin.

8. Use $A(-3, 0)$ and $B(9, -9)$. Find (a) AB, (b) the coordinates of the midpoint of $\overline{AB}$, (c) an equation for $\overleftrightarrow{AB}$, and (d) the image of $\overline{AB}$ after the translation $(x, y) \rightarrow (x - 4, y)$. **(Review pp. 19, 35, 165–167, 422)** See margin.

7. $JL = \sqrt{145}$, $m\angle J \approx 48.4°$, $m\angle L \approx 41.6°$

8. a. 15
b. $\left(3, -4\frac{1}{2}\right)$
c. $y = -\frac{3}{4}x - \frac{9}{4}$
d. the segment with endpoints $A'(-7, 0)$ and $B'(5, -9)$

STUDY STRATEGY

Here's a study strategy!

Answer Your Questions

Use a red pen to write a large question mark next to any part of a homework question you don't understand. Be sure to get your questions answered by the teacher or another student. Then write a check mark through the question mark when you are able to complete an exercise with which you had difficulty.

10.1 Tangents to Circles

What you should learn

GOAL 1 Identify segments and lines related to circles.

GOAL 2 Use properties of a tangent to a circle.

Why you should learn it

▼ You can use properties of tangents of circles to find **real-life** distances, such as the radius of the silo in **Example 5**.

REAL LIFE

CALIFORNIA STANDARDS AND ASSESSMENT

CA Standards: 7, 21

GOAL 1 COMMUNICATING ABOUT CIRCLES

A **circle** is the set of all points in a plane that are equidistant from a given point, called the **center** of the circle. A circle with center P is called "circle P", or $\odot P$.

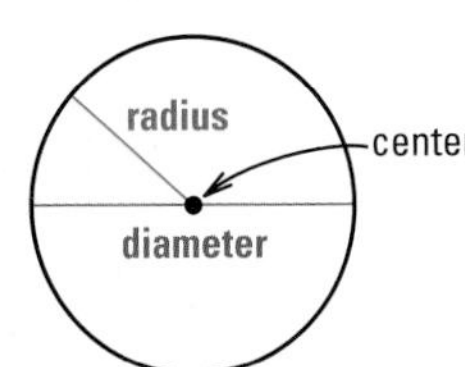

The distance from the center to a point on the circle is the **radius** of the circle. Two circles are **congruent** if they have the same radius.

The distance across the circle, through its center, is the **diameter** of the circle. The diameter is twice the radius.

The terms *radius* and *diameter* describe segments as well as measures. A **radius** is a segment whose endpoints are the center of the circle and a point on the circle. $\overline{QP}$, $\overline{QR}$, and $\overline{QS}$ are radii of $\odot Q$ below. All radii of a circle are congruent.

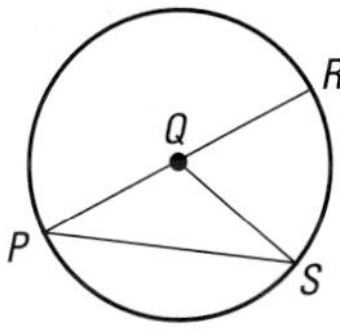

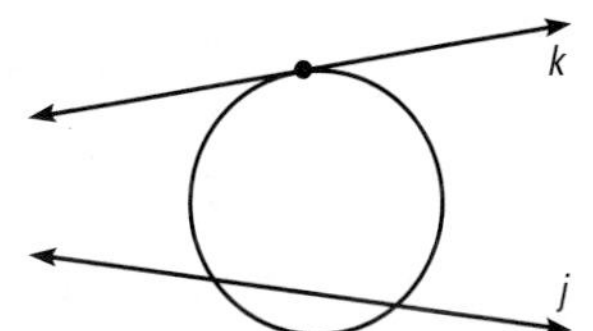

A **chord** is a segment whose endpoints are points on the circle. $\overline{PS}$ and $\overline{PR}$ are chords.

A **diameter** is a chord that passes through the center of the circle. $\overline{PR}$ is a diameter.

A **secant** is a line that intersects a circle in two points. Line j is a secant.

A **tangent** is a line in the plane of a circle that intersects the circle in exactly one point. Line k is a tangent.

EXAMPLE 1 *Identifying Special Segments and Lines*

Tell whether the line or segment is best described as a *chord*, a *secant*, a *tangent*, a *diameter*, or a *radius* of $\odot C$.

a. $\overline{AD}$ **b.** $\overline{CD}$

c. $\overleftrightarrow{EG}$ **d.** $\overline{HB}$

SOLUTION

a. $\overline{AD}$ is a diameter because it contains the center C.

b. $\overline{CD}$ is a radius because C is the center and D is a point on the circle.

c. $\overleftrightarrow{EG}$ is a tangent because it intersects the circle in one point.

d. $\overline{HB}$ is a chord because its endpoints are on the circle.

1 PLAN

PACING
Basic: 2 days
Average: 2 days
Advanced: 2 days
Block Schedule: 1 block

LESSON OPENER
APPLICATION
An alternative way to approach Lesson 10.1 is to use the Application Lesson Opener:

- Blackline Master (*Chapter 10 Resource Book*, p. 12)
- Transparency (p. 61)

MEETING INDIVIDUAL NEEDS

- ***Chapter 10 Resource Book***
  Prerequisite Skills Review (p. 5)
  Practice Level A (p. 16)
  Practice Level B (p. 17)
  Practice Level C (p. 18)
  Reteaching with Practice (p. 19)
  Absent Student Catch-Up (p. 21)
  Challenge (p. 23)
- ***Resources in Spanish***
- ***Personal Student Tutor***

NEW-TEACHER SUPPORT
See the Tips for New Teachers on pp. 1–2 of the *Chapter 10 Resource Book* for additional notes about Lesson 10.1.

WARM-UP EXERCISES

Transparency Available

Solve the equation.

1. $2x = x + 5$ 5
2. $3w + 4 = 5w - 8$ 6
3. $h^2 + 4 = 40$ 6; −6
4. $m^2 - 16 = 32$ $4\sqrt{3}$; $-4\sqrt{3}$
5. $(y + 2)^2 + 4 = 29$ 3; −7

ENGLISH LEARNERS
Students must have a clear understanding of key vocabulary terms. You may want to have English learners make note cards of key terms and keep these at hand as they work through the chapter.

2 TEACH

EXTRA EXAMPLE 1

Tell whether the segment is best described as a *chord*, a *secant*, a *tangent*, a *diameter*, or a *radius*.

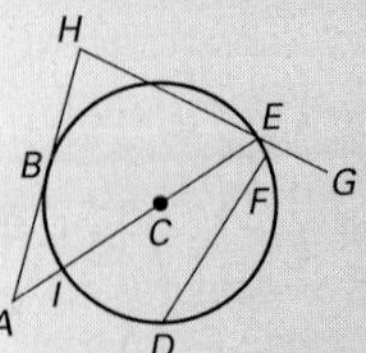

a. $\overline{AH}$ tangent **b.** $\overline{EI}$ diameter
c. $\overline{DF}$ chord **d.** $\overline{CE}$ radius

EXTRA EXAMPLE 2

Tell whether the common tangent is *internal* or *external.* external

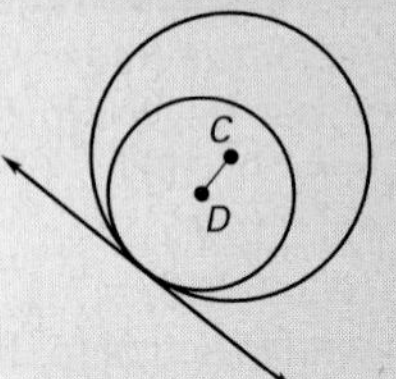

EXTRA EXAMPLE 3

Give the center and radius of each circle. Describe the intersection of the two circles and describe all common tangents.

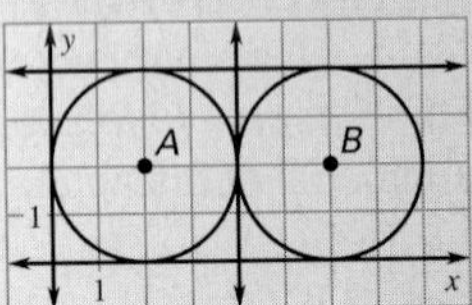

See below.

CHECKPOINT EXERCISES

For use after Example 1:

1. Tell whether the line or segment is best described as a *chord,* a *secant,* a *tangent,* a *diameter,* or a *radius* of ⊙*C*.

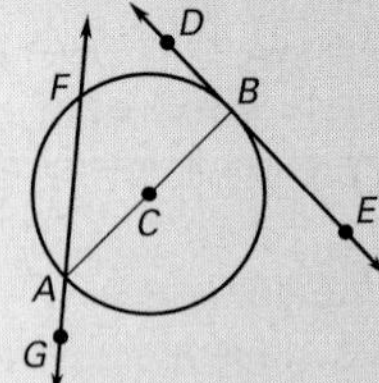

See answer at right.

Checkpoint Exercises for Examples 2 and 3 on next page.

In a plane, two circles can intersect in two points, one point, or no points. Coplanar circles that intersect in one point are called **tangent circles**. Coplanar circles that have a common center are called **concentric**.

2 points of intersection

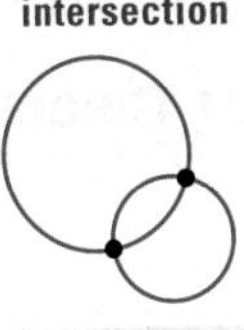

1 point of intersection (tangent circles)

Internally tangent

Externally tangent

No points of intersection

Concentric circles

A line or segment that is tangent to two coplanar circles is called a **common tangent**. A *common internal tangent* intersects the segment that joins the centers of the two circles. A *common external tangent* does not intersect the segment that joins the centers of the two circles.

EXAMPLE 2 *Identifying Common Tangents*

Tell whether the **common tangents** are *internal* or *external*.

a.

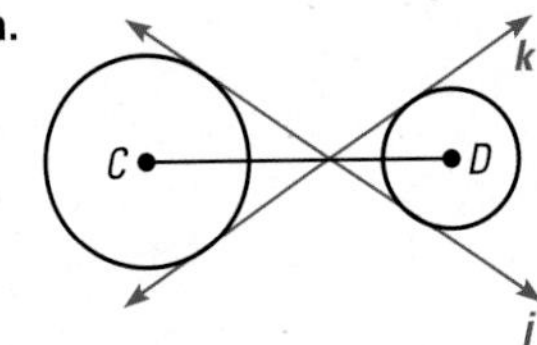

b.

SOLUTION

a. The lines j and k intersect $\overline{CD}$, so they are common internal tangents.

b. The lines m and n do not intersect $\overline{AB}$, so they are common external tangents.

In a plane, the **interior of a circle** consists of the points that are inside the circle. The **exterior of a circle** consists of the points that are outside the circle.

EXAMPLE 3 *Circles in Coordinate Geometry*

Give the center and the radius of each circle. Describe the intersection of the two circles and describe all common tangents.

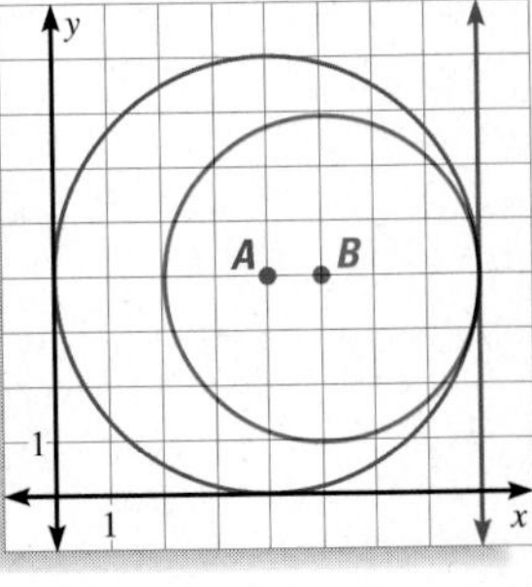

SOLUTION

The center of ⊙A is $A(4, 4)$ and its radius is 4. The center of ⊙B is $B(5, 4)$ and its radius is 3. The two circles have only one point of intersection. It is the point $(8, 4)$. The vertical line $x = 8$ is the only common tangent of the two circles.

STUDENT HELP

HOMEWORK HELP
Visit our Web site www.mcdougallittell.com for extra examples.

Extra Example 3 *Sample answer:*
center ⊙*A*: (2, 2); radius 2
center ⊙*B*: (6, 2); radius 2
common tangents: $x = 4$; $y = 4$; $y = 0$

Checkpoint Exercises *Sample answer:*
1. $\overline{AB}$: diameter; $\overline{CB}$: radius; $\overleftrightarrow{DE}$: tangent; $\overleftrightarrow{GF}$: secant

GOAL 2 USING PROPERTIES OF TANGENTS

The point at which a tangent line intersects the circle to which it is tangent is the **point of tangency**. You will justify the following theorems in the exercises.

THEOREMS

THEOREM 10.1

If a line is tangent to a circle, then it is perpendicular to the radius drawn to the point of tangency.

If ℓ is tangent to $\odot Q$ at P, then $\ell \perp \overline{QP}$.

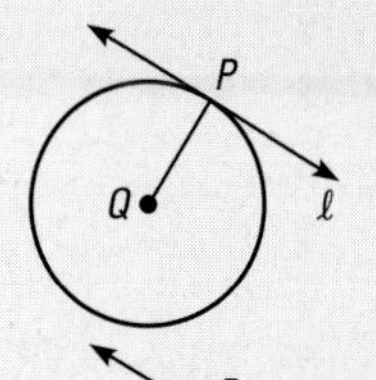

THEOREM 10.2

In a plane, if a line is perpendicular to a radius of a circle at its endpoint on the circle, then the line is tangent to the circle.

If $\ell \perp \overline{QP}$ at P, then ℓ is tangent to $\odot Q$.

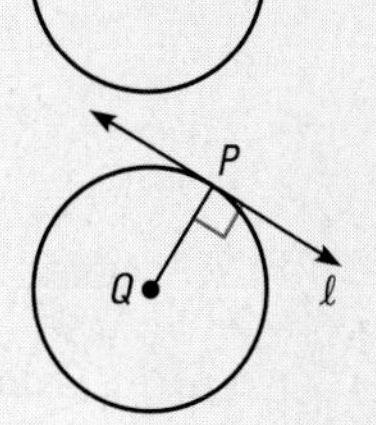

STUDENT HELP

Study Tip

A secant can look like a tangent if it intersects the circle in two points that are close together.

EXAMPLE 4 *Verifying a Tangent to a Circle*

You can use the Converse of the Pythagorean Theorem to tell whether $\overleftrightarrow{EF}$ is tangent to $\odot D$.

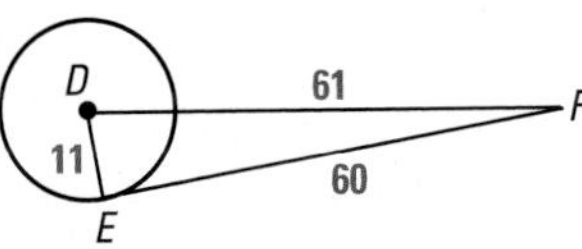

Because $11^2 + 60^2 = 61^2$, $\triangle DEF$ is a right triangle and $\overline{DE}$ is perpendicular to $\overline{EF}$. So, by Theorem 10.2, $\overleftrightarrow{EF}$ is tangent to $\odot D$.

EXAMPLE 5 *Finding the Radius of a Circle*

You are standing at C, 8 feet from a grain silo. The distance from you to a point of tangency on the tank is 16 feet. What is the radius of the silo?

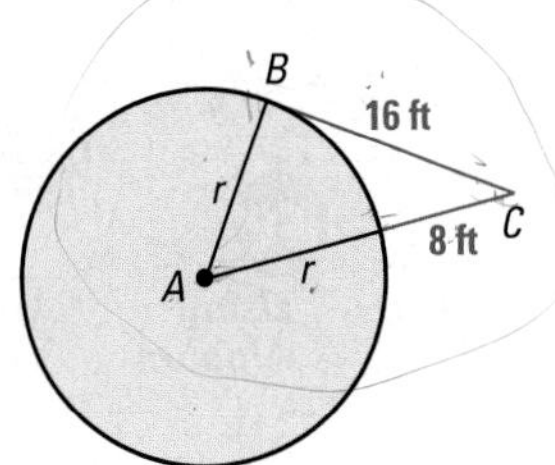

SOLUTION

Tangent $\overleftrightarrow{BC}$ is perpendicular to radius $\overline{AB}$ at B, so $\triangle ABC$ is a right triangle. So, you can use the Pythagorean Theorem.

$(r + 8)^2 = r^2 + 16^2$	**Pythagorean Theorem**
$r^2 + 16r + 64 = r^2 + 256$	**Square of binomial**
$16r + 64 = 256$	**Subtract r^2 from each side.**
$16r = 192$	**Subtract 64 from each side.**
$r = 12$	**Divide.**

▶ The radius of the silo is 12 feet.

STUDENT HELP

Skills Review

For help squaring a binomial, see p. 798.

CHECKPOINT EXERCISES

For use after Examples 2 and 3:

2. Give the center and radius of each circle. Describe all common tangents.

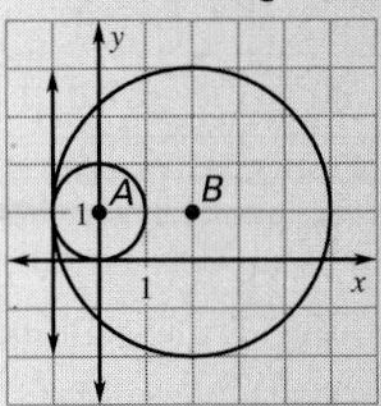

center $\odot A$: (0, 1); radius 1
center $\odot B$: (2, 1); radius 3
common tangents: $x = -1$

EXTRA EXAMPLE 4

Is $\overline{CE}$ tangent to $\odot D$? Explain.

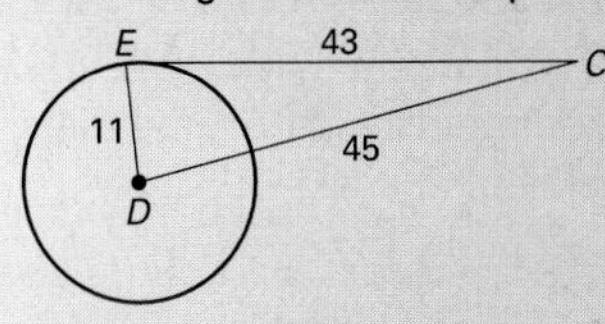

no; $45^2 \neq 43^2 + 11^2$

EXTRA EXAMPLE 5

You are standing 14 feet from a water tower. The distance from you to a point of tangency on the tower is 28 feet. What is the radius of the water tower? **21 ft**

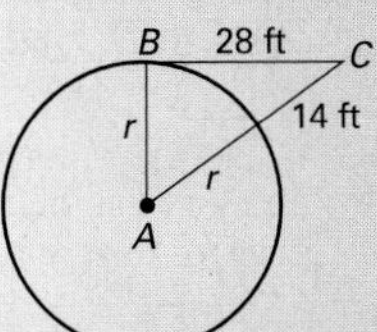

CHECKPOINT EXERCISES

For use after Examples 4 and 5:

1. $\overline{BC}$ is tangent to $\odot A$. Find the radius of the circle. **10**

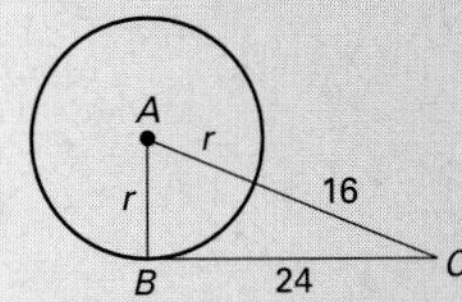

Extra Example 6

Given: $\overline{CB}$ is tangent to $\odot A$ at B. $\overline{CD}$ is tangent to $\odot A$ at D.
Prove: $\triangle ABC \cong \triangle ADC$

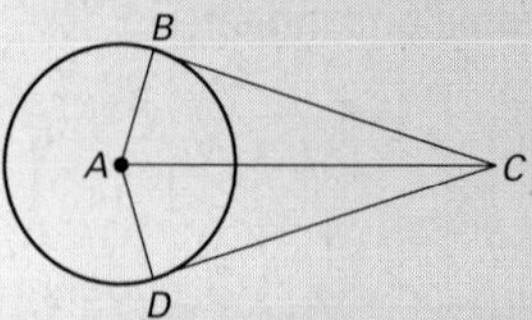

Since $\overline{CB}$ and $\overline{CD}$ are both tangent to $\odot A$, we have $\overline{CB} \cong \overline{CD}$. (If 2 segments from the same exterior point are tangent to a $\odot$, then they are $\cong$.) Since $\overline{AB}$ and $\overline{AD}$ are radii, they are $\cong$. (Def. of $\odot$). Also, $\overline{AC} \cong \overline{AC}$ by the reflexive property. So, $\triangle ABC \cong \triangle ADC$ by SSS.

Extra Example 7

$\overline{AB}$ is tangent to $\odot C$ at B. $\overline{AD}$ is tangent to $\odot C$ at D. Find the value of x. 5 or −5

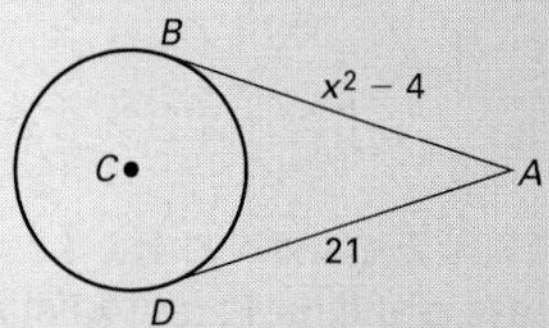

Checkpoint Exercises

For use after Examples 6 and 7:

1. $\overline{AB}$ is tangent to $\odot C$ at B. $\overline{AD}$ is tangent to $\odot C$ at D. Find the value of x. 6 or −6

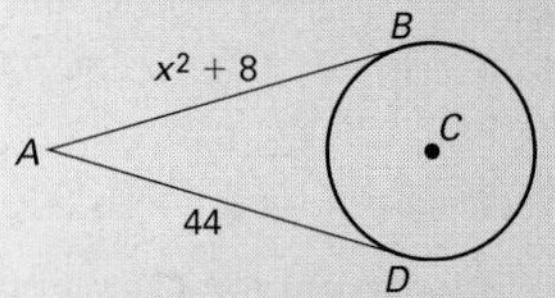

Closure Question

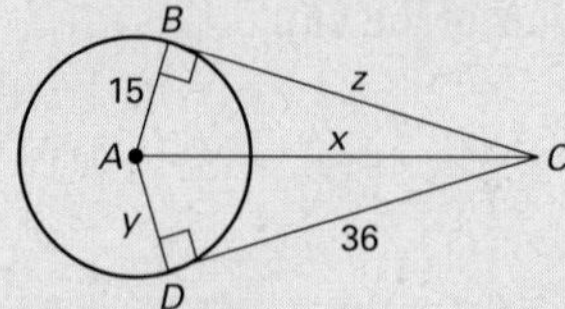

Find the values of x, y, and z in the diagram. $x = 39$; $y = 15$, $z = 36$

From a point in a circle's exterior, you can draw exactly two different tangents to the circle. The following theorem tells you that the segments joining the external point to the two points of tangency are congruent.

THEOREM

THEOREM 10.3

If two segments from the same exterior point are tangent to a circle, then they are congruent.

If $\overleftrightarrow{SR}$ and $\overleftrightarrow{ST}$ are tangent to $\odot P$, then $\overline{SR} \cong \overline{ST}$.

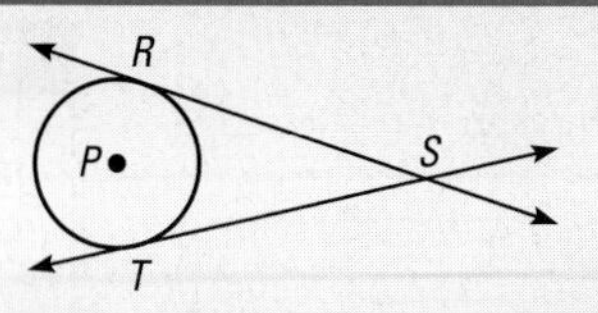

EXAMPLE 6 *Proof of Theorem 10.3*

GIVEN ▶ $\overleftrightarrow{SR}$ is tangent to $\odot P$ at R.
$\overleftrightarrow{ST}$ is tangent to $\odot P$ at T.

PROVE ▶ $\overline{SR} \cong \overline{ST}$

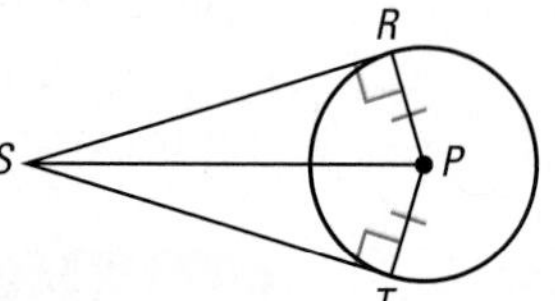

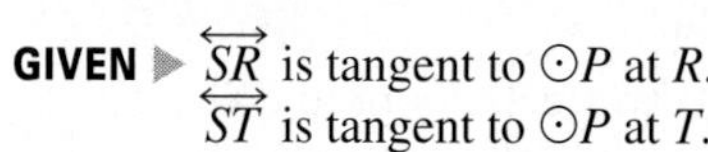

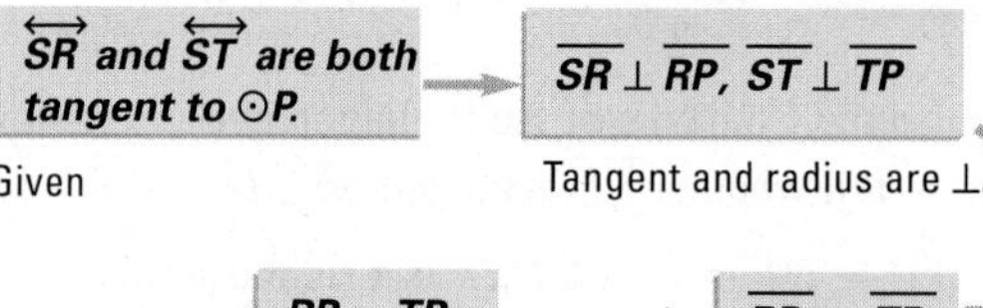

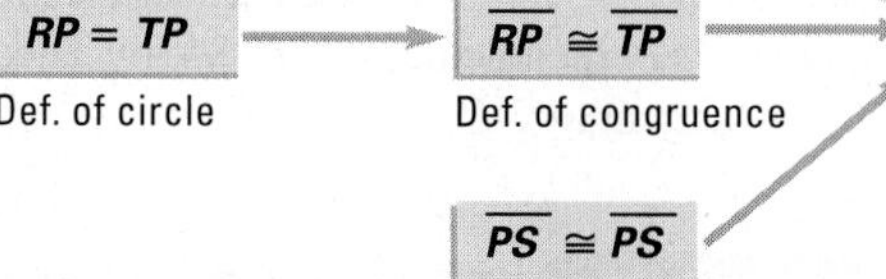

EXAMPLE 7 *Using Properties of Tangents*

$\overleftrightarrow{AB}$ is tangent to $\odot C$ at B.
$\overleftrightarrow{AD}$ is tangent to $\odot C$ at D.

Find the value of x.

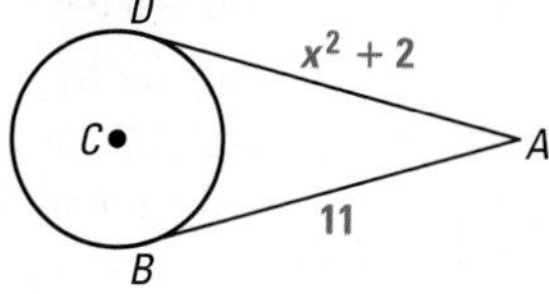

Solution

$AB = AD$	**Two tangent segments from the same point are ≅.**
$11 = x^2 + 2$	**Substitute.**
$9 = x^2$	**Subtract 2 from each side.**
$\pm 3 = x$	**Find the square roots of 9.**

▶ The value of x is 3 or −3.

GUIDED PRACTICE

Vocabulary Check ✓

1. Sketch a circle. Then sketch and label a *radius*, a *diameter*, and a *chord*. See margin.
2. How are chords and secants of circles alike? How are they different? See margin.

Concept Check ✓

3. $\overleftrightarrow{XY}$ is tangent to $\odot C$ at point P. What is $m\angle CPX$? Explain. See margin.
4. The diameter of a circle is 13 cm. What is the radius of the circle? 6.5 cm

Skill Check ✓

5. In the diagram at the right, $AB = BD = 5$ and $AD = 7$. Is $\overleftrightarrow{BD}$ tangent to $\odot C$? Explain. See margin.

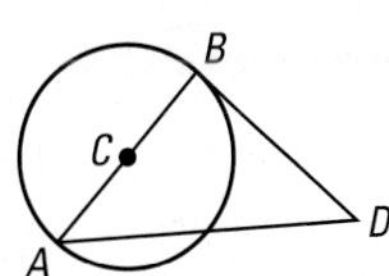

2. Both intersect a ⊙ in 2 points; a secant is a line, a chord is a segment with endpoints on the ⊙.

3. 90°; if a line is tangent to a ⊙, then it is ⊥ to the radius drawn to the point of tangency.

$\overleftrightarrow{AB}$ is tangent to $\odot C$ at A and $\overleftrightarrow{DB}$ is tangent to $\odot C$ at D. Find the value of x.

6. 4

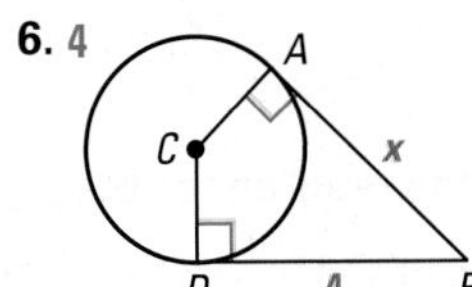

7. 2

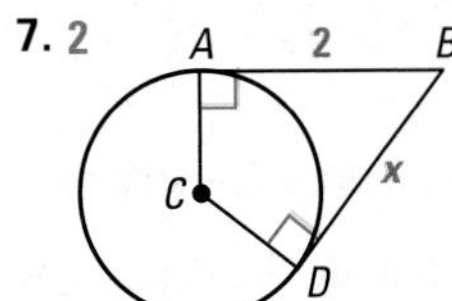

8. 5

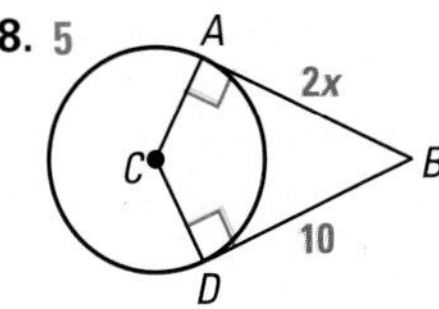

PRACTICE AND APPLICATIONS

STUDENT HELP

Extra Practice to help you master skills is on p. 821.

FINDING RADII **The diameter of a circle is given. Find the radius.**

9. $d = 15$ cm 7.5 cm
10. $d = 6.7$ in. 3.35 in.
11. $d = 3$ ft 1.5 ft
12. $d = 8$ cm 4 cm

FINDING DIAMETERS **The radius of $\odot C$ is given. Find the diameter of $\odot C$.**

13. $r = 26$ in. 52 in.
14. $r = 62$ ft 124 ft
15. $r = 8.7$ in. 17.4 in.
16. $r = 4.4$ cm 8.8 cm

17. **CONGRUENT CIRCLES** Which two circles below are congruent? Explain your reasoning.

17. C and G; the diameter of $\odot G$ is 45, so the radius is $\frac{45}{2} = 22.5$, which is the radius of $\odot C$.

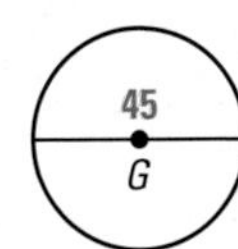

MATCHING TERMS **Match the notation with the term that best describes it.**

18. $\overline{AB}$ B	A. Center	
19. H E	B. Chord	
20. $\overleftrightarrow{HF}$ F	C. Diameter	
21. $\overline{CH}$ D	D. Radius	
22. C A	E. Point of tangency	
23. $\overline{HB}$ C	F. Common external tangent	
24. $\overleftrightarrow{AB}$ H	G. Common internal tangent	
25. $\overleftrightarrow{DE}$ G	H. Secant	

STUDENT HELP

HOMEWORK HELP

Example 1: Exs. 18–25, 42–45
Example 2: Exs. 26–31
Example 3: Exs. 32–35
Example 4: Exs. 36–39
Example 5: Exs. 40, 41
Example 6: Exs. 49–53
Example 7: Exs. 46–48

3 APPLY

ASSIGNMENT GUIDE

BASIC
Day 1: pp. 599–600 Exs. 9–35
Day 2: pp. 600–602 Exs. 36–49, 54–56, 58–70 even

AVERAGE
Day 1: pp. 599–600 Exs. 9–35
Day 2: pp. 600–602 Exs. 36–49, 54–56, 58–70 even

ADVANCED
Day 1: pp. 599–600 Exs. 9–35
Day 2: pp. 600–602 Exs. 36–57, 58–70 even

BLOCK SCHEDULE
pp. 599–602 Exs. 9–49, 54–56, 58–70 even

EXERCISE LEVELS

Level A: *Easier*
9–28

Level B: *More Difficult*
29–52, 54–56

Level C: *Most Difficult*
53, 57

✓ HOMEWORK CHECK

To quickly check student understanding of key concepts, go over the following exercises: Exs. 14, 26, 30, 36, 44, 46, 49, 55. See also the Daily Homework Quiz:

- Blackline Master (*Chapter 10 Resource Book,* p. 26)
- Transparency (p. 72)

! COMMON ERROR

EXERCISES 18 AND 24

Students may confuse the notation for chords and secants. Emphasize that a secant is a line, while a chord is a segment. $\overline{AB}$ is a chord, while $\overleftrightarrow{AB}$ is a secant.

1, 5. See Additional Answers beginning on page AA1.

MATHEMATICAL REASONING
EXERCISE 39 The following statement and its converse are both true: A tangent is perpendicular to a radius drawn to the point of tangency. Ask students to rewrite the statement as a biconditional. A tangent is perpendicular to a radius if and only if the radius is drawn to the point of tangency.

TEACHING TIPS
EXERCISE 40 Remind students that they need to square a binomial to solve this problem. Example 5 on page 597 is a similar problem.

APPLICATION NOTE
EXERCISES 40–41 Golf is played in many countries throughout the world. Professional golfers come not only from the United States, but also from Great Britain, Spain, Japan, Mexico, and Fiji. The Ryder Cup, an international golf championship, is held every other year.

29. 2 internal, 2 external

30. none
31. 2 external

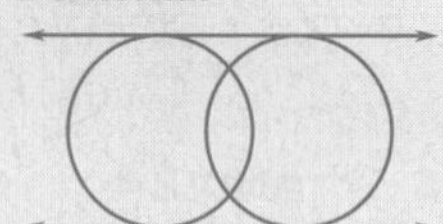

36. No; $5^2 + 14^2 \neq 15^2$, so by the Converse of the Pythagorean Thm., $\triangle ABC$ is not a right $\triangle$, so $\overline{AB}$ is not $\perp$ to $\overline{AC}$. Then $\overleftrightarrow{AB}$ is not tangent to $\odot C$.

37. No; $5^2 + 15^2 \neq 17^2$, so by the Converse of the Pythagorean Thm., $\triangle ABC$ is not a right $\triangle$, so $\overline{AB}$ is not $\perp$ to $\overline{AC}$. Then $\overleftrightarrow{AB}$ is not tangent to $\odot C$.

38. Yes; $BC = 12 + 8 = 20$ and $12^2 + 16^2 = 20^2$, so by the Converse of the Pythagorean Thm., $\triangle ABC$ is a right $\triangle$, and $\overline{AB} \perp \overline{AC}$. Then $\overleftrightarrow{AB}$ is tangent to $\odot C$.

39. Yes; $BD = 10 + 10 = 20$ and $20^2 + 21^2 = 29^2$, so by the Converse of the Pythagorean Thm., $\triangle ABD$ is a right $\triangle$, and $\overline{AB} \perp \overline{BD}$. Then $\overleftrightarrow{AB}$ is tangent to $\odot C$.

IDENTIFYING TANGENTS **Tell whether the common tangent(s) are *internal* or *external*.**

26. external

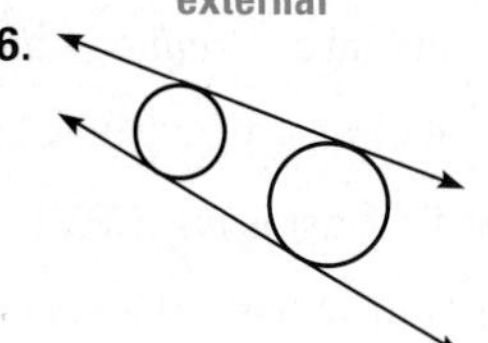

27. internal

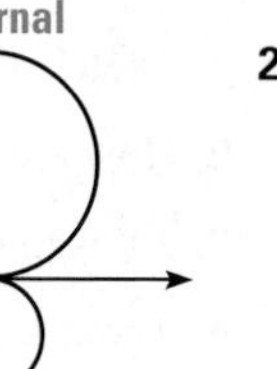

28. internal

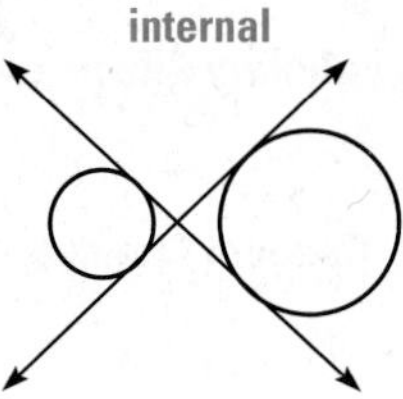

DRAWING TANGENTS **Copy the diagram. Tell how many common tangents the circles have. Then sketch the tangents.** See margin.

29.

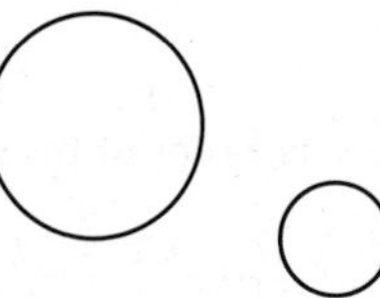

30.

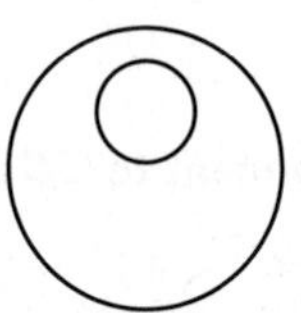

31.

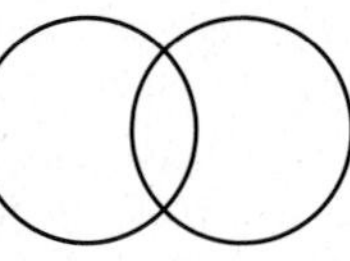

COORDINATE GEOMETRY **Use the diagram at the right.**

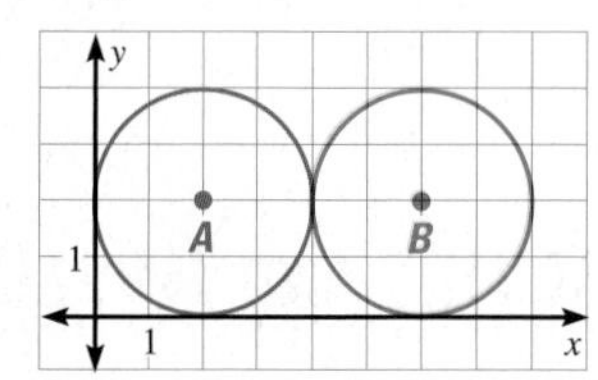

32. What are the center and radius of $\odot A$? (2, 2), 2

33. What are the center and radius of $\odot B$? (6, 2), 2

34. Describe the intersection of the two circles. the single point (4, 2)

35. Describe all the common tangents of the two circles. the lines with equations $y = 0$, $y = 4$, and $x = 4$

DETERMINING TANGENCY **Tell whether $\overleftrightarrow{AB}$ is tangent to $\odot C$. Explain your reasoning.** 36–39. See margin.

36.

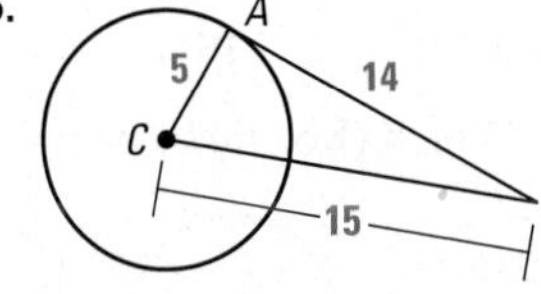

37.

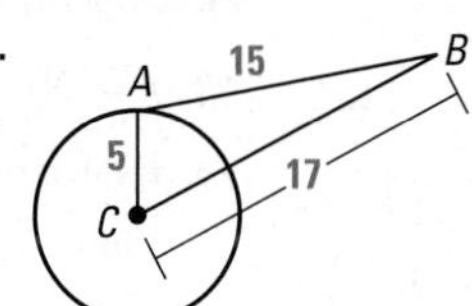

38.

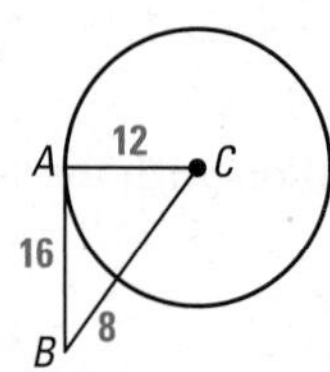

39.

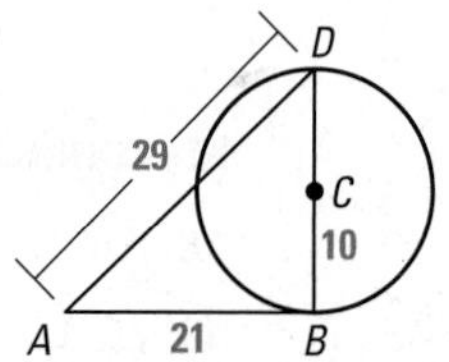

FOCUS ON PEOPLE

TIGER WOODS At age 15 Tiger Woods became the youngest golfer ever to win the U.S. Junior Amateur Championship, and at age 21 he became the youngest Masters champion ever.

GOLF **In Exercises 40 and 41, use the following information.**
A green on a golf course is in the shape of a circle. A golf ball is 8 feet from the edge of the green and 28 feet from a point of tangency on the green, as shown at the right. Assume that the green is flat.

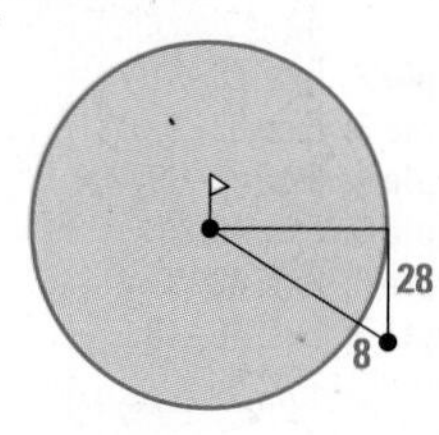

40. What is the radius of the green? 45 ft

41. How far is the golf ball from the cup at the center? 53 ft

Mexcaltitlán Island, Mexico

MEXCALTITLÁN The diagram shows the layout of the streets on Mexcaltitlán Island.

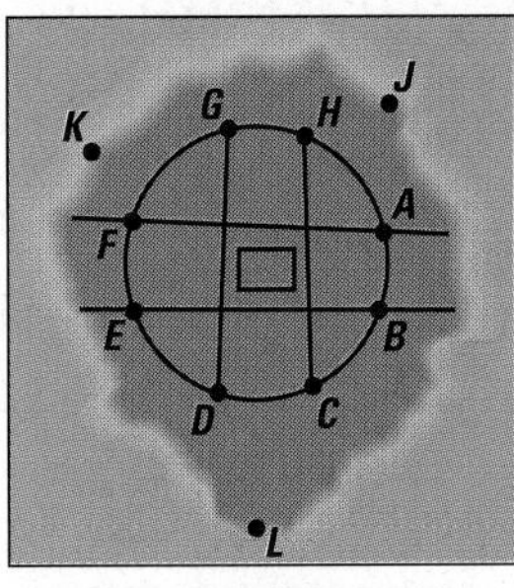

42. Name two secants. $\overleftrightarrow{FA}$ and $\overleftrightarrow{EB}$

43. Name two chords. any two of $\overline{GD}$, $\overline{HC}$, $\overline{FA}$, $\overline{EB}$

44. Is the diameter of the circle greater than HC? Explain. See margin.

45. If $\triangle LJK$ were drawn, one of its sides would be tangent to the circle. Which side is it? $\overleftrightarrow{JK}$

USING ALGEBRA $\overleftrightarrow{AB}$ and $\overleftrightarrow{AD}$ are tangent to $\odot C$. Find the value of x.

46. 5

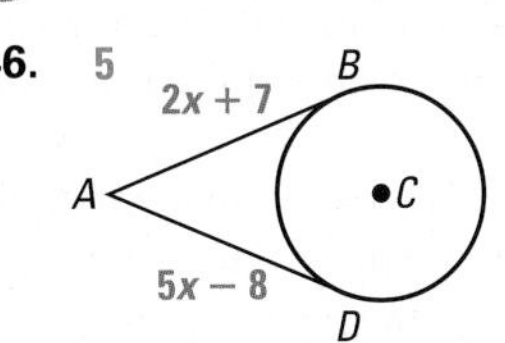

47. −1, 1

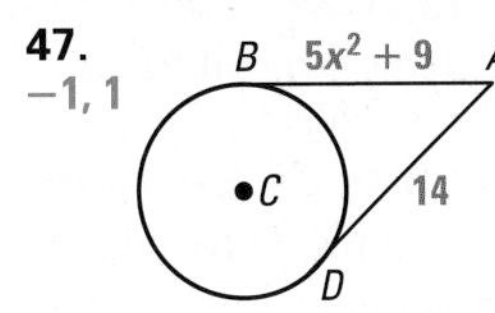

48. −2, 2

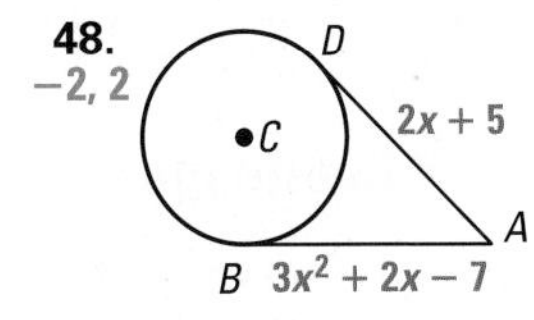

49. **PROOF** Write a proof.

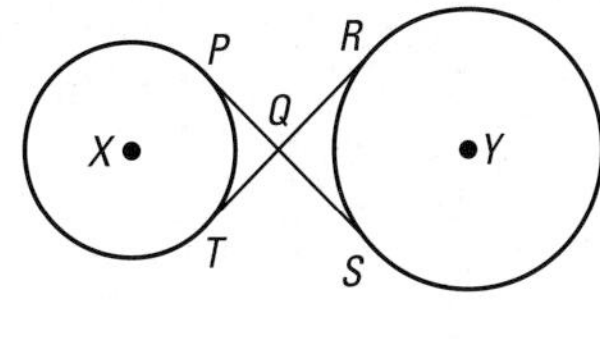

GIVEN ▶ $\overleftrightarrow{PS}$ is tangent to $\odot X$ at P.
$\overleftrightarrow{PS}$ is tangent to $\odot Y$ at S.
$\overleftrightarrow{RT}$ is tangent to $\odot X$ at T.
$\overleftrightarrow{RT}$ is tangent to $\odot Y$ at R.

PROVE ▶ $PS \cong RT$

PROVING THEOREM 10.1 In Exercises 50–52, you will use an indirect argument to prove Theorem 10.1.

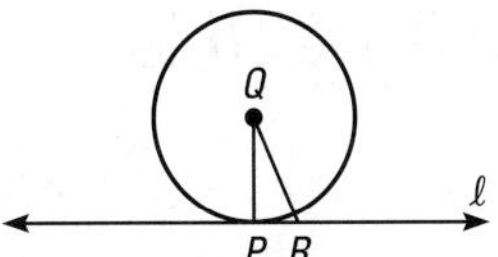

GIVEN ▶ ℓ is tangent to $\odot Q$ at P.

PROVE ▶ $\ell \perp \overline{QP}$

50. Assume ℓ and $\overline{QP}$ are not perpendicular. Then the perpendicular segment from Q to ℓ intersects ℓ at some other point R. Because ℓ is a tangent, R cannot be in the interior of $\odot Q$. So, how does QR compare to QP? Write an inequality. $QR > QP$

51. $\overline{QR}$ is the perpendicular segment from Q to ℓ, so $\overline{QR}$ is the shortest segment from Q to ℓ. Write another inequality comparing QR to QP. $QR < QP$

52. Use your results from Exercises 50 and 51 to complete the indirect proof of Theorem 10.1. See margin.

53. **PROVING THEOREM 10.2** Write an indirect proof of Theorem 10.2. (*Hint:* The proof is like the one in Exercises 50–52.) See margin.

GIVEN ▶ ℓ is in the plane of $\odot Q$.
$\ell \perp$ radius $\overline{QP}$ at P.

PROVE ▶ ℓ is tangent to $\odot Q$.

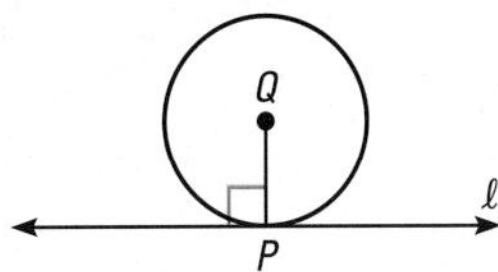

4. Yes; the diameter is the longest chord of the $\odot$. (Let P be the center of the $\odot$ and consider $\triangle HPC$. By the $\triangle$ Inequality, $HP + CP > HC$. But $HP = r$ and $CP = r$, so $HP + CP = 2r =$ the diameter of the $\odot$.)

9. $\overleftrightarrow{PS}$ is tangent to $\odot X$ at P, $\overleftrightarrow{PS}$ is tangent to $\odot Y$ at S, $\overleftrightarrow{RT}$ is tangent to $\odot X$ at T, and $\overleftrightarrow{RT}$ is tangent to $\odot Y$ at R. Then $\overline{PQ} \cong \overline{TQ}$ and $\overline{QS} \cong \overline{QR}$. (2 tangent segments with the same ext. endpoint are $\cong$.) By the def. of cong., $PQ = TQ$ and $QS = QR$, so $PQ + QS = TQ + QR$ by the addition prop. of equality. Then by the Segment Addition Post. and the Substitution Prop., $PS = RT$ or $\overline{PS} \cong \overline{RT}$.

2. QR cannot be both greater than QP and less than QP, so the assumption that ℓ and $\overline{QP}$ are not $\perp$ must be false. Then $\ell \perp \overline{QP}$.

3. *Sample proof:* Assume that ℓ is not tangent to P, that is, there is another point X on ℓ that is also on $\odot Q$. X is on $\odot Q$ so $QX = QP$. But the $\perp$ segment from Q to ℓ is the shortest such segment, so $QX > QP$. QX cannot be both equal to and greater than QP. The assumption that such a point X exists must be false. Then ℓ is tangent to P.

! COMMON ERROR

EXERCISE 53 Students often start an indirect proof with the negation of one of the given statements. Emphasize that the given statements are never changed. They should start by supposing line l is not tangent to $\odot Q$.

54.

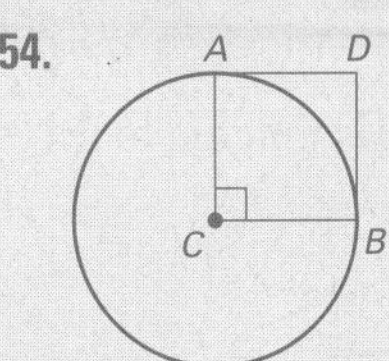

55. Square; $\overline{BD}$ and $\overline{AD}$ are tangent to $\odot C$ at A and B, respectively, so $\angle A$ and $\angle B$ are right $\angle$s. Then by the Interior Angles of a Quadrilateral Thm., $\angle D$ is also a right $\angle$. Then $CABD$ is a rectangle. Opp. sides of a $\square$ are $\cong$, so $\overline{CA} \cong \overline{BD}$ and $\overline{AD} \cong \overline{CB}$. But $\overline{CA}$ and $\overline{CB}$ are radii, so $\overline{CA} \cong \overline{CB}$ and by the Transitive Prop. of Cong., all 4 sides of $CABD$ are $\cong$. $CABD$ is both a rectangle and a rhombus, so it is a square by the Square Corollary.

57. See Additional Answers beginning on page AA1.

ADDITIONAL PRACTICE AND RETEACHING

For Lesson 10.1:

- Practice Levels A, B, and C (*Chapter 10 Resource Book*, p. 16)
- Reteaching with Practice (*Chapter 10 Resource Book*, p. 19)
- See Lesson 10.1 of the *Personal Student Tutor*

For more Mixed Review:

- Search the *Test and Practice Generator* for key words or specific lessons.

4 ASSESS

DAILY HOMEWORK QUIZ

Transparency Available

The radius of $\odot C$ is given. Find the diameter of $\odot C$.

1. 13 ft 26 ft

2. 3.2 in. 6.4 in.

Tell whether $\overline{AB}$ is tangent to $\odot C$.

3.

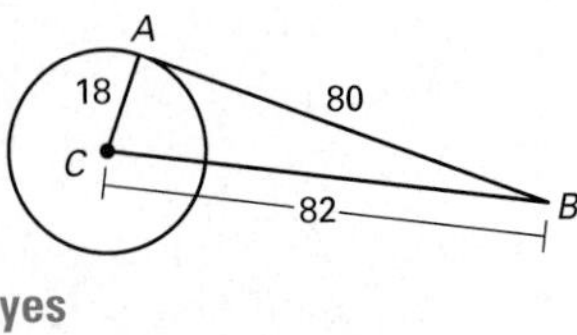

yes

$\overline{AB}$ and $\overline{AD}$ are tangent to $\odot C$. Find the value of x.

4.

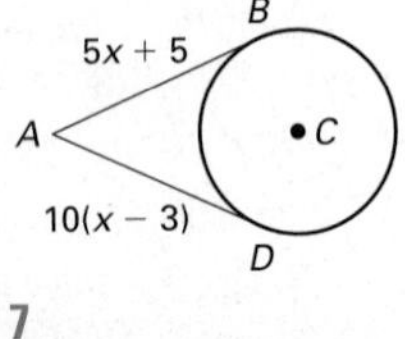

7

EXTRA CHALLENGE NOTE

Challenge problems for Lesson 10.1 are available in **blackline** format in the *Chapter 10 Resource Book*, p. 23 and at **www.mcdougallittell.com.**

ADDITIONAL TEST PREPARATION

1. OPEN ENDED Draw a pair of circles with exactly 3 common tangents. Show the tangents.
Sample answer:

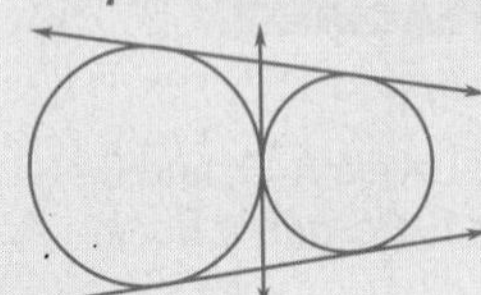

LOGICAL REASONING In $\odot C$, radii $\overline{CA}$ and $\overline{CB}$ are perpendicular. $\overleftrightarrow{BD}$ and $\overleftrightarrow{AD}$ are tangent to $\odot C$.

54. Sketch $\odot C$, $\overline{CA}$, $\overline{CB}$, $\overline{BD}$, and $\overline{AD}$. See margin on page 601.

55. What type of quadrilateral is *CADB*? Explain. See margin on page 601.

Test Preparation

56. MULTI-STEP PROBLEM In the diagram, line j is tangent to $\odot C$ at P.

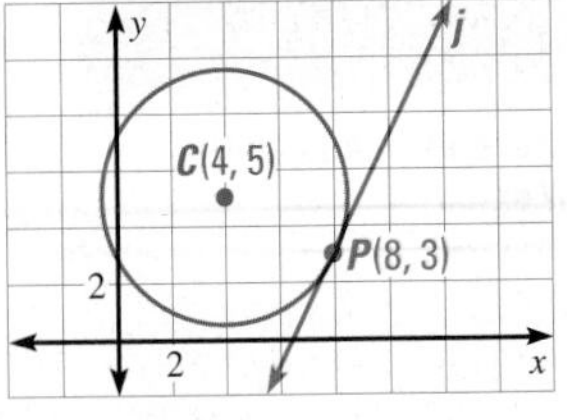

a. What is the slope of radius $\overline{CP}$? $-\frac{1}{2}$

b. What is the slope of j? Explain. 2; perpendicular lines have slopes that are opposite reciprocals.

c. Write an equation for j. $y = 2x - 13$

d. *Writing* Explain how to find an equation for a line tangent to $\odot C$ at a point other than P. See margin.

★ Challenge

56. d. Let Q be the point on $\odot C$. Find the slope of $\overline{CQ}$. Take the opposite reciprocal of this slope to get the slope of the tangent. Use this slope and the coordinates for Q to get the equation.

57. CIRCLES OF APOLLONIUS The Greek mathematician Apollonius (c. 200 B.C.) proved that for any three circles with no common points or common interiors, there are eight ways to draw a circle that is tangent to the given three circles. The red, blue, and green circles are given. Two ways to draw a circle that is tangent to the given three circles are shown below. Sketch the other six ways. See margin on page 601.

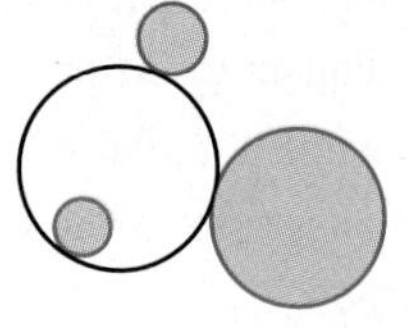

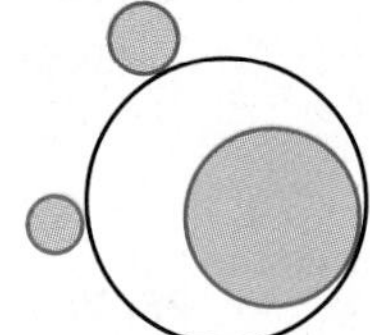

EXTRA CHALLENGE

www.mcdougallittell.com

MIXED REVIEW

58. TRIANGLE INEQUALITIES The lengths of two sides of a triangle are 4 and 10. Use an inequality to describe the length of the third side. **(Review 5.5)**
Let x be the length of the third side; $6 < x < 14$.

PARALLELOGRAMS Show that the vertices represent the vertices of a parallelogram. Use a different method for each proof. (Review 6.3)
59–60. Sample answers are given.

59. $P(5, 0)$, $Q(2, 9)$, $R(-6, 6)$, $S(-3, -3)$

60. $P(4, 3)$, $Q(6, -8)$, $R(10, -3)$, $S(8, 8)$

SOLVING PROPORTIONS Solve the proportion. (Review 8.1)

61. $\frac{x}{11} = \frac{3}{5}$ $6\frac{3}{5}$ **62.** $\frac{x}{6} = \frac{9}{2}$ 27 **63.** $\frac{x}{7} = \frac{12}{3}$ 28 **64.** $\frac{33}{x} = \frac{18}{42}$ 77

65. $\frac{10}{3} = \frac{8}{x}$ $2\frac{2}{5}$ **66.** $\frac{3}{x+2} = \frac{4}{x}$ −8 **67.** $\frac{2}{x-3} = \frac{3}{x}$ 9 **68.** $\frac{5}{x-1} = \frac{9}{2x}$ −9

SOLVING TRIANGLES Solve the right triangle. Round decimals to the nearest tenth. (Review 9.6)

69. A, B, C; AB = 14, BC = 6

70.

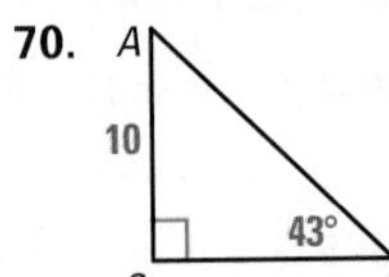

71. C, A, B; AC = 8, AB = 14

59. Since slope of $\overline{PS} = \frac{3}{8} =$ slope of $\overline{QR}$, $\overline{PS} \parallel \overline{QR}$. Since slope of $\overline{PQ} = -3 =$ slope of $\overline{SR}$, $\overline{PQ} \parallel \overline{SR}$. Then *PQRS* is a ▱ by def.

60. Since $PS = \sqrt{41} = QR$, $\overline{PS} \cong \overline{QR}$. Since slope of $\overline{PS} = \frac{5}{4} =$ slope of $\overline{QR}$, $\overline{PS} \parallel \overline{QR}$. Since one pair of opp. sides of *PQRS* is both ∥ and ≅, *PQRS* is a ▱.

69. $m\angle A \approx 23.2°$, $m\angle C \approx 66.8°$, $AC \approx 15.2$

70. $m\angle A = 47°$, $AB \approx 14.7$, $BC \approx 10.7$

71. $BC \approx 11.5$, $m\angle A \approx 55.2°$, $m\angle B \approx 34.8°$

10.2 Arcs and Chords

What *you should learn*

GOAL 1 Use properties of arcs of circles, as applied in **Exs. 49–51**.

GOAL 2 Use properties of chords of circles, as applied in **Ex. 52**.

Why *you should learn it*

▼ To find the centers of **real-life** arcs, such as the arc of an ax swing in **Example 6**.

REAL LIFE

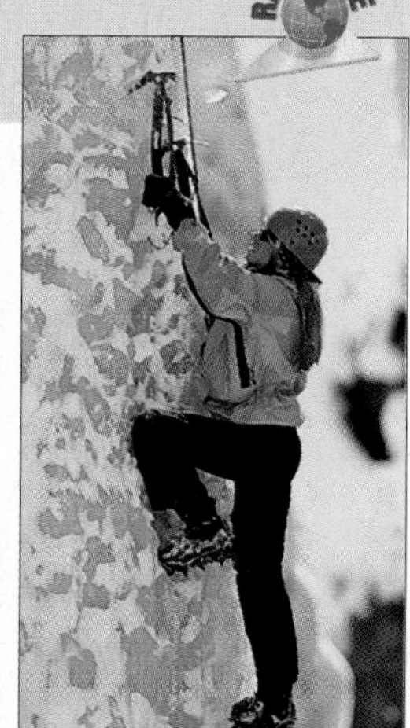

CALIFORNIA STANDARDS AND ASSESSMENT

CA Standards: 4, 7, 16, 21

GOAL 1 USING ARCS OF CIRCLES

In a plane, an angle whose vertex is the center of a circle is a **central angle** of the circle.

If the measure of a central angle, $\angle APB$, is less than $180°$, then A and B and the points of $\odot P$ in the interior of $\angle APB$ form a **minor arc** of the circle. The points A and B and the points of $\odot P$ in the *exterior* of $\angle APB$ form a **major arc** of the circle. If the endpoints of an arc are the endpoints of a diameter, then the arc is a **semicircle.**

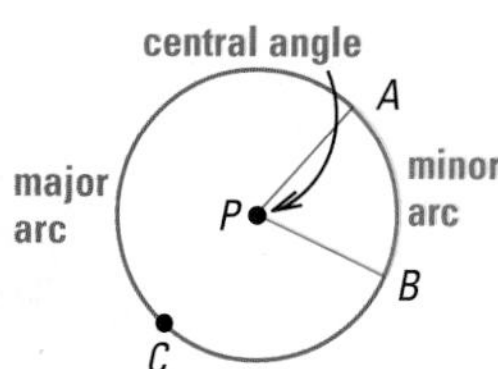

NAMING ARCS Arcs are named by their endpoints. For example, the minor arc associated with $\angle APB$ above is $\overparen{AB}$. Major arcs and semicircles are named by their endpoints and by a point on the arc. For example, the major arc associated with $\angle APB$ above is $\overparen{ACB}$. $\overparen{EGF}$ below is a semicircle.

MEASURING ARCS The **measure of a minor arc** is defined to be the measure of its central angle. For instance, $m\overparen{GF} = m\angle GHF = 60°$. "$m\overparen{GF}$" is read "the measure of arc GF." You can write the measure of an arc next to the arc. The measure of a semicircle is $180°$.

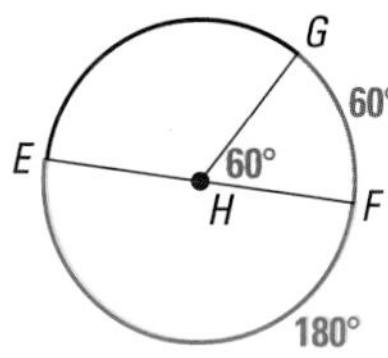

The **measure of a major arc** is defined as the difference between $360°$ and the measure of its associated minor arc. For example, $m\overparen{GEF} = 360 - 60° = 300°$. The measure of a whole circle is $360°$.

EXAMPLE 1 *Finding Measures of Arcs*

Find the measure of each arc of $\odot R$.

a. $\overparen{MN}$

b. $\overparen{MPN}$

c. $\overparen{PMN}$

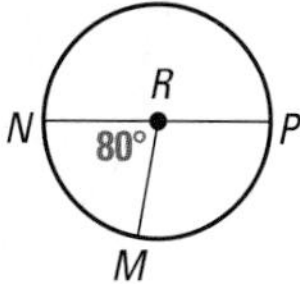

SOLUTION

a. $\overparen{MN}$ is a minor arc, so $m\overparen{MN} = m\angle MRN = 80°$

b. $\overparen{MPN}$ is a major arc, so $m\overparen{MPN} = 360° - 80° = 280°$

c. $\overparen{PMN}$ is a semicircle, so $m\overparen{PMN} = 180°$

1 PLAN

PACING
Basic: 2 days
Average: 2 days
Advanced: 2 days
Block Schedule: 1 block

LESSON OPENER
APPLICATION
An alternative way to approach Lesson 10.2 is to use the Application Lesson Opener:

- Blackline Master (*Chapter 10 Resource Book,* p. 27)
- Transparency (p. 62)

MEETING INDIVIDUAL NEEDS

- ***Chapter 10 Resource Book***
  Prerequisite Skills Review (p. 5)
  Practice Level A (p. 28)
  Practice Level B (p. 29)
  Practice Level C (p. 30)
  Reteaching with Practice (p. 31)
  Absent Student Catch-Up (p. 33)
  Challenge (p. 36)
- ***Resources in Spanish***
- ***Personal Student Tutor***

NEW-TEACHER SUPPORT
See the Tips for New Teachers on pp. 1–2 of the *Chapter 10 Resource Book* for additional notes about Lesson 10.2.

WARM-UP EXERCISES

Transparency Available

Solve the equation.

1. $3x = x + 50$ 25
2. $y + 5y + 66 = 360$ 49
3. $x + 14x = 180$ 12
4. $a^2 + 16 = 25$ 3; –3
5. $3w + 4w + 5w = 360$ 30

2 TEACH

MOTIVATING THE LESSON

Sketch a pie chart. Ask students where they have seen pie charts. Explain that finding measures of arcs to be able to make pie charts is a focus of this lesson.

EXTRA EXAMPLE 1

Find the measure of each arc.

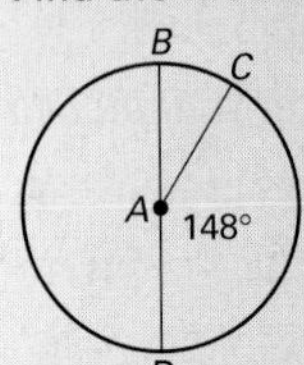

a. $\overset{\frown}{CD}$ 148°
b. $\overset{\frown}{CDB}$ 328°
c. $\overset{\frown}{BCD}$ 180°

EXTRA EXAMPLE 2

Find the measure of each arc.

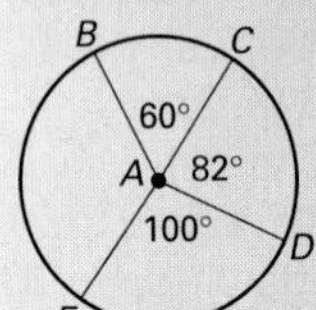

a. $\overset{\frown}{BD}$ 142°
b. $\overset{\frown}{BED}$ 218°
c. $\overset{\frown}{BE}$ 118°

EXTRA EXAMPLE 3

Find the measures of $\overset{\frown}{AB}$ and $\overset{\frown}{CD}$. Are the arcs congruent?

a.

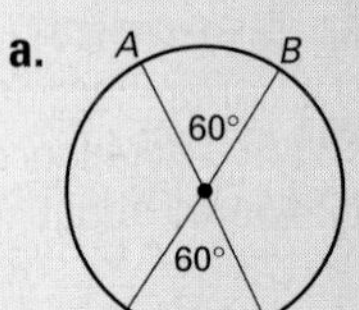

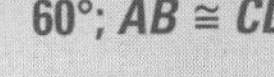

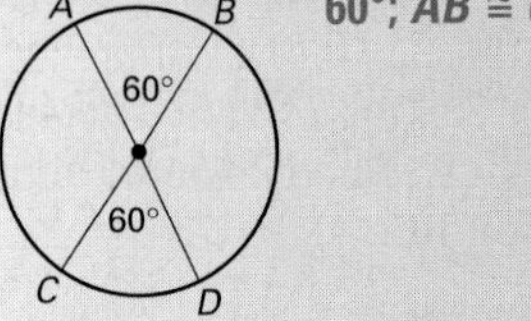

60°; $\overset{\frown}{AB} \cong \overset{\frown}{CD}$

b.

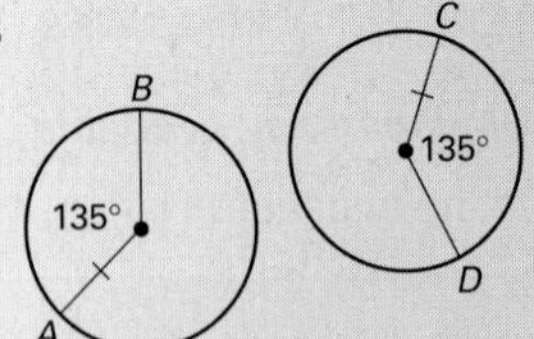

135°; $\overset{\frown}{AB} \cong \overset{\frown}{CD}$

c.

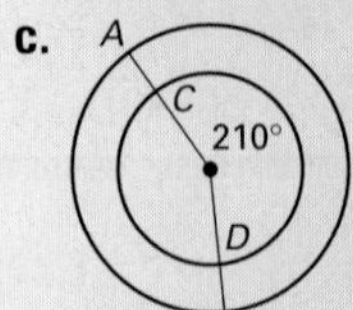

150°; $\overset{\frown}{AB} \ncong \overset{\frown}{CD}$

Checkpoint Exercises for Examples 1–3 on next page.

Two arcs of the same circle are *adjacent* if they intersect at exactly one point. You can add the measures of adjacent arcs.

POSTULATE

POSTULATE 26 ***Arc Addition Postulate***

The measure of an arc formed by two adjacent arcs is the sum of the measures of the two arcs.

$$m\overset{\frown}{ABC} = m\overset{\frown}{AB} + m\overset{\frown}{BC}$$

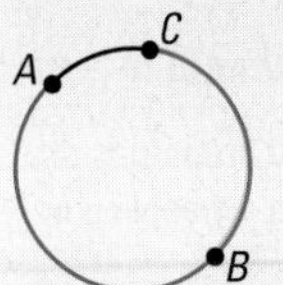

EXAMPLE 2 Finding Measures of Arcs

Find the measure of each arc.

a. $\overset{\frown}{GE}$ **b.** $\overset{\frown}{GEF}$ **c.** $\overset{\frown}{GF}$

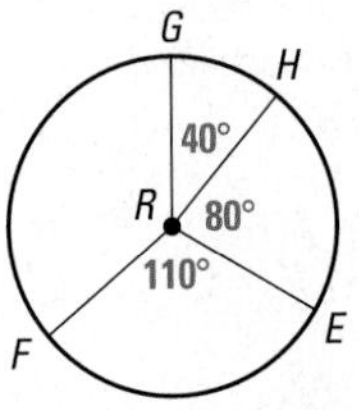

SOLUTION

a. $m\overset{\frown}{GE} = m\overset{\frown}{GH} + m\overset{\frown}{HE} = 40° + 80° = 120°$

b. $m\overset{\frown}{GEF} = m\overset{\frown}{GE} + m\overset{\frown}{EF} = 120° + 110° = 230°$

c. $m\overset{\frown}{GF} = 360° - m\overset{\frown}{GEF} = 360° - 230° = 130°$

....

Two arcs of the same circle or of congruent circles are **congruent arcs** if they have the same measure. So, two minor arcs of the same circle or of congruent circles are congruent if their central angles are congruent.

EXAMPLE 3 Identifying Congruent Arcs

Find the measures of the blue arcs. Are the arcs congruent?

a.

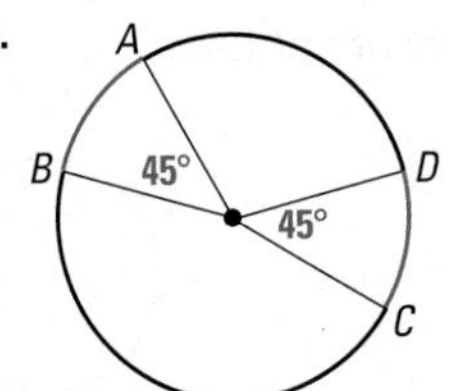

b.

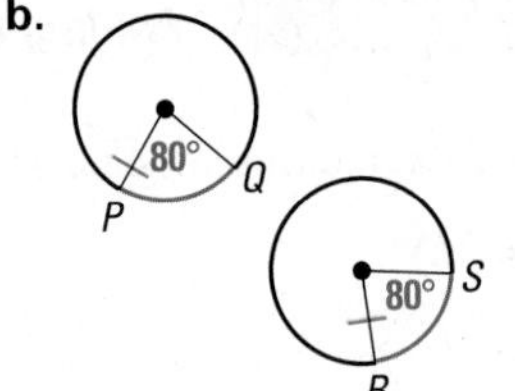

c.

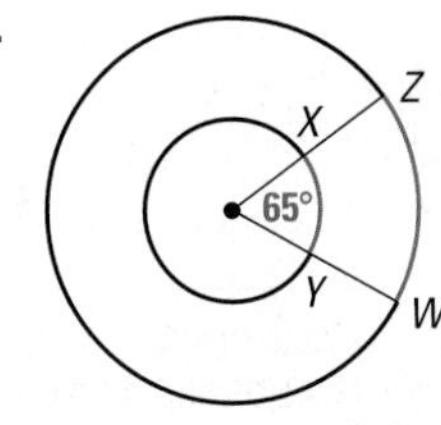

SOLUTION

a. $\overset{\frown}{AB}$ and $\overset{\frown}{DC}$ are in the same circle and $m\overset{\frown}{AB} = m\overset{\frown}{DC} = 45°$. So, $\overset{\frown}{AB} \cong \overset{\frown}{DC}$.

b. $\overset{\frown}{PQ}$ and $\overset{\frown}{RS}$ are in congruent circles and $m\overset{\frown}{PQ} = m\overset{\frown}{RS} = 80°$. So, $\overset{\frown}{PQ} \cong \overset{\frown}{RS}$.

c. $m\overset{\frown}{XY} = m\overset{\frown}{ZW} = 65°$, but $\overset{\frown}{XY}$ and $\overset{\frown}{ZW}$ are not arcs of the same circle or of congruent circles, so $\overset{\frown}{XY}$ and $\overset{\frown}{ZW}$ are *not* congruent.

GOAL 2 USING CHORDS OF CIRCLES

A point Y is called the *midpoint* of $\overparen{XYZ}$ if $\overparen{XY} \cong \overparen{YZ}$. Any line, segment, or ray that contains Y *bisects* $\overparen{XYZ}$. You will prove Theorems 10.4–10.6 in the exercises.

THEOREMS ABOUT CHORDS OF CIRCLES

THEOREM 10.4

In the same circle, or in congruent circles, two minor arcs are congruent if and only if their corresponding chords are congruent.

$\overparen{AB} \cong \overparen{BC}$ if and only if $\overline{AB} \cong \overline{BC}$.

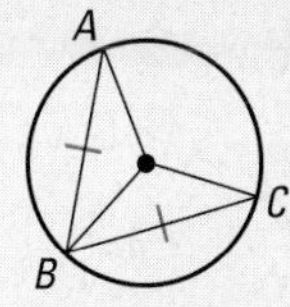

THEOREM 10.5

If a diameter of a circle is perpendicular to a chord, then the diameter bisects the chord and its arc.

$\overline{DE} \cong \overline{EF}$, $\overparen{DG} \cong \overparen{GF}$

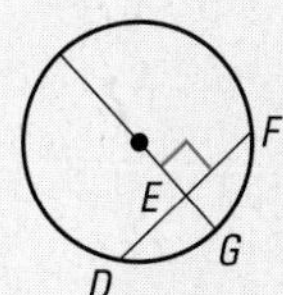

THEOREM 10.6

If one chord is a perpendicular bisector of another chord, then the first chord is a diameter.

$\overline{JK}$ is a diameter of the circle.

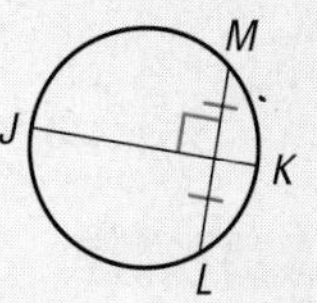

EXAMPLE 4 *Using Theorem 10.4*

Using Algebra

You can use Theorem 10.4 to find $m\overparen{AD}$.

Because $\overline{AD} \cong \overline{DC}$, $\overparen{AD} \cong \overparen{DC}$. So, $m\overparen{AD} = m\overparen{DC}$.

$2x = x + 40$ **Substitute.**

$x = 40$ **Subtract x from each side.**

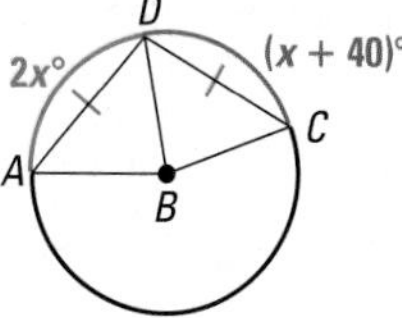

EXAMPLE 5 *Finding the Center of a Circle*

Theorem 10.6 can be used to locate a circle's center, as shown below.

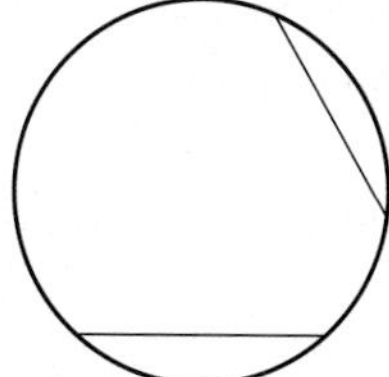

❶ Draw any two chords that are not parallel to each other.

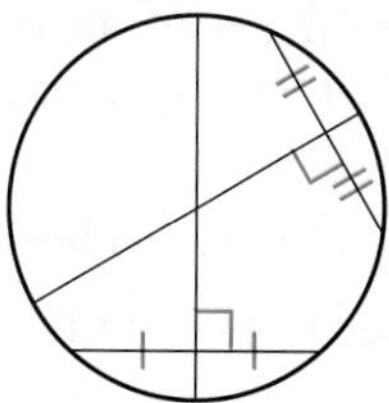

❷ Draw the perpendicular bisector of each chord. These are diameters.

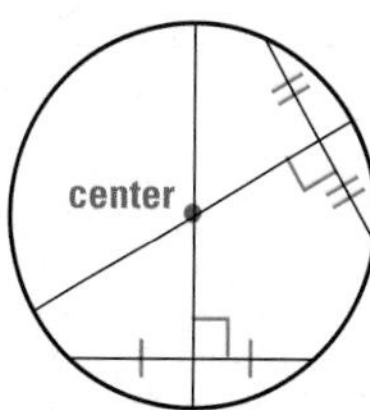

❸ The perpendicular bisectors intersect at the circle's center.

CHECKPOINT EXERCISES

For use after Examples 1–3:

1. Find the measure of each arc of $\odot A$.

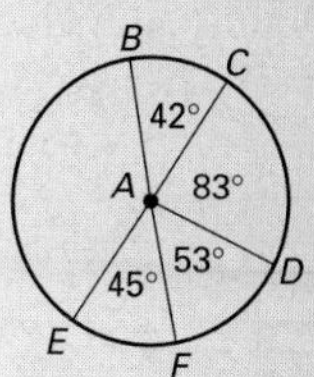

a. $\overparen{BD}$ 125°
b. $\overparen{BE}$ 137°
c. $\overparen{BED}$ 235°

EXTRA EXAMPLE 4

Use Theorem 10.4 to find $m\overparen{BC}$.

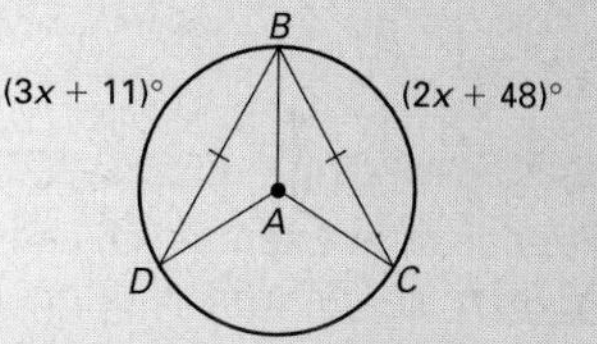

122°

EXTRA EXAMPLE 5

Locate the center of the following circle using the chords shown.

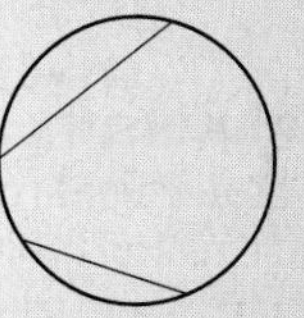

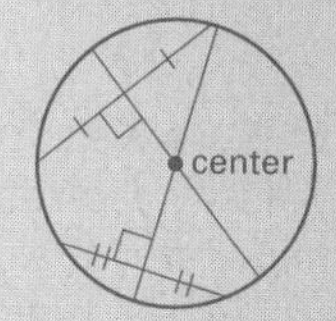

CHECKPOINT EXERCISES

For use after Examples 4 and 5:

1. Find $m\overparen{ED}$. 104°

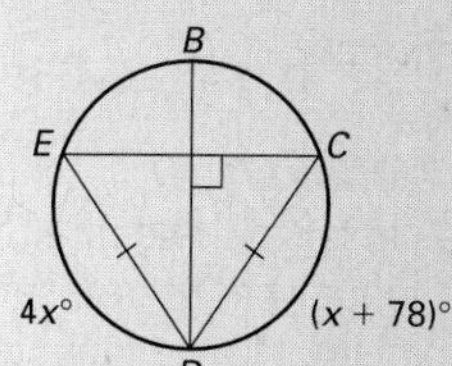

Extra Example 6

The top of a window is in the shape of a circular arc, as shown. Find the center of the circle used to form the arc.

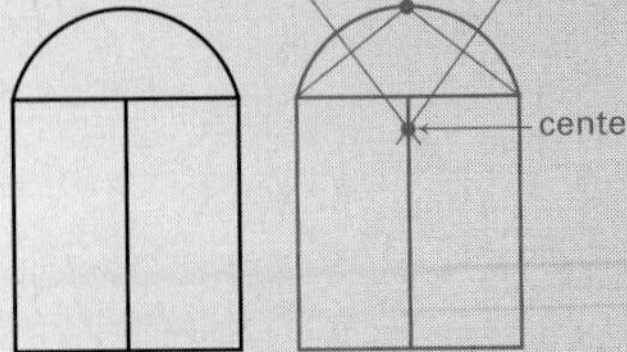

Extra Example 7

$AB = 12$, $DE = 12$, and $CE = 7$. Find CG. $\sqrt{13}$

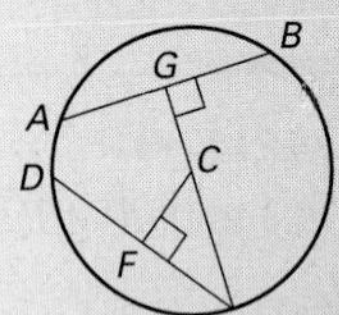

Checkpoint Exercises

For use after Examples 6 and 7:

1. $AD = 40$, $CD = 25$. Find CG. 15

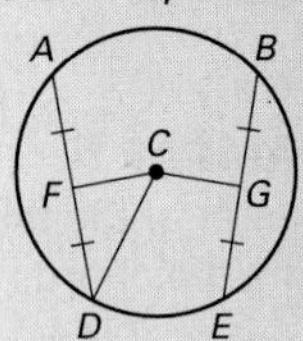

Focus on Vocabulary

Classify each arc as a major arc, a minor arc, or as a semicircle: 180°, 62°, 240°. **semicircle; minor; major**

Closure Question

Find the length of a chord of a circle with radius 8 that is a distance of 5 from the center. $2\sqrt{39}$

Daily Puzzler

Which is closer to the center of a circle? A longer chord or a shorter chord? Explain. **The longer chord because it is closer to the length of the diameter (the longest chord), which passes through the center.**

EXAMPLE 6 Using Properties of Chords

Masonry Hammer A masonry hammer has a hammer on one end and a curved pick on the other. The pick works best if you swing it along a circular curve that matches the shape of the pick. Find the center of the circular swing.

Solution

Draw a segment $\overline{AB}$, from the top of the masonry hammer to the end of the pick. Find the midpoint C, and draw a perpendicular bisector $\overline{CD}$. Find the intersection of $\overline{CD}$ with the line formed by the handle.

▶ So, the center of the swing lies at E.

You are asked to prove Theorem 10.7 in Exercises 61 and 62.

Student Help

Look Back
Remember that the distance from a point to a line is the length of the perpendicular segment from the point to the line. (p. 266)

THEOREM

THEOREM 10.7

In the same circle, or in congruent circles, two chords are congruent if and only if they are equidistant from the center.

$\overline{AB} \cong \overline{CD}$ if and only if $\overline{EF} \cong \overline{EG}$.

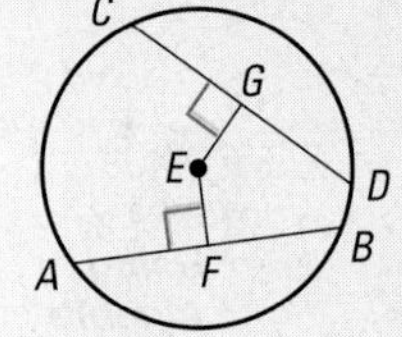

EXAMPLE 7 Using Theorem 10.7

$AB = 8$, $DE = 8$, and $CD = 5$. Find CF.

Solution

Because $\overline{AB}$ and $\overline{DE}$ are congruent chords, they are equidistant from the center. So, $\overline{CF} \cong \overline{CG}$. To find CG, first find DG.

$\overline{CG} \perp \overline{DE}$, so $\overline{CG}$ bisects $\overline{DE}$. Because $DE = 8$, $DG = \frac{8}{2} = 4$.

Then use DG to find CG.

$DG = 4$ and $CD = 5$, so $\triangle CGD$ is a 3-4-5 right triangle. So, $CG = 3$.

Finally, use CG to find CF.

▶ Because $\overline{CF} \cong \overline{CG}$, $CF = CG = 3$.

GUIDED PRACTICE

Vocabulary Check ✓

1. The measure of an arc is 170°. Is the arc a *major arc*, a *minor arc*, or a *semicircle*? minor arc

Concept Check ✓

2. In the figure at the right, what is $m\widehat{KL}$? What is $m\widehat{MN}$? Are $\widehat{KL}$ and $\widehat{MN}$ congruent? Explain.
72°; 72°; no; $\widehat{KL}$ and $\widehat{MN}$ are not arcs of the same ⊙ nor of ≅ ⊙s.

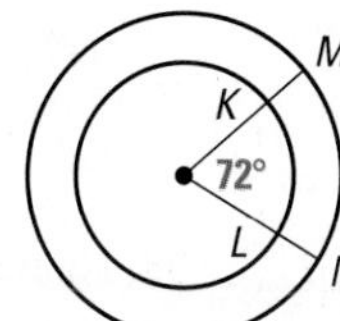

Skill Check ✓

Find the measure in ⊙*T*.

3. $m\widehat{RS}$ 60°
4. $m\widehat{RPS}$ 300°
5. $m\widehat{PQR}$ 180°
6. $m\widehat{QS}$ 100°
7. $m\widehat{QSP}$ 220°
8. $m\angle QTR$ 40°

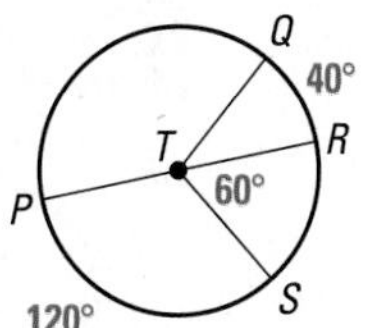

What can you conclude about the diagram? State a postulate or theorem that justifies your answer.

9.

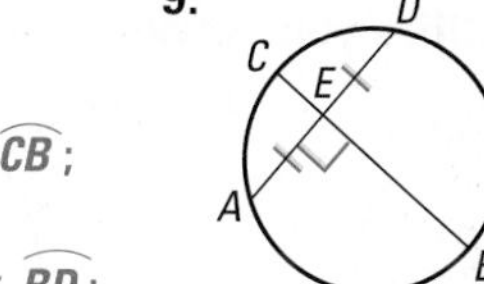

10.

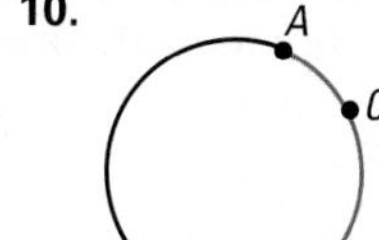

11.

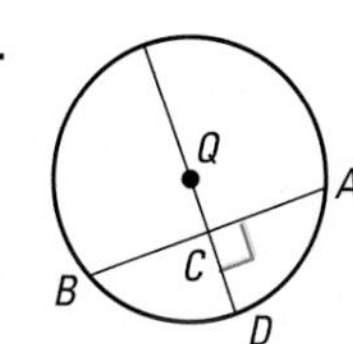

9. $\overline{BC}$ is a diameter; a chord that is the ⊥ bisector of another chord is a diameter.
10. *Sample answer:* $m\widehat{AB} = m\widehat{AC} + m\widehat{CB}$; Arc Addition Post.
11. $\overline{AC} \cong \overline{BC}$ and $\widehat{AD} \cong \widehat{BD}$; a diameter ⊥ to a chord bisects the chord and its arc.

PRACTICE AND APPLICATIONS

STUDENT HELP
Extra Practice to help you master skills is on p. 821.

UNDERSTANDING THE CONCEPT **Determine whether the arc is a *minor arc*, a *major arc*, or a *semicircle* of ⊙*R*.**

12. $\widehat{PQ}$ minor arc
13. $\widehat{SU}$ minor arc
14. $\widehat{PQT}$ semicircle
15. $\widehat{QT}$ minor arc
16. $\widehat{TUQ}$ major arc
17. $\widehat{TUP}$ semicircle
18. $\widehat{QUT}$ major arc
19. $\widehat{PUQ}$ major arc

Q
P
R
S
T
U

MEASURING ARCS AND CENTRAL ANGLES $\overline{KN}$ **and** $\overline{JL}$ **are diameters. Copy the diagram. Find the indicated measure.**

STUDENT HELP
HOMEWORK HELP
Example 1: Exs. 12–29
Example 2: Exs. 30–34, 49, 50
Example 3: Ex. 35
continued on p. 608

20. $m\widehat{KL}$ 60°
21. $m\widehat{MN}$ 55°
22. $m\widehat{LNK}$ 300°
23. $m\widehat{MKN}$ 305°
24. $m\widehat{NJK}$ 180°
25. $m\widehat{JML}$ 180°
26. $m\angle JQN$ 60°
27. $m\angle MQL$ 65°
28. $m\widehat{JN}$ 60°
29. $m\widehat{ML}$ 65°
30. $m\widehat{JM}$ 115°
31. $m\widehat{LN}$ 120°

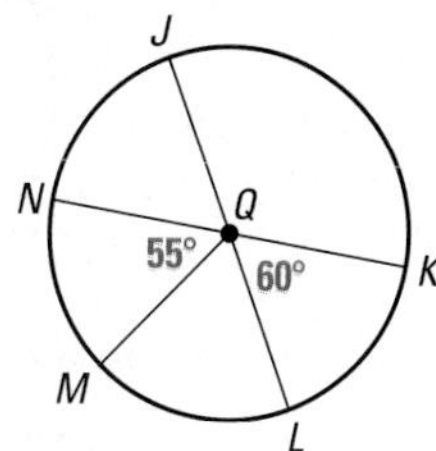

3 APPLY

ASSIGNMENT GUIDE

BASIC
Day 1: pp. 607–608 Exs. 12–38
Day 2: pp. 608–611 Exs. 39–48, 54–57, 63–68, 70–77

AVERAGE
Day 1: pp. 607–608 Exs. 12–38
Day 2: pp. 608–611 Exs. 39–51, 53–57, 59, 63–68, 70–77

ADVANCED
Day 1: pp. 607–608 Exs. 12–38
Day 2: pp. 608–611 Exs. 39–51, 53–57, 59, 63–77

BLOCK SCHEDULE
pp. 607–611 Exs. 12–51, 53–57, 59, 63–68, 70–77

EXERCISE LEVELS

Level A: *Easier*
12–19
Level B: *More Difficult*
20–60, 63–68
Level C: *Most Difficult*
61, 62, 69

✓ HOMEWORK CHECK

To quickly check student understanding of key concepts, go over the following exercises: Exs. 16, 22, 32, 38, 40, 44, 46, 56, 64. See also the Daily Homework Quiz:

- Blackline Master (*Chapter 10 Resource Book,* p. 39)
- Transparency (p. 73)

! COMMON ERROR

EXERCISES 12–19 Students often confuse minor arcs with major arcs. Major arcs and semicircles are labeled with three letters to avoid confusion.

MATHEMATICAL REASONING EXERCISE 37 In the same circle, congruent chords intercept congruent minor arcs. This exercise demonstrates that diameters intercept congruent semicircles. Name them. $\widehat{AMB}, \widehat{ANB}, \widehat{NBM}, \widehat{NAM}$

35. $\widehat{AC} \cong \widehat{KL}$ and $\widehat{ABC} \cong \widehat{KML}$; $\odot D$ and $\odot N$ are $\cong$ (both have radius 4). By the Arc Add. Post., $m\widehat{AC} = m\widehat{AE} + m\widehat{EC} = 70° + 75° = 145°$. $m\widehat{KL} = 145°$ and since $\odot D \cong \odot N$, $\widehat{AC} \cong \widehat{KL}$; $m\widehat{ABC} = 360° - m\widehat{AC} = 360° - 145° = 215°$. $m\widehat{KML} = m\widehat{KM} + m\widehat{ML} = 130° + 85° = 215°$ by the Arc Add. Post. Since $\odot D \cong \odot N$, $\widehat{ABC} \cong \widehat{KML}$.

STUDENT HELP

HOMEWORK HELP
continued from p. 607

Example 4: Exs. 36–38
Example 5: Exs. 52, 54
Example 6: Exs. 52, 54
Example 7: Exs. 39–47

39. $\widehat{AB} \cong \widehat{CB}$; 2 arcs are $\cong$ if and only if their corresp. chords are $\cong$.

40. $\overline{AB} \cong \overline{CD}$; 2 arcs are $\cong$ if and only if their corresp. chords are $\cong$.

41. $\overline{AB} \cong \overline{AC}$; in a $\odot$, 2 chords are $\cong$ if and only if they are equidistant from the center.

42. 10; in a $\odot$, 2 chords are $\cong$ if and only if they are equidistant from the center.

43. 40°: a diameter that is $\perp$ to a chord bisects the chord and its arc.

44. 170°; 2 arcs are $\cong$ if and only if their corresp. chords are $\cong$. (By the Arc Addition Post., $m\widehat{BD} = 110° + 60° = 170°$. The chords corresp. to $\widehat{EC}$ and $\widehat{BD}$ are $\cong$ by the addition property of equality and the Segment Addition Post.)

45. 15; in a $\odot$, 2 chords are $\cong$ if and only if they are equidistant from the center.

46. 7; a diameter that is $\perp$ to a chord bisects the chord and its arc.

47. 40°; Vertical Angles Thm., def. of minor arc

FINDING ARC MEASURES Find the measure of the red arc.

32. 145°
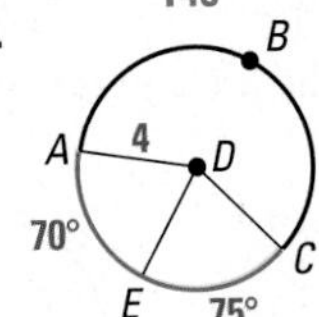

33. 145°
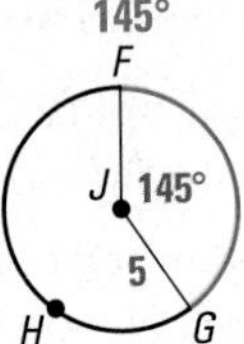

34. 145°
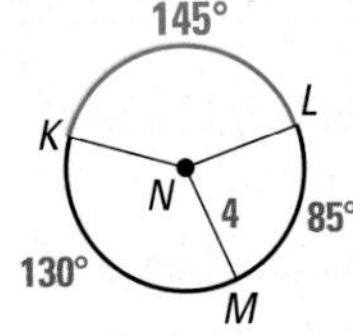

35. Name two pairs of congruent arcs in Exercises 32–34. Explain your reasoning. See margin.

USING ALGEBRA Use $\odot P$ to find the value of x. Then find the measure of the red arc.

36. 70; 110°
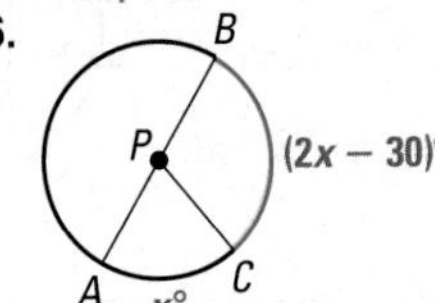

37. 36; 144°
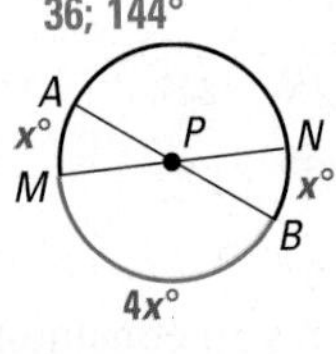

38. 15; 195°
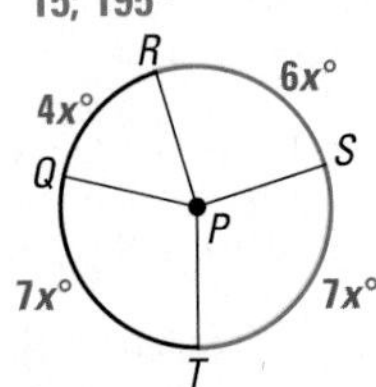

LOGICAL REASONING What can you conclude about the diagram? State a postulate or theorem that justifies your answer. See margin.

39.
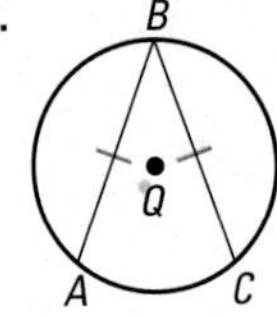

40.
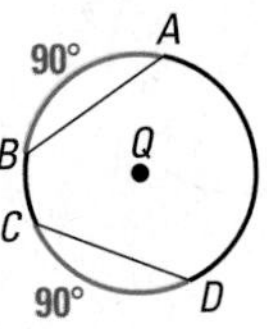

41.
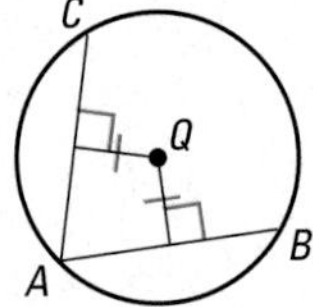

MEASURING ARCS AND CHORDS Find the measure of the red arc or chord in $\odot A$. Explain your reasoning. See margin.

42.
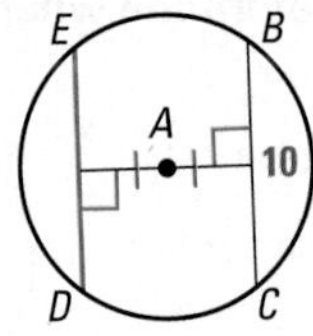

43.
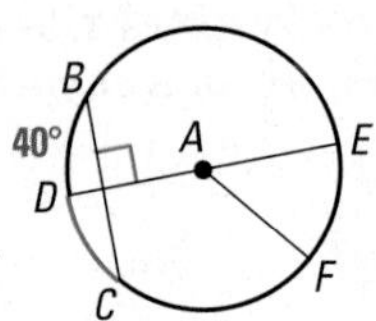

44.
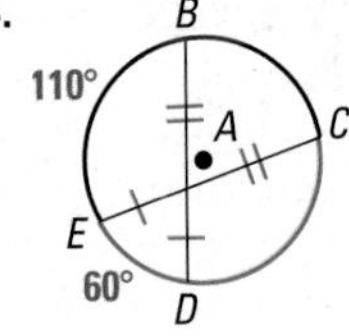

MEASURING ARCS AND CHORDS Find the value of x in $\odot C$. Explain your reasoning. See margin.

45.
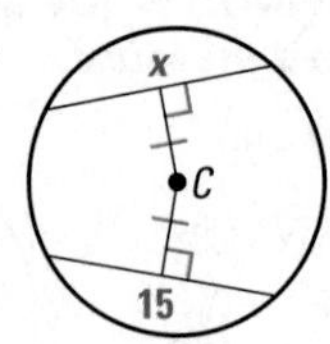

46.
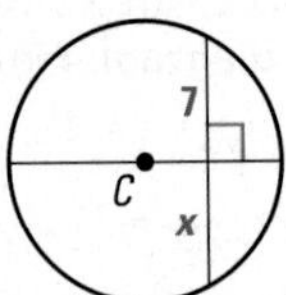

47.
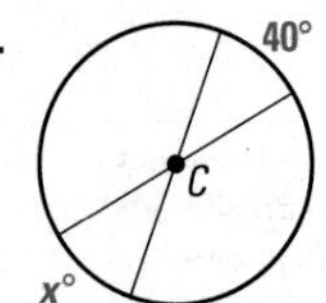

48. **SKETCHING** Draw a circle with two noncongruent chords. Is the shorter chord's midpoint farther from the center or closer to the center than the longer chord's midpoint? Check drawings; farther from the center.

52. The searcher is constructing a chord of the signal's ⊙ and the ⊥ bisector of the chord, a diameter of the circle (Theorem 10.6). By locating the midpoint of the diameter, the searcher locates the center of the ⊙ and, so, the beacon.

53. This follows from the definition of the measure of a minor arc. (The measure of a minor arc is the measure of its central ∠.) If 2 minor arcs in the same ⊙ or ≅ ⊙s are ≅, then their central ∠s are ≅. Conversely, if 2 central ∠s of the same ⊙ or ≅ ⊙s are ≅, then the measures of the associated arcs are ≅.

TIME ZONE WHEEL **In Exercises 49–51, use the following information.** The time zone wheel shown at the right consists of two concentric circular pieces of cardboard fastened at the center so the smaller wheel can rotate. To find the time in Tashkent when it is 4 P.M. in San Francisco, you rotate the small wheel until 4 P.M. and San Francisco line up as shown. Then look at Tashkent to see that it is 6 A.M. there. The arcs between cities are congruent.

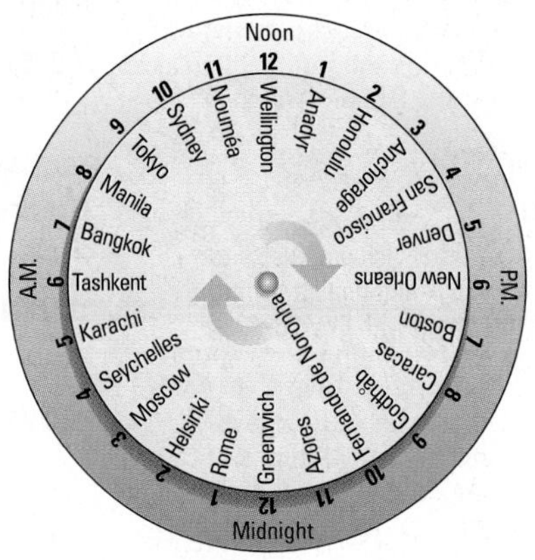

49. What is the arc measure for each time zone on the wheel? 15°

50. What is the measure of the minor arc from the Tokyo zone to the Anchorage zone? 90°

51. If two cities differ by 180° on the wheel, then it is 3:00 P.M. in one city if and only if it is _?_ in the other city. 3:00 A.M.

52. **AVALANCHE RESCUE BEACON** An avalanche rescue beacon is a small device carried by backcountry skiers that gives off a signal that can be picked up only within a circle of a certain radius. During a practice drill, a ski patrol uses steps similar to the following to locate a beacon buried in the snow. Write a paragraph explaining why this procedure works. ▶ Source: The Mountaineers
See margin.

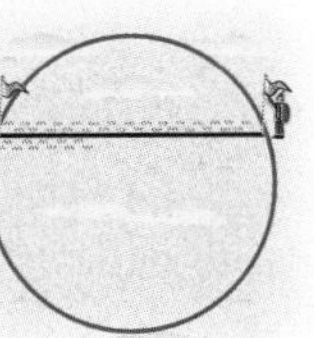

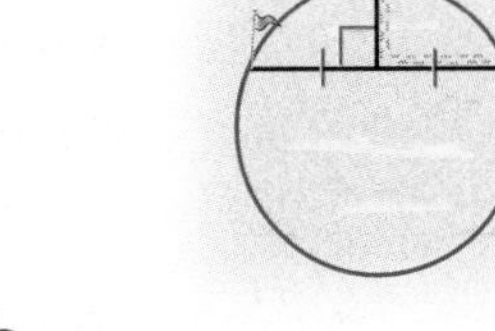

1 Walk until the signal disappears, turn around, and pace the distance in a straight line until the signal disappears again.

2 Pace back to the halfway point, and walk away from the line at a 90° angle until the signal disappears.

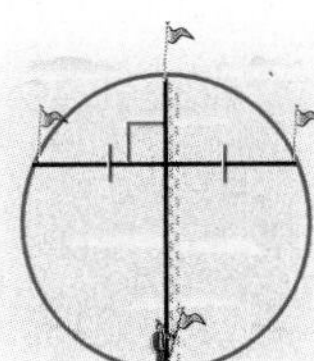

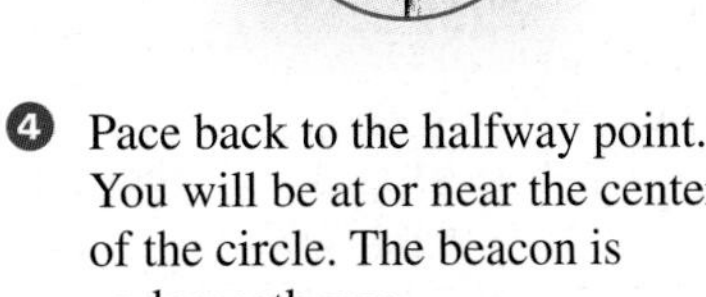

3 Turn around and pace the distance in a straight line until the signal disappears again.

4 Pace back to the halfway point. You will be at or near the center of the circle. The beacon is underneath you.

53. **LOGICAL REASONING** Explain why two minor arcs of the same circle or of congruent circles are congruent if and only if their central angles are congruent. See margin.

FOCUS ON CAREERS

REAL LIFE **EMTS** Some Emergency Medical Technicians (EMTs) train specifically for wilderness emergencies. These EMTs must be able to improvise with materials they have on hand.

INTERNET **CAREER LINK**
www.mcdougallittell.com

CAREER NOTE

EXERCISE 52 Additional information about emergency medical technicians is available at **www.mcdougallittell.com.**

ENGLISH LEARNERS

EXERCISE 52 English learners typically develop the ability to explain processes orally before they develop the ability to write paragraphs explaining such processes. To help students write explanations of why the steps presented work, you might have them work in a group to act out each step, and then discuss what the paragraph should include.

TEACHING TIPS

EXERCISE 54 This construction can be used to find the center of circles on a much larger scale. Ask students to think of examples where this construction might be useful. *Sample answer:* finding the center of a large circle on a gym floor

STUDENT HELP NOTES

Homework Help Students can find help for Exs. 56–62 at **www.mcdougallittell.com.** The information can be printed out for students who don't have access to the Internet.

61–63. See Additional Answers beginning on page AA1.

ADDITIONAL PRACTICE AND RETEACHING

For Lesson 10.2:

- Practice Levels A, B, and C (*Chapter 10 Resource Book,* p. 28)
- Reteaching with Practice (*Chapter 10 Resource Book,* p. 31)
- See Lesson 10.2 of the *Personal Student Tutor*

For more Mixed Review:

- Search the *Test and Practice Generator* for key words or specific lessons.

54. Draw two chords that are not $\parallel$ and construct their $\perp$ bisectors. The center of the $\odot$ is the intersection of the $\perp$ bisectors.

55. Yes; construct the $\perp$s from the center of the $\odot$ to each chord. Use a compass to compare the lengths of the segments.

56. $\overline{PA}$, $\overline{PB}$, $\overline{PC}$, and $\overline{PD}$ are all radii of $\odot P$, so $\overline{PA} \cong \overline{PB} \cong \overline{PC} \cong \overline{PD}$. Since $\overline{AB} \cong \overline{CD}$, $\triangle APB \cong \triangle CPD$ by the SSS Cong. Post. Then corresp. $\angle$s APB and CPD are $\cong$ and $\widehat{AB} \cong \widehat{DC}$ by the def. of $\cong$ arcs.

57. Since $\widehat{AB} \cong \widehat{DC}$, $\angle APB \cong \angle CPD$ by the def. of $\cong$ arcs. $\overline{PA}$, $\overline{PB}$, $\overline{PC}$, and $\overline{PD}$ are all radii of $\odot P$, so $\overline{PA} \cong \overline{PB} \cong \overline{PC} \cong \overline{PD}$. Then $\triangle APB \cong \triangle CPD$ by the SAS Cong. Post. so corresp. sides $\overline{AB}$ and $\overline{DC}$ are $\cong$.

59. Draw radii $\overline{LG}$, $\overline{LH}$. $\overline{LG} \cong \overline{LH}$, $\overline{LJ} \cong \overline{LJ}$, and, since $\overline{EF} \perp \overline{GH}$, $\triangle LGJ \cong \triangle LHJ$ by the HL Cong. Thm. Then corresp. sides $\overline{GJ}$ and $\overline{JH}$ are $\cong$, as are corresp. $\angle$s GLJ and HLJ. By the def. of $\cong$ arcs, $\widehat{GE} \cong \widehat{EH}$.

60. Let $\overline{EF}$ be the $\perp$ bisector of $\overline{GH}$ and assume that L is not on $\overline{EF}$. Draw radii $\overline{GL}$ and $\overline{LH}$. Then $\overline{GL} \cong \overline{LH}$ and $\overline{LJ} \cong \overline{LJ}$. By def. of $\perp$ bisector, $\overline{GJ} \cong \overline{JH}$. So $\triangle GLJ \cong \triangle HLJ$ by the SSS Cong. Post. Then $\angle$s GJL and LJH are right angles and $\overline{LJ} \perp \overline{GH}$. Then $\overleftrightarrow{EF}$ and $\overleftrightarrow{JL}$ are 2 lines $\perp$ the same line and intersect in point J. This contradicts the fact that, in a plane, 2 lines $\perp$ to the same line are $\parallel$. The assumption that L is not on $\overline{EF}$ must be incorrect, so L is on $\overline{EF}$ and $\overline{EF}$ is a diameter of $\odot L$.

STUDENT HELP

HOMEWORK HELP Visit our Web site www.mcdougallittell.com for help with Exs. 56–62.

54. **CONSTRUCTION** Trace a circular object like a cup or can. Then use a compass and straightedge to find the center of the circle. Explain your steps.

55. **CONSTRUCTION** Construct a large circle with two congruent chords. Are the chords the same distance from the center? How can you tell? See margin.

PROVING THEOREM 10.4 **In Exercises 56 and 57, you will prove Theorem 10.4 for the case in which the two chords are in the same circle. Write a plan for a proof.** 56, 57. See margin.

56. **GIVEN** ▶ $\overline{AB}$ and $\overline{DC}$ are in $\odot P$.
$\overline{AB} \cong \overline{DC}$

PROVE ▶ $\widehat{AB} \cong \widehat{DC}$

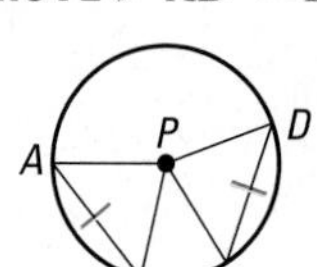

57. **GIVEN** ▶ $\overline{AB}$ and $\overline{DC}$ are in $\odot P$.
$\widehat{AB} \cong \widehat{DC}$

PROVE ▶ $\overline{AB} \cong \overline{DC}$

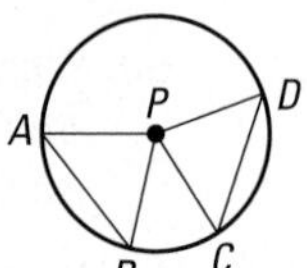

58. **JUSTIFYING THEOREM 10.4** Explain how the proofs in Exercises 56 and 57 would be different if $\overline{AB}$ and $\overline{DC}$ were in congruent circles rather than the same circle. You would have to use the def. of $\cong$ $\odot$s and the Transitive Prop. of Cong. to show that the appropriate sides and $\angle$s are $\cong$.

PROVING THEOREMS 10.5 AND 10.6 **Write a proof.** 59, 60. See margin.

59. **GIVEN** ▶ $\overline{EF}$ is a diameter of $\odot L$.
$\overline{EF} \perp \overline{GH}$

PROVE ▶ $\overline{GJ} \cong \overline{JH}$, $\widehat{GE} \cong \widehat{EH}$

Plan for Proof Draw $\overline{LG}$ and $\overline{LH}$. Use congruent triangles to show $\overline{GJ} \cong \overline{JH}$ and $\angle GLE \cong \angle HLE$. Then show $\widehat{GE} \cong \widehat{EH}$.

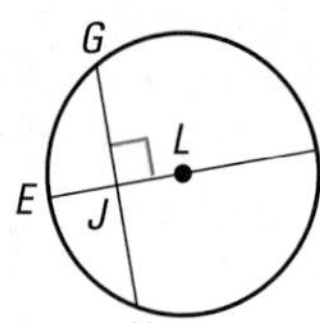

60. **GIVEN** ▶ $\overline{EF}$ is the $\perp$ bisector of $\overline{GH}$.

PROVE ▶ $\overline{EF}$ is a diameter of $\odot L$.

Plan for Proof Use indirect reasoning. Assume center L is not on $\overline{EF}$. Prove that $\triangle GLJ \cong \triangle HLJ$, so $\overline{JL} \perp \overline{GH}$. Then use the Perpendicular Postulate.

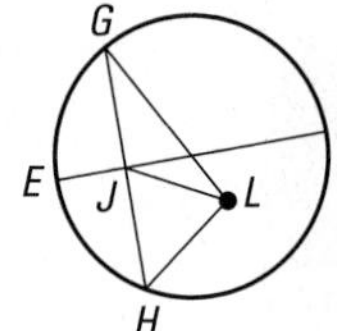

PROVING THEOREM 10.7 **Write a proof.** 61, 62. See margin.

61. **GIVEN** ▶ $\overline{PE} \perp \overline{AB}$, $\overline{PF} \perp \overline{DC}$,
$\overline{PE} \cong \overline{PF}$

PROVE ▶ $\overline{AB} \cong \overline{DC}$

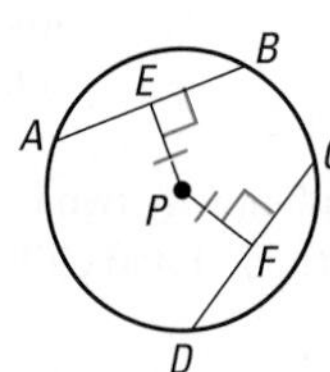

62. **GIVEN** ▶ $\overline{PE} \perp \overline{AB}$, $\overline{PF} \perp \overline{DC}$,
$\overline{AB} \cong \overline{DC}$

PROVE ▶ $\overline{PE} \cong \overline{PF}$

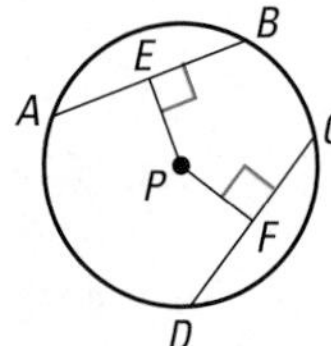

POLAR COORDINATES In Exercises 63–67, use the following information.

A *polar coordinate system* locates a point in a plane by its distance from the origin O and by the measure of a central angle. For instance, the point $A(2, 30°)$ at the right is 2 units from the origin and $m\angle XOA = 30°$. Similarly, the point $B(4, 120°)$ is 4 units from the origin and $m\angle XOB = 120°$.

63. Use polar graph paper or a protractor and a ruler to graph points A and B. Also graph $C(4, 210°)$, $D(4, 330°)$, and $E(2, 150°)$. See margin.

64. Find $m\widehat{AE}$. 120° **65.** Find $m\widehat{BC}$. 90° **66.** Find $m\widehat{BD}$. 150° **67.** Find $m\widehat{BCD}$. 210°

68. MULTI-STEP PROBLEM You want to find the radius of a circular object. First you trace the object on a piece of paper. See margin.

a. Explain how to use two chords that are not parallel to each other to find the radius of the circle.

b. Explain how to use two tangent lines that are not parallel to each other to find the radius of the circle.

c. *Writing* Would the methods in parts (a) and (b) work better for small objects or for large objects? Explain your reasoning.

69. The plane at the right intersects the sphere in a circle that has a diameter of 12. If the diameter of the sphere is 18, what is the value of x? Give your answer in simplified radical form. $3\sqrt{5}$

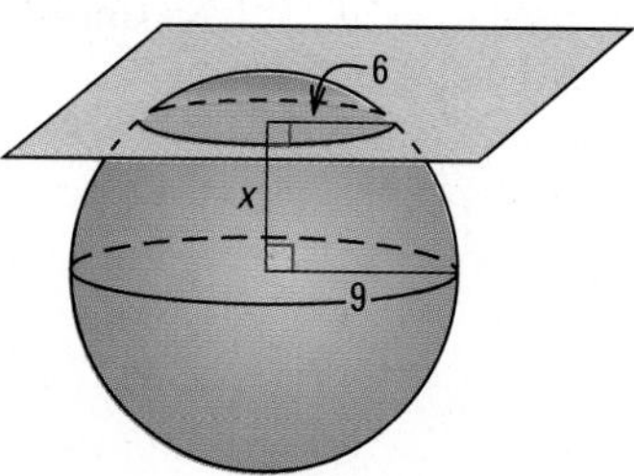

EXTRA CHALLENGE
www.mcdougallittell.com

68. a. Construct the perpendicular bisector of each chord. The point at which the bisectors intersect is the center of the circle. Connect the center with any point on the circle and measure the segment drawn.

Test Preparation

b. Construct lines ⊥ to the two tangents at the points of tangency. The intersection of the ⊥s is the center of the circle. Draw a segment from the center to any point on the circle and measure the segment.

MIXED REVIEW

INTERIOR OF AN ANGLE Plot the points in a coordinate plane and sketch $\angle ABC$. Write the coordinates of a point that lies in the interior and a point that lies in the exterior of $\angle ABC$. (Review 1.4 for 10.3) 70–73. See margin.

70. $A(4, 2)$, $B(0, 2)$, $C(3, 0)$

71. $A(-2, 3)$, $B(0, 0)$, $C(4, -1)$

72. $A(-2, -3)$, $B(0, -1)$, $C(2, -3)$

73. $A(-3, 2)$, $B(0, 0)$, $C(3, 2)$

COORDINATE GEOMETRY The coordinates of the vertices of parallelogram $PQRS$ are given. Decide whether $\square PQRS$ is best described as a *rhombus*, a *rectangle*, or a *square*. Explain your reasoning. (Review 6.4 for 10.3) 74, 75. See margin.

74. $P(-2, 1)$, $Q(-1, 4)$, $R(0, 1)$, $S(-1, -2)$

75. $P(-1, 2)$, $Q(2, 5)$, $R(5, 2)$, $S(2, -1)$

74. Rhombus; $PQ = QR = RS = PS = \sqrt{10}$; $PQRS$ is a rhombus by the Rhombus Corollary.

75. Square; $PQ = QR = RS = PS = 3\sqrt{2}$ so $PQRS$ is a rhombus by the Rhombus Corollary; $PR = QS = 6$, so $PQRS$ is a rectangle. (A $\square$ is a rectangle if and only if its diagonals are ≅.) Then $PQRS$ is a square by the Square Corollary.

GEOMETRIC MEAN Find the geometric mean of the numbers. (Review 8.2)

76. 9, 16 12 **77.** 8, 32 16 **78.** 4, 49 14 **79.** 9, 36 18

4 ASSESS

DAILY HOMEWORK QUIZ

Transparency Available

Determine whether the arc is a *minor arc*, a *major arc*, or a *semicircle* of $\odot K$.

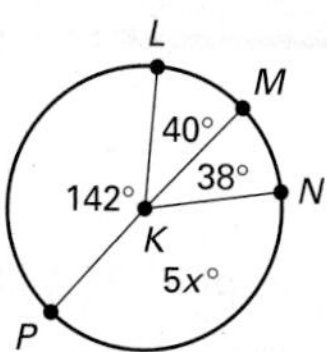

1. $\widehat{PLM}$ major arc

2. $\widehat{NL}$ minor arc

Find the indicated value.

3. $m\widehat{LN}$ 78°

4. $m\widehat{PLN}$ 220°

5. x 28

EXTRA CHALLENGE NOTE

Challenge problems for Lesson 10.2 are available in **blackline** format in the *Chapter 10 Resource Book*, p. 36 and at **www.mcdougallittell.com.**

ADDITIONAL TEST PREPARATION

1. WRITING Describe the properties of congruent chords of a circle. Congruent chords intercept congruent arcs and they are equidistant from the center of the circle.

68c. The object would have to be small enough to be traced on a piece of paper and to allow you to do constructions. If it were too small, however, it would be difficult to perform the constructions accurately.

70–73. See Additional Answers beginning on page AA1.

1 Planning the Activity

PURPOSE
Find the measure of an inscribed angle.

MATERIALS
- compass
- straightedge
- protractor

PACING
- Exploring the Concept — 10 min
- Investigate — 10 min
- Conjecture — 5 min

LINK TO LESSON
When students find the measure of inscribed angles in Example 1 of Lesson 10.3, ask them to redraw the diagram to include the corresponding central angle. Then give its measure.

2 Managing the Activity

ALTERNATIVE APPROACH
To save time, assign 3 groups of students a central angle measure for them to use. Draw the table on an overhead transparency and have each group complete the part of the table for their circle.

3 Closing the Activity

KEY DISCOVERY
An inscribed angle's measure is one-half the measure of the arc intercepted by the corresponding central angle. All inscribed angles that intercept the same arc are congruent.

ACTIVITY ASSESSMENT
Find the measure of $\angle A$ if $m\widehat{BC} = 132°$. 66°

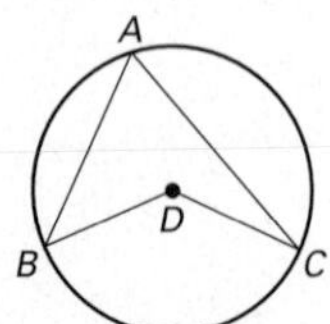

ACTIVITY 10.3
Developing Concepts

Investigating Inscribed Angles

GROUP ACTIVITY
Work with a partner.

MATERIALS
- paper
- pencil
- compass
- straightedge
- protractor

QUESTION An angle in a circle is an *inscribed angle* if its vertex is on the circle and its sides contain chords of the circle. How is the measure of an inscribed angle related to the measure of the corresponding central angle?

EXPLORING THE CONCEPT Steps 1–3. Check drawings.

Follow the steps to construct an inscribed angle.

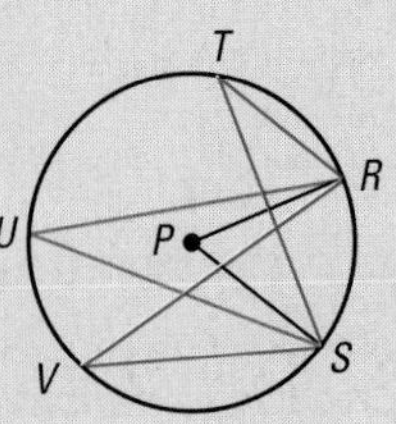

1. Construct a circle. Label its center P.
2. Use a straightedge to construct a central angle. Label it $\angle RPS$.
3. Locate three points on $\odot P$ in the exterior of $\angle RPS$ and label them T, U, and V. Use a straightedge to draw the inscribed angles $\angle RTS$, $\angle RUS$, and $\angle RVS$.

INVESTIGATE See margin.

1. Use a protractor to measure $\angle RPS$, $\angle RTS$, $\angle RUS$, and $\angle RVS$. Make a table similar to the one below. Record the angle measures for Circle 1 in the table.

	$m\angle RPS$	$m\angle RTS$	$m\angle RUS$	$m\angle RVS$
Circle 1	?	?	?	?
Circle 2	?	?	?	?
Circle 3	?	?	?	?

2. Repeat Steps 1 through 3 using different central angles. Record the measures in your table.

1, 2. Answers will vary, but in each case, $m\angle RTS = m\angle RUS = m\angle RVS = \frac{1}{2}m\angle RPS$.

MAKE A CONJECTURE

3. Use the results in your table to make a conjecture about how the measure of an inscribed angle is related to the measure of the corresponding central angle.

3. The measure of an inscribed $\angle$ is half the measure of the corresp. central $\angle$.

EXTENSION

CRITICAL THINKING The star divides the circle into congruent arcs. Use the conjecture you made in Exercise 3 to find the measures of the angles that form the points of the star. Explain your reasoning. Then use a protractor to measure the angles to verify your conjecture.

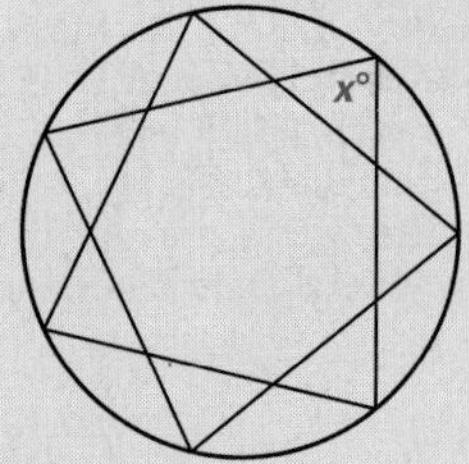

Extension: About 77°; the star divides the $\odot$ into 7 $\cong$ arcs, so each has measure $\frac{360°}{7}$. Each inscribed $\angle$ corresp. to an arc with measure $3 \cdot \frac{360°}{7} = \frac{1080°}{7}$. Then $x = \frac{1}{2} \cdot \frac{1080°}{7} = \frac{540°}{7} = 77\frac{1}{7}° \approx 77°$.

10.3 Inscribed Angles

What you should learn

GOAL 1 Use inscribed angles to solve problems.

GOAL 2 Use properties of inscribed polygons.

Why you should learn it

▼ To solve **real-life** problems, such as finding the different seats in a theater that will give you the same viewing angle, as in **Example 4**.

REAL LIFE

GOAL 1 USING INSCRIBED ANGLES

An **inscribed angle** is an angle whose vertex is on a circle and whose sides contain chords of the circle. The arc that lies in the interior of an inscribed angle and has endpoints on the angle is called the **intercepted arc** of the angle.

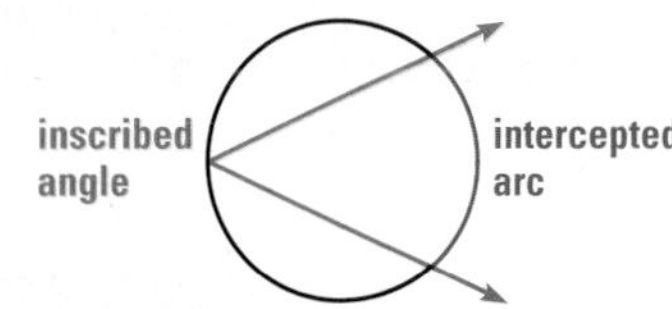

THEOREM

THEOREM 10.8 ***Measure of an Inscribed Angle***

If an angle is inscribed in a circle, then its measure is half the measure of its intercepted arc.

$m\angle ADB = \frac{1}{2}m\widehat{AB}$

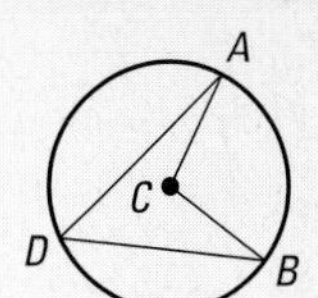

EXAMPLE 1 *Finding Measures of Arcs and Inscribed Angles*

Find the measure of the blue arc or angle.

a. 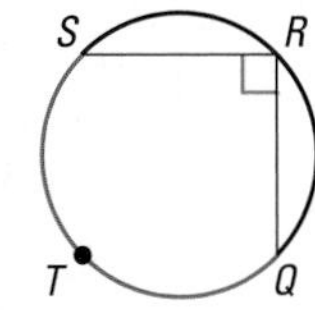

b. 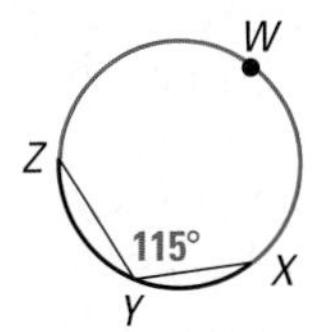

c. 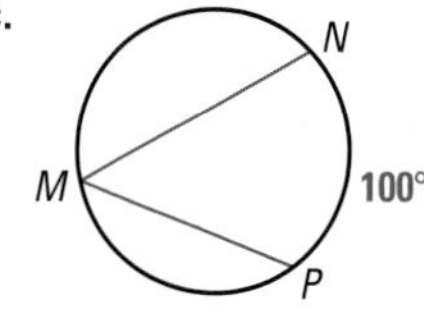

SOLUTION

a. $m\widehat{QTS} = 2m\angle QRS = 2(90°) = 180°$

b. $m\widehat{ZWX} = 2m\angle ZYX = 2(115°) = 230°$

c. $m\angle NMP = \frac{1}{2}m\widehat{NP} = \frac{1}{2}(100°) = 50°$

EXAMPLE 2 *Comparing Measures of Inscribed Angles*

Find $m\angle ACB$, $m\angle ADB$, and $m\angle AEB$.

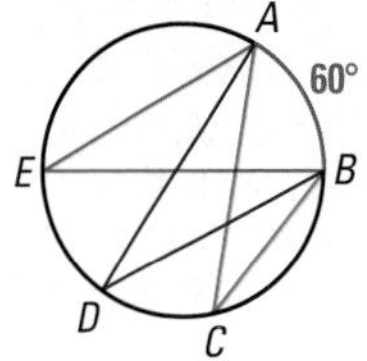

SOLUTION

The measure of each angle is half the measure of $\widehat{AB}$. $m\widehat{AB} = 60°$, so the measure of each angle is 30°.

CALIFORNIA STANDARDS AND ASSESSMENT

CA Standards: 4, 7, 16, 21
SAT9 Task 1: Obj. 1
SAT9 Task 2: Obj. 1

1 PLAN

PACING

Basic: 2 days
Average: 2 days
Advanced: 2 days
Block Schedule: 1 block

LESSON OPENER
GEOMETRY SOFTWARE

An alternative way to approach Lesson 10.3 is to use the Geometry Software Lesson Opener:

- Blackline Master (*Chapter 10 Resource Book,* p. 40)
- Transparency (p. 63)

MEETING INDIVIDUAL NEEDS

- ***Chapter 10 Resource Book***
  Prerequisite Skills Review (p. 5)
  Practice Level A (p. 42)
  Practice Level B (p. 43)
  Practice Level C (p. 44)
  Reteaching with Practice (p. 45)
  Absent Student Catch-Up (p. 47)
  Challenge (p. 49)
- ***Resources in Spanish***
- ***Personal Student Tutor***

NEW-TEACHER SUPPORT

See the Tips for New Teachers on pp. 1–2 of the *Chapter 10 Resource Book* for additional notes about Lesson 10.3.

WARM-UP EXERCISES

Transparency Available

Solve the equation or system of equations.

1. $x + 3x = 90$ 22.5
2. $2x + 8x = 180$ 18
3. $2x + 3x + 80 + 120 = 360$ 32
4. $x + y = 60$
   $5x - y = 180$ (40, 20)

2 TEACH

MOTIVATING THE LESSON
Ask students if they have ever been to a theater with seats arranged in an arc. This pattern may improve the viewing angle for the screen. A viewing angle is an example of an inscribed angle, the focus of this lesson.

EXTRA EXAMPLE 1
Find the measure of the arc or angle.

a. $m\widehat{ADC}$ 180°

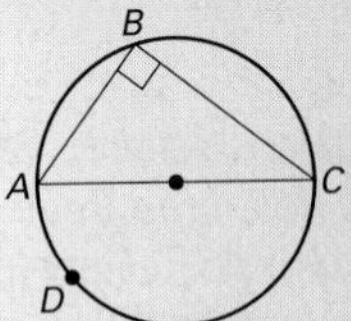

b. $m\widehat{AC}$ 140°

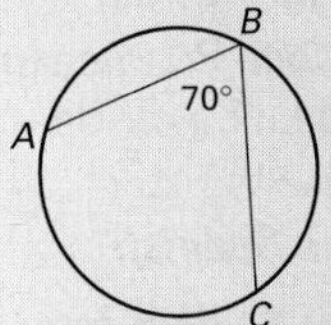

c. $m\angle ABC$ 98°

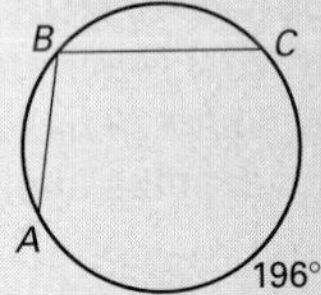

EXTRA EXAMPLE 2
Find $m\angle ABE$, $m\angle ACE$, and $m\angle ADE$. 45°; 45°; 45°

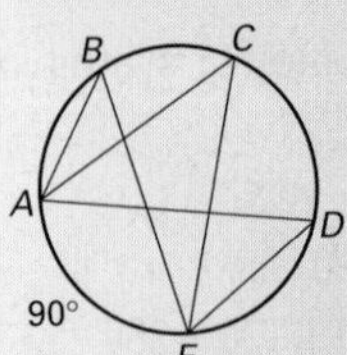

EXTRA EXAMPLE 3
It is given that $m\angle B = 44°$. What is $m\angle C$? 44°

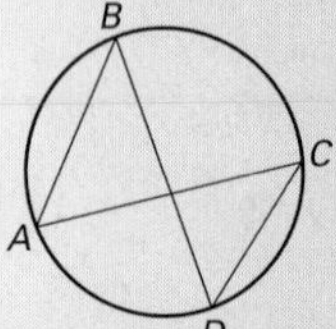

Example 2 suggests the following theorem. You are asked to prove Theorem 10.8 and Theorem 10.9 in Exercises 35–38.

THEOREM

THEOREM 10.9

If two inscribed angles of a circle intercept the same arc, then the angles are congruent.

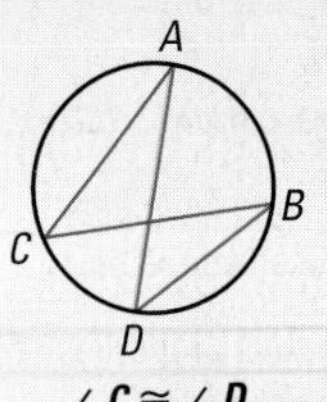

EXAMPLE 3 *Finding the Measure of an Angle*

It is given that $m\angle E = 75°$. What is $m\angle F$?

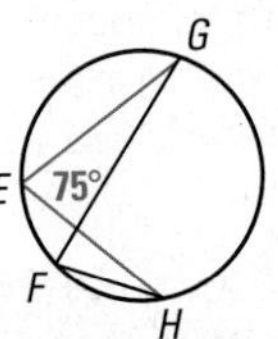

SOLUTION

$\angle E$ and $\angle F$ both intercept $\widehat{GH}$, so $\angle E \cong \angle F$.

▶ So, $m\angle F = m\angle E = 75°$.

EXAMPLE 4 *Using the Measure of an Inscribed Angle*

THEATER DESIGN When you go to the movies, you want to be close to the movie screen, but you don't want to have to move your eyes too much to see the edges of the picture. If E and G are the ends of the screen and you are at F, $m\angle EFG$ is called your *viewing angle*.

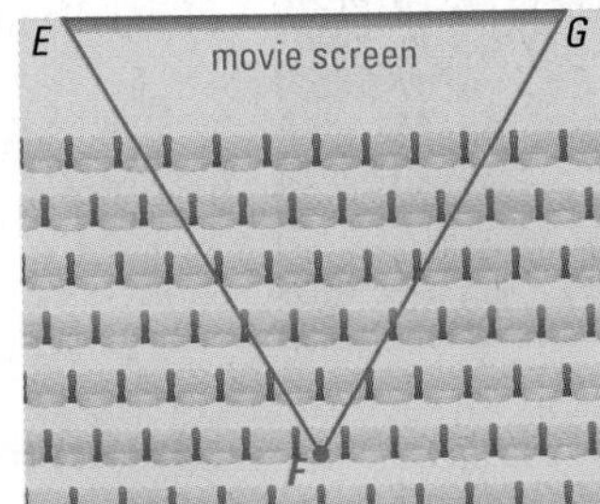

You decide that the middle of the sixth row has the best viewing angle. If someone is sitting there, where else can you sit to have the same viewing angle?

SOLUTION

Draw the circle that is determined by the endpoints of the screen and the sixth row center seat. Any other location on the circle will have the same viewing angle.

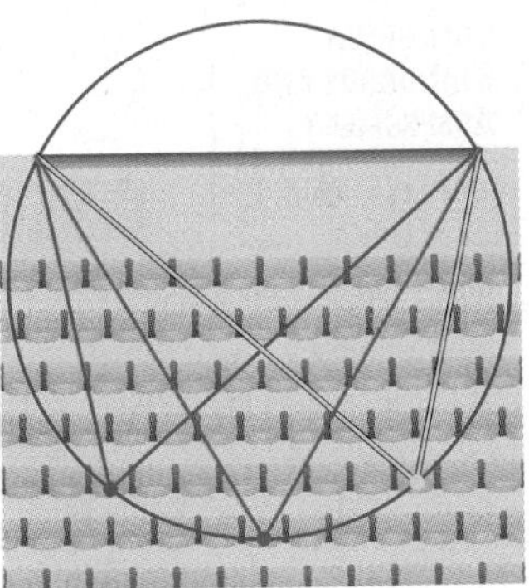

FOCUS ON APPLICATIONS

THEATER DESIGN In Ancient Greece, stages were often part of a circle and the seats were on concentric circles.

Extra Example 4 and Checkpoint Exercises for Examples 1–4 on next page.

GOAL 2 USING PROPERTIES OF INSCRIBED POLYGONS

If all of the vertices of a polygon lie on a circle, the polygon is **inscribed** in the circle and the circle is **circumscribed** about the polygon. The polygon is an *inscribed polygon* and the circle is a *circumscribed circle*. You are asked to justify Theorem 10.10 and part of Theorem 10.11 in Exercises 39 and 40. A complete proof of Theorem 10.11 appears on page 840.

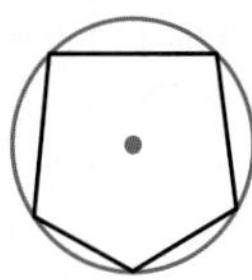

THEOREMS ABOUT INSCRIBED POLYGONS

THEOREM 10.10

If a right triangle is inscribed in a circle, then the hypotenuse is a diameter of the circle. Conversely, if one side of an inscribed triangle is a diameter of the circle, then the triangle is a right triangle and the angle opposite the diameter is the right angle.

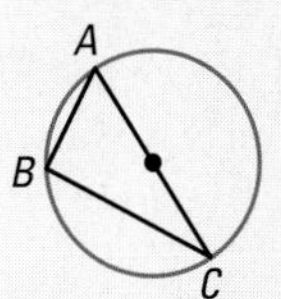

$\angle B$ is a right angle if and only if $\overline{AC}$ is a diameter of the circle.

THEOREM 10.11

A quadrilateral can be inscribed in a circle if and only if its opposite angles are supplementary.

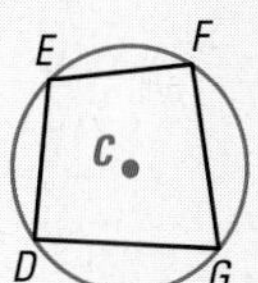

D, E, F, and G lie on some circle, $\odot C$, if and only if $m\angle D + m\angle F = 180°$ and $m\angle E + m\angle G = 180°$.

EXAMPLE 5 *Using Theorems 10.10 and 10.11*

Find the value of each variable.

a.

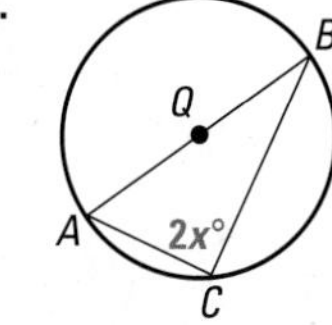

b.

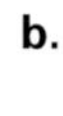

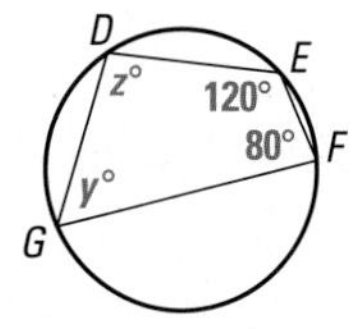

SOLUTION

a. $\overline{AB}$ is a diameter. So, $\angle C$ is a right angle and $m\angle C = 90°$.

$2x° = 90°$

$x = 45$

b. $DEFG$ is inscribed in a circle, so opposite angles are supplementary.

$m\angle D + m\angle F = 180°$	$m\angle E + m\angle G = 180°$
$z + 80 = 180$	$120 + y = 180$
$z = 100$	$y = 60$

EXTRA EXAMPLE 4

When you go to a sports arena, you want to be close to the playing field, but you don't want to have to move your eyes too much to see the action on each end of the arena. In the diagram, $m\angle ABC$ is called your viewing angle. You decide that the middle of the twelfth row has the best viewing angle. If someone is sitting there, where else can you sit to have the same viewing angle?

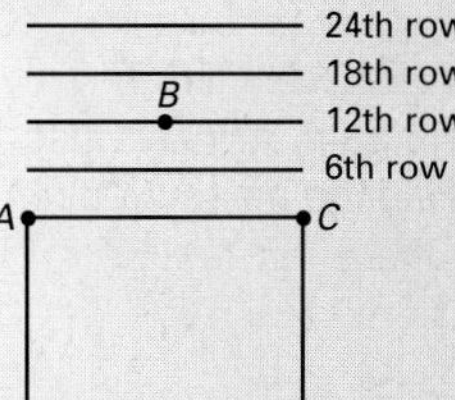

Draw the circle that is determined by the endpoints of the arena and the twelfth row center seat. Any other location on the circle will have the same viewing angle.

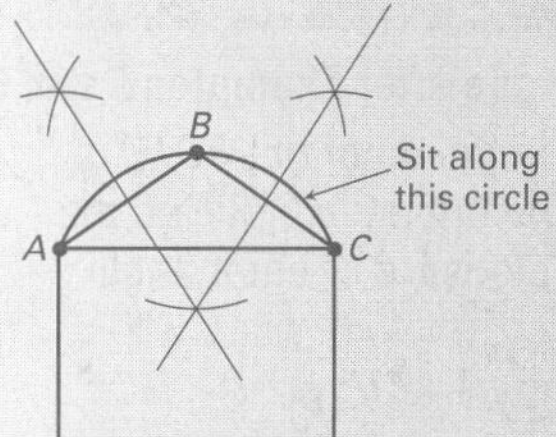

CHECKPOINT EXERCISES

For use after Examples 1–4:

1. It is given that $m\overset{\frown}{AD} = 164°$. What is $m\angle C$? **82°**

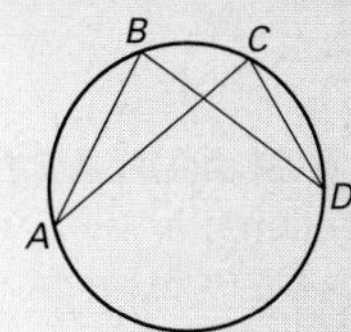

Extra Example 5 and Checkpoint Exercises for Example 5 on next page.

EXTRA EXAMPLE 5

Find the value of each variable.

a. 30

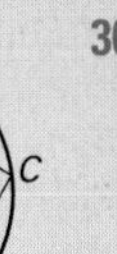

b. $x = 95$; $y = 100$

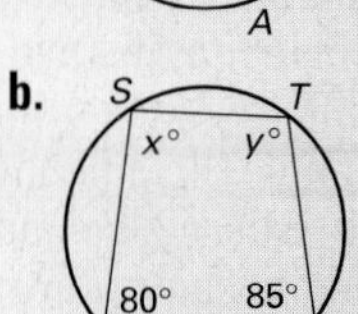

EXTRA EXAMPLE 6

In the diagram, $ABCD$ is inscribed in $\odot P$. Find the measure of each angle. $m\angle A = 60°$; $m\angle B = 114°$; $m\angle C = 120°$; $m\angle D = 66°$

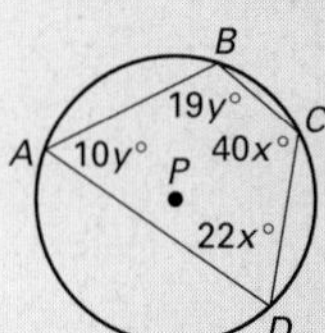

CHECKPOINT EXERCISES

For use after Examples 5 and 6:

1. In the diagram, $RSTU$ is inscribed in $\odot P$. Find the measure of each angle. $m\angle R = 116°$; $m\angle S = 96°$; $m\angle T = 64°$; $m\angle U = 84°$

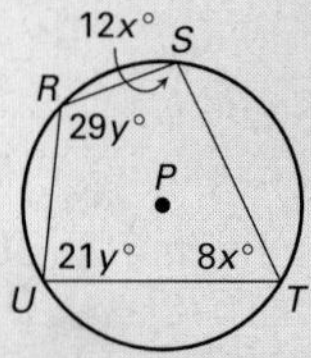

FOCUS ON VOCABULARY

Define inscribed angle.
An inscribed angle is an angle whose vertex is on the circle and whose sides contain chords.

CLOSURE QUESTION

Explain why the diagonals of a rectangle inscribed in a circle are diameters of the circle. Since the angle opposite the chord (diagonal) is 90°, the diagonals are chords whose endpoints intercept an arc of 180°. The only chords that intercept arcs of 180° are diameters.

STUDENT HELP

Skills Review
For help with solving systems of equations, see p. 796.

EXAMPLE 6 Using an Inscribed Quadrilateral

In the diagram, $ABCD$ is inscribed in $\odot P$. Find the measure of each angle.

SOLUTION

$ABCD$ is inscribed in a circle, so opposite angles are supplementary.

$$3x + 3y = 180 \qquad 5x + 2y = 180$$

To solve this system of linear equations, you can solve the first equation for y to get $y = 60 - x$. Substitute this expression into the second equation.

$5x + 2y = 180$	Write second equation.
$5x + 2(60 - x) = 180$	Substitute $60 - x$ for y.
$5x + 120 - 2x = 180$	Distributive property
$3x = 60$	Subtract 120 from each side.
$x = 20$	Divide each side by 3.
$y = 60 - 20 = 40$	Substitute and solve for y.

▶ $x = 20$ and $y = 40$, so $m\angle A = 80°$, $m\angle B = 60°$, $m\angle C = 100°$, and $m\angle D = 120°$.

GUIDED PRACTICE

Vocabulary Check ✓

1. Draw a circle and an inscribed angle, $\angle ABC$. Name the intercepted arc of $\angle ABC$. Label additional points on your sketch if you need to. See margin.

Concept Check ✓

2. Determine whether the quadrilateral can be inscribed in a circle. Explain your reasoning. No; opp. ∠s are not supp.

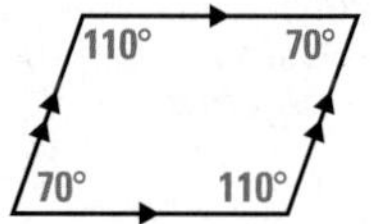

Skill Check ✓

Find the measure of the blue arc. See margin.

3. 40°

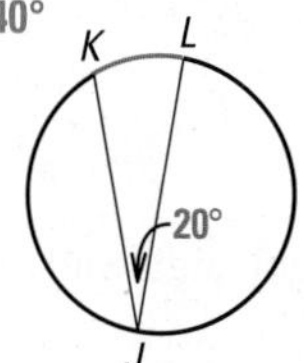

4. 180°

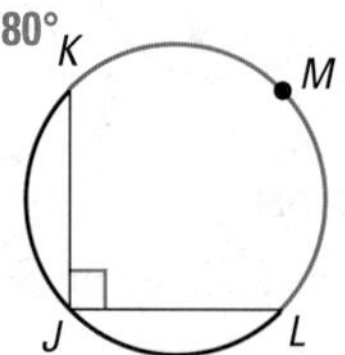

5. 210°

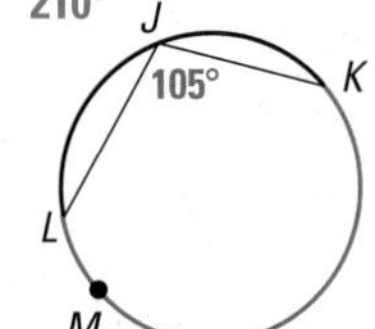

Find the value of each variable. See margin.

6.

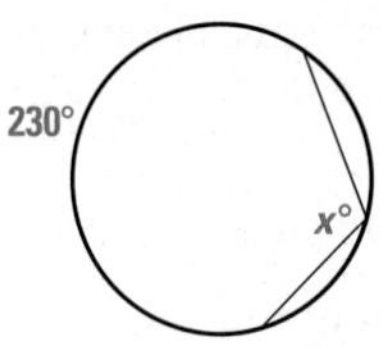

$x = 115$

7.

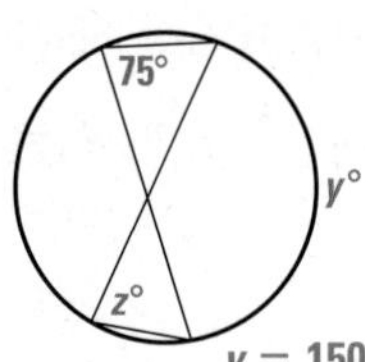

$y = 150$, $z = 75$

8.

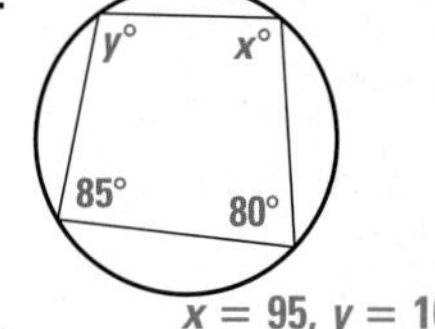

$x = 95$, $y = 100$

PRACTICE AND APPLICATIONS

STUDENT HELP

Extra Practice to help you master skills is on p. 821.

15. 47; inscribed ∠s that intercept the same arc have the same measure.

16. $x = 90$; the segment shown is a diameter; $y = 50$; △ Sum Theorem

17. $x = 45$, $y = 40$; inscribed ∠s that intercept the same arc have the same measure.

21. $x = 30$, $y = 20$, $m\angle A = m\angle B = m\angle C = 60°$

22. $x = 25$, $y = 5$; $m\angle A = 130°$, $m\angle B = 75°$, $m\angle C = 50°$, $m\angle D = 105°$

23. $x = 9$, $y = 6$; $m\angle A = 54°$, $m\angle B = 36°$, $m\angle C = 126°$, $m\angle D = 144°$

24. Yes; both pairs of opp. ∠s are right ∠s and, so, are supp.

25. Yes; both pairs of opp. ∠s are right ∠s and, so, are supp.

26. No; both pairs of opp. ∠s are supp. only if the ▱ is a rectangle.

27. No; both pairs of opp. ∠s of a kite may be, but are not always, supp.

28. No; both pairs of opp. ∠s of a rhombus may be, but are not always, supp.

29. Yes; both pairs of opp. ∠s of an isosceles trapezoid are supp.

STUDENT HELP

HOMEWORK HELP

Example 1: Exs. 9–14, 19–21
Example 2: Exs. 15, 17
Example 3: Exs. 15, 17
Example 4: Exs. 15, 17
Example 5: Exs. 15–20, 24–29, 31–34
Example 6: Exs. 21–23

ARC AND ANGLE MEASURES Find the measure of the blue arc or angle.

9.

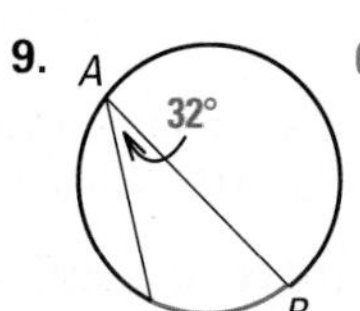

10.

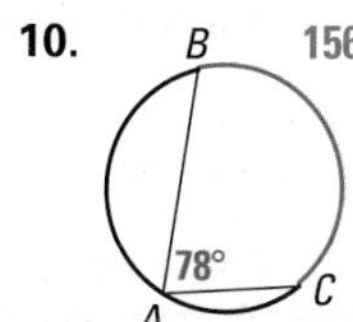

11.

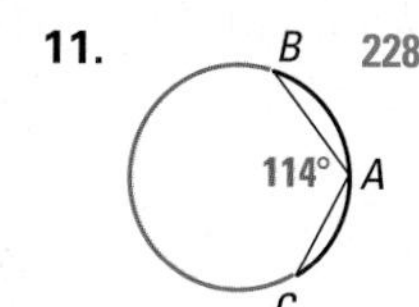

12.

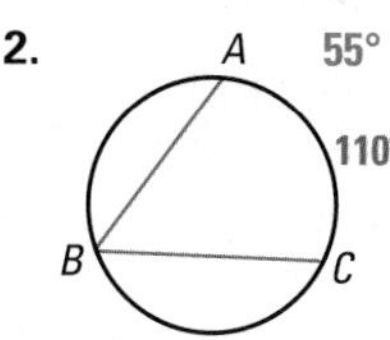

13.

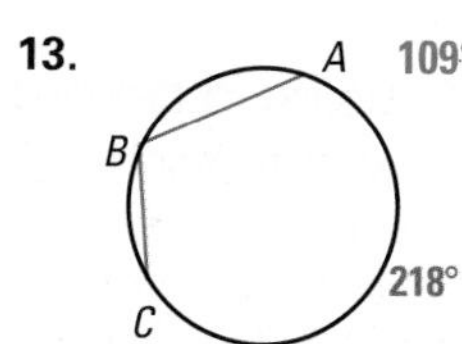

14.

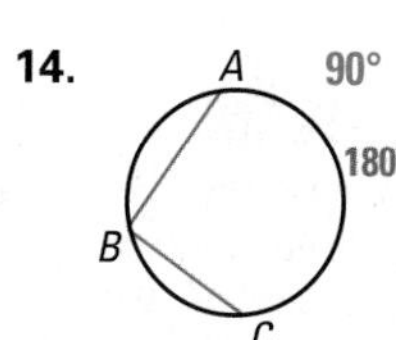

USING ALGEBRA Find the value of each variable. Explain. 15–17. See margin.

15.

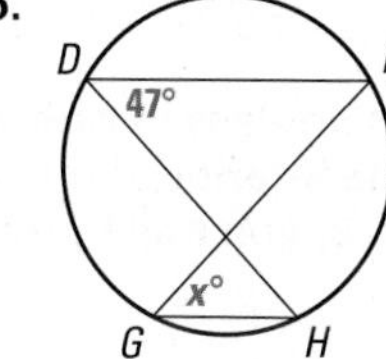

16.

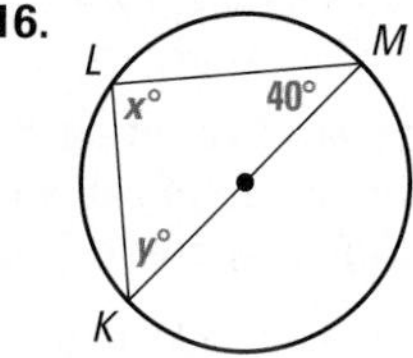

17.

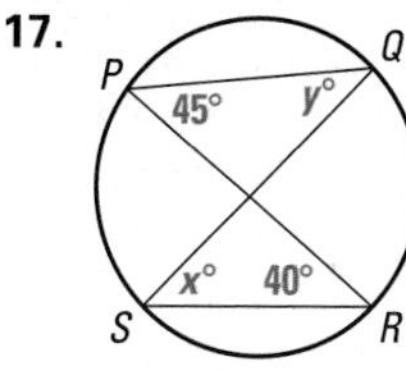

USING ALGEBRA Find the values of x, y, and z.

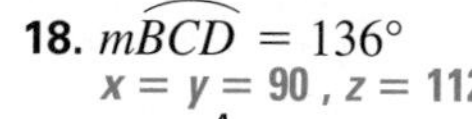

18. $m\overparen{BCD} = 136°$
$x = y = 90$, $z = 112$

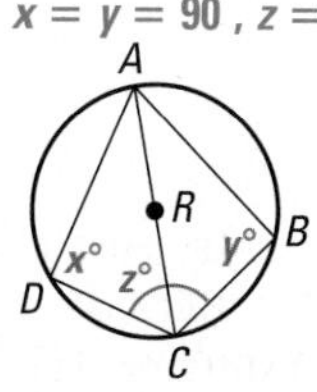

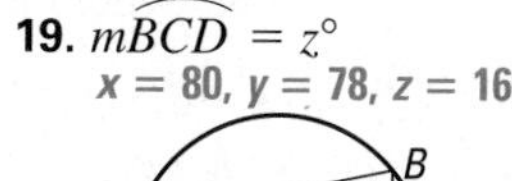

19. $m\overparen{BCD} = z°$
$x = 80$, $y = 78$, $z = 160$

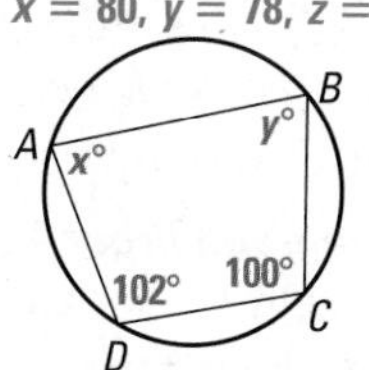

20. $m\overparen{ABC} = z°$
$x = 65$, $y = 90$, $z = 180$

A, B, C, D, 115°, $y°$, $x°$

USING ALGEBRA Find the values of x and y. Then find the measures of the interior angles of the polygon. 21–23. See margin.

21.

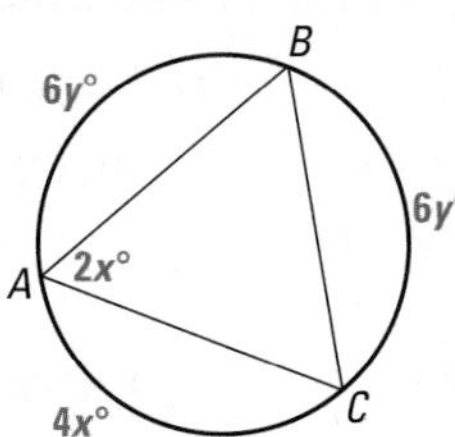

22.

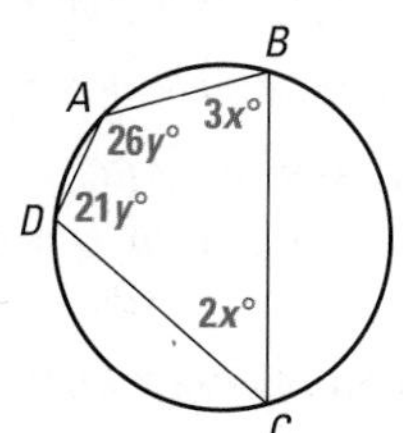

23.

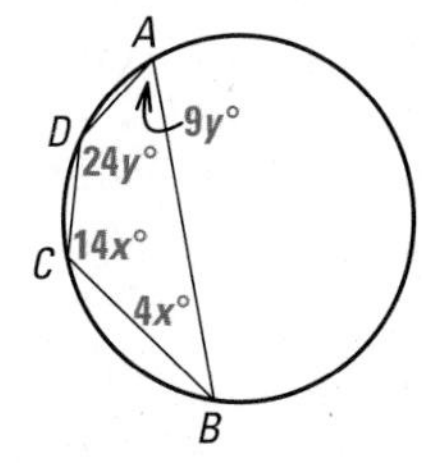

LOGICAL REASONING Can the quadrilateral always be inscribed in a circle? Explain your reasoning. 24–29. See margin.

24. square
25. rectangle
26. parallelogram
27. kite
28. rhombus
29. isosceles trapezoid

3 APPLY

ASSIGNMENT GUIDE

BASIC

Day 1: p. 617 Exs. 9–29

Day 2: pp. 618–620 Exs. 30–33, 35–38, 42, 43, 48–58 even, 59–62, Quiz 1 Exs. 1–9

AVERAGE

Day 1: p. 617 Exs. 9–29

Day 2: pp. 618–620 Exs. 30–33, 35–38, 41–43, 48–58 even, 59–62, Quiz 1 Exs. 1–9

ADVANCED

Day 1: p. 617 Exs. 9–29

Day 2: pp. 618–620 Exs. 30–33, 35–47, 48–58 even, 59–62, Quiz 1 Exs. 1–9

BLOCK SCHEDULE

pp. 617–620 Exs. 9–33, 35–38, 41–43, 48–58 even, 59–62, Quiz 1 Exs. 1–9

EXERCISE LEVELS

Level A: *Easier*
9–14

Level B: *More Difficult*
15–37, 42, 43

Level C: *Most Difficult*
38–41, 44–47

✓ HOMEWORK CHECK

To quickly check student understanding of key concepts, go over the following exercises: Exs. 10, 16, 18, 22, 28, 30, 32, 36, 38. See also the Daily Homework Quiz:

- Blackline Master (*Chapter 10 Resource Book,* p. 53)
- Transparency (p. 74)

1. See Additional Answers beginning on page AA1.

STUDENT HELP NOTES

Software Help Instructions for several software packages are available in **blackline** format in the *Chapter 10 Resource Book*, p. 41 and at **www.mcdougallittell.com.**

TEACHING TIPS

EXERCISE 36 Ask students to draw radii $\overline{AQ}$ and $\overline{CQ}$ and use the Arc Addition Postulate to help them plan this proof.

ENGLISH LEARNERS

EXERCISE 35 Note that the task of inserting terms into incomplete sentences in a paragraph may prove challenging for English learners. You might work with students in a small group, reading aloud each sentence and discussing with them what term would complete it correctly.

38. Given: $\odot O$ with inscribed $\angle$s C and D, both intercepting $\widehat{AB}$

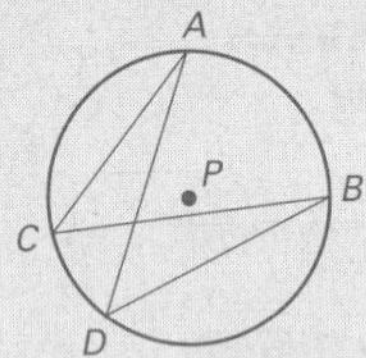

Prove: $\angle C \cong \angle D$
Proof: By the Measure of an Inscribed Angle Thm., $m\angle C = \frac{1}{2}m\widehat{AB}$ and $m\angle D = \frac{1}{2}m\widehat{AB}$. By the transitive prop. of equality, $m\angle C = m\angle D$. Then by the def. of cong., $\angle C \cong \angle D$.

39. Given: Circle O with inscribed $\triangle ABC$, $\overline{AC}$ is a diameter of circle O

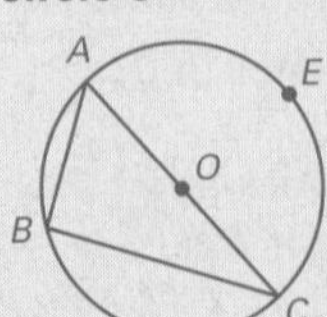

Prove: $\triangle ABC$ is a right $\triangle$
Use the Arc Addition Postulate to show that $m\widehat{AEC} = m\widehat{ABC}$ and thus $m\widehat{ABC} = 180°$. Then use the Measure of an Incribed Angle Thm. to show $m\angle B = 90°$, so that $\angle B$ is a right $\angle$ and $\triangle ABC$ is a right $\triangle$.

Answer continued on next page.

30. Draw $\overline{AC}$ and then construct a $\perp$ to $\overline{AC}$ through A; a line $\perp$ to a radius of a $\odot$ at its endpoint is tangent to the $\odot$.

33. $\overline{AB}$; a line $\perp$ to a radius of a $\odot$ at its endpoint is tangent to the $\odot$.

STUDENT HELP

SOFTWARE HELP
Visit our Web site www.mcdougallittell.com to see instructions for several software applications.

36. Draw the diameter containing $\overline{QB}$ intersecting the $\odot$ at point D. By the proof in Ex. 35, $m\angle ABD = \frac{1}{2}m\widehat{AD}$ and $m\angle DBC = \frac{1}{2}m\widehat{DC}$. By the Arc Addition Post., $m\widehat{AC} = m\widehat{AD} + m\widehat{DC}$ and by the Angle Addition Post., $m\angle ABC = m\angle ABD + m\angle DBC$. Then by repeated application of the Substitution Prop., $m\angle ABC = \frac{1}{2}m\widehat{AC}$.

37. Draw the diameter containing $\overline{QB}$ intersecting the $\odot$ at point D. By the proof in Ex. 35, $m\angle ABD = \frac{1}{2}m\widehat{AD}$, and $m\angle DBC = \frac{1}{2}m\widehat{DC}$. By the Arc Addition Post., $m\widehat{AD} = m\widehat{AC} + m\widehat{CD}$ so $m\widehat{AC} = m\widehat{AD} - m\widehat{CD}$ by the subtraction prop. of equality. By the Angle Addition Post., $m\angle ABD = m\angle ABC + m\angle CBD$, so $m\angle ABC = m\angle ABD - m\angle CBD$ by the subtraction prop. of equality. Then by repeated application of the Substitution Prop., $m\angle ABC = \frac{1}{2}m\widehat{AC}$.

30. **CONSTRUCTION** Construct a $\odot C$ and a point A on $\odot C$. Construct the tangent to $\odot C$ at A. Explain why your construction works.

CONSTRUCTION In Exercises 31–33, you will construct a tangent to a circle from a point outside the circle.

31. Construct a $\odot C$ and a point outside the circle, A. Draw $\overline{AC}$ and construct its midpoint M. Construct $\odot M$ with radius MC. What kind of chord is $\overline{AC}$? **diameter**

32. $\odot C$ and $\odot M$ have two points of intersection. Label one of the points B. Draw $\overline{AB}$ and $\overline{CB}$. What is $m\angle CBA$? How do you know? **90°; $\overline{AC}$ is a diameter of $\odot M$.**

33. Which segment is tangent to $\odot C$ from A? Explain.

34. **USING TECHNOLOGY** Use geometry software to construct $\odot Q$, diameter $\overline{AB}$, and point C on $\odot Q$. Construct $\overline{AC}$ and $\overline{CB}$. Measure the angles of $\triangle ABC$. Drag point C along $\odot Q$. Record and explain your observations.
Sample answer: **$m\angle C = 90°$; when $\overleftrightarrow{CQ} \perp \overline{AB}$, $m\angle A = m\angle B = 45°$. As you drag C toward A, $m\angle A$ increases and $m\angle B$ decreases. As you drag C away from A, $m\angle A$ decreases and $m\angle B$ increases.**

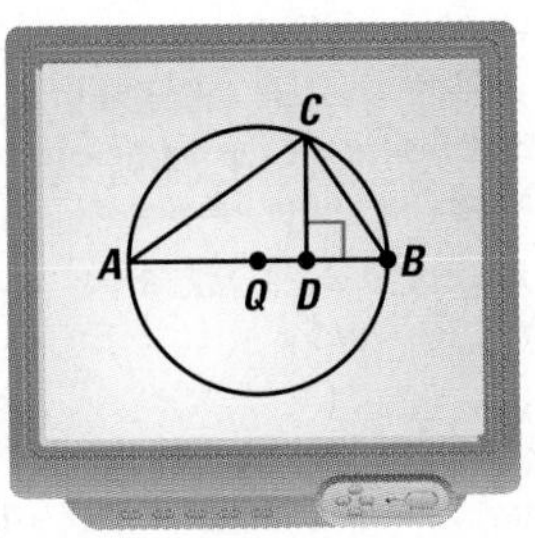

PROVING THEOREM 10.8 If an angle is inscribed in $\odot Q$, the center Q can be on a side of the angle, in the interior of the angle, or in the exterior of the angle. To prove Theorem 10.8, you must prove each of these cases.

35. Fill in the blanks to complete the proof.

GIVEN ▶ $\angle ABC$ is inscribed in $\odot Q$. Point Q lies on $\overline{BC}$.

PROVE ▶ $m\angle ABC = \frac{1}{2}m\widehat{AC}$

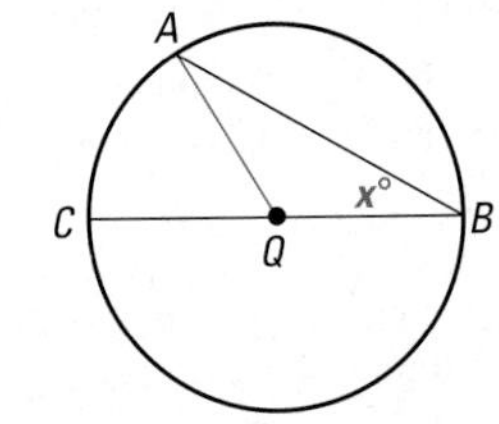

$\overline{QB}$; isosceles; base $\angle$s; $\angle A \cong \angle B$; Exterior Angle; $2x°$; $2x°$; 2; $\frac{1}{2}m\widehat{AC}$; $\frac{1}{2}m\widehat{AC}$

Paragraph Proof Let $m\angle ABC = x°$. Because $\overline{QA}$ and $\overline{QB}$ are both radii of $\odot Q$, $\overline{QA} \cong$ __?__ and $\triangle AQB$ is __?__. Because $\angle A$ and $\angle B$ are __?__ of an isosceles triangle, __?__. So, by substitution, $m\angle A = x°$.

By the __?__ Theorem, $m\angle AQC = m\angle A + m\angle B =$ __?__. So, by the definition of the measure of a minor arc, $m\widehat{AC} =$ __?__. Divide each side by __?__ to show that $x° =$ __?__. Then, by substitution, $m\angle ABC =$ __?__.

36. Write a plan for a proof. **See margin.**

GIVEN ▶ $\angle ABC$ is inscribed in $\odot Q$. Point Q is in the interior of $\angle ABC$.

PROVE ▶ $m\angle ABC = \frac{1}{2}m\widehat{AC}$

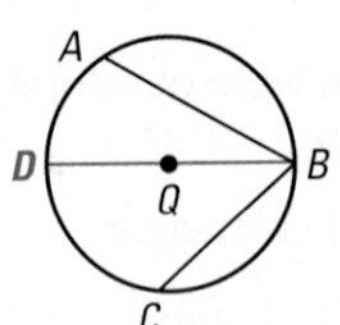

37. Write a plan for a proof. **See margin.**

GIVEN ▶ $\angle ABC$ is inscribed in $\odot Q$. Point Q is in the exterior of $\angle ABC$.

PROVE ▶ $m\angle ABC = \frac{1}{2}m\widehat{AC}$

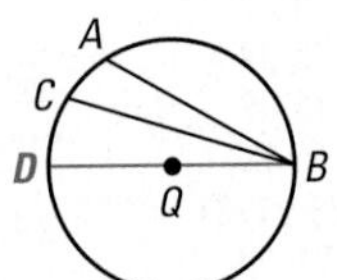

38. **PROVING THEOREM 10.9** Write a proof of Theorem 10.9. First draw a diagram and write GIVEN and PROVE statements. See margin.

39. **PROVING THEOREM 10.10** Theorem 10.10 is written as a conditional statement and its converse. Write a plan for a proof of each statement. See margin.

40. **PROVING THEOREM 10.11** Draw a diagram and write a proof of part of Theorem 10.11. See margin.

GIVEN ▶ *DEFG* is inscribed in a circle.

PROVE ▶ $m\angle D + m\angle F = 180°, m\angle E + m\angle G = 180°$

41. **CARPENTER'S SQUARE** A carpenter's square is an L-shaped tool used to draw right angles. Suppose you are making a copy of a wooden plate. You trace the plate on a piece of wood. How could you use a carpenter's square to find the center of the circle?

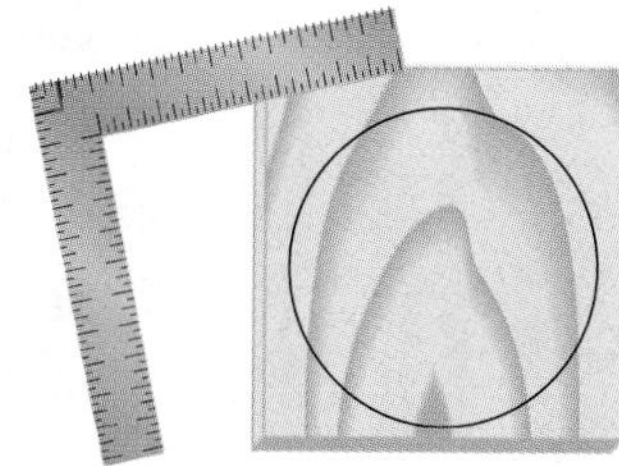

41. *Sample answer:* Use the carpenter's square to draw two diameters of the circle. (Position the vertex of the tool on the circle and mark the 2 points where the sides intersect the ⊙. Repeat, placing the vertex at a different point on the ⊙. The center is the point where the diameters intersect.)

Test Preparation

42. **MULTIPLE CHOICE** In the diagram at the right, if $\angle ACB$ is a central angle and $m\angle ACB = 80°$, what is $m\angle ADB$? B

Ⓐ 20 Ⓑ 40 Ⓒ 80 Ⓓ 100 Ⓔ 160

43. **MULTIPLE CHOICE** In the diagram at the right, what is the value of x? C

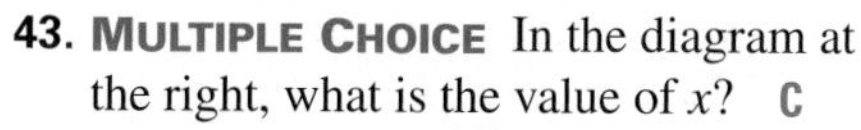

Ⓐ $\frac{48}{11}$ Ⓑ 12 Ⓒ 16 Ⓓ 18 Ⓔ 24

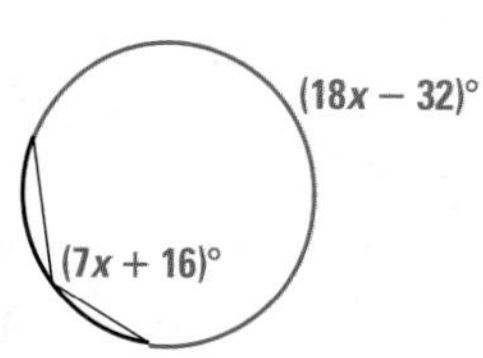

★ Challenge

CUTTING BOARD In Exercises 44–47, use the following information. You are making a circular cutting board. To begin, you glue eight 1 inch by 2 inch boards together, as shown at the right. Then you draw and cut a circle with an 8 inch diameter from the boards.

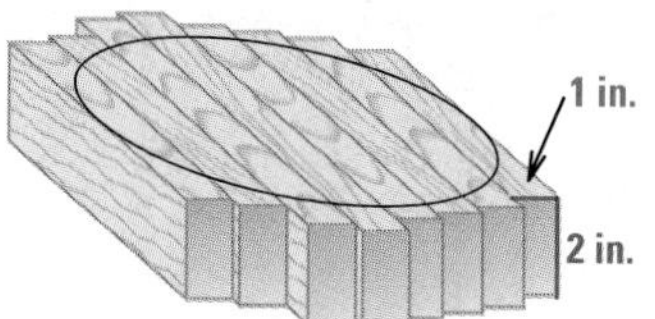

44. $\overline{FH}$ is a diameter of the circular cutting board. What kind of triangle is $\triangle FGH$? right

45. How is GJ related to FJ and JH? State a theorem to justify your answer.

46. Find FJ, JH, and JG. What is the length of the seam of the cutting board that is labeled $\overline{GK}$? 6 in.; 2 in., $2\sqrt{3} \approx 3.5$ in.; $4\sqrt{3} \approx 6.9$ in.

47. Find the length of $\overline{LM}$. $2\sqrt{7} \approx 5.3$ in.

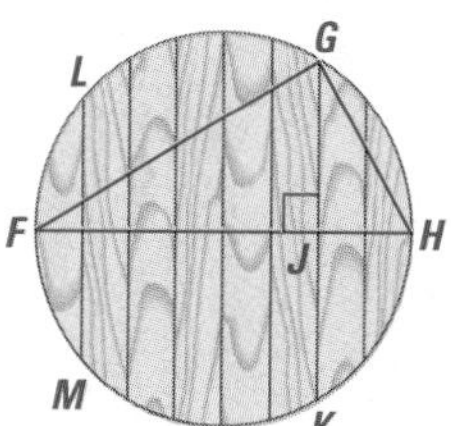

45. *GJ* is the geometric mean of *FJ* and *JH*; in a right △, the altitude drawn to the hypotenuse divides the hypotenuse into 2 segments. The length of the altitude is the geometric mean of the lengths of the 2 segments.

EXTRA CHALLENGE

▶ www.mcdougallittell.com

Given: Circle *O* with inscribed $\triangle ABC$, $\angle B$ is a right ∠
Prove: $\overline{AC}$ is a diameter of circle *O*
Use the Measure of an Inscribed Angle Thm., to show the inscribed right ∠ intercepts an arc with measure 2(90°) = 180°. Since $\overline{AC}$ intercepts an arc that is half of the measure of the circle, it must be a diameter.

40. Given: ⊙*C* with inscribed quad. *DEFG*

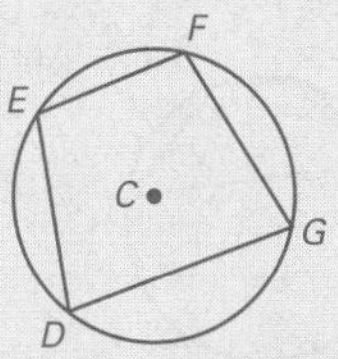

Prove: $m\angle D + m\angle F = 180°$, $m\angle E + m\angle G = 180°$
Proof: By the Arc Addition Postulate, $m\widehat{EDG} + m\widehat{EFG} = 360°$ and $m\widehat{DEF} + m\widehat{FGD} = 360°$. Using the Measure of an Inscribed Angle Thm., $m\widehat{EDG} = 2m\angle F$, $m\widehat{EFG} = 2m\angle D$, $m\widehat{DEF} = 2m\angle G$, and $m\widehat{FGD} = 2m\angle E$. By the Substitution Prop., $2m\angle D + 2m\angle F = 360°$, so $m\angle D + m\angle F = 180°$. Similarly, $m\angle E + m\angle G = 180°$.

TEACHING TIPS

EXERCISE 41 Refer students to Example 5, p. 605 for help finding the center of a circle.

ADDITIONAL PRACTICE AND RETEACHING

For Lesson 10.3:

- Practice Levels A, B, and C (*Chapter 10 Resource Book*, p. 42)
- Reteaching with Practice (*Chapter 10 Resource Book*, p. 45)
- See Lesson 10.3 of the *Personal Student Tutor*

For more Mixed Review:

- Search the *Test and Practice Generator* for key words or specific lessons.

4 ASSESS

DAILY HOMEWORK QUIZ

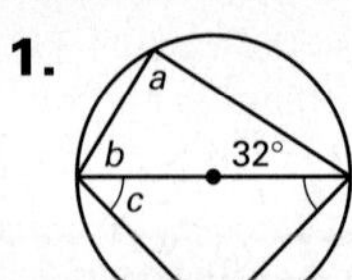

Transparency Available

Find the value of each variable.

1.

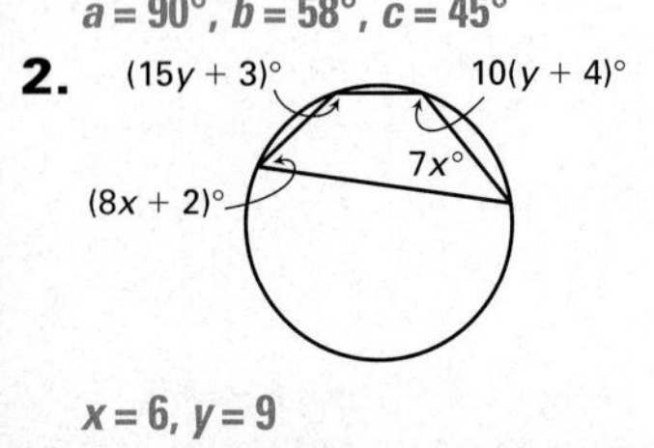

$a = 90°$, $b = 58°$, $c = 45°$

2. $x = 6$, $y = 9$

EXTRA CHALLENGE NOTE

Challenge problems for Lesson 10.3 are available in **blackline** format in the *Chapter 10 Resource Book,* p. 49 and at **www.mcdougallittell.com.**

ADDITIONAL TEST PREPARATION

1. **WRITING** Describe how to find the angles of an inscribed quadrilateral with congruent angles and sides. Since the opposite angles of the quadrilateral are congruent and supplementary, the angles must all be right angles.

ADDITIONAL RESOURCES

An alternative Quiz for Lessons 10.1–10.3 is available in the *Chapter 10 Resource Book,* p. 50.

54–57. See Additional Answers beginning on page AA1.

MIXED REVIEW

WRITING EQUATIONS **Write an equation in slope-intercept form of the line that passes through the given point and has the given slope.** (Review 3.6)

48. $(-2, -6)$, $m = -1$ $y = -x - 8$
49. $(5, 1)$, $m = 2$ $y = 2x - 9$
50. $(3, 3)$, $m = 0$ $y = 3$
51. $(0, 7)$, $m = \frac{4}{3}$ $y = \frac{4}{3}x + 7$
52. $(-8, 4)$, $m = -\frac{1}{2}$ $y = -\frac{1}{2}x$
53. $(-5, -12)$, $m = -\frac{4}{5}$ $y = -\frac{4}{5}x - 16$

SKETCHING IMAGES **Sketch the image of $\triangle PQR$ after a composition using the given transformations in the order in which they appear. $\triangle PQR$ has vertices $P(-5, 4)$, $Q(-2, 1)$, and $R(-1, 3)$.** (Review 7.5) 54–57. See margin.

54. **translation:** $(x, y) \to (x + 6, y)$
    reflection: in the x-axis
55. **translation:** $(x, y) \to (x + 8, y + 1)$
    reflection: in the line $y = 1$
56. **reflection:** in the line $x = 3$
    translation: $(x, y) \to (x - 1, y - 7)$
57. **reflection:** in the y-axis
    rotation: 90° clockwise about the origin

58. What is the length of an altitude of an equilateral triangle whose sides have lengths of $26\sqrt{2}$? (Review 9.4) $13\sqrt{6}$

FINDING TRIGONOMETRIC RATIOS **$\triangle ABC$ is a right triangle in which $AB = 4\sqrt{3}$, $BC = 4$, and $AC = 8$.** (Review 9.5 for 10.4)

59. $\sin A =$ _?_ $\frac{1}{2}$
60. $\cos A =$ _?_ $\frac{\sqrt{3}}{2}$
61. $\sin C =$ _?_ $\frac{\sqrt{3}}{2}$
62. $\tan C =$ _?_ $\sqrt{3}$

QUIZ 1

Self-Test for Lessons 10.1–10.3

$\overleftrightarrow{AB}$ is tangent to $\odot C$ at A and $\overleftrightarrow{DB}$ is tangent to $\odot C$ at D. Find the value of x. Write the postulate or theorem that justifies your answer. (Lesson 10.1)

1.

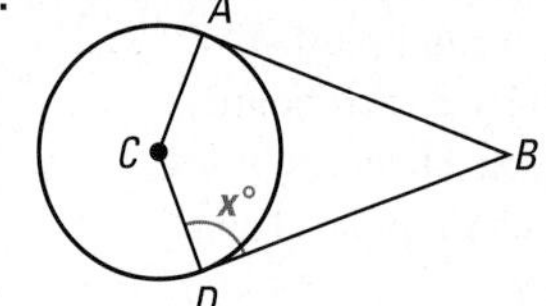

2.

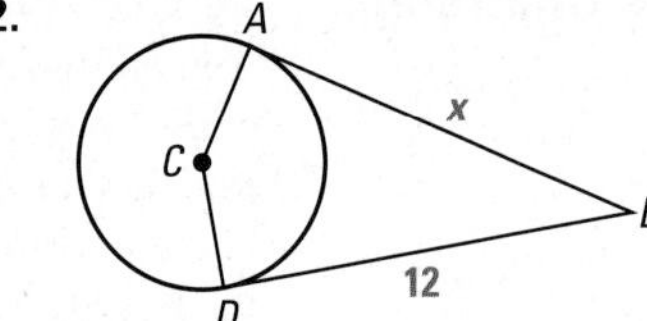

1. 90; a tangent line is ⊥ to the radius drawn to the point of tangency.
2. 12; 2 tangent segs. with the same ext. endpoint are ≅.

Find the measure of the arc of $\odot Q$. (Lesson 10.2)

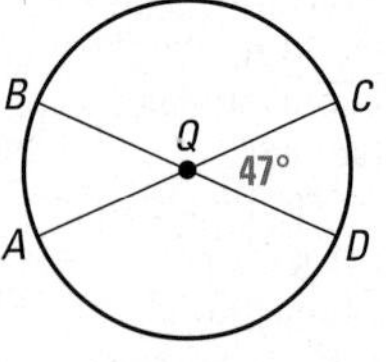

3. $\overset{\frown}{AB}$ 47°
4. $\overset{\frown}{BC}$ 133°
5. $\overset{\frown}{ABD}$ 227°
6. $\overset{\frown}{BCA}$ 313°
7. $\overset{\frown}{ADC}$ 180°
8. $\overset{\frown}{CD}$ 47°

9. If an angle that has a measure of 42.6° is inscribed in a circle, what is the measure of its intercepted arc? (Lesson 10.3) 85.2°

10.4 Other Angle Relationships in Circles

What you should learn

GOAL 1 Use angles formed by tangents and chords to solve problems in geometry.

GOAL 2 Use angles formed by lines that intersect a circle to solve problems.

Why you should learn it

▼ To solve **real-life** problems, such as finding from how far away you can see fireworks, as in **Ex. 35**.

REAL LIFE

CALIFORNIA STANDARDS AND ASSESSMENT

CA Standards: 7, 21
SAT9 Task 1: Obj. 1
SAT9 Task 2: Obj. 1

GOAL 1 USING TANGENTS AND CHORDS

You know that the measure of an angle inscribed in a circle is half the measure of its intercepted arc. This is true even if one side of the angle is tangent to the circle. You will be asked to prove Theorem 10.12 in Exercises 37–39.

THEOREM

THEOREM 10.12

If a tangent and a chord intersect at a point on a circle, then the measure of each angle formed is one half the measure of its intercepted arc.

$m\angle 1 = \frac{1}{2}m\widehat{AB}$ $\qquad$ $m\angle 2 = \frac{1}{2}m\widehat{BCA}$

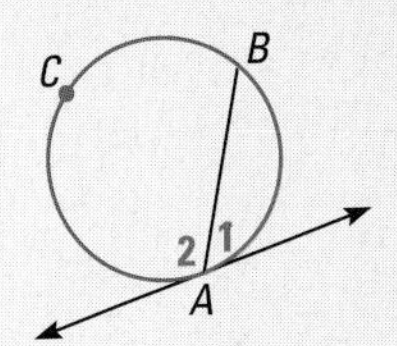

EXAMPLE 1 Finding Angle and Arc Measures

Line m is tangent to the circle. Find the measure of the red angle or arc.

a.

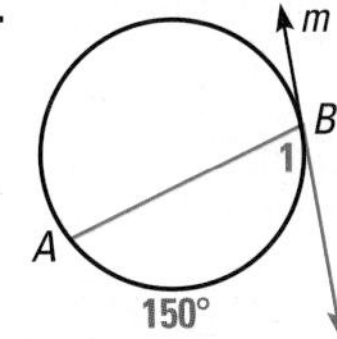

b.

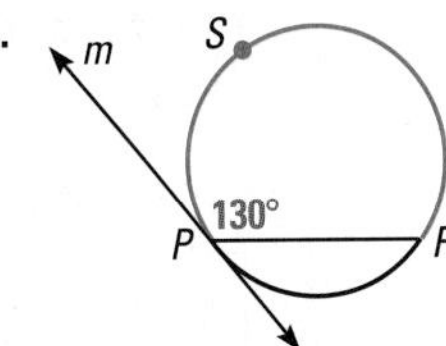

SOLUTION

a. $m\angle 1 = \frac{1}{2}(150°) = 75°$

b. $m\widehat{RSP} = 2(130°) = 260°$

EXAMPLE 2 Finding an Angle Measure

In the diagram below, $\overleftrightarrow{BC}$ is tangent to the circle. Find $m\angle CBD$.

SOLUTION

$$m\angle CBD = \frac{1}{2}m\widehat{DAB}$$

$$5x = \frac{1}{2}(9x + 20)$$

$$10x = 9x + 20$$

$$x = 20$$

A
C
(9x + 20)°
5x°
B
D

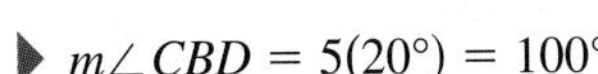

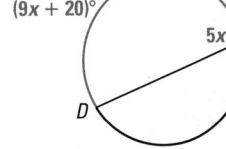

▶ $m\angle CBD = 5(20°) = 100°$

1 PLAN

PACING

Basic: 1 day
Average: 1 day
Advanced: 1 day
Block Schedule: 0.5 block with 10.5

LESSON OPENER
VISUAL APPROACH

An alternative way to approach Lesson 10.4 is to use the Visual Approach Lesson Opener:

- Blackline Master (*Chapter 10 Resource Book,* p. 54)
- Transparency (p. 64)

MEETING INDIVIDUAL NEEDS

- ***Chapter 10 Resource Book***
  Prerequisite Skills Review (p. 5)
  Practice Level A (p. 56)
  Practice Level B (p. 57)
  Practice Level C (p. 58)
  Reteaching with Practice (p. 59)
  Absent Student Catch-Up (p. 61)
  Challenge (p. 63)
- ***Resources in Spanish***
- ***Personal Student Tutor***

NEW-TEACHER SUPPORT

See the Tips for New Teachers on pp. 1–2 of the *Chapter 10 Resource Book* for additional notes about Lesson 10.4.

WARM-UP EXERCISES

Transparency Available

Solve the equation.

1. $4c = 180$ 45

2. $\frac{1}{2}(3x + 42) = 27$ 4

3. $8y = \frac{1}{2}(5y + 55)$ 5

4. $120 = \frac{1}{2}[(360 - x) - x]$ 60

2 TEACH

EXTRA EXAMPLE 1

Line m is tangent to the circle. Find $m\widehat{RST}$. 204°

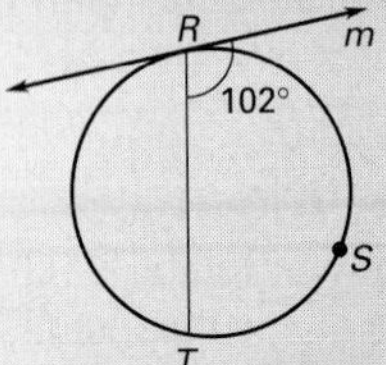

EXTRA EXAMPLE 2

$\overleftrightarrow{BC}$ is tangent to the circle. Find $m\angle CBD$. 75°

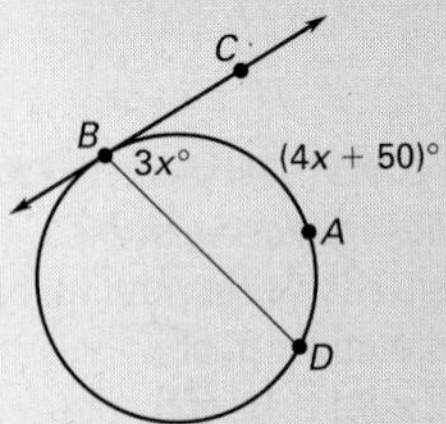

EXTRA EXAMPLE 3

Find the value of x. 80

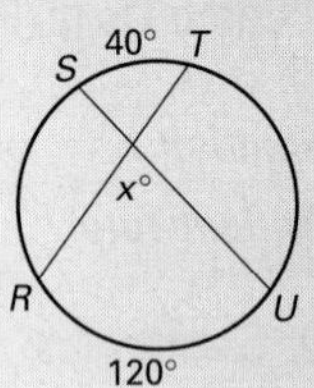

CHECKPOINT EXERCISES

For use after Examples 1 and 2:

1. $\overleftrightarrow{BC}$ is tangent to the circle. Find $m\angle CBD$. 120°

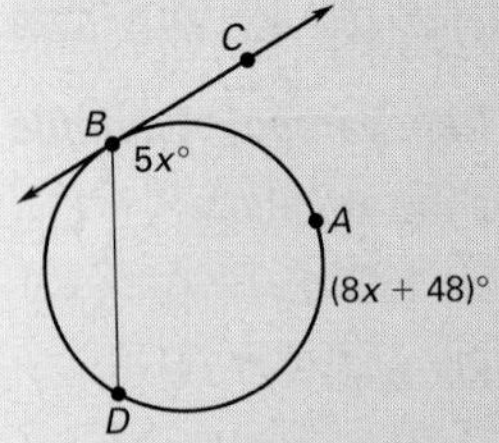

For use after Example 3:

2. Find the value of x. 145

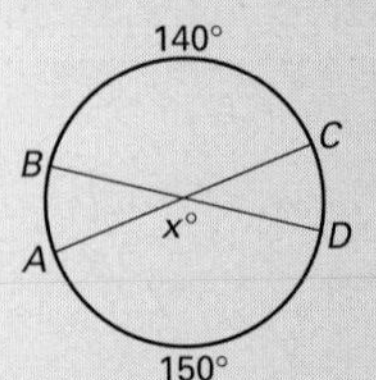

GOAL 2 LINES INTERSECTING INSIDE OR OUTSIDE A CIRCLE

If two lines intersect a circle, there are three places where the lines can intersect.

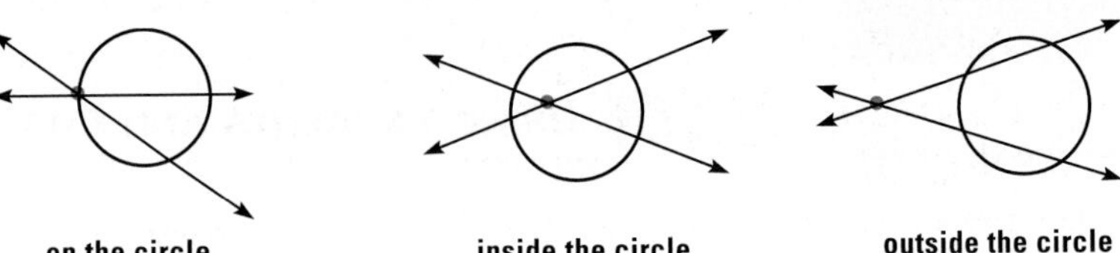

You know how to find angle and arc measures when lines intersect *on* the circle. You can use Theorems 10.13 and 10.14 to find measures when the lines intersect *inside* or *outside* the circle. You will prove these theorems in Exercises 40 and 41.

THEOREMS

THEOREM 10.13

If two chords intersect in the *interior* of a circle, then the measure of each angle is one half the *sum* of the measures of the arcs intercepted by the angle and its vertical angle.

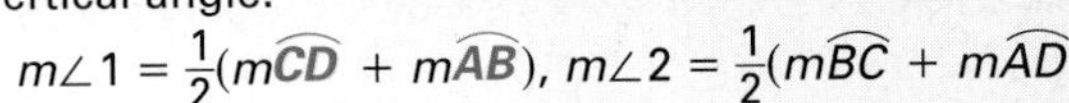

$m\angle 1 = \frac{1}{2}(m\widehat{CD} + m\widehat{AB}),\ m\angle 2 = \frac{1}{2}(m\widehat{BC} + m\widehat{AD})$

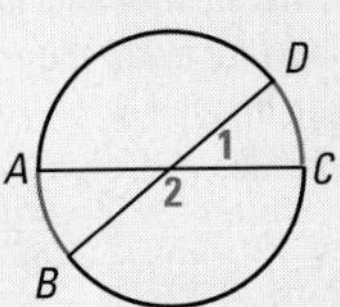

THEOREM 10.14

If a tangent and a secant, two tangents, or two secants intersect in the *exterior* of a circle, then the measure of the angle formed is one half the *difference* of the measures of the intercepted arcs.

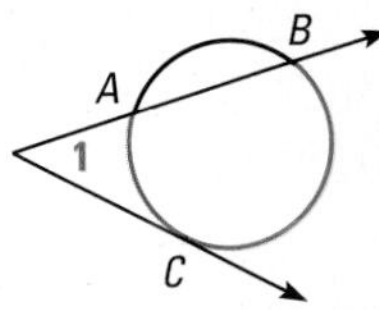

$m\angle 1 = \frac{1}{2}(m\widehat{BC} - m\widehat{AC})$

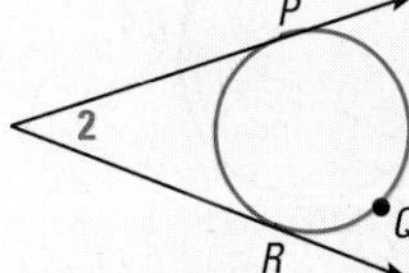

$m\angle 2 = \frac{1}{2}(m\widehat{PQR} - m\widehat{PR})$

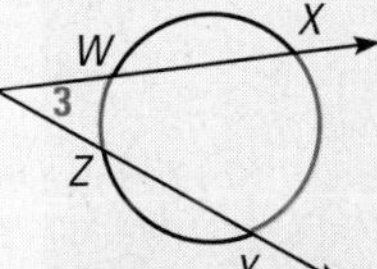

$m\angle 3 = \frac{1}{2}(m\widehat{XY} - m\widehat{WZ})$

EXAMPLE 3 *Finding the Measure of an Angle Formed by Two Chords*

Find the value of x.

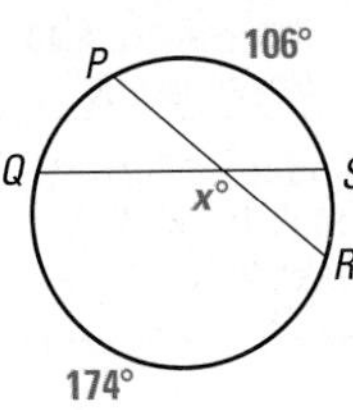

SOLUTION

$x° = \frac{1}{2}(m\widehat{PS} + m\widehat{RQ})$ **Apply Theorem 10.13.**

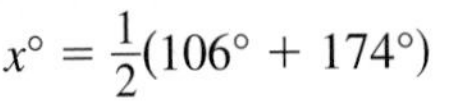

$x° = \frac{1}{2}(106° + 174°)$ **Substitute.**

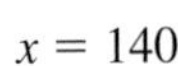

$x = 140$ **Simplify.**

STUDENT HELP

HOMEWORK HELP Visit our Web site www.mcdougallittell.com for extra examples.

EXAMPLE 4 *Using Theorem 10.14*

Find the value of x.

a.

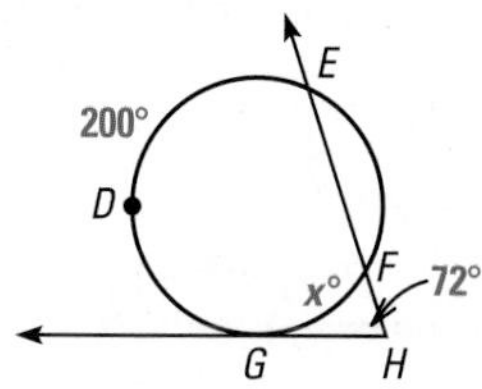

b.

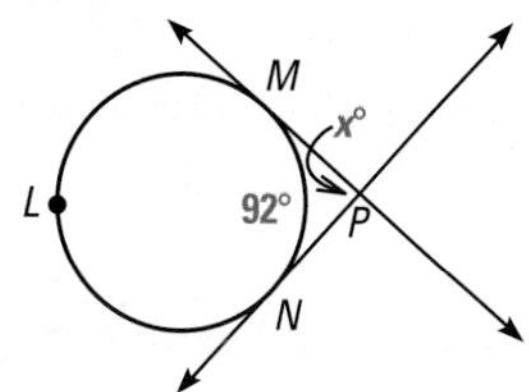

SOLUTION

a. $m\angle GHF = \frac{1}{2}(m\widehat{EDG} - m\widehat{GF})$ **Apply Theorem 10.14.**

$72° = \frac{1}{2}(200° - x°)$ **Substitute.**

$144 = 200 - x$ **Multiply each side by 2.**

$x = 56$ **Solve for x.**

b. Because $\widehat{MN}$ and $\widehat{MLN}$ make a whole circle, $m\widehat{MLN} = 360° - 92° = 268°$.

$x = \frac{1}{2}(m\widehat{MLN} - m\widehat{MN})$ **Apply Theorem 10.14.**

$= \frac{1}{2}(268 - 92)$ **Substitute.**

$= \frac{1}{2}(176)$ **Subtract.**

$= 88$ **Multiply.**

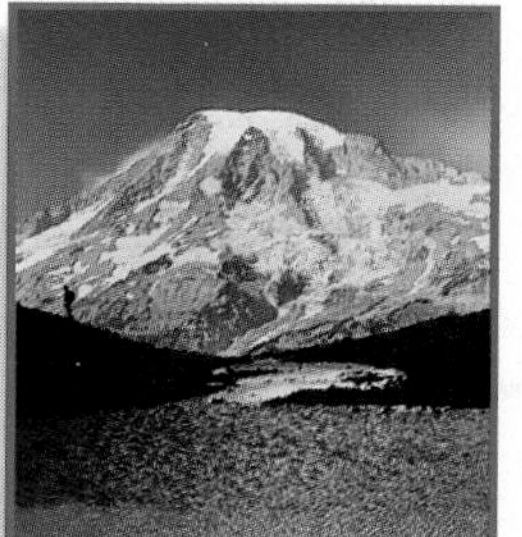

Mount Rainier, Washington

EXAMPLE 5 *Describing the View from Mount Rainier*

REAL LIFE VIEWS You are on top of Mount Rainier on a clear day. You are about 2.73 miles above sea level. Find the measure of the arc $\widehat{CD}$ that represents the part of Earth that you can see.

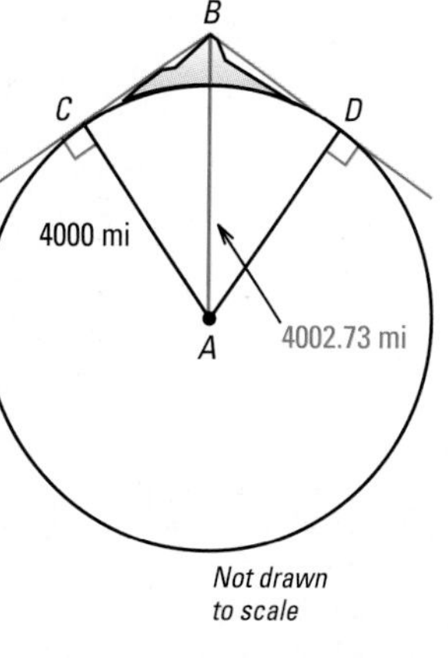

SOLUTION

$\overrightarrow{BC}$ and $\overrightarrow{BD}$ are tangent to Earth. You can solve right $\triangle BCA$ to see that $m\angle CBA \approx 87.9°$. So, $m\angle CBD \approx 175.8°$. Let $m\widehat{CD} = x°$.

$175.8 \approx \frac{1}{2}[(360 - x) - x]$ **Apply Theorem 10.14.**

$175.8 \approx \frac{1}{2}(360 - 2x)$ **Simplify.**

$175.8 \approx 180 - x$ **Distributive property**

$x \approx 4.2$ **Solve for x.**

▶ From the peak, you can see an arc of about 4°.

STUDENT HELP

Look Back
For help with solving a right triangle, see pp. 567–569.

EXTRA EXAMPLE 4

Find the value of x. 100

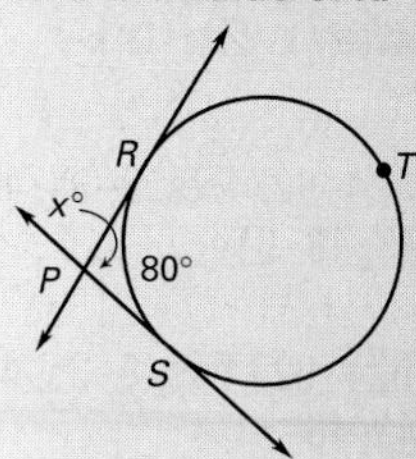

EXTRA EXAMPLE 5

You are standing on top of a tall building about 0.22 miles above sea level. Find the measure of $\widehat{CD}$. 1.2°

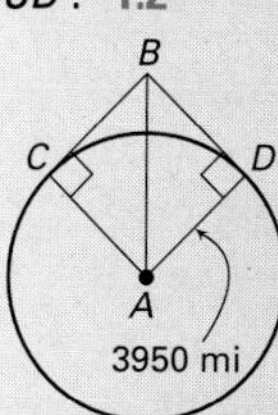

CHECKPOINT EXERCISES

For use after Examples 4 and 5:

1. Find the value of x.

a.

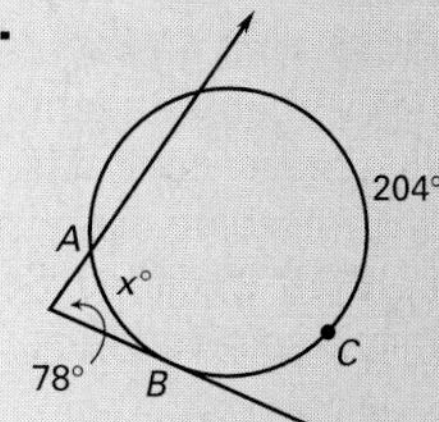

b.

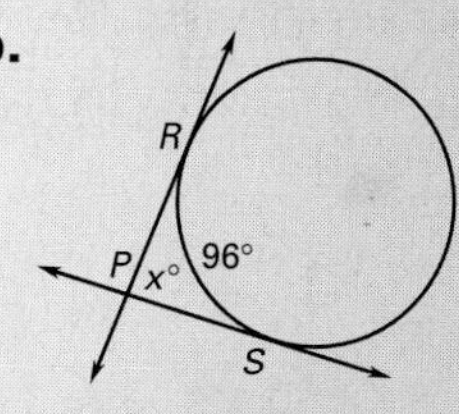

a. 48; b. 84

CLOSURE QUESTION

Find the values of x and y. 124; 80

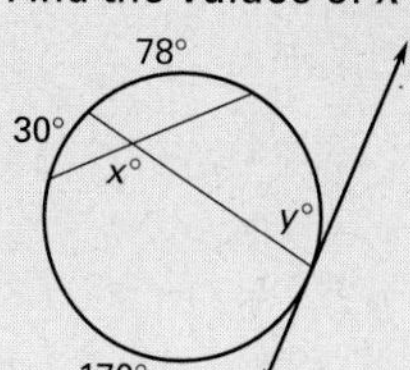

3 APPLY

ASSIGNMENT GUIDE

BASIC
Day 1: pp. 624–627 Exs. 8–34, 40, 42, 43, 46–51

AVERAGE
Day 1: pp. 624–627 Exs. 8–35, 40, 42, 43, 46–51

ADVANCED
Day 1: pp. 624–627 Exs. 8–35, 37–40, 42–51

BLOCK SCHEDULE WITH 10.5
pp. 624–627 Exs. 8–35, 40, 42, 43, 46–51

EXERCISE LEVELS

Level A: *Easier*
8–13

Level B: *More Difficult*
14–37, 40, 42, 43

Level C: *Most Difficult*
38, 39, 41, 44, 45

✔ HOMEWORK CHECK

To quickly check student understanding of key concepts, go over the following exercises: Exs. 8, 16, 18, 28, 30, 40. See also the Daily Homework Quiz:

- Blackline Master (*Chapter 10 Resource Book,* p. 66)
- Transparency (p. 75)

GUIDED PRACTICE

Concept Check ✓

1. If a chord of a circle intersects a tangent to the circle at the point of tangency, what is the relationship between the angles formed and the intercepted arcs? **The measure of each ∠ is half the measure of the intercepted arc.**

Skill Check ✓

Find the indicated measure or value.

2. $m\widehat{STU}$ 210°

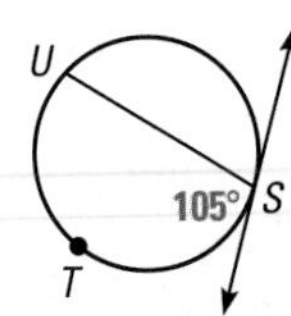

3. $m\angle 1$ 60°

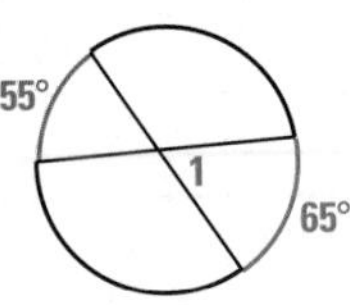

4. $m\angle DBR$ 65°

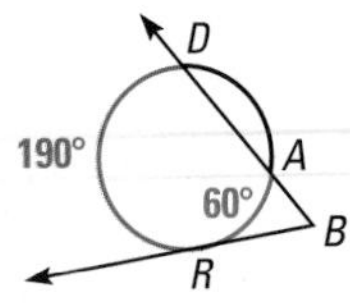

5. $m\angle RQU$ 90°

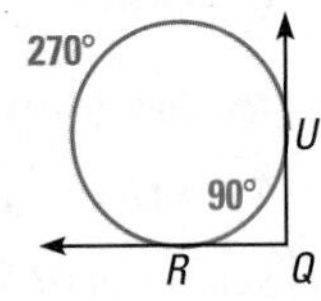

6. $m\angle N$ 22.5°

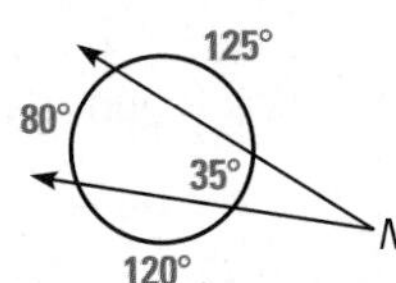

7. $m\angle 1$ 88°

PRACTICE AND APPLICATIONS

STUDENT HELP
Extra Practice to help you master skills is on p. 822.

FINDING MEASURES **Find the indicated measure.**

8. $m\angle 1$ 110°

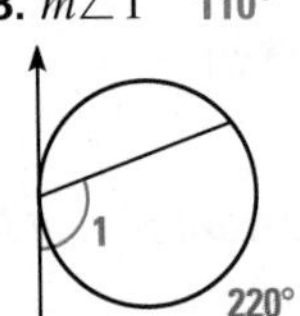

9. $m\widehat{GHJ}$ 280°

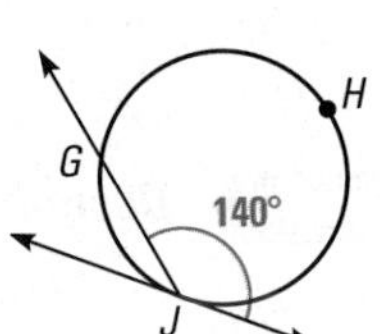

10. $m\angle 2$ 90°

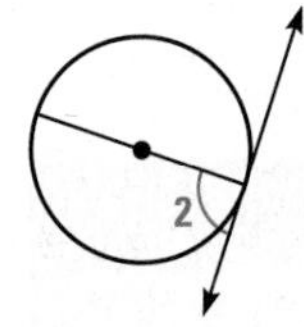

11. $m\widehat{DE}$ 72°

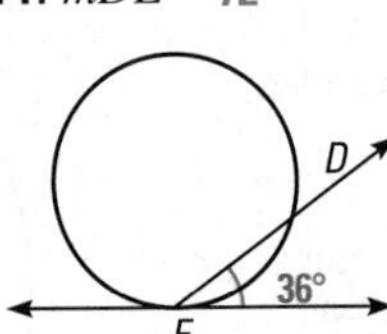

12. $m\widehat{ABC}$ 252°

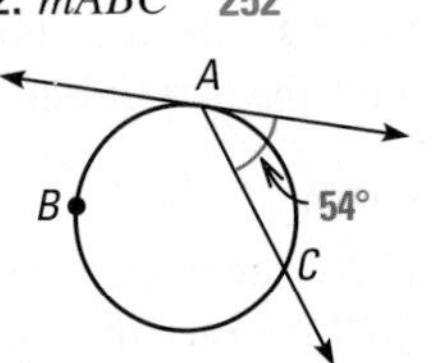

13. $m\angle 3$ 110°

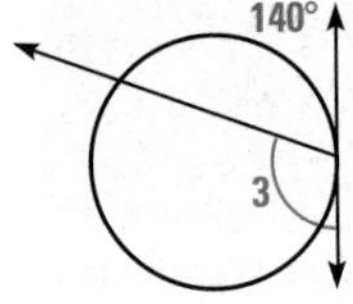

USING ALGEBRA **Find the value of *x*.**

STUDENT HELP
HOMEWORK HELP
Example 1: Exs. 8–13
Example 2: Exs. 14–16
Example 3: Exs. 17–25
Example 4: Exs. 26–28
Example 5: Ex. 35

14. $m\widehat{AB} = x°$ 168

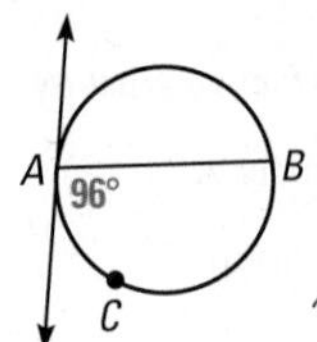

15. $m\widehat{PQ} = (5x + 17)°$ 25.4

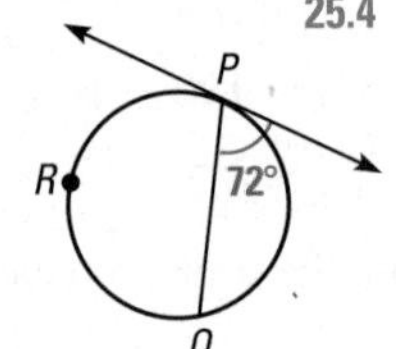

16. $m\widehat{HJK} = (10x + 50)°$ 18

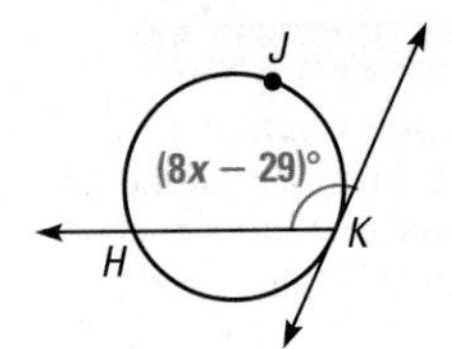

FINDING ANGLE MEASURES Find $m\angle 1$.

17. 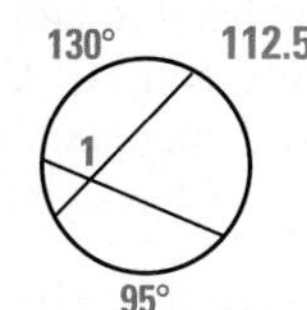

18. 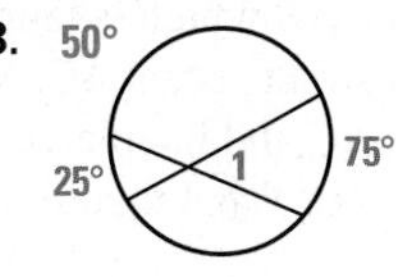

19. 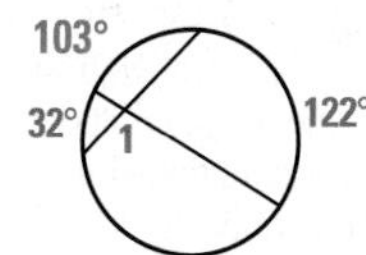

20. 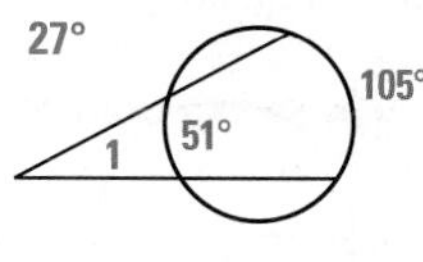

21. 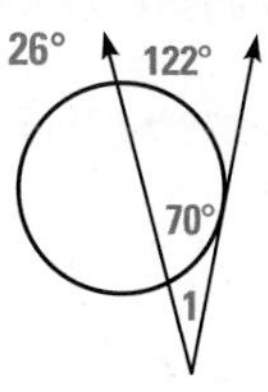

22. 45° 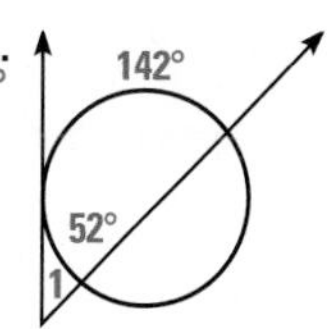

23. 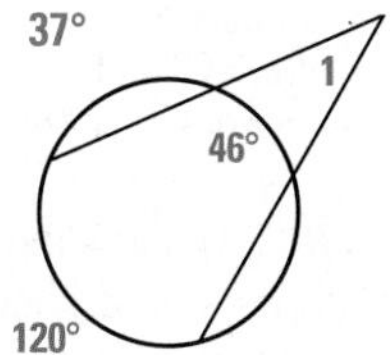

24. 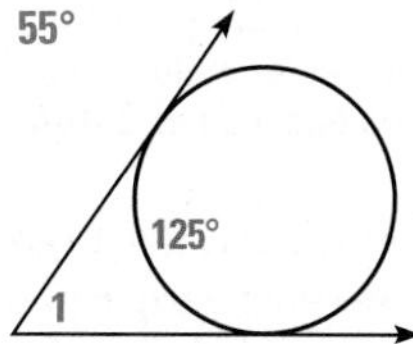

25. 55° 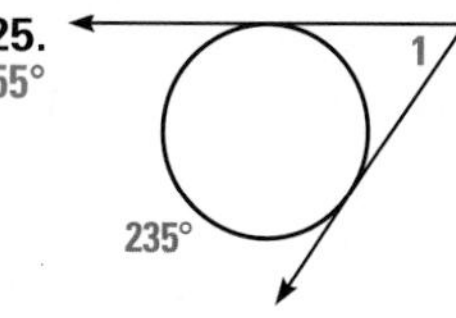

 **USING ALGEBRA** Find the value of *a*.

26. 15 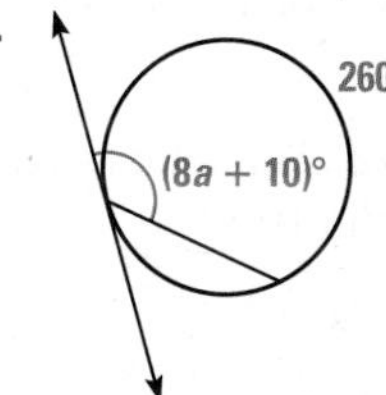

27. 5 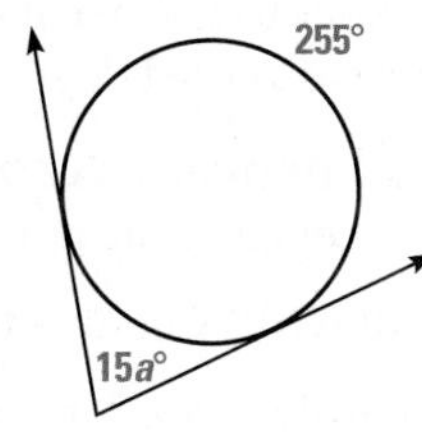

28. 40 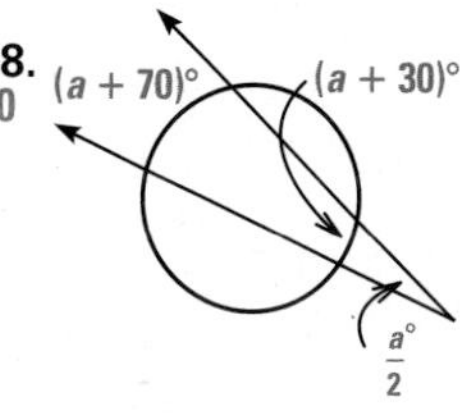

FINDING ANGLE MEASURES Use the diagram at the right to find the measure of the angle.

29. $m\angle 1$ 60°	30. $m\angle 2$ 60°
31. $m\angle 3$ 30°	32. $m\angle 4$ 90°
33. $m\angle 5$ 30°	34. $m\angle 6$ 60°

STUDENT HELP

INTERNET APPLICATION LINK
Visit our Web site www.mcdougallittell.com.

35. **FIREWORKS** You are watching fireworks over San Diego Bay *S* as you sail away in a boat. The highest point the fireworks reach *F* is about 0.2 mile above the bay and your eyes *E* are about 0.01 mile above the water. At point *B* you can no longer see the fireworks because of the curvature of Earth. The radius of Earth is about 4000 miles and $\overline{FE}$ is tangent to Earth at *T*. Find $m\widehat{SB}$. Give your answer to the nearest tenth of a degree. 0.7°

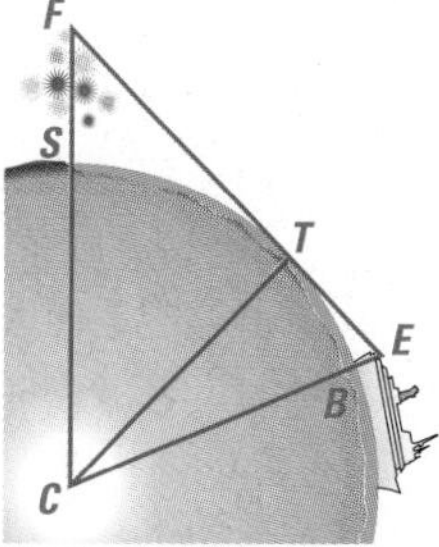

Not drawn to scale

! COMMON ERROR
EXERCISES 17–25 Students may forget whether they need to find one-half the sum or the difference to find $m\angle 1$. Refer students back to the theorems on page 622. Also, remind students that if the angle is inside the circle they need to find the sum and if it is outside the circle they need to find the difference.

APPLICATION NOTE
Additional information about fireworks is available at **www.mcdougallittell.com.**

STUDENT HELP NOTES

Software Help Instructions for several software packages are available in **blackline** format in the *Chapter 10 Resource Book,* p. 55 and at **www.mcdougallittell.com.**

41. See Additional Answers beginning on page AA1.

ADDITIONAL PRACTICE AND RETEACHING

For Lesson 10.4:

- Practice Levels A, B, and C (*Chapter 10 Resource Book,* p. 56)
- Reteaching with Practice (*Chapter 10 Resource Book,* p. 59)
- See Lesson 10.4 of the *Personal Student Tutor*

For more Mixed Review:

- Search the *Test and Practice Generator* for key words or specific lessons.

STUDENT HELP

SOFTWARE HELP Visit our Web site www.mcdougallittell.com to see instructions for several software applications.

36. $m\angle BAC = \frac{1}{2}m\overset{\frown}{AC}$; Thm. 10.12

37. Diameter; 90°; a tangent line is ⊥ to the radius drawn to the point of tangency.

38. Draw $\overline{BQ}$ intersecting the ⊙ at P and let X be a point on the upper semicircle. Show that $m\angle ABC = m\angle ABQ + m\angle QBC$. Then $m\angle ABQ = 90° = \frac{1}{2}(180°) = \frac{1}{2}m\overset{\frown}{BXP}$, and $m\angle QBC = \frac{1}{2}m\overset{\frown}{PC}$, so by the Arc Addition Post., $m\angle ABC = \frac{1}{2}m\overset{\frown}{BPC}$.

39. The proof would be similar, using the Angle Addition and Arc Addition Postulates, but you would be subtracting $m\angle PBC$ and $m\overset{\frown}{PC}$ instead of adding.

36. **TECHNOLOGY** Use geometry software to construct and label circle O, $\overline{AB}$ which is tangent to $\odot O$ at point A, and any point C on $\odot O$. Then construct secant $\overline{AC}$. Measure $\angle BAC$ and $\overset{\frown}{AC}$. Compare the measures of $\angle BAC$ and its intercepted arc as you drag point C on the circle. What do you notice? What theorem from this lesson have you illustrated? **See margin.**

PROVING THEOREM 10.12 The proof of Theorem 10.12 can be split into three cases, as shown in the diagrams. **37–39. See margin.**

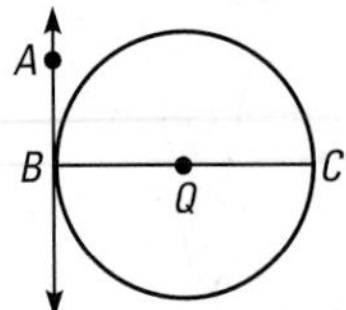

Case 1
The center of the circle is on one side of $\angle ABC$.

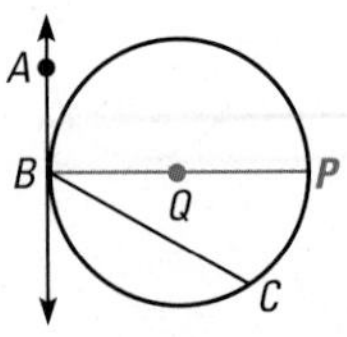

Case 2
The center of the circle is in the interior of $\angle ABC$.

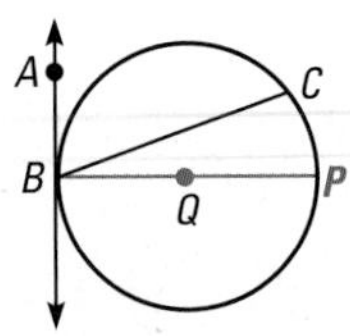

Case 3
The center of the circle is in the exterior of $\angle ABC$.

37. In Case 1, what type of chord is $\overline{BC}$? What is the measure of $\angle ABC$? What theorem earlier in this chapter supports your conclusion?

38. Write a plan for a proof of Case 2 of Theorem 10.12. (*Hint:* Use the auxiliary line and the Angle Addition Postulate.)

39. Describe how the proof of Case 3 of Theorem 10.12 is different from the proof of Case 2.

40. **PROVING THEOREM 10.13** Fill in the blanks to complete the proof of Theorem 10.13.

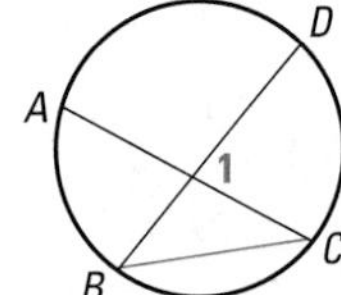

GIVEN ▶ Chords $\overline{AC}$ and $\overline{BD}$ intersect.

PROVE ▶ $m\angle 1 = \frac{1}{2}(m\overset{\frown}{DC} + m\overset{\frown}{AB})$

Statements	Reasons
1. Chords $\overline{AC}$ and $\overline{BD}$ intersect.	**1.** ? Given.
2. Draw $\overline{BC}$.	**2.** ? Through any 2 pts. there is exactly 1 line.
3. $m\angle 1 = m\angle DBC + m\angle$? **ACB**	**3.** ? Ext. ∠ Thm.
4. $m\angle DBC = \frac{1}{2}m\overset{\frown}{DC}$	**4.** ? Measure of an inscribed ∠ Thm.
5. $m\angle ACB = \frac{1}{2}m\overset{\frown}{AB}$	**5.** ? Measure of an inscribed ∠ Thm.
6. $m\angle 1 = \frac{1}{2}m\overset{\frown}{DC} + \frac{1}{2}m\overset{\frown}{AB}$	**6.** ? Substitution Prop.
7. $m\angle 1 = \frac{1}{2}(m\overset{\frown}{DC} + m\overset{\frown}{AB})$	**7.** ? Distributive Prop.

41. **JUSTIFYING THEOREM 10.14** Look back at the diagrams for Theorem 10.14 on page 622. Copy the diagram for the case of a tangent and a secant and draw $\overline{BC}$. Explain how to use the Exterior Angle Theorem in the proof of this case. Then copy the diagrams for the other two cases, draw appropriate auxiliary segments, and write plans for the proofs of the cases. **See margin.**

Test Preparation

42. **MULTIPLE CHOICE** The diagram at the right is not drawn to scale. $\overline{AB}$ is any chord of the circle. The line is tangent to the circle at point A. Which of the following must be true? E

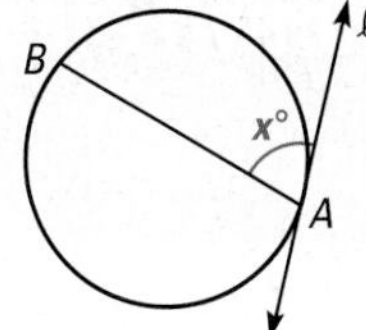

Ⓐ $x < 90°$ Ⓑ $x \le 90°$ Ⓒ $x = 90°$

Ⓓ $x > 90°$ Ⓔ Cannot be determined from given information

43. **MULTIPLE CHOICE** In the figure at the right, which relationship is *not* true? C

Ⓐ $m\angle 1 = \frac{1}{2}(m\widehat{CD} + m\widehat{AB})$

Ⓑ $m\angle 1 = \frac{1}{2}(m\widehat{EF} - m\widehat{CD})$

Ⓒ $m\angle 2 = \frac{1}{2}(m\widehat{BD} - m\widehat{AC})$

Ⓓ $m\angle 3 = \frac{1}{2}(m\widehat{EF} - m\widehat{CD})$

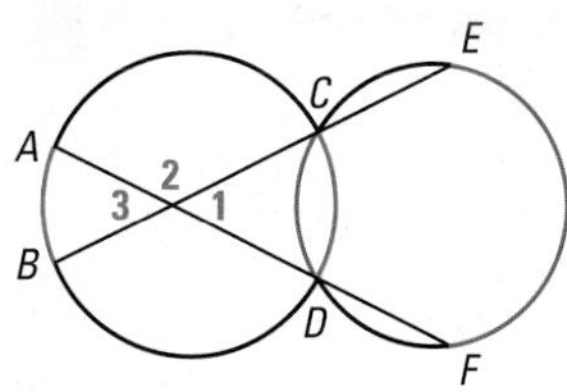

★ **Challenge**

44. **PROOF** Use the plan to write a paragraph proof. See margin.

GIVEN ▶ $\angle R$ is a right angle. Circle P is inscribed in $\triangle QRS$. T, U, and V are points of tangency.

PROVE ▶ $r = \frac{1}{2}(QR + RS - QS)$

Plan for Proof Prove that $TPVR$ is a square. Then show that $\overline{QT} \cong \overline{QU}$ and $\overline{SU} \cong \overline{SV}$. Finally, use the Segment Addition Postulate and substitution.

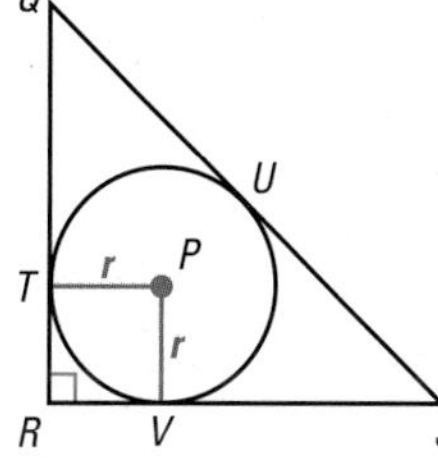

EXTRA CHALLENGE

www.mcdougallittell.com

45. **FINDING A RADIUS** Use the result from Exercise 44 to find the radius of an inscribed circle of a right triangle with side lengths of 3, 4, and 5. 1

MIXED REVIEW

USING SIMILAR TRIANGLES Use the diagram at the right and the given information. (Review 9.1)

46. $MN = 9$, $PM = 12$, $LP = \underline{\ ?\ }$ 20

47. $LM = 4$, $LN = 9$, $LP = \underline{\ ?\ }$ 6

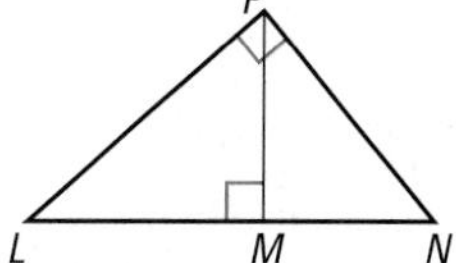

48. **FINDING A RADIUS** You are 10 feet from a circular storage tank. You are 22 feet from a point of tangency on the tank. Find the tank's radius. (Review 10.1) 19.2 ft

USING ALGEBRA $\overline{AB}$ and $\overline{AD}$ are tangent to $\odot L$. Find the value of x. (Review 10.1)

49. 25

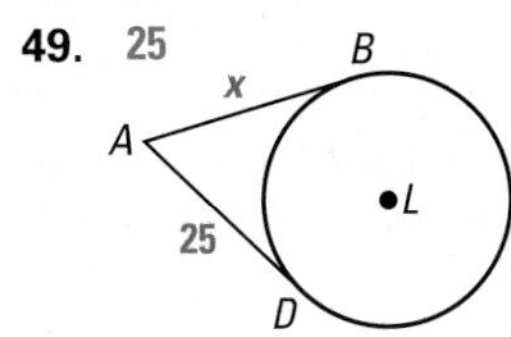

50. 8

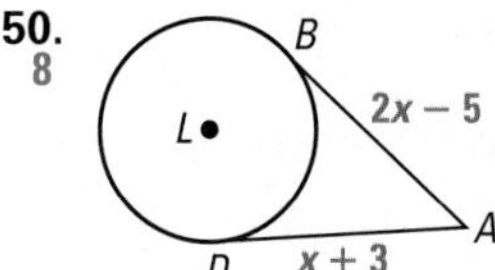

51. 2

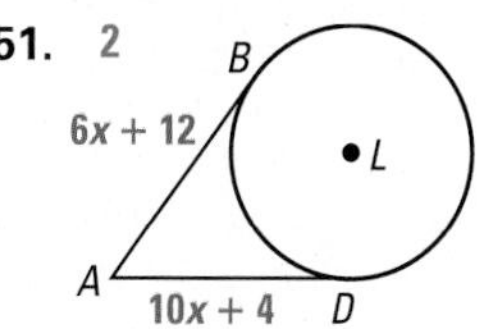

4 ASSESS

DAILY HOMEWORK QUIZ

Transparency Available

Find the value of x.

1. $m\widehat{HJK} = (20x - 4)°$

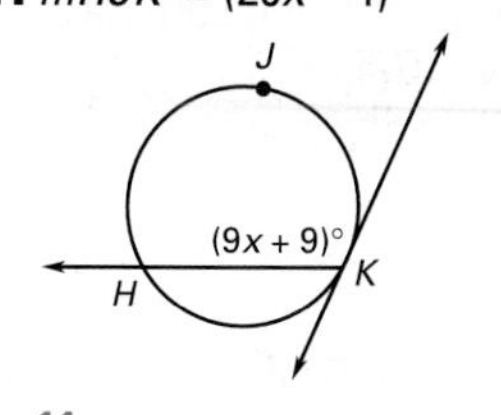

11

2.

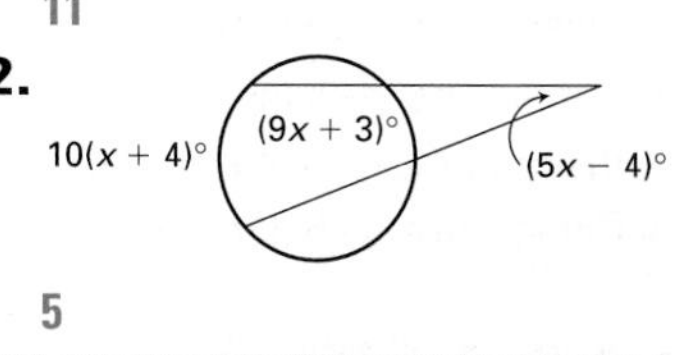

5

EXTRA CHALLENGE NOTE

Challenge problems for Lesson 10.4 are available in **blackline** format in the *Chapter 10 Resource Book*, p. 63 and at **www.mcdougallittell.com.**

ADDITIONAL TEST PREPARATION

2. **OPEN ENDED** Draw a tangent and a chord intersecting at a point on a circle. Estimate the angle between them. Label each angle and intercepted arc with its measure. *Sample answer:*

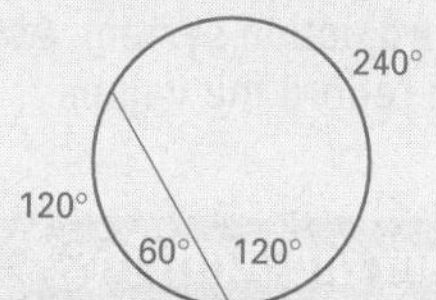

44. See Additional Answers beginning on page AA1.

1 Planning the Activity

PURPOSE
To find the lengths of segments in a circle.

MATERIALS
- Geometry drawing software
- Software Help (*Chapter 10 Resource Book,* p. 68)

PACING
- Construct — 5 min
- Investigate — 5 min
- Conjecture — 5 min
- Investigate — 5 min
- Conjecture — 5 min

LINK TO LESSON
The results of this activity will help students better understand the theorems in Lesson 10.5.

2 Managing the Activity

CLASSROOM MANAGEMENT
If students have difficulty generalizing the relationships for the segments of intersecting chords, have students record the segment lengths and make another construction.

ALTERNATIVE APPROACH
To save time, do this activity as a demonstration with an overhead computer projection system. Ask students to record the values.

3 Closing the Activity

KEY DISCOVERY
If two chords or two secants as labeled in this activity intersect in a point E, then $EA \cdot EB = EC \cdot ED$.

ACTIVITY ASSESSMENT
Find the value of x. 5

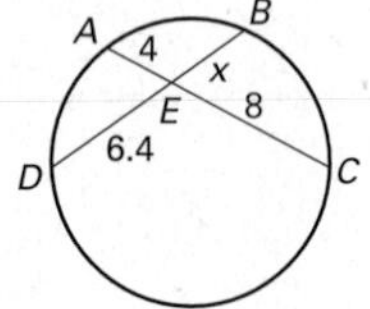

ACTIVITY 10.5
Using Technology

Investigating Segment Lengths

You can use geometry software to explore the lengths of segments in a circle.

STUDENT HELP
INTERNET SOFTWARE HELP
Visit our Web site www.mcdougallittell.com to see instructions for several software applications.

CONSTRUCT Follow the steps to construct a circle and two intersecting lines.

Steps 1-4. Check drawings.

1. Draw a circle.
2. On the circle, draw and label points A, B, C, and D.
3. Draw lines $\overleftrightarrow{AB}$ and $\overleftrightarrow{CD}$.
4. Draw the point of intersection of $\overleftrightarrow{AB}$ and $\overleftrightarrow{CD}$. Label it point E.

INVESTIGATE

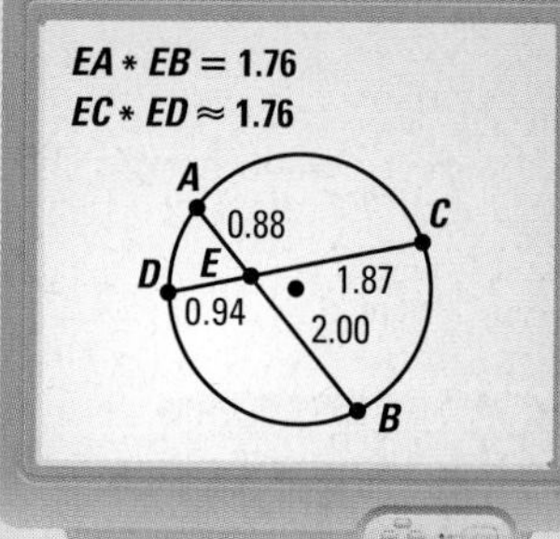

1. Drag points A, B, C, and D. Can you rearrange the points so that point E is outside the circle? on the circle? inside the circle? yes; yes; yes
2. Draw $\overline{EA}$, $\overline{EC}$, $\overline{EB}$, and $\overline{ED}$. Hide $\overleftrightarrow{AB}$ and $\overleftrightarrow{CD}$. Check drawings.
3. Rearrange the points A, B, C, and D so that point E is inside the circle. Measure $\overline{EA}$, $\overline{EC}$, $\overline{EB}$, and $\overline{ED}$. Calculate $EA \cdot EB$ and $EC \cdot ED$. What do you notice? $EA \cdot EB \approx EC \cdot ED$
4. Drag points A, B, C, and D, keeping point E inside the circle. What do you notice about $EA \cdot EB$ and $EC \cdot ED$? $EA \cdot EB \approx EC \cdot ED$

CONJECTURE

5. Make a conjecture about the lengths of the segments of intersecting chords. See margin.

INVESTIGATE

6. Drag points A, B, C, and D so that point E is outside the circle. What do you notice about $EA \cdot EB$ and $EC \cdot ED$? $EA \cdot EB \approx EC \cdot ED$

CONJECTURE

7. Make a conjecture about the lengths of the segments of secants from a point outside a circle to the circle. See margin.

5. If 2 chords intersect inside a ⊙, the product of the lengths of the segments of one chord is equal to the product of the lengths of the segments of the other chord.

7. If 2 secant segments to a ⊙ have a common endpoint outside the ⊙, then the product of the lengths of one secant segment and its external segment is equal to the product of the lengths of the other secant segment and its external segment.

Extension: Tangent; $(EA)^2 \approx EC \cdot ED$; If a secant segment and a tangent segment have a common endpoint outside the ⊙, the square of the length of the tangent segment is equal to the product of the lengths of the secant segment and its external segment.

EXTENSION

CRITICAL THINKING Move point A until it is in the same place as point B. What kind of line is $\overleftrightarrow{EA}$? What is the relationship between EA, EC, and ED? Make and test a conjecture. See margin.

10.5 Segment Lengths in Circles

What you should learn

GOAL 1 Find the lengths of segments of chords.

GOAL 2 Find the lengths of segments of tangents and secants.

Why you should learn it

▼ To find **real-life** measures, such as the radius of an aquarium tank in **Example 3**.

CALIFORNIA STANDARDS AND ASSESSMENT

CA Standards: 4, 7, 21
SAT9 Task 1: Obj. 26
SAT9 Task 2: Obj. 26

GOAL 1 FINDING LENGTHS OF SEGMENTS OF CHORDS

When two chords intersect in the interior of a circle, each chord is divided into two segments which are called *segments of a chord*. The following theorem gives a relationship between the lengths of the four segments that are formed.

THEOREM

THEOREM 10.15

If two chords intersect in the interior of a circle, then the product of the lengths of the segments of one chord is equal to the product of the lengths of the segments of the other chord.

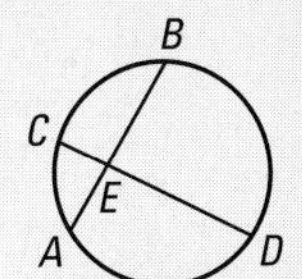

$EA \cdot EB = EC \cdot ED$

You can use similar triangles to prove Theorem 10.15.

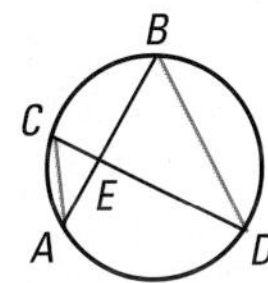

GIVEN ▶ $\overline{AB}$, $\overline{CD}$ are chords that intersect at E.

PROVE ▶ $EA \cdot EB = EC \cdot ED$

Paragraph Proof Draw $\overline{DB}$ and $\overline{AC}$. Because $\angle C$ and $\angle B$ intercept the same arc, $\angle C \cong \angle B$. Likewise, $\angle A \cong \angle D$. By the AA Similarity Postulate, $\triangle AEC \sim \triangle DEB$. So, the lengths of corresponding sides are proportional.

$\frac{EA}{ED} = \frac{EC}{EB}$ — The lengths of the sides are proportional.

$EA \cdot EB = EC \cdot ED$ — Cross Product Property

EXAMPLE 1 *Finding Segment Lengths*

Chords $\overline{ST}$ and $\overline{PQ}$ intersect inside the circle. Find the value of x.

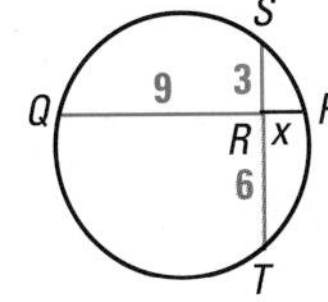

SOLUTION

$RQ \cdot RP = RS \cdot RT$	Use Theorem 10.15.
$9 \cdot x = 3 \cdot 6$	Substitute.
$9x = 18$	Simplify.
$x = 2$	Divide each side by 9.

1 PLAN

PACING

Basic: 2 days
Average: 2 days
Advanced: 2 days
Block Schedule: 0.5 block with 10.4; 0.5 block with 10.6

LESSON OPENER ACTIVITY

An alternative way to approach Lesson 10.5 is to use the Activity Lesson Opener:

- Blackline Master (*Chapter 10 Resource Book*, p. 67)
- Transparency (p. 65)

MEETING INDIVIDUAL NEEDS

- ***Chapter 10 Resource Book***
  Prerequisite Skills Review (p. 5)
  Practice Level A (p. 70)
  Practice Level B (p. 71)
  Practice Level C (p. 72)
  Reteaching with Practice (p. 73)
  Absent Student Catch-Up (p. 75)
  Challenge (p. 77)
- ***Resources in Spanish***
- ***Personal Student Tutor***

NEW-TEACHER SUPPORT

See the Tips for New Teachers on pp. 1–2 of the *Chapter 10 Resource Book* for additional notes about Lesson 10.5.

WARM-UP EXERCISES

Transparency Available

Solve each equation.

1. $8x = 12 \cdot 4$ 6
2. $8(10 + 8) = 6(y + 6)$ 18

3. $10^2 = 6(2x + 8)$ $4\frac{1}{3}$
4. $12^2 = x(x + 6)$ $-3 \pm 3\sqrt{17}$

2 TEACH

MOTIVATING THE LESSON

The length of a bridge with semicircular arch supports is an application of a tangent or secant segment. Ask students to draw simple bridges and compare them. Finding the lengths of segments relating to circles is the focus of this lesson.

EXTRA EXAMPLE 1

Chords $\overline{AB}$ and $\overline{CD}$ intersect inside the circle. Find the value of x. 6

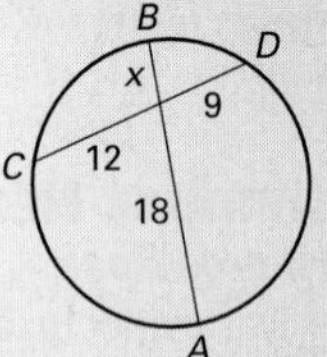

EXTRA EXAMPLE 2

Find the value of x. 7.25

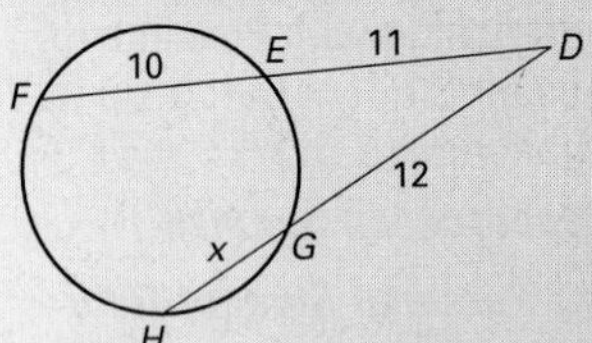

CHECKPOINT EXERCISES

For use after Examples 1 and 2:

1. Find the values of x and y. $22\frac{7}{8}$; 7

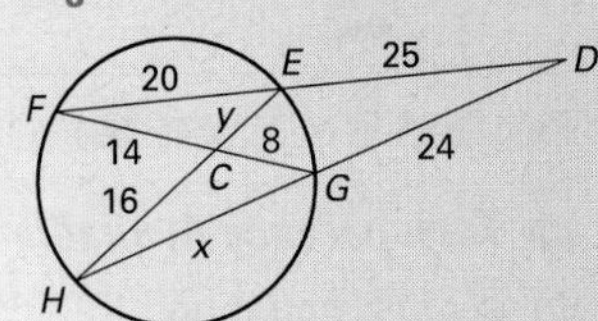

GOAL 2 USING SEGMENTS OF TANGENTS AND SECANTS

In the figure shown below, $\overline{PS}$ is called a **tangent segment** because it is tangent to the circle at an endpoint. Similarly, $\overline{PR}$ is a **secant segment** and $\overline{PQ}$ is the **external segment** of $\overline{PR}$.

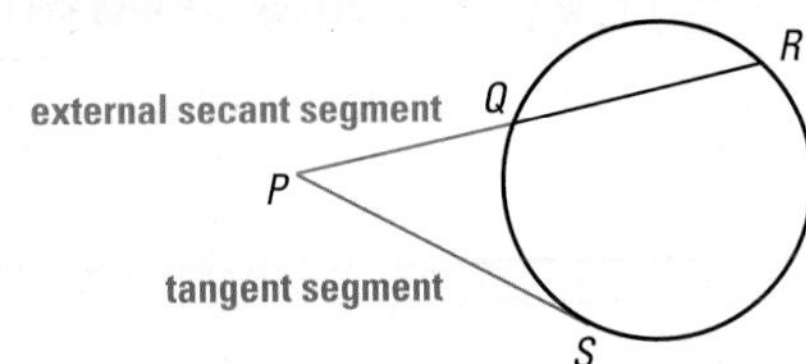

You are asked to prove the following theorems in Exercises 31 and 32.

THEOREMS

THEOREM 10.16

If two secant segments share the same endpoint outside a circle, then the product of the length of one secant segment and the length of its external segment equals the product of the length of the other secant segment and the length of its external segment.

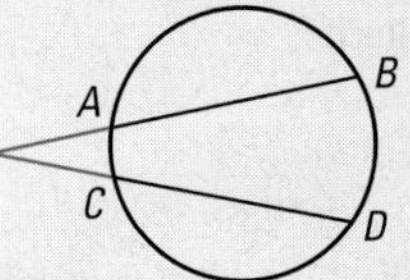

$EA \cdot EB = EC \cdot ED$

THEOREM 10.17

If a secant segment and a tangent segment share an endpoint outside a circle, then the product of the length of the secant segment and the length of its external segment equals the square of the length of the tangent segment.

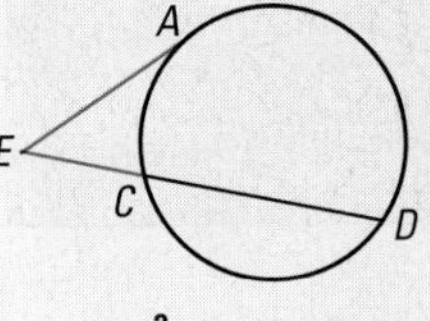

$(EA)^2 = EC \cdot ED$

EXAMPLE 2 Finding Segment Lengths

Using Algebra

Find the value of x.

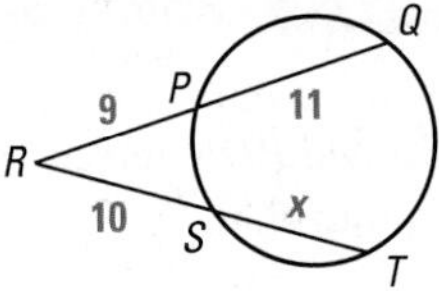

SOLUTION

$RP \cdot RQ = RS \cdot RT$	Use Theorem 10.16.
$9 \cdot (11 + 9) = 10 \cdot (x + 10)$	Substitute.
$180 = 10x + 100$	Simplify.
$80 = 10x$	Subtract 100 from each side.
$8 = x$	Divide each side by 10.

FOCUS ON APPLICATIONS

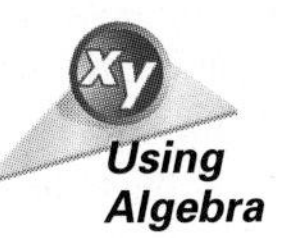

AQUARIUM TANK The Caribbean Coral Reef Tank at the New England Aquarium is a circular tank 24 feet deep. The 200,000 gallon tank contains an elaborate coral reef and many exotic fishes.

APPLICATION LINK
www.mcdougallittell.com

In Lesson 10.1, you learned how to use the Pythagorean Theorem to estimate the radius of a grain silo. Example 3 shows you another way to estimate the radius of a circular object.

EXAMPLE 3 *Estimating the Radius of a Circle*

AQUARIUM TANK You are standing at point C, about 8 feet from a circular aquarium tank. The distance from you to a point of tangency on the tank is about 20 feet. Estimate the radius of the tank.

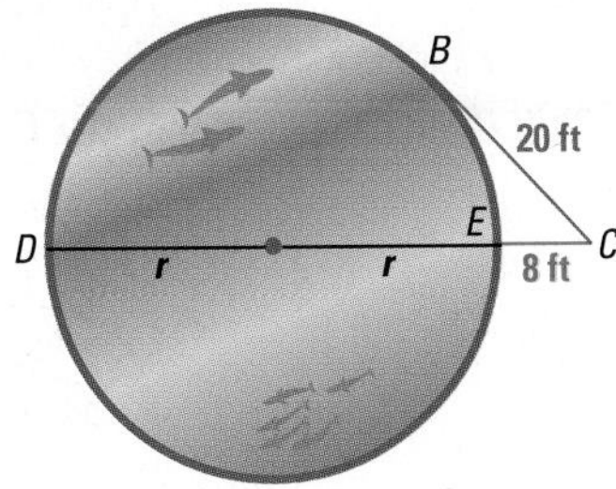

SOLUTION

You can use Theorem 10.17 to find the radius.

$(CB)^2 = CE \cdot CD$	**Use Theorem 10.17.**
$20^2 \approx 8 \cdot (2r + 8)$	**Substitute.**
$400 \approx 16r + 64$	**Simplify.**
$336 \approx 16r$	**Subtract 64 from each side.**
$21 \approx r$	**Divide each side by 16.**

▶ So, the radius of the tank is about 21 feet.

EXAMPLE 4 *Finding Segment Lengths*

Using Algebra

Use the figure at the right to find the value of x.

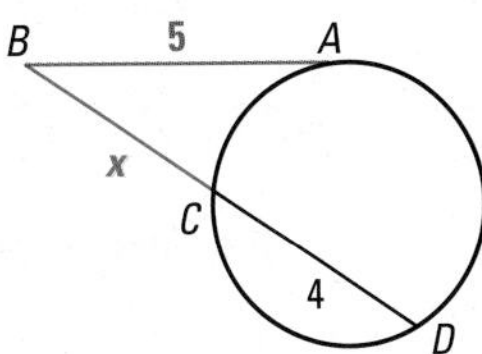

SOLUTION

$(BA)^2 = BC \cdot BD$	**Use Theorem 10.17.**
$5^2 = x \cdot (x + 4)$	**Substitute.**
$25 = x^2 + 4x$	**Simplify.**
$0 = x^2 + 4x - 25$	**Write in standard form.**
$x = \dfrac{-4 \pm \sqrt{4^2 - 4(1)(-25)}}{2}$	**Use Quadratic Formula.**
$x = -2 \pm \sqrt{29}$	**Simplify.**

Use the positive solution, because lengths cannot be negative.

▶ So, $x = -2 + \sqrt{29} \approx 3.39$.

Daily Puzzler *Sample answer:*

No. If $\overline{BC}$ were a diameter, it would be perpendicular to $\overline{BA}$ and the Pythagorean Theorem would apply with $x = \sqrt{495}$. Since $495 + 576 \neq 1089$, $\overline{BC}$ can't be perpendicular. It is therefore not a diameter.

EXTRA EXAMPLE 3

You are standing 18 feet from a circular display case. The distance from you to a point of tangency on the case is about 32 feet. Estimate the radius of the display case. **about 19.4 ft**

EXTRA EXAMPLE 4

Find the value of x. **20.3**

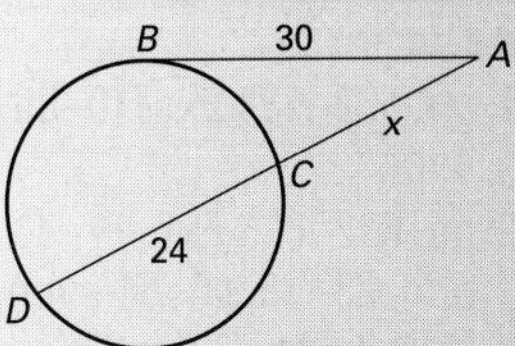

CHECKPOINT EXERCISES

For use after Examples 3 and 4:

1. Find the value of x. **18**

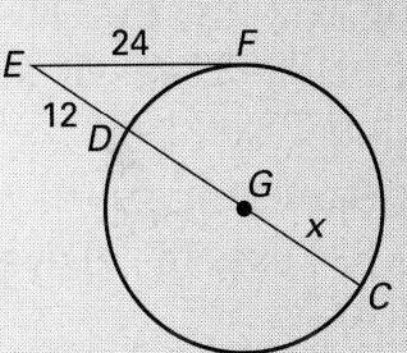

FOCUS ON VOCABULARY

What is a tangent segment? **A segment tangent to a circle at one endpoint of the segment.**

CLOSURE QUESTION

Describe how to find the length of the segments of a circle formed by two secants intersecting at an external point. **The product of one secant segment and its external segment is equal to the product of the other secant segment and its external segment.**

DAILY PUZZLER

Is $\overline{BC}$ a diameter of the circle? Explain.

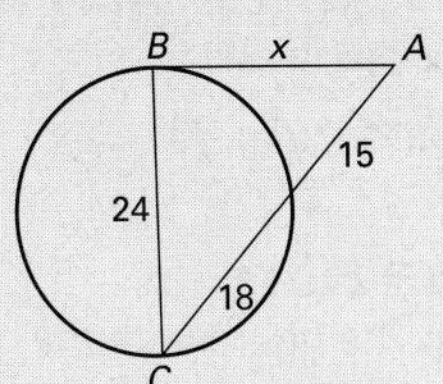

See answer at left.

3 APPLY

ASSIGNMENT GUIDE

BASIC
Day 1: pp. 632–634 Exs. 10–30 even
Day 2: pp. 632–635 Exs. 11–31 odd, 33–35, 40–54 even, Quiz 2 Exs. 1–7

AVERAGE
Day 1: pp. 632–634 Exs. 10–30 even
Day 2: pp. 632–635 Exs. 11–31 odd, 33–35, 40–54 even, Quiz 2 Exs. 1–7

ADVANCED
Day 1: pp. 632–634 Exs. 10–32 even
Day 2: pp. 632–635 Exs. 11–31 odd, 33–39, 40–54 even, Quiz 2 Exs. 1–7

BLOCK SCHEDULE
pp. 632–634 Exs. 10–30 even (with 10.4)
pp. 632–635 Exs. 11–31 odd, 33–35, 40–54 even, Quiz 2 Exs. 1–7 (with 10.6)

EXERCISE LEVELS

Level A: *Easier*
10–12
Level B: *More Difficult*
13–35
Level C: *Most Difficult*
36–39

✔ HOMEWORK CHECK

To quickly check student understanding of key concepts, go over the following exercises: Exs. 10, 14, 16, 18, 22, 26, 30. See also the Daily Homework Quiz:

- Blackline Master (*Chapter 10 Resource Book,* p. 81)
- Transparency (p. 76)

APPLICATION NOTE

EXERCISE 9 The figure with the most area for a given perimeter is a circle. Cylindrical cages provide the most volume (habitat space) for a given height because the base is a circle.

GUIDED PRACTICE

Vocabulary Check ✔

1. Sketch a circle with a secant segment. Label each endpoint and point of intersection. Then name the external segment. **Check students' drawings.**

Concept Check ✔

2. How are the lengths of the segments in the figure at the right related to each other? $GH \cdot HK = FH \cdot HJ$

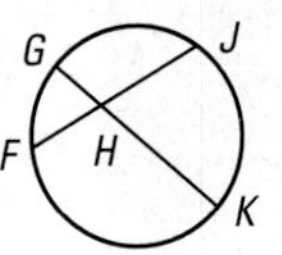

Skill Check ✔

Fill in the blanks. Then find the value of *x*.

3. $x \cdot \underline{?} = 10 \cdot \underline{?}$
15; 18; 12

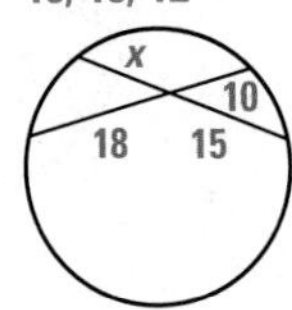

4. $\underline{?} \cdot x = \underline{?} \cdot 40$
12; 15; 50

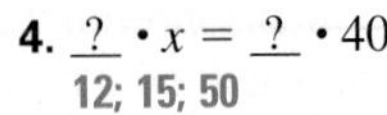

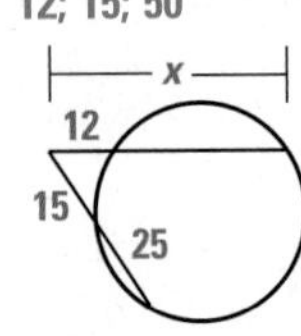

5. $6 \cdot \underline{?} = 8 \cdot \underline{?}$
16; $x + 8$; 4

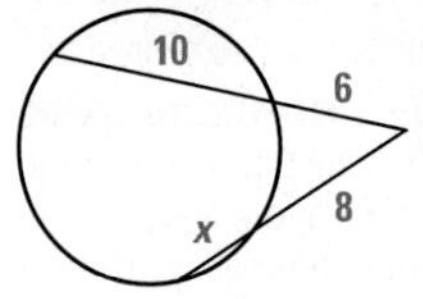

6. $4^2 = 2 \cdot (\underline{?} + x)$
2; 6

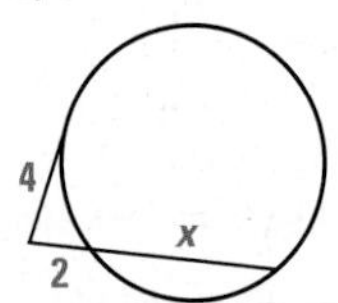

7. $x^2 = 4 \cdot \underline{?}$
9; 6

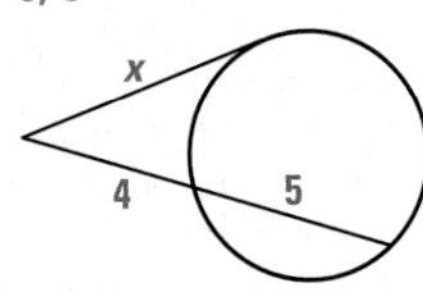

8. $x \cdot \underline{?} = \underline{?}$
$x + 3$; 2^2; 1

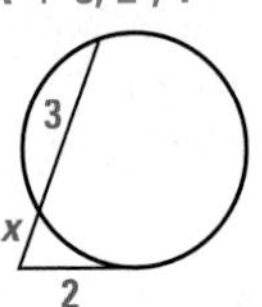

9. **ZOO HABITAT** A zoo has a large circular aviary, a habitat for birds. You are standing about 40 feet from the aviary. The distance from you to a point of tangency on the aviary is about 60 feet. Describe how to estimate the radius of the aviary. **The segment from you to the center of the aviary is a secant segment that shares an endpoint with the segment that is tangent to the aviary. Let *x* be the length of the internal secant segment (twice the radius of the aviary) and use Thm. 10.17. Since $40(40 + x) \approx 60^2$, the radius is about $\frac{50}{2} = 25$ ft.**

PRACTICE AND APPLICATIONS

STUDENT HELP
Extra Practice to help you master skills is on p. 822.

FINDING SEGMENT LENGTHS **Fill in the blanks. Then find the value of *x*.**

10. $x \cdot \underline{?} = 12 \cdot \underline{?}$
9; 15; 20

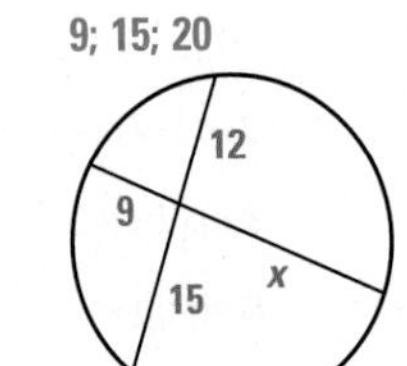

11. $x \cdot \underline{?} = \underline{?} \cdot 50$
45; 27; 30

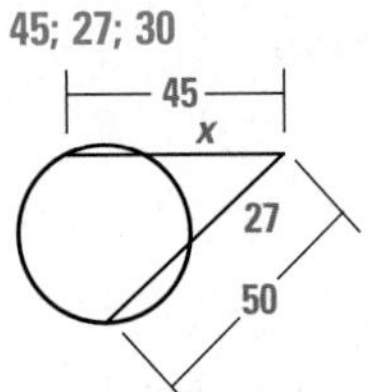

12. $x^2 = 9 \cdot \underline{?}$
16; 12

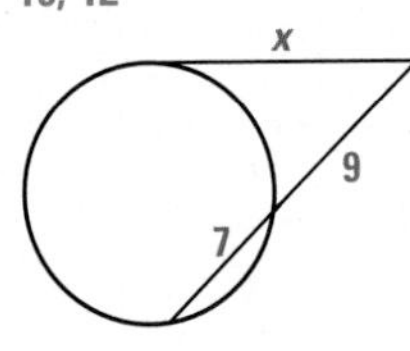

STUDENT HELP
HOMEWORK HELP
Example 1: Exs. 10, 14–17, 26–29
Example 2: Exs. 11, 13, 18, 19, 24, 25

FINDING SEGMENT LENGTHS **Find the value of *x*.**

13. 13

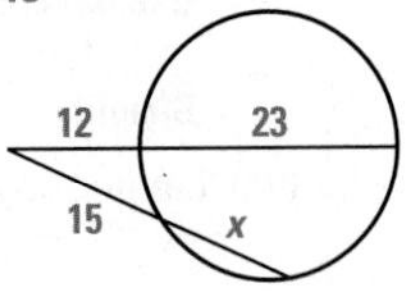

14. 28

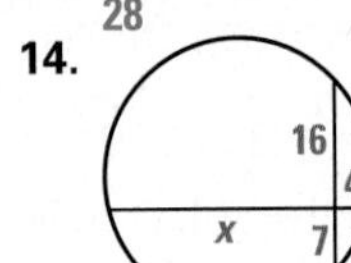

15. 8.5

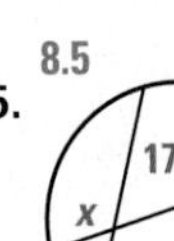

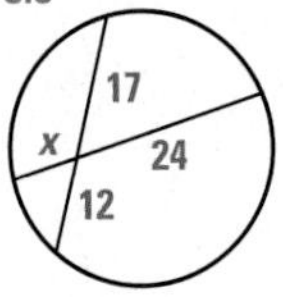

STUDENT HELP

HOMEWORK HELP
Example 3: Exs. 12, 20–23, 25–27
Example 4: Exs. 12, 20–23, 25–27

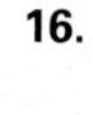

FINDING SEGMENT LENGTHS Find the value of *x*.

16.

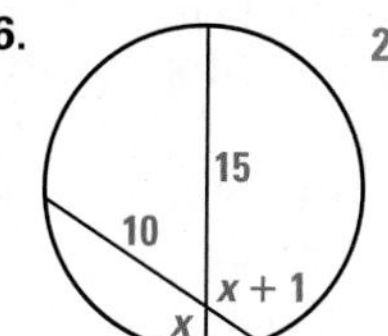

17.

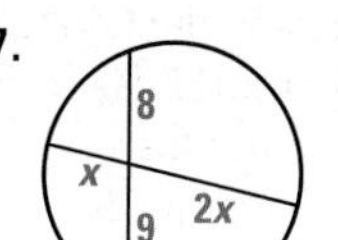

18.

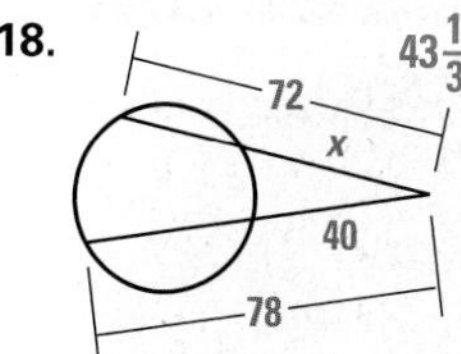

19.

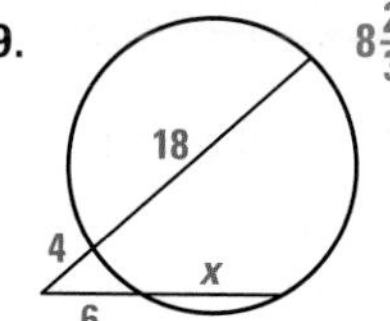

20. 24

21. 4

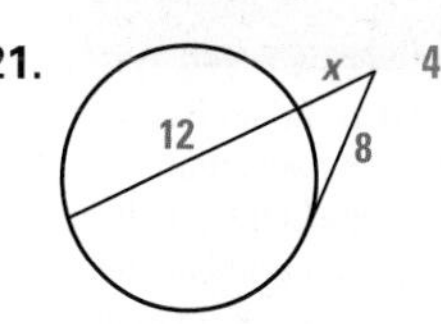

STUDENT HELP

HOMEWORK HELP
Visit our Web site www.mcdougallittell.com for help with using the Quadratic Formula in Exs. 21–27.

22. 8

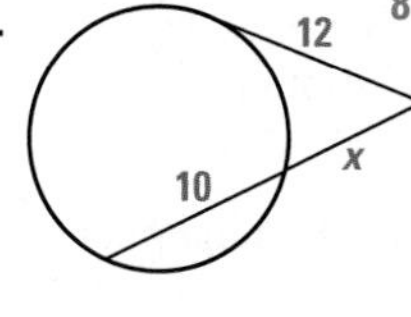

23.

$\frac{-9 + \sqrt{565}}{2} \approx 7.38$

24.

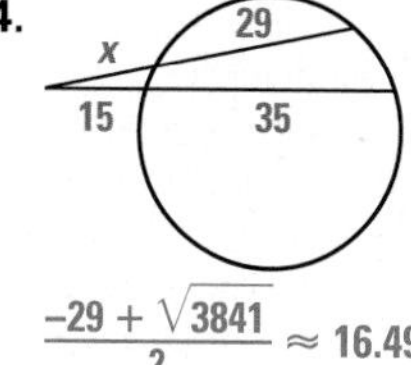

$\frac{-29 + \sqrt{3841}}{2} \approx 16.49$

USING ALGEBRA Find the values of *x* and *y*.

25.

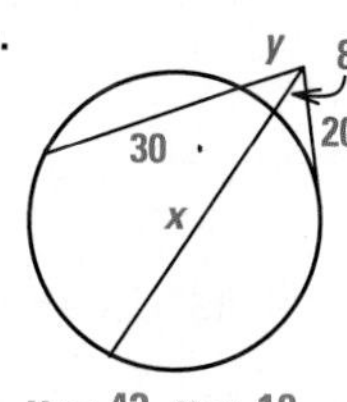

$x = 42,\ y = 10$

26.

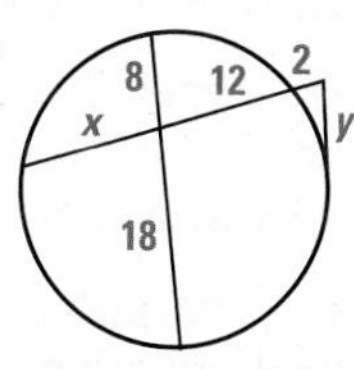

$x = 12,\ y = 2\sqrt{13} \approx 7.21$

27.

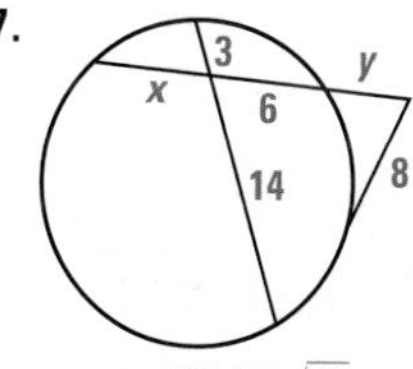

$x = 7,\ y = \frac{-13 + 5\sqrt{17}}{2} \approx 3.81$

28. **DESIGNING A LOGO** Suppose you are designing an animated logo for a television commercial. You want sparkles to leave point C and move to the circle along the segments shown. You want each of the sparkles to reach the circle at the same time. To calculate the speed for each sparkle, you need to know the distance from point C to the circle along each segment. What is the distance from C to N? 18

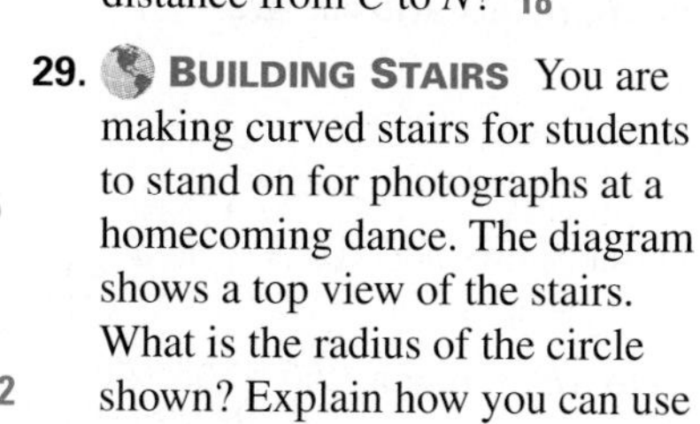

29. 4.875 ft; the diameter through *A* bisects the chord into two 4.5 ft segments. Use Thm. 10.15 to find the length of the part of the diameter containing *A*. Add this length to 3 and divide by 2 to get the radius.

29. **BUILDING STAIRS** You are making curved stairs for students to stand on for photographs at a homecoming dance. The diagram shows a top view of the stairs. What is the radius of the circle shown? Explain how you can use Theorem 10.15 to find the answer.

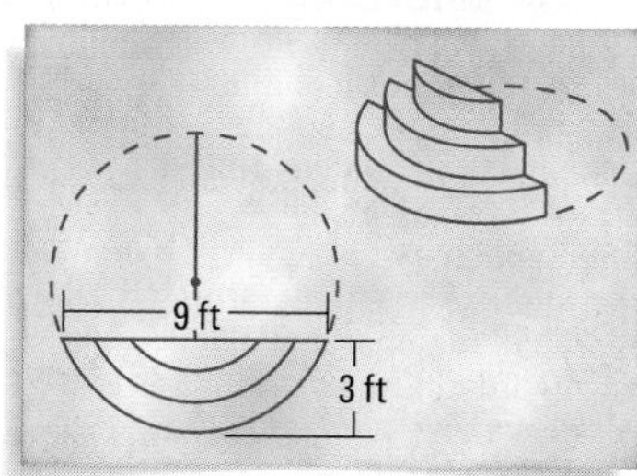

! COMMON ERROR

EXERCISE 19 Watch for students who find $x = 12$ because they calculate using the equation $4 \times 18 = 6 \times x$ instead of the equation $4(18 + 4) = 6(6 + x)$.

STUDENT HELP NOTES

Homework Help Students can find help for Exs. 21–27 at **www.mcdougallittell.com.** The information can be printed out for students who don't have access to the Internet.

TEACHING TIPS

EXERCISE 29 Remind students that a diameter that is perpendicular to a chord bisects the chord. Since the stairs are built symmetrically, the diameter is perpendicular to the chord.

APPLICATION NOTE

EXERCISE 30 The GPS provides signals that can be used to compute velocity and time as well as position. Additional information about the Global Positioning System is available at **www.mcdougallittell.com.**

32. Draw $\overline{AD}$ and $\overline{AC}$. $\angle ADE$ is an inscribed $\angle$, so $m\angle ADE = \frac{1}{2}m\widehat{AC}$. $\angle CAE$ is formed by a tangent and a chord, so $m\angle CAE = \frac{1}{2}m\widehat{AC}$. Then $\angle ADE \cong \angle CAE$. Since $\angle E \cong \angle E$ by the Reflexive Prop. of Cong., $\triangle ACE \sim \triangle DAE$ by the AA Similarity Post. Then since lengths of corresp. sides of ~ ⚠s are proportional, $\frac{EA}{EC} = \frac{ED}{EA}$. By the Cross Product Prop., $(EA)^2 = EC \cdot ED$.

ADDITIONAL PRACTICE AND RETEACHING

For Lesson 10.5:

- Practice Levels A, B, and C (*Chapter 10 Resource Book*, p. 70)
- Reteaching with Practice (*Chapter 10 Resource Book*, p. 73)
- See Lesson 10.5 of the *Personal Student Tutor*

For more Mixed Review:

- Search the *Test and Practice Generator* for key words or specific lessons.

FOCUS ON APPLICATIONS

GPS Some cars have navigation systems that use GPS to tell you where you are and how to get where you want to go.

APPLICATION LINK www.mcdougallittell.com

31. Draw $\overline{AD}$ and $\overline{BC}$. Then inscribed angles $\angle EBC$ and $\angle EDA$ intercept the same arc, so $\angle EBC \cong \angle EDA$. $\angle E \cong \angle E$ by the Reflexive Prop. of Cong., so $\triangle BCE \sim \triangle DAE$ by the AA Similarity Post. Then since lengths of corresp. sides of ~⚠ are proportional, $\frac{EA}{EC} = \frac{ED}{EB}$. By Cross Product Prop., $EA \cdot EB = EC \cdot ED$.

Test Preparation

35. The distances over which most inhabitants of Earth are able to see are relatively short and the curvature of Earth over such distances is so small as to be unnoticeable.

39. *Sample answer:* If tangent segments to 2 intersecting ⊙s share a common endpoint outside the 2 ⊙s, the tangent segments are ≅. The conjecture is not true in general. Let *A* be the common endpoint and *C* and *D* the points of intersection as shown in the figure. The conjecture is true if and only if *A*, *C*, and *D* are collinear.

★ Challenge

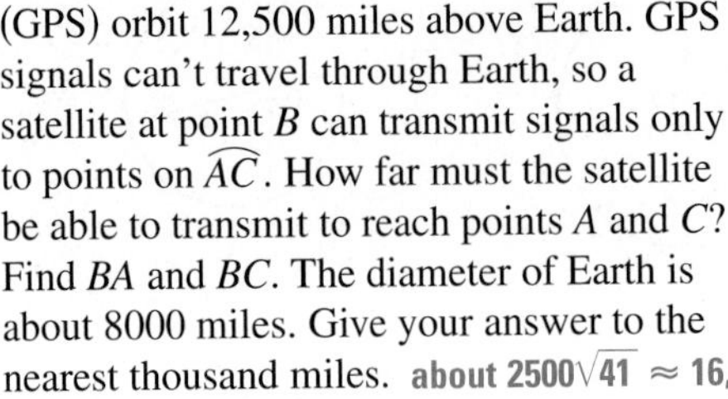

EXTRA CHALLENGE

www.mcdougallittell.com

30. **GLOBAL POSITIONING SYSTEM** Satellites in the Global Positioning System (GPS) orbit 12,500 miles above Earth. GPS signals can't travel through Earth, so a satellite at point *B* can transmit signals only to points on $\widehat{AC}$. How far must the satellite be able to transmit to reach points *A* and *C*? Find *BA* and *BC*. The diameter of Earth is about 8000 miles. Give your answer to the nearest thousand miles. about $2500\sqrt{41} \approx 16{,}008$ mi

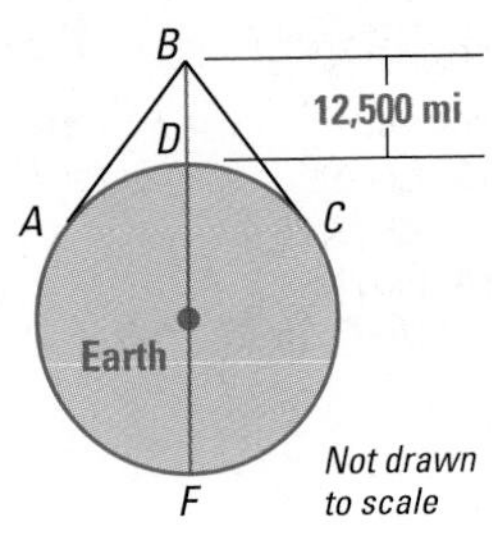

31. **PROVING THEOREM 10.16** Use the plan to write a paragraph proof. See margin.

GIVEN ▶ $\overline{EB}$ and $\overline{ED}$ are secant segments.

PROVE ▶ $EA \cdot EB = EC \cdot ED$

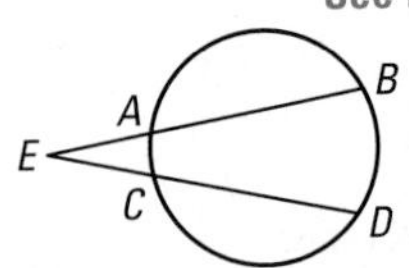

Plan for Proof Draw $\overline{AD}$ and $\overline{BC}$, and show that $\triangle BCE$ and $\triangle DAE$ are similar. Use the fact that corresponding sides of similar triangles are proportional.

32. **PROVING THEOREM 10.17** Use the plan to write a paragraph proof. See margin.

GIVEN ▶ $\overline{EA}$ is a tangent segment and $\overline{ED}$ is a secant segment.

PROVE ▶ $(EA)^2 = EC \cdot ED$

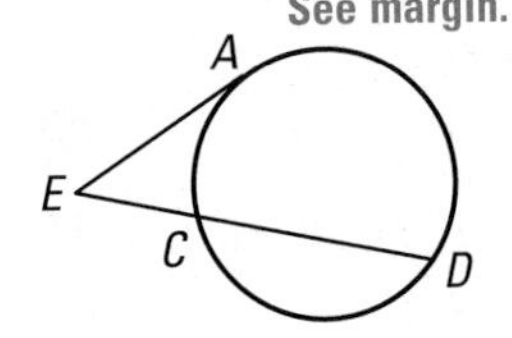

Plan for Proof Draw $\overline{AD}$ and $\overline{AC}$. Use the fact that corresponding sides of similar triangles are proportional.

MULTI-STEP PROBLEM In Exercises 33–35, use the following information.

A person is standing at point *A* on a beach and looking 2 miles down the beach to point *B*, as shown at the right. The beach is very flat but, because of Earth's curvature, the ground between *A* and *B* is *x* mi higher than $\overline{AB}$.

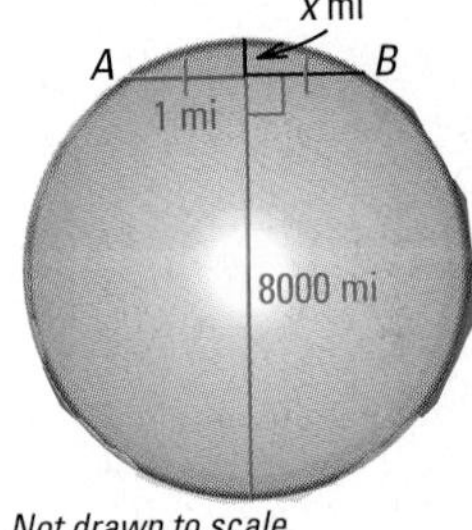

33. Find the value of *x*. about 0.000125 mi

34. Convert your answer to inches. Round to the nearest inch. 8 in.

35. *Writing* Why do you think people historically thought that Earth was flat? See margin.

In the diagram at the right, $\overrightarrow{AB}$ and $\overrightarrow{AE}$ are tangents.

36. Write an equation that shows how *AB* is related to *AC* and *AD*. $(AB)^2 = AC \cdot AD$

37. Write an equation that shows how *AE* is related to *AC* and *AD*. $(AE)^2 = AC \cdot AD$

38. How is *AB* related to *AE*? Explain. $AB = AE$; $(AB)^2 = (AE)^2$ and AB and AE are both positive.

39. Make a conjecture about tangents to intersecting circles. Then test your conjecture by looking for a counterexample. See margin.

MIXED REVIEW

FINDING DISTANCE AND MIDPOINT **Find *AB* to the nearest hundredth. Then find the coordinates of the midpoint of $\overline{AB}$.** (Review 1.3, 1.5 for 10.6)

40. $A(2, 5), B(-3, 3)$ 5.39; $\left(-\frac{1}{2}, 4\right)$

41. $A(6, -4), B(0, 4)$ 10; (3, 0)

42. $A(-8, -6), B(1, 9)$ 17.49, $\left(-\frac{7}{2}, \frac{3}{2}\right)$

43. $A(-1, -5), B(-10, 7)$ 15; $\left(-\frac{11}{2}, 1\right)$

44. $A(0, -11), B(8, 2)$ 15.26, $\left(4, -\frac{9}{2}\right)$

45. $A(5, -2), B(-9, -2)$ 14, (−2, −2)

WRITING EQUATIONS **Write an equation of a line perpendicular to the given line at the given point.** (Review 3.7 for 10.6)

46. $y = -2x - 5, (-2, -1)$ $y = \frac{1}{2}x$

47. $y = \frac{2}{3}x + 4, (6, 8)$ $y = -\frac{3}{2}x + 17$

48. $y = -x + 9, (0, 9)$ $y = x + 9$

49. $y = 3x - 10, (2, -4)$ $y = -\frac{1}{3}x - \frac{10}{3}$

50. $y = \frac{1}{5}x + 1, (-10, -1)$ $y = -5x - 51$

51. $y = -\frac{7}{3}x - 5, (-6, 9)$ $y = \frac{3}{7}x + \frac{81}{7}$

DRAWING TRANSLATIONS **Quadrilateral *ABCD* has vertices *A*(−6, 8), *B*(−1, 4), *C*(−2, 2), and *D*(−7, 3). Draw its image after the translation.** (Review 7.4 for 10.6) 52–54. See margin.

52. $(x, y) \rightarrow (x + 7, y)$

53. $(x, y) \rightarrow (x - 2, y + 3)$

54. $(x, y) \rightarrow \left(x, y - \frac{11}{2}\right)$

QUIZ 2

Self-Test for Lessons 10.4 and 10.5

Find the value of *x*. (Lesson 10.4)

1. 202

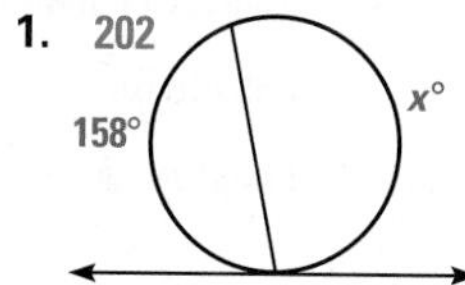

2. 139

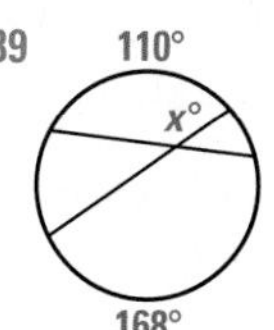

3. 26

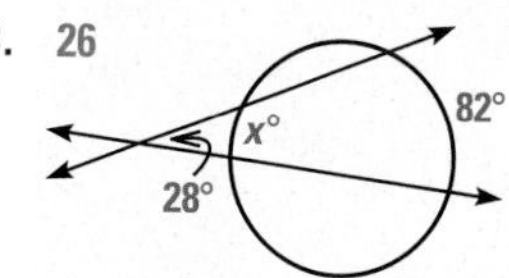

Find the value of *x*. (Lesson 10.5)

4. $6\frac{1}{4}$

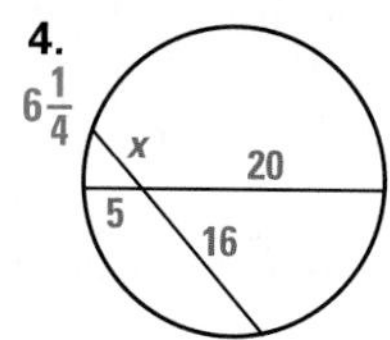

5. 6

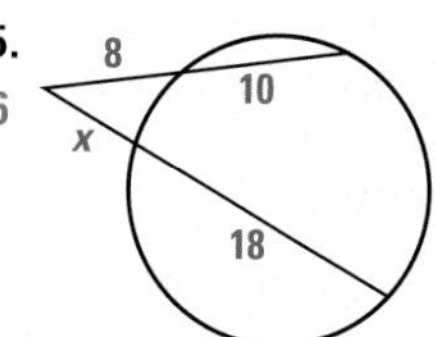

6. 5

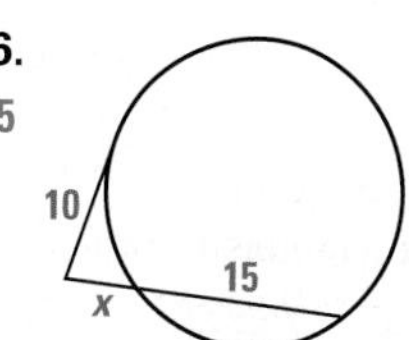

7. **SWIMMING POOL** You are standing 20 feet from the circular wall of an above ground swimming pool and 49 feet from a point of tangency. Describe two different methods you could use to find the radius of the pool. What is the radius? (Lesson 10.5)

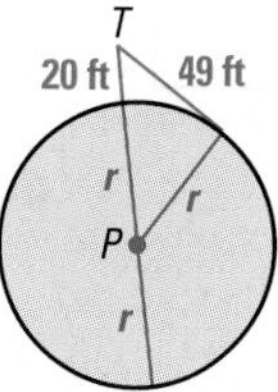

7. Solve $20(2r + 20) = 49^2$ (Thm. 10.17) or solve $(r + 20)^2 = r^2 + 49^2$ (the Pythagorean Theorem); 50.025 ft.

4 ASSESS

DAILY HOMEWORK QUIZ

Transparency Available

Find the values of *x* and *y*.

1. 6

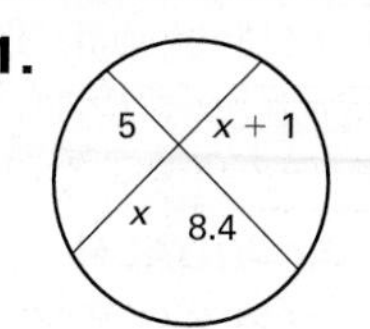

2. 8

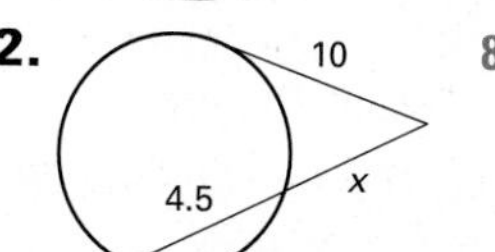

EXTRA CHALLENGE NOTE

Challenge problems for Lesson 10.5 are available in **blackline** format in the *Chapter 10 Resource Book,* p. 77 and at **www.mcdougallittell.com.**

ADDITIONAL TEST PREPARATION

1. WRITING Describe how to find the length of the tangent segment in the figure below. Solve $(AB)^2 = BC \cdot BD$ to find *AB*.

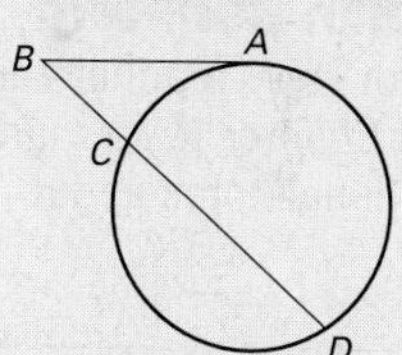

ADDITIONAL RESOURCES

An alternative Quiz for Lessons 10.4–10.5 is available in the *Chapter 10 Resource Book,* p. 78.

52–54. See Additional Answers beginning on page AA1.

1 PLAN

PACING
Basic: 1 day
Average: 1 day
Advanced: 1 day
Block Schedule: 0.5 block with 10.5

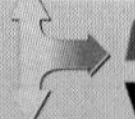

LESSON OPENER
VISUAL APPROACH
An alternative way to approach Lesson 10.6 is to use the Visual Approach Lesson Opener:

- Blackline Master (*Chapter 10 Resource Book*, p. 82)
- Transparency (p. 66)

MEETING INDIVIDUAL NEEDS

- ***Chapter 10 Resource Book***
  Prerequisite Skills Review (p. 5)
  Practice Level A (p. 86)
  Practice Level B (p. 87)
  Practice Level C (p. 88)
  Reteaching with Practice (p. 89)
  Absent Student Catch-Up (p. 91)
  Challenge (p. 94)
- ***Resources in Spanish***
- ***Personal Student Tutor***

NEW-TEACHER SUPPORT
See the Tips for New Teachers on pp. 1–2 of the *Chapter 10 Resource Book* for additional notes about Lesson 10.6.

WARM-UP EXERCISES

Transparency Available

Find the distance between each pair of points. Leave answers in simplest radical form.

1. (0, 4), (0, −8) 12
2. (1, 5), (4, 1) 5
3. (−1, 2), (4, 1) $\sqrt{26}$
4. (0, 0), (4, 4) $4\sqrt{2}$
5. (−3, −2), (2, 0) $\sqrt{29}$

10.6 Equations of Circles

What you should learn

GOAL 1 Write the equation of a circle.

GOAL 2 Use the equation of a circle and its graph to solve problems.

Why you should learn it

▼ To solve **real-life** problems, such as determining cellular phone coverage, as in **Exs. 41 and 42.**

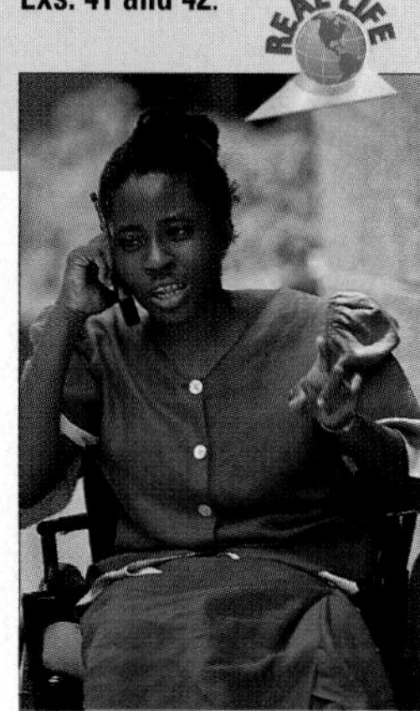

CALIFORNIA STANDARDS AND ASSESSMENT

CA Standards: 17
SAT9 Task 1: Obj. 1
SAT9 Task 2: Obj. 1

GOAL 1 FINDING EQUATIONS OF CIRCLES

You can write an equation of a circle in a coordinate plane if you know its radius and the coordinates of its center. Suppose the radius of a circle is r and the center is (h, k). Let (x, y) be any point on the circle. The distance between (x, y) and (h, k) is r, so you can use the Distance Formula.

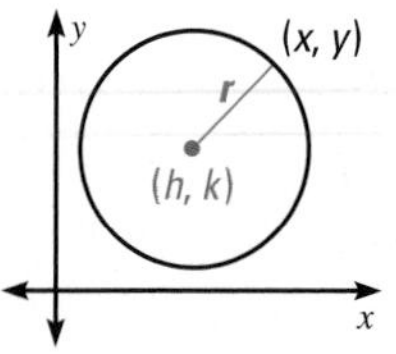

$$\sqrt{(x-h)^2 + (y-k)^2} = r$$

Square both sides to find the **standard equation of a circle** with radius r and center (h, k).

Standard equation of a circle: $(x-h)^2 + (y-k)^2 = r^2$

If the center is the origin, then the standard equation is $x^2 + y^2 = r^2$.

EXAMPLE 1 *Writing a Standard Equation of a Circle*

Write the standard equation of the circle with center $(-4, 0)$ and radius 7.1.

SOLUTION

$(x-h)^2 + (y-k)^2 = r^2$ **Standard equation of a circle**

$[x-(-4)]^2 + (y-0)^2 = 7.1^2$ **Substitute.**

$(x+4)^2 + y^2 = 50.41$ **Simplify.**

EXAMPLE 2 *Writing a Standard Equation of a Circle*

The point (1, 2) is on a circle whose center is (5, −1). Write the standard equation of the circle.

SOLUTION

Find the radius. The radius is the distance from the point (1, 2) to the center (5, −1).

$r = \sqrt{(5-1)^2 + (-1-2)^2}$ **Use the Distance Formula.**

$r = \sqrt{4^2 + (-3)^2}$ **Simplify.**

$r = 5$ **Simplify.**

Substitute $(h, k) = (5, -1)$ and $r = 5$ into the standard equation of a circle.

$(x-5)^2 + (y-(-1))^2 = 5^2$ **Standard equation of a circle**

$(x-5)^2 + (y+1)^2 = 25$ **Simplify.**

GOAL 2 GRAPHING CIRCLES

If you know the equation of a circle, you can graph the circle by identifying its center and radius.

STUDENT HELP

Study Tip
You can sketch the graph of the circle in Example 3 without a compass by first plotting the four points shown in red. Then sketch a circle through the points.

EXAMPLE 3 *Graphing a Circle*

The equation of a circle is $(x+2)^2+(y-3)^2=9$. Graph the circle.

Rewrite the equation to find the center and radius:

$$(x+2)^2+(y-3)^2=9$$

$$[x-(-2)]^2+(y-3)^2=3^2$$

The center is $(-2, 3)$ and the radius is 3. To graph the circle, place the point of a compass at $(-2, 3)$, set the radius at 3 units, and swing the compass to draw a full circle.

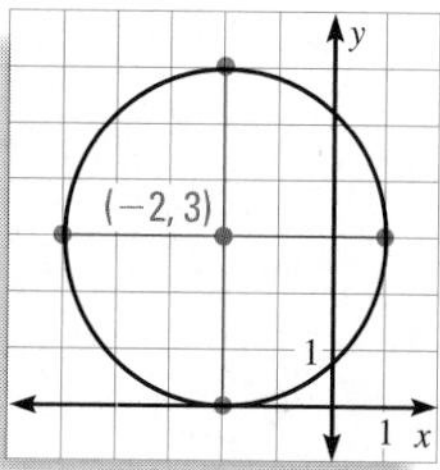

EXAMPLE 4 *Applying Graphs of Circles*

REAL LIFE **THEATER LIGHTING** A bank of lights is arranged over a stage. Each light illuminates a circular area on the stage. A coordinate plane is used to arrange the lights, using the corner of the stage as the origin. The equation $(x-13)^2+(y-4)^2=16$ represents one of the disks of light.

a. Graph the disk of light.

b. Three actors are located as follows: Henry is at (11, 4), Jolene is at (8, 5), and Martin is at (15, 5). Which actors are in the disk of light?

SOLUTION

a. Rewrite the equation to find the center and radius:

$$(x-13)^2+(y-4)^2=16$$

$$(x-13)^2+(y-4)^2=4^2$$

The center is (13, 4) and the radius is 4. The circle is shown below.

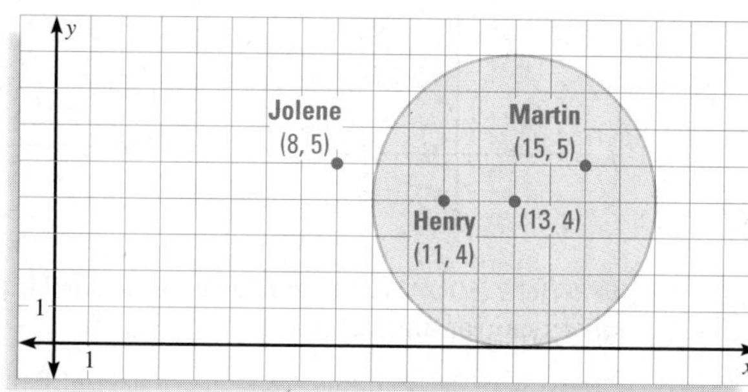

b. The graph shows that Henry and Martin are both in the disk of light.

2 TEACH

EXTRA EXAMPLE 1
Write the standard equation of a circle with center (−5, 0) and radius 4.8. $(x+5)^2+y^2=23.04$

EXTRA EXAMPLE 2
The point (2, 1) is on a circle whose center is (4, −3). Write the standard equation of the circle. $(x-4)^2+(y+3)^2=20$

EXTRA EXAMPLE 3
Graph $(x-3)^2+(y+1)^2=4$.

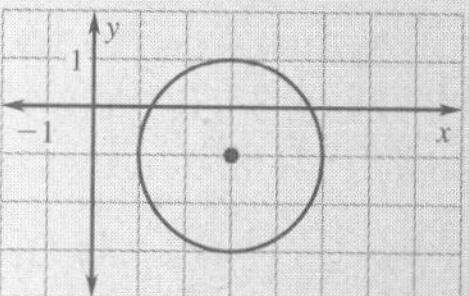

EXTRA EXAMPLE 4
The equation of a circle is $(x-13)^2+(y-6)^2=9$. Three points are located as follows: *A*(5, 6), *B*(14, 8), and *C*(20, 9). Which point is in the circle? *B*

CHECKPOINT EXERCISES

For use after Examples 1–4:

1. Write the standard equation of a circle with center (−2, 1) and radius 3.7. $(x+2)^2+(y-1)^2=13.69$

2. The point (3, 3) is on a circle whose center is (3, −1). Write the standard equation of the circle. $(x-3)^2+(y+1)^2=16$

CLOSURE QUESTION
The point (0, −1) is on a circle whose center is (−4, 1). Write the standard equation of the circle. $(x+4)^2+(y-1)^2=20$

3 APPLY

ASSIGNMENT GUIDE

BASIC

Day 1: pp. 638–640 Exs. 8–40 even, 47, 49, 50, 54–62 even

AVERAGE

Day 1: pp. 638–640 Exs. 8–40 even, 41, 42, 47–49, 50, 54–62 even

ADVANCED

Day 1: pp. 638–640 Exs. 8–40 even, 41–49, 50–53, 54–62 even

BLOCK SCHEDULE WITH 10.5

pp. 638–640 Exs. 8–40 even, 41, 42, 47–49, 50, 54–62 even

EXERCISE LEVELS

Level A: *Easier*
7–12

Level B: *More Difficult*
13–42, 47, 49, 50

Level C: *Most Difficult*
43–46, 48, 51–53

✓ HOMEWORK CHECK

To quickly check student understanding of key concepts, go over the following exercises: Exs. 10, 16, 22, 24, 32, 36, 47. See also the Daily Homework Quiz:

- Blackline Master (*Chapter 10 Resource Book*, p. 97)
- Transparency (p. 77)

GUIDED PRACTICE

Vocabulary Check ✓

1. The standard form of an equation of a circle is ___?___.
$(x - h)^2 + (y - k)^2 = r^2$, where (h, k) is the center of the ⊙ and r is the radius.

Concept Check ✓

2. Describe how to graph the circle $(x - 3)^2 + (y - 4)^2 = 9$.
Open a compass to a radius of 3, put the point of the compass at (3, 4), and draw the circle.

Skill Check ✓

Give the coordinates of the center and the radius. Write an equation of the circle in standard form.

3.

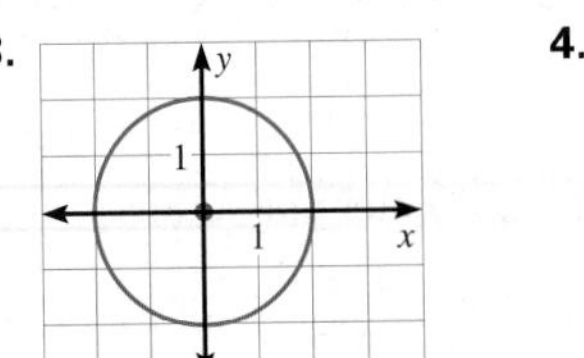

(0, 0), 2; $x^2 + y^2 = 4$

4.

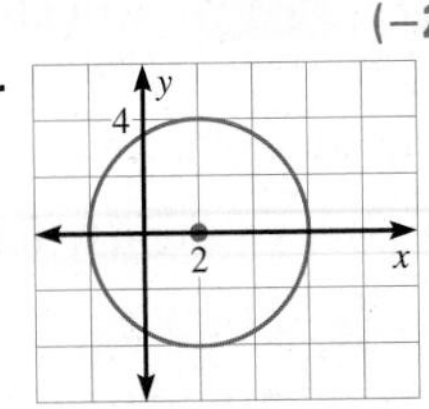

(2, 0), 4; $(x - 2)^2 + y^2 = 16$

5.

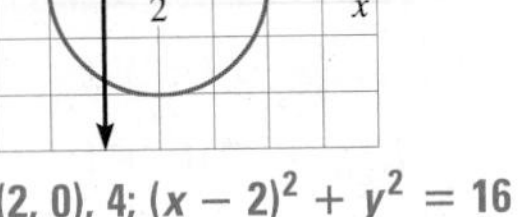

(−2, 2), 2; $(x + 2)^2 + (y - 2)^2 = 4$

6. $P(-1, 3)$ is on a circle whose center is $C(0, 0)$. Write an equation of $\odot C$.
$x^2 + y^2 = 10$

PRACTICE AND APPLICATIONS

STUDENT HELP

Extra Practice to help you master skills is on p. 822.

USING STANDARD EQUATIONS **Give the center and radius of the circle.**

7. $(x - 4)^2 + (y - 3)^2 = 16$ (4, 3), 4

8. $(x - 5)^2 + (y - 1)^2 = 25$ (5, 1), 5

9. $x^2 + y^2 = 4$ (0, 0), 2

10. $(x + 2)^2 + (y - 3)^2 = 36$ (−2, 3), 6

11. $(x + 5)^2 + (y + 3)^2 = 1$ (−5, −3), 1

12. $\left(x - \frac{1}{2}\right)^2 + \left(y + \frac{3}{4}\right)^2 = \frac{1}{4}$ $\left(\frac{1}{2}, -\frac{3}{4}\right), \frac{1}{2}$

USING GRAPHS **Give the coordinates of the center, the radius, and the equation of the circle.**

13.

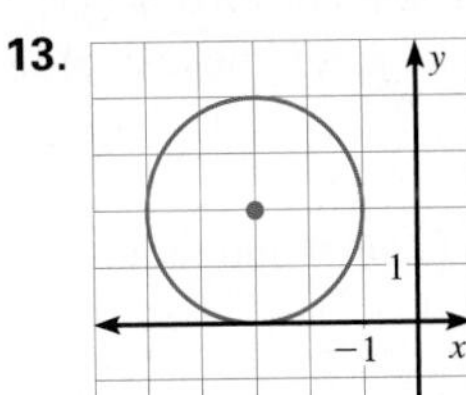

(−3, 2), 2, $(x + 3)^2 + (y - 2)^2 = 4$

14.

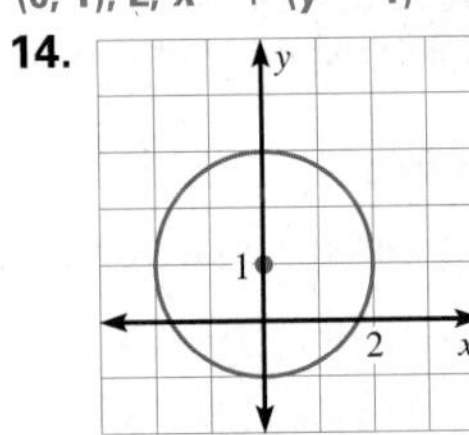

(0, 1), 2, $x^2 + (y - 1)^2 = 4$

15.

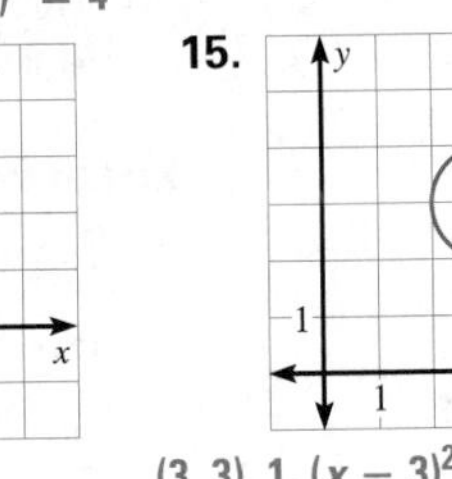

(3, 3), 1, $(x - 3)^2 + (y - 3)^2 = 1$

16.

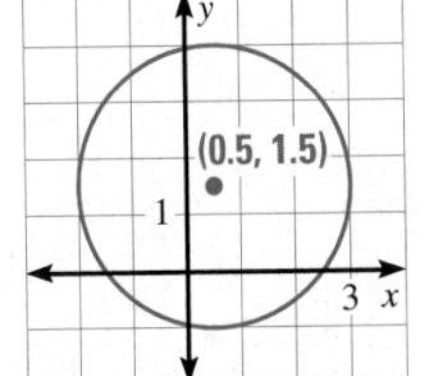

16. (0.5, 1.5), 2.5, $(x - 0.5)^2 + (y - 1.5)^2 = 6.25$

17.

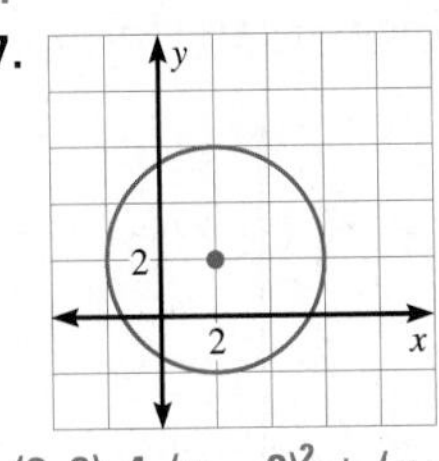

(2, 2), 4, $(x - 2)^2 + (y - 2)^2 = 16$

18.

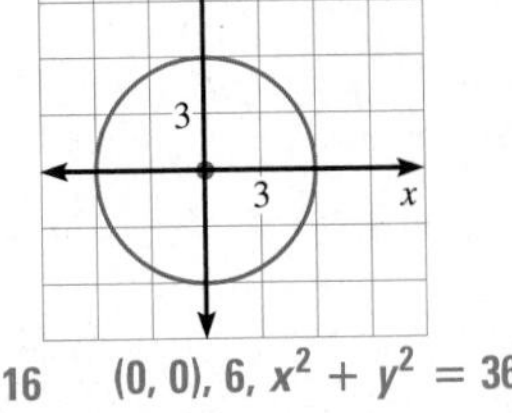

(0, 0), 6, $x^2 + y^2 = 36$

STUDENT HELP

HOMEWORK HELP
Example 1: Exs. 13–22
Example 2: Exs. 23–26
Example 3: Exs. 27–40
Example 4: Exs. 33–42

WRITING EQUATIONS **Write the standard equation of the circle with the given center and radius.**

19. center (0, 0), radius 1 $x^2 + y^2 = 1$

20. center (4, 0), radius 4 $(x - 4)^2 + y^2 = 16$

21. center (3, −2), radius 2
$(x - 3)^2 + (y + 2)^2 = 4$

22. center (−1, −3), radius 6
$(x + 1)^2 + (y + 3)^2 = 36$

WRITING EQUATIONS Use the given information to write the standard equation of the circle.

23. The center is (0, 0), a point on the circle is (0, 3). $x^2 + y^2 = 9$

24. The center is (1, 2), a point on the circle is (4, 6). $(x - 1)^2 + (y - 2)^2 = 25$

25. The center is (3, 2), a point on the circle is (5, 2). $(x - 3)^2 + (y - 2)^2 = 4$

26. The center is (−5, 3) and the diameter is 8. $(x + 5)^2 + (y - 3)^2 = 16$

GRAPHING CIRCLES Graph the equation. 27–32. See margin.

27. $x^2 + y^2 = 25$

28. $x^2 + (y - 4)^2 = 1$

29. $(x + 3)^2 + y^2 = 9$

30. $(x - 3)^2 + (y - 4)^2 = 16$

31. $(x + 5)^2 + (y - 1)^2 = 49$

32. $\left(x - \frac{1}{2}\right)^2 + \left(y + \frac{1}{2}\right)^2 = \frac{1}{4}$

USING GRAPHS The equation of a circle is $(x - 2)^2 + (y + 3)^2 = 4$. Tell whether each point is *on* the circle, in the *interior* of the circle, or in the *exterior* of the circle.

33. (0, 0) exterior
34. (2, −4) interior
35. (0, −3) on
36. (3, −1) exterior
37. (1, −4) interior
38. (2, −5) on
39. (2, 0) exterior
40. (2.5, −3) interior

CELL PHONES In Exercises 41 and 42, use the following information.
A cellular phone network uses towers to transmit calls. Each tower transmits to a circular area. On a grid of a city, the coordinates of the location and the radius each tower covers are as follows (integers represent miles): Tower A is at (0, 0) and covers a 3 mile radius, Tower B is at (5, 3) and covers a 2.5 mile radius, and Tower C is at (2, 5) and covers a 2 mile radius.

41. Write the equations that represent the transmission boundaries of the towers. Graph each equation. See margin.

42. Tell which towers, if any, transmit to a phone located at $J(1, 1)$, $K(4, 2)$, $L(3.5, 4.5)$, $M(2, 2.8)$, or $N(1, 6)$. J: A; K: B; L: B and C; M: none; N: C

REULEAUX POLYGONS The figure at the right is called a *Reuleaux polygon*. It is not a true polygon because its sides are not straight. $\triangle ABC$ is equilateral.

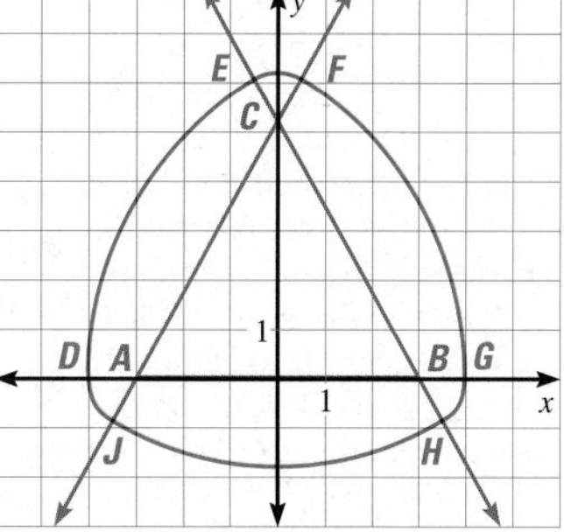

43. $\widehat{JD}$ lies on a circle with center A and radius AD. Write an equation of this circle. $(x + 3)^2 + y^2 = 1$

44. $\widehat{DE}$ lies on a circle with center B and radius BD. Write an equation of this circle. $(x - 3)^2 + y^2 = 49$

45. CONSTRUCTION The remaining arcs of the polygon are constructed in the same way as $\widehat{JD}$ and $\widehat{DE}$ in Exercises 43 and 44. Construct a Reauleaux polygon on a piece of cardboard. Check results.

46. Cut out the Reauleaux polygon from Exercise 45. Roll it on its edge like a wheel and measure its height when it is in different orientations. Explain why a Reuleaux polygon is said to have constant width. See margin.

46. The height is always the same, no matter what the orientation. The width (or height) is always the same.

FOCUS ON APPLICATIONS

Exhaust out — Fuel/air in — Burning gas expands — Reuleaux triangle

REAL LIFE The Wankel engine is an engine with a triangular rotor that is based on a Reuleaux triangle. It has been used in sports cars, snowmobiles, and hybrid electric vehicles.

INTERNET APPLICATION LINK www.mcdougallittell.com

! COMMON ERROR
EXERCISES 7–12, 19–32 Students may forget that the standard equation of a circle involves subtraction signs and consequently may use a point as the center whose coordinates are the opposites of the current center. Refer these students back to Examples 1–3 on pages 636 and 637.

APPLICATION NOTE
EXERCISE 46 The Wankel engine does not need a crankshaft to convert vertical forces to a rotating force because of the shape of the rotor. This gives it much power without a mechanical energy loss. Additional information about the Wankel Engine is available at **www.mcdougallittell.com.**

27–32, 41. See Additional Answers beginning on page AA1.

ADDITIONAL PRACTICE AND RETEACHING

For Lesson 10.6:
- Practice Levels A, B, and C (*Chapter 10 Resource Book,* p. 86)
- Reteaching with Practice (*Chapter 10 Resource Book,* p. 89)
- See Lesson 10.6 of the *Personal Student Tutor*

For more Mixed Review:
- Search the *Test and Practice Generator* for key words or specific lessons.

4 ASSESS

DAILY HOMEWORK QUIZ

Transparency Available

Give the center and radius of the circle.

1. $(x+3)^2+(y-5)^2=36$
   $(-3, 5), 6$
2. $(x-4)^2+(y+1)^2=49$
   $(4, -1), 7$

Write the standard equation of the circle with the given information.

3. center (1, 0), radius 2
   $(x-1)^2+y^2=4$
4. center (3, –2); a point on the circle is (3, 4)
   $(x-3)^2+(y+2)^2=36$

EXTRA CHALLENGE NOTE

Challenge problems for Lesson 10.6 are available in **blackline** format in the *Chapter 10 Resource Book,* p. 94 and at **www.mcdougallittell.com.**

ADDITIONAL TEST PREPARATION

1. **OPEN ENDED** Write an equation in standard form of a circle with radius 5 that is not centered at the origin. Name its center.
   Sample answer:
   $(x-3)^2+(y+2)^2=25$; $(3, -2)$

47. See Additional Answers beginning on page AA1.

47. **TRANSLATIONS** Sketch the circle whose equation is $x^2 + y^2 = 16$. Then sketch the image of the circle after the translation $(x, y) \rightarrow (x - 2, y - 4)$. What is the equation of the image? See margin for graph. $(x + 2)^2 + (y + 4)^2 = 16$

48. **WRITING AN EQUATION** A circle has a center (p, q) and is tangent to the x-axis. Write the standard equation of the circle. $(x - p)^2 + (y - q)^2 = q^2$

Test Preparation

49. **MULTIPLE CHOICE** What is the standard form of the equation of a circle with center $(-3, 1)$ and radius 2? D

    Ⓐ $(x - 3)^2 + (y - 1)^2 = 2$ Ⓑ $(x + 3)^2 + (y - 1)^2 = 2$
    Ⓒ $(x - 3)^2 + (y - 1)^2 = 4$ Ⓓ $(x + 3)^2 + (y - 1)^2 = 4$

50. **MULTIPLE CHOICE** The center of a circle is $(-3, 0)$ and its radius is 5. Which point does *not* lie on the circle? C

    Ⓐ (2, 0) Ⓑ (0, 4) Ⓒ (−3, 0) Ⓓ (−3, −5) Ⓔ (−8, 0)

★ Challenge

51. **CRITICAL THINKING** ⊙A and ⊙B are externally tangent. Suppose you know the equation of ⊙A, the coordinates of the single point of intersection of ⊙A and ⊙B, and the radius of ⊙B. Do you know enough to find the equation of ⊙B? Explain. See margin.

USING ALGEBRA Find the missing coordinate of the center of the circle with the given characteristics.

52. The center is $(1, b)$, the radius is 3, and a point on the circle is $(-2, 0)$. 0

53. The center is $(-3, b)$, the radius is 5, and a point on the circle is $(2, -2)$. −2

EXTRA CHALLENGE
www.mcdougallittell.com

MIXED REVIEW

51. Yes; Let P be the point of intersection and r the radius of ⊙B. Since the ⊙ are externally tangent, $\overline{AP}$ and $\overline{PB}$ are ⊥ to the tangent line at P. Thus point B lies on the line through A and P. Point B also lies on the circle with center P and radius r. Use these facts to write two equations in terms of the coordinates of point B and solve this system. Point B is the solution to this system that lies outside circle A. Use the coordinates of point B and the radius to write the equation for circle B.

61. No; P is not equidistant from the sides of ∠A.

62. Yes; P is equidistant from the sides of ∠A.

IDENTIFYING QUADRILATERALS What kind(s) of quadrilateral could *ABCD* be? *ABCD* is not drawn to scale. (Review 6.6)

54. ▱, rectangle, rhombus, kite

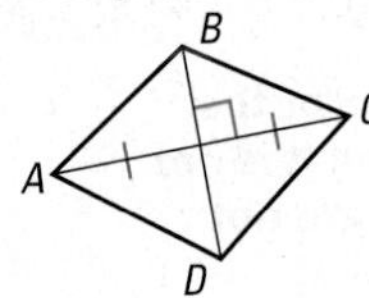

55. ▱, rectangle, rhombus, kite, isosceles trapezoid

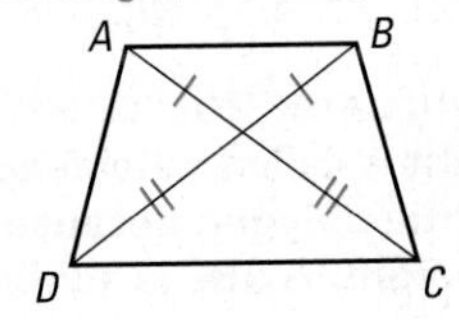

56. ▱, rectangle, rhombus, kite

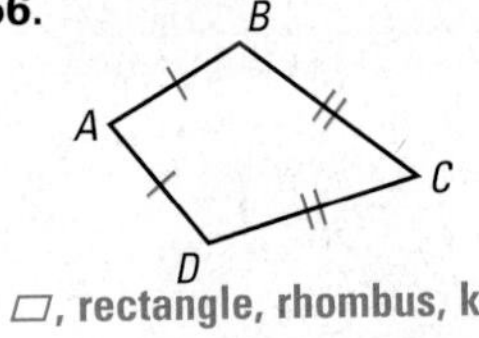

VECTORS Write the component form of vector $\overrightarrow{PQ}$. Use the component form to find the magnitude of $\overrightarrow{PQ}$ to the nearest tenth. (Review 9.7)

57. $P = (0, 0), Q = (-6, 7)$ $\langle -6, 7\rangle$; 9.2
58. $P = (3, -4), Q = (-11, 2)$ $\langle -14, 6\rangle$; 15.2
59. $P = (-6, -6), Q = (9, -5)$ $\langle 15, 1\rangle$; 15.0
60. $P = (5, 6), Q = (-3, 7)$ $\langle -8, 1\rangle$; 8.1

ANGLE BISECTORS Does P lie on the bisector of ∠A? Explain your reasoning. (Review 5.1) 61–62. See margin.

61.

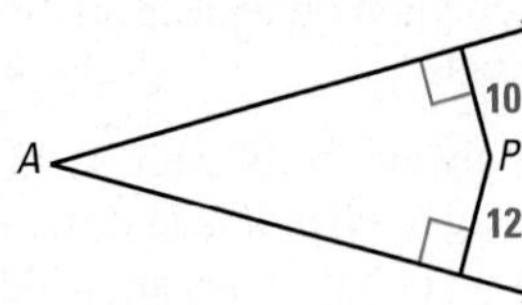

62.

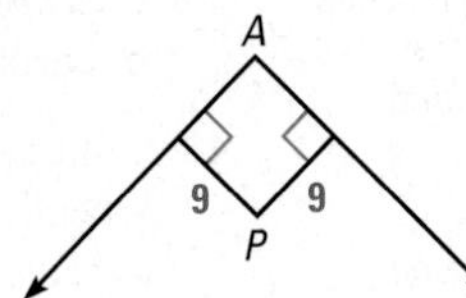

ACTIVITY 10.7

Using Technology

Investigating Points Equidistant from a Point and a Line

STUDENT HELP

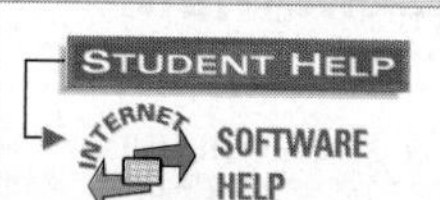

SOFTWARE HELP

Visit our Web site www.mcdougallittell.com to see instructions for several software applications.

Point P and line k lie in a plane. Which points in the plane are equidistant from P and k? You can use geometry software to find out.

▶ **CONSTRUCT** **Follow the steps to construct a line k, a point P not on k, and two points that are equidistant from P and k.**

Steps 1-4. Check drawings.

1. Draw a line k and a point P not on k. Near the corner of the screen, draw a segment and label it $\overline{AB}$.

2. Construct a line perpendicular to k. Label the intersection C. Construct a circle with center C and radius AB. The circle intersects the line perpendicular to k in two points. Choose the point that is on the same side of k as P and label it D. Construct a line through D parallel to k. Label this line m. Hide $\overleftrightarrow{CD}$, $\odot C$, C, and D.

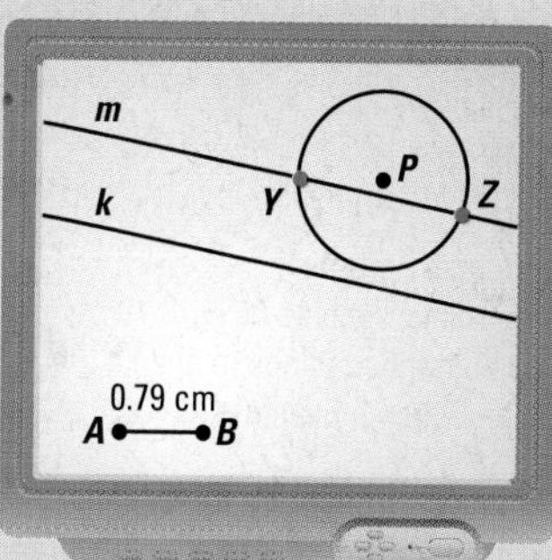

3. Construct a circle with center P and radius AB.

4. Draw the intersection points of circle P and line m. Label the points Y and Z.

▶ **INVESTIGATE**

1. Is Y equidistant from P and k? How do you know? Is Z equidistant from P and k? How do you know?

2. Drag point B. What happens to m? What happens to circle P? Do Y and Z remain equidistant from P and k?

3. Use the *Trace* feature to trace Y and Z as you slowly drag B. What shape is formed? You should recognize it from your algebra class.
parabola

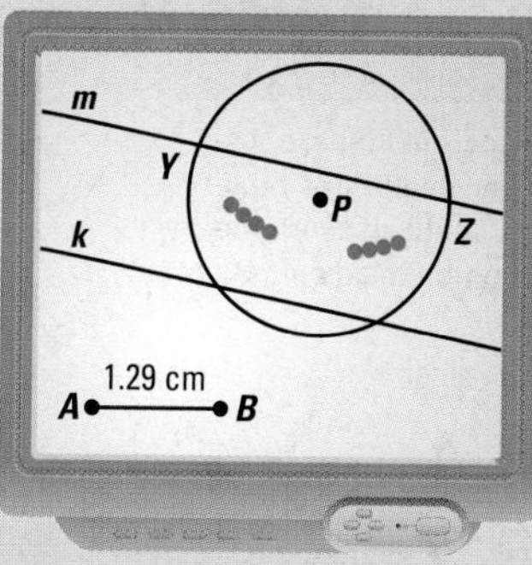

1. Yes; m and k are $\|$ and the distance from m to k is AB, so Y is AB units from k. $\odot P$ has radius AB, so Y is AB units from P. This is also true of point Z.

2. If B is dragged to the right, m moves up and circle P gets larger. If B is dragged to the left, m moves down and circle P gets smaller; yes.

▶ **CONJECTURE**

4. Make a conjecture about the points in a plane that are equidistant from a line and a point in the plane.
The set of points in a plane that are equidistant from a line and a point in the plane is a parabola.

EXTENSION

CRITICAL THINKING Use the *Coordinate* feature of the geometry software to find the coordinates of some points that are equidistant from the line $y = -\frac{1}{4}$ and the point $\left(0, \frac{1}{4}\right)$. Make and test a conjecture.

Extension: The locus of points equidistant from $\left(0, \frac{1}{4}\right)$ and the line $y = -\frac{1}{4}$ is the parabola with equation $y = x^2$.

1 Planning the Activity

PURPOSE
To find points equidistant from a line and a point not on the line.

MATERIALS
- Geometry drawing software
- Software Help (*Chapter 10 Resource Book,* p. 99)

PACING
- Construct — 10 min
- Investigate — 10 min
- Conjecture — 5 min

▶ **LINK TO LESSON**
Students may wish to use the software to verify the results of Examples 2 and 3 in Lesson 10.7.

2 Managing the Activity

COOPERATIVE LEARNING
Ask pairs of students to do this construction. Have them switch roles and repeat the construction with a different line and point not on the line.

ALTERNATIVE APPROACH
To save time, do this activity as a demonstration. Use a computer projection system to show the results. Ask students to make the conjecture.

3 Closing the Activity

★ ***KEY DISCOVERY***
The points equidistant from a line and a point not on that line trace out a parabola.

ACTIVITY ASSESSMENT
JOURNAL Describe the points in a plane that are equidistant from a line and a point in the plane.
Sample answer: If the point is on the line, the points equidistant from that point and the line form a circle. If the point is not on the line, the points equidistant from that point and the line trace out a parabola.

1 PLAN

PACING
Basic: 2 days
Average: 2 days
Advanced: 2 days
Block Schedule: 1 block

LESSON OPENER ACTIVITY
An alternative way to approach Lesson 10.7 is to use the Activity Lesson Opener:

- Blackline Master (*Chapter 10 Resource Book,* p. 98)
- Transparency (p. 67)

MEETING INDIVIDUAL NEEDS
- ***Chapter 10 Resource Book***
  Prerequisite Skills Review (p. 5)
  Practice Level A (p. 102)
  Practice Level B (p. 103)
  Practice Level C (p. 104)
  Reteaching with Practice (p. 105)
  Absent Student Catch-Up (p. 107)
  Challenge (p. 110)
- ***Resources in Spanish***
- ***Personal Student Tutor***

NEW-TEACHER SUPPORT
See the Tips for New Teachers on pp. 1–2 of the *Chapter 10 Resource Book* for additional notes about Lesson 10.7.

WARM-UP EXERCISES

Transparency Available

Fill in the blank.

1. Two lines intersect in a ____. **point**

2. Two lines in a plane that don't intersect are ____. **parallel**

3. The point (0, 0) is the ____ of the circle $x^2 + y^2 = 25$. **center**

4. The point (1, 4) is in the ____ of the circle with equation $x^2 + y^2 = 25$. **interior**

10.7 Locus

What you should learn

GOAL 1 Draw the locus of points that satisfy a given condition.

GOAL 2 Draw the locus of points that satisfy two or more conditions.

Why you should learn it

▼ To use **real-life** constraints, such as using seismograph readings to find an epicenter in **Example 4** and **Ex. 29**.

REAL LIFE

In ancient China, a seismometer like this one could measure the direction to an epicenter.

CALIFORNIA STANDARDS AND ASSESSMENT

CA Standards: 7

GOAL 1 DRAWING A LOCUS SATISFYING ONE CONDITION

A **locus** in a plane is the set of all points in a plane that satisfy a given condition or a set of given conditions. The word *locus* is derived from the Latin word for "location." The plural of locus is *loci*, pronounced "low-sigh."

A locus is often described as the path of an object moving in a plane. For instance, the reason that many clock faces are circular is that the locus of the end of a clock's minute hand is a circle.

EXAMPLE 1 *Finding a Locus*

Draw point C on a piece of paper. Draw and describe the locus of all points on the paper that are 3 inches from C.

SOLUTION

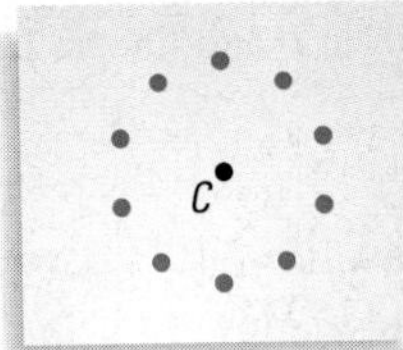

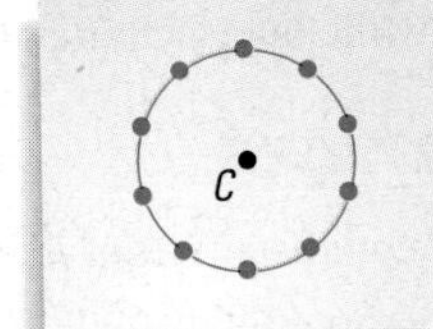

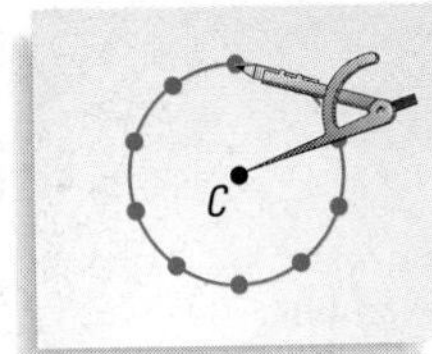

❶ Draw point C. Locate several points 3 inches from C.

❷ Recognize a pattern: the points lie on a circle.

❸ Draw the circle.

▶ The locus of points on the paper that are 3 inches from C is a circle with center C and a radius of 3 inches.

CONCEPT SUMMARY **FINDING A LOCUS**

To find the locus of points that satisfy a given condition, use the following steps.

❶ Draw any figures that are given in the statement of the problem.
❷ Locate several points that satisfy the given condition.
❸ Continue drawing points until you can recognize the pattern.
❹ Draw the locus and describe it in words.

GOAL 2 LOCI SATISFYING TWO OR MORE CONDITIONS

To find the locus of points that satisfy two or more conditions, first find the locus of points that satisfy each condition alone. Then find the intersection of these loci.

EXAMPLE 2 Drawing a Locus Satisfying Two Conditions

Points A and B lie in a plane. What is the locus of points in the plane that are equidistant from points A and B and are a distance of AB from B?

SOLUTION

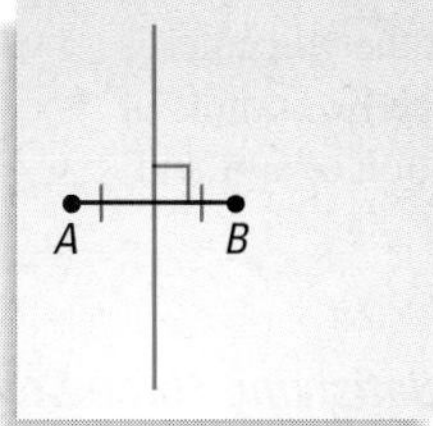

The locus of all points that are equidistant from A and B is the perpendicular bisector of $\overline{AB}$.

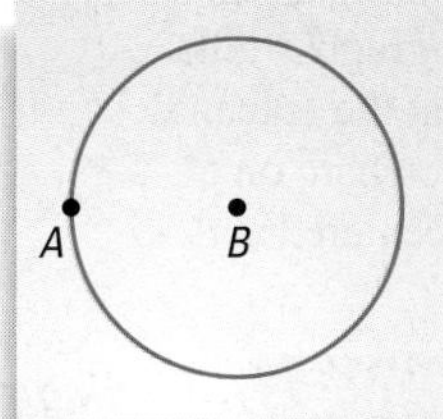

The locus of all points that are a distance of AB from B is the circle with center B and radius AB.

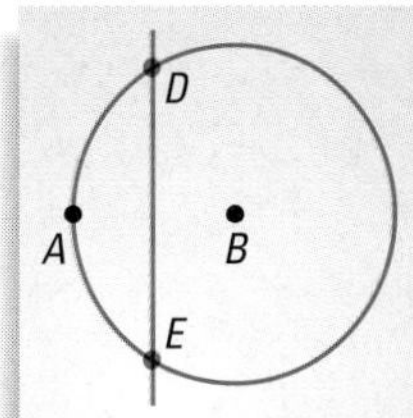

These loci intersect at D and E. So D and E are the locus of points that satisfy both conditions.

EXAMPLE 3 Drawing a Locus Satisfying Two Conditions

Point P is in the interior of $\angle ABC$. What is the locus of points in the interior of $\angle ABC$ that are equidistant from both sides of $\angle ABC$ and 2 inches from P? How does the location of P within $\angle ABC$ affect the locus?

SOLUTION

The locus of points equidistant from both sides of $\angle ABC$ is the angle bisector. The locus of points 2 inches from P is a circle. The intersection of the angle bisector and the circle depends on the location of P. The locus can be 2 points, 1 point, or 0 points.

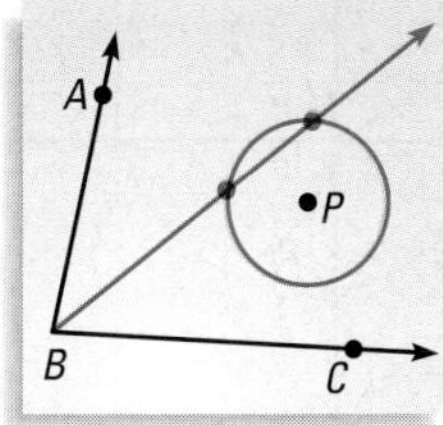

The locus is 2 points.

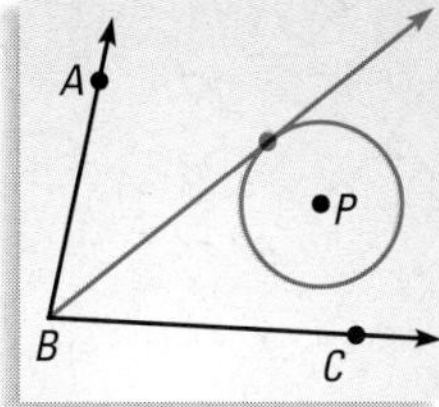

The locus is 1 point.

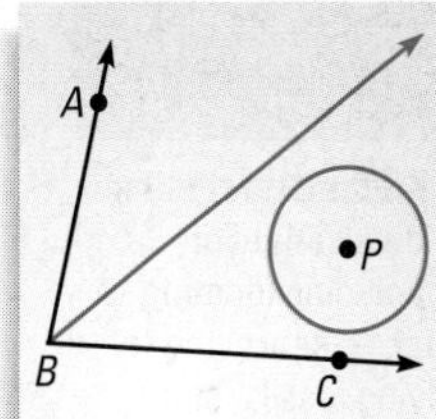

The locus is 0 points.

Extra Example 3 *Sample answer:*
The locus of points 2 cm from X is a circle with center X and radius 2 cm. The locus of points 3 cm from Y is a circle with center Y and radius 3 cm. If X is more than 5 cm from Y, the locus is 0 points; if X is 5 cm from Y, the locus is 1 point; if X is less than 5 cm from Y, the locus is 2 points.

2 TEACH

MOTIVATING THE LESSON

Ask students to describe the path of Earth around the sun. Their description is the locus of points satisfying a condition, the subject of this lesson.

EXTRA EXAMPLE 1

Draw a line k on a piece of paper. Draw and describe the locus of points on the paper that are 1 inch from the line.

two lines parallel to k and 1 in. from k

EXTRA EXAMPLE 2

Given $\triangle ABC$, what is the locus of points in the plane equidistant from $\overline{AB}$ and $\overline{AC}$ and also equidistant from A and B? **The locus of all points equidistant from $\overline{AB}$ and $\overline{AC}$ is the bisector of $\angle A$. The locus of all points equidistant from A and B is the perpendicular bisector of $\overline{AB}$. These loci intersect in one point.**

EXTRA EXAMPLE 3

What is the locus of points 2 cm from point X and 3 cm from point Y? **See below.**

CHECKPOINT EXERCISES

For use after Examples 1–3:

1. Describe the locus of points equidistant from the vertices of a square. **the intersection point of the diagonals.**
2. Point A is in the same plane as parallel lines m and n. What is the locus of points 4 inches from A and equidistant from m and n? **The locus of points 4 inches from A is a circle with center A and radius 4 inches. The locus of points equidistant from m and n is a third line halfway between m and n and parallel to them. The locus can be 0, 1, or 2 points.**

EXTRA EXAMPLE 4

You are given readings from three seismographs. At $A(2, 4)$, the epicenter is 2 miles away. At $B(2, 0.5)$, the epicenter is 2.5 miles away. At $C(-1, 1)$ the epicenter is 3 miles away. Where is the epicenter?
about (2, 2)

CHECKPOINT EXERCISES

For use after Example 4:

1. You are given readings from three seismographs. At $A(2, -1)$, the epicenter is 4 miles away. At $B(1, 2)$, the epicenter is 2 miles away. At $C(-4, 1)$ the epicenter is 3 miles away. Where is the epicenter? **about (−1, 1.5)**

FOCUS ON VOCABULARY

Define locus. **The locus in a plane is the set of all points in the plane that satisfy given conditions.**

CLOSURE QUESTION

Find the locus of points in the interior of a right angle and equidistant from the sides of the angle.
the angle bisector

DAILY PUZZLER

Three circles, each with radius 2 units, have centers at (4, 2), (6, 2), and (5, 0). Draw the locus of points that falls within all three circles.

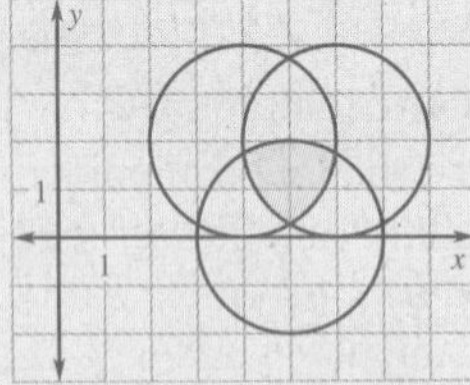

MULTIPLE REPRESENTATIONS

Loci can be represented verbally and geometrically. The Solution of Example 4 shows how the verbal representation of three circles can be translated into a geometric model.

EARTHQUAKES The *epicenter* of an earthquake is the point on Earth's surface that is directly above the earthquake's origin. A seismograph can measure the distance to the epicenter, but not the direction to the epicenter. To locate the epicenter, readings from three seismographs in different locations are needed.

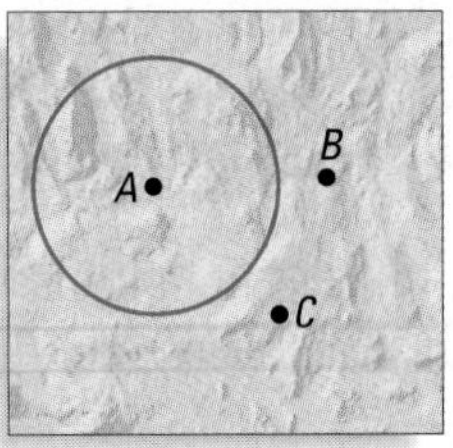

The reading from seismograph A tells you that the epicenter is somewhere on a circle centered at A.

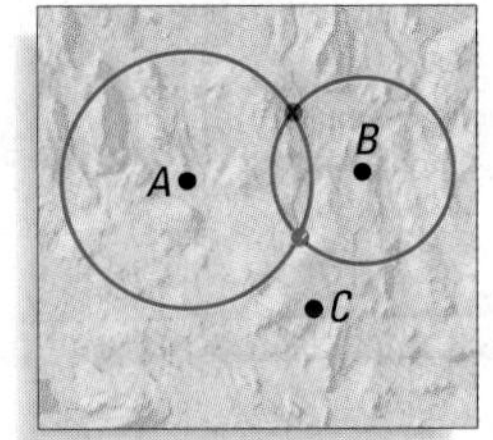

The reading from B tells you that the epicenter is one of the two points of intersection of $\odot A$ and $\odot B$.

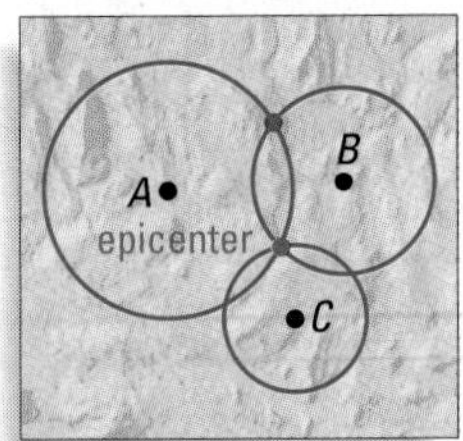

The reading from C tells you which of the two points of intersection is the epicenter.

EXAMPLE 4 ***Finding a Locus Satisfying Three Conditions***

LOCATING AN EPICENTER You are given readings from three seismographs.

- At $A(-5, 5)$, the epicenter is 4 miles away.
- At $B(-4, -3.5)$, the epicenter is 5 miles away.
- At $C(1, 1.5)$, the epicenter is 7 miles away.

Where is the epicenter?

SOLUTION

Each seismograph gives you a locus that is a circle.

Circle A has center $(-5, 5)$ and radius 4.

Circle B has center $(-4, -3.5)$ and radius 5.

Circle C has center $(1, 1.5)$ and radius 7.

Draw the three circles in a coordinate plane. The point of intersection of the three circles is the epicenter.

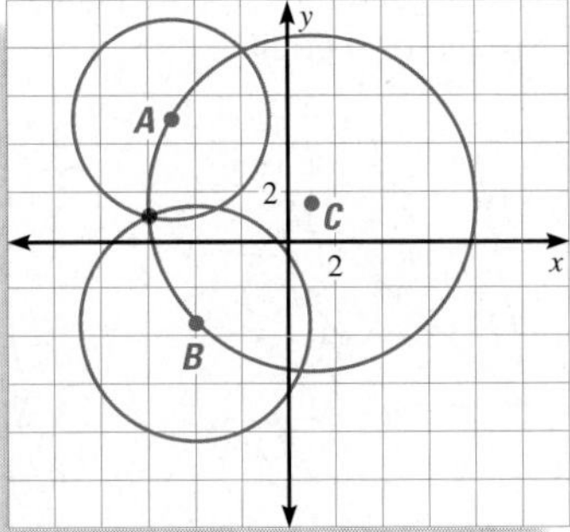

▶ The epicenter is at about $(-6, 1)$.

FOCUS ON CAREERS

GEOSCIENTISTS do a variety of things, including locating earthquakes, searching for oil, studying fossils, and mapping the ocean floor.

CAREER LINK
www.mcdougallittell.com

GUIDED PRACTICE

Vocabulary Check ✓

1. The radius of $\odot C$ is 3 inches. The locus of points in the plane that are more than 3 inches from C is the _?_ of $\odot C$. exterior

Concept Check ✓

2. Draw two points A and B on a piece of paper. Draw and describe the locus of points on the paper that are equidistant from A and B. See margin for figure. the segment that represents points of the ⊥ bisector that lie on the paper

Skill Check ✓

Match the object with the locus of point *P*.

A. Arc **B.** Circle **C.** Parabola **D.** Line segment

3. B

4. A

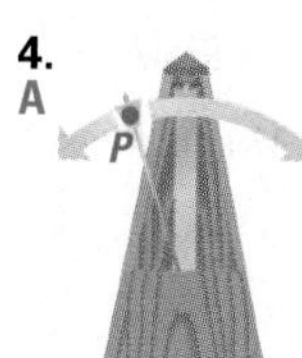

5. D

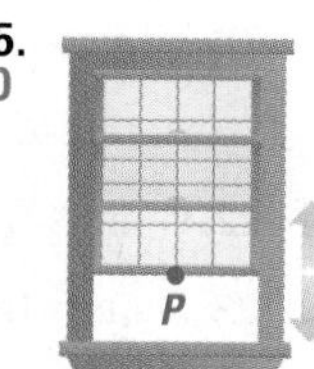

6. C

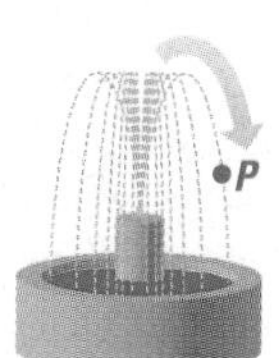

7. What is the locus of points in the coordinate plane that are equidistant from $A(0, 0)$ and $B(6, 0)$ and 5 units from A? Make a sketch. See margin for figure. the two points on the intersection of the ⊥ bisector of $\overline{AB}$ and $\odot A$ with radius 5
8. Points C and D are in a plane. What is the locus of points in the plane that are 3 units from C and 5 units from D? 2 points, 1 point, or no points, depending on whether the distance between C and D is less than, equal to, or greater than 8

PRACTICE AND APPLICATIONS

STUDENT HELP

Extra Practice to help you master skills is on p. 822.

LOGICAL REASONING **Draw the figure. Then sketch and describe the locus of points on the paper that satisfy the given condition.** 9–12. See margin for figures.

9. Point P, the locus of points that are 1 inch from P $\odot P$ with radius 1 in.
10. Line k, the locus of points that are 1 inch from k lines m and n on opp. sides of k, each ∥ to k and 1 in. from k
11. Point C, the locus of points that are no more than 1 inch from C $\odot C$ with radius 1 in. and the interior of $\odot C$
12. Line j, the locus of points that are at least 1 inch from j lines m and n on opp. sides of j, each ∥ to j and 1 in. from j, and all the points on the paper above m or below n

LOGICAL REASONING **Copy the figure. Then sketch and describe the locus of points on the paper that satisfy the given condition(s).** 13–15. See margin for figures.

13. equidistant from j and k

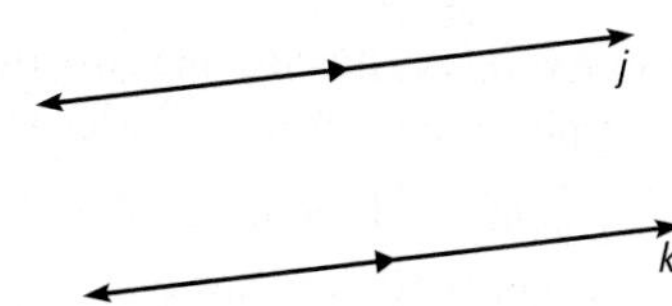

a line ∥ to both j and k and halfway between them

14. in the interior of $\angle A$ and equidistant from both sides of $\angle A$

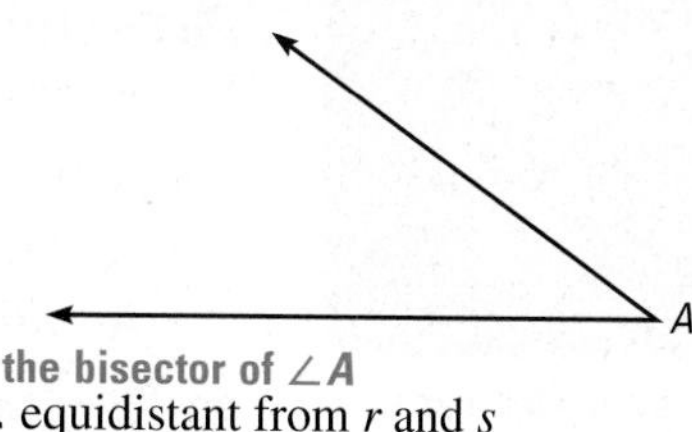

the bisector of $\angle A$

15. midpoint of a radius of $\odot C$

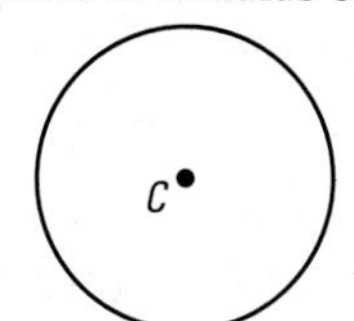

a $\odot$ with center C and radius half that of the original $\odot$

16. equidistant from r and s

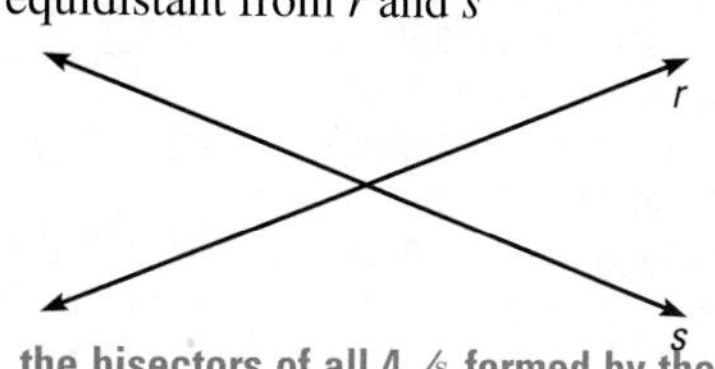

the bisectors of all 4 ∠s formed by the intersection of r and s

STUDENT HELP

HOMEWORK HELP

Example 1: Exs. 9–23
Example 2: Exs. 14, 24, 25
Example 3: Exs. 26, 27, 31
Example 4: Exs. 19–25, 28–30

3 APPLY

ASSIGNMENT GUIDE

BASIC
Day 1: pp. 645–647 Exs. 10–26 even, 28–30
Day 2: pp. 645–648 Exs. 9–27 odd, 33, 34, 36–45, Quiz 3 Exs. 1–8

AVERAGE
Day 1: pp. 645–647 Exs. 10–26 even, 28–30
Day 2: pp. 645–648 Exs. 9–27 odd, 33, 34, 36–45, Quiz 3 Exs. 1–8

ADVANCED
Day 1: pp. 645–647 Exs. 10–26 even, 28–30
Day 2: pp. 645–648 Exs. 9–27 odd, 32–45, Quiz 3 Exs. 1–8

BLOCK SCHEDULE
pp. 645–648 Exs. 9–30, 33, 34, 36–45, Quiz 3 Exs. 1–8

EXERCISE LEVELS

Level A: *Easier* 9–12
Level B: *More Difficult* 13–34
Level C: *Most Difficult* 35

✓ HOMEWORK CHECK

To quickly check student understanding of key concepts, go over the following exercises: Exs. 10, 12, 16, 18, 20, 24, 26, 30. See also the Daily Homework Quiz:

- Blackline Master (*Chapter 11 Resource Book*, p. 11)
- Transparency (p. 79)

2, 7, 9–16. See Additional Answers beginning on page AA1.

! COMMON ERROR
EXERCISE 17 Watch for students who sketch only one set of points for *P*. There are two possible solutions for this exercise. *P* can be on either side of $\overline{AB}$.

APPLICATION NOTE
EXERCISES 28–30 The intensity of an earthquake can be measured using the Richter Scale. The magnitude of a quake is determined from the logarithm of the amplitude of the waves recorded by various seismographs. The magnitude formula is adjusted to compensate for the variation in distance from the seismographs to the epicenter.

17. 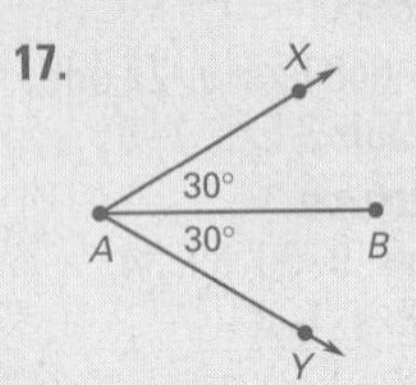

18. 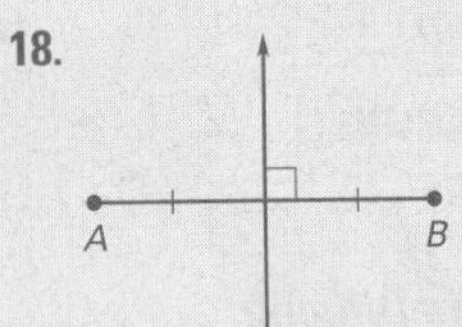

24. 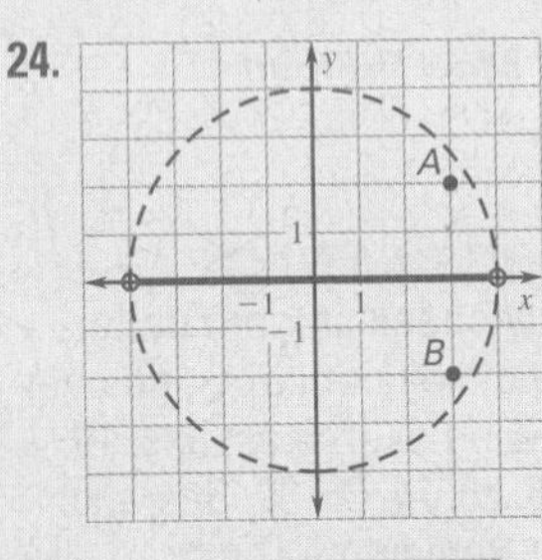

25. 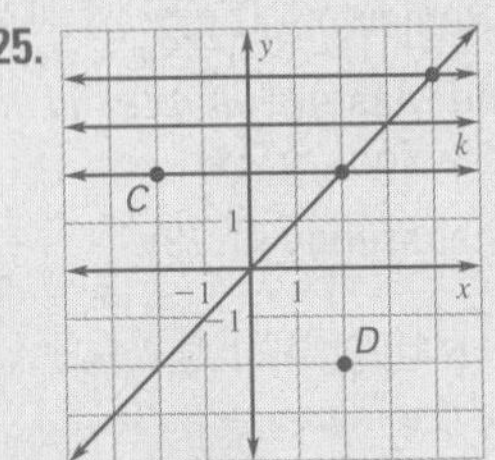

26–27. See Additional Answers beginning on page AA1.

17. all points except *A* on two rays, $\overrightarrow{AX}$ and $\overrightarrow{AY}$, such that $m\angle XAY = 60°$ and $\overline{AB}$ is the bisector of $\angle XAY$

18. the ⊥ bisector of $\overline{AB}$

24. the points on the *x*-axis with *x*-coordinate greater than −4 and less than 4

25. 2 points, (2, 2) and (4, 4), the intersections of $y = x$ with $y = 2$ and $y = 4$

26. Let *d* be the distance from *R* to *k*; the locus of points is 4 points if $d < 1$, 3 points if $d = 1$, 2 points if $1 < d < 3$, 1 point if $d = 3$, and 0 points if $d > 3$.

27. Let *d* be the distance from *R* to the ⊥ bisector of $\overline{PQ}$; the locus of points is 2 points if $d < 4$, 1 point if $d = 4$, and 0 points if $d > 4$.

30. No; the distance between the epicenter, (0, −6), and your friend's location, (−3, 20) = $\sqrt{(0-(-3))^2 + (-6-20)^2} = \sqrt{685} \approx 26$ mi.

FOCUS ON APPLICATIONS

SAN ANDREAS FAULT In 1857, an earthquake on this fault made a river run upstream and flung the water out of a lake, stranding fish miles away.

CRITICAL THINKING **Draw $\overline{AB}$. Then sketch and describe the locus of points on the paper that satisfy the given condition.**

17. the locus of points *P* such that $\angle PAB$ is 30°

18. the locus of points *Q* such that $\triangle QAB$ is an isosceles triangle with base $\overline{AB}$

USING ALGEBRA **Use the graph at the right to write equation(s) for the locus of points in the coordinate plane that satisfy the given condition.**

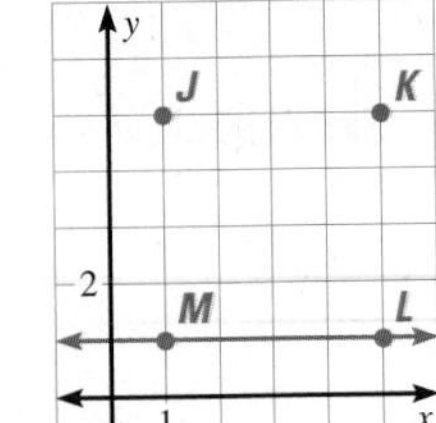

19. equidistant from *J* and *K* $x = 3$

20. equidistant from *J* and *M* $y = 3$

21. equidistant from *M* and *K* $y = -x + 6$

22. 3 units from *K* $(x-5)^2 + (y-5)^2 = 9$

23. 3 units from $\overleftrightarrow{ML}$ $y = -2, y = 4$

COORDINATE GEOMETRY **Copy the graph. Then sketch and describe the locus of points in the plane that satisfy the given conditions. Explain your reasoning.** 24, 25. See margin.

24. equidistant from *A* and *B* and less than 4 units from the origin

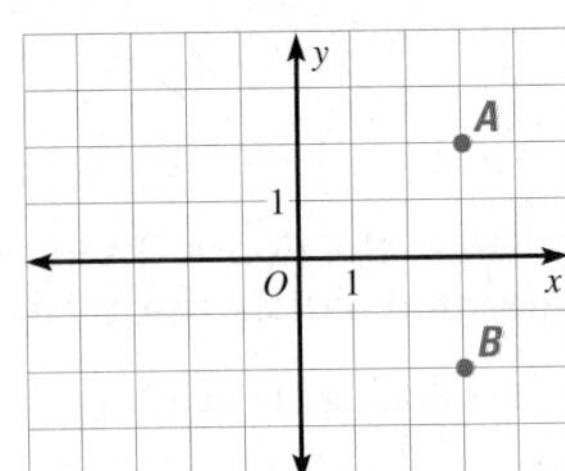

25. equidistant from *C* and *D* and 1 unit from line *k*

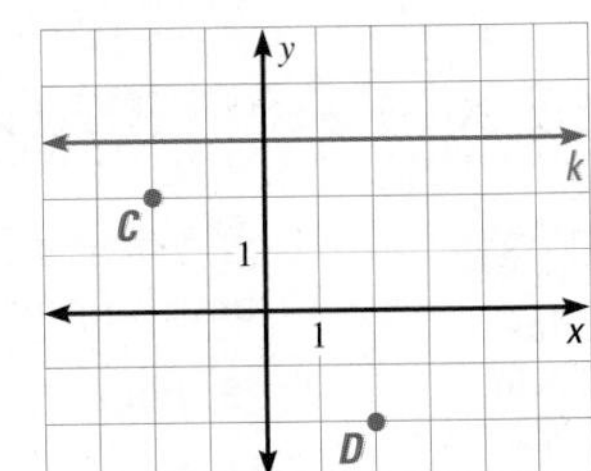

LOGICAL REASONING **Sketch and describe the locus. How do the positions of the given points affect the locus?** 26, 27. See margin.

26. Point *R* and line *k* are in a plane. What is the locus of points in the plane that are 1 unit from *k* and 2 units from *R*?

27. Noncollinear points *P*, *Q*, and *R* are in a plane. What is the locus of points in the plane that are equidistant from *P* and *Q* and 4 units from *R*?

EARTHQUAKES **In Exercises 28–30, use the following information.**
You are given seismograph readings from three locations.

- At $A(-5, 6)$, the epicenter is 13 miles away.
- At $B(6, 2)$, the epicenter is 10 miles away.
- At $O(0, 0)$, the epicenter is 6 miles away.

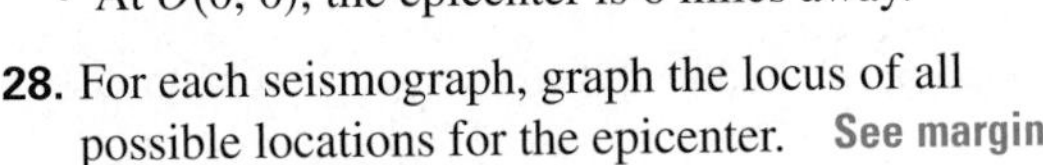

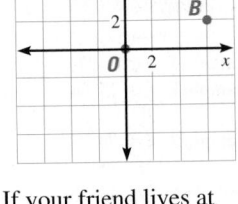

28. For each seismograph, graph the locus of all possible locations for the epicenter. See margin.

29. Where is the epicenter? (0, −6)

30. People could feel the earthquake up to 14 miles away. If your friend lives at (−3, 20), could your friend feel the earthquake? Explain your reasoning. See margin.

31. Let d be the distance from P to k. If $0 < d < 4$, the locus is 2 points. If $d = 4$, the locus is 1 point. If $d > 4$, the locus is 0 points.

31.  **TECHNOLOGY** Using geometry software, construct and label a line k and a point P not on k. Construct the locus of points that are 2 units from P. Construct the locus of points that are 2 units from k. What is the locus of points that are 2 units from P and 2 units from k? Drag P and k to determine how the location of P and k affects the locus.

32. **CRITICAL THINKING** Given points A and B, describe the locus of points P such that $\triangle APB$ is a right triangle. See margin.

Test Preparation

32. the ⊙ with center at the midpoint of $\overline{AB}$ and radius $\frac{1}{2}AB$

33. **MULTIPLE CHOICE** What is the locus of points in the coordinate plane that are 3 units from the origin? D

(A) The line $x = 3$ (B) The line $y = 3$ (C) The circle $x^2 + y^2 = 3$

(D) The circle $x^2 + y^2 = 9$ (E) None of the above

34. **MULTIPLE CHOICE** Circles C and D are externally tangent. The radius of circle C is 6 centimeters and the radius of circle D is 9 centimeters. What is the locus of all points that are a distance of CD from point C? C

(A) Circle with center C and a radius of 3 centimeters

(B) Circle with center D and a radius of 3 centimeters

(C) Circle with center C and a radius of 15 centimeters

(D) Circle with center D and a radius of 15 centimeters

★ Challenge

35. **DOG LEASH** A dog's leash is tied to a stake at the corner of its doghouse, as shown at the right. The leash is 9 feet long. Make a scale drawing of the doghouse and sketch the locus of points that the dog can reach. See margin.

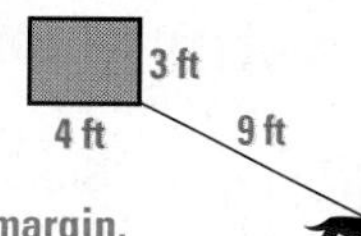

MIXED REVIEW

FINDING ANGLE MEASURES **Find the value of x.** (Review 4.1, 4.6, 6.1 for 11.1)

36. 22

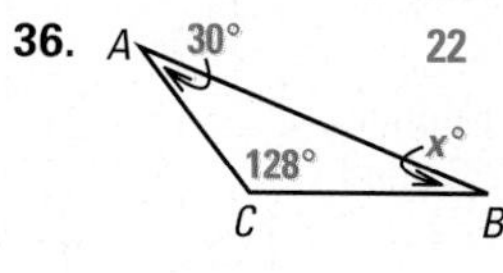

37. 69

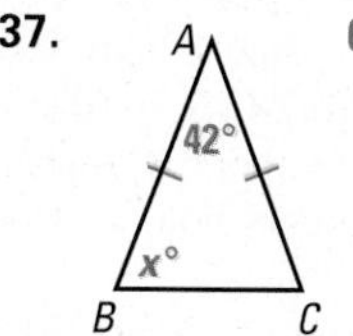

38. 70

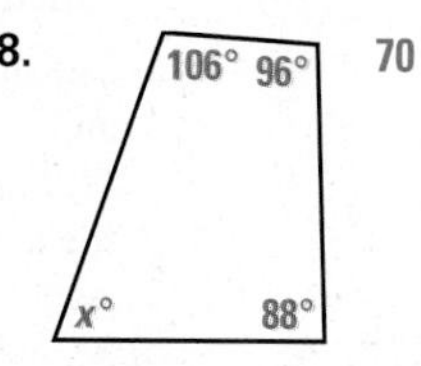

FINDING LENGTHS **Find the value of x.** (Review 10.5)

39. 17.5

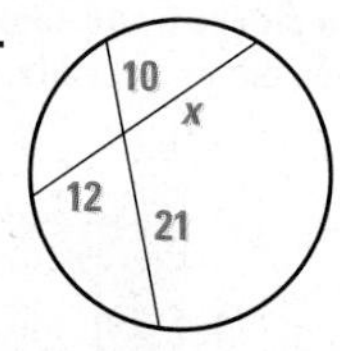

40. 17

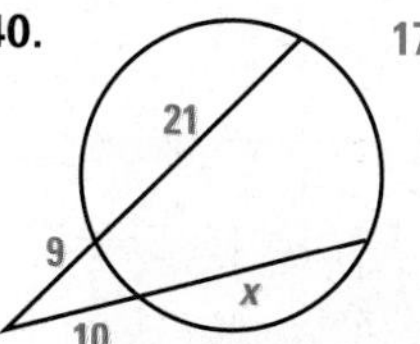

41. 24

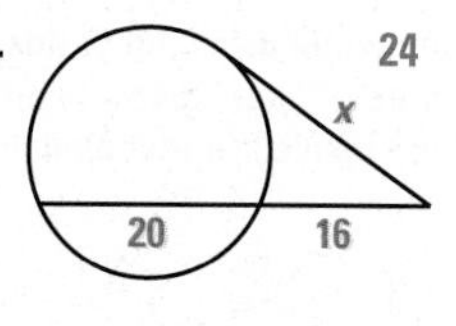

DRAWING GRAPHS **Graph the equation.** (Review 10.6) 42–45. See margin.

42. $x^2 + y^2 = 81$

43. $(x + 6)^2 + (y - 4)^2 = 9$

44. $x^2 + (y - 7)^2 = 100$

45. $(x - 4)^2 + (y - 5)^2 = 1$

28.

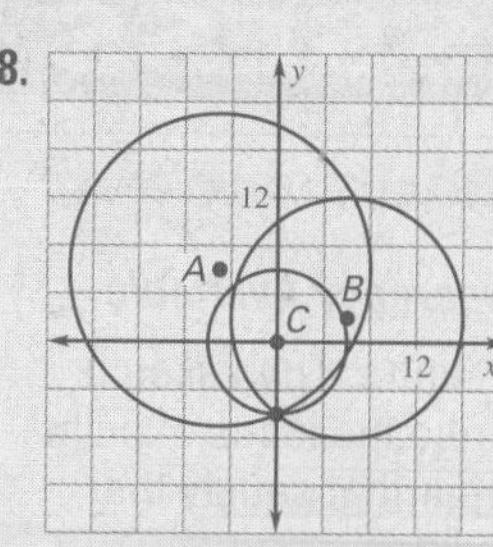

35.

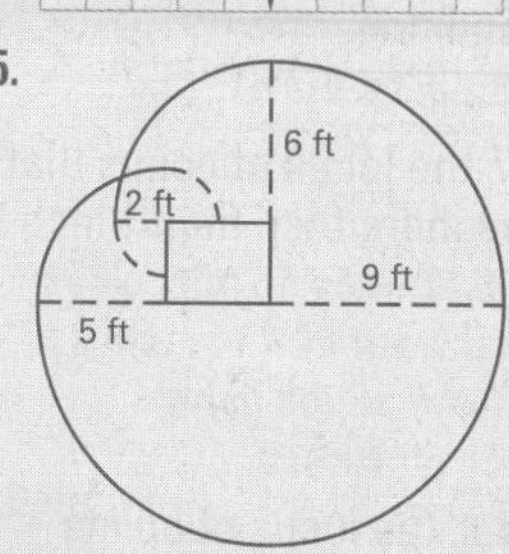

42–45. See Additional Answers beginning on page AA1.

ADDITIONAL PRACTICE AND RETEACHING

For Lesson 10.7:

- Practice Levels A, B, and C (*Chapter 10 Resource Book*, p. 102)
- Reteaching with Practice (*Chapter 10 Resource Book*, p. 105)
- See Lesson 10.7 of the *Personal Student Tutor*

For more Mixed Review:

- Search the *Test and Practice Generator* for key words or specific lessons.

4 ASSESS

DAILY HOMEWORK QUIZ

Transparency Available

Draw the figure. Then sketch and describe the locus of points on the paper that satisfy the given condition.
Check students' drawings.

1. Line f, the locus of points that are no more than than 1 inch from f. 2 lines on opp. sides of f, each parallel to f and 1 in. from f and all the points between the lines
2. Point p, the locus of points that are 1 cm or more from p. circle p with radius 1 cm and all points outside the circle
3. Points $A(1, 2)$ and $B(3, -2)$, the locus of points equidistant from A and B line with slope $\frac{1}{2}$ passing through (2, 0)

EXTRA CHALLENGE NOTE

Challenge problems for Lesson 10.7 are available in **blackline** format in the *Chapter 10 Resource Book*, p. 110 and at **www.mcdougallittell.com.**

ADDITIONAL TEST PREPARATION

1. **WRITING** Summarize how to find a locus of points that satisfy a given condition. Draw figures given in the problem. Locate several points that match the given condition. Continue drawing points until you recognize a pattern. Draw the locus and describe it.

MATH & HISTORY NOTE

A **blackline** master with additional Math & History exercises is available in the the *Chapter 10 Resource Book*, p. 109.

QUIZ 3

Self-Test for Lessons 10.6 and 10.7

6. the points that are in both the exterior of the ⊙ with center P and radius 6 units and the interior of the ⊙ with center P and radius 9 units
7. a set of points formed by 2 rays on opposite sides of $\overrightarrow{AB}$, each $\parallel$ to $\overrightarrow{AB}$ and 4 cm from it, and a semicircle with center A and radius 4 cm
8. the points that are on the field and on or outside the ⊙ whose center is the center of the field and whose radius is 10 yd

Graph the equation. (Lesson 10.6) 1–4. See margin.

1. $x^2 + y^2 = 100$
2. $(x + 3)^2 + (y + 3)^2 = 49$
3. $(x - 1)^2 + y^2 = 36$
4. $(x + 4)^2 + (y - 7)^2 = 25$
5. The point $(-3, -9)$ is on a circle whose center is $(2, -2)$. What is the standard equation of the circle? (Lesson 10.6) $(x - 2)^2 + (y + 2)^2 = 74$
6. Draw point P on a piece of paper. Draw and describe the locus of points on the paper that are more than 6 units and less than 9 units from P. (Lesson 10.7) See margin.
7. Draw the locus of all points in a plane that are 4 centimeters from a ray $\overrightarrow{AB}$. (Lesson 10.7) See margin.
8. **SOCCER** In a soccer game, play begins with a kick-off. All players not involved in the kick-off must stay at least 10 yards from the ball. The ball is in the center of the field. Sketch a 50 yard by 100 yard soccer field with a ball in the center. Then draw and describe the locus of points at which the players not involved in the kick-off can stand. (Lesson 10.7) See margin.

MATH & History — History of Timekeeping

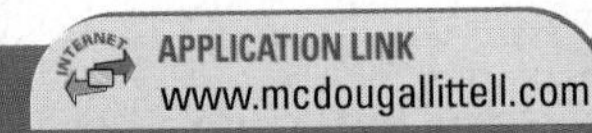

THEN

SCHOLARS BELIEVE THAT the practice of dividing a circle into 360 equal parts has its origins in ancient Babylon. Around 1000 B.C., the Babylonians divided the day (one rotation of Earth) into 12 equal time units. Each unit was divided into 30 smaller units. So one of Earth's rotations was divided into $12 \times 30 = 360$ equal parts.

1. Before the introduction of accurate clocks, other civilizations divided the time between sunrise and sunset into 12 equal "temporary hours." These hours varied in length, depending on the time of year.

   The table at the right shows the times of sunrise and sunset in New York City. To the nearest minute, find the length of a temporary hour on June 21 and the length of a temporary hour on December 21.
   75 min, 46 min

New York City		
Date	**Sunrise**	**Sunset**
June 21	4:25 A.M.	7:30 P.M.
Dec. 21	7:16 A.M.	4:31 P.M.

NOW

TODAY, a day is divided into 24 hours. Atomic clocks are used to give the correct time with an accuracy of better than one second in six million years.

As water drips out of this clock, "hour" markers on the inside are revealed.

c. 1500 B.C.

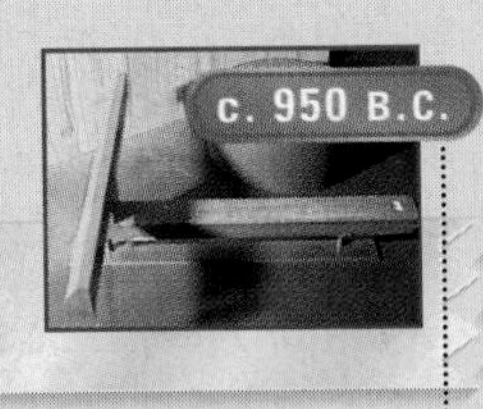

c. 950 B.C.

This shadow clock divides the morning into six parts.

Accurate clocks made safe navigation at sea possible.

1757

1963

Atomic clocks use the resonances of atoms.

CHAPTER 10

Chapter Summary

WHAT did you learn?	*WHY did you learn it?*
Identify segments and lines related to circles. **(10.1)**	Lay the foundation for work with circles.
Use properties of tangents of circles. **(10.1)**	Find real-life distances, such as the radius of a silo. **(p. 597)**
Use properties of arcs and chords of circles. **(10.2)**	Solve real-life problems such as analyzing a procedure used to locate an avalanche rescue beacon. **(p. 609)**
Use properties of inscribed angles and inscribed polygons of circles. **(10.3)**	Reach conclusions about angles in real-life objects, such as your viewing angle at the movies. **(p. 614)**
Use angles formed by tangents, chords, and secants. **(10.4)**	Estimate distances, such as the maximum distance at which fireworks can be seen. **(p. 625)**
Find the lengths of segments of tangents, chords, and lines that intersect a circle. **(10.5)**	Find real-life distances, such as the distance a satellite transmits a signal. **(p. 634)**
Find and graph the equation of a circle. **(10.6)**	Solve real-life problems, such as determining cellular phone coverage. **(p. 639)**
Draw loci in a plane that satisfy one or more conditions. **(10.7)**	Make conclusions based on real-life constraints, such as using seismograph readings to locate the epicenter of an earthquake. **(p. 644)**

How does Chapter 10 fit into the BIGGER PICTURE of geometry?

In this chapter, you learned that circles have many connections with other geometric figures. For instance, you learned that a quadrilateral can be inscribed in a circle if and only if its opposite angles are supplementary. Circles also occur in natural settings, such as the ripples in a pond, and in manufactured structures, such as a cross section of a storage tank. The properties of circles that you studied in this chapter will help you solve problems related to mathematics and the real world.

STUDY STRATEGY

Did you answer your questions?

Your record of questions about difficult exercises, following the study strategy on page 594, may resemble this one.

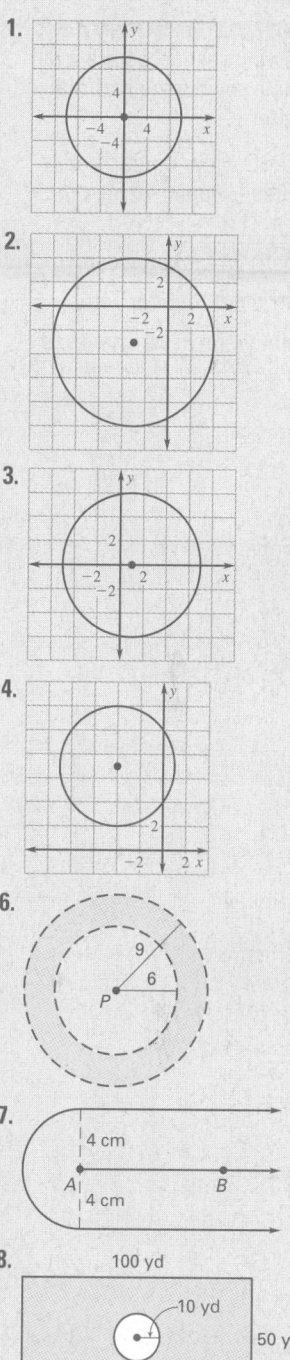

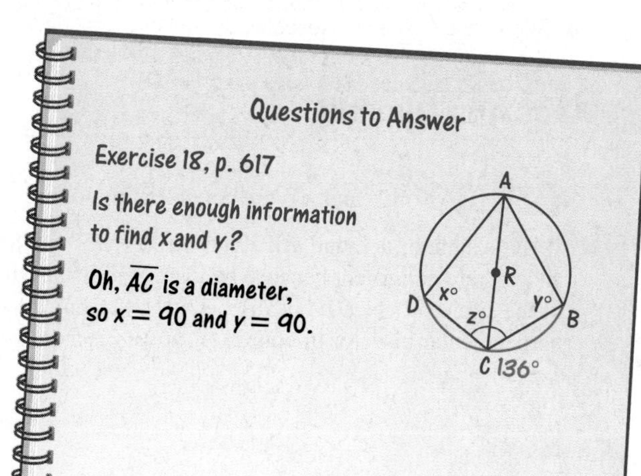

Questions to Answer
Exercise 18, p. 617
Is there enough information to find x and y?
Oh, $\overline{AC}$ is a diameter, so x = 90 and y = 90.
A
R
D
x°
y°
z°
B
C 136°

1.

2.

3.

4.

6.

7.

8.

649

ADDITIONAL RESOURCES
The following resources are available to help review the material in this chapter.

- Chapter Review Games and Activities (*Chapter 10 Resource Book*, p. 111)
- *Geometry in Motion video*
- *Personal Student Tutor*
- Cumulative Review, Chs. 1–10 (*Chapter 10 Resource Book*, p. 123)

CHAPTER 10

Chapter Review

VOCABULARY

- circle, p. 595
- center of circle, p. 595
- radius of circle, p. 595
- congruent circles, p. 595
- diameter of circle, p. 595
- chord, secant, tangent, p. 595
- tangent circles, p. 596
- concentric circles, p. 596
- common tangent, p. 596
- interior of a circle, p. 596
- exterior of a circle, p. 596
- point of tangency, p. 597
- central angle, p. 603
- minor arc and its measure, p. 603
- major arc and its measure, p. 603
- semicircle, p. 603
- congruent arcs, p. 604
- inscribed angle, p. 613
- intercepted arc, p. 613
- inscribed polygon, p. 615
- circumscribed circle, p. 615
- tangent segment, p.
- secant segment, p. 6
- external segment, p
- standard equation o circle, p. 636
- locus, p. 642

10.1 TANGENTS TO CIRCLES

Exam pp.

EXAMPLES In $\odot R$, R is the center. $\overline{RJ}$ is a radius, and $\overline{JL}$ is a diameter. $\overline{MP}$ is a chord, and $\overleftrightarrow{MP}$ is a secant. $\overleftrightarrow{KS}$ is a tangent and so it is perpendicular to the radius $\overline{RS}$. $\overline{KS} \cong \overline{KP}$ because they are two tangents from the same exterior point.

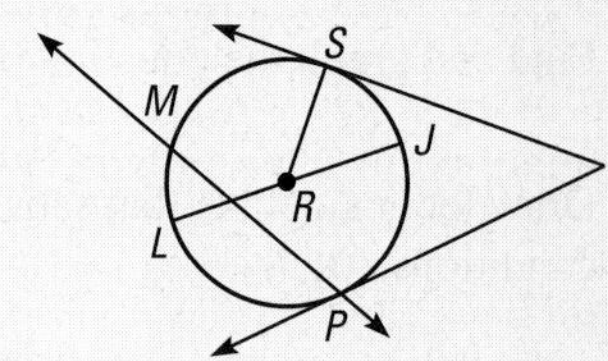

Name a point, segment, line, or circle that represents the phrase.

1. Diameter of $\odot P$ **$\overline{BN}$**
2. Point of tangency of $\odot Q$ **C, D, or R**
3. Chord of $\odot P$ **$\overline{BN}$ or $\overline{BF}$**
4. Center of larger circle **P**
5. Radius of $\odot Q$ **$\overline{QE}$**
6. Common tangent **$\overleftrightarrow{SB}$**
7. Secant **$\overleftrightarrow{BF}$**
8. Point of tangency of $\odot P$ and $\odot Q$ **R**
9. Is $\angle PBC$ a right angle? Explain.
   Yes; a tangent is $\perp$ to the radius drawn to the point of tangency.
10. Show that $\triangle SCD$ is isosceles.
    Since $\overline{SC}$ and $\overline{SD}$ are tangent segments with the same exterior endpoint, $\overline{SC} \cong \overline{SD}$ and $\triangle SCD$ is isosceles.

10.2 ARCS AND CHORDS

Exam pp.

EXAMPLES $\widehat{WX}$ and $\widehat{XY}$ are congruent minor arcs with measure 75°. $\widehat{WYX}$ is a major arc, and $m\widehat{WYX} = 360° - 75° = 285°$. Chords $\overline{TU}$ and $\overline{UY}$ are congruent because they are equidistant from the center of the circle. $\widehat{TU} \cong \widehat{UY}$ because $\overline{TU} \cong \overline{UY}$. Chord $\overline{WZ}$ is a perpendicular bisector of chord $\overline{UY}$, so $\overline{WZ}$ is a diameter.

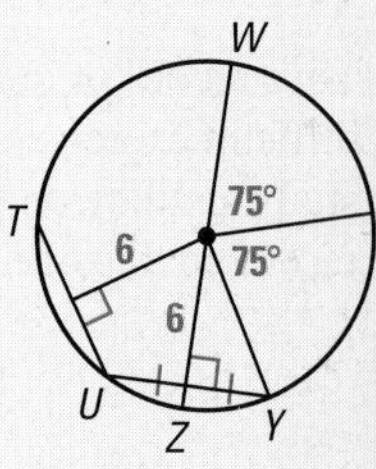

Use $\odot Q$ in the diagram to find the measure of the indicated arc. $\overline{AD}$ is a diameter, and $m\widehat{CE} = 121°$.

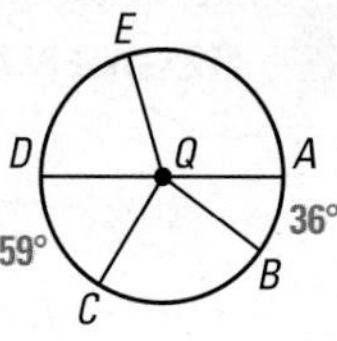

11. $\widehat{DE}$ 62° **12.** $\widehat{AE}$ 118° **13.** $\widehat{AEC}$ 239°

14. $\widehat{BC}$ 85° **15.** $\widehat{BDC}$ 275° **16.** $\widehat{BDA}$ 324°

10.3 INSCRIBED ANGLES

Examples on pp. 613–616

EXAMPLES $\angle ABC$ and $\angle ADC$ are congruent inscribed angles, each with measure $\frac{1}{2} \cdot m\widehat{AEC} = 90°$. Because $\triangle ADC$ is an inscribed right triangle, $\overline{AC}$ is a diameter. The quadrilateral can be inscribed in a circle because its opposite angles are supplementary.

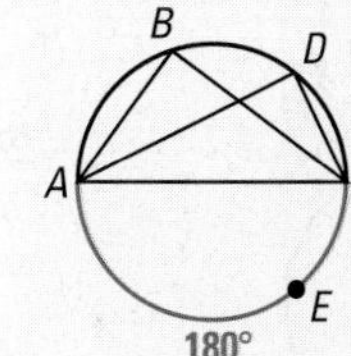

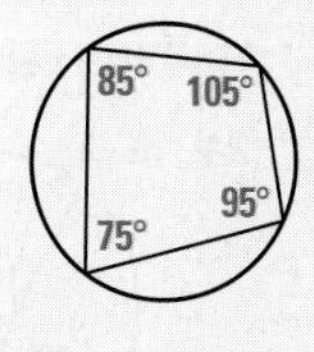

Kite *ABCD* is inscribed in $\odot P$. Decide whether the statement is *true* or *false*. Explain your reasoning.

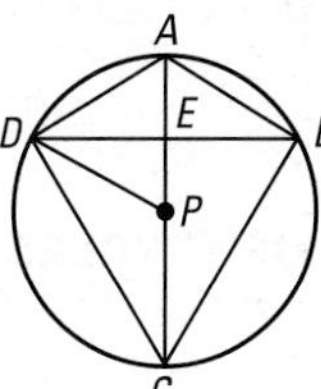

17. $\angle ABC$ and $\angle ADC$ are right angles. See margin.

18. $m\angle ACD = \frac{1}{2} \cdot m\angle AED$ See margin.

19. $m\angle DAB + m\angle BCD = 180°$
True; *ABCD* is inscribed in a $\odot$, so opp. $\angle$s are supp.

10.4 OTHER ANGLE RELATIONSHIPS IN CIRCLES

Examples on pp. 621–623

EXAMPLES

$m\angle ABD = \frac{1}{2} \cdot 120°$
$= 60°$

$m\angle CED = \frac{1}{2}(30° + 40°)$
$= 35°$

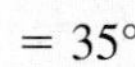

$m\angle CED = \frac{1}{2}(100° - 20°)$
$= 40°$

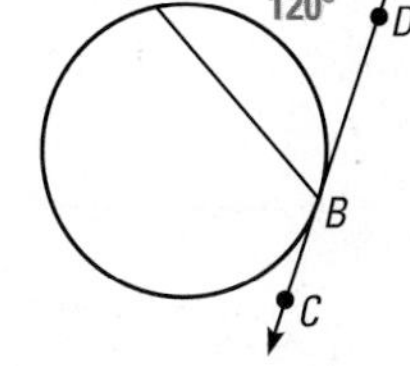

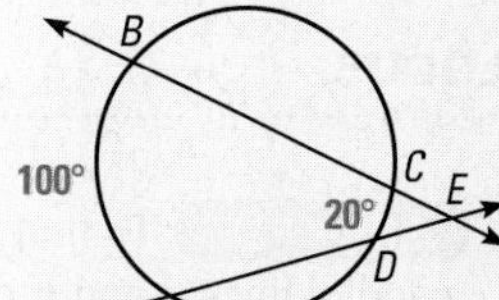

Find the value of *x*.

20. 112

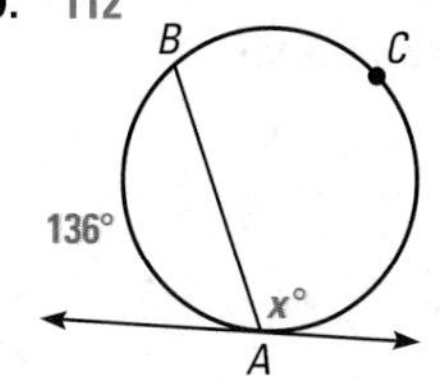

21. 55

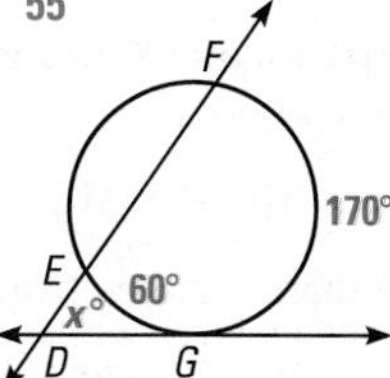

22. 64

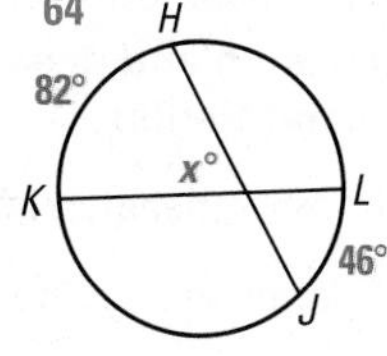

23. 94

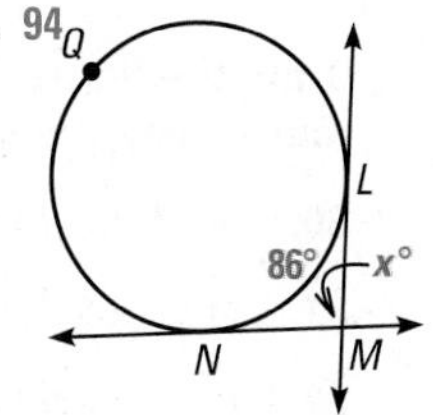

17. True; the sides of the $\triangle$s opp. the inscribed $\angle$s are diameters, so the inscribed $\angle$s are right $\angle$s.

18. False; in kite *ABCD*, the diagonals are $\perp$ so $\overline{AC} \perp \overline{DB}$. Then $m\angle AED = 90°$. If $m\angle ACD = \frac{1}{2}m\angle AED = \frac{1}{2}(90°) = 45°$, then $m\angle DAE = 45°$ as well. *ABCD* is a kite so $\overline{AD} \cong \overline{AB}$. Then $\triangle AED \cong \triangle AEB$ (HL Cong. Thm.) and $m\angle BAE = 45°$. This would make $\angle DAB$ a right angle and so make $\overline{DB}$ a diameter, which would mean that *E* and *D* would be the same point and the diagonals of *ABCD* would bisect each other. That contradicts the given that *ABCD* is a kite. So the assumption that $m\angle ACD = \frac{1}{2} m\angle AED$ must be false.

27.
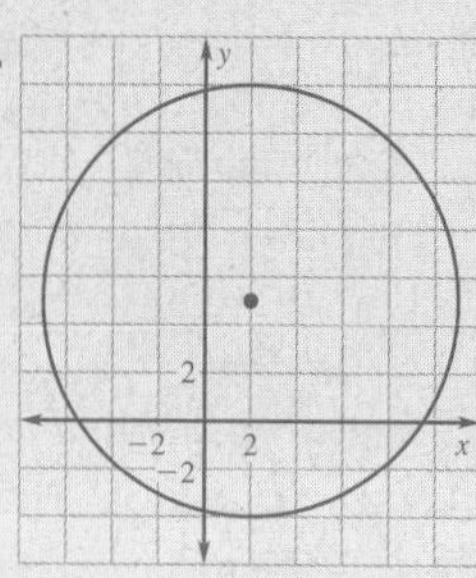

28.
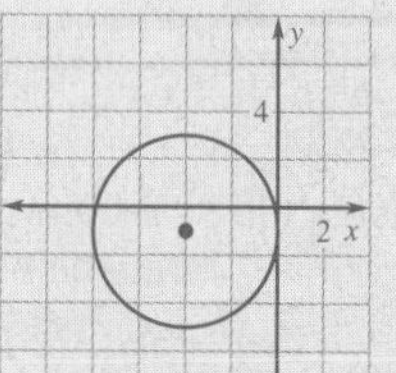

29.
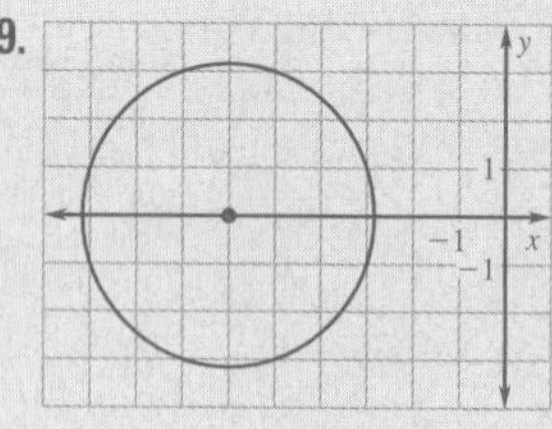

30.
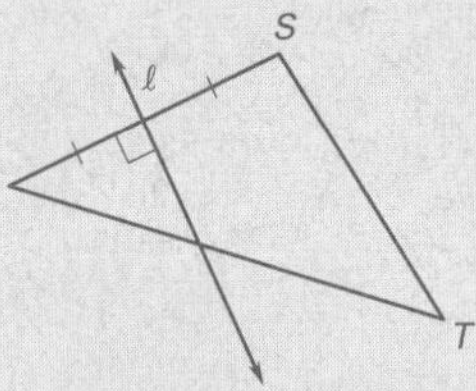

31.
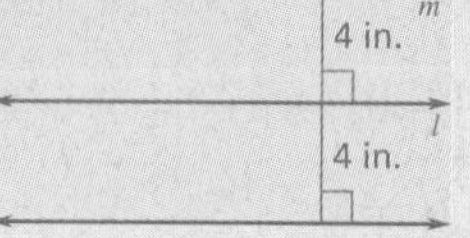

32.
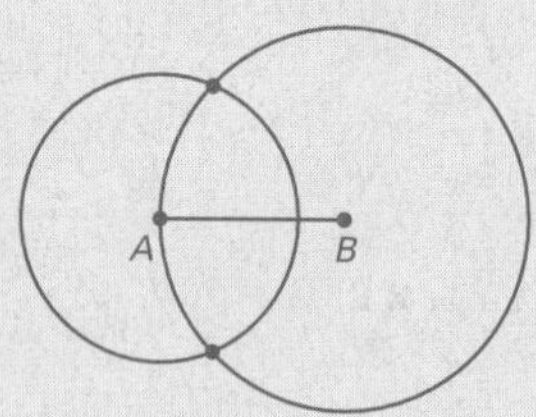

10.5 SEGMENT LENGTHS IN CIRCLES

Examples on pp. 629–631

EXAMPLES $\overline{GE}$ is a tangent segment.

$BF \cdot FE = AF \cdot FD$

$GC \cdot GB = GD \cdot GA$

$(GE)^2 = GD \cdot GA$

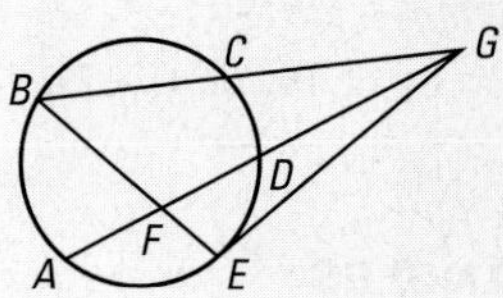

Find the value of *x*.

24. 5

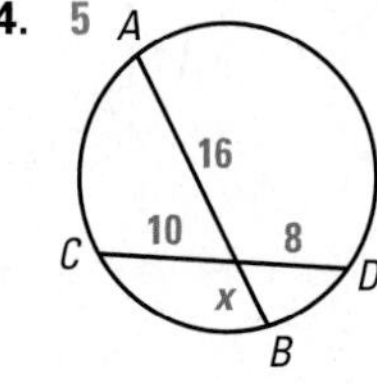

25. 34.4

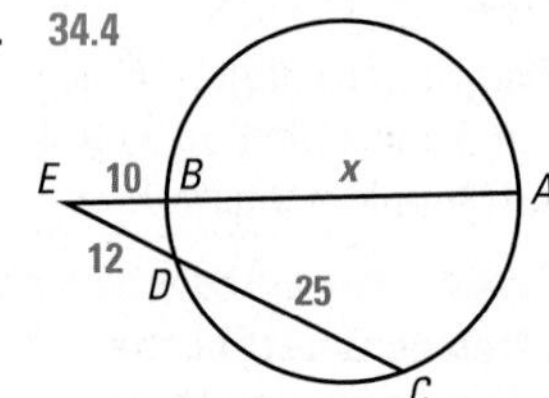

26. 10

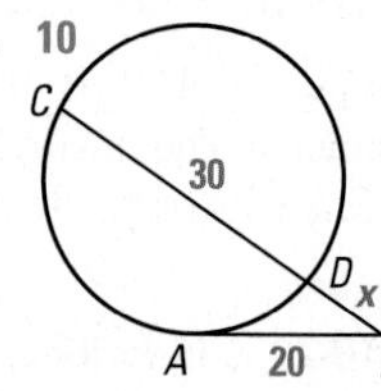

10.6 EQUATIONS OF CIRCLES

Examples on pp. 636–637

EXAMPLE $\odot C$ has center $(-3, -1)$ and radius 2. Its standard equation is

$$[x - (-3)]^2 + [y - (-1)]^2 = 2^2, \text{ or } (x + 3)^2 + (y + 1)^2 = 4.$$

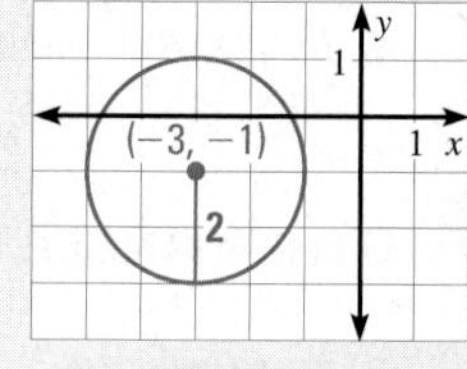

Write the standard equation of the circle. Then graph the equation. 27–29. See margin for figures.

27. Center (2, 5), radius 9
$(x - 2)^2 + (y - 5)^2 = 81$

28. Center $(-4, -1)$, radius 4
$(x + 4)^2 + (y + 1)^2 = 16$

29. Center $(-6, 0)$, radius $\sqrt{10}$
$(x + 6)^2 + y^2 = 10$

10.7 LOCUS

Examples on pp. 642–644

EXAMPLE To find the locus of points equidistant from two parallel lines, *r* and *s*, draw 2 parallel lines, *r* and *s*. Locate several points that are equidistant from *r* and *s*. Identify the pattern. The locus is a line parallel to *r* and *s* and halfway between them.

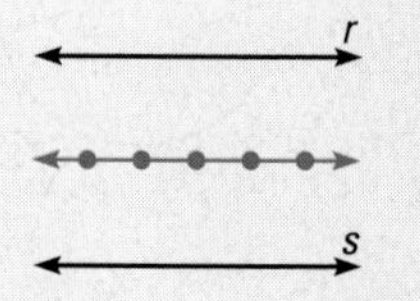

Draw the figure. Then sketch and describe the locus of points on the paper that satisfy the given condition(s). 30–32. See margin for figures.

30. $\triangle RST$, the locus of points that are equidistant from R and S the $\perp$ bisector of $\overline{RS}$

31. Line ℓ, the locus of points that are no more than 4 inches from ℓ 2 lines *m* and *n* on opp. sides of ℓ, each $\parallel$ to ℓ and 4 in. from ℓ, and all the points between *m* and *n*

32. $\overline{AB}$ with length 4 cm, the locus of points 3 cm from A and 4 cm from B
2 points, the intersection of $\odot A$ with radius 3 cm and $\odot B$ with radius 4 cm

CHAPTER 10

Chapter Test

Use the diagram at the right.

1. Which theorems allow you to conclude that $\overline{JK} \cong \overline{MK}$? **2 tangent segments with the same ext. endpoint are ≅; the HL Cong. Thm.**
2. Find the lengths of $\overline{JK}$, $\overline{MP}$, and $\overline{PK}$. **$JK = 4\sqrt{3}$; $MP = 3$; $PK = 4\sqrt{3} + 3$**
3. Show that $\widehat{JL} \cong \widehat{LM}$. **See margin.**
4. Find the measures of $\widehat{JM}$ and $\widehat{JN}$. **120°, about 156.9°**

Use the diagram at the right.

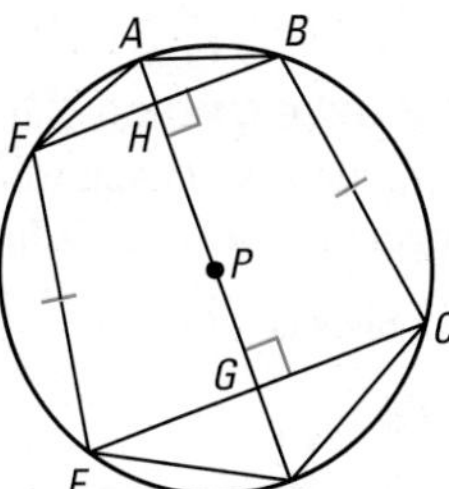

5. Show that $\widehat{AF} \cong \widehat{AB}$ and $\overline{FH} \cong \overline{BH}$. **$\overline{AD} \perp \overline{FB}$; a diameter ⊥ to a chord bisects the chord and its arc.**
6. Show that $\widehat{FE} \cong \widehat{BC}$. **In the same circle, 2 minor arcs with ≅ chords are ≅.**
7. Suppose you were given that $PH = PG$. What could you conclude? **$\overline{FB} \cong \overline{EC}$ and $\widehat{FB} \cong \widehat{EC}$**

Find the measure of each numbered angle in ⊙*P*.

8. 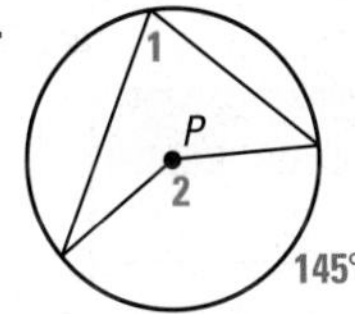

$m\angle 1 = 72.5°$, $m\angle 2 = 145°$

9. 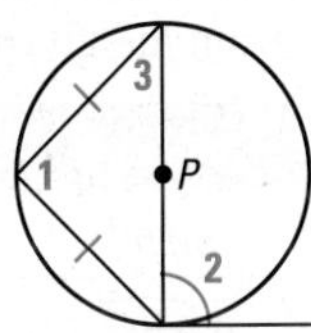

$m\angle 1 = m\angle 2 = 90°$, $m\angle 3 = 45°$

10. 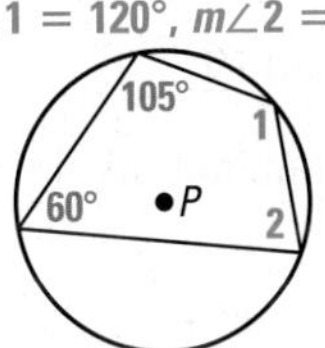

$m\angle 1 = 120°$, $m\angle 2 = 75°$

11. 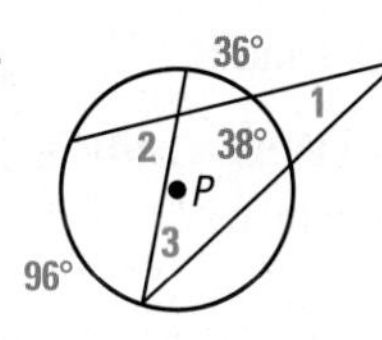

$m\angle 1 = 29°$, $m\angle 2 = 66°$, $m\angle 3 = 37°$

12. Sketch a pentagon *ABCDE* inscribed in a circle. Describe the relationship between (a) $\angle CDE$ and $\angle CAE$ and (b) $\angle CBE$ and $\angle CAE$. **See margin for figure. a. supp. b. cong.**

In the diagram at the right $\overline{CA}$ is tangent to the circle at *A*.

13. If $AG = 2$, $GD = 9$, and $BG = 3$, find GF. **6**
14. If $CF = 12$, $CB = 3$, and $CD = 9$, find CE. **4**
15. If $BF = 9$ and $CB = 3$, find CA. **6**
16. Graph the circle with equation $(x - 4)^2 + (y + 6)^2 = 64$. **See margin.**
17. Sketch and describe the locus of points in the coordinate plane that are equidistant from (0, 3) and (3, 0) and 4 units from the point (4, 0). **See margin.**
18. **ROCK CIRCLE** This circle of rock is in the Ténéré desert in the African country of Niger. The circle is about 60 feet in diameter. About a mile away to the north, south, east, and west, stone arrows point away from the circle. It's not known who created the circle or why. Suppose the center of the circle is at (30, 30) on a grid measured in units of feet. Write an equation for the circle. **See margin.**

19. **DOG RUN** A dog on a leash is able to move freely along a cable that is attached to the ground. The leash allows the dog to move anywhere within 3.5 feet from any point on the 10-foot straight cable. Draw and describe the locus of points that the dog can reach. **See margin.**

19. 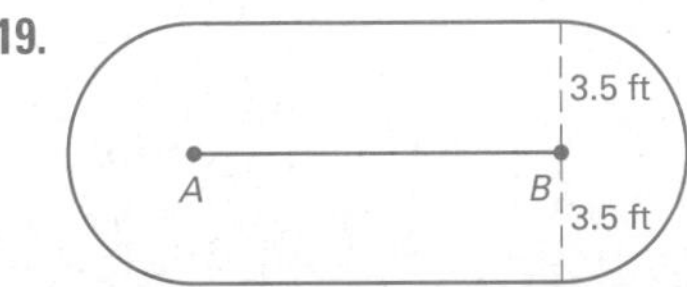

Let *A* and *B* be the ends of the cable. The locus consists of the points on or inside a region bounded by two semicircles with centers *A* and *B* and radius 3.5 ft and two segments on opp. sides of $\overline{AB}$, both ∥ to $\overline{AB}$ and 3.5 ft from $\overline{AB}$.

ADDITIONAL RESOURCES

- ***Chapter 10 Resource Book***
  Chapter Test (3 levels) (p. 112)
  SAT/ACT Chapter Test (p. 118)
  Alternative Assessment (p. 119)
- ***Test and Practice Generator***

3. $\overline{HJ}$ and $\overline{HM}$ are ≅ since they are both radii of ⊙*H*. △*HJK* and △*HMK* are right △s as a tangent line is perpendicular to the radius drawn to the point of tangency and, since $\overline{HK} \cong \overline{HK}$, △*HJK* ≅ △*HMK* by the HL Cong. Thm. Then corresp. ∠s *JHK* and *MHK* are ≅ and $\widehat{JL} \cong \widehat{LM}$ by the def. of the measure of a minor arc and the def. of cong.

12. 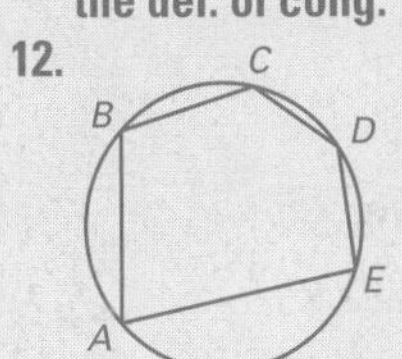

16. 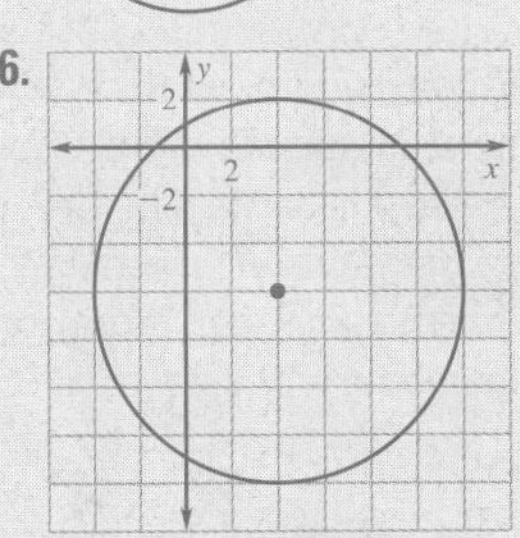

17. 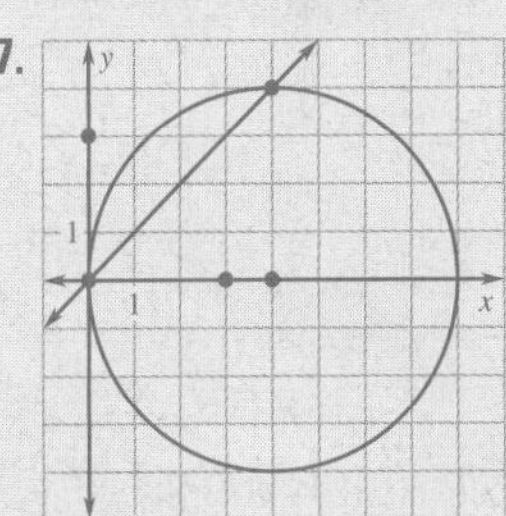

2 points, (0, 0) and (4, 4), on the intersection of the ⊙ with center (4, 0) and radius 4 and the line $y = x$

18. $(x - 30)^2 + (y - 30)^2 = 900$

ADDITIONAL RESOURCES

- ***Chapter 10 Resource Book***
  Chapter Test (3 levels) (p. 112)
  SAT/ACT Chapter Test (p. 118)
  Alternative Assessment (p. 119)
- ***Test and Practice Generator***

21.

A B

22.

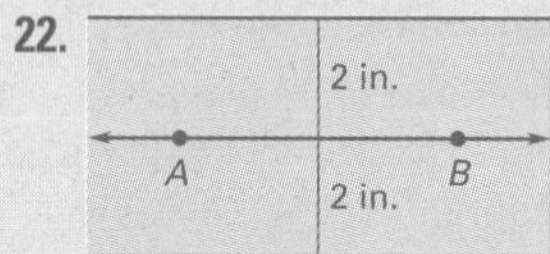

23.

2 in.
A B
2 in.

26. **Farther away; you want to increase the measure of the arc that is presently 30° to 40°. The measure of that arc decreases as you move closer and increases as you move farther away.**

27.

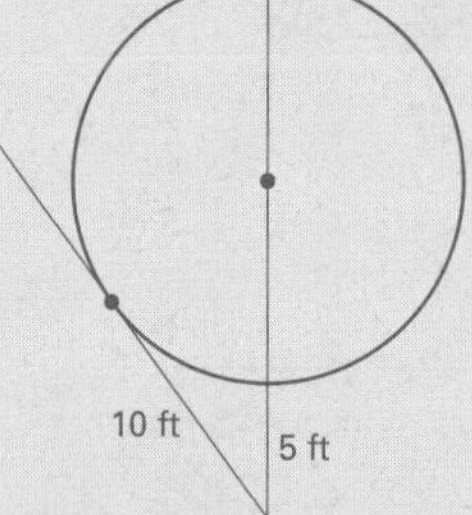

28. **7.5 ft, 15 ft; the radius may be found using the Pythagorean Thm. or Thm. 10.17. (If a secant segment and a tangent segment share an endpoint outside a ⊙, then the product of the length of the secant segment and the length of its external segment equals the square of the length of the tangent segment.)**

654

CHAPTER 10 Chapter Standardized Test

TEST-TAKING STRATEGY Read each test question carefully. Always look for shortcuts that will allow you to work through a problem more quickly.

1. **MULTIPLE CHOICE** How many common tangents do the circles at the right have? D

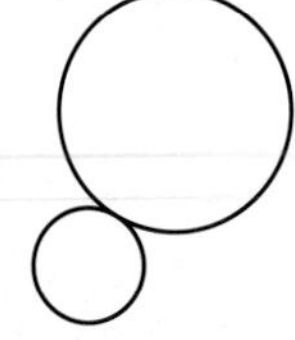

Ⓐ 0 Ⓑ 1 Ⓒ 2 Ⓓ 3 Ⓔ 4

2. **MULTIPLE CHOICE** Suppose $\overline{AB}$ is a diameter of $\odot O$, line r is tangent to $\odot O$ at A, and line s is tangent to $\odot O$ at B. Which statements are true? C

I. r bisects $\overline{AB}$. **II.** $OA = 2 \cdot AB$

III. $r \parallel s$

Ⓐ I only Ⓑ II only Ⓒ III only Ⓓ I and II Ⓔ II and III

3. **MULTIPLE CHOICE** Use the diagram to find the value of x. E

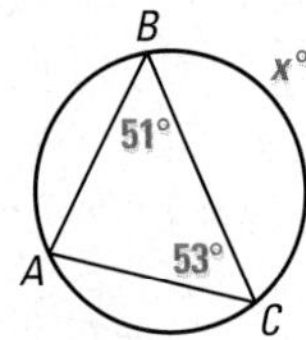

Ⓐ 38 Ⓑ 106 Ⓒ 114 Ⓓ 76 Ⓔ 152

4. **MULTIPLE CHOICE** Find the length of a chord that is 21 cm from the center of a circle with radius 29 cm. B

Ⓐ 20 cm Ⓑ 40 cm Ⓒ 42 cm Ⓓ 8 cm Ⓔ 16 cm

5. **MULTIPLE CHOICE** If $m\angle A = 42°$, find the value of y in the diagram. B

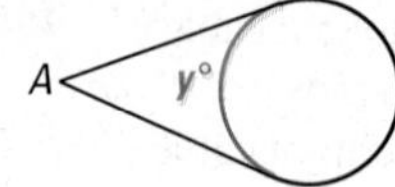

Ⓐ 42 Ⓑ 138 Ⓒ 318 Ⓓ 222 Ⓔ cannot be determined

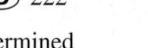

QUANTITATIVE COMPARISON **In Exercises 6 and 7, use the diagram to choose the statement that is true. $\overleftrightarrow{KF}$ is tangent to the circle.**

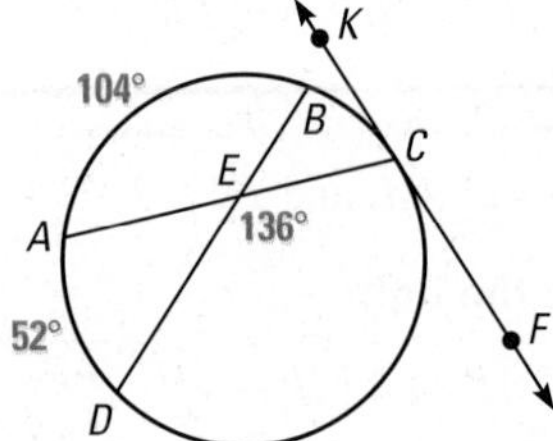

Ⓐ The quantity in column A is greater.

Ⓑ The quantity in column B is greater.

Ⓒ The two quantities are equal.

Ⓓ The relationship cannot be determined from the given information.

	Column A	Column B	
6.	$m\widehat{DC}$	168°	C
7.	$m\widehat{ABC}$	$m\angle FCA$	A

8. **MULTIPLE CHOICE** A diameter of a circle has endpoints $(-4, 8)$ and $(6, 2)$. What is an equation of the circle? A

Ⓐ $(x - 1)^2 + (y - 5)^2 = 34$

Ⓑ $(x + 1)^2 + (y + 5)^2 = 34$

Ⓒ $(x - 6)^2 + (y - 2)^2 = 136$

Ⓓ $(x - 1)^2 + (y - 5)^2 = 136$

Ⓔ $(x + 1)^2 + (y - 5)^2 = 34$

9. **MULTIPLE CHOICE** Describe the locus of all points in the coordinate plane that are equidistant from points $(-3, 1)$ and $(1, 9)$ and 2 units from the line $x = -7$. D

Ⓐ $(-5, 7)$

Ⓑ The line $y = -5$

Ⓒ $(-5, 8)$ and $(-9, 10)$

Ⓓ $(-5, 7)$ and $(-9, 9)$

Ⓔ $(-7, 8)$

MULTI-STEP PROBLEM Quadrilateral *EFGH* is inscribed in a circle. $m\angle E = x^2 + 15$, $m\angle F = 27x$, and $m\angle G = 6x^2 - 10$.

10. Find the value of x. 5

11. Find the measure of each angle of the quadrilateral. $m\angle E = 40°$, $m\angle F = 135°$, $m\angle G = 140°$, $m\angle H = 45°$

12. If $m\widehat{GH} = 30°$, find the measures of $\widehat{EF}$, $\widehat{FG}$, and $\widehat{EH}$. $m\widehat{EF} = 40°$, $m\widehat{FG} = 50°$, $m\widehat{EH} = 240°$

MULTI-STEP PROBLEM The points $A(0, 0)$, $B(3, 0)$, and $C(0, 4)$ lie on $\odot P$.

13. Explain why $\overline{BC}$ is a diameter of $\odot P$. $\triangle ABC$ is inscribed in the $\odot$ and $\overline{BC}$ is the hypotenuse of the $\triangle$. (The hypotenuse of an inscribed right $\triangle$ is a diameter.)

14. Find the coordinates of point P and the radius of $\odot P$. $\left(\frac{3}{2}, 2\right)$; $\frac{5}{2}$

15. Write an equation of $\odot P$. $\left(x - \frac{3}{2}\right)^2 + (y - 2)^2 = \frac{25}{4}$

16. What is the locus of points in the coordinate plane that are equidistant from A, B, and C? the point $\left(\frac{3}{2}, 2\right)$

MULTI-STEP PROBLEM In Exercises 17–20, use the diagram at the right. $\overrightarrow{CJ}$ is tangent to $\odot E$ at C and $\overline{KH}$ is tangent to $\odot E$ at H.

17. Find the length of the segment, the measure of the arc, or the measure of the angle. Round your answer to two decimal places, if necessary.

a. GF 3 **b.** KH 24 **c.** $m\widehat{BGD}$ 180°

d. $m\widehat{BC}$ 90° **e.** $m\angle CDB$ 45° **f.** $m\angle BCJ$ 45°

18. Name two congruent arcs. Justify your answer. $\widehat{BC}$ and $\widehat{DC}$; 2 arcs are $\cong$ if their corresponding chords are $\cong$.

19. If $m\angle BFD = 120°$, find $m\widehat{AG}$. 60°

20. If $m\angle K = 16°$, find the measures of $\widehat{BH}$ and $\widehat{HD}$. $m\widehat{BH} = 106°$, $m\widehat{HD} = 74°$

MULTI-STEP PROBLEM Sketch and describe the locus. 21–23. See margin for figures.

21. The locus of points that are equidistant from A and B. the $\perp$ bisector of $\overline{AB}$

22. The locus of points that are 2 inches or less from $\overleftrightarrow{AB}$. a part of the plane bounded by two parallel lines on either side of $\overleftrightarrow{AB}$ that are 4 inches apart

23. The locus of points that are equidistant from A and B and are 2 inches or less from $\overleftrightarrow{AB}$. the 4 in. segment of the $\perp$ bisector of $\overline{AB}$ with 2 in. on either side of $\overline{AB}$

MULTI-STEP PROBLEM In Exercises 24–26, use the diagram. Television cameras are positioned at *A*, *B*, and *Q*. The stage is an arc of $\odot Q$.

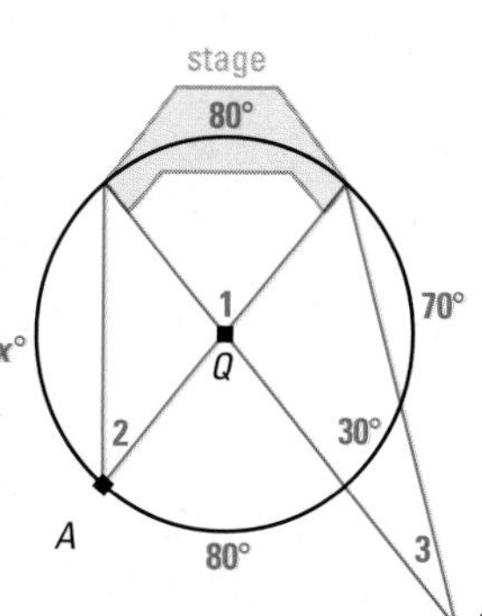

24. Find the value of x. 100

25. Find the measures of $\angle 1$, $\angle 2$, and $\angle 3$. $m\angle 1 = 80°$, $m\angle 2 = 40°$, $m\angle 3 = 25°$

26. *Writing* Suppose you are operating the camera located at point B. If you want a 20° angle of the stage, should you move closer to the stage or farther away? Explain. See margin.

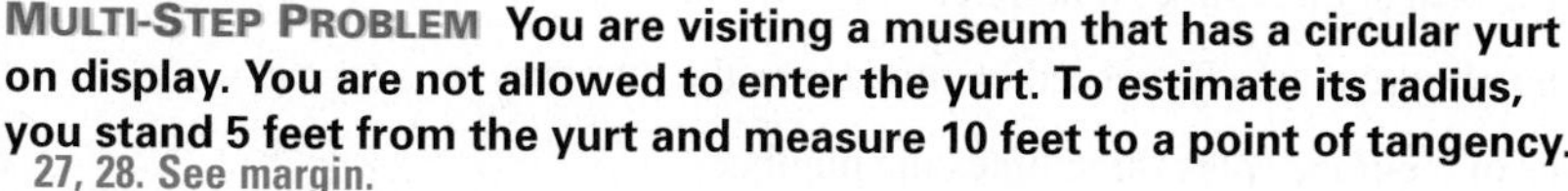

MULTI-STEP PROBLEM You are visiting a museum that has a circular yurt on display. You are not allowed to enter the yurt. To estimate its radius, you stand 5 feet from the yurt and measure 10 feet to a point of tangency. 27, 28. See margin.

27. Sketch a diagram to model the problem.

28. Find the radius and diameter of the yurt. Explain your method.

EXTRA EXAMPLE 1

Given the formula for the area of a regular polygon, solve for n.

$A = \frac{1}{2}ans.$ $n = \frac{2A}{as}$

EXTRA EXAMPLE 2

a. Write an expression for eleven more than twice a number. $2x + 11$

b. Write an equation for 6 more than a number is 5 less than twice the number, then solve. $x + 6 = 2x - 5$; 11

c. $(4\sqrt{13})^2$ 208

CHECKPOINT EXERCISES

For use after Example 1:

1. Given the formula for the area of a sector, solve for r.

$A = \frac{x}{360} \cdot \pi r^2$ $r = \sqrt{\frac{360A}{x\pi}}$

For use after Example 2:

2. a. Write an expression for 5 greater than a number. $x + 5$

b. Write an equation for twelve is 3 times a number decreased by 3, then solve. $12 = 3x - 3$; 5

CHAPTER 10

Algebra Review

EXAMPLE 1 Solving Literal Equations

Given the formula for the surface area of a right cylinder, solve for h.

$S = 2\pi r^2 + 2\pi rh$

$$S = 2\pi r(r + h) \qquad \text{or} \qquad S - 2\pi r^2 = 2\pi rh$$

$$\frac{S}{2\pi r} = r + h \qquad \frac{(S - 2\pi r^2)}{2\pi r} = h$$

$$\frac{S}{2\pi r} - r = h$$

EXERCISES

Solve the literal equation for the indicated variable. Assume variables are positive.

1. $A = \ell w$; w $\frac{A}{\ell}$
2. $V = \frac{4}{3}\pi r^3$; r $\sqrt[3]{\frac{3V}{4\pi}}$, or $\frac{\sqrt[3]{6\pi^2 V}}{2\pi}$
3. $A = \frac{1}{2}bh$; h $\frac{2A}{b}$
4. $A = \frac{1}{2}h(b_1 + b_2)$; b_1 $\frac{2A}{h} - b_2$
5. $A = \pi r^2$; r $\frac{\sqrt{A\pi}}{\pi}$
6. $C = 2\pi r$; r $\frac{C}{2\pi}$
7. $V = s^3$; s $\sqrt[3]{V}$
8. $P = 2\ell + 2w$; ℓ $\frac{P - 2w}{2}$
9. $V = \ell wh$; h $\frac{V}{\ell w}$
10. $V = \pi r^2 h$; h $\frac{V}{\pi r^2}$
11. $S = 6s^2$; s $\frac{\sqrt{6S}}{6}$
12. $a^2 + b^2 = c^2$; b $\sqrt{c^2 - a^2}$

EXAMPLE 2 Algebraic Expressions

a. Write an expression for seven less than a number.
$x - 7$

b. Write an equation for three less than six times a number is five times the same number plus 5, then solve.
$6x - 3 = 5x + 5$
$x - 3 = 5$
$x = 8$

EXERCISES

Write the expression or equation. Solve the equations.

13. Five plus a number $5 + x$
14. A number squared increased by the square root of 2 $x^2 + \sqrt{2}$
15. Twice a number decreased by fourteen $2x - 14$
16. Six less than three times a number $3x - 6$
17. A number plus two decreased by nine times the number $x + 2 - 9x$
18. Half of a number plus three times the number $\frac{x}{2} + 3x$
19. The product of five and a number decreased by seven equals thirteen. $5x - 7 = 13$; 4
20. Sixteen less than twice a number is 10. $2x - 16 = 10$; 13

21. Twice a number increased by the product of the number and fourteen results in forty-eight. $2x + 14x = 48$; 3

22. Half of a number is three times the sum of the number and five. $\frac{x}{2} = 3(x + 5)$; -6

EXAMPLE 3 ***Percent Problems***

a. What number is 12% of 75?
$$x = 0.12(75)$$
$$x = 9$$

b. 6 is what percent of 40?
$$6 = 40p$$
$$0.15 = p$$
$$p = 15\%$$

EXERCISES

Solve.

23. What number is 30% of 120? 36

24. What distance is 15% of 340 miles? 51 miles

25. What number is 71% of 200? 142

26. How much money is 50% of \$25? \$12.50

27. 34 is what percent of 136? 25%

28. 11 dogs is what percent of 50 dogs? 22%

29. 200 is what percent of 50? 400%

30. 8 weeks is what percent of a year? about 15%

31. 3 is 30% of what number? 10

32. 16 meters is 64% of what distance? 25 meters

33. If sales tax is 8%, how much tax is charged on a \$25.95 purchase? \$2.08

34. 15 out of 18 players on a team came to a tournament. What percent of the players were absent? about 17%

EXAMPLE 4 ***Simplifying Rational Expressions***

Simplify.

a. $\dfrac{8x^2 + 12x}{4x^2 + 16x}$

$\dfrac{4x(2x + 3)}{4x(x + 4)}$

$\dfrac{2x + 3}{x + 4}$

b. $\dfrac{y^2 - 9}{y^2 + 6y + 9}$

$\dfrac{(y + 3)(y - 3)}{(y + 3)(y + 3)}$

$\dfrac{y - 3}{y + 3}$

EXERCISES

Simplify.

35. $\dfrac{5x}{10x^2}$ $\dfrac{1}{2x}$

36. $\dfrac{16a^3}{8a}$ $2a^2$

37. $\dfrac{(5x^2 + x)}{(5x + 1)}$ x

38. $\dfrac{9w^3 + 27w}{3w^3 + 9w}$ 3

39. $\dfrac{5a + 10}{5a - 40}$ $\dfrac{a + 2}{a - 8}$

40. $\dfrac{5x^2 + 15x}{30x^2 - 5x}$ $\dfrac{x + 3}{6x - 1}$

41. $\dfrac{14d^2 - 2d}{6d^2 + 8d}$ $\dfrac{7d - 1}{3d + 4}$

42. $\dfrac{2y - 12}{24 - 2y}$ $\dfrac{y - 6}{12 - y}$

43. $\dfrac{36s^2 - 4s}{4s^2 - 12s}$ $\dfrac{9s - 1}{s - 3}$

44. $\dfrac{-5h + 1}{h + 1}$ $\dfrac{-5h + 1}{h + 1}$

45. $\dfrac{t^2 - 1}{t^2 + 2t + 1}$ $\dfrac{t - 1}{t + 1}$

46. $\dfrac{m^2 - 4m + 4}{m^2 - 4}$ $\dfrac{m - 2}{m + 2}$

EXTRA EXAMPLE 3

a. 50 is 25% of what number? 200

b. What number is 40% of 15? 6

EXTRA EXAMPLE 4

Simplify.

a. $\dfrac{3x^2 - 3x}{2x - 2}$ $\dfrac{3x}{2}$

b. $\dfrac{x^2 + 3x - 10}{x^2 - 25}$ $\dfrac{x - 2}{x - 5}$

CHECKPOINT EXERCISES

For use after Example 1:

1. a. 7 is 20% of what number? 35

b. 9 inches is what percent of 1 foot? 75%

For use after Extra Example 4:

2. a. $\dfrac{4y + 4}{8y + 12}$ $\dfrac{y + 1}{2y + 3}$

b. $\dfrac{x^2 + 6x + 9}{x^2 + 3x}$ $\dfrac{x + 3}{x}$

CHAPTER 11

PLANNING THE CHAPTER

Area of Polygons and Circles

TASK 1

GOALS

LESSON	GOALS	NCTM	ITED	SAT9	Terra-Nova	Local
11.1 *pp. 661–668*	GOAL 1 Find the measures of interior and exterior angles of polygons. GOAL 2 Use measures of angles of polygons to solve real-life problems.	1, 2, 3, 4, 6, 8, 9, 10	MIM, MIGE, RQGE	1, 27	11, 13, 14, 16, 17, 18, 49, 51	12, 13
11.2 *pp. 669–675*	GOAL 1 Find the area of an equilateral triangle. GOAL 2 Find the area of a regular polygon.	1, 2, 3, 4	MCE, SAPE, MIM, MIGE	29	10, 11, 13, 14, 16, 49, 51	8, 10, 16, 19
11.3 *pp. 676–682*	CONCEPT ACTIVITY: 11.3 *Investigate area relationships in similar figures.* GOAL 1 Compare perimeters and areas of similar figures. GOAL 2 Use perimeters and areas of similar figures to solve real-life problems.	1, 2, 3, 4, 6, 8, 9, 10	MCE, SAPE, MIM, MIGE, MIRA, RQGE	1, 29	10, 11, 13, 14, 16, 17, 18, 48, 49, 51	4, 8, 11, 21
11.4 *pp. 683–690*	GOAL 1 Find the circumference of a circle and the length of a circular arc. GOAL 2 Use circumference and arc length to solve real-life problems. TECHNOLOGY ACTIVITY: 11.4 *Explore perimeters of regular polygons using a spreadsheet.*	1, 2, 3, 4, 6, 8, 9, 10	MIM, MIGE, RQGE	1, 31	11, 13, 14, 16, 17, 18, 49, 51	8, 19, 21
11.5 *pp. 691–698*	GOAL 1 Find the area of a circle and a sector of a circle. GOAL 2 Use areas of circles and sectors to solve real-life problems.	1, 2, 3, 4, 6, 8, 9, 10	MCE, SAPE, MIM, MIGE, RQGE	1, 29	10, 11, 13, 14, 16, 17, 18, 48, 49, 51, 52	8, 19, 21
11.6 *pp. 699–706*	GOAL 1 Find a geometric probability. GOAL 2 Uses geometric probability to solve real-life problems. TECHNOLOGY ACTIVITY: 11.6 *Explore experimental probability using a graphing calculator simulation.*	1, 2, 3, 4, 5, 6, 8, 9, 10	SAPP, MIM, MIP, MIGE, RQGE, MIPE	1, 15, 29, 41	11, 13, 14, 15, 16, 17, 18, 48, 49, 50, 51, 52	8, 10

RESOURCES

Chapter Resource Booklets

Chapter Support

Tips for New Teachers	p. 1
Parent Guide for Student Success	p. 3
Prerequisite Skills Review	p. 5
Strategies for Reading Mathematics	p. 7

Lesson Support

Lesson Support	11.1	11.2	11.3	11.4	11.5	11.6
Lesson Plans (regular and block)	p. 9	p. 23	p. 38	p. 53	p. 67	p. 83
Warm-Up Exercises and Daily Quiz	p. 11	p. 25	p. 40	p. 55	p. 69	p. 85
Activity Support Masters			p. 41			
Lesson Openers	p. 12	p. 26	p. 42	p. 56	p. 70	p. 86
Technology Activities & Keystrokes	p. 13	p. 27		p. 57	p. 71	p. 87
Practice (3 levels)	p. 14	p. 30	p. 43	p. 59	p. 75	p. 89
Reteaching with Practice	p. 17	p. 33	p. 46	p. 62	p. 78	p. 92
Quick Catch-Up for Absent Students	p. 19	p. 35	p. 48	p. 64	p. 80	p. 94
Cooperative Learning Activities	p. 20					
Interdisciplinary Applications	p. 21		p. 49		p. 81	
Real-Life Applications		p. 36		p. 65		p. 95
Math & History Applications			p. 50			
Challenge: Skills and Applications	p. 22	p. 37	p. 51	p. 66	p. 82	p. 96

Review and Assessment

Quizzes	pp. 52, 97
Chapter Review Games and Activities	p. 98
Chapter Test (3 levels)	pp. 99–104
SAT/ACT Chapter Test	p. 105
Alternative Assessment with Math Journal	p. 106
Project with Rubric	p. 108
Cumulative Review	p. 110
Resource Book Answers	p. A1

Transparencies

	11.1	11.2	11.3	11.4	11.5	11.6
Warm-Up Exercises and Daily Quiz	p. 79	p. 80	p. 81	p. 82	p. 83	p. 84
Alternative Lesson Opener Transparencies	p. 68	p. 69	p. 70	p. 71	p. 72	p. 73
Examples/Standardized Test Practice	✓	✓	✓	✓	✓	✓
Answer Transparencies	✓	✓	✓	✓	✓	✓

Technology

- Electronic Teaching Tools
- Online Lesson Planner
- Internet Support
- Personal Student Tutor
- Test and Practice Generator
- Geometry in Motion video
- Electronic Lesson Presentations (Lesson 11.5)

Additional Resources

- Basic Skills Workbook: Diagnosis and Remediation
- Worked-Out Solution Key
- Resources in Spanish
- Standardized Test Practice Workbook
- Practice Workbook with Examples

Correlations to the California Curriculum

Correlations to California Standards
See Teacher's Edition pp. CA9–CA11

Correlations to SAT9
Task 1: See Teacher's Edition pp. CA12–CA14
Task 2: See Teacher's Edition pp. CA15–CA17

CHAPTER 11

PACING THE CHAPTER

Resource Key
- STUDENT EDITION
- CHAPTER 11 RESOURCE BOOK
- TEACHER'S EDITION

REGULAR SCHEDULE

Day 1

11.1

STARTING OPTIONS
- Prereq. Skills Review
- Strategies for Reading
- Homework Check
- Warm-Up or Daily Quiz

TEACHING OPTIONS
- Motivating the Lesson
- Les. Opener (Visual)
- Examples 1–5
- Guided Practice Exs.

APPLY/HOMEWORK
- See Assignment Guide.
- See the CRB: Practice, Reteach, Apply, Extend

ASSESSMENT OPTIONS
- Checkpoint Exercises

Day 2

11.1 *(cont.)*

STARTING OPTIONS
- Homework Check

TEACHING OPTIONS
- Examples 1–5
- Closure Question

APPLY/HOMEWORK
- See Assignment Guide.
- See the CRB: Practice, Reteach, Apply, Extend

ASSESSMENT OPTIONS
- Checkpoint Exercises
- Daily Quiz (11.1)
- Stand. Test Practice

Day 3

11.2

STARTING OPTIONS
- Homework Check
- Warm-Up or Daily Quiz

TEACHING OPTIONS
- Motivating the Lesson
- Les. Opener (Activity)
- Technology Activity
- Examples 1–3
- Guided Practice Exs. 1–6

APPLY/HOMEWORK
- See Assignment Guide.
- See the CRB: Practice, Reteach, Apply, Extend

ASSESSMENT OPTIONS
- Checkpoint Exercises, pp. 670–671

Day 4

11.2 *(cont.)*

STARTING OPTIONS
- Homework Check

TEACHING OPTIONS
- Example 4
- Closure Question
- Guided Practice Exs. 7–8

APPLY/HOMEWORK
- See Assignment Guide.
- See the CRB: Practice, Reteach, Apply, Extend

ASSESSMENT OPTIONS
- Checkpoint Exercises, p. 671
- Daily Quiz (11.2)
- Stand. Test Practice

Day 5

11.3

STARTING OPTIONS
- Homework Check
- Warm-Up or Daily Quiz

TEACHING OPTIONS
- Motivating the Lesson
- Concept Act. & Wksht.
- Les. Opener (Spreadsheet)
- Examples 1–3
- Guided Practice Exs.

APPLY/HOMEWORK
- See Assignment Guide.
- See the CRB: Practice, Reteach, Apply, Extend

ASSESSMENT OPTIONS
- Checkpoint Exercises

Day 6

11.3 *(cont.)*

STARTING OPTIONS
- Homework Check

TEACHING OPTIONS
- Examples 1–3
- Closure Question

APPLY/HOMEWORK
- See Assignment Guide.
- See the CRB: Practice, Reteach, Apply, Extend

ASSESSMENT OPTIONS
- Checkpoint Exercises
- Daily Quiz (11.3)
- Stand. Test Practice
- Quiz (11.1–11.3)

Day 9

11.5

STARTING OPTIONS
- Homework Check
- Warm-Up or Daily Quiz

TEACHING OPTIONS
- Motivating the Lesson
- Les. Opener (Application)
- Technology Activity
- Examples 1–6
- Closure Question
- Guided Practice Exs.

APPLY/HOMEWORK
- See Assignment Guide.
- See the CRB: Practice, Reteach, Apply, Extend

ASSESSMENT OPTIONS
- Checkpoint Exercises
- Daily Quiz (11.5)
- Stand. Test Practice

Day 10

11.6

STARTING OPTIONS
- Homework Check
- Warm-Up or Daily Quiz

TEACHING OPTIONS
- Les. Opener (Activity)
- Examples 1–2
- Guided Practice Exs. 1–3

APPLY/HOMEWORK
- See Assignment Guide.
- See the CRB: Practice, Reteach, Apply, Extend

ASSESSMENT OPTIONS
- Checkpoint Exercises, p. 700

Day 11

11.6 *(cont.)*

STARTING OPTIONS
- Homework Check

TEACHING OPTIONS
- Examples 3–4
- Technology Activity
- Closure Question
- Guided Practice Exs. 4–8

APPLY/HOMEWORK
- See Assignment Guide.
- See the CRB: Practice, Reteach, Apply, Extend

ASSESSMENT OPTIONS
- Checkpoint Exercises, pp. 700–701
- Daily Quiz (11.6)
- Stand. Test Practice
- Quiz (11.4–11.6)

Day 12

Review

DAY 12 START OPTIONS
- Homework Check

REVIEWING OPTIONS
- Chapter 11 Summary
- Chapter 11 Review
- Chapter Review Games and Activities

APPLY/HOMEWORK
- Chapter 11 Test (practice)
- Ch. Standardized Test (practice)

Day 13

Assess

DAY 13 START OPTIONS
- Homework Check

ASSESSMENT OPTIONS
- Chapter 11 Test
- SAT/ACT Ch. 11 Test
- Alternative Assessment

APPLY/HOMEWORK
- Skill Review, p. 718

Day 7

11.4

Starting Options
- Homework Check
- Warm-Up or Daily Quiz

Teaching Options
- Les. Opener (Application)
- Examples 1–3
- Guided Practice Exs. 1–11

Apply/Homework
- See Assignment Guide.
- See the CRB: Practice, Reteach, Apply, Extend

Assessment Options
- Checkpoint Exercises, p. 684

Day 8

11.4 *(cont.)*

Starting Options
- Homework Check

Teaching Options
- Examples 4–5
- Technology Activity
- Closure Question
- Guided Practice Exs. 12–14

Apply/Homework
- See Assignment Guide.
- See the CRB: Practice, Reteach, Apply, Extend

Assessment Options
- Checkpoint Exercises, p. 685
- Daily Quiz (11.4)
- Stand. Test Practice

BLOCK SCHEDULE

Day 1

11.1

Day 1 Start Options
- Prereq. Skills Review
- Strategies for Reading
- Homework Check
- Warm-Up or Daily Quiz

Teaching 11.1 Options
- Motivating the Lesson
- Les. Opener (Visual)
- Examples 1–5
- Closure Question
- Guided Practice Exs.

Apply/Homework
- See Assignment Guide.
- See the CRB: Practice, Reteach, Apply, Extend

Assessment Options
- Checkpoint Exercises
- Daily Quiz (Les. 11.1)
- Stand. Test Practice

Day 2

11.2

Day 2 Start Options
- Homework Check
- Warm-Up or Daily Quiz

Teaching 11.2 Options
- Motivating the Lesson
- Les. Opener (Activity)
- Technology Activity
- Examples 1–4
- Closure Question
- Guided Practice Exs.

Apply/Homework
- See Assignment Guide.
- See the CRB: Practice, Reteach, Apply, Extend

Assessment Options
- Checkpoint Exercises
- Daily Quiz (Les. 11.2)
- Stand. Test Practice

Day 3

11.3

Day 3 Start Options
- Homework Check
- Warm-Up or Daily Quiz

Teaching 11.3 Options
- Motivating the Lesson
- Concept Act. & Wksht.
- Les. Opener (Spreadsheet)
- Examples 1–3
- Closure Question
- Guided Practice Exs.

Apply/Homework
- See Assignment Guide.
- See the CRB: Practice, Reteach, Apply, Extend

Assessment Options
- Checkpoint Exercises
- Daily Quiz (Les. 11.3)
- Stand. Test Practice
- Quiz (11.1–11.3)

Day 4

11.4

Day 4 Start Options
- Homework Check
- Warm-Up or Daily Quiz

Teaching 11.4 Options
- Les. Opener (Appl.)
- Examples 1–5
- Technology Activity
- Closure Question
- Guided Practice Exs.

Apply/Homework
- See Assignment Guide.
- See the CRB: Practice, Reteach, Apply, Extend

Assessment Options
- Checkpoint Exercises
- Daily Quiz (Les. 11.4)
- Stand. Test Practice

Day 5

11.5 & 11.6

Day 5 Start Options
- Homework Check
- Warm-Up (Les. 11.5) or Daily Quiz (Les. 11.4)

Teaching 11.5 Options
- Motivating the Lesson
- Les. Opener (Appl.)
- Technology Activity
- Examples 1–6
- Closure Question
- Guided Practice Exs.

Beginning 11.6 Options
- Warm-Up (Les. 11.6)
- Les. Opener (Activity)
- Examples 1–2
- Guided Practice Exs. 1–3

Apply/Homework
- See Assignment Guide.
- See the CRB: Practice, Reteach, Apply, Extend

Assessment Options
- Checkpoint Exercises
- Daily Quiz (Les. 11.5)
- Stand. Test Prac. (11.5)

Day 6

11.6 & Review

Day 6 Start Options
- Homework Check
- Daily Quiz (Les. 11.5)

Finishing 11.6 Options
- Examples 3–4
- Technology Activity
- Closure Question
- Guided Practice Exs. 4–8

Reviewing Options
- Chapter 11 Summary
- Chapter 11 Review
- Chapter Review Games and Activities

Apply/Homework
- See Assignment Guide.
- See the CRB: Practice, Reteach, Apply, Extend
- Chapter 11 Test (practice)
- Ch. Standardized Test (practice)

Assessment Options
- Checkpoint Exercises
- Daily Quiz (Les. 11.6)
- Stand. Test Practice
- Quiz (11.4–11.6)

Day 7

Assess & 12.1

(Day 7 = Ch. 12 Day 1)

Assessment Options
- Chapter 11 Test
- SAT/ACT Ch. 11 Test
- Alternative Assessment

Ch. 12 Start Options
- Skill Review, p. 718
- Prereq. Skills Review
- Strategies for Reading

Teaching 12.1 Options
- Warm-Up (Les. 12.1)
- Motivating the Lesson
- Les. Opener (Activity)
- Examples 1–6
- Closure Question
- Guided Practice Exs.

Apply/Homework
- See Assignment Guide.
- See the CRB: Practice, Reteach, Apply, Extend

Assessment Options
- Checkpoint Exercises
- Daily Quiz (Les. 12.1)
- Stand. Test Practice

CHAPTER 11 MEETING INDIVIDUAL NEEDS

BEFORE THE CHAPTER

The *Chapter 11 Resource Book* has the following materials to distribute and use before the chapter:

- **Parent Guide for Student Success**
- **Prerequisite Skills Review**
- **Strategies for Reading Mathematics (pictured below)**

STRATEGIES FOR READING *Pages 7–8*

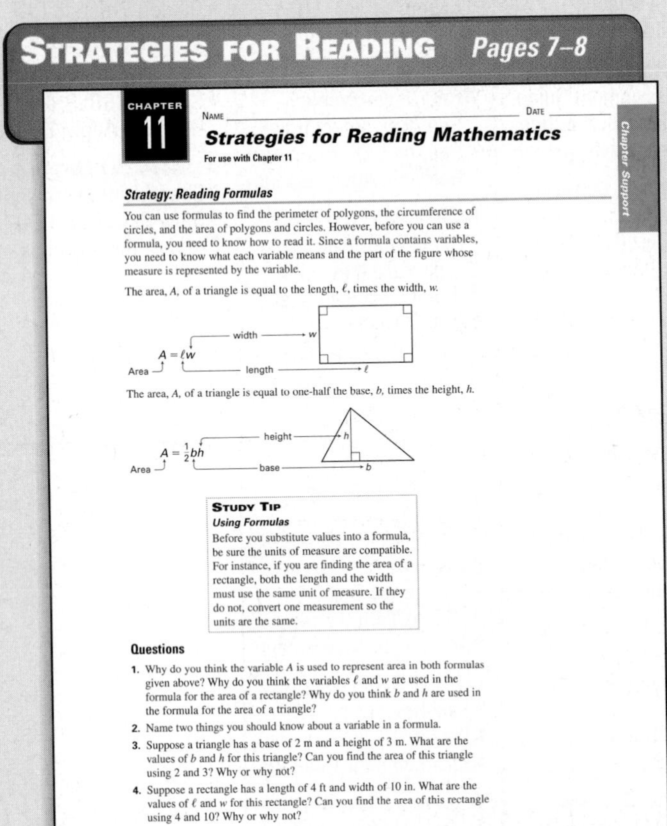

CHAPTER 11 NAME ______ DATE ______

Strategies for Reading Mathematics

For use with Chapter 11

Chapter Support

Strategy: Reading Formulas

You can use formulas to find the perimeter of polygons, the circumference of circles, and the area of polygons and circles. However, before you can use a formula, you need to know how to read it. Since a formula contains variables, you need to know what each variable means and the part of the figure whose measure is represented by the variable.

The area, A, of a triangle is equal to the length, ℓ, times the width, w.

The area, A, of a triangle is equal to one-half the base, b, times the height, h.

STUDY TIP
Using Formulas
Before you substitute values into a formula, be sure the units of measure are compatible. For instance, if you are finding the area of a rectangle, both the length and the width must use the same unit of measure. If they do not, convert one measurement so the units are the same.

Questions

1. Why do you think the variable A is used to represent area in both formulas given above? Why do you think the variables ℓ and w are used in the formula for the area of a rectangle? Why do you think b and h are used in the formula for the area of a triangle?
2. Name two things you should know about a variable in a formula.
3. Suppose a triangle has a base of 2 m and a height of 3 m. What are the values of b and h for this triangle? Can you find the area of this triangle using 2 and 3? Why or why not?
4. Suppose a rectangle has a length of 4 ft and width of 10 in. What are the values of ℓ and w for this rectangle? Can you find the area of this rectangle using 4 and 10? Why or why not?

STRATEGIES FOR READING MATHEMATICS These two pages give students tips about reading and using formulas as they prepare for Chapter 11 and provide a visual glossary of key vocabulary words in the chapter, such as center of a polygon and arc length.

DURING EACH LESSON

The *Chapter 11 Resource Book* has the following alternatives for introducing the lesson:

- **Lesson Openers (pictured below)**
- **Technology Activities with Keystrokes**

LESSON OPENER *Page 70*

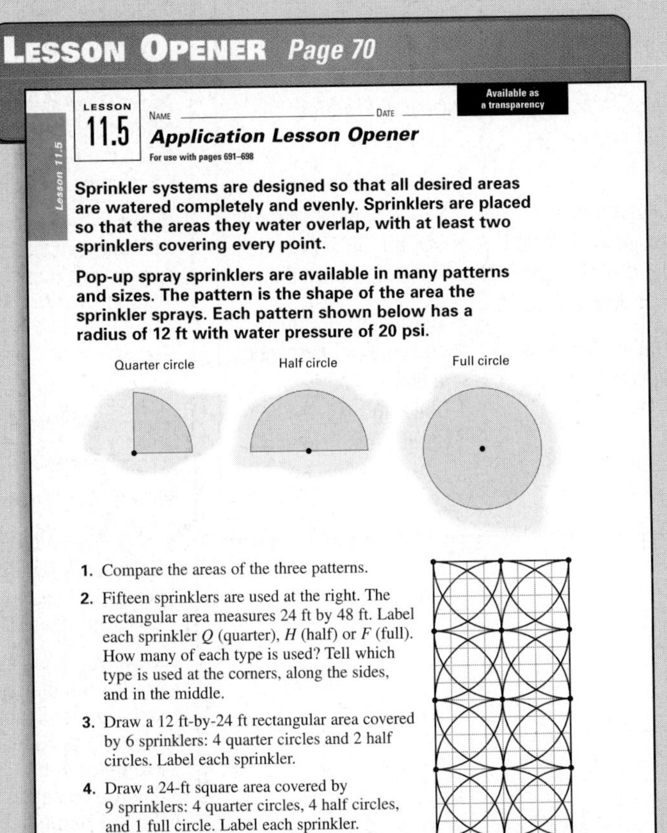

LESSON 11.5 NAME ______ DATE ______

Available as a transparency

Lesson 11.5

Application Lesson Opener

For use with pages 691–698

Sprinkler systems are designed so that all desired areas are watered completely and evenly. Sprinklers are placed so that the areas they water overlap, with at least two sprinklers covering every point.

Pop-up spray sprinklers are available in many patterns and sizes. The pattern is the shape of the area the sprinkler sprays. Each pattern shown below has a radius of 12 ft with water pressure of 20 psi.

1. Compare the areas of the three patterns.
2. Fifteen sprinklers are used at the right. The rectangular area measures 24 ft by 48 ft. Label each sprinkler Q (quarter), H (half) or F (full). How many of each type is used? Tell which type is used at the corners, along the sides, and in the middle.
3. Draw a 12 ft-by-24 ft rectangular area covered by 6 sprinklers: 4 quarter circles and 2 half circles. Label each sprinkler.
4. Draw a 24-ft square area covered by 9 sprinklers: 4 quarter circles, 4 half circles, and 1 full circle. Label each sprinkler.

APPLICATION LESSON OPENER This Lesson Opener provides an alternative way to start Lesson 11.5 in the form of a real-life application. Students see how area of a circle relates to sprinkler system patterns.

TECHNOLOGY RESOURCE

Students and teachers can look to the Application Links and the Career Links at www.mcdougallittell.com for more information about selected applications in Chapter 11.

Following Each Lesson

The *Chapter 11 Resource Book* has a variety of materials to follow-up each lesson. They include the following:

- **Practice (3 levels)**
- **Reteaching with Practice**
- **Quick Catch-Up for Absent Students**
- **Interdisciplinary Applications (pictured below)**
- **Real-Life Applications**

Application *Page 81*

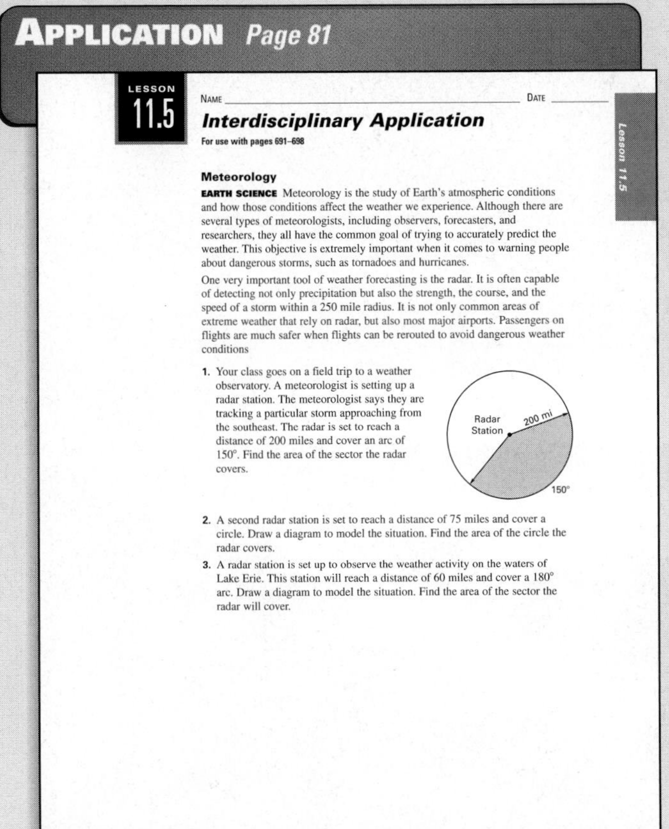

LESSON 11.5

NAME ______ DATE ______

Interdisciplinary Application

For use with pages 691–698

Meteorology

EARTH SCIENCE Meteorology is the study of Earth's atmospheric conditions and how those conditions affect the weather we experience. Although there are several types of meteorologists, including observers, forecasters, and researchers, they all have the common goal of trying to accurately predict the weather. This objective is extremely important when it comes to warning people about dangerous storms, such as tornadoes and hurricanes.

One very important tool of weather forecasting is the radar. It is often capable of detecting not only precipitation but also the strength, the course, and the speed of a storm within a 250 mile radius. It is not only common areas of extreme weather that rely on radar, but also most major airports. Passengers on flights are much safer when flights can be rerouted to avoid dangerous weather conditions

1. Your class goes on a field trip to a weather observatory. A meteorologist is setting up a radar station. The meteorologist says they are tracking a particular storm approaching from the southeast. The radar is set to reach a distance of 200 miles and cover an arc of 150°. Find the area of the sector the radar covers.

2. A second radar station is set to reach a distance of 75 miles and cover a circle. Draw a diagram to model the situation. Find the area of the circle the radar covers.
3. A radar station is set up to observe the weather activity on the waters of Lake Erie. This station will reach a distance of 60 miles and cover a 180° arc. Draw a diagram to model the situation. Find the area of the sector the radar will cover.

Lesson 11.5

Interdisciplinary Application This application makes a connection between meteorology and area of a circle, the topic of Lesson 11.5.

Assessing the Chapter

The *Chapter 11 Resource Book* has the following review and assessment materials:

- **Quizzes**
- **Chapter Review Games and Activities**
- **Chapter Test (3 levels)**
- **SAT/ACT Chapter Test**
- **Alternative Assessment with Rubric and Math Journal**
- **Project with Rubric (pictured below)**
- **Cumulative Review**

Project with Rubric *Pages 108–109*

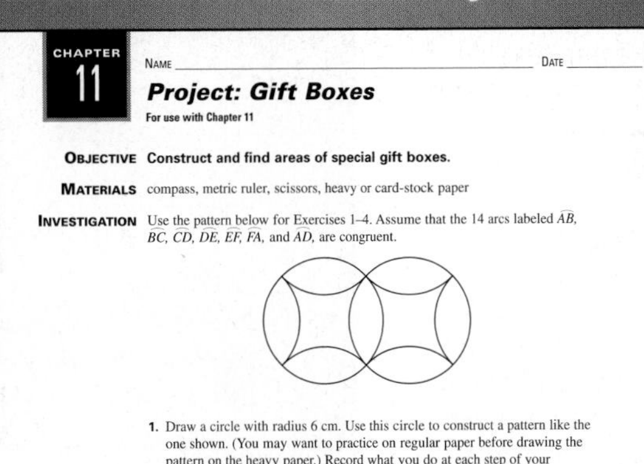

CHAPTER 11

NAME ______ DATE ______

Project: Gift Boxes

For use with Chapter 11

Objective Construct and find areas of special gift boxes.

Materials compass, metric ruler, scissors, heavy or card-stock paper

Investigation Use the pattern below for Exercises 1–4. Assume that the 14 arcs labeled $\widehat{AB}$, $\widehat{BC}$, $\widehat{CD}$, $\widehat{DE}$, $\widehat{EF}$, $\widehat{FA}$, and $\widehat{AD}$, are congruent.

1. Draw a circle with radius 6 cm. Use this circle to construct a pattern like the one shown. (You may want to practice on regular paper before drawing the pattern on the heavy paper.) Record what you do at each step of your construction. (*Hint:* You need to figure out how to locate the centers of the circles that form the arcs.)
2. Press firmly along each arc with a pen. You will be creasing along the arcs.
3. Cut around the outer perimeter of the circles. Fold the sides of the box carefully along the arcs, with the pen marks on the inside. Your gift box is complete.
4. Construct two more gift boxes: one with radius 9 cm and one with radius 12 cm.
5. Organize a table of information for the three boxes as shown below.

Radius	*Area*	$\frac{\textit{radius}}{\textit{initial radius of 6 cm}}$	$\frac{\textit{area}}{\textit{area using radius of 6 cm}}$
6 cm		–	–
9 cm		$\frac{9}{6} = \frac{3}{2}$	
12 cm			

6. Find the area of the paper required for each box. Show your calculations. Record the results in your table.
7. Complete the last two columns of the table. Are the ratios of the areas between the figures what you would expect? Why or why not?

Present Your Results Write a report to go along with your gift boxes. Include the directions for your construction, the table of information for the three boxes, your calculations, and your discussion of the relationship between the areas.

Review and Assess

Project with Rubric The Project for Chapter 11 provides students with the opportunity to apply the concepts they have learned in the chapter in a new way. In this project, students use what they have learned about constructions and area to create and find areas of unusual boxes. Teacher's notes and a scoring rubric are provided on a separate sheet.

CHAPTER OVERVIEW

CHAPTER GOALS

Chapter 11 explores many topics which relate to the area of polygons and circles. The chapter begins by finding the measures of the interior and exterior angles of polygons. These angle measures are then used to find the area of an equilateral triangle and other polygons. Perimeters and areas of similar figures are investigated. Next, students are introduced to the circumference of a circle and the length of a circular arc. This leads to finding the area of a circle and the area of a sector of a circle. Finally geometric probability is introduced. Throughout the chapter, real-life problems involving area, perimeter, circumference, arc length, and geometric probability are solved.

APPLICATION NOTE

Students may be fascinated by these hexagonal basaltic columns. Ask them to think of other examples of naturally occurring polygons. A common example is the hexagonal-shaped honeycomb. Also, flower blossoms often contain pentagon and hexagon designs. Spider webs are another common example. The crystals of many common substances, such as salt, exhibit polygonal shapes.

Additional information about basaltic columns is available at **www.mcdougallittell.com.**

AREA OF POLYGONS AND CIRCLES

▶ *Where do hexagons occur in nature?*

CHAPTER 11

APPLICATION: Area of Columns

Basaltic columns are geological formations that result from rapidly cooling lava.

Most basaltic columns are hexagonal, or six sided. The Giant's Causeway in Ireland, pictured here, features hexagonal columns ranging in size from 15 to 20 inches across and up to 82 feet high.

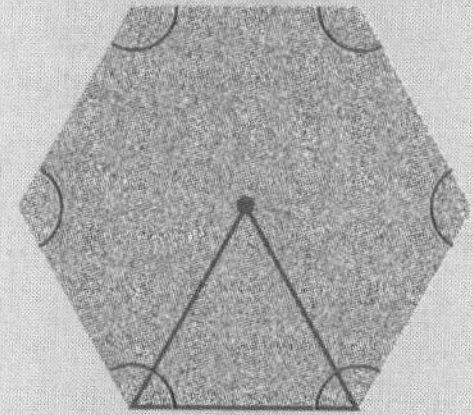

Think & Discuss

1. A regular hexagon, like the one above, can be divided into equilateral triangles by drawing segments to connect the center to each vertex. How many equilateral triangles make up the hexagon? 6
2. Find the sum of the angles in a hexagon by adding together the base angles of the equilateral triangles. 720°

Learn More About It

You will learn more about the shape of the top of a basaltic column in Exercise 34 on p. 673.

APPLICATION LINK Visit www.mcdougallittell.com for more information about basaltic columns.

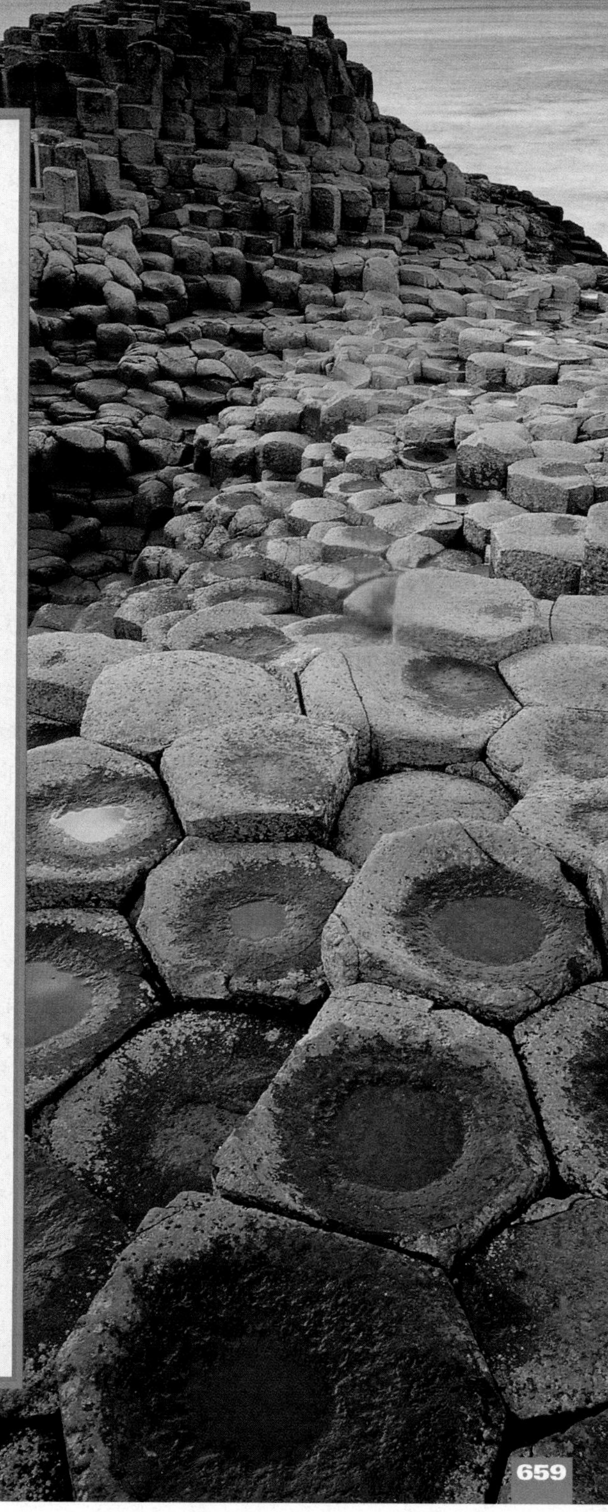

PROJECTS

A project covering Chapters 10 and 11 appears on pages 714–715 of the Student Edition. An additional project for Chapter 11 is available in the *Chapter 11 Resource Book,* p. 108.

TECHNOLOGY

Software

- *Electronic Teaching Tools*
- *Online Lesson Planner*
- *Personal Student Tutor*
- *Test and Practice Generator*
- *Electronic Lesson Presentations (Lesson 11.5)*

Video

- *Geometry in Motion*

Internet Connections
www.mcdougallittell.com

- **Application Links**
  659, 671, 678, 682, 697, 703
- **Student Help**
  662, 674, 680, 684, 690, 692, 700, 706
- **Career Links**
  674, 701
- **Extra Challenge**
  675, 681, 689, 698, 704

PREPARE

DIAGNOSTIC TOOLS

The **Skill Review** exercises can help you diagnose whether students have the following skills needed in Chapter 11:

- Find angle measures in polygons.
- Find the area of equilateral triangles.
- Find side lengths in similar triangles.
- Use trigonometry to find the measures of acute angles in a triangle.

The following resources are available for students who need additional help with these skills:

- Prerequisite Skills Review (*Chapter 11 Resource Book*, p. 5; *Warm-Up Transparencies*, p. 78)
- Reteaching with Practice (Chapter Resource Books for Lessons 4.1, 6.1, 8.3, 8.4, 9.4, 9.6, 10.2, and 10.3)
- *Personal Student Tutor*

ADDITIONAL RESOURCES

The following resources are provided to help you prepare for the upcoming chapter and customize review materials:

- ***Chapter 11 Resource Book***
  Tips for New Teachers (p. 1)
  Parent Guide (p. 3)
  Lesson Plans (every lesson)
  Lesson Plans for Block Scheduling (every lesson)
- ***Electronic Teaching Tools***
- ***Online Lesson Planner***
- ***Test and Practice Generator***

1. 48 in.^{2}
2. 44°; 123°, 101°, 136°
3a. $\frac{3}{2}$
b. $\frac{2}{3}$
4. 43.6°, 46.4°

CHAPTER 11

Study Guide

PREVIEW

What's the chapter about?

Chapter 11 is about **areas of polygons and circles**. In Chapter 11, you'll learn

- how to find angle measures and areas of polygons.
- how to compare perimeters and areas of similar figures.
- how to find the circumference and area of a circle and to find other measures related to circles.

KEY VOCABULARY

▶ **Review**
- **polygon, p. 322**
- ***n*-gon, p. 322**
- **convex polygon, p. 323**
- **regular polygon, p. 323**
- **similar polygons, p. 473**
- **trigonometric ratio, p. 558**
- **circle, p. 595**
- **center of a circle, p. 595**
- **radius of a circle, p. 595**
- **measure of an arc, p. 603**

▶ **New**
- **apothem of a polygon, p. 670**
- **central angle of a regular polygon, p. 671**
- **circumference, p. 683**
- **arc length, p. 683**
- **sector of a circle, p. 692**
- **probability, p. 699**
- **geometric probability, p. 699**

PREPARE

Are you ready for the chapter?

SKILL REVIEW Do these exercises to review key skills that you'll apply in this chapter. See the given **reference page** if there is something you don't understand.

1. Find the area of a triangle with height 8 in. and base 12 in. **(Review p. 51)** 48 in.^{2}
2. In $\triangle ABC$, $m\angle A = 57°$ and $m\angle C = 79°$. Find the measure of $\angle B$ and the measure of an exterior angle at each vertex. **(Review pp. 196–197)** 44°; 123°, 101°, 136°
3. If $\triangle DEF \sim \triangle XYZ$, $DF = 8$, and $XZ = 12$, find each ratio.
   a. $\frac{XY}{DE}$ $\frac{3}{2}$ **b.** $\frac{\text{Perimeter of } \triangle DEF}{\text{Perimeter of } \triangle XYZ}$ **(Review pp. 475, 480)** $\frac{2}{3}$
4. A right triangle has sides of length 20, 21, and 29. Find the measures of the acute angles of the triangle to the nearest tenth. **(Review pp. 567–568)** 43.6°, 46.4°

STUDY STRATEGY

Here's a study strategy!

A *concept map* is a diagram that highlights the connections between ideas. Drawing a concept map for a chapter can help you focus on the important ideas and on how they are related.

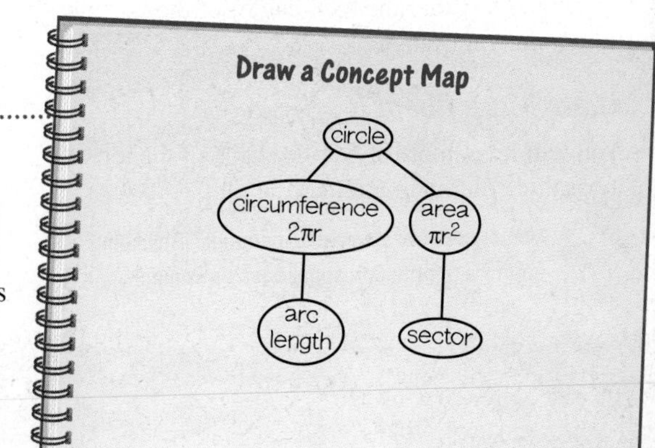

11.1 Angle Measures in Polygons

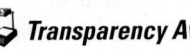

What you should learn

GOAL 1 Find the measures of interior and exterior angles of polygons.

GOAL 2 Use measures of angles of polygons to solve **real-life** problems.

Why you should learn it

▼ To solve **real-life** problems, such as finding the measures of the interior angles of a home plate marker of a softball field in **Example 4**.

REAL LIFE

GOAL 1 MEASURES OF INTERIOR AND EXTERIOR ANGLES

You have already learned that the name of a polygon depends on the number of sides in the polygon: triangle, quadrilateral, pentagon, hexagon, and so forth. The sum of the measures of the interior angles of a polygon also depends on the number of sides.

In Lesson 6.1, you found the sum of the measures of the interior angles of a quadrilateral by dividing the quadrilateral into two triangles. You can use this triangle method to find the sum of the measures of the interior angles of any convex polygon with n sides, called an n-gon.

ACTIVITY Developing Concepts

Investigating the Sum of Polygon Angle Measures

Draw examples of 3-sided, 4-sided, 5-sided, and 6-sided convex polygons. In each polygon, draw all the diagonals from one vertex. Notice that this divides each polygon into triangular regions.

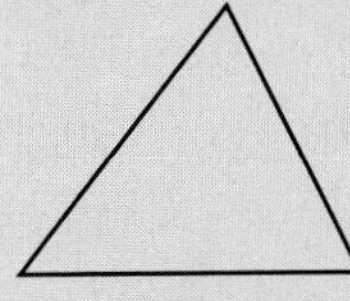
Triangle

Quadrilateral

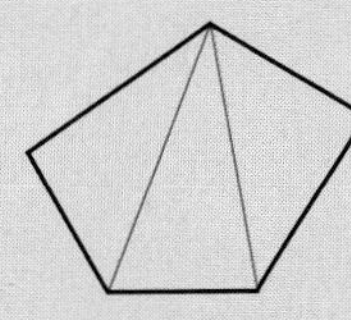
Pentagon

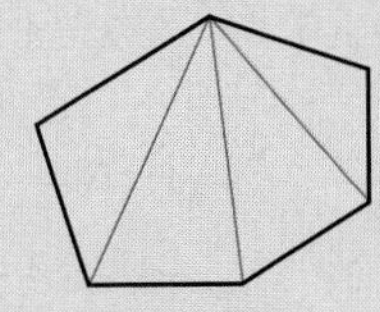
Hexagon

Complete the table below. What is the pattern in the sum of the measures of the interior angles of any convex n-gon?

Polygon	Number of sides	Number of triangles	Sum of measures of interior angles
Triangle	3	1	$1 \cdot 180° = 180°$
Quadrilateral	?	?	$2 \cdot 180° = 360°$
Pentagon	?	?	?
Hexagon	?	?	?
⋮	⋮	⋮	⋮
n-gon	n	?	?

Answers (margin): Quadrilateral: 4; 2 — Pentagon: 5; 3; $3 \cdot 180° = 540°$ — Hexagon: 6; 4; $4 \cdot 180° = 720°$ — n-gon: $n - 2$; $(n - 2) \cdot 180°$

CALIFORNIA STANDARDS AND ASSESSMENT

CA Standards: 12, 13
SAT9 Task 1: Objs. 1, 24
SAT9 Task 2: Objs. 1, 27

1 PLAN

PACING
Basic: 2 days
Average: 2 days
Advanced: 2 days
Block Schedule: 1 block

LESSON OPENER
VISUAL APPROACH
An alternative way to approach Lesson 11.1 is to use the Visual Approach Lesson Opener:
- Blackline Master (*Chapter 11 Resource Book,* p. 12)
- Transparency (p. 68)

MEETING INDIVIDUAL NEEDS
- ***Chapter 11 Resource Book***
  Prerequisite Skills Review (p. 5)
  Practice Level A (p. 14)
  Practice Level B (p. 15)
  Practice Level C (p. 16)
  Reteaching with Practice (p. 17)
  Absent Student Catch-Up (p. 19)
  Challenge (p. 22)
- ***Resources in Spanish***
-  ***Personal Student Tutor***

NEW-TEACHER SUPPORT
See the Tips for New Teachers on pp. 1–2 of the *Chapter 11 Resource Book* for additional notes about Lesson 11.1.

WARM-UP EXERCISES

Transparency Available

Given the following angle measures in $\triangle ABC$, find $m\angle C$.

1. $m\angle A = 28°$, $m\angle B = 112°$ **40°**
2. $m\angle A = 42°$, $m\angle B = 90°$ **48°**
3. $m\angle A = 60°$, $m\angle B = 60°$ **60°**
4. What is a name for a regular polygon that is also a triangle? **equilateral or equiangular triangle**

2 TEACH

MOTIVATING THE LESSON
Ask students what is the sum of the measures of the interior angles of a any triangle. Then ask for the sum of the measures of the interior angles of any rectangle. Ask if they think that the sum of the measures of the interior angles in any polygon can be determined given the number of sides. Explain that students will investigate this question in today's lesson.

ACTIVITY NOTE
This activity leads students to discover the Polygon Interior Angles Theorem.

EXTRA EXAMPLE 1
Find the value of x in the diagram shown.

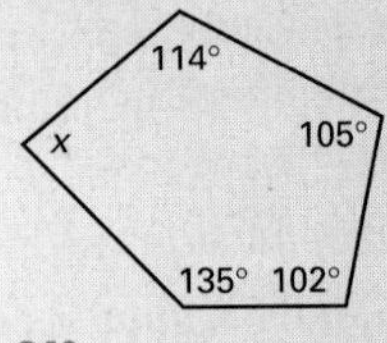

84°

EXTRA EXAMPLE 2
The measure of each interior angle of a regular polygon is 165°. How many sides does the polygon have? 24

CHECKPOINT EXERCISES

For use after Example 1:

1. A heptagon has four interior angles that measure 160° each and two interior angles that are right angles. What is the measure of the other interior angle? 80°

For use after Example 2:

2. Find the measure of each angle in a regular 11-gon. about 147.3°

STUDENT HELP

Look Back
For help with *regular* polygons, see p. 323.

You may have found in the activity that the sum of the measures of the interior angles of a convex n-gon is $(n - 2) \cdot 180°$. This relationship can be used to find the measure of each interior angle in a *regular* n-gon, because the angles are all congruent. Exercises 43 and 44 ask you to write proofs of the following results.

THEOREMS ABOUT INTERIOR ANGLES

THEOREM 11.1 ***Polygon Interior Angles Theorem***

The sum of the measures of the interior angles of a convex n-gon is $(n - 2) \cdot 180°$.

COROLLARY TO THEOREM 11.1

The measure of each interior angle of a regular n-gon is

$\frac{1}{n} \cdot (n - 2) \cdot 180°$, or $\frac{(n - 2) \cdot 180°}{n}$.

EXAMPLE 1 *Finding Measures of Interior Angles of Polygons*

Find the value of x in the diagram shown.

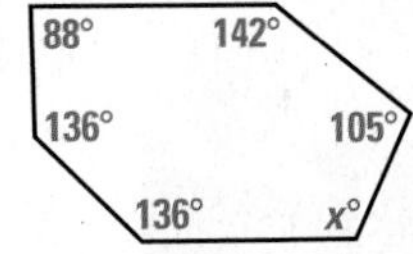

SOLUTION

The sum of the measures of the interior angles of any hexagon is $(6 - 2) \cdot 180° = 4 \cdot 180° = 720°$.

Add the measures of the interior angles of the hexagon.

$136° + 136° + 88° + 142° + 105° + x° = 720°$	**The sum is 720°.**
$607 + x = 720$	**Simplify.**
$x = 113$	**Subtract 607 from each side.**

▶ The measure of the sixth interior angle of the hexagon is 113°.

EXAMPLE 2 *Finding the Number of Sides of a Polygon*

The measure of each interior angle of a regular polygon is 140°. How many sides does the polygon have?

SOLUTION

$\frac{1}{n} \cdot (n - 2) \cdot 180° = 140°$	**Corollary to Theorem 11.1**
$(n - 2) \cdot 180 = 140n$	**Multiply each side by n.**
$180n - 360 = 140n$	**Distributive property**
$40n = 360$	**Addition and subtraction properties of equality**
$n = 9$	**Divide each side by 40.**

▶ The polygon has 9 sides. It is a regular nonagon.

STUDENT HELP

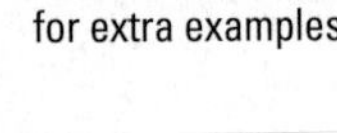

HOMEWORK HELP
Visit our Web site www.mcdougallittell.com for extra examples.

The diagrams below show that the sum of the measures of the *exterior* angles of any convex polygon is 360°. You can also find the measure of each exterior angle of a *regular* polygon. Exercises 45 and 46 ask for proofs of these results.

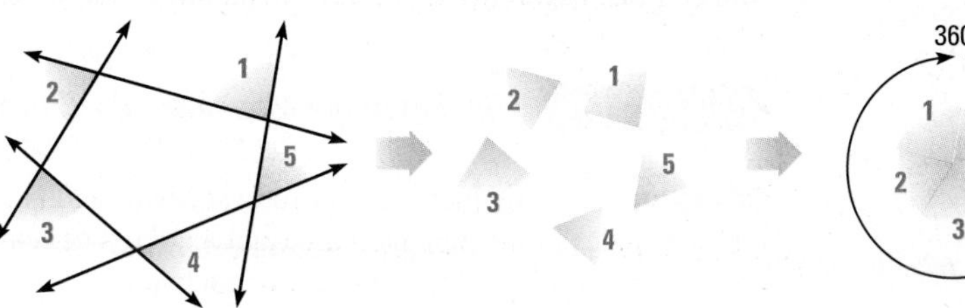

❶ Shade one exterior angle at each vertex.

❷ Cut out the exterior angles.

❸ Arrange the exterior angles to form 360°.

THEOREMS ABOUT EXTERIOR ANGLES

THEOREM 11.2 ***Polygon Exterior Angles Theorem***

The sum of the measures of the exterior angles of a convex polygon, one angle at each vertex, is 360°.

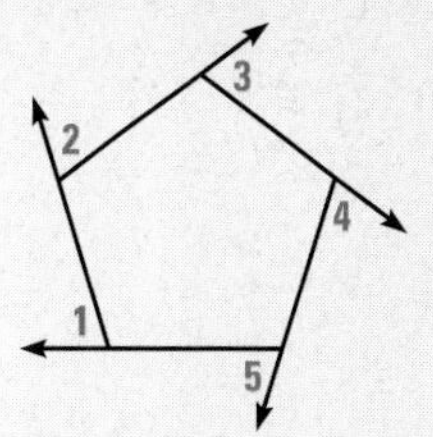

COROLLARY TO THEOREM 11.2

The measure of each exterior angle of a regular n-gon is $\frac{1}{n} \cdot 360°$, or $\frac{360°}{n}$.

EXAMPLE 3 ***Finding the Measure of an Exterior Angle***

Using Algebra

Find the value of x in each diagram.

a.

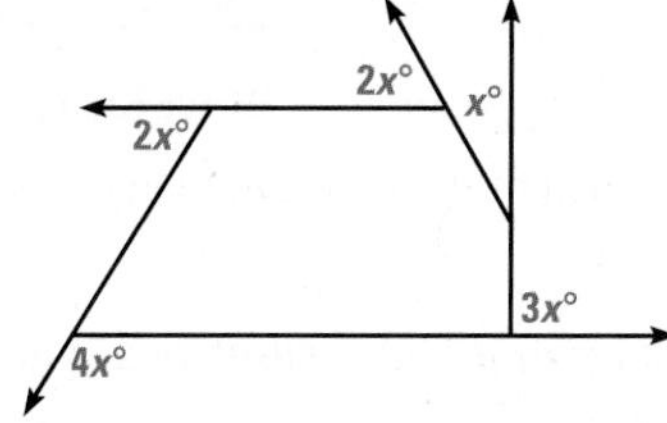

b.

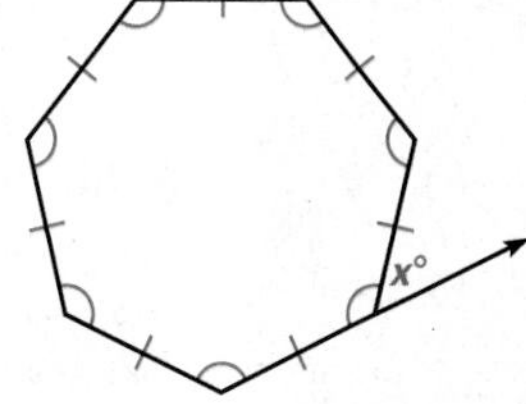

SOLUTION

a. $2x° + x° + 3x° + 4x° + 2x° = 360°$ **Use Theorem 11.2.**

$12x = 360$ **Combine like terms.**

$x = 30$ **Divide each side by 12.**

b. $x° = \frac{1}{7} \cdot 360°$ **Use $n = 7$ in the Corollary to Theorem 11.2.**

≈ 51.4 **Use a calculator.**

▶ The measure of each exterior angle of a regular heptagon is about 51.4°.

MATHEMATICAL REASONING

Point out to students how the activity on page 661 uses inductive reasoning to arrive at the conjecture that forms Theorem 11.1. Remind students that for this conjecture to become a theorem it must be proven. Students will provide a deductive proof for one case of Theorem 11.1 in Exercise 43.

STUDENT HELP NOTES

- **Look Back** As student look back to page 323, remind them that *regular* polygons have congruent interior angles and congruent sides.
- **Homework Help** Students can find extra examples at **www.mcdougallittell.com** that parallel the examples in the student edition.

EXTRA EXAMPLE 3

Find the value of the variable in each diagram.

a.

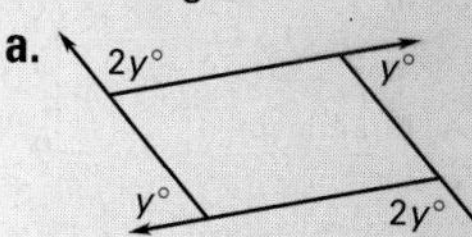

60

b.

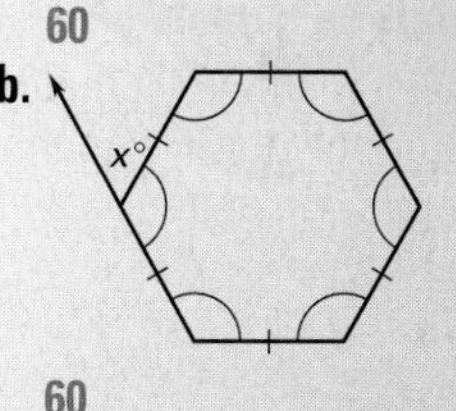

60

CHECKPOINT EXERCISES

For use after Example 3:

1. The measure of each exterior angle of a regular polygon is 40°. How many sides does the polygon have? 9

EXTRA EXAMPLE 4
The sign on a building has a long narrow hexagon shape. Four of the interior angles measure 140° each. The remaining two interior angles at each end of the sign are congruent. What is the measure of each angle? 80°

EXTRA EXAMPLE 5
If you were designing a sign for a new building, would it be possible to make a sign that is a regular polygon with each angle having a measure of (**a**) 160° (**b**) 115°? yes; no

CHECKPOINT EXERCISES

For use after Example 4:

1. Shown below is the floor plan of an outdoor theater stage. The stage has two right angles and two angles that measure 135° each. The remaining interior angles are congruent. What is the measure of each of these angles?

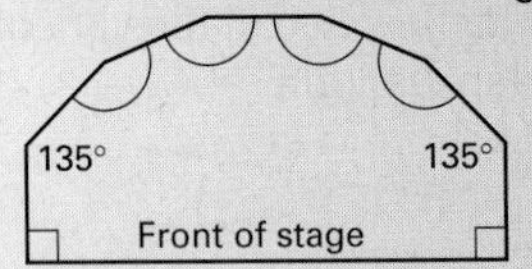

157.5°

For use after Example 5:

2. Can a stage be built that is a regular polygon with each angle having a measure of 175°? yes

FOCUS ON VOCABULARY
What is an exterior angle of a polygon? An exterior angle is the angle formed by one of the sides of a polygon and the ray created by extending an adjacent side of the polygon.

CLOSURE QUESTION
Explain in words how to find the measure of each interior angle and each exterior angle in a regular polygon. See right.

DAILY PUZZLER
One interior angle of a 16-gon measures 157.5°. Is this a regular 16-gon? Explain. See right.

GOAL 2 USING ANGLE MEASURES IN REAL LIFE

You can use Theorems 11.1 and 11.2 and their corollaries to find angle measures.

EXAMPLE 4 *Finding Angle Measures of a Polygon*

SOFTBALL A home plate marker for a softball field is a pentagon. Three of the interior angles of the pentagon are right angles. The remaining two interior angles are congruent. What is the measure of each angle?

SOLUTION

PROBLEM SOLVING STRATEGY

DRAW A SKETCH Sketch and label a diagram for the home plate marker. It is a nonregular pentagon. The right angles are $\angle A$, $\angle B$, and $\angle D$. The remaining angles are congruent. So $\angle C \cong \angle E$. The sum of the measures of the interior angles of the pentagon is 540°.

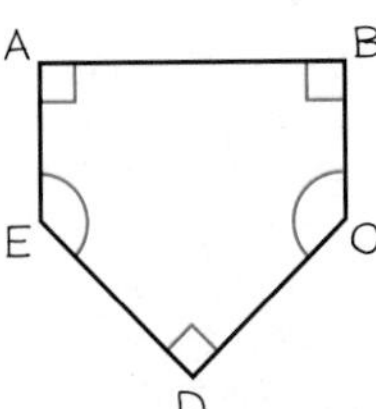

VERBAL MODEL [Sum of measures of interior angles] = 3 · [Measure of each right angle] + 2 · [Measure of $\angle C$ and $\angle E$]

LABELS

Sum of measures of interior angles = **540** (degrees)

Measure of each right angle = **90** (degrees)

Measure of $\angle C$ and $\angle E$ = x (degrees)

REASONING

$540 = 3 \cdot 90 + 2x$ **Write the equation.**

$540 = 270 + 2x$ **Simplify.**

$270 = 2x$ **Subtract 270 from each side.**

$135 = x$ **Divide each side by 2.**

▶ So, the measure of each of the two congruent angles is 135°.

FOCUS ON PEOPLE

JOAN JOYCE set a number of softball pitching records from 1956–1975. She delivered 40 pitches to slugger Ted Williams during an exhibition game in 1962. Williams only connected twice, for one foul ball and one base hit.

EXAMPLE 5 *Using Angle Measures of a Regular Polygon*

SPORTS EQUIPMENT If you were designing the home plate marker for some new type of ball game, would it be possible to make a home plate marker that is a regular polygon with each interior angle having a measure of (**a**) 135°? (**b**) 145°?

SOLUTION

a. Solve the equation $\frac{1}{n} \cdot (n-2) \cdot 180° = 135°$ for n. You get $n = 8$.

▶ Yes, it would be possible. A polygon can have 8 sides.

b. Solve the equation $\frac{1}{n} \cdot (n-2) \cdot 180° = 145°$ for n. You get $n \approx 10.3$.

▶ No, it would not be possible. A polygon cannot have 10.3 sides.

Closure Question *Sample answer:*
To find the measure of each interior angle, multiply 2 less than the number of sides by 180° and then divide that result by the number of sides. To find the measure of each exterior angle, divide 360° by the number of sides.

Daily Puzzler *Sample answer:*
Not necessarily. In a regular 16-gon each interior angle is 157.5°. It is possible for only one of the angles to measure 157.5° as long as the sum of the measures of all the angles is 2520°.

GUIDED PRACTICE

Vocabulary Check ✓

1. Name an *interior angle* and an *exterior angle* of the polygon shown at the right.
$\angle A$, $\angle B$, $\angle BCD$, $\angle D$, or $\angle AED$; $\angle AEF$, $\angle BCG$, or $\angle DCH$

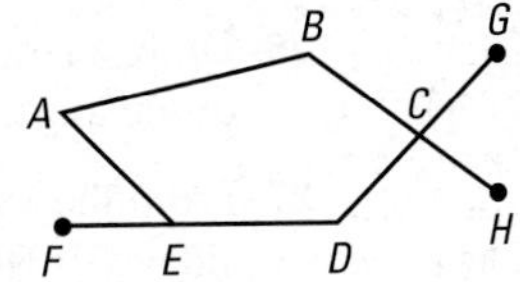

Concept Check ✓

2. How many exterior angles are there in an n-gon? Are they all considered when using the Polygon Exterior Angles Theorem? Explain.
$2n$ (2 at each vertex); no, only one at each vertex

Skill Check ✓

Find the value of x.

3. 95

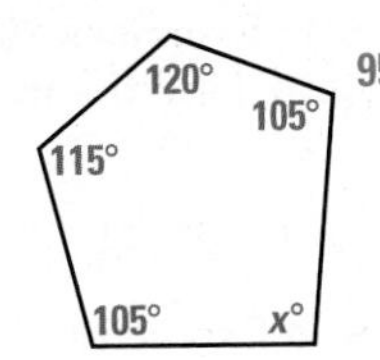

4. 120

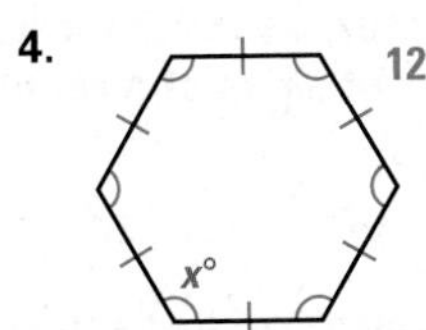

5. 45

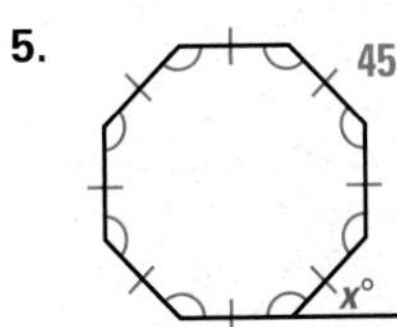

PRACTICE AND APPLICATIONS

STUDENT HELP

Extra Practice to help you master skills is on p. 823.

SUMS OF ANGLE MEASURES **Find the sum of the measures of the interior angles of the convex polygon.**

6. 10-gon 1440°
7. 12-gon 1800°
8. 15-gon 2340°
9. 18-gon 2880°
10. 20-gon 3240°
11. 30-gon 5040°
12. 40-gon 6840°
13. 100-gon 17,640°

ANGLE MEASURES **In Exercises 14–19, find the value of x.**

14. 127

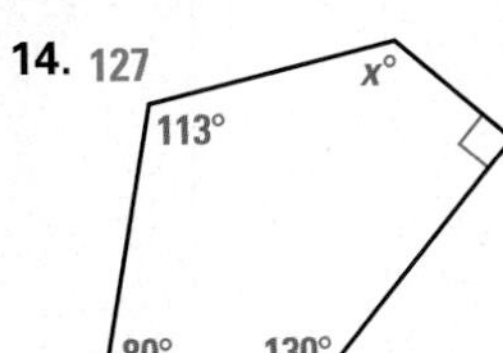

15. 101

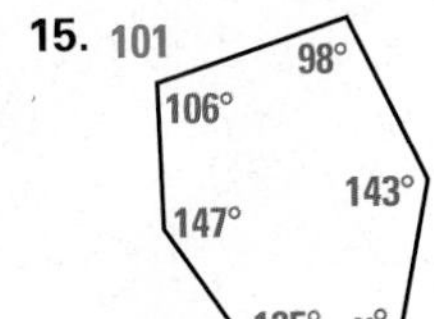

16. 80

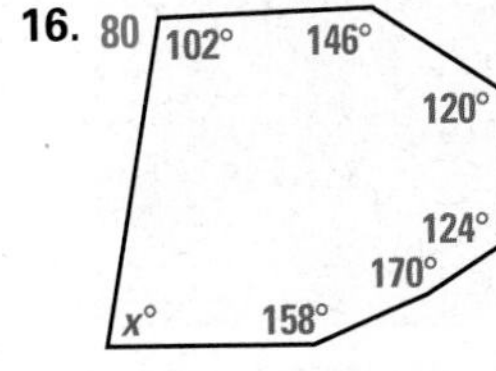

17. 108

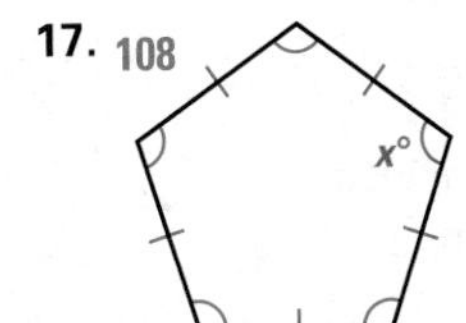

18. about 128.6

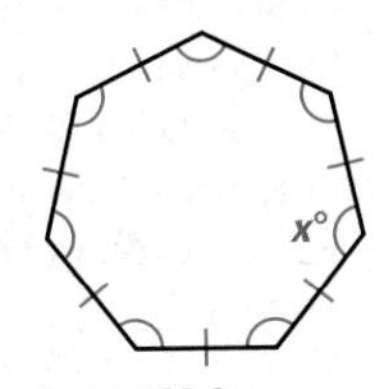

19. 135

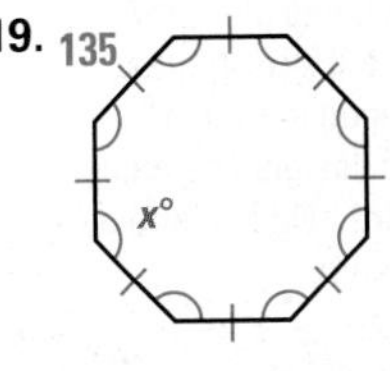

20. A convex quadrilateral has interior angles that measure 80°, 110°, and 80°. What is the measure of the fourth interior angle? 90°

21. A convex pentagon has interior angles that measure 60°, 80°, 120°, and 140°. What is the measure of the fifth interior angle? 140°

DETERMINING NUMBER OF SIDES **In Exercises 22–25, you are given the measure of each interior angle of a regular n-gon. Find the value of n.**

22. 144° 10
23. 120° 6
24. 140° 9
25. 157.5° 16

STUDENT HELP

HOMEWORK HELP
Example 1: Exs. 6–16, 20, 21
Example 2: Exs. 17–19, 22–28
Example 3: Exs. 29–38
Example 4: Exs. 39, 40, 49, 50
Example 5: Exs. 51–54

3 APPLY

ASSIGNMENT GUIDE

BASIC
Day 1: pp. 665–666 Exs. 6–40 even
Day 2: pp. 665–668 Exs. 7–41 odd, 49–56, 58–61, 63–73 odd

AVERAGE
Day 1: pp. 665–666 Exs. 6–40 even
Day 2: pp. 665–668 Exs. 7–43 odd, 49–61, 63–73 odd

ADVANCED
Day 1: pp. 665–666 Exs. 6–40 even
Day 2: pp. 665–668 Exs. 7–41 odd, 43–45, 49–62, 63–73 odd

BLOCK SCHEDULE
pp. 665–668 Exs. 6–41, 43, 49–61, 63–73 odd

EXERCISE LEVELS

Level A: ***Easier***
6–13

Level B: ***More Difficult***
14–42, 47–61

Level C: ***Most Difficult***
43–46, 62

✓ HOMEWORK CHECK

To quickly check student understanding of key concepts, go over the following exercises: Exs. 8, 14, 20, 22, 26, 30, 34, 38, 51, 56. See also the Daily Homework Quiz:

- Blackline Master (*Chapter 11 Resource Book*, p. 25)
- Transparency (p. 80)

! COMMON ERROR

EXERCISES 22–25 Students may make some algebraic errors when solving these problems. Point out that after they set up the equation, they should multiply both sides by n.

! COMMON ERROR

EXERCISES 29–38 Students may use the formulas for interior angles to do these exercises. Point out that if they are using exterior angles, they should be using the formulas on page 663 not the ones on page 662.

39. The yellow hexagon is regular with interior angles measuring 120° each; the yellow pentagons each have two interior angles that measure 90° and three interior angles that measure 120°; the triangles are equilateral with all interior angles measuring 60°.

40. The yellow decagon is regular with each interior angle measuring 144°; the yellow pentagons each have two interior angles measuring 90°, two interior angles measuring 108° and one interior angle measuring 144°; the red quadrilaterals have one angle measuring 144° and three angles measuring 72° each.

43. Draw all the diagonals of *ABCDE* that have *A* as one endpoint. The diagonals, $\overline{AC}$ and $\overline{AD}$, divide *ABCDE* into 3 △s. By the Angle Addition Post., $m\angle BAE = m\angle BAC + m\angle CAD + m\angle DAE$. Similarly, $m\angle BCD = m\angle BCA + m\angle ACD$ and $m\angle CDE = m\angle CDA + m\angle ADE$. Then the sum of the measures of the interior ∠s of *ABCDE* is equal to the sum of the measures of ∠s of △*ABC*, △*ACD*, and △*ADE*. By the △ Sum Thm., the sum of the measures of each △ is 180°, so the sum of the measures of the interior ∠s of *ABCDE* is $3 \cdot 180° = (5-2) \cdot 180°$.

41. ∠3 and ∠8 are a linear pair, so $m\angle 3 = 140°$; ∠2 and ∠7 are a linear pair, so $m\angle 7 = 80°$; $m\angle 1 = 80°$ by the Polygon Interior Angles Thm.; ∠1 and ∠6 are a linear pair, so $m\angle 6 = 100°$; ∠4 and ∠9 are a linear pair, as are ∠5 and ∠10, so $m\angle 9 = m\angle 10 = 70°$.

42. According to the Polygon Interior Angles Thm., the sum of the measures of the interior ∠s of a convex polygon is dependent only on the number of sides. Therefore, the sums of the measures of the interior ∠s of any two polygons with the same number of sides are equal. It does not matter whether one or both of the polygons are regular or whether the two are similar.

FOCUS ON APPLICATIONS

REAL LIFE **STAINED GLASS** is tinted glass that has been cut into shapes and arranged to form a picture or design. The pieces of glass are held in place by strips of lead.

44. Let *A* be a regular *n*-gon and $x°$ the measure of each interior ∠. By the Polygon Interior Angles Thm., the sum of the measures of the interior ∠s of *A* is $(n-2) \cdot 180°$. That is, $n \cdot x° = (n-2) \cdot 180°$, or $x° = \frac{(n-2) \cdot 180°}{n}$.

CONSTRUCTION Use a compass, protractor, and ruler to check the results of Example 2 on page 662. 26–28. Check drawings.

26. Draw a large angle that measures 140°. Mark congruent lengths on the sides of the angle.

27. From the end of one of the congruent lengths in Exercise 26, draw the second side of another angle that measures 140°. Mark another congruent length along this new side.

28. Continue to draw angles that measure 140° until a polygon is formed. Verify that the polygon is regular and has 9 sides.

DETERMINING ANGLE MEASURES In Exercises 29–32, you are given the number of sides of a regular polygon. Find the measure of each exterior angle.

29. 12 30° **30.** 11 about 32.7° **31.** 21 about 17.1° **32.** 15 24°

DETERMINING NUMBER OF SIDES In Exercises 33–36, you are given the measure of each exterior angle of a regular *n*-gon. Find the value of *n*.

33. 60° 6 **34.** 20° 18 **35.** 72° 5 **36.** 10° 36

37. A convex hexagon has exterior angles that measure 48°, 52°, 55°, 62°, and 68°. What is the measure of the exterior angle of the sixth vertex? 75°

38. What is the measure of each exterior angle of a regular decagon? 36°

STAINED GLASS WINDOWS In Exercises 39 and 40, the purple and green pieces of glass are in the shape of regular polygons. Find the measure of each interior angle of the red and yellow pieces of glass. 39, 40. See margin.

39.

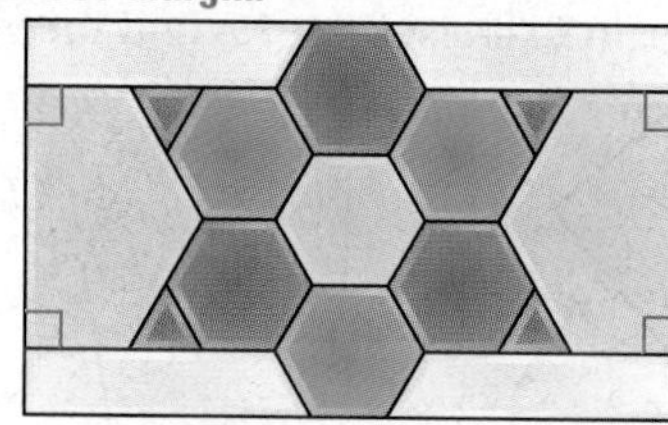

40.

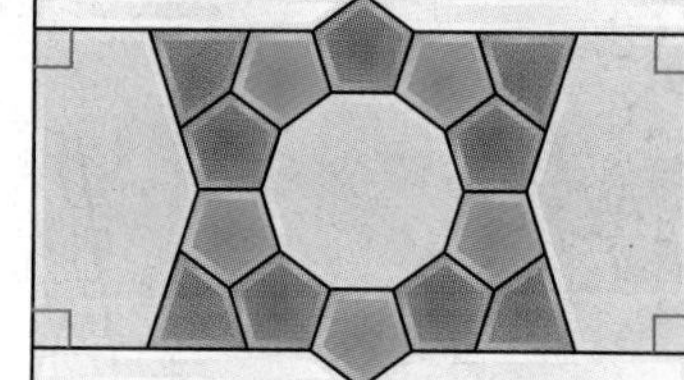

41. FINDING MEASURES OF ANGLES In the diagram at the right, $m\angle 2 = 100°$, $m\angle 8 = 40°$, $m\angle 4 = m\angle 5 = 110°$. Find the measures of the other labeled angles and explain your reasoning. See margin.

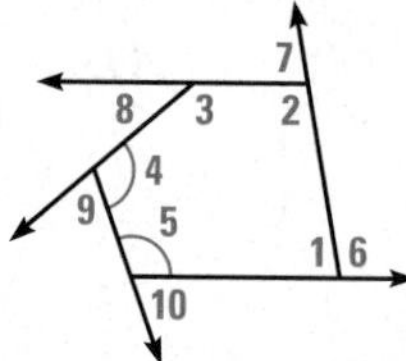

42. *Writing* Explain why the sum of the measures of the interior angles of any two *n*-gons with the same number of sides (two octagons, for example) is the same. Do the *n*-gons need to be regular? Do they need to be similar? See margin.

43. PROOF Use *ABCDE* to write a paragraph proof to prove Theorem 11.1 for pentagons. See margin.

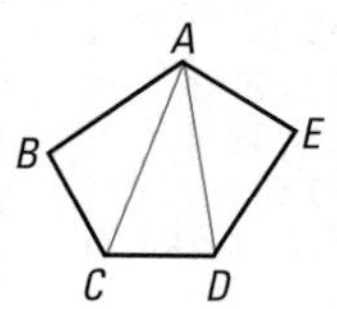

44. PROOF Use a paragraph proof to prove the Corollary to Theorem 11.1.

45. **PROOF** Use this plan to write a paragraph proof of Theorem 11.2.
Plan for Proof In a convex n-gon, the sum of the measures of an interior angle and an adjacent exterior angle at any vertex is 180°. Multiply by n to get the sum of all such sums at each vertex. Then subtract the sum of the interior angles derived by using Theorem 11.1.

46. **PROOF** Use a paragraph proof to prove the Corollary to Theorem 11.2. See margin.

TECHNOLOGY In Exercises 47 and 48, use geometry software to construct a polygon. At each vertex, extend one of the sides of the polygon to form an exterior angle.

47. Measure each exterior angle and verify that the sum of the measures is 360°. Check results.

48. Move any vertex to change the shape of your polygon. What happens to the measures of the exterior angles? What happens to their sum? See margin.

49. **HOUSES** Pentagon $ABCDE$ is an outline of the front of a house. Find the measure of each angle. $m\angle A = m\angle E = 90°$, $m\angle B = m\angle C = m\angle D = 120°$

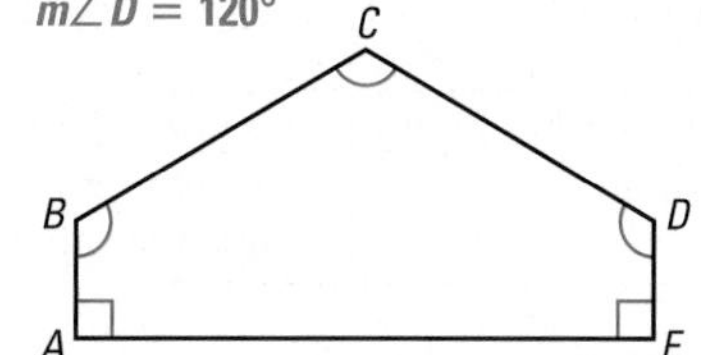

50. **TENTS** Heptagon $PQRSTUV$ is an outline of a camping tent. Find the unknown angle measures. $m\angle P = m\angle V = 70°$, $m\angle S = 140°$

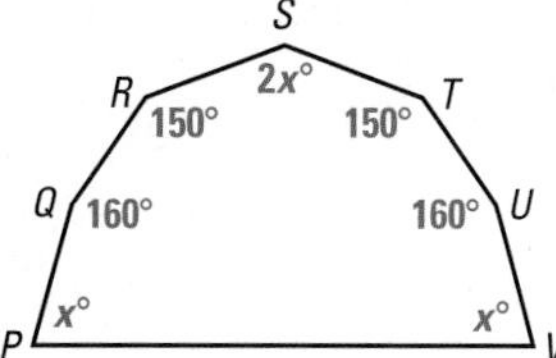

POSSIBLE POLYGONS Would it be possible for a regular polygon to have interior angles with the angle measure described? Explain. 51–54. See margin.

51. 150°
52. 90°
53. 72°
54. 18°

USING ALGEBRA In Exercises 55 and 56, you are given a function and its graph. In each function, n is the number of sides of a polygon and $f(n)$ is measured in degrees. How does the function relate to polygons? What happens to the value of $f(n)$ as n gets larger and larger? 55, 56. See margin.

55. $f(n) = \dfrac{180n - 360}{n}$

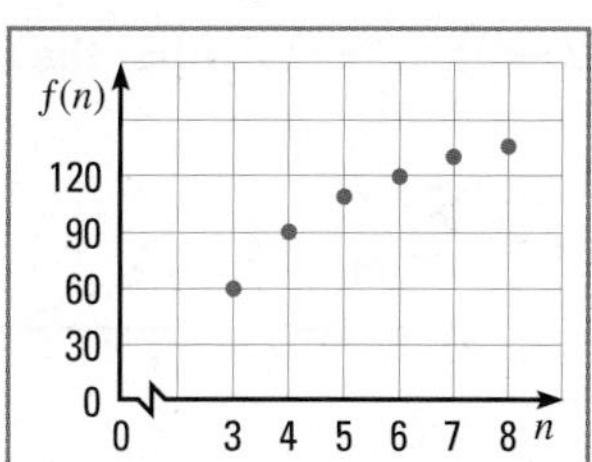

56. $f(n) = \dfrac{360}{n}$

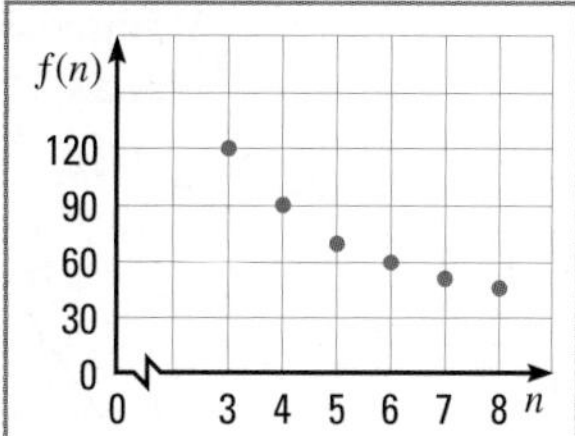

57. **LOGICAL REASONING** You are shown part of a convex n-gon. The pattern of congruent angles continues around the polygon. Use the Polygon Exterior Angles Theorem to find the value of n. 10

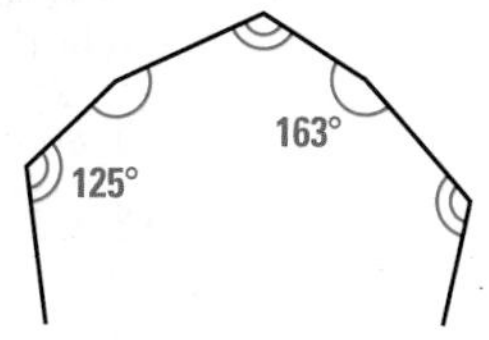

45. Let A be a convex n-gon. Each interior ∠ and one of the exterior ∠s at that vertex form a linear pair, so the sum of their measures is 180°. Then the sum of the measures of the interior ∠ and one exterior ∠ at each vertex is $n \cdot 180°$. By the Polygon Interior Angles Thm., the sum of the measures of the interior ∠s of A is $(n-2) \cdot 180°$. So the sum of the measures of the exterior ∠s of A, one at each vertex, is $n \cdot 180° - (n-2) \cdot 180° = n \cdot 180° - n \cdot 180° + 360° = 360°$.

46. Let A be a regular convex n-gon. Since all the interior ∠s are ≅ and each interior ∠ and one of the exterior ∠s at that vertex form a linear pair, the exterior ∠s are also ≅ by the Congruent Supplements Thm. Let $x°$ be the measure of each exterior ∠. Then $n \cdot x° = 360°$ and $x° = \dfrac{360°}{n}$.

48. If the measure of an interior ∠ increases, the measure of the corresp. exterior ∠ decreases. If the measure of an interior ∠ decreases, the measure of the corresp. exterior ∠ increases. The sum of the measures of the exterior ∠s is always 360°.

51. Yes; if $\dfrac{(n-2) \cdot 180°}{n} = 150°$, then $n = 12$. A regular 12-gon (dodecagon) has interior ∠s with measure 150°.

52. Yes; a square is a regular polygon with interior ∠s of 90°.

53. No; if $\dfrac{(n-2) \cdot 180°}{n} = 72°$, then $n = 3\frac{1}{3}$. It is not possible for a polygon to have $3\frac{1}{3}$ sides.

54. No; if $\dfrac{(n-2) \cdot 180°}{n} = 18°$, then $n = 2\frac{2}{9}$. It is not possible for a polygon to have $2\frac{2}{9}$ sides.

55. $f(n)$ is the measure of each interior ∠ of a regular n-gon; as n gets larger and larger, $f(n)$ increases, becoming closer and closer to 180°.

56. $f(n)$ is the measure of each exterior ∠ of a regular n-gon; as n gets larger and larger, $f(n)$ gets smaller and smaller.

ADDITIONAL PRACTICE AND RETEACHING

For Lesson 11.1:

- Practice Levels A, B, and C (*Chapter 11 Resource Book,* p. 14)
- Reteaching with Practice (*Chapter 11 Resource Book,* p. 17)
- See Lesson 11.1 of the *Personal Student Tutor*

For more Mixed Review:

- Search the *Test and Practice Generator* for key words or specific lessons.

4 ASSESS

DAILY HOMEWORK QUIZ

Transparency Available

1. Find the sum of the measures of the interior angles in a convex 16-gon. 2520°
2. Find the value of *x*.

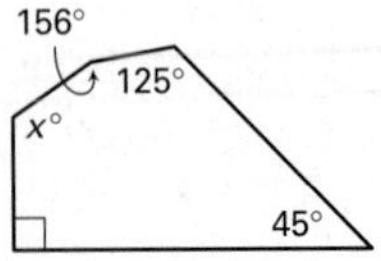

124°

3. The measure of each interior angle of a regular polygon is 162°. How many sides does the polygon have? 20
4. The measure of each exterior angle of a regular polygon is 6°. How many sides does the polygon have? 60

EXTRA CHALLENGE NOTE

Challenge problems for Lesson 11.1 are available in **blackline** format in the *Chapter 11 Resource Book,* p. 22 and at **www.mcdougallittell.com.**

ADDITIONAL TEST PREPARATION

1. **WRITING** Explain how to find the sum of the measures of the interior angles of a polygon using triangles. **Use diagonals to divide the polygon into triangular regions. The sum of the angles in each triangle is 180°. Multiply the number of triangles by 180° to get the sum of the measures of the interior angles in the polygon.**

Test Preparation

QUANTITATIVE COMPARISON In Exercises 58–61, choose the statement that is true about the given quantities.

Ⓐ The quantity in column A is greater.

Ⓑ The quantity in column B is greater.

Ⓒ The two quantities are equal.

Ⓓ The relationship cannot be determined from the given information.

	Column A	Column B	
58.	The sum of the interior angle measures of a decagon	The sum of the interior angle measures of a 15-gon	B
59.	The sum of the exterior angle measures of an octagon	8(45°)	C
60.	$m\angle 1$ 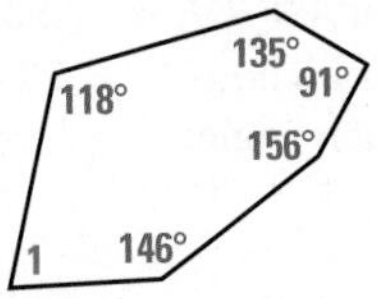	$m\angle 2$ 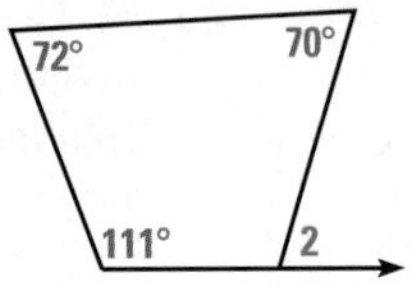	A
61.	Number of sides of a polygon with an exterior angle measuring 72°	Number of sides of a polygon with an exterior angle measuring 144°	D

★ **Challenge**

62. Polygon *STUVWXYZ* is a regular octagon. Suppose sides $\overline{ST}$ and $\overline{UV}$ are extended to meet at a point *R*. Find the measure of $\angle TRU$. 90°

MIXED REVIEW

FINDING AREA Find the area of the triangle described. (Review 1.7 for 11.2)

63. base: 11 inches; height: 5 inches 27.5 in.^{2}

64. base: 43 meters; height: 11 meters 236.5 m^2

65. vertices: *A*(2, 0), *B*(7, 0), *C*(5, 15) 37.5 sq. units

66. vertices: *D*(−3, 3), *E*(3, 3), *F*(−7, 11) 24 sq. units

VERIFYING RIGHT TRIANGLES Tell whether the triangle is a right triangle. (Review 9.3)

67. no

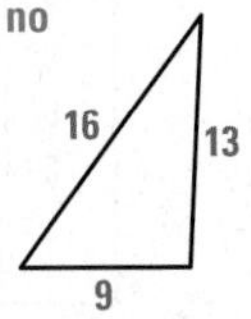

68. yes

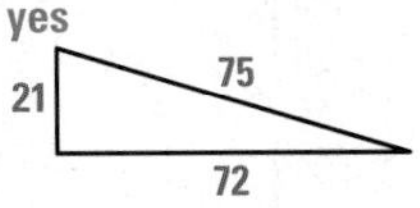

69. no

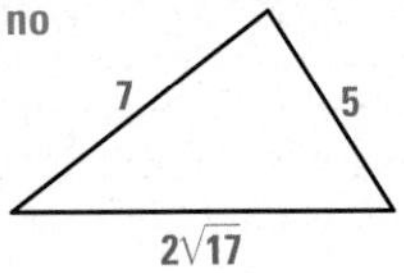

FINDING MEASUREMENTS $\overline{GD}$ and $\overline{FH}$ are diameters of circle *C*. Find the indicated arc measure. (Review 10.2)

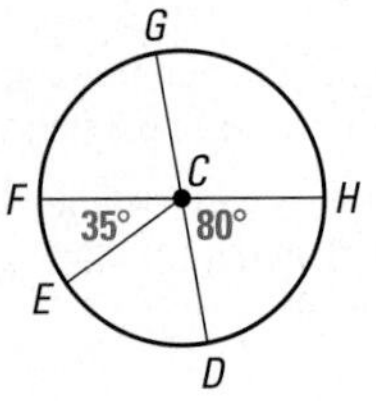

70. $m\widehat{DH}$ 80°

71. $m\widehat{ED}$ 65°

72. $m\widehat{EH}$ 145°

73. $m\widehat{EHG}$ 245°

11.2 Areas of Regular Polygons

What you should learn

GOAL 1 Find the area of an equilateral triangle.

GOAL 2 Find the area of a regular polygon, such as the area of a dodecagon in **Example 4**.

Why you should learn it

▼ To solve **real-life** problems, such as finding the area of a hexagonal mirror on the Hobby-Eberly Telescope in **Exs. 45 and 46**.

REAL LIFE

GOAL 1 FINDING THE AREA OF AN EQUILATERAL TRIANGLE

The area of *any* triangle with base length b and height h is given by $A = \frac{1}{2}bh$. The following formula for equilateral triangles, however, uses only the side length.

THEOREM

THEOREM 11.3 ***Area of an Equilateral Triangle***

The area of an equilateral triangle is one fourth the square of the length of the side times $\sqrt{3}$.

$$A = \frac{1}{4}\sqrt{3}s^2$$

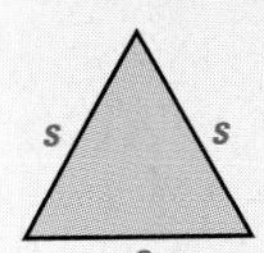

EXAMPLE 1 ***Proof of Theorem 11.3***

Prove Theorem 11.3. Refer to the figure below.

SOLUTION

GIVEN ▶ $\triangle ABC$ is equilateral.

PROVE ▶ Area of $\triangle ABC$ is $A = \frac{1}{4}\sqrt{3}s^2$.

Paragraph Proof Draw the altitude from B to side $\overline{AC}$. Then $\triangle ABD$ is a 30°-60°-90° triangle. From Lesson 9.4, the length of $\overline{BD}$, the side opposite the 60° angle in $\triangle ABD$, is $\frac{\sqrt{3}}{2}s$. Using the formula for the area of a triangle,

$$A = \frac{1}{2}bh = \frac{1}{2}(s)\left(\frac{\sqrt{3}}{2}s\right) = \frac{1}{4}\sqrt{3}s^2.$$

EXAMPLE 2 ***Finding the Area of an Equilateral Triangle***

Find the area of an equilateral triangle with 8 inch sides.

SOLUTION

Use $s = 8$ in the formula from Theorem 11.3.

$$A = \frac{1}{4}\sqrt{3}s^2 = \frac{1}{4}\sqrt{3}(8^2) = \frac{1}{4}\sqrt{3}(64) = \frac{1}{4}(64)\sqrt{3} = 16\sqrt{3} \text{ square inches}$$

▶ Using a calculator, the area is about 27.7 square inches.

STUDENT HELP

Study Tip

Be careful with radical signs. Notice in Example 1 that $\sqrt{3}s^2$ and $\sqrt{3s^2}$ do not mean the same thing.

CALIFORNIA STANDARDS AND ASSESSMENT

CA Standards: 8, 10, 16, 19
SAT9 Task 1: Obj. 23
SAT9 Task 2: Obj. 29

1 PLAN

PACING

Basic: 2 days
Average: 2 days
Advanced: 2 days
Block Schedule: 1 block

LESSON OPENER ACTIVITY

An alternative way to approach Lesson 11.2 is to use the Activity Lesson Opener:

- Blackline Master (*Chapter 11 Resource Book*, p. 26)
- Transparency (p. 69)

MEETING INDIVIDUAL NEEDS

- ***Chapter 11 Resource Book***
  Prerequisite Skills Review (p. 5)
  Practice Level A (p. 30)
  Practice Level B (p. 31)
  Practice Level C (p. 32)
  Reteaching with Practice (p. 33)
  Absent Student Catch-Up (p. 35)
  Challenge (p. 37)
- ***Resources in Spanish***
- ***Personal Student Tutor***

NEW-TEACHER SUPPORT

See the Tips for New Teachers on pp. 1–2 of the *Chapter 11 Resource Book* for additional notes about Lesson 11.2.

WARM-UP EXERCISES

Transparency Available

Use the figure to find each measure.

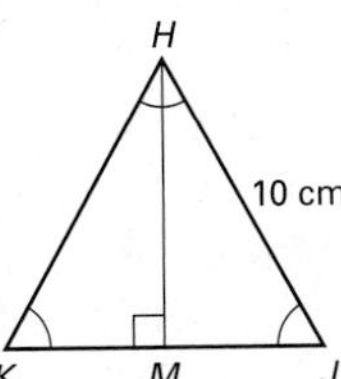

1. KJ 10 cm
2. $m\angle K$ 60°
3. $m\angle KHM$ 30°
4. HM $5\sqrt{3}$ cm

2 TEACH

MOTIVATING THE LESSON
Remind students that in the last lesson they divided polygons into triangles in order to derive a formula for finding the sum of the angle measures of polygons. In today's lesson, regular polygons will again be divided into triangles to find formulas for their areas.

ACTIVITY NOTE
In this activity, students use paper folding to see that a regular hexagon can be divided into 6 congruent equilateral triangles.

EXTRA EXAMPLE 1
Prove that the area of an isosceles triangle with base b, and base angles that measure 45° is one-fourth the square of the base.

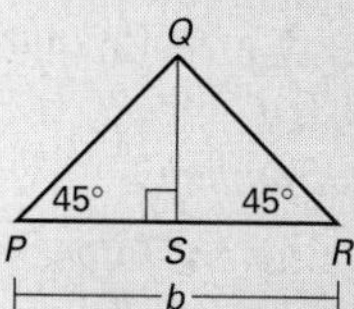

Sample answer:
Given: Isosceles triangle PQR with $m\angle P = m\angle Q = 45°$.
Prove: Area of $\triangle PQR$ is $A = \frac{1}{4}b^2$.
Draw the altitude from Q to PR; so $m\angle PSQ = 90°$. Then $\triangle PQS$ is a 45°-45°-90° triangle. Likewise, $\triangle QSR$ is a 45°-45°-90° triangle. From Lesson 9.4, $QS = PS = SR$. Since $b = PS + SR$, by substitution, $b = 2QS$, or $QS = \frac{1}{2}b$. Using the formula for the area of a triangle, $A = \frac{1}{2}bh = \frac{1}{2}(b)\left(\frac{1}{2}b\right) = \frac{1}{4}b^2$.

EXTRA EXAMPLE 2
Find the area of an equilateral triangle with 10 cm sides.
$25\sqrt{3}$ cm^2

CHECKPOINT EXERCISES
For use after Examples 1 and 2:
1. Find the area of an equilateral triangle whose perimeter is 6 in. $\sqrt{3}$ in.^{2}

GOAL 2 FINDING THE AREA OF A REGULAR POLYGON

You can use equilateral triangles to find the area of a regular hexagon.

ACTIVITY Developing Concepts

Investigating the Area of a Regular Hexagon

Use a protractor and ruler to draw a regular hexagon. Cut out your hexagon. Fold and draw the three lines through opposite vertices. The point where these lines intersect is the *center* of the hexagon.

1. How many triangles are formed? What kind of triangles are they?
   6; equilateral
2. Measure a side of the hexagon. Find the area of one of the triangles. What is the area of the entire hexagon? Explain your reasoning.
   Let s = the length of a side; $\frac{s^2\sqrt{3}}{4}$; $\frac{3s^2\sqrt{3}}{2}$; there are 6 △, so the total area is $6 \cdot \frac{s^2\sqrt{3}}{4} = \frac{3s^2\sqrt{3}}{2}$.

Think of the hexagon in the activity above, or another regular polygon, as inscribed in a circle.

The **center of the polygon** and **radius of the polygon** are the center and radius of its circumscribed circle, respectively.

The distance from the center to any side of the polygon is called the **apothem of the polygon**. The apothem is the height of a triangle between the center and two consecutive vertices of the polygon.

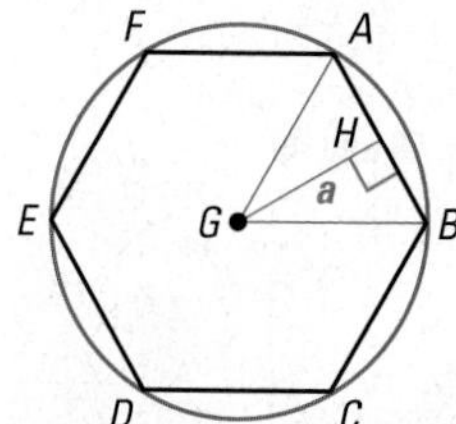

Hexagon *ABCDEF* with center *G*, radius *GA*, and apothem *GH*

STUDENT HELP

Study Tip
In a regular polygon, the length of each side is the same. If this length is s and there are n sides, then the perimeter P of the polygon is $n \cdot s$, or $P = ns$.

As in the activity, you can find the area of any regular n-gon by dividing the polygon into congruent triangles.

$$A = \text{area of one triangle} \cdot \text{number of triangles}$$
$$= \left(\frac{1}{2} \cdot \text{apothem} \cdot \text{side length } s\right) \cdot \text{number of sides}$$
$$= \frac{1}{2} \cdot \text{apothem} \cdot \text{number of sides} \cdot \text{side length } s$$
$$= \frac{1}{2} \cdot \text{apothem} \cdot \text{perimeter of polygon}$$

The number of congruent triangles formed will be the same as the number of sides of the polygon.

This approach can be used to find the area of any regular polygon.

THEOREM

THEOREM 11.4 ***Area of a Regular Polygon***
The area of a regular n-gon with side length s is half the product of the apothem a and the perimeter P, so $A = \frac{1}{2}aP$, or $A = \frac{1}{2}a \cdot ns$.

A **central angle of a regular polygon** is an angle whose vertex is the center and whose sides contain two consecutive vertices of the polygon. You can divide 360° by the number of sides to find the measure of each central angle of the polygon.

EXAMPLE 3 *Finding the Area of a Regular Polygon*

A regular pentagon is inscribed in a circle with radius 1 unit. Find the area of the pentagon.

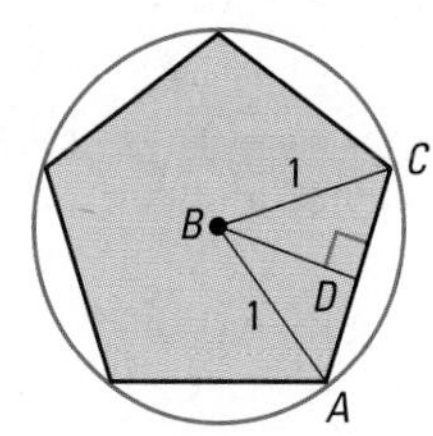

SOLUTION

To apply the formula for the area of a regular pentagon, you must find its apothem and perimeter.

The measure of central $\angle ABC$ is $\frac{1}{5} \cdot 360°$, or 72°.

In isosceles triangle $\triangle ABC$, the altitude to base $\overline{AC}$ also bisects $\angle ABC$ and side $\overline{AC}$. The measure of $\angle DBC$, then, is 36°. In right triangle $\triangle BDC$, you can use trigonometric ratios to find the lengths of the legs.

$$\cos 36° = \frac{BD}{BC} = \frac{BD}{1} = BD \qquad \sin 36° = \frac{DC}{BC} = \frac{DC}{1} = DC$$

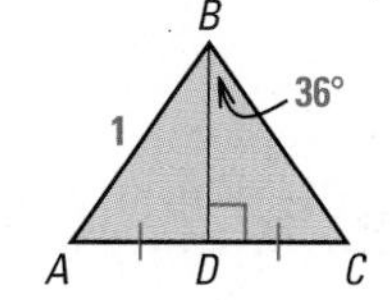

▶ So, the pentagon has an apothem of $a = BD = \cos 36°$ and a perimeter of $P = 5(AC) = 5(2 \cdot DC) = 10 \sin 36°$. The area of the pentagon is

$$A = \frac{1}{2}aP = \frac{1}{2}(\cos 36°)(10 \sin 36°) \approx 2.38 \text{ square units.}$$

STUDENT HELP

Look Back
For help with trigonometric ratios, see p. 558.

EXAMPLE 4 *Finding the Area of a Regular Dodecagon*

PENDULUMS The enclosure on the floor underneath the Foucault Pendulum at the Houston Museum of Natural Sciences in Houston, Texas, is a regular dodecagon with a side length of about 4.3 feet and a radius of about 8.3 feet. What is the floor area of the enclosure?

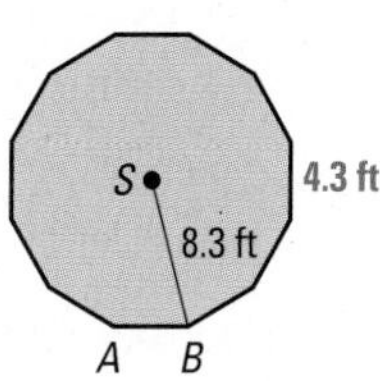

SOLUTION

A dodecagon has 12 sides. So, the perimeter of the enclosure is

$P \approx 12(4.3) = 51.6$ feet.

In $\triangle SBT$, $BT = \frac{1}{2}(BA) = \frac{1}{2}(4.3) = 2.15$ feet. Use the Pythagorean Theorem to find the apothem ST.

$a = \sqrt{8.3^2 - 2.15^2} \approx 8$ feet

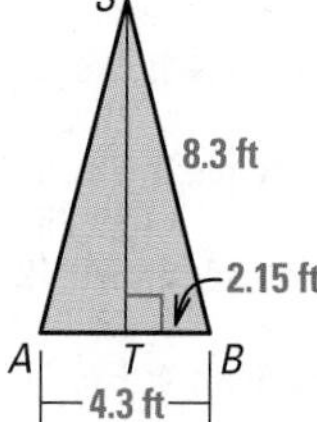

▶ So, the floor area of the enclosure is

$A = \frac{1}{2}aP \approx \frac{1}{2}(8)(51.6) = 206.4$ square feet.

FOCUS ON APPLICATIONS

FOUCAULT PENDULUMS swing continuously in a straight line. Watching the pendulum, though, you may think its path shifts. Instead, it is Earth and you that are turning. The floor under this pendulum in Texas rotates fully about every 48 hours.

APPLICATION LINK
www.mcdougallittell.com

EXTRA EXAMPLE 3
A regular octagon is inscribed in a circle with radius 4 units. Find the area of the octagon. **about 45.25 square units**

EXTRA EXAMPLE 4
The bottom of a glass is a regular 12-gon with a side length of about 1.2 cm and a radius of 2.3 cm. What is the area of the bottom of the glass? **about 16 cm²**

CHECKPOINT EXERCISES
For use after Examples 3 and 4:

1. What is the area of a regular 9-gon with a side length of 6 in.? **222.5 in.²**

APPLICATION NOTE
EXAMPLE 4 Additional information about pendulums is available at **www.mcdougallittell.com.**

FOCUS ON VOCABULARY
What is the difference between the *apothem* and the *radius* of a regular polygon? **The apothem is the distance from the center of the polygon to any side whereas the radius is the distance from the center to any vertex.**

CLOSURE QUESTION
You are given the radius of a regular polygon. Describe how you would find its area. ***Sample answer:*** **First divide 360° by 2 times the number of sides in the polygon to find the measure of the vertex ∠ formed by one radius and a segment whose length is the apothem. Use this ∠ and the cosine and sine ratios to find the lengths of the legs of the △ formed by the radius and segment whose length is the apothem. The length of one leg is the apothem and the length of the other side times two is the length of the side of the polygon. Multiply the side length by the number of sides to get the perimeter, and then use the formula $A = \frac{1}{2}aP$ to get the area of the polygon.**

DAILY PUZZLER
An equilateral triangle has an area of $\frac{9\sqrt{3}}{4}$ cm². What is its side length? **3 cm**

3 APPLY

ASSIGNMENT GUIDE

BASIC
Day 1: pp. 672–673 Exs. 9–29
Day 2: pp. 673–675 Exs. 30–44, 48–52, 54–64

AVERAGE
Day 1: pp. 672–673 Exs. 9–29
Day 2: pp. 673–675 Exs. 30–52, 54–64

ADVANCED
Day 1: pp. 672–673 Exs. 9–29
Day 2: pp. 673–675 Exs. 30–64

BLOCK SCHEDULE
pp. 672–675 Exs. 9–52, 54–64

EXERCISE LEVELS

Level A: *Easier*
9–15
Level B: *More Difficult*
16–52
Level C: *Most Difficult*
53

HOMEWORK CHECK

To quickly check student understanding of key concepts, go over the following exercises: Exs. 10, 18, 20, 22, 26, 28, 32, 38, 44. See also the Daily Homework Quiz:

- Blackline Master (*Chapter 11 Resource Book,* p. 40)
- Transparency (p. 81)

GUIDED PRACTICE

Vocabulary Check ✓

In Exercises 1–4, use the diagram shown.

1. Identify the *center* of polygon *ABCDE*. **J**
2. Identify the *radius* of the polygon. **5**
3. Identify a *central angle* of the polygon. **∠BJC**
4. Identify a segment whose length is the *apothem*. $\overline{JK}$

Concept Check ✓

5. In a regular polygon, how do you find the measure of each central angle? **Divide 360° by the number of sides.**

Skill Check ✓

6. What is the area of an equilateral triangle with 3 inch sides? $\frac{9\sqrt{3}}{4} \approx 3.9$ in.^{2}

STOP SIGN **The stop sign shown is a regular octagon. Its perimeter is about 80 inches and its height is about 24 inches.**

STOP
ARRÊT

7. What is the measure of each central angle? **45°**
8. Find the apothem, radius, and area of the stop sign. **about 12 in., about 13 in., about 480 in.^{2}**

PRACTICE AND APPLICATIONS

STUDENT HELP
Extra Practice to help you master skills is on p. 823.

FINDING AREA **Find the area of the triangle.**

9. 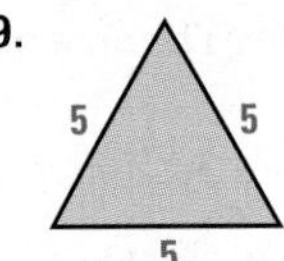

$\frac{25\sqrt{3}}{4} \approx 10.8$ sq. units

10. 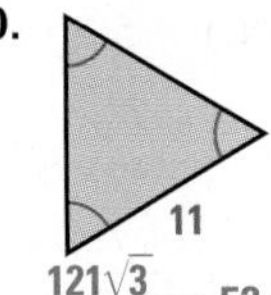

$\frac{121\sqrt{3}}{4} \approx 52.4$ sq. units

11. 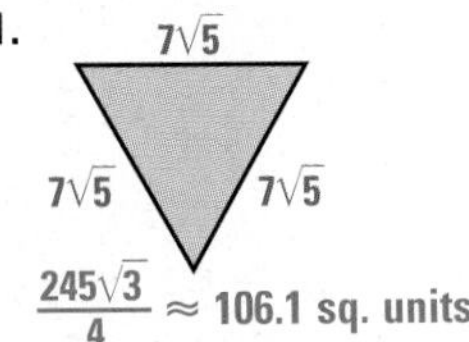

$\frac{245\sqrt{3}}{4} \approx 106.1$ sq. units

MEASURES OF CENTRAL ANGLES **Find the measure of a central angle of a regular polygon with the given number of sides.**

12. 9 sides **40°**
13. 12 sides **30°**
14. 15 sides **24°**
15. 180 sides **2°**

FINDING AREA **Find the area of the inscribed regular polygon shown.**

16. 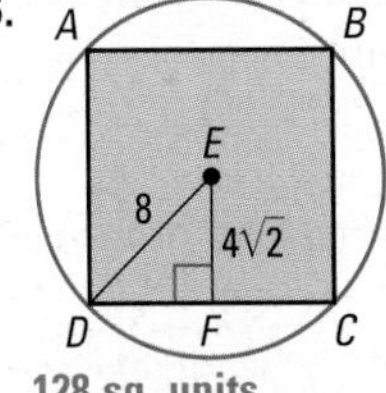

128 sq. units

17. 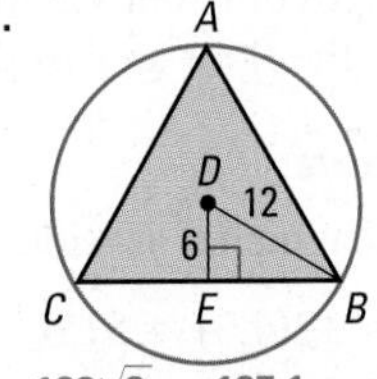

$108\sqrt{3} \approx 187.1$ sq. units

18. 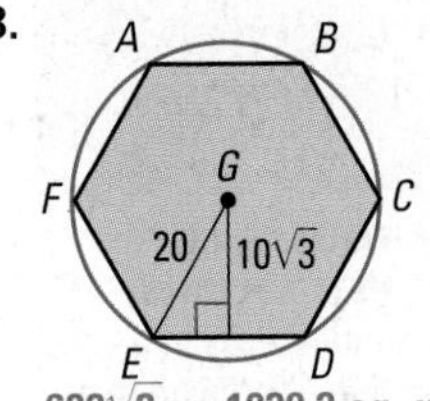

$600\sqrt{3} \approx 1039.2$ sq. units

STUDENT HELP
HOMEWORK HELP
Example 1: Exs. 9–11, 17, 19, 25, 33
Example 2: Exs. 9–11, 17, 19, 25, 33
Example 3: Exs. 12–24, 26, 34
Example 4: Exs. 34, 45–49

PERIMETER AND AREA **Find the perimeter and area of the regular polygon.**

19. 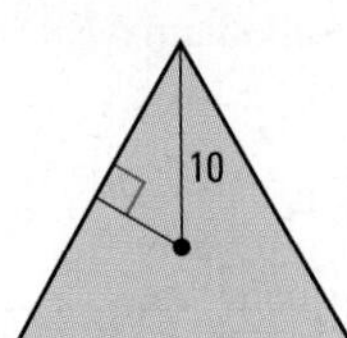

$30\sqrt{3} \approx 52.0$ units; $75\sqrt{3} \approx 129.9$ sq. units

20. 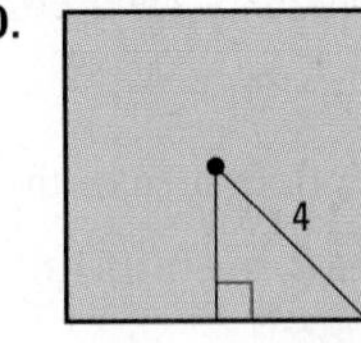

$16\sqrt{2}$ units; 32 sq. units

21. 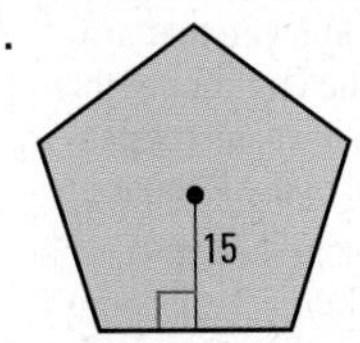

150 tan 36° ≈ 109.0 units; 1125 tan 36° ≈ 817.36 sq. units

PERIMETER AND AREA In Exercises 22–24, find the perimeter and area of the regular polygon.

22\.

23\.

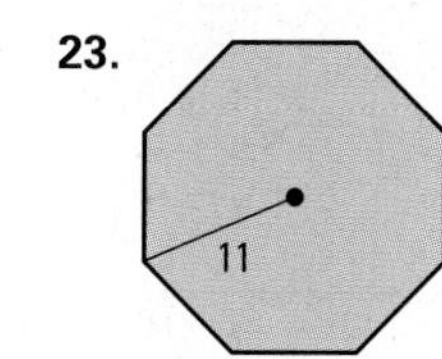

24\.

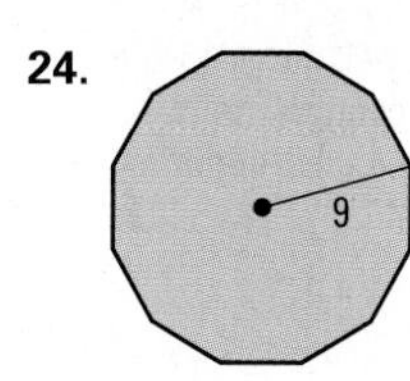

25\. **AREA** Find the area of an equilateral triangle that has a height of 15 inches. $75\sqrt{3} \approx 129.9$ in.^{2}

26\. **AREA** Find the area of a regular dodecagon (or 12-gon) that has 4 inch sides. 48(tan 75°) ≈ 179.14 in.^{2}

LOGICAL REASONING Decide whether the statement is *true* or *false*. Explain your choice.

27\. The area of a regular polygon of fixed radius r increases as the number of sides increases. See margin.

28\. The apothem of a regular polygon is always less than the radius. See margin.

29\. The radius of a regular polygon is always less than the side length. False; for example, the radius of a regular hexagon is equal to the side length.

AREA In Exercises 30–32, find the area of the regular polygon. The area of the portion shaded in red is given. Round answers to the nearest tenth.

30\. Area = $16\sqrt{3}$

$96\sqrt{3} \approx 166.3$

31\. Area = 4 tan 67.5°

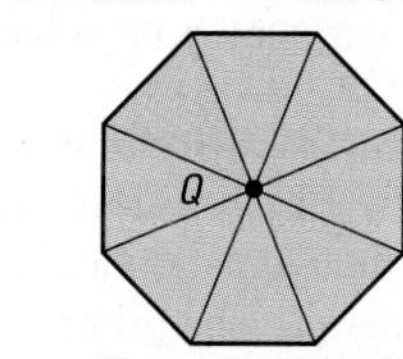

32 tan 67.5° ≈ 77.3

32\. Area = tan 54°

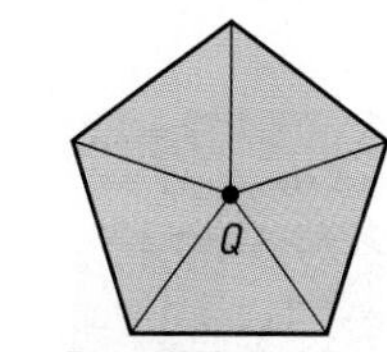

5 tan 54° ≈ 6.9

33\. **USING THE AREA FORMULAS** Show that the area of a regular hexagon is six times the area of an equilateral triangle with the same side length.

(*Hint*: Show that for a hexagon with side lengths s, $\frac{1}{2}aP = 6 \cdot \left(\frac{1}{4}\sqrt{3}s^2\right)$.)

34\. **BASALTIC COLUMNS** Suppose the top of one of the columns along the Giant's Causeway (see p. 659) is in the shape of a regular hexagon with a diameter of 18 inches. What is its apothem? $4.5\sqrt{3} \approx 7.8$ in.

CONSTRUCTION In Exercises 35–39, use a straightedge and a compass to construct a regular hexagon and an equilateral triangle.

35–37. Check drawings.

35\. Draw $\overline{AB}$ with a length of 1 inch. Open the compass to 1 inch and draw a circle with that radius.

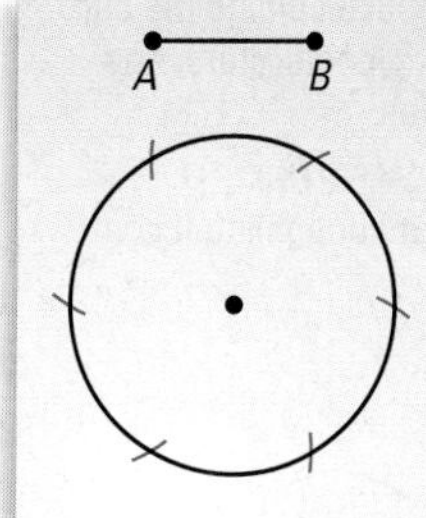

36\. Using the same compass setting, mark off equal parts along the circle.

37\. Connect the six points where the compass marks and circle intersect to draw a regular hexagon.

38\. What is the area of the hexagon? $\frac{3\sqrt{3}}{2} \approx 2.60$ in.^{2}

39\. *Writing* Explain how you could use this construction to construct an equilateral triangle. Draw segments connecting 3 of the compass marks, skipping every second mark.

22\. 42 units; $\frac{147\sqrt{3}}{2} \approx$ 127. 31 sq. units

23\. 176 sin 22.5° ≈ 67.35 units; 968(sin 22.5°)(cos 22.5°) ≈ 342.24 sq. units

24\. 216 sin 15° ≈ 55.9 units; 972(sin 15°)(cos 15°) = 243 sq. units

27\. True; let θ be the measure of a central angle, n the number of sides, r the radius, and P the perimeter. As n grows bigger θ will become smaller, so the apothem, which is given by by $r \cos \frac{\theta}{2}$ will get larger. The perimeter of the polygon, which is given by $n\left(2r\sin \frac{\theta}{2}\right)$ will grow larger, too. Although the factor involving the sine will get smaller, the increase in n more than makes up for it. Consequently, the area, which is given by $\frac{1}{2}aP$ will increase.

28\. True; the apothem is a leg length in a right △ of which the radius is the length of the hypotenuse.

33\. Let s = the length of a side of the hexagon and of the equilateral triangle. The apothem of the hexagon is $\frac{1}{2}\sqrt{3}s$ and the perimeter of the hexagon is $6s$. The area of the hexagon, then, is $A = \frac{1}{2}aP = \frac{1}{2}\left(\frac{1}{2}\sqrt{3}s\right) \cdot 6s$, or $\frac{3}{2}\sqrt{3}s^2$. The area of an equilateral triangle with side length s is $A = \frac{1}{4}\sqrt{3}s^2$. Six of these equilateral triangles together (forming the hexagon), then, would have area $6 \cdot \frac{s^2\sqrt{3}}{4} = \frac{3s^2\sqrt{3}}{2}$. The two results are the same.

TEACHING TIPS

EXERCISES 16–21 Students may come up with slightly different answers to these problems. To get the most accurate answer possible, have students carry trigonometric expressions or radical expressions through until the very last step, then round, as is shown in Example 3 on page 671.

! COMMON ERROR

EXERCISES 22–24 Students might use the central angle when using trigonometry to find the apothem and side length. Point out that the acute angle in the triangle formed by a radius and a segment whose length is the apothem is half the measure of the central angle of the polygon. Also, students might forget to double the length of the leg of this triangle to get the side length. This error would result in an area that is half the actual area of the polygon.

STUDENT HELP NOTES

Homework Help Students can find help for Exs. 40–44 at **www.mcdougallittell.com.** The information can be printed out for students who don't have access to the Internet.

CAREER NOTE
EXERCISES 45 AND 46
Additional information about astronomers is available at **www.mcdougallittell.com.**

ENGLISH LEARNERS
EXERCISES 45–46
Understanding terminology in word problems can be difficult for English learners. For Exercises 45–46, students may have difficulty understanding what a *primary mirror* is, and thus have trouble interpeting the photograph.

ADDITIONAL PRACTICE AND RETEACHING

For Lesson 11.2:

- Practice Levels A, B, and C (*Chapter 11 Resource Book*, p. 30)
- Reteaching with Practice (*Chapter 11 Resource Book*, p. 33)
- See Lesson 11.2 of the *Personal Student Tutor*

For more Mixed Review:

- Search the *Test and Practice Generator* for key words or specific lessons.

674

STUDENT HELP

HOMEWORK HELP
Visit our Web site www.mcdougallittell for help with construction in Exs. 40–44.

CONSTRUCTION In Exercises 40–44, use a straightedge and a compass to construct a regular pentagon as shown in the diagrams below.
40–44. Check drawings.

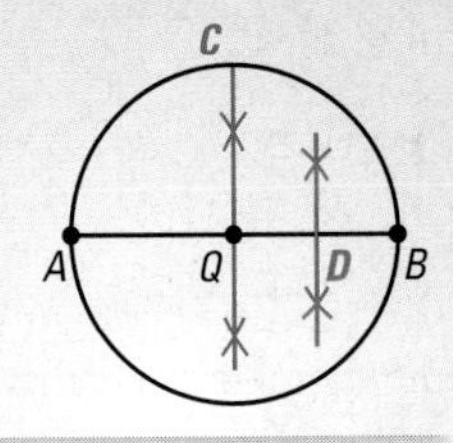

Exs. 40, 41

Ex. 42

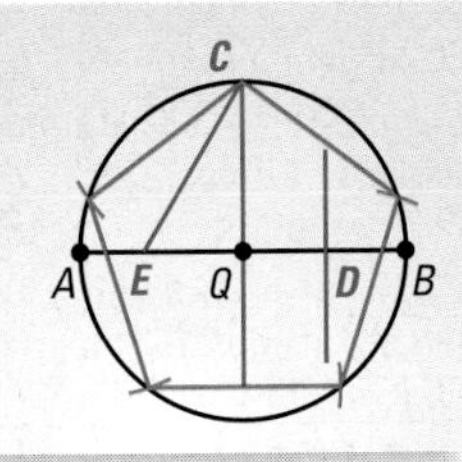

Exs. 43, 44

40. Draw a circle with center Q. Draw a diameter $\overline{AB}$. Construct the perpendicular bisector of $\overline{AB}$ and label its intersection with the circle as point C.

41. Construct point D, the midpoint of $\overline{QB}$.

42. Place the compass point at D. Open the compass to the length DC and draw an arc from C so it intersects $\overline{AB}$ at a point, E. Draw $\overline{CE}$.

43. Open the compass to the length CE. Starting at C, mark off equal parts along the circle.

44. Connect the five points where the compass marks and circle intersect to draw a regular pentagon. What is the area of your pentagon?
Check results.

TELESCOPES In Exercises 45 and 46, use the following information.
The Hobby-Eberly Telescope in Fort Davis, Texas, is the largest optical telescope in North America. The primary mirror for the telescope consists of 91 smaller mirrors forming a hexagon shape. Each of the smaller mirror parts is itself a hexagon with side length 0.5 meter.

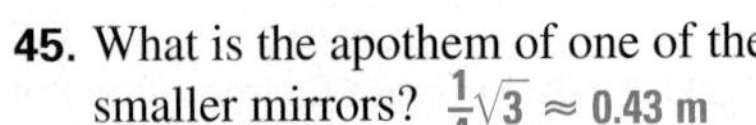

45. What is the apothem of one of the smaller mirrors? $\frac{1}{4}\sqrt{3} \approx 0.43$ m

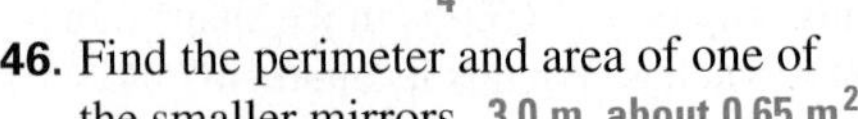

46. Find the perimeter and area of one of the smaller mirrors. 3.0 m, about 0.65 m^2

FOCUS ON CAREERS

ASTRONOMERS use physics and mathematics to study the universe, including the sun, moon, planets, stars, and galaxies.

CAREER LINK
www.mcdougallittell.com

TILING In Exercises 47–49, use the following information.
You are tiling a bathroom floor with tiles that are regular hexagons, as shown. Each tile has 6 inch sides. You want to choose different colors so that no two adjacent tiles are the same color.

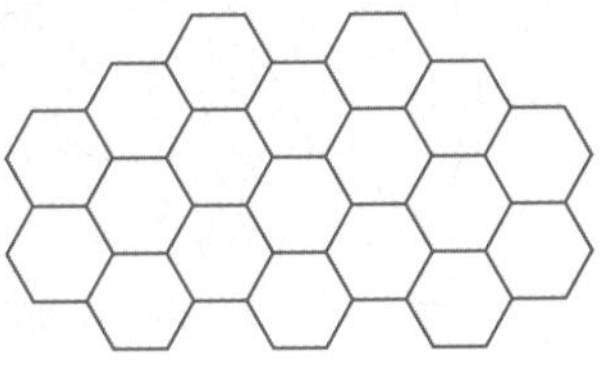

47. What is the minimum number of colors that you can use? 3 colors

48. What is the area of each tile? $54\sqrt{3} \approx 93.5$ in.^{2}

49. The floor that you are tiling is rectangular. Its width is 6 feet and its length is 8 feet. At least how many tiles of each color will you need?
about 25 tiles

Test Preparation

QUANTITATIVE COMPARISON In Exercises 50–52, choose the statement that is true about the given quantities.

Ⓐ The quantity in column A is greater.

Ⓑ The quantity in column B is greater.

Ⓒ The two quantities are equal.

Ⓓ The relationship cannot be determined from the given information.

	Column A	Column B	
	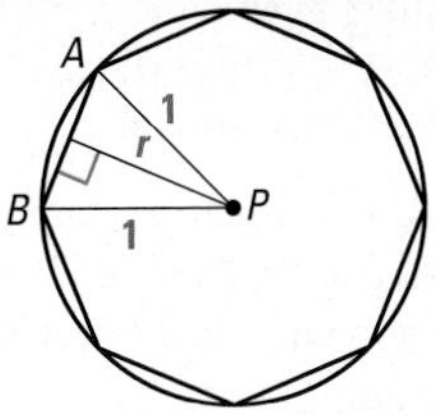 (octagon inscribed in circle with center P; A, B, $PA = 1$, $PB = 1$, apothem r)	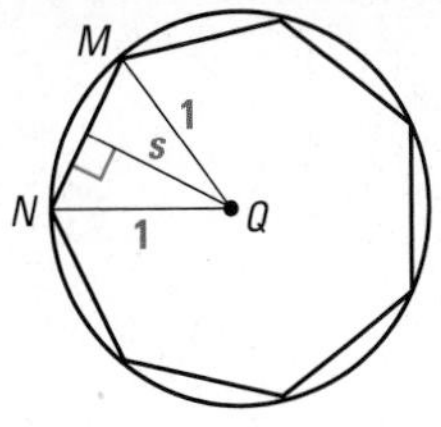 (heptagon inscribed in circle with center Q; M, N, $QM = 1$, $QN = 1$, apothem s)	
50.	$m\angle APB$	$m\angle MQN$	B
51.	Apothem r	Apothem s	A
52.	Perimeter of octagon with center P	Perimeter of heptagon with center Q	A

★ Challenge

53. USING DIFFERENT METHODS Find the area of $ABCDE$ by using two methods. First, use the formula $A = \frac{1}{2}aP$, or $A = \frac{1}{2}a \cdot ns$. Second, add the areas of the smaller polygons. Check that both methods yield the same area.

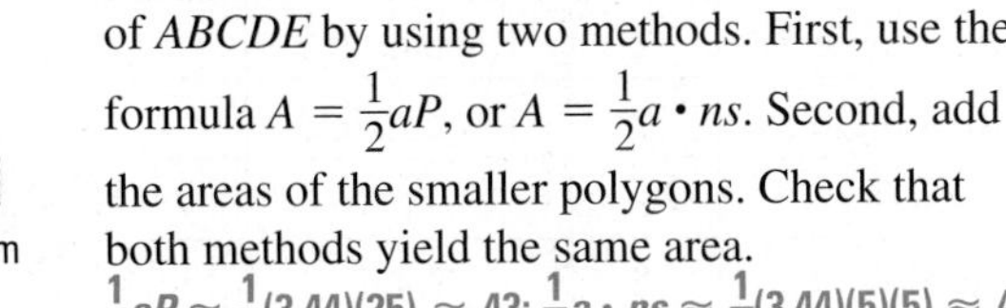

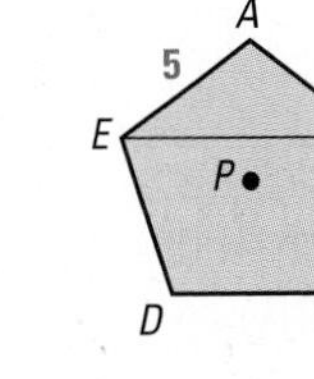

$\frac{1}{2}aP \approx \frac{1}{2}(3.44)(25) \approx 43$; $\frac{1}{2}a \cdot ns \approx \frac{1}{2}(3.44)(5)(5) \approx 43$; area of $\triangle ABE$ + area of $EDCB \approx 11.9 + 31.1 \approx 43$

EXTRA CHALLENGE
www.mcdougallittell.com

MIXED REVIEW

SOLVING PROPORTIONS Solve the proportion. (Review 8.1 for 11.3)

54. $\frac{x}{6} = \frac{11}{12}$ $\frac{11}{2}$ **55.** $\frac{20}{4} = \frac{15}{x}$ 3 **56.** $\frac{12}{x+7} = \frac{13}{x}$ -91 **57.** $\frac{x+6}{9} = \frac{x}{11}$ -33

USING SIMILAR POLYGONS In the diagram shown, $\triangle ABC \sim \triangle DEF$. Use the figures to determine whether the statement is true. (Review 8.3 for 11.3)

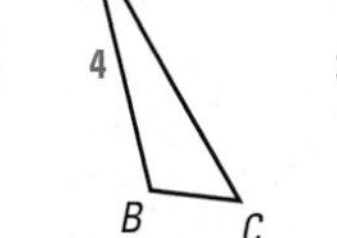

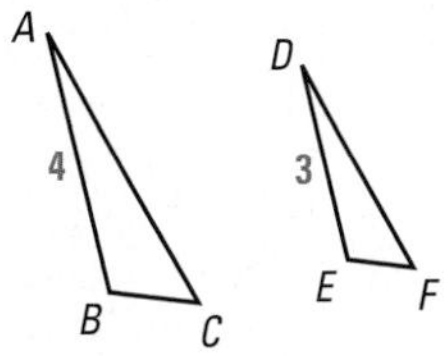

58. $\frac{AC}{BC} = \frac{DF}{EF}$ true **59.** $\frac{DF}{AC} = \frac{EF + DE + DF}{BC + AB + AC}$ true

60. $\angle B \cong \angle E$ true **61.** $\overline{BC} \cong \overline{EF}$ false

FINDING SEGMENT LENGTHS Find the value of *x*. (Review 10.5)

62. 6

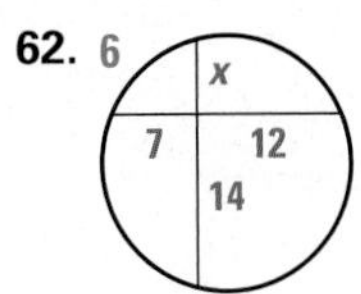

63. 7

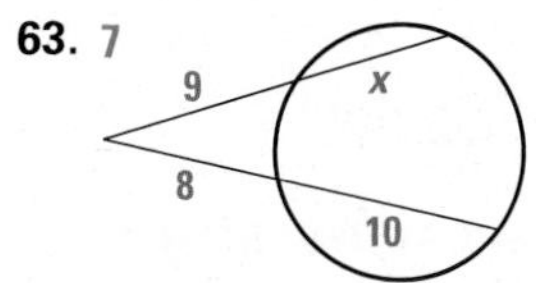

64. 12

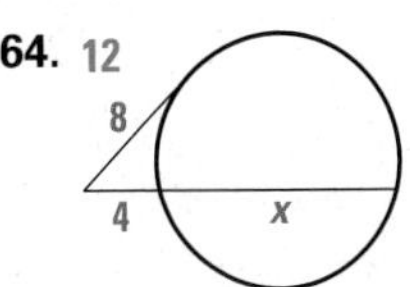

4 ASSESS

DAILY HOMEWORK QUIZ

Transparency Available

1. Find the area of the triangle.

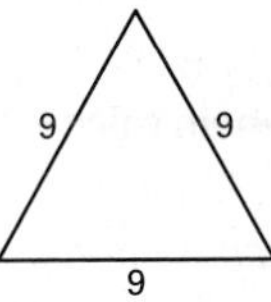

$\frac{81\sqrt{3}}{4} \approx 35.1$ square units

2. Find the measure of the central angle of a regular polygon with 10 sides. 36°

3. Find the area of the inscribed regular polygon shown.

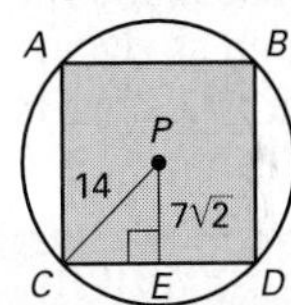

392 square units

4. Find the area of a regular hexagon that has 4-inch sides. $24\sqrt{3} \approx 41.6$

EXTRA CHALLENGE NOTE

Challenge problems for Lesson 11.2 are available in **blackline** format in the *Chapter 11 Resource Book,* p. 37 and at **www.mcdougallittell.com.**

ADDITIONAL TEST PREPARATION

1. OPEN ENDED Draw a regular polygon and show how to find its area. Check student's work.

2. WRITING Explain why you might use the Pythagorean Theorem when finding the area of a regular polygon.
Sample answer: If you know the radius and side length of the regular polygon, you can use the Pythagorean Theorem with the radius and half the side length to find the apothem.

1 Planning the Activity

PURPOSE
To investigate the relationship between the areas and scale factors of two similar polygons.

MATERIALS
- graph paper, pencil, ruler
- Activity Support Master (*Chapter 11 Resource Book,* p. 41)

PACING
- Exploring the Concept — 15 min
- Drawing Conclusions — 15 min

LINK TO LESSON
Students should recall the results of the activity when studying Examples 1 and 3 in Lesson 11.3.

2 Managing the Activity

CLASSROOM MANAGEMENT
In Step 1, be sure students use grid lines for all the sides of their polygon; otherwise it will be difficult to find the area of the polygon or to construct the similar polygon. When drawing the similar polygon in Step 4, students should begin at one vertex and expand the sides connecting that vertex. They can then continue to an adjacent vertex and so on to form the similar figure.

3 Closing the Activity

★ ***KEY DISCOVERY***
If the ratio of corresponding sides of two similar polygons is 1:2, the ratio of their areas is 1:4.

ACTIVITY ASSESSMENT
Suppose you draw two similar figures whose ratio of corresponding side lengths is 1:2 and you know the area of the smaller figure. How will you find the area of the larger figure? **Multiply the area of the smaller figure by 4.**

ACTIVITY 11.3
Developing Concepts

GROUP ACTIVITY
Work with a partner.

MATERIALS
- graph paper
- pencil
- ruler

Area Relationships in Similar Figures

▶ **QUESTION** **How does the ratio of the areas of any two similar polygons compare to the scale factor?**

▶ **EXPLORING THE CONCEPT**

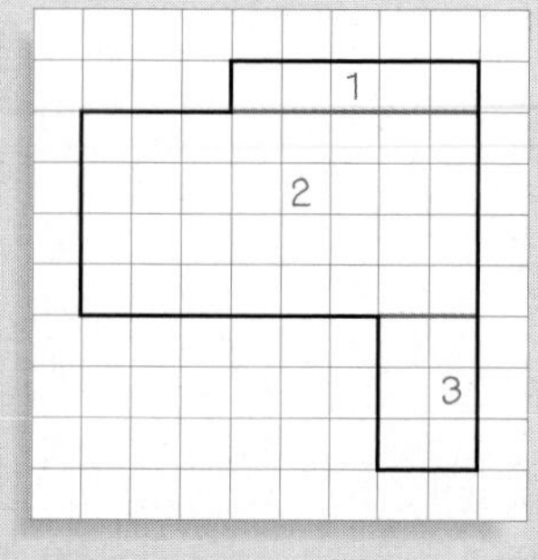

1. On a piece of graph paper draw a polygon. Use grid lines as sides of the polygon. An example is shown.

2. Divide your polygon into several rectangles. Calculate the area of each rectangle. Create a table like the one shown below to record the area of each rectangle.

3. Add the areas of the rectangles to find the total area of the polygon. Record your results.

Original polygon	Area	Similar polygon	Area
Rectangle 1	?	Rectangle 1	?
Rectangle 2	?	Rectangle 2	?
Rectangle 3	?	Rectangle 3	?
⋮	⋮	⋮	⋮
Total	?	Total	?

4. On another piece of graph paper draw a polygon that is similar to your original polygon. The ratio of the side lengths of the second polygon to the first polygon should be 2:1.

5. Repeat **Steps 2** and **3** to find the area of the similar polygon.

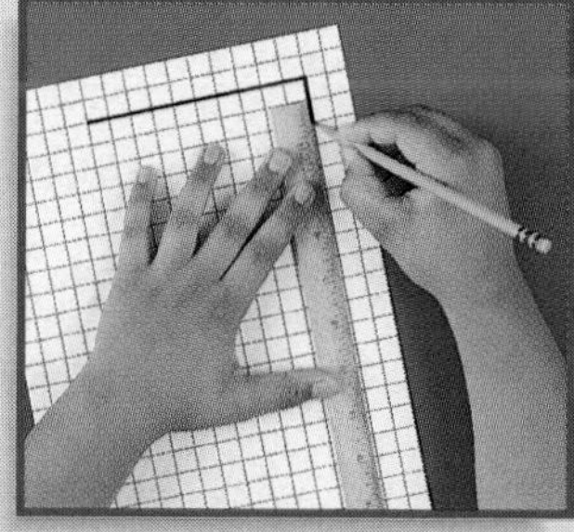

▶ **DRAWING CONCLUSIONS**

1. Use a ratio to compare the area of the similar polygon to the area of the original polygon.

2. Make a conjecture about the relationship between the scale factor of two similar polygons and the ratio of their areas.

1. **Areas will vary; the ratio of the area of the similar polygon to the area of the original polygon is the square of the scale factor of the similar polygon and should be 4:1.**
2. **The ratio of the areas of two similar polygons is the square of the scale factor.**

EXTENSION

CRITICAL THINKING Compare and discuss your conjecture with your partner. Work together to create a new pair of similar polygons to test the conjecture. **Check students' results.**

11.3 Perimeters and Areas of Similar Figures

What you should learn

GOAL 1 Compare perimeters and areas of similar figures.

GOAL 2 Use perimeters and areas of similar figures to solve **real-life** problems, as applied in **Example 2**.

Why you should learn it

▼ To solve **real-life** problems, such as finding the area of the walkway around a polygonal pool in **Exs. 25–27**.

REAL LIFE

Frank Lloyd Wright included this triangular pool and walkway in his design of *Taliesin West* in Scottsdale, Arizona.

GOAL 1 COMPARING PERIMETER AND AREA

For any polygon, the *perimeter of the polygon* is the sum of the lengths of its sides and the *area of the polygon* is the number of square units contained in its interior.

In Lesson 8.3, you learned that if two polygons are *similar*, then the ratio of their perimeters is the same as the ratio of the lengths of their corresponding sides. In Activity 11.3 on page 676, you may have discovered that the ratio of the areas of two similar polygons is *not* this same ratio, as shown in Theorem 11.5. Exercise 22 asks you to write a proof of this theorem for rectangles.

THEOREM

THEOREM 11.5 ***Areas of Similar Polygons***

If two polygons are similar with the lengths of corresponding sides in the ratio of $a:b$, then the ratio of their areas is $a^2:b^2$.

$$\frac{\text{Side length of Quad. I}}{\text{Side length of Quad. II}} = \frac{a}{b}$$

$$\frac{\text{Area of Quad. I}}{\text{Area of Quad. II}} = \frac{a^2}{b^2}$$

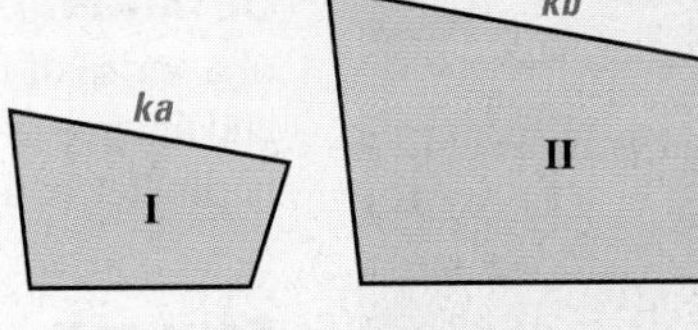

Quad. I ~ Quad. II

EXAMPLE 1 *Finding Ratios of Similar Polygons*

Pentagons *ABCDE* and *LMNPQ* are similar.

a. Find the ratio (red to blue) of the perimeters of the pentagons.

b. Find the ratio (red to blue) of the areas of the pentagons.

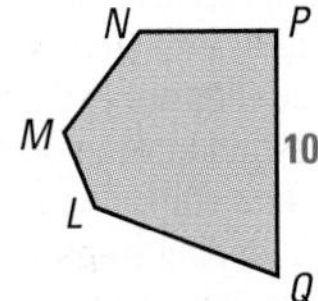

SOLUTION

The ratio of the lengths of corresponding sides in the pentagons is $\frac{5}{10} = \frac{1}{2}$, or 1:2.

a. The ratio of the perimeters is also 1:2. So, the perimeter of pentagon *ABCDE* is half the perimeter of pentagon *LMNPQ*.

b. Using Theorem 11.5, the ratio of the areas is $1^2:2^2$, or 1:4. So, the area of pentagon *ABCDE* is one fourth the area of pentagon *LMNPQ*.

STUDENT HELP

Study Tip
The ratio "*a* to *b*," for example, can be written using a fraction bar $\left(\frac{a}{b}\right)$ or a colon $(a:b)$.

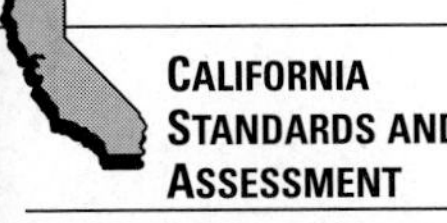

CALIFORNIA STANDARDS AND ASSESSMENT

CA Standards: 4, 8, 11, 21
SAT9 Task 1: Objs. 1, 23
SAT9 Task 2: Objs. 1, 29

1 PLAN

PACING
Basic: 2 days
Average: 2 days
Advanced: 2 days
Block Schedule: 1 block

LESSON OPENER
SPREADSHEET
An alternative way to approach Lesson 11.3 is to use the Spreadsheet Lesson Opener:
- Blackline Master (*Chapter 11 Resource Book*, p. 42)
- Transparency (p. 70)

MEETING INDIVIDUAL NEEDS
- ***Chapter 11 Resource Book***
  Prerequisite Skills Review (p. 5)
  Practice Level A (p. 43)
  Practice Level B (p. 44)
  Practice Level C (p. 45)
  Reteaching with Practice (p. 46)
  Absent Student Catch-Up (p. 48)
  Challenge (p. 51)
- ***Resources in Spanish***
-  ***Personal Student Tutor***

NEW-TEACHER SUPPORT
See the Tips for New Teachers on pp. 1–2 of the *Chapter 11 Resource Book* for additional notes about Lesson 11.3.

WARM-UP EXERCISES

Transparency Available

Polygons *ABCD* and *HJKL* are similar.

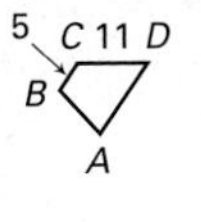

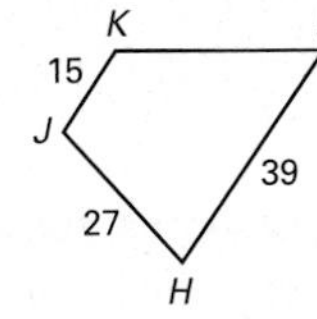

1. What is the ratio of the side lengths of *ABCD* to *HJKL*? 1:3
2. Find *KL*. 33
3. Find *AB*. 9
4. What is the ratio of their perimeters? 1:3

2 TEACH

MOTIVATING THE LESSON

Ask students to recall the relationship between the side lengths and the perimeters of two similar polygons. Ask if they think their areas might also be related. In today's lesson this relationship is explored.

EXTRA EXAMPLE 1

The ratio of corresponding sides of two similar hexagons is 3:2.

a. Find the ratio of their perimeters. 3:2

b. Find the ratio of their areas. 9:4

EXTRA EXAMPLE 2

A rectangular tablecloth is 60 in. by 120 in. A rectangular place mat made from the same cloth is 12 in. by 24 in. and costs $5. Compare the areas of the place mat and tablecloth to find a reasonable cost for the tablecloth. $125

EXTRA EXAMPLE 3

A store sells trampolines that are all regular hexagons. One trampoline has a side length of about 4.5 ft and an area of about 52.6 ft^2. Find the area of the trampoline whose perimeter is 67.5 ft. about 328.8 ft^2

CHECKPOINT EXERCISES

For use after Examples 1–3:

1. Two similar polygons have perimeters 7 cm and 28 cm respectively. Find the area of the smaller figure if the area of the larger is 48 cm^2. 3 cm^2

CLOSURE QUESTION

How can you find the area of a polygon if you know its perimeter and the perimeter and area of a similar polygon? **The ratio of their areas is the square of the ratio of their perimeters. Set up an equation using the ratio and the known area to find the unknown area.**

GOAL 2 USING PERIMETER AND AREA IN REAL LIFE

EXAMPLE 2 *Using Areas of Similar Figures*

COMPARING COSTS You are buying photographic paper to print a photo in different sizes. An 8 inch by 10 inch sheet of the paper costs $.42. What is a reasonable cost for a 16 inch by 20 inch sheet?

SOLUTION

Because the ratio of the lengths of the sides of the two rectangular pieces of paper is 1 : 2, the ratio of the areas of the pieces of paper is $1^2 : 2^2$, or 1 : 4. Because the cost of the paper should be a function of its area, the larger piece of paper should cost about four times as much, or $1.68.

EXAMPLE 3 *Finding Perimeters and Areas of Similar Polygons*

OCTAGONAL FLOORS A trading pit at the Chicago Board of Trade is in the shape of a series of regular octagons. One octagon has a side length of about 14.25 feet and an area of about 980.4 square feet. Find the area of a smaller octagon that has a perimeter of about 76 feet.

SOLUTION

All regular octagons are similar because all corresponding angles are congruent and the corresponding side lengths are proportional.

Draw and label a sketch.

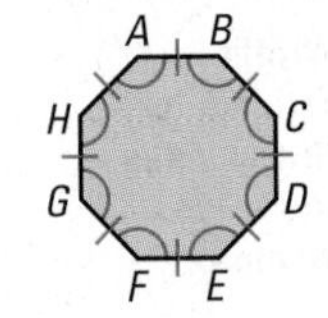

Find the ratio of the side lengths of the two octagons, which is the same as the ratio of their perimeters.

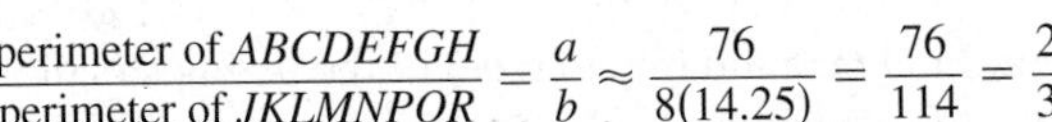

$$\frac{\text{perimeter of } ABCDEFGH}{\text{perimeter of } JKLMNPQR} = \frac{a}{b} \approx \frac{76}{8(14.25)} = \frac{76}{114} = \frac{2}{3}$$

Calculate the area of the smaller octagon. Let A represent the area of the smaller octagon. The ratio of the areas of the smaller octagon to the larger is $a^2 : b^2 = 2^2 : 3^2$, or 4 : 9.

$$\frac{A}{980.4} = \frac{4}{9} \qquad \textbf{Write proportion.}$$

$$9A = 980.4 \cdot 4 \qquad \textbf{Cross product property}$$

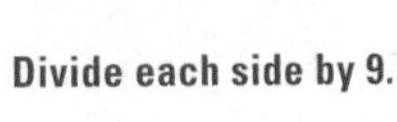

$$A = \frac{3921.6}{9} \qquad \textbf{Divide each side by 9.}$$

$$A \approx 435.7 \qquad \textbf{Use a calculator.}$$

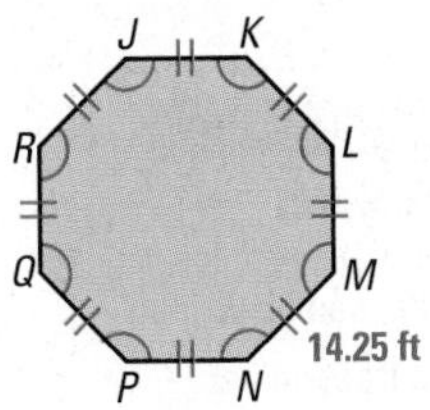

▶ The area of the smaller octagon is about 435.7 square feet.

FOCUS ON APPLICATIONS

CHICAGO BOARD OF TRADE

Commodities such as grains, coffee, and financial securities are exchanged at this marketplace. Associated traders stand on the descending steps in the same "pie-slice" section of an octagonal pit. The different levels allow buyers and sellers to see each other as orders are yelled out.

APPLICATION LINK
www.mcdougallittell.com

GUIDED PRACTICE

Vocabulary Check ✓

1. If two polygons are *similar* with the lengths of corresponding sides in the ratio of $a:b$, then the ratio of their perimeters is __?__ and the ratio of their areas is __?__. $a:b$; $a^2:b^2$

Concept Check ✓

Tell whether the statement is *true* or *false*. Explain.

2. Any two regular polygons with the same number of sides are similar. True; all corresp. ∠s are ≅ and all side lengths are proportional.
3. Doubling the side length of a square doubles the area. See margin.

3. False; the ratio of the lengths of corresp. sides is 1:2, so the ratio of the areas is 1:4. Doubling the side length of a square quadruples the area.

Skill Check ✓

In Exercises 4 and 5, the red and blue figures are similar. Find the ratio (red to blue) of their perimeters and of their areas.

4. 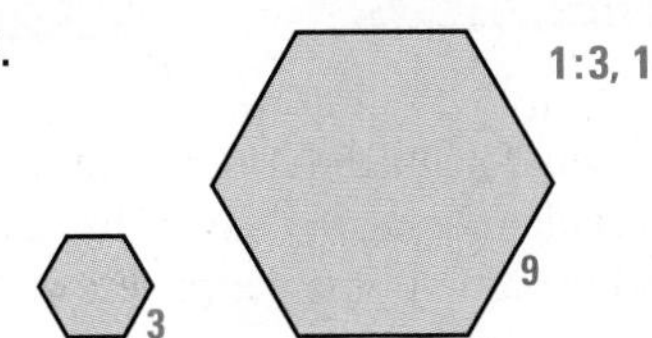

1:3, 1:9

5. 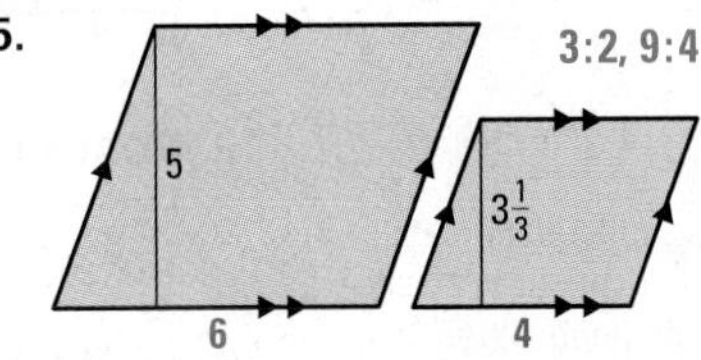

3:2, 9:4

6. PHOTOGRAPHY Use the information from Example 2 on page 678 to find a reasonable cost for a sheet of 4 inch by 5 inch photographic paper. about $.11

PRACTICE AND APPLICATIONS

STUDENT HELP

Extra Practice to help you master skills is on p. 823.

FINDING RATIOS In Exercises 7–10, the polygons are similar. Find the ratio (red to blue) of their perimeters and of their areas.

7. 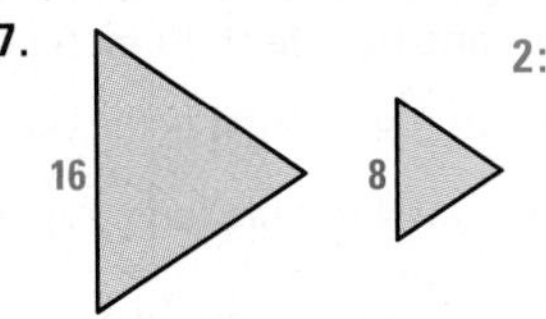

2:1, 4:1

8. 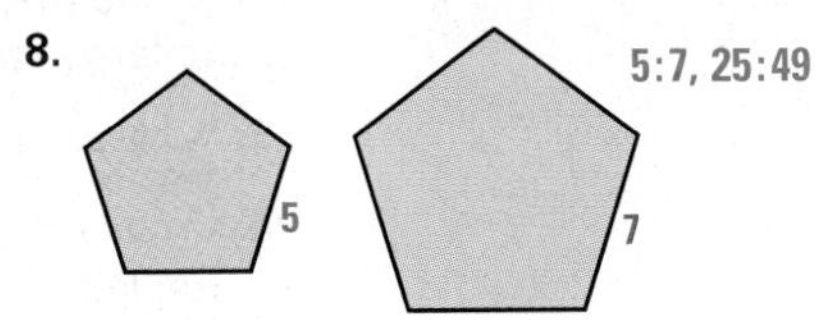

5:7, 25:49

9. 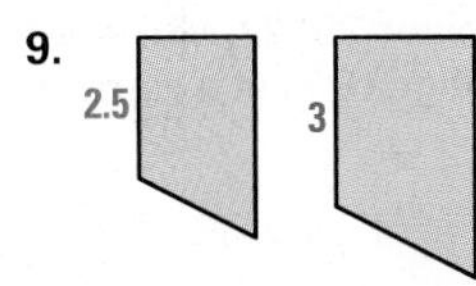

5:6, 25:36

10. 5:3, 25:9
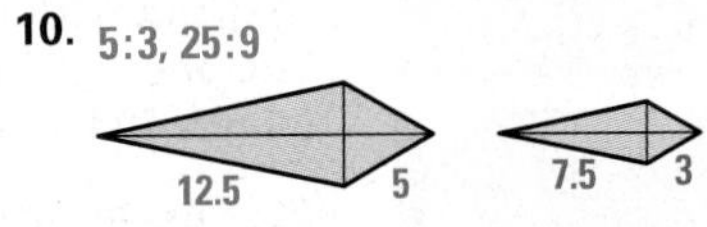

LOGICAL REASONING In Exercises 11–13, complete the statement using *always, sometimes,* or *never*.

11. Two similar hexagons __?__ have the same perimeter. sometimes
12. Two rectangles with the same area are __?__ similar. sometimes
13. Two regular pentagons are __?__ similar. always
14. HEXAGONS The ratio of the lengths of corresponding sides of two similar hexagons is 2:5. What is the ratio of their areas? 4:25
15. OCTAGONS A regular octagon has an area of 49 m^2. Find the scale factor of this octagon to a similar octagon that has an area of 100 m^2. 7:10

STUDENT HELP

HOMEWORK HELP
Example 1: Exs. 7–10, 14–18
Example 2: Exs. 23, 24
Example 3: Exs. 25–28

3 APPLY

ASSIGNMENT GUIDE

BASIC
Day 1: pp. 679–680 Exs. 8–20 even, 23–27
Day 2: pp. 679–682 Exs. 7–21 odd, 28, 29, 34–41, Quiz 1 Exs. 1–7

AVERAGE
Day 1: pp. 679–680 Exs. 8–20 even, 23–27
Day 2: pp. 679–682 Exs. 7–21 odd, 28, 29, 34–41, Quiz 1 Exs. 1–7

ADVANCED
Day 1: pp. 679–680 Exs. 8–20 even, 23–27
Day 2: pp. 679–682 Exs. 7–21 odd, 22, 28–41, Quiz 1 Exs. 1–7

BLOCK SCHEDULE
pp. 679–682 Exs. 7–21, 23–29, 34–41, Quiz 1 Exs. 1–7

EXERCISE LEVELS

Level A: *Easier* 7–13
Level B: *More Difficult* 14–29
Level C: *Most Difficult* 30–33

✓ HOMEWORK CHECK

To quickly check student understanding of key concepts, go over the following exercises: Exs. 8, 14, 16, 18, 20, 24, 27. See also the Daily Homework Quiz:

- Blackline Master (*Chapter 11 Resource Book,* p. 55)
- Transparency (p. 82)

! COMMON ERROR

EXERCISE 16 Students may forget to square the numbers in the ratio of side lengths to find the ratio of areas. Or, students may not set up the proportion correctly. Encourage students to think about their answer and make sure that it makes sense in the context of the problem.

STUDENT HELP NOTES

Homework Help Students can find help for Exs. 19–21 at **www.mcdougallittell.com.** The information can be printed out for students who don't have access to the Internet.

ADDITIONAL PRACTICE AND RETEACHING

For Lesson 11.3:

- Practice Levels A, B, and C (*Chapter 11 Resource Book,* p. 43)
- Reteaching with Practice (*Chapter 11 Resource Book,* p. 46)
- See Lesson 11.3 of the *Personal Student Tutor*

For more Mixed Review:

- Search the *Test and Practice Generator* for key words or specific lessons.

17. Since $\overline{AB}$ is parallel to $\overline{DC}$, $\angle A \cong \angle C$ and $\angle B \cong \angle D$ by the Alternate Interior Angles Thm. So $\triangle CDE \sim \triangle ABE$ by the AA Similarity Postulate; 98 square units

18. $\overline{AB} \parallel \overline{DC}$ and $\overline{LK} \parallel \overline{AB}$, so $\overline{DC} \parallel \overline{LK}$ since 2 lines $\parallel$ to the same line are $\parallel$. Then $\angle K \cong \angle C$ and $\angle A \cong \angle J$ and all the corresp. $\triangle$ are $\cong$. The ratio of the lengths of any 2 corresp. sides is $\frac{1}{3}$, so ratio of areas $= \frac{1}{9}$; 137.7 in.^{2}

STUDENT HELP

HOMEWORK HELP Visit our Web site www.mcdougallittell.com for help with scale factors in Exs. 19–21.

22. Let $ABCD$ and $EFGH$ be similar rectangles with the lengths of corresp. sides in the ratio $a:b$. Let $a\ell$ be the length of $ABCD$ and aw the width, and let $b\ell$ be the length of $EFGH$ and bw the width. Then $\frac{\text{area of } ABCD}{\text{area of } EFGH} = \frac{a\ell(aw)}{b\ell(bw)} = \frac{a^2}{b^2}$.

FOCUS ON APPLICATIONS

FORT JEFFERSON is in the Dry Tortugas National Park 70 miles west of Key West, Florida. The fort has been used as a prison, a navy base, a seaplane port, and an observation post.

16. **RIGHT TRIANGLES** $\triangle ABC$ is a right triangle whose hypotenuse $\overline{AC}$ is 8 inches long. Given that the area of $\triangle ABC$ is 13.9 square inches, find the area of similar triangle $\triangle DEF$ whose hypotenuse $\overline{DF}$ is 20 inches long. 86.875 in.^{2}

17. **FINDING AREA** Explain why $\triangle CDE$ is similar to $\triangle ABE$. Find the area of $\triangle CDE$.

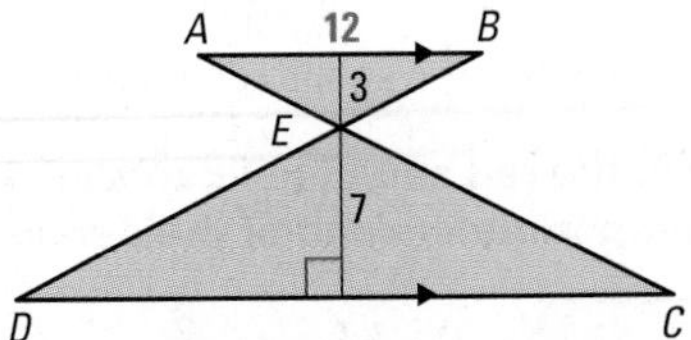

18. **FINDING AREA** Explain why $\square JBKL \sim \square ABCD$. The area of $\square JBKL$ is 15.3 square inches. Find the area of $\square ABCD$.

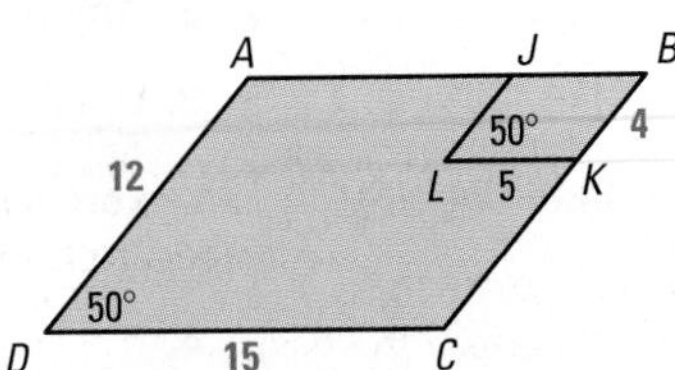

19. **SCALE FACTOR** Regular pentagon $ABCDE$ has a side length of $6\sqrt{5}$ centimeters. Regular pentagon $QRSTU$ has a perimeter of 40 centimeters. Find the ratio of the perimeters of $ABCDE$ to $QRSTU$. $3\sqrt{5}:4$

20. **SCALE FACTOR** A square has a perimeter of 36 centimeters. A smaller square has a side length of 4 centimeters. What is the ratio of the areas of the larger square to the smaller one? 81:16

21. **SCALE FACTOR** A regular nonagon has an area of 90 square feet. A similar nonagon has an area of 25 square feet. What is the ratio of the perimeters of the first nonagon to the second? $3\sqrt{10}:5$

22. **PROOF** Prove Theorem 11.5 for rectangles.

RUG COSTS Suppose you want to be sure that a large rug is priced fairly. The price of a small rug (29 inches by 47 inches) is $79 and the price of the large rug (4 feet 10 inches by 7 feet 10 inches) is $299.

23. What are the areas of the two rugs? What is the ratio of the areas? 1363 in.^{2} and 5452 in.^{2}; 1:4

24. Compare the rug costs. Do you think the large rug is a good buy? Explain. The price is reasonable; it is slightly less than 4 times the cost of the smaller rug.

TRIANGULAR POOL In Exercises 25–27, use the following information. The pool at *Taliesin West* (see page 677) is a right triangle with legs of length 40 feet and 41 feet.

25. Find the area of the triangular pool, $\triangle DEF$. 820 ft^2

26. The walkway bordering the pool is 40 inches wide, so the scale factor of the similar triangles is about 1.3 : 1. Find AB. about 52 ft

27. Find the area of $\triangle ABC$. What is the area of the walkway? about 1385.8 ft^2; about 565.8 ft^2

Not drawn to scale

A, D, 40, 41, E, F, B, C

$\triangle ABC \sim \triangle DEF$

28. **FORT JEFFERSON** The outer wall of Fort Jefferson, which was originally constructed in the mid-1800s, is in the shape of a hexagon with an area of about 466,170 square feet. The length of one side is about 477 feet. The inner courtyard is a similar hexagon with an area of about 446,400 square feet. Calculate the length of a corresponding side in the inner courtyard to the nearest foot. about 467 ft

Test Preparation

29\. e. Since $\overline{AB}$ and $\overline{DE}$ are corresp. sides of ~ △, the ratio of their lengths is the scale factor. Then you can write and solve a proportion; $\frac{22.5}{13z - 10} = \frac{15}{2}$. $z = 1$

29\. **MULTI-STEP PROBLEM** Use the following information about similar triangles $\triangle ABC$ and $\triangle DEF$.

The scale factor of $\triangle ABC$ to $\triangle DEF$ is 15:2.

The area of $\triangle ABC$ is $25x$. The area of $\triangle DEF$ is $x - 5$.

The perimeter of $\triangle ABC$ is $8 + y$. The perimeter of $\triangle DEF$ is $3y - 19$.

a. Use the scale factor to find the ratio of the area of $\triangle ABC$ to the area of $\triangle DEF$. 225:4

b. Write and solve a proportion to find the value of x. $\frac{25x}{x-5} = \frac{225}{4}$; 9

c. Use the scale factor to find the ratio of the perimeter of $\triangle ABC$ to the perimeter of $\triangle DEF$. 15:2

d. Write and solve a proportion to find the value of y. $\frac{8+y}{3y-19} = \frac{15}{2}$; 7

e. *Writing* Explain how you could find the value of z if $AB = 22.5$ and the length of the corresponding side $\overline{DE}$ is $13z - 10$. See margin.

★ Challenge

30\. $\triangle PVQ$ and $\triangle RVT$, $\triangle TUS$ and $\triangle TQR$, $\triangle QVR$ and $\triangle UVP$; all pairs are ~ by the AA Similarity Post.

Use the figure shown at the right. *PQRS* is a parallelogram.

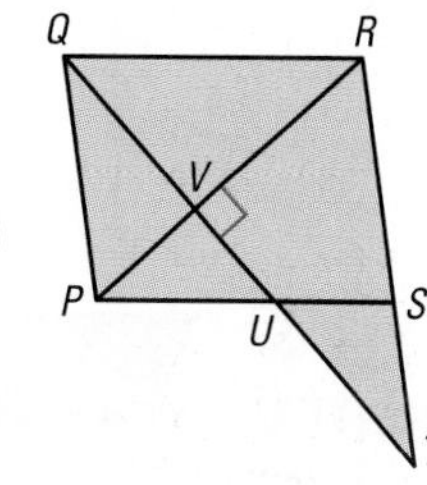

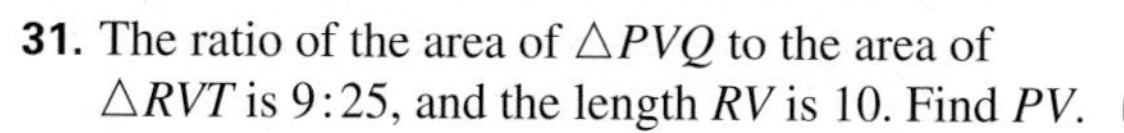

30\. Name three pairs of similar triangles and explain how you know that they are similar.

31\. The ratio of the area of $\triangle PVQ$ to the area of $\triangle RVT$ is 9:25, and the length RV is 10. Find PV. 6

32\. If VT is 15, find VQ, VU, and UT. 9, $5\frac{2}{5}$, $9\frac{3}{5}$

33\. Find the ratio of the areas of each pair of similar triangles that you found in Exercise 30.
$\triangle PVQ$ and $\triangle RVT$: 9:25; $\triangle TUS$ and $\triangle TQR$: 4:25; $\triangle QVR$ and $\triangle UVP$: 25:9

EXTRA CHALLENGE
www.mcdougallittell.com

MIXED REVIEW

FINDING MEASURES In Exercises 34–37, use the diagram shown at the right. (Review 10.2 for 11.4)

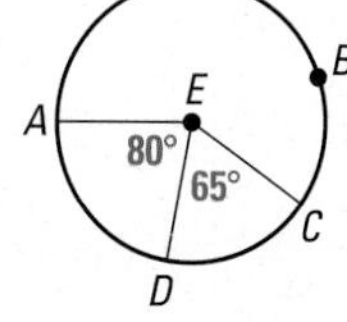

34\. Find $m\widehat{AD}$. 80°

35\. Find $m\angle AEC$. 145°

36\. Find $m\widehat{AC}$. 145°

37\. Find $m\widehat{ABC}$. 215°

38\. **USING AN INSCRIBED QUADRILATERAL** In the diagram shown at the right, quadrilateral $RSTU$ is inscribed in circle P. Find the values of x and y, and use them to find the measures of the angles of $RSTU$. (Review 10.3)
$x = 10$, $y = 5$, $m\angle R = 100°$, $m\angle S = 85°$, $m\angle T = 80°$, $m\angle U = 95°$

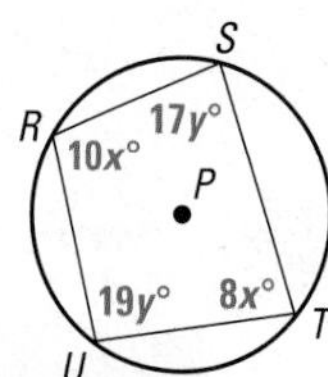

FINDING ANGLE MEASURES Find the measure of ∠1. (Review 10.4 for 11.4)

39\. 80°

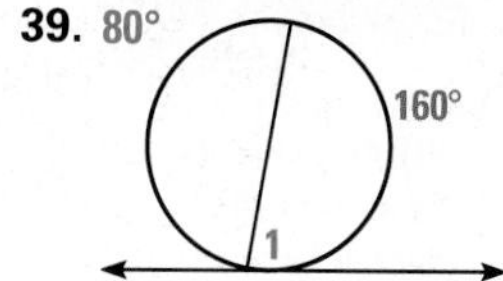

40\. 80°

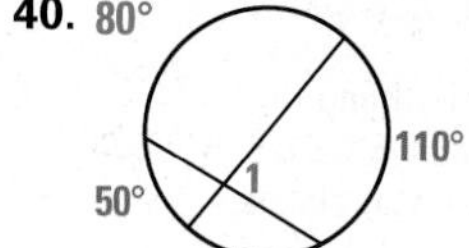

41\. 43°

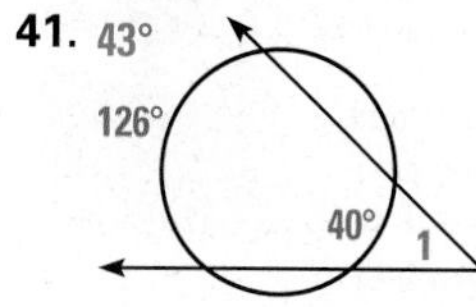

Additional Test Preparation:

1\. Check students' work. The area should be 9 times the area of their polygon.

2\. *Sample answer:* Find the ratio of their side lengths. Use this to find the ratio of their areas. The ratio of their prices should be proportional to the ratio of their areas.

4 ASSESS

DAILY HOMEWORK QUIZ

Transparency Available

1\. The polygons are similar. Find the ratio (grey to white) of their perimeters and their areas.

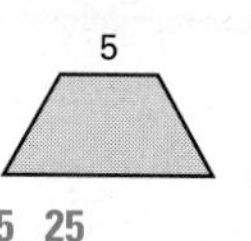

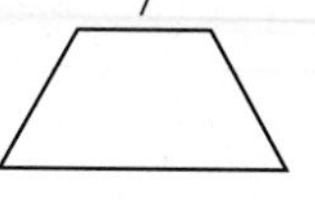

$\frac{5}{7}$, $\frac{25}{49}$

2\. Determine whether $\triangle ACD$ is similar to $\triangle AEB$. If it is, find the area of $\triangle AEB$.

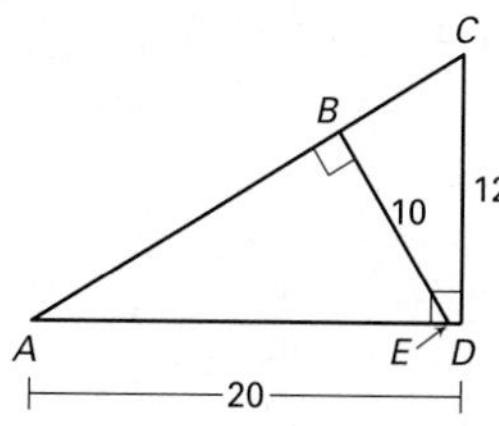

$\triangle ACD$ is similar to $\triangle AEB$. Area of $\triangle AEB$ is $83\frac{1}{3}$.

3\. The price of a small tablecloth (4 ft by 5 ft) is \$45 and the price of a large tablecloth (96 in. by 120 in.) is \$95. Compare the costs. Is the large tablecloth a good buy? Explain. The price is very reasonable; it is almost half the cost of 4 times the cost of the smaller tablecloth.

EXTRA CHALLENGE NOTE

Challenge problems for Lesson 11.3 are available in **blackline** format in the *Chapter 11 Resource Book,* p. 51 and at **www.mcdougallittell.com.**

ADDITIONAL TEST PREPARATION

1\. **OPEN ENDED** Draw a regular polygon and find its area. What is the area of a similar polygon whose side length is three times as long as the side length of your original polygon. See left.

2\. **WRITING** Explain how you can determine if two products that are similar polygons are fairly priced. See left.

ADDITIONAL RESOURCES

An alternative Quiz for Lessons 11.1–11.3 is available in the *Chapter 11 Resource Book,* p. 52.

A **blackline** master with additional Math & History exercises is available in the *Chapter 11 Resource Book,* p. 50.

QUIZ 1

Self-Test for Lessons 11.1–11.3

1. Find the sum of the measures of the interior angles of a convex 20-gon. **(Lesson 11.1)** 3240°

2. What is the measure of each exterior angle of a regular 25-gon? **(Lesson 11.1)** 14.4°

3. Find the area of an equilateral triangle with a side length of 17 inches. **(Lesson 11.2)** $\frac{289\sqrt{3}}{4} \approx 125.1$ in.^{2}

4. Find the area of a regular nonagon with an apothem of 9 centimeters. **(Lesson 11.2)** $729 \tan 20° \approx 265.3$ cm^2

In Exercises 5 and 6, the polygons are similar. Find the ratio (red to blue) of their perimeters and of their areas. (Lesson 11.3)

5. $\frac{4}{3}, \frac{16}{9}$

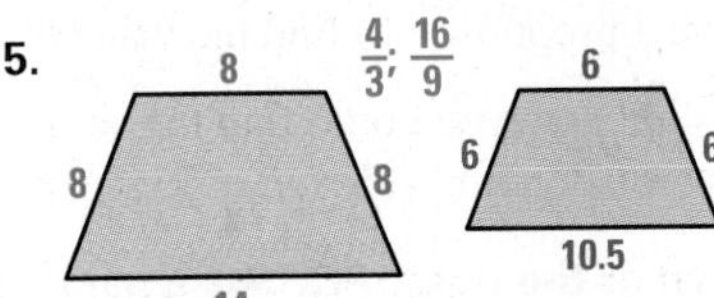

8
8
8
14
6
6
6
10.5

6. $\frac{13}{20}, \frac{169}{400}$

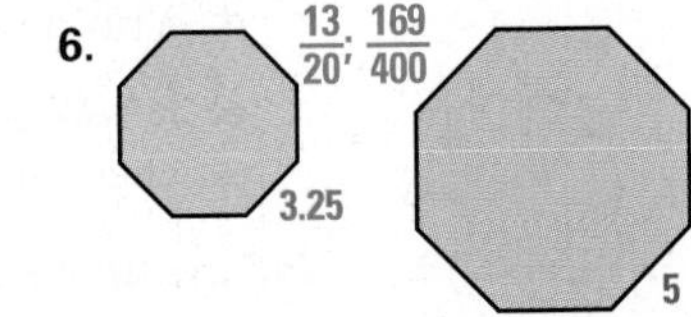

3.25
5

7. **CARPET** You just carpeted a 9 foot by 12 foot room for \$480. The carpet is priced by the square foot. About how much would you expect to pay for the same carpet in another room that is 21 feet by 28 feet? **(Lesson 11.3)** about \$2613

MATH & History

History of Approximating Pi

APPLICATION LINK
www.mcdougallittell.com

THEN

THOUSANDS OF YEARS AGO, people first noticed that the circumference of a circle is the product of its diameter and a value that is a little more than three. Over time, various methods have been used to find better approximations of this value, called π (*pi*).

1. In the third century B.C., Archimedes approximated the value of π by calculating the perimeters of inscribed and circumscribed regular polygons of a circle with diameter 1 unit. Copy the diagram and follow the steps below to use his method.
   - Find the perimeter of the **inscribed** hexagon in terms of the length of the diameter of the circle.
   - Draw a radius of the **circumscribed** hexagon. Find the length of one side of the hexagon. Then find its perimeter.
   - Write an inequality that approximates the value of π: $3 < \pi < 3.46$

$$\text{perimeter of inscribed hexagon} < \pi < \text{perimeter of circumscribed hexagon}$$

diameter 1 unit

NOW

MATHEMATICIANS use computers to calculate the value of π to billions of decimal places.

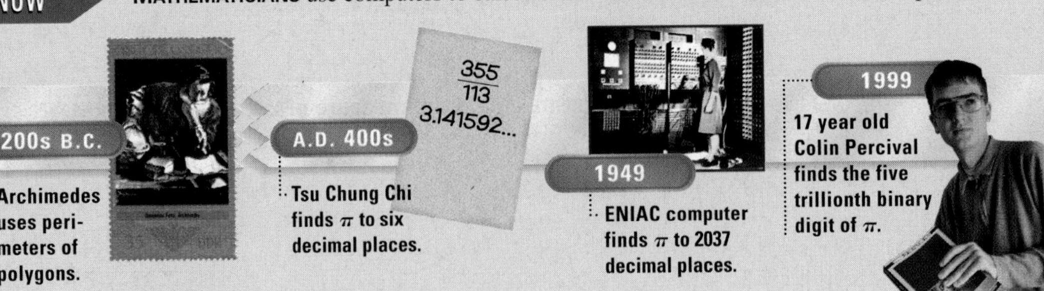

200s B.C.
Archimedes uses perimeters of polygons.
A.D. 400s
355/113
3.141592...
Tsu Chung Chi finds π to six decimal places.
1949
ENIAC computer finds π to 2037 decimal places.
1999
17 year old Colin Percival finds the five trillionth binary digit of π.

11.4 Circumference and Arc Length

What you should learn

GOAL 1 Find the circumference of a circle and the length of a circular arc.

GOAL 2 Use circumference and arc length to solve **real-life** problems such as finding the distance around a track in **Example 5**.

Why you should learn it

▼ To solve **real-life** problems, such as finding the number of revolutions a tire needs to make to travel a given distance in **Example 4** and **Exs. 39–41**.

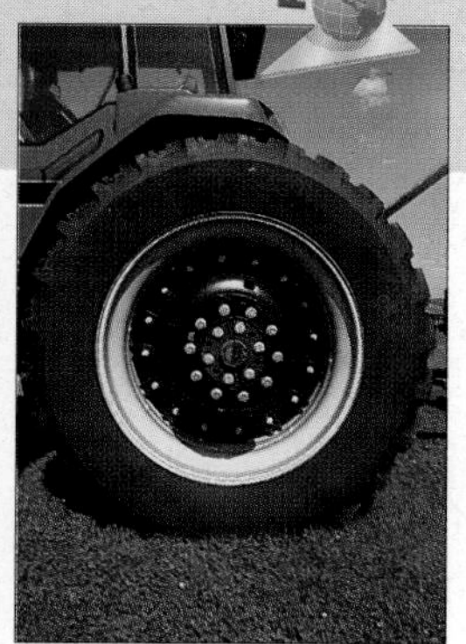

CALIFORNIA STANDARDS AND ASSESSMENT

CA Standards: 8, 19, 21
SAT9 Task 1: Objs. 1, 28
SAT9 Task 2: Objs. 1, 31

GOAL 1 FINDING CIRCUMFERENCE AND ARC LENGTH

The **circumference** of a circle is the distance around the circle. For all circles, the ratio of the circumference to the diameter is the same. This ratio is known as π, or *pi*.

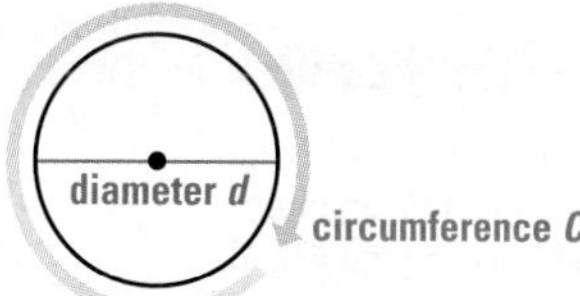

THEOREM

THEOREM 11.6 *Circumference of a Circle*

The circumference C of a circle is $C = \pi d$ or $C = 2\pi r$, where d is the diameter of the circle and r is the radius of the circle.

EXAMPLE 1 *Using Circumference*

Find (**a**) the circumference of a circle with radius 6 centimeters and (**b**) the radius of a circle with circumference 31 meters. Round decimal answers to two decimal places.

SOLUTION

a. $C = 2\pi r$

$= 2 \cdot \pi \cdot 6$

$= 12\pi$ **Use a calculator.**

≈ 37.70

▶ So, the circumference is about 37.70 centimeters.

b. $C = 2\pi r$

$31 = 2\pi r$

$\frac{31}{2\pi} = r$ **Use a calculator.**

$4.93 \approx r$

▶ So, the radius is about 4.93 meters.

An **arc length** is a portion of the circumference of a circle. You can use the measure of the arc (in degrees) to find its length (in linear units).

COROLLARY

ARC LENGTH COROLLARY

In a circle, the ratio of the length of a given arc to the circumference is equal to the ratio of the measure of the arc to 360°.

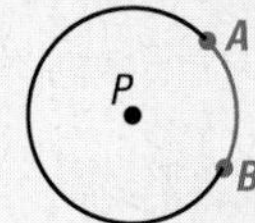

$$\frac{\text{Arc length of } \widehat{AB}}{2\pi r} = \frac{m\widehat{AB}}{360^\circ}, \text{ or Arc length of } \widehat{AB} = \frac{m\widehat{AB}}{360^\circ} \cdot 2\pi r$$

1 PLAN

PACING
Basic: 2 days
Average: 2 days
Advanced: 2 days
Block Schedule: 1 block

LESSON OPENER APPLICATION
An alternative way to approach Lesson 11.4 is to use the Application Lesson Opener:
- Blackline Master (*Chapter 11 Resource Book*, p. 56)
- Transparency (p. 71)

MEETING INDIVIDUAL NEEDS
- ***Chapter 11 Resource Book***
  Prerequisite Skills Review (p. 5)
  Practice Level A (p. 59)
  Practice Level B (p. 60)
  Practice Level C (p. 61)
  Reteaching with Practice (p. 62)
  Absent Student Catch-Up (p. 64)
  Challenge (p. 66)
- ***Resources in Spanish***
- ***Personal Student Tutor***

NEW-TEACHER SUPPORT
See the Tips for New Teachers on pp. 1–2 of the *Chapter 11 Resource Book* for additional notes about Lesson 11.4.

WARM-UP EXERCISES

Transparency Available

Find the measure of each arc.

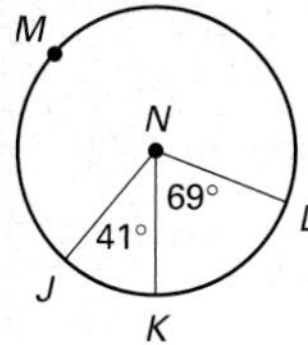

1. $\widehat{JK}$ 41° **2.** $\widehat{JL}$ 110°
3. $\widehat{JML}$ 250° **4.** $\widehat{JMK}$ 319°

2 TEACH

EXTRA EXAMPLE 1

Solve for a stool with a circular seat.

a. Find the circumference of a seat with a radius of 9 in.
about 56.5 in.

b. Find the radius of the seat with circumference 52 in.
about 8.3 in.

EXTRA EXAMPLE 2

Find the length of $\widehat{JK}$. (Use $\pi \approx 3.14$.)

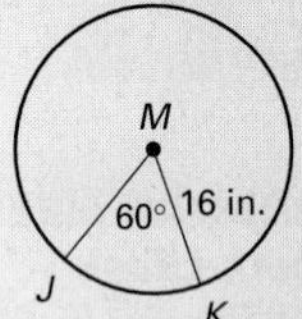

about 16.75 in.

EXTRA EXAMPLE 3

Find the indicated measure. (Use $\pi \approx 3.14$.)

a. $m\widehat{LM}$

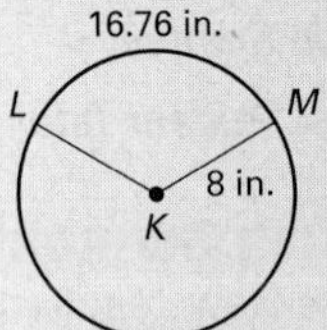

about 120°

b. circumference

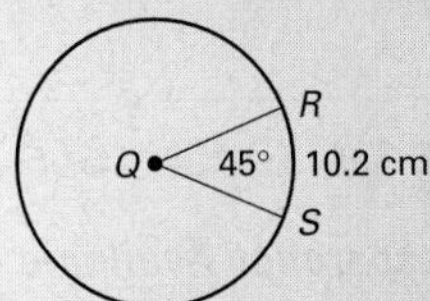

about 81.6 cm

CHECKPOINT EXERCISES

For use after Examples 1–3:

1. Find $m\widehat{TUV}$ if the arc length of $\widehat{TUV}$ is 27 ft.

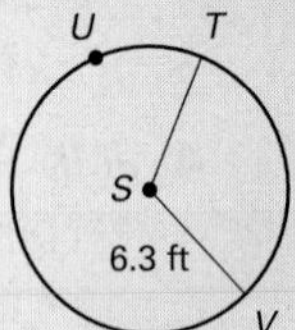

about 245.7°

The length of a **semicircle** is one half the circumference, and the length of a **90° arc** is one quarter of the circumference.

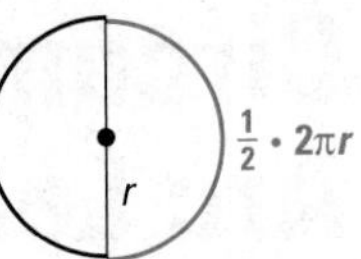

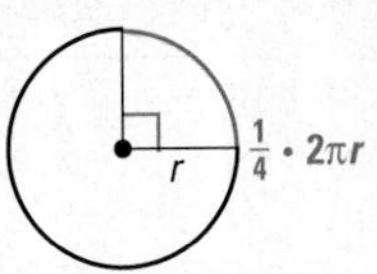

EXAMPLE 2 Finding Arc Lengths

Find the length of each arc.

a.

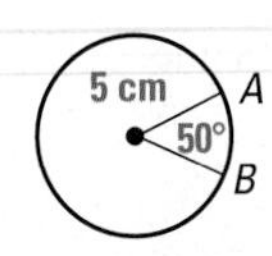

b.

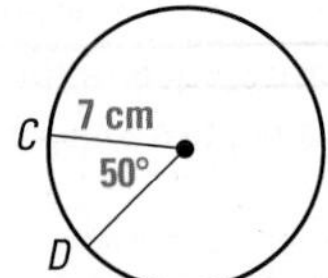

c.

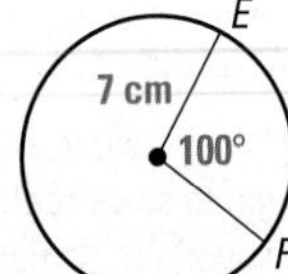

SOLUTION

a. Arc length of $\widehat{AB} = \frac{50°}{360°} \cdot 2\pi(5) \approx 4.36$ centimeters

b. Arc length of $\widehat{CD} = \frac{50°}{360°} \cdot 2\pi(7) \approx 6.11$ centimeters

c. Arc length of $\widehat{EF} = \frac{100°}{360°} \cdot 2\pi(7) \approx 12.22$ centimeters

....

In parts (a) and (b) in Example 2, note that the arcs have the same measure, but different lengths because the circumferences of the circles are not equal.

> **STUDENT HELP**
> **Study Tip**
> Throughout this chapter, you should use the π key on a calculator, then round decimal answers to two decimal places unless instructed otherwise.

EXAMPLE 3 Using Arc Lengths

Find the indicated measure.

a. Circumference

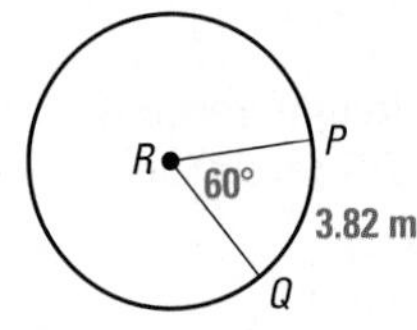

b. $m\widehat{XY}$

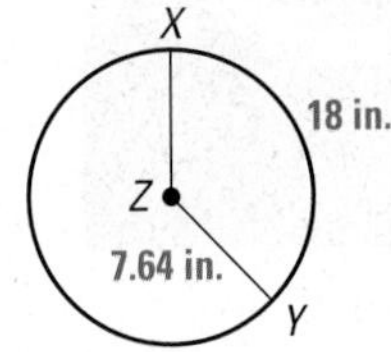

SOLUTION

a.
$$\frac{\text{Arc length of } \widehat{PQ}}{2\pi r} = \frac{m\widehat{PQ}}{360°}$$
$$\frac{3.82}{2\pi r} = \frac{60°}{360°}$$
$$\frac{3.82}{2\pi r} = \frac{1}{6}$$
$$3.82(6) = 2\pi r$$
$$22.92 = 2\pi r$$

▶ So, $C = 2\pi r \approx 22.92$ meters.

b.
$$\frac{\text{Arc length of } \widehat{XY}}{2\pi r} = \frac{m\widehat{XY}}{360°}$$
$$\frac{18}{2\pi(7.64)} = \frac{m\widehat{XY}}{360°}$$
$$360° \cdot \frac{18}{2\pi(7.64)} = m\widehat{XY}$$
$$135° \approx m\widehat{XY}$$

▶ So, $m\widehat{XY} \approx 135°$.

> **STUDENT HELP**
> INTERNET
> **HOMEWORK HELP**
> Visit our Web site www.mcdougallittell.com for extra examples.

GOAL 2 CIRCUMFERENCE

EXAMPLE 4 *Comparing Circumferences*

TIRE REVOLUTIONS Tires from two different automobiles are shown below. How many revolutions does each tire make while traveling 100 feet? Round decimal answers to one decimal place.

SOLUTION

Tire A has a diameter of $14 + 2(5.1)$, or 24.2 inches. Its circumference is $\pi(24.2)$, or about 76.03 inches.

Tire B has a diameter of $15 + 2(5.25)$, or 25.5 inches. Its circumference is $\pi(25.5)$, or about 80.11 inches.

Divide the distance traveled by the tire circumference to find the number of revolutions made. First convert 100 feet to 1200 inches.

Tire A: $\frac{100 \text{ ft}}{76.03 \text{ in.}} = \frac{1200 \text{ in.}}{76.03 \text{ in.}}$

≈ 15.8 revolutions

Tire B: $\frac{100 \text{ ft}}{80.11 \text{ in.}} = \frac{1200 \text{ in.}}{80.11 \text{ in.}}$

≈ 15.0 revolutions

EXAMPLE 5 *Finding Arc Length*

TRACK The track shown has six lanes. Each lane is 1.25 meters wide. There is a 180° arc at each end of the track. The radii for the arcs in the first two lanes are given.

a. Find the distance around Lane 1.

b. Find the distance around Lane 2.

$r_1 = 29.00$ m
$r_2 = 30.25$ m
$s = 108.9$ m

SOLUTION

The track is made up of two semicircles and two straight sections with length s. To find the total distance around each lane, find the sum of the lengths of each part. Round decimal answers to one decimal place.

a. Distance $= 2s + 2\pi r_1$
$= 2(108.9) + 2\pi(29.00)$
≈ 400.0 meters

b. Distance $= 2s + 2\pi r_2$
$= 2(108.9) + 2\pi(30.25)$
≈ 407.9 meters

FOCUS ON PEOPLE

JACOB HEILVEIL was born in Korea and now lives in the United States. He was the top American finisher in the 10,000 meter race at the 1996 Paralympics held in Atlanta, Georgia.

EXTRA EXAMPLE 4

Tires from two different bicycles are shown. How many revolutions does each tire make while traveling 25 ft?

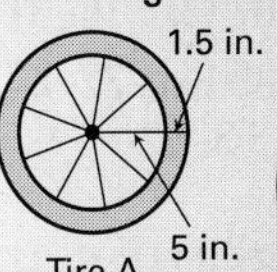

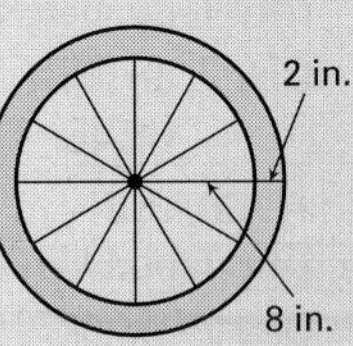

Tire A: about 7.3 rev., Tire B: about 4.8 rev.

EXTRA EXAMPLE 5

The top view of a child's toy has 5 boxes that nest together as shown. The distance between the rims of each of the successive boxes is 0.75 cm. There is a 180° arc at two ends of each box. The radii for the first two boxes are given.

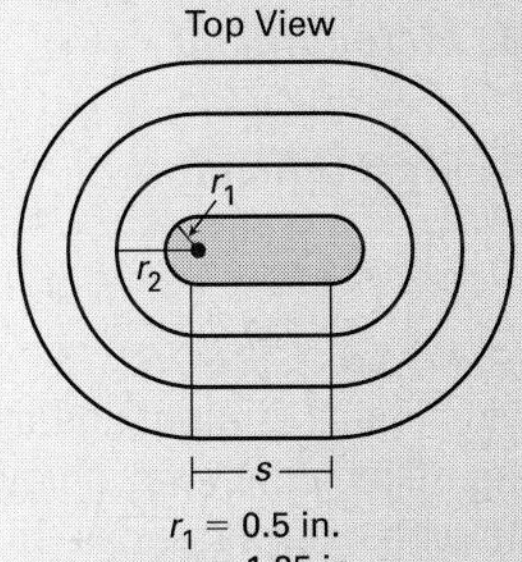

a. Find the distance around the rim of the smallest box. about 7.1 in.

b. Find the distance around the rim of the second smallest box. about 11.9 in.

CHECKPOINT EXERCISES

For use after Examples 4 and 5:

1. A tire has an inside diameter of 22 in. and is 5 in. thick. How many revolutions will it make while driving 1 mi? (1 mi = 5280 ft) about 631 rev.

CLOSURE QUESTION

What proportion can you use to find the arc length of a given arc? $\frac{\text{arc length}}{2\pi r} = \frac{\text{arc measure}}{360°}$

3 APPLY

ASSIGNMENT GUIDE

BASIC
Day 1: pp. 686–687 Exs. 15–31
Day 2: pp. 687–689 Exs. 32–41, 44, 46–49, 52–62

AVERAGE
Day 1: pp. 686–687 Exs. 15–31
Day 2: pp. 687–689 Exs. 32–49, 52–62

ADVANCED
Day 1: pp. 686–687 Exs. 15–31
Day 2: pp. 687–689 Exs. 32–62

BLOCK SCHEDULE
pp. 686–689 Exs. 15–31, 32–49, 52–62

EXERCISE LEVELS

Level A: *Easier*
15–19

Level B: *More Difficult*
20–49

Level C: *Most Difficult*
50, 51

✓ HOMEWORK CHECK

To quickly check student understanding of key concepts, go over the following exercises: Exs. 16, 20, 26, 30, 34, 38, 40, 44. See also the Daily Homework Quiz:

- Blackline Master (*Chapter 11 Resource Book,* p. 69)
- Transparency (p. 83)

GUIDED PRACTICE

Unless otherwise noted, answers are rounded to two decimal places.

Vocabulary Check ✓

1. What is the difference between *arc measure* and *arc length*? See margin.

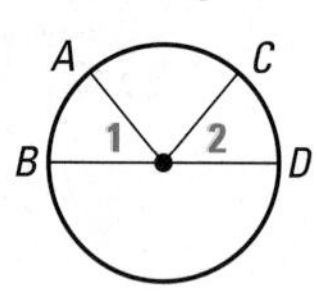

Concept Check ✓

2. In the diagram, $\overline{BD}$ is a diameter and $\angle 1 \cong \angle 2$. Explain why $\widehat{AB}$ and $\widehat{CD}$ have the same length. See margin.

Skill Check ✓

1. Arc measure is the measure of the central ∠ of an arc; arc length is the portion of the circumference of the ⊙ determined by the arc.
2. length of $\widehat{AB} = \frac{m\angle 1}{360°} \cdot 2\pi r = \frac{m\angle 2}{360°} \cdot 2\pi r =$ length of $\widehat{CD}$

In Exercises 3–8, match the measure with its value.

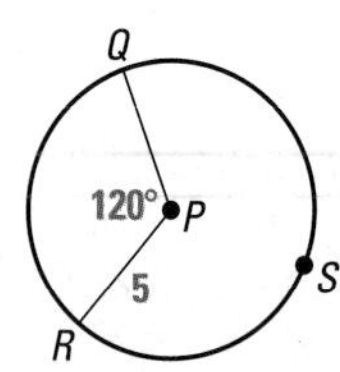

A. $\frac{10}{3}\pi$ **B.** 10π **C.** $\frac{20}{3}\pi$

D. 10 **E.** 5π **F.** 120°

3. $m\widehat{QR}$ F

4. Diameter of ⊙P D

5. Length of $\widehat{QSR}$ C

6. Circumference of ⊙P B

7. Length of $\widehat{QR}$ A

8. Length of semicircle of ⊙P E

Is the statement *true* or *false*? If it is false, provide a counterexample.

9. Two arcs with the same measure have the same length.
False; the arcs must be arcs of the same ⊙ or of ≅ ⊙s.

10. If the radius of a circle is doubled, its circumference is multiplied by 4.
False; its circumference is doubled.

11. Two arcs with the same length have the same measure.
False; the arcs must be arcs of the same ⊙ or of ≅ ⊙s.

FANS **Find the indicated measure.**

12. Length of $\widehat{AB}$

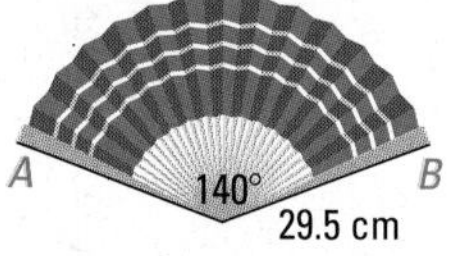

about 72.1 cm

13. Length of $\widehat{CD}$

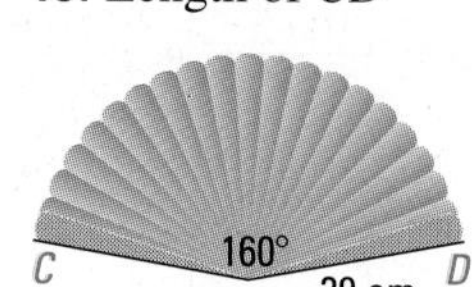

about 81.0 cm

14. $m\widehat{EF}$

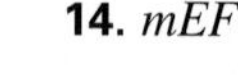

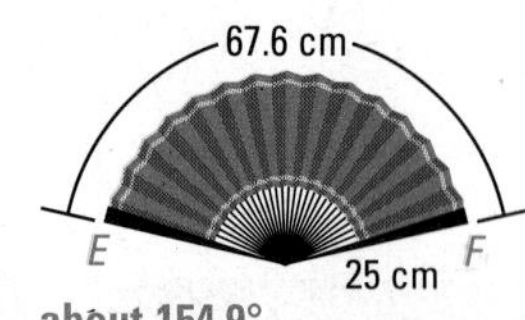

about 154.9°

PRACTICE AND APPLICATIONS

STUDENT HELP

Extra Practice to help you master skills is on p. 824.

USING CIRCUMFERENCE **In Exercises 15 and 16, find the indicated measure.**

15. Circumference 31.42 in.

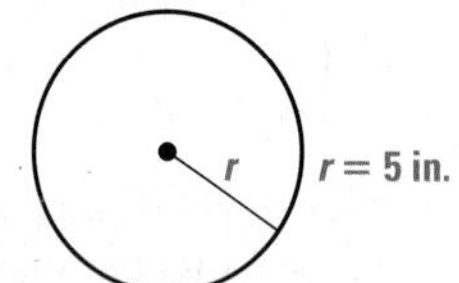

16. Radius 7.00 ft

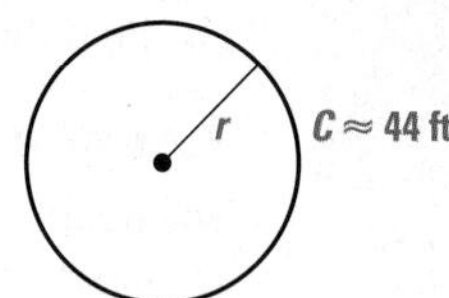

17. Find the circumference of a circle with diameter 8 meters. 25.13 m

18. Find the circumference of a circle with radius 15 inches. (Leave your answer in terms of π.) 30π in.

19. Find the radius of a circle with circumference 32 yards. 5.09 yd

STUDENT HELP

HOMEWORK HELP
Example 1: Exs. 15–19
Example 2: Exs. 20–23
Example 3: Exs. 24–29
Example 4: Exs. 39–41
Example 5: Exs. 42–46

FINDING ARC LENGTHS **In Exercises 20–22, find the length of $\widehat{AB}$.**

20.

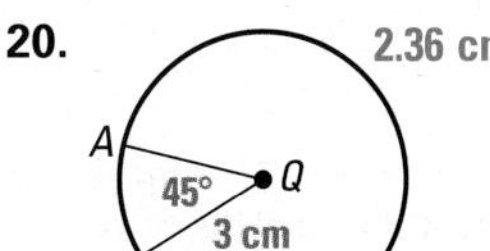

21.

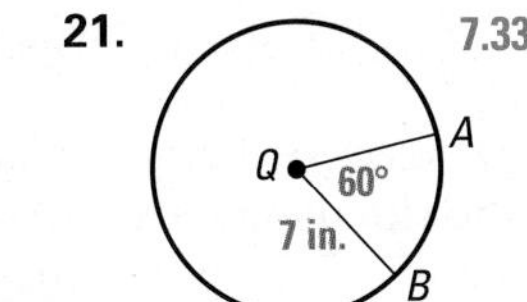

22.

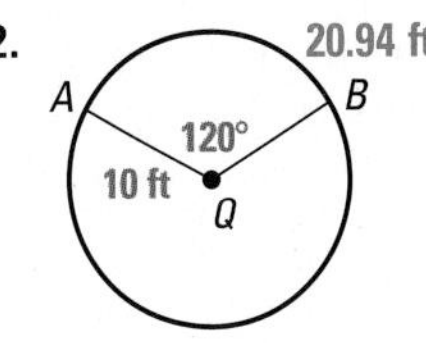

23. FINDING VALUES Complete the table.

Answers	Radius	?	3	0.6	3.5	?	$3\sqrt{3}$
12; 5.1	$m\widehat{AB}$	45°	30°	?	192°	90°	?
120°; about 107°	Length of $\widehat{AB}$	3π	?	0.4π	?	2.55π	3.09π
0.5π; about 3.73π							

FINDING MEASURES **Find the indicated measure.**

24. Length of $\widehat{XY}$

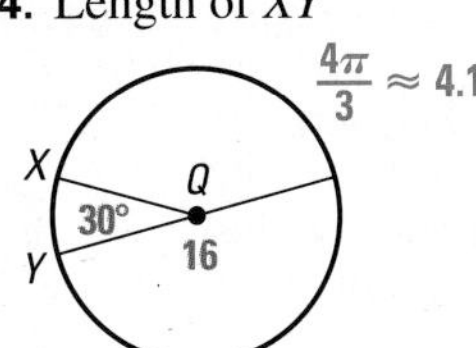

25. Circumference

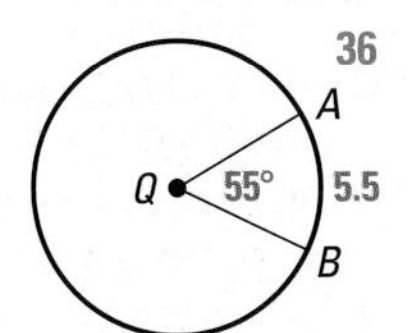

26. Radius

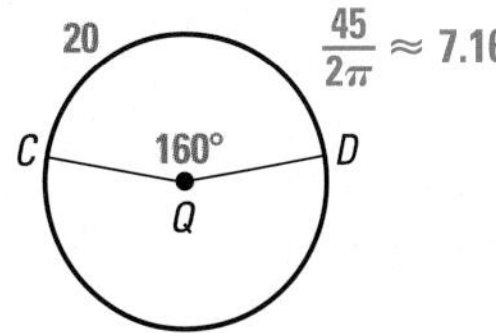

27. Length of $\widehat{AB}$

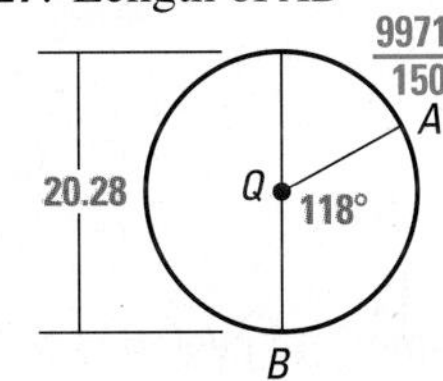

28. Circumference

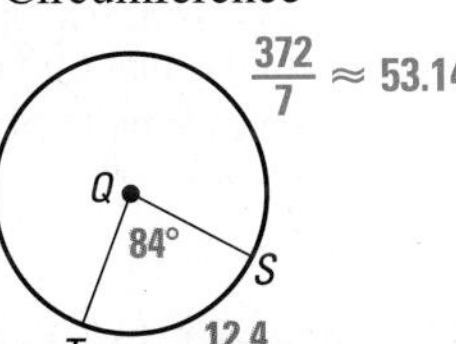

29. Radius

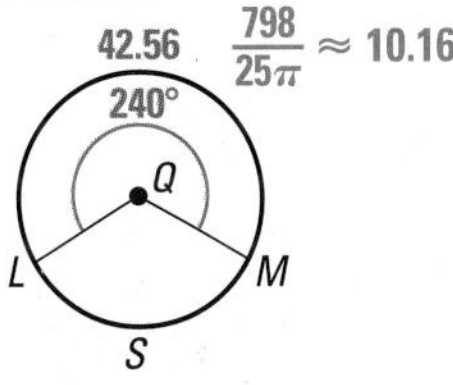

CALCULATING PERIMETERS **In Exercises 30–32, the region is bounded by circular arcs and line segments. Find the perimeter of the region.**

30.

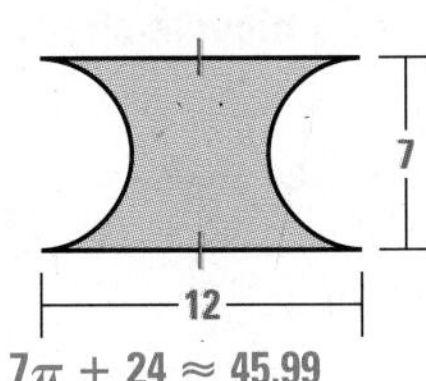

31.

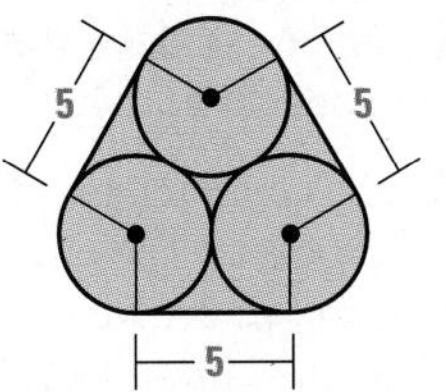

32.

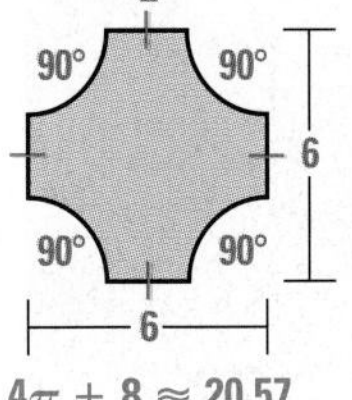

USING ALGEBRA **Find the values of *x* and *y*.**

33.

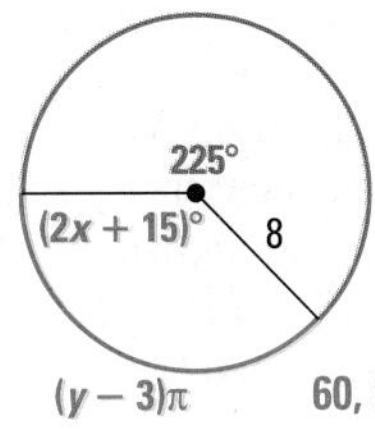

34.

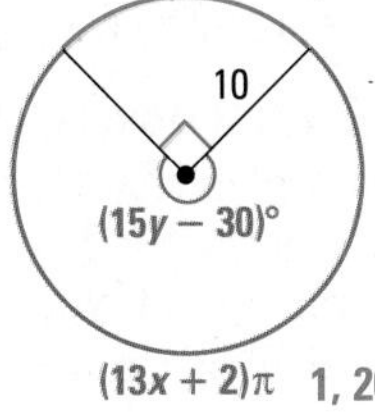

35.

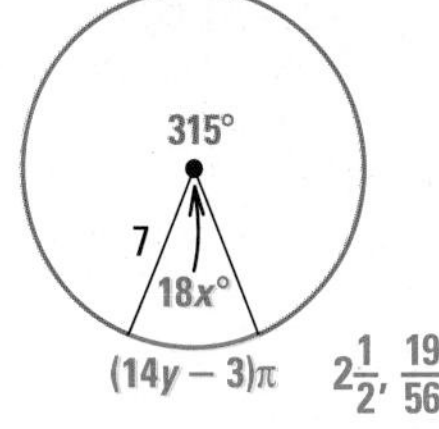

! COMMON ERROR
EXERCISES 15–19 Students should test their answers to problems involving circumference to help them avoid needless errors. Point out that as π is just slightly more than 3, 2π is slightly more than 6. Thus, the circumference of any circle is slightly more than 6 times the radius. For example in Ex. 15, the circumference should be slightly more than 6 times 5, or 30 in.

! COMMON ERROR
EXERCISES 25–28 Encourage students to compare these problems to those with angles that divide evenly into 360° to check that their answers are reasonable. For example, in Ex. 25, 55° is a little less that 60° which is $\frac{1}{6}$ of the circle. Thus the circumference should be about 6 times the arc length of $\widehat{AB}$, or about 6(5.5) = 33.

ENGLISH LEARNERS

EXERCISES 39–41 Keep in mind that the language contained in word problems is often specialized, and can be difficult for English learners. In the paragraph preceding Exercises 39–41, the meanings of the terms *rim* and *sidewall* may not be familiar to some students. You might display a photo of an auto tire and point out the rim and sidewall.

USING ALGEBRA Find the circumference of the circle whose equation is given. (Leave your answer in terms of π.)

36. $x^2 + y^2 = 9$ 6π **37.** $x^2 + y^2 = 28$ $4\pi\sqrt{7}$ **38.** $(x + 1)^2 + (y - 5)^2 = 4$ 4π

AUTOMOBILE TIRES In Exercises 39–41, use the table below. The table gives the rim diameters and sidewall widths of three automobile tires.

	Rim diameter	Sidewall width
Tire A	15 in.	4.60 in.
Tire B	16 in.	4.43 in.
Tire C	17 in.	4.33 in.

39. Find the diameter of each automobile tire.
A: 24.2 in., B: 24.9 in., C: 25.7

40. How many revolutions does each tire make while traveling 500 feet?
A: about 78.92 revolutions, B: about 76.70 revolutions, C: about 74.31 revolutions

41. A student determines that the circumference of a tire with a rim diameter of 15 inches and a sidewall width of 5.5 inches is 64.40 inches. Explain the error.
The sidewall width must be added twice to the rim diameter to get the tire diameter.

GO-CART TRACK Use the diagram of the go-cart track for Exercises 42 and 43. Turns 1, 2, 4, 5, 6, 8, and 9 all have a radius of 3 meters. Turns 3 and 7 each have a radius of 2.25 meters.

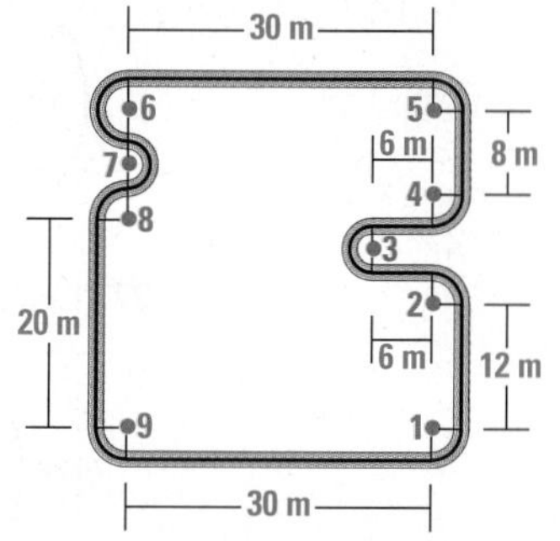

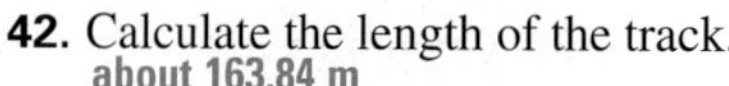

42. Calculate the length of the track.
about 163.84 m

43. How many laps do you need to make to travel 1609 meters (about 1 mile)? about 9.8 laps

44. about 293.22 mi (from Chap. 10, you can see an arc of about 4.2° from Mt. Rainier; length of arc $\frac{4.2°}{360°} \cdot 2 \cdot \pi \cdot (4000 \text{ mi}) \approx 293.22$ mi)

44. **MOUNT RAINIER** In Example 5 on page 623 of Lesson 10.4, you calculated the measure of the arc of Earth's surface seen from the top of Mount Rainier. Use that information to calculate the distance in miles that can be seen looking in one direction from the top of Mount Rainier.
See margin.

FOCUS ON APPLICATIONS

MT. RAINIER, at 14,410 ft high, is the tallest mountain in Washington State.

BICYCLES Use the diagram of a bicycle chain for a fixed gear bicycle in Exercises 45 and 46.

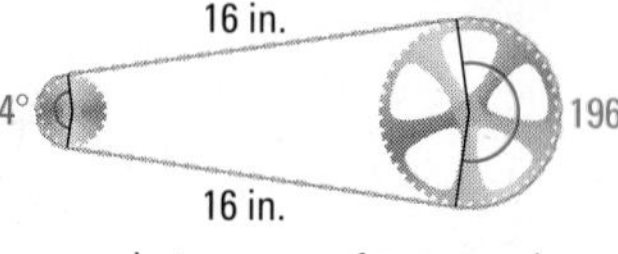

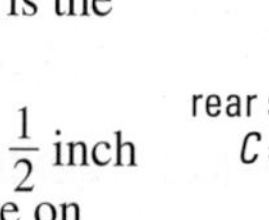

rear sprocket $C = 8$ in. front sprocket $C = 22$ in.

45. The chain travels along the front and rear sprockets. The circumference of each sprocket is given. About how long is the chain? about 47.62 in.

46. On a chain, the teeth are spaced in $\frac{1}{2}$ inch intervals. How many teeth are there on this chain? about 95 teeth

47. **ENCLOSING A GARDEN** Suppose you have planted a circular garden adjacent to one of the corners of your garage, as shown at the right. If you want to fence in your garden, how much fencing do you need?
about 37.70 ft

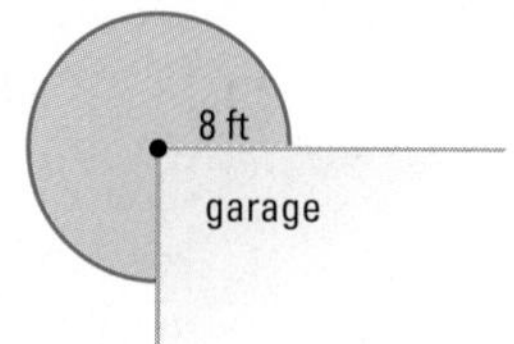

ADDITIONAL PRACTICE AND RETEACHING

For Lesson 11.4:

- Practice Levels A, B, and C (*Chapter 11 Resource Book*, p. 59)
- Reteaching with Practice (*Chapter 11 Resource Book*, p. 62)
- See Lesson 11.4 of the *Personal Student Tutor*

For more Mixed Review:

- Search the *Test and Practice Generator* for key words or specific lessons.

Test Preparation

48\. **MULTIPLE CHOICE** In the diagram shown, $\overline{YZ}$ and $\overline{WX}$ each measure 8 units and are diameters of $\odot T$. If $\widehat{YX}$ measures 120°, what is the length of $\widehat{XZ}$? B

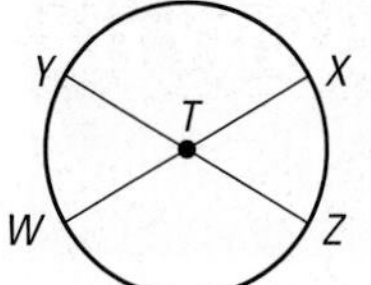

Ⓐ $\frac{2}{3}\pi$ Ⓑ $\frac{4}{3}\pi$ Ⓒ $\frac{8}{3}\pi$

Ⓓ 4π Ⓔ 8π

49\. **MULTIPLE CHOICE** In the diagram shown, the ratio of the length of $\widehat{PQ}$ to the length of $\widehat{RS}$ is 2 to 1. What is the ratio of x to y? B

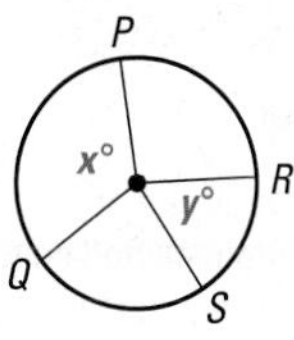

Ⓐ 4 to 1 Ⓑ 2 to 1 Ⓒ 1 to 1

Ⓓ 1 to 2 Ⓔ 1 to 4

★ **Challenge**

CALCULATING ARC LENGTHS Suppose $\overline{AB}$ is divided into four congruent segments and semicircles with radius r are drawn.

50\. What is the sum of the four arc lengths if the radius of each arc is r? $4\pi r$

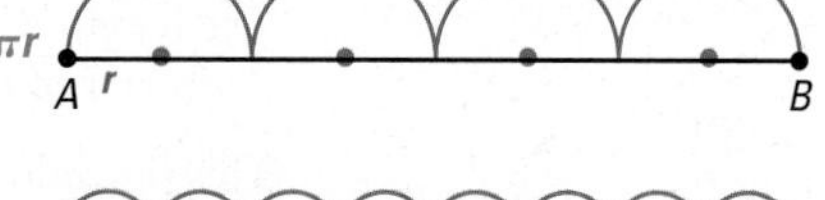

51\. Imagine that $\overline{AB}$ is divided into n congruent segments and that semicircles are drawn. What would the sum of the arc lengths be for 8 segments? 16 segments? n segments? Does the number of segments matter? $4\pi r$, $4\pi r$, $4\pi r$, no

EXTRA CHALLENGE

www.mcdougallittell.com

MIXED REVIEW

FINDING AREA In Exercises 52–55, the radius of a circle is given. Use the formula $A = \pi r^2$ to calculate the area of the circle. (Review 1.7 for 11.5)

52\. $r = 9$ ft $81\pi \approx 254.47$ ft^2

53\. $r = 3.3$ in. $10.89\pi \approx 34.21$ in.^{2}

54\. $r = \frac{27}{5}$ cm $\frac{729\pi}{25} \approx 91.61$ cm^2

55\. $r = 4\sqrt{11}$ m $176\pi \approx 552.92$ m^2

56\. **USING ALGEBRA** Line n_1 has the equation $y = \frac{2}{3}x + 8$. Line n_2 is parallel to n_1 and passes through the point $(9, -2)$. Write an equation for n_2. (Review 3.6)

56\. $y = \frac{2}{3}x - 8$

USING PROPORTIONALITY THEOREMS In Exercises 57 and 58, find the value of the variable. (Review 8.6)

57\. $2\frac{11}{12}$

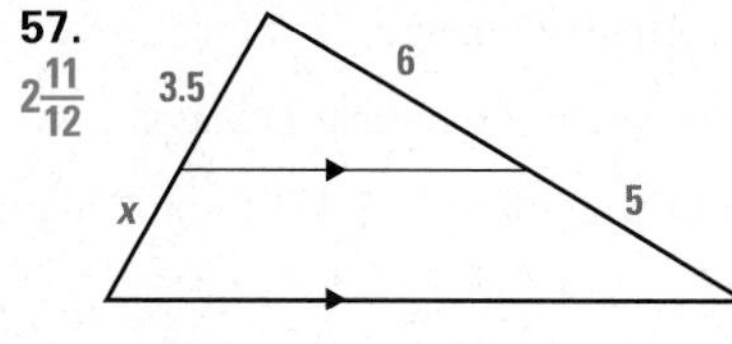

58\. 36

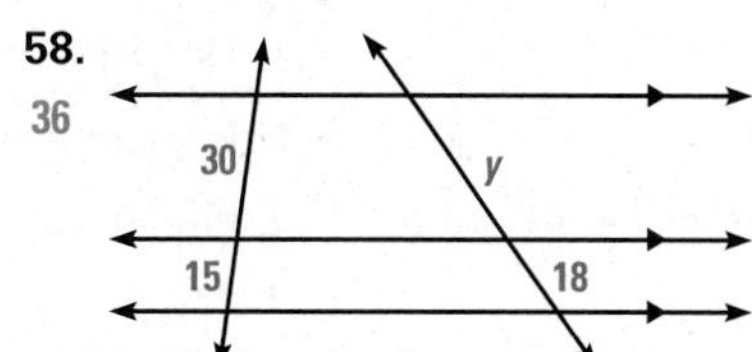

CALCULATING ARC MEASURES You are given the measure of an inscribed angle of a circle. Find the measure of its intercepted arc. (Review 10.3)

59\. 48° 96°

60\. 88° 176°

61\. 129° 258°

62\. 15.5° 31°

4 ASSESS

DAILY HOMEWORK QUIZ

Transparency Available

1\. Find the circumference of a circle with a diameter 6 inches. (Use $\pi \approx 3.14$.) 18.84 in.

2\. Find the circumference of a circle with a radius 20 meters. (Leave your answer in terms of π.) 40π

3\. Find the length of $\widehat{AB}$ (Use $\pi \approx 3.14$.)

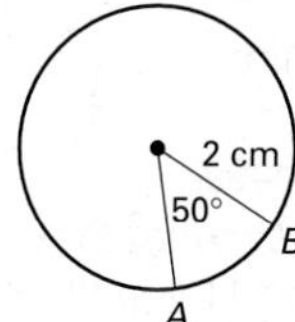

1.74 cm

4\. Find the circumference.

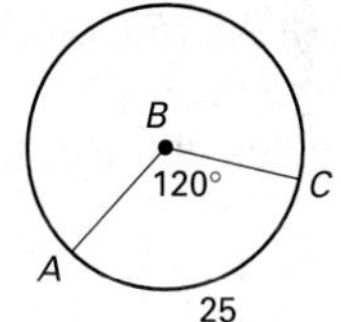

75

5\. Find the circumference of the circle whose equation is $x^2 + y^2 = 81$. 18π

EXTRA CHALLENGE NOTE

Challenge problems for Lesson 11.4 are available in **blackline** format in the *Chapter 11 Resource Book*, p. 66 and at **www.mcdougallittell.com.**

ADDITIONAL TEST PREPARATION

1\. **WRITING** Can you find the radius of a circle if you know the arc length and arc measure of one of its arcs? Explain. Yes, set up the proportion $\frac{\text{arc length}}{2\pi r} = \frac{\text{arc measure}}{360°}$; then solve for r.

2\. **OPEN ENDED** Draw a tire for a child's toy and label its dimensions in inches. How many revolutions will this tire make in 200 ft? Check student's work.

1 Planning the Activity

PURPOSE
To investigate the perimeters of regular polygons inscribed in a circle with radius 1 unit.

MATERIALS
- a computer with spreadsheet software
- Software Help (*Chapter 11 Resource Book,* p. 57)

PACING
- Activity — 20 min

LINK TO LESSON
Have students use what they learned in Lesson 11.4 to find the circumference, rounded to two decimal places, of the circle in this activity. They should see that the perimeters of the regular polygons get closer to this value as the number of sides of the polygon increases.

2 Managing the Activity

ALTERNATIVE APPROACH
This activity can be done using the List feature on a graphing calculator. Enter the number of sides, 1 through 24, in L_1. The list the corresponding perimeters in L_2 using the formula $L_2 = 2L_1 \sin\left(\frac{180}{L_1}\right)$.

3 Closing the Activity

KEY DISCOVERY
The perimeter of a polygon inscribed in a circle with radius 1 unit increases as the number of sides increases. The perimeter seems to approach the circumference of the circle.

ACTIVITY ASSESSMENT
Suppose you inscribed a 50-gon into a circle with radius 2 units. What is a good estimate of the perimeter of this polygon? about 12.6 units

ACTIVITY 11.4
Using Technology

Perimeters of Regular Polygons

You can use a spreadsheet to explore the perimeters of regular polygons that are inscribed in a circle with radius 1 unit.

Visit our Web site at www.mcdougallittell.com to see instructions for several software applications.

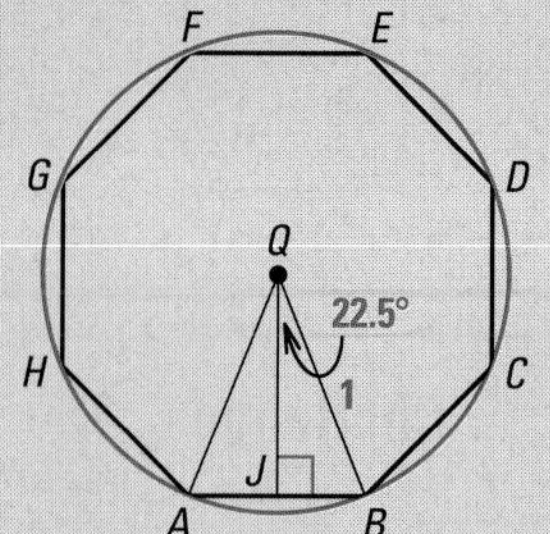

The regular octagon shown at the right is inscribed in a circle with radius 1 unit.

The measure of the interior angle $\angle AQB$ is $\frac{1}{8} \cdot 360°$ or $45°$, so the measure of $\angle JQB$ is $22.5°$.

You can find the length of $\overline{JB}$ using a sine ratio.

$$\sin 22.5° = \frac{JB}{QB} = \frac{JB}{1} = JB$$

The length of each side of the octagon is $s = AB = 2(JB) = 2 \cdot \sin 22.5°$. The perimeter of the octagon is $P = 8s = 8(2 \cdot \sin 22.5°) = 16 \cdot \sin 22.5°$.

This procedure used for an octagon can be generalized to conclude that the perimeter of a regular n-gon inscribed in a circle of radius 1 is

$$P = 2n \sin \frac{180°}{n}.$$

CONSTRUCT **Use a spreadsheet to construct a table.**
Steps 1–3. Check results.

1. Use a spreadsheet to make a table with two columns. The first column is for the number of sides, n, of the regular polygon. In cell A3, start with a value of 3. In cell A4 use the formula =A3+1.

Polygon Perimeter

	A	B
1	Number of sides	Perimeter
2	n	2*n*sin(180/n)
3	3	=2*A3*sin(pi()/A3)
4	=A3+1	=2*A4*sin(pi()/A4)

2. The second column is for the perimeter of the regular polygon. In cell B3 use the formula =2*A3*sin(180/A3). If your spreadsheet uses radian measure, you may need to use "pi()" instead of "180" so that the formula is =2*A3*sin(pi()/A3).

3. Use the Fill Down feature to create more rows. You may need to select Row 4 and drag down to highlight rows before using the Fill Down command.

INVESTIGATE

1. Describe how the perimeter changes as n increases.
It increases, getting closer and closer to 2π.
2. Explain why the perimeter of a regular hexagon is 6.
3. Find the perimeter of a regular 12-gon, 15-gon, 18-gon, and 24-gon.
(Answers are given to the nearest hundredth.) 6.21, 6.24, 6.25, 6.27

2. $n = 6$; $p = 2(6)\sin\left(\frac{180°}{6}\right) = 12 \sin 30°$; $\sin 30° = 0.5$; $p = 12(0.5) = 6$

EXTENSION

Critical Thinking Modify your spreadsheet so that the number of sides increases by 100 instead of 1. (Use =A3+100 in cell A4.) Does the perimeter of the polygon approach 2π, the circumference of the circle with radius 1 unit? yes

11.5 Areas of Circles and Sectors

What you should learn

GOAL 1 Find the area of a circle and a sector of a circle.

GOAL 2 Use areas of circles and sectors to solve **real-life** problems, such as finding the area of a boomerang in **Example 6**.

Why you should learn it

▼ To solve **real-life** problems, such as finding the area of portions of tree trunks that are used to build Viking ships in **Exs. 38 and 39**.

CALIFORNIA STANDARDS AND ASSESSMENT

CA Standards: 8, 19, 21
SAT9 Task 1: Objs. 1, 23
SAT9 Task 2: Objs. 1, 29

GOAL 1 AREAS OF CIRCLES AND SECTORS

The diagrams below show regular polygons inscribed in circles with radius r. Exercise 42 on page 697 demonstrates that as the number of sides increases, the area of the polygon approaches the value πr^2.

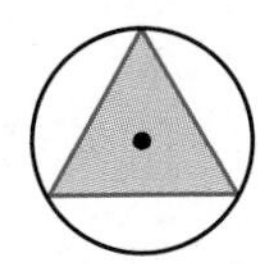
3-gon

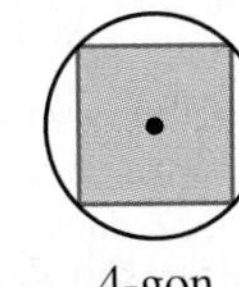
4-gon

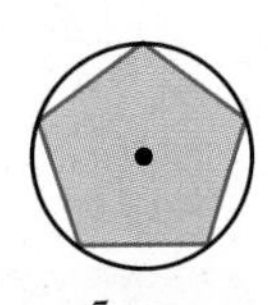
5-gon

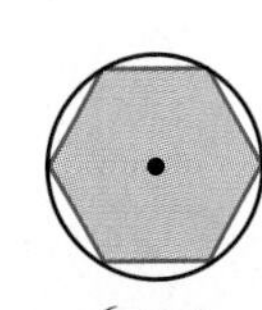
6-gon

THEOREM

THEOREM 11.7 *Area of a Circle*

The area of a circle is π times the square of the radius, or $A = \pi r^2$.

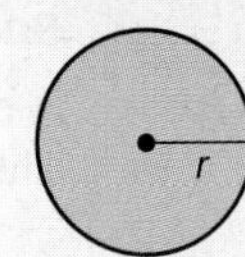

EXAMPLE 1 *Using the Area of a Circle*

a. Find the area of $\odot P$.

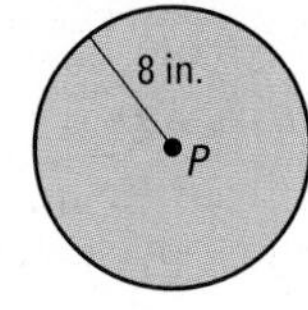

b. Find the diameter of $\odot Z$.

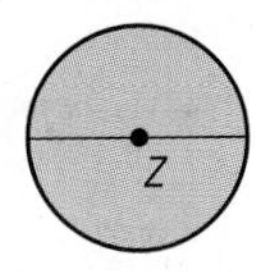

Area of $\odot Z = 96$ cm^2

SOLUTION

a. Use $r = 8$ in the area formula.

$A = \pi r^2$

$= \pi \cdot 8^2$

$= 64\pi$

≈ 201.06

▶ So, the area is 64π, or about 201.06, square inches.

b. The diameter is twice the radius.

$A = \pi r^2$

$96 = \pi r^2$

$\frac{96}{\pi} = r^2$

$30.56 \approx r^2$

$5.53 \approx r$ **Find the square roots.**

▶ The diameter of the circle is about 2(5.53), or about 11.06, centimeters.

1 PLAN

PACING
Basic: 1 day
Average: 1 day
Advanced: 1 day
Block Schedule: 0.5 block with 11.6

LESSON OPENER APPLICATION

An alternative way to approach Lesson 11.5 is to use the Application Lesson Opener:

- Blackline Master (*Chapter 11 Resource Book,* p. 70)
- Transparency (p. 72)

MEETING INDIVIDUAL NEEDS

- ***Chapter 11 Resource Book***
  Prerequisite Skills Review (p. 5)
  Practice Level A (p. 75)
  Practice Level B (p. 76)
  Practice Level C (p. 77)
  Reteaching with Practice (p. 78)
  Absent Student Catch-Up (p. 80)
  Challenge (p. 82)
- ***Resources in Spanish***
- ***Personal Student Tutor***

NEW-TEACHER SUPPORT

See the Tips for New Teachers on pp. 1–2 of the *Chapter 11 Resource Book* for additional notes about Lesson 11.5.

WARM-UP EXERCISES

Transparency Available

Find the area of each figure.

1. a square with sides 12 in. **144 in.^{2}**
2. an equilateral triangle with sides 5 cm **about 10.8 cm^2**
3. a pentagon with apothem 2 ft and side length 2.9 ft **14.5 ft^2**
4. a hexagon with radius 16 yd **about 665 yd^2**

2 TEACH

MOTIVATING THE LESSON

Ask students to describe the shape of a slice of a circular pizza. Then have them use the vocabulary of circles to describe the boundaries of the slice. Explain that a slice of pizza is an example of a sector. In today's lesson, students will learn to find the areas of sectors.

EXTRA EXAMPLE 1

Find the area of the circle with the given information.

a. radius 3 m about 28.3 m^2

b. diameter 18 ft about 254.5 ft^2

EXTRA EXAMPLE 2

Find the area of the sector shown below.

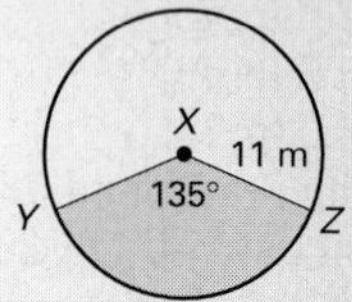

about 142.5 m^2

EXTRA EXAMPLE 3

L and M are two points on a $\odot R$ with radius 50 cm and $m\angle LRM = 150°$. Find the areas of the sectors formed by $\angle LRM$. about 4581 cm^2 and about 3272 cm^2

CHECKPOINT EXERCISES

For use after Examples 1 and 2:

1. Find the area of a circle whose diameter is 30 in. about 706.9 in.^{2}

For use after Examples 2 and 3:

2. S and R are two points on $\odot W$ with radius 5 m and $m\angle SWR = 45°$. Find the areas of the sectors formed by $\angle SWR$. about 9.8 m^2 and about 68.7 m^2

STUDENT HELP NOTES

Homework Help Students can find extra examples at **www.mcdougallittell.com** that parallel the examples in the student edition.

A **sector of a circle** is the region bounded by two radii of the circle and their intercepted arc. In the diagram, sector APB is bounded by $\overline{AP}$, $\overline{BP}$, and $\overset{\frown}{AB}$. The following theorem gives a method for finding the area of a sector.

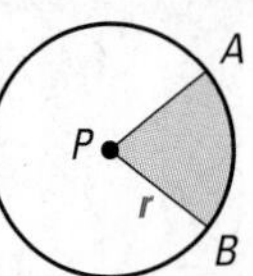

THEOREM

THEOREM 11.8 ***Area of a Sector***

The ratio of the area A of a sector of a circle to the area of the circle is equal to the ratio of the measure of the intercepted arc to 360°.

$$\frac{A}{\pi r^2} = \frac{m\overset{\frown}{AB}}{360°}, \text{ or } A = \frac{m\overset{\frown}{AB}}{360°} \cdot \pi r^2$$

EXAMPLE 2 *Finding the Area of a Sector*

Find the area of the sector shown at the right.

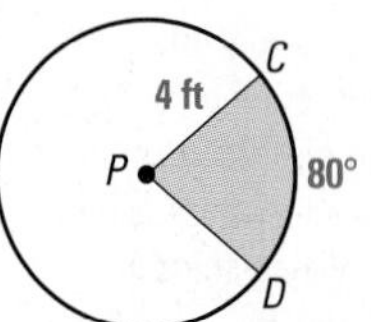

SOLUTION

Sector CPD intercepts an arc whose measure is 80°. The radius is 4 feet.

$A = \frac{m\overset{\frown}{CD}}{360°} \cdot \pi r^2$ **Write the formula for the area of a sector.**

$= \frac{80°}{360°} \cdot \pi \cdot 4^2$ **Substitute known values.**

≈ 11.17 **Use a calculator.**

▶ So, the area of the sector is about 11.17 square feet.

EXAMPLE 3 *Finding the Area of a Sector*

A and B are two points on a $\odot P$ with radius 9 inches and $m\angle APB = 60°$. Find the areas of the sectors formed by $\angle APB$.

SOLUTION

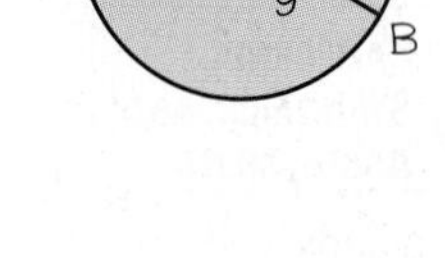

Draw a diagram of $\odot P$ and $\angle APB$. Shade the sectors.

Label a point Q on the major arc.

Find the measures of the minor and major arcs.

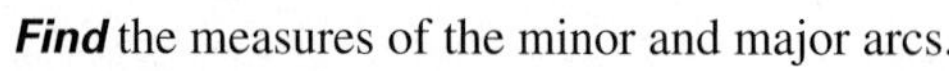

Because $m\angle APB = 60°$, $m\overset{\frown}{AB} = 60°$ and $m\overset{\frown}{AQB} = 360° - 60° = 300°$.

Use the formula for the area of a sector.

Area of small sector $= \frac{60°}{360°} \cdot \pi \cdot 9^2 = \frac{1}{6} \cdot \pi \cdot 81 \approx 42.41$ square inches

Area of larger sector $= \frac{300°}{360°} \cdot \pi \cdot 9^2 = \frac{5}{6} \cdot \pi \cdot 81 \approx 212.06$ square inches

STUDENT HELP

HOMEWORK HELP
Visit our Web site www.mcdougallittell.com for extra examples.

GOAL 2 USING AREAS OF CIRCLES AND REGIONS

You may need to divide a figure into different regions to find its area. The regions may be polygons, circles, or sectors. To find the area of the entire figure, add or subtract the areas of the separate regions as appropriate.

EXAMPLE 4 *Finding the Area of a Region*

Find the area of the shaded region shown at the right.

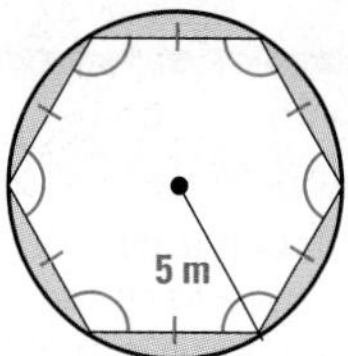

SOLUTION

The diagram shows a regular hexagon inscribed in a circle with radius 5 meters. The shaded region is the part of the circle that is outside of the hexagon.

Area of shaded region	=	Area of circle	−	Area of hexagon

$$= \pi r^2 - \frac{1}{2}aP$$

$$= \pi \cdot 5^2 - \frac{1}{2} \cdot \left(\frac{5}{2}\sqrt{3}\right) \cdot (6 \cdot 5)$$

The apothem of a hexagon is $\frac{1}{2}$ · side length · $\sqrt{3}$.

$$= 25\pi - \frac{75}{2}\sqrt{3}$$

▶ So, the area of the shaded region is $25\pi - \frac{75}{2}\sqrt{3}$, or about 13.59 square meters.

EXAMPLE 5 *Finding the Area of a Region*

WOODWORKING You are cutting the front face of a clock out of wood, as shown in the diagram. What is the area of the front of the case?

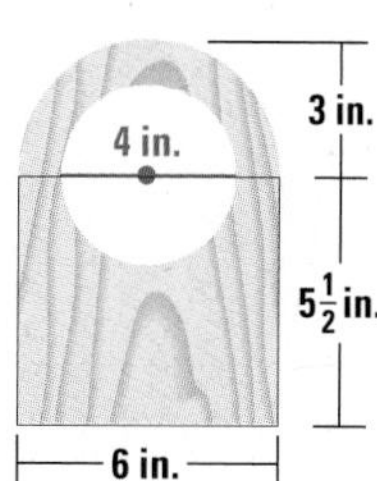

SOLUTION

The front of the case is formed by a rectangle and a sector, with a circle removed. Note that the intercepted arc of the sector is a semicircle.

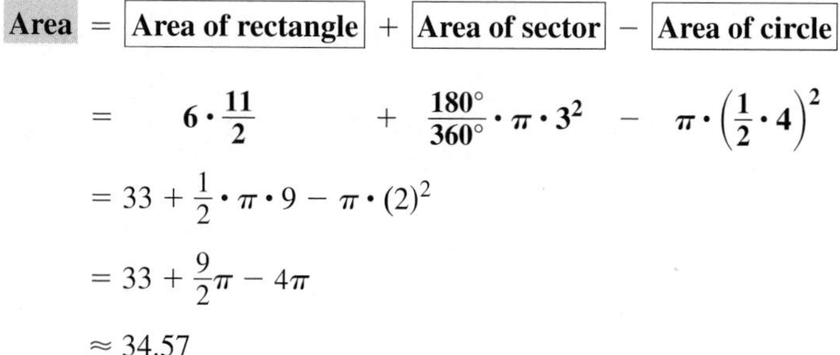

Area	=	Area of rectangle	+	Area of sector	−	Area of circle

$$= 6 \cdot \frac{11}{2} + \frac{180°}{360°} \cdot \pi \cdot 3^2 - \pi \cdot \left(\frac{1}{2} \cdot 4\right)^2$$

$$= 33 + \frac{1}{2} \cdot \pi \cdot 9 - \pi \cdot (2)^2$$

$$= 33 + \frac{9}{2}\pi - 4\pi$$

$$\approx 34.57$$

▶ The area of the front of the case is about 34.57 square inches.

EXTRA EXAMPLE 4

Find the area of the shaded region shown below.

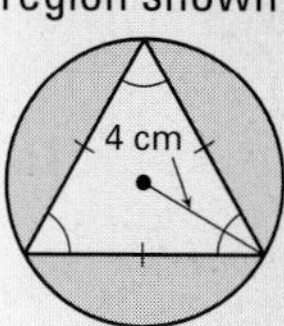

$16\pi - 12\sqrt{3}$, or about 29.5 cm^2

EXTRA EXAMPLE 5

You are cutting the front face of a grandfather clock out of wood, as shown in the diagram. What is the area of the front of the case?

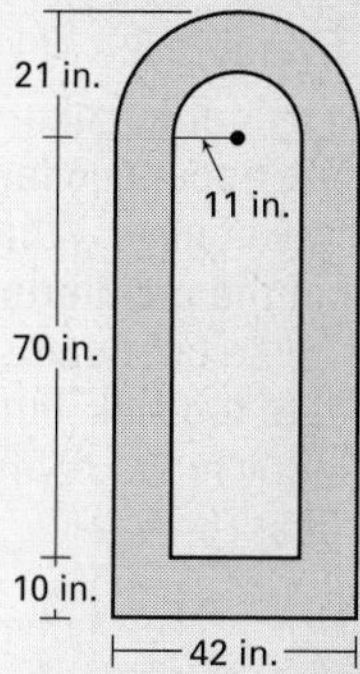

$1820 + 160\pi$, or about 2322.7 $in.^2$

CHECKPOINT EXERCISES

For use after Examples 4 and 5:

1. Find the area of the shaded region below.

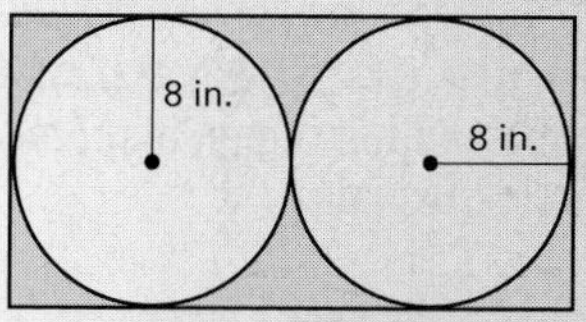

$512 - 128\pi$, or about 110.1 $in.^2$

MULTIPLE REPRESENTATIONS

In Examples 4 and 5, area is represented visually and numerically. Numbers for areas that involve circles or parts of circles invariably involve the use of π, and may involve radicals as well. While giving an exact answer is algebraically precise, an approximate answer can be more useful.

EXTRA EXAMPLE 6

Find the area of the countertop.

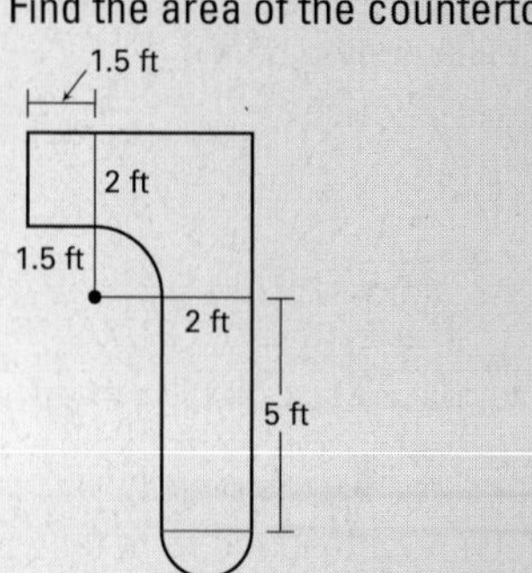

$25.25 - 0.0625\pi$, or about 25.05 ft^2

CHECKPOINT EXERCISES

For use after Example 6:

1. A hole is to be cut out of a countertop to accommodate the sink shown below. What is the area of the countertop that needs to be cut out to accommodate the sink if the sink fits exactly in the hole?

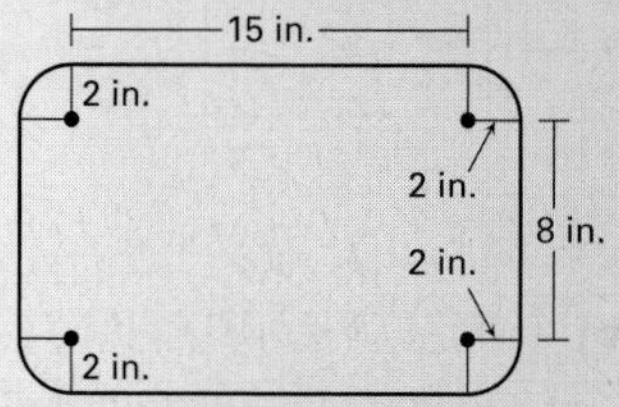

$212 + 4\pi$, or about 224.6 in.^{2}

FOCUS ON VOCABULARY

Is the shaded region a *sector* of the circle? Explain.

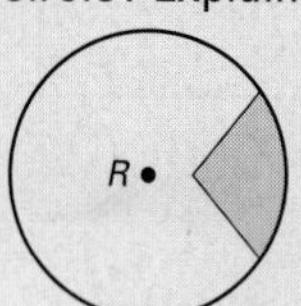

No; two of the boundaries of a sector must be radii.

CLOSURE QUESTION

Describe how to find the area of a sector of a circle. See right.

DAILY PUZZLER

A square is inscribed in a circle with radius 10 in. Inscribed in the square is another circle. Find the area of the region between the square and the smaller circle.
$200 - 50\pi$, or about 42.9 in.^{2}.

FOCUS ON APPLICATIONS

REAL LIFE **BOOMERANGS** are slightly curved at the ends and travel in an arc when thrown. Small boomerangs used for sport make a full circle and return to the thrower.

Complicated shapes may involve a number of regions. In Example 6, the curved region is a portion of a ring whose edges are formed by concentric circles. Notice that the area of a portion of the ring is the difference of the areas of two sectors.

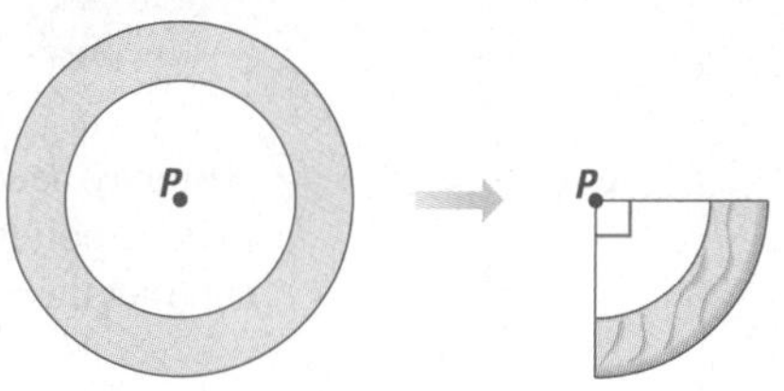

EXAMPLE 6 *Finding the Area of a Boomerang*

BOOMERANGS Find the area of the boomerang shown. The dimensions are given in inches. Give your answer in terms of π and to two decimal places.

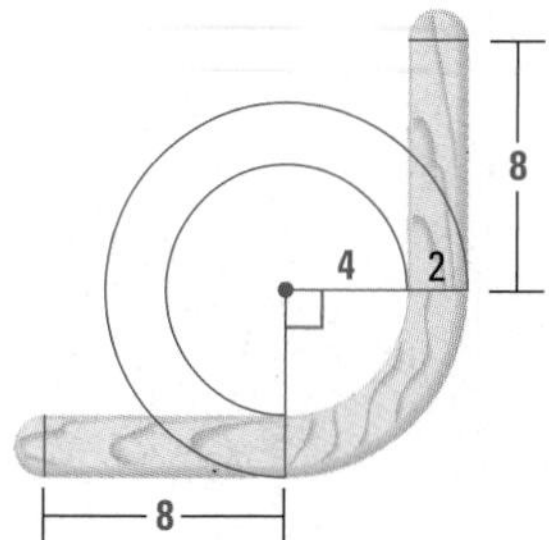

SOLUTION

Separate the boomerang into different regions. The regions are two semicircles (at the ends), two rectangles, and a portion of a ring. Find the area of each region and add these areas together.

PROBLEM SOLVING STRATEGY

DRAW AND LABEL A SKETCH Draw and label a sketch of each region in the boomerang.

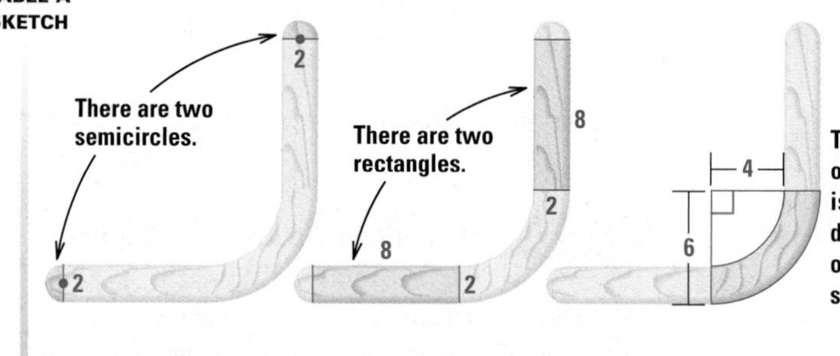

VERBAL MODEL Area of boomerang $= 2 \cdot$ Area of semicircle $+ 2 \cdot$ Area of rectangle $+$ Area of portion of ring

LABELS

Area of semicircle $= \frac{1}{2} \cdot \pi \cdot 1^2$ (square inches)

Area of rectangle $= 8 \cdot 2$ (square inches)

Area of portion of ring $= \frac{1}{4} \cdot \pi \cdot 6^2 - \frac{1}{4} \cdot \pi \cdot 4^2$ (square inches)

REASONING

$$\text{Area of boomerang} = 2\left(\frac{1}{2} \cdot \pi \cdot 1^2\right) + 2(8 \cdot 2) + \left(\frac{1}{4} \cdot \pi \cdot 6^2 - \frac{1}{4} \cdot \pi \cdot 4^2\right)$$

$$= 2\left(\frac{1}{2} \cdot \pi \cdot 1\right) + 2 \cdot 16 + \left(\frac{1}{4} \cdot \pi \cdot 36 - \frac{1}{4} \cdot \pi \cdot 16\right)$$

$$= \pi + 32 + (9\pi - 4\pi)$$

$$= 6\pi + 32$$

▶ So, the area of the boomerang is $(6\pi + 32)$, or about 50.85 square inches.

Closure Question *Sample answer:*
Find the measure of the intercepted arc. Then divide this measure by 360° and multiply it by the area of the circle.

GUIDED PRACTICE

Vocabulary Check ✓

1. Describe the boundaries of a *sector of a circle*.
2 radii of a ⊙ and their intercepted arc

Concept Check ✓

2. In Example 5 on page 693, explain why the expression $\pi \cdot \left(\frac{1}{2} \cdot 4\right)^2$ represents the area of the circle cut from the wood. See margin.

Skill Check ✓

2. The diameter is 4, so the radius is half that, or $\frac{1}{2} \cdot 4$. Then the area is $\pi r^2 = \pi\left(\frac{1}{2} \cdot 4\right)^2$.

In Exercises 3–8, find the area of the shaded region.

3. 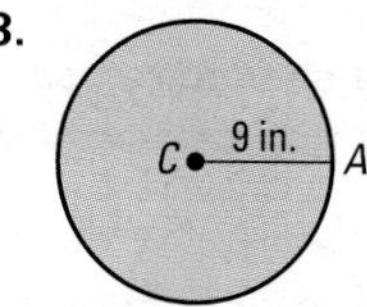

$81\pi \approx 254.47$ in.^{2}

4. 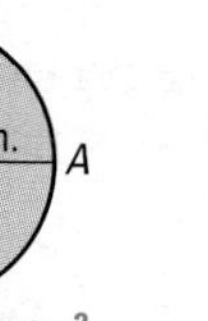 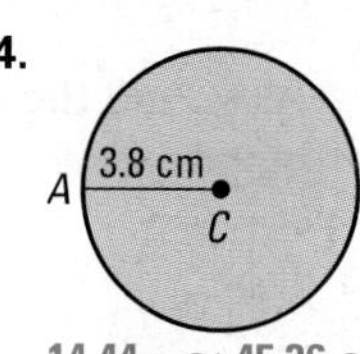

$14.44\pi \approx 45.36$ cm^2

5. 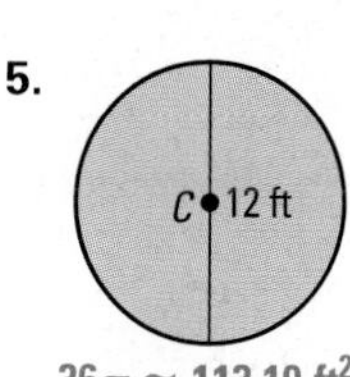

$36\pi \approx 113.10$ ft^2

6.
A
6 ft
C
110°
B

$11\pi \approx 34.56$ ft^2

7. 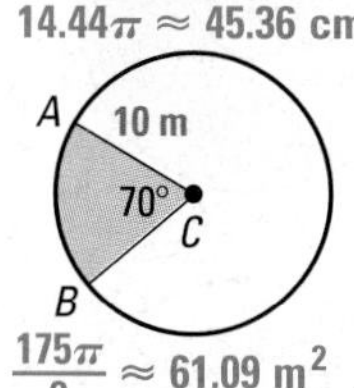

$\frac{175\pi}{9} \approx 61.09$ m^2

8. 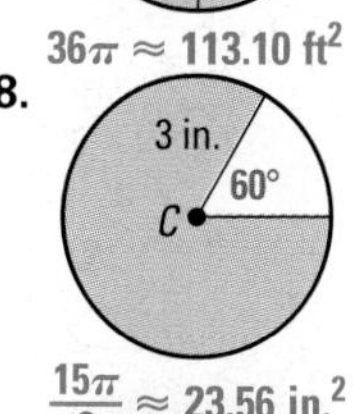

$\frac{15\pi}{2} \approx 23.56$ in.^{2}

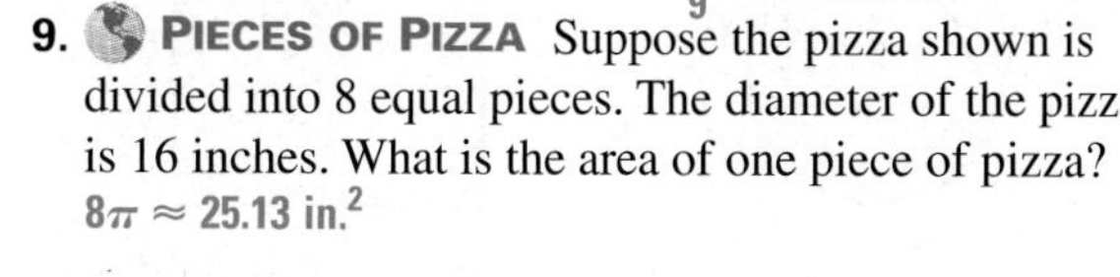

9. **PIECES OF PIZZA** Suppose the pizza shown is divided into 8 equal pieces. The diameter of the pizza is 16 inches. What is the area of one piece of pizza? $8\pi \approx 25.13$ in.^{2}

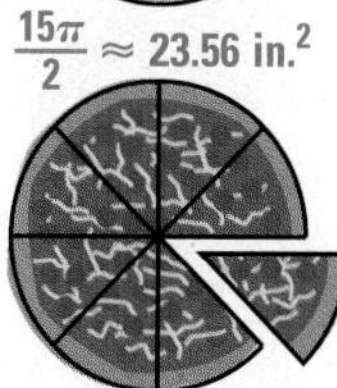

PRACTICE AND APPLICATIONS

STUDENT HELP

Extra Practice to help you master skills is on p. 824.

FINDING AREA In Exercises 10–18, find the area of the shaded region.

10. 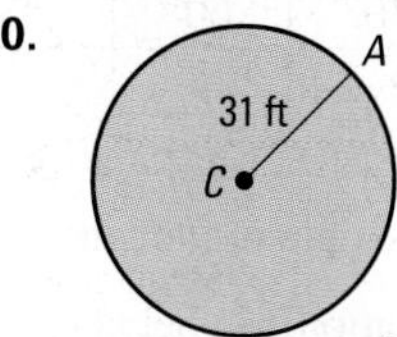

$961\pi \approx 3019.07$ ft^2

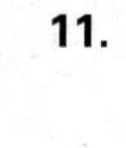

11. 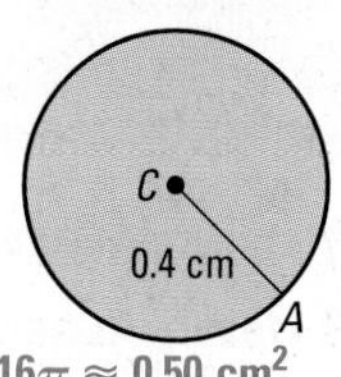

$0.16\pi \approx 0.50$ cm^2

12. 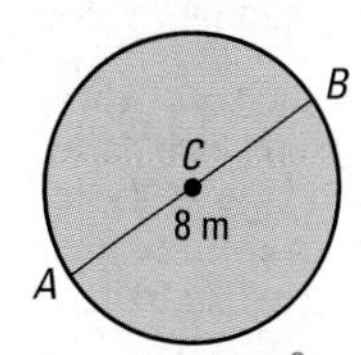

$16\pi \approx 50.27$ m^2

13.
C
20 in.

$100\pi \approx 314.16$ in.^{2}

14.
A
60°
C
11 ft
B

$\frac{121\pi}{6} \approx 63.36$ ft^2

15. 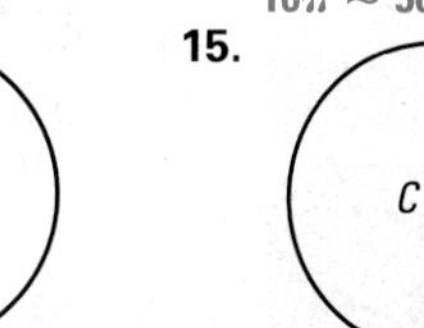

$\frac{49\pi}{18} \approx 8.55$ in.^{2}

16.
A
10 cm
C
293°
B

$\frac{1465\pi}{18} \approx 255.69$ cm^2

17.
4.6 m
C

$\frac{529\pi}{75} \approx 22.16$ m^2

18. 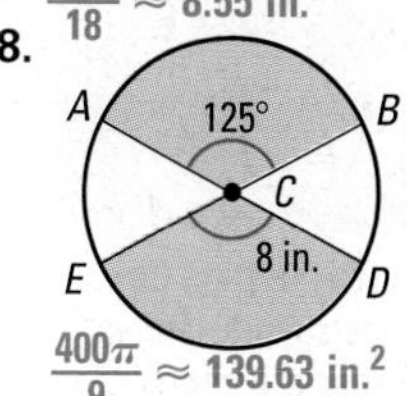

$\frac{400\pi}{9} \approx 139.63$ in.^{2}

STUDENT HELP

HOMEWORK HELP
Example 1: Exs. 10–13, 19, 20
Example 2: Exs. 14–18, 21, 22, 29
Example 3: Exs. 14–18, 21, 22, 29
Example 4: Exs. 23–28, 35–37
Example 5: Exs. 23–28, 35–37
Example 6: Exs. 38–40

19. **USING AREA** What is the area of a circle with diameter 20 feet? $100\pi \approx 314.16$ ft^2

20. **USING AREA** What is the radius of a circle with area 50 square meters? $\frac{5\sqrt{2\pi}}{\pi} \approx 3.99$ m

3 APPLY

ASSIGNMENT GUIDE

BASIC
Day 1: pp. 695–698 Exs. 10–28 even, 30–32, 35–37, 40, 41, 43–44, 46–60 even

AVERAGE
Day 1: pp. 695–698 Exs. 10–28 even, 30–37, 40, 41, 43–44, 46–60 even

ADVANCED
Day 1: pp. 695–698 Exs. 10–28 even, 30–37, 40, 41, 43–45, 46–60 even

BLOCK SCHEDULE WITH 11.6
pp. 695–698 Exs. 10–28 even, 30–37, 40, 41, 43–44, 46–60 even

EXERCISE LEVELS

Level A: *Easier*
10–13

Level B: *More Difficult*
14–44

Level C: *Most Difficult*
42, 45

✓ HOMEWORK CHECK

To quickly check student understanding of key concepts, go over the following exercises: Exs. 14, 20, 24, 32, 36, 40. See also the Daily Homework Quiz:

- Blackline Master (*Chapter 11 Resource Book,* p. 85)
- Transparency (p. 84)

! COMMON ERROR

EXERCISES 10–18 Students may confuse the formulas for area of a circle or sector with those for circumference or arc length. Tell them that area is measured in *square* units, so the radius is *squared* in the area formulas.

MATHEMATICAL REASONING

EXERCISES 31 AND 32 Ask students to write the equation representing the relationship in Ex. 31 in terms of π. Remind them that π is a constant so that this is a linear equation. Then have them write the equation for the relationship in Ex. 32. Students should see that this is another linear function.

ENGLISH LEARNERS

EXERCISE 34 Note that sentences with several consecutive prepositional phrases can present problems for some English learners. You might paraphrase the first sentence in Exercise 34 so that students understand the relationship between the boat and the beam of light.

30.

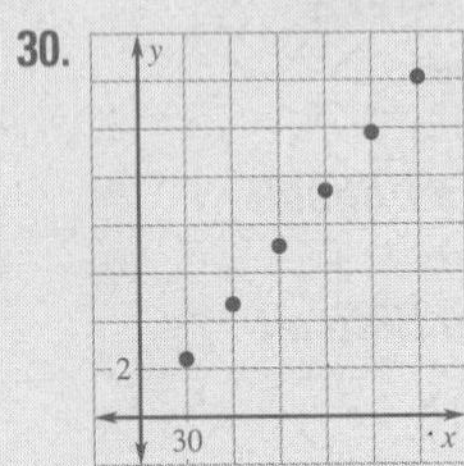

25. $16\pi - 80 \cos 36° \sin 36° \approx 12.22 \text{ ft}^2$

31. Yes; it appears that the points lie along a line. You can also write a linear equation, $y = \frac{\pi}{40}x$.

32. Yes; no; the areas would change because the radius of the ⊙ changes; the relationship between x and y would be linear, with $y = \frac{5\pi}{72}x$.

FOCUS ON APPLICATIONS

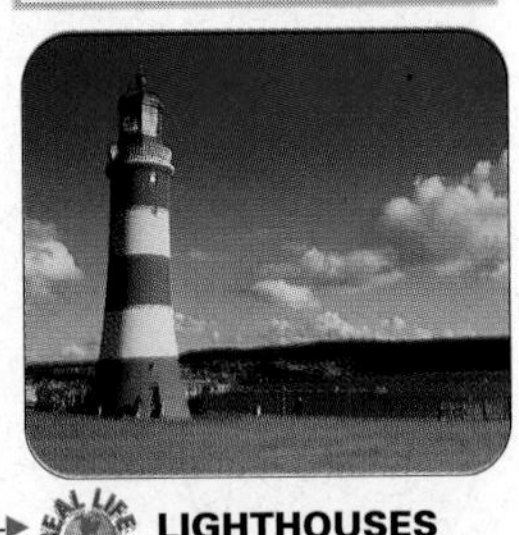

LIGHTHOUSES use special lenses that increase the intensity of the light projected. Some lenses are 8 feet high and 6 feet in diameter.

USING AREA **Find the indicated measure. The area given next to the diagram refers to the shaded region only.**

21. Find the radius of ⊙C. 13.00 in.

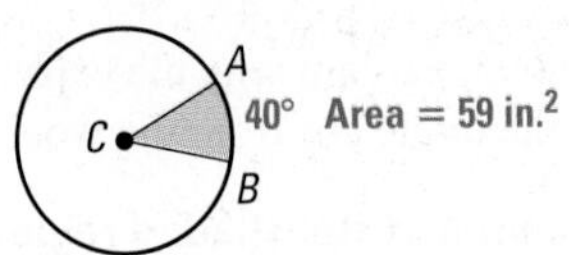

22. Find the diameter of ⊙G. 21.00 m

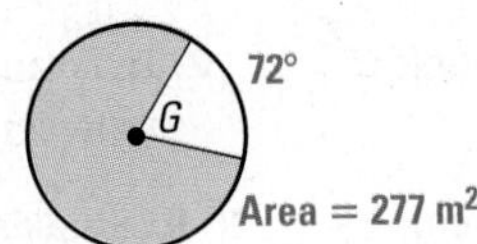

FINDING AREA **Find the area of the shaded region.**

23.

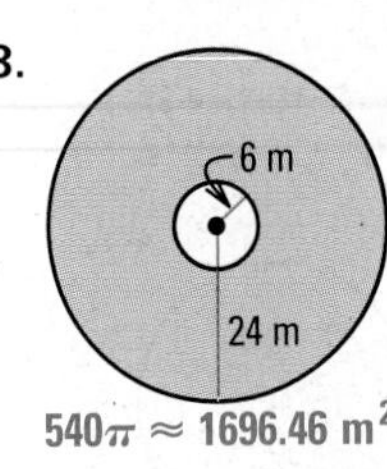

$540\pi \approx 1696.46 \text{ m}^2$

24.

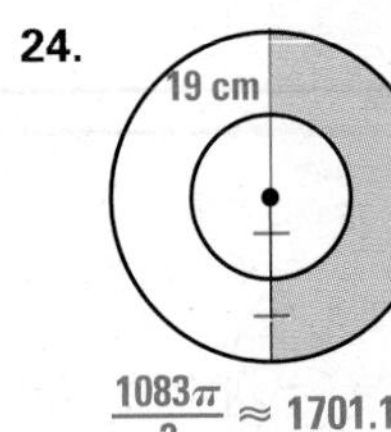

$\frac{1083\pi}{2} \approx 1701.17 \text{ cm}^2$

25.

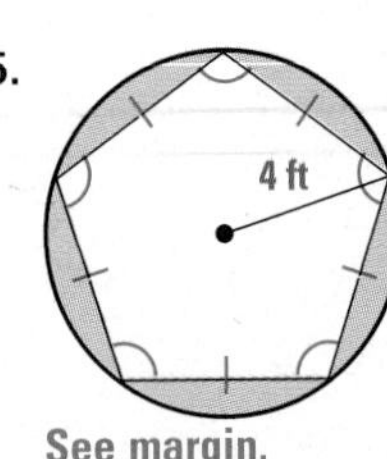

See margin.

26.

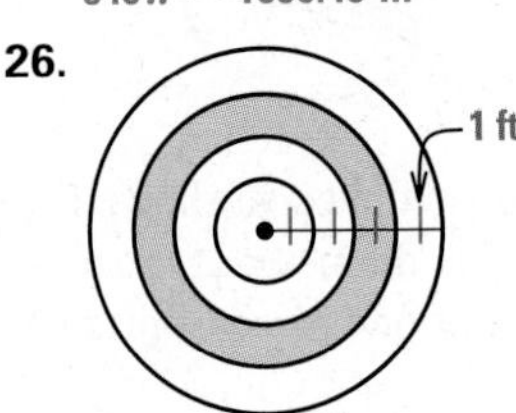

$5\pi \approx 15.71 \text{ ft}^2$

27.

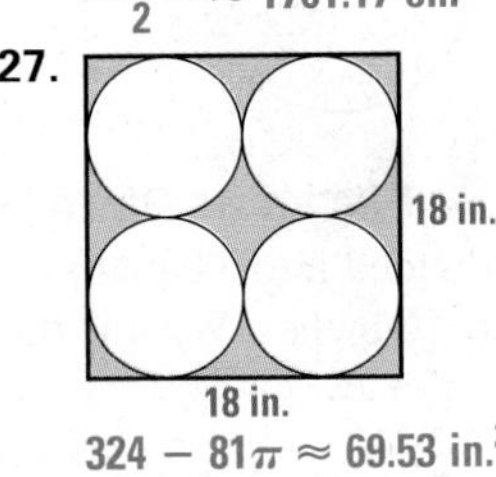

$324 - 81\pi \approx 69.53 \text{ in.}^2$

28.

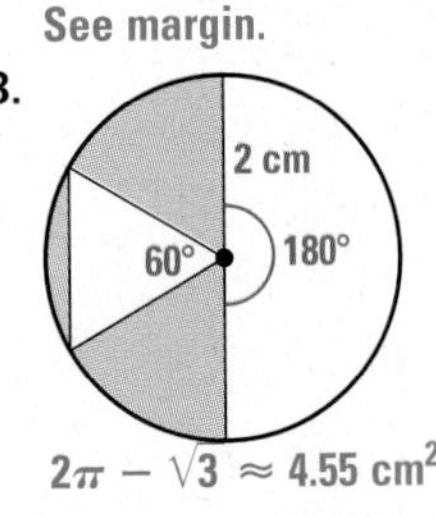

$2\pi - \sqrt{3} \approx 4.55 \text{ cm}^2$

FINDING A PATTERN **In Exercises 29–32, consider an arc of a circle with a radius of 3 inches.**

29. Copy and complete the table. Round your answers to the nearest tenth.

Measure of arc, x	30°	60°	90°	120°	150°	180°
Area of corresponding sector, y	?	?	?	?	?	?
	2.4	4.7	7.1	9.4	11.8	14.1

30. **USING ALGEBRA** Graph the data in the table. See margin.

31. **USING ALGEBRA** Is the relationship between x and y linear? Explain. See margin.

32. **LOGICAL REASONING** If Exercises 29–31 were repeated using a circle with a 5 inch radius, would the areas in the table change? Would your answer to Exercise 31 change? Explain your reasoning. See margin.

LIGHTHOUSES **The diagram shows a projected beam of light from a lighthouse.**

33. What is the area of water that can be covered by the light from the lighthouse? 692.72 mi²

34. Suppose a boat traveling along a straight line is illuminated by the lighthouse for approximately 28 miles of its route. What is the closest distance between the lighthouse and the boat? about 11.31 mi

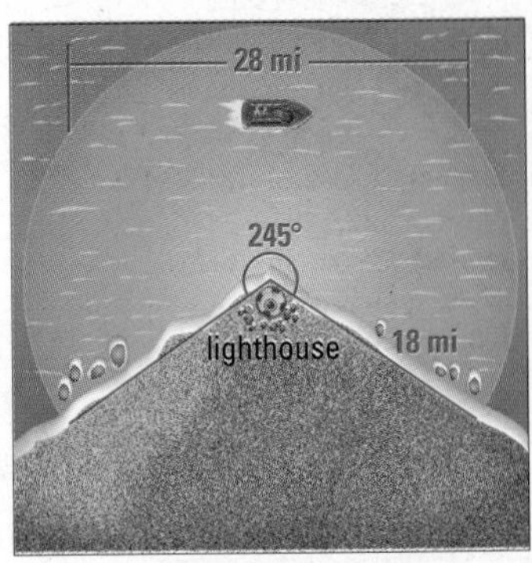

39. You would need to know the length of the diagonals of the kite, the measure of the central angle of the sector, and the radius of the sector.

USING AREA In Exercises 35–37, find the area of the shaded region in the circle formed by a chord and its intercepted arc. (*Hint:* Find the difference between the areas of a sector and a triangle.)

35.

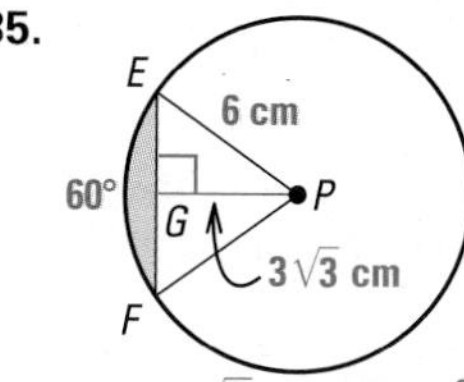

$6\pi - 9\sqrt{3} \approx 3.26$ cm^2

36.

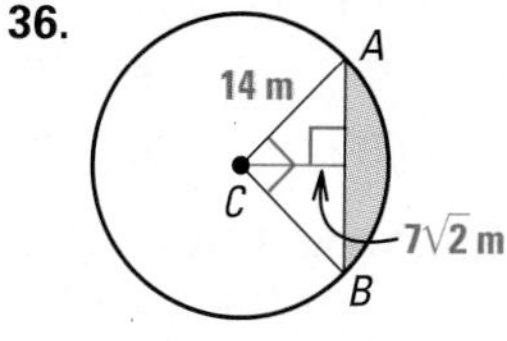

$49\pi - 98 \approx 55.94$ m^2

37.

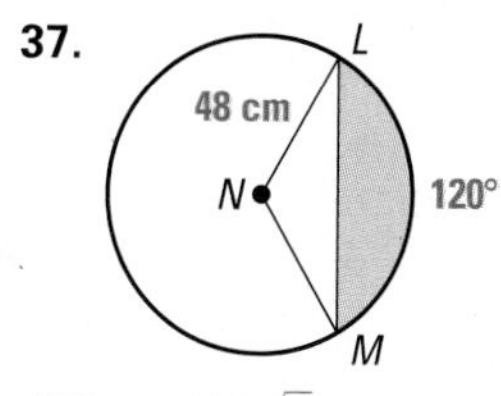

$768\pi - 576\sqrt{3} \approx 1415.08$ cm^2

FOCUS ON APPLICATIONS

VIKING LONGSHIPS
The planks in the hull of a longship were cut in a radial pattern from a single green log, providing uniform resiliency and strength.

APPLICATION LINK
www.mcdougallittell.com

VIKING LONGSHIPS Use the information below for Exercises 38 and 39.
When Vikings constructed *longships*, they cut hull-hugging frames from curved trees. Straight trees provided angled knees, which were used to brace the frames.

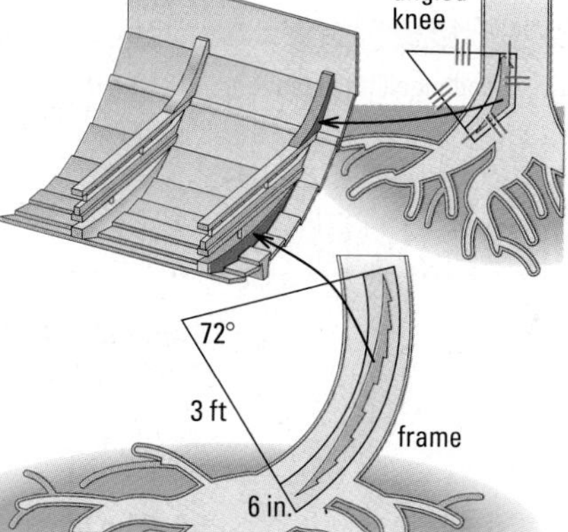

38. Find the area of a cross-section of the frame piece shown in red. 2.04 ft^2 or 294.05 in.^{2}

39. *Writing* The angled knee piece shown in blue has a cross section whose shape results from subtracting a sector from a kite. What measurements would you need to know to find its area? See margin.

40. **WINDOW DESIGN** The window shown is in the shape of a semicircle with radius 4 feet. The distance from S to T is 2 feet, and the measure of $\widehat{AB}$ is 45°. Find the area of the glass in the region $ABCD$. $1.5\pi \approx 4.71$ ft^2

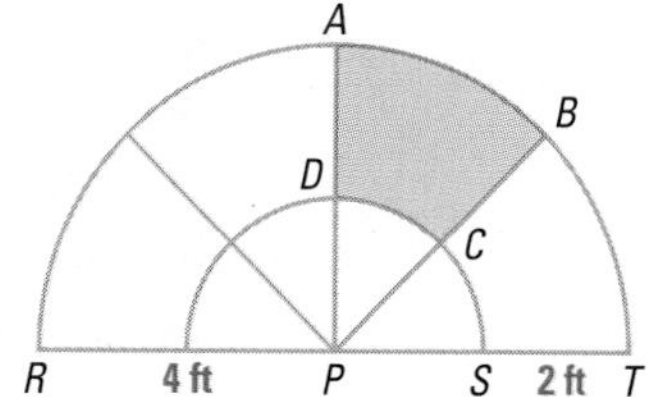

41. No; the area of the ⊙ is quadrupled and the circumference is doubled. $A = \pi r^2$ and $C = 2\pi r$, $\pi(2r)^2 = 4\pi r^2 = 4A$ and $2\pi(2r) = 2(2\pi r) = 2C$.

41. **LOGICAL REASONING** Suppose a circle has a radius of 4.5 inches. If you double the radius of the circle, does the area of the circle double as well? What happens to the circle's circumference? Explain.

42. **TECHNOLOGY** The area of a regular n-gon inscribed in a circle with radius 1 unit can be written as

$$A = \frac{1}{2}\left(\cos\left(\frac{180°}{n}\right)\right)\left(2n \cdot \sin\left(\frac{180°}{n}\right)\right).$$

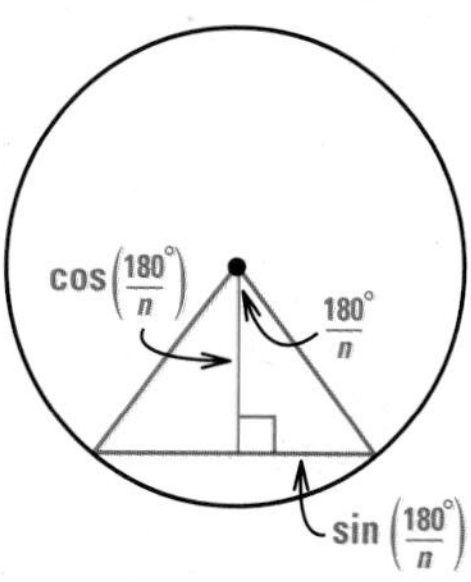

Use a spreadsheet to make a table. The first column is for the number of sides n and the second column is for the area of the n-gon. Fill in your table up to a 16-gon. What do you notice as n gets larger and larger?
The areas of the polygons approach the value of π, the area of the ⊙.

STUDENT HELP

Look Back
to Activity 11.4 on p. 690 for help with spreadsheets.

APPLICATION NOTE
EXERCISES 38 AND 39
Additional information about Viking longships is available at **www.mcdougallittell.com.**

STUDENT HELP NOTES

Look Back As students look back to Activity 11.4 on page 690, remind them to enter formulas in the first few rows of the spreadsheet so that the rest of the spreadsheet can be filled in using the Fill Down command.

ADDITIONAL PRACTICE AND RETEACHING

For Lesson 11.5:
- Practice Levels A, B, and C (*Chapter 11 Resource Book,* p. 75)
- Reteaching with Practice (*Chapter 11 Resource Book,* p. 78)
- See Lesson 11.5 of the *Personal Student Tutor*

For more Mixed Review:
- Search the *Test and Practice Generator* for key words or specific lessons.

4 ASSESS

DAILY HOMEWORK QUIZ

Transparency Available

1. What is the area of a circle with radius 9 cm? 81π cm^2
2. Find the area of the shaded region.

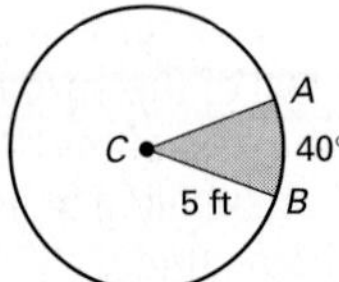

about 8.7 ft^2

3. Find the area of the shaded region.

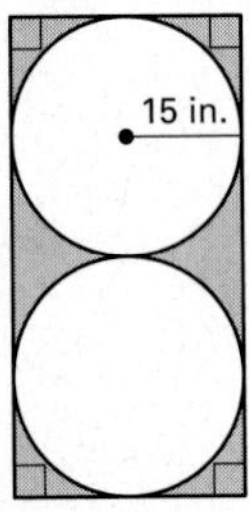

$1800 - 450\pi$ in.^{2}

4. What is the radius of a circle with area 100π square meters? 10 m

EXTRA CHALLENGE NOTE

Challenge problems for Lesson 11.5 are available in **blackline** format in the *Chapter 11 Resource Book*, p. 82 and at **www.mcdougallittell.com.**

ADDITIONAL TEST PREPARATION

1. **OPEN ENDED** Draw a circle. Then draw and label a sector of that circle so that the area of the sector is 4π. *Sample answer:* a circle with radius 4 units and the sector with the measure of the intercepted arc 90°
2. **WRITING** How is the procedure for finding the area of a sector similar to finding arc length? See answer at right.

Test Preparation

⊙Q and ⊙P are tangent. Use the diagram for Exercises 43 and 44.

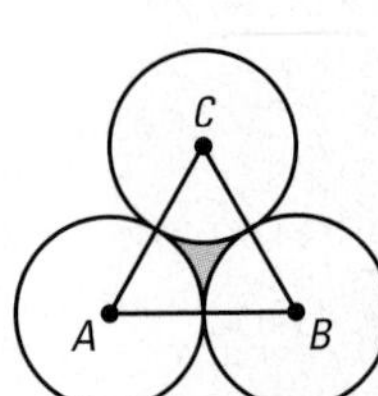

43. **MULTIPLE CHOICE** If ⊙Q is cut away, what is the remaining area of ⊙P? C

(A) 6π (B) 9π (C) 27π (D) 60π (E) 180π

44. **MULTIPLE CHOICE** What is the area of the region shaded in red? D

(A) 0.3 (B) 1.8π (C) 6π (D) 10.8π (E) 108π

★ Challenge

EXTRA CHALLENGE
www.mcdougallittell.com

45. **FINDING AREA** Find the area between the three congruent tangent circles. The radius of each circle is 6 centimeters. (*Hint:* $\triangle ABC$ is equilateral.) $36\sqrt{3} - 18\pi \approx 5.81$ cm^2

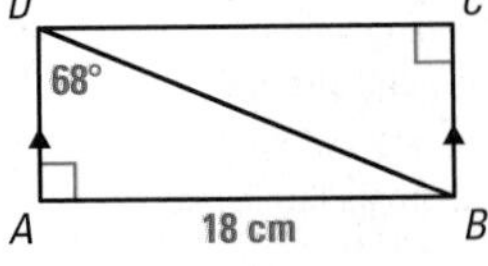

MIXED REVIEW

SIMPLIFYING RATIOS In Exercises 46–49, simplify the ratio. (Review 8.1 for 11.6)

46. $\frac{8 \text{ cats}}{20 \text{ cats}}$ $\frac{2}{5}$
47. $\frac{6 \text{ teachers}}{32 \text{ teachers}}$ $\frac{3}{16}$
48. $\frac{12 \text{ inches}}{63 \text{ inches}}$ $\frac{4}{21}$
49. $\frac{52 \text{ weeks}}{143 \text{ weeks}}$ $\frac{4}{11}$
50. The length of the diagonal of a square is 30. What is the length of each side? (Review 9.4) $15\sqrt{2}$

FINDING MEASURES Use the diagram to find the indicated measure. Round decimals to the nearest tenth. (Review 9.6)

D, C, 68°, A, 18 cm, B

51. BD 19.4 cm
52. DC 18 cm
53. $m\angle DBC$ 68°
54. BC 7.3 cm

WRITING EQUATIONS Write the standard equation of the circle with the given center and radius. (Review 10.6)

55. center $(-2, -7)$, radius 6
56. center $(0, -9)$, radius 10
57. center $(-4, 5)$, radius 3.2
58. center $(8, 2)$, radius $\sqrt{11}$

55. $(x + 2)^2 + (y + 7)^2 = 36$
56. $x^2 + (y + 9)^2 = 100$
57. $(x + 4)^2 + (y - 5)^2 = 10.24$
58. $(x - 8)^2 + (y - 2)^2 = 11$

FINDING MEASURES Find the indicated measure. (Review 11.4)

59. Circumference

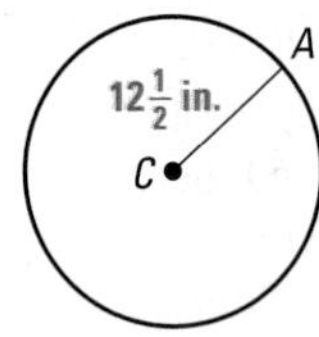

$25\pi \approx 78.5$ in.

60. Length of $\widehat{AB}$

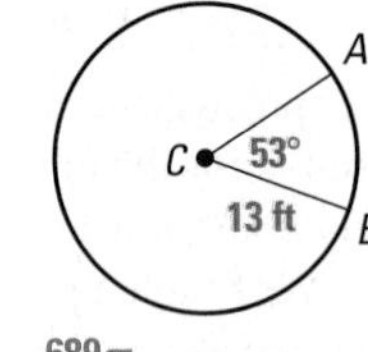

$\frac{689\pi}{180} \approx 12.0$ ft

61. Radius

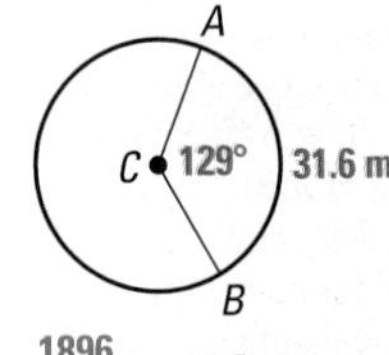

$\frac{1896}{43\pi} \approx 14.0$ m

Additional Test Preparation:

2. *Sample answer:* In both procedures you first find the ratio of the circle represented by the sector or arc. Then you multiply this ratio by the area of the circle to find the area of the sector, or by the circumference of the circle to find the arc length of the intercepted arc.

11.6 Geometric Probability

What you should learn

GOAL 1 Find a geometric probability.

GOAL 2 Use geometric probability to solve **real-life** problems, as applied in **Example 2**.

Why you should learn it

▼ Geometric probability is one model for calculating **real-life** probabilities, such as the probability that a bus will be waiting outside a hotel in **Ex. 28**.

REAL LIFE

GOAL 1 FINDING A GEOMETRIC PROBABILITY

A **probability** is a number from 0 to 1 that represents the chance that an event will occur. Assuming that all outcomes are equally likely, an event with a probability of 0 *cannot* occur. An event with a probability of 1 is *certain* to occur, and an event with a probability of 0.5 is just as likely to occur as not.

In an earlier course, you may have evaluated probabilities by counting the number of favorable outcomes and dividing that number by the total number of possible outcomes. In this lesson, you will use a related process in which the division involves geometric measures such as length or area. This process is called **geometric probability**.

GEOMETRIC PROBABILITY

PROBABILITY AND LENGTH

Let $\overline{AB}$ be a segment that contains the segment $\overline{CD}$. If a point K on $\overline{AB}$ is chosen at random, then the probability that it is on $\overline{CD}$ is as follows:

$$P(\text{Point } K \text{ is on } \overline{CD}) = \frac{\text{Length of } \overline{CD}}{\text{Length of } \overline{AB}}$$

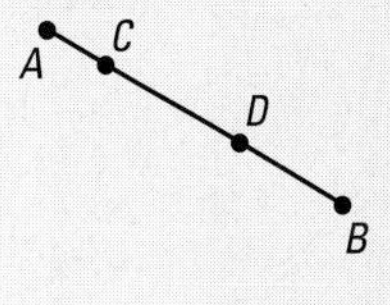

PROBABILITY AND AREA

Let J be a region that contains region M. If a point K in J is chosen at random, then the probability that it is in region M is as follows:

$$P(\text{Point } K \text{ is in region } M) = \frac{\text{Area of } M}{\text{Area of } J}$$

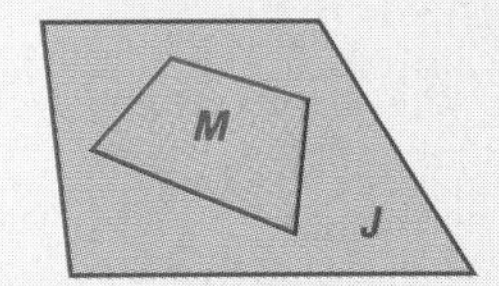

EXAMPLE 1 *Finding a Geometric Probability*

Find the probability that a point chosen at random on $\overline{RS}$ is on $\overline{TU}$.

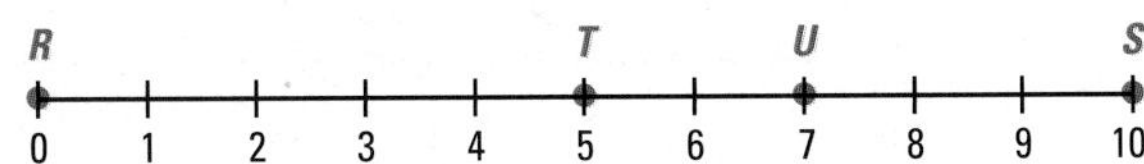

SOLUTION

$$P(\text{Point is on } \overline{TU}) = \frac{\text{Length of } \overline{TU}}{\text{Length of } \overline{RS}} = \frac{2}{10} = \frac{1}{5}$$

▶ The probability can be written as $\frac{1}{5}$, 0.2, or 20%.

STUDENT HELP

Study Tip
When applying a formula for geometric probability, it is important that every point on the segment or in the region is equally likely to be chosen.

CALIFORNIA STANDARDS AND ASSESSMENT

CA Standards: 8, 10
SAT9 Task 1: Objs. 1, 14, 23, 25, 37
SAT9 Task 2: Objs. 1, 15, 29, 41

1 PLAN

PACING
Basic: 2 days
Average: 2 days
Advanced: 2 days
Block Schedule: 0.5 block with 11.5
0.5 block with Ch. Rev.

LESSON OPENER ACTIVITY
An alternative way to approach Lesson 11.6 is to use the Activity Lesson Opener:
- Blackline Master (*Chapter 11 Resource Book*, p. 86)
- Transparency (p. 73)

MEETING INDIVIDUAL NEEDS
- ***Chapter 11 Resource Book***
  Prerequisite Skills Review (p. 5)
  Practice Level A (p. 89)
  Practice Level B (p. 90)
  Practice Level C (p. 91)
  Reteaching with Practice (p. 92)
  Absent Student Catch-Up (p. 94)
  Challenge (p. 96)
- ***Resources in Spanish***
-  ***Personal Student Tutor***

NEW-TEACHER SUPPORT
See the Tips for New Teachers on pp. 1–2 of the *Chapter 11 Resource Book* for additional notes about Lesson 11.6.

WARM-UP EXERCISES
Transparency Available
Find the area of each figure.

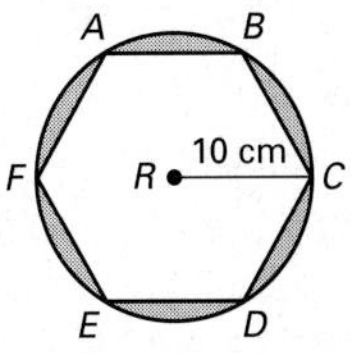

1. $\odot R$ **100π cm², or about 314 cm²**
2. hexagon $ABCDEF$ **$150\sqrt{3}$ cm², or about 260 cm²**
3. the shaded region **$100\pi - 150\sqrt{3}$ cm², or about 54 cm²**

2 TEACH

EXTRA EXAMPLES 1–2

Each circular hole on the target has a radius of 0.5 ft. If a beanbag is equally likely to land on any point on the target, find the probability that the beanbag goes through one of the holes.

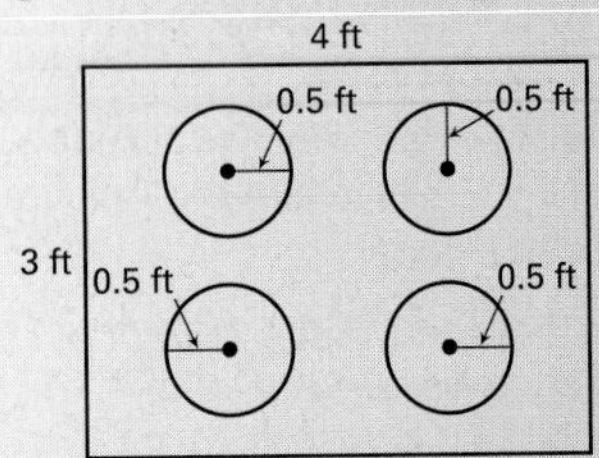

$\frac{\pi}{12} \approx 0.26$, or about 26%

EXTRA EXAMPLE 3

You ride to work on a bus. The buses come every 15 min and the ride to work is 31 min. You arrive at the bus stop at 8:24 A.M. What is the probability that you will be at work at 9:00 A.M.?

$\frac{1}{3} \approx 0.33$ or 33%

CHECKPOINT EXERCISES

For use after Examples 1 and 2:

1. Find the probability that a randomly chosen point in the figure below lies in the shaded region.

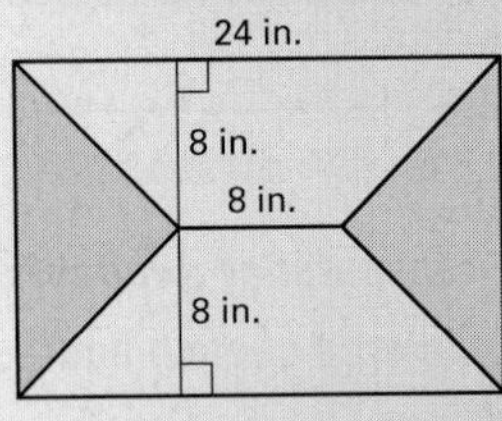

$\frac{1}{3} \approx 0.33$, or 33%

For use after Example 3:

2. Buses pick up passengers at the airport every 33 min. The ride home on the bus takes 22 min. If you get to the bus stop at 7:11 P.M., what is the probability that you can get home by 8:00 P.M.?

$\frac{9}{11} \approx 0.82$, or 82%

GOAL 2 USING GEOMETRIC PROBABILITY IN REAL LIFE

EXAMPLE 2 Using Areas to Find a Geometric Probability

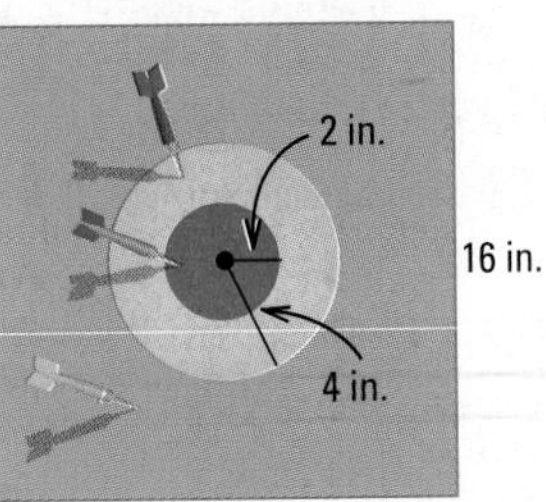

DART BOARD A dart is tossed and hits the dart board shown. The dart is equally likely to land on any point on the dart board. Find the probability that the dart lands in the red region.

SOLUTION

Find the ratio of the area of the red region to the area of the dart board.

$$P(\text{Dart lands in red region}) = \frac{\text{Area of red region}}{\text{Area of dart board}} = \frac{\pi(2^2)}{16^2} = \frac{4\pi}{256} \approx 0.05$$

▶ The probability that the dart lands in the red region is about 0.05, or 5%.

EXAMPLE 3 Using a Segment to Find a Geometric Probability

TRANSPORTATION You are visiting San Francisco and are taking a trolley ride to a store on Market Street. You are supposed to meet a friend at the store at 3:00 P.M. The trolleys run every 10 minutes and the trip to the store is 8 minutes. You arrive at the trolley stop at 2:48 P.M. What is the probability that you will arrive at the store by 3:00 P.M.?

Logical Reasoning

SOLUTION

To begin, find the greatest amount of time you can afford to wait for the trolley and still get to the store by 3:00 P.M.

Because the ride takes 8 minutes, you need to catch the trolley no later than 8 minutes before 3:00 P.M., or in other words by 2:52 P.M.

So, you can afford to wait 4 minutes (2:52 − 2:48 = 4 min). You can use a line segment to model the probability that the trolley will come within 4 minutes.

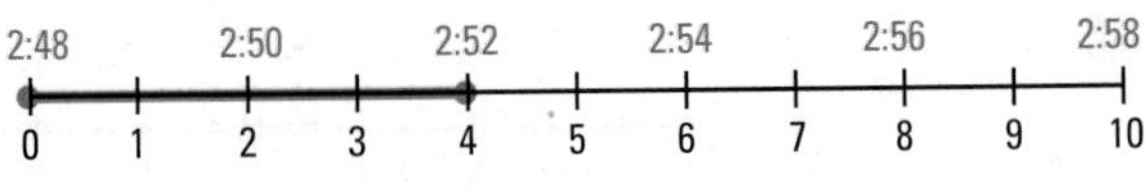

$$P(\text{Get to store by 3:00}) = \frac{\text{Favorable waiting time}}{\text{Maximum waiting time}} = \frac{4}{10} = \frac{2}{5}$$

▶ The probability is $\frac{2}{5}$, or 40%.

STUDENT HELP

HOMEWORK HELP
Visit our Web site www.mcdougallittell.com for extra examples.

EMPLOYMENT COUNSELORS help people make decisions about career choices. A counselor evaluates a client's interests and skills and works with the client to locate and apply for appropriate jobs.

CAREER LINK
www.mcdougallittell.com

EXAMPLE 4 *Finding a Geometric Probability*

JOB LOCATION You work for a temporary employment agency. You live on the west side of town and prefer to work there. The work assignments are spread evenly throughout the rectangular region shown. Find the probability that an assignment chosen at random for you is on the west side of town.

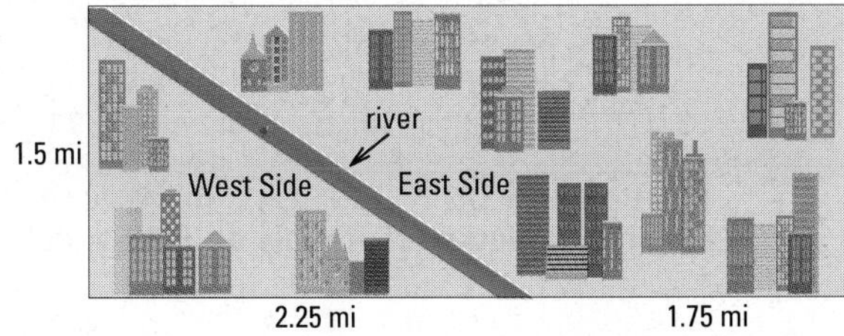

SOLUTION

The west side of town is approximately triangular. Its area is $\frac{1}{2} \cdot 2.25 \cdot 1.5$, or about 1.69 square miles. The area of the rectangular region is $1.5 \cdot 4$, or 6 square miles. So, the probability that the assignment is on the west side of town is

$$P(\text{Assignment is on west side}) = \frac{\text{Area of west side}}{\text{Area of rectangular region}} \approx \frac{1.69}{6} \approx 0.28.$$

▶ So, the probability that the work assignment is on the west side is about 28%.

GUIDED PRACTICE

Vocabulary Check ✓

1. Explain how a *geometric probability* is different from a *probability* found by dividing the number of favorable outcomes by the total number of possible outcomes. See margin.

Concept Check ✓

Determine whether you would use the *length method* or *area method* to find the geometric probability. Explain your reasoning.

2. The probability that an outcome lies in a triangular region
A triangular region is two-dimensional, so I would use the area method.
3. The probability that an outcome occurs within a certain time period
A period of time can be modeled using a segment, so I would use the length method.

Skill Check ✓

In Exercises 4–7, K is chosen at random on $\overline{AF}$. Find the probability that K is on the indicated segment.

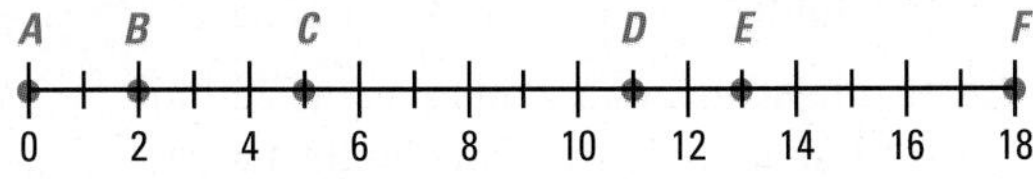

4. $\overline{AB}$ $\frac{1}{9} \approx 11\%$
5. $\overline{BD}$ $\frac{1}{2} = 50\%$
6. $\overline{BF}$ $\frac{8}{9} \approx 89\%$
7. Explain the relationship between your answers to Exercises 4 and 6.
8. Find the probability that a point chosen at random in the trapezoid shown lies in either of the shaded regions. $\frac{9}{23} \approx 39\%$

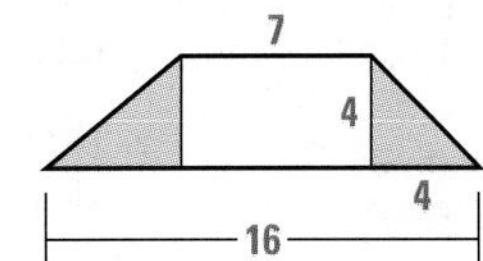

1. Geometric probabilities are determined by comparing geometric measures, such as dividing the length or area of a part of a segment or figure by the length or area of the entire segment or figure.

7. $\overline{AB}$ and $\overline{BF}$ do not overlap and $AB + BF = AF$. So any point K on $\overline{AF}$ must be on one of the two parts. Therefore, the sum of the two probabilities is 1.

EXTRA EXAMPLE 4

The shaded area in the diagram of your backyard below shows the area that you can see from your window. If a child is equally likely to play in any part of the backyard, what is the probability that you will be able to see him from the window?

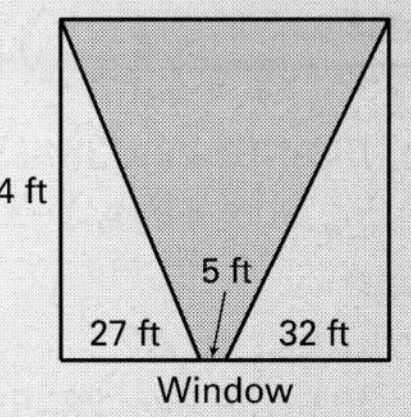

about 0.54 , or 54%

CHECKPOINT EXERCISES

For use after Examples 1 and 2:

1. You are acting on the stage shown in the diagram below. In order to be clearly seen by the audience, you need to stay in the triangular portion of the stage. If you are equally likely to be in any part of the stage, what is the probability that you will *not* be clearly seen by the audience?

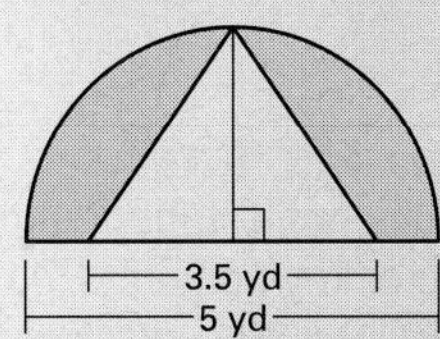

about $\frac{5\pi - 7}{5\pi}$, 0.55, or 55%

FOCUS ON VOCABULARY

What is used to find *geometric probability*? Geometric probability is found by using a ratio of geometric measures such as lengths or areas.

CLOSURE QUESTION

Explain how to find the probability that a randomly chosen point lies in a desired part of a segment. Find the length of the entire segment and of the desired segment. Divide the length of the desired segment by the length of the entire segment.

3 APPLY

ASSIGNMENT GUIDE

BASIC
Day 1: p. 702 Exs. 9–25
Day 2: pp. 703–705 Exs. 26–34, 36–39, 43, 45–52, Quiz 2 Exs. 1–7

AVERAGE
Day 1: p. 702 Exs. 9–25
Day 2: pp. 703–705 Exs. 26–43, 45–52, Quiz 2 Exs. 1–7

ADVANCED
Day 1: p. 702 Exs. 9–25
Day 2: pp. 703–705 Exs. 26–52, Quiz 2 Exs. 1–7

BLOCK SCHEDULE
p. 702 Exs. 9–25 (with 11.5)
pp. 703–705 Exs. 26–43, 45–52, Quiz 2 Exs. 1–7 (with Ch. Rev.)

EXERCISE LEVELS
Level A: *Easier*
9–16
Level B: *More Difficult*
17–43
Level C: *Most Difficult*
44

✔ HOMEWORK CHECK
To quickly check student understanding of key concepts, go over the following exercises: Exs. 10, 14, 20, 22, 24, 30, 36, 38. See also the Daily Homework Quiz:

- Blackline Master (*Chapter 12 Resource Book,* p. 11)
- Transparency (p. 86)

PRACTICE AND APPLICATIONS

STUDENT HELP
Extra Practice to help you master skills is on p. 824.

PROBABILITY ON A SEGMENT **In Exercises 9–12, find the probability that a point *A*, selected randomly on $\overline{GN}$, is on the given segment.**

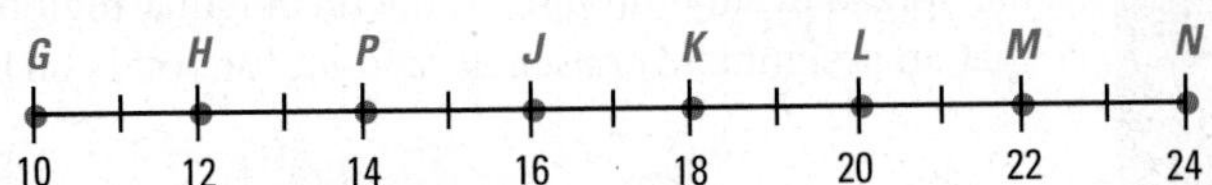

9. $\overline{GH}$ about 14% **10.** $\overline{JL}$ about 29% **11.** $\overline{JN}$ about 57% **12.** $\overline{GJ}$ about 43%

PROBABILITY ON A SEGMENT **In Exercises 13–16, find the probability that a point *K*, selected randomly on $\overline{PU}$, is on the given segment.**

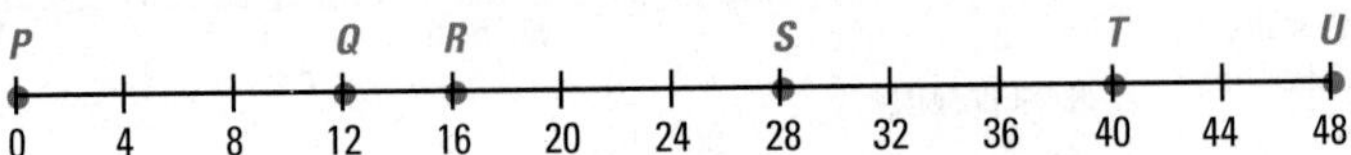

13. $\overline{PQ}$ 25% **14.** $\overline{PS}$ about 58% **15.** $\overline{SU}$ about 42% **16.** $\overline{PU}$ 100%

FINDING A GEOMETRIC PROBABILITY **Find the probability that a randomly chosen point in the figure lies in the shaded region.**

17. $\frac{4-\pi}{4} \approx 21.5\%$

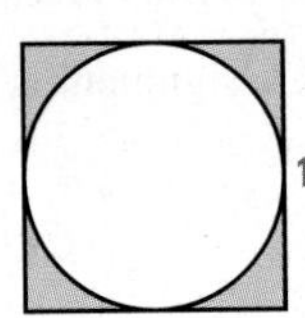

18.

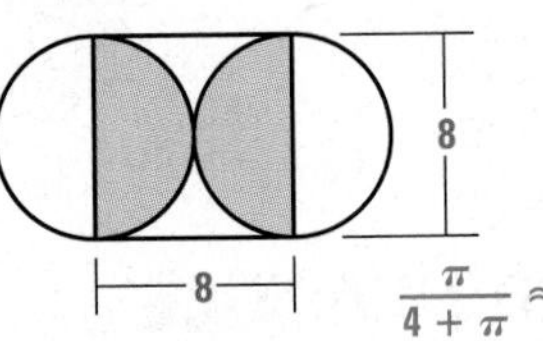

$\frac{\pi}{4+\pi} \approx 44.0\%$

19. $\frac{1}{4} = 25\%$

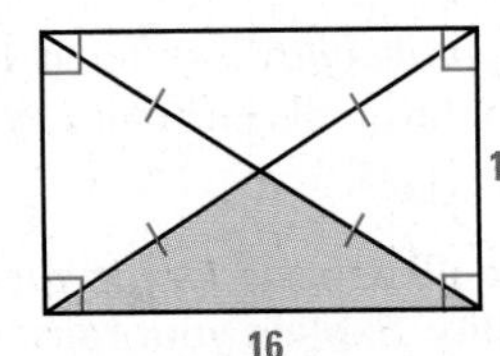

20.

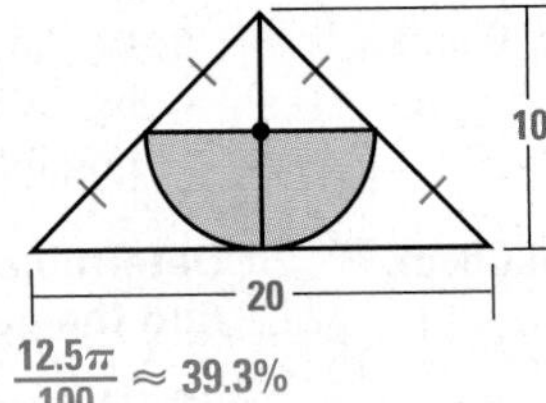

$\frac{12.5\pi}{100} \approx 39.3\%$

TARGETS **A regular hexagonal shaped target with sides of length 14 centimeters has a circular bull's eye with a diameter of 3 centimeters. In Exercises 21–23, darts are thrown and hit the target at random.**

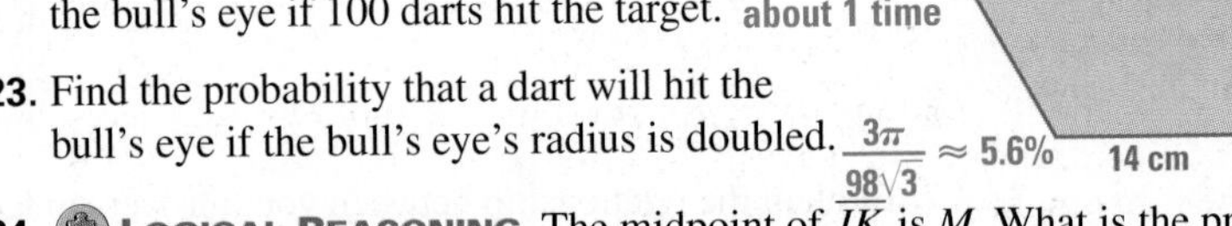

21. What is the probability that a dart that hits the target will hit the bull's eye? $\frac{3\pi}{392\sqrt{3}} \approx 1.4\%$

22. Estimate how many times a dart will hit the bull's eye if 100 darts hit the target. about 1 time

23. Find the probability that a dart will hit the bull's eye if the bull's eye's radius is doubled. $\frac{3\pi}{98\sqrt{3}} \approx 5.6\%$

24. **LOGICAL REASONING** The midpoint of $\overline{JK}$ is M. What is the probability that a randomly selected point on $\overline{JK}$ is closer to M than to J or to K? $\frac{1}{2} = 50\%$

25. **LOGICAL REASONING** A circle with radius $\sqrt{2}$ units is circumscribed about a square with side length 2 units. Find the probability that a randomly chosen point will be inside the circle but outside the square. $\frac{\pi-2}{\pi} \approx 36\%$

STUDENT HELP
HOMEWORK HELP
Example 1: Exs. 9–16
Example 2: Exs. 17–23, 29–34
Example 3: Exs. 26–28
Example 4: Exs. 40–42

26. **FIRE ALARM** Suppose that your school day begins at 7:30 A.M. and ends at 3:00 P.M. You eat lunch at 11:00 A.M. If there is a fire drill at a random time during the day, what is the probability that it begins before lunch? $\frac{7}{15} \approx 46.7\%$

27. **PHONE CALL** You are expecting a call from a friend anytime between 6:00 P.M. and 7:00 P.M. Unexpectedly, you have to run an errand for a relative and are gone from 5:45 P.M. until 6:10 P.M. What is the probability that you missed your friend's call? $\frac{1}{6} \approx 16.7\%$

28. **TRANSPORTATION** Buses arrive at a resort hotel every 15 minutes. They wait for three minutes while passengers get on and get off, and then the buses depart. What is the probability that there is a bus waiting when a hotel guest walks out of the door at a randomly chosen time? $\frac{1}{5} = 20\%$

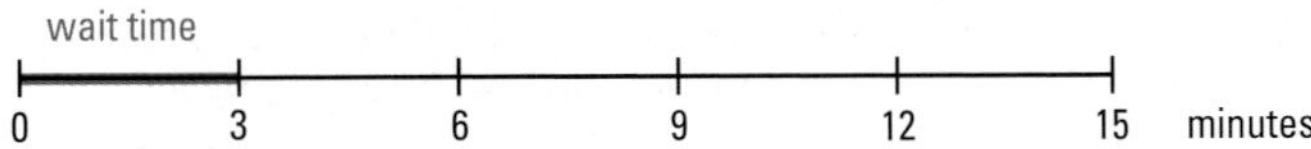

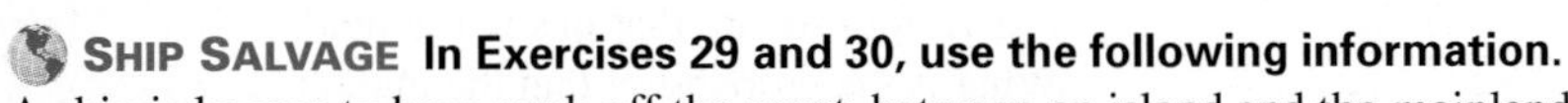

FOCUS ON APPLICATIONS

SHIP SALVAGE Searchers for sunken items such as ships, planes, or even a space capsule, use charts, sonar, and video cameras in their search and recovery expeditions.

APPLICATION LINK
www.mcdougallittell.com

SHIP SALVAGE In Exercises 29 and 30, use the following information.
A ship is known to have sunk off the coast, between an island and the mainland as shown. A salvage vessel anchors at a random spot in this rectangular region for divers to search for the ship.

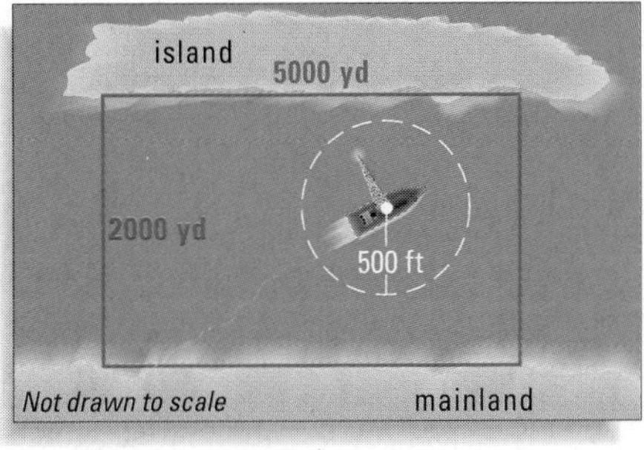

29. Find the approximate area of the rectangular region where the ship sank. 10,000,000 yd^2

30. The divers search 500 feet in all directions from a point on the ocean floor directly below the salvage vessel. Estimate the probability that the divers will find the sunken ship on the first try. about 0.9%

ARCHERY In Exercises 31–35, use the following information.
Imagine that an arrow hitting the target shown is equally likely to hit any point on the target. The 10-point circle has a 4.8 inch diameter and each of the other rings is 2.4 inches wide. Find the probability that the arrow hits the region described.

31. The 10-point region 1%

32. The yellow region 4%

33. The white region 36%

34. The 5-point region 11%

35. **CRITICAL THINKING** Does the geometric probability model hold true when an expert archer shoots an arrow? Explain your reasoning.

10 9 8 7 6 5 4 3 2 1

35. No; an expert archer has the skill to aim, so that it is no longer true that every point on the target has an equal probability of being hit.

36. **USING ALGEBRA** If $0 < y < 1$ and $0 < x < 1$, find the probability that $y < x$. Begin by sketching the graph, and then use the *area method* to find the probability. $\frac{1}{2} = 50\%$

! COMMON ERROR
EXERCISE 17 Students often give this probability as the area of the circle divided by the area of the square. Stress that they must first subtract the area of the circle from the area of the square to get the shaded area and then divide by the area of the square to get the probability.

APPLICATION NOTE
EXERCISE 29 AND 30
Additional information about a career in ship salvage is available at **www.mcdougallittell.com.**

36.
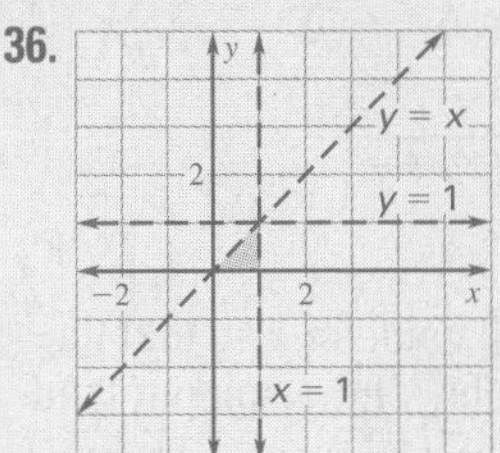

ADDITIONAL PRACTICE AND RETEACHING

For Lesson 11.6:
- Practice Levels A, B, and C (*Chapter 11 Resource Book*, p. 89)
- Reteaching with Practice (*Chapter 11 Resource Book*, p. 92)
- See Lesson 11.6 of the *Personal Student Tutor*

For more Mixed Review:
- Search the *Test and Practice Generator* for key words or specific lessons.

4 ASSESS

DAILY HOMEWORK QUIZ

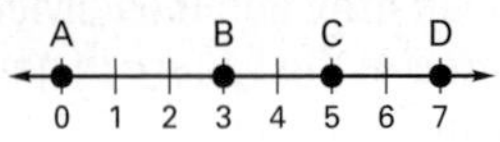
Transparency Available

1. Find the probability that a point chosen on $\overline{AD}$ is on $\overline{BC}$.

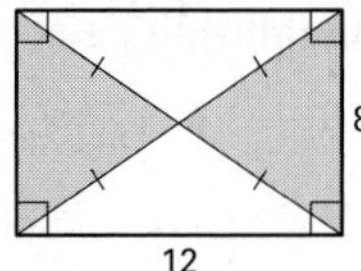

$\frac{2}{7}$, 0.29, or 29%

2. Find the probability that a randomly chosen point in the figure lies in the shaded region.

$\frac{1}{2}$ or 50%

3. Find the value of x so that the probability of the spinner landing on a grey sector is $\frac{1}{9}$.

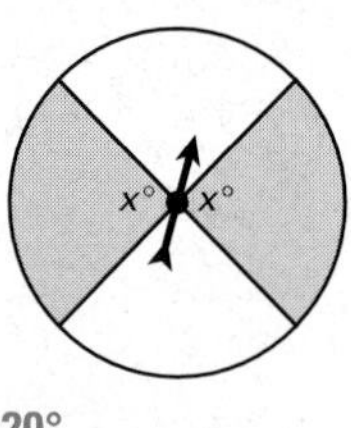

20°

EXTRA CHALLENGE NOTE
Challenge problems for Lesson 11.6 are available in **blackline** format in the *Chapter 11 Resource Book,* p. 96 and at **www.mcdougallittell.com.**

ADDITIONAL TEST PREPARATION

1. **OPEN ENDED** Draw a target constructed of polygons and circles. Then shade part of the target and find the probability that a randomly chosen point on the target is in the shaded region. Check students' work.

USING ALGEBRA **Find the value of x so that the probability of the spinner landing on a blue sector is the value given.**

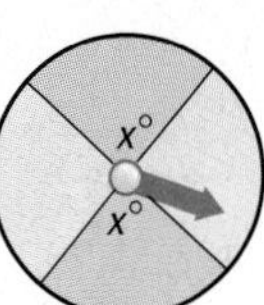

37. $\frac{1}{3}$ 60° **38.** $\frac{1}{4}$ 45° **39.** $\frac{1}{6}$ 30°

BALLOON RACE **In Exercises 40–42, use the following information.**
In a "Hare and Hounds" balloon race, one balloon (the hare) leaves the ground first. About ten minutes later, the other balloons (the hounds) leave. The hare then lands and marks a square region as the target. The hounds each try to drop a marker in the target zone.

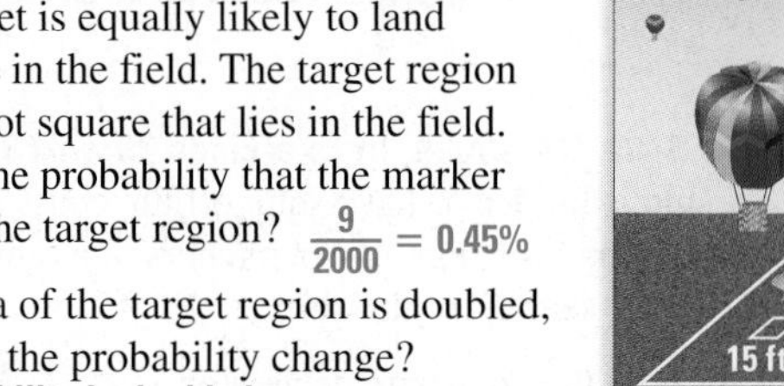

40. Suppose that a hound's marker dropped onto a rectangular field that is 200 feet by 250 feet is equally likely to land anywhere in the field. The target region is a 15 foot square that lies in the field. What is the probability that the marker lands in the target region? $\frac{9}{2000} = 0.45\%$

41. If the area of the target region is doubled, how does the probability change? The probability is doubled.

42. If each side of the target region is doubled, how does the probability change? The probability is quadrupled.

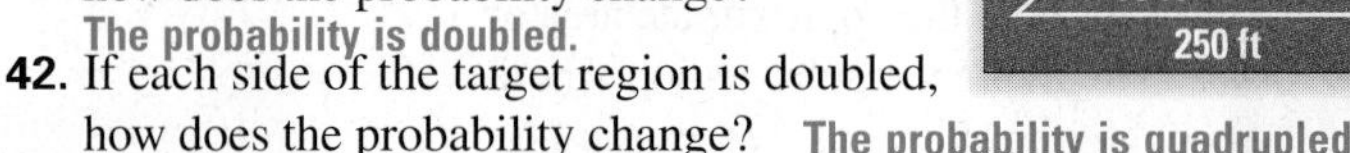

Test Preparation

43. MULTI-STEP PROBLEM Use the following information.
You organize a fund-raiser at your school. You fill a large glass jar that has a 25 centimeter diameter with water. You place a dish that has a 5 centimeter diameter at the bottom of the jar. A person donates a coin by dropping it in the jar. If the coin lands in the dish, the person wins a small prize.

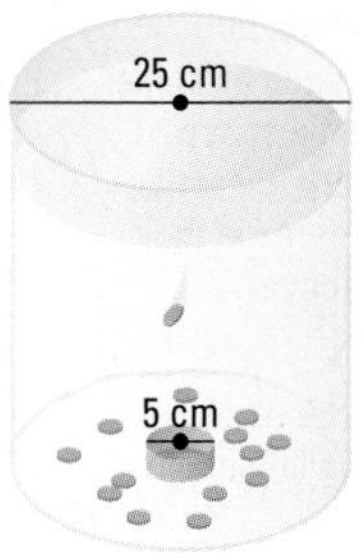

a. Calculate the probability that a coin dropped, with an equally likely chance of landing anywhere at the bottom of the jar, lands in the dish. 0.04 or 4%

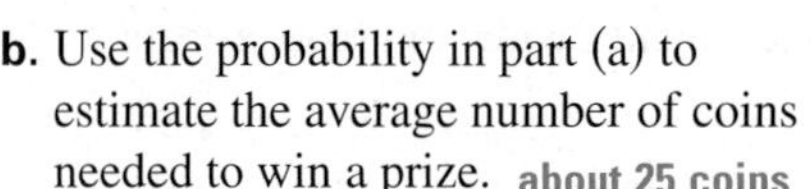

b. Use the probability in part (a) to estimate the average number of coins needed to win a prize. about 25 coins

c. From past experience, you expect about 250 people to donate 5 coins each. How many prizes should you buy? about 50 prizes

d. *Writing* Suppose that instead of the dish, a circle with a diameter of 5 centimeters is painted on the bottom of the jar, and any coin touching the circle wins a prize. Will the probability change? Explain.

43. d. Yes; the target area is larger, so the probability increases.

★ **Challenge**

44. **USING ALGEBRA** Graph the lines $y = x$ and $y = 3$ in a coordinate plane. A point is chosen randomly from within the boundaries $0 < y < 4$ and $0 < x < 4$. Find the probability that the coordinates of the point are a solution of this system of inequalities: $\frac{9}{32} \approx 28\%$

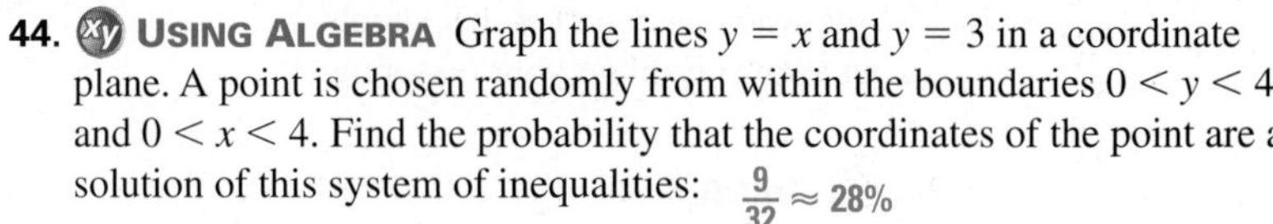

$$y < 3$$
$$y > x$$

EXTRA CHALLENGE
www.mcdougallittell.com

MIXED REVIEW

DETERMINING TANGENCY **Tell whether $\overleftrightarrow{AB}$ is tangent to $\odot C$. Explain your reasoning.** (Review 10.1) 45–47. See margin.

45. No; since $11^2 = 121 \neq 100 + 16$, $\triangle ABC$ is not a right $\triangle$. Then $\overline{CB}$ is not $\perp$ to $\overleftrightarrow{AB}$ and $\overleftrightarrow{AB}$ is not tangent to the $\odot$.

46. Yes; $13^2 = 169 = 25 + 144$, so $\triangle ABC$ is a right $\triangle$ and $\overline{CB} \perp \overleftrightarrow{AB}$. Then $\overleftrightarrow{AB}$ is tangent to the $\odot$.

47. Yes; $25^2 = 625 = 49 + 576$, so $\triangle ABC$ is a right $\triangle$ and $\overline{CA} \perp \overleftrightarrow{AB}$. Then $\overleftrightarrow{AB}$ is tangent to the $\odot$.

45.

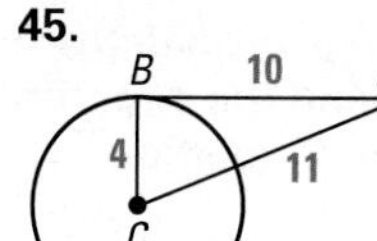

46.

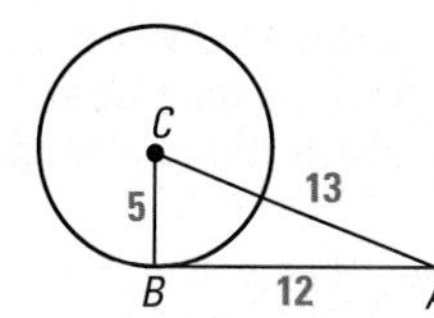

47.

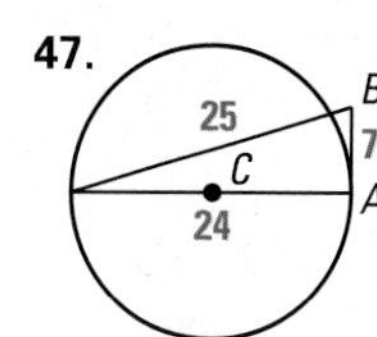

DESCRIBING LINES **In Exercises 48–51, graph the line with the circle $(x - 2)^2 + (y + 4)^2 = 16$. Is the line a *tangent* or a *secant*?** (Review 10.6)
48–51. See margin for graphs.

48. $x = -y$ secant

49. $y = 0$ tangent

50. $x = 6$ tangent

51. $y = x - 1$ secant

52. **LOCUS** Find the locus of all points in the coordinate plane that are equidistant from points (3, 2) and (1, 2) and within $\sqrt{2}$ units of the point (1, −1). (Review 10.7)
points on the $\perp$ bisector of the segment with endpoints (3, 2) and (1, 2) that are on or inside the $\odot$ with center (1, −1) and radius $\sqrt{2}$ (all points (2, y) where $-2 < y < 0$)

QUIZ 2

Self-Test for Lessons 11.4–11.6

Find the indicated measure. (Lesson 11.4)

1. Circumference

2. Length of $\overset{\frown}{AB}$

3. Radius

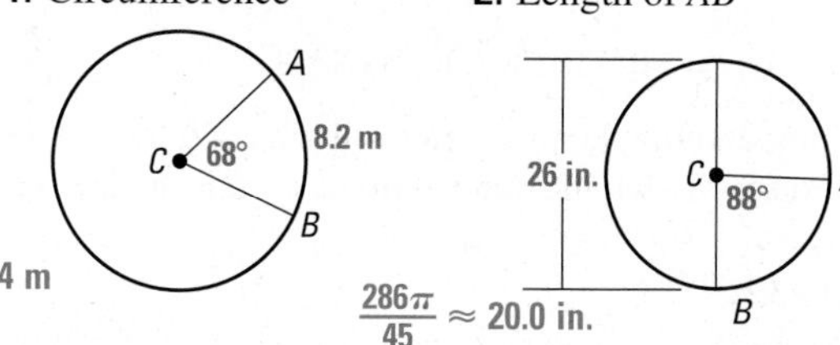

$\frac{738}{17} \approx 43.4$ m

$\frac{286\pi}{45} \approx 20.0$ in.

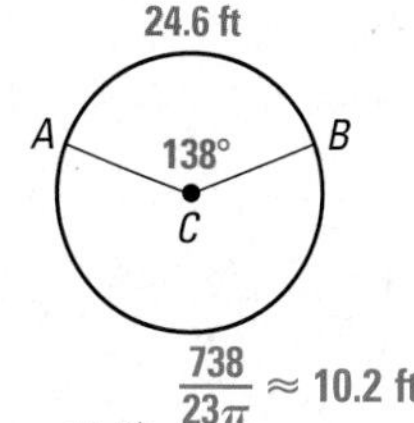

$\frac{738}{23\pi} \approx 10.2$ ft

In Exercises 4–6, find the area of the shaded region. (Lesson 11.5)

4.

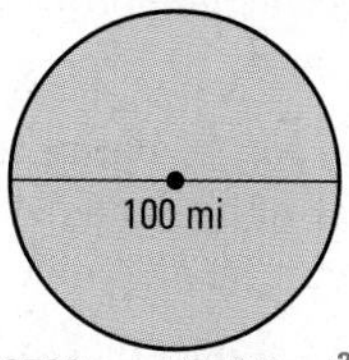

100 mi

$2500\pi \approx 7854.0$ mi^2

5.

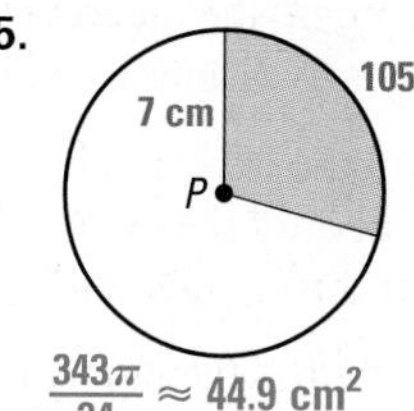

$\frac{343\pi}{24} \approx 44.9$ cm^2

6.

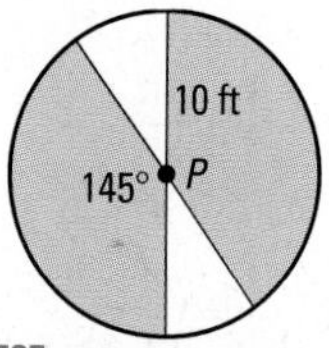

10 ft
145°
P

$\frac{725\pi}{9} \approx 253.1$ ft^2

7. **TARGETS** A square target with 20 cm sides includes a triangular region with equal side lengths of 5 cm. A dart is thrown and hits the target at random. Find the probability that the dart hits the triangle. (Lesson 11.6)
$\frac{\sqrt{3}}{64} \approx 2.7\%$

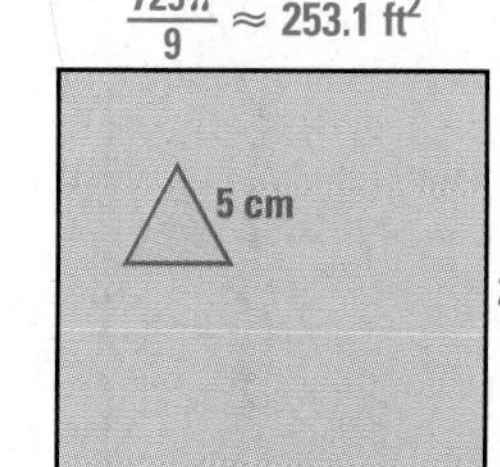

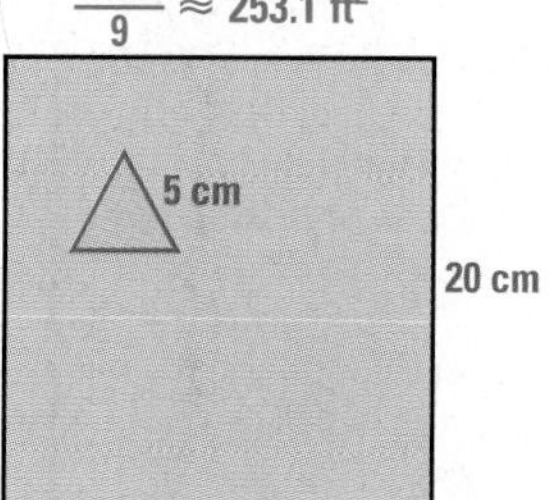

ADDITIONAL RESOURCES

An alternative Quiz for Lessons 11.4–11.6 is available in the *Chapter 11 Resource Book*, p. 97.

44.

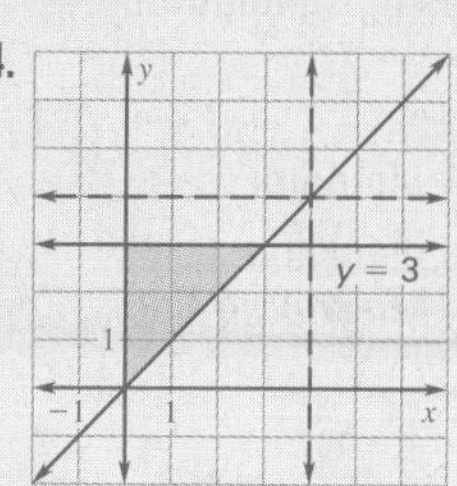

48.

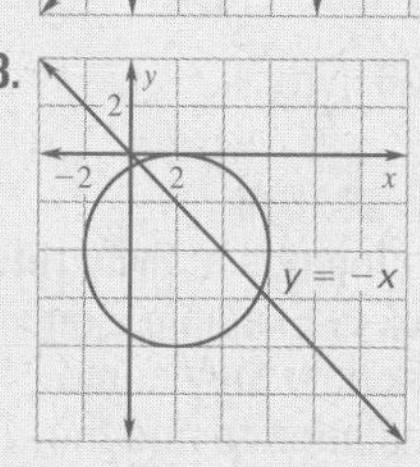

49.

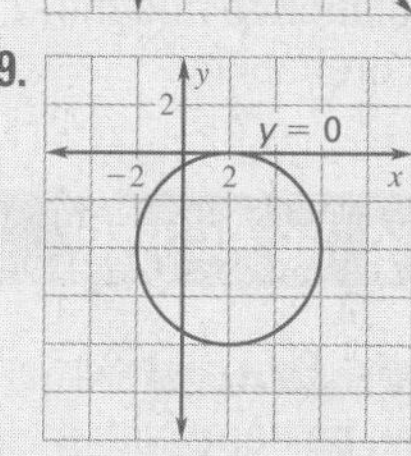

50.

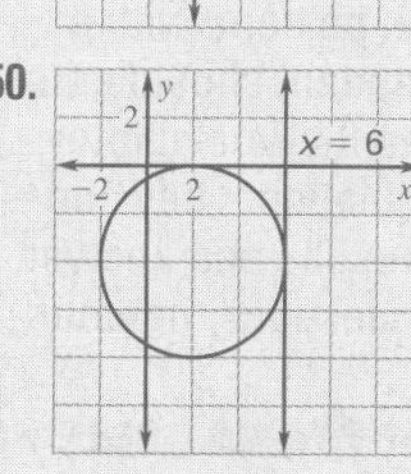

51.

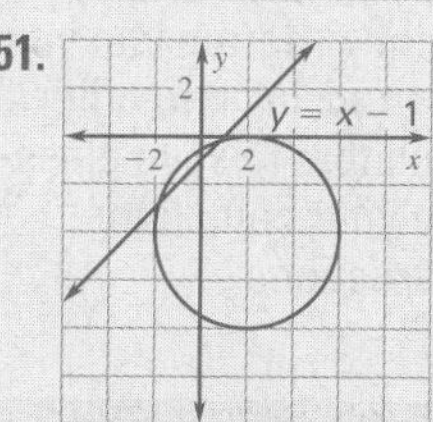

1 Planning the Activity

PURPOSE
To investigate experimental probability using simulation.

MATERIALS
- graphing calculator
- Keystroke blackline (*Chapter 11 Resource Book*, p. 87)

PACING
- Activity — 20 min

LINK TO LESSON
After completing this activity refer students back to Example 2 on page 700. Ask how they could alter this simulation to find the experimental probability.

2 Managing the Activity

COOPERATIVE LEARNING
This activity can be done with a partner. Each student should enter the program into their calculator and run the simulation. They can then compare results and answer the remaining questions together.

CLASSROOM MANAGEMENT
You can enter the program into your own calculator and link it to other student's calculators to save classroom time. See your calculator manual for instructions.

3 Closing the Activity

KEY DISCOVERY
The experimental probability approaches the theoretical probability as the number of hits increases.

ACTIVITY ASSESSMENT
Why is the probability obtained in Step 6 an experimental probability?
It is found by simulating an experiment rather than calculating it theoretically.

ACTIVITY 11.6
Using Technology

Investigating Experimental Probability

In Lesson 11.6 you found the *theoretical probability* of a dart landing in a region on a dart board. You can also find the *experimental probability* of this event using a graphing calculator simulation.

STUDENT HELP

KEYSTROKE HELP
Visit our Web site www.mcdougallittell.com to see keystrokes for several models of calculators.

INVESTIGATE

1. Calculate the theoretical probability that a randomly thrown dart that lands on the dart board shown below will land in the region shaded red. $\frac{\pi}{16} \approx 19.6\%$
2. To find the experimental probability, you can physically throw a dart many times and record the results. You can also use a graphing calculator program that simulates throwing a dart as many times as you like. You can simulate this experiment on a TI-82 or TI-83 graphing calculator using the following program.

```
PROGRAM: DARTS
:ClrHome
:Input "HOW MANY THROWS?",N
:0 → H
:For (I, 1, N)
:rand → X
:rand → Y
:If (X² + Y²) < 0.25
:H + 1 → H
:End
:Disp "NUMBER OF HITS",H
```

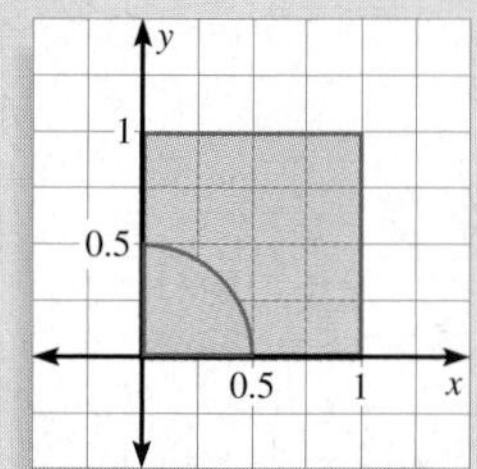

3. Enter and run the program to simulate 40 throws. Determine the proportion of darts thrown that landed in the region shaded red.

CONJECTURE

1. Explain why "If $(X^2 + Y^2) < 0.25$" is in the program.
   If $x^2 + y^2 < 0.25$, then (x, y) is the region shaded red.
2. Compare the theoretical and experimental probabilities you found in **Steps 1**, **2**, and **3**. Answers will vary.
3. Find the experimental probability for the entire class by combining the number of throws and the number of hits and determining the proportion of dart throws that landed in the region shaded red. Answers will vary.
4. How does the number of trials affect the relationship between the theoretical and experimental probabilities?
   The greater the number of trials, the closer the experimental and theoretical probabilities will be.

EXTENSION

CRITICAL THINKING The results of a calculator simulation tend to be more reliable than those of a human-generated simulation. Explain why a calculator simulation would be easier and more accurate than a human-generated one.

Extension: *Sample answer:* It would be easier because it would not involve the physical actions of tossing and retrieving the darts and recording the results. It would be more accurate because it would not involve such variables as skill level, effort, or physical factors such as air currents.

CHAPTER 11

Chapter Summary

WHAT did you learn?	WHY did you learn it?
Find the measures of the interior and exterior angles of polygons. **(11.1)**	Find the measures of angles in real-world objects, such as a home plate marker. **(p. 664)**
Find the areas of equilateral triangles and other regular polygons. **(11.2)**	Solve problems by finding real-life areas, such as the area of a hexagonal mirror in a telescope. **(p. 674)**
Compare perimeters and areas of similar figures. **(11.3)**	Solve real-life problems, such as estimating a reasonable cost for photographic paper. **(p. 678)**
Find the circumference of a circle and the length of an arc of a circle. **(11.4)**	Find real-life distances, such as the distance around a track. **(p. 685)**
Find the areas of circles and sectors. **(11.5)**	Find areas of real-life regions containing circles or parts of circles, such as the area of the front of a case for a clock. **(p. 693)**
Find a geometric probability. **(11.6)**	Estimate the likelihood that an event will occur, such as the likelihood that divers will find a sunken ship on their first dive. **(p. 703)**

How does Chapter 11 fit into the BIGGER PICTURE of geometry?

The word *geometry* is derived from Greek words meaning "land measurement." The ability to measure angles, arc lengths, perimeters, circumferences, and areas allows you to calculate measurements required to solve problems in the real world. Keep in mind that a region that lies in a plane has two types of measures. The perimeter or circumference of a region is a *one*-dimensional measure that uses units such as centimeters or feet. The area of a region is a *two*-dimensional measure that uses units such as square centimeters or square feet. In the next chapter, you will study a *three*-dimensional measure called *volume*.

STUDY STRATEGY

Did your concept map help you organize your work?

The concept map you made, following the **Study Strategy** on page 660, may include these ideas.

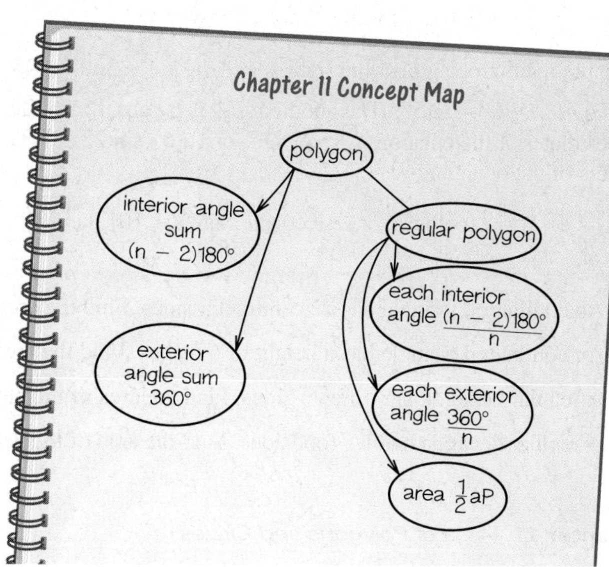

ADDITIONAL RESOURCES

The following resources are available to help review the material in this chapter.

- Chapter Review Games and Activities (*Chapter 11 Resource Book,* p. 98)
- *Geometry in Motion video*
- *Personal Student Tutor*
- Cumulative Review, Chs. 1–11 (*Chapter 11 Resource Book,* p. 110)

CHAPTER 11 Chapter Review

VOCABULARY

- center of a polygon, p. 670
- radius of a polygon, p. 670
- apothem of a polygon, p. 670
- central angle of a regular polygon, p. 671
- circumference, p. 683
- arc length, p. 683
- sector of a circle, p. 692
- probability, p. 699
- geometric probability, p. 699

11.1 ANGLE MEASURES IN POLYGONS

Examples on pp. 661–664

EXAMPLES If a regular polygon has 15 sides, then the sum of the measures of its interior angles is $(15 - 2) \cdot 180° = 2340°$. The measure of each interior angle is $\frac{1}{15} \cdot 2340° = 156°$. The measure of each exterior angle is $\frac{1}{15} \cdot 360° = 24°$.

In Exercises 1–4, you are given the number of sides of a regular polygon. Find the measure of each interior angle and each exterior angle.

1. 9 **140°, 40°** **2.** 13 **about 152.3°, about 27.7°** **3.** 16 **157.5°, 22.5°** **4.** 24 **165°, 15°**

In Exercises 5–8, you are given the measure of each interior angle of a regular *n*-gon. Find the value of *n*.

5. 172° **45** **6.** 135° **8** **7.** 150° **12** **8.** 170° **36**

11.2 AREAS OF REGULAR POLYGONS

Examples on pp. 669–671

EXAMPLES The area of an equilateral triangle with sides of length 14 inches is

$A = \frac{1}{4}\sqrt{3}(14^2) = \frac{1}{4}\sqrt{3}(196) = 49\sqrt{3} \approx 84.9 \text{ in.}^2$

In the regular octagon at the right, $m\angle ABC = \frac{1}{8} \cdot 360° = 45°$ and $m\angle DBC = 22.5°$. The apothem BD is $6 \cdot \cos 22.5°$. The perimeter of the octagon is $8 \cdot 2 \cdot DC$, or $16(6 \cdot \sin 22.5°)$. The area of the octagon is

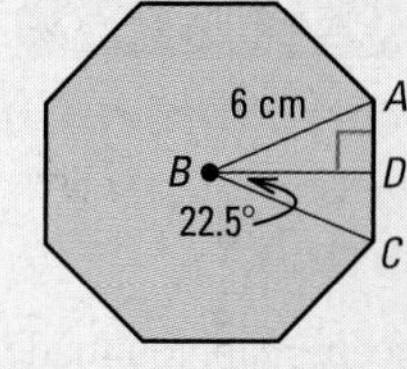

$A = \frac{1}{2}aP = \frac{1}{2}(6 \cos 22.5°) \cdot 16(6 \sin 22.5°) \approx 101.8 \text{ cm}^2$.

9. An equilateral triangle has 12 centimeter sides. Find the area of the triangle. $\mathbf{36\sqrt{3} \approx 62.4 \text{ cm}^2}$

10. An equilateral triangle has a height of 6 inches. Find the area of the triangle. $\mathbf{12\sqrt{3} \approx 20.8 \text{ in.}^2}$

11. A regular hexagon has 5 meter sides. Find the area of the hexagon. $\mathbf{\frac{75\sqrt{3}}{2} \approx 65.0 \text{ m}^2}$

12. A regular decagon has 1.5 foot sides. Find the area of the decagon. $\mathbf{\frac{45}{8 \tan 18°} \approx 17.3 \text{ ft}^2}$

11.3 PERIMETERS AND AREAS OF SIMILAR FIGURES

Examples on pp. 677–678

EXAMPLE The two pentagons at the right are similar. Their corresponding sides are in the ratio 2:3, so the ratio of their areas is $2^2:3^2 = 4:9$.

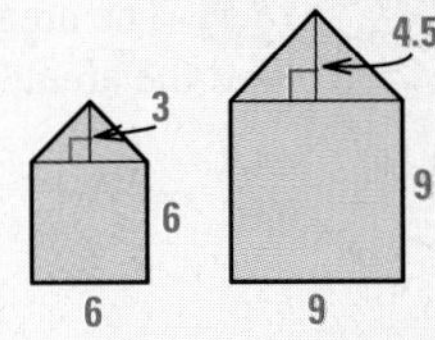

$$\frac{\text{Area (smaller)}}{\text{Area (larger)}} = \frac{6 \cdot 6 + \frac{1}{2}(3 \cdot 6)}{9 \cdot 9 + \frac{1}{2}(4.5 \cdot 9)} = \frac{45}{101.25} = \frac{4}{9}$$

Complete the statement using *always, sometimes,* or *never.*

13. If the ratio of the perimeters of two rectangles is 3:5, then the ratio of their areas is __?__ 9:25. **sometimes**

14. Two parallelograms are __?__ similar. **sometimes**

15. Two regular dodecagons with perimeters in the ratio 4 to 7 __?__ have areas in the ratio 16 to 49. **always**

In the diagram at the right, $\triangle ADG$, $\triangle BDF$, and $\triangle CDE$ are similar.

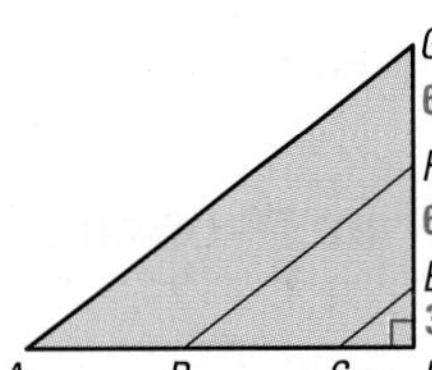

16. Find the ratio of the perimeters and of the areas of $\triangle CDE$ and $\triangle BDF$. **1:3, 1:9**

17. Find the ratio of the perimeters and of the areas of $\triangle ADG$ and $\triangle BDF$. **5:3, 25:9**

11.4 CIRCUMFERENCE AND ARC LENGTH

Examples on pp. 683–685

EXAMPLES The circumference of the circle at the right is $C = 2\pi(9) = 18\pi$.

The length of $\widehat{AB} = \frac{m\widehat{AB}}{360°} \cdot 2\pi r = \frac{60°}{360°} \cdot 18\pi = 3\pi$.

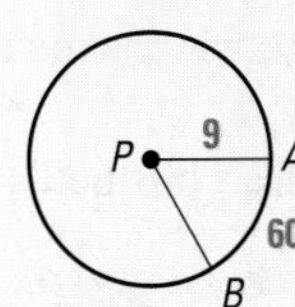

In Exercises 18–20, find the circumference of $\odot P$ and the length of $\widehat{AB}$.

18.

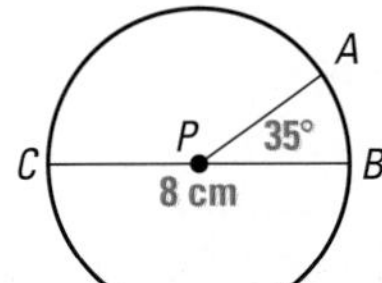

about 25.1 cm, about 2.4 cm

19.

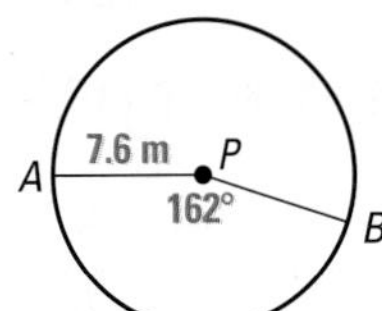

about 47.8 m, about 21.5 m

20.

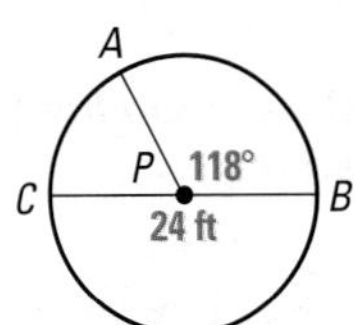

about 75.4 ft, about 24.7 ft

21. Find the radius of a circle with circumference 12 inches. **about 1.91 in.**

22. Find the diameter of a circle with circumference 15π meters. **15 m**

11.5 Areas of Circles and Sectors

Examples on pp. 691–694

EXAMPLES The area of $\odot P$ at the right is $A = \pi(12^2) = 144\pi$. To find the area A of the shaded sector of $\odot P$, use

$$\frac{A}{\pi r^2} = \frac{m\widehat{AB}}{360^\circ}, \text{ or } A = \frac{m\widehat{AB}}{360^\circ} \cdot \pi r^2 = \frac{90^\circ}{360^\circ} \cdot 144\pi = 36\pi.$$

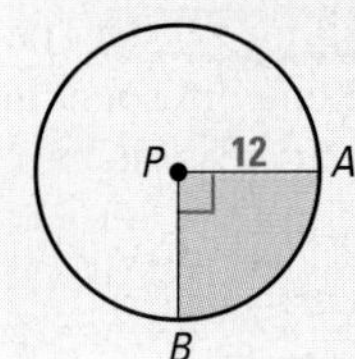

In Exercises 23–26, find the area of the shaded region.

23. 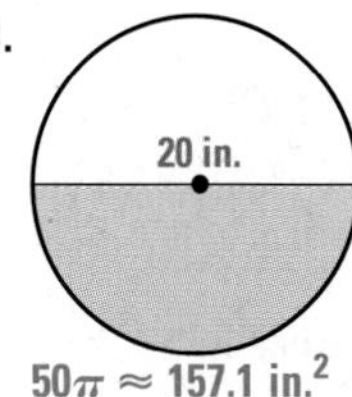

$50\pi \approx 157.1$ in.^{2}

24. 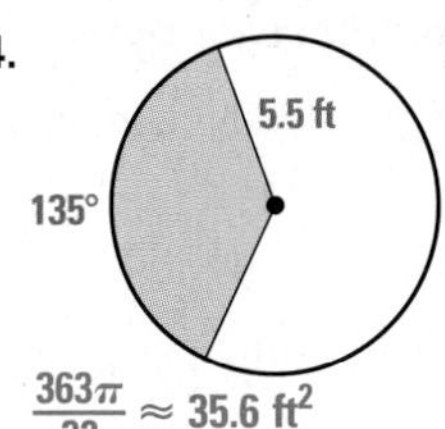

$\frac{363\pi}{32} \approx 35.6$ ft^2

25. 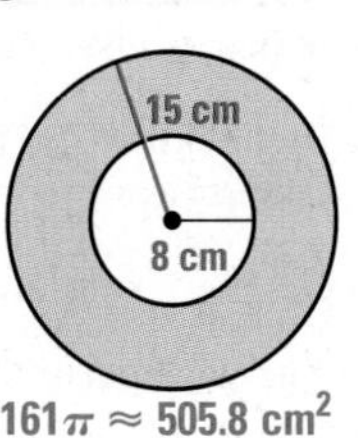

$161\pi \approx 505.8$ cm^2

26. 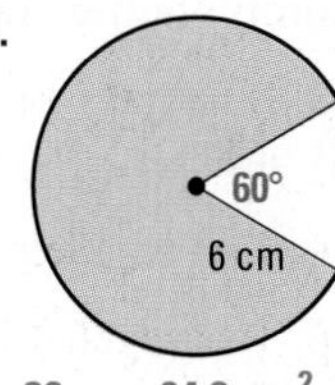

$30\pi \approx 94.2$ cm^2

27. What is the area of a circle with diameter 28 feet? $196\pi \approx 615.75$ ft^2

28. What is the radius of a circle with area 40 square inches? $\sqrt{\frac{40}{\pi}} \approx 3.57$ in.

11.6 Geometric Probability

Examples on pp. 699–701

EXAMPLES The probability that a randomly chosen point on $\overline{AB}$ is on $\overline{CD}$ is

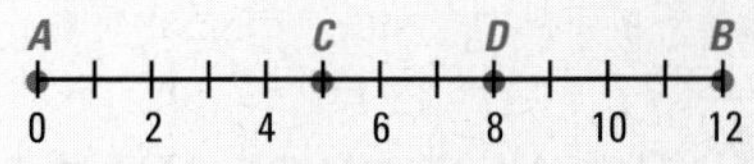

$$P(\text{Point is on } \overline{CD}) = \frac{\text{Length of } \overline{CD}}{\text{Length of } \overline{AB}} = \frac{3}{12} = \frac{1}{4}.$$

Suppose a circular target has radius 12 inches and its bull's eye has radius 2 inches. If a dart that hits the target hits it at a random point, then

$$P(\text{Dart hits bull's eye}) = \frac{\text{Area of bull's eye}}{\text{Area of target}} = \frac{4\pi}{144\pi} = \frac{1}{36}.$$

Find the probability that a point A, selected randomly on $\overline{JN}$, is on the given segment.

29. $\overline{LM}$ $\frac{3}{10} = 30\%$

30. $\overline{JL}$ $\frac{1}{2} = 50\%$

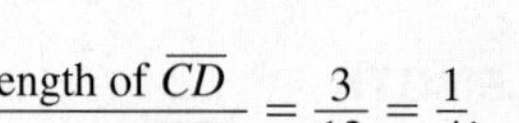

31. $\overline{KM}$ $\frac{3}{5} = 60\%$

Find the probability that a randomly chosen point in the figure lies in the shaded region.

32. 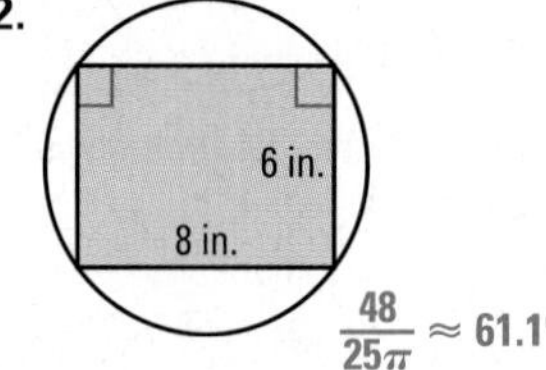

$\frac{48}{25\pi} \approx 61.1\%$

33. 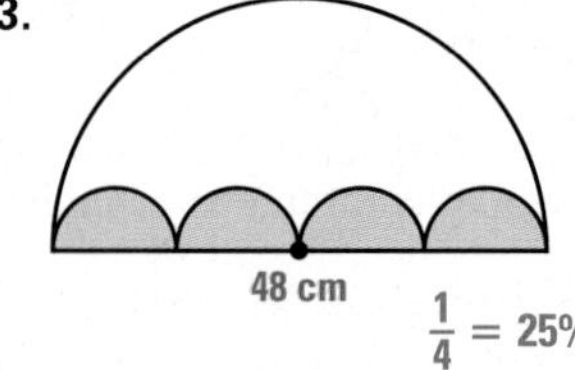

$\frac{1}{4} = 25\%$

34. 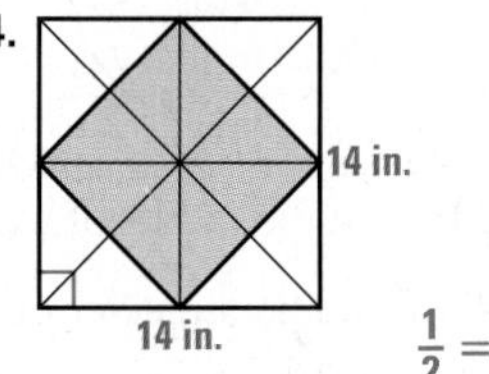

$\frac{1}{2} = 50\%$

CHAPTER 11 Chapter Test

ADDITIONAL RESOURCES

- ***Chapter 11 Resource Book***
  Chapter Test (3 levels) (p. 99)
  SAT/ACT Chapter Test (p. 105)
  Alternative Assessment (p. 106)
- ***Test and Practice Generator***

In Exercises 1 and 2, use the figure at the right.

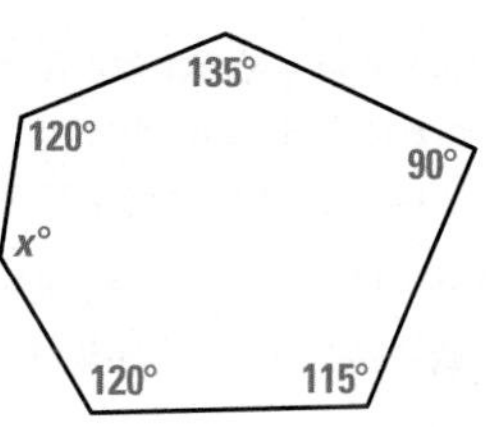

1. What is the value of x? 140
2. Find the sum of the measures of the exterior angles, one at each vertex. 360°
3. What is the measure of each interior angle of a regular 30-gon? 168°
4. What is the measure of each exterior angle of a regular 27-gon? $13\frac{1}{3}°$

In Exercises 5–8, find the area of the regular polygon to two decimal places.

5. An equilateral triangle with perimeter 30 feet 43.30 ft^2
6. A regular pentagon with apothem 8 inches 232.49 in.^{2}
7. A regular hexagon with 9 centimeter sides 210.44 cm^2
8. A regular nonagon (9-gon) with radius 1 meter 2.89 m^2

Rhombus *ABCD* has sides of length 8 centimeters. *EFGH* is a similar rhombus with sides of length 6 centimeters.

9. Find the ratio of the perimeters of $ABCD$ to $EFGH$. Then find the ratio of their areas. 4:3; 16:9
10. The area of $ABCD$ is 56 square centimeters. Find the area of $EFGH$. 31.5 cm^2

Use the diagram of $\odot R$.

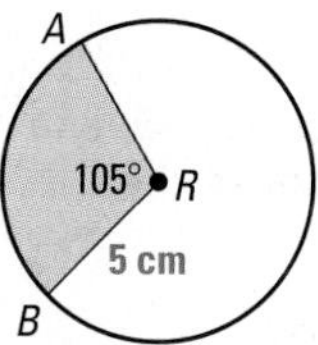

11. Find the circumference and the area of $\odot R$. $10\pi \approx 31.42$ cm, $25\pi \approx 78.54$ cm^2
12. Find the length of $\widehat{AB}$. $\frac{35\pi}{12} \approx 9.16$ cm
13. Find the area of the sector ARB. $\frac{175\pi}{24} \approx 22.91$ cm^2

Find the area of the shaded region.

14. 30 ft $\frac{225\pi}{2} \approx 353.43$ ft^2

15. 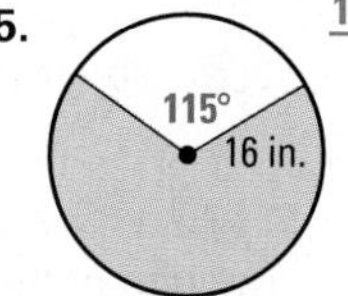

$\frac{1568\pi}{9} \approx 547.34$ in.^{2}

16. 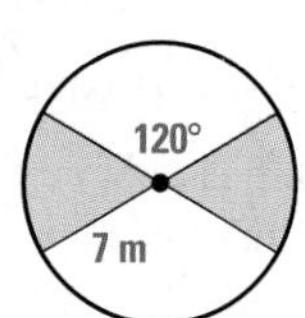

$\frac{49\pi}{3} \approx 51.3$ m^2

In Exercises 17 and 18, a point is chosen randomly in the 20 inch by 20 inch square at the right.

20 in.
20 in.

17. Find the probability that the point is inside the circle. $\frac{\pi}{4} \approx 78.5\%$
18. Find the probability that the point is in the shaded area. $\frac{1}{8} = 12.5\%$
19. **WATER-SKIER** A boat that is pulling a water-skier drives in a circle that has a radius of 80 feet. The skier is moving outside the path of the boat in a circle that has a radius of 110 feet. Find the distance traveled by the boat when it has completed a full circle. How much farther has the skier traveled? $160\pi \approx 502.7$ ft; about 188.5 ft farther
20. **WAITING TIME** You are expecting friends to come by your house any time between 6:00 P.M. and 8:00 P.M. Meanwhile, a problem at work has delayed you. If you get home at 6:20 P.M., what is the probability that your friends are already there? $\frac{1}{6} \approx 16.7\%$

ADDITIONAL RESOURCES

- ***Chapter 11 Resource Book***
  Chapter Test (3 levels) (p. 99)
  SAT/ACT Chapter Test (p. 105)
  Alternative Assessment (p. 106)
- ***Test and Practice Generator***

CHAPTER 11

Chapter Standardized Test

TEST-TAKING STRATEGY Do not panic if you run out of time before answering all of the questions. You can still receive a high test score without answering every question.

1. **MULTIPLE CHOICE** A regular polygon has an interior angle with a measure of 160°. How many sides does the polygon have? C

   Ⓐ 14 Ⓑ 16 Ⓒ 18 Ⓓ 20 Ⓔ 22

2. **MULTIPLE CHOICE** What is the value of x? A

   Ⓐ 56 Ⓑ 59 Ⓒ 62 Ⓓ 67 Ⓔ 72

QUANTITATIVE COMPARISON In Exercises 3–5, use the two regular polygons shown to choose the statement that is true.

Ⓐ The quantity in column A is greater.

Ⓑ The quantity in column B is greater.

Ⓒ The two quantities are equal.

Ⓓ The relationship cannot be determined from the given information.

Polygon A

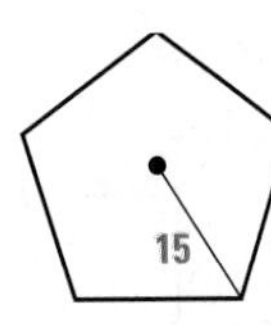

Polygon B

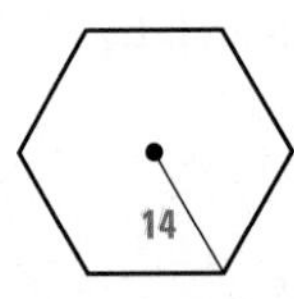

	Column A	Column B	
3.	Apothem of polygon A	Apothem of polygon B	A
4.	Perimeter of polygon A	Perimeter of polygon B	A
5.	Area of polygon A	Area of polygon B	A

6. **MULTIPLE CHOICE** A regular octagon has sides of length 12 cm. Another regular octagon has sides of length 18 cm. Find the ratio of the area of the smaller octagon to the area of the larger octagon. A

   Ⓐ 4:9 Ⓑ 2:3 Ⓒ 12:18 Ⓓ 18:12 Ⓔ 9:4

In Exercises 7 and 8, use the diagram below.

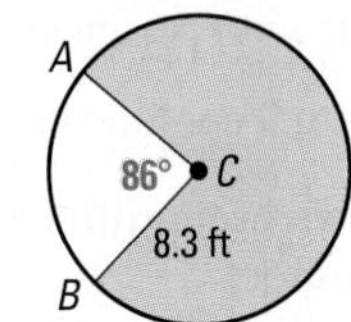

7. **MULTIPLE CHOICE** What is the length of $\widehat{AB}$? B

   Ⓐ about 12.10 ft Ⓑ about 12.46 ft
   Ⓒ about 13.56 ft Ⓓ about 14.81 ft
   Ⓔ about 21.64 ft

8. **MULTIPLE CHOICE** What is the area of the shaded region? E

   Ⓐ about 51.70 ft^2 Ⓑ about 84.50 ft^2
   Ⓒ about 160.27 ft^2 Ⓓ about 162.72 ft^2
   Ⓔ about 164.72 ft^2

9. **MULTIPLE CHOICE** What is the area of the shaded region in the diagram below? C

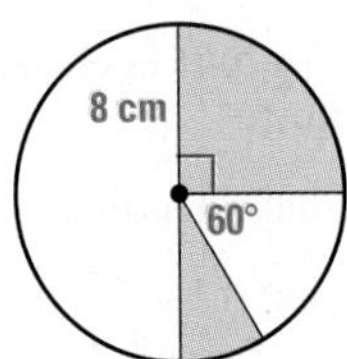

   Ⓐ about 33.51 cm^2 Ⓑ about 50.27 cm^2
   Ⓒ about 67.02 cm^2 Ⓓ about 83.78 cm^2
   Ⓔ about 100.53 cm^2

10. **MULTIPLE CHOICE** $\odot P$ and $\odot Q$ are tangent. If a point is chosen at random in $\odot P$, what is the probability that the chosen point lies in the shaded region? **C**

Ⓐ 25% Ⓑ 50% Ⓒ 75%

Ⓓ $133\frac{1}{3}\%$ Ⓔ 200%

11. **MULTIPLE CHOICE** Suppose that in a one-hour television program, 24 minutes are used for advertising. If you start watching the program at a random time during the show, what is the probability that you tune in during a commercial? **A**

Ⓐ 0.4 Ⓑ 0.6 Ⓒ about 0.67

Ⓓ 0.24 Ⓔ cannot be determined

MULTI-STEP PROBLEM In the diagram at the right, the polygon is a regular octagon inscribed in a circle.

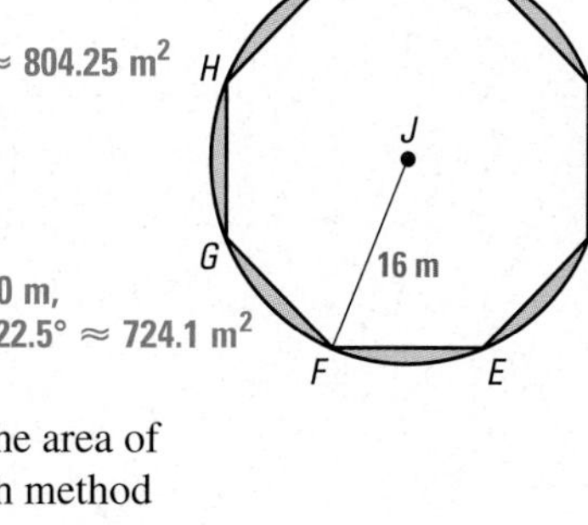

12. Find the circumference and the area of $\odot J$. **$32\pi \approx 100.53$ m, $256\pi \approx 804.25$ m²**

13. What is the measure of each interior angle of the octagon? **135°**

14. What is the measure of each exterior angle? **45°**

15. Find the perimeter and the area of the octagon. **256 sin 22.5° ≈ 98.0 m, 2048 cos 22.5° sin 22.5° ≈ 724.1 m²**

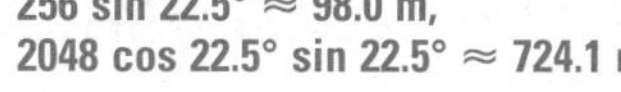

16. Find the length of $\widehat{AB}$. **$4\pi \approx 12.57$ m**

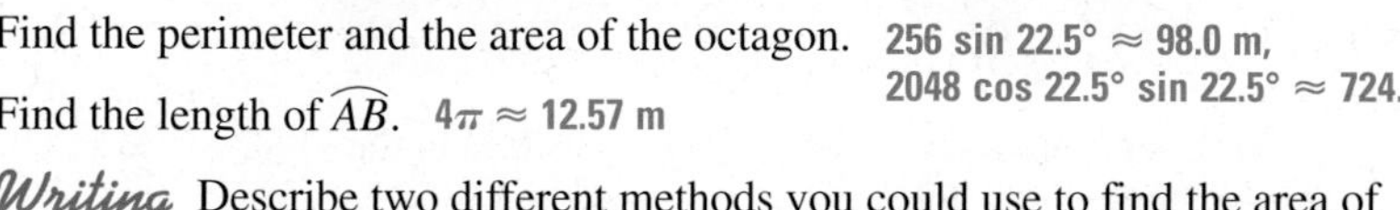

17. *Writing* Describe two different methods you could use to find the area of the shaded region. Does each method yield the same result? Which method do you prefer? Explain your answer by comparing the methods. **See margin.**

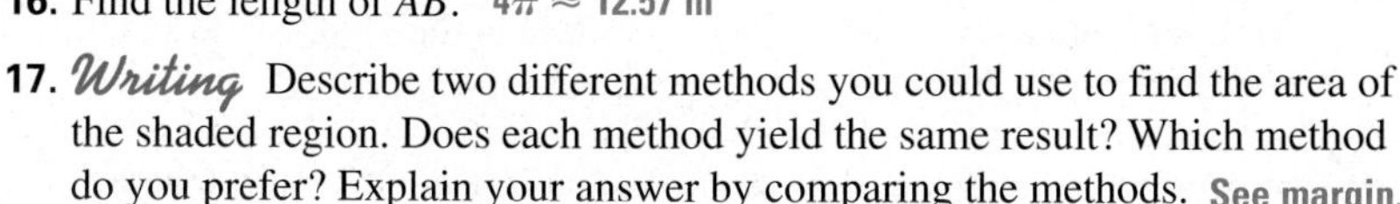

MULTI-STEP PROBLEM In Exercises 18–22, use the following information.
Suppose you are at a carnival playing a game in which you throw darts and hit the dart board shown at the right. A dart is equally likely to hit any point on the dart board. The red regions are congruent trapezoids.

18. Find the radius, the circumference, and the area of the green circular region. **3 in., $6\pi \approx 18.85$ in., $9\pi \approx 28.27$ in.²**

19. What is the probability that a dart lands in the green circular region? **$\frac{9\pi}{864} \approx 3\%$**

20. What is the probability that a dart lands in the blue rectangular region? **$\frac{55}{432} \approx 13\%$**

21. Suppose you win a prize if your dart hits a red, green, or blue region. If you throw a dart that hits the board, what is the probability that you win a prize? **$\frac{215 + 9\pi}{864} \approx 28\%$**

22. Suppose you win a prize if your dart hits a red, green, or blue region. If you throw a dart that hits the board, what is the probability that you do not win a prize? **about 72%**

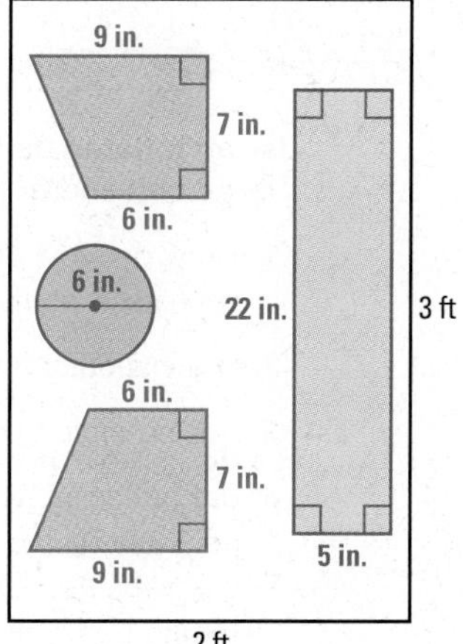

17. *Sample answer:* Subtract the area of the hexagon from the area of the circle or determine the area of one of the small shaded areas and multiply by 8. The methods yield the same answer, because in the second, you are finding $\frac{1}{8}$ the area of the hexagon, subtracting it from $\frac{1}{8}$ the area of the circle, and multiplying by 8, which uses the same principles as the first method.

PROJECT OVERVIEW

PROJECT GOALS

- Use planes and lines in the geometry of a sphere.
- Compare the geometry of a sphere with Euclidean Geometry.
- Use triangles in the geometry of a sphere.

MANAGING THE PROJECT

CLASSROOM MANAGEMENT

The Chapter 11 Project may be completed by individual students or by students working with partners. If students work with a partner, they should discuss and agree upon the answers to Exercises 1–10. The partners should take turns drawing and measuring the lines and triangles. The partners can divide-up parts of the display to complete individually but should initially discuss the display together.

GUIDING STUDENT'S WORK

This project can be completed as a class demonstration. If possible, give each student a balloon or ball and rubber bands to draw their own circle and triangles as the investigation proceeds.

CONCLUDING THE PROJECT

Have each student or group present their display to the class. Encourage other students to ask questions of the presenters. You might arrange to show the displays in a hallway or foyer of your school. Any reports written for the Extension can also be included.

PROJECT for Chapters 10 and 11

Geometry on a Sphere

OBJECTIVE **Explore lines and triangles on a sphere, and compare geometry on a sphere to Euclidean geometry.**

Materials: round balloon and markers (or ball and rubber bands), protractor

A DIFFERENT UNDERSTANDING OF PLANE AND LINE

In Euclidean geometry, you can think of a plane as a flat surface that extends forever, and you can think of a line that lies in a plane as a set of points that extends forever in two directions.

Geometry on a sphere is different: a *plane* is a spherical surface and a *line* is a special kind of circle on that surface.

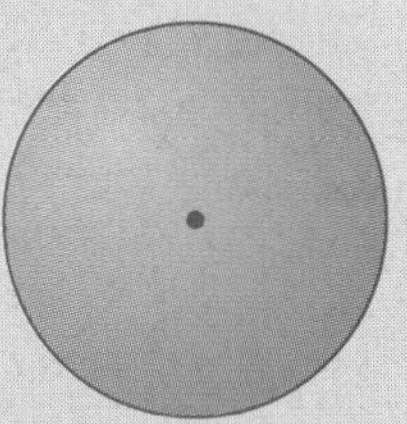
a **plane** in the geometry of a sphere

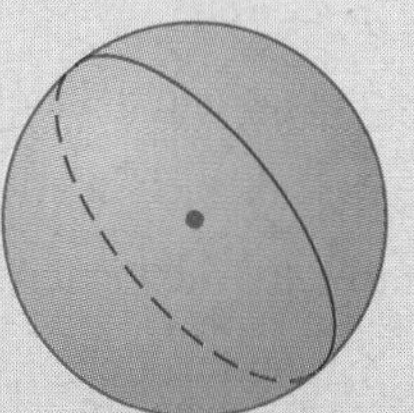
a **line** in the geometry of a sphere

A *line* on a sphere can be defined as a *great circle*, that is, a circle on the sphere whose center is the center of the sphere. Circles on the sphere that do not have the same center as the sphere are not considered lines.

If you imagine Earth as a sphere, then the equator is an example of a great circle. Circles of longitude, which pass through the north and south poles, are also great circles.

INVESTIGATION

Use an inflated balloon as a sphere and use a marker to draw lines, or use a large ball and fit rubber bands around it to represent lines.

1. Draw one line on a sphere. If a point lies on the line, does the point that is opposite it on the sphere also lie on the line? yes
2. Draw another line on a sphere. Do your two lines intersect? yes
3. Is it possible to draw two lines on the sphere that do not intersect? No; any two great circles must intersect.
4. In Euclidean geometry, the Parallel Postulate states that given a line and a point not on the line, there is exactly one line through the point parallel to the given line. Does the Parallel Postulate apply to geometry on a sphere? Explain. No; there are no parallel lines in geometry on a sphere.
5. Is it possible to draw two lines on a sphere that intersect to form right angles? Yes; for example, a line of longitude and the equator on a globe.

TRIANGLES ON A SPHERE

If you draw three lines on a sphere, you can divide the sphere into eight 3-sided regions, which can be considered *triangles* in the geometry of a sphere.

INVESTIGATION

6. Draw three lines on a sphere. Find a triangular region enclosed by three lines. Measure the angles of the triangle with a protractor. **Check students' work.**
7. What is the sum of the angles of the triangle you drew on the sphere? **Check students' work. The sum should be larger than 180°.**
8. Draw three lines on a sphere so that the triangular region formed is equiangular. What are the measures of the angles? **The angles will have measures between 60° and 180°.**
9. Is it possible to draw a 60°-60°-60° triangle on a sphere? a 90°-90°-90° triangle? a 120°-120°-120° triangle? **no; yes; yes**
10. What is the range of values for the sum of the angles of a triangle on a sphere? **The sum of the angles is between 180° and 540°.**

PRESENT YOUR RESULTS

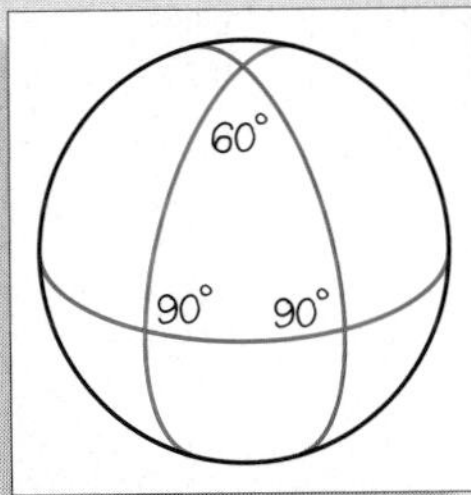

Make a bulletin board display of your results.

- Include a description of how *plane* and *line* are viewed differently in Euclidean geometry and the geometry of a sphere.
- Include drawings or balloons with markings of lines that intersect on a sphere.
- Summarize your results about the angles of triangles on a sphere.

EXTENSION

These mathematicians investigated non-Euclidean geometries, such as elliptic geometry and hyperbolic geometry. Research and write a report about one of them. How did the mathematician's work challenge the Parallel Postulate?

- Carl Friedrich Gauss (1777–1855)
- Nikolay Lobachevsky (1792–1856)
- János Bolyai (1802–1860)
- G. F. Bernhard Riemann (1826–1866)
- Felix Klein (1849–1925)
- David Hilbert (1862–1943)

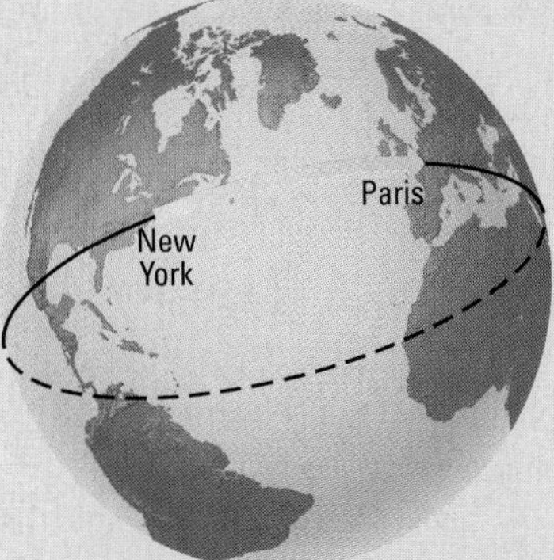

Pilots save time and fuel by using great circle routes to travel between cities on the globe.

GRADING THE PROJECT
RUBRIC FOR CHAPTER PROJECT

4 Students' bulletin board display shows an understanding of lines, planes, and triangles in spherical geometry and how they differ from those in Euclidean geometry. The drawings or balloons are labeled and show various intersecting lines.

3 Students' bulletin board display contains all the required elements but may be lacking in some details. The drawings or balloons are included but may not be carefully done. The written elements may not explain each part well.

2 The bulletin board display contains serious errors or is incomplete. Not all of the questions are answered in the written part of the display.

1 The bulletin board display shows that the student does not have an understanding of the material presented. The drawings or balloons are missing or are incorrect. The written portion of the display is incomplete or not understandable. The project should be returned with a new deadline for completion. The student should speak with the teacher as soon as possible so that he or she understands the purpose and format of the project.

CHAPTER 12

PLANNING THE CHAPTER

Surface Area and Volume

GOALS

Lesson	Goals	NCTM	ITED	SAT9 (TASK 1)	Terra-Nova	Local
12.1 *pp. 719–726*	GOAL 1 Use properties of polyhedra. GOAL 2 Use Euler's Theorem in real-life situations.	3, 7, 8, 9, 10	MIGE		14, 17, 18	8, 9
12.2 *pp. 727–734*	CONCEPT ACTIVITY: 12.2 *Investigate surface area.* GOAL 1 Find the surface area of a prism. GOAL 2 Find the surface area of a cylinder.	1, 2, 3, 4	MCWN, MCE, SAPE, MIM, MIGE	6	10, 11, 13, 14, 16, 49, 51, 52	8, 9
12.3 *pp. 735–742*	GOAL 1 Find the surface area of pyramid. GOAL 2 Find the surface area of a cone.	1, 2, 3, 4	MCWN, MCE, SAPE, MIM, MIGE	6	10, 11, 13, 14, 16, 49, 51	8, 9
12.4 *pp. 743–750*	GOAL 1 Use volume postulates. GOAL 2 Find the volume of prisms and cylinders in real life. TECHNOLOGY ACTIVITY: 12.4 *Find the minimum surface area of a solid with a given volume using a spreadsheet.*	1, 2, 3, 4, 7, 8, 9, 10	MCWN, MCE, SAPE, MIM, MIGE	5, 6	10, 11, 13, 14, 16, 17, 18, 49, 51, 52	8, 9
12.5 *pp. 751–758*	CONCEPT ACTIVITY: 12.5 *Investigate how the volume of a pyramid is related to the volume of a prism.* GOAL 1 Find the volume of pyramids and cones. GOAL 2 Find the volume of pyramids and cones in real life.	1, 2, 3, 4, 9, 10	MCWN, MCE, SAPE, MIM, MIGE	5, 6	10, 11, 13, 14, 16, 49, 51, 52	8, 9
12.6 *pp. 759–765*	GOAL 1 Find the surface area of a sphere. GOAL 2 Find the volume of a sphere in real life.	1, 2, 3, 4, 9, 10	MCWN, MCE, SAPE, MIM, MIGE	5, 6	10, 11, 13, 14, 16, 49, 51, 52	8, 9
12.7 *pp. 766–772*	GOAL 1 Find and use the scale factor of similar solids. GOAL 2 Use similar solids to solve real-life problems.	1, 2, 3, 4, 6, 8, 9, 10	MCWN, MIM, MIGE, MIRA, RQGE	1	11, 13, 14, 16, 17, 18, 49, 51, 52	8, 9, 11

RESOURCES

Chapter Resource Booklets

Chapter Support

Tips for New Teachers	p. 1	Prerequisite Skills Review	p. 5
Parent Guide for Student Success	p. 3	Strategies for Reading Mathematics	p. 7

Lesson Support

Lesson Support	12.1	12.2	12.3	12.4	12.5	12.6	12.7
Lesson Plans (regular and block)	p. 9	p. 21	p. 34	p. 51	p. 65	p. 78	p. 94
Warm-Up Exercises and Daily Quiz	p. 11	p. 23	p. 36	p. 53	p. 67	p. 80	p. 96
Activity Support Masters		p. 24					
Lesson Openers	p. 12	p. 25	p. 37	p. 54	p. 68	p. 81	p. 97
Technology Activities & Keystrokes			p. 38	p. 55		p. 82	
Practice (3 levels)	p. 13	p. 26	p. 41	p. 57	p. 69	p. 86	p. 98
Reteaching with Practice	p. 16	p. 29	p. 44	p. 60	p. 72	p. 89	p. 101
Quick Catch-Up for Absent Students	p. 18	p. 31	p. 46	p. 62	p. 74	p. 91	p. 103
Cooperative Learning Activities							p. 104
Interdisciplinary Applications	p. 19		p. 47		p. 75		p. 105
Real-Life Applications		p. 32		p. 63		p. 92	
Math & History Applications			p. 48				
Challenge: Skills and Applications	p. 20	p. 33	p. 49	p. 64	p. 76	p. 93	p. 106

Review and Assessment

Quizzes	pp. 50, 77	Alternative Assessment with Math Journal	p. 115
Chapter Review Games and Activities	p. 107	Project with Rubric	p. 117
Chapter Test (3 levels)	pp. 108–113	Cumulative Review	p. 119
SAT/ACT Chapter Test	p. 114	Resource Book Answers	p. A1

Transparencies

	12.1	12.2	12.3	12.4	12.5	12.6	12.7
Warm-Up Exercises and Daily Quiz	p. 86	p. 87	p. 88	p. 89	p. 90	p. 91	p. 92
Alternative Lesson Opener Transparencies	p. 74	p. 75	p. 76	p. 77	p. 78	p. 79	p. 80
Examples/Standardized Test Practice	✓	✓	✓	✓	✓	✓	✓
Answer Transparencies	✓	✓	✓	✓	✓	✓	✓

Technology

- Electronic Teaching Tools
- Online Lesson Planner
- Internet Support
- Personal Student Tutor
- Test and Practice Generator
- Geometry in Motion video
- Electronic Lesson Presentations (Lesson 12.4)

Additional Resources

- Basic Skills Workbook: Diagnosis and Remediation
- Worked-Out Solution Key
- Resources in Spanish
- Standardized Test Practice Workbook
- Practice Workbook with Examples

Correlations to the California Curriculum

Correlations to California Standards
See Teacher's Edition pp. CA9–CA11

Correlations to SAT9
Task 1: See Teacher's Edition pp. CA12–CA14
Task 2: See Teacher's Edition pp. CA15–CA17

CHAPTER 12

PACING THE CHAPTER

Resource Key
- STUDENT EDITION
- CHAPTER 12 RESOURCE BOOK
- TEACHER'S EDITION

REGULAR SCHEDULE

Day 1

12.1

STARTING OPTIONS
- Prereq. Skills Review
- Strategies for Reading
- Homework Check
- Warm-Up or Daily Quiz

TEACHING OPTIONS
- Motivating the Lesson
- Les. Opener (Activity)
- Examples 1–6
- Closure Question
- Guided Practice Exs.

APPLY/HOMEWORK
- See Assignment Guide.
- See the CRB: Practice, Reteach, Apply, Extend

ASSESSMENT OPTIONS
- Checkpoint Exercises
- Daily Quiz (12.1)
- Stand. Test Practice

Day 2

12.2

STARTING OPTIONS
- Homework Check
- Warm-Up or Daily Quiz

TEACHING OPTIONS
- Motivating the Lesson
- Concept Act. & Wksht.
- Les. Opener (Visual)
- Examples 1–4
- Closure Question
- Guided Practice Exs.

APPLY/HOMEWORK
- See Assignment Guide.
- See the CRB: Practice, Reteach, Apply, Extend

ASSESSMENT OPTIONS
- Checkpoint Exercises
- Daily Quiz (12.2)
- Stand. Test Practice

Day 3

12.3

STARTING OPTIONS
- Homework Check
- Warm-Up or Daily Quiz

TEACHING OPTIONS
- Motivating the Lesson
- Les. Opener (Application)
- Technology Activity
- Examples 1–3
- Guided Practice Exs.

APPLY/HOMEWORK
- See Assignment Guide.
- See the CRB: Practice, Reteach, Apply, Extend

ASSESSMENT OPTIONS
- Checkpoint Exercises

Day 4

12.3 *(cont.)*

STARTING OPTIONS
- Homework Check

TEACHING OPTIONS
- Examples 1–3
- Closure Question

APPLY/HOMEWORK
- See Assignment Guide.
- See the CRB: Practice, Reteach, Apply, Extend

ASSESSMENT OPTIONS
- Checkpoint Exercises
- Daily Quiz (12.3)
- Stand. Test Practice
- Quiz (12.1–12.3)

Day 5

12.4

STARTING OPTIONS
- Homework Check
- Warm-Up or Daily Quiz

TEACHING OPTIONS
- Motivating the Lesson
- Les. Opener (Application)
- Examples 1–3
- Guided Practice Exs. 1–6

APPLY/HOMEWORK
- See Assignment Guide.
- See the CRB: Practice, Reteach, Apply, Extend

ASSESSMENT OPTIONS
- Checkpoint Exercises, pp. 744–745

Day 6

12.4 *(cont.)*

STARTING OPTIONS
- Homework Check

TEACHING OPTIONS
- Example 4
- Technology Activity
- Closure Question
- Guided Practice Exs. 7–9

APPLY/HOMEWORK
- See Assignment Guide.
- See the CRB: Practice, Reteach, Apply, Extend

ASSESSMENT OPTIONS
- Checkpoint Exercises, p. 745
- Daily Quiz (12.4)
- Stand. Test Practice

Day 9

12.6

STARTING OPTIONS
- Homework Check
- Warm-Up or Daily Quiz

TEACHING OPTIONS
- Motivating the Lesson
- Les. Opener (Technology)
- Technology Activity
- Examples 1–4
- Closure Question
- Guided Practice Exs.

APPLY/HOMEWORK
- See Assignment Guide.
- See the CRB: Practice, Reteach, Apply, Extend

ASSESSMENT OPTIONS
- Checkpoint Exercises
- Daily Quiz (12.6)
- Stand. Test Practice

Day 10

12.7

STARTING OPTIONS
- Homework Check
- Warm-Up or Daily Quiz

TEACHING OPTIONS
- Les. Opener (Activity)
- Examples 1–4
- Guided Practice Exs.

APPLY/HOMEWORK
- See Assignment Guide.
- See the CRB: Practice, Reteach, Apply, Extend

ASSESSMENT OPTIONS
- Checkpoint Exercises, pp. 767–768

Day 11

12.7 *(cont.)*

STARTING OPTIONS
- Homework Check

TEACHING OPTIONS
- Example 5
- Closure Question

APPLY/HOMEWORK
- See Assignment Guide.
- See the CRB: Practice, Reteach, Apply, Extend

ASSESSMENT OPTIONS
- Checkpoint Exercises, p. 768
- Daily Quiz (12.7)
- Stand. Test Practice
- Quiz (12.6–12.7)

Day 12

Review

DAY 12 START OPTIONS
- Homework Check

REVIEWING OPTIONS
- Chapter 12 Summary
- Chapter 12 Review
- Chapter Review Games and Activities

APPLY/HOMEWORK
- Chapter 12 Test (practice)
- Ch. Standardized Test (practice)

Day 13

Assess

DAY 13 START OPTIONS
- Homework Check

ASSESSMENT OPTIONS
- Chapter 12 Test
- SAT/ACT Ch. 12 Test
- Alternative Assessment

Day 7

12.5

Starting Options
- Homework Check
- Warm-Up or Daily Quiz

Teaching Options
- Motivating the Lesson
- Concept Activity
- Les. Opener (Visual)
- Examples 1–3
- Guided Practice Exs.

Apply/Homework
- See Assignment Guide.
- See the CRB: Practice, Reteach, Apply, Extend

Assessment Options
- Checkpoint Exercises, p. 753

Day 8

12.5 *(cont.)*

Starting Options
- Homework Check

Teaching Options
- Examples 4–5
- Closure Question

Apply/Homework
- See Assignment Guide.
- See the CRB: Practice, Reteach, Apply, Extend

Assessment Options
- Checkpoint Exercises, p. 754
- Daily Quiz (12.5)
- Stand. Test Practice
- Quiz (12.4–12.5)

BLOCK SCHEDULE

Day 1

Assess & 12.1

(Day 1 = Ch. 11 Day 7)

Assessment Options
- Chapter 11 Test
- SAT/ACT Ch. 11 Test
- Alternative Assessment

Ch. 12 Start Options
- Skill Review, p. 718
- Prereq. Skills Review
- Strategies for Reading

Teaching 12.1 Options
- Warm-Up (Les. 12.1)
- Motivating the Lesson
- Les. Opener (Activity)
- Examples 1–6
- Closure Question
- Guided Practice Exs.

Apply/Homework
- See Assignment Guide.
- See the CRB: Practice, Reteach, Apply, Extend

Assessment Options
- Checkpoint Exercises
- Daily Quiz (Les. 12.1)
- Stand. Test Practice

Day 2

12.2 & 12.3

Day 2 Start Options
- Homework Check
- Warm-Up (Les. 12.2) or Daily Quiz (Les. 12.1)

Teaching 12.2 Options
- Motivating the Lesson
- Concept Act. & Wksht.
- Les. Opener (Visual)
- Examples 1–4
- Closure Question
- Guided Practice Exs.

Beginning 12.3 Options
- Warm-Up (Les. 12.3)
- Motivating the Lesson
- Les. Opener (Appl.)
- Technology Activity
- Examples 1–3
- Guided Practice Exs.

Apply/Homework
- See Assignment Guide.
- See the CRB: Practice, Reteach, Apply, Extend

Assessment Options
- Checkpoint Exercises
- Daily Quiz (Les. 12.2)
- Stand. Test Prac. (12.2)

Day 3

12.3 & 12.4

Day 3 Start Options
- Homework Check
- Daily Quiz (Les. 12.2)

Finishing 12.3 Options
- Examples 1–3
- Closure Question

Beginning 12.4 Options
- Warm-Up (Les. 12.4)
- Motivating the Lesson
- Les. Opener (Appl.)
- Examples 1–3
- Guided Practice Exs. 1–6

Apply/Homework
- See Assignment Guide.
- See the CRB: Practice, Reteach, Apply, Extend

Assessment Options
- Checkpoint Exercises
- Daily Quiz (Les. 12.3)
- Stand. Test Prac. (12.3)
- Quiz (12.1–12.3)

Day 4

12.4 & 12.5

Day 4 Start Options
- Homework Check
- Daily Quiz (Les. 12.3)

Finishing 12.4 Options
- Example 4
- Technology Activity
- Closure Question
- Guided Practice Exs. 7–9

Beginning 12.5 Options
- Warm-Up (Les. 12.5)
- Motivating the Lesson
- Concept Activity
- Les. Opener (Visual)
- Examples 1–3
- Guided Practice Exs. 1–7

Apply/Homework
- See Assignment Guide.
- See the CRB: Practice, Reteach, Apply, Extend

Assessment Options
- Checkpoint Exercises
- Daily Quiz (Les. 12.4)
- Stand. Test Prac. (12.4)

Day 5

12.5 & 12.6

Day 5 Start Options
- Homework Check
- Daily Quiz (Les. 12.4)

Finishing 12.5 Options
- Examples 4–5
- Closure Question

Teaching 12.6 Options
- Warm-Up (Les. 12.6)
- Motivating the Lesson
- Les. Opener (Tech.)
- Technology Activity
- Examples 1–4
- Closure Question
- Guided Practice Exs.

Apply/Homework
- See Assignment Guide.
- See the CRB: Practice, Reteach, Apply, Extend

Assessment Options
- Checkpoint Exercises
- Daily Quiz (12.5, 12.6)
- Stand. Test Practice
- Quiz (12.4–12.5)

Day 6

12.7

Day 6 Start Options
- Homework Check
- Warm-Up or Daily Quiz

Teaching 12.7 Options
- Les. Opener (Activity)
- Examples 1–5
- Closure Question
- Guided Practice Exs.

Apply/Homework
- See Assignment Guide.
- See the CRB: Practice, Reteach, Apply, Extend

Assessment Options
- Checkpoint Exercises
- Daily Quiz (Les. 12.7)
- Stand. Test Practice
- Quiz (12.6–12.7)

Day 7

Review/Assess

Day 7 Start Options
- Homework Check

Reviewing Options
- Chapter 12 Summary
- Chapter 12 Review
- Chapter Review Games and Activities
- Chapter 12 Test (practice)
- Ch. Standardized Test (practice)

Assessment Options
- Chapter 12 Test
- SAT/ACT Ch. 12 Test
- Alternative Assessment

CHAPTER 12 MEETING INDIVIDUAL NEEDS

BEFORE THE CHAPTER

The *Chapter 12 Resource Book* has the following materials to distribute and use before the chapter:

- **Parent Guide for Student Success (pictured below)**
- **Prerequisite Skills Review**
- **Strategies for Reading Mathematics**

PARENT GUIDE *Pages 3–4*

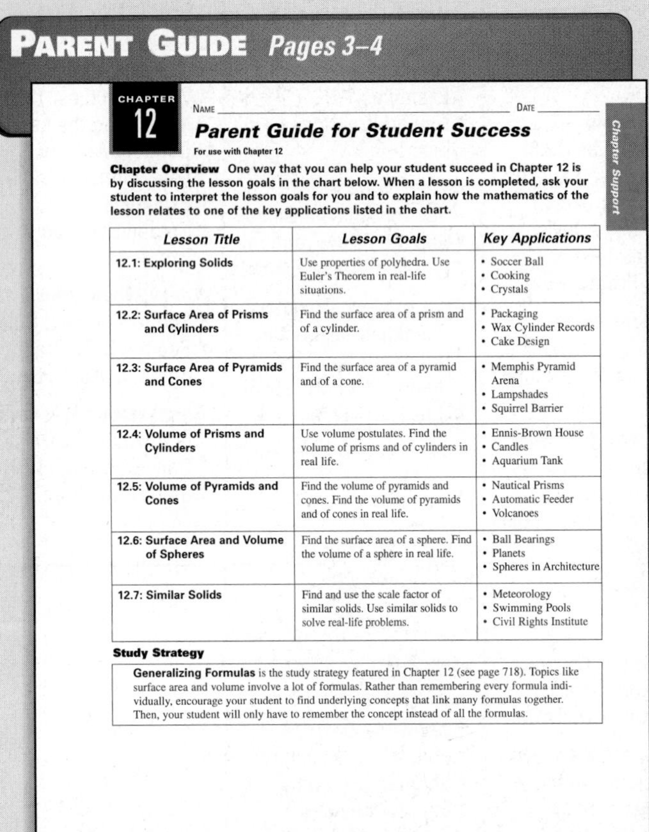

CHAPTER 12 NAME _______ DATE _______

Parent Guide for Student Success

For use with Chapter 12

Chapter Support

Chapter Overview One way that you can help your student succeed in Chapter 12 is by discussing the lesson goals in the chart below. When a lesson is completed, ask your student to interpret the lesson goals for you and to explain how the mathematics of the lesson relates to one of the key applications listed in the chart.

Lesson Title	*Lesson Goals*	*Key Applications*
12.1: Exploring Solids	Use properties of polyhedra. Use Euler's Theorem in real-life situations.	• Soccer Ball • Cooking • Crystals
12.2: Surface Area of Prisms and Cylinders	Find the surface area of a prism and of a cylinder.	• Packaging • Wax Cylinder Records • Cake Design
12.3: Surface Area of Pyramids and Cones	Find the surface area of a pyramid and of a cone.	• Memphis Pyramid Arena • Lampshades • Squirrel Barrier
12.4: Volume of Prisms and Cylinders	Use volume postulates. Find the volume of prisms and of cylinders in real life.	• Ennis-Brown House • Candles • Aquarium Tank
12.5: Volume of Pyramids and Cones	Find the volume of pyramids and cones. Find the volume of pyramids and of cones in real life.	• Nautical Prisms • Automatic Feeder • Volcanoes
12.6: Surface Area and Volume of Spheres	Find the surface area of a sphere. Find the volume of a sphere in real life.	• Ball Bearings • Planets • Spheres in Architecture
12.7: Similar Solids	Find and use the scale factor of similar solids. Use similar solids to solve real-life problems.	• Meteorology • Swimming Pools • Civil Rights Institute

Study Strategy

Generalizing Formulas is the study strategy featured in Chapter 12 (see page 718). Topics like surface area and volume involve a lot of formulas. Rather than remembering every formula individually, encourage your student to find underlying concepts that link many formulas together. Then, your student will only have to remember the concept instead of all the formulas.

PARENT GUIDE FOR STUDENT SUCCESS The first page summarizes the content of Chapter 12. Parents are encouraged to have their students explain how the material relates to key applications in the chapter, such as cooking. The second page (not shown) provides exercises and an activity that parents can do with their students. In the activity, parents and students use grid paper to make boxes and find volumes.

DURING EACH LESSON

The *Chapter 12 Resource Book* has the following alternatives for introducing the lesson:

- **Lesson Openers (pictured below)**
- **Technology Activities with Keystrokes**

LESSON OPENER *Page 25*

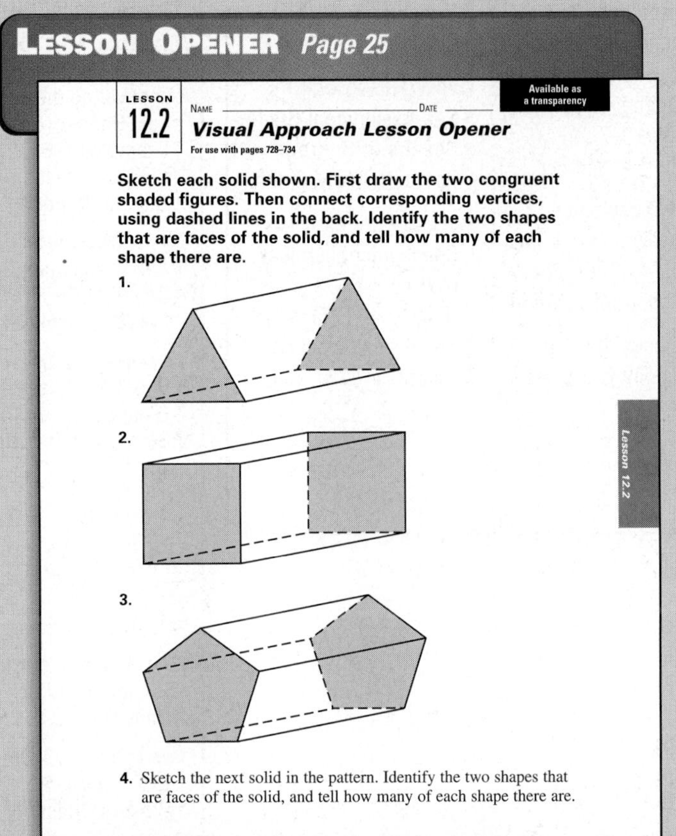

LESSON 12.2 NAME _______ DATE _______

Available as a transparency

Visual Approach Lesson Opener

For use with pages 728–734

Lesson 12.2

Sketch each solid shown. First draw the two congruent shaded figures. Then connect corresponding vertices, using dashed lines in the back. Identify the two shapes that are faces of the solid, and tell how many of each shape there are.

1.

2.

3.

4. Sketch the next solid in the pattern. Identify the two shapes that are faces of the solid, and tell how many of each shape there are.

VISUAL APPROACH LESSON OPENER This Lesson Opener uses visuals as an alternative way to start Lesson 12.2. Students sketch solids as an introduction to surface area.

Following Each Lesson

The *Chapter 12 Resource Book* has a variety of materials to follow-up each lesson. They include the following:

- **Practice (3 levels)**
- **Reteaching with Practice (pictured below)**
- **Quick Catch-Up for Absent Students**
- **Interdisciplinary Applications**
- **Real-Life Applications**

Reteaching with Practice *Pages 60–61*

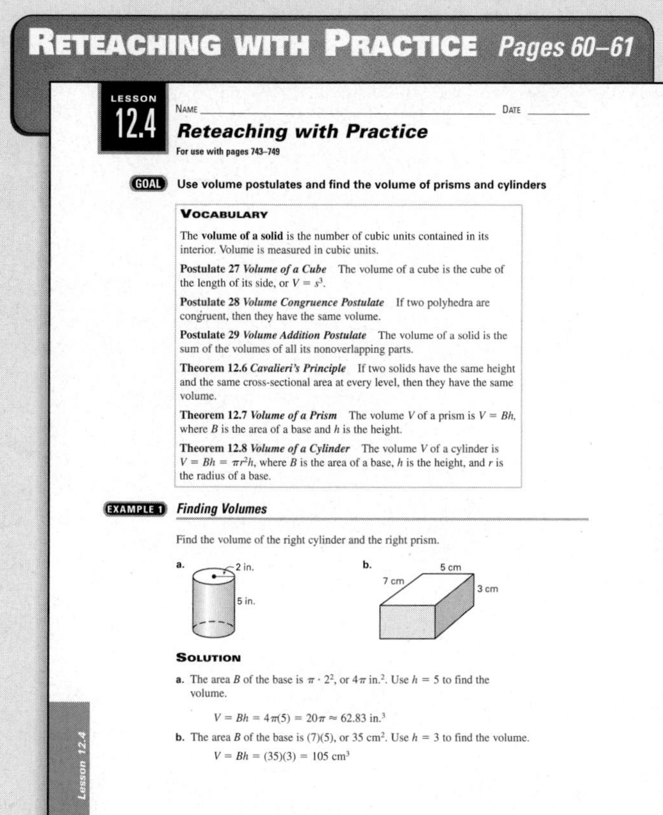

LESSON 12.4 NAME ______ DATE ______

Reteaching with Practice

For use with pages 743–749

GOAL **Use volume postulates and find the volume of prisms and cylinders**

Vocabulary

The **volume of a solid** is the number of cubic units contained in its interior. Volume is measured in cubic units.

Postulate 27 ***Volume of a Cube*** The volume of a cube is the cube of the length of its side, or $V = s^3$.

Postulate 28 ***Volume Congruence Postulate*** If two polyhedra are congruent, then they have the same volume.

Postulate 29 ***Volume Addition Postulate*** The volume of a solid is the sum of the volumes of all its nonoverlapping parts.

Theorem 12.6 ***Cavalieri's Principle*** If two solids have the same height and the same cross-sectional area at every level, then they have the same volume.

Theorem 12.7 ***Volume of a Prism*** The volume V of a prism is $V = Bh$, where B is the area of a base and h is the height.

Theorem 12.8 ***Volume of a Cylinder*** The volume V of a cylinder is $V = Bh = \pi r^2 h$, where B is the area of a base, h is the height, and r is the radius of a base.

EXAMPLE 1 ***Finding Volumes***

Find the volume of the right cylinder and the right prism.

a.

b.

Solution

a. The area B of the base is $\pi \cdot 2^2$, or 4π in.^{2}. Use $h = 5$ to find the volume.

$V = Bh = 4\pi(5) = 20\pi \approx 62.83$ in.^{3}

b. The area B of the base is (7)(5), or 35 cm^2. Use $h = 3$ to find the volume.

$V = Bh = (35)(3) = 105$ cm^3

Lesson 12.4

Reteaching with Practice On this two-page worksheet, additional examples and practice reinforce the key concept of Lesson 12.4: volume of prisms and cylinders.

Technology Resource

Students can use the Personal Student Tutor to find additional reteaching and practice for the skills in Lesson 12.4 and in the rest of Chapter 12.

Assessing the Chapter

The *Chapter 12 Resource Book* has the following review and assessment materials:

- **Quizzes**
- **Chapter Review Games and Activities**
- **Chapter Test (3 levels)**
- **SAT/ACT Chapter Test**
- **Alternative Assessment with Rubric and Math Journal**
- **Project with Rubric**
- **Cumulative Review (pictured below)**

Cumulative Review *Pages 119–120*

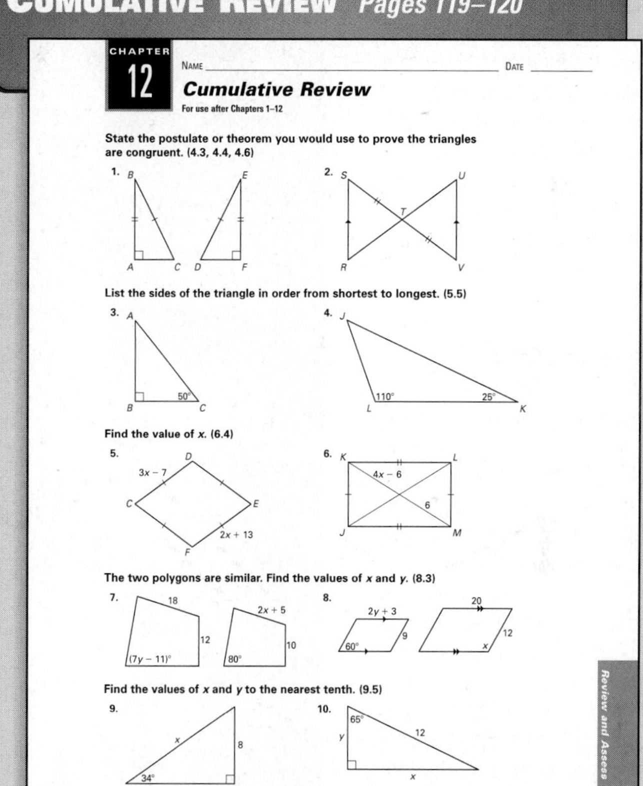

CHAPTER 12 NAME ______ DATE ______

Cumulative Review

For use after Chapters 1–12

State the postulate or theorem you would use to prove the triangles are congruent. (4.3, 4.4, 4.6)

1. **2.**

List the sides of the triangle in order from shortest to longest. (5.5)

3. **4.**

Find the value of *x*. (6.4)

5. **6.**

The two polygons are similar. Find the values of *x* and *y*. (8.3)

7. **8.**

Find the values of *x* and *y* to the nearest tenth. (9.5)

9. **10.**

Review and Assess

Cumulative Review The content of Chapters 1–12 is reviewed in this two-page cumulative review. Lesson references with each cluster of exercises guide students to the places in the textbook where they can go to review each concept.

Technology Resource

Teachers can use the Time-Saving Test and Practice Generator to create customized review materials covering Chapters 1–12.

CHAPTER OVERVIEW

Chapter Goals

In this chapter students will investigate the surface area and volume of solids. First, they will learn to distinguish polyhedra from other solids and to classify polyhedra. They will identify the Platonic solids and use Euler's Theorem. Students will use nets to help them explore the surface area of prisms and cylinders. They will use the Pythagorean theorem to identify the surface area of pyramids, and use proportions involving circles to identify the surface area of cones. They will then develop methods for finding the volume of prisms and cylinders, including using Cavalieri's Principle. Students will find the volume of pyramids and cones. After learning to find the surface area and volume of spheres, students will investigate similar solids, including scale factors and how surface area and volume relate to the dimensions of similar solids.

Application Note

The first planetariums were mechanical models of the solar system. They were also called *orreries*, after Charles Boyle, the fourth Earl of Orrery in Ireland. The clockwork-driven orreries showed the planets from Mercury through Saturn revolving around the sun.

Today, planetariums use a projection system inside a dome to show the sun, the moon, the planets, and the stars. The projection system produces images of the moon and planets in correct positions and phases. Other astronomical features, like galaxies and eclipses, can also be superimposed onto the dome.

Additional information about spherical buildings is available at **www.mcdougallittell.com.**

SURFACE AREA AND VOLUME

How are geometric solids used in planetarium design?

CHAPTER 12

APPLICATION: Spherical Buildings

Planetariums create space shows by projecting images of the moon, stars, and planets onto the interior surface of a dome, or *hemisphere*. The planetarium in these architectural drawings is shaped like a ball, or *sphere*.

When constructing the dome of a planetarium, the builders need to estimate the amount of material needed to cover the interior surface of the dome. The diagram below shows the radius r of the dome of a planetarium.

Think & Discuss

1. Use the formula $2\pi r^2$ to find the amount of material needed to cover the interior of a hemisphere with a radius of 40 feet. $3200\pi \approx 10{,}053$ ft^2
2. Describe any other buildings that are shaped like spheres or hemispheres. *Sample answers:* domed stadium, igloo

Learn More About It

You will investigate spherical buildings in Exercises 38–40 on p. 764.

APPLICATION LINK Visit www.mcdougallittell.com for more information about spheres in architecture.

PROJECT

A project for Chapter 12 is available in the *Chapter 12 Resource Book*, p. 117.

TECHNOLOGY

Software
- *Electronic Teaching Tools*
- *Online Lesson Planner*
- *Personal Student Tutor*
- *Test and Practice Generator*
- *Electronic Lesson Presentations (Lesson 12.4)*

Video
- *Geometry in Motion*

Internet Connections
www.mcdougallittell.com
- **Application Links** 717, 722, 742, 763
- **Student Help** 725, 730, 739, 747, 750, 756, 760, 764
- **Career Links** 725, 733, 757, 768
- **Extra Challenge** 726, 734, 741, 749, 757, 765, 771

PREPARE

DIAGNOSTIC TOOLS

The **Skill Review** exercises can help you diagnose whether students have the following skills needed in Chapter 12:

- Find the scale factor of similar polygons.
- Calculate the area of a regular polygon.

The following resources are available for students who need additional help with these skills:

- Prerequisite Skills Review (*Chapter 12 Resource Book*, p. 5; *Warm-Up Transparencies*, p. 85)
- Reteaching with Practice (Chapter Resource Books for Lessons 8.3 and 11.2)
- *Personal Student Tutor*

ADDITIONAL RESOURCES

The following resources are provided to help you prepare for the upcoming chapter and customize review materials:

- ***Chapter 12 Resource Book***
  Tips for New Teachers (p. 1)
  Parent Guide (p. 3)
  Lesson Plans (every lesson)
  Lesson Plans for Block Scheduling (every lesson)
- ***Electronic Teaching Tools***
- ***Online Lesson Planner***
- ***Test and Practice Generator***

CHAPTER 12

Study Guide

PREVIEW

What's the chapter about?

Chapter 12 is about **surface area and volume of solids**. Surface area and volume are the measurements used to describe three-dimensional geometric figures. In Chapter 12, you'll learn

- how to calculate the surface area and volume of various solids.
- how to use surface area and volume in real-life situations, such as finding the amount of wax needed to make a candle.

KEY VOCABULARY

▶ Review
- equilateral triangle, p. 194
- polygon, p. 322
- convex, p. 323
- nonconvex, p. 323
- ratio, p. 457
- scale factor, p. 474
- locus, p. 642

▶ New
- polyhedron, p. 719
- Platonic solids, p. 721
- prism, p. 728
- cylinder, p. 730
- pyramid, p. 735
- circular cone, p. 737
- sphere, p. 759
- similar solids, p. 766

PREPARE

Are you ready for the chapter?

SKILL REVIEW Do these exercises to review key skills that you'll apply in this chapter. See the given **reference page** if there is something you don't understand.

STUDENT HELP

Study Tip
"Student Help" boxes throughout the chapter give you study tips and tell you where to look for extra help in this book and on the Internet.

Find the scale factor of the similar polygons. (Review p. 474)

1. 2:1

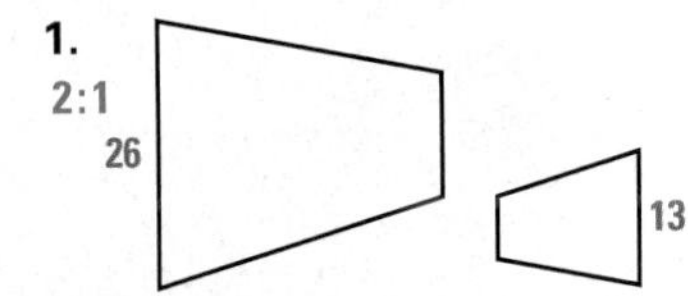

2. 3:4

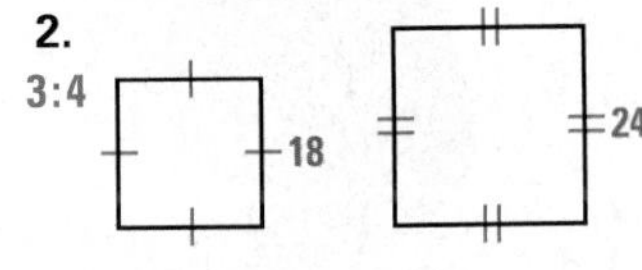

Calculate the area of the regular polygon. (Review pp. 669–671)

3.

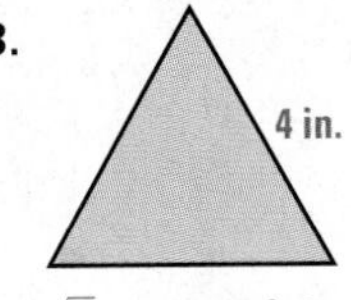

$4\sqrt{3} \approx 6.9$ in.^{2}

4.

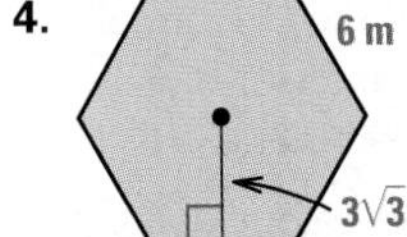

$54\sqrt{3} \approx 93.5$ m^2

5.

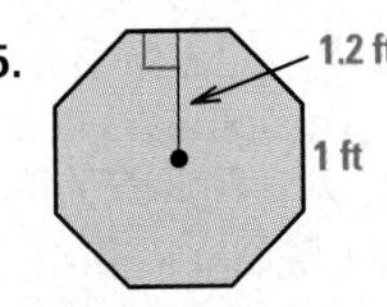

4.8 ft^2

STUDY STRATEGY

Here's a study strategy!

Generalizing Formulas

When faced with having to remember many formulas, try to find an underlying concept that links some or all of the formulas together. Then, you only have to remember the concept instead of all the formulas.

12.1

Exploring Solids

What you should learn

GOAL 1 Use properties of polyhedra.

GOAL 2 Use Euler's Theorem in **real-life** situations, such as analyzing the molecular structure of salt in **Example 5**.

Why you should learn it

▼ You can use properties of polyhedra to classify various crystals, as in **Exs. 39–41**.

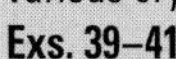

GOAL 1 USING PROPERTIES OF POLYHEDRA

A **polyhedron** is a solid that is bounded by polygons, called **faces**, that enclose a single region of space. An **edge** of a polyhedron is a line segment formed by the intersection of two faces. A **vertex** of a polyhedron is a point where three or more edges meet. The plural of polyhedron is *polyhedra*, or polyhedrons.

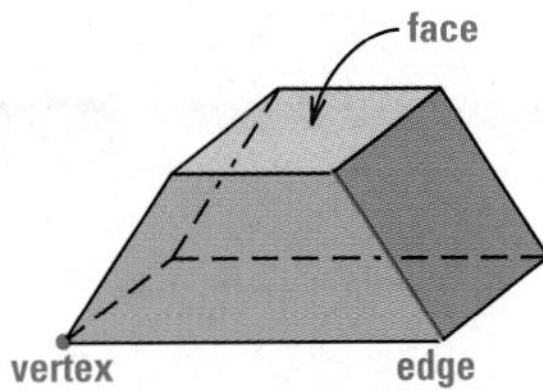

EXAMPLE 1 *Identifying Polyhedra*

Decide whether the solid is a polyhedron. If so, count the number of faces, vertices, and edges of the polyhedron.

a. 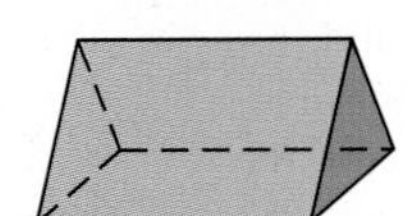

b. 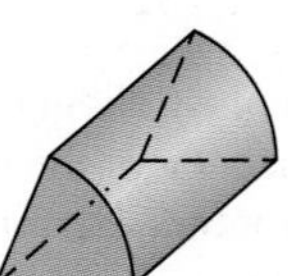

c. 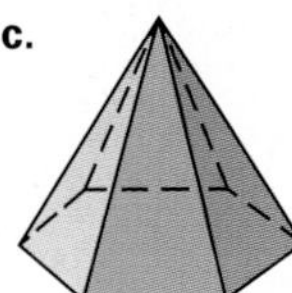

SOLUTION

a. This is a polyhedron. It has 5 faces, 6 vertices, and 9 edges.

b. This is not a polyhedron. Some of its faces are not polygons.

c. This is a polyhedron. It has 7 faces, 7 vertices, and 12 edges.

CONCEPT SUMMARY — TYPES OF SOLIDS

Of the five solids below, the prism and pyramid are polyhedra. The cone, cylinder, and sphere are not polyhedra.

Prism

Pyramid

Cone

Cylinder

Sphere

CALIFORNIA STANDARDS AND ASSESSMENT

CA Standards: 8, 9

1 PLAN

PACING

Basic: 1 day
Average: 1 day
Advanced: 1 day
Block Schedule: 0.5 block with Ch. 11 Assess.

LESSON OPENER ACTIVITY

An alternative way to approach Lesson 12.1 is to use the Activity Lesson Opener:

- Blackline Master (*Chapter 12 Resource Book,* p. 12)
- Transparency (p. 74)

MEETING INDIVIDUAL NEEDS

- ***Chapter 12 Resource Book***
  Prerequisite Skills Review (p. 5)
  Practice Level A (p. 13)
  Practice Level B (p. 14)
  Practice Level C (p. 15)
  Reteaching with Practice (p. 16)
  Absent Student Catch-Up (p. 18)
  Challenge (p. 20)
- ***Resources in Spanish***
- ***Personal Student Tutor***

NEW-TEACHER SUPPORT

See the Tips for New Teachers on pp. 1–2 of the *Chapter 12 Resource Book* for additional notes about Lesson 12.1.

WARM-UP EXERCISES

 ***Transparency Available***

State the number of sides of each polygon.

1. nonagon 9
2. hexagon 6
3. decagon 10
4. dodecagon 12
5. n-gon n

2 TEACH

MOTIVATING THE LESSON

Ask students who has gem or mineral crystals. Tell them that the shapes of the crystals are characteristic of each mineral. The crystal faces are polygons. The crystals themselves are examples of three-dimensional solids called *polyhedra*.

EXTRA EXAMPLE 1

Decide whether the solid is a polyhedron. If so, count the number of faces, vertices, and edges of the polyhedron.

a.

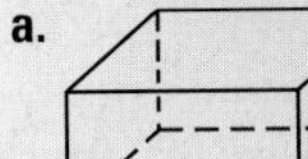

yes; 6 faces, 8 vertices, 12 edges

b.

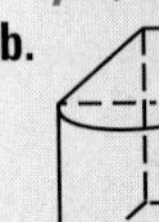

not a polyhedron

EXTRA EXAMPLE 2

Is the decahedron convex? Is it regular?

a. yes; no

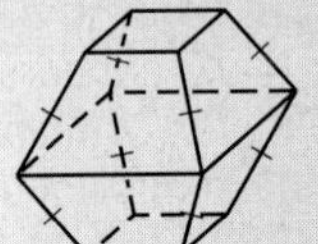

b. no; no

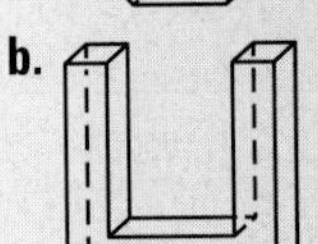

CHECKPOINT EXERCISES

For use after Examples 1 and 2:

1. Count the number of faces, vertices, and edges of the polyhedron. Is it convex? Is it regular?

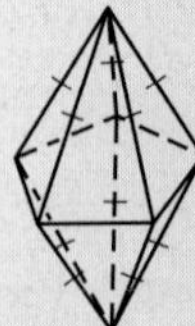

10 faces, 7 vertices, 15 edges; yes; no

A polyhedron is **regular** if all of its faces are congruent regular polygons. A polyhedron is **convex** if any two points on its surface can be connected by a segment that lies entirely inside or on the polyhedron. If this segment goes outside the polyhedron, then the polyhedron is *nonconvex*, or *concave*.

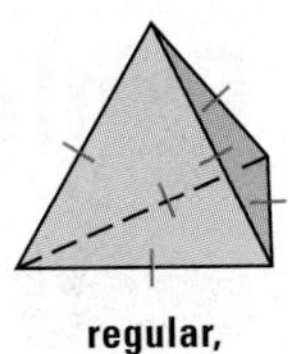

regular, convex

nonregular, nonconvex

EXAMPLE 2 Classifying Polyhedra

Is the octahedron convex? Is it regular?

a.

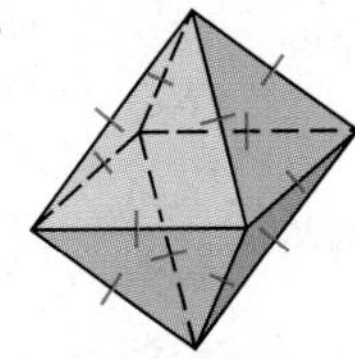

convex, regular

b.

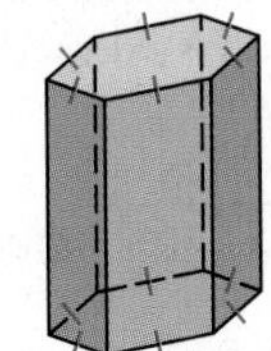

convex, nonregular

c.

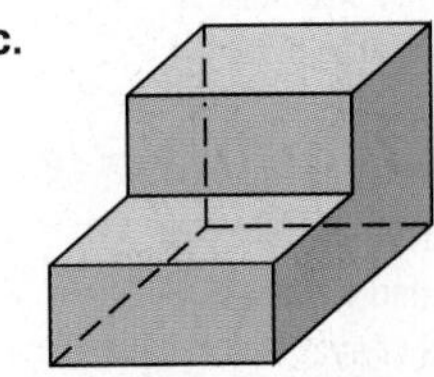

nonconvex, nonregular

....

Imagine a plane slicing through a solid. The intersection of the plane and the solid is called a **cross section**. For instance, the diagram shows that the intersection of a plane and a sphere is a circle.

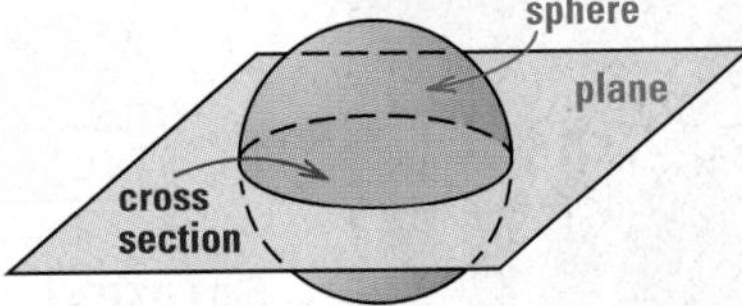

EXAMPLE 3 Describing Cross Sections

Describe the shape formed by the intersection of the plane and the cube.

STUDENT HELP

Study Tip
When sketching a cross section of a polyhedron, first sketch the solid. Then, locate the vertices of the cross section and draw the sides of the polygon.

a.

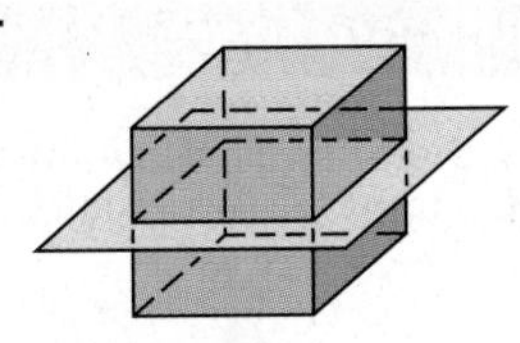

b.

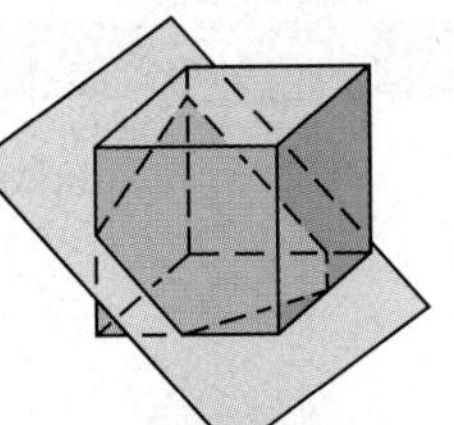

c.

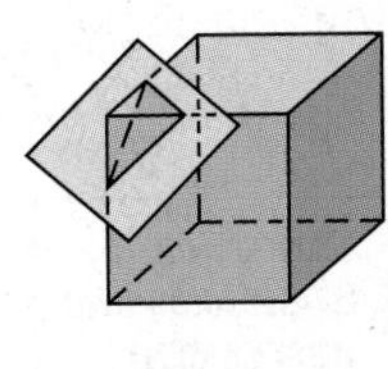

SOLUTION

a. This cross section is a square.

b. This cross section is a pentagon.

c. This cross section is a triangle.

....

The square, pentagon, and triangle cross sections of a cube are described in Example 3. Some other cross sections are the rectangle, trapezoid, and hexagon.

GOAL 2 USING EULER'S THEOREM

> **STUDENT HELP**
> **Study Tip**
> Notice that four of the Platonic solids end in "hedron." *Hedron* is Greek for "side" or "face." A cube is sometimes called a *hexahedron*.

There are five regular polyhedra, called *Platonic solids*, after the Greek mathematician and philosopher Plato. The **Platonic solids** are a regular **tetrahedron** (4 faces), a cube (6 faces), a regular **octahedron** (8 faces), a regular **dodecahedron** (12 faces), and a regular **icosahedron** (20 faces).

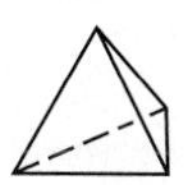
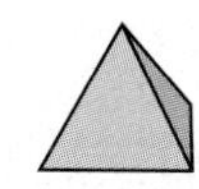

Regular tetrahedron
4 faces, 4 vertices, 6 edges

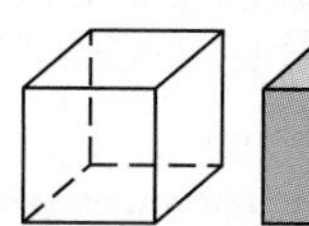
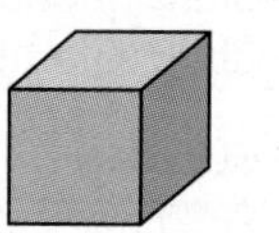

Cube
6 faces, 8 vertices, 12 edges

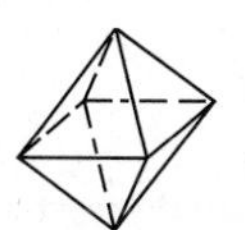
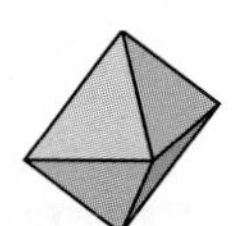

Regular octahedron
8 faces, 6 vertices, 12 edges

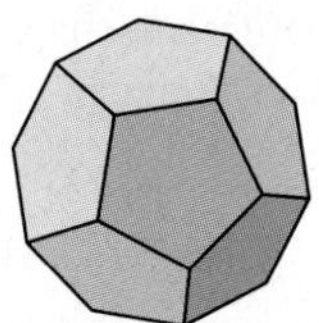

Regular dodecahedron
12 faces, 20 vertices, 30 edges

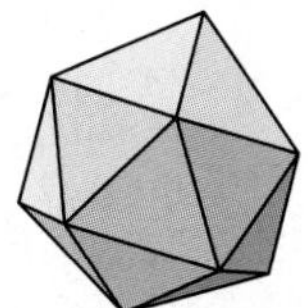

Regular icosahedron
20 faces, 12 vertices, 30 edges

Notice that the sum of the number of faces and vertices is two more than the number of edges in the solids above. This result was proved by the Swiss mathematician Leonhard Euler (1707–1783).

> **THEOREM**
>
> **THEOREM 12.1** *Euler's Theorem*
>
> The number of faces (F), vertices (V), and edges (E) of a polyhedron are related by the formula $F + V = E + 2$.

EXAMPLE 4 *Using Euler's Theorem*

The solid has 14 faces; 8 triangles and 6 octagons. How many vertices does the solid have?

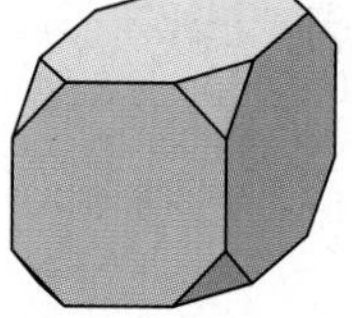

SOLUTION

On their own, 8 triangles and 6 octagons have $8(3) + 6(8)$, or 72 edges. In the solid, each side is shared by exactly two polygons. So, the number of edges is one half of 72, or 36. Use Euler's Theorem to find the number of vertices.

$F + V = E + 2$	Write Euler's Theorem.
$14 + V = 36 + 2$	Substitute.
$V = 24$	Solve for V.

▶ The solid has 24 vertices.

EXTRA EXAMPLE 3

Describe the shape formed by the intersection of the plane and the cube.

a. 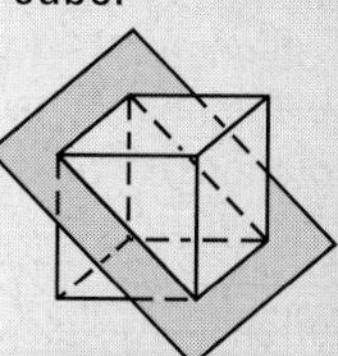

rectangle

b. 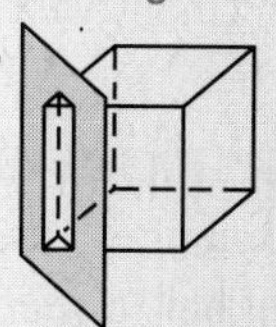

rectangle

c. 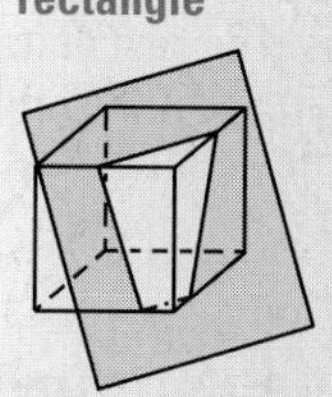

trapezoid

EXTRA EXAMPLE 4

A solid has 10 faces: 4 triangles, 1 square, 4 hexagons, and 1 octagon. How many vertices does the solid have? 16

CHECKPOINT EXERCISES

For use after Examples 3 and 4:

1. A solid has 11 faces: 5 quadrilaterals and 6 pentagons. How many vertices does the solid have? 16

TEACHING TIP

The Euler Formula applies to polyhedra that are topologically equivalent to a sphere; in other words polyhedra without holes. This lesson is restricted to such polyhedra. Challenge Worksheet 12.1 in the Chapter 12 Resource Book presents a discussion of how the formula can be modified to apply to polyhedra with holes.

EXTRA EXAMPLE 5

Some quartz crystals are pointed on both ends, and have 14 vertices and 30 edges. If you plan to put a label on one of the faces of a crystal, how many faces do you have to choose from? **18**

EXTRA EXAMPLE 6

A paper model of a geodesic dome is composed of 180 triangular faces. How many vertices does it have? **92**

CHECKPOINT EXERCISES

For use after Examples 5 and 6:

1. Like a soccer ball, a *snub dodecahedron* has 12 pentagonal faces. The rest of its 92 faces are triangles. How many vertices does the solid have? **66**

FOCUS ON VOCABULARY

What makes a polyhedron a *regular polyhedron*? **having congruent regular polygons for all its faces**

CLOSURE QUESTION

How can you find the number of vertices of a polyhedron if you know the number of faces and edges? **See sample answer below.**

DAILY PUZZLER

Can any diamond-shaped dodecahedron with triangular faces like the one shown be regular (a regular hexagon forms the "girdle")? Explain.

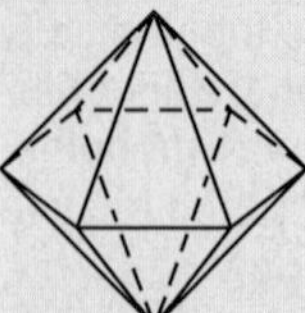

No. *Sample answer:* Connecting opposite vertices of a regular hexagon forms six triangles. A hexagon's interior angles measure 120°, so the base angles of each triangle measure 60°. So, the six triangles are equilateral. But this figure is two dimensional. If you try to "pull" the vertices apart, the triangles will be stretched so they are no longer equilateral.

EXAMPLE 5 *Finding the Number of Edges*

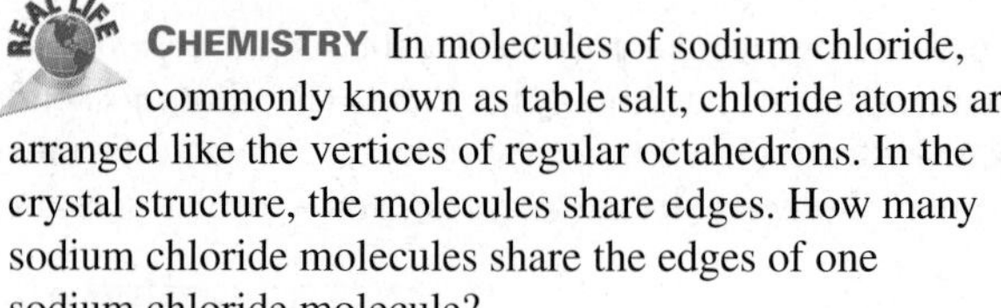

CHEMISTRY In molecules of sodium chloride, commonly known as table salt, chloride atoms are arranged like the vertices of regular octahedrons. In the crystal structure, the molecules share edges. How many sodium chloride molecules share the edges of one sodium chloride molecule?

SOLUTION

To find the number of molecules that share edges with a given molecule, you need to know the number of edges of the molecule.

You know that the molecules are shaped like regular octahedrons. So, they each have 8 faces and 6 vertices. You can use Euler's Theorem to find the number of edges, as shown below.

$F + V = E + 2$ **Write Euler's Theorem.**

$8 + 6 = E + 2$ **Substitute.**

$12 = E$ **Simplify.**

▶ So, 12 other molecules share the edges of the given molecule.

FOCUS ON APPLICATIONS

GEODESIC DOME The dome has the same underlying structure as a soccer ball, but the faces are subdivided into triangles.

APPLICATION LINK www.mcdougallittell.com

EXAMPLE 6 *Finding the Number of Vertices*

SPORTS A soccer ball resembles a polyhedron with 32 faces; 20 are regular hexagons and 12 are regular pentagons. How many vertices does this polyhedron have?

SOLUTION

Each of the 20 hexagons has 6 sides and each of the 12 pentagons has 5 sides. Each edge of the soccer ball is shared by two polygons. Thus, the total number of edges is as follows:

$E = \frac{1}{2}(6 \cdot 20 + 5 \cdot 12)$ **Expression for number of edges**

$= \frac{1}{2}(180)$ **Simplify inside parentheses.**

$= 90$ **Multiply.**

Knowing the number of edges, 90, and the number of faces, 32, you can apply Euler's Theorem to determine the number of vertices.

$F + V = E + 2$ **Write Euler's Theorem.**

$32 + V = 90 + 2$ **Substitute.**

$V = 60$ **Simplify.**

▶ So, the polyhedron has 60 vertices.

Closure Question *Sample answer:*
Use the formula $F + V = E + 2$, solving for V to get $V = E + 2 - F$, where V represents the number of vertices, F the number of faces, and E the number of edges of the polyhedron.

Guided Practice

Vocabulary Check ✓

Concept Check ✓

Skill Check ✓

1. Define *polyhedron* in your own words. *Sample answer:* A polyhedron is a solid figure bounded by faces that are polygons and enclose a single region of space.
2. Is a regular octahedron convex? Are all the Platonic solids convex? Explain.

2. Yes; yes; any 2 points on the surface of any Platonic solid can be connected by a line segment that lies entirely inside or on the solid.

3. Yes; the figure is a solid that is bounded by polygons that enclose a single region of space.

4. Yes; the figure is a solid that is bounded by polygons that enclose a single region of space.

5. No; it does not have faces that are polygons.

Decide whether the solid is a polyhedron. Explain.

3. 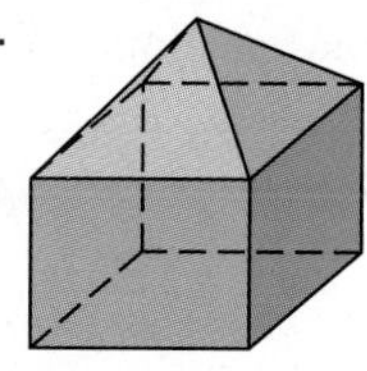

4. 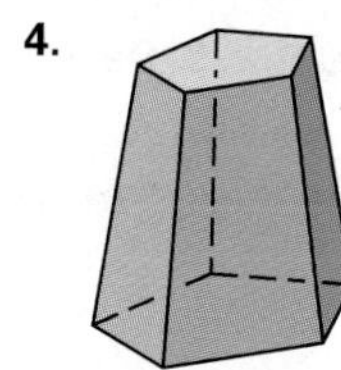

5. 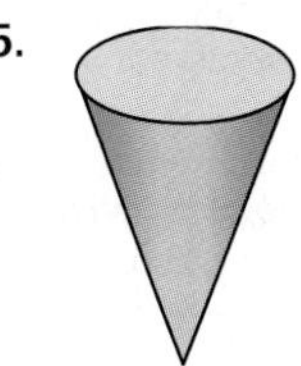

Use Euler's Theorem to find the unknown number.

6. Faces: __?__ 8
   Vertices: 6
   Edges: 12

7. Faces: 5
   Vertices: __?__ 6
   Edges: 9

8. Faces: __?__ 7
   Vertices: 10
   Edges: 15

9. Faces: 20
   Vertices: 12
   Edges: __?__ 30

Practice and Applications

STUDENT HELP

Extra Practice to help you master skills is on p. 825.

10. No; some of its faces are not polygons.

11. Yes; the figure is a solid that is bounded by polygons that enclose a single region of space.

12. Yes; the figure is a solid that is bounded by polygons that enclose a single region of space.

IDENTIFYING POLYHEDRA **Tell whether the solid is a polyhedron. Explain your reasoning.**

10. 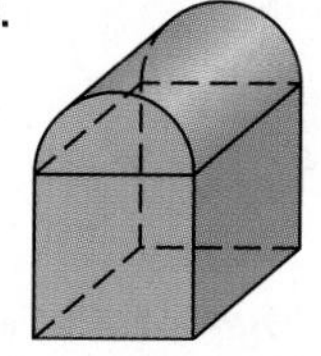

11. 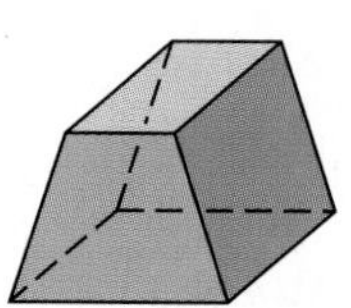

12. 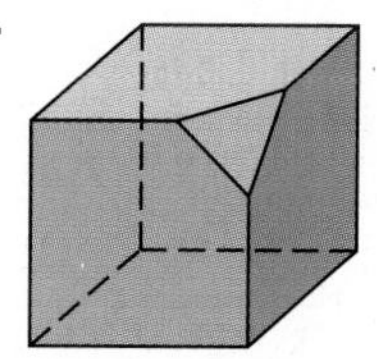

ANALYZING SOLIDS **Count the number of faces, vertices, and edges of the polyhedron.**

13. 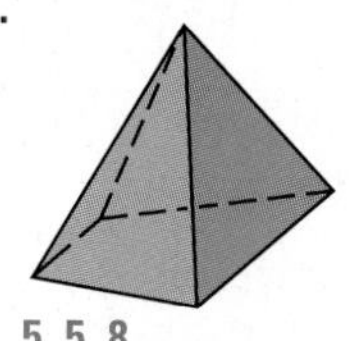

5, 5, 8

14. 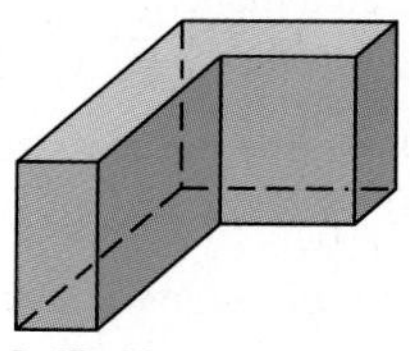

8, 12, 18

15. 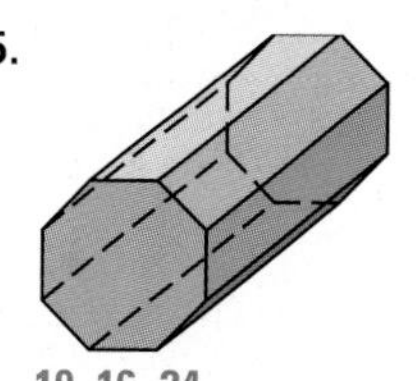

10, 16, 24

STUDENT HELP

HOMEWORK HELP

Example 1: Exs. 10–15
Example 2: Exs. 16–24
Example 3: Exs. 25–35
Example 4: Exs. 36–52
Example 5: Ex. 53
Example 6: Exs. 47–52

ANALYZING POLYHEDRA **Decide whether the polyhedron is regular and/or convex. Explain.** 16–18. See margin.

16. 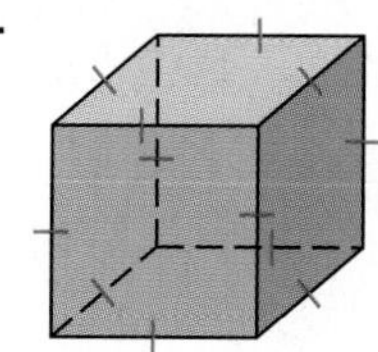

17. 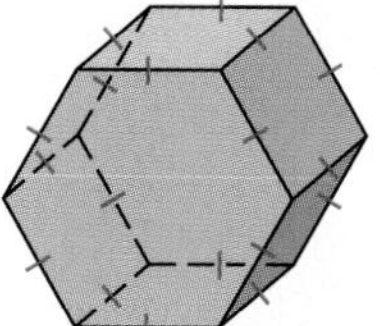

18. 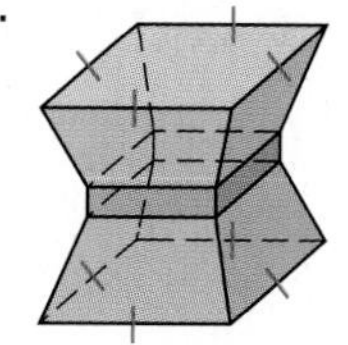

3 APPLY

Assignment Guide

BASIC
Day 1: pp. 723–726 Exs. 10–30 even, 32–35, 43–52, 54, 55, 60–70 even

AVERAGE
Day 1: pp. 723–726 Exs. 10–30 even, 32–35, 42–52, 54, 55, 60–70 even

ADVANCED
Day 1: pp. 723–726 Exs. 10–30 even, 32–35, 42–52, 54–59, 60–70 even

BLOCK SCHEDULE
(with Ch. 11 Assess) pp. 723–726 Exs. 10–30 even, 32–35, 42–52, 54, 55, 60–70 even

Exercise Levels

Level A: *Easier*
10–18, 25–31, 36–41, 60–62, 68–70

Level B: *More Difficult*
19–24, 32–35, 43–55, 63–67

Level C: *Most Difficult*
42, 56–69

✓ Homework Check

To quickly check student understanding of key concepts, go over the following exercises: Exs. 10, 14, 18, 24, 28, 34, 44, 48. See also the Daily Homework Quiz:

- Blackline Master (*Chapter 12 Resource Book,* p. 23)
- Transparency (p. 87)

! Common Error

EXERCISE 17 Some students may think the polyhedron is regular because all of its faces are regular polygons. In this case, however, they are not all *congruent*, as is required.

16–18. See next page.

TEACHING TIPS

EXERCISES 25–28 To help students visualize cross sections when a plane intersects a solid, demonstrate with actual objects that can be cut. For example, you could use solids made of styrofoam or clay (cut with a very fine wire).

MATHEMATICAL REASONING

EXERCISE 26 The idea of intersecting a cone by a plane at various angles can be used to introduce the conic sections: the circle, ellipse, parabola, and hyperbola. For the hyperbola, use two cones sharing the same vertical axis, touching only at their vertices.

16. Regular, convex; the 6 faces of the polyhedron are ≅ squares; any two points on the surface of the polyhedron can be connected by a line segment that lies entirely inside or on the polyhedron.
17. Not regular, convex; the faces of the polyhedron are not congruent (two are hexagons and six are squares); any two points on the surface of the polyhedron can be connected by a line segment that lies entirely inside or on the polyhedron.
18. Not regular, not convex; the faces of the polyhedron are not congruent (two are squares, eight are trapezoids, and four are rectangles); some of the segments connecting a vertex of one square face to a vertex of the other lie outside the polyhedron.

33. yes;

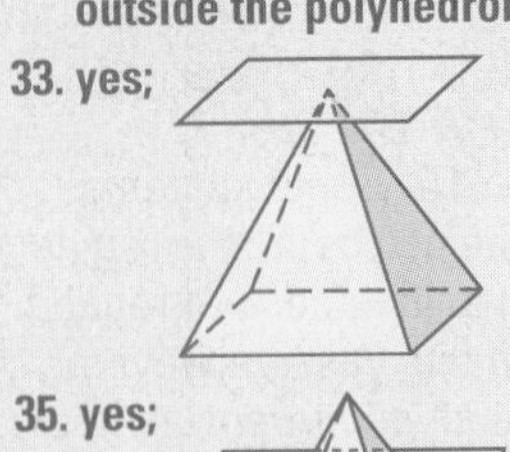

35. yes;

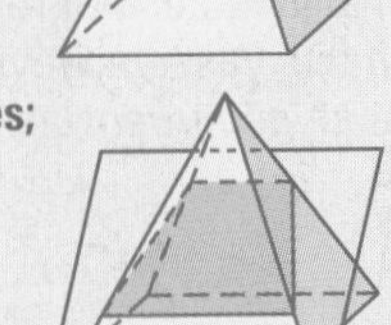

19. False; see the octahedron in part (b) of Example 2 on page 720.
20. False; each face of a polyhedron is a polygon, so each face has at least 3 sides and therefore must intersect with at least 3 other faces. Thus a polyhedron must have at least 4 faces.
21. True; the faces are ≅ squares.
22. True; see the regular tetrahedron on page 721.
23. False; it does not have polygonal faces.
24. True; see the pyramid on page 719.

LOGICAL REASONING **Determine whether the statement is *true* or *false*. Explain your reasoning.**

19. Every convex polyhedron is regular.

20. A polyhedron can have exactly 3 faces.

21. A cube is a regular polyhedron.

22. A polyhedron can have exactly 4 faces.

23. A cone is a regular polyhedron.

24. A polyhedron can have exactly 5 faces.

CROSS SECTIONS **Describe the cross section.**

25. circle

26. circle

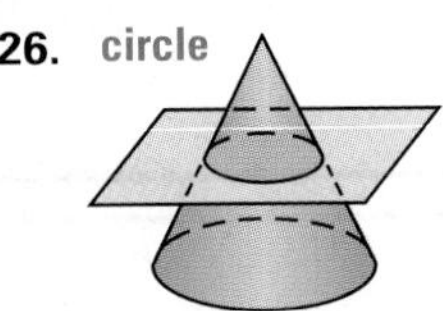

27. pentagon

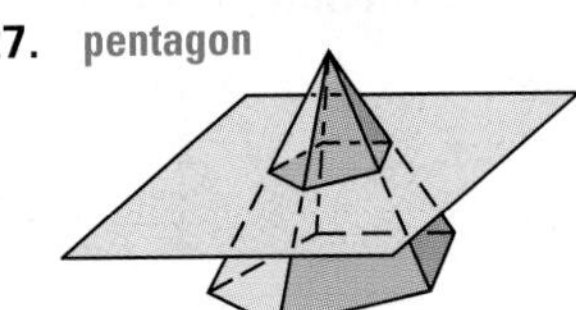

28. rectangle

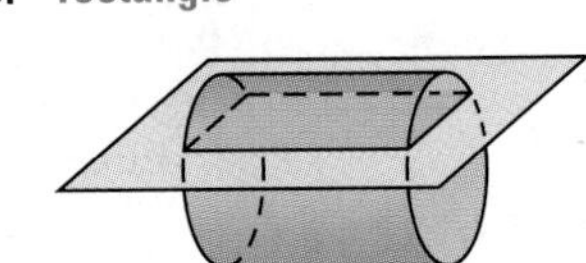

COOKING **Describe the shape that is formed by the cut made in the food shown.**

29. Carrot circle

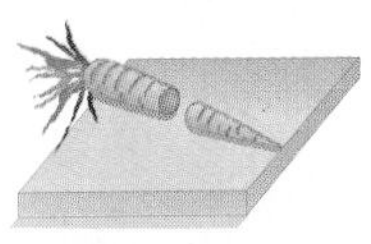

30. Cheese rectangle or square

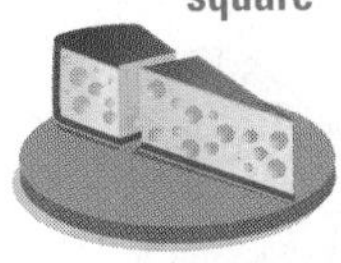

31. Cake rectangle

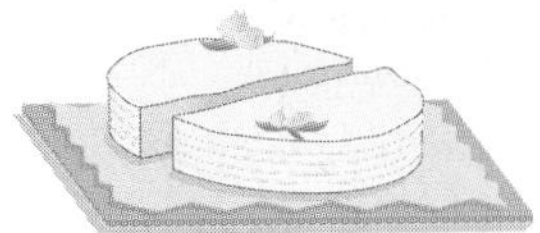

CRITICAL THINKING **In the diagram, the bottom face of the pyramid is a square.**

32. Name the cross section shown. pentagon

33. Can a plane intersect the pyramid at a point? If so, sketch the intersection. See margin.

34. Describe the cross section when the pyramid is sliced by a plane parallel to its bottom face. square

35. Is it possible to have an isosceles trapezoid as a cross section of this pyramid? If so, draw the cross section. See margin.

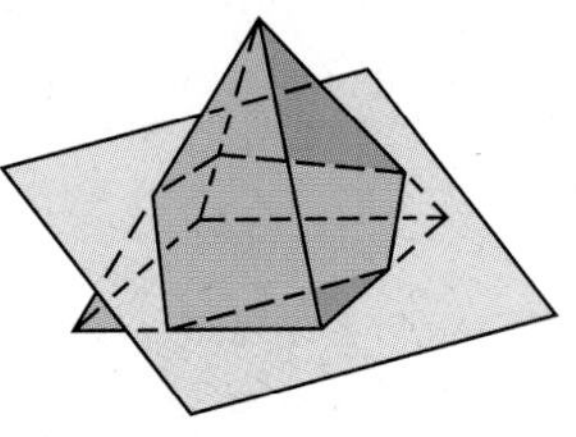

POLYHEDRONS **Name the regular polyhedron.**

36.

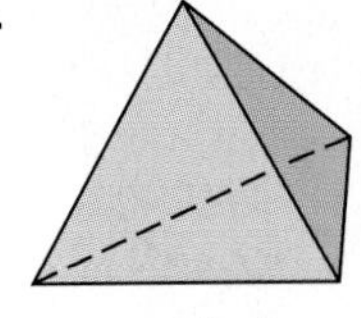

tetrahedron

37.

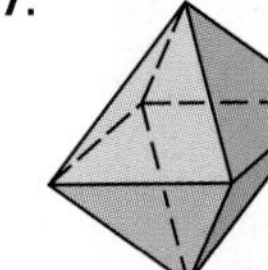

octahedron

38.

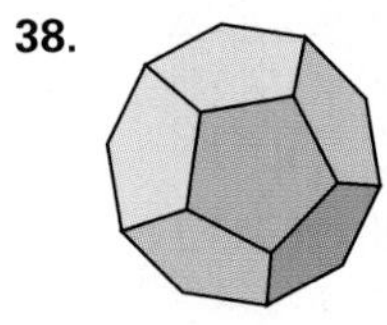

dodecahedron

FOCUS ON CAREERS

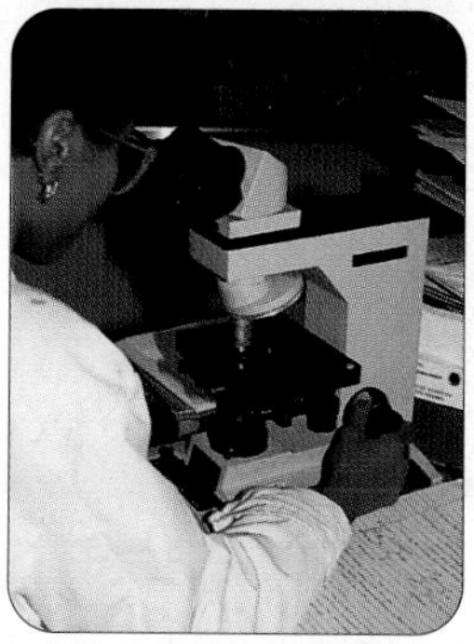

MINERALOGY By studying the arrangement of atoms in a crystal, mineralogists are able to determine the chemical and physical properties of the crystal.

CAREER LINK
www.mcdougallittell.com

CRYSTALS **In Exercises 39–41, name the Platonic solid that the crystal resembles.**

39. Cobaltite **dodecahedron** **40.** Fluorite **octahedron** **41.** Pyrite **cube**

42. **VISUAL THINKING** Sketch a cube and describe the figure that results from connecting the centers of adjoining faces. **regular octahedron**

EULER'S THEOREM **In Exercises 43–45, find the number of faces, edges, and vertices of the polyhedron and use them to verify Euler's Theorem.**
43–45. See margin.

43.

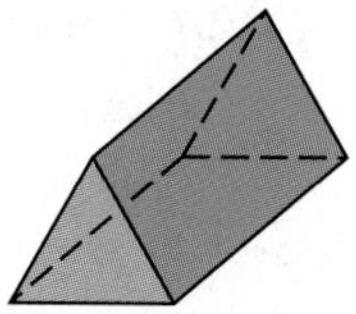

44.

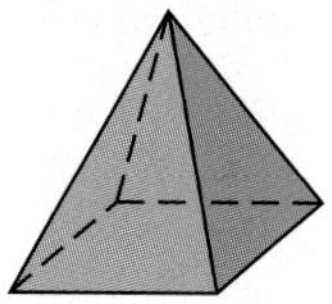

45.

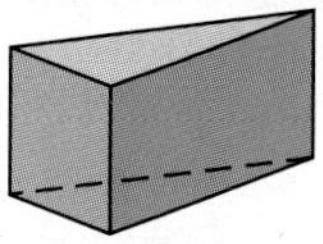

46. **MAKING A TABLE** Make a table of the number of faces, vertices, and edges for the Platonic solids. Use it to show Euler's Theorem is true for each solid. **See margin.**

USING EULER'S THEOREM **In Exercises 47–52, calculate the number of vertices of the solid using the given information.**

47. 20 faces; all triangles **12 vertices**

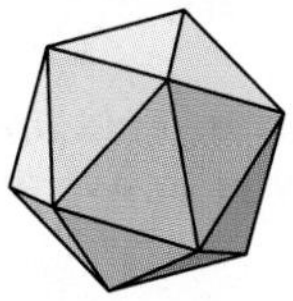

48. 14 faces; 8 triangles and 6 squares **12 vertices**

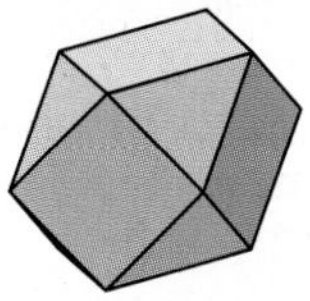

49. 14 faces; 8 hexagons and 6 squares **24 vertices**

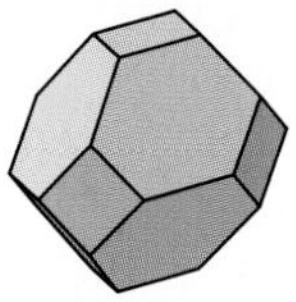

50. 26 faces; 18 squares and 8 triangles **24 vertices**

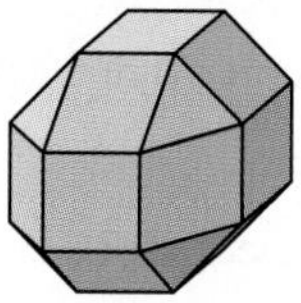

51. 8 faces; 4 hexagons and 4 triangles **12 vertices**

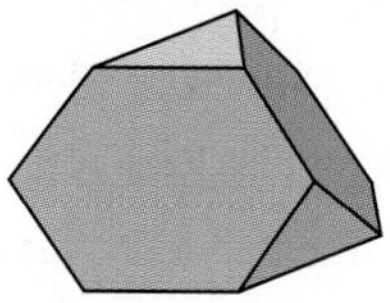

52. 12 faces; all pentagons **20 vertices**

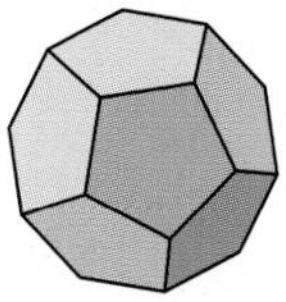

53. **SCIENCE CONNECTION** In molecules of cesium chloride, chloride atoms are arranged like the vertices of cubes. In its crystal structure, the molecules share faces to form an array of cubes. How many cesium chloride molecules share the faces of a given cesium chloride molecule? **6 molecules**

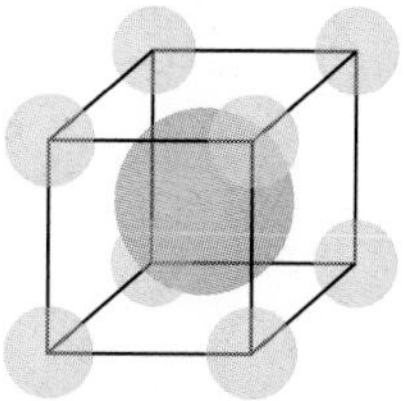

STUDENT HELP

HOMEWORK HELP
Visit our Web site www.mcdougallittell.com for help with problem solving in Exs. 47–52.

43. 5 faces, 6 vertices, 9 edges; $5 + 6 = 9 + 2$

44. 5 faces, 5 vertices, 8 edges; $5 + 5 = 8 + 2$

45. 5 faces, 6 vertices, 9 edges; $5 + 6 = 9 + 2$

CAREER NOTE
EXERCISES 39–41
Additional information about mineralogists is available at **www.mcdougallittell.com.**

STUDENT HELP NOTES

Homework Help Students can find help for Exs. 47–52 at **www.mcdougallittell.com.** The information can be printed out for students who don't have access to the Internet.

42.

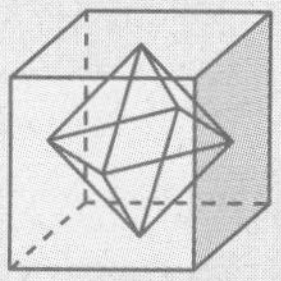

46. For each solid, the number of faces, vertices, edges, and the verification of Euler's Theorem are given in that order.
tetrahedron: 4, 4, 6, $4 + 4 = 6 + 2$
cube: 6, 8, 12, $6 + 8 = 12 + 2$
octahedron: 8, 6, 12, $8 + 6 = 12 + 2$
dodecahedron: 12, 20, 30, $12 + 20 = 30 + 2$
icosahedron: 20, 12, 30, $20 + 12 = 30 + 2$

ADDITIONAL PRACTICE AND RETEACHING

For Lesson 12.1:

- Practice Levels A, B, and C (*Chapter 12 Resource Book*, p. 13)
- Reteaching with Practice (*Chapter 12 Resource Book*, p. 16)
- See Lesson 12.1 of the *Personal Student Tutor*

For more Mixed Review:

- Search the *Test and Practice Generator* for key words or specific lessons.

4 ASSESS

DAILY HOMEWORK QUIZ

Transparency Available

1. Determine whether the statement *A cylinder is a convex polyhedron* is true or false. Explain your reasoning.
False; a cylinder is not a polyhedron because its faces are not polygons.

2. Describe the cross section.

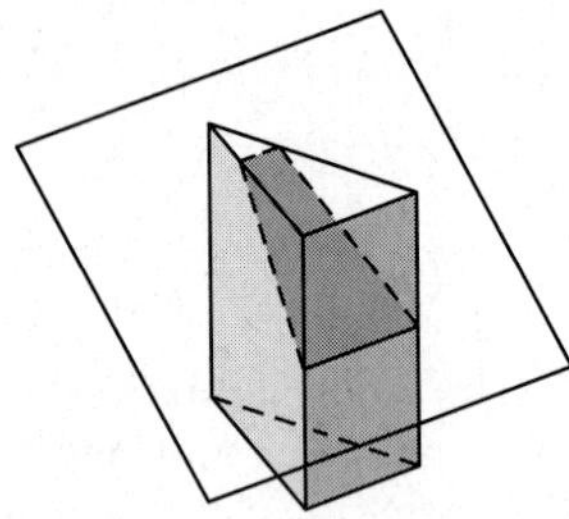

trapezoid

3. Find the number of faces, edges, and vertices of the polyhedron and use them to verify Euler's Theorem.

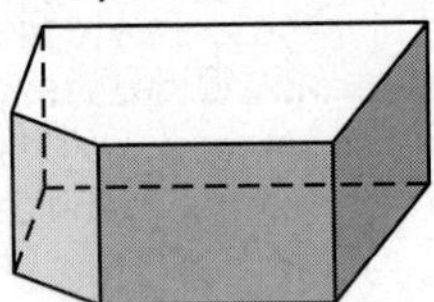

7, 15, 10; 7 + 10 = 15 + 2

4. A solid has 14 faces: 6 octagons and 8 triangles. How many vertices does it have? 24

EXTRA CHALLENGE NOTE

Challenge problems for Lesson 12.1 are available in **blackline** format in the *Chapter 12 Resource Book*, p. 20 and at **www.mcdougallittell.com.**

ADDITIONAL TEST PREPARATION

1. WRITING Use Euler's Theorem to explain why there can be no polyhedron with six vertices and seven edges.
See sample answer at right.

56–59. See Additional Answers beginning on page AA1.

Test Preparation

54. MULTIPLE CHOICE A polyhedron has 18 edges and 12 vertices. How many faces does it have? C

Ⓐ 4 Ⓑ 6 Ⓒ 8 Ⓓ 10 Ⓔ 12

55. MULTIPLE CHOICE In the diagram, Q and S are the midpoints of two edges of the cube. What is the length of $\overline{QS}$, if each edge of the cube has length h? B

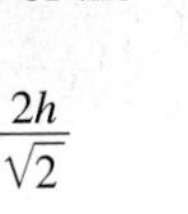

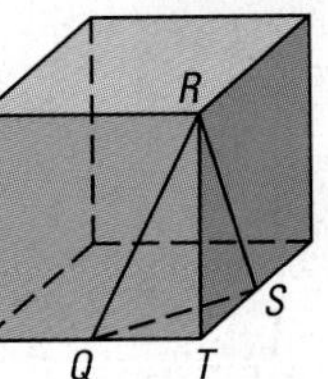

Ⓐ $\frac{h}{2}$ Ⓑ $\frac{h}{\sqrt{2}}$ Ⓒ $\frac{2h}{\sqrt{2}}$

Ⓓ $\sqrt{2}h$ Ⓔ $2h$

★ Challenge

SKETCHING CROSS SECTIONS **Sketch the intersection of a cube and a plane so that the given shape is formed.** 56–59. See margin.

EXTRA CHALLENGE
www.mcdougallittell.com

56. An equilateral triangle

57. A regular hexagon

58. An isosceles trapezoid

59. A rectangle

MIXED REVIEW

FINDING AREA OF QUADRILATERALS **Find the area of the figure.** (Review 6.7 for 12.2)

60. 96 in.^{2}
8 in.
12 in.

61. 280 ft^2
14 ft
16 ft
21 ft

62. 735 m^2
15 m
32 m
17 m
15 m

FINDING AREA OF REGULAR POLYGONS **Find the area of the regular polygon described. Round your answer to two decimal places.** (Review 11.2 for 12.2)

63. An equilateral triangle with a perimeter of 48 meters and an apothem of 4.6 meters. 110.40 m^2

64. A regular octagon with a perimeter of 28 feet and an apothem of 4.22 feet. 59.08 ft^2

65. An equilateral triangle whose sides measure 8 centimeters. 27.71 cm^2

66. A regular hexagon whose sides measure 4 feet. 41.57 ft^2

67. A regular dodecagon whose sides measure 16 inches. 2866.22 in.^{2}

FINDING AREA **Find the area of the shaded region. Round your answer to two decimal places.** (Review 11.5)

68.
115°
7 cm

49.17 cm^2

69.
43 ft

5808.80 ft^2

70.

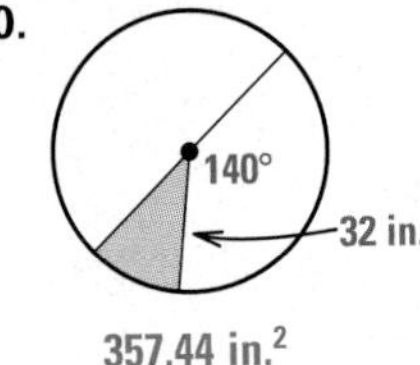

357.44 in.^{2}

Additional Test Preparation *Sample answer:*
1. By Euler's Theorem, $F + V = E + 2$, so $F + 6 = 7 + 2$, which gives $F = 3$. Since you cannot enclose any region in three-dimensional space with only three polygons, the polyhedron cannot exist.

ACTIVITY 12.2

Developing Concepts

Investigating Surface Area

GROUP ACTIVITY
Work with a partner.

MATERIALS
- graph paper
- pencil
- scissors

QUESTION **A *net* is a pattern that can be folded to form a polyhedron. How can a net be used to find the surface area of a polyhedron?**

EXPLORING THE CONCEPT

1 Copy the net below on graph paper. Be sure to label the sections of the net.

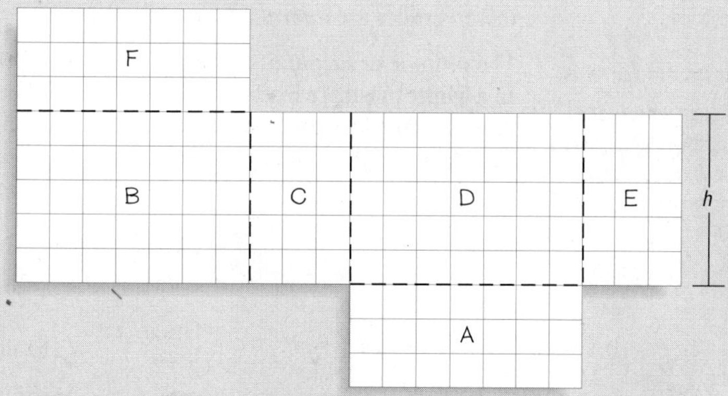

2 Cut out the net and fold it along the dotted lines to form a polyhedron. Describe the polyhedron. Is it regular? Is it convex?

INVESTIGATE

1. The *surface area* of a polyhedron is the sum of the areas of its faces. Find the surface area of the polyhedron you just made. (Each square on the graph paper measures 1 unit by 1 unit.) **142 sq. units**

2. Lay the net flat again and find the following measures.

   A: the area of rectangle A **21 sq. units**

   P: the perimeter of rectangle A **20 units**

   h: the height of rectangles B, C, D, and E **5 units**

3. Using the values from Exercise 2, find $2A + Ph$. Compare this value to the surface area you found in Exercise 1. What do you notice?
   142 sq. units; the values are the same.

MAKE A CONJECTURE

4. Make a conjecture about how to find the surface area of a rectangular solid.

4. Identify one side of the rectangular solid as the base and find its area A and perimeter P. Then find the height h of the solid and use the formula $A = 2A + Ph$.

EXTENSION

CRITICAL THINKING Use graph paper to draw the net of another rectangular solid. Fold the net to make sure that it forms a rectangular solid. Use your conjecture from Exercise 4 to calculate the surface area of the solid.
Answers will vary.

Activity Assessment *Sample answer:*
Find the sum of the surface areas of the faces, or multiply the area of the base by 2 and add it to the perimeter of the base multiplied by the height.

1 Planning the Activity

PURPOSE
To use a net to find the surface area of a polyhedron.

MATERIALS
- graph paper
- scissors
- Activity Support Master (*Chapter 12 Resource Book,* p. 24)

PACING
- Exploring the Concept — 10 min
- Investigate — 15 min

LINK TO LESSON
On page 729 of Lesson 12.2, the method for finding the area of a right prism explored in this activity is formalized.

2 Managing the Activity

COOPERATIVE LEARNING
Have pairs work together to find values for A, P, and h in Question 2. Pairs can compare their values with those of others to ensure they are using the correct values.

ALTERNATIVE APPROACH
Have pairs of students make their own net for a different rectangular solid than the one shown. Have them show that the formula derived for the surface area of a polyhedron is valid for this new solid.

3 Closing the Activity

KEY DISCOVERY
The surface area of a rectangular solid can be found by adding twice the area of the base to the product of the perimeter of the base and the height.

ACTIVITY ASSESSMENT
JOURNAL Explain two ways to find the total surface area of a rectangular solid.
See sample answer at left.

1 PLAN

PACING
Basic: 1 day
Average: 1 day
Advanced: 1 day
Block Schedule: 0.5 block with 12.3

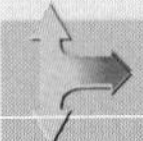

LESSON OPENER
VISUAL APPROACH
An alternative way to approach Lesson 12.2 is to use the Visual Approach Lesson Opener:

- Blackline Master (*Chapter 12 Resource Book,* p. 25)
- Transparency (p. 75)

MEETING INDIVIDUAL NEEDS
- ***Chapter 12 Resource Book***
  Prerequisite Skills Review (p. 5)
  Practice Level A (p. 26)
  Practice Level B (p. 27)
  Practice Level C (p. 28)
  Reteaching with Practice (p. 29)
  Absent Student Catch-Up (p. 31)
  Challenge (p. 33)
- ***Resources in Spanish***
-  ***Personal Student Tutor***

NEW-TEACHER SUPPORT
See the Tips for New Teachers on pp. 1–2 of the *Chapter 12 Resource Book* for additional notes about Lesson 12.2.

WARM-UP EXERCISES
Transparency Available
Find the area of each polygon.
1. triangle: base = 12 ft, height = 9 ft 54 ft^2
2. parallelogram: base = 10 cm, height = 15 cm 150 cm^2
3. square: side = 16 in. 256 in.^2
4. rectangle: length = 10.2 m, width = 5.5 m 56.1 m^2

12.2 Surface Area of Prisms and Cylinders

What you should learn

GOAL 1 Find the surface area of a prism.

GOAL 2 Find the surface area of a cylinder.

Why you should learn it

▼ You can find the surface area of **real-life** objects, such as the cylinder records used on phonographs during the late 1800s. See **Ex. 43**.

CALIFORNIA STANDARDS AND ASSESSMENT
CA Standards: 8, 9
SAT9 Task 1: Obj. 2
SAT9 Task 2: Obj. 6

STUDENT HELP
Study Tip
When sketching prisms, first draw the two bases. Then connect the corresponding vertices of the bases.

GOAL 1 FINDING THE SURFACE AREA OF A PRISM

A **prism** is a polyhedron with two congruent faces, called **bases**, that lie in parallel planes. The other faces, called **lateral faces**, are parallelograms formed by connecting the corresponding vertices of the bases. The segments connecting these vertices are *lateral edges.*

The *altitude* or *height* of a prism is the perpendicular distance between its bases. In a **right prism**, each lateral edge is perpendicular to both bases. Prisms that have lateral edges that are not perpendicular to the bases are **oblique prisms**. The length of the oblique lateral edges is the *slant height* of the prism.

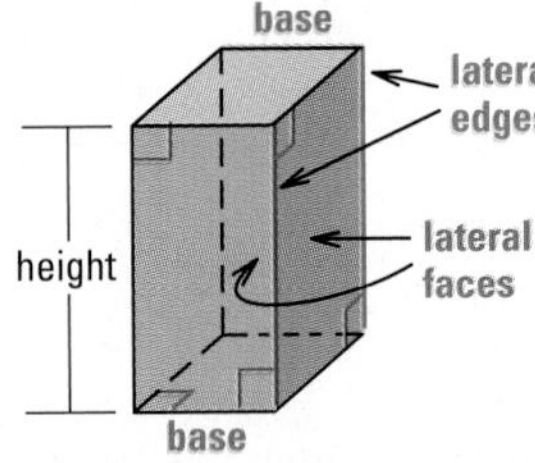

Right rectangular prism

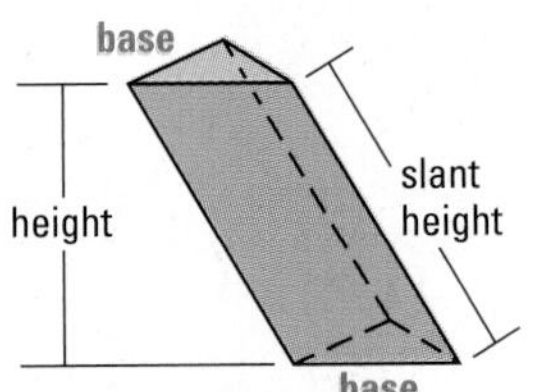

Oblique triangular prism

Prisms are classified by the shapes of their bases. For example, the figures above show one rectangular prism and one triangular prism. The **surface area** of a polyhedron is the sum of the areas of its faces. The **lateral area** of a polyhedron is the sum of the areas of its lateral faces.

EXAMPLE 1 *Finding the Surface Area of a Prism*

Find the surface area of a right rectangular prism with a height of 8 inches, a length of 3 inches, and a width of 5 inches.

SOLUTION

Begin by sketching the prism, as shown. The prism has 6 faces, two of each of the following:

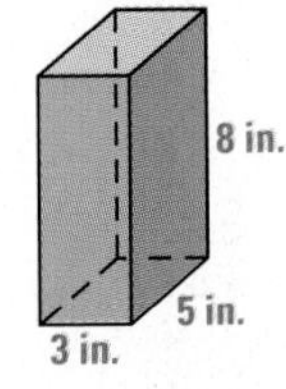

Faces	Dimensions	Area of faces
Left and right	8 in. by 5 in.	40 in.^2
Front and back	8 in. by 3 in.	24 in.^2
Top and bottom	3 in. by 5 in.	15 in.^2

▶ The surface area of the prism is $S = 2(40) + 2(24) + 2(15) = 158\text{ in.}^2$

Imagine that you cut some edges of a right hexagonal prism and unfolded it. The two-dimensional representation of all of the faces is called a **net**.

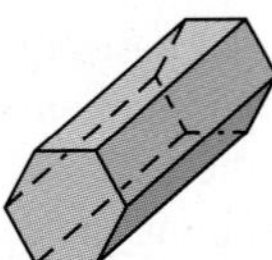

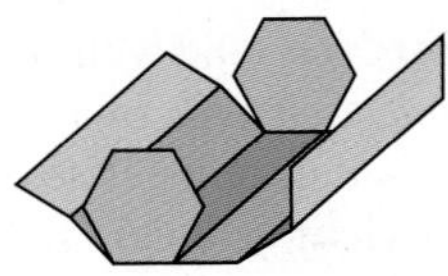

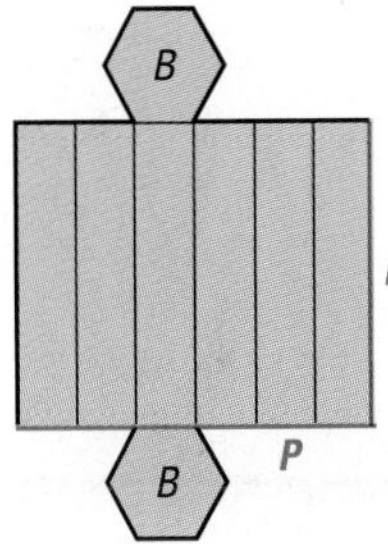

In the net of the prism, notice that the lateral area (the sum of the areas of the lateral faces) is equal to the perimeter of the base multiplied by the height.

THEOREM

THEOREM 12.2 ***Surface Area of a Right Prism***

The surface area S of a right prism can be found using the formula $S = 2B + Ph$, where B is the area of a base, P is the perimeter of a base, and h is the height.

EXAMPLE 2 *Using Theorem 12.2*

Find the surface area of the right prism.

a.

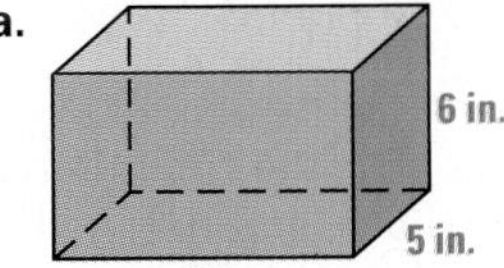

b.

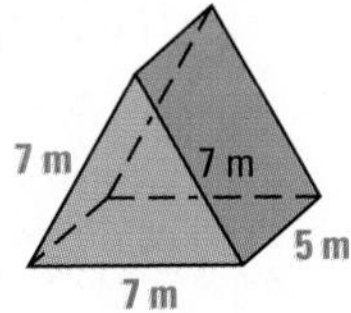

SOLUTION

a. Each base measures 5 inches by 10 inches with an area of

$$B = 5(10) = 50 \text{ in.}^2$$

The perimeter of the base is $P = 30$ in. and the height is $h = 6$ in.

▶ So, the surface area is

$$S = 2B + Ph = 2(50) + 30(6) = 280 \text{ in.}^2$$

b. Each base is an equilateral triangle with a side length, s, of 7 meters. Using the formula for the area of an equilateral triangle, the area of each base is

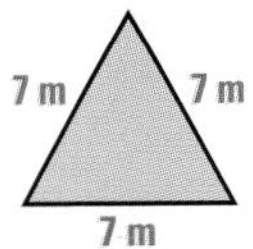

$$B = \frac{1}{4}\sqrt{3}\,(s^2) = \frac{1}{4}\sqrt{3}\,(7^2) = \frac{49}{4}\sqrt{3} \text{ m}^2.$$

The perimeter of each base is $P = 21$ m and the height is $h = 5$ m.

▶ So, the surface area is

$$S = 2B + Ph = 2\left(\frac{49}{4}\sqrt{3}\right) + 21(5) \approx 147 \text{ m}^2.$$

STUDENT HELP

Study Tip
The prism in part (a) has three pairs of parallel, congruent faces. Any pair can be called bases, whereas the prism in part (b) has only one pair of parallel, congruent faces that can be bases.

STUDENT HELP

Look Back
For help with finding the area of an equilateral triangle, see p. 669.

2 TEACH

MOTIVATING THE LESSON
Have empty cereal boxes and metal cans on hand. Ask students how they can find how much cardboard is needed to make a box and how much metal is needed for a can. Tell them that by learning to find *surface areas* of cylinders and rectangular solids, they can solve these problems.

EXTRA EXAMPLE 1
Find the surface area of a right rectangular prism with a height of 2 feet, a length of 5 feet, and a width of 4 feet. **76 ft^2**

EXTRA EXAMPLE 2
Find the surface area of the right prism.

a.

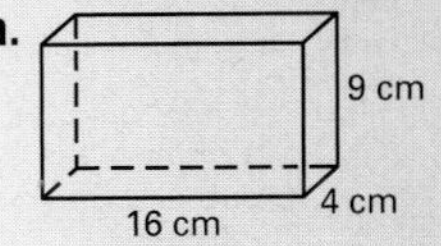

488 cm^2

b.

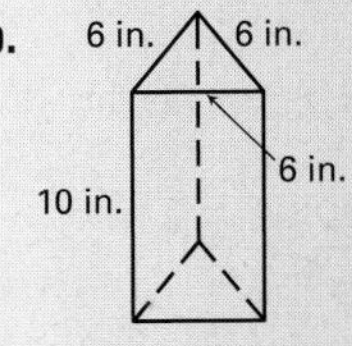

$18\sqrt{3} + 180 \approx 211.2 \text{ in.}^2$

CHECKPOINT EXERCISES

For use after Examples 1 and 2:

1. Find the surface area of a right triangular prism with a height of 11 meters, and bases that are triangles with sides of 3 meters, 4 meters, and 5 meters. **144 m^2**

STUDENT HELP NOTES

Look Back As students look back to p. 669 for help with finding the area of an equilateral triangle, remind them that an equilateral triangle can be divided into two congruent 30°-60°-90° right triangles. The special triangle relationships then make it easy to find the height.

EXTRA EXAMPLE 3

Find the surface area of the right cylinder.

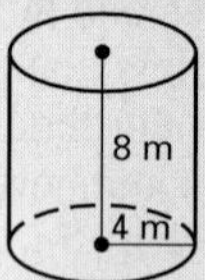

$96\pi \approx 301.59\ m^2$

CHECKPOINT EXERCISES

For use after Example 3:

1. Find the surface area of a right cylinder that has a diameter of 10 in. and a height of 10 in. $150\pi \approx 471.24\ in.^2$

GOAL 2 FINDING THE SURFACE AREA OF A CYLINDER

A **cylinder** is a solid with congruent circular bases that lie in parallel planes. The *altitude*, or *height*, of a cylinder is the perpendicular distance between its bases. The radius of the base is also called the *radius* of the cylinder. A cylinder is called a **right cylinder** if the segment joining the centers of the bases is perpendicular to the bases.

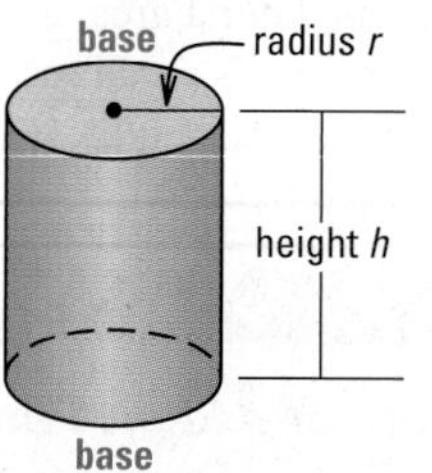

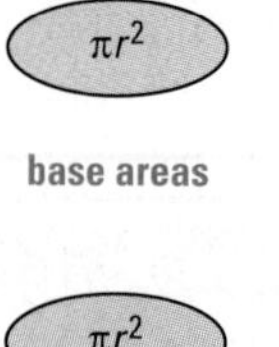

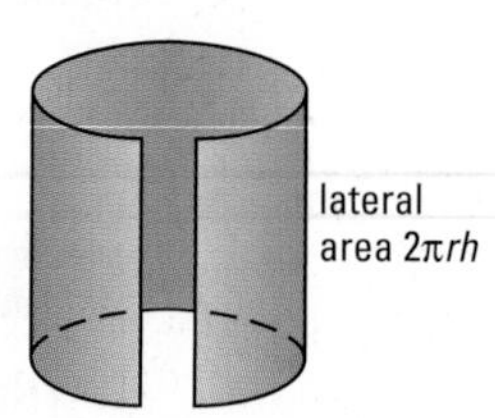

The **lateral area of a cylinder** is the area of its curved surface. The lateral area is equal to the product of the circumference and the height, which is $2\pi rh$. The entire **surface area of a cylinder** is equal to the sum of the lateral area and the areas of the two bases.

THEOREM

THEOREM 12.3 ***Surface Area of a Right Cylinder***

The surface area S of a right cylinder is

$$S = 2B + Ch = 2\pi r^2 + 2\pi rh,$$

where B is the area of a base, C is the circumference of a base, r is the radius of a base, and h is the height.

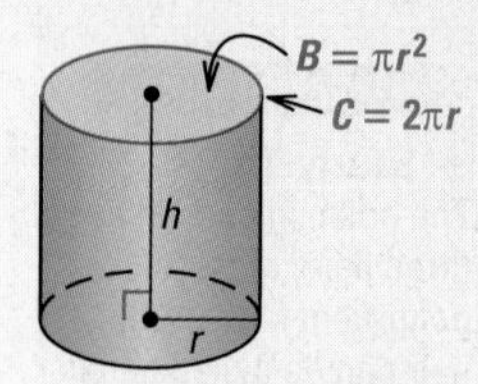

EXAMPLE 3 *Finding the Surface Area of a Cylinder*

STUDENT HELP

HOMEWORK HELP
Visit our Web site www.mcdougallittell.com for extra examples.

Find the surface area of the right cylinder.

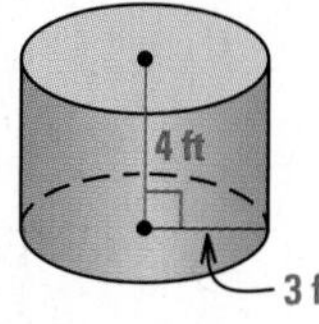

SOLUTION

Each base has a radius of 3 feet, and the cylinder has a height of 4 feet.

$S = 2\pi r^2 + 2\pi rh$	**Formula for surface area of cylinder**
$= 2\pi(3^2) + 2\pi(3)(4)$	**Substitute.**
$= 18\pi + 24\pi$	**Simplify.**
$= 42\pi$	**Add.**
≈ 131.95	**Use a calculator.**

▶ The surface area is about 132 square feet.

EXAMPLE 4 *Finding the Height of a Cylinder*

Find the height of a cylinder which has a radius of 6.5 centimeters and a surface area of 592.19 square centimeters.

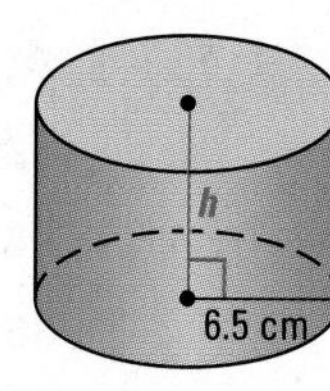

SOLUTION

Use the formula for the surface area of a cylinder and solve for the height h.

$S = 2\pi r^2 + 2\pi rh$	Formula for surface area
$592.19 = 2\pi(6.5)^2 + 2\pi(6.5)h$	Substitute 6.5 for r.
$592.19 = 84.5\pi + 13\pi h$	Simplify.
$592.19 - 84.5\pi = 13\pi h$	Subtract 84.5π from each side.
$326.73 \approx 13\pi h$	Simplify.
$8 \approx h$	Divide each side by 13π.

▶ The height is about 8 centimeters.

1. Sample answer: All the faces of a prism are polygons; the bases of a cylinder are ⊙s and one of its surfaces is curved. Both are space figures with two ≅ faces in ∥ planes. The surface area of both can be determined by adding the area of the bases to the area of the lateral surface(s).

GUIDED PRACTICE

Vocabulary Check ✓

1. Describe the differences between a prism and a cylinder. Describe their similarities. See margin.

Concept Check ✓

2. Sketch a triangular prism. Then sketch a net of the triangular prism. Describe how to find its lateral area and surface area. See margin.

Skill Check ✓

Give the mathematical name of the solid.

3. Soup can cylinder

4. Door stop triangular prism

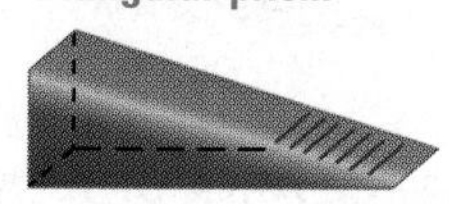

5. Shoe box rectangular prism

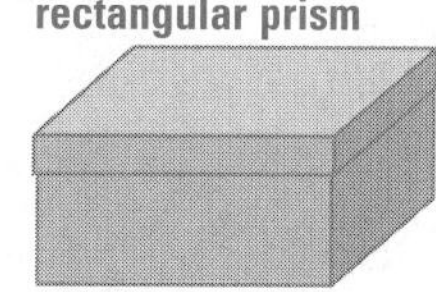

6–10. Three answers are given. The first considers the top and bottom as the bases, the second, the front and back, and the third, the right and left sides.

Use the diagram to find the measurement of the right rectangular prism.

6. Perimeter of a base 22 cm; 16 cm; 26 cm
7. Length of a lateral edge 5 cm; 8 cm; 3 cm
8. Lateral area of the prism 110 cm^2; 128 cm^2; 78 cm^2
9. Area of a base 24 cm^2; 15 cm^2; 40 cm^2
10. Surface area of the prism 158 cm^2

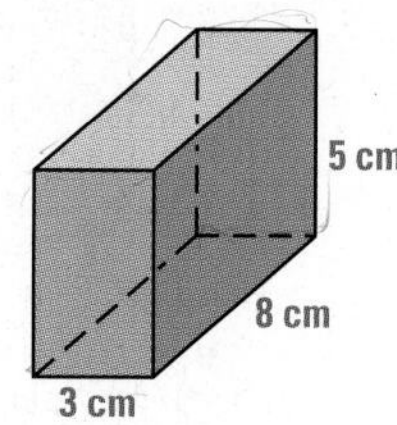

Make a sketch of the described solid. 11, 12. See margin.

11. Right rectangular prism with a 3.4 foot square base and a height of 5.9 feet
12. Right cylinder with a diameter of 14 meters and a height of 22 meters

EXTRA EXAMPLE 4

Find the height of a cylinder that has a radius of 9.5 inches and a surface area of 925.2 square inches. about 6 in.

✓ *CHECKPOINT EXERCISES*

For use after Example 4:

1. Find the surface area of a right cylinder with a radius of 12 meters and a height of 4.5 meters. $396\pi \approx 1244.07$ m^2

STUDENT HELP NOTES

Homework Help Students can find extra examples at **www.mcdougallittell.com** that parallel the examples in the student edition.

FOCUS ON VOCABULARY

Compare a *right* prism with an *oblique* prism. *Sample answer:* In a right prism, the lateral edges are perpendicular to both bases. In an oblique prism, the lateral edges are not perpendicular to both bases, so the prism appears to be slanted.

CLOSURE QUESTION

How do you find the surface area of a right prism? of a right cylinder? *Sample answer:* For the prism, double the area of the base, and add to it the perimeter of a base times the height. For the cylinder, double the area of a base ($2 \times \pi r^2$), and add to it the circumference of a base ($2\pi r$) times the height.

DAILY PUZZLER

If you "stretch" a prism so that its length doubles, but its base remains unchanged, does its surface area double? Explain or give an example. No; for example, a square prism with a base edge of 5 and a height of 4 has a surface area of 130. Changing the height to 8 changes the surface area to 210.

2, 11, 12. See Additional Answers beginning on page AA1.

3 APPLY

Assignment Guide

Basic
Day 1: pp. 732–734 Exs. 18–42 even, 45–47, 50–60

Average
Day 1: pp. 732–734 Exs. 18–42 even, 44–47, 50–60

Advanced
Day 1: pp. 732–734 Exs. 18–42 even, 44–60

Block Schedule with 12.3
pp. 732–734 Exs. 18–42 even, 44–47, 50–60

Exercise Levels

Level A: *Easier*
13–19

Level B: *More Difficult*
20–47, 50–60

Level C: *Most Difficult*
48, 49

Homework Check

To quickly check student understanding of key concepts, go over the following exercises: Exs. 14, 18, 22, 28, 32, 36, 38. See also the Daily Homework Quiz:

- Blackline Master (*Chapter 12 Resource Book,* p. 36)
- Transparency (p. 88)

Teaching Tips

Exercises 17–25 As students work with nets, encourage them to use or make a physical model if they are having trouble seeing how a net will fold. Also, if students are having trouble keeping track of all of the faces of a solid when finding surface area, encourage them to draw a net of the solid and find the total area of all the bases and faces.

English Learners

Exercises 6–10 If students have not yet absorbed the terminology for elements of three-dimensional solids, point out on the figure each element named in Exercises 6–10 before asking students to find the measurements.

Practice and Applications

Student Help
Extra Practice to help you master skills is on p. 825.

Studying Prisms **Use the diagram at the right.**

13. Give the mathematical name of the solid. right hexagonal prism
14. How many lateral faces does the solid have? 6
15. What kind of figure is each lateral face? rectangle
16. Name four lateral edges. any 4 of $\overline{AP}$, $\overline{BQ}$, $\overline{CR}$, $\overline{DS}$, $\overline{ET}$, or $\overline{FV}$

Analyzing Nets **Name the solid that can be folded from the net.**

17. 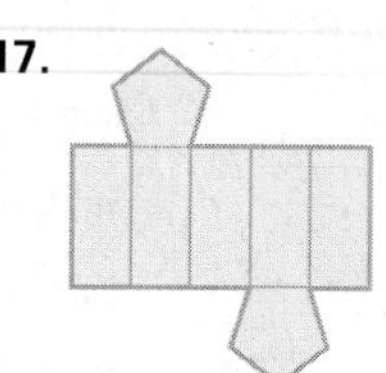
pentagonal prism

18. 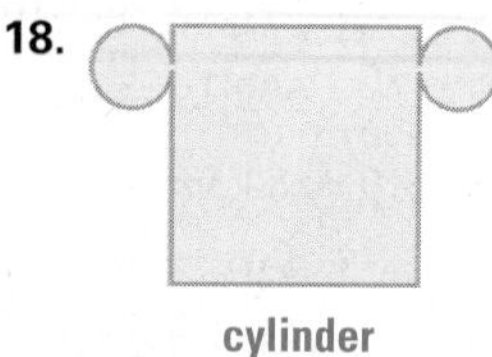
cylinder

19. 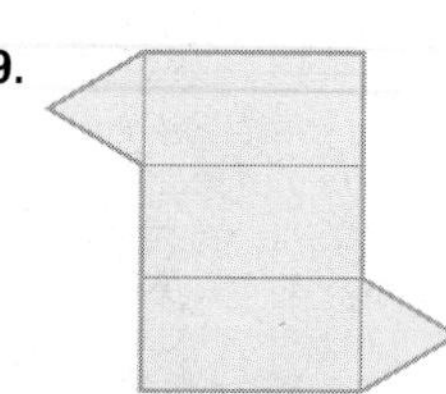
triangular prism

Surface Area of a Prism **Find the surface area of the right prism. Round your result to two decimal places.**

20. 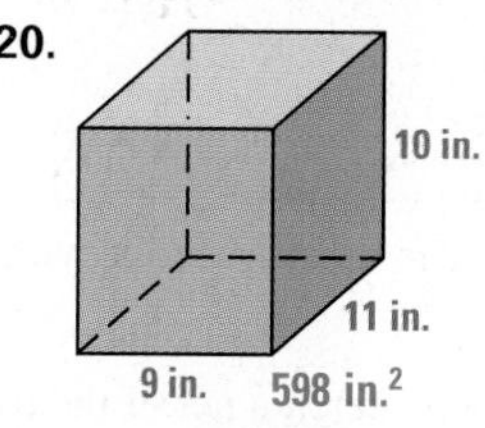

598 in.^{2}

21. 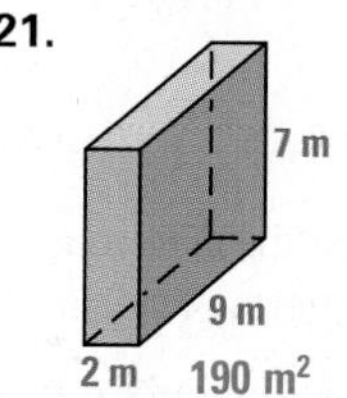

190 m^2

22. 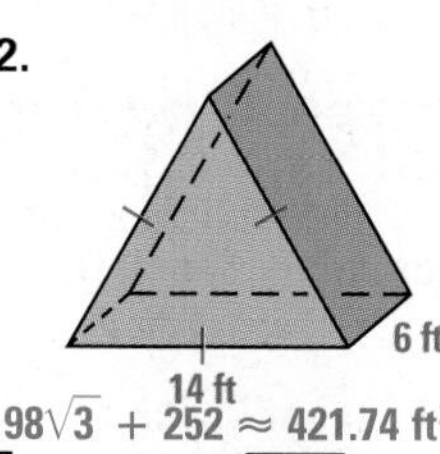

$98\sqrt{3} + 252 \approx 421.74$ ft^2

23. 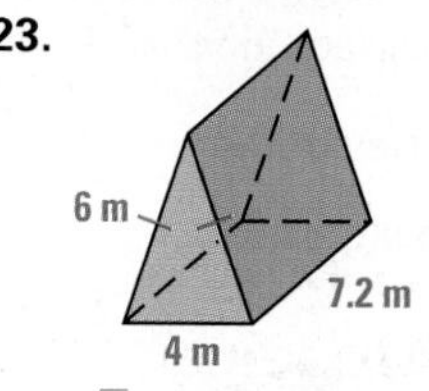

$16\sqrt{2} + 115.2 \approx 137.83$ m^2

24. 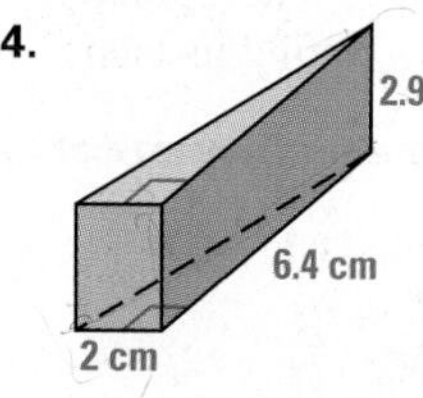

56.61 cm^2

25. 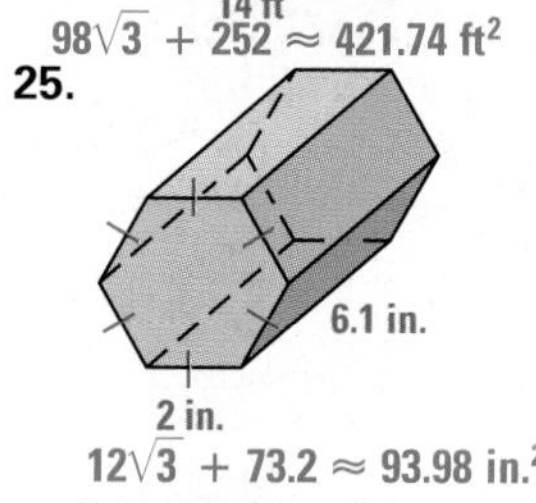

$12\sqrt{3} + 73.2 \approx 93.98$ in.^{2}

Surface Area of a Cylinder **Find the surface area of the right cylinder. Round the result to two decimal places.**

26. 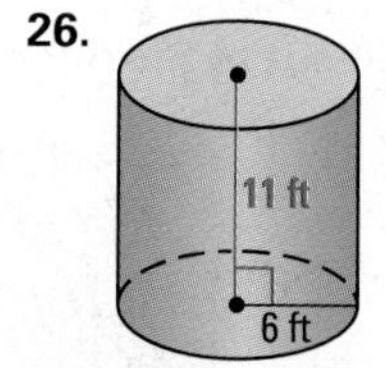

$204\pi \approx 640.88$ ft^2

27. 8 cm, 8 cm
$256\pi \approx 804.25$ cm^2

28. 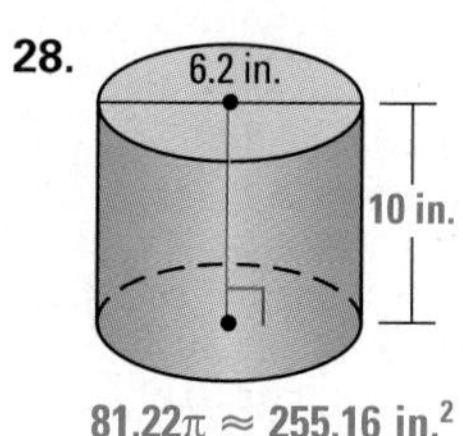

$81.22\pi \approx 255.16$ in.^{2}

Student Help
Homework Help
Example 1: Exs. 13–16, 20–25
Example 2: Exs. 20–25, 29–31, 35–37
Example 3: Exs. 26–28
Example 4: Exs. 32–34

Visual Thinking **Sketch the described solid and find its surface area.** 29–31. See margin.

29. Right rectangular prism with a height of 10 feet, length of 3 feet, and width of 6 feet
30. Right regular hexagonal prism with all edges measuring 12 millimeters
31. Right cylinder with a diameter of 2.4 inches and a height of 6.1 inches

29–31. See Additional Answers beginning on page AA1.

USING ALGEBRA **Solve for the variable given the surface area S of the right prism or right cylinder. Round the result to two decimal places.**

32. $S = 298\text{ ft}^2$ 11 ft

33. $S = 870\text{ m}^2$ 27 m

34. $S = 1202\text{ in.}^2$ 18.01 in.

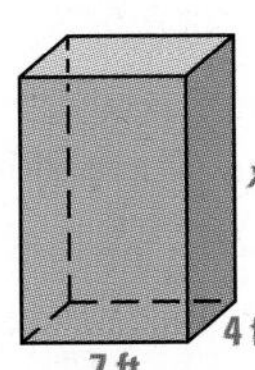

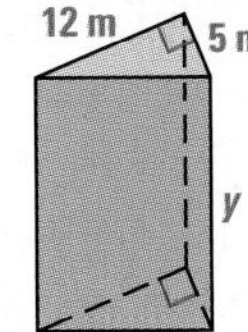

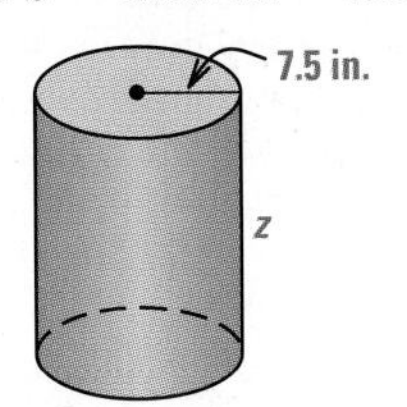

LOGICAL REASONING **Find the surface area of the right prism when the height is 1 inch, and then when the height is 2 inches. When the height doubles, does the surface area double?** 35–37. See margin.

35.

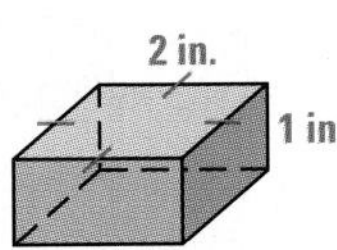

36.

3 in.
1 in.

37.

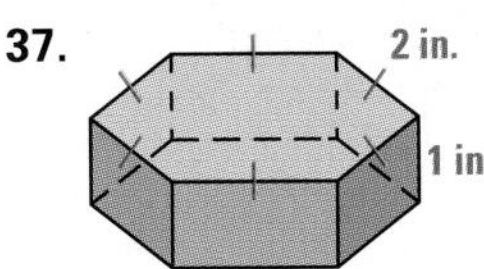

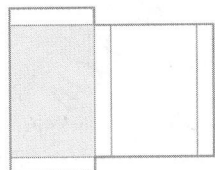

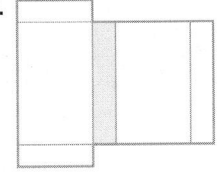

PACKAGING **In Exercises 38–40, sketch the box that results after the net has been folded. Use the shaded face as a base.** 38–40. See margin.

38.

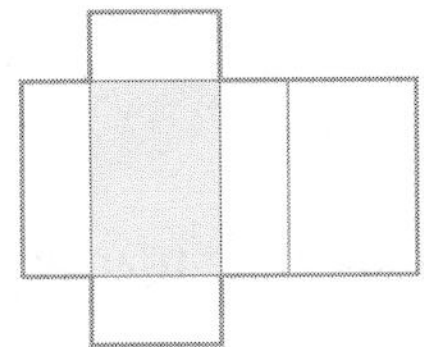

39.

40.

41. CRITICAL THINKING If you were to unfold a cardboard box, the cardboard would not match the net of the original solid. What sort of differences would there be? Why do these differences exist?

42. ARCHITECTURE Each tower of the World Trade Center in New York City is 414 meters high. The bases are squares with sides that are 64 meters. What is the surface area of each tower (including both bases)? $114{,}176\text{ m}^2$

43. WAX CYLINDER RECORDS The first versions of phonograph records were hollow wax cylinders. Grooves were cut into the lateral surface of the cylinder, and the cylinder was rotated on a phonograph to reproduce the sound. In the late 1800's, a standard sized cylinder was about 2 inches in diameter and 4 inches long. Find the exterior lateral area of the cylinder described. $8\pi \approx 25\text{ in.}^2$

44. CAKE DESIGN Two layers of a cake are right regular hexagonal prisms as shown in the diagram. Each layer is 3 inches high. Calculate the area of the cake that will be frosted. If one can of frosting will cover 130 square inches of cake, how many cans do you need? (*Hint:* The bottom of each layer will not be frosted and the entire top of the bottom layer will be frosted.) $219\sqrt{3} + 288 \approx 667\text{ in.}^2$; 6 cans

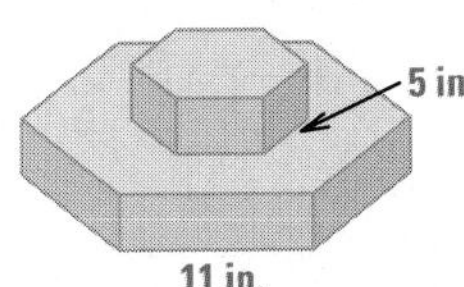

FOCUS ON CAREERS

REAL LIFE **ARCHITECTS** use the surface area of a building to help them calculate the amount of building materials needed to cover the outside of a building.

41. At least two sides would be longer or wider than the corresponding sides of the folded box. Several sides have to fold over to enclose the box and make its structure more rigid.

! COMMON ERROR

EXERCISES 26–28 As students find the surface area of a cylinder, alert them to avoid several common errors: forgetting to include the areas of both bases, using a diameter instead of a radius, using the square of the radius value in both expressions, or multiplying the height by the area of a base instead of by its circumference.

CAREER NOTE

EXERCISES 38–40
Additional information about architects is available at **www.mcdougallittell.com.**

35. 16 in.^2; 24 in.^2; no

36. $\frac{9\sqrt{3}}{2} + 9 \approx 16.8\text{ in.}^2$;

$\frac{9\sqrt{3}}{2} + 18 \approx 25.8\text{ in.}^2$; no

37. $12\sqrt{3} + 12 \approx 32.8\text{ in.}^2$;

$12\sqrt{3} + 24 \approx 44.8\text{ in.}^2$; no

38.

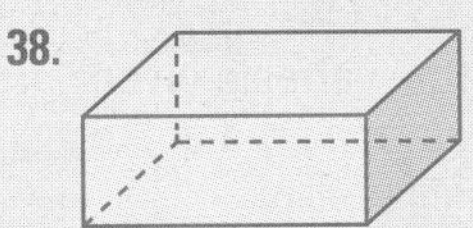

39, 40. See Additional Answers beginning on page AA1.

ADDITIONAL PRACTICE AND RETEACHING

For Lesson 12.2:

- Practice Levels A, B, and C (*Chapter 12 Resource Book,* p. 26)
- Reteaching with Practice (*Chapter 12 Resource Book,* p. 29)
- See Lesson 12.2 of the *Personal Student Tutor*

For more Mixed Review:

- Search the *Test and Practice Generator* for key words or specific lessons.

4 ASSESS

DAILY HOMEWORK QUIZ

Transparency Available

1. How many lateral faces and how many lateral edges does an oblique octagonal prism have? 8, 8
2. Find the surface area of the right prism. Round your result to two decimal places.

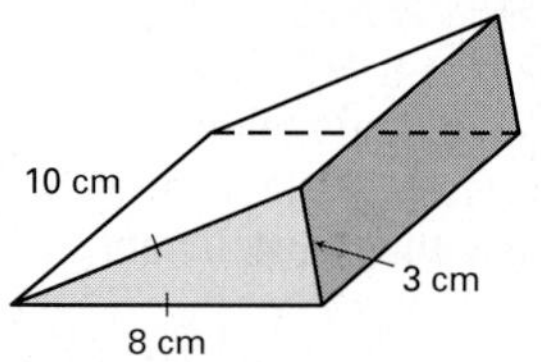

213.57 cm^2

3. Find the surface area of a right cylinder that has a base diameter of 8 inches and a height of 15 inches. Round your result to two decimal places. 477.52 $in.^2$
4. Solve for the variable given that the surface area of the right prism is 208 m^2.

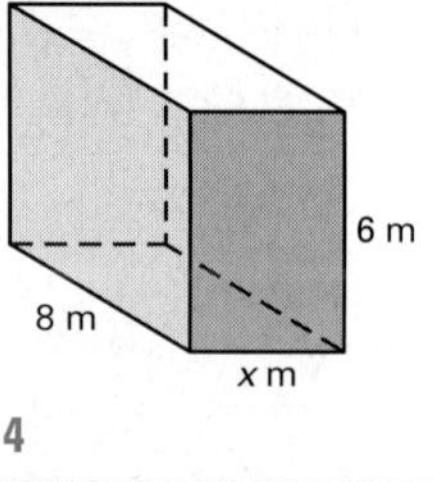

4

EXTRA CHALLENGE NOTE

Challenge problems for Lesson 12.2 are available in **blackline** format in the *Chapter 12 Resource Book,* p. 33 and at **www.mcdougallittell.com.**

ADDITIONAL TEST PREPARATION

1. **WRITING** Explain how the formula $S = 2B + Ph$ applies to finding the surface areas both of right prisms and of right cylinders.
See sample answer at right.

Test Preparation

47. Let r, h, and S be the radius, height, and surface area of the original cylinder. Then the surface area of the larger cylinder is $2\pi(2r)^2 + 2\pi(2r)(2h) = 8\pi r^2 + 8\pi rh = 4(2\pi r^2 + 2\pi rh) = 4S$.

MULTI-STEP PROBLEM **Use the following information.**
A canned goods company manufactures cylindrical cans resembling the one at the right.

45. Find the surface area of the can. $\frac{33\pi}{2} \approx 52$ $in.^2$
46. Find the surface area of a can whose radius and height are twice that of the can shown. $66\pi \approx 207$ $in.^2$
47. *Writing* Use the formula for the surface area of a right cylinder to explain why the answer in Exercise 46 is not twice the answer in Exercise 45.

★ Challenge

FINDING SURFACE AREA **Find the surface area of the solid. Remember to include both lateral areas. Round the result to two decimal places.**

48. 196 cm^2

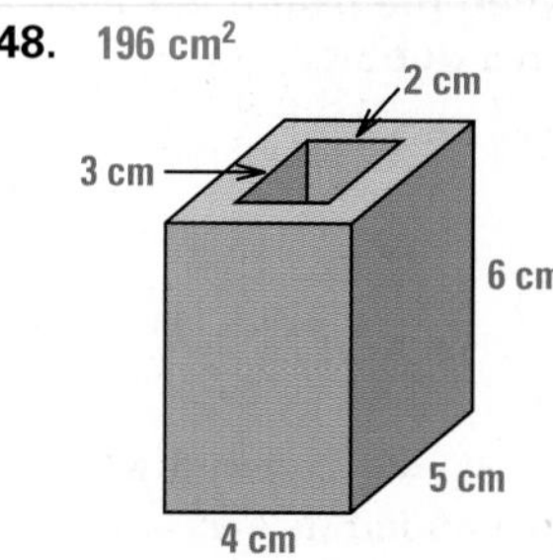

49. $28\pi \approx 87.96$ $in.^2$

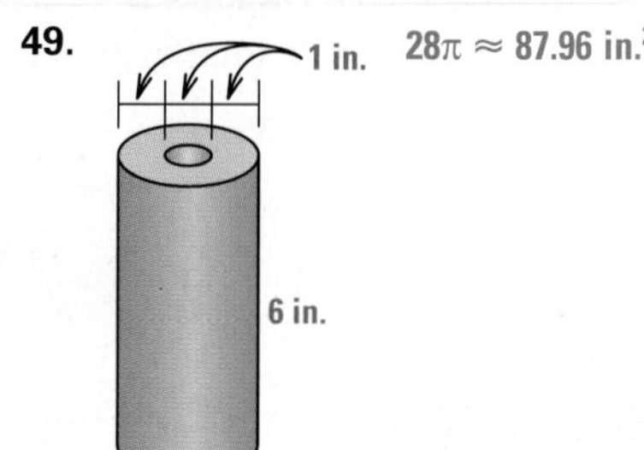

EXTRA CHALLENGE
www.mcdougallittell.com

MIXED REVIEW

EVALUATING TRIANGLES **Solve the right triangle. Round your answers to two decimal places.** (Review 9.6)

50. $m\angle A = 61°$, $BC \approx 9.02$, $AB \approx 10.31$
51. $m\angle A = 58°$, $BC \approx 16.80$, $AB \approx 19.81$
52. $m\angle B = 44°$, $BC \approx 12.43$, $AB \approx 17.27$

50. 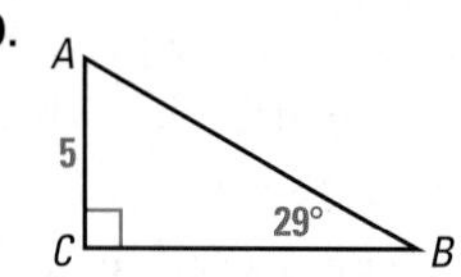

51. 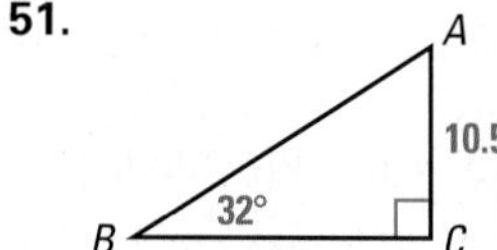

52. 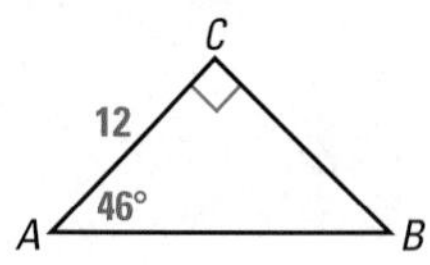

FINDING AREA **Find the area of the regular polygon or circle. Round the result to two decimal places.** (Review 11.2, 11.5 for 12.3)

53. $1805 \cos 36° \sin 36° \approx 858.33$ m^2
54. $196\pi \approx 615.75$ ft^2
55. $96\sqrt{3} \approx 166.28$ $in.^2$

53. 19 m

54. 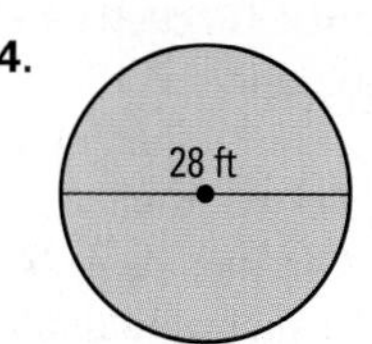

55. 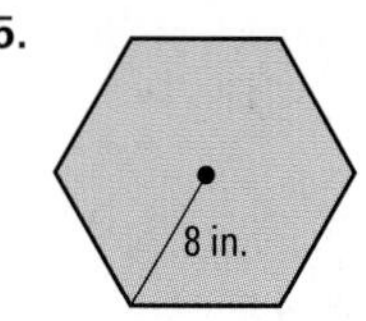

FINDING PROBABILITY **Find the probability that a point chosen at random on $\overline{PW}$ is on the given segment.** (Review 11.6)

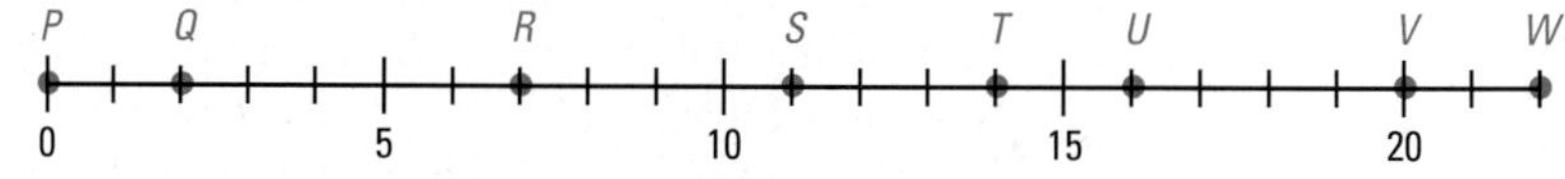

56. $\overline{QS}$ $\frac{9}{22} \approx 41\%$
57. $\overline{PU}$ $\frac{8}{11} \approx 73\%$
58. $\overline{QU}$ $\frac{7}{11} \approx 64\%$
59. $\overline{TW}$ $\frac{4}{11} \approx 36\%$
60. $\overline{PV}$ $\frac{10}{11} \approx 91\%$

Additional Test Preparation *Sample answer:*
1. Since B represents the area of a base, $2B$ gives the total area of both bases either of a prism or a cylinder. To find B, use the area formula appropriate to a base with a given shape. Then Ph, the perimeter times the height, represents the lateral area of either a prism or cylinder. In the case of a cylinder, the perimeter is actually the circumference C.

12.3 Surface Area of Pyramids and Cones

What you should learn

GOAL 1 Find the surface area of a pyramid.

GOAL 2 Find the surface area of a cone.

Why you should learn it

▼ To find the surface area of solids in **real life**, such as the Pyramid Arena in Memphis, Tennessee, shown below and in **Example 1**.

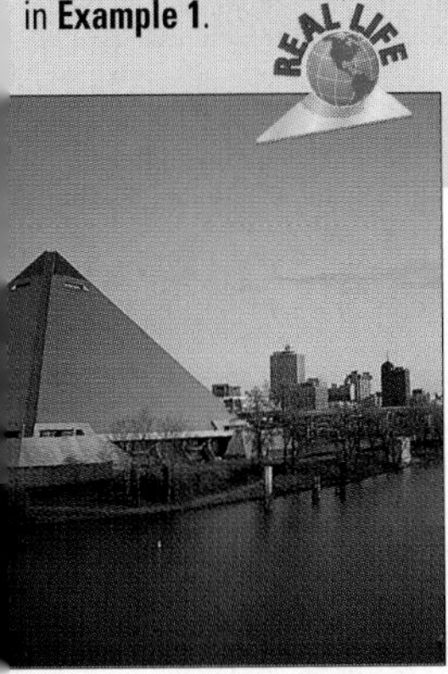

GOAL 1 FINDING THE SURFACE AREA OF A PYRAMID

A **pyramid** is a polyhedron in which the *base* is a polygon and the *lateral faces* are triangles with a common *vertex*. The intersection of two lateral faces is a *lateral edge*. The intersection of the base and a lateral face is a *base edge*. The *altitude*, or *height*, of the pyramid is the perpendicular distance between the base and the vertex.

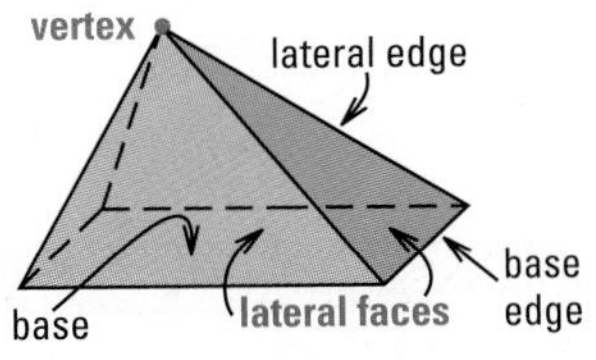

Pyramid

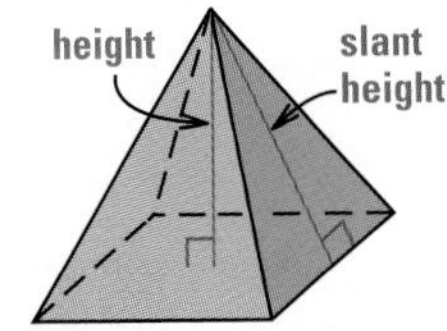

Regular pyramid

A **regular pyramid** has a regular polygon for a base and its height meets the base at its center. The *slant height* of a regular pyramid is the altitude of any lateral face. A nonregular pyramid does not have a slant height.

EXAMPLE 1 *Finding the Area of a Lateral Face*

ARCHITECTURE The lateral faces of the Pyramid Arena in Memphis, Tennessee, are covered with steel panels. Use the diagram of the arena at the right to find the area of each lateral face of this regular pyramid.

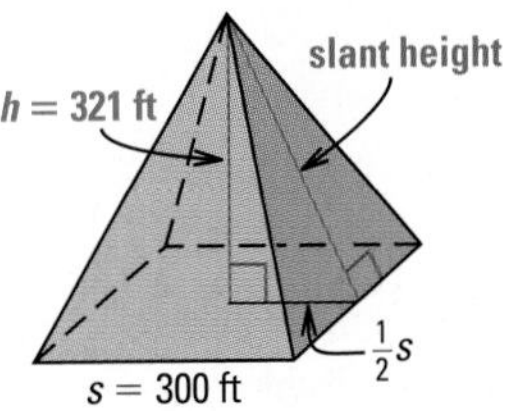

SOLUTION

To find the slant height of the pyramid, use the Pythagorean Theorem.

321 ft | slant height | $\frac{1}{2}s = 150$ ft

$$(\text{Slant height})^2 = h^2 + \left(\frac{1}{2}s\right)^2 \quad \textbf{Write formula.}$$

$$(\text{Slant height})^2 = 321^2 + 150^2 \quad \textbf{Substitute.}$$

$$(\text{Slant height})^2 = 125{,}541 \quad \textbf{Simplify.}$$

$$\text{Slant height} = \sqrt{125{,}541} \quad \textbf{Take the positive square root.}$$

$$\text{Slant height} \approx 354.32 \quad \textbf{Use a calculator.}$$

▶ So, the area of each lateral face is $\frac{1}{2}$(base of lateral face)(slant height), or about $\frac{1}{2}(300)(354.32)$, which is about 53,148 square feet.

STUDENT HELP

Study Tip

A *regular pyramid* is considered a regular polyhedron only if *all* its faces, including the base, are congruent. So, the only pyramid that is a regular polyhedron is the regular triangular pyramid, or *tetrahedron*. See page 721.

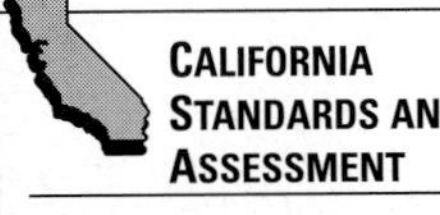

CALIFORNIA STANDARDS AND ASSESSMENT

CA Standards: 8, 9
SAT9 Task 1: Obj. 2
SAT9 Task 2: Obj. 6

1 PLAN

PACING

Basic: 2 days
Average: 2 days
Advanced: 2 days
Block Schedule: 0.5 block with 12.2
0.5 block with 12.4

LESSON OPENER APPLICATION

An alternative way to approach Lesson 12.3 is to use the Application Lesson Opener:

- Blackline Master (*Chapter 12 Resource Book*, p. 37)
- Transparency (p. 76)

MEETING INDIVIDUAL NEEDS

- ***Chapter 12 Resource Book***
  Prerequisite Skills Review (p. 5)
  Practice Level A (p. 41)
  Practice Level B (p. 42)
  Practice Level C (p. 43)
  Reteaching with Practice (p. 44)
  Absent Student Catch-Up (p. 46)
  Challenge (p. 49)
- ***Resources in Spanish***
- ***Personal Student Tutor***

NEW-TEACHER SUPPORT

See the Tips for New Teachers on pp. 1–2 of the *Chapter 12 Resource Book* for additional notes about Lesson 12.3.

WARM-UP EXERCISES

Transparency Available

Find the surface area of the solid.

1. right rectangular prism: length = 2 cm, width = 3 cm, height = 10 cm **112 cm²**
2. right cylinder: height = 12 ft, radius = 5 ft **$170\pi \approx 534.07$ ft²**
3. right pentagonal prism: area of a base = 62 m², perimeter of a base = 30 m, height = 5 m **274 m²**
4. right cylinder: height = 6 in., diameter = 3 in. **$22.5\pi \approx 70.69$ in.²**

2 TEACH

MOTIVATING THE LESSON

Ask students who has had a drink of water or a snow cone in a cone-shaped paper cup. When such a cup is unfolded, it forms a sector of a circle. Tell students that by finding the area of the sector, which is really finding the *lateral surface area* of a cone, they can find how much paper is used to make the cup.

EXTRA EXAMPLE 1

A wooden jewelry box is in the shape of a regular pyramid. Use the diagram of the box to find the area of each lateral face.

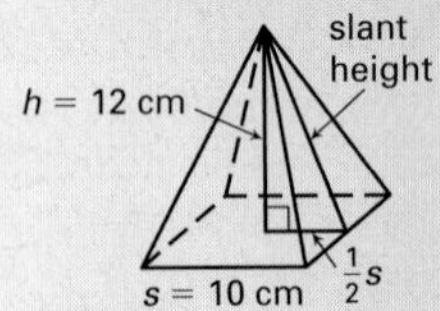

65 cm²

EXTRA EXAMPLE 2

Find the surface area of the regular pyramid shown.

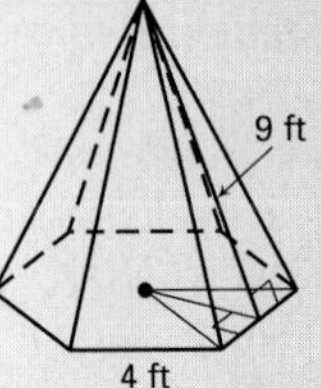

about 149.6 ft²

CHECKPOINT EXERCISES

For use after Examples 1 and 2:

1. A regular pentagonal pyramid has a base with sides of length 18 inches, an apothem of about 12.4 inches, and a slant height of 24 inches. Find the surface area of the pyramid. about 1638 in.²

STUDENT HELP

Study Tip
When sketching the net of a pyramid, first sketch the base. Then sketch the lateral faces.

A regular hexagonal pyramid and its net are shown at the right. Let b represent the length of a base edge, and let ℓ represent the slant height of the pyramid.

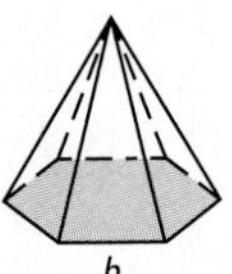

The area of each lateral face is $\frac{1}{2}b\ell$ and the perimeter of the base is $P = 6b$. So, the surface area is as follows:

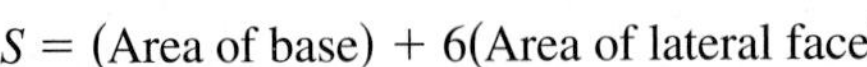

$S = (\text{Area of base}) + 6(\text{Area of lateral face})$

$S = B + 6\left(\frac{1}{2}b\ell\right)$ **Substitute.**

$S = B + \frac{1}{2}(6b)\ell$ **Rewrite $6\left(\frac{1}{2}b\ell\right)$ as $\frac{1}{2}(6b)\ell$.**

$S = B + \frac{1}{2}P\ell$ **Substitute P for $6b$.**

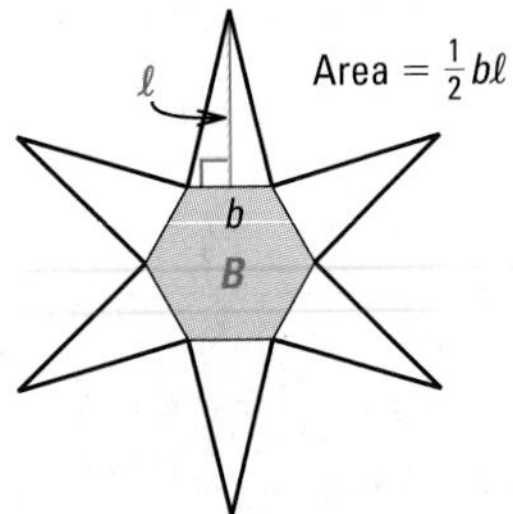

THEOREM

THEOREM 12.4 ***Surface Area of a Regular Pyramid***

The surface area S of a regular pyramid is $S = B + \frac{1}{2}P\ell$, where B is the area of the base, P is the perimeter of the base, and ℓ is the slant height.

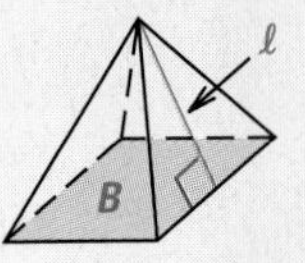

EXAMPLE 2 *Finding the Surface Area of a Pyramid*

To find the surface area of the regular pyramid shown, start by finding the area of the base.

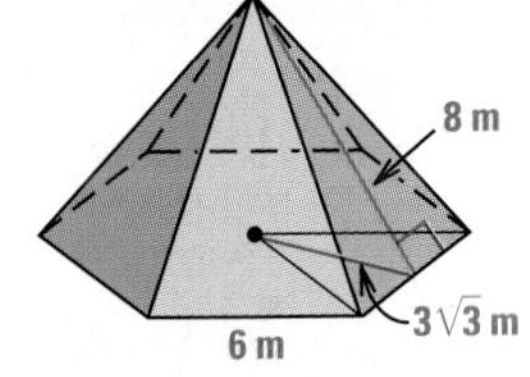

STUDENT HELP

Look Back
For help with finding the area of regular polygons see pp. 669–671.

Use the formula for the area of a regular polygon, $\frac{1}{2}(\text{apothem})(\text{perimeter})$. A diagram of the base is shown at the right. After substituting, the area of the base is $\frac{1}{2}(3\sqrt{3})(6 \cdot 6)$, or $54\sqrt{3}$ square meters.

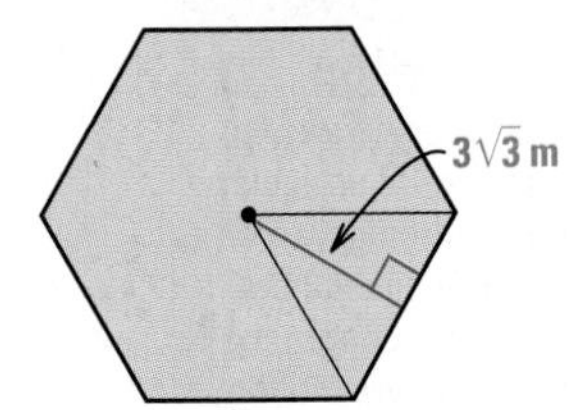

Now you can find the surface area, using $54\sqrt{3}$ for the area of the base, B.

$S = B + \frac{1}{2}P\ell$ **Write formula.**

$= 54\sqrt{3} + \frac{1}{2}(36)(8)$ **Substitute.**

$= 54\sqrt{3} + 144$ **Simplify.**

≈ 237.5 **Use a calculator.**

▶ So, the surface area is about 237.5 square meters.

GOAL 2 FINDING THE SURFACE AREA OF A CONE

A **circular cone**, or **cone**, has a circular *base* and a *vertex* that is not in the same plane as the base. The *altitude*, or *height*, is the perpendicular distance between the vertex and the base. In a **right cone**, the height meets the base at its center and the *slant height* is the distance between the vertex and a point on the base edge.

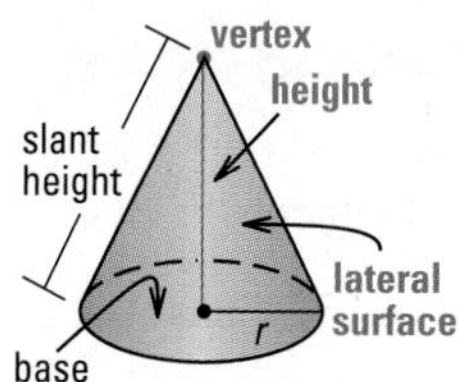

The **lateral surface** of a cone consists of all segments that connect the vertex with points on the base edge. When you cut along the slant height and lie the cone flat, you get the net shown at the right. In the net, the circular base has an area of πr^2 and the lateral surface is the sector of a circle. You can find the area of this sector by using a proportion, as shown below.

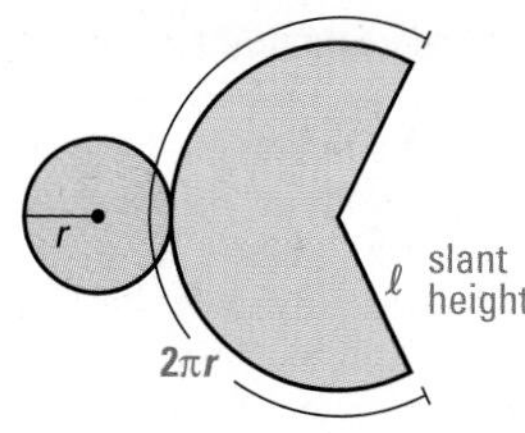

$$\frac{\text{Area of sector}}{\text{Area of circle}} = \frac{\text{Arc length}}{\text{Circumference of circle}}$$ **Set up proportion.**

$$\frac{\text{Area of sector}}{\pi\ell^2} = \frac{2\pi r}{2\pi\ell}$$ **Substitute.**

$$\text{Area of sector} = \pi\ell^2 \cdot \frac{2\pi r}{2\pi\ell}$$ **Multiply each side by $\pi\ell^2$.**

$$\text{Area of sector} = \pi r\ell$$ **Simplify.**

The surface area of a cone is the sum of the base area and the lateral area, $\pi r\ell$.

THEOREM

THEOREM 12.5 ***Surface Area of a Right Cone***

The surface area S of a right cone is $S = \pi r^2 + \pi r\ell$, where r is the radius of the base and ℓ is the slant height.

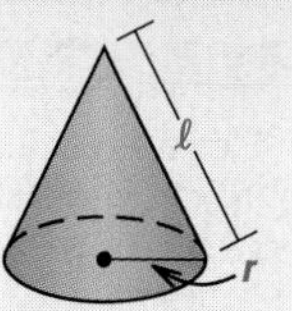

EXAMPLE 3 *Finding the Surface Area of a Right Cone*

To find the surface area of the right cone shown, use the formula for the surface area.

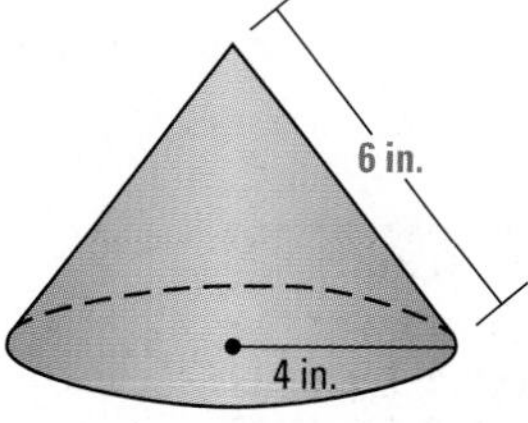

$S = \pi r^2 + \pi r\ell$ **Write formula.**

$= \pi 4^2 + \pi(4)(6)$ **Substitute.**

$= 16\pi + 24\pi$ **Simplify.**

$= 40\pi$ **Simplify.**

▶ The surface area is 40π square inches, or about 125.7 square inches.

EXTRA EXAMPLE 3

Find the surface area of the right cone shown.
65π in.^{2}, or about 204.2 in.^{2}

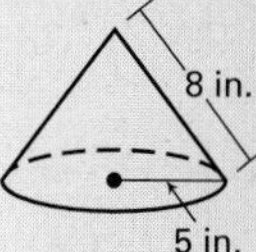

CHECKPOINT EXERCISES

For use after Example 3:

1. Find the surface area of a right cone with a radius of 12 feet and a slant height of 16 feet.
336π ft^2, or about 1055.6 ft^2

FOCUS ON VOCABULARY

What is meant by the *slant height* of a pyramid or cone?
Sample answer: The slant height is the length of a segment extending from the vertex of the pyramid or cone to the edge of the base. In a pyramid, the segment must be perpendicular to a base edge, which makes it an altitude of a lateral face of the pyramid.

CLOSURE QUESTION

Describe how to find the surface area of a right regular pyramid.
Sample answer: Use the formula $S = B + \frac{1}{2}Pl$, where B represents the area of the base, or one half the apothem times the perimeter, P represents the perimeter of the base, and l represents the slant height, which is the altitude of each lateral face.

DAILY PUZZLER

Each circle in the figure is tangent to the other two circles and tangent to the triangle at two points. If each circle has a radius of 4 centimeters, what is the perimeter of the triangle?

$24 + 24\sqrt{3}$ cm

ASSIGNMENT GUIDE

BASIC

Day 1: pp. 738–741 Exs. 14–38 even, 44–46

Day 2: pp. 738–742 Exs. 15–39 odd, 43, 50–53, Quiz 1 Exs. 1–6

AVERAGE

Day 1: pp. 738–741 Exs. 14–38 even, 44–46

Day 2: pp. 738–742 Exs. 15–43 odd, 50–53, Quiz 1 Exs. 1–6

ADVANCED

Day 1: pp. 738–741 Exs. 14–38 even, 44–46

Day 2: pp. 738–742 Exs. 15–43 odd, 50–53, Quiz 1 Exs. 1–6

BLOCK SCHEDULE

pp. 738–741 Exs. 14–38 even, 44–46 (with 12.2)
pp. 738–742 Exs. 15–43 odd, 50–53, Quiz 1 Exs. 1–6 (with 12.4)

EXERCISE LEVELS

Level A: ***Easier***
14–16

Level B: ***More Difficult***
17–31, 35–46, 50–53

Level C: ***Most Difficult***
32–34, 47–49

✓ HOMEWORK CHECK

To quickly check student understanding of key concepts, go over the following exercises: Exs. 14, 18, 20, 24, 26, 30, 34, 36, 43. See also the Daily Homework Quiz:

- Blackline Master (*Chapter 12 Resource Book,* p. 53)
- Transparency (p. 89)

! COMMON ERROR

EXERCISE 19 Students may have trouble finding the base area. Remind them that the base is a regular hexagon, so each interior angle measures 120°. They should see that each triangle formed by joining the center of the base to the ends of a base edge is equilateral, which will make it easy to find the apothem.

GUIDED PRACTICE

Vocabulary Check ✓

1. Describe the differences between pyramids and cones. Describe their similarities. See margin.

Concept Check ✓

2. Can a pyramid have rectangles for lateral faces? Explain. No; all the faces of any pyramid are △.

Skill Check ✓

Match the expression with the correct measurement.

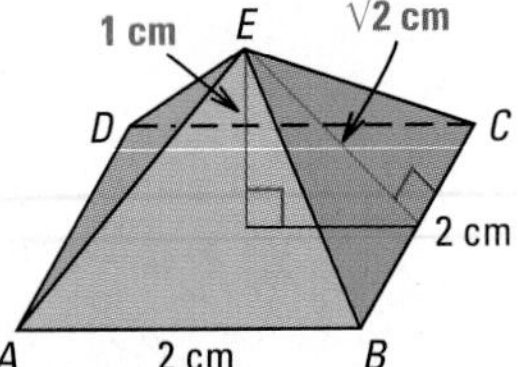

3. Area of base C **A.** $4\sqrt{2}$ cm^2
4. Height E **B.** $\sqrt{2}$ cm
5. Slant height B **C.** 4 cm^2
6. Lateral area A **D.** $(4 + 4\sqrt{2})$ cm^2
7. Surface area D **E.** 1 cm

1. *Sample answer:* All the faces of a pyramid are polygons and two lateral faces intersect in a lateral edge. A cone has no lateral faces. Its base is a ⊙ and its lateral surface is curved, so it has no lateral edges. Both are space figures with a vertex and a base. The altitude of each is the ⊥ distance from the vertex to the plane containing the base.

In Exercises 8–11, sketch a right cone with $r = 3$ ft and $h = 7$ ft.

8. Find the area of the base. about 28.27 ft^2
9. Find the slant height. about 7.62 ft
10. Find the lateral area. about 71.82 ft^2
11. Find the surface area. about 100.09 ft^2

Find the surface area of the regular pyramid described.

12. The base area is 9 square meters, the perimeter of the base is 12 meters, and the slant height is 2.5 meters. 24 m^2
13. The base area is $25\sqrt{3}$ square inches, the perimeter of the base is 30 inches, and the slant height is 12 inches. $25\sqrt{3} + 180 \approx 223.30$ in.^{2}

PRACTICE AND APPLICATIONS

STUDENT HELP
Extra Practice to help you master skills is on p. 825.

AREA OF A LATERAL FACE **Find the area of a lateral face of the regular pyramid. Round the result to one decimal place.**

14. 50.6 m^2

12 m
8 m
8 m

15. 270.6 in.^{2}

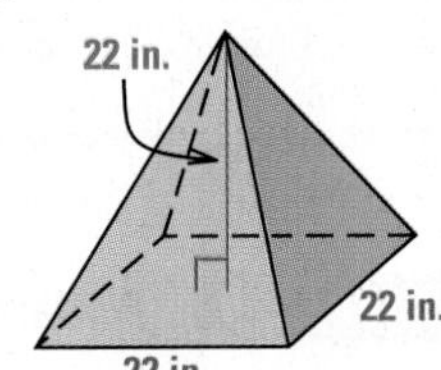

16. 14.8 ft^2

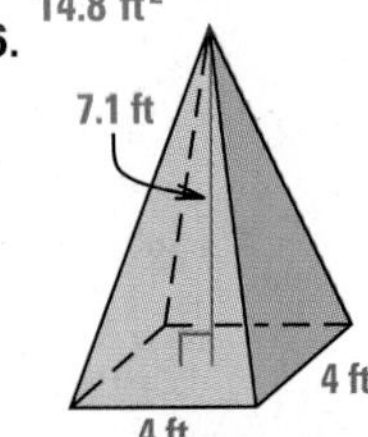

SURFACE AREA OF A PYRAMID **Find the surface area of the regular pyramid.**

STUDENT HELP
HOMEWORK HELP
Example 1: Exs. 14–16
Example 2: Exs. 17–19
Example 3: Exs. 20–25

17.

17 mm
11.2 mm

506.24 mm^2

18.

13 cm
8 cm

$16\sqrt{3} + 36\sqrt{17} \approx 176.14$ cm^2

19.

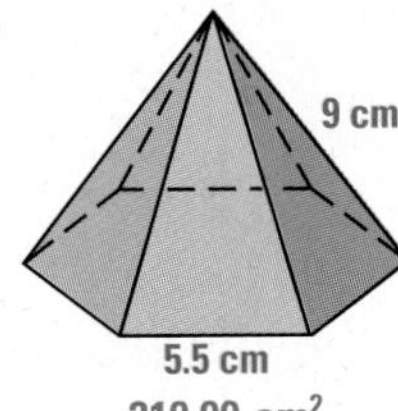

219.99 cm^2

FINDING SLANT HEIGHT Find the slant height of the right cone.

20. 14 in.; 8 in. — $2\sqrt{65} \approx 16.1$ in.

21. 9.2 cm; 5.6 cm — $2\sqrt{29} \approx 10.8$ cm

22. $\sqrt{2}$ ft; 2 ft — $\sqrt{6} \approx 2.4$ ft

SURFACE AREA OF A CONE Find the surface area of the right cone. Leave your answers in terms of π.

23. 24. 25.

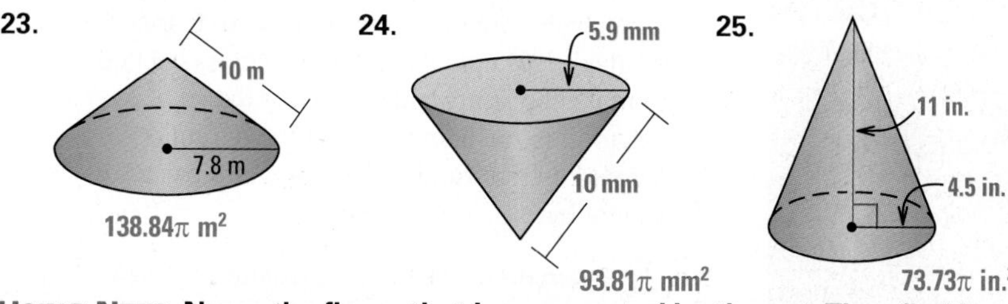

USING NETS Name the figure that is represented by the net. Then find its surface area. Round the result to one decimal place. See margin.

26. 27.

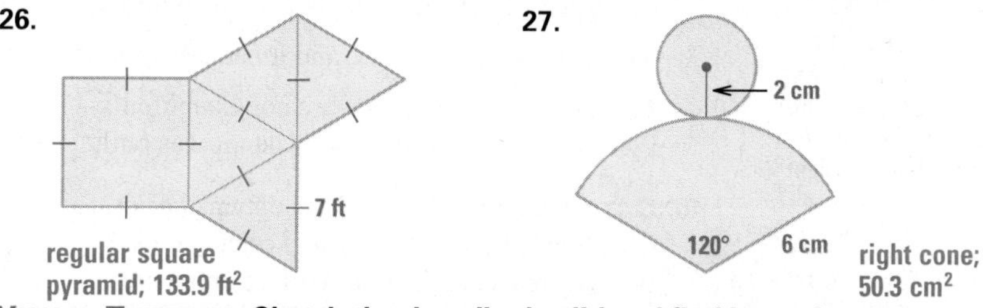

VISUAL THINKING Sketch the described solid and find its surface area. Round the result to one decimal place. 28–31. See margin.

28. A regular pyramid has a triangular base with a base edge of 8 centimeters, a height of 12 centimeters, and a slant height of 12.2 centimeters.

29. A regular pyramid has a hexagonal base with a base edge of 3 meters, a height of 5.8 meters, and a slant height of 6.2 meters.

30. A right cone has a diameter of 11 feet and a slant height of 7.2 feet.

31. A right cone has a radius of 9 inches and a height of 12 inches.

STUDENT HELP

HOMEWORK HELP Visit our Web site www.mcdougallittell.com for help with Exs. 32–34.

COMPOSITE SOLIDS Find the surface area of the solid. The pyramids are regular and the prisms, cylinders, and cones are right. Round the result to one decimal place.

32. 33. 34.

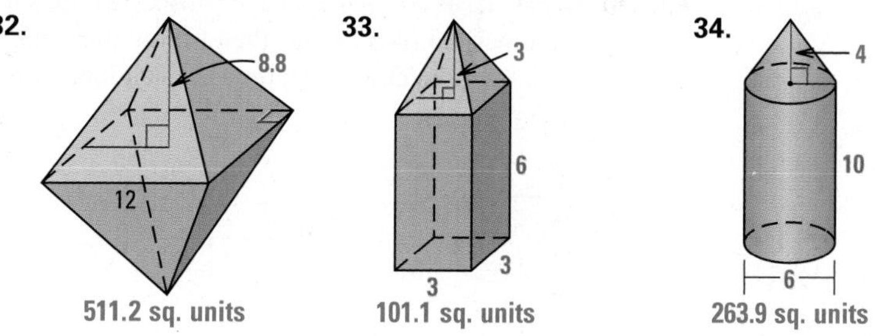

MATHEMATICAL REASONING

EXERCISES 23–25 The formula for the surface area of a right cone, $S = \pi r^2 + \pi rl$, can be derived from that for a regular pyramid, $S = B + \frac{1}{2}Pl$. The term πr^2 corresponds to B because it is the area of the circular base cone. The circumference of the circle is $2\pi r$, so $\frac{1}{2}Pl$ is $\frac{1}{2}(2\pi r)l$, or πrl. This makes sense because as the number of sides of the regular pyramid's base increases, the base becomes more and more circular in shape.

STUDENT HELP NOTES

Homework Help Students can find help for Exs. 32–34 at **www.mcdougallittell.com.** The information can be printed out for students who don't have access to the Internet.

ENGLISH LEARNERS

EXERCISES 32–34 Some students may be confused by the phrase *the prisms, cylinders, and cones are right.* Explain that here *right* does not mean "correct."

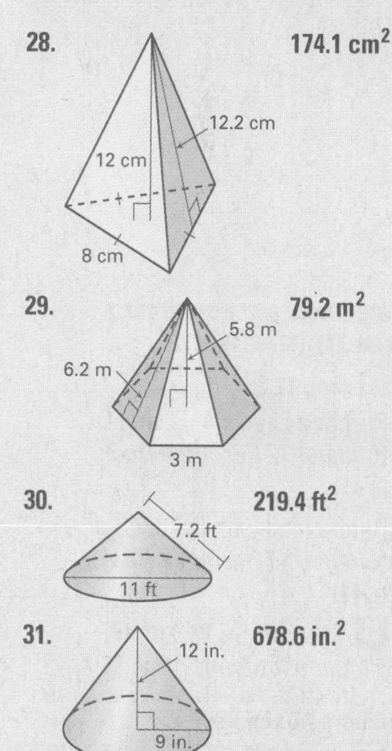

ENGLISH LEARNERS
EXERCISE 41 Many English phrases formed by the use of a noun as an adjective preceding another noun are ambiguous and present particular problems to English learners unfamiliar with their meanings. You might explain that a *squirrel barrier* is a barrier constructed to keep squirrels out of something.

USING ALGEBRA In Exercises 35–37, find the missing measurements of the solid. The pyramids are regular and the cones are right.

35. $P = 72$ cm
$p = 9$ cm, $q = 15$ cm

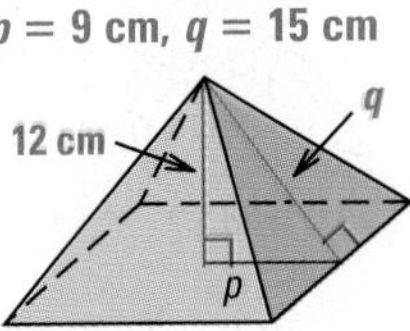

36. $S = 75.4$ in.^{2}
$y \approx 5$ in., $x \approx 4$ in.

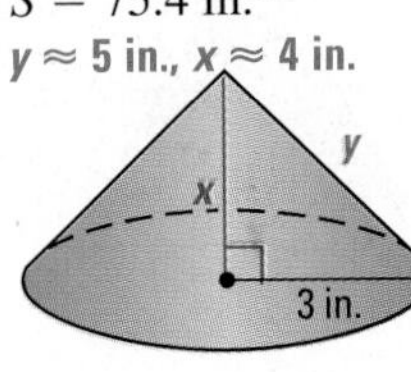

37. $S = 333$ m^2, $P = 42$ m
$l \approx 9.8$ m, $h \approx 7.7$ m

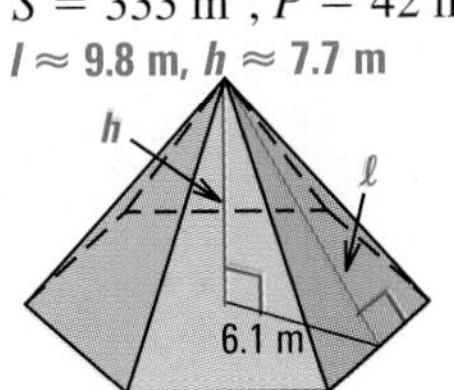

FOCUS ON APPLICATIONS

LAMPSHADES Many stained-glass lampshades are shaped like cones or pyramids. These shapes help direct the light down.

38. **LAMPSHADES** Some stained-glass lampshades are made out of decorative pieces of glass. Estimate the amount of glass needed to make the lampshade shown at the right by calculating the lateral area of the pyramid formed by the framing. The pyramid has a square base. about 1277 cm^2

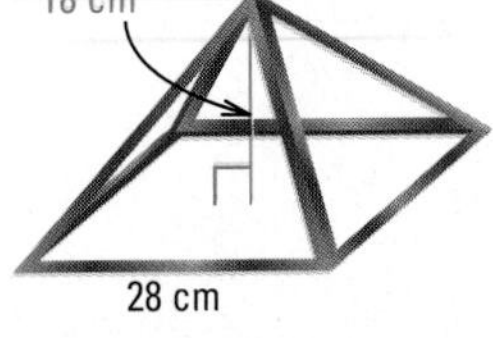

39. **PYRAMIDS** The three pyramids of Giza, Egypt, were built as regular square pyramids. The pyramid in the middle of the photo is Chephren's Pyramid and when it was built its base edge was $707\frac{3}{4}$ feet, and it had a height of 471 feet. Find the surface area of Chephren's Pyramid, including its base, when it was built. about 1,334,817 ft^2

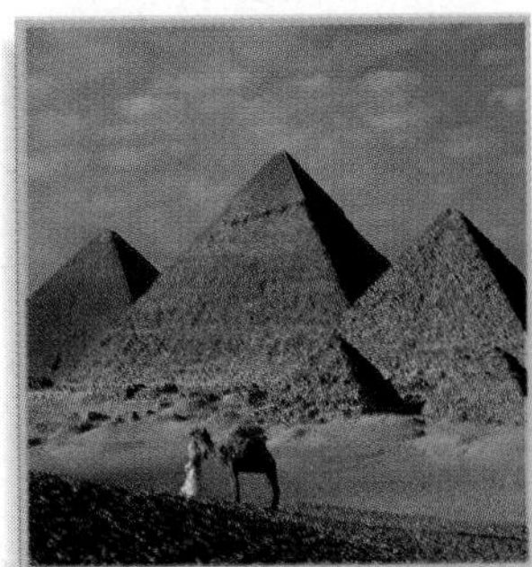

40. **DATA COLLECTION** Find the dimensions of Chephren's Pyramid today and calculate its surface area. Compare this surface area with the surface area you found in Exercise 39.

40. about 1,295,603 ft^2; *sample answer:* The surface area is about 39,214 ft^2 less, a decrease of about 3%.

41. **SQUIRREL BARRIER** Some bird feeders have a metal cone that prevents squirrels from reaching the bird seed, as shown. You are planning to manufacture this metal cone. The slant height of the cone is 12 inches and the radius is 8 inches. Approximate the amount of sheet metal you need. about 302 in.^{2}

42. **CRITICAL THINKING** A regular hexagonal pyramid with a base edge of 9 feet and a height of 12 feet is inscribed in a right cone. Find the lateral area of the cone. about 424 ft^2

43. **PAPER CUP** To make a paper drinking cup, start with a circular piece of paper that has a 3 inch radius, then follow the steps below. How does the surface area of the cup compare to the original paper circle? Find $m\angle ABC$.

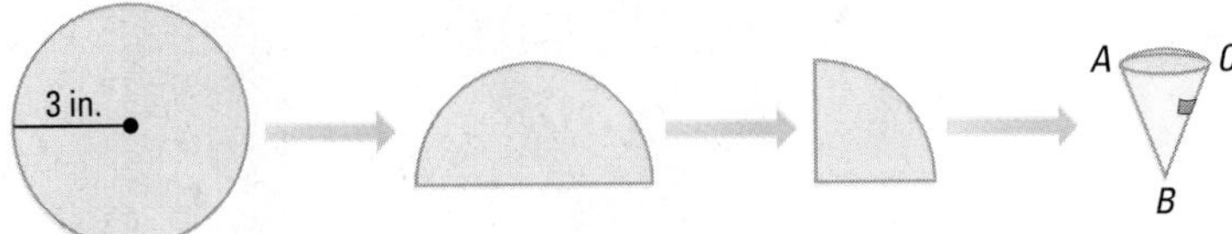

43. The surface area of the cup is $\frac{1}{4}$ the surface area of the original paper ⊙; about 29°.

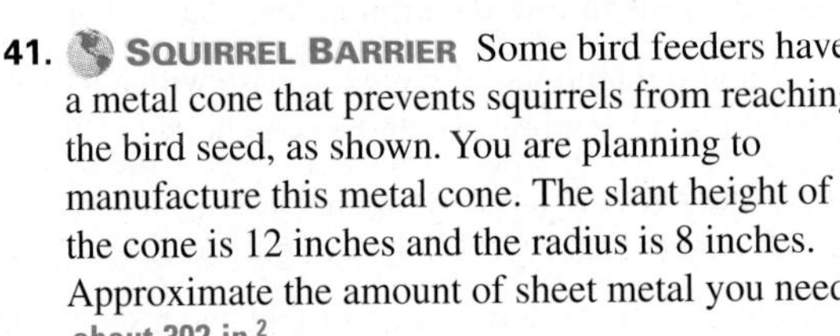

ADDITIONAL PRACTICE AND RETEACHING

For Lesson 12.3:
- Practice Levels A, B, and C (*Chapter 12 Resource Book,* p. 41)
- Reteaching with Practice (*Chapter 12 Resource Book,* p. 44)
- See Lesson 12.3 of the *Personal Student Tutor*

For more Mixed Review:
- Search the *Test and Practice Generator* for key words or specific lessons.

Test Preparation

QUANTITATIVE COMPARISON Choose the statement that is true about the given quantities.

Ⓐ The quantity in column A is greater.

Ⓑ The quantity in column B is greater.

Ⓒ The two quantities are equal.

Ⓓ The relationship cannot be determined from the given information.

	Column A	Column B	
	4, 3, 4	4, 3	
44.	Area of base	Area of base	B
45.	Lateral edge length	Slant height	C
46.	Lateral area	Lateral area	B

★ Challenge

INSCRIBED PYRAMIDS Each of three regular pyramids are inscribed in a right cone whose radius is 1 unit and height is $\sqrt{2}$ units. The dimensions of each pyramid are listed in the table and the square pyramid is shown.

Base	Base edge	Slant height
Square	1.414	1.58
Hexagon	1	1.65
Octagon	0.765	1.68

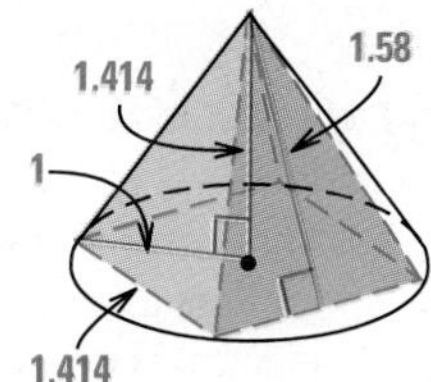

47. Find the surface area of the cone. $\pi(1 + \sqrt{3}) \approx$ **8.58 square units**

48. Find the surface area of each of the three pyramids.

48. square: 6.47 sq. units; hexagon: 7.55 sq. units; octagon: 7.97 sq. units

49. What happens to the surface area as the number of sides of the base increases? If the number of sides continues to increase, what number will the surface area approach? **It increases; $\pi(1 + \sqrt{3})$ (the surface area of the cone)**

EXTRA CHALLENGE
www.mcdougallittell.com

MIXED REVIEW

FINDING AREA In Exercises 50–52, find the area of the regular polygon. Round your result to two decimal places. **(Review 11.2 for 12.4)**

50. 21 — **190.96 sq. units**

51.

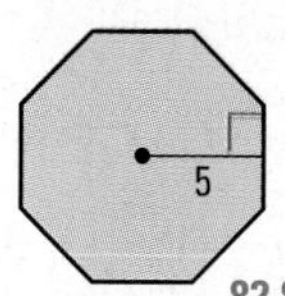

82.84 sq. units

52.

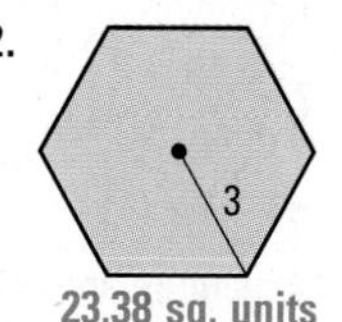

23.38 sq. units

53. AREA OF A SEMICIRCLE A semicircle has an area of 190 square inches. Find the approximate length of the radius. **(Review 11.5 for 12.4)** **about 11 in.**

Additional Test Preparation *Sample answer:*

1. Halve the diameter to find the radius r. Then use the Pythagorean Theorem to find the slant height l: $l = \sqrt{h^2 + r^2}$. Then substitute these values in the formula for the surface area of a right cone, $S = \pi r^2 + \pi r l$, and solve for S.

4 ASSESS

DAILY HOMEWORK QUIZ

Transparency Available

1. Find the surface area of the regular pyramid.

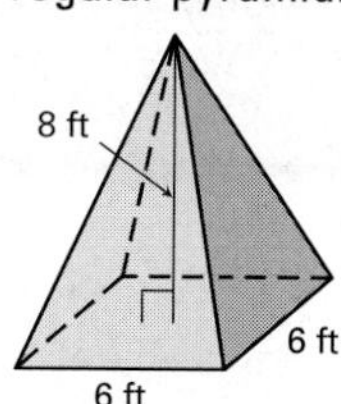

$36 + 12\sqrt{73} \approx 138.53 \text{ ft}^2$

2. Find the slant height of a right cone that has a height of 15 mm and a radius of 9 mm. **$3\sqrt{34} \approx 17.49$ mm**

3. Find the surface area of a right cone that has a height of 12 in. and a radius of 9 in. Leave your answer in terms of π. **$216\pi \text{ in.}^2$**

4. Find the missing measurements of the regular triangular pyramid if $S = 225 \text{ m}^2$ and $P = 30$ m.

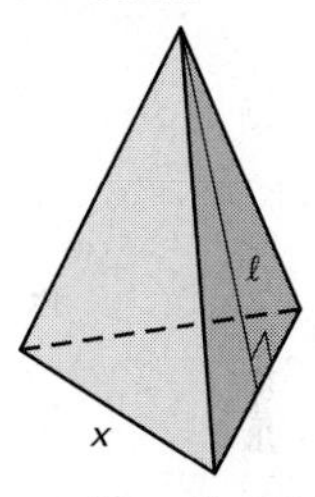

$x = 10$ m, $l \approx 12.11$ m

EXTRA CHALLENGE NOTE

Challenge problems for Lesson 12.3 are available in **blackline** format in the *Chapter 12 Resource Book,* p. 49 and at **www.mcdougallittell.com.**

ADDITIONAL TEST PREPARATION

1. WRITING If you know the diameter d and height h of a right cone, how can you find the cone's surface area? **See sample answer at left.**

ADDITIONAL RESOURCES

An alternative Quiz for Lessons 12.1–12.3 is available in the *Chapter 12 Resource Book,* p. 50.

A **blackline** master with additional Math & History exercises is available in the *Chapter 12 Resource Book,* p. 48.

QUIZ 1

Self-Test for Lessons 12.1–12.3

1. regular, convex; 4 vertices
2. not regular, convex; 8 vertices
3. not regular, not convex; 12 vertices

State whether the polyhedron is regular and/or convex. Then calculate the number of vertices of the solid using the given information. (Lesson 12.1)

1. 4 faces; all triangles

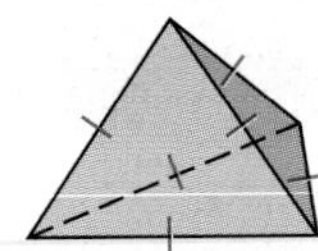

2. 8 faces; 4 triangles and 4 trapezoids

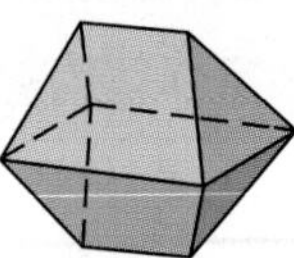

3. 8 faces; 2 hexagons and 6 rectangles

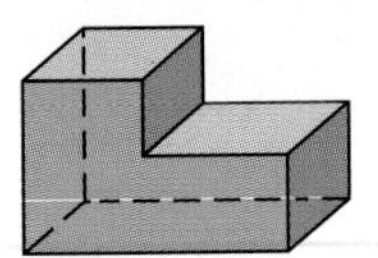

Find the surface area of the solid. Round your result to two decimal places. (Lesson 12.2 and 12.3)

4.

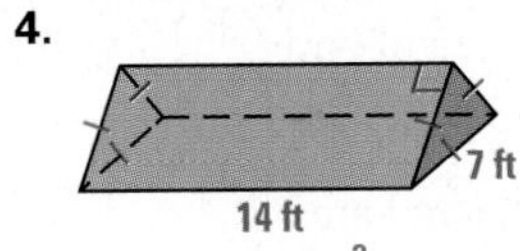

336.44 ft^2

5.

305.91 m^2

6.

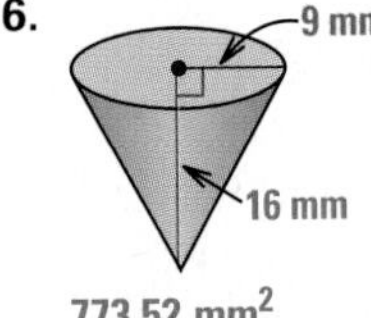

773.52 mm^2

MATH & History

History of Containers

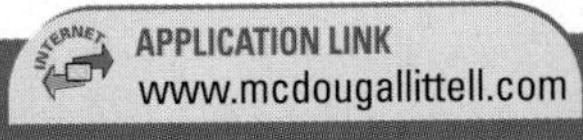

THEN

THROUGHOUT HISTORY, people have created containers for items that were important to store, such as liquids and grains. In ancient civilizations, large jars called *amphorae* were used to store water and other liquids.

NOW

TODAY, containers are no longer used just for the bare necessities. People use containers of many shapes and sizes to store a variety of objects.

1. How much paper is required to construct a paper grocery bag using the pattern at the right? 760 $in.^2$
2. The sections on the left side of the pattern are folded to become the rectangular base of the bag. Find the dimensions of the base. Then find the surface area of the completed bag. 6 in. by 12 in.; 648 $in.^2$

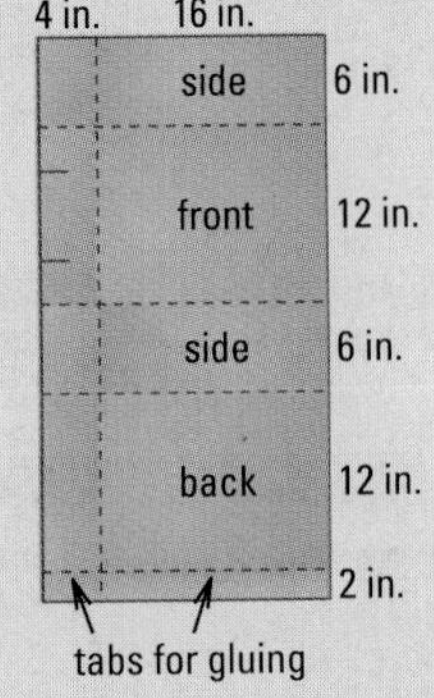

c. 525 B.C.

Amphorae are used in Ancient Greece to store water and oils.

1810

Tin containers are first used to package food.

1870

Margaret Knight patents machine to make paper bags.

1990s

Water bottles come in all shapes and sizes.

12.4 Volume of Prisms and Cylinders

What you should learn

GOAL 1 Use volume postulates.

GOAL 2 Find the volume of prisms and cylinders in **real life**, such as the concrete block in **Example 4**.

Why you should learn it

▼ Learning to find the volumes of prisms and cylinders is important in **real life**, such as in finding the volume of a fish tank in **Exs. 7–9, and 46**.

REAL LIFE

GOAL 1 EXPLORING VOLUME

The **volume of a solid** is the number of cubic units contained in its interior. Volume is measured in cubic units, such as cubic meters (m^3).

VOLUME POSTULATES

POSTULATE 27 *Volume of a Cube*

The volume of a cube is the cube of the length of its side, or $V = s^3$.

POSTULATE 28 *Volume Congruence Postulate*

If two polyhedra are congruent, then they have the same volume.

POSTULATE 29 *Volume Addition Postulate*

The volume of a solid is the sum of the volumes of all its nonoverlapping parts.

EXAMPLE 1 *Finding the Volume of a Rectangular Prism*

The box shown is 5 units long, 3 units wide, and 4 units high. How many unit cubes will fit in the box? What is the volume of the box?

unit cube 1 1 1

4 units

3 units

5 units

SOLUTION

The base of the box is 5 units by 3 units. This means 5 • 3, or 15 unit cubes, will cover the base.

Three more layers of 15 cubes each can be placed on top of the lower layer to fill the box. Because the box contains 4 layers with 15 cubes in each layer, the box contains a total of 4 • 15, or 60 unit cubes.

▶ Because the box is completely filled by the 60 cubes and each cube has a volume of 1 cubic unit, it follows that the volume of the box is 60 • 1, or 60 cubic units.

In Example 1, the area of the base, 15 square units, multiplied by the height, 4 units, yields the volume of the box, 60 cubic units. So, the volume of the prism can be found by multiplying the area of the base by the height. This method can also be used to find the volume of a cylinder.

CALIFORNIA STANDARDS AND ASSESSMENT

CA Standards: 8, 9
SAT9 Task 1: Objs. 2, 4
SAT9 Task 2: Objs. 5, 6

1 PLAN

PACING

Basic: 2 days
Average: 2 days
Advanced: 2 days
Block Schedule: 0.5 block with 12.3
0.5 block with 12.5

LESSON OPENER
APPLICATION

An alternative way to approach Lesson 12.4 is to use the Application Lesson Opener:

- Blackline Master (*Chapter 12 Resource Book*, p. 54)
- Transparency (p. 77)

MEETING INDIVIDUAL NEEDS

- ***Chapter 12 Resource Book***
  Prerequisite Skills Review (p. 5)
  Practice Level A (p. 57)
  Practice Level B (p. 58)
  Practice Level C (p. 59)
  Reteaching with Practice (p. 60)
  Absent Student Catch-Up (p. 62)
  Challenge (p. 64)
- ***Resources in Spanish***
- ***Personal Student Tutor***

NEW-TEACHER SUPPORT

See the Tips for New Teachers on pp. 1–2 of the *Chapter 12 Resource Book* for additional notes about Lesson 12.4.

WARM-UP EXERCISES

Transparency Available

Find the area of each figure.

1. a square with sides of length 4
   16 units²
2. a circle with a radius of 7 cm
   49π, or about 153.9 cm²
3. an equilateral triangle with sides of length 4 meters
   $4\sqrt{3}$, or about 6.93 m²
4. a regular hexagon with sides of length 2 feet
   $6\sqrt{3}$, or about 10.4 ft²

2 TEACH

MOTIVATING THE LESSON
Have a new box of cereal or other food that tends to settle during shipping. Ask students what a phrase like "This package is shipped by weight, not by volume" means. Point out that while surface area can be used to find the amount of cardboard needed to make a box, the *volume* of a box tells how much it can hold.

EXTRA EXAMPLE 1
The box shown is 2 units long, 6 units wide, and 3 units high. How many unit cubes will fit in the box? What is the volume of the box?

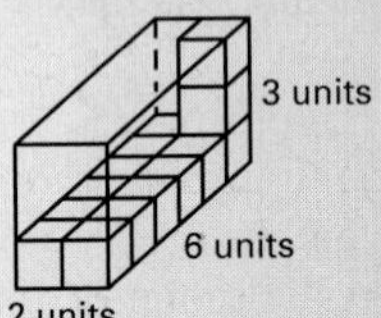

36 cubes; 36 cubic units

EXTRA EXAMPLE 2
Find the volume of the right prism and the right cylinder.

a.

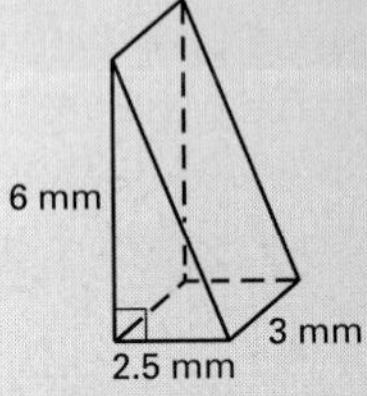

22.5 mm^3

b.

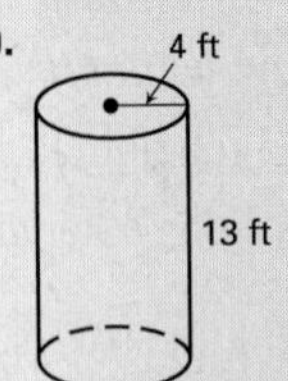

$208\pi \approx 653.45 \text{ ft}^3$

CHECKPOINT EXERCISES
For use after Examples 1 and 2:
1. Find the volume of a right hexagonal prism with a base area of 24 square inches and a height of 10 inches. 240 in.^2

GOAL 2 FINDING VOLUMES OF PRISMS AND CYLINDERS

THEOREM

THEOREM 12.6 ***Cavalieri's Principle***
If two solids have the same height and the same cross-sectional area at every level, then they have the same volume.

Theorem 12.6 is named after mathematician Bonaventura Cavalieri (1598–1647). To see how it can be applied, consider the solids below. All three have cross sections with equal areas, B, and all three have equal heights, h. By Cavalieri's Principle, it follows that each solid has the same volume.

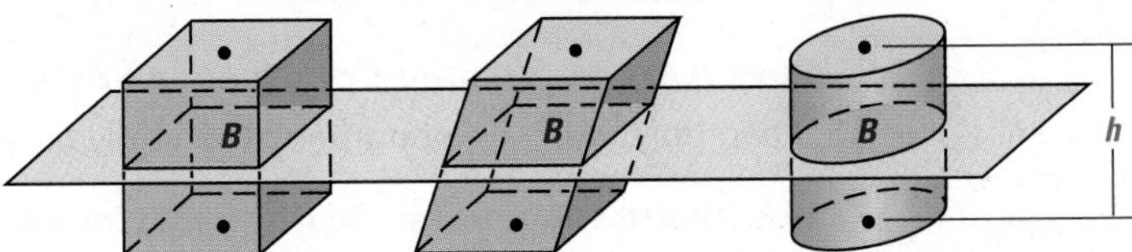

VOLUME THEOREMS

THEOREM 12.7 ***Volume of a Prism***
The volume V of a prism is $V = Bh$, where B is the area of a base and h is the height.

THEOREM 12.8 ***Volume of a Cylinder***
The volume V of a cylinder is $V = Bh = \pi r^2 h$, where B is the area of a base, h is the height, and r is the radius of a base.

EXAMPLE 2 *Finding Volumes*

Find the volume of the right prism and the right cylinder.

a.

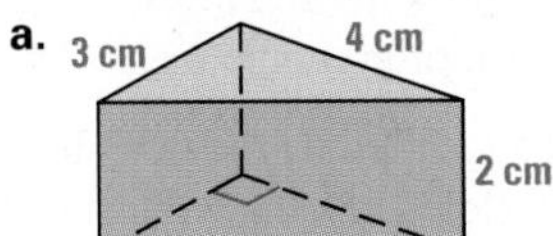

b.

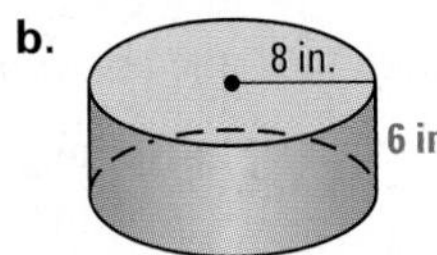

SOLUTION

a. The area B of the base is $\frac{1}{2}(3)(4)$, or 6 cm^2. Use $h = 2$ to find the volume.

$$V = Bh = 6(2) = 12 \text{ cm}^3$$

b. The area B of the base is $\pi \cdot 8^2$, or $64\pi \text{ in.}^2$ Use $h = 6$ to find the volume.

$$V = Bh = 64\pi(6) = 384\pi \approx 1206.37 \text{ in.}^3$$

EXAMPLE 3 *Using Volumes*

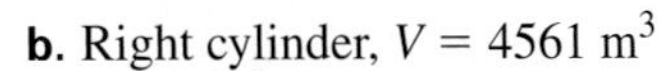

Use the measurements given to solve for x.

a. Cube, $V = 100 \text{ ft}^3$

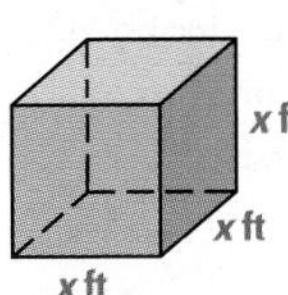

b. Right cylinder, $V = 4561 \text{ m}^3$

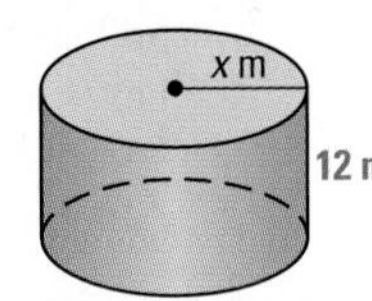

SOLUTION

a. A side length of the cube is x feet.

$V = s^3$ — **Formula for volume of cube**

$100 = x^3$ — **Substitute.**

$4.64 \approx x$ — **Take the cube root.**

▶ So, the height, width, and length of the cube are about 4.64 feet.

b. The area of the base is πx^2 square meters.

$V = Bh$ — **Formula for volume of cylinder**

$4561 = \pi x^2(12)$ — **Substitute.**

$4561 = 12\pi x^2$ — **Rewrite.**

$\frac{4561}{12\pi} = x^2$ — **Divide each side by 12π.**

$11 \approx x$ — **Find the positive square root.**

▶ So, the radius of the cylinder is about 11 meters.

STUDENT HELP

KEYSTROKE HELP

If your calculator does not have a cube root key, you can raise a number to the $\frac{1}{3}$ to find its cube root. For example, the cube root of 8 can be found as follows:

EXAMPLE 4 *Using Volumes in Real Life*

CONSTRUCTION Concrete weighs 145 pounds per cubic foot. To find the weight of the concrete block shown, you need to find its volume. The area of the base can be found as follows:

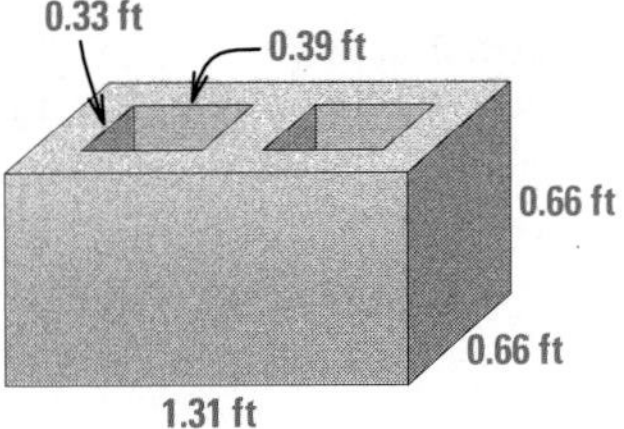

$$B = \boxed{\text{Area of large rectangle}} - 2 \cdot \boxed{\text{Area of small rectangle}}$$

$$= (1.31)(0.66) - 2(0.33)(0.39)$$

$$\approx 0.61 \text{ ft}^2$$

Using the formula for the volume of a prism, the volume is

$$V = Bh \approx 0.61(0.66) \approx 0.40 \text{ ft}^3.$$

▶ To find the weight of the block, multiply the pounds per cubic foot, 145 lb/ft^3, by the number of cubic feet, 0.40 ft^3.

$$\text{Weight} = \frac{145 \text{ lb}}{1 \text{ ft}^3} \cdot 0.4 \text{ ft}^3 \approx 58 \text{ lb}$$

FOCUS ON APPLICATIONS

CONSTRUCTION The Ennis-Brown House, shown above, was designed by Frank Lloyd Wright. It was built using concrete blocks.

EXTRA EXAMPLE 3

Use the measurements given to solve for *x*.

a. Rectangular prism, $V = 396 \text{ cm}^3$

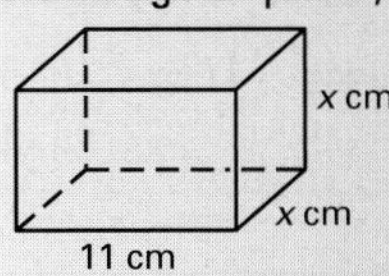

6 cm

b. Right cylinder, $V = 277 \text{ ft}^3$, diameter = x ft, height = 5 ft
about 8.4 ft

EXTRA EXAMPLE 4

Concrete is used to fill around two bricks as shown. Find the volume and the weight of the concrete used if concrete weighs 0.084 pounds per cubic inch.

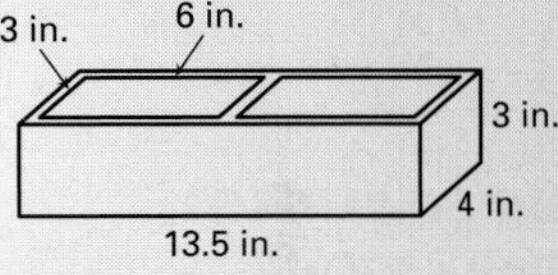

54 in.^3; about 4.54 lb

CHECKPOINT EXERCISES

For use after Examples 3 and 4:

1. A right triangular prism has base edges of length 5 cm, 12 cm, and 13 cm. Its volume is 222 cm^3. What is its height? 7.4 cm

FOCUS ON VOCABULARY

What type of units is the *volume* of a solid measured in? cubic units

CLOSURE QUESTION

How do you find the volume of a prism or cylinder with height *h*? Multiply *h* by the area of a base *B*. In the case of a cylinder with a base radius of *r*, $B = \pi r^2$.

DAILY PUZZLER

Three faces of a box have the areas shown. What is the volume of the box? 1536 units^3

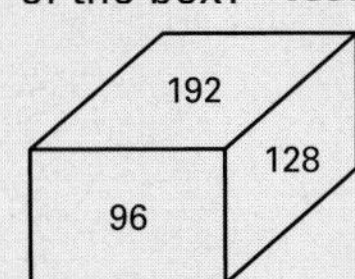

3 APPLY

ASSIGNMENT GUIDE

BASIC
Day 1: pp. 746–747 Exs. 10–33
Day 2: pp. 748–749 Exs. 34–49, 51–60

AVERAGE
Day 1: pp. 746–747 Exs. 10–33
Day 2: pp. 748–749 Exs. 34–49, 51–60

ADVANCED
Day 1: pp. 746–747 Exs. 10–33
Day 2: pp. 748–749 Exs. 34–61

BLOCK SCHEDULE
pp. 746–747 Exs. 10–33 (with 12.3)
pp. 748–749 Exs. 34–49, 51–60 (with 12.5)

EXERCISE LEVELS

Level A: *Easier*
10–14
Level B: *More Difficult*
15–49, 51–60
Level C: *Most Difficult*
50

✔ HOMEWORK CHECK

To quickly check student understanding of key concepts, go over the following exercises: Exs. 10, 15, 16, 20, 26, 30, 32, 36, 42. See also the Daily Homework Quiz:

- Blackline Master (*Chapter 12 Resource Book,* p. 67)
- Transparency (p. 90)

GUIDED PRACTICE

Vocabulary Check ✓

1. Surface area is measured in ___?___ and volume is measured in ___?___.
square units; cubic units

Concept Check ✓

2. Each stack of memo papers shown contains 500 sheets of paper. Explain why the stacks have the same volume. Then calculate the volume, given that each sheet of paper is 3 inches by 3 inches by 0.01 inches. **See margin.**

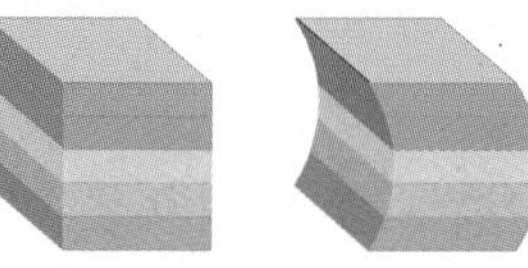

2. The two stacks have the same height and the same cross-sectional area at every level. Therefore, by Cavalieri's Principle, the two stacks have the same volume; 45 in.^{3}.

Skill Check ✓

Use the diagram to complete the table.

	ℓ	w	h	Volume	
3.	17	3	5	?	255
4.	?	8	10	160	2
5.	4.8	6.1	?	161.04	5.5
6.	$6t$	?	$3t$	$54t^3$	$3t$

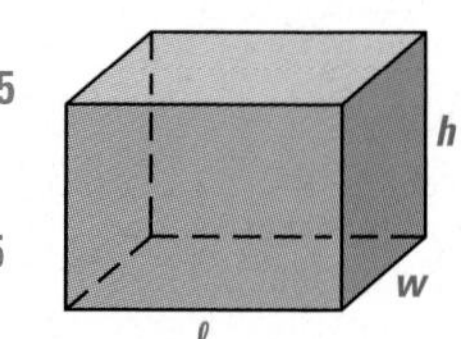

FISH TANKS **Find the volume of the tank.** **See margin.**

7.
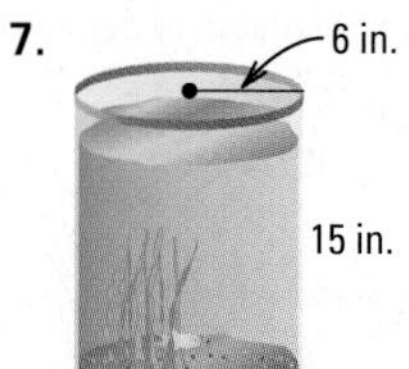

$540\pi \approx 1696$ in.^{3}

8.
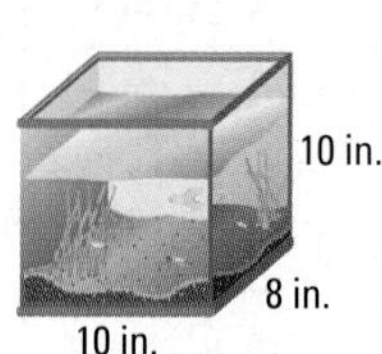

800 in.^{3}

9.
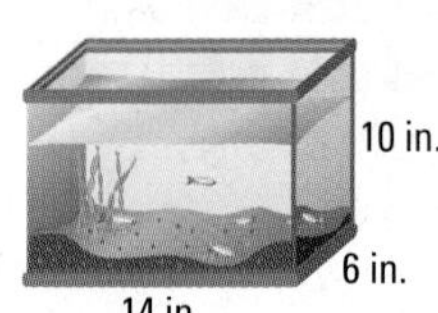

840 in.^{3}

PRACTICE AND APPLICATIONS

STUDENT HELP
Extra Practice to help you master skills is on p. 826.

USING UNIT CUBES **Find the number of unit cubes that will fit in the box. Explain your reasoning.**

10.
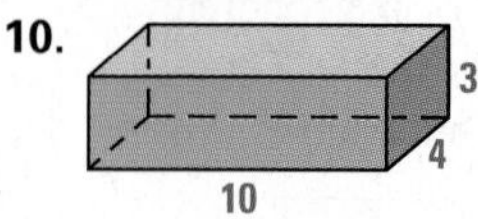

120 unit cubes; 3 layers of 4 rows of 10 cubes each

11.
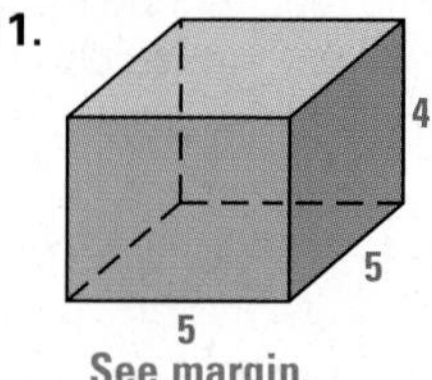

See margin.

11. 100 unit cubes; 4 layers of 5 rows of 5 cubes each

12.
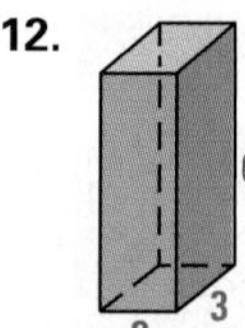

36 unit cubes; 6 layers of 3 rows of 2 cubes each

STUDENT HELP
HOMEWORK HELP
Example 1: Exs. 10–12
Example 2: Exs. 13–27
Example 3: Exs. 28–33
Example 4: Exs. 34–37

VOLUME OF A PRISM **Find the volume of the right prism.**

13.
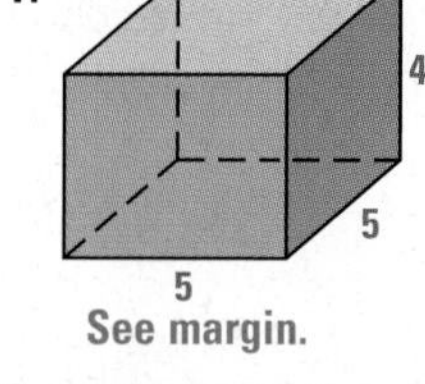

512 in.^{3}

14. 12 cm, 5 cm, 4 cm
240 cm^3

15.
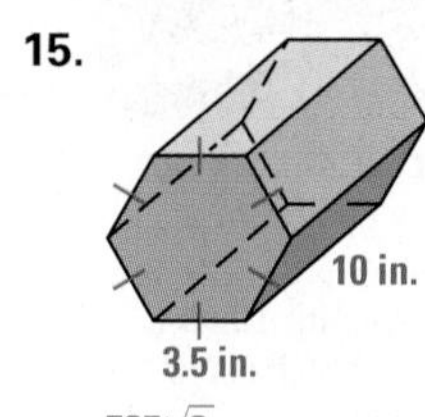

$\frac{735\sqrt{3}}{4} \approx 318.26$ in.^{3}

VOLUME OF A CYLINDER Find the volume of the right cylinder. Round the result to two decimal places.

16. 6785.84 m^3

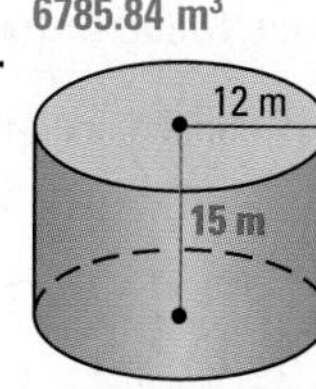

17. 288.40 ft^3

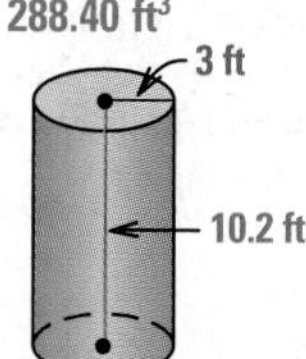

18. 381.00 cm^3

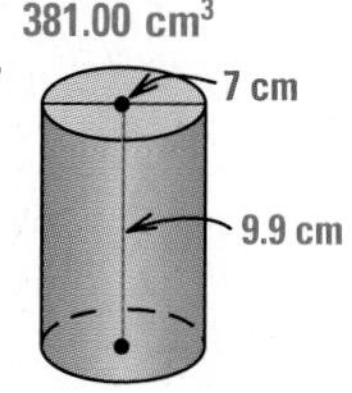

VISUAL THINKING Make a sketch of the solid and find its volume. Round the result to two decimal places. 19–24. Check sketches.

19. A prism has a square base with 4 meter sides and a height of 15 meters. 240 m^3

20. A pentagonal prism has a base area of 24 square feet and a height of 3 feet. 72 ft^3

21. A prism has a height of 11.2 centimeters and an equilateral triangle for a base, where each base edge measures 8 centimeters. 310.38 cm^3

22. A cylinder has a radius of 4 meters and a height of 8 meters. 402.12 m^3

23. A cylinder has a radius of 21.4 feet and a height of 33.7 feet. 48,484.99 ft^3

24. A cylinder has a diameter of 15 inches and a height of 26 inches. 4594.58 $in.^3$

STUDENT HELP

INTERNET HOMEWORK HELP Visit our Web site www.mcdougallittell.com for help with Exs. 25–27.

VOLUMES OF OBLIQUE SOLIDS Use Cavalieri's Principle to find the volume of the oblique prism or cylinder.

25. 924 m^3

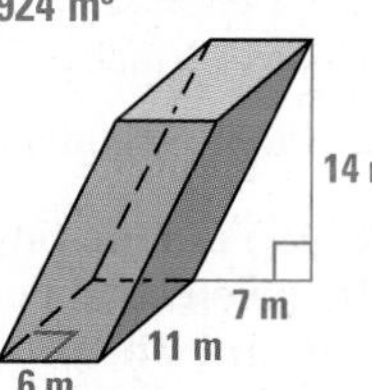

26. $200\pi \approx 628.32$ ft^3

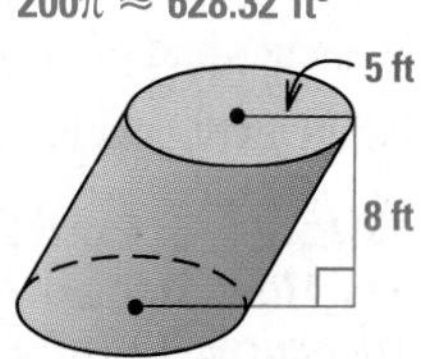

27. $\frac{135\sqrt{3}}{2} \approx 116.91$ cm^3

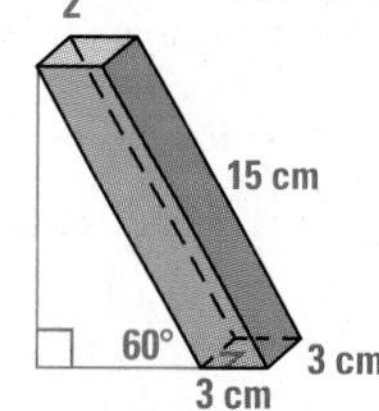

USING ALGEBRA Solve for the variable using the given measurements. The prisms and the cylinders are right.

28. Volume = 560 ft^3

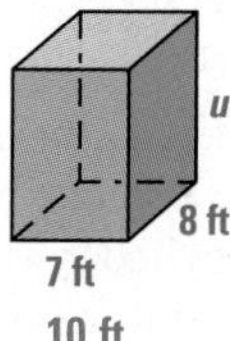

10 ft

29. Volume = 2700 yd^3

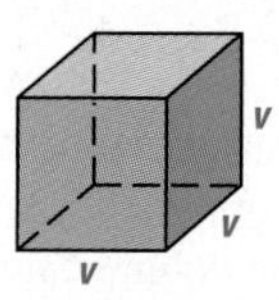

$3\sqrt[3]{100} \approx 13.92$ yd

30. Volume = 80 cm^3

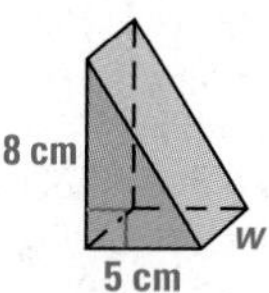

4 cm

31. Volume = 72.66 $in.^3$

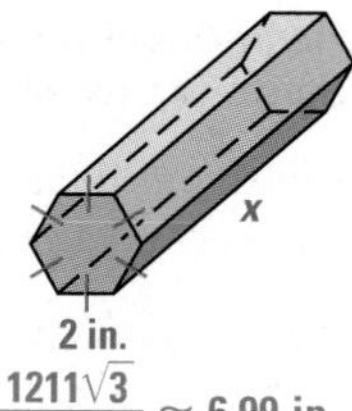

$\frac{1211\sqrt{3}}{300} \approx 6.99$ in.

32. Volume = 3000 ft^3

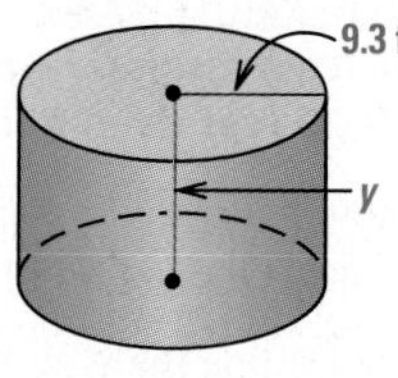

$\frac{100,000}{2883\pi} \approx 11.04$ ft

33. Volume = 1696.5 m^3

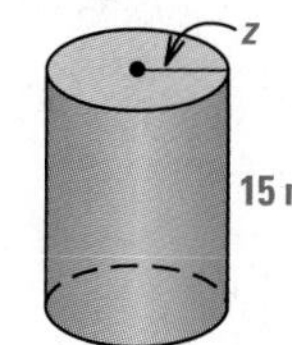

$\sqrt{\frac{1131}{10\pi}} \approx 6.00$ m

MATHEMATICAL REASONING

EXERCISES 16–18 Though a cylinder doesn't have straight edges like a rectangular prism, its volume is still measured in *cubic* units, as is true for any solid. Have students imagine filling a cylinder with unit cubes. They will notice that not all the space will be filled. Then have them imagine filling the cylinder with cubes with side lengths only half of those of the unit cubes. Point out that these cubes will fill more of the space. By continuing to use smaller and smaller cubes, the sum of the volumes of the cubes will get closer and closer to the volume of the cylinder. So, as for a rectangular prism, the volume of a cylinder can be thought of as the sum of the volumes of little cubes each with a volume given by the three-dimensional product of its length, width, and height.

STUDENT HELP NOTES

Homework Help Students can find help for Exs. 25–27 at **www.mcdougallittell.com.** The information can be printed out for students who don't have access to the Internet.

! COMMON ERROR

EXERCISE 27 Some students may multiply the base area of the prism by the slant height. Remind them that the volume of an oblique prism or cylinder is the product of the base area and the height of the solid, not its slant height. In this exercise, students must use the Pythagorean Theorem to find the height, given the slant height.

ADDITIONAL PRACTICE AND RETEACHING

For Lesson 12.4:

- Practice Levels A, B, and C (*Chapter 12 Resource Book*, p. 57)
- Reteaching with Practice (*Chapter 12 Resource Book*, p. 60)
- See Lesson 12.4 of the *Personal Student Tutor*

For more Mixed Review:

- Search the *Test and Practice Generator* for key words or specific lessons.

34. **CONCRETE BLOCK** In Example 4 on page 745, find the volume of the entire block and subtract the volume of the two rectangular prisms. How does your answer compare with the volume found in Example 4?
The answer is the same, about 0.4 ft^3.

FINDING VOLUME **Find the volume of the entire solid. The prisms and cylinders are right.**

35. 150 ft^3

5 ft, 2 ft, 3 ft, 2 ft, 6 ft, 10 ft

36. 821.88 m^3

1.8 m, 3 m, 9 m, 7.8 m, 12.4 m

37. $605\pi \approx 1900.66$ in.^{3}

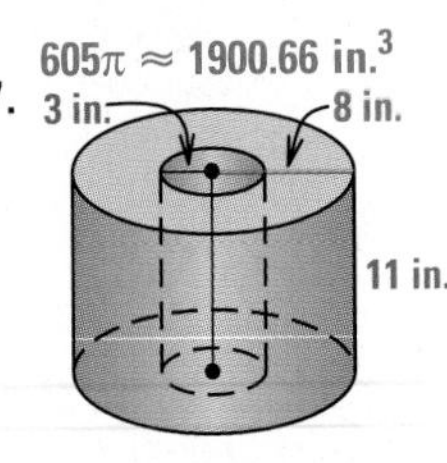

CONCRETE **In Exercises 38–40, determine the number of yards of concrete you need for the given project. To builders, a "yard" of concrete means a cubic yard. (A cubic yard is equal to (36 in.)^3, or 46,656 in.^{3}.)**

38. A driveway that is 30 feet long, 18 feet wide, and 4 inches thick $6\frac{2}{3}$ yd

39. A tennis court that is 100 feet long, 50 feet wide, and 6 inches thick about 92.6 yd

40. A circular patio that has a radius of 24 feet and is 8 inches thick about 44.7 yd

41. **LOGICAL REASONING** Take two sheets of paper that measure $8\frac{1}{2}$ inches by 11 inches and form two cylinders; one with the height as $8\frac{1}{2}$ inches and one with the height as 11 inches. Do the cylinders have the same volume? Explain.

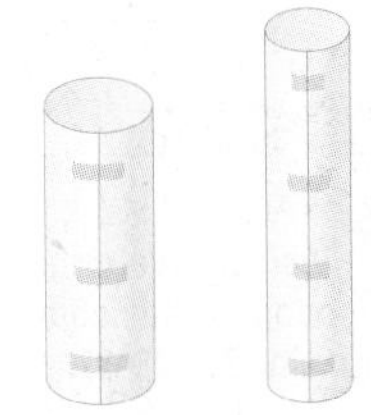

41. No; the circumference of the base of the shorter cylinder is 11 in., so the radius is about 1.75 in. and the volume is about 82 in.^{3}. The circumference of the base of the taller cylinder is 8.5 in., so the radius is about 1.35 in. and the volume is about 63 in.^{3}.

CANDLES **In Exercises 42–44, you are melting a block of wax to make candles. How many candles of the given shape can be made using a block that measures 10 cm by 9 cm by 20 cm? The prisms and cylinder are right.**

42. 2 candles

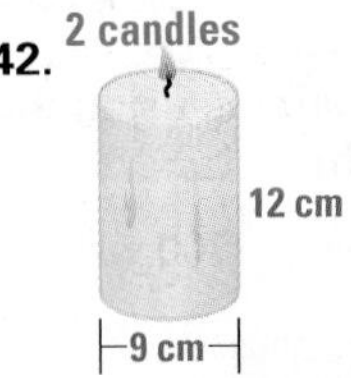

43. 7 candles

44. 6 candles

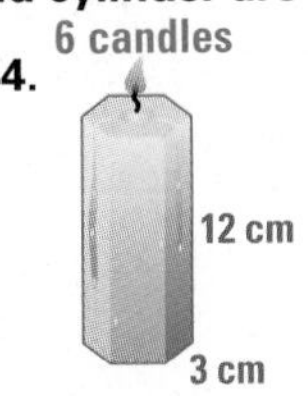

45. **CANNED GOODS** Find the volume and surface area of a prism with a height of 4 inches and a 3 inch by 3 inch square base. Compare the results with the volume and surface area of a cylinder with a height of 5.1 inches and a diameter of 3 inches. Use your results to explain why canned goods are usually packed in cylindrical containers.

45. Prism: volume = 36 in.^{3}, surface area = 66 in.^{2}; cylinder: volume $\approx$ 36 in.^{3}, surface area $\approx$ 62.2 in.^{2}; the cylinder and the prism hold about the same amount. The cylinder has smaller surface area, so less metal would be needed and it would be cheaper to produce a cylindrical can than one shaped like a prism.

AQUARIUM TANK **The Caribbean Coral Reef Tank at the New England Aquarium is a cylindrical tank that is 23 feet deep and 40 feet in diameter, as shown.**

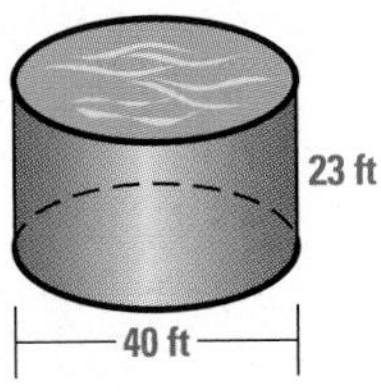

46. How many gallons of water are needed to fill the tank? (One gallon of water equals 0.1337 cubic foot.)
about 216,175 gal

47. Determine the weight of the water in the tank. (One gallon of salt water weighs about 8.56 pounds.)
about 1,850,458 lb

Test Preparation

48. MULTIPLE CHOICE If the volume of the rectangular prism at the right is 1, what does x equal? A

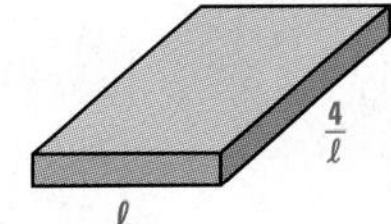

Ⓐ $\frac{1}{4}$ Ⓑ $\frac{\ell}{4}$ Ⓒ ℓ

Ⓓ 4 Ⓔ 4ℓ

49. MULTIPLE CHOICE What is the volume of a cylinder with a radius of 6 and a height of 10? E

Ⓐ 60π Ⓑ 90π Ⓒ 120π Ⓓ 180π Ⓔ 360π

★ Challenge

50. Suppose that a 3 inch by 5 inch index card is rotated around a horizontal line and a vertical line to produce two different solids, as shown. Which solid has a greater volume? Explain your reasoning.

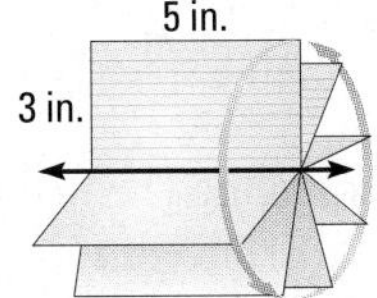

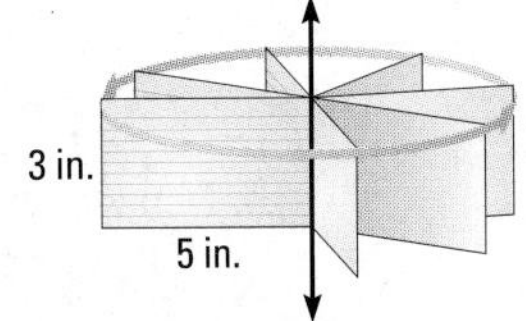

EXTRA CHALLENGE
www.mcdougallittell.com

Let H be the solid produced by rotating the card around a horizontal line and V the solid produced by rotating the card around a vertical line. V has greater volume. H has radius 3 in. and height 5 in., so the volume of H is 45π, or about 141 in.^{3}. V has radius 5 in. and height 3 in., so the volume of V is 75π, or about 236 in.^{3}.

MIXED REVIEW

USING RATIOS Find the measures of the angles in the triangle whose angles are in the given extended ratio. (Review 8.1)

51. 2:5:5 30°, 75°, 75°

52. 1:2:3 30°, 60°, 90°

53. 3:4:5 45°, 60°, 75°

FINDING AREA In Exercises 54–56, find the area of the figure. Round your result to two decimal places. (Review 11.2, 11.5 for 12.5)

54.

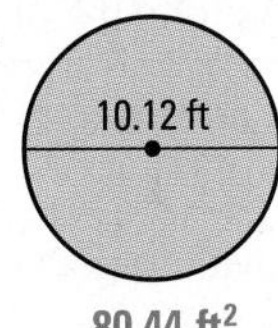

80.44 ft^2

55.

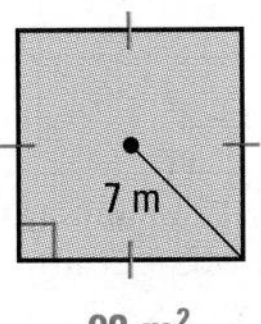

98 m^2

56.

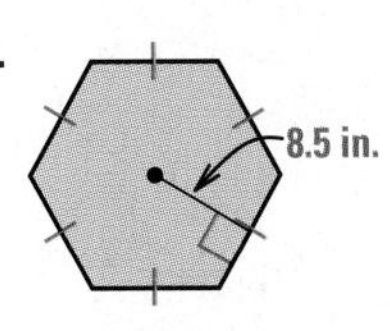

250.28 in.^{2}

57. SURFACE AREA OF A PRISM A right rectangular prism has a height of 13 inches, a length of 1 foot, and a width of 3 inches. Sketch the prism and find its surface area. (Review 12.2) Check drawings; 462 in.^{2}

SURFACE AREA Find the surface area of the solid. The cone is right and the pyramids are regular. (Review 12.3) See margin.

58.

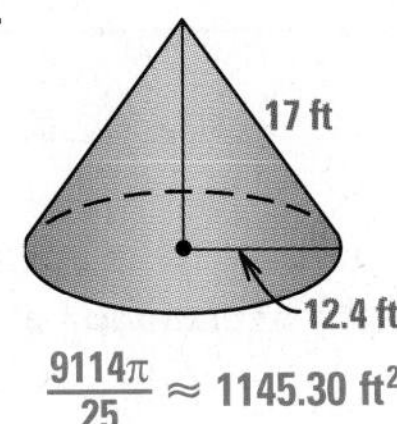

$\frac{9114\pi}{25} \approx 1145.30$ ft^2

59.

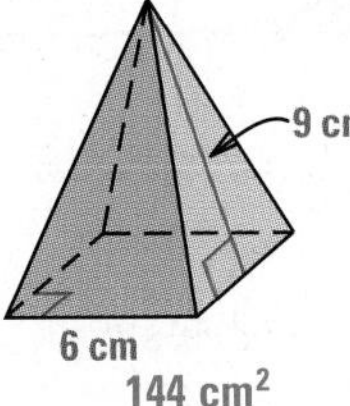

144 cm^2

60.

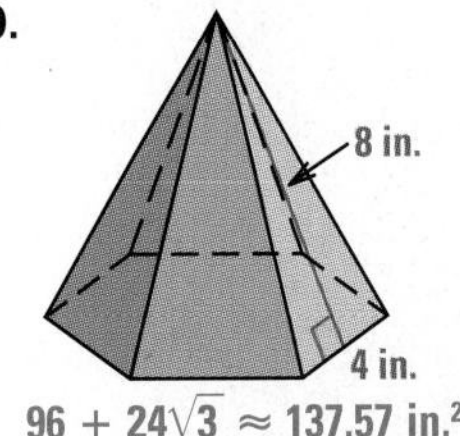

$96 + 24\sqrt{3} \approx 137.57$ in.^{2}

Additional Test Preparation *Sample answer:* 1.

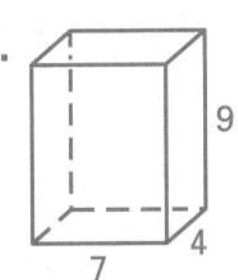

4 ASSESS

DAILY HOMEWORK QUIZ

Transparency Available

1. Find the volume of the right prism.

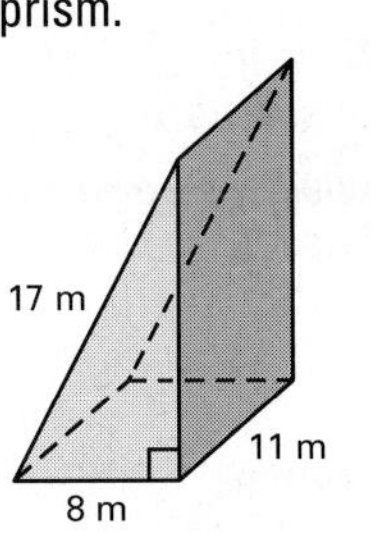

660 m^3

2. Find the volume of a right cylinder that has a diameter of 12 yd and a height of 11 yd. Round the result to one decimal place. 1244.1 yd^3

3. A heptagonal prism has a base area of 24 in.^{2} and a height of 5 in. What is its volume? 120 in.^{3}

4. Use Cavalieri's Principle to find the volume of the oblique cylinder. Leave the result in terms of π.

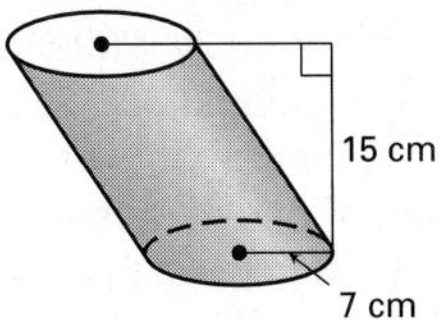

735π cm^3

5. A right rectangular prism has a volume of 385 m^3. Its bases have sides of length 5 m and 7 m. What is its height? 11 m

EXTRA CHALLENGE NOTE

Challenge problems for Lesson 12.4 are available in **blackline** format in the *Chapter 12 Resource Book,* p. 64 and at **www.mcdougallittell.com.**

ADDITIONAL TEST PREPARATION

1. OPEN ENDED Draw a right rectangular prism that has a volume of 252 cubic units. Label its length, width, and height. See sample answer at left.

1 Planning the Activity

PURPOSE
To use a spreadsheet to find the minimum surface area of a solid with a given volume.

MATERIALS
- spreadsheet software
- Software Help (*Chapter 12 Resource Book,* p. 55)

PACING
- Activity — 25 min

LINK TO LESSON
Students can use a spreadsheet to find the dimensions of the cylinder of least surface area with the same volume as the one in Lesson 12.4, Example 2, and compare the results with those from the activity.

2 Managing the Activity

CLASSROOM MANAGEMENT
You may want to complete the activity simultaneously with students to help troubleshoot. You may also want to pair computer-savvy students with those of lesser computer skills to help keep the class together.

3 Closing the Activity

KEY DISCOVERY
Cylinders can have the same volume but different surface areas. For a given volume, you can find values of h and r that minimize the surface area. This occurs in the activity when the radius is about half the height.

ACTIVITY ASSESSMENT
How can you find the minimum surface area of a cylindrical solid with a fixed volume?
See sample answer at right.

ACTIVITY 12.4

Using Technology

Minimizing Surface Area

A spreadsheet can be used to find the minimum surface area of a solid with a given volume.

EXPLORING THE CONCEPT

A canned goods manufacturer needs to design a cylindrical container with a volume of 72 cm^3. To use the least amount of material, the dimensions of the container must be chosen so the surface area is a minimum. Find the dimensions.

The dimensions you must find are the radius and the height for the given volume. You can vary the radius and find the resulting height and surface area. A spreadsheet is helpful in organizing the data.

STUDENT HELP
INTERNET SOFTWARE HELP
Visit our Web site www.mcdougallittell.com to see instructions for several software applications.

USE A SPREADSHEET

1. Make a table with four columns. The first column is for the given volume. Cell A2 stores the volume V. In cell A3, use the formula =A2.
2. The second column is for the radius. Cell B2 stores the starting value for the radius r. In cell B3, use the formula =B2+0.05 to increase the radius in increments of 0.05 centimeter.
3. The third column is for the height. In cell C2, use the formula =A2/(PI()*B2^2). Your spreadsheet might use a different expression for π.
4. The fourth column is for the surface area. In cell D2, use the formula =2*PI()*B2^2+2*PI()*B2*C2.

	A	B	C	D
1	Volume V	Radius r	Height $h = \frac{V}{\pi r^2}$	Surface area $SA = 2\pi r^2 + 2\pi rh$
2	V	r	= A2/(PI()*B2^2)	= 2*PI()*B2^2 + 2*PI()*B2*C2
3	= A2	= B2 + 0.05	= A3/(PI()*B3^2)	= 2*PI()*B3^2 + 2*PI()*B3*C3

5. Fill in Cells C3 and D3 as shown above. Then use the Fill Down feature to create more rows. Replace the V in cell A2 with 72 and replace the r in cell B2 with 2. Your spreadsheet should resemble the one below.

	A	B	C	D
1	Volume V	Radius r	Height $h = \frac{V}{\pi r^2}$	Surface area $SA = 2\pi r^2 + 2\pi rh$
2	72	2.00	5.73	97.14
3	72	2.05	5.45	96.60
4	72	2.10	5.20	96.32

MAKE A CONJECTURE

1. From the data in your spreadsheet, which dimensions yield a minimum surface area for the given volume? Explain how you know.

1. $r = 2.25$, $h = 4.53$; for values between 2.00 and 2.25, S decreases and for values greater than 2.25, S increases.

Activity Assessment *Sample answer:*
Vary the radius or height incrementally while calculating the other dimension from this value and the volume. Calculate the surface area for each pair of dimensions using the formula, and find the smallest value.

ACTIVITY 12.5

Developing Concepts

Investigating Volume

GROUP ACTIVITY
Work with a partner.

MATERIALS
- poster board
- ruler
- scissors
- tape
- unpopped popcorn, uncooked rice, or dried beans

▶ **QUESTION** **How is the volume of a pyramid related to the volume of a prism with the same base and height?**

▶ **EXPLORING THE CONCEPT**

1. Use a ruler to draw the two nets shown below on poster board. $\left(\text{Use } 1\frac{7}{16} \text{ inches to approximate } \sqrt{2} \text{ inches.}\right)$

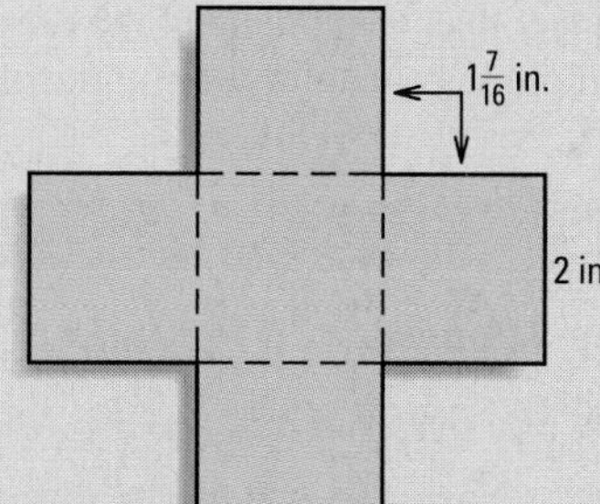

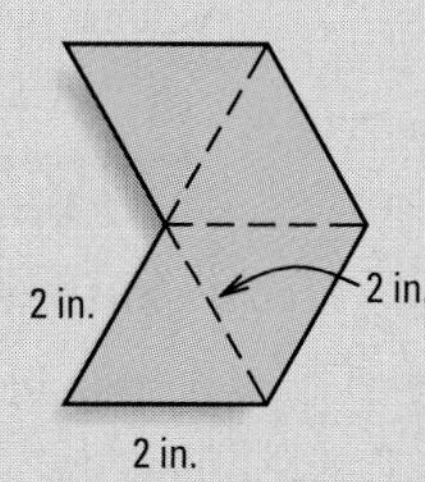

2. Cut out the nets. Fold along the dotted lines to form an open prism and an open pyramid, as shown below. Tape each solid to hold it in place, making sure that the edges do not overlap.

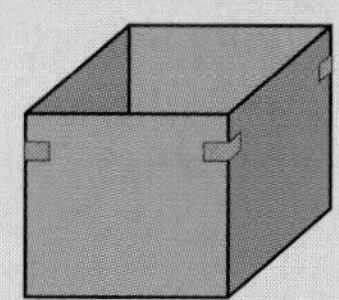

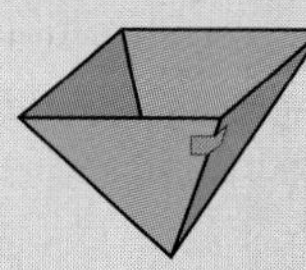

▶ **INVESTIGATE**

1. Compare the area of the base of the pyramid to the area of the base of the prism. Fitting the pyramid inside the prism will help. What do you notice?
2. Compare the heights of the solids. What do you notice?

▶ **MAKE A CONJECTURE**

3. Compare the volumes of the solids visually. Which solid has a greater volume? About how many times greater is the volume?
4. Fill the pyramid with unpopped popcorn, uncooked rice, or dried beans and pour it into the prism. Repeat this as many times as needed to fill the prism. How many times did you fill the pyramid? What does this tell you about the volume of the solids?

1. The areas of the bases are the same: 4 in.^{2}
2. The heights are the same.
3. The volume of the prism is greater; *sample answer:* about 3 times greater
4. The pyramid was filled about 3 times. So, the volume of the prism is about 3 times the volume of the pyramid.

Extension: The volume of a pyramid with base of area B and height h is equal to $\frac{1}{3}Bh$.

EXTENSION

CRITICAL THINKING Use your results to write a formula for the volume of a pyramid that uses the formula for the volume of a prism.

1 Planning the Activity

PURPOSE
To compare the volume of a pyramid and prism with the same base and height.

MATERIALS
- poster board
- ruler
- scissors
- tape
- unpopped popcorn, uncooked rice, or dried beans

PACING
- Activity — 20 min

▶ ***LINK TO LESSON***
Theorem 12.9 of Lesson 12.5 formalizes the results of this investigation.

2 Managing the Activity

CLASSROOM MANAGEMENT
In each pair, one student can construct the prism while the other constructs the pyramid. Emphasize the importance of making accurate measurements for the nets and folding and taping carefully. Otherwise, it will be hard to make accurate volume comparisons.

3 Closing the Activity

★ ***KEY DISCOVERY***
The volume of a pyramid is one third the volume of a prism with the same base and height.

ACTIVITY ASSESSMENT
The volume V of a pyramid is given by $V = Bh$, where B is the area of the base and h is the height. Use this fact and the results of the activity to write a formula for the volume of a pyramid. $V = \frac{1}{3}Bh$

1 PLAN

PACING
Basic: 2 days
Average: 2 days
Advanced: 2 days
Block Schedule: 0.5 block with 12.4
0.5 block with 12.6

LESSON OPENER
VISUAL APPROACH
An alternative way to approach Lesson 12.5 is to use the Visual Approach Lesson Opener:

- Blackline Master (*Chapter 12 Resource Book,* p. 68)
- Transparency (p. 78)

MEETING INDIVIDUAL NEEDS

- ***Chapter 12 Resource Book***
  Prerequisite Skills Review (p. 5)
  Practice Level A (p. 69)
  Practice Level B (p. 70)
  Practice Level C (p. 71)
  Reteaching with Practice (p. 72)
  Absent Student Catch-Up (p. 74)
  Challenge (p. 76)
- ***Resources in Spanish***
- ***Personal Student Tutor***

NEW-TEACHER SUPPORT
See the Tips for New Teachers on pp. 1–2 of the *Chapter 12 Resource Book* for additional notes about Lesson 12.5.

WARM-UP EXERCISES

Transparency Available

Find the volume of the solid.

1. cube, side lengths of 9
   729 units^3
2. cylinder, radius of 3 and height of 8 $72\pi \approx 226.19$ units^3
3. cylinder, diameter of 12 and height of 2 $72\pi \approx 226.19$ units^3
4. rectangular prism, length of 6, width of 11, height of 4
   264 units^3
5. triangular prism, base edges of length 4, height of 4
   $16\sqrt{3} \approx 27.71$ units^3

12.5 Volume of Pyramids and Cones

What you should learn

GOAL 1 Find the volume of pyramids and cones.

GOAL 2 Find the volume of pyramids and cones in **real life**, such as the nautical prism in **Example 4**.

Why you should learn it

▼ Learning to find volumes of pyramids and cones is important in **real life**, such as in finding the volume of a volcano shown below and in **Ex. 34**.

REAL LIFE

Mount St. Helens

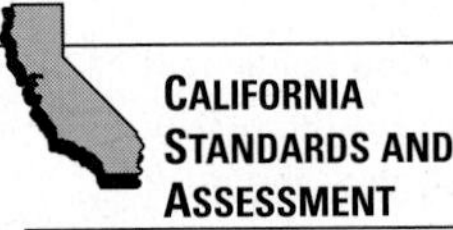
CALIFORNIA STANDARDS AND ASSESSMENT
CA Standards: 8, 9
SAT9 Task 1: Objs. 2, 4
SAT9 Task 2: Objs. 5, 6

GOAL 1 FINDING VOLUMES OF PYRAMIDS AND CONES

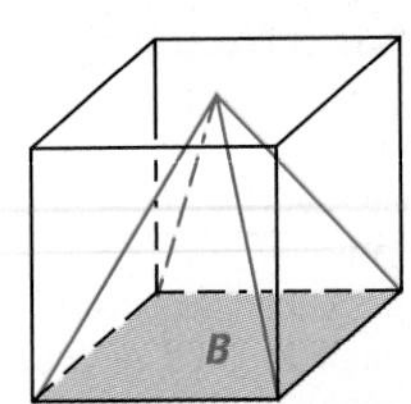

In Lesson 12.4, you learned that the volume of a prism is equal to Bh, where B is the area of the base and h is the height. From the figure at the right, it is clear that the volume of the pyramid with the same base area B and the same height h must be less than the volume of the prism. The volume of the pyramid is one third the volume of the prism.

THEOREMS

THEOREM 12.9 ***Volume of a Pyramid***

The volume V of a pyramid is $V = \frac{1}{3}Bh$, where B is the area of the base and h is the height.

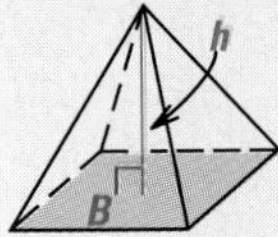

THEOREM 12.10 ***Volume of a Cone***

The volume V of a cone is $V = \frac{1}{3}Bh = \frac{1}{3}\pi r^2 h$, where B is the area of the base, h is the height, and r is the radius of the base.

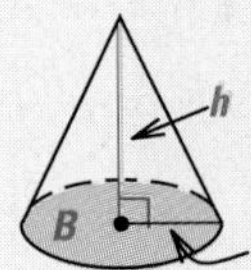

EXAMPLE 1 *Finding the Volume of a Pyramid*

Find the volume of the pyramid with the regular base.

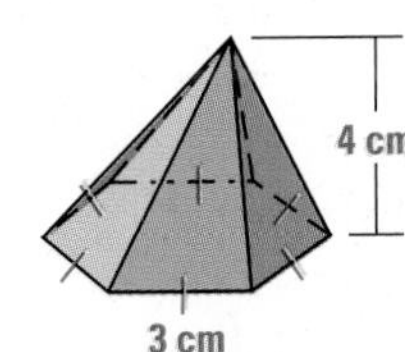

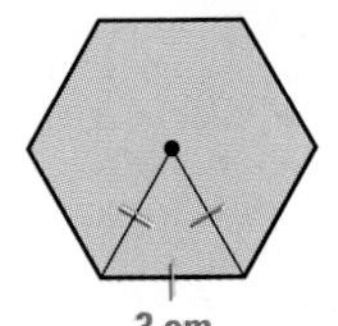

SOLUTION

The base can be divided into six equilateral triangles. Using the formula for the area of an equilateral triangle, $\frac{1}{4}\sqrt{3} \cdot s^2$, the area of the base B can be found as follows:

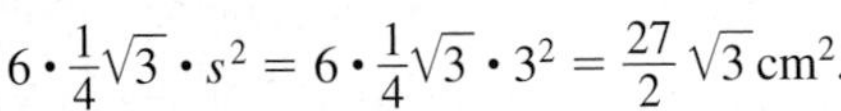

$$6 \cdot \frac{1}{4}\sqrt{3} \cdot s^2 = 6 \cdot \frac{1}{4}\sqrt{3} \cdot 3^2 = \frac{27}{2}\sqrt{3}\text{ cm}^2.$$

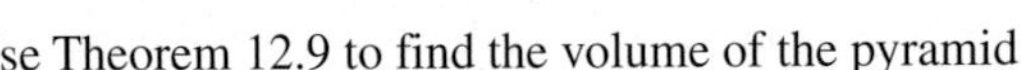

Use Theorem 12.9 to find the volume of the pyramid.

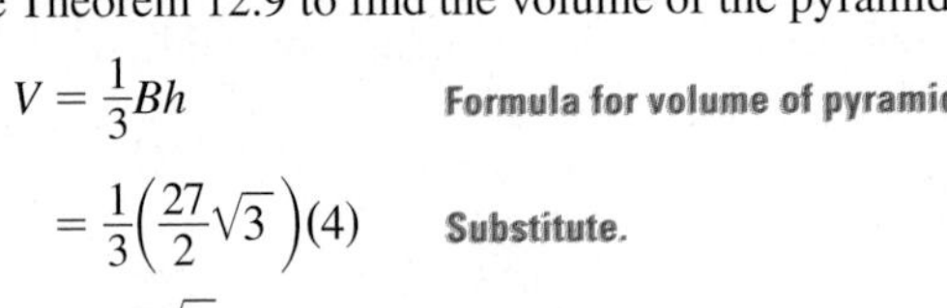

$$V = \frac{1}{3}Bh \qquad \textbf{Formula for volume of pyramid}$$

$$= \frac{1}{3}\left(\frac{27}{2}\sqrt{3}\right)(4) \qquad \textbf{Substitute.}$$

$$= 18\sqrt{3} \qquad \textbf{Simplify.}$$

▶ So, the volume of the pyramid is $18\sqrt{3}$, or about 31.2 cubic centimeters.

> **STUDENT HELP**
>
> **Study Tip**
> The formulas given in Theorems 12.9 and 12.10 apply to all pyramids and cones, whether right or oblique. This follows from Cavalieri's Principle, stated in Lesson 12.4.

EXAMPLE 2 *Finding the Volume of a Cone*

Find the volume of each cone.

a. Right circular cone

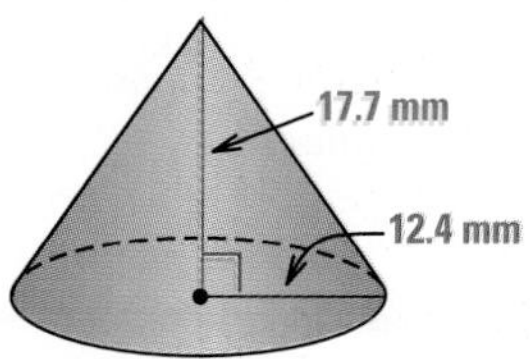

b. Oblique circular cone

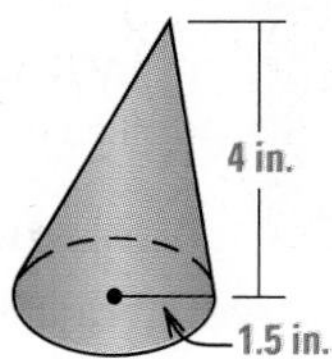

SOLUTION

a. Use the formula for the volume of a cone.

$V = \frac{1}{3}Bh$	**Formula for volume of cone**
$= \frac{1}{3}(\pi r^2)h$	**Base area equals πr^2.**
$= \frac{1}{3}(\pi 12.4^2)(17.7)$	**Substitute.**
$\approx 907.18\pi$	**Simplify.**

▶ So, the volume of the cone is about 907.18π, or 2850 cubic millimeters.

b. Use the formula for the volume of a cone.

$V = \frac{1}{3}Bh$	**Formula for volume of cone**
$= \frac{1}{3}(\pi r^2)h$	**Base area equals πr^2.**
$= \frac{1}{3}(\pi 1.5^2)(4)$	**Substitute.**
$= 3\pi$	**Simplify.**

▶ So, the volume of the cone is 3π, or about 9.42 cubic inches.

EXAMPLE 3 *Using the Volume of a Cone*

Use the given measurements to solve for x.

13 ft

x

Volume = 2614 ft³

SOLUTION

$V = \frac{1}{3}\pi r^2 h$	**Formula for volume**
$2614 = \frac{1}{3}(\pi x^2)(13)$	**Substitute.**
$7842 = 13\pi x^2$	**Multiply each side by 3.**
$192 \approx x^2$	**Divide each side by 13π.**
$13.86 \approx x$	**Find positive square root.**

▶ So, the radius of the cone is about 13.86 feet.

> **STUDENT HELP**
>
> **Study Tip**
> To eliminate the fraction in an equation, you can multiply each side by the reciprocal of the fraction. This was done in Example 3.

2 TEACH

MOTIVATING THE LESSON
Have students imagine buying popcorn in a conical cup or in a cylindrical cup with the same height and same size opening. How should the costs compare? By comparing the volumes of cylinders and cones, students can answer the question.

EXTRA EXAMPLE 1
Find the volume of the pyramid with the regular base.

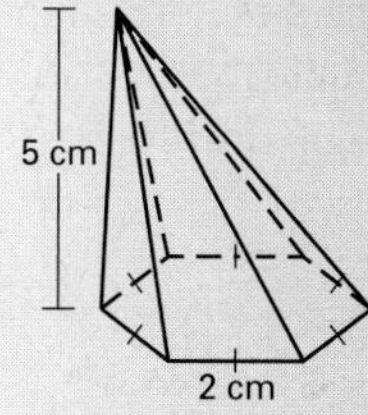

$10\sqrt{3}$, or about 17.3 cm³

EXTRA EXAMPLE 2
Find the volume of each cone.
a. Right circular cone

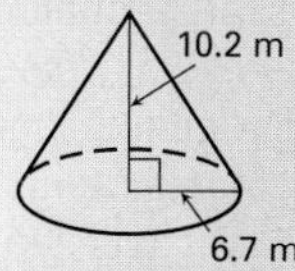

about 152.63π, or about 479 m³

b. Oblique circular cone

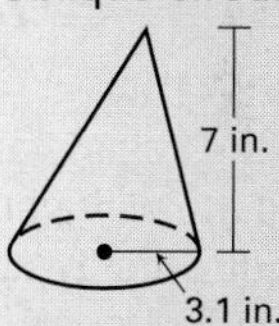

about 22.42π, or about 70.4 in.³

EXTRA EXAMPLE 3
Use the given measurements to solve for x.

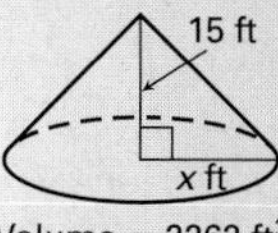

Volume = 2262 ft³

about 12 ft

CHECKPOINT EXERCISES
For use after Examples 1–3:
1. Find the volume of a right circular cone with a diameter of 12 feet and a height of 4 feet. **48π, or about 150.8 ft³**

EXTRA EXAMPLE 4

The bases of the prism and pyramid in the light fixture shown are regular hexagons. Find the volume of the fixture.

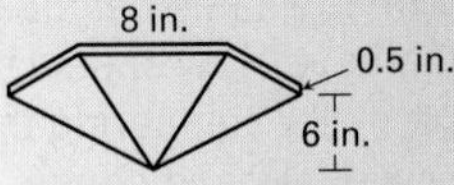

about 415.7 $in.^3$

EXTRA EXAMPLE 5

Coolant is being poured through the funnel into a radiator at a rate of 198 milliliters per second and flows out of the funnel at a rate of 60 milliliters per second. Estimate the time it will take for the funnel to overflow.

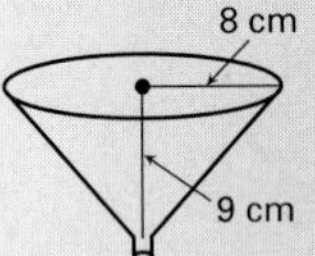

about 4.37 sec

CHECKPOINT EXERCISES

For use after Examples 4 and 5:

1. Grain feeds into a conical bin at a rate of 2.5 ft^3/sec. The bin is 8 feet high, and its circular top has a radius of 5 feet. How long will it take to fill the bin? about 83.8 sec

CLOSURE QUESTION

Compare finding the volume of a right pyramid or cone with finding the volume of an oblique pyramid or cone. See sample answer below.

DAILY PUZZLER

The cone shown holds 2 gallons. If it is filled with 1 gallon of fluid, what will x be?

$\left(\text{HINT: } \dfrac{\frac{1}{3}\pi R^2 H}{\frac{1}{3}\pi r^2 h} = 2; \dfrac{R}{r} = \dfrac{H}{h} = \dfrac{12}{x}\right)$

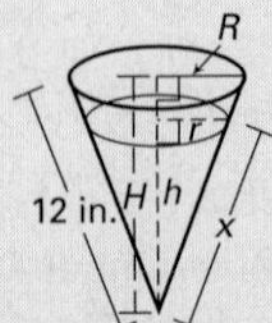

about 9.52 in.

FOCUS ON APPLICATIONS

NAUTICAL PRISMS Before electricity, nautical prisms were placed in the decks of sailing ships. By placing the hexagonal face flush with the deck, the prisms would draw light to the lower regions of the ship.

GOAL 2 USING VOLUME IN REAL-LIFE PROBLEMS

EXAMPLE 4 *Finding the Volume of a Solid*

NAUTICAL PRISMS A nautical prism is a solid piece of glass, as shown. Find its volume.

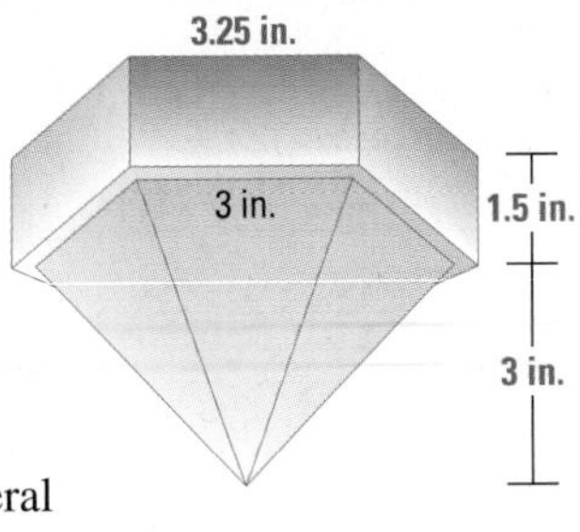

SOLUTION

To find the volume of the entire solid, add the volumes of the prism and the pyramid. The bases of the prism and the pyramid are regular hexagons made up of six equilateral triangles. To find the area of each base, B, multiply the area of one of the equilateral triangles by 6, or $6\left(\frac{\sqrt{3}}{4}s^2\right)$, where s is the base edge.

Volume of prism	$= 6\left(\frac{\sqrt{3}}{4}s^2\right)h$	Formula for volume of prism
	$= 6\left(\frac{\sqrt{3}}{4}(3.25)^2\right)(1.5)$	Substitute.
	≈ 41.16	Use a calculator.
Volume of pyramid	$= \frac{1}{3} \cdot 6\left(\frac{\sqrt{3}}{4}s^2\right)h$	Formula for volume of pyramid
	$= \frac{1}{3} \cdot 6\left(\frac{\sqrt{3}}{4} \cdot 3^2\right)(3)$	Substitute.
	≈ 23.38	Use a calculator.

▶ The volume of the nautical prism is **41.16** + **23.38** or 64.54 cubic inches.

EXAMPLE 5 *Using the Volume of a Cone*

AUTOMOBILES If oil is being poured into the funnel at a rate of 147 milliliters per second and flows out of the funnel at a rate of 42 milliliters per second, estimate the time it will take for the funnel to overflow. (1 mL = 1 cm^3)

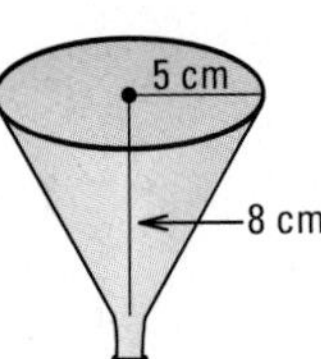

SOLUTION

First, find the approximate volume of the funnel.

$$V = \frac{1}{3}\pi r^2 h = \frac{1}{3}\pi(5^2)(8) \approx 209 \text{ cm}^3 = 209 \text{ mL}$$

The rate of accumulation of oil in the funnel is 147 − 42 = 105 mL/s. To find the time it will take for the oil to fill the funnel, divide the volume of the funnel by the rate of accumulation of oil in the funnel as follows:

$$209 \text{ mL} \div \frac{105 \text{ mL}}{1 \text{ s}} = 209 \text{ mL} \times \frac{1 \text{ s}}{105 \text{ mL}} \approx 2 \text{ s}$$

▶ The funnel will overflow after about 2 seconds.

Closure Question ***Sample answer:*** Whether the pyramid or cone is right or oblique, you use the formula $V = \frac{1}{3}Bh$, where B represents the area of the base and h represents the height. For a cone of radius r, the formula can be expanded as $V = \frac{1}{3}\pi r^2 h$.

GUIDED PRACTICE

Vocabulary Check ✓

1. The volume of a cone with radius r and height h is $\frac{1}{3}$ the volume of a __?__ with radius r and height h. cylinder

Concept Check ✓

Do the two solids have the same volume? Explain your answer. 2, 3. See margin.

2.

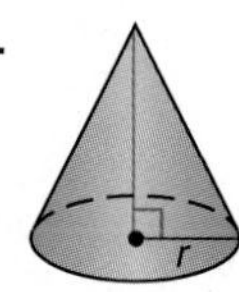

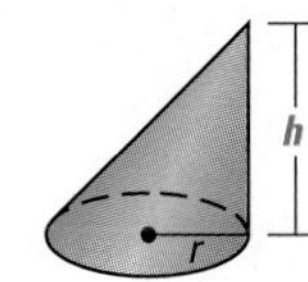

3.

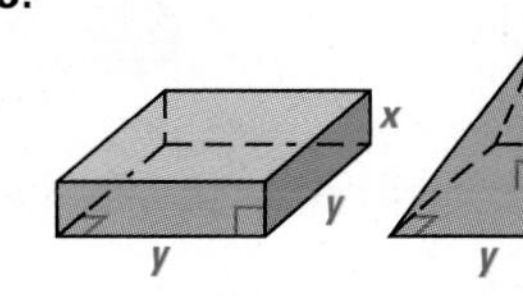

Skill Check ✓

In Exercises 4–6, find (a) the area of the base of the solid and (b) the volume of the solid.

4.a. 25 cm^2
b. $\frac{100}{3} \approx 33.3$ cm^3
5.a. $4\pi \approx 12.6$ ft^2
b. $\frac{16\pi}{3} \approx 16.8$ ft^3
6.a. $\frac{121\sqrt{3}}{4} \approx 52.4$ m^2
b. $\frac{847\sqrt{3}}{6} \approx 244.5$ m^3

4.

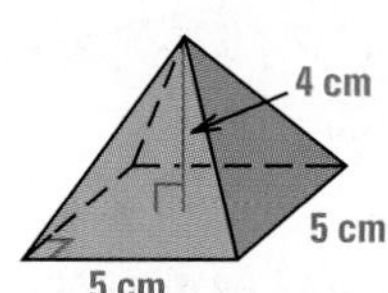

5.

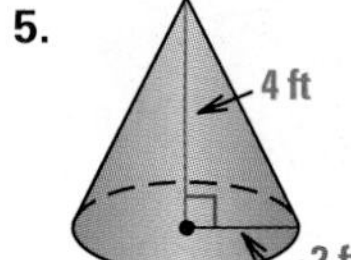

6. 14 m, 11 m

7. **CRITICAL THINKING** You are given the radius and the slant height of a right cone. Explain how you can find the height of the cone. The height of the cone is the length of one leg of a right △ with hypotenuse equal to the slant height and one leg the radius of the base, so use the Pythagorean Theorem to determine the height.

PRACTICE AND APPLICATIONS

STUDENT HELP

Extra Practice to help you master skills is on p. 826.

FINDING BASE AREAS **Find the area of the base of the solid.**

8.

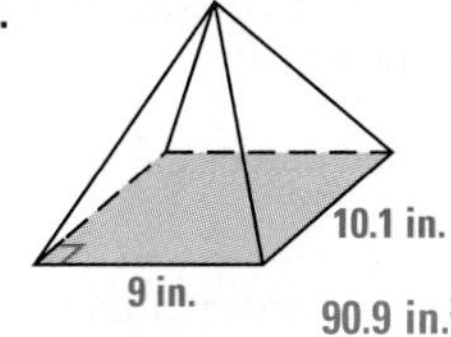

90.9 in.^{2}

9.

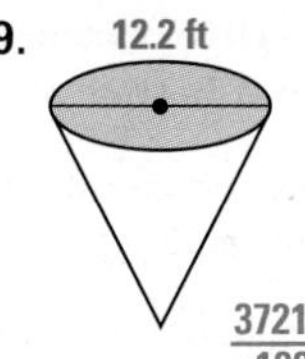

$\frac{3721\pi}{100} \approx 116.9$ ft^2

10. Regular base

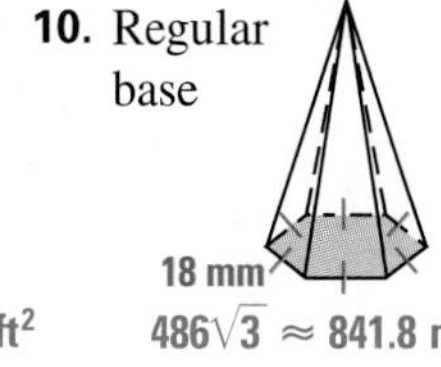

$486\sqrt{3} \approx 841.8$ mm^2

VOLUME OF A PYRAMID **Find the volume of the pyramid. Each pyramid has a regular polygon for a base.**

11. 400 cm^3

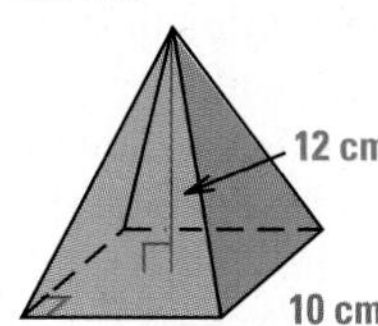

12. $\frac{245}{3} \approx 81.7$ m^3

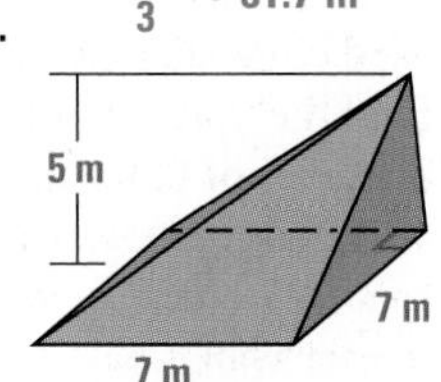

13. $\frac{67{,}183\sqrt{3}}{750} \approx 155.2$ ft^3

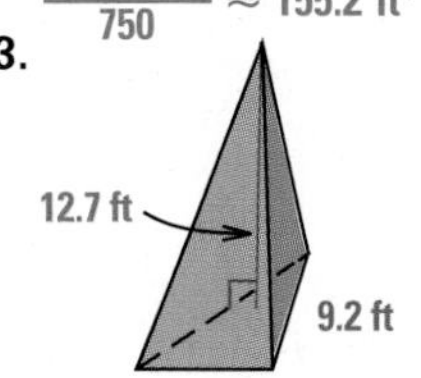

14.

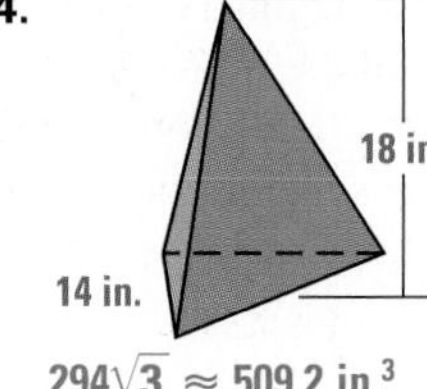

$294\sqrt{3} \approx 509.2$ in.^{3}

15.

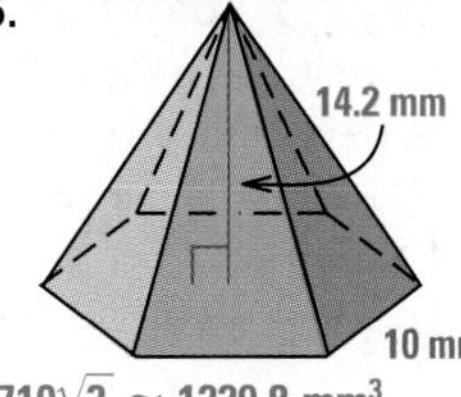

$710\sqrt{3} \approx 1229.8$ mm^3

16.

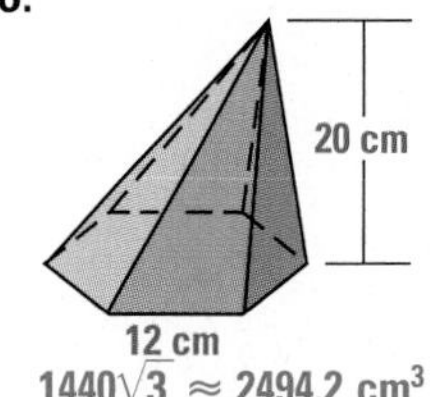

$1440\sqrt{3} \approx 2494.2$ cm^3

STUDENT HELP

HOMEWORK HELP
Example 1: Exs. 11–16
Example 2: Exs. 17–19
Example 3: Exs. 20–22
Example 4: Exs. 23–28
Example 5: Ex. 29

3 APPLY

ASSIGNMENT GUIDE

BASIC
Day 1: pp. 755–756 Exs. 8–22
Day 2: pp. 756–758 Exs. 23–37, 40–51, Quiz 2 Exs. 1–7

AVERAGE
Day 1: pp. 755–756 Exs. 8–22
Day 2: pp. 756–758 Exs. 23–37, 40–51, Quiz 2 Exs. 1–7

ADVANCED
Day 1: pp. 755–756 Exs. 8–22
Day 2: pp. 756–758 Exs. 23–51, Quiz 2 Exs. 1–7

BLOCK SCHEDULE
pp. 755–756 Exs. 8–22 (with 12.4)
pp. 756–758 Exs. 23–37, 40–51, Quiz 2 Exs. 1–7 (with 12.6)

EXERCISE LEVELS

Level A: *Easier*
8–10, 40–47
Level B: *More Difficult*
11–33, 35–37, 48–51
Level C: *Most Difficult*
34, 38, 39

✓ HOMEWORK CHECK

To quickly check student understanding of key concepts, go over the following exercises: Exs. 10, 14, 18, 20, 24, 25, 27, 32. See also the Daily Homework Quiz:

- Blackline Master (*Chapter 12 Resource Book*, p. 80)
- Transparency (p. 91)

2. Yes; both have radius r and height h, so both have volume $\frac{1}{3}\pi r^2 h$.
3. Yes; the volume of the prism is $y \cdot y \cdot x = xy^2$; the volume of the pyramid is $\frac{1}{3} \cdot y^2 \cdot 3x = xy^2$.

! COMMON ERROR

EXERCISE 17 Some students may multiply the base area by the slant height instead of by the height. Remind them that the slant height is used in the formula for the surface area of a cone, but that the height is used in the volume formula. Encourage students to write out formulas to avoid mistakes.

STUDENT HELP NOTES

Homework Help Students can find help for Exs. 23–25 at **www.mcdougallittell.com.** The information can be printed out for students who don't have access to the Internet.

VOLUME OF A CONE **Find the volume of the cone. Round your result to two decimal places.**

17. 48.97 ft³

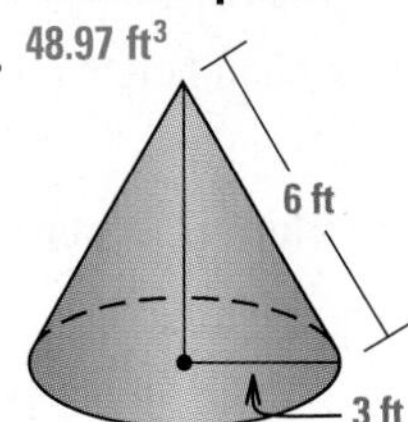

18. 526.27 cm³

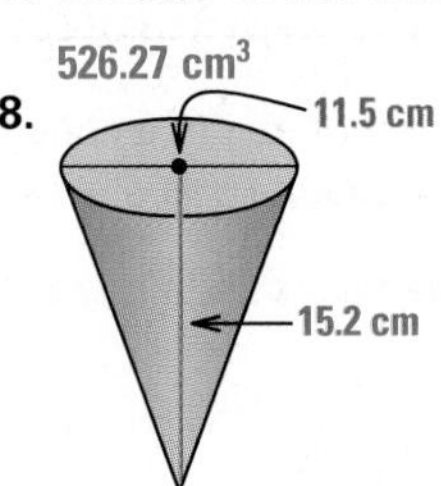

19. 667.06 in.³

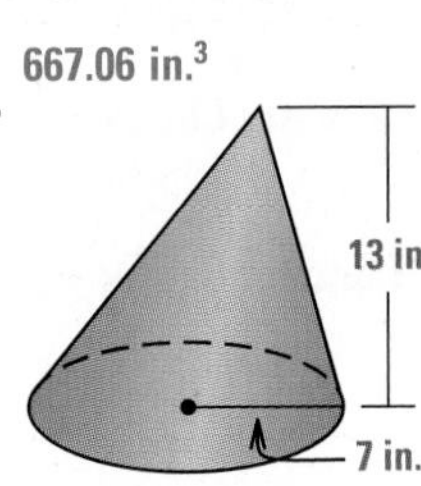

USING ALGEBRA **Solve for the variable using the given information.**

20. Volume $= 270\ \text{m}^3$ 10 m

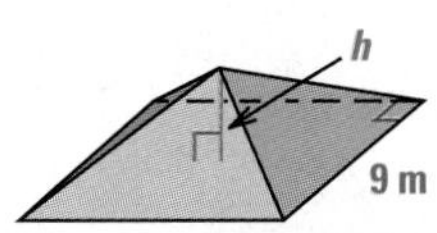

21. Volume $= 100\pi\ \text{in.}^3$ 5 in.

r
12 in.

22. Volume $= 5\sqrt{3}\ \text{cm}^3$ 5 cm

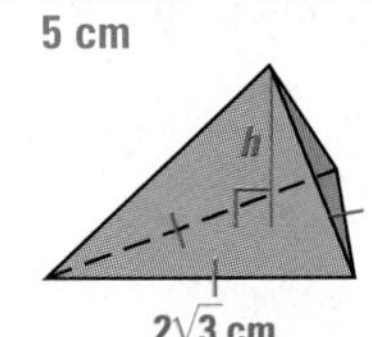

2√3 cm

STUDENT HELP

HOMEWORK HELP Visit our Web site www.mcdougallittell.com for help with Exs. 23–25.

COMPOSITE SOLIDS **Find the volume of the solid. The prisms, pyramids, and cones are right. Round the result to two decimal places.**

23.

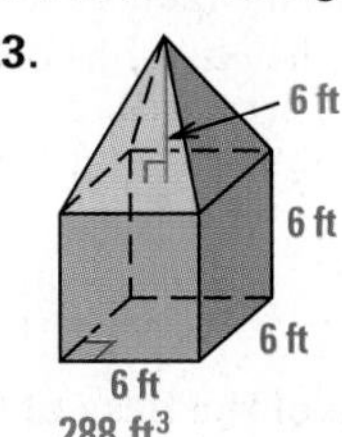

288 ft³

24.

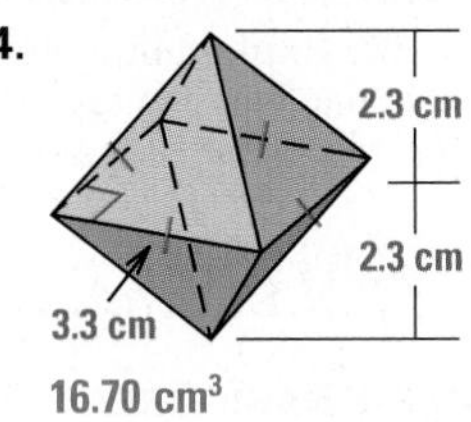

16.70 cm³

25.

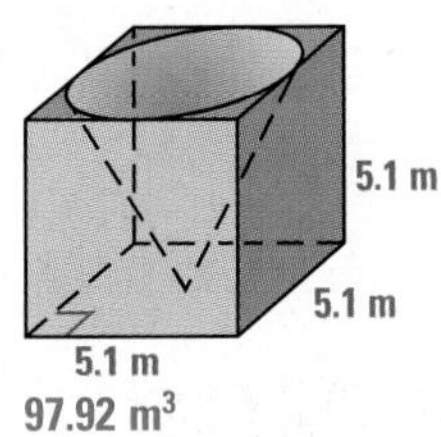

97.92 m³

AUTOMATIC FEEDER **In Exercises 26 and 27, use the diagram of the automatic pet feeder. (1 cup = 14.4 in.³)**

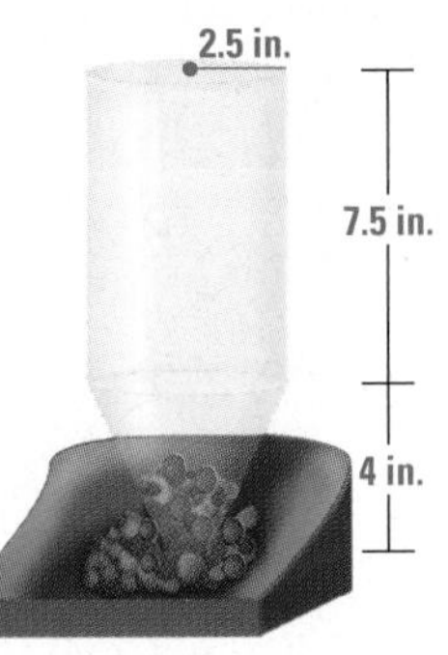

26. Calculate the amount of food that can be placed in the feeder. about 12 c

27. If a cat eats half of a cup of food, twice per day, will the feeder hold enough food for three days? yes

28. **ANCIENT CONSTRUCTION** Early civilizations in the Andes Mountains in Peru used cone-shaped adobe bricks to build homes. Find the volume of an adobe brick with a diameter of 8.3 centimeters and a slant height of 10.1 centimeters. Then calculate the amount of space 27 of these bricks would occupy in a mud mortar wall. about 166 cm³; about 4482 cm³

29. SCIENCE CONNECTION During a chemistry lab, you use a funnel to pour a solvent into a flask. The radius of the funnel is 5 centimeters and its height is 10 centimeters. If the solvent is being poured into the funnel at a rate of 80 milliliters per second and the solvent flows out of the funnel at a rate of 65 milliliters per second, how long will it be before the funnel overflows? $(1\ \text{mL} = 1\ \text{cm}^3)$ about 17.5 sec

FOCUS ON CAREERS

VOLCANOLOGY Volcanologists collect and interpret data about volcanoes to help them predict when a volcano will erupt.

CAREER LINK
www.mcdougallittell.com

36. No; it takes the sand slightly more than an hour (about 62 min) to fall from one part of the glass to the other.

USING NETS In Exercises 30–32, use the net to sketch the solid. Then find the volume of the solid. Round the result to two decimal places.

30. 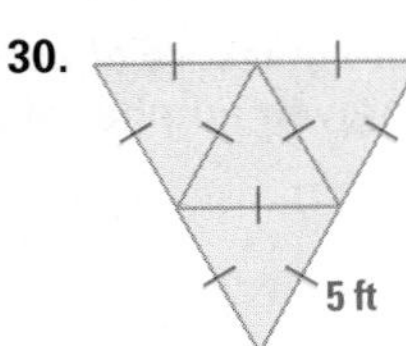

14.73 ft³

31. 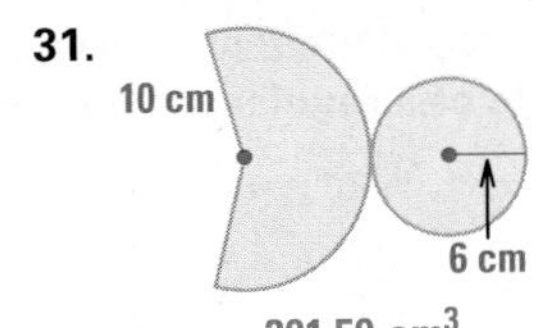

301.59 cm³

32. 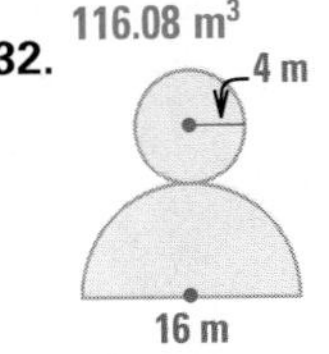

116.08 m³

33. **FINDING VOLUME** In the diagram at the right, a regular square pyramid with a base edge of 4 meters is inscribed in a cone with a height of 6 meters. Use the dimensions of the pyramid to find the volume of the cone. $16\pi \approx 50.3$ m³

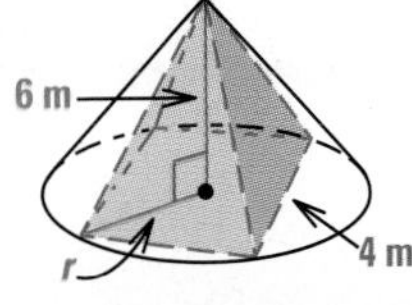

34. **VOLCANOES** Before 1980, Mount St. Helens was cone shaped with a height of about 1.83 miles and a base radius of about 3 miles. In 1980, Mount St. Helens erupted. The tip of the cone was destroyed, as shown, reducing the volume by 0.043 cubic mile. The cone-shaped tip that was destroyed had a radius of about 0.4 mile. How tall is the volcano today? (*Hint:* Find the height of the destroyed cone-shaped tip.) about 1.58 mi

MULTI-STEP PROBLEM Use the diagram of the hourglass below.

35. Find the volume of the cone-shaped pile of sand. about 62.12 in.³

36. The sand falls through the opening at a rate of one cubic inch per minute. Is the hourglass a true "hour"-glass? Explain. (1 hr = 60 min) See margin.

37. *Writing* The sand in the hourglass falls into a conical shape with a one-to-one ratio between the radius and the height. Without doing the calculations, explain how to find the radius and height of the pile of sand that has accumulated after 30 minutes.

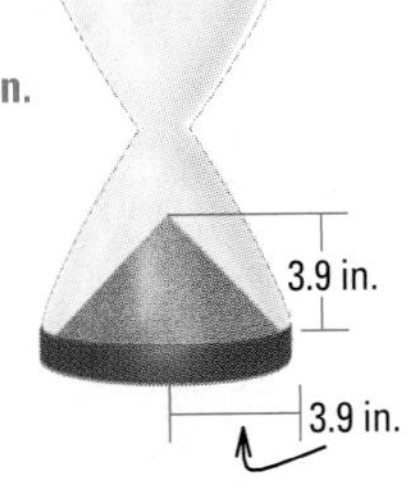

Test Preparation

37. Assume that half the sand has accumulated after 30 min. Let r be the radius of the pile containing all the sand and r_1 the radius of the pile containing half. $\frac{1}{3}\pi(r_1)^3 = \frac{1}{2}\left(\frac{1}{3}\pi r^3\right)$, so $(r_1)^3 = \frac{1}{2}(r^3)$ and $r_1 = \sqrt[3]{\frac{1}{2}} \cdot r$.

★ Challenge

FRUSTUMS A *frustum* of a cone is the part of the cone that lies between the base and a plane parallel to the base, as shown. Use the information below to complete Exercises 38 and 39.

One method for calculating the volume of a frustum is to add the areas of the two bases to their geometric mean, then multiply the result by $\frac{1}{3}$ the height.

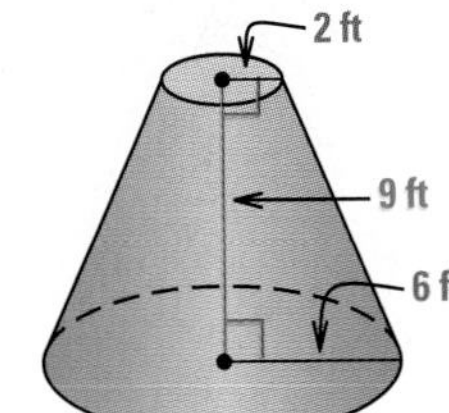

38. Use the measurements in the diagram to calculate the volume of the frustum. 156π ft³

39. Write a formula for the volume of a frustum that has bases with radii r_1 and r_2 and a height h.
$V = \frac{1}{3}(r_1^2 + r_2^2 + r_1r_2)h\pi$

STUDENT HELP

Look Back
For help with finding geometric means, see p. 466.

CAREER NOTE
EXERCISE 33
Additional information about volcanologists is available at **www.mcdougallittell.com.**

STUDENT HELP NOTES

Look Back As students look back to p. 466 for help with finding geometric means, remind them that the geometric mean of two numbers derives from a proportion: the first number is to the geometric mean as the geometric mean is to the second number.

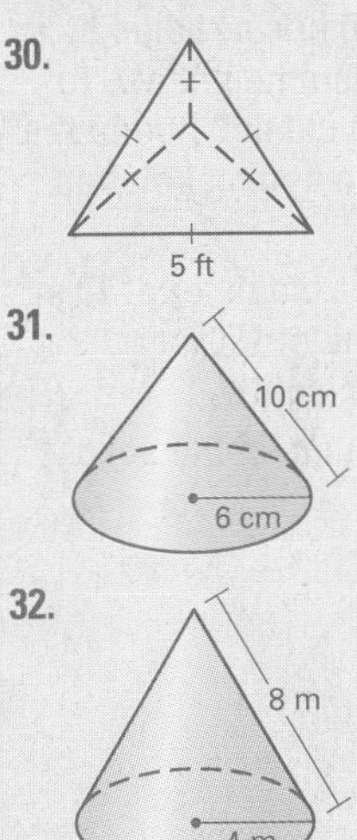

ADDITIONAL PRACTICE AND RETEACHING

For Lesson 12.5:
- Practice Levels A, B, and C (*Chapter 12 Resource Book,* p. 69)
- Reteaching with Practice (*Chapter 12 Resource Book,* p. 72)
- See Lesson 12.5 of the *Personal Student Tutor*

For more Mixed Review:
- Search the *Test and Practice Generator* for key words or specific lessons.

4 ASSESS

DAILY HOMEWORK QUIZ

Transparency Available

1. Find the volume of the pyramid with the regular base.

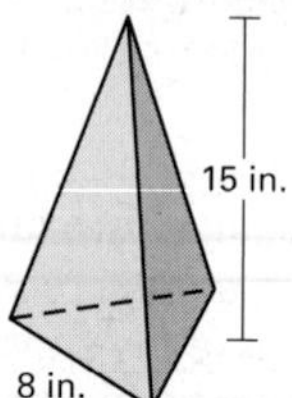

$80\sqrt{3} \approx 138.56$ in.^{3}

2. A right cone has a radius of 6 ft and a slant height of 9 ft. What is its volume? Round the result to two decimal places. 252.89 ft^3

3. A cone has a diameter of 10 in. and a volume of 150π m^3. What is its height? 18 m

4. Find the volume of the solid. 192 cm^3

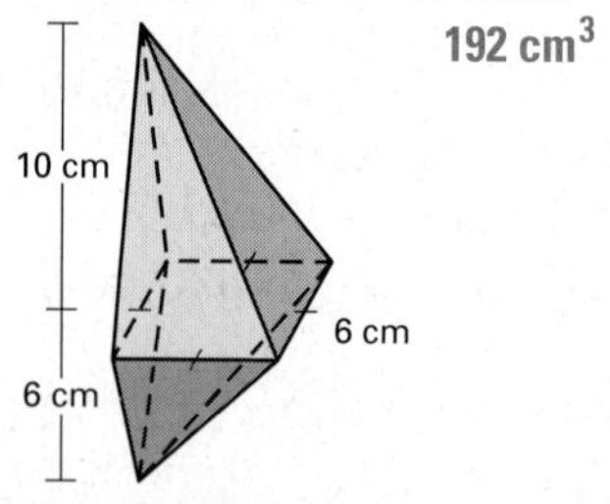

EXTRA CHALLENGE NOTE

Challenge problems for Lesson 12.5 are available in **blackline** format in the *Chapter 12 Resource Book,* p. 76 and at **www.mcdougallittell.com.**

ADDITIONAL TEST PREPARATION

1. WRITING Cone B has the same height as Cone A, but twice the base diameter. Cone C has the same base diameter as Cone A, but twice the height. Do Cones B and C have the same volume? Explain. See right.

ADDITIONAL RESOURCES

An alternative Quiz for Lessons 12.4 and 12.5 is available in the *Chapter 12 Resource Book,* p. 77.

MIXED REVIEW

FINDING ANGLE MEASURES Find the measure of each interior and exterior angle of a regular polygon with the given number of sides. (Review 11.1)

40. 9 140°, 40° **41.** 10 144°, 36° **42.** 19 $161\frac{1}{19}°$, $18\frac{18}{19}°$

43. 22 $163\frac{7}{11}°$, $16\frac{4}{11}°$ **44.** 25 165.6°, 14.4° **45.** 30 168°, 12°

FINDING THE AREA OF A CIRCLE Find the area of the described circle. (Review 11.5 for 12.6)

46. The diameter of the circle is 25 inches. $\frac{625\pi}{4} \approx 490.87$ in.^{2}

47. The radius of the circle is 16.3 centimeters. $\frac{26{,}569\pi}{100} \approx 834.69$ cm^2

48. The circumference of the circle is 48π feet. $576\pi \approx 1809.56$ ft^2

49. The length of a 36° arc of the circle is 2π meters. $100\pi \approx 314.16$ m^2

USING EULER'S THEOREM Calculate the number of vertices of the solid using the given information. (Review 12.1)

50. 32 faces; 12 octagons and 20 triangles 48 vertices

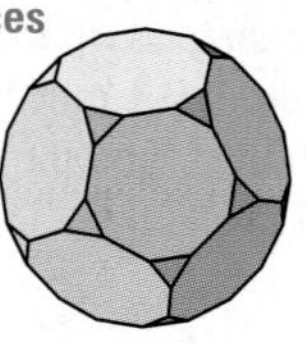

51. 14 faces; 6 squares and 8 hexagons 24 vertices

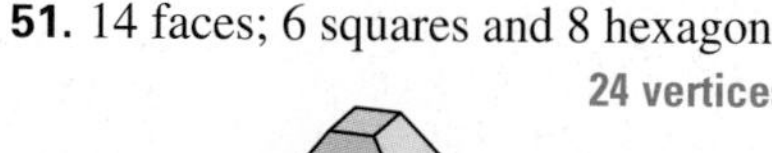

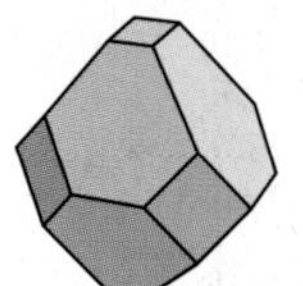

QUIZ 2

Self-Test for Lessons 12.4 and 12.5

In Exercises 1–6, find the volume of the solid. (Lessons 12.4 and 12.5)

1. 1080 in.^{3}

2. 1020 ft^3

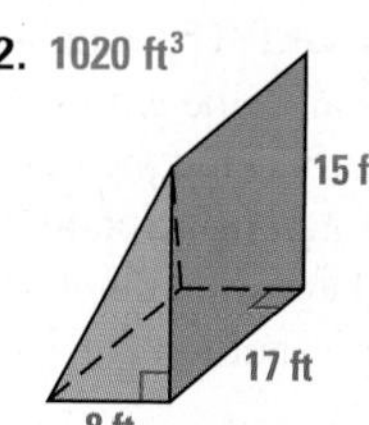

3. $350\pi \approx 1099.56$ cm^3

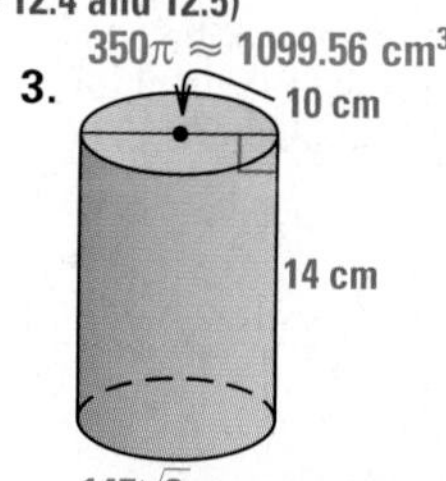

4. $\frac{243\pi}{4} \approx 190.85$ m^3

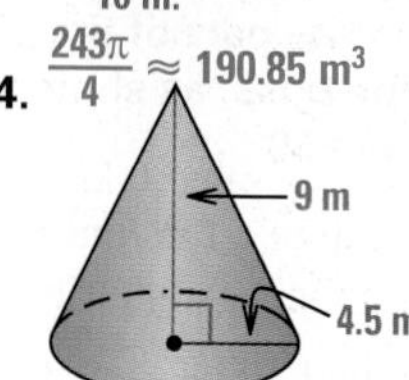

5. 21,168 mm^3

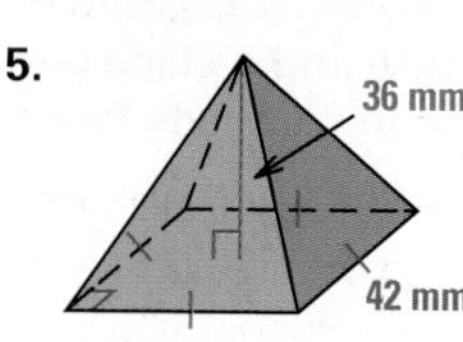
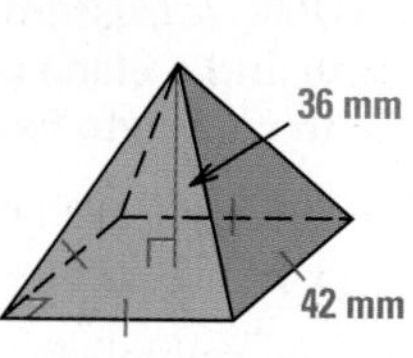

6. $\frac{147\sqrt{3}}{4} \approx 63.65$ in.^{3}

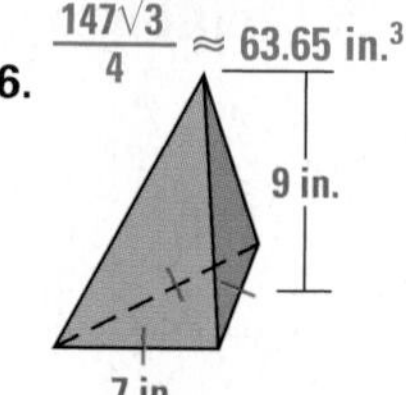

7. STORAGE BUILDING A road-salt storage building is composed of a regular octagonal pyramid and a regular octagonal prism as shown. Find the volume of salt that the building can hold. (Lesson 12.5) about 5633 ft^3

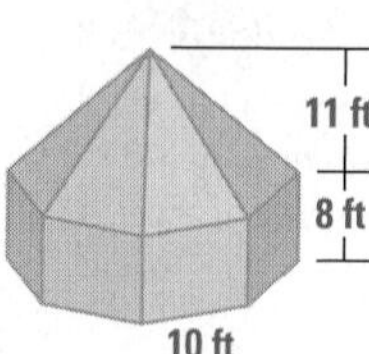

Additional Test Preparation *Sample answer:*

1. No; *Sample answer:* If the volume of Cone A is $\frac{1}{3}\pi r^2 h$, then the volume of Cone B is $\frac{1}{3}\pi(2r)^2 h = 4 \cdot \frac{1}{3}\pi r^2 h$, because the radius is twice that of A. The volume of Cone C is $\frac{1}{3}\pi r^2(2h) = 2 \cdot \frac{1}{3}\pi r^2 h$, because the height is twice that of A. So, Cone B has twice the volume of Cone C.

12.6 Surface Area and Volume of Spheres

What you should learn

GOAL 1 Find the surface area of a sphere.

GOAL 2 Find the volume of a sphere in **real life**, such as the ball bearing in **Example 4**.

Why you should learn it

▼ You can find the surface area and volume of **real-life** spherical objects, such as the planets and moons in **Exs. 18 and 19**.

REAL LIFE

Saturn

California Standards and Assessment

CA Standards: 8, 9
SAT9 Task 1: Objs. 2, 4
SAT9 Task 2: Objs. 5, 6

GOAL 1 Finding the Surface Area of a Sphere

In Lesson 10.7, a circle was described as the locus of points in a plane that are a given distance from a point. A **sphere** is the locus of points in *space* that are a given distance from a point. The point is called the **center of the sphere**. A **radius of a sphere** is a segment from the center to a point on the sphere.

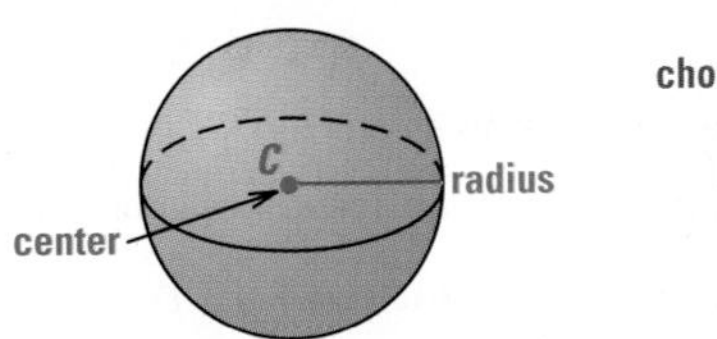

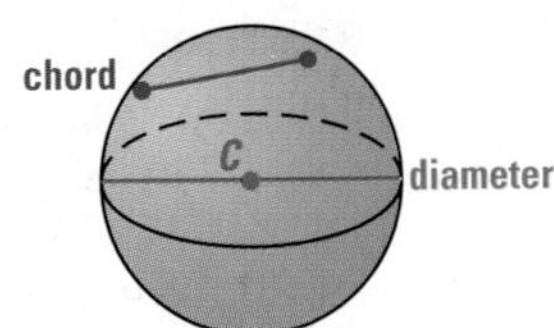

A **chord of a sphere** is a segment whose endpoints are on the sphere. A **diameter** is a chord that contains the center. As with circles, the terms radius and diameter also represent distances, and the diameter is twice the radius.

THEOREM

THEOREM 12.11 *Surface Area of a Sphere*

The surface area S of a sphere with radius r is $S = 4\pi r^2$.

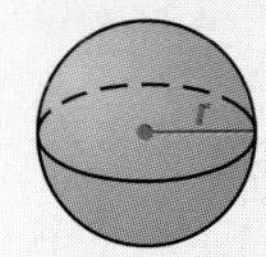

EXAMPLE 1 *Finding the Surface Area of a Sphere*

Find the surface area. When the radius doubles, does the surface area double?

a.

b.

Solution

a. $S = 4\pi r^2 = 4\pi(2)^2 = 16\pi \text{ in.}^2$

b. $S = 4\pi r^2 = 4\pi(4)^2 = 64\pi \text{ in.}^2$

The surface area of the sphere in part (b) is four times greater than the surface area of the sphere in part (a) because $16\pi \cdot 4 = 64\pi$.

▶ So, when the radius of a sphere doubles, the surface area does *not* double.

1 PLAN

Pacing

Basic: 1 day
Average: 1 day
Advanced: 1 day
Block Schedule: 0.5 block with 12.5

Lesson Opener Technology

An alternative way to approach Lesson 12.6 is to use the Technology Lesson Opener:

- Blackline Master (*Chapter 12 Resource Book*, p. 81)
- Transparency (p. 79)

Meeting Individual Needs

- ***Chapter 12 Resource Book***
  Prerequisite Skills Review (p. 5)
  Practice Level A (p. 86)
  Practice Level B (p. 87)
  Practice Level C (p. 88)
  Reteaching with Practice (p. 89)
  Absent Student Catch-Up (p. 91)
  Challenge (p. 93)
- ***Resources in Spanish***
- ***Personal Student Tutor***

New-Teacher Support

See the Tips for New Teachers on pp. 1–2 of the *Chapter 12 Resource Book* for additional notes about Lesson 12.6.

Warm-Up Exercises

Transparency Available

Find the volume of the figure.

1. right cylinder, radius of 10 and height of 4 **$400\pi \approx 1257$ units^3**
2. right cone, base diameter of 18, height of 8 **$216\pi \approx 678.6$ units^3**

Find the surface area of the figure.

3. right cylinder, radius of 9 and height of 11 **$360\pi \approx 1131$ units^2**
4. right cone, radius of 5, slant height of 6 **$55\pi \approx 172.8$ units^2**

2 TEACH

MOTIVATING THE LESSON

Cookie dough often comes in a cylindrical package. If the directions say to divide and roll the dough into 1 inch balls, ask students how to find how many cookies the package will make. To find out, they will have to understand how to find the volume of spheres.

EXTRA EXAMPLE 1

Find the surface area. When the radius triples, does the surface area triple?

a.

64π cm^2

b.

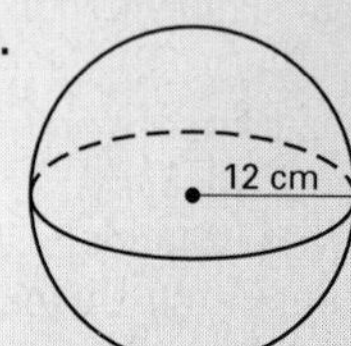

576π cm^2; no

EXTRA EXAMPLE 2

The circumference of a great circle of a sphere is 15.5π meters. What is the surface area of the sphere? 240.25π, or about 755 m^2

EXTRA EXAMPLE 3

A leather ball has a radius of 5 inches. Estimate the amount of leather used to cover the ball. about 314 in.^{2}

CHECKPOINT EXERCISES

For use after Example 1:

1. Find the surface area of a globe with a diameter of 20 inches. 400π, or about 1257 in.^{2} (about 8.7 ft^2)

For use after Examples 2 and 3:

2. The great circle formed by the equator of Mars has a circumference of about 13,300 miles. Estimate the surface area of Mars. about 56,300,000 mi^2

If a plane intersects a sphere, the intersection is either a single point or a circle. If the plane contains the center of the sphere, then the intersection is a **great circle** of the sphere. Every great circle of a sphere separates a sphere into two congruent halves called **hemispheres**.

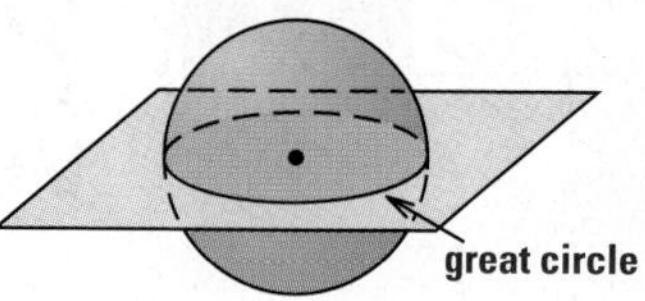

EXAMPLE 2 *Using a Great Circle*

STUDENT HELP

HOMEWORK HELP
Visit our Web site www.mcdougallittell.com for extra examples.

The circumference of a great circle of a sphere is 13.8π feet. What is the surface area of the sphere?

13.8π ft

SOLUTION

Begin by finding the radius of the sphere.

$C = 2\pi r$ Formula for circumference of circle

$13.8\pi = 2\pi r$ Substitute 13.8π for C.

$6.9 = r$ Divide each side by 2π.

Using a radius of 6.9 feet, the surface area is

$$S = 4\pi r^2 = 4\pi(6.9)^2 = 190.44\pi \text{ ft}^2.$$

▶ So, the surface area of the sphere is 190.44π, or about 598 ft^2.

EXAMPLE 3 *Finding the Surface Area of a Sphere*

BASEBALL A baseball and its leather covering are shown. The baseball has a radius of about 1.45 inches.

a. Estimate the amount of leather used to cover the baseball.

b. The surface of a baseball is sewn from two congruent shapes, each of which resembles two joined circles. How does this relate to the formula for the surface area of a sphere?

$r = 1.45$ in.

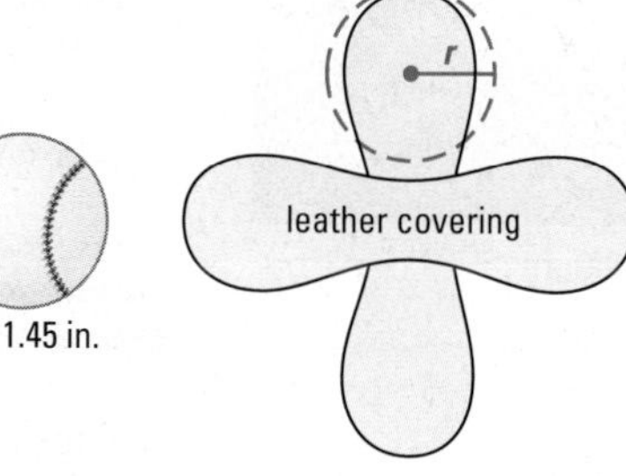

SOLUTION

a. Because the radius r is about 1.45 inches, the surface area is as follows:

$S = 4\pi r^2$ Formula for surface area of sphere

$\approx 4\pi(1.45)^2$ Substitute 1.45 for r.

≈ 26.4 in.^{2} Use a calculator.

b. Because the covering has two pieces, each resembling two joined circles, then the entire covering consists of four circles with radius r. The area of a circle of radius r is $A = \pi r^2$. So, the area of the covering can be approximated by $4\pi r^2$. This is the same as the formula for the surface area of a sphere.

GOAL 2 FINDING THE VOLUME OF A SPHERE

Imagine that the interior of a sphere with radius r is approximated by n pyramids, each with a base area of B and a height of r, as shown. The volume of each pyramid is $\frac{1}{3}Br$ and the sum of the base areas is nB. The surface area of the sphere is approximately equal to nB, or $4\pi r^2$. So, you can approximate the volume V of the sphere as follows.

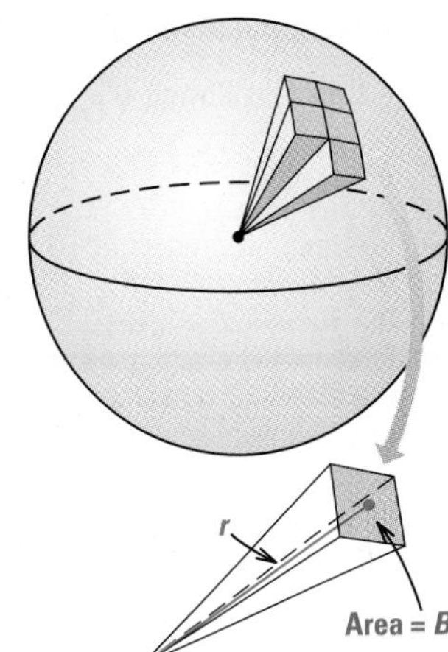

$V \approx n\frac{1}{3}Br$	**Each pyramid has a volume of $\frac{1}{3}Br$.**
$= \frac{1}{3}(nB)r$	**Regroup factors.**
$\approx \frac{1}{3}(4\pi r^2)r$	**Substitute $4\pi r^2$ for nB.**
$= \frac{4}{3}\pi r^3$	**Simplify.**

STUDENT HELP

Study Tip
If you understand how a formula is derived, then it will be easier for you to remember the formula.

THEOREM

THEOREM 12.12 ***Volume of a Sphere***

The volume V of a sphere with radius r is $V = \frac{4}{3}\pi r^3$.

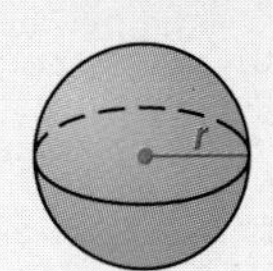

EXAMPLE 4 *Finding the Volume of a Sphere*

BALL BEARINGS To make a steel ball bearing, a cylindrical *slug* is heated and pressed into a spherical shape with the same volume. Find the radius of the ball bearing below.

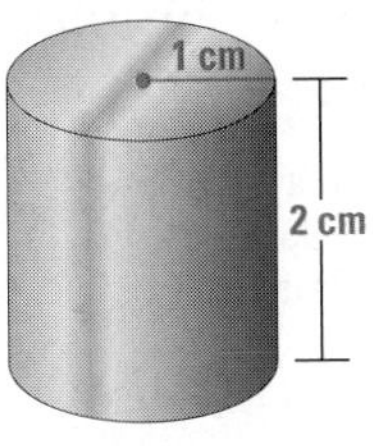

slug

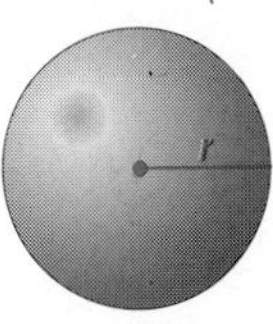

ball bearing

SOLUTION

To find the volume of the slug, use the formula for the volume of a cylinder.

$$V = \pi r^2 h = \pi(1^2)(2) = 2\pi \text{ cm}^3$$

To find the radius of the ball bearing, use the formula for the volume of a sphere and solve for r.

$V = \frac{4}{3}\pi r^3$	**Formula for volume of sphere**
$2\pi = \frac{4}{3}\pi r^3$	**Substitute 2π for V.**
$6\pi = 4\pi r^3$	**Multiply each side by 3.**
$1.5 = r^3$	**Divide each side by 4π.**
$1.14 \approx r$	**Use a calculator to take the cube root.**

▶ So, the radius of the ball bearing is about 1.14 centimeters.

FOCUS ON PEOPLE

IN-LINE SKATING Ball bearings help the wheels of an in-line skate turn smoothly. The two brothers above, Scott and Brennan Olson, pioneered the design of today's in-line skates.

EXTRA EXAMPLE 4
What is the radius of a sphere molded from the cylinder of modeling clay shown?

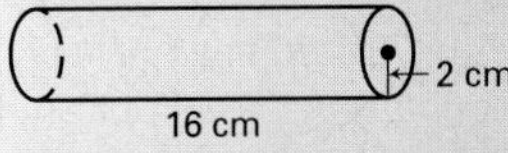

about 3.63 cm

CHECKPOINT EXERCISES
For use after Example 4:
1. You melt a 4 inch diameter sphere of wax and pour it into a cylindrical 2 inch diameter candle mold. How tall can you make the candle? $10\frac{2}{3}$ in.

FOCUS ON VOCABULARY
What is a *great circle* of a sphere? ***Sample answer:*** **It is the intersection of a plane with a sphere such that the plane contains the sphere's center. The diameter of a great circle is the diameter of the sphere.**

CLOSURE QUESTION
How can you find the surface area of a sphere? the volume of a sphere? **Use the formulas $S = 4\pi r^2$ and $V = \frac{4}{3}\pi r^3$, where r is the radius of the sphere.**

DAILY PUZZLER
Eight congruent spheres are packed into a cube with edge length x so that each sphere is tangent to three faces of the cube and three other spheres as shown. What is the ratio of the total volume of the spheres to the volume of the cube? $\frac{\pi}{6}$

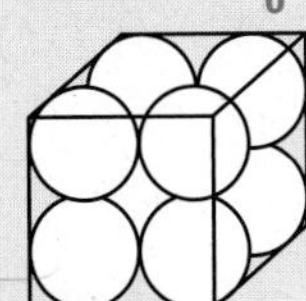

3 APPLY

ASSIGNMENT GUIDE

BASIC
Day 1: pp. 762–765 Exs. 10–17, 20–29, 35, 36, 45–48, 50–57

AVERAGE
Day 1: pp. 762–765 Exs. 10–18, 20–29, 35–40, 45–48, 50–57

ADVANCED
Day 1: pp. 762–765 Exs. 10–18, 20–29, 35–40, 44–57

BLOCK SCHEDULE WITH 12.5
pp. 762–765 Exs. 10–18, 20–29, 35–40, 45–48, 50–57

EXERCISE LEVELS

Level A: *Easier*
10–12

Level B: *More Difficult*
13–43, 45–48, 50–57

Level C: *Most Difficult*
44, 49

✓ HOMEWORK CHECK

To quickly check student understanding of key concepts, go over the following exercises: Exs. 12, 22, 24, 28, 36. See also the Daily Homework Quiz:

- Blackline Master (*Chapter 12 Resource Book*, p. 96)
- Transparency (p. 92)

GUIDED PRACTICE

Vocabulary Check ✓

Concept Check ✓

Skill Check ✓

1. The locus of points in space that are __?__ from a __?__ is called a sphere. **equidistant; point**

2. **ERROR ANALYSIS** Melanie is asked to find the volume of a sphere with a diameter of 10 millimeters. Explain her error(s).

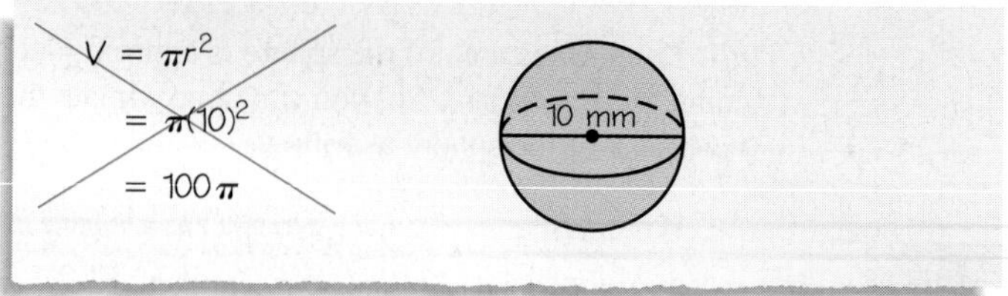

2. She used the formula for the area of a ⊙ with radius r rather than the formula for the volume of a sphere with radius r, and used the diameter rather than the radius.

In Exercises 3–8, use the diagram of the sphere, whose center is *P*.
3, 4. Sample answers are given.

3. Name a chord of the sphere. $\overline{QS}$, $\overline{RT}$, or $\overline{TS}$

4. Name a segment that is a radius of the sphere. $\overline{PQ}$, $\overline{PR}$, or $\overline{PS}$

5. Name a segment that is a diameter of the sphere. $\overline{QS}$

6. Find the circumference of the great circle that contains Q and S. $6\pi \approx 18.85$ units

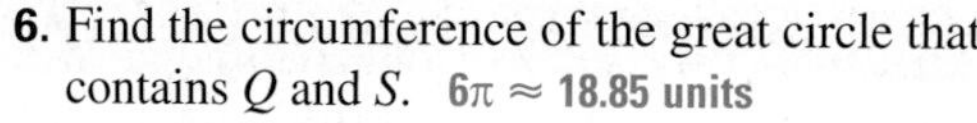

7. Find the surface area of the sphere. $36\pi \approx 113.10$ sq. units

8. Find the volume of the sphere. $36\pi \approx 113.10$ cu. units

9. **CHEMISTRY** A helium atom is approximately spherical with a radius of about 0.5×10^{-8} centimeter. What is the volume of a helium atom? about 5.24×10^{-25} cm³

PRACTICE AND APPLICATIONS

STUDENT HELP
Extra Practice to help you master skills is on p. 826.

FINDING SURFACE AREA **Find the surface area of the sphere. Round your result to two decimal places.**

10. 530.93 m² (6.5 m)

11. 4071.50 cm² (18 cm)

12. 186.27 ft²

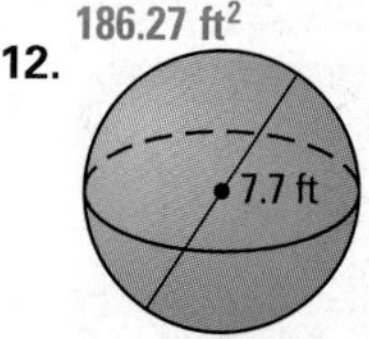

USING A GREAT CIRCLE **In Exercises 13–16, use the sphere below. The center of the sphere is *C* and its circumference is 7.4π inches.**

STUDENT HELP
HOMEWORK HELP
Example 1: Exs. 10–12
Example 2: Exs. 13–16
Example 3: Ex. 17
Example 4: Exs. 20–22, 41–43

13. What is half of the sphere called? a hemisphere

14. Find the radius of the sphere. 3.7 in.

15. Find the diameter of the sphere. 7.4 in.

16. Find the surface area of half of the sphere. $27.38\pi \approx 86.02$ in.²

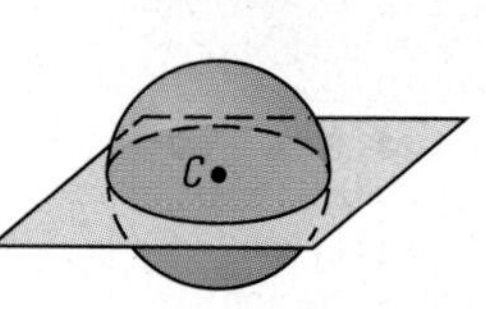

17. **SPORTS** The diameter of a softball is 3.8 inches. Estimate the amount of leather used to cover the softball. about 45.4 in.²

FOCUS ON APPLICATIONS

PLANETS Jupiter is the largest planet in our solar system. It has a diameter of 88,730 miles, or 142,800 kilometers.

APPLICATION LINK www.mcdougallittell.com

18. **PLANETS** The circumference of Earth at the equator (great circle of Earth) is 24,903 miles. The diameter of the moon is 2155 miles. Find the surface area of Earth and of the moon to the nearest hundred. How does the surface area of the moon compare to the surface area of Earth? See margin.

19. **DATA COLLECTION** Research to find the diameters of Neptune and its two moons, Triton and Nereid. Use the diameters to find the surface area of each. See margin.

FINDING VOLUME **Find the volume of the sphere. Round your result to two decimal places.**

20. 44,602.24 cm^3

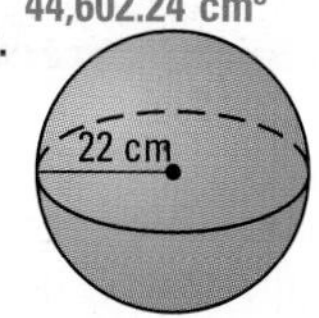

21. 65.45 $in.^3$

2.5 in.

22. 3156.55 mm^3

18.2 mm

USING A TABLE **Copy and complete the table below. Leave your answers in terms of π.**

	Radius of sphere	Circumference of great circle	Surface area of sphere	Volume of sphere
23.	7 mm	?	?	?
24.	?	?	144π in.^{2}	?
25.	?	10π cm	?	?
26.	?	?	?	$\frac{4000\pi}{3}$ m^3

23. 14π mm; 196π mm^2; $\frac{1372\pi}{3}$ mm^3

24. 6 in.; 12π in.; 288π in.^{3}

25. 5 cm; 100π cm^2; $\frac{500\pi}{3}$ cm^3

26. 10 m; 20π m; 400π m^2

COMPOSITE SOLIDS **Find (a) the surface area of the solid and (b) the volume of the solid. The cylinders and cones are right. Round your results to two decimal places.**

27.

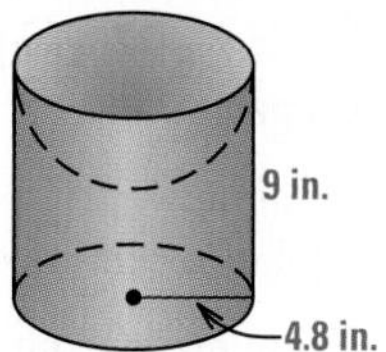

28.

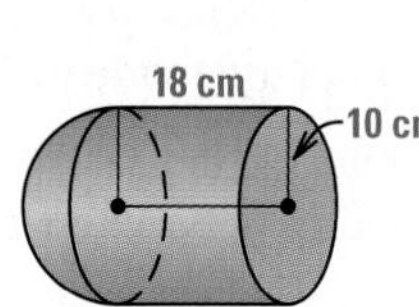

29.

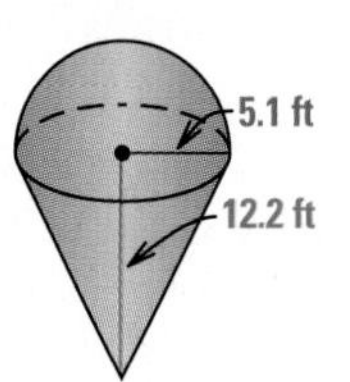

27. a. 488.58 $in.^2$
 b. 419.82 $in.^3$

28. a. 2073.45 cm^2
 b. 7749.26 cm^3

29. a. 375.29 ft^2
 b. 610.12 ft^3

TECHNOLOGY **In Exercises 30–33, consider five spheres whose radii are 1 meter, 2 meters, 3 meters, 4 meters, and 5 meters.**

30. Find the volume and surface area of each sphere. Leave your results in terms of π. See margin.

31. Use your answers to Exercise 30 to find the ratio of the volume to the surface area, $\frac{V}{S}$, for each sphere. $\frac{1}{3}, \frac{2}{3}, 1, \frac{4}{3}, \frac{5}{3}$

32. Use a graphing calculator to plot the graph of $\frac{V}{S}$ as a function of the radius. What do you notice? Check graphs; the graph is linear.

33. *Writing* If the radius of a sphere triples, does its surface area triple? Explain your reasoning. See margin.

33. No; let r be the radius of a sphere and S its surface area. If the radius is tripled, then the surface area is $4\pi(3r)^2 = 4\pi(9r^2) = 9(4\pi r^2) = 9S$. The surface area is multiplied by 9. (Another way to consider this is to note that surface area is a function of r^2, not of r, so tripling the value of r multiplies the value of S by $3^2 = 9$.)

APPLICATION NOTE

EXERCISE 18 Additional information about planets is available at **www.mcdougallittell.com.**

! COMMON ERROR

EXERCISE 26 Dealing with the units may be confusing for some students when working backwards from cubic meters. Simplifying the equation $\frac{4}{3}\pi r^3 = \frac{4000\pi}{3}$ m^3 gives $r^3 = 1000$ m^3. When students take the cube root of both sides, they can treat m like a variable, so $\sqrt[3]{m^3} = m$, and $r = 10$ m. This makes sense because the radius is a one-dimensional length.

GRAPHING CALCULATOR NOTE

EXERCISES 30–32 Students can use the table features of a graphing calculator to help with Exercises 30 and 31 by setting the table to an initial value of 1 with a step of 1, and then entering the formulas for volume and surface area as the first two functions. The third function can then be entered from the variables list as the ratio of the previously defined functions. Students can graph the third function directly for Exercise 32. Students can verify that the graph makes sense by writing the ratio of the formulas explicitly and simplifying.

18. about 197,402,900 mi^2, about 14,589,600 mi^2; the surface area of the earth is about 13.5 times the surface area of the moon. (Answers may vary due to rounding.)

19. The diameters of Neptune and its moons Triton and Nereid are, respectively, about 30,775 mi, about 1680 mi, and about 211 mi. Then the surface areas are about 2,975,404,400 mi^2, about 8,866,800 mi^2, and 139,900 mi^2.

30. See next page.

STUDENT HELP NOTES

Homework Help Students can find help for Exs. 35 and 36 at **www.mcdougallittell.com.** The information can be printed out for students who don't have access to the Internet.

30.

Radius of sphere (m)	Surface area (m^2)	Volume (m^3)
1	4π	$\frac{4}{3}\pi$
2	16π	$10\frac{2}{3}\pi$
3	36π	36π
4	64π	$85\frac{1}{3}\pi$
5	100π	$166\frac{2}{3}\pi$

34.

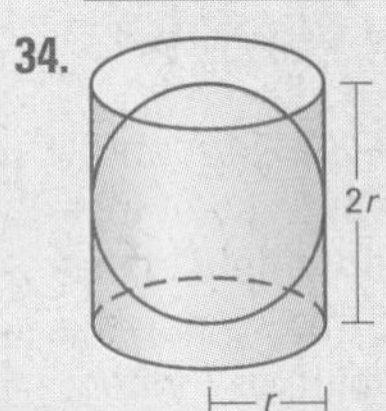

ADDITIONAL PRACTICE AND RETEACHING

For Lesson 12.6:

- Practice Levels A, B, and C (*Chapter 12 Resource Book,* p. 86)
- Reteaching with Practice (*Chapter 12 Resource Book,* p. 89)
- See Lesson 12.6 of the *Personal Student Tutor*

For more Mixed Review:

- Search the *Test and Practice Generator* for key words or specific lessons.

34. VISUAL THINKING A sphere with radius r is inscribed in a cylinder with height $2r$. Make a sketch and find the volume of the cylinder in terms of r. $2\pi r^3$

STUDENT HELP

HOMEWORK HELP Visit our Web site www.mcdougallittell.com for help with Exs. 35 and 36.

USING ALGEBRA In Exercises 35 and 36, solve for the variable. Then find the area of the intersection of the sphere and the plane.

35. $y = 2$; $4\pi \approx 12.57$ sq. units

36. $z = 12$; $144\pi \approx 452.39$ sq. units

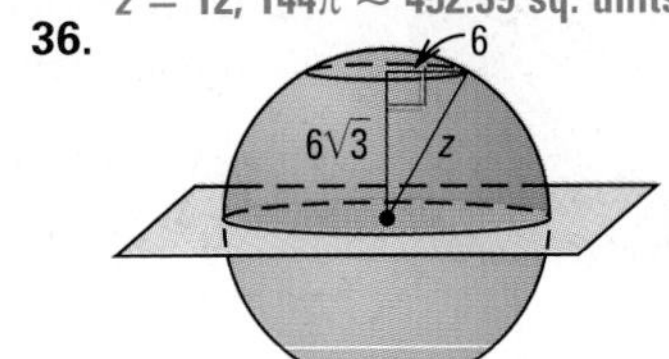

37. CRITICAL THINKING Sketch the intersection of a sphere and a plane that does not pass through the center of the sphere. If you know the circumference of the circle formed by the intersection, can you find the surface area of the sphere? Explain. No; you need to know the distance from the center of the sphere to the plane.

SPHERES IN ARCHITECTURE The spherical building below has a diameter of 165 feet.

38. $27{,}225\pi \approx 85{,}530$ ft^2; no; *Sample answer:* the surface does not appear to be smooth, so it is possible that the building is not actually a sphere.

38. Find the surface area of a sphere with a diameter of 165 feet. Looking at the surface of the building, do you think its surface area is the same? Explain.

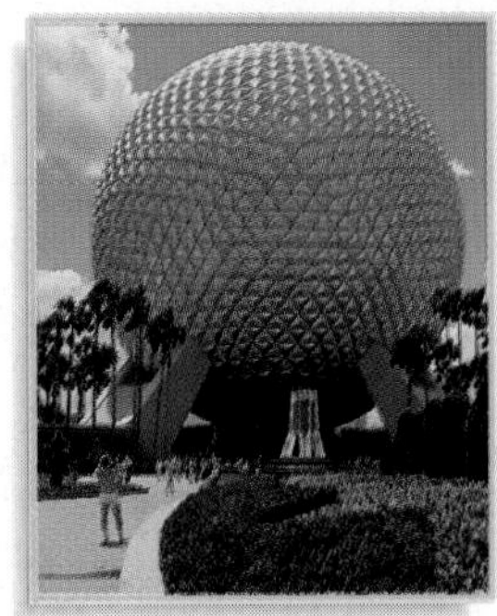

39. The surface of the building consists of 1000 (nonregular) triangular pyramids. If the lateral area of each pyramid is about 267.3 square feet, estimate the actual surface area of the building. about 267,300 ft^2

40. Estimate the volume of the building using the formula for the volume of a sphere. about 2,352,071 ft^3

BALL BEARINGS In Exercises 41–43, refer to the description of how ball bearings are made in Example 4 on page 761.

41–43. Answers are rounded to 2 decimal places.

41. Find the radius of a steel ball bearing made from a cylindrical slug with a radius of 3 centimeters and a height of 6 centimeters. 3.43 cm

42. Find the radius of a steel ball bearing made from a cylindrical slug with a radius of 2.57 centimeters and a height of 4.8 centimeters. 2.88 cm

43. If a steel ball bearing has a radius of 5 centimeters, and the radius of the cylindrical slug it was made from was 4 centimeters, then what was the height of the cylindrical slug? 10.42 cm

44. COMPOSITION OF ICE CREAM In making ice cream, a mix of solids, sugar, and water is frozen. Air bubbles are whipped into the mix as it freezes. The air bubbles are about 1×10^{-2} centimeter in diameter. If one quart, 946.34 cubic centimeters, of ice cream has about 1.446×10^9 air bubbles, what percent of the ice cream is air? (*Hint:* Start by finding the volume of one air bubble.) about 80%

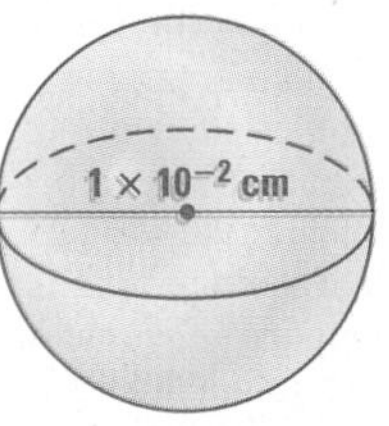

Air bubble

Test Preparation

MULTI-STEP PROBLEM **Use the solids below.**

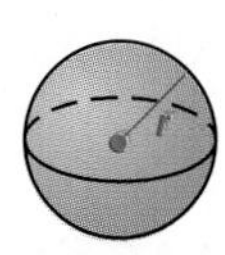

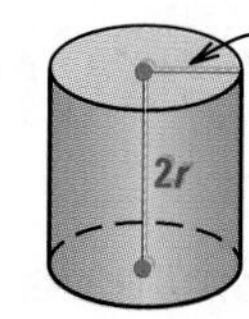

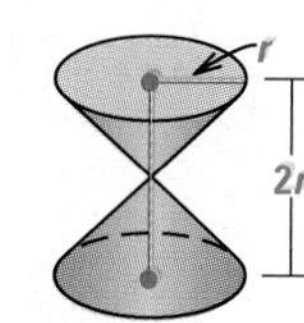

45. Write an expression for the volume of the sphere in terms of r. $\frac{4}{3}\pi r^3$

46. Write an expression for the volume of the cylinder in terms of r. $2\pi r^3$

47. Write an expression for the volume of the solid composed of two cones in terms of r. $\frac{2}{3}\pi r^3$

48. Compare the volumes of the cylinder and the cones to the volume of the sphere. What do you notice?

48. The volume of the cylinder is greater than the volumes of both other solids; the volume of the cylinder is equal to the sum of the volumes of the sphere and the double-cone shaped solid.

★ Challenge

49. A cone is inscribed in a sphere with a radius of 5 centimeters, as shown. The distance from the center of the sphere to the center of the base of the cone is x. Write an expression for the volume of the cone in terms of x. (*Hint:* Use the radius of the sphere as part of the height of the cone.)
$\frac{\pi}{3}(25 - x^2)(x + 5)$ or $\frac{\pi}{3}(125 + 25x - 5x^2 - x^3)$

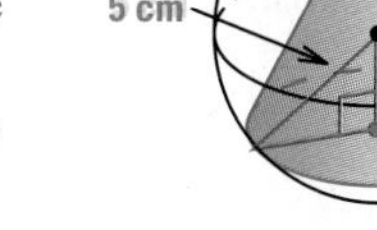

EXTRA CHALLENGE
www.mcdougallittell.com

MIXED REVIEW

CLASSIFYING PATTERNS **Name the isometries that map the frieze pattern onto itself.** **(Review 7.6)**

50. translation

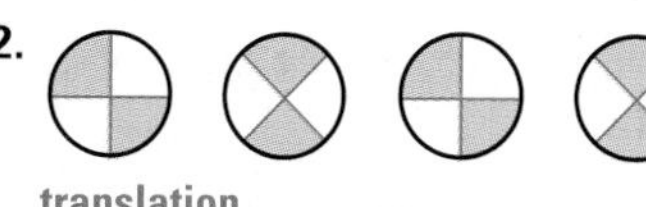

51. translation, vertical line reflection, 180° rotation, glide reflection

52. translation

53. translation, 180° rotation

FINDING AREA **In Exercises 54–56, determine whether $\triangle ABC$ is similar to $\triangle EDC$. If so, then find the area of $\triangle ABC$.** **(Review 8.4, 11.3 for 12.7)**

54. yes; about 19.43 sq. units

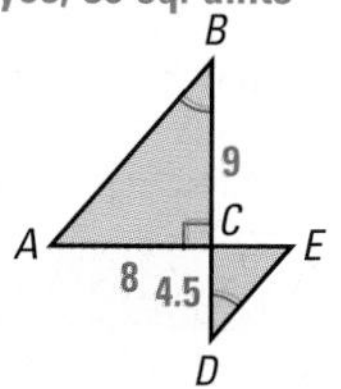

55. yes; 36 sq. units

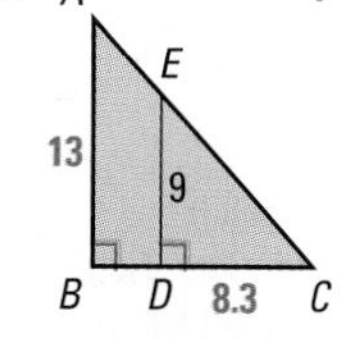

56. yes; $\frac{14,027}{180} \approx$ 77.93 sq. units

A, E, 13, 9, B, D, 8.3, C

57. MEASURING CIRCLES The tire at the right has an outside diameter of 26.5 inches. How many revolutions does the tire make when traveling 100 feet? **(Review 11.4)** about 14.4 revolutions

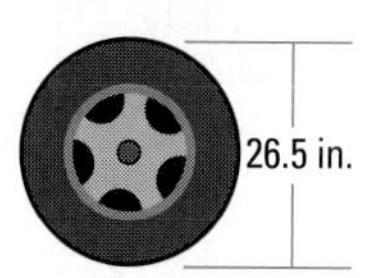

4 ASSESS

DAILY HOMEWORK QUIZ

Transparency Available

1. Find the surface area of a sphere with a radius of 5 m. Round the result to two decimal places. 314.16 m^2
2. Find the volume of a sphere with a diameter of 9.5 ft. Round the result to two decimal places. 448.92 ft^3
3. Find the surface area and volume of a sphere with a radius of 3 cm. Leave the results in terms of π. $36\pi \text{ cm}^2$, $36\pi \text{ cm}^3$
4. Solve for the variable. Then find the area of the intersection of the sphere and the plane.

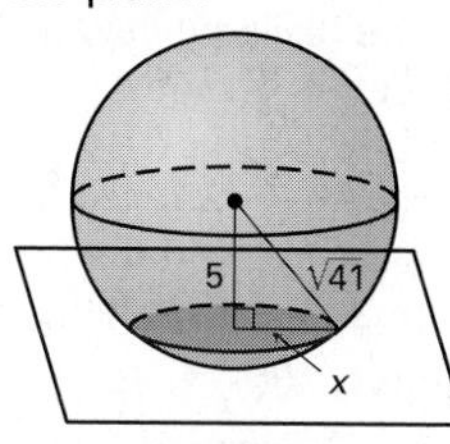

4; $16\pi \approx 50.27$ sq. units

EXTRA CHALLENGE NOTE

Challenge problems for Lesson 12.6 are available in **blackline** format in the *Chapter 12 Resource Book*, p. 93 and at **www.mcdougallittell.com.**

ADDITIONAL TEST PREPARATION

1. **WRITING** What effect does doubling the radius of a sphere have on its volume? Explain.
It multiplies it by 8. The original volume is $\frac{4}{3}\pi r^3$. The new volume is $\frac{4}{3}\pi(2r)^3 = 8 \cdot \frac{4}{3}\pi r^3$.
2. **WRITING** Is there a sphere with a volume of $288\pi \text{ ft}^3$ and a surface area of $256\pi \text{ ft}^2$? Explain.
See sample answer at left.

Additional Test Preparation ***Sample answer:***

2. No; solving $V = 288\pi = \frac{4}{3}\pi r^3$ for r gives $r = 6$ ft. Solving $S = 256\pi = 4\pi r^2$ for r gives $r = 8$ ft. In each case, there is only one possible radius for a given volume or surface area. Since these radii do not agree, they describe two spheres of different sizes.

1 PLAN

PACING
Basic: 2 days
Average: 2 days
Advanced: 2 days
Block Schedule: 1 block

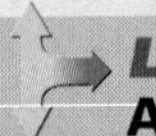

LESSON OPENER ACTIVITY

An alternative way to approach Lesson 12.7 is to use the Activity Lesson Opener:

- Blackline Master (*Chapter 12 Resource Book*, p. 97)
- Transparency (p. 80)

MEETING INDIVIDUAL NEEDS

- ***Chapter 12 Resource Book***
  Prerequisite Skills Review (p. 5)
  Practice Level A (p. 98)
  Practice Level B (p. 99)
  Practice Level C (p. 100)
  Reteaching with Practice (p. 101)
  Absent Student Catch-Up (p. 103)
  Challenge (p. 106)
- ***Resources in Spanish***
- 

NEW-TEACHER SUPPORT

See the Tips for New Teachers on pp. 1–2 of the *Chapter 12 Resource Book* for additional notes about Lesson 12.7.

WARM-UP EXERCISES

Transparency Available

1. Find the surface area and volume of a square prism with a base edge of 1 and a height of 2. 10 units^2, 2 units^3
2. Find the surface area and volume of a square prism with a base edge of 3 and a height of 6. 90 units^2, 54 units^3
3. Find the surface area and volume in terms of π of a right cone with a radius of 3 and a height of 4.
   24π units^2, 12π units^3

12.7 Similar Solids

What you should learn

GOAL 1 Find and use the scale factor of similar solids.

GOAL 2 Use similar solids to solve **real-life** problems, such as finding the lift power of the weather balloon in **Example 4**.

Why you should learn it

▼ You can use similar solids when building a model, such as the model planes below and the model car in **Exs. 25–27**.

CALIFORNIA STANDARDS AND ASSESSMENT

CA Standards: 8, 9, 11
SAT9 Task 1: Obj. 1
SAT9 Task 2: Obj. 1

GOAL 1 COMPARING SIMILAR SOLIDS

Two solids with equal ratios of corresponding *linear* measures, such as heights or radii, are called **similar solids**. This common ratio is called the *scale factor* of one solid to the other solid. Any two cubes are similar; so are any two spheres. Here are other examples of similar and nonsimilar solids.

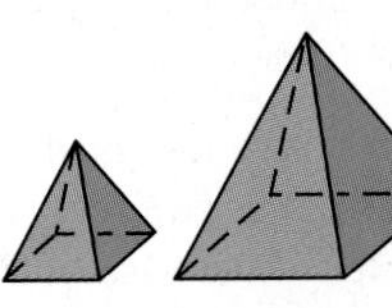
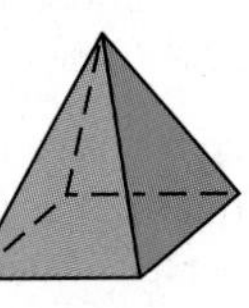

Similar pyramids

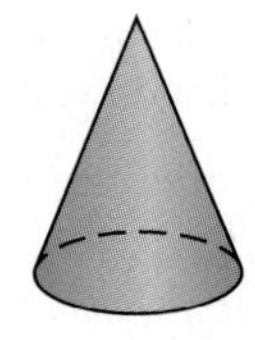
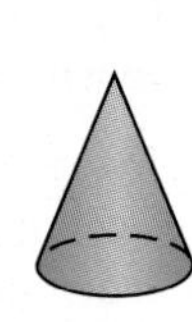

Similar cones

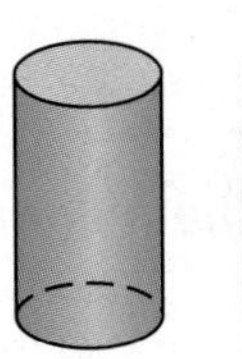
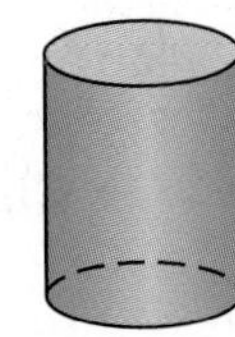

Nonsimilar cylinders

EXAMPLE 1 *Identifying Similar Solids*

Decide whether the two solids are similar. If so, compare the surface areas and volumes of the solids.

a.

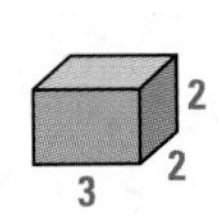

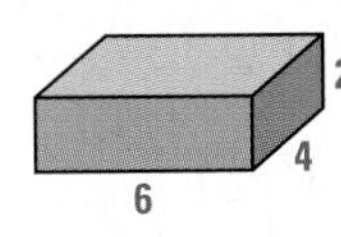

b.

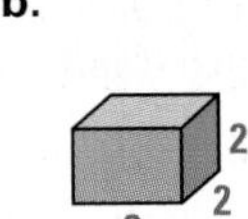

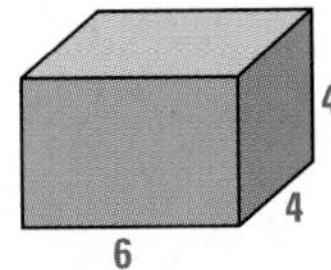

SOLUTION

a. The solids are not similar because the ratios of corresponding linear measures are not equal, as shown.

lengths: $\frac{3}{6} = \frac{1}{2}$ **widths:** $\frac{2}{4} = \frac{1}{2}$ **heights:** $\frac{2}{2} = \frac{1}{1}$

b. The solids are similar because the ratios of corresponding linear measures are equal, as shown. The solids have a scale factor of 1:2.

lengths: $\frac{3}{6} = \frac{1}{2}$ **widths:** $\frac{2}{4} = \frac{1}{2}$ **heights:** $\frac{2}{4} = \frac{1}{2}$

The surface area and volume of the solids are as follows:

Prism	Surface area	Volume
Smaller	$S = 2B + Ph = 2(6) + 10(2) = 32$	$V = Bh = 6(2) = 12$
Larger	$S = 2B + Ph = 2(24) + 20(4) = 128$	$V = Bh = 24(4) = 96$

▶ The ratio of side lengths is 1:2, the ratio of surface areas is 32:128, or 1:4, and the ratio of volumes is 12:96, or 1:8.

THEOREM

THEOREM 12.13 ***Similar Solids Theorem***

If two similar solids have a scale factor of $a:b$, then corresponding areas have a ratio of $a^2:b^2$, and corresponding volumes have a ratio of $a^3:b^3$.

The term *areas* in the theorem above can refer to any pair of corresponding areas in the similar solids, such as lateral areas, base areas, and surface areas.

EXAMPLE 2 *Using the Scale Factor of Similar Solids*

The prisms are similar with a scale factor of 1:3. Find the surface area and volume of prism G given that the surface area of prism F is 24 square feet and the volume of prism F is 7 cubic feet.

SOLUTION

Begin by using Theorem 12.13 to set up two proportions.

$$\frac{\text{Surface area of } F}{\text{Surface area of } G} = \frac{a^2}{b^2} \qquad \frac{\text{Volume of } F}{\text{Volume of } G} = \frac{a^3}{b^3}$$

$$\frac{24}{\text{Surface area of } G} = \frac{1^2}{3^2} \qquad \frac{7}{\text{Volume of } G} = \frac{1^3}{3^3}$$

$$\text{Surface area of } G = 216 \qquad \text{Volume of } G = 189$$

STUDENT HELP

Look Back
For help with solving a proportion with an unknown, see p. 459.

▶ So, the surface area of prism G is 216 square feet and the volume of prism G is 189 cubic feet.

✓**CHECK** Check your answers by substituting back into the original proportions.

$$\frac{\text{Surface area of } F}{\text{Surface area of } G} = \frac{24}{216} = \frac{1}{9} \qquad \frac{\text{Volume of } F}{\text{Volume of } G} = \frac{7}{189} = \frac{1}{27}$$

EXAMPLE 3 *Finding the Scale Factor of Similar Solids*

To find the scale factor of the two cubes, find the ratio of the two volumes.

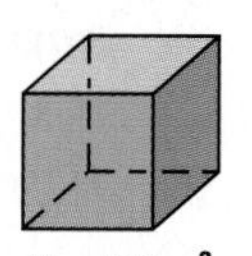

$V = 512\ m^3$

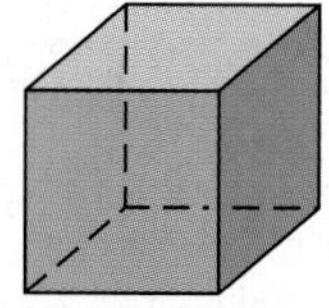
$V = 1728\ m^3$

$\frac{a^3}{b^3} = \frac{512}{1728}$ **Write ratio of volumes.**

$\frac{a}{b} = \frac{8}{12}$ **Use a calculator to take the cube root.**

$= \frac{2}{3}$ **Simplify.**

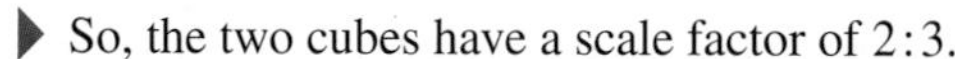

▶ So, the two cubes have a scale factor of 2:3.

2 TEACH

EXTRA EXAMPLE 1

Decide whether the two solids are similar. If so, compare the surface areas and volumes of the solids.

a.

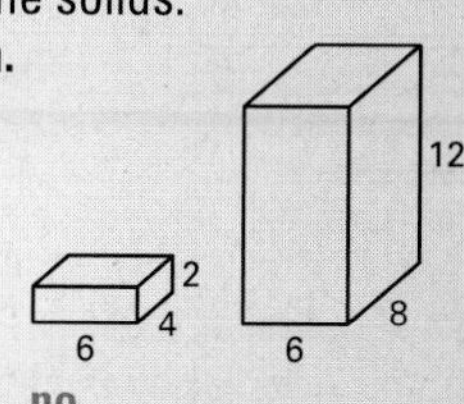

no

b.

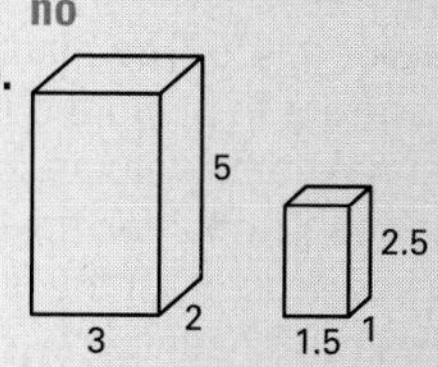

Yes; the ratio of side lengths is 2:1; the surface areas of 62 and 15.5 are in a ratio of 4:1, and the volumes of 30 and 3.75 are in a ratio of 8:1.

EXTRA EXAMPLE 2

Two rectangular prisms are similar with a scale factor $A:B$ of 1:4. Find the surface area and volume of prism B given that the surface area of prism A is 28 square feet and the volume of prism A is 8 cubic feet.
448 ft^2, 512 ft^3

EXTRA EXAMPLE 3

Two cubes have volumes of 64 m^3 and 1000 m^3. Find the scale factor of the cubes by finding the ratio of the volumes. 2:5

CHECKPOINT EXERCISES

For use after Examples 1 and 2:

1. Two spheres have diameters of 56 and 70. What are the ratios of their surface areas and their volumes?
16:25 and 64:125

For use after Example 3:

2. Two similar cones have surface areas of 384π ft^2 and 216π ft^2. Find the scale factor of the cones by finding the ratio of the surface areas.
4:3

EXTRA EXAMPLE 4

Find the missing measures in the table, given that the ratio of the lift powers equals the ratio of the volumes of the balloons.

Diameter	Volume	Lift power
4 ft	___ ft^3	2 lb
10 ft	___ ft^3	___ lb

first row: 10.7π;
second row: 166.7π, 31.25

EXTRA EXAMPLE 5

Two similar punch bowls have a scale factor of 4:5. The amount of concentrate to be added is proportional to the volume. How much concentrate does the smaller bowl require if the larger bowl requires 32 ounces?
about 16.4 oz

CHECKPOINT EXERCISES

For use after Examples 4 and 5:

1. Two fish tanks are similar. One holds 5 gallons and the other holds 10 gallons. If the length of the 5 gallon tank is 14 inches, what is the length of the 10 gallon tank?
about 17.64 in.

FOCUS ON VOCABULARY

What does it mean for two solids to be *similar*?
See sample answer below.

CLOSURE QUESTION

If the dimensions of a solid are increased by a factor of *x*, what happens to the surface area of the solid? to its volume? The surface area increases by a factor of x^2; the volume increases by a factor of x^3.

DAILY PUZZLER

One cylindrical water tank has a radius of 8 meters and is filled to a depth of 25 meters. Another has a radius of 6 meters and is empty. How much water will be in the smaller tank when the depth is the same in both tanks? about 1810 m^3

USING SIMILARITY IN REAL LIFE

FOCUS ON CAREERS

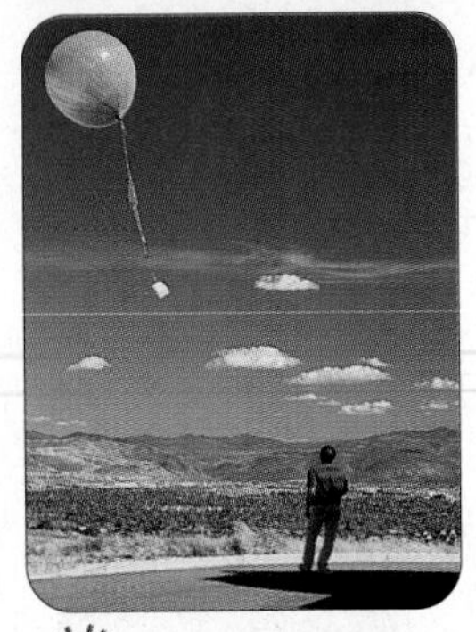

METEOROLOGY Meteorologists rely on data collected from weather balloons and radar to make predictions about the weather.

CAREER LINK
www.mcdougallittell.com

EXAMPLE 4 *Using Volumes of Similar Solids*

METEOROLOGY The lift power of a weather balloon is the amount of weight the balloon can lift. Find the missing measures in the table below, given that the ratio of the lift powers is equal to the ratio of the volumes of the balloons.

Diameter	Volume	Lift power
8 ft	? ft^3	17 lb
16 ft	? ft^3	? lb

SOLUTION

Find the volume of the smaller balloon, whose radius is 4 feet.

smaller balloon $\quad V = \frac{4}{3}\pi r^3 = \frac{4}{3}\pi(4)^3 \approx 85.3\pi \text{ ft}^3$

The scale factor of the two balloons is $\frac{8}{16}$, or 1:2. So, the ratio of the volumes is $1^3:2^3$, or 1:8. To find the volume of the larger balloon, multiply the volume of the smaller balloon by 8.

larger balloon $\quad V \approx 8(85.3\pi) \approx 682.4\pi \text{ ft}^3$

The ratio of the lift powers is 1:8. To find the lift power of the larger balloon, multiply the lift power of the smaller balloon by 8, as follows: 8(17) = 136 lb.

Diameter	Volume	Lift power
8 ft	85.3π ft^3	17 lb
16 ft	682.4π ft^3	136 lb

EXAMPLE 5 *Comparing Similar Solids*

SWIMMING POOLS Two swimming pools are similar with a scale factor of 3:4. The amount of a chlorine mixture to be added is proportional to the volume of water in the pool. If two cups of the chlorine mixture are needed for the smaller pool, how much of the chlorine mixture is needed for the larger pool?

SOLUTION

Using the scale factor, the ratio of the volume of the smaller pool to the volume of the larger pool is as follows:

$$\frac{a^3}{b^3} = \frac{3^3}{4^3} = \frac{27}{64} \approx \frac{1}{2.4}$$

The ratio of the volumes of the mixtures is 1:2.4. The amount of the chlorine mixture for the larger pool can be found by multiplying the amount of the chlorine mixture for the smaller pool by 2.4 as follows: 2(2.4) = 4.8 c.

▶ So, the larger pool needs 4.8 cups of the chlorine mixture.

STUDENT HELP

Study Tip
To rewrite a fraction so that it has a 1 in the numerator, divide both the numerator and the denominator by the numerator. For example,

$\frac{27}{64} = \frac{27 \div 27}{64 \div 27} \approx \frac{1}{2.4}$.

Focus on Vocabulary *Sample answer:* They have the same shape but not necessarily the same size; the ratios of corresponding linear measures are equal. This common ratio is the scale factor.

GUIDED PRACTICE

Vocabulary Check ✓

1. If two solids are similar with a scale factor of $p:q$, then corresponding areas have a ratio of __?__, and corresponding volumes have a ratio of __?__. $p^2:q^2$; $p^3:q^3$

Concept Check ✓

2. Yes; the ratios of corresponding linear dimensions are equal.
3. No; the ratios of corresponding linear dimensions are not equal. $\left(\frac{6}{3} \neq \frac{4}{4}\right)$

Determine whether the pair of solids are similar. Explain your reasoning.

2.
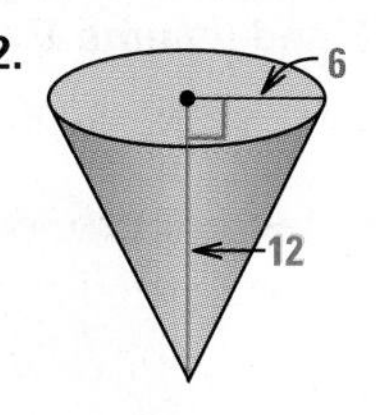

3.
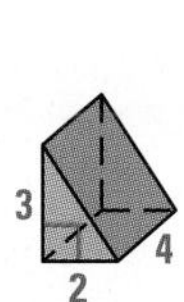

Skill Check ✓

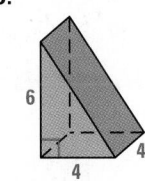

In Exercises 4–6, match the right prism with a similar right prism.

A.
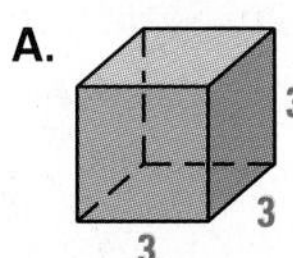

B.
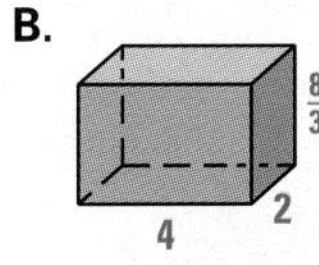

C.
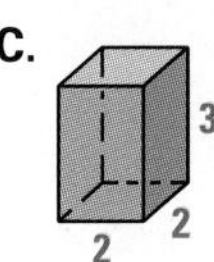

4. B
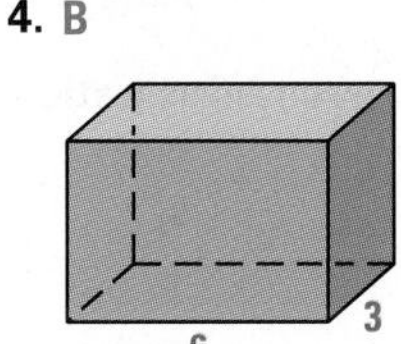

5. C
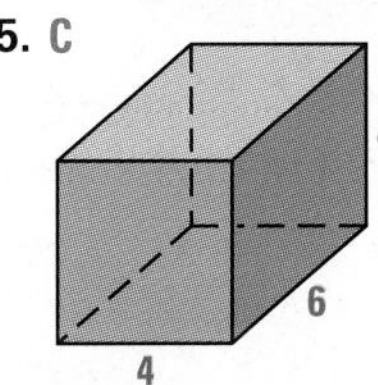

6. A
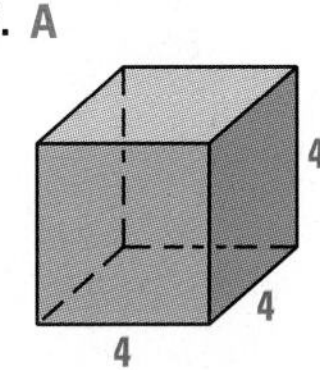

7. Two cubes have volumes of 216 cubic inches and 1331 cubic inches. Find their scale factor. 6:11

8. Two spheres have a scale factor of 1:3. The smaller sphere has a surface area of 36π square meters. Find the surface area of the larger sphere. 324π m^2

PRACTICE AND APPLICATIONS

STUDENT HELP

Extra Practice to help you master skills is on p. 826.

IDENTIFYING SIMILAR SOLIDS **Decide whether the solids are similar.**

9. not similar
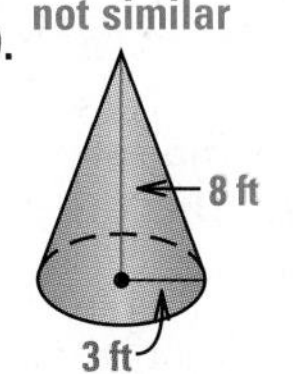

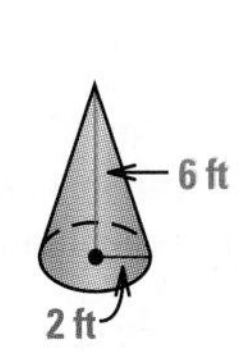

10. similar
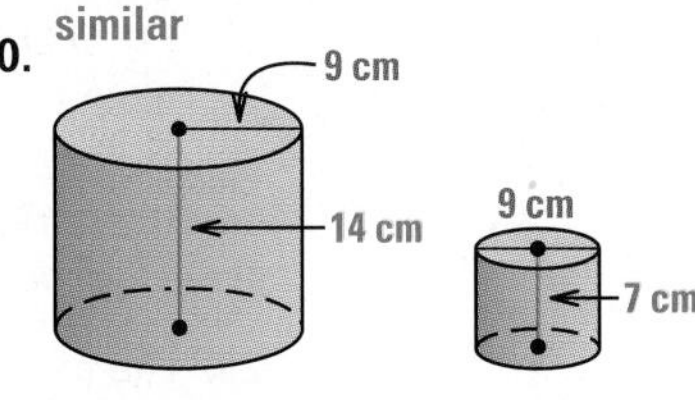

11. similar
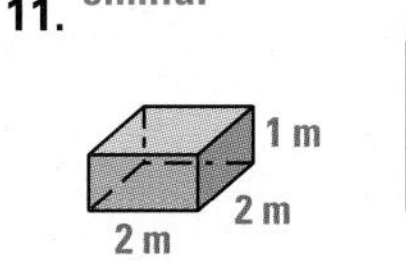

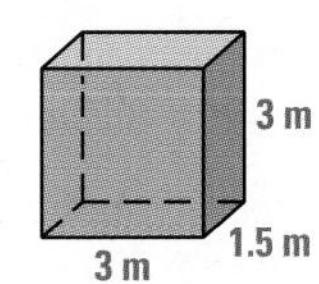

12. similar
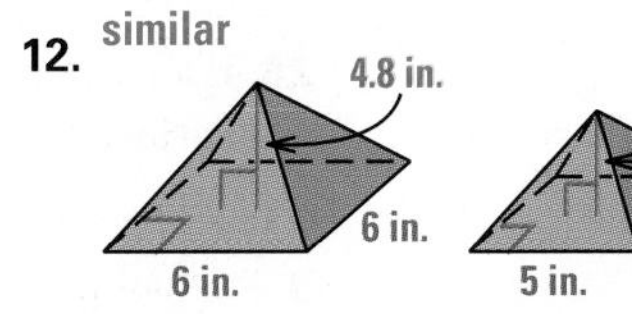

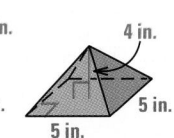

3 APPLY

ASSIGNMENT GUIDE

BASIC

Day 1: pp. 769–772 Exs. 10–24 even, 25–29, 39–44

Day 2: pp. 769–772 Exs. 9–23 odd, 30–36, 45–49, Quiz 3 Exs. 1–8

AVERAGE

Day 1: pp. 769–772 Exs. 10–24 even, 25–29, 39–44

Day 2: pp. 769–772 Exs. 9–23 odd, 30–36, 45–49, Quiz 3 Exs. 1–8

ADVANCED

Day 1: pp. 769–772 Exs. 10–24 even, 25–29, 39–44

Day 2: pp. 769–772 Exs. 9–23 odd, 30–38, 45–49, Quiz 3 Exs. 1–8

BLOCK SCHEDULE

pp. 769–772 Exs. 9–36, 39–49, Quiz 3 Exs. 1–8

EXERCISE LEVELS

Level A: *Easier*
9–16, 39–44

Level B: *More Difficult*
17–36, 45–49

Level C: *Most Difficult*
37, 38

✓ HOMEWORK CHECK

To quickly check student understanding of key concepts, go over the following exercises: Exs. 10, 18, 20, 24, 26, 30, 32, 34. See also the Daily Homework Quiz:

- Transparency (p. 93)

MATHEMATICAL REASONING

EXERCISE 23 Remind students to simplify ratios if possible before taking a square root or cube root. In this exercise, students will need to simplify $\frac{36\pi}{121.5\pi}$. Most will quickly see to divide out the common factor π, but may be unsure how to simplify $\frac{36}{121.5}$. Point out that multiplying both the numerator and denominator by 2 is a way of multiplying the fraction by 1. This gives $\frac{72}{243}$. Students should then realize they can divide out the common factor 9 to obtain the perfect cube $\frac{8}{27}$.

STUDENT HELP

HOMEWORK HELP
Example 1: Exs. 9–16
Example 2: Exs. 17–20
Example 3: Exs. 21–24
Example 5: Ex. 34

LOGICAL REASONING Complete the statement using *always, sometimes,* or *never.*

13. Two cubes are __?__ similar. always

14. Two cylinders are __?__ similar. sometimes

15. A solid is __?__ similar to itself. always

16. A pyramid is __?__ similar to a cone. never

USING SCALE FACTOR The solid is similar to a larger solid with the given scale factor. Find the surface area S and volume V of the larger solid.

17. Scale factor $1:2$ 112π cm^2, 160π cm^3

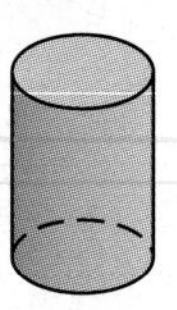

$S = 28\pi$ cm^2
$V = 20\pi$ cm^3

18. Scale factor $1:3$ 1129.5 m^2, 2349 m^3

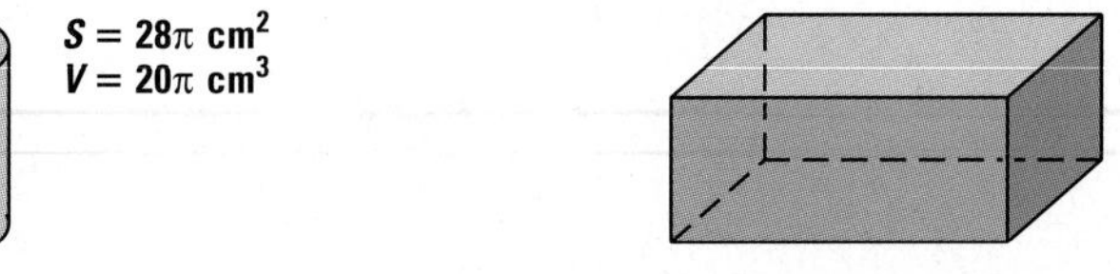

$S = 125.5$ m^2
$V = 87$ m^3

19. Scale factor $1:4$ 384π ft^2, 768π ft^3

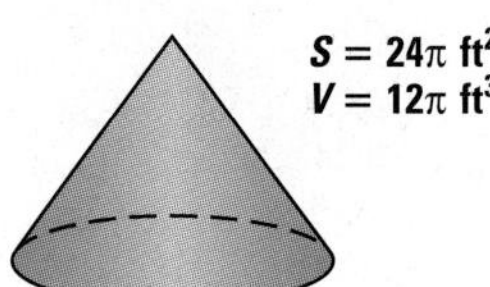

$S = 24\pi$ ft^2
$V = 12\pi$ ft^3

20. Scale factor $2:5$ 2250 in.^{2}, 6250 in.^{3}

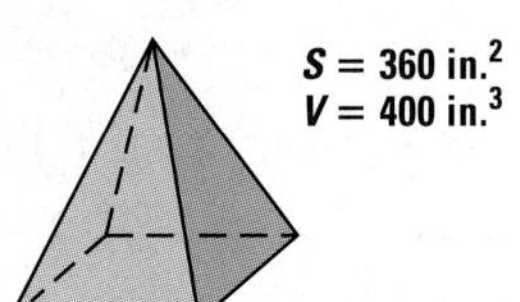

$S = 360$ in.^{2}
$V = 400$ in.^{3}

FINDING SCALE FACTOR Use the given information about the two similar solids to find their scale factor.

21. 1:2

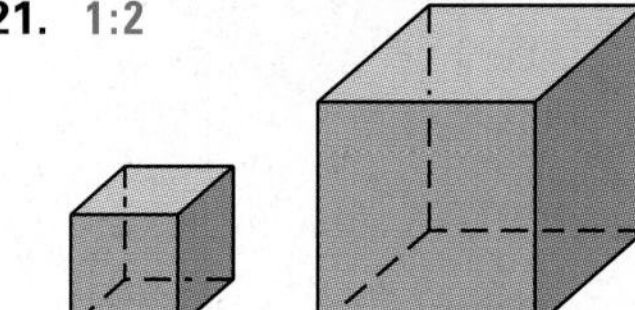

$V = 27$ ft^3 $V = 216$ ft^3

22. 3:5

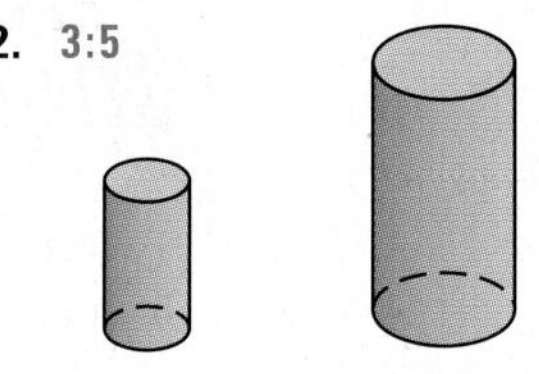

$V = 27\pi$ cm^3 $V = 125\pi$ cm^3

23. 2:3

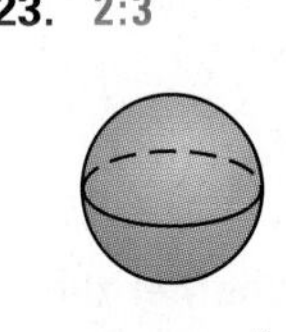

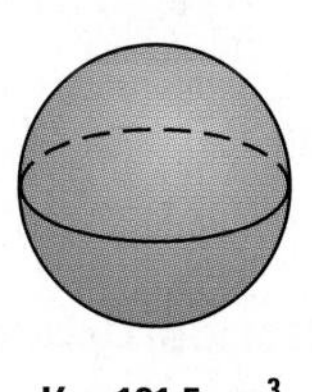

$V = 36\pi$ m^3 $V = 121.5\pi$ m^3

24. 1:4

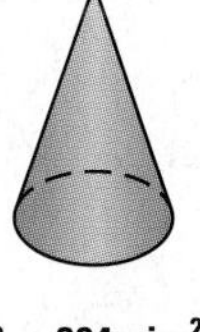

$S = 24\pi$ in.^{2} $S = 384\pi$ in.^{2}

MODEL CAR The scale factor of the model car at the right to the actual car is 1:16. Use the scale factor to complete the exercises.

25. The model has a height of 5.5 inches. What is the height of the actual car? 88 in.

26. Each tire of the model has a surface area of 12.9 square inches. What is the surface area of each tire of the actual car? 3302.4 in.^{2}

27. The model's engine has a volume of 2 cubic inches. Find the volume of the actual car's engine. 8192 in.^{3}

ARCHITECTURE The Civil Rights Institute, in Birmingham, Alabama, was completed in 1992. Its roof is in the shape of a hemisphere.

CRITICAL THINKING Decide whether the statement is true. Explain your reasoning. 28, 29. See margin.

28. If sphere A has a radius of x and sphere B has a radius of y, then the corresponding volumes have a ratio of $x^3 : y^3$.

29. If cube A has an edge length of x and cube B has an edge length of y, then the corresponding surface areas have a ratio of $x^2 : y^2$.

28. True; all spheres are similar; the scale factor of A to B is $x : y$, so the ratio of their volumes is $x^3 : y^3$.

29. True; all cubes are similar; the scale factor of A to B is $x : y$, so the ratio of their surface areas is $x^2 : y^2$.

ARCHITECTURE In Exercises 30–33, you are building a scale model of the Civil Rights Institute shown at the left.

30. You decide that 0.125 inch in your model will correspond to 12 inches of the actual building. What is your scale factor? The scale factor of the model to the actual building is 1:96.

31. The dome of the building is a hemisphere with a diameter of $50\frac{2}{3}$ feet. Find the surface area of the hemisphere. about 4032 ft²

32. Use your results from Exercises 30 and 31 to find the surface area of the dome of your model. $(1 \text{ ft}^2 = 144 \text{ in.}^2)$ about 63 in.²

33. Use your results from Exercises 30 and 31 to find the volume of the actual dome. What is the volume of your model's dome? about 34,051 ft³, about 67 in.³

34. **MAKING JUICE** Two similar cylindrical juice containers have a scale factor of 2:3. To make juice in the smaller container, you use $\frac{1}{2}$ cup of concentrated juice and fill the rest with water. Find the amount of concentrated juice needed to make juice in the larger container. (*Hint:* Start by finding the ratio of the volumes of the containers.) $1\frac{11}{16}$ c

Test Preparation

35. **MULTIPLE CHOICE** The dimensions of the right rectangular prism shown are doubled. How many times larger is the volume of the new prism? E

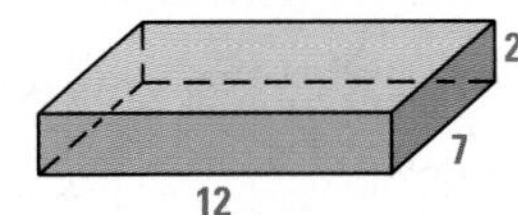

Ⓐ $\frac{1}{4}$ Ⓑ $\frac{1}{2}$ Ⓒ 2 Ⓓ 4 Ⓔ 8

36. **MULTIPLE CHOICE** What is the ratio of the surface areas of the spheres shown? D

Ⓐ $\frac{\sqrt{2}}{\sqrt{5}}$ Ⓑ $\frac{2}{5}$ Ⓒ $\frac{\sqrt{8}}{\sqrt{125}}$

Ⓓ $\frac{4}{25}$ Ⓔ $\frac{8}{125}$

★ Challenge

37. **SPORTS** Twelve basketballs, each with a diameter of 9.55 inches, fill a crate. Estimate the number of volleyballs it would take to fill the crate. The diameter of a volleyball is 8.27 inches. Explain why your answer is an estimate and not an exact number. See margin.

37. About 18; the answer is an estimate because it is calculated from the ratio of the volumes of the basketballs and volleyballs and does not account for the spaces between the balls.

38. **CRITICAL THINKING** Two similar cylinders have surface areas of 96π square feet and 150π square feet. The height of each cylinder is equal to its diameter. Find the dimensions of one cylinder and use their scale factor to find the dimensions of the other cylinder. See margin.

38. The smaller cylinder has a radius of 4 ft, a height of 8 ft, and a volume of 128π ft³. The larger cylinder has a radius of 5 ft, a height of 10 ft, and a volume of 250π ft³.

www.mcdougallittell.com

ADDITIONAL PRACTICE AND RETEACHING

For Lesson 12.7:

- Practice Levels A, B, and C (*Chapter 12 Resource Book,* p. 98)
- Reteaching with Practice (*Chapter 12 Resource Book,* p. 101)
- See Lesson 12.7 of the *Personal Student Tutor*

For more Mixed Review:

- Search the *Test and Practice Generator* for key words or specific lessons.

4 ASSESS

DAILY HOMEWORK QUIZ

Transparency Available

1. Decide whether the solids are similar.

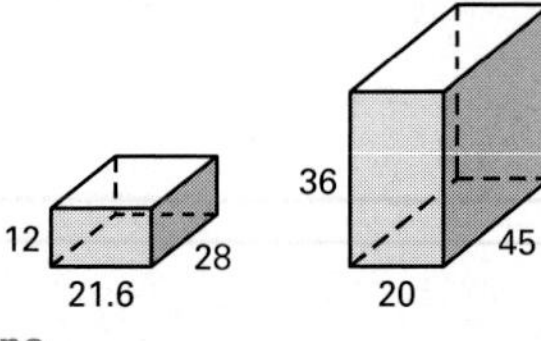

no

2. Two similar cylinders have a scale factor of 2:3. The smaller cylinder has a surface area of 128π m^2 and a volume of 192π m^3. Find the surface area and volume of the larger cylinder. 288π cm^3; 648π cm^3
3. Two regular triangular pyramids have volumes of 297 in.^{3} and 704 in.^{3}. What is their scale factor? 3:4
4. A model of a refinery has a scale of 1 inch to 8 feet. A storage cylinder in the refinery has a surface area of 2304 ft^2. What is the surface area of the cylinder in the model? 0.25 ft^2

EXTRA CHALLENGE NOTE

Challenge problems for Lesson 12.7 are available in **blackline** format in the *Chapter 12 Resource Book*, p. 106 and at **www.mcdougallittell.com.**

ADDITIONAL TEST PREPARATION

1. **OPEN ENDED** Choose two noncongruent, similar solids. Give the linear dimensions of the solids, and find the surface area and volume of the smaller solid. Then use the scale factor to find the surface area and volume of the larger solid.
See sample answer at right.

5, 6. See next page.

MIXED REVIEW

TRANSFORMATIONS Use the diagram of the isometry to complete the statement. (Review 7.1)

39. $\overline{BC} \rightarrow$ ___?___ $\overline{LK}$
40. $\overline{AB} \rightarrow$ ___?___ $\overline{JL}$
41. ___?___ $\rightarrow \overline{KJ}$ $\overline{CA}$
42. $\angle BCA \rightarrow$ ___?___ $\angle LKJ$
43. ___?___ $\rightarrow \angle LJK$ $\angle BAC$
44. $\triangle ABC \rightarrow$ ___?___ $\triangle JLK$

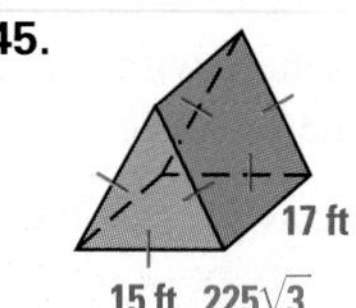

FINDING SURFACE AREA In Exercises 45–47, find the surface area of the solid. (Review 12.2, 12.3, and 12.6)

45. 17 ft, 15 ft. $\frac{225\sqrt{3}}{2} + 765 \approx 959.86$ ft^2

46. 21.4 m, 18 m. $709.2\pi \approx 2228.02$ m^2

47. 32.8 in. $\frac{26{,}896\pi}{25} \approx 3379.85$ in.^{2}

48. The volume of a cylinder is about 14,476.46 cubic meters. If the cylinder has a height of 32 meters, what is its diameter? (Review 12.4) about 24 m

49. The volume of a cone is about 40,447.07 cubic inches. If the cone has a radius of 22.8 inches, what is its height? (Review 12.5) about 74.3 in.

QUIZ 3

Self-Test for Lessons 12.6 and 12.7

You are given the diameter d of a sphere. Find the surface area and volume of the sphere. Round your result to two decimal places. (Lesson 12.6)

1. $d = 20$ cm 1256.64 cm^2, 4188.79 cm^3
2. $d = 3.76$ in. 44.41 in.^{2}, 27.83 in.^{3}
3. $d = 10.8$ ft 366.44 ft^2, 659.58 ft^3
4. $d = 30\sqrt{5}$ m 14,137.17 m^2, 158,058.33 m^3

In Exercises 5 and 6, you are given two similar solids. Find the missing measurement. Then calculate the surface area and volume of each solid. (Lesson 12.7) 5, 6. See margin.

5.

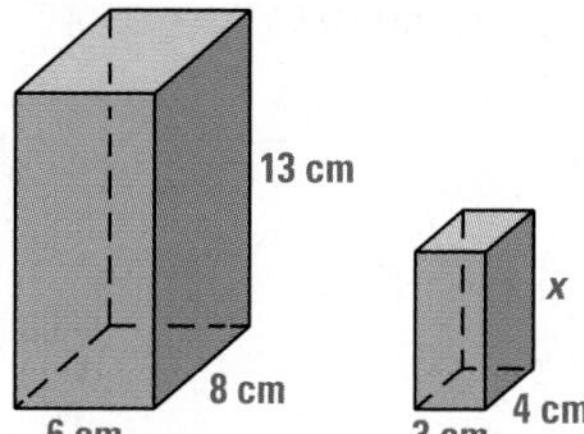

6.

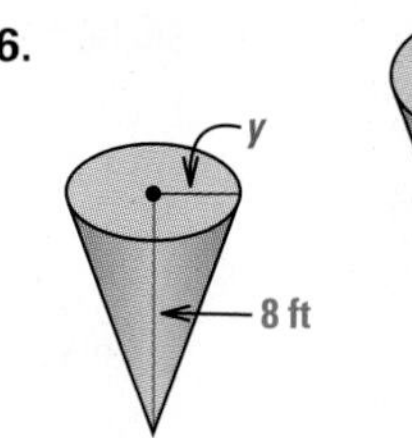

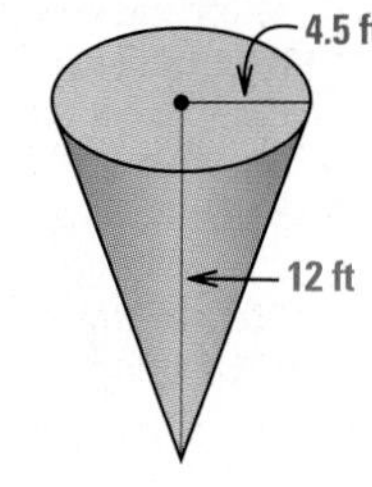

7. $40{,}000\pi \approx 125{,}663.71$ ft^2, $\frac{4{,}000{,}000\pi}{3} \approx 4{,}188{,}790.21$ ft^3

8. 5 ft, $100\pi \approx 314.16$ ft^2, $\frac{500\pi}{3} \approx 523.60$ ft^3

7. **WORLD'S FAIR** The Trylon and Perisphere were the symbols of the New York World's Fair in 1939–40. The Perisphere, shown at the left, was a spherical structure with a diameter of 200 feet. Find the surface area and volume of the Perisphere. (Lesson 12.6) See margin.

8. **SCALE MODEL** The scale factor of a model of the Perisphere to the actual Perisphere is 1:20. Use the information in Exercise 7 and the scale factor to find the radius, surface area, and volume of the model. (Lesson 12.7) See margin.

Additional Test Preparation *Sample answer:*

1. Regular triangular prism A has a base edge of 2 cm and a height of 4 cm; prism B has a base edge of 3 cm and a height of 6 cm. For A, $S = 24 + 2\sqrt{3} \approx 27.46$ cm^2 and $V = 4\sqrt{3} \approx 6.93$ cm^3. The scale factor is 2:3, so for B, $S = \frac{9}{4}(24 + 2\sqrt{3}) = 54 + \frac{9}{2}\sqrt{3} \approx 61.79$ cm^2 and $V = \frac{27}{8}(4\sqrt{3}) = \frac{27}{2}\sqrt{3} \approx 23.38$ cm^3.

CHAPTER 12 Chapter Summary

WHAT did you learn?	*WHY did you learn it?*
Use properties of polyhedra. **(12.1)**	Classify crystals by their shape. **(p. 725)**
Find the surface area of prisms and cylinders. **(12.2)**	Determine the surface area of a wax cylinder record. **(p. 733)**
Find the surface area of pyramids and cones. **(12.3)**	Find the area of each lateral face of a pyramid, such as the Pyramid Arena in Tennessee. **(p. 735)**
Find the volume of prisms and cylinders. **(12.4)**	Find the volume of a fish tank, such as the tank at the New England Aquarium. **(p. 748)**
Find the volume of pyramids and cones. **(12.5)**	Find the volume of a volcano, such as Mount St. Helens. **(p. 757)**
Find the surface area and volume of a sphere. **(12.6)**	Find the surface area of a planet, such as Earth. **(p. 763)**
Find the surface area and volume of similar solids. **(12.7)**	Use the scale factor of a model car to determine dimensions on the actual car. **(p. 770)**

How does Chapter 12 fit into the BIGGER PICTURE of geometry?

Solids can be assigned three types of measure. For instance, the height and radius of a cylinder are one-dimensional measures. The surface area of a cylinder is a two-dimensional measure, and the volume of a cylinder is a three-dimensional measure. Assigning measures to plane regions and to solids is one of the primary goals of geometry. In fact, the word geometry means "Earth measure."

STUDY STRATEGY

How did generalizing formulas help you?

The list of similar concepts you made, following the **Study Strategy** on p. 718, may resemble this one.

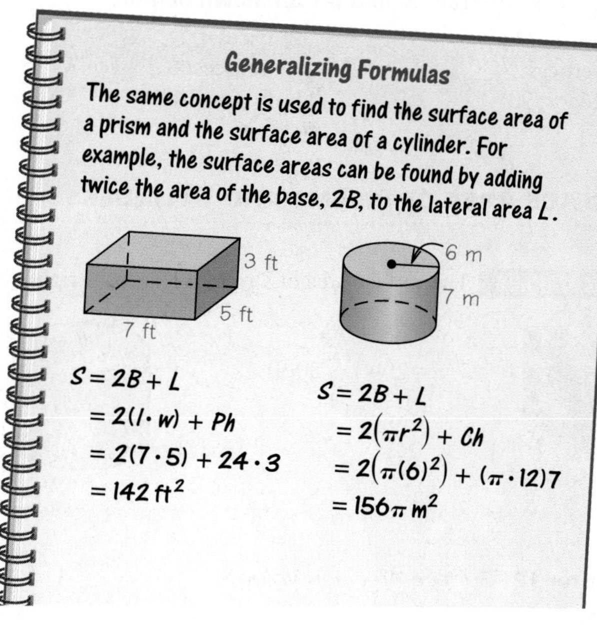

Generalizing Formulas
The same concept is used to find the surface area of a prism and the surface area of a cylinder. For example, the surface areas can be found by adding twice the area of the base, 2B, to the lateral area L.
3 ft
5 ft
7 ft
6 m
7 m
$S = 2B + L$
$= 2(l \cdot w) + Ph$
$= 2(7 \cdot 5) + 24 \cdot 3$
$= 142\ \text{ft}^2$
$S = 2B + L$
$= 2(\pi r^2) + Ch$
$= 2(\pi(6)^2) + (\pi \cdot 12)7$
$= 156\pi\ \text{m}^2$

5. 6.5 cm; larger prism: 460 cm^2, 624 cm^3; smaller prism: 115 cm^2, 78 cm^3
6. 3 ft; smaller cone: $9\pi + 3\pi\sqrt{73} \approx 108.80\ \text{ft}^2$, $24\pi \approx 75.40\ \text{ft}^3$; larger cone: $\frac{81\pi + 27\pi\sqrt{73}}{4} \approx 244.80\ \text{ft}^2$, $81\pi \approx 254.47\ \text{ft}^3$

773

ADDITIONAL RESOURCES

The following resources are available to help review the material in this chapter.

- Chapter Review Games and Activities (*Chapter 12 Resource Book*, p. 107)
- *Geometry in Motion video*
- *Personal Student Tutor*
- Cumulative Review, Chs. 1–12 (*Chapter 12 Resource Book*, p. 119)

CHAPTER 12

Chapter Review

VOCABULARY

- polyhedron, p. 719
- face, p. 719
- edge, p. 719
- vertex, p. 719
- regular polyhedron, p. 720
- convex, p. 720
- cross section, p. 720
- Platonic solids, p. 721
- tetrahedron, p. 721
- octahedron, p. 721
- dodecahedron, p. 721
- icosahedron, p. 721
- prism, p. 728
- bases, p. 728
- lateral faces, p. 728
- right prism, p. 728
- oblique prism, p. 728
- surface area of a polyhedron, p. 728
- lateral area of a polyhedron, p. 728
- net, p. 729
- cylinder, p. 730
- right cylinder, p. 730
- lateral area of a cylinder, p. 730
- surface area of a cylinder, p. 730
- pyramid, p. 735
- regular pyramid, p. 735
- circular cone, p. 737
- lateral surface of a cone, p. 737
- right cone, p. 737
- volume of a solid, p. 743
- sphere, p. 759
- center of a sphere, p. 759
- radius of a sphere, p. 759
- chord of a sphere, p. 759
- diameter of a sphere, p. 759
- great circle, p. 760
- hemisphere, p. 760
- similar solids, p. 766

12.1 EXPLORING SOLIDS

Examples on pp. 719–722

EXAMPLE The solid at the right has 6 faces and 10 edges. The number of vertices can be found using Euler's Theorem.

$F + V = E + 2$

$6 + V = 10 + 2$

$V = 6$

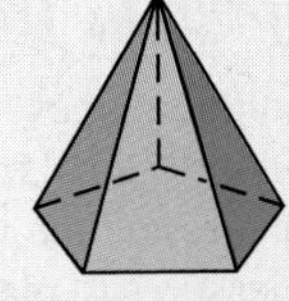

Use Euler's Theorem to find the unknown number.

1. Faces: 32
Vertices: ___?___ 60
Edges: 90

2. Faces: ___?___ 6
Vertices: 6
Edges: 10

3. Faces: 5
Vertices: 5
Edges: ___?___ 8

12.2 SURFACE AREA OF PRISMS AND CYLINDERS

Examples on pp. 728–731

EXAMPLES The surface area of a right prism and a right cylinder are shown.

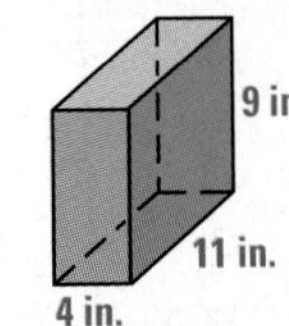

$S = 2B + Ph$

$= 2(44) + 30(9)$

$= 358 \text{ in.}^2$

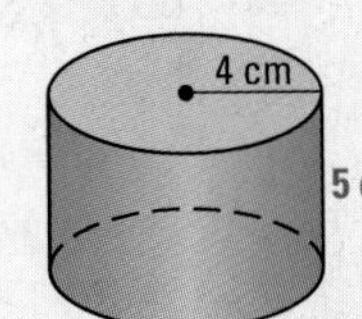

$S = 2\pi r^2 + 2\pi rh$

$= 2\pi(4^2) + 2\pi(4)(5)$

$\approx 226.2 \text{ cm}^2$

Find the surface area of the right prism or right cylinder. Round your result to two decimal places.

4. 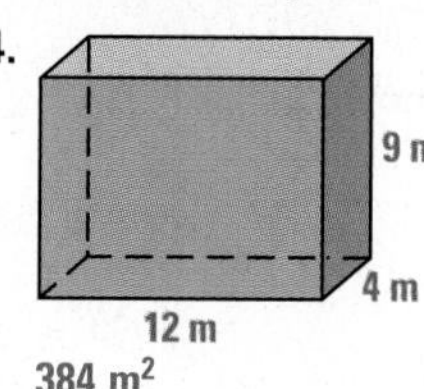

384 m^2

5. 414.69 ft^2 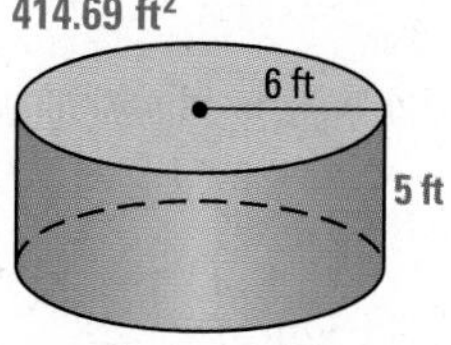

6. 812.10 $in.^2$ 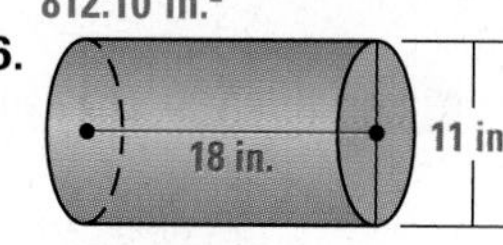

12.3 SURFACE AREA OF PYRAMIDS AND CONES

Examples on pp. 735–737

EXAMPLES The surface area of a regular pyramid and a right cone are shown.

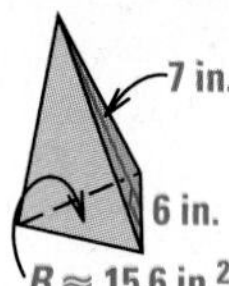

$S = B + \frac{1}{2}P\ell$

$\approx 15.6 + \frac{1}{2}(18)(7)$

$\approx 78.6 \text{ in.}^2$

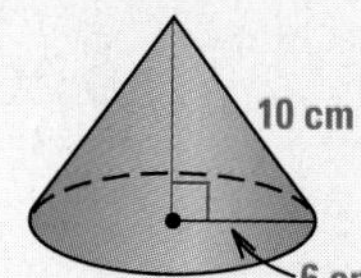

$S = \pi r^2 + \pi r\ell$

$= \pi(6)^2 + \pi(6)(10)$

$\approx 301.6 \text{ cm}^2$

Find the surface area of the regular pyramid or right cone. Round your result to two decimal places.

7. 96 cm^2 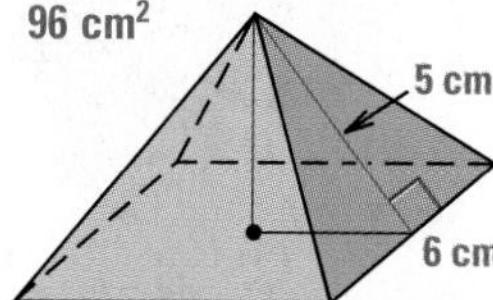

8. 263.89 $in.^2$ 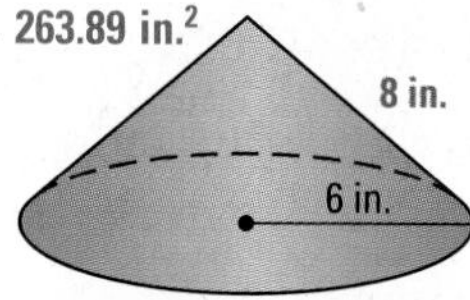

9. 124.71 $in.^2$ 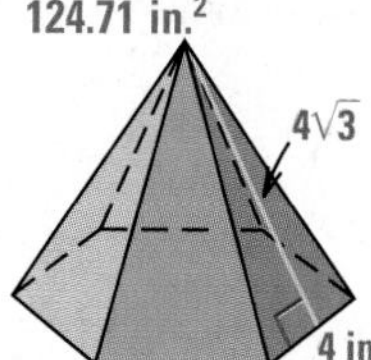

12.4 VOLUME OF PRISMS AND CYLINDERS

Examples on pp. 743–745

EXAMPLES The volume of a rectangular prism and a right cylinder are shown.

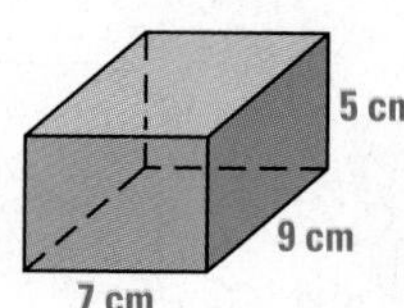

$V = Bh = (7 \cdot 9)(5) = 315 \text{ cm}^3$

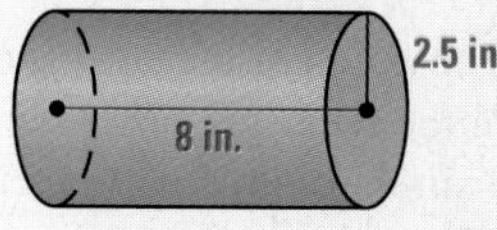

$V = \pi r^2 h = \pi(2.5^2)(8) \approx 157.1 \text{ in.}^3$

Find the volume of the described solid.

10. A side of a cube measures 8 centimeters. 512 cm^3

11. A right prism has a height of 37.2 meters and regular hexagonal bases, each with a base edge of 21 meters. $\frac{123{,}039\sqrt{3}}{5} \approx 42{,}621.96 \text{ m}^3$

12. A right cylinder has a radius of 3.5 inches and a height of 8 inches. $98\pi \approx 307.88 \text{ in.}^3$

12.5 VOLUME OF PYRAMIDS AND CONES

Examples on pp. 752–754

EXAMPLES The volume of a right pyramid and a right cone are shown.

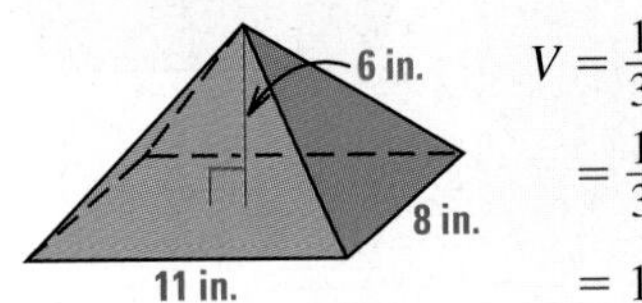

$V = \frac{1}{3}Bh$
$= \frac{1}{3}(11 \cdot 8)(6)$
$= 176 \text{ in.}^3$

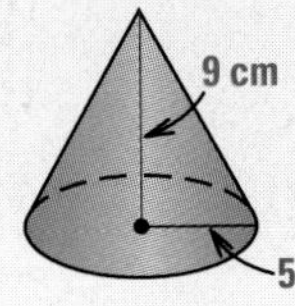

$V = \frac{1}{3}\pi r^2 h$
$= \frac{1}{3}\pi(5^2)(9)$
$\approx 235.6 \text{ cm}^3$

Find the volume of the pyramid or cone.

13.

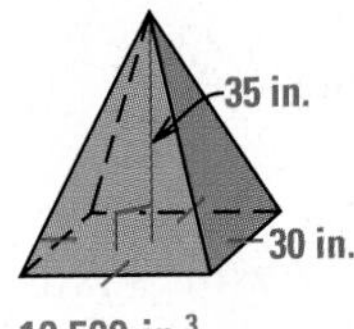

$10{,}500 \text{ in.}^3$

14.

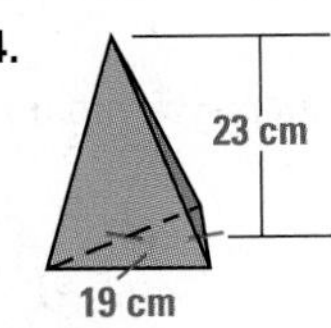

$\frac{8303\sqrt{3}}{12} \approx 1198.43 \text{ cm}^3$

15.

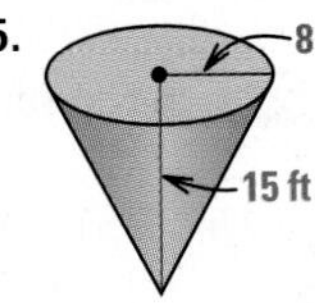

$320\pi \approx 1005.31 \text{ ft}^3$

12.6 SURFACE AREA AND VOLUME OF SPHERES

Examples on pp. 759–761

EXAMPLES The surface area and volume of the sphere are shown.

$S = 4\pi r^2 = 4\pi(7^2) \approx 615.8 \text{ in.}^2$

$V = \frac{4}{3}\pi r^3 = \frac{4}{3}\pi(7^3) \approx 1436.8 \text{ in.}^3$

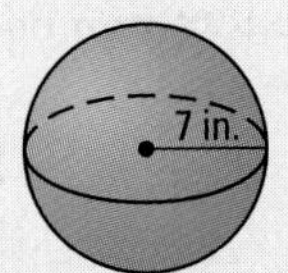

16. Find the surface area and volume of a sphere with a radius of 14 meters. $784\pi \approx 2463.01 \text{ m}^2, \frac{10{,}976\pi}{3} \approx 11{,}494.04 \text{ m}^3$

17. Find the surface area and volume of a sphere with a radius of 0.5 inch. $\pi \approx 3.14 \text{ in.}^2, \frac{\pi}{6} \approx 0.52 \text{ in.}^3$

12.7 SIMILAR SOLIDS

Examples on pp. 766–768

EXAMPLES The ratios of the corresponding linear measurements of the two right prisms are equal, so the solids are similar with a scale factor of 3:4.

lengths: $\frac{15}{20} = \frac{3}{4}$ **widths:** $\frac{12}{16} = \frac{3}{4}$ **heights:** $\frac{21}{28} = \frac{3}{4}$

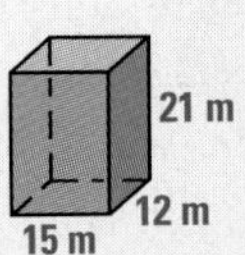

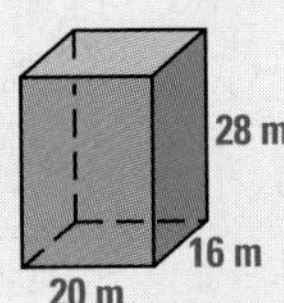

Decide whether the solids are similar. If so, find their scale factor.

18. yes; 2:1

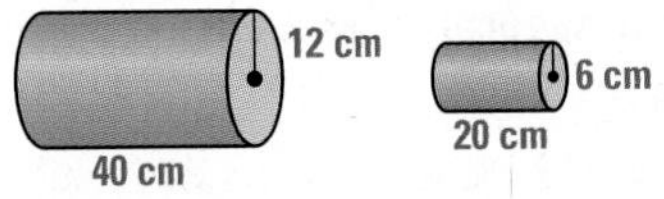

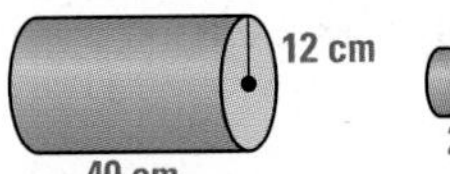

19. no

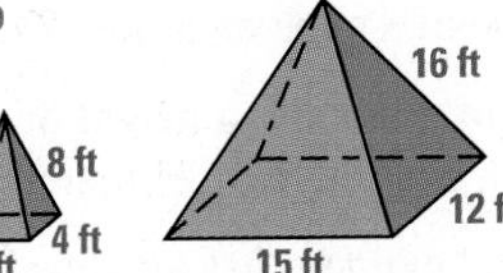

CHAPTER 12

Chapter Test

Determine the number of faces, vertices, and edges of the solids.

1. 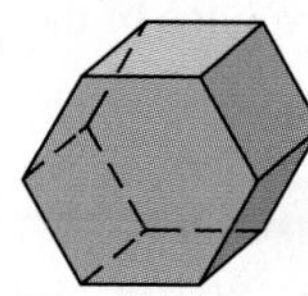
8 faces, 12 vertices, 18 edges

2. 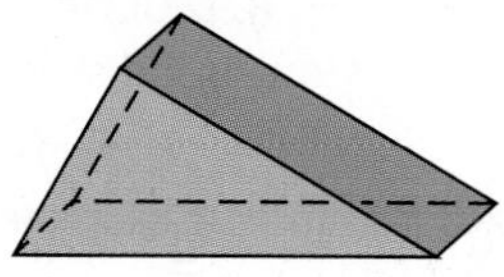
5 faces, 6 vertices, 9 edges

3. 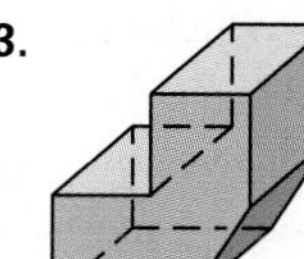
9 faces, 14 vertices, 21 edges

USING ALGEBRA Sketch the solid described and find its missing measurement. (*B* is the base area, *P* is the base perimeter, *h* is the height, *S* is the surface area, *r* is the radius, and ℓ is the slant height.) 4–8. Check drawings.

4. Right rectangular prism: $B = 44$ m^2, $P = 30$ m, $h = 7$ m, $S =$ __?__ 298 m^2

5. Right cylinder: $r = 8.6$ in., $h =$ __?__, $S = 784\pi$ in.^{2} 36.98 in.

6. Regular pyramid: $B = 100$ ft^2, $P = 40$ ft, $\ell =$ __?__, $S = 340$ ft^2 12 ft

7. Right cone: $r = 12$ yd, $\ell = 17$ yd, $S =$ __?__ $348\pi \approx 1093.27$ yd^2

8. Sphere: $r = 34$ cm, $S =$ __?__ $4624\pi \approx 14{,}526.72$ cm^2

In Exercises 9–11, find the volume of the right solid.

9. 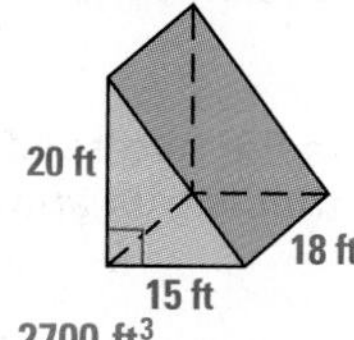

2700 ft^3

10. 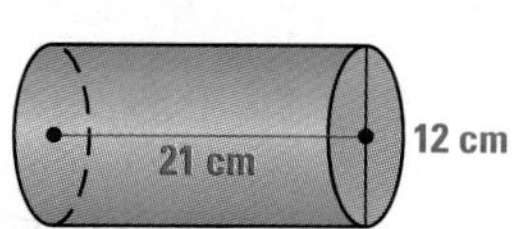

$756\pi \approx 2375.04$ cm^3

11. 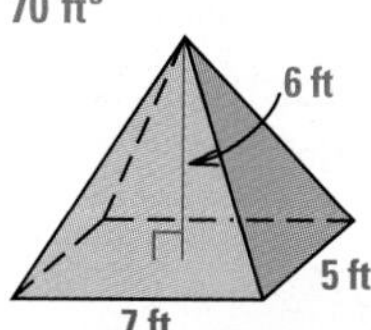

70 ft^3

12. Draw a net for each solid in Exercises 9–11. Label the dimensions of the net. See margin.

13. The scale factor of two spheres is 1 : 5. The radius of the smaller sphere is 3 centimeters. What is the volume of the larger sphere? $4500\pi \approx 14{,}137.17$ cm^3

14. Describe the possible intersections of a plane and a sphere. See margin.

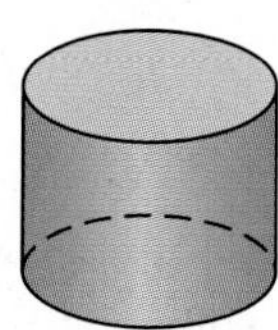

$V = 8\pi$ m^3 $V = 27\pi$ m^3

15. What is the scale factor of the two cylinders at the right? 2:3

16. **CANNED GOODS** Find the volume and surface area of a prism with a height of 6 inches and a 4 inch by 4 inch square base. Compare the results with the volume and surface area of a cylinder with a height of 7.64 inches and a diameter of 4 inches. Prism: 96 in.^{3}, 128 in.^{2}; cylinder: $30.56\pi \approx 96$ in.^{3}, $38.56\pi \approx 121.14$ in.^{2}; the volumes are nearly equal, but the prism has slightly greater surface area.

SILOS Suppose you are building a silo. The shape of your silo is a right prism with a regular 15-gon for a base, as shown. The height of your silo is 59 feet.

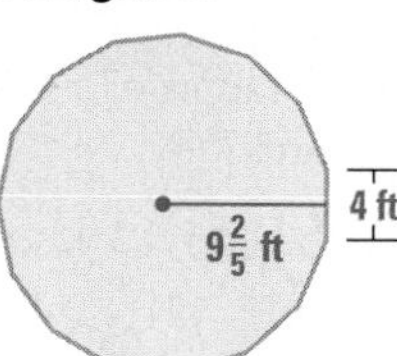

17. What is the area of the floor of your silo? 282 ft^2

18. Find the lateral area and volume of your silo. 3540 ft^2, 16,638 ft^3

19. What are the lateral area and volume of a larger silo that is in a 1 : 1.25 ratio with yours? about 5531 ft^2, about 32,496 ft^3

ADDITIONAL RESOURCES
- ***Chapter 12 Resource Book***
  Chapter Test (3 levels) (p. 108)
  SAT/ACT Chapter Test (p. 114)
  Alternative Assessment (p. 115)
- ***Test and Practice Generator***

12.

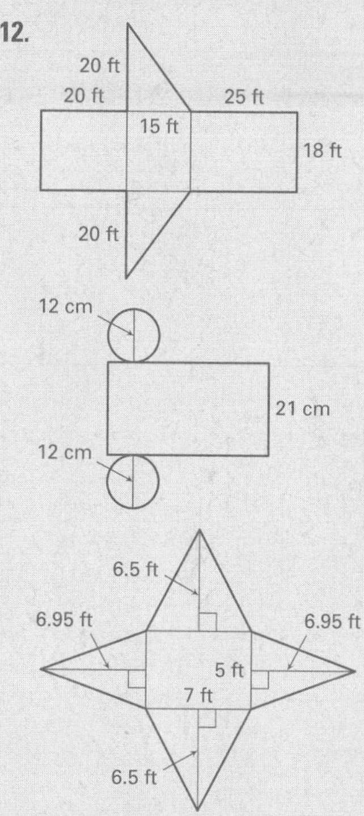

14. A plane may intersect a sphere in a point or in a circle. If the plane contains a diameter of the sphere, the intersection is a great circle.

ADDITIONAL RESOURCES

- ***Chapter 12 Resource Book***
  Chapter Test (3 levels) (p. 108)
  SAT/ACT Chapter Test (p. 114)
  Alternative Assessment (p. 115)
- ***Test and Practice Generator***

CHAPTER 12

Chapter Standardized Test

TEST-TAKING STRATEGY It is important to remember that your SAT score will not solely determine your acceptance into a college or university. Do not put added pressure on yourself to do well. If you are not satisfied with your SAT score, remember that you can take it again.

1. **MULTIPLE CHOICE** Which of the figures shown below are *not* convex? B

I. 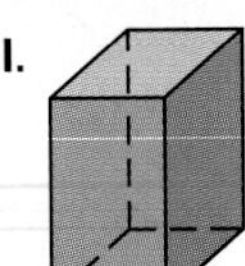

II. 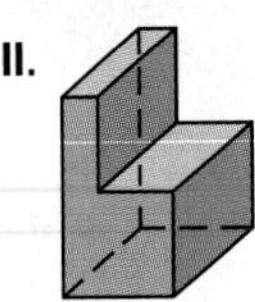

III. 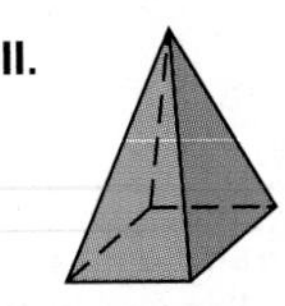

Ⓐ I only Ⓑ II only Ⓒ III only

Ⓓ I and III Ⓔ I, II, and III

2. **MULTIPLE CHOICE** A right rectangular prism has a width of 6.8 meters and a length of 28 meters. If the surface area of the prism is 2608 square meters, what is its height? E

Ⓐ 20 m Ⓑ 22.5 m Ⓒ 24.8 m

Ⓓ 30 m Ⓔ 32 m

3. **MULTIPLE CHOICE** What is the lateral area of the right cylinder below? D

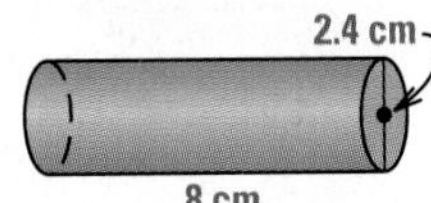

Ⓐ 2.4π cm^2 Ⓑ 9.6π cm^2 Ⓒ 11.5π cm^2

Ⓓ 19.2π cm^2 Ⓔ 38.4π cm^2

4. **MULTIPLE CHOICE** The right triangular prism below has a volume of 1650 cubic meters. What is the value of x? C

Ⓐ 8 m

Ⓑ 8.5 m

Ⓒ 10 m

Ⓓ 12 m

Ⓔ 12.5 m

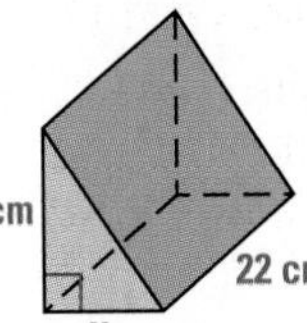

5. **MULTIPLE CHOICE** What is the radius of a sphere whose volume is 972π cubic yards? B

Ⓐ 6 yd Ⓑ 9 yd Ⓒ 12 yd

Ⓓ 14 yd Ⓔ 18 yd

6. **MULTIPLE CHOICE** What is the volume of the solid shown below? D

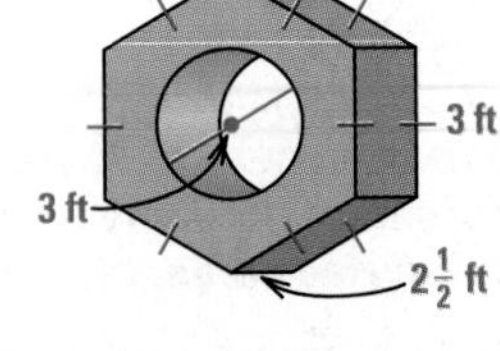

Ⓐ 34.75 ft^3

Ⓑ 36 ft^3

Ⓒ 38.58 ft^3

Ⓓ 40.79 ft^3

Ⓔ 42.22 ft^3

7. **MULTIPLE CHOICE** What is the ratio of the volumes of the right cones shown below? E

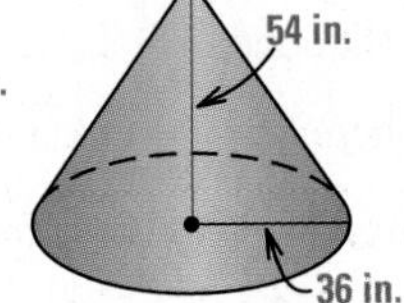

Ⓐ 2:5

Ⓑ 1:3

Ⓒ 3:20

Ⓓ 1:9

Ⓔ 1:27

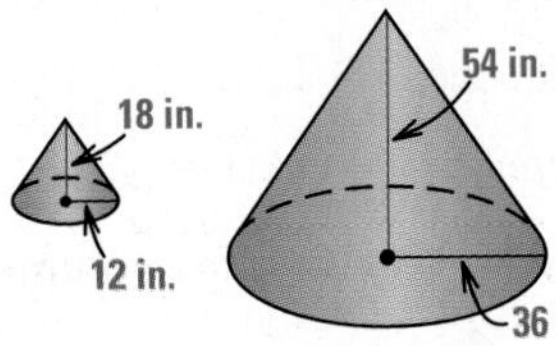

QUANTITATIVE COMPARISON **Use the two solids shown to choose the statement that is true about the quantities.**

Ⓐ The quantity in column A is greater.

Ⓑ The quantity in column B is greater.

Ⓒ The two quantities are equal.

Ⓓ The relationship cannot be determined from the given information.

	Column A	Column B
	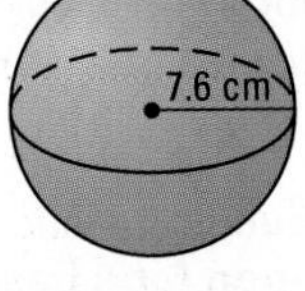 7.6 cm	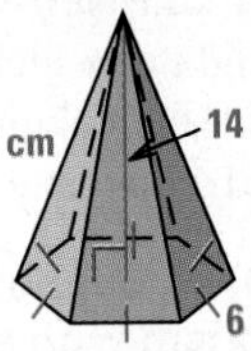 15.2 cm, 14 cm, 6 cm
8. A	Circumference of a great circle of the sphere	Perimeter of a lateral face of the pyramid
9. A	Surface area of the sphere	Surface area of the pyramid

10. MULTIPLE CHOICE The side lengths of a cube are doubled. How many times larger is the surface area of the new cube? C

(A) 2 times (B) 3 times (C) 4 times (D) 8 times (E) 16 times

11. MULTIPLE CHOICE The scale factor of two cylinders is 1 : 4. The radius of a base of the smaller cylinder is 4 feet and its height is 5 feet. What is the volume of the larger cylinder? D

(A) 320π ft^3 (B) 1280π ft^3 (C) 2560π ft^3 (D) 5120π ft^3 (E) 6480π ft^3

MULTI-STEP PROBLEM Use the diagram of the storage building shown.

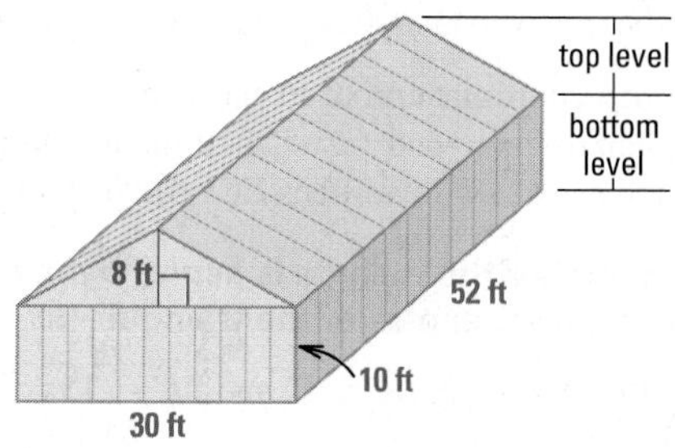

12. You decide to cover the roof with 8 foot by 4 foot plywood sheets. Estimate the number of sheets of plywood you need. Explain how you calculated your answer. See margin.

13. Find the volume of the entire storage building. 21,840 ft^3

14. What is the surface area of the top level of the building? Include the floor separating the top level from the bottom level. 3568 ft^2

MULTI-STEP PROBLEM Terry plans to use 12 sliced peaches for a peach cobbler. The cylindrical soufflé dish she will bake it in has a diameter of 18 centimeters and a height of 9 centimeters.

15. What is the volume of Terry's soufflé dish? $729\pi \approx 2290.22$ cm^3

16. The 12 sliced peaches fill a bowl with a diameter of 20 centimeters. Given that the bowl is a hemisphere, how can you determine whether the peaches will fit in the soufflé dish? Find the volume of the bowl $\left(\frac{2000}{3}\pi \approx 2094.40 \text{ cm}^3\right)$ and compare it to the volume of the soufflé dish.

17. How many peaches should she use to make two single servings in custard cups that have diameters of 7 centimeters and heights of 3.5 centimeters? about $1\frac{1}{2}$ peaches

18. *Writing* Mark says that to reduce the volume of a dessert by half, a baking dish with dimensions that are half the dimensions of the original dish must be used. Is Mark correct? Explain. No; each dimension must be $\frac{1}{\sqrt[3]{2}}$ times the dimensions of the original dish. Then the ratio of the volumes will be $1^3 : \frac{1}{(\sqrt[3]{2})^3} = 1:2$.

MULTI-STEP PROBLEM Use the similar cylindrical weights shown.

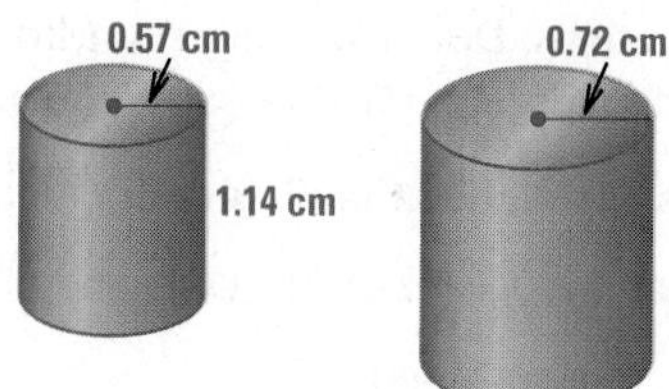

19. What is the scale factor of the smaller cylinder to the larger cylinder? about 1:1.26

20. What is the height of the larger cylindrical weight? about 1.44 cm

21. Find the surface area of the smaller cylinder. Use the scale factor from Exercise 19 to find the surface area of the larger cylinder. about 6.12 cm^2, about 9.72 cm^2

22. Find the volume of the smaller cylinder. Use the scale factor from Exercise 19 to find the volume of the larger cylinder. about 1.16 cm^3, about 2.32 cm^3

23. A third cylindrical weight is larger than the two shown. This third weight is similar to the larger weight with a scale factor of 1:3. Use your results from Exercises 21 and 22 to find the surface area and volume of the third weight. about 87.48 cm^2, about 62.64 cm^3

12. About 56 sheets; the length of each side of the roof is $\sqrt{8^2 + 15^2} = 17$ ft. The total area of the roof is $2 \times 17 \times 52 = 1768$ ft^2. The area of each sheet is 32 ft^2; $\frac{1768}{32} = 55.25$.

ADDITIONAL RESOURCES

A Cumulative Review covering Chapters 1–12 is available in the *Chapter 12 Resource Book,* p. 119.

2. 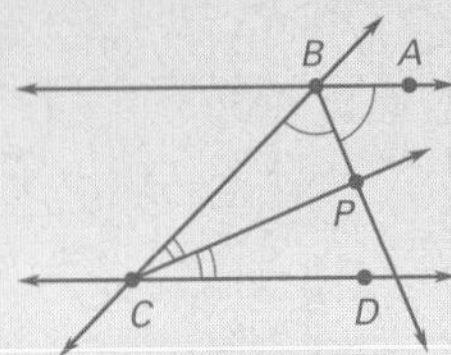

A right triangle; $\angle ABC$ and $\angle BCD$ are supplementary, so $m\angle PBC + m\angle BCP = \frac{1}{2}(m\angle ABC) + \frac{1}{2}(m\angle BCD) = \frac{1}{2}(m\angle ABC + m\angle BCD) = \frac{1}{2} \cdot 180° = 90°$. By the Triangle Sum Theorem, the measure of the third angle is 90°.

6. Statements (Reasons)
   1. $j \parallel k$ (Given)
   2. $\angle 1$ and $\angle 2$ are supplementary. (Consec. Int. ⦞ Thm.)
   3. $m\angle 1 = 73°$ (Given)
   4. $m\angle 2 = 107°$ (Def. of supplementary ⦞)

7. Statements (Reasons)
   1. *ABDE* and *CDEF* are parallelograms. (Given)
   2. $\overline{AB} \parallel \overline{DE}$ and $\overline{CF} \parallel \overline{DE}$ (Def. of parallelogram)
   3. $\overline{AB} \parallel \overline{CF}$ (Two lines $\parallel$ to the same line are $\parallel$.)
   4. $\angle 4 \cong \angle 5$ (Corresp. ⦞ Post.)
   5. $m\angle 4 = m\angle 5$ (Def. of $\cong$ ⦞)
   6. $\overline{BD} \parallel \overline{AE}$ (Def. of parallelogram)
   7. $\angle 5$ and $\angle 6$ are supplements. (Consec. Int. ⦞ Thm.)
   8. $m\angle 5 + m\angle 6 = 180°$ (Def. of supplementary ⦞)
   9. $m\angle 4 + m\angle 6 = 180°$ (Subst. prop. of =)
   10. $\angle 4$ and $\angle 6$ are supplements. (Def. of supplementary ⦞)

10. 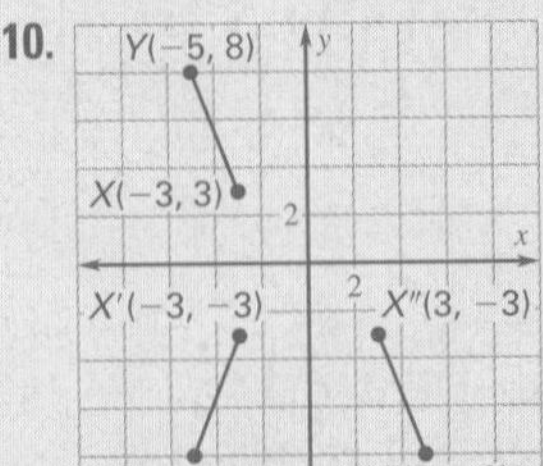

11. *Sample answer:* $\angle ABC \cong \angle ADE$ and $\angle ACB \cong \angle AED$ by the Corresp. ⦞ Post. Also, $\angle A \cong \angle A$ by the Reflex. Prop. of Cong., so $\triangle ABC \sim \triangle ADE$.

CHAPTER 12 Cumulative Practice *for Chapters 1–12*

1. Two lines intersect to form vertical angles with measures of $(4x - 2)°$ and $6(x - 3)°$. Find the measures of the four angles formed at the intersection of the two lines. **(2.6)** 30°, 30°, 150°, 150°

2. Sketch two parallel lines intersected by a transversal. Then sketch the bisectors of two consecutive interior angles. What kind of triangle is formed by the transversal and the two bisectors? Explain your answer. **(3.3, 4.1)** See margin.

3. Write a coordinate proof to show that in a right triangle, the length of the median to the hypotenuse is half the length of the hypotenuse. Use $\triangle RST$, which is right with vertices $R(0, 0)$, $S(2h, 0)$, and $T(0, 2k)$. **(4.7, 5.3)** Let *M* be the midpoint of $\overline{TS}$. By the Midpoint Formula, $M = (h, k)$. Then $RM = \sqrt{(h-0)^2 + (k-0)^2} = \sqrt{h^2 + k^2}$. Since $TS = \sqrt{(2h-0)^2 + (0-2k)^2} = 2\sqrt{h^2 + k^2}$, $RM = \frac{1}{2}TS$.

Decide whether the triangle is *acute, right,* or *obtuse.* Name the largest and the smallest angles of the triangle. (5.5, 9.3)

4. $\triangle ABC$, $AB = 12$, $BC = 8$, and $AC = 15$ obtuse; $\angle B$, $\angle A$

5. $\triangle XYZ$, $XY = 10$, $YZ = 8$, and $XZ = 6$ right; $\angle Z$, $\angle Y$

TWO-COLUMN PROOF **Write a two-column proof. (3.3, 6.2)** 6–7. See margin.

6. **GIVEN** ▶ $j \parallel k$, $m\angle 1 = 73°$

   PROVE ▶ $m\angle 2 = 107°$

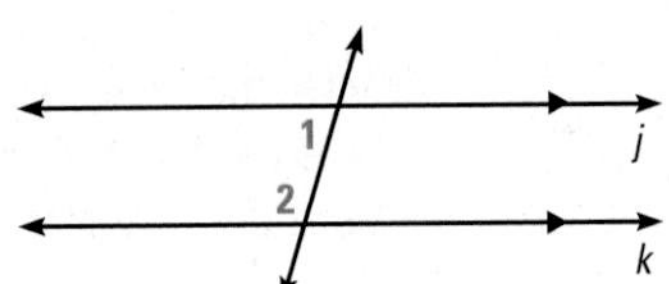

7. **GIVEN** ▶ *ABDE* and *CDEF* are ▱s.

   PROVE ▶ $\angle 4$ and $\angle 6$ are supplementary.

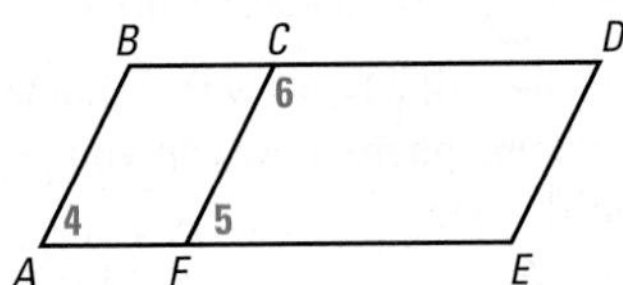

In Exercises 8 and 9, use *always, sometimes,* or *never* to complete the statement.

8. The sides of a rhombus are __?__ congruent. **(6.4)** always

9. A trapezoid __?__ has rotational symmetry. **(6.5, 7.3)** never

10. A segment has endpoints $X(-3, 3)$ and $Y(-5, 8)$. The segment is reflected in the *x*-axis and then in the *y*-axis. Sketch the image of the segment after the two reflections. Describe a single transformation that would map $\overline{XY}$ to the final image. **(7.2, 7.3, 7.5)** 180° rotation about the origin

In Exercises 11–13, use the diagram.

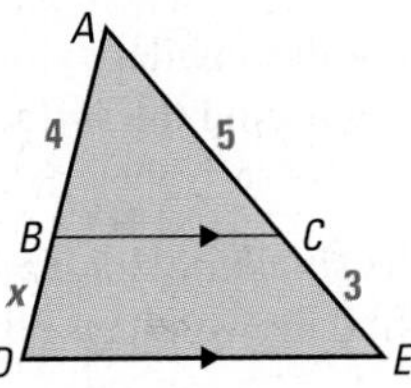

11. Show that $\triangle ABC \sim \triangle ADE$. **(8.4)** See margin.

12. Find the value of *x*. **(8.6)** $2\frac{2}{5}$

13. Find the ratio of the perimeter of $\triangle ABC$ to the perimeter of $\triangle ADE$. Then find the ratio of their areas. **(11.3)** 5:8; 25:64

A right triangle has legs of lengths 7 and 24.

14. Find the lengths of the hypotenuse and the altitude to the hypotenuse. **(9.1, 9.2)** 25, 6.72

15. Find the measures of the acute angles of the triangle. **(9.6)** about 73.7°, about 16.3°

In $\odot Q$, $\overline{EF} \perp \overline{DB}$, $m\angle AQB = 50°$, and $m\angle F = 40°$. Find the measure of the angle or the arc. (10.2, 10.3, 10.4)

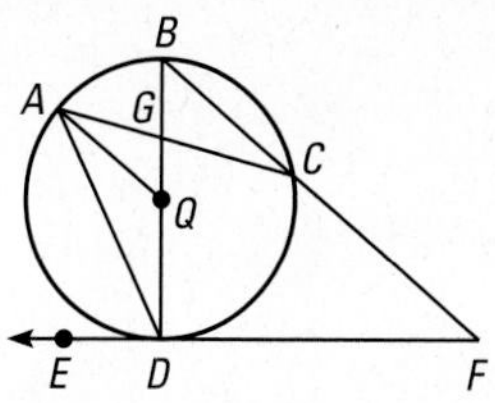

16. $\widehat{AD}$ 130°
17. $\angle ADB$ 25°
18. $\angle ACB$ 25°
19. $\angle EDB$ 90°
20. $\angle EDA$ 65°
21. $\widehat{DC}$ 100°
22. $\widehat{BC}$ 80°
23. $\widehat{ABD}$ 230°
24. $\angle BGC$ 105°

Suppose *A* is in the exterior of $\odot P$, and $\overline{AB}$ and $\overline{AC}$ are tangent to $\odot P$.

25. What can you conclude about $\angle BAC$ and $\angle BPC$? Explain. (10.1)

25. They are supplementary angles; *ABPC* is a quadrilateral with 2 right ∆s (tangents ⊥ to radii at point of tangency), so the sum of the measures of the other 2 ∆s is 180°.

26. What special kind of quadrilateral is *BACP*? Explain. (6.5, 10.1) Kite; 2 pairs of sides are ≅, but opp. sides are not ≅.

In Exercises 27–29, use the diagram at the right. (10.5)

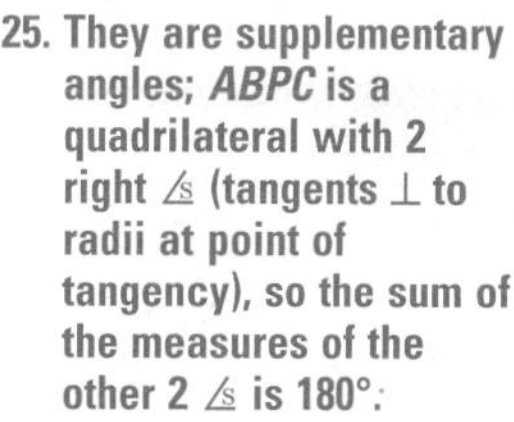
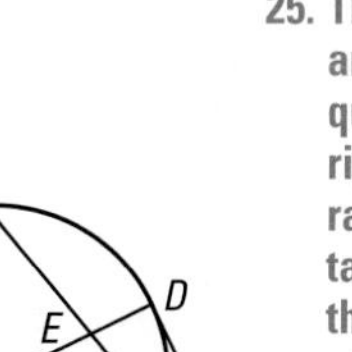

27. Find AE if $EB = 6$, $CE = 18$, and $ED = 4$. 12

28. Find BC if $DF = 6$ and $FB = 4$. 5

29. Find CE if $AE = 10$, $EB = 7$, and $ED = 3.5$. 20

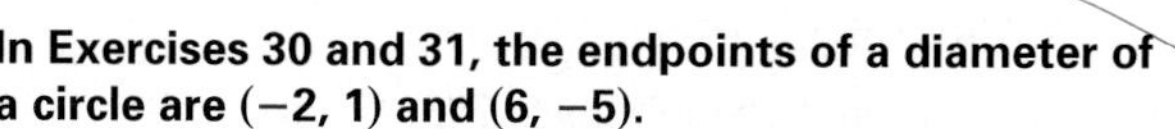

In Exercises 30 and 31, the endpoints of a diameter of a circle are (−2, 1) and (6, −5).

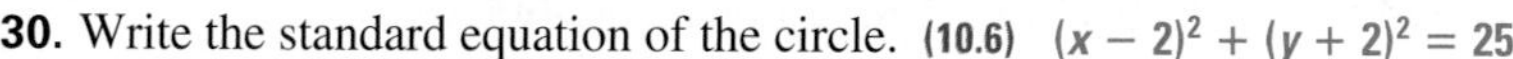

30. Write the standard equation of the circle. (10.6) $(x - 2)^2 + (y + 2)^2 = 25$

31. Find the circumference of the circle. Use $\pi \approx 3.14$. (11.4) 31.4

In Exercises 32 and 33, describe the locus of points in a plane. (10.7)

32. Points that are equidistant from the vertices of a regular hexagon. the center of the hexagon (the intersection of the ⊥ bisectors of the sides)

33. Points that are equidistant from two perpendicular lines, *j* and *k*. the bisectors of the right ∆s formed

34. What is the sum of the measures of the interior angles of a convex polygon with 25 sides? (11.1) 4140°

35. Find the area of a regular octagon whose perimeter is 240 centimeters. (11.2) 1800 tan 67.5° ≈ 4345.58 cm²

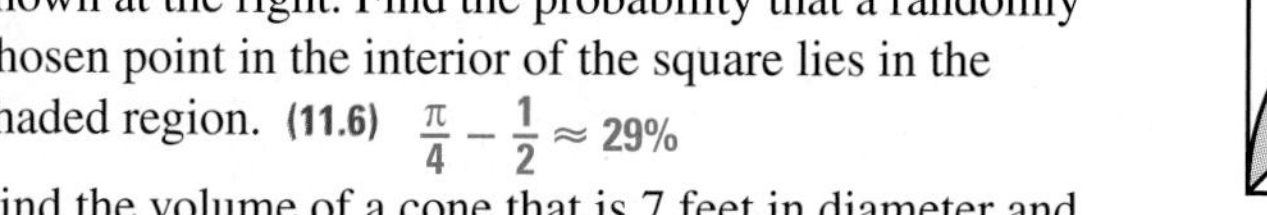

36. A quarter circle and a diagonal are drawn inside a square, shown at the right. Find the probability that a randomly chosen point in the interior of the square lies in the shaded region. (11.6) $\frac{\pi}{4} - \frac{1}{2} \approx 29\%$

Ex. 36

37. Find the volume of a cone that is 7 feet in diameter and 6 feet high. (12.5) See margin.

37. $\frac{49\pi}{2} \approx 76.97$ ft³

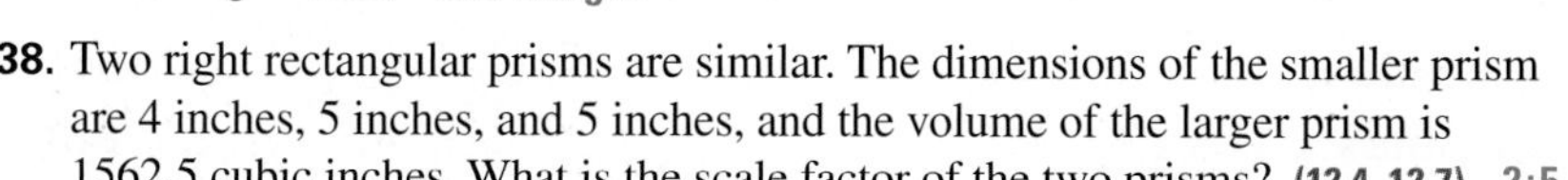

38. Two right rectangular prisms are similar. The dimensions of the smaller prism are 4 inches, 5 inches, and 5 inches, and the volume of the larger prism is 1562.5 cubic inches. What is the scale factor of the two prisms? (12.4, 12.7) 2:5

39. **TABLE** A square table has hinged leaves that can be raised to enlarge the table. When all four leaves are up, the table top is a circle. If the area of the square table is 16 square feet, what is the area of the round table? (9.4, 11.5) $8\pi \approx 25.13$ ft²

40. **HONEYCOMB** A cell of a honeycomb is a right regular hexagonal prism with base edges of 0.25 inch and a height of 0.75 inch. Find the lateral area of one cell. (12.2) 1.125 in.²

41. **TABLE TENNIS** The diameter of a table tennis ball is 1.5 inches. Find its surface area to the nearest tenth. (12.6) 7.1 in.²

Contents of Student Resources

Skills Review Handbook

PROBLEM SOLVING

One of your primary goals in mathematics should be to become a good problem solver. It will help to approach every problem with an organized plan.

STEP 1 **UNDERSTAND THE PROBLEM.**
Read the problem carefully. Decide what information you are given and what you need to find. Check whether some of the information given is unnecessary, or whether you need additional information to solve the problem. Supply missing facts, if possible.

STEP 2 **MAKE A PLAN TO SOLVE THE PROBLEM.**
Choose a strategy. (You can get ideas from the list on page 784.) Choose the correct operations. Decide if you will use a tool such as a calculator, a graph, or a spreadsheet.

STEP 3 **CARRY OUT THE PLAN TO SOLVE THE PROBLEM.**
Use the strategy and any tools you have chosen. Estimate before you calculate, if possible. Do any necessary calculations. Answer the question that the problem asks.

STEP 4 **CHECK TO SEE IF YOUR ANSWER IS REASONABLE.**
Reread the problem. See if your answer agrees with the given information and with your estimate if you calculated one.

EXAMPLE In how many ways can two students be chosen to receive an award from a list of ten nominees?

SOLUTION

1. You are given the number of nominated students and the number of students to be chosen. You need to determine how many ways there are to do this.
2. Some strategies to consider are the following: make an organized list, look for a pattern, and solve a simpler problem.
3. Consider the problem when fewer students are nominated. Look for a pattern.

Number of students	2: A, B	3: A, B, C	4: A, B, C, D	5: A, B, C, D, E
Number of ways to choose 2 students	**1**	**3**: AB; AC; BC	**6**: AB; AC; AD; BC; BD; CD	**10**: AB; AC; AD; AE; BC; BD; BE; CD; CE; DE
Pattern	**1**	**1 + 2**	**1 + 2 + 3**	**1 + 2 + 3 + 4**

Continue the pattern to find the number of ways to choose 2 out of 10 students.

▶ There are $1 + 2 + 3 + 4 + 5 + 6 + 7 + 8 + 9 = 45$ ways to choose two students from a list of ten to receive an award.

4. You can check your solution by using an organized list.

Step 2 of the problem-solving plan on the previous page asks you to select a strategy. When you solve a problem, you may want to consider these strategies.

PROBLEM SOLVING STRATEGIES

- **Guess, check, and revise.** Use when you do not seem to have enough information.
- **Draw a diagram or a graph.** Use when words describe a visual representation.
- **Make a table or an organized list.** Use when you have data or choices to organize.
- **Use an equation or a formula.** Use when you know a relationship between quantities.
- **Use a proportion.** Use when you know that two ratios are equal.
- **Look for a pattern.** Use when you can examine several cases.
- **Break the problem into simpler parts.** Use when you have a multi-step problem.
- **Solve a simpler problem.** Use when smaller numbers make the problem easier to understand.
- **Work backwards.** Use when you are looking for a fact leading to a known result.
- **Act out the situation.** Use when visualizing the problem is helpful.

PRACTICE

Solve, if possible.

1. During the month of May, Rosa made deposits of $128.50 and $165.19 into her checking account. She wrote checks for $55.12, $25, and $83.98. If her account balance at the end of May was $327.05, what was her balance at the beginning of May? **$197.46**
2. You make 20 silk flower arrangements and plan to sell them at a craft show. Each flower arrangement costs $12 in materials, and your booth at the craft show costs $30. If you sell the arrangements for $24 each, how many must you sell to make at least $100 profit? **at least 16 flower arrangements**
3. A store sells sweatshirts in small, medium, large, and extra large. A customer can choose a long sleeve sweatshirt or sweatshirt with a hood There are four choices of colors: white, blue, gray, and black. How many different kinds of sweatshirts are available at the store? **32 kinds**
4. If 4.26 lb of chicken costs $6.77, what would 3.75 lb of chicken cost? **$5.96**
5. Roger bought some 33¢ stamps and some 20¢ stamps, and spent $4.50. How many of each type of stamp did he buy? **10 33¢ stamps and 6 20¢ stamps**
6. Anita, Betty, Carla, and Dominique are competing in a race. In how many different orders can the four athletes cross the finish line? **24 different orders**
7. Stan and Margaret Wu are planning to paint their living room walls. The living room is 18 ft long and 12 ft wide, and the walls are 10 ft high. If a can of paint costs $8.75, what will it cost to paint the living room walls? **not enough information (You need to know how much area a can of paint will cover.)**

Positive and Negative Numbers

You can use a number line to find the sum of two numbers. Add a positive number by moving to the right. Add a negative number by moving to the left.

EXAMPLES

a. To find the sum $-4 + 3$, start at -4. Go 3 units to the right. End at -1. So, $-4 + 3 = -1$.

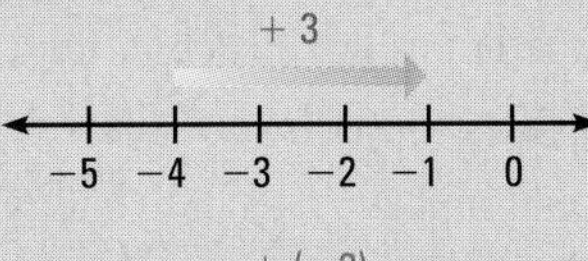

b. To find the sum $-2 + (-3)$, start at -2. Go 3 units to the left. End at -5. So, $-2 + (-3) = -5$.

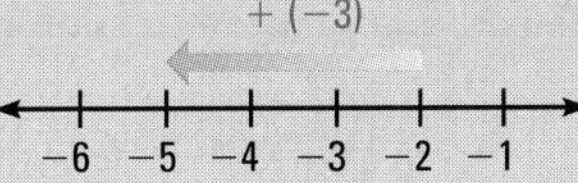

To subtract a number, add its opposite.

EXAMPLES

a. $7 - 9 = 7 + (-9) = -2$

b. $2.1 - (-5.5) = 2.1 + 5.5 = 7.6$

When you multiply or divide numbers, use these rules.

- The product or quotient of two numbers with the same sign is positive.
- The product or quotient of two numbers with opposite signs is negative.

EXAMPLES

a. $-2(4) = -8$

b. $-\frac{1}{2}\left(-\frac{2}{3}\right) = \frac{1 \cdot 2}{2 \cdot 3} = \frac{1}{3}$

c. $18 \div (-9) = -2$

d. $\frac{-3.5}{-7} = 0.5$

Practice

Add, subtract, multiply, or divide.

1. $0 + (-3.3)$ **−3.3**
2. $-7 + (-2)$ **−9**
3. $5.2 + (-2.5)$ **2.7**
4. $\frac{1}{2} + \left(-\frac{1}{2}\right)$ **0**
5. $-\frac{1}{3} + \left(-\frac{3}{4}\right)$ $-1\frac{1}{12}$
6. $-75 + 48$ **−27**
7. $-1 - (-1)$ **0**
8. $\frac{1}{2} - \left(-\frac{1}{2}\right)$ **1**
9. $8 - 9$ **−1**
10. $8 - (-9)$ **17**
11. $-4.8 - 3.2$ **−8**
12. $24 - 67$ **−43**
13. $(-3)(-3)$ **9**
14. $-8 \cdot 9$ **−72**
15. $7 \cdot 0 \cdot (-12)$ **0**
16. $(-4)(-4)(-4)$ **−64**
17. $6\left(-\frac{1}{6}\right)$ **−1**
18. $-\frac{1}{4} \cdot 20$ **−5**
19. $0.65(-0.24)$ **−0.156**
20. $-120(-46)$ **5520**
21. $-33 \div 11$ **−3**
22. $0 \div (-1)$ **0**
23. $45 \div (-5)$ **−9**
24. $\frac{-108}{8}$ **−13.5**
25. $7.2 \div (-2.5)$ **−2.88**
26. $\frac{-128}{-16}$ **8**
27. $-\frac{1}{3} \div (-10)$ $\frac{1}{30}$
28. $-\frac{7}{12} \div \frac{2}{3}$ $-\frac{7}{8}$

EVALUATING EXPRESSIONS

To evaluate a **numerical expression** involving more than one operation, follow the *order of operations.*

- First do operations that occur within grouping symbols.
- Then evaluate *powers* (expressions with exponents, such as $3^2 = 3 \cdot 3$).
- Then do multiplications and divisions in order from left to right.
- Finally, do additions and subtractions in order from left to right.

EXAMPLES Evaluate the expression.

a. $2 - (4 - 7)^2 \div (-6)$ **b.** $\frac{(2 + 4)^2}{2 + 4^2}$

SOLUTION **a.** $2 - (4 - 7)^2 \div (-6) = 2 - (-3)^2 \div (-6) = 2 - 9 \div (-6) = 2 - (-1.5) = 3.5$

b. A fraction bar acts as a grouping symbol. Simplify the numerator and the denominator. Then divide.

$$\frac{(2 + 4)^2}{2 + 4^2} = \frac{6^2}{2 + 16} = \frac{36}{18} = 2$$

To evaluate a **variable expression,** substitute values for the variables, and simplify the resulting numerical expression using the order of operations.

EXAMPLES Evaluate the expression when $x = 3$.

a. $x(2x - 8)$ **b.** $\frac{12}{x} + \frac{1}{2}x$

SOLUTION **a.** $x(2x - 8) = \mathbf{3}(2 \cdot \mathbf{3} - 8) = 3(6 - 8) = 3(-2) = -6$

b. $\frac{12}{x} + \frac{1}{2}x = \frac{12}{\mathbf{3}} + \frac{1}{2} \cdot \mathbf{3} = 4 + 1.5 = 5.5$

PRACTICE

Evaluate the expression.

1. $8^2 + (-6)^2$ 100 **2.** $-4 \cdot 5 - 8 \div 2$ −24 **3.** $-7 + 2^3 - 9$ −8 **4.** $18 \div [(4 - 7) + 5]$ 9

5. $9(7 - 2)^2$ 225 **6.** $\frac{3}{4} \cdot 24 + 4^2 - 1$ 33 **7.** $156 - 3^2 \cdot 5 - 8^2$ 47 **8.** $4.2 \div (0.7 \div 0.1)$ 0.6

9. $17^2 - 15^2$ 64 **10.** $\frac{5 + 7 \cdot 3}{6 + 7}$ 2 **11.** $\frac{2 - 9}{8 - 8^2}$ $\frac{1}{8}$ **12.** $[(1 - 7)^2 + 4] \div 8$ 5

Evaluate the expression when $x = -4$ and $y = 3$.

13. $-3x^2$ −48 **14.** $(-3x)^2$ 144 **15.** $\frac{x + 2}{x - 2}$ $\frac{1}{3}$ **16.** $\frac{1}{2}x^3$ −32

17. $x(x + 7)$ −12 **18.** $20 - \frac{16}{x}$ 24 **19.** $x^2 - x + 5$ 25 **20.** $(x + 3)(x - 3)$ 7

21. $xy \div (x + y)$ 12 **22.** $5(2y - x)$ 50 **23.** $-2x^2 + y^2$ −23 **24.** $-2(x + 4y)^2$ −128

786

THE DISTRIBUTIVE PROPERTY

Here are four forms of the **distributive property**:

$a(b + c) = ab + ac$ and $(b + c)a = ba + ca$

$a(b - c) = ab - ac$ and $(b - c)a = ba - ca$

EXAMPLES

a. $x(x + 4) = x \cdot x + 4x = x^2 + 4x$

b. $-(2a - 3b) = -1(2a - 3b) = -1 \cdot 2a - (-1)(3b) = -2a + 3b$

c. $5 - 3(n - 2) = 5 - (3 \cdot n - 3 \cdot 2) = 5 - 3n - (-6) = 5 - 3n + 6 = 11 - 3n$

When an expression is written as a sum, the parts that are added are the **terms** of the expression. **Like terms** are constant terms or terms that have the same variable raised to the same power. The distributive property allows you to combine like terms that have variables by adding coefficients. An expression is *simplified* if it has no grouping symbols and if all the like terms have been combined.

EXAMPLES

a. $-4x + 7x = (-4 + 7)x = 3x$

b. $2(x + y) - x(4 - y) = 2x + 2y - 4x + xy = (2 - 4)x + 2y + xy = -2x + 2y + xy$

c. $4x^2 + 5x - 7 + 2 - 3x^2 = (4 - 3)x^2 + 5x + (-7 + 2) = x^2 + 5x - 5$

PRACTICE

Use the distributive property to rewrite the expression without parentheses.

1. $2(a + 4)$ $2a + 8$

2. $(2k + 1)7$ $14k + 7$

3. $-(-3x + 2)$ $3x - 2$

4. $(7 - 2z)z$ $7z - 2z^2$

5. $y(y - 9)$ $y^2 - 9y$

6. $(j - 1)(-3)$ $-3j + 3$

7. $\frac{1}{2}(8n - 14)$ $4n - 7$

8. $(3k + 5)(-k)$ $-3k^2 - 5k$

9. $4b(b + 2)$ $4b^2 + 8b$

10. $(10 + c)d$ $10d + cd$

11. $8x(2x - 9y)$ $16x^2 - 72xy$

12. $(4t - q)(-3t)$ $-12t^2 + 3tq$

13. $2r(s + t)$ $2rs + 2rt$

14. $(b + c - 1)6$ $6b + 6c - 6$

15. $7(-x^2 + 3x - 2)$ $-7x^2 + 21x - 14$

16. $-\frac{2}{3}x(6x + 9y - 12)$ $-4x^2 - 6xy + 8x$

Simplify the expression.

17. $-m + 4 + 7m$ $6m + 4$

18. $6x - 9x + x$ $-2x$

19. $3z + 6 - 3z - 7$ -1

20. $\frac{1}{5}d + \frac{2}{7}d$ $\frac{17}{35}d$

21. $18g^3 + 9g^2 + g^3$ $19g^3 + 9g^2$

22. $3.1 + 7.5y - 8y$ $3.1 - 0.5y$

23. $6xy + 2x - 3y - 5xy$ $xy + 2x - 3y$

24. $2.5(4z - 18) + 12$ $10z - 33$

25. $6h - 3h(h + 1)$ $3h - 3h^2$

26. $3 - (2x - 7)$ $10 - 2x$

27. $8 + 3(y - 4)$ $3y - 4$

28. $9k - 2(3k - 5) - 10$ $3k$

29. $5(r + 1) - (r - 3)$ $4r + 8$

30. $x(2x - 6) + x^2$ $3x^2 - 6x$

31. $2(n + 8) + 3n(n - 5)$ $3n^2 - 13n + 16$

RECIPROCALS

The product of a nonzero number and its **reciprocal** is 1.

The reciprocal of a is $\frac{1}{a}$, and the reciprocal of $\frac{a}{b}$ is $\frac{b}{a}$. Zero has no reciprocal.

EXAMPLES $-\frac{3}{7}$ and $-\frac{7}{3}$ are reciprocals because $-\frac{3}{7}\left(-\frac{7}{3}\right) = 1$.

6 and $\frac{1}{6}$ are reciprocals because $6 \cdot \frac{1}{6} = 1$.

PRACTICE

Find the reciprocal of the number.

1. 12 $\frac{1}{12}$ **2.** -99 $-\frac{1}{99}$ **3.** $\frac{1}{4}$ 4 **4.** $-\frac{5}{2}$ $-\frac{2}{5}$ **5.** $-\frac{1}{10}$ -10

6. 1 $\frac{1}{1}$ **7.** $\frac{6}{13}$ $\frac{13}{6}$ **8.** -1 -1 **9.** 0.2 5 **10.** -0.75 $-\frac{4}{3}$

RATIOS

If a and b are two quantities measured in the *same* units, then the **ratio of a to b** is $\frac{a}{b}$, usually written in simplest form. The ratio of a to b can also be written as $a : b$. Because a ratio is a quotient, its denominator cannot be zero.

EXAMPLE $\frac{9 \text{ inches}}{2 \text{ feet}} = \frac{9 \text{ inches}}{2 \cdot 12 \text{ inches}} = \frac{9}{24} = \frac{3}{8}$

Notice that to simplify a ratio with different units, you rewrite the ratio so that the numerator and denominator have the same units. Then simplify if possible.

EXAMPLE Suppose there are 18 boys in a class of 30 students. To find the ratio of girls to boys, compute the number of girls, $30 - 18 = 12$. Then $\frac{\text{girls}}{\text{boys}} = \frac{12}{18} = \frac{2}{3}$.

PRACTICE

Simplify the ratio.

1. $\frac{48 \text{ miles}}{120 \text{ miles}}$ $\frac{2}{5}$ **2.** $\frac{72 \text{ cm}}{1.5 \text{ m}}$ $\frac{12}{25}$ **3.** $\frac{9 \text{ yards}}{15 \text{ feet}}$ $\frac{9}{5}$ **4.** $\frac{12 \text{ ounces}}{2 \text{ pounds}}$ $\frac{3}{8}$

5. $\frac{3 \text{ ft}}{36 \text{ in.}}$ $\frac{1}{1}$ **6.** $\frac{980 \text{ g}}{2 \text{ kg}}$ $\frac{49}{100}$ **7.** $\frac{40 \text{ km}}{500 \text{ m}}$ $\frac{80}{1}$ **8.** $\frac{5 \text{ mi}}{6200 \text{ ft}}$ $\frac{132}{31}$

Find the ratio of girls to boys in a class, given the number of boys and the total number of students.

9. 15 boys, 28 students $\frac{13}{15}$ **10.** 12 boys, 27 students $\frac{5}{4}$ **11.** 12 boys, 20 students $\frac{2}{3}$

Solving Linear Equations (Single-Step)

The equations $\frac{1}{2}x = 4$ and $3t - 1 = 4t$ are examples of **linear** equations.

When the variable in a single-variable equation is replaced by a number and the resulting statement is true, the number is a **solution** of the equation. You can *solve an equation* by writing an *equivalent* equation that has the variable alone on one side. One way to do this is to add or subtract the same number *from each side* of the equation.

EXAMPLES Solve the equation.

a. $x + 6 = -2$

b. $y - 7 = 3$

SOLUTION

a. $x + 6 = -2$

$x + 6 - \mathbf{6} = -2 - \mathbf{6}$ **Subtract 6 from each side.**

$x = -8$ **Simplify.**

b. $y - 7 = 3$

$y - 7 + \mathbf{7} = 3 + \mathbf{7}$ **Add 7 to each side.**

$y = 10$ **Simplify.**

Another way to solve a linear equation is to multiply or divide each side by the same nonzero number. Notice the use of reciprocals in the example below.

EXAMPLE Solve the equation $8 = \frac{4}{3}a$.

SOLUTION

$8 = \frac{4}{3}a$

$\mathbf{\frac{3}{4}} \cdot 8 = \mathbf{\frac{3}{4}} \cdot \frac{4}{3}a$ **Multiply each side by the reciprocal.**

$6 = a$ **Simplify.**

Check your solution by substituting it in the original equation.

Practice

Solve the equation.

1. $x + 12 = 25$ 13 **2.** $k - 6 = 0$ 6 **3.** $-36 = -9s$ 4 **4.** $\frac{1}{5}n = 5$ 25

5. $-32h = 4$ $-\frac{1}{8}$ **6.** $4.6 + z = 3.6$ -1 **7.** $-\frac{3}{4}d = 24$ -32 **8.** $0.02v = 8$ 400

9. $w - 5 = -13$ -8 **10.** $4z = 132$ 33 **11.** $-6 = c + 4$ -10 **12.** $-\frac{4}{7}p = -8$ 14

13. $\frac{2}{3}y = 7$ $\frac{21}{2}$ **14.** $37 = r - (-9)$ 28 **15.** $\frac{1}{2}x = -40$ -80 **16.** $-m = 5$ -5

17. $\frac{n}{3} = 6$ 18 **18.** $330 = -15f$ -22 **19.** $y + 7 = -16$ -23 **20.** $-4.2z = 42$ -10

21. $t - \frac{1}{8} = \frac{5}{8}$ $\frac{3}{4}$ **22.** $\frac{9}{2}x = -1$ $-\frac{2}{9}$ **23.** $120 = -120b$ -1 **24.** $0 = 6.4k$ 0

SOLVING LINEAR EQUATIONS (MULTI-STEP)

Solving a linear equation may require several steps. You may need to simplify one or both sides of the equation, use the distributive property, or collect variable terms on one side of the equation.

EXAMPLES Solve the equation.

a. $\frac{1}{5}x + 7 = 3$

b. $5 - 2(r + 6) = 1$

SOLUTION

a. $\frac{1}{5}x + 7 = 3$

$\frac{1}{5}x + 7 - 7 = 3 - 7$ **Subtract 7 from each side.**

$\frac{1}{5}x = -4$ **Simplify.**

$5 \cdot \frac{1}{5}x = 5(-4)$ **Multiply by the reciprocal.**

$x = -20$ **Simplify.**

CHECK

$\frac{1}{5}(-20) + 7 = 3$ ✓

b. $5 - 2(r + 6) = 1$

$5 - 2r - 12 = 1$ **Distributive property**

$-2r - 7 = 1$ **Simplify.**

$-2r - 7 + 7 = 1 + 7$ **Add 7 to each side.**

$-2r = 8$ **Simplify.**

$\frac{-2r}{-2} = \frac{8}{-2}$ **Divide each side by −2.**

$r = -4$ **Simplify.**

PRACTICE

Solve the equation.

1. $3y - 4 = 20$ 8

2. $\frac{c}{7} + 2 = 1$ −7

3. $6 - \frac{3a}{2} = -6$ 8

4. $3r - (2r + 1) = 21$ 22

5. $5(z + 3) = 12$ −0.6, or $-\frac{3}{5}$

6. $44 = 5g - 8 - g$ 13

7. $75 + 7x = 2x$ −15

8. $14r + 81 = -r$ −5.4, or $-\frac{27}{5}$

9. $3n - 1 = 5n - 9$ 4

10. $12r - 5 = 7r$ 1

11. $4 - 6p = 2p - 3$ $\frac{7}{8}$

12. $7(b - 3) = 8b + 2$ −23

13. $60c - 54(c - 2) = 0$ −18

14. $22d - (6 + 2d) = 4$ $\frac{1}{2}$

15. $s - (-4s + 2) = 13$ 3

16. $-\frac{1}{2}(16 - 2h) = 11$ 19

17. $1 + j = 2(2j + 1)$ $-\frac{1}{3}$

18. $4x + 2(x - 3) = 0$ 1

19. $\frac{1}{4}y + 27 = 41$ 56

20. $\frac{3 + m}{2} = 5$ 7

21. $\frac{x + (-2)}{2} = -6$ −10

22. $\frac{8 + x}{2} = 10$ 12

23. $2 \cdot 3.14 \cdot r = 157$ 25

24. $\frac{1}{2} \cdot 9 \cdot h = 94.5$ 21

25. $12 \cdot b \cdot 13 = 338$ $\frac{13}{6}$

26. $4(t - 7) + 6 = 30$ 13

27. $7y - 84 = 2y + 61$ 29

28. $85 = \frac{1}{2}(226 - x)$ 56

29. $104 = \frac{1}{2}[(360 - x) - x]$ 76

30. $18(x + 18) = 21^2$ 6.5

31. $18^2 = 15(x + 15)$ 6.6

32. $12 - 23c = 7(9 - c)$ $-\frac{51}{16}$

33. $2.7(z - 7) + 6 = 2.1(3z + 1)$ $-\frac{25}{6}$

34. $7(4h + 1) - 2(2h - 3) = -23$ −1.5

35. $4(5n + 7) - 3n = 3(4n - 9)$ −11

36. $4.7(2f - 0.5) = -6(1.6f - 8.3f)$ $-\frac{47}{616}$

SOLVING INEQUALITIES

You can solve a linear inequality in one variable in much the same way you solve a linear equation in one variable.

EXAMPLES Solve the inequality.

a.

$$x + 18 > 24$$
$$x + 18 - 18 > 24 - 18$$
$$x > 6$$

b.

$x + (2x - 5) > x + 3$	
$3x - 5 > x + 3$	**Simplify.**
$3x - 5 + 5 > x + 3 + 5$	**Add 5 to each side.**
$3x > x + 8$	**Simplify.**
$-x + 3x > -x + x + 8$	**Add $-x$ to each side.**
$2x > 8$	**Combine like terms.**
$\frac{2x}{2} > \frac{8}{2}$	**Divide each side by 2.**
$x > 4$	**Simplify.**

A **solution of an inequality** is a number that produces a true statement when it is substituted for the variable in the inequality.

EXAMPLE Decide whether 3 is a solution of the inequality $3x - 8 < 10$.

SOLUTION $3(3) - 8 < 10$ **Substitute.**

$1 < 10$ **Simplify.**

So, 3 is a solution of the inequality.

PRACTICE

Solve the inequality.

1. $24 + 32 > x$ $x < 56$

2. $16 + x > 21$ $x > 5$

3. $x + 7.8 > 15.1$ $x > 7.3$

4. $x < 125 + 175$ $x < 300$

5. $x + \frac{7}{2} < \frac{11}{2}$ $x < 2$

6. $55 < 5 + x$ $x > 50$

7. $x + 3x > 2x + 6$ $x > 3$

8. $(x + 4) + (x + 6) > 3x - 1$ $x < 11$

9. $(2x - 1) + (x + 3) > 18 - x$ $x > 4$

Check whether the given number is a solution of the inequality.

10. $m + 12 > 30$; 16 no

11. $n - 3 < 6$; 2 yes

12. $5 + 2p > 10$; 3 yes

13. $3r - 4 < 0$; 0.5 yes

14. $10s - 2 > 40$; 4 no

15. $6t - 2 < 4t$; 3 no

16. $7u + 7 < 38$; 5 no

17. $8(w - 3) > 95$; 15 yes

18. $6.2x - 3.7 < -14$; -2.2 yes

19. Name three solutions of the inequality $(2x - 3) + (x + 5) > x + 8$. Is 3 a solution? Explain. Examples: 4, 4.5, and 10. No; when $x = 3$, $(2x - 3) + (x + 5) = x + 8$.

13–28. 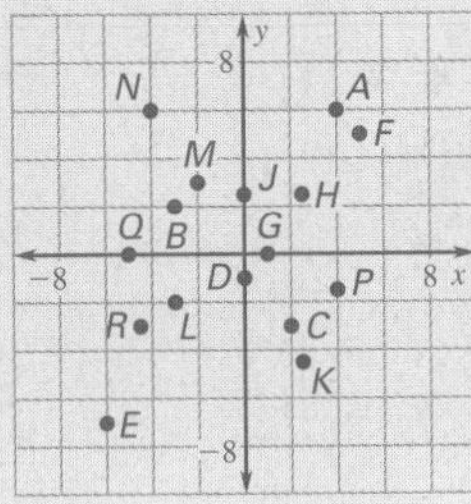

PLOTTING POINTS

A **coordinate plane** is formed by a horizontal ***x*-axis** and a vertical ***y*-axis** that intersect at the **origin,** forming right angles. Each point in a coordinate plane corresponds to an **ordered pair** of real numbers. Point $W(3, -2)$, shown on the graph, has an ***x*-coordinate** of 3 and a ***y*-coordinate** of -2.

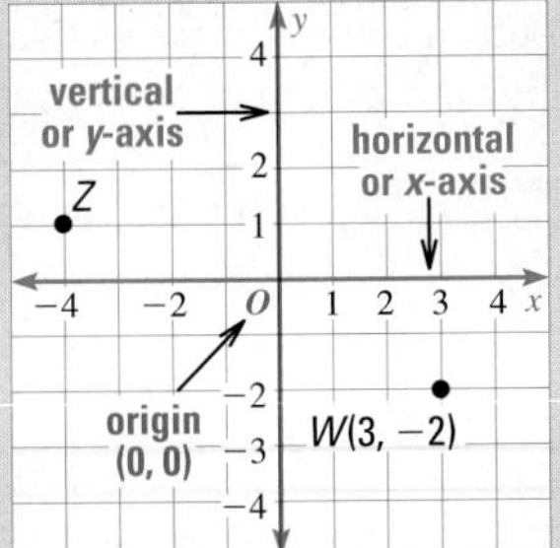

EXAMPLE Use the graph to name the coordinates of point Z.

SOLUTION

The x-coordinate of Z is -4 and the y-coordinate is 1.
So, the ordered pair corresponding to Z is $(-4, 1)$.

EXAMPLES Plot each point in a coordinate plane.

a. $P(-5, 2)$ **b.** $Q(3, 0)$

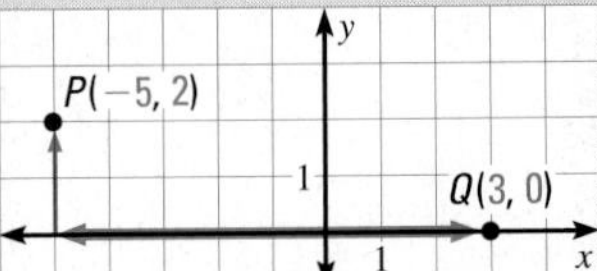

SOLUTION **a.** To plot the point $P(-5, 2)$, start at the origin. Move 5 units to the left and 2 units up.

b. To plot the point $Q(3, 0)$, start at the origin. Move 3 units to the right and 0 units up.

PRACTICE

Give the coordinates of each of the following points.

1. A (−1, 0) **2.** B (2, 3)

3. C (2, −2) **4.** D (−5, −3)

5. E (−5, 3) **6.** F (−1, −2)

7. G (5, −2) **8.** H (4, 2)

9. J (−2, 5) **10.** K (−4, 1)

11. M (1, 1) **12.** N (−4, −1)

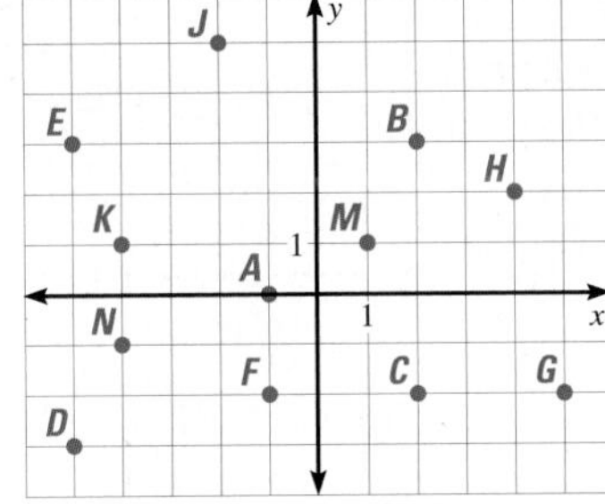

Plot each point in a coordinate plane. 13–28. See margin.

13. $A(4, 6)$ **14.** $B(-3, 2)$ **15.** $C(2, -3)$ **16.** $D(0, -1)$

17. $E(-6, -7)$ **18.** $F(5, 5)$ **19.** $G(1, 0)$ **20.** $H\left(\frac{5}{2}, \frac{5}{2}\right)$

21. $J(0, 2.5)$ **22.** $K\left(\frac{5}{2}, -\frac{9}{2}\right)$ **23.** $L(-3, -2)$ **24.** $M(-2, 3)$

25. $N(-4, 6)$ **26.** $P\left(4, -\frac{3}{2}\right)$ **27.** $Q(-5, 0)$ **28.** $R\left(-\frac{9}{2}, -3\right)$

LINEAR EQUATIONS AND THEIR GRAPHS

A **solution** of an equation in two variables x and y is an ordered pair (x, y) that makes the equation true. Equations like $2x + 3y = -6$, $y = 5x - 1$, and $y = 3$ are **linear equations**. Their graphs are lines.

EXAMPLE Graph the equation $y - 4x = 2$.

SOLUTION You can use a table of values to graph the equation $y - 4x = 2$. Rewrite the equation in *function form* by solving for y: $y - 4x = 2$, so $y = 4x + 2$. Choose a few values of x. Substitute to find the corresponding y-value.

x	$y = 4x + 2$	(x, y)
-1	$y = 4(-1) + 2 = -2$	$(-1, -2)$
0	$y = 4 \cdot 0 + 2 = 2$	$(0, 2)$
1	$y = 4 \cdot 1 + 2 = 6$	$(1, 6)$

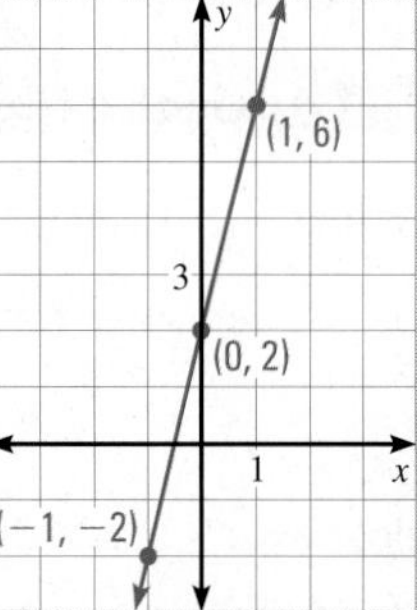

Plot the points in the table. Draw a line through the points.

EXAMPLE Graph the equation $3x - 4y = 12$.

SOLUTION You can quickly draw a graph of an equation such as $3x - 4y = 12$ by using the *intercepts*. The **x-intercept** is the x-coordinate of a point where the graph crosses the x-axis. The **y-intercept** is the y-coordinate of a point where the graph crosses the y-axis.

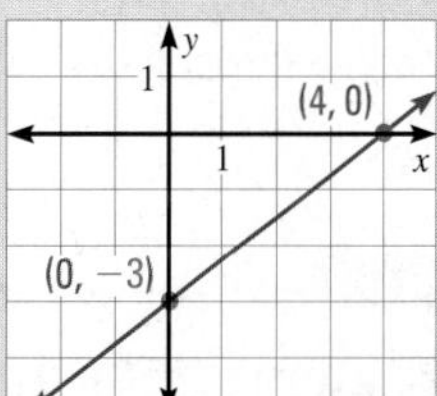

Substitute 0 for x: $3 \cdot 0 - 4y = 12$; $y = -3$, and so the y-intercept is -3.

Substitute 0 for y: $3x - 4 \cdot 0 = 12$; $x = 4$, and so the x-intercept is 4.

Now you can graph the equation $3x - 4y = 12$ by plotting the points (4, 0) and (0, −3) and then drawing a line through the points.

PRACTICE

Use a table of values to graph the equation. 1–8. See margin.

1. $y = -2x + 3$ **2.** $y = 3x - 5$ **3.** $y = \frac{1}{3}x - 2$ **4.** $y = 2.5 + 1.5x$

5. $y = -\frac{3}{4}x$ **6.** $4x + y = -8$ **7.** $x - 3y = 6$ **8.** $y = \frac{3}{2}(x + 1)$

Use the x-intercept and the y-intercept to graph the equation. Label the points where the line crosses the coordinate axes. 9–16. See margin.

9. $x + 5y = -10$ **10.** $-5x + 6y = 30$ **11.** $3x - 8y = -48$ **12.** $y = -(2x - 1)$

13. $y = 4x + 1$ **14.** $y = -x - 2$ **15.** $y = 5 - \frac{1}{2}x$ **16.** $y = 0.75x + 1.25$

9–16. See Additional Answers beginning on page AA1.

1.
2.

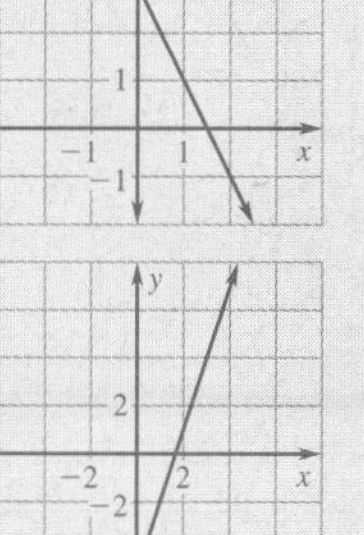

3.

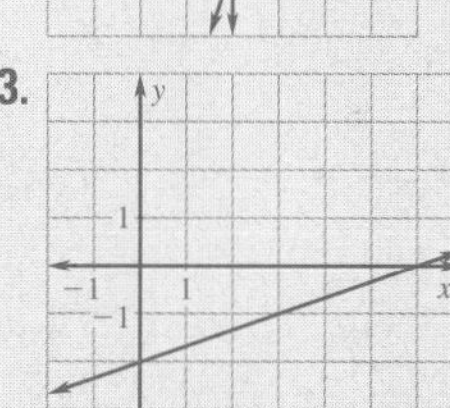

4.

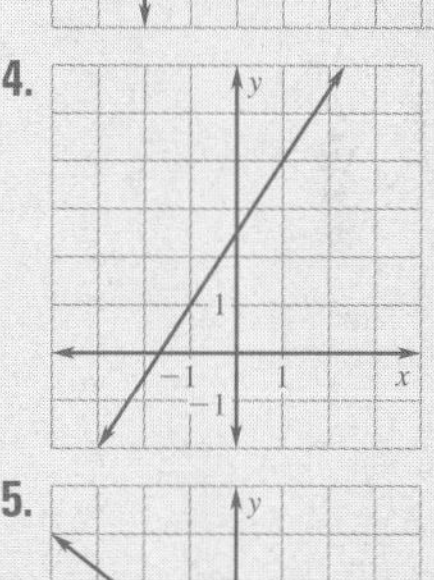

5.

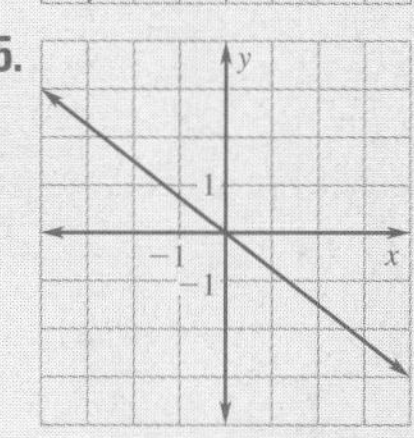

6.

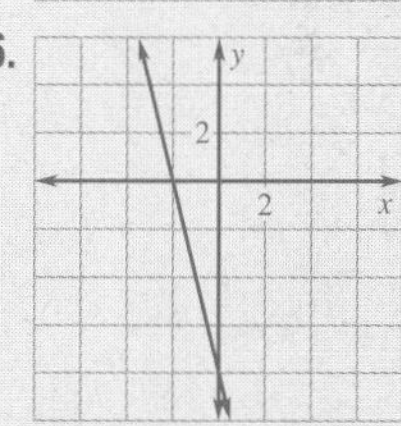

7.

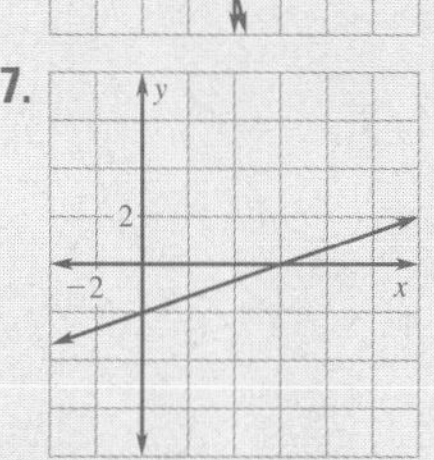

8.

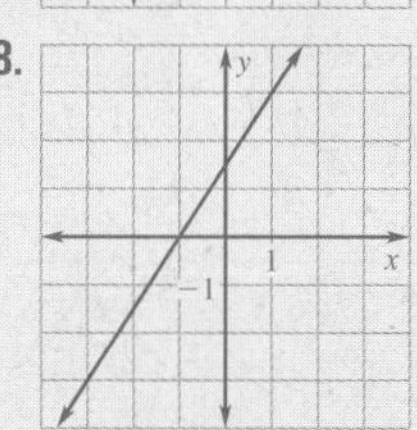

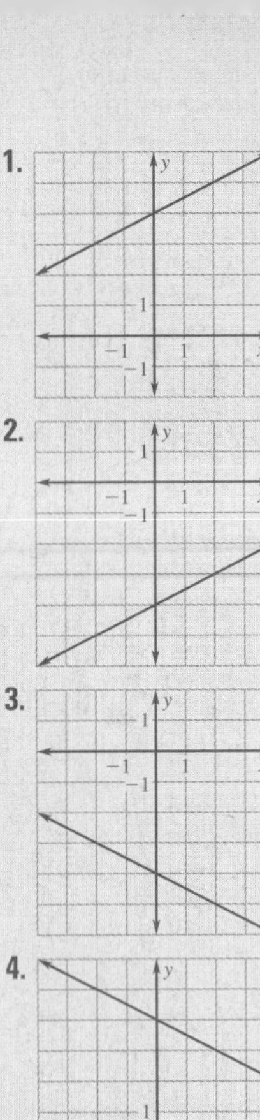

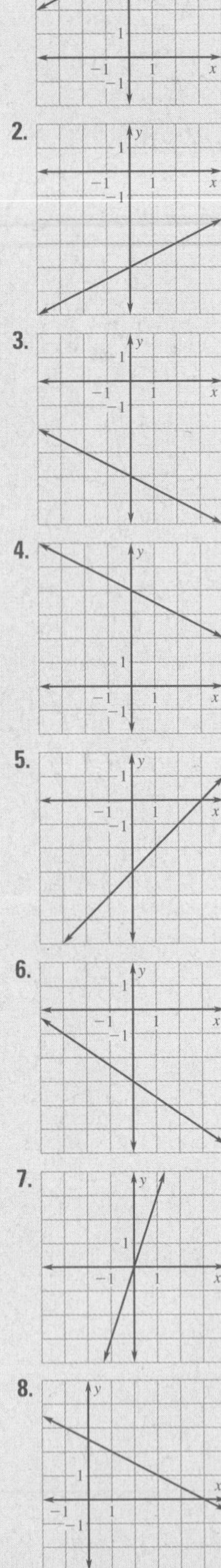

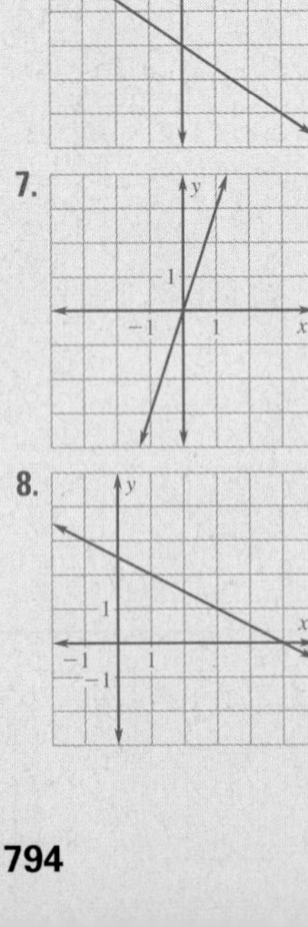

SLOPE-INTERCEPT FORM

Another way to draw the graph of a linear equation is to use the slope and the y-intercept. Recall that the slope of a nonvertical line is $m = \frac{\text{rise}}{\text{run}} = \frac{\text{change in } y}{\text{change in } x}$.

The linear equation $y = mx + b$ is written in **slope-intercept form**. The slope of the line is m and the y-intercept is b.

EXAMPLE Graph the equation $\frac{1}{2}x + 2y = 4$.

SOLUTION To graph the equation $\frac{1}{2}x + 2y = 4$, write the equation in slope-intercept form:

$$2y = -\frac{1}{2}x + 4;\ y = -\frac{1}{4}x + 2.$$

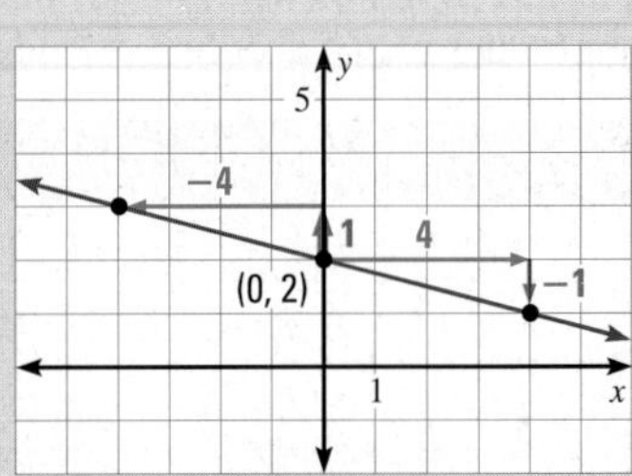

The slope m is $-\frac{1}{4}$, and the y-intercept b is 2.

Plot the point (0, 2).

Draw a *slope triangle* to locate a second point on the line:

$$m = -\frac{1}{4} = \frac{\text{rise}}{\text{run}}.$$

Draw a line through the two points.

EXAMPLES Graph $x = 3$ and $y = -1$.

SOLUTION

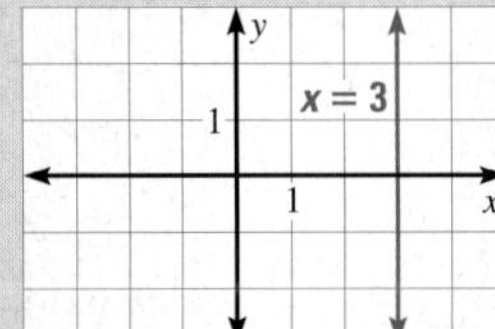

The graph of $x = 3$ is a vertical line.

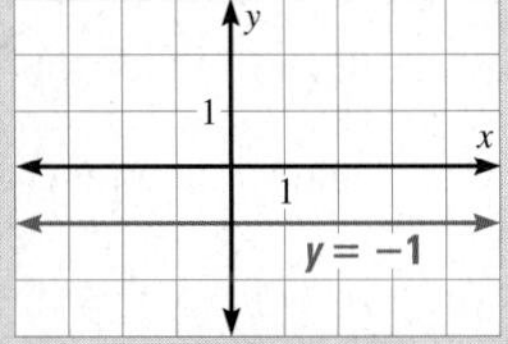

The graph of $y = -1$ is a horizontal line.

PRACTICE

Use the slope and the y-intercept to graph the equation. 1–13. See margin.

1. $y = \frac{1}{2}x + 4$ **2.** $y = \frac{1}{2}x - 4$ **3.** $y = -\frac{1}{2}x - 4$ **4.** $y = -\frac{1}{2}x + 4$

5. $x - y - 3 = 0$ **6.** $2x + 3y = -9$ **7.** $3x - y = 0$ **8.** $x + 2y = 5$

9. $-4x = 8$ **10.** $0.25y = 3$ **11.** $-y - 3x = 4$ **12.** $2x = 6 - 3y$

13. Graph the equation $x = -2$. Explain why the graph has no slope and no y-intercept.

14. Graph the equation $y = 3$. Find the slope of the graph. Name three different ordered pairs that are solutions of the graph. See margin for graph.
The slope is 0. *Sample answer:* (−2, 3), (0, 3), and (1, 3)

9–14. See Additional Answers beginning on page AA1.

WRITING LINEAR EQUATIONS

The slope of a nonvertical line is $m = \frac{\text{rise}}{\text{run}} = \frac{\text{change in } y}{\text{change in } x}$.

Given the slope and the y-intercept of a line, the slope and a point on a line, or two points on a line, you can use the slope-intercept form to write an equation of the line.

EXAMPLE Write an equation of a line that has a slope of $\frac{1}{2}$ and passes through the point $(-4, -3)$.

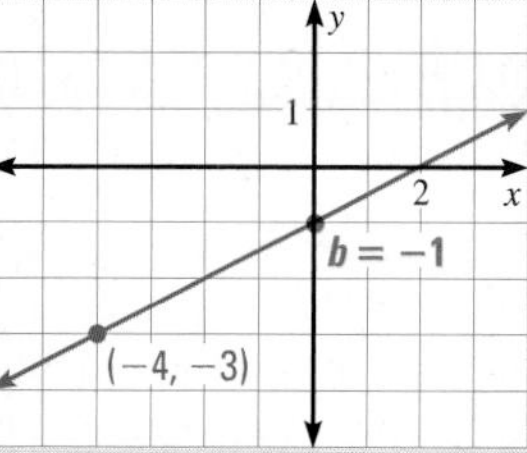

SOLUTION

$y = mx + b$	**Write slope formula.**
$-3 = \frac{1}{2}(-4) + b$	**Substitute.**
$-1 = b$	**Simplify.**

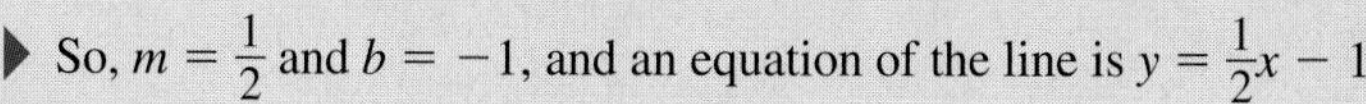

So, $m = \frac{1}{2}$ and $b = -1$, and an equation of the line is $y = \frac{1}{2}x - 1$.

EXAMPLE Write an equation of a line that passes through the points $(4, 0)$ and $(-5, 3)$.

SOLUTION First find the slope of the line.

$$m = \frac{y_2 - y_1}{x_2 - x_1} = \frac{3 - 0}{-5 - 4} = -\frac{1}{3}$$

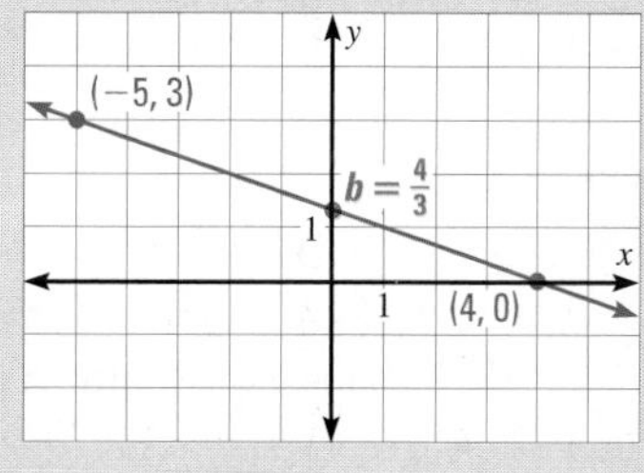

Then substitute the slope and the coordinates of either point into the slope-intercept formula to find the y-intercept. Let $m = -\frac{1}{3}$, $x = 4$, and $y = 0$.

$0 = -\frac{1}{3} \cdot 4 + b$	**Substitute.**
$b = \frac{4}{3}$	**Simplify.**

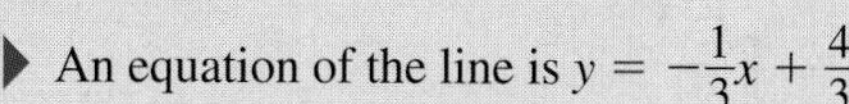

An equation of the line is $y = -\frac{1}{3}x + \frac{4}{3}$.

PRACTICE

Write an equation in slope-intercept form of the line that passes through the given point and has the given slope. 1–12. See margin.

1. $(0, -4)$, $m = 1$ **2.** $(0, 8)$, $m = -3$ **3.** $(0, -0.75)$, $m = 2.5$ **4.** $(0, 1.6)$, $m = 0$

5. $(0, 0)$, $m = 0.7$ **6.** $(0, -24)$, $m = 50$ **7.** $(1, -5)$, $m = 2$ **8.** $(3, 0)$, $m = -4$

9. $(-6, -6)$, $m = 12$ **10.** $(-9, 7)$, $m = -1$ **11.** $(3, -11)$, $m = 0$ **12.** $(0.5, -1.5)$, $m = 2$

Write an equation in slope-intercept form of the line that passes through the given points. 13–24. See margin.

13. $(1, 3), (7, 4)$ **14.** $(0, -3), (-5, 0)$ **15.** $(-6, -7), (-5, 1)$ **16.** $(4, 2), (7, -4)$

17. $(2, 0), (-6, -5)$ **18.** $(11, -1), (-1, -7)$ **19.** $(-5, 4), (2, -3)$ **20.** $(4, -9), (8, -9)$

21. $(1.4, 2.7), (3.9, 1.1)$ **22.** $(0, 11), (16, 87)$ **23.** $(0.5, 2), (-1.25, 0.5)$ **24.** $(58, 20), (80, 108)$

1. $y = x - 4$
2. $y = -3x + 8$
3. $y = \frac{5}{2}x - \frac{3}{4}$
4. $y = 1.6$
5. $y = 0.7x$
6. $y = 50x - 24$
7. $y = 2x - 7$
8. $y = -4x + 12$
9. $y = 12x + 66$
10. $y = -x - 2$
11. $y = -11$
12. $y = 2x - \frac{5}{2}$
13. $y = \frac{1}{6}x + \frac{17}{6}$
14. $y = -\frac{3}{5}x - 3$
15. $y = 8x + 41$
16. $y = -2x + 10$
17. $y = \frac{5}{8}x - \frac{5}{4}$
18. $y = \frac{1}{2}x - \frac{13}{2}$
19. $y = -x - 1$
20. $y = -9$
21. $y = -0.64x + 3.596$
22. $y = 4.75x + 11$
23. $y = \frac{6}{7}x + \frac{11}{7}$
24. $y = 4x - 212$

SOLVING SYSTEMS OF EQUATIONS

EXAMPLE Use substitution to solve the linear system:

$3x + 2y = 16$ **Equation 1**

$x + 3y = 10$ **Equation 2**

SOLUTION

Solve for x in Equation 2 since it is easy to isolate x: $x = 10 - 3y$.

Substitute $10 - 3y$ for x in Equation 1: $3(10 - 3y) + 2y = 16$.

Solve for y to get $y = 2$. Then $x = 10 - 3y = 10 - 3 \cdot 2 = 4$.

The solution is (4, 2). One way to check this solution is to substitute 4 for x and 2 for y in each of the original equations. Another way is to graph the original equations in the same coordinate plane to see if the graphs intersect at the point (4, 2).

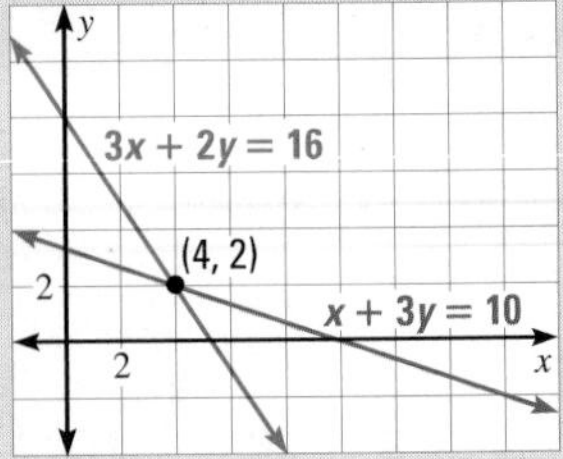

EXAMPLE Use linear combinations to solve the linear system.

$4x - 3y = -5$

$7x + 2y = -16$

SOLUTION The goal is to obtain coefficients that are opposites for one of the variables.

$4x - 3y = -5$ **Multiply by 2.** → $8x - 6y = -10$

$7x + 2y = -16$ **Multiply by 3.** → $\underline{21x + 6y = -48}$

$29x = -58$ **Add the equations.**

$x = -2$ **Solve for x.**

Substitute -2 for x: $4(-2) - 3y = -5$. Solve to get $y = -1$.

▶ The solution is $(-2, -1)$. Check this in the original equations.

PRACTICE

Use substitution to solve the system of linear equations.

1. $2x - 3y = -16$, $y = 5x + 1$ (1, 6)

2. $3x + y = -6$, $x = 0.5y - 3$ (−2.4, 1.2)

3. $7x - y = 0$, $x - y = 12$ (−2, −14)

4. $x + y = 8$, $2x + 5y = 3$ $\left(12\frac{1}{3}, -4\frac{1}{3}\right)$

5. $9x + 4y = 3$, $x + 8y = 6$ $\left(0, \frac{3}{4}\right)$

6. $3x + 5y = -8$, $4x - y = -3$ (−1, −1)

7. $x - 0.5y = 6$, $0.5x + 0.2y = 8$ $\left(\frac{104}{9}, \frac{100}{9}\right)$

8. $3x + y = 6$, $5(x + y) = 22$ (0.8, 3.6)

Use linear combinations to solve the system of linear equations.

9. $4x - 5y = 18$, $3x + 10y = -3$ (3, −1.2)

10. $7x + y = 8.5$, $-4x - 3y = 0$ $\left(1\frac{1}{2}, -2\right)$

11. $3x - 2y = -6$, $7x - 6y = 12$ (−15, −19.5)

12. $8x + 7y = 56$, $7x + 3y = 45$ (5.88, 1.28)

13. $5x + 9y = -6$, $2x - 6y = 6$ $\left(\frac{3}{8}, -\frac{7}{8}\right)$

14. $8x + y = -8$, $-2x - 3y = 35$ $\left(\frac{1}{2}, -12\right)$

15. $8x - 4y = 15$, $7x + 9y = 25$ (2.35, 0.95)

16. $13x - 5y = 10$, $3x - 2y = 14$ $\left(-\frac{50}{11}, -\frac{152}{11}\right)$

PROPERTIES OF EXPONENTS

An expression like 5^3 is called a **power**. The **exponent** 3 represents the number of times the **base** 5 is used as a factor: $5^3 = 5 \cdot 5 \cdot 5$ (3 factors of 5). To simplify expressions involving exponents, you often use properties of exponents. Let a and b be numbers and let m and n be integers.

- **Product of powers property:** $a^m \cdot a^n = a^{m+n}$ — **Example:** $4^2 \cdot 4^5 = 4^{2+5} = 4^7$
- **Power of a power property:** $(a^m)^n = a^{m \cdot n}$ — **Example:** $(x^4)^3 = x^{4 \cdot 3} = x^{12}$
- **Power of a product property:** $(a \cdot b)^m = a^m \cdot b^m$ — **Example:** $(-3k)^4 = (-3)^4 \cdot k^4 = 81\,k^4$
- If $a \neq 0$, then $a^0 = 1$. — **Example:** $5^0 = 1$
- If $a \neq 0$, then $a^{-n} = \frac{1}{a^n}$. — **Example:** $x^{-5} = \frac{1}{x^5}$
- **Quotient of powers property:** If $a \neq 0$, then $\frac{a^m}{a^n} = a^{m-n}$. — **Example:** $\frac{7^6}{7} = 7^{6-1} = 7^5 = 16{,}807$
- **Power of a quotient property:** If $b \neq 0$, then $\left(\frac{a}{b}\right)^m = \frac{a^m}{b^m}$. — **Example:** $\left(\frac{z}{3}\right)^4 = \frac{z^4}{3^4} = \frac{z^4}{81}$

EXAMPLES Simplify the expression.

a. $(-3xy^2)^3 \cdot y$ **b.** $\frac{1}{r^7} \cdot r^4$ **c.** $\frac{1}{x^6} \cdot \left(\frac{x}{2}\right)^6$

SOLUTION

a. $(-3xy^2)^3 \cdot y = (-3)^3 \cdot x^3 \cdot (y^2)^3 \cdot y^1 = -27x^3 \cdot y^{6+1} = -27x^3y^7$

b. $\frac{1}{r^7} \cdot r^4 = \frac{r^4}{r^7} = r^{4-7} = r^{-3} = \frac{1}{r^3}$

c. $\frac{1}{x^6} \cdot \left(\frac{x}{2}\right)^6 = \frac{1}{x^6} \cdot \frac{x^6}{2^6} = \frac{x^6}{64x^6} = \frac{1}{64}$

PRACTICE

Simplify the expression. The simplified expression should have no negative exponents.

1. $\left(-\frac{2}{3}\right)^3$ $-\frac{8}{27}$

2. $x^3 \cdot x \cdot x^3$ x^7

3. $\left(\frac{1}{2}ab\right)^5$ $\frac{1}{32}a^5b^5$

4. $2n^4 \cdot (3n)^2$ $18n^6$

5. $(rst)^0$ 1

6. $\left(8^{-1}\right)^{-3}$ 512

7. $4x^{-3} \cdot y^{-6}$ $\frac{4}{x^3y^6}$

8. $c \cdot c^{-9}$ $\frac{1}{c^8}$

9. $4^3 \cdot 4^6$ 262,144

10. $(3 \cdot a^2 \cdot 6)^2$ $324a^4$

11. $\left(\frac{5}{m}\right)^3$ $\frac{125}{m^3}$

12. $\frac{(-3)^5}{-3^5}$ 1

13. $(2b)^3 \cdot b$ $8b^4$

14. $(5x \cdot x^3)^4$ $625x^{16}$

15. $\left(\frac{x^4}{x^3}\right)^2$ x^2

16. $c^6 \cdot \frac{1}{c^9}$ $\frac{1}{c^3}$

17. $\frac{1}{a^{-4}}$ a^4

18. $\frac{2x^0}{8y^{-7}}$ $\frac{y^7}{4}$

19. $\left(2a^{-2}bc^3\right)^{-1}$ $\frac{a^2}{2bc^3}$

20. $\left(\frac{r}{3s}\right)^{-3}$ $\frac{27s^3}{r^3}$

21. $\left(5ab^3\right)^2 \cdot (-7b^2c)$ $-175a^2b^8c$

22. $w^5 \cdot \left(\frac{7}{w^4}\right)^2$ $\frac{49}{w^3}$

23. $4y^3z \cdot \left(\frac{y}{2z}\right)^{-3}$ $32z^4$

24. $\left(3c^{-4}d^5\right)^{-2} \cdot 12cd^{-4}$ $\frac{4c^9}{3d^{14}}$

MULTIPLYING BINOMIALS

To multiply binomials, use the distributive property. Each term in the first binomial is multiplied by each term in the second binomial. The **FOIL** method can help you remember the pattern of the distributive property. **FOIL** stands for **F** irst, **O** uter, **I** nner, and **L** ast, which is the order in which you multiply terms.

EXAMPLE $(x + 1)(2x - 4) = x(2x) + x(-4) + 1(2x) + 1(-4)$ **Multiply using FOIL.**

$= 2x^2 - 4x + 2x - 4$ **Simplify.**

$= 2x^2 - 2x - 4$ **Add like terms.**

PRACTICE

Simplify.

1. $(x + 1)(x + 1)$ $x^2 + 2x + 1$
2. $(4b + 1)(2 + b)$ $4b^2 + 9b + 2$
3. $(3c + 3)(c - 1)$ $3c^2 - 3$
4. $(t + 3)(2t - 3)$ $2t^2 + 3t - 9$
5. $(a + 5)(4a - 7)$ $4a^2 + 13a - 35$
6. $(5d + 3)(d - 2)$ $5d^2 - 7d - 6$
7. $(2f - 4)(2f + 4)$ $4f^2 - 16$
8. $(1 - 2g)(g + 3)$ $-2g^2 - 5g + 3$
9. $(6h + 3)(h + 1)$ $6h^2 + 9h + 3$

SQUARING BINOMIALS

One way to square a binomial is to use a pattern for the square of a binomial.

Patterns for the Square of a Binomial: $(a + b)^2 = a^2 + 2ab + b^2$

$(a - b)^2 = a^2 - 2ab + b^2$

EXAMPLES $(k + 9)^2 = k^2 + 2(k)(9) + 9^2$

$= k^2 + 18k + 81$

$(x - 4)^2 = x^2 - 2(x)(4) + 4^2$

$= x^2 - 8x + 16$

If you have trouble remembering the patterns, you can always use the distributive property to find the square of a binomial.

EXAMPLE $(r + 3)^2 = (r + 3)(r + 3)$

$= r(r + 3) + 3(r + 3)$ **Distributive property**

$= r^2 + 3r + 3r + 9$ **Distributive property**

$= r^2 + 6r + 9$ **Combine like terms.**

PRACTICE

Find the product by squaring the binomial.

1. $(x + 2)^2$ $x^2 + 4x + 4$
2. $(x - 1)^2$ $x^2 - 2x + 1$
3. $(x + 8)^2$ $x^2 + 16x + 64$
4. $(10 + x)^2$ $100 + 20x + x^2$, or $x^2 + 20x + 100$
5. $(n - 5)^2$ $n^2 - 10n + 25$
6. $(x - 0.5)^2$ $x^2 - x + 0.25$
7. $(15 - x)^2$ $225 - 30x + x^2$, or $x^2 - 30x + 225$
8. $(y + 12)^2$ $y^2 + 24y + 144$

798

RADICAL EXPRESSIONS

If $a^2 = b$, then b is a **square root** of a. Every positive number has two square roots: a positive square root and a negative square root. For example,

$4^2 = 16$ and $(-4)^2 = 16$, so the square roots of 16 are 4 and -4. We write:

$$\sqrt{16} = 4 \text{ and } -\sqrt{16} = -4.$$

Zero has just one square root: $\sqrt{0} = 0$.

EXAMPLES $11^2 = 121$, so $-\sqrt{121} = -11$ $\quad$ $\left(\frac{1}{5}\right)^2 = \frac{1}{25}$, so $\sqrt{\frac{1}{25}} = \frac{1}{5}$

$\sqrt{-4}$ is undefined, because the square of every real number is either positive or zero.

$\sqrt{5 + 4} = \sqrt{9} = 3$. Begin by simplifying an expression under the square root symbol.

When you simplify a radical expression, you will often use the following properties of radicals.

If a and b are positive numbers, then $\sqrt{ab} = \sqrt{a} \cdot \sqrt{b}$ and $\sqrt{\frac{a}{b}} = \frac{\sqrt{a}}{\sqrt{b}}$.

EXAMPLES Simplify the expression.

a. $\sqrt{56}$ **b.** $\sqrt{6} \cdot \sqrt{15}$ **c.** $\frac{\sqrt{150}}{\sqrt{2}}$ **d.** $\frac{5}{\sqrt{8}}$

SOLUTION

a. $\sqrt{56} = \sqrt{4} \cdot \sqrt{14} = 2\sqrt{14}$

b. $\sqrt{6} \cdot \sqrt{15} = \sqrt{6 \cdot 15} = \sqrt{90} = \sqrt{9 \cdot 10} = \sqrt{9} \cdot \sqrt{10} = 3\sqrt{10}$

c. $\frac{\sqrt{150}}{\sqrt{2}} = \sqrt{\frac{150}{2}} = \sqrt{75} = \sqrt{25 \cdot 3} = \sqrt{25} \cdot \sqrt{3} = 5\sqrt{3}$

d. $\frac{5}{\sqrt{8}} = \frac{5}{2\sqrt{2}} = \frac{5}{2\sqrt{2}} \cdot \frac{\sqrt{2}}{\sqrt{2}} = \frac{5\sqrt{2}}{4}$ **Do not leave a square root in a denominator.**

PRACTICE

Find all square roots of the number or write *no square roots*. Check the results by squaring each root.

1. 64 8 and -8 **2.** -36 no square roots **3.** $\frac{49}{81}$ $\frac{7}{9}$ and $-\frac{7}{9}$ **4.** $\frac{7}{100}$ $\frac{\sqrt{7}}{10}$ and $-\frac{\sqrt{7}}{10}$ **5.** 0.09 0.3 and -0.3

Simplify the expression. Give the exact value in simplified form.

6. $\sqrt{36 + 64}$ 10 **7.** $\sqrt{4 + 9}$ $\sqrt{13} \approx 3.61$ **8.** $\sqrt{16 + 16}$ $4\sqrt{2} \approx 5.66$ **9.** $\sqrt{(-1)^2 + 7^2}$ $5\sqrt{2} \approx 7.07$

Simplify the expression. Give the exact value in simplified form.

10. $-\sqrt{0}$ 0 **11.** $-\sqrt{196}$ -14 **12.** $\sqrt{54}$ $3\sqrt{6} \approx 7.35$ **13.** $\sqrt{60}$ $2\sqrt{15} \approx 7.75$

14. $\sqrt{7} \cdot \sqrt{3}$ $\sqrt{21} \approx 4.58$ **15.** $\sqrt{12} \cdot \sqrt{6}$ $6\sqrt{2} \approx 8.49$ **16.** $\sqrt{10} \cdot \sqrt{15}$ $5\sqrt{6} \approx 12.25$ **17.** $\sqrt{120 \cdot 105}$ $30\sqrt{14} \approx 112.25$

18. $\frac{\sqrt{147}}{\sqrt{3}}$ 7 **19.** $\frac{\sqrt{20}}{\sqrt{500}}$ $\frac{1}{5} = 0.2$ **20.** $\frac{\sqrt{48}}{\sqrt{6}}$ $2\sqrt{2} \approx 2.83$ **21.** $\frac{\sqrt{6}}{\sqrt{96}}$ $\frac{1}{4} = 0.25$

22. $\frac{4}{\sqrt{3}}$ $\frac{4\sqrt{3}}{3} \approx 2.31$ **23.** $\frac{6}{\sqrt{2}}$ $3\sqrt{2} \approx 4.24$ **24.** $\frac{5}{\sqrt{20}}$ $\frac{\sqrt{5}}{2} \approx 1.12$ **25.** $\frac{4}{\sqrt{27}}$ $\frac{4\sqrt{3}}{9} \approx 0.77$

SOLVING $AX^2 + C = 0$

A **quadratic equation** is an equation that can be written in the **standard form** $ax^2 + bx + c = 0$ where $a \neq 0$.

When $b = 0$, the quadratic equation has the form $ax^2 + c = 0$. In this case, you can solve for x. Solving $ax^2 + c = 0$ for x^2 you get $x^2 = \frac{-c}{a}$ and the following rules apply.

- If $\frac{-c}{a} > 0$, then $x^2 = \frac{-c}{a}$ has two solutions, $x = \sqrt{\frac{-c}{a}}$ and $x = -\sqrt{\frac{-c}{a}}$.
- If $\frac{-c}{a} = 0$, then $x^2 = \frac{-c}{a}$ has one solution, $x = 0$.
- If $\frac{-c}{a} < 0$, $x^2 = \frac{-c}{a}$ has no real solution.

EXAMPLES Solve the equation.

a. $3x^2 - 1 = 23$ **b.** $12 - x^2 = 13$ **c.** $4 + 2n^2 = 4$

SOLUTION

a.
$$3x^2 - 1 = 23$$
$$3x^2 = 24$$
$$x^2 = 8$$
$$x = \pm\sqrt{8}$$
$$x = \pm 2\sqrt{2}$$

b.
$$12 - x^2 = 13$$
$$-x^2 = 1$$
$$x^2 = -1$$
no real solution

c.
$$4 + 2n^2 = 4$$
$$2n^2 = 0$$
$$n^2 = 0$$
$$n = 0$$

EXAMPLE Solve $(x + 2)^2 = x^2 + 9$.

SOLUTION

$$(x + 2)^2 = x^2 + 9$$

$x^2 + 4x + 4 = x^2 + 9$ **See page 798 for help with squaring a binomial.**

$4x = 5$ **The given equation simplifies to a linear equation.**

$x = 1.25$ **Simplify.**

PRACTICE

Solve the equation or write *no solution*. Round solutions to the nearest hundredth.

1. $x^2 = 625$ 25, −25

2. $x^2 = -9$ no solution

3. $x^2 + 6 = 11$ $\sqrt{5} \approx 2.24, -\sqrt{5} \approx -2.24$

4. $4x^2 = 0$ 0

5. $-8 + 3r^2 = 4$ 2, −2

6. $\frac{1}{2}k^2 + 3 = 245$ 22, −22

7. $7a^2 + 25 = -6$ no solution

8. $4x^2 - 2 = 1$ $\frac{\sqrt{3}}{2} \approx 0.87, -\frac{\sqrt{3}}{2} \approx -0.87$

9. $(x + 5)^2 = x^2 + 49$ 2.4

10. $x^2 + 81 = (x + 6)^2$ 3.75

11. $(x + 1)^2 = 27 + x^2$ 13

12. $(x + 4)^2 = (x - 4)^2 + 96$ 6

SOLVING $AX^2 + BX + C = 0$

You can solve any quadratic equation by using the **quadratic formula**. This formula, which you used in Algebra, states that the solutions of the quadratic equation $ax^2 + bx + c = 0$ are

$$x = \frac{-b \pm \sqrt{b^2 - 4ac}}{2a} \text{ when } a \neq 0 \text{ and } b^2 - 4ac \geq 0.$$

EXAMPLE Solve $x^2 - 4x - 12 = 0$ by using the quadratic formula.

SOLUTION Substitute $a = 1$, $b = -4$, and $c = -12$ in the quadradic formula.

$$x = \frac{-b \pm \sqrt{b^2 - 4ac}}{2a} = \frac{4 \pm \sqrt{(-4)^2 - 4(1)(-12)}}{2 \cdot 1} = \frac{4 \pm \sqrt{64}}{2}$$

▶ The solutions are $\frac{4 + 8}{2} = 6$ and $\frac{4 - 8}{2} = -2$.

Check your solutions by substituting each solution into the original equation.

$6^2 - 4(6) - 12 = 0$ | $(-2)^2 - 4(-2) - 12 = 0$

$36 - 24 - 12 = 0$ ✓ | $4 + 8 - 12 = 0$ ✓

EXAMPLE Solve $2x^2 + 6x = 1$ by using the quadratic formula.

SOLUTION

Begin by writing the equation in *standard form*: $2x^2 + 6x - 1 = 0$.

Substitute $a = 2$, $b = 6$, and $c = -1$ in the quadratic formula.

$$x = \frac{-b \pm \sqrt{b^2 - 4ac}}{2a} = \frac{-6 \pm \sqrt{6^2 - 4 \cdot 2(-1)}}{2 \cdot 2} = \frac{-6 \pm \sqrt{44}}{4} = \frac{-6 \pm 2\sqrt{11}}{4} = \frac{-3 \pm \sqrt{11}}{2}$$

▶ The solutions are $\frac{-3 + \sqrt{11}}{2} \approx 0.16$ and $\frac{-3 - \sqrt{11}}{2} \approx -3.16$.

PRACTICE

Use the quadratic formula to solve each equation. Round solutions to the nearest hundredth.

1. $x^2 + 5x + 4 = 0$ **−4, −1**
2. $x^2 - x - 6 = 0$ **3, −2**
3. $x^2 + 6x = 0$ **0, −6**
4. $a^2 + 8 = 6a$ **4, 2**
5. $z^2 = 9z - 1$ **See margin.**
6. $-25 = x^2 + 10x$ **−5**
7. $2x^2 + 4x + 1 = 0$ **See margin.**
8. $4c^2 = 4c - 1$ **0.5**
9. $-8m + 3m^2 = -1$ **See margin.**
10. $3x^2 + 6x + 2 = 0$ **See margin.**
11. $5y^2 = 1 + 5y$ **See margin.**
12. $4x^2 - 3x = 7$ **1.75, −1**

13. Solve the quadratic equation $x^2 - 3x + 2 = 0$. Then graph the function $y = x^2 - 3x + 2$ in a coordinate plane. Describe the relationship between the solutions of the quadratic equation and the x-intercepts of the graph. **1, 2; See margin for graph. The solutions of the quadratic equation are the same as the x-intercepts of the graph.**

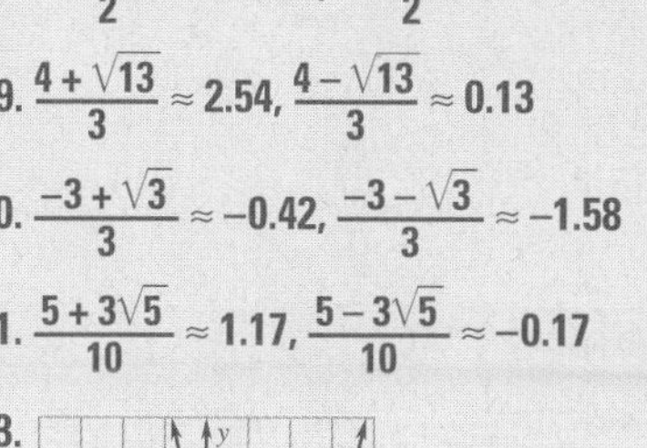
5. $\frac{9+\sqrt{77}}{2} \approx 8.89, \frac{9-\sqrt{77}}{2} \approx 0.11$

7. $\frac{-2+\sqrt{2}}{2} \approx -0.29, \frac{-2-\sqrt{2}}{2} \approx -1.71$

9. $\frac{4+\sqrt{13}}{3} \approx 2.54, \frac{4-\sqrt{13}}{3} \approx 0.13$

10. $\frac{-3+\sqrt{3}}{3} \approx -0.42, \frac{-3-\sqrt{3}}{3} \approx -1.58$

11. $\frac{5+3\sqrt{5}}{10} \approx 1.17, \frac{5-3\sqrt{5}}{10} \approx -0.17$

13.

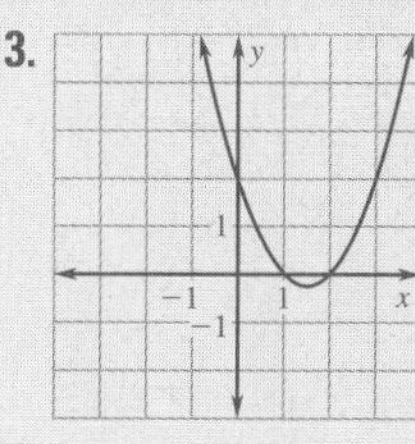

801

SOLVING FORMULAS

A **formula** is an algebraic equation that relates two or more real-life quantities. You can solve a formula for one of the variables by rewriting the formula so that the required variable is isolated on one side of the equation.

EXAMPLE The formula for the perimeter of the figure shown is $P = 2r + \pi r$. Solve the formula for r.

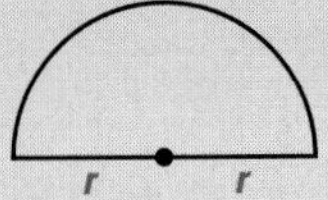

SOLUTION $P = 2r + \pi r$

$P = (2 + \pi)r$ **Distributive property**

$\frac{P}{2 + \pi} = r$ **Divide each side by $(2 + \pi)$.**

EXAMPLE Rewrite the equation $2x + 3y = -6$ so that y is a function of x.

SOLUTION $2x + 3y = -6$

$3y = -2x - 6$

$y = \frac{-2x - 6}{3}$ or $y = -\frac{2}{3}x - 2$

PRACTICE

Solve the formula for the indicated variable.

1. Area of a parallelogram: $A = bh$. Solve for b. $b = \frac{A}{h}$
2. Volume of a pyramid: $V = \frac{1}{3}Bh$. Solve for h. $h = \frac{3V}{B}$
3. Perimeter of a triangle: $P = a + b + c$. Solve for b. $b = P - a - c$
4. Circumference of a circle: $C = 2\pi r$. Solve for r. $r = \frac{C}{2\pi}$
5. Perimeter of a parallelogram: $P = 2(a + b)$. Solve for a. $a = \frac{P - 2b}{2}$
6. Sum of the measures of the interior angles of a convex polygon with n sides: $S = (n - 2)180$. Solve for n. $n = \frac{S + 360}{180}$
7. Surface area of a rectangular solid: $S = 2\ell w + 2\ell h + 2wh$. Solve for ℓ. $\ell = \frac{S - 2wh}{2w + 2h}$
8. Surface area of a right cylinder: $S = 2\pi r^2 + 2\pi rh$. Solve for h. $h = \frac{S - 2\pi r^2}{2\pi r}$
9. Surface area of a right cone: $S = \pi r^2 + \pi r\ell$. Solve for ℓ. $\ell = \frac{S - \pi r^2}{\pi r}$
10. Area of a trapezoid: $A = \frac{1}{2}hb_1 + \frac{1}{2}hb_2$. Solve for h. $h = \frac{2A}{b_1 + b_2}$

Rewrite the equation so that *y* is a function of *x*.

11. $3x + y = 9$ $y = 9 - 3x$
12. $5x - y = 0$ $y = 5x$
13. $2y + 6 = 3 - x$ $y = -\frac{1}{2}x - \frac{3}{2}$
14. $\frac{1}{2}x + 4y = -8$ $y = -\frac{1}{8}x - 2$
15. $6x - 7y = 42$ $y = \frac{6}{7}x - 6$
16. $1.5x + 0.2y = 3$ $y = -\frac{15}{2}x + 15$
17. $ax + by = c$ $y = \frac{c - ax}{b}$
18. $ax^2 - by = c$ $y = \frac{ax^2 - c}{b}$

Extra Practice

CHAPTER 1

Describe a pattern in the sequence of numbers. Predict the next number. (Lesson 1.1)

1. 16, 8, 4, 2, 1, . . . multiply by $\frac{1}{2}$; $\frac{1}{2}$

2. 1, 2, 4, 7, 11, . . . add 1, add 2, add 3, add 4,...; 16

3. 1, 5, 25, 125, . . . powers of 5; 625

4. 7, 2, 2, 8, 2, 2, 9, 2, 2, . . . add 1, 2, 2, add 1; 10

5. 32, 48, 72, 108, . . . multiply by 1.5; 162

6. 2, −6, 18, −54, . . . multiply by −3; 162

7. Complete the conjecture based on the pattern you observe in the specific cases. **(Lesson 1.1)**

Conjecture: Any negative number cubed is __?__. negative

$-1^3 = -1$ $\quad$ $-7^3 = -343$
$-3^3 = -27$ $\quad$ $-9^3 = -729$
$-5^3 = -125$ $\quad$ $-11^3 = -1331$

8. Show that $n^{n+1} > (n+1)^n$ for the values $n = 3$, 4, and 5. Then show that the values $n = 1$ and $n = 2$ are counterexamples to the conjecture that $n^{n+1} > (n+1)^n$. **(Lesson 1.1)** $3^4 = 81 > 4^3 = 64$; $4^5 = 1024 > 5^4 = 625$; $5^6 = 15{,}625 > 6^5 = 7776$; $1^2 = 1 \not> 2^1 = 2$; $2^3 = 8 \not> 3^2 = 9$

Sketch the points, lines, segments, planes, and rays. (Lesson 1.2) 9–13. Check sketches.

9. Draw four collinear points A, B, C, and D.

10. Draw two opposite rays $\overrightarrow{MN}$ and $\overrightarrow{MP}$.

11. Draw a plane that contains two intersecting lines.

12. Draw three points E, F, and G that are coplanar, but are not collinear.

13. Draw two points, R and S. Then sketch $\overrightarrow{RS}$. Add a point T on the ray so that S is between R and T.

In the diagram of the collinear points, $AE = 24$, C is the midpoint of $\overline{AE}$, $AB = 8$, and $DE = 5$. Find each length. (Lesson 1.3)

A B C D E

14. BC 4

15. AD 19

16. BD 11

17. AC 12

18. CD 7

19. BE 16

Use the Distance Formula to decide whether $\overline{HM} \cong \overline{ML}$. (Lesson 1.3)

20. $H(-1, 3)$, $M(1, 7)$, $L(3, 3)$ yes

21. $H(3, -1)$, $M(8, 2)$, $L(3, 5)$ yes

22. $H(-5, 2)$, $M(-4, 6)$, $L(-6, 2)$ no

Name the vertex and sides of the angle, then write two names for the angle. (Lesson 1.4)

23.

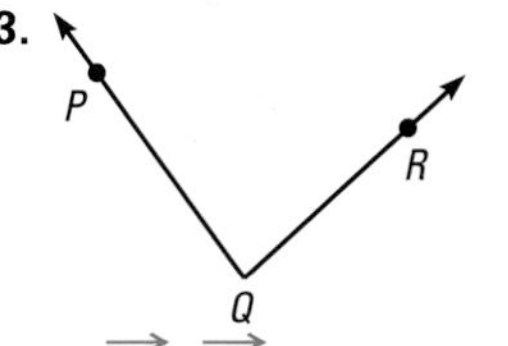

Q; $\overrightarrow{QP}$, $\overrightarrow{QR}$; ∠PQR, ∠RQP

24.

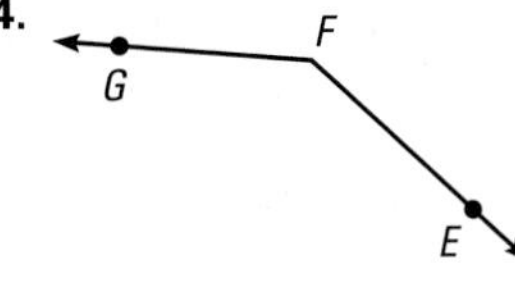

F; $\overrightarrow{FG}$, $\overrightarrow{FE}$; ∠GFE, ∠EFG

25.

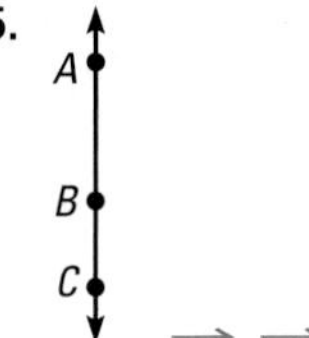

B; $\overrightarrow{BA}$, $\overrightarrow{BC}$; ∠ABC, ∠CBA

Use the Angle Addition Postulate to find the measure of the unknown angle. (Lesson 1.4)

26. $m\angle STR = \underline{\ ?\ }$ 70°

R
110°
S T

27. $m\angle HJK = \underline{\ ?\ }$ 65°

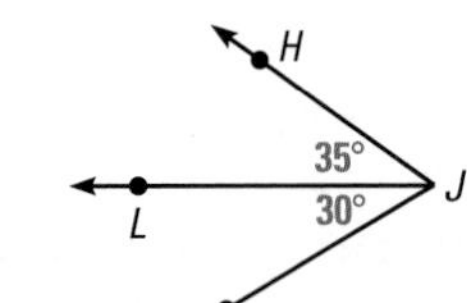

28. $m\angle DEF = \underline{\ ?\ }$ 90°

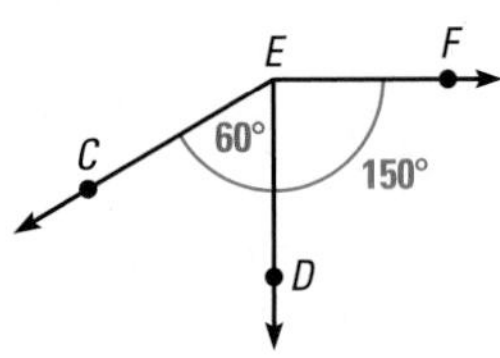

State whether the angle appears to be *acute, right, obtuse,* or *straight.* Then estimate its measure. (Lesson 1.4)

29.

obtuse; ≈150°

30.

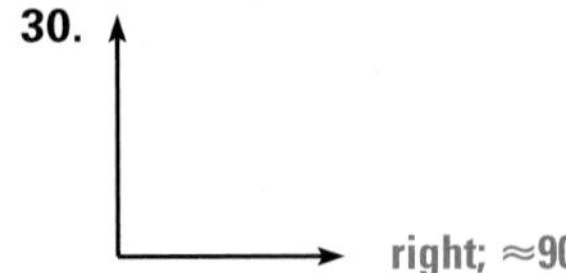

right; ≈90°

31.

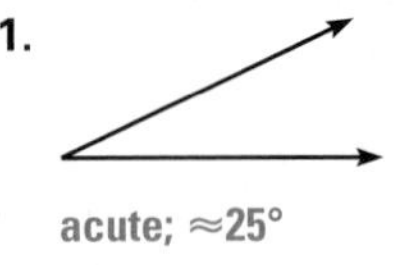

acute; ≈25°

Find the coordinates of the midpoint of a segment with the given endpoints. (Lesson 1.5)

32. $P(-4, 2)$
$Q(8, -4)$ (2, −1)

33. $P(-1, 3.5)$
$Q(7, -5.5)$ (3, −1)

34. $P(-12, 4)$
$Q(-3, -6)$ (−7.5, −1)

$\overrightarrow{XY}$ **is the angle bisector of** $\angle UXB$. **Find** $m\angle UXY$. (Lesson 1.5)

35. 42°

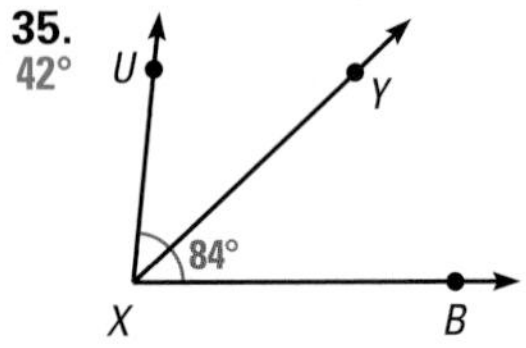

36. 25°

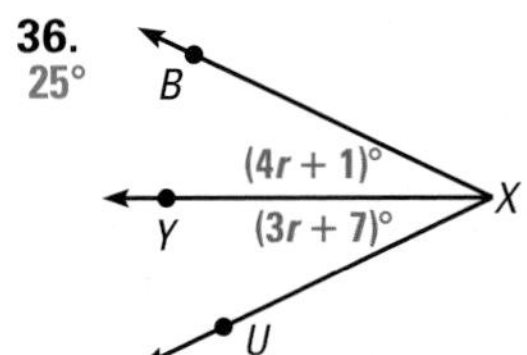

37. 74°

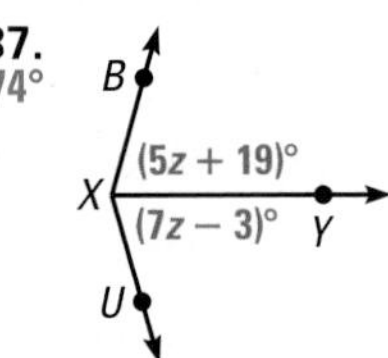

Find the measure of each angle. (Lesson 1.6)

38. Two vertical angles are complementary. Find the measure of each angle. 45°

39. The measure of one angle of a linear pair is 3 times the measure of the other angle. Find the measures of the two angles. 45°, 135°

40. The supplement of an angle is 130°. Find the complement of the angle. 40°

Find the perimeter (or circumference) and area of the figure. (Where necessary, use $\pi \approx 3.14$.) (Lesson 1.7)

41.

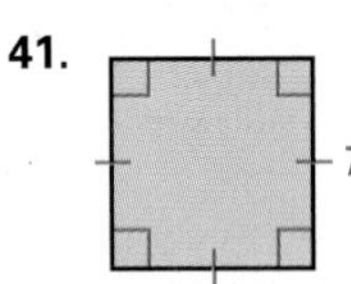

28; 49

42.

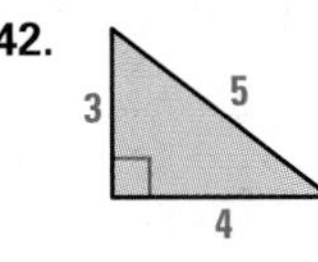

12; 6

43.

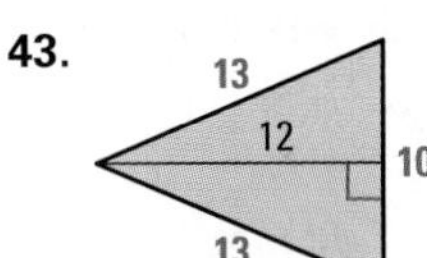

36; 60

44.

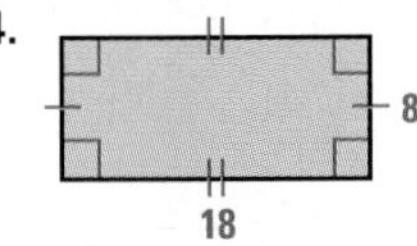

52; 144

45.

5

31.4; 78.5

46.

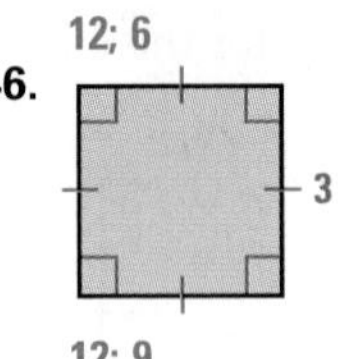

12; 9

47.

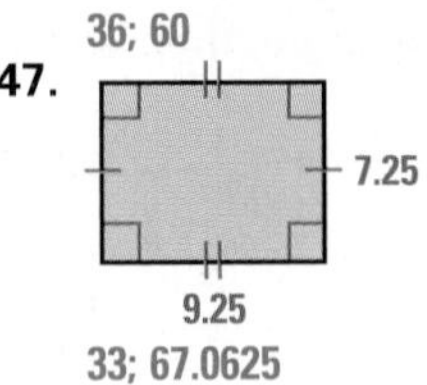

33; 67.0625

48.

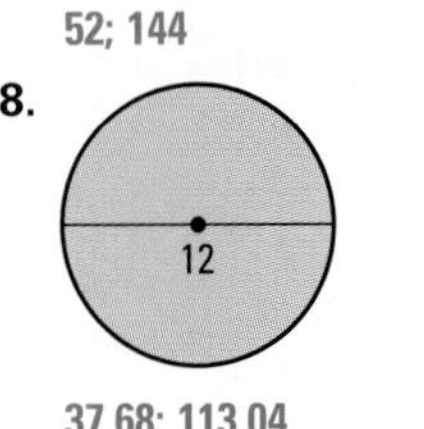

37.68; 113.04

CHAPTER 2

Rewrite the conditional statement in if-then form. (Lesson 2.1)

1. It must be true if you read it in a newspaper. If you read it in a newspaper, then it must be true.
2. An apple a day keeps the doctor away. If you have an apple a day, then it will keep the doctor away.
3. The square of an odd number is odd. If a number is odd, then its square is odd.

Write the inverse, converse, and contrapositive of the conditional statement. (Lesson 2.1)

4. If $x = 12$, then $x^2 = 144$. If $x \neq 12$, then $x^2 \neq 144$; If $x^2 = 144$, then $x = 12$; If $x^2 \neq 144$, then $x \neq 12$.
5. If you are indoors, then you are not caught in a rainstorm. See margin.
6. If four points are collinear, then they are coplanar. If four points are not collinear, then they are not coplanar; If 4 points are coplanar, then they are collinear; If four points are not coplanar, then they are not collinear.
7. If two angles are vertical angles, then they are congruent. See margin.

Write the converse of the true statement. Decide whether the converse is *true* or *false*. If false, provide a counterexample. (Lesson 2.1)

8. If two angles form a linear pair, then they are supplementary. See margin.
9. If $2x - 5 = 7$, then $x = 6$. If $x = 6$, then $2x - 5 = 7$; true.

Rewrite the biconditional statement as a conditional statement and its converse. (Lesson 2.2)

10. Two segments have the same length if and only if they are congruent. If two segments have the same length, then they are congruent; If two segments are congruent, then they have the same length.
11. Two angles are right angles if and only if they are supplementary. If two angles are right angles, then they are supplementary; If two angles are supplementary then they are right angles.
12. $x = 10$ if and only if $x^2 = 100$. If $x = 10$, then $x^2 = 100$; If $x^2 = 100$, then $x = 10$.

Determine whether the statement can be combined with its converse to form a true biconditional statement. (Lesson 2.2)

13. If $\angle ABC$ is a right angle, then $\overline{AB} \perp \overline{BC}$. yes
14. If $\angle 1$ and $\angle 2$ are adjacent, supplementary angles, then $\angle 1$ and $\angle 2$ form a linear pair. yes
15. If two angles are vertical angles, then they are congruent. no

Using *p*, *q*, *r*, and *s* below, write the symbolic statement in words. (Lesson 2.3) 16–21. See margin.

p: We go shopping. **r: We stop at the bank.**
q: We need a shopping list. **s: We see our friends.**

16. $p \to q$
17. $\sim r \to \sim s$
18. $r \to s$
19. $p \leftrightarrow q$
20. $\sim p \to \sim s$
21. $p \leftrightarrow r$

Given that the statement is of the form $p \to q$, write p and q. Then write the inverse and the contrapositive of $p \to q$ both symbolically and in words. (Lesson 2.3) 22–24. See margin.

22. If it is hot, May will go to the beach.
23. If the hockey team wins the game tonight, they will play in the championship.
24. If John misses the bus, then he will be late for school.

5. If you are not indoors, then you are caught in a rainstorm; If you are not caught in a rainstorm, then you are indoors; If you are caught in a rainstorm, then you are not indoors.
7. If two angles are not vertical angles, then they are not congruent; If two angles are congruent, then they are vertical angles; If two angles are not congruent, then they are not vertical angles.
8. If two angles are supplementary, then they form a linear pair; false. For example, two consecutive angles of a parallelogram are supplementary, but they do not form a linear pair.
16. If we go shopping, then we need a shopping list.
17. If we don't stop at the bank, then we won't see our friends.
18. If we stop at the bank, then we see our friends.
19. We go shopping if and only if we need a shopping list.
20. If we don't go shopping, then we won't see our friends.
21. We go shopping if and only if we stop at the bank.
22. p: It is hot. q: May will go to the beach.
    $\sim p \to \sim q$; If it is not hot, May will not go to the beach.
    $\sim q \to \sim p$; If May does not go to the beach, then it is not hot.
23. p: The hockey team wins the game tonight. q: They will play in the Championship Round.
    $\sim p \to \sim q$; If the hockey team doesn't win the game tonight, they won't play in the Championship Round.
    $\sim q \to \sim p$; If the hockey team doesn't play in the Championship Round, then they didn't win the game tonight.
24. p: John misses the bus. q: He will be late for school.
    $\sim p \to \sim q$; If John doesn't miss the bus, then he won't be late for school.
    $\sim q \to \sim p$; If John isn't late for school, then he did not miss the bus.

37. Statements (Reasons)
1. $\angle 1 \cong \angle 3$ (Vertical angles are congruent)
2. $\angle 4 \cong \angle 2$ (Vertical angles are congruent)
3. $\angle 1$ and $\angle 4$ are complementary (Given)
4. $m\angle 1 + m\angle 4 = 90°$ (Definition of complementary)
5. $m\angle 1 = m\angle 3$ (Definition of congruence)
6. $m\angle 4 = m\angle 2$ (Definition of congruence)
7. $m\angle 3 + m\angle 2 = 90°$ (Substitution property of equality)
8. $\angle 3$ and $\angle 2$ are complementary (Definition of complementary)

Use the property to complete the statement. (Lesson 2.4)

25. Reflexive property of equality: $AB = \underline{\ ?\ }$. AB

26. Symmetric property of equality: If $ED = DF$, then $\underline{\ ?\ }$. $DF = ED$

27. Transitive property of equality: If $AB = AC$ and $AC = DF$, then $\underline{\ ?\ }$. $AB = DF$

28. Division property of equality: If $2x = 3y$, then $\frac{2x}{z} = \underline{\ ?\ }$. $\frac{3y}{z}$

29. Subtraction property of equality: If $x = 6$, then $x - 4 = \underline{\ ?\ }$. $6 - 4$ (or 2)

Copy and complete the proof using the diagram and the given information. (Lesson 2.5)

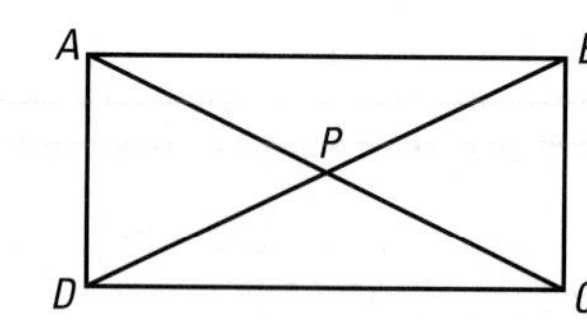

30. GIVEN ▶ $\overline{PD} \cong \overline{PC}$, P is the midpoint of $\overline{AC}$ and $\overline{BD}$

PROVE ▶ $\overline{AP} \cong \overline{BP}$

Statements	Reasons
1. P is the midpoint of $\overline{AC}$ and $\overline{BD}$.	1. ? Given
2. $AP = PC$	2. ? Definition of a midpoint
3. $BP = PD$	3. ? Definition of a midpoint
4. ? $\overline{PD} \cong \overline{PC}$	4. Given
5. $PD = PC$	5. ? Definition of congruent segments
6. ? $AP = BP$	6. Transitive property of equality
7. $\overline{AP} \cong \overline{BP}$	7. Definition of congruent segments

In Exercises 31–32, use the diagram to complete the statement. (Lesson 2.6)

31. $\angle 2$ and $\underline{\ ?\ }$ are vertical angles. $\angle 6$

32. $\angle QWR$ is supplementary to $\underline{\ ?\ }$. $\angle VWQ$ or $\angle RWU$

33. In the diagram, suppose that $\angle 3$ and $\angle 4$ are complementary and that $\angle 4$ and $\angle 5$ are complementary. Prove that $\angle 3 \cong \angle 5$. (Lesson 2.6)
$\angle 3 \cong \angle 5$ by the Congruent Complements Theorem

Solve for each variable. (Lesson 2.6)

34.

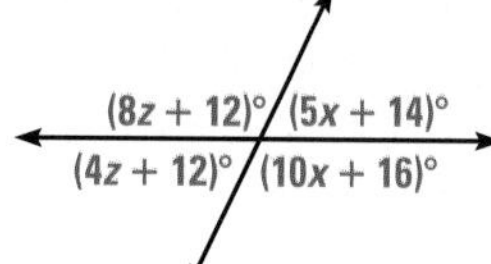

$z = 13$; $x = 10$

35.

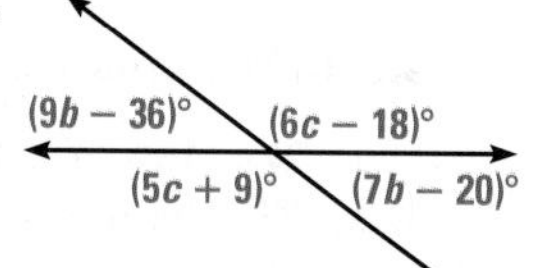

$b = 8$; $c = 27$

36.

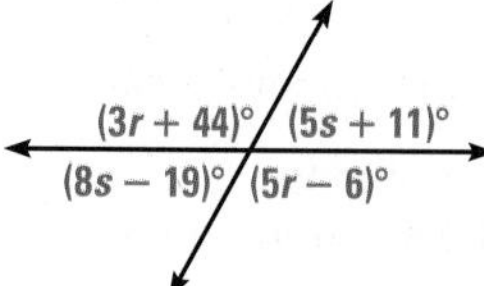

$r = 25$; $s = 10$

37. Write a two-column proof. (Lesson 2.6)

GIVEN ▶ $\angle 1$ and $\angle 4$ are complementary, $\angle DBE$ is a right angle.

PROVE ▶ $\angle 2$ and $\angle 3$ are complementary.
See margin.

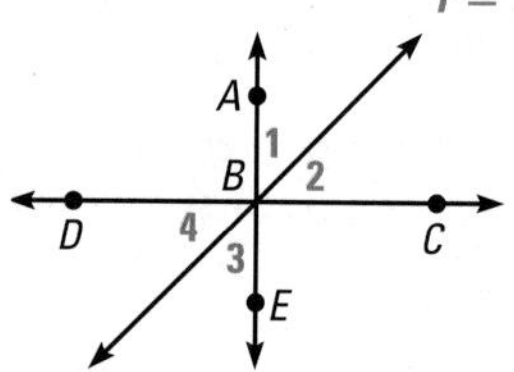

CHAPTER 3

Think of each segment in the diagram as part of a line. Fill in the blank with *parallel, skew,* or *perpendicular.* (Lesson 3.1)

1. $\overleftrightarrow{HA}$ and $\overleftrightarrow{EC}$ are __?__. parallel
2. $\overleftrightarrow{FD}$ and $\overleftrightarrow{AD}$ are __?__. perpendicular
3. $\overleftrightarrow{AD}$ and $\overleftrightarrow{GB}$ are __?__. skew

Think of each segment in the diagram as part of a line. There may be more than one right answer. (Lesson 3.1)

4. Name a line parallel to $\overleftrightarrow{AD}$. *Sample answers: $\overleftrightarrow{HF}$, $\overleftrightarrow{BC}$, $\overleftrightarrow{GE}$*
5. Name a line perpendicular to $\overleftrightarrow{GB}$. *Sample answers: $\overleftrightarrow{AB}$, $\overleftrightarrow{BC}$, $\overleftrightarrow{GE}$, $\overleftrightarrow{HG}$*
6. Name a line skew to $\overleftrightarrow{EC}$. *Sample answers: $\overleftrightarrow{GH}$, $\overleftrightarrow{AB}$, $\overleftrightarrow{HF}$, $\overleftrightarrow{AD}$*
7. Name a plane parallel to *GBC*. *Sample answers: HAD, ADF, DFH, FHA*

Complete the statement with *corresponding, alternate interior, alternate exterior,* or *consecutive interior.* (Lesson 3.1)

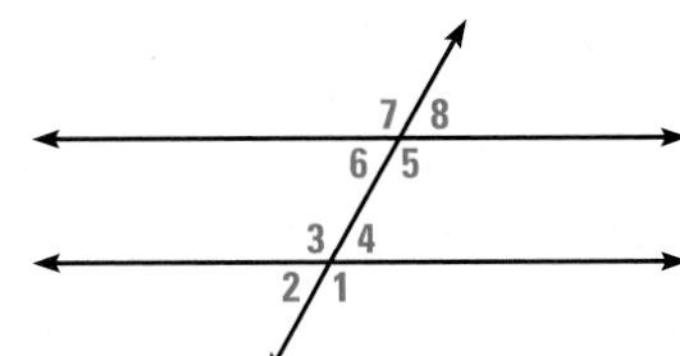

8. $\angle 3$ and $\angle 7$ are __?__ angles. corresponding
9. $\angle 4$ and $\angle 6$ are __?__ angles. alternate interior
10. $\angle 8$ and $\angle 2$ are __?__ angles. alternate exterior
11. $\angle 4$ and $\angle 5$ are __?__ angles. consecutive interior
12. $\angle 5$ and $\angle 1$ are __?__ angles. corresponding

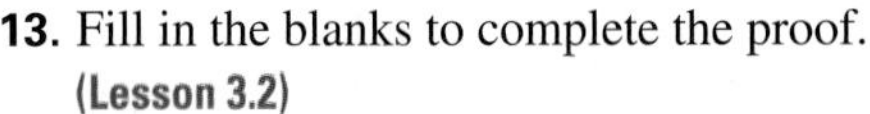

13. Fill in the blanks to complete the proof. (Lesson 3.2)

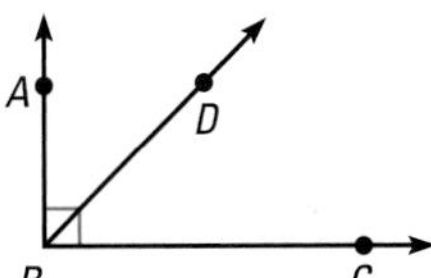

GIVEN ▶ $\overline{AB} \perp \overline{BC}$, $\overrightarrow{BD}$ bisects $\angle ABC$

PROVE ▶ $m\angle ABD = 45°$

Statements	Reasons
1. $\overline{AB} \perp \overline{BC}$	1. __?__ Given
2. __?__ $\angle ABC$ is a right $\angle$.	2. Definition of perpendicular lines
3. $m\angle ABC = 90°$	3. __?__ Definition of right $\angle$
4. $\overrightarrow{BD}$ bisects $\angle ABC$	4. __?__ Given
5. $m\angle ABD = m\angle DBC$	5. __?__ Definition of $\angle$ bisector
6. $m\angle ABD + m\angle DBC = 90°$	6. __?__ If 2 sides of 2 adj. acute $\angle$s are $\perp$, then the $\angle$s are complementary.
7. $m\angle ABD +$ __?__ $= 90°$ $m\angle ABD$	7. Substitution property of equality
8. $2(m\angle ABD) = 90°$	8. __?__ Distributive property
9. $m\angle ABD = 45°$	9. __?__ Division property of equality

23. Corresponding angles are congruent.
24. Consecutive angles are supplementary.
25. Alternate interior angles are congruent.
26. All slopes are 1; $\overleftrightarrow{AB} \parallel \overleftrightarrow{CD} \parallel \overleftrightarrow{EF}$
27. $\overleftrightarrow{AB}$: 0; $\overleftrightarrow{CD}$: $-\frac{1}{3}$; $\overleftrightarrow{EF}$: $-\frac{11}{14}$; none
28. All lines are vertical; $\overleftrightarrow{AB} \parallel \overleftrightarrow{CD} \parallel \overleftrightarrow{EF}$

Find the values of *x* and *y*. Explain your reasoning. (Lesson 3.3)

14.

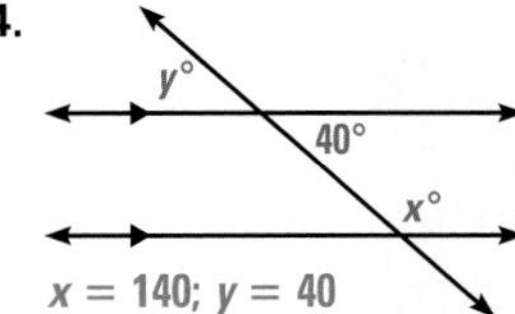

$x = 140$; $y = 40$

15.

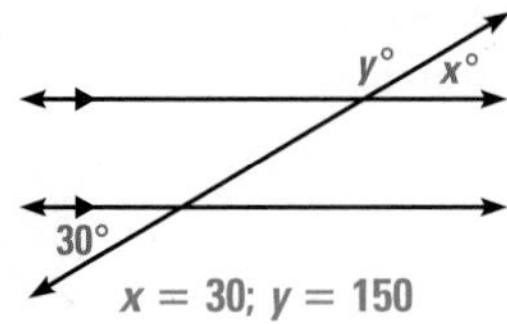

$x = 30$; $y = 150$

16.

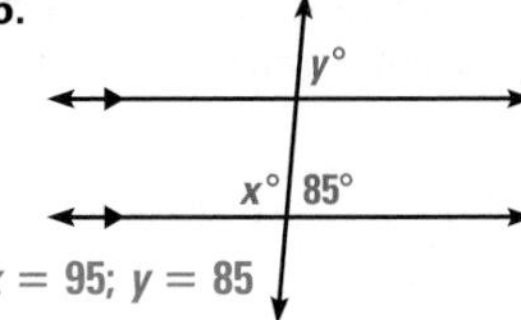

$x = 95$; $y = 85$

17.

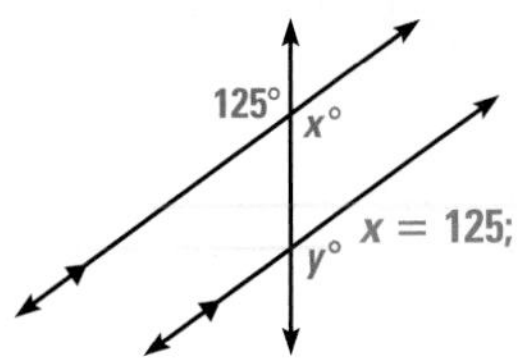

$x = 125$; $y = 125$

18.

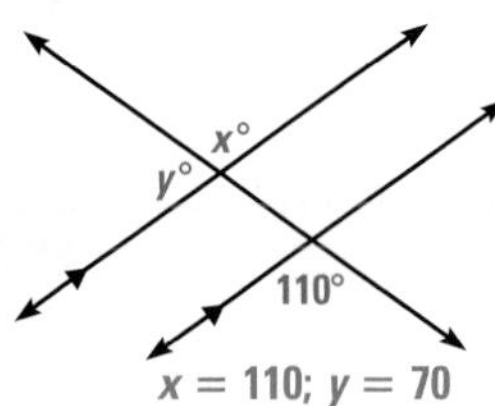

$x = 110$; $y = 70$

19.

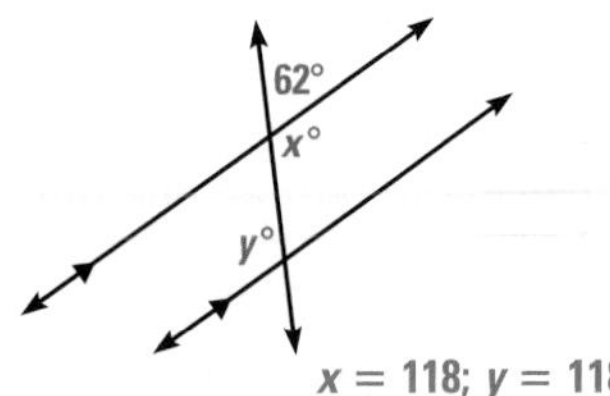

$x = 118$; $y = 118$

Which lines, if any, are parallel? Explain. (Lesson 3.4)

20.

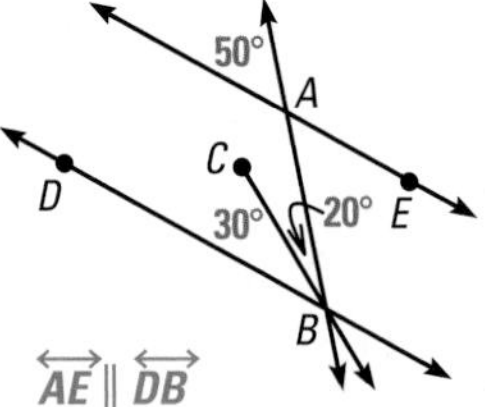

$\overleftrightarrow{AE} \parallel \overleftrightarrow{DB}$

21.

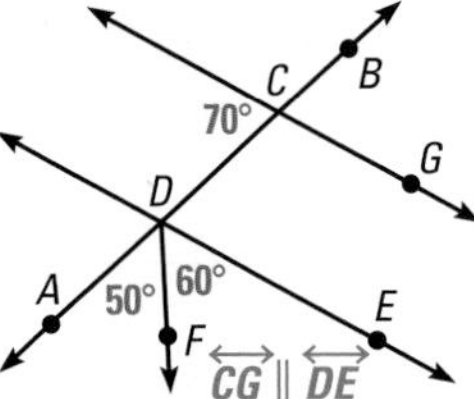

$\overleftrightarrow{CG} \parallel \overleftrightarrow{DE}$

22.

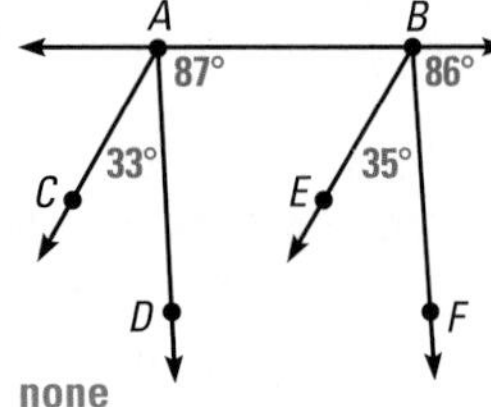

none

Explain how you would show that $a \parallel b$. State any theorems or postulates that you would use. (Lesson 3.5) 23–25. See margin.

23.

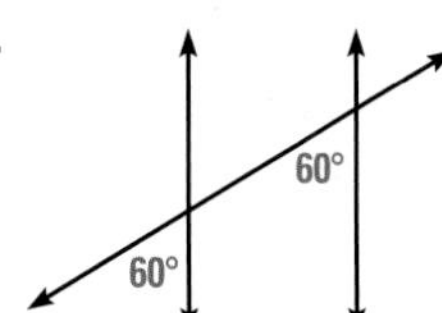

24.

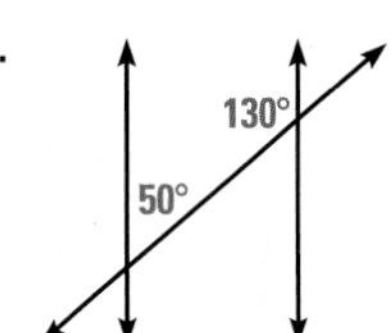

25.

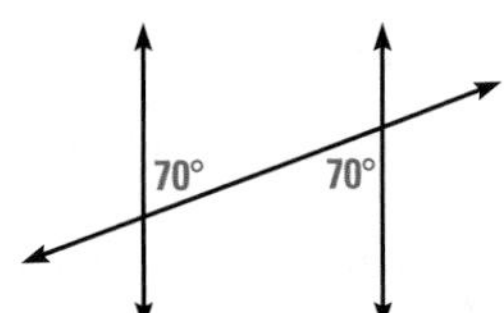

Find the slopes of $\overleftrightarrow{AB}$, $\overleftrightarrow{CD}$, and $\overleftrightarrow{EF}$. Which lines are parallel, if any? (Lesson 3.6) 26–28. See margin.

26. $A(3, 7)$, $B(1, 5)$
$C(4, 1)$, $D(9, 6)$
$E(2, 5)$, $F(-8, -5)$

27. $A(-4, 1)$, $B(3, 1)$
$C(-2, -1)$, $D(4, -3)$
$E(-10, 3)$, $F(4, -8)$

28. $A(-3, 2)$, $B(-3, 5)$
$C(7, -1)$, $D(7, 7)$
$E(4, -11)$, $F(4, -6)$

Write an equation of the line that passes through point *P* and is parallel to the line with the given equation. (Lesson 3.6)

29. $P(-4, -5)$, $y = 6x - 7$ — $y = 6x + 19$

30. $P(2, -3)$, $y = -\frac{1}{2}x + 4$ — $y = -\frac{1}{2}x - 2$

31. $P(-9, 8)$, $x = -12$ — $x = -9$

Decide whether lines p_1 and p_2 are perpendicular. (Lesson 3.7)

32. line p_1: $-7y + 3x = 6$
line p_2: $-9y - 21x = 3$ yes

33. line p_1: $3y + 12x = 15$
line p_2: $8y - 2x = 9$ yes

34. line p_1: $16y - 2x = 11$
line p_2: $-12x - 2y = 6$ no

Line *j* is perpendicular to the line with the given equation and line *j* passes through *P*. Write an equation of line *j*. (Lesson 3.7)

35. $y = -2x + 1$, $P(4, -1)$ — $y = \frac{1}{2}x - 3$

36. $2x + 5y = 20$, $P(4, 10)$ — $y = \frac{5}{2}x$

37. $y = \frac{1}{2}x + 6$, $P(-2, -7)$ — $y = -2x - 11$

CHAPTER 4

In Exercises 1–4, the variable expressions represent the angle measures of a triangle. Find the measure of each angle. Then classify the triangle by its angles. (Lesson 4.1)

1. $m\angle E = x^\circ$
$m\angle F = 3x^\circ$
$m\angle G = 5x^\circ$
20, 60, 100; obtuse

2. $m\angle H = 60^\circ$
$m\angle K = x^\circ$
$m\angle L = x^\circ$
60, 60; equiangular

3. $m\angle P = x^\circ$
$m\angle Q = (2x + 10)^\circ$
$m\angle R = (x + 10)^\circ$
40, 90, 50; right

4. $m\angle S = (2x)^\circ$
$m\angle T = (2x - 4)^\circ$
$m\angle U = (2x - 2)^\circ$
62, 58, 60; acute

5. The measure of an exterior angle of a right triangle is 135°. Find the measures of the interior angles of the triangle. (Lesson 4.1) 90°, 45°, 45°

Identify any figures that can be proved congruent. For those that can be proved congruent, write a congruence statement. (Lesson 4.2)

6. $\triangle ABC \cong \triangle FED$

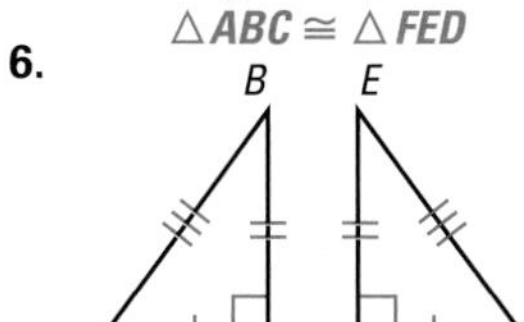

7.

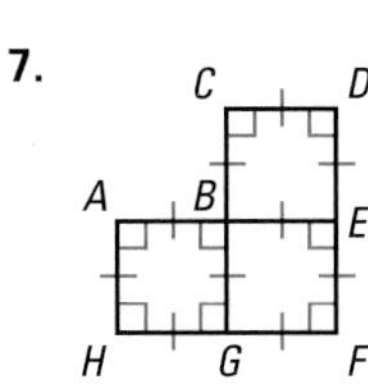

ABGH ≅ BEFG ≅ CDEB; AEFH ≅ CGFD

8.

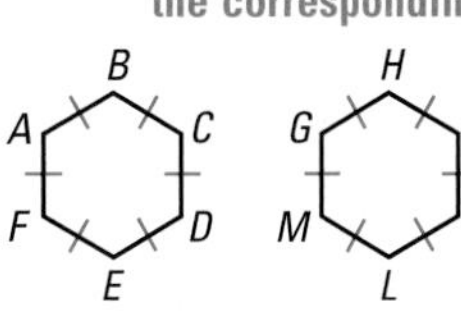

8. none; corresponding sides are congruent, but no information is given about the corresponding angles.

9. Use the triangles in Exercise 6 above. Identify all pairs of congruent corresponding angles and corresponding sides. (Lesson 4.2) $\angle A, \angle F$; $\angle B, \angle E$; $\angle C, \angle D$
$\overline{AB}, \overline{FE}$; $\overline{BC}, \overline{ED}$; $\overline{AC}, \overline{FD}$

Use the given information to find the value of *x*. (Lesson 4.2)

10. $\angle Q \cong \angle T$, $\angle R \cong \angle H$
7

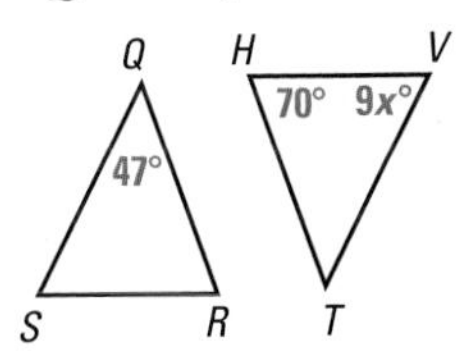

11. $\angle E \cong \angle K$, $\angle F \cong \angle M$
13

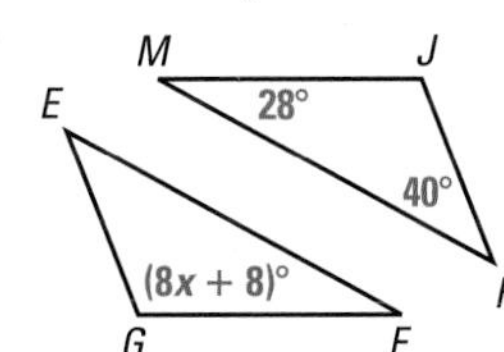

12. $\angle A \cong \angle C$, $\angle BDA \cong \angle BDC$
6

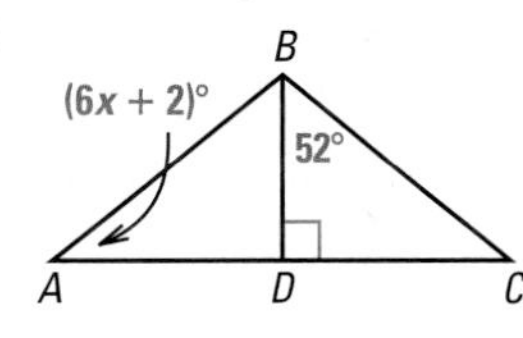

Decide whether enough information is given to prove that the triangles are congruent. If there is enough information, state the congruence postulate you would use. (Lesson 4.3)

13. $\triangle XVY$, $\triangle ZVW$

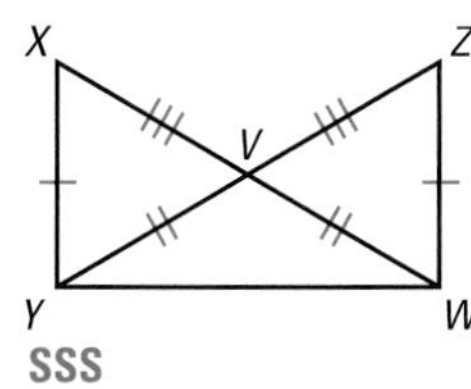

SSS

14. $\triangle MPN$, $\triangle QPR$

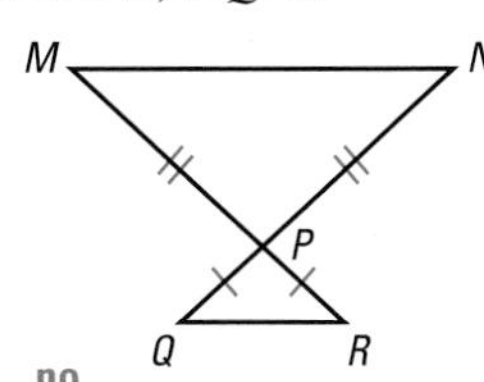

no

15. $\triangle BCE \cong \triangle DCE$

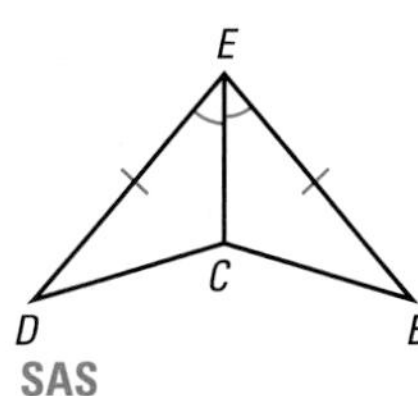

SAS

16. Use the diagram in Exercise 13. Prove that $\triangle XYW \cong \triangle ZWY$. See margin.

Is it possible to prove that the triangles are congruent? If so, state the congruence postulate or theorem you would use. (Lesson 4.4)

17.

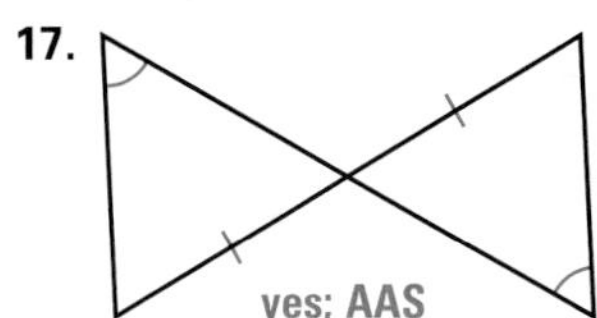

yes; AAS

18.

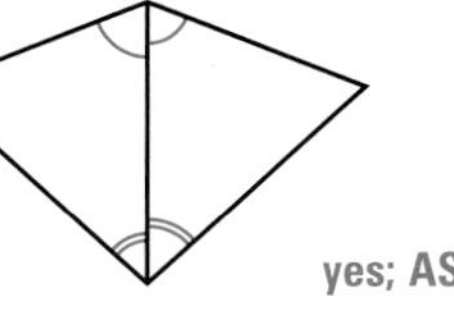

yes; ASA

19. no

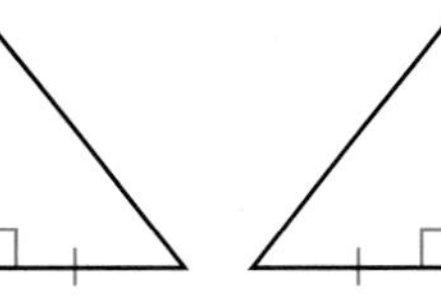

16. Statements (Reasons)
1. $\overline{XV} \cong \overline{ZV}$, $\overline{VY} \cong \overline{VW}$ (Given)
2. $XV = ZV$, $VY = VW$ (Definition of congruent segments)
3. $XV + VW = XW$, $ZV + VY = ZY$ (Segment Addition Postulate)
4. $ZV + VY = XW$ (Substitution property of equality)
5. $XW = ZY$ (Substitution property of equality)
6. $\overline{XW} \cong \overline{ZY}$ (Definition of congruent segments)
7. $\overline{XY} \cong \overline{ZW}$ (Given)
8. $\overline{YW} \cong \overline{YW}$ (Reflexive property of equality)
9. $\triangle XYW \cong \triangle ZWY$ (SSS Congruence Postulate)

20. Statements (Reasons)
1. $\overline{AD} \parallel \overline{BC}$ (Given)
2. $\angle ADE \cong \angle CBE$ (If 2 ∥ lines are cut by a transv., then alt. int. $\measuredangle$ are ≅.)
3. $\angle AED \cong \angle CEB$ (Vertical $\measuredangle$ are ≅.)
4. $\overline{AC}$ bisects $\overline{BD}$ (Given)
5. $\overline{BE} \cong \overline{ED}$ (Def. of segment bisector)
6. $\triangle AED \cong \triangle CEB$ (ASA Congruence Postulate)

24. Paragraph proof: Given that $\triangle BAF \cong \triangle FBD$, $\angle AFB \cong \angle BDF$ by corresp. parts of ≅ $\triangle$ are ≅.

25. Paragraph proof: Given that $\triangle CBD \cong \triangle BAF$, $\overline{BC} \cong \overline{AB}$ by corresp. parts of ≅ $\triangle$ are ≅.

26. Paragraph proof: Given that $\triangle FBD \cong \triangle DFE$, $\overline{FD} \cong \overline{DE}$ by corresponding parts of ≅ $\triangle$ are ≅.

30. *Sample answer:*

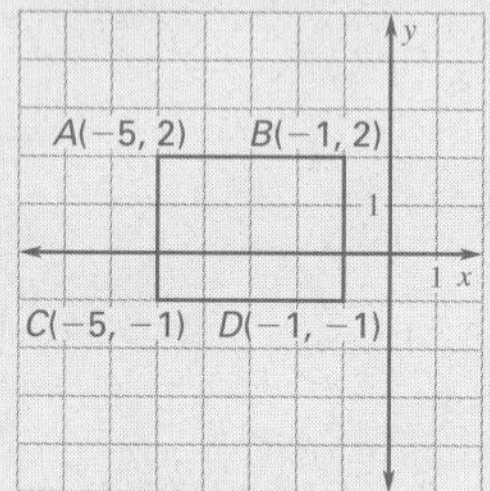

31. *Sample answer:*

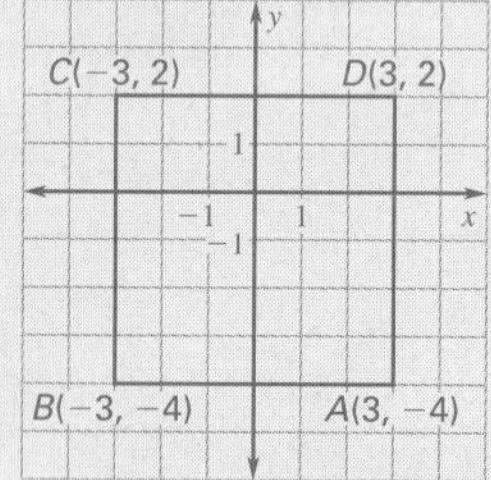

Write a two-column proof or a paragraph proof. (Lesson 4.4)

20. GIVEN ▶ $\overline{AD} \parallel \overline{BC}$, $\overline{AC}$ bisects $\overline{BD}$

PROVE ▶ $\triangle AED \cong \triangle CEB$ See margin.

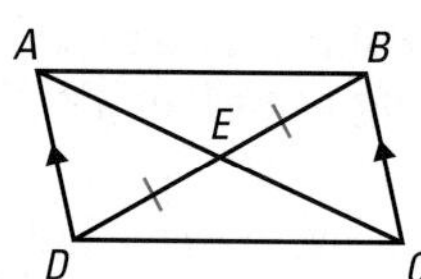

State which postulate or theorem you can use to prove that the triangles are congruent. Then explain how proving that the triangles are congruent proves the given statement. (Lesson 4.5)

21. PROVE ▶ $\overline{AB} \cong \overline{CD}$

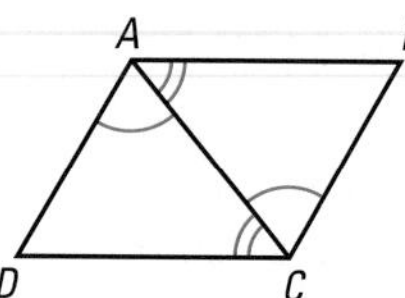

ASA; Corresp. parts of ≅ $\triangle$ are ≅.

22. PROVE ▶ $\angle GEF \cong \angle GHJ$

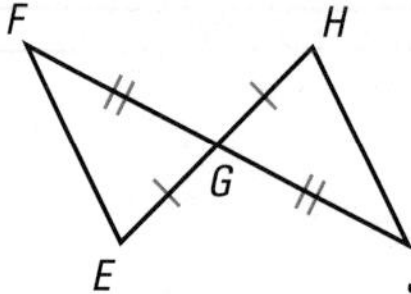

SAS; corresp. parts of ≅ $\triangle$ are ≅.

23. PROVE ▶ $\angle RQT \cong \angle RST$

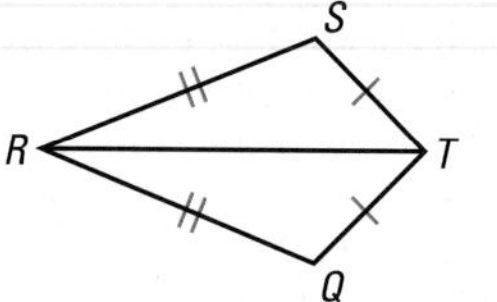

SSS; corresp. parts of ≅ $\triangle$ are ≅.

Use the diagram and the information given below. (Lesson 4.5) 24–26. See margin.

GIVEN ▶ $\triangle CBD \cong \triangle BAF$
$\triangle BAF \cong \triangle FBD$
$\triangle FBD \cong \triangle DFE$

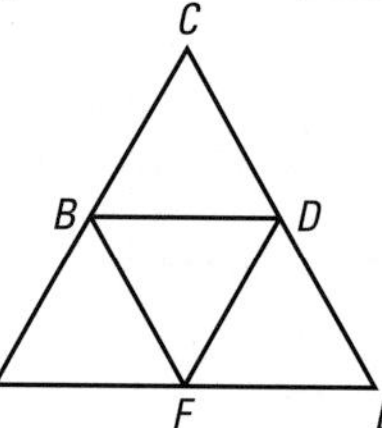

24. PROVE ▶ $\angle AFB \cong \angle BDF$

25. PROVE ▶ $\overline{BC} \cong \overline{AB}$

26. PROVE ▶ $\overline{FD} \cong \overline{DE}$

Find the values of *x* and *y*. (Lesson 4.6)

27.

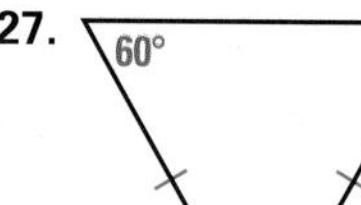

$x = 60$; $y = 60$

28.

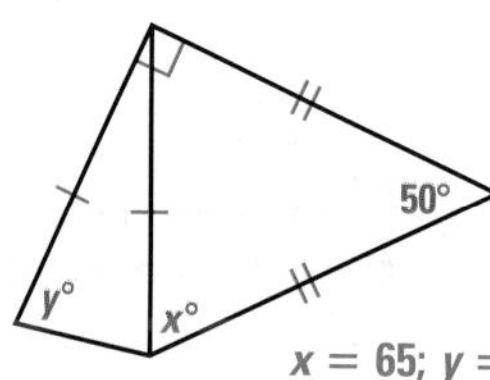

$x = 65$; $y = 77.5$

29. $x = 45$; $y = 45$

Place the figure in a coordinate plane. Label the vertices and give the coordinates of each vertex. (Lesson 4.7) 30, 31. See margin.

30. A 4 unit by 3 unit rectangle with one vertex at $(-5, 2)$

31. A square with side length 6 and one vertex at $(3, -4)$

In the diagram, $\triangle EFG$ is a right triangle. Its base is 80 units and its height is 60 units. (Lesson 4.7)

32. Give the coordinates of points F and G. $F(-30, -20)$; $G(-30, 40)$

33. Find the length of the hypotenuse of $\triangle EFG$. 100

Place the figure in a coordinate plane and find the given information. (Lesson 4.7)

34. A rectangle with length 6 units and width 3 units; find the length of a diagonal of the rectangle. $3\sqrt{5}$

35. An isosceles right triangle with legs of 7 units; find the length of the hypotenuse. $7\sqrt{2}$

CHAPTER 5

Use the diagram shown. **(Lesson 5.1)**

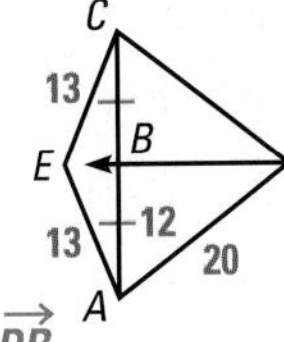

1. In the diagram, $\overrightarrow{DB} \perp \overline{AC}$ and $\overline{BA} \cong \overline{BC}$. Find BC. **12**

2. In the diagram, $\overrightarrow{DB} \perp \overline{AC}$ and $\overline{BA} \cong \overline{BC}$. Find DC. **20**

3. In the diagram, $\overrightarrow{DB}$ is the perpendicular bisector of $\overline{AC}$. Because $EA = EC = 13$, what can you conclude about the point E? **E is on $\overrightarrow{DB}$.**

Use the diagram shown. **(Lesson 5.1)**

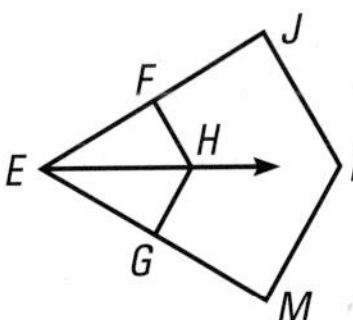

4. In the diagram, $m\angle FEH = m\angle GEH = 30°$, $m\angle HGE = m\angle HFE = 90°$, and $HF = 5$. Find HG. **5**

5. In the diagram, $\overrightarrow{EH}$ bisects $\angle JEM$, $m\angle EJK = m\angle EMK = 90°$ and $JK = MK = 10$. What can you conclude about point K? **K is on $\overrightarrow{EH}$**

In each case, find the indicated measure. **(Lesson 5.2)**

6. The perpendicular bisectors of $\triangle ABC$ meet at point D. Find AC. **16**

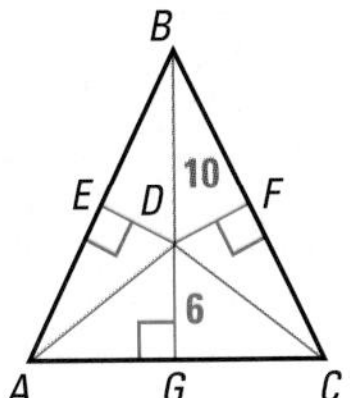

7. The perpendicular bisectors of $\triangle EFG$ meet at point H. Find HJ. **9**

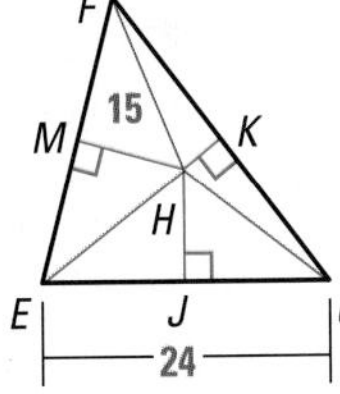

8. The angle bisectors of $\triangle RST$ meet at point Q. Find WS. **24**

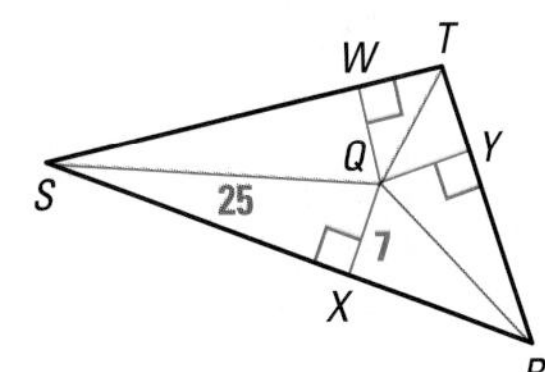

9. The angle bisectors of $\triangle AEC$ meet at point G. Find GF. **10**

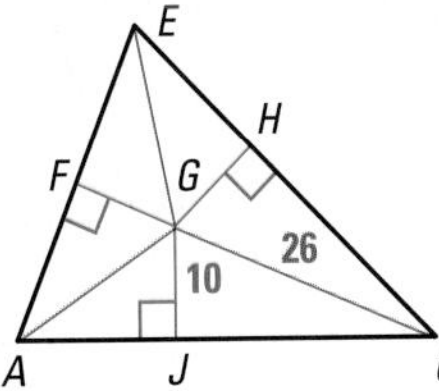

Use the figure below and the given information. **(Lesson 5.3)**
T is the centroid of $\triangle ABC$, $BT = 14$, $XC = 24$, and $TZ = 8.5$.

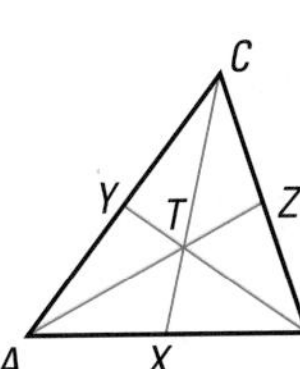

10. Find the length of $\overline{BY}$. **21**

11. Find the length of $\overline{TX}$. **8**

12. Find the length of $\overline{AT}$. **17**

Draw and label a large triangle of the given type and construct altitudes. Verify Theorem 5.8 by showing that the lines containing the altitudes are concurrent and label the orthocenter. **(Lesson 5.3)** **13–15. Check sketches.**

13. an isosceles $\triangle MNP$

14. an equilateral $\triangle DEF$
The orthocenter should be equidistant from the three vertices of the triangle.

15. a right isosceles $\triangle STR$
The orthocenter should be at the vertex of the right angle of the triangle.

Use $\triangle ABC$, where X, Y, and Z are midpoints of the sides. (Lesson 5.4)

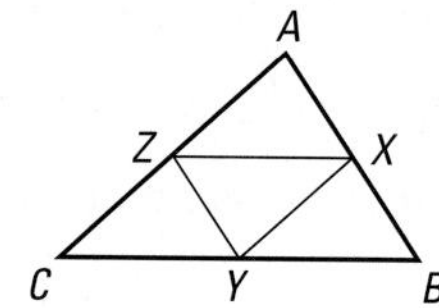

16. $\overline{CB} \parallel$ __?__. $\overline{ZX}$

17. $\overline{XY} \parallel$ __?__. $\overline{AC}$

18. If $AB = 8$, then $YZ =$ __?__. 4

19. If $AC = 10$, then $XY =$ __?__. 5

20. If $XZ = 6$, then $BC =$ __?__. 12

21. If $YZ = 4x - 11$ and $AB = 3x + 3$, then $YZ =$ __?__. 9

22. If $AZ = 4x - 5$ and $XY = 2x + 1$, then $AC =$ __?__. 14

Name the shortest and longest sides of the triangle. (Lesson 5.5)

23.

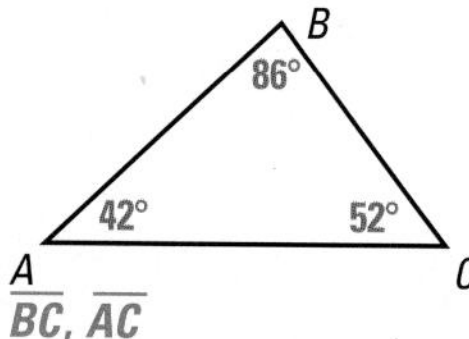

$\overline{BC}$, $\overline{AC}$

24.

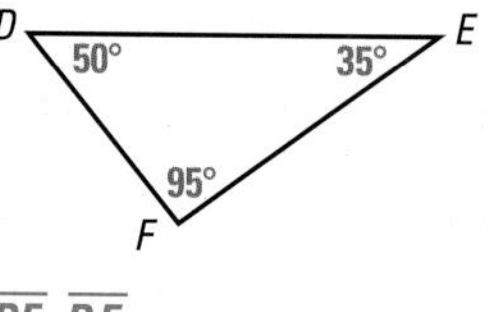

$\overline{DF}$, $\overline{DE}$

25.

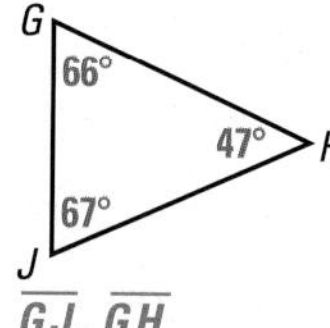

$\overline{GJ}$, $\overline{GH}$

Name the smallest and largest angles of the triangle. (Lesson 5.5)

26.

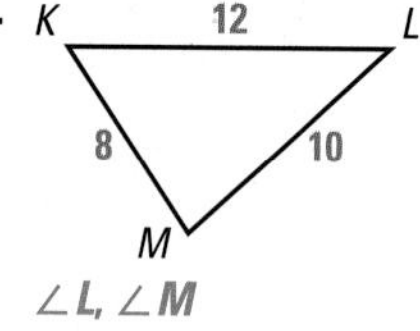

$\angle L$, $\angle M$

27.

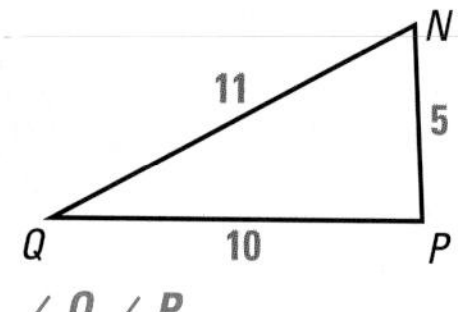

$\angle Q$, $\angle P$

28.

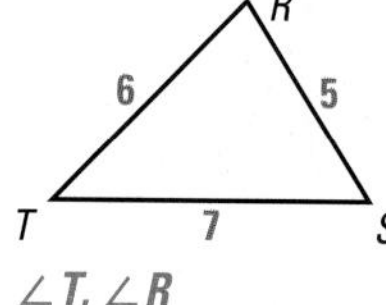

$\angle T$, $\angle R$

Complete with $>$, $<$, or $=$. (Lesson 5.6)

29. $AC \ \underline{?}\ DF$ $\quad <$

30. $QS \ \underline{?}\ TU$ $\quad <$

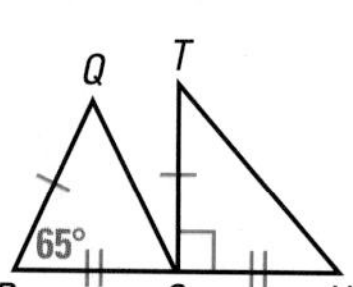

31. $m\angle 1 \ \underline{?}\ m\angle 2$ $\quad =$

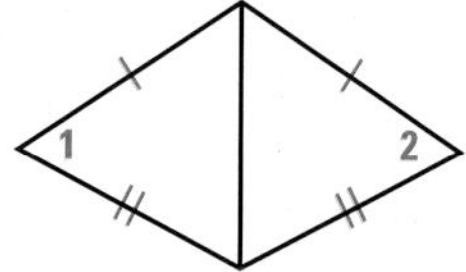

32. $MN \ \underline{?}\ PR$ $\quad >$

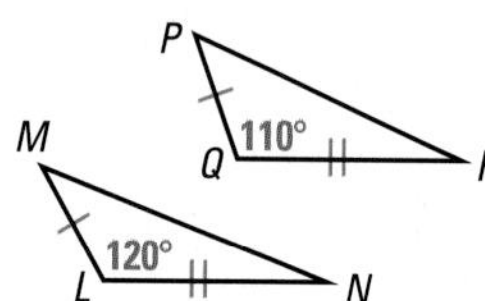

33. $m\angle 1 \ \underline{?}\ m\angle 2$ $\quad =$

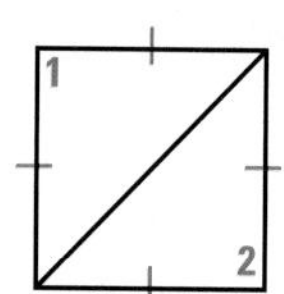

34. $m\angle 1 \ \underline{?}\ m\angle 2$ $\quad >$

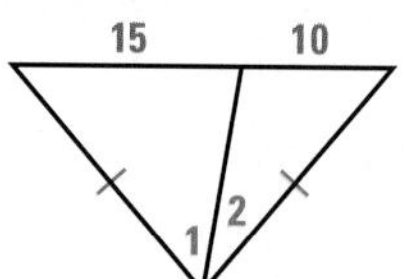

35. $JK \ \underline{?}\ ST$ $\quad =$

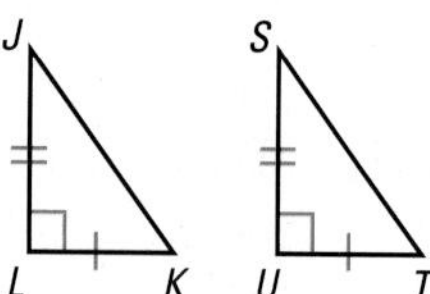

36. $XY \ \underline{?}\ WV$ $\quad <$

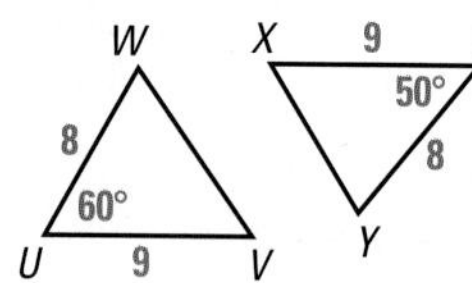

37. $m\angle 1 \ \underline{?}\ m\angle 2$ $\quad <$

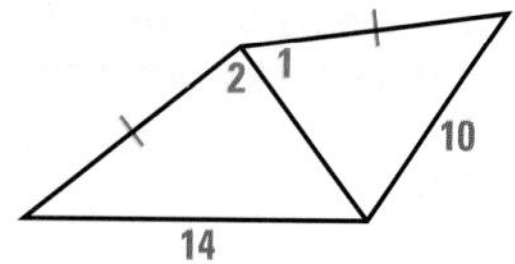

CHAPTER 6

Decide whether the figure is a polygon. If it is, use the number of sides to tell what kind of polygon the shape is. Then state whether the polygon is *convex* or *concave*. (Lesson 6.1)

1.  no

2. 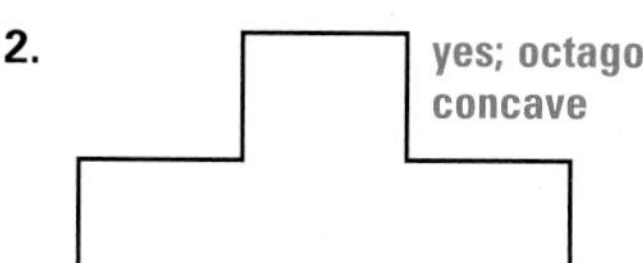 yes; octagon; concave

3. 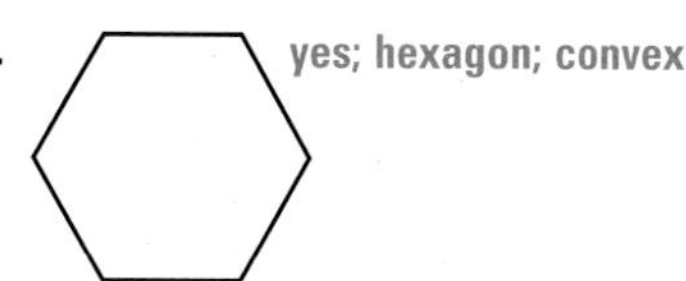 yes; hexagon; convex

4. 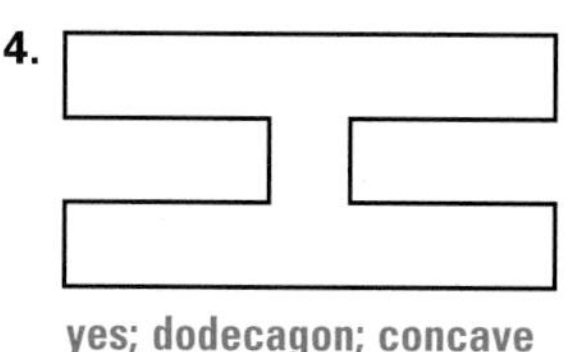
yes; dodecagon; concave

5. 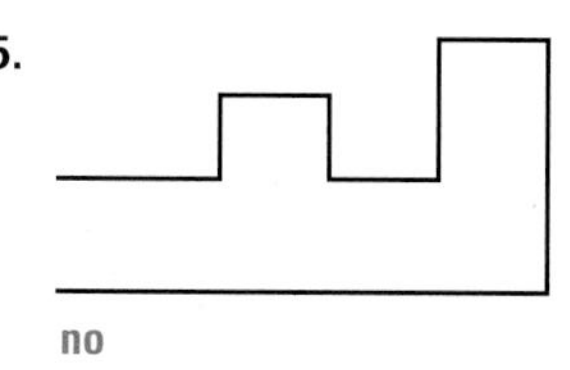
no

6. 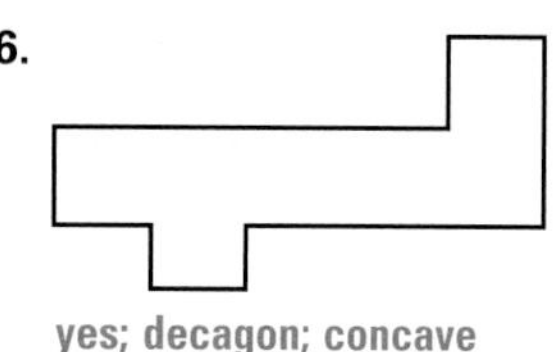
yes; decagon; concave

Use the information in the diagram to solve for x. (Lesson 6.1)

7. 25 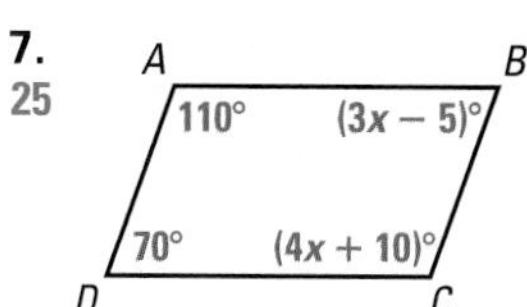

8. 14 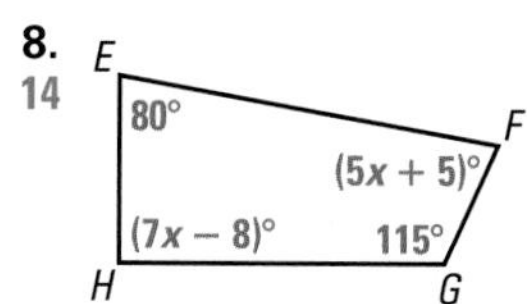

9. 13 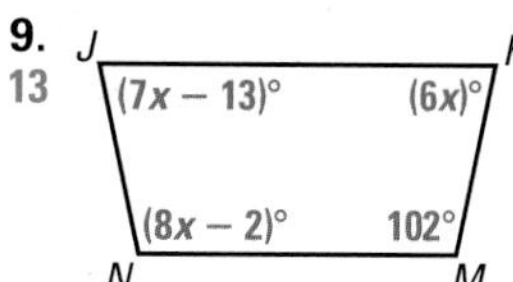

Use the diagram of parallelogram $VWXY$ at the right. Complete each statement, and give a reason for your answer. (Lesson 6.2) 10–17. See margin.

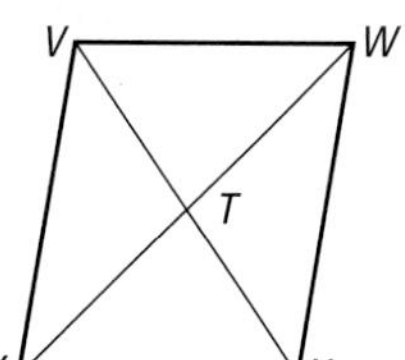

10. $\overline{VW} \cong$ ___?___

11. $\angle VWX \cong$ ___?___

12. $\overline{XW} \cong$ ___?___

13. $\overline{VT} \cong$ ___?___

14. $\angle XYW \cong$ ___?___

15. $\overline{WX} \parallel$ ___?___

16. $\angle VYX$ is supplementary to ___?___ and ___?___.

17. Point T is the midpoint of ___?___ and ___?___.

Are you given enough information to determine whether the quadrilateral is a parallelogram? Explain. (Lesson 6.3)

18. 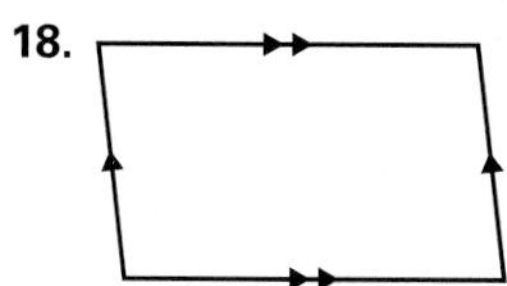
yes; opposite sides are parallel.

19. 
yes; opposite angles are congruent.

20. 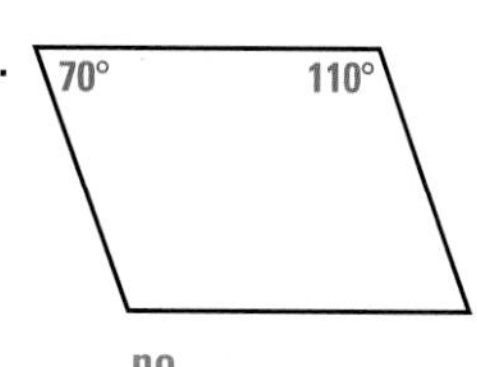

no

Prove that the points represent the vertices of a parallelogram. (Lesson 6.3) 21–24. See margin.

21. $A(2, 4), B(4, -3), C(9, -6), D(7, 1)$

22. $E(-7, -1), F(-1, -2), G(-4, -9), H(-10, -8)$

23. $R(-5, 5), S(6, 4), T(2, -5), U(-9, -4)$

24. $M(-7, -3), N(6, 10), P(8, 4), Q(-5, -9)$

10. $\overline{YX}$; If a quadrilateral is a parallelogram, then its opposite sides are congruent.
11. $\angle VYX$; If a quadrilateral is a parallelogram, then its opposite angles are congruent.
12. $\overline{VY}$; If a quadrilateral is a parallelogram, then its opposite sides are congruent.
13. $\overline{TX}$; If a quadrilateral is a parallelogram, then its diagonals bisect each other.
14. $\angle YWV$; If two ∥ lines are cut by a transversal, then alt. int. ∠s are ≅.
15. $\overline{VY}$; If a quadrilateral is a parallelogram, then its opposite sides are parallel.
16. $\angle YVW$ and $\angle YXW$; If a quadrilateral is a parallelogram, then its consecutive angles are supplementary.
17. $\overline{VX}$, and $\overline{YW}$; If a quadrilateral is a parallelogram, then its diagonals bisect each other.
21. *Sample answer:* The slope of $\overline{AD}$ = slope of $\overline{BC} = -\frac{3}{5}$ and the slope of $\overline{AB}$ = slope of $\overline{DC} = -\frac{7}{2}$. If opposite sides of a quadrilateral are parallel, then it is a parallelogram.
22. *Sample answer:* Because $EF = HG = \sqrt{37}$, then $\overline{EF} \cong \overline{HG}$ by definition of congruence. Similarly, $EH = FG = \sqrt{58}$, and $\overline{EH} \cong \overline{FG}$. If both pairs of opposite sides of a quadrilateral are congruent, then the quadrilateral is a parallelogram.
23. *Sample answer:* The slope of $\overline{RS}$ = slope of $\overline{UT} = -\frac{1}{11}$. Since $RS = UT = \sqrt{122}$, $\overline{RS} \cong \overline{UT}$ by definition of congruence. If one pair of opposite sides of a quadrilateral are congruent and parallel, then the quadrilateral is a parallelogram.
24. *Sample answer:* The slope of $\overline{MQ}$ = slope of $\overline{NP} = -3$. Since $MQ = NP = 2\sqrt{10}$, $\overline{MQ} \cong \overline{NP}$ by definition of congruence. If one pair of opposite sides of a quadrilateral are congruent and parallel, then the quadrilateral is a parallelogram.

List each quadrilateral for which the statement is true. (Lesson 6.4)

25. Adjacent angles are supplementary. parallelogram, rhombus, rectangle, square

26. Adjacent angles are congruent. rectangle, square

27. Adjacent sides are perpendicular. rectangle, square

28. Diagonals are congruent. rectangle, square

29. Adjacent sides are congruent. rhombus, square

30. Opposite sides are parallel. parallelogram, rhombus, rectangle, square

It is given that *PQRS* is a parallelogram. Graph ▱*PQRS*. Decide whether it is a *rectangle*, a *rhombus*, a *square*, or *none of the above*. Justify your answer using theorems about quadrilaterals. (Lesson 6.4)

31. $P(6, 7), Q(-2, 1), R(6, -5), S(14, 1)$ rhombus

32. $P(-6, 5), Q(4, 11), R(7, 7), S(-3, 1)$ none of the above

33. $P(-2, 7), Q(4, 7), R(4, 1), S(-2, 1)$ square

34. $P(-7, -2), Q(-2, -2), R(-2, -7), S(-7, -7)$ square

Find the missing angle measures. (Lesson 6.5)

35.

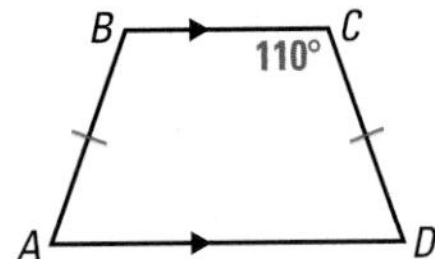

$m\angle A = 70°$; $m\angle B = 110°$; $m\angle D = 70°$

36.

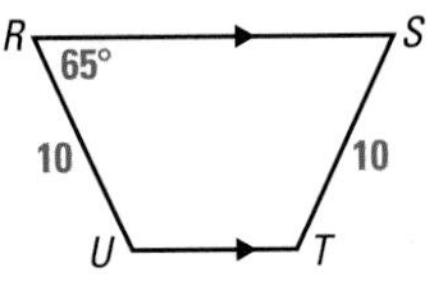

$m\angle S = 65°$; $m\angle T = 115°$; $m\angle U = 115°$

37.

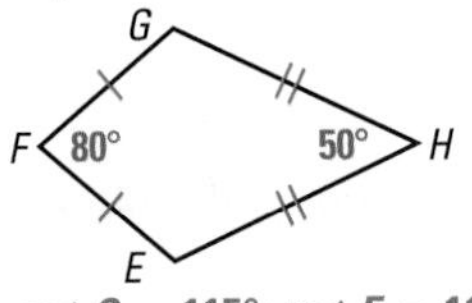

$m\angle G = 115°$; $m\angle E = 115°$

Find the value of *x*. (Lesson 6.5)

38. 22

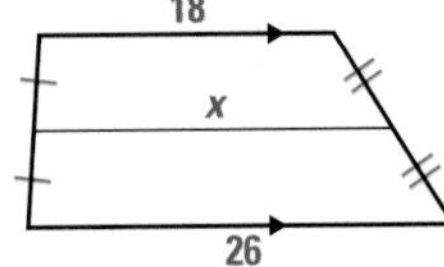

39. 23

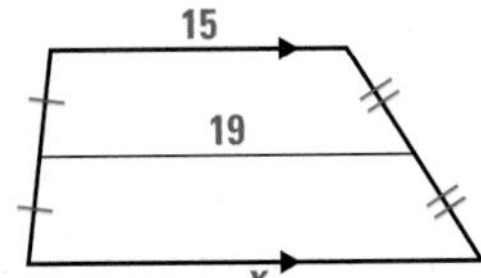

40. 8

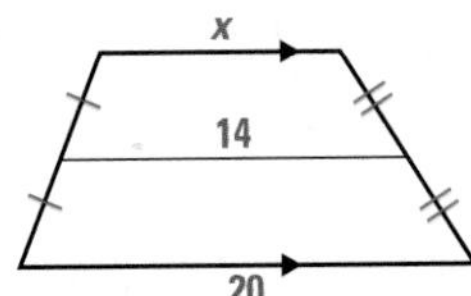

What are the lengths of the sides of the kite? (Lesson 6.5)

41.

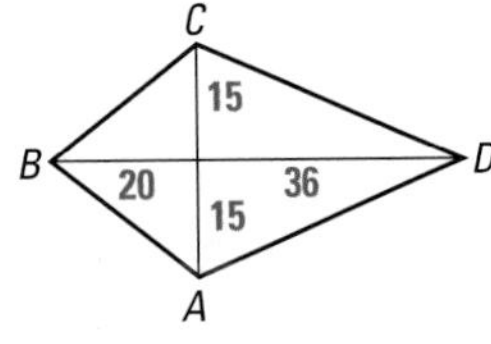

$AB = 25$, $BC = 25$, $AD = 39$, $CD = 39$

42.

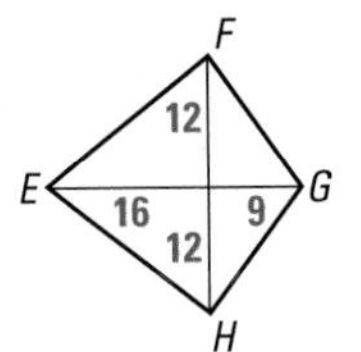

$EF = 20$, $EH = 20$, $FG = 15$, $HG = 15$

43.

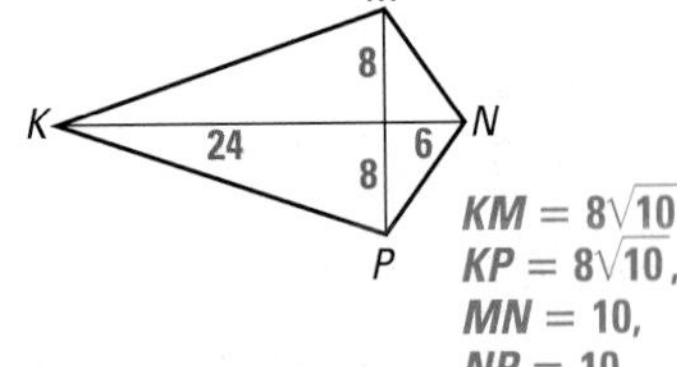

$KM = 8\sqrt{10}$, $KP = 8\sqrt{10}$, $MN = 10$, $NP = 10$

What kind of quadrilateral could *EFGH* be? *EFGH* is not drawn to scale. (Lesson 6.6)

44.

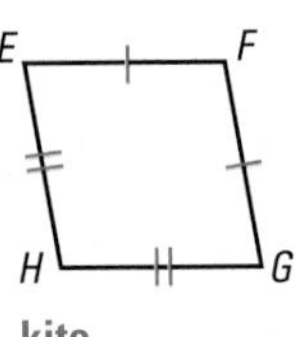

kite

45.

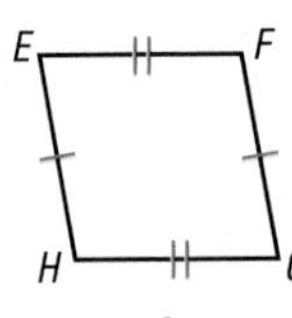

rectangle or parallelogram

46.

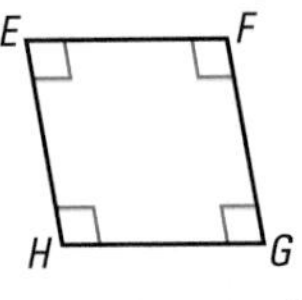

square or a rectangle

Find the area of the polygon. (Lesson 6.7)

47. 160

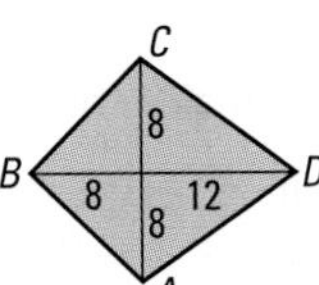

48. 25

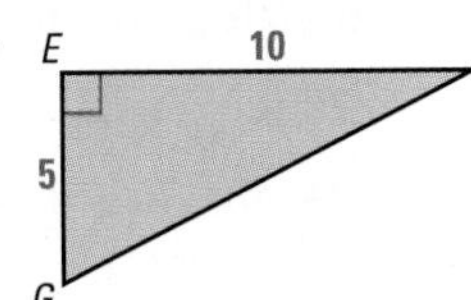

49. 55

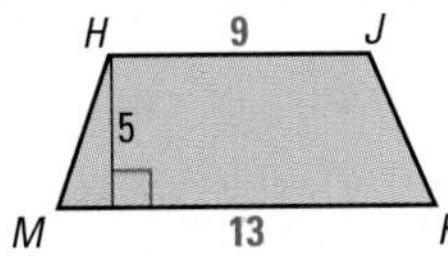

CHAPTER 7

Use the graph of the transformation below. **(Lesson 7.1)**

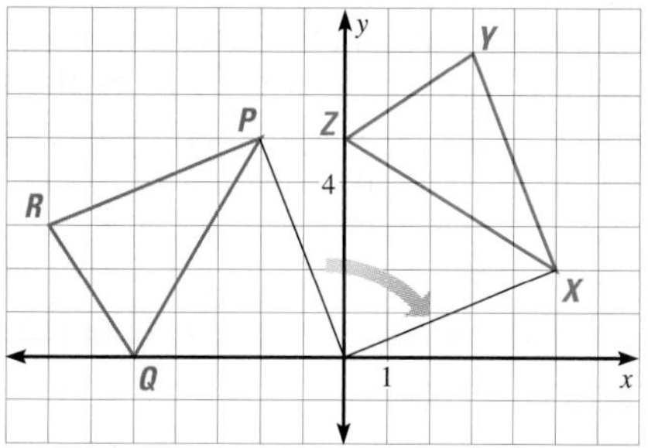

1. Name the image of Q. Z
2. Name and describe the transformation. 90° clockwise rotation about the origin
3. Name two sides with the same length. *Sample answers*: $\overline{QR} \cong \overline{ZY}$; $\overline{RP} \cong \overline{YX}$; $\overline{PQ} \cong \overline{XZ}$
4. Name two angles with the same measure. *Sample answers*: $\angle R \cong \angle Y$; $\angle P \cong \angle X$; $\angle Q \cong \angle Z$
5. Name the coordinates of the preimage of point Y. $(-7, 3)$
6. Show two corresponding sides have the same length, using the Distance Formula. See margin.

Name and describe the transformation. Then name the coordinates of the vertices of the image. **(Lesson 7.1)**

7. translation; slide 8 units to the right; $E(3, 1)$, $F(3, 3)$, $G(6, 3)$, $H(6, 1)$

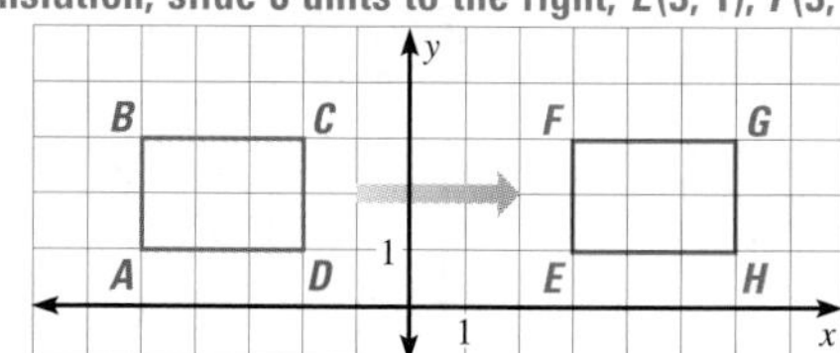

8.

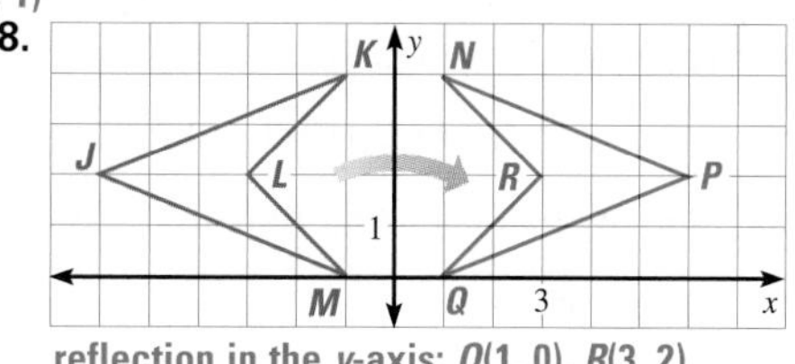

reflection in the y-axis; $Q(1, 0)$, $R(3, 2)$, $N(1, 4)$, $P(6, 2)$

Use the diagrams to complete the statement. **(Lesson 7.1)**

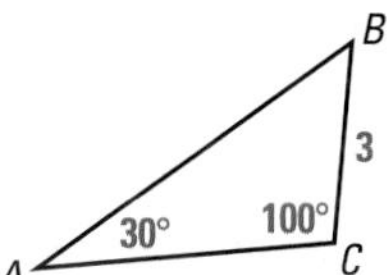

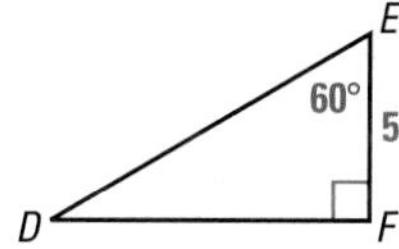

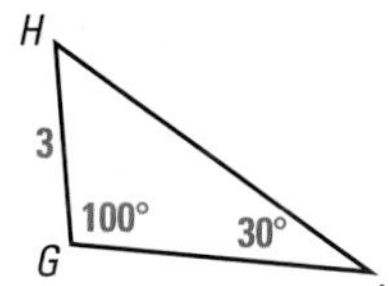

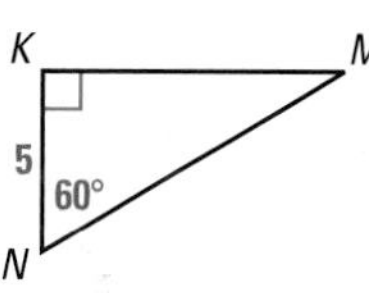

9. $\triangle CBA \rightarrow$ __?__ $\triangle GHJ$
10. $\triangle DEF \rightarrow$ __?__ $\triangle MNK$
11. __?__ $\rightarrow \triangle KNM$ $\triangle FED$

Use the diagram at the right to name the image of $\triangle ABC$ after the reflection. If the reflection does not appear in the diagram, write *not shown*. **(Lesson 7.2)**

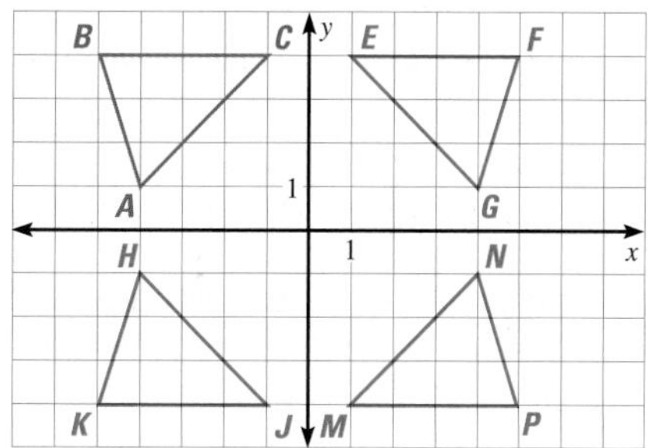

12. Reflection in the x-axis $\triangle HKJ$
13. Reflection in the y-axis $\triangle GFE$
14. Reflection in the line $y = x$ not shown
15. Reflection in the x-axis, followed by a reflection in the y-axis $\triangle NPM$

Find the coordinates of the reflection without using a coordinate plane. Then check your answer by plotting the image and preimage on a coordinate plane. **(Lesson 7.2)**

16. $M(5, 2)$ reflected in the x-axis $(5, -2)$
17. $N(-2, 4)$ reflected in the y-axis $(2, 4)$
18. $P(1, -8)$ reflected in the y-axis $(-1, -8)$
19. $Q(1, 12)$ reflected in the x-axis $(1, -12)$

6. *Sample Answers:*

$RQ = \sqrt{(-7-(-5))^2 + (3-0)^2} = \sqrt{13}$,
$YZ = \sqrt{(3-0)^2 + (7-5)^2} = \sqrt{13}$;
$RP = \sqrt{(-7-(-2))^2 + (3-5)^2} = \sqrt{29}$,
$YX = \sqrt{(3-5)^2 + (7-2)^2} = \sqrt{29}$;
$PQ = \sqrt{(-2-(-5))^2 + (5-0)^2} = \sqrt{34}$,
$XZ = \sqrt{(5-0)^2 + (2-5)^2} = \sqrt{34}$

35.

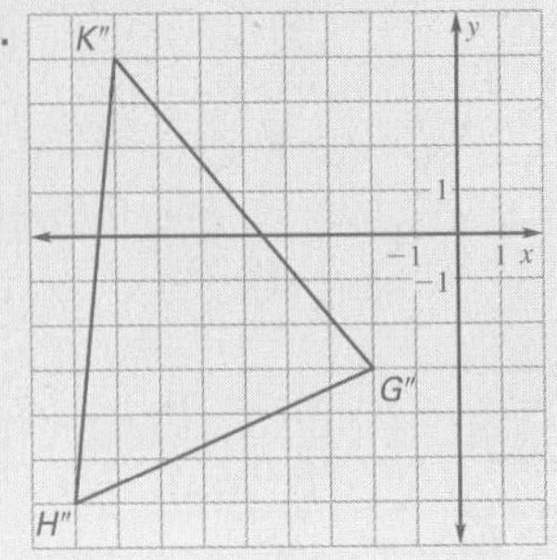

36.

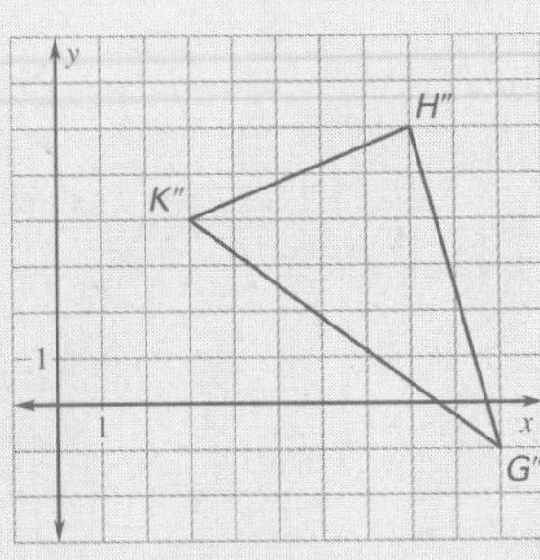

Find point *C* on the *x*-axis so *AC* + *BC* is a minimum. (Lesson 7.2)

20. $A(1, 2), B(12, 5)$ (4, 0)

21. $A(3, 7), B(11, 7)$ (7, 0)

22. $A(-2, 7), B(-9, 5)$ (−6, 0)

Name the coordinates of the vertices of the image after a clockwise rotation of the given number of degrees about the origin. (Lesson 7.3)

23. 90° *H′*(2, 0), *E′*(5, −2), *F′*(5, −5), *G′*(2, −7)

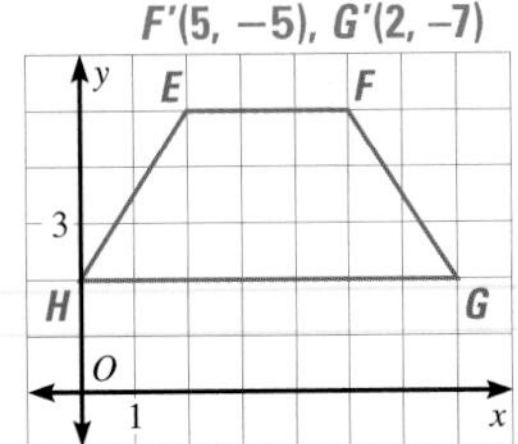

24. 270° *A′*(2, −2), *B′*(−1, −2), *C′*(2, 3)

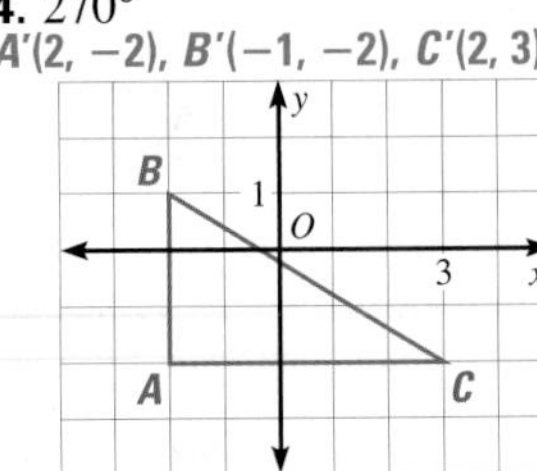

25. 180° *J′*(4, −4), *K′*(1, −2), *M′*(4, 0), *N′*(7, −2)

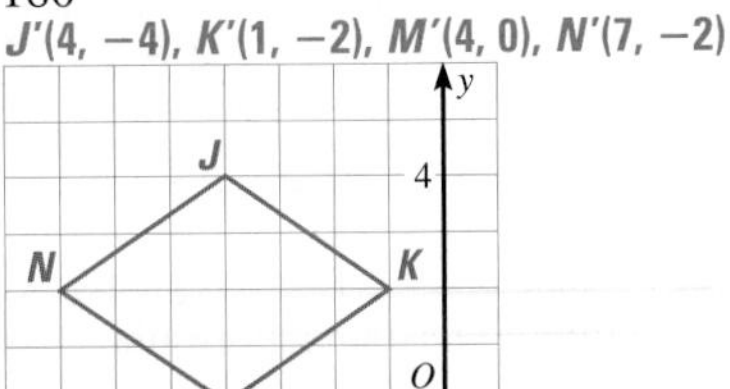

In the diagram, *a* ∥ *b*, △*JKM* is reflected in line *a* and △*J′K′M′* is reflected in line *b*. (Lesson 7.4)

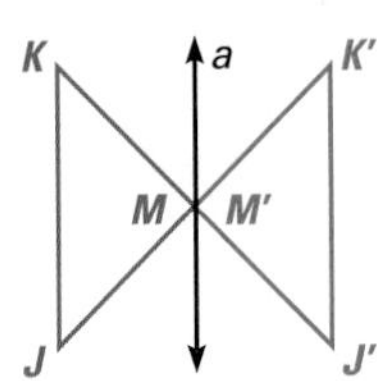

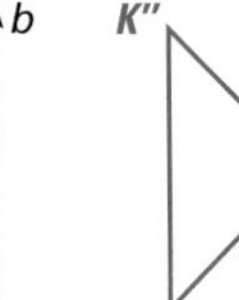

26. A translation of △*JKM* maps onto which triangle? △*J″K″M″*

27. Which lines are perpendicular to $\overleftrightarrow{KK''}$? *a*, *b*

28. Name two segments parallel to $\overleftrightarrow{MM''}$. $\overline{KK''}$, $\overline{JJ''}$

Copy figure *RSTV* and draw its image after the translation. Then describe the translation using a vector in component form. (Lesson 7.4) Check sketches.

29. $(x, y) \rightarrow (x - 3, y + 5)$ ⟨−3, 5⟩

30. $(x, y) \rightarrow (x + 1, y - 4)$ ⟨1, −4⟩

31. $(x, y) \rightarrow (x - 7, y + 7)$ ⟨−7, 7⟩

32. $(x, y) \rightarrow (x + 2, y - 6)$ ⟨2, −6⟩

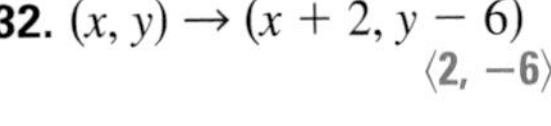

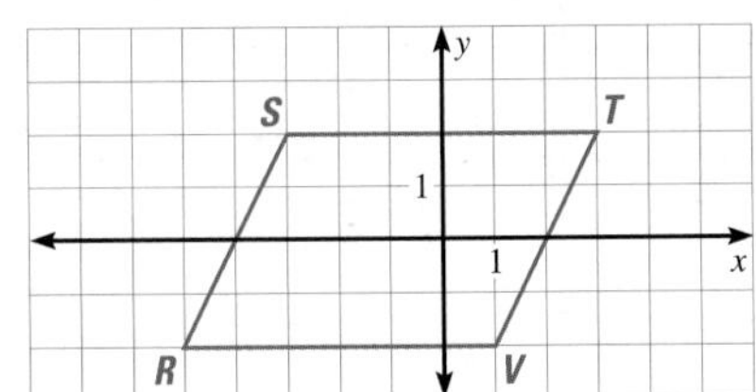

Sketch the image of *A*(−6, −2) after the described glide reflection. (Lesson 7.5)

33. Translation: $(x, y) \rightarrow (x + 1, y + 3)$
Reflection: in the x-axis (−5, −1)

34. Translation: $(x, y) \rightarrow (x + 4, y - 3)$
Reflection: in $x = -4$ (−6, −5)

Sketch the image of △*GHK* after a composition using the given transformations in the order they appear. (Lesson 7.5) 35, 36. See margin.

35. $G(5, 3), H(-2, 6), K(-1, -4)$
Translation: $(x, y) \rightarrow (x - 7, y)$
Reflection: in the x-axis

36. $G(2, 1), H(0, -6), K(-5, -4)$
Translation: $(x, y) \rightarrow (x + 8, y)$
Reflection: in the x-axis

Describe each frieze pattern according to the following seven categories: T, TR, TG, TV, THG, TRVG, and TRHVG. (Lesson 7.6)

37. TR

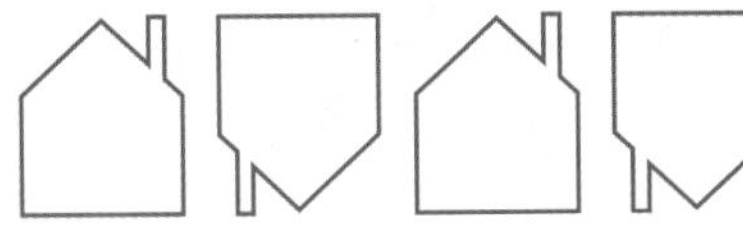

38. THG

CHAPTER 8

Rewrite the fraction so that the numerator and denominator have the same units. Then simplify. (Lesson 8.1)

1. $\frac{5 \text{ m}}{250 \text{ cm}}$ $\frac{2}{1}$ **2.** $\frac{15 \text{ ft}}{4 \text{ yd}}$ $\frac{5}{4}$ **3.** $\frac{15 \text{ in.}}{2 \text{ ft}}$ $\frac{5}{8}$ **4.** $\frac{10 \text{ km}}{900 \text{ m}}$ $\frac{100}{9}$

Use ratios to solve the following problems. (Lesson 8.1)

5. The measures of the angles in a quadrilateral are in the extended ratio of 3:4:5:6. Find the measures of the angles. 60°, 80°, 100°, 120°

6. The perimeter of isosceles triangle *ABC* is 35 cm. The extended ratio of *AB*:*BC*:*AC* is *x*:3*x*:3*x*. Find the lengths of the three sides. 5, 15, 15

Solve the proportion. (Lesson 8.1)

7. $\frac{a}{21} = \frac{1}{3}$ 7 **8.** $\frac{-5}{b} = \frac{20}{8}$ −2 **9.** $\frac{-2}{6} = \frac{c}{-9}$ 3

10. $\frac{7}{d+5} = \frac{28}{8}$ −3 **11.** $\frac{2}{-9} = \frac{f-3}{9}$ 1 **12.** $\frac{11}{1} = \frac{g+6}{g-4}$ 5

Complete the sentence. (Lesson 8.2)

13. If $\frac{x}{10} = \frac{30}{y}$, then $\frac{x}{30} = \frac{?}{?}$. $\frac{10}{y}$ **14.** If $\frac{9}{4} = \frac{x}{y}$, then $\frac{13}{4} = \frac{?}{?}$. $\frac{x+y}{y}$

15. If $\frac{9}{x} = \frac{12}{y}$, then $\frac{3}{4} = \frac{?}{?}$. $\frac{x}{y}$ **16.** If $\frac{z}{12} = \frac{y}{8}$, then $\frac{z+12}{12} = \frac{?}{?}$. $\frac{y+8}{8}$

Find the geometric mean of the two numbers. (Lesson 8.2)

17. 4 and 9 6 **18.** 1 and 4 2 **19.** 2.5 and 10 5

20. 9 and 16 12 **21.** 256 and 4 32 **22.** 100 and 10,000 1000

Use the diagram and the given information to find the unknown length. (Lesson 8.2)

23. GIVEN ▶ $\frac{PS}{SR} = \frac{PT}{TQ}$, find *SR*. 6.25 **24.** GIVEN ▶ $\frac{CE}{EG} = \frac{DF}{FH}$, find *CE*. 7.5

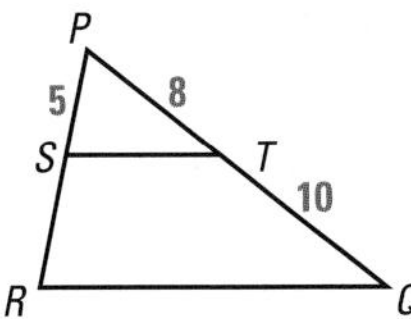

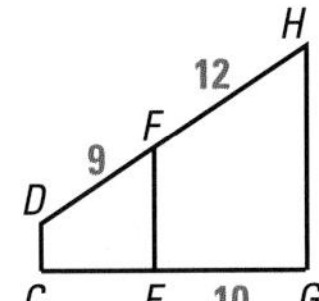

In the diagram, *PQRS* ~ *TVWX*. (Lesson 8.3)

25. Find the scale factor of *PQRS* to *TVWX*. 3:2

26. Find the scale factor of *TVWX* to *PQRS*. 2:3

27. Find the values of *u*, *y*, and *z*. $u = 9$, $y = 4$, $z = 10$

28. Find the perimeter of each polygon. *PQRS* = 39, *TVWX* = 26

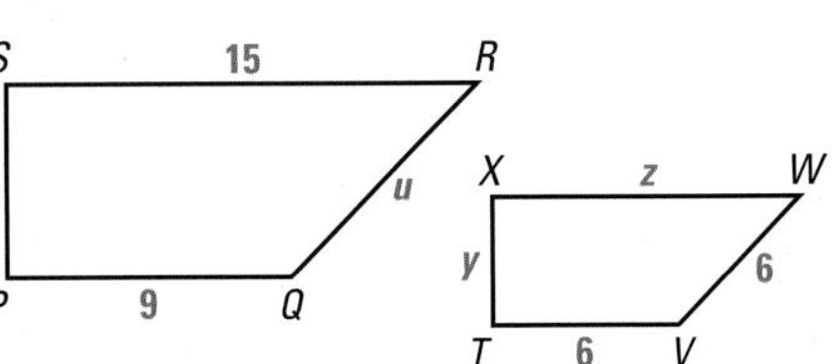

817

Determine whether the triangles can be proved similar. If they are similar, write a similarity statement. If they are not similar, explain why. (Lesson 8.4)

29.

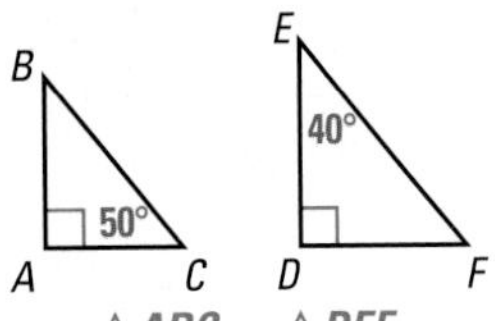

yes; $\triangle ABC \sim \triangle DEF$

30.

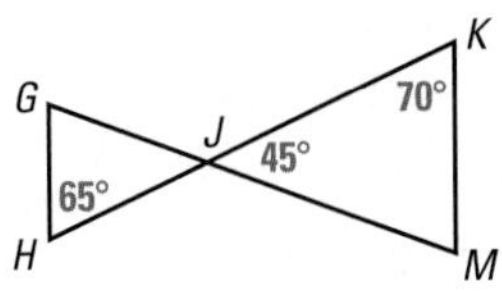

yes; $\triangle GHJ \sim \triangle KMJ$

31.

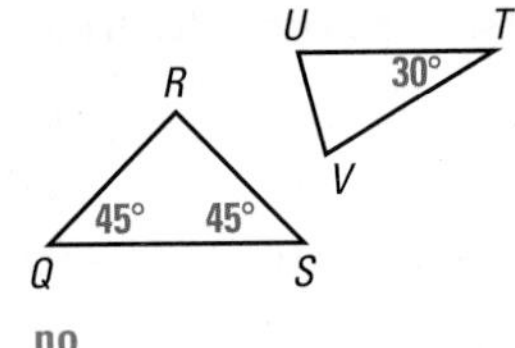

no

Find coordinates for point *Z* so that $\triangle OWX \sim \triangle OYZ$. (Lesson 8.4)

32. $O(0, 0)$, $W(4, 0)$, $X(0, 3)$, $Y(12, 0)$ (0, 9)

33. $O(0, 0)$, $W(2, 0)$, $X(0, 5)$, $Y(5, 0)$ (0, 12.5)

34. $O(0, 0)$, $W(-4, 0)$, $X(0, 2)$, $Y(-6, 0)$ (0, 3)

35. $O(0, 0)$, $W(-1, 0)$, $X(0, -4)$, $Y(-3, 0)$ (0, −12)

Are the triangles similar? If so, state the similarity and the postulate or theorem that justifies your answer. (Lesson 8.5)

36.

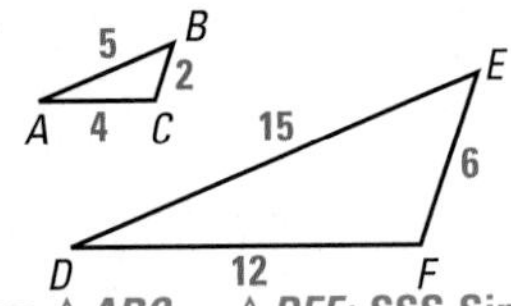

yes; $\triangle ABC \sim \triangle DEF$; SSS Sim. Thm.

37.

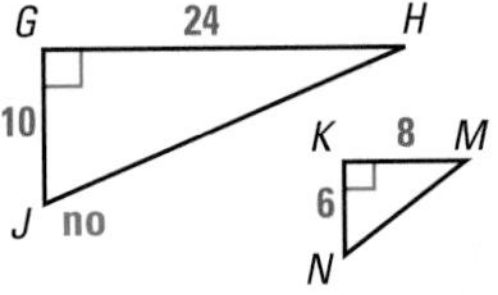

no

38.

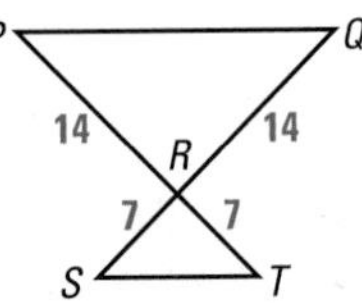

yes; $\triangle PQR \sim \triangle STR$; SAS Similarity Theorem

Determine whether the triangles are similar. If they are, write a similarity statement and solve for the variable. (Lesson 8.5)

39. yes; $\triangle ACE \sim \triangle BCD$; 12

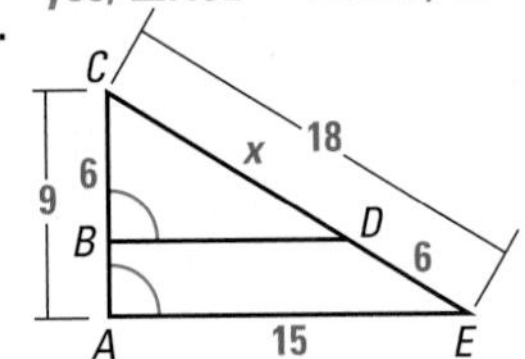

40. yes; $\triangle MNR \sim \triangle MPQ$; 15

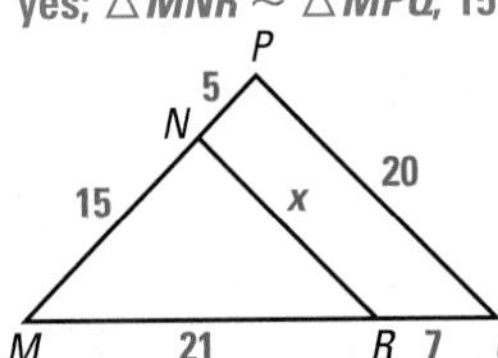

41. yes; $\triangle EFG \sim \triangle HJK$; 8

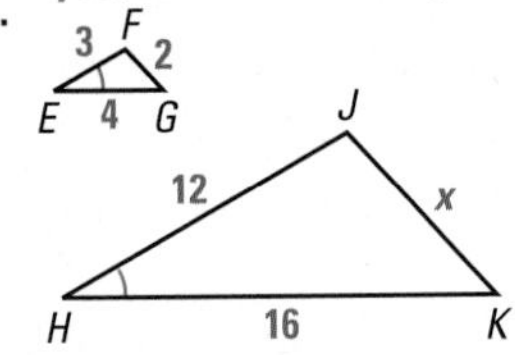

Determine whether the given information implies that $\overline{QS} \parallel \overline{PT}$. Explain. (Lesson 8.6)

42. no; $\frac{7}{18} \neq \frac{8}{20}$

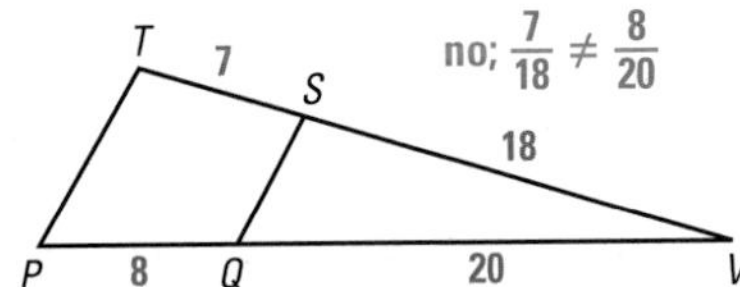

43. yes; $\frac{4}{8} = \frac{1}{2}$

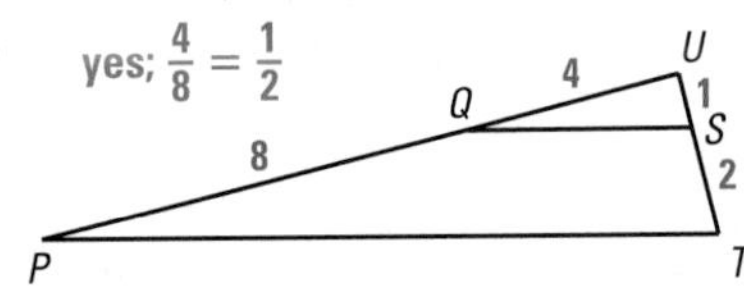

Find the value of the variable. (Lesson 8.6)

44. 8

A 4 C 3 B

x 6

D

45. 20

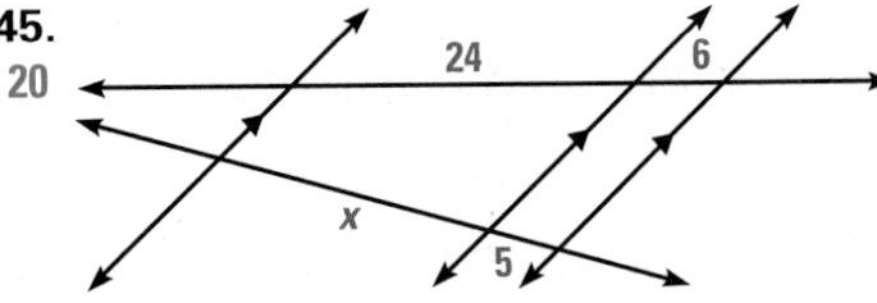

Use the origin as the center of the dilation and the given scale factor to find the coordinates of the vertices of the image of the polygon. (Lesson 8.7)

46. $A(-2, 3)$, $B(-1, 5)$, $C(3, 3)$, $D(2, -4)$, $k = 2$
A′(−4, 6), B′(−2, 10), C′(6, 6), D′(4, −8)

47. $A(2, 0)$, $B(5, 3)$, $C(4, 5)$, $D(1, 3)$, $k = 5$
A′(10, 0), B′(25, 15), C′(20, 25), D′(5, 15)

48. $A(3, -6)$, $B(6, -6)$, $C(6, 9)$, $D(-3, 9)$, $k = \frac{1}{3}$
A′(1, −2), B′(2, −2), C′(2, 3), D′(−1, 3)

49. $A(4, -4)$, $B(6, 4)$, $C(2, 8)$, $D(-8, -4)$, $k = \frac{1}{4}$
A′(1, −1), B′(1.5, 1), C′(0.5, 2), D′(−2, −1)

CHAPTER 9

Write similarity statements for the three similar triangles in the diagram. Then complete the proportion. (Lesson 9.1)

1. $\frac{AD}{AC} = \frac{?}{AB}$

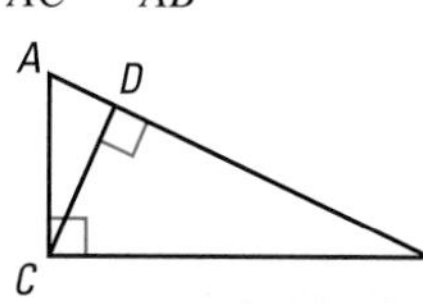

$\triangle ABC \sim \triangle ACD \sim \triangle CBD$; AC

2. $\frac{?}{EH} = \frac{EH}{GH}$

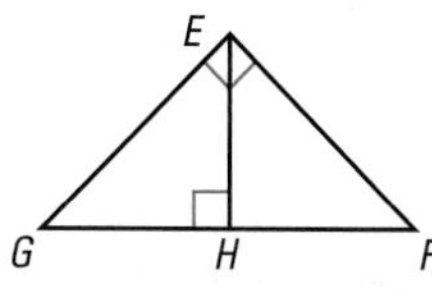

$\triangle GFE \sim \triangle GEH \sim \triangle EFH$; FH

3. $\frac{JM}{KJ} = \frac{KJ}{?}$

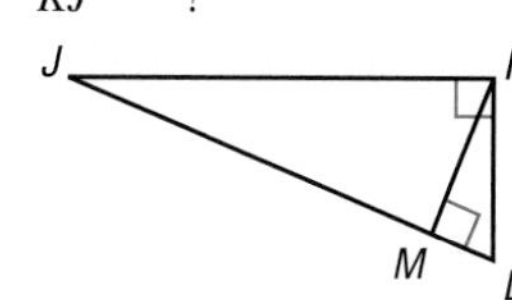

$\triangle JLK \sim \triangle JKM \sim \triangle KLM$; JL

Find the value of the variable. (Lesson 9.1)

4. 27

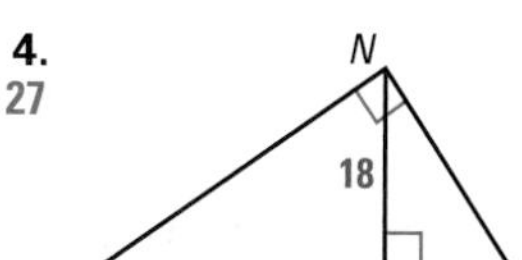

5. 10

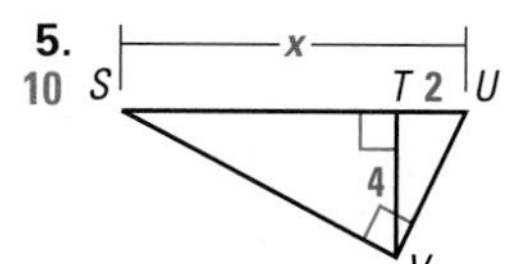

6. 40

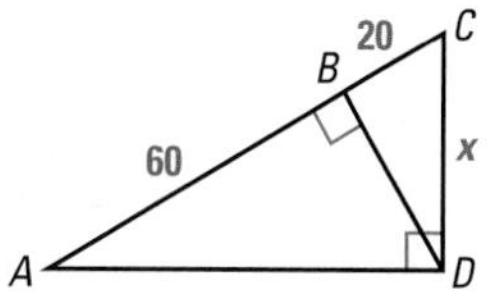

20 C B x 60 A D

Find the unknown side length. Simplify answers that are radicals. Tell whether the side lengths form a Pythagorean triple. (Lesson 9.2)

7. $\sqrt{61}$; no

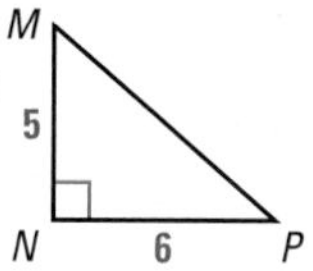

M 5 N 6 P

8. 24; yes

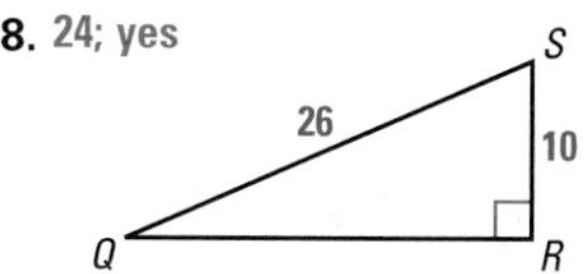

9. 50; yes

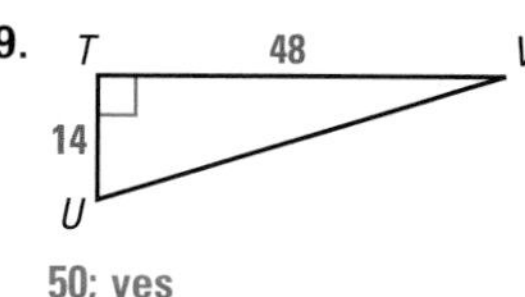

The variables *r* and *s* represent the lengths of the legs of a right triangle, and *t* represents the length of the hypotenuse. The values of *r*, *s*, and *t* form a Pythagorean Triple. Find the unknown value. (Lesson 9.2)

10. $r = 7, t = 25$ 24

11. $r = 5, s = 12$ 13

12. $s = 25, t = 65$ 60

13. $r = 49, s = 168$ 175

14. $s = 198, t = 202$ 40

15. $r = 21, t = 35$ 28

Find the area of the figure. Round decimal answers to the nearest tenth. (Lesson 9.2)

16. 24 cm^2

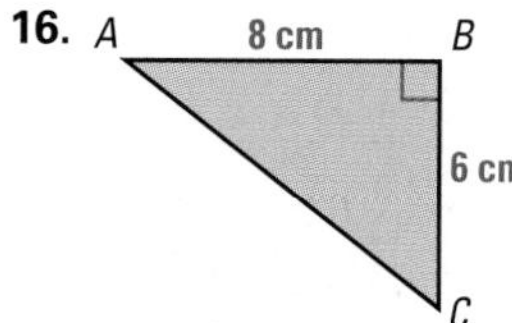

17. about 91.2 cm^2

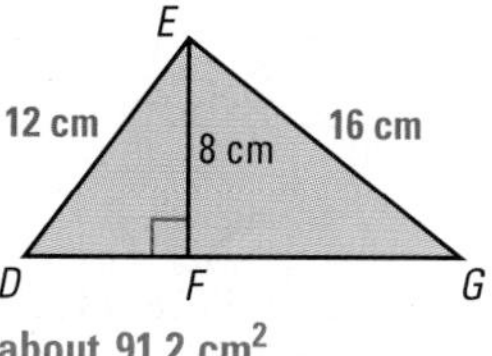

18. about 39.6 cm^2

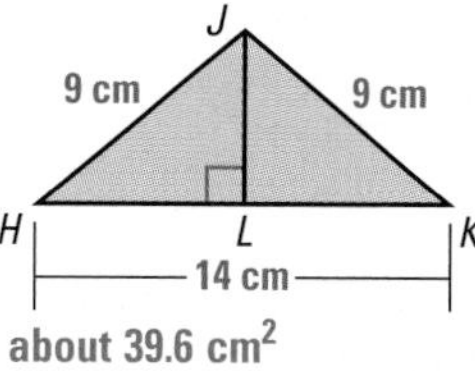

Tell whether the triangle is a right triangle. (Lesson 9.3)

19. yes

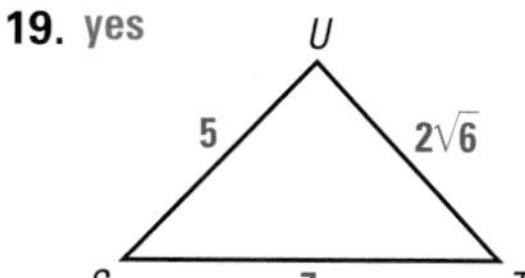

20. no

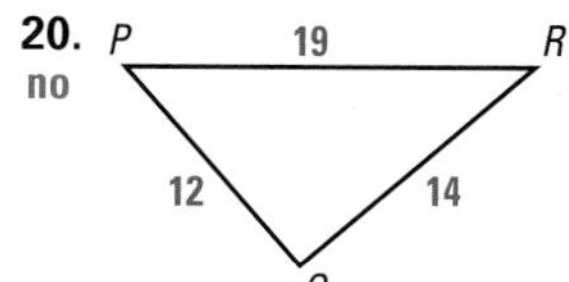

21. yes

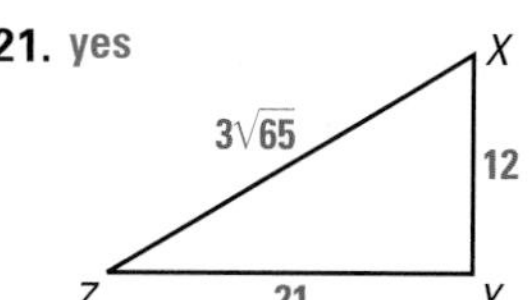

31. sin $S = 0.8615$, cos $S = 0.5077$, tan $S = 1.6970$; sin $T = 0.5077$, cos $T = 0.8615$, tan $T = 0.5893$

32. sin $U = 0.7809$, cos $U = 0.6247$, tan $U = 1.25$; sin $V = 0.6247$, cos $V = 0.7809$, tan $V = 0.8$

33. sin $X = 0.7241$, cos $X = 0.6897$, tan $X = 1.05$; sin $Z = 0.6897$, cos $Z = 0.7241$, tan $Z = 0.9524$

Decide whether the numbers can represent the side lengths of a triangle. If they can, classify the triangle as *right, acute,* or *obtuse*. (Lesson 9.3)

22. 17, 18, 19 yes; acute **23.** 15, 36, 39 yes; right **24.** 3, 5, 8 no

25. 7, 9, 12 yes; obtuse **26.** 100, 300, 500 no **27.** $\sqrt{91}$, 12, 20 yes; obtuse

Find the value of each variable. Write answers in simplest radical form. (Lesson 9.4)

28.

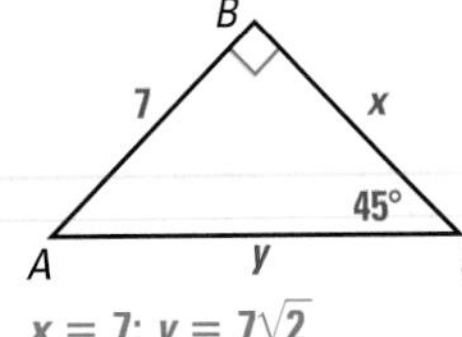

$x = 7$; $y = 7\sqrt{2}$

29.

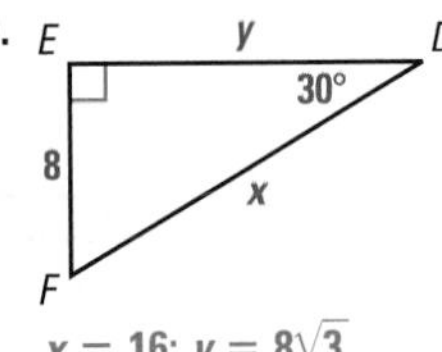

$x = 16$; $y = 8\sqrt{3}$

30.

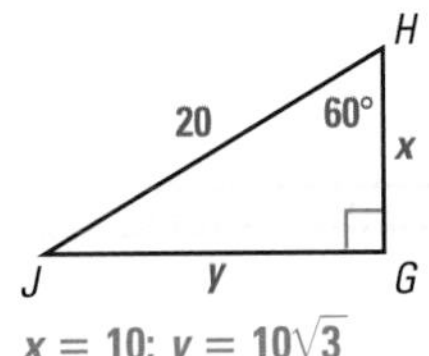

$x = 10$; $y = 10\sqrt{3}$

Find the sine, the cosine, and the tangent of the acute angles of the triangle. Express each value as a decimal rounded to four places. (Lesson 9.5) 31–33. See margin.

31.

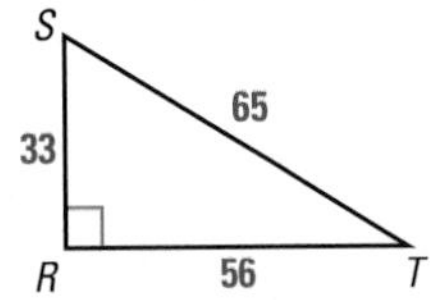

32.

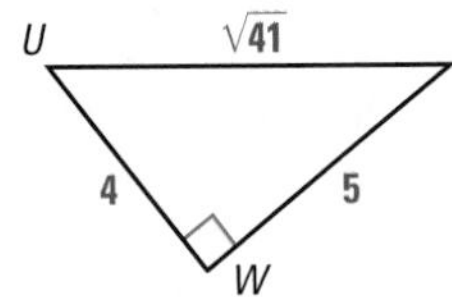

33.

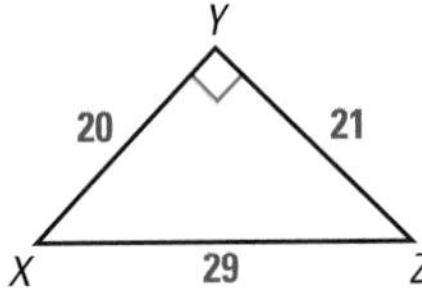

Find the value of each variable. Round decimals to the nearest tenth. (Lesson 9.5)

34.

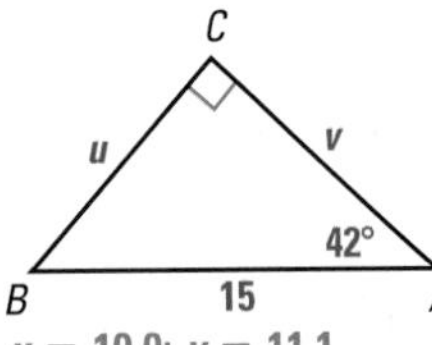

$u = 10.0$; $v = 11.1$

35.

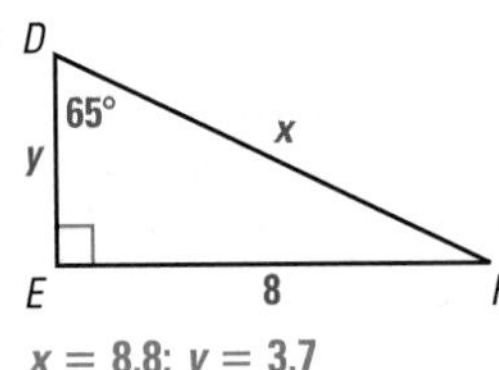

$x = 8.8$; $y = 3.7$

36.

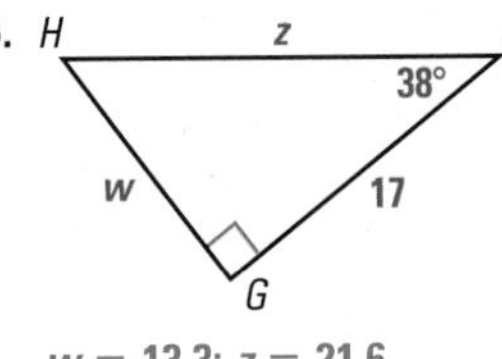

$w = 13.3$; $z = 21.6$

Solve the right triangle. Round decimals to the nearest tenth. (Lesson 9.6)

37.

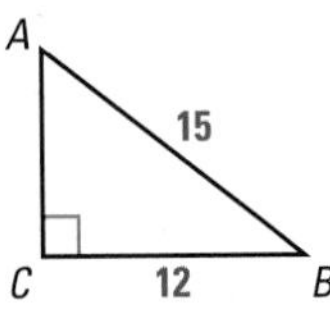

$AC = 9$, $m\angle A = 53.1°$, $m\angle B = 36.9°$

38.

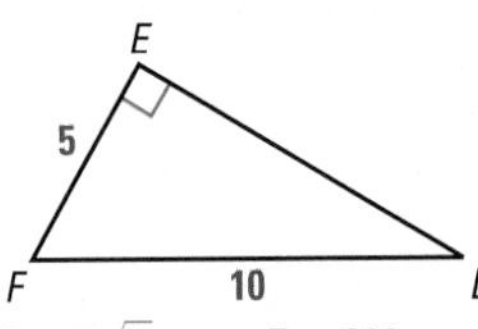

$ED = 5\sqrt{3}$, $m\angle F = 60°$, $m\angle D = 30°$

39.

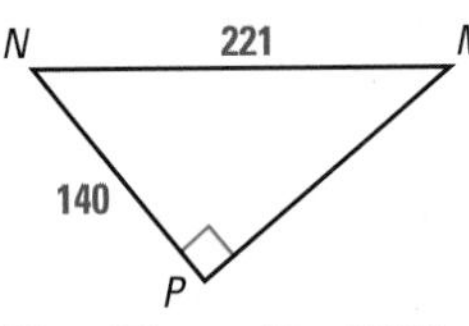

$MP = 171$, $m\angle N = 50.7°$, $m\angle M = 39.3°$

Draw vector $\overrightarrow{PQ}$ in a coordinate plane. Write the component form of the vector and find its magnitude. Round your answer to the nearest tenth. (Lesson 9.7)

40. $P(2, 3)$, $Q(5, 7)$ $\langle 3, 4\rangle$; 5 **41.** $P(-1, -5)$, $Q(3, 6)$ $\langle 4, 11\rangle$; 11.7 **42.** $P(-4, 3)$, $Q(2, -8)$ $\langle 6, -11\rangle$; 12.5

Let $\vec{a} = \langle 3, 5\rangle$, $\vec{b} = \langle -7, 2\rangle$, $\vec{c} = \langle 1, -6\rangle$, and $\vec{d} = \langle 2, 9\rangle$. Find the given sum. (Lesson 9.7)

43. $\vec{a} + \vec{b}$ $\langle -4, 7\rangle$ **44.** $\vec{a} + \vec{c}$ $\langle 4, -1\rangle$ **45.** $\vec{c} + \vec{d}$ $\langle 3, 3\rangle$ **46.** $\vec{b} + \vec{c}$ $\langle -6, -4\rangle$

CHAPTER 10

Match the notation with the term that best describes it. **(Lesson 10.1)**

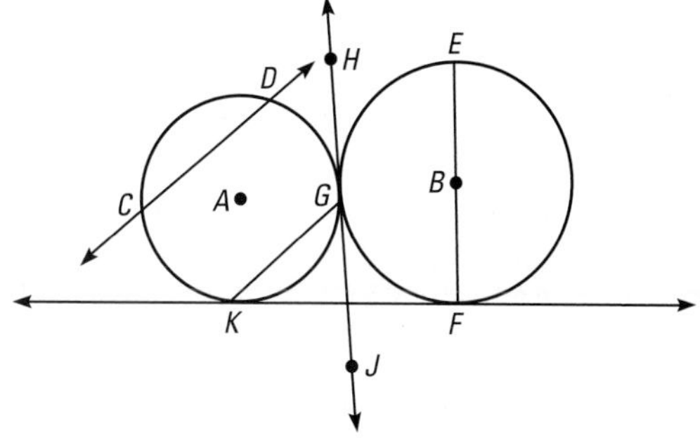

1. $\overline{EF}$ D

2. G E

3. $\overleftrightarrow{HJ}$ G

4. $\overline{BF}$ C

5. A H

6. $\overleftrightarrow{KF}$ F

7. $\overleftrightarrow{CD}$ A

8. $\overline{GK}$ B

A. Secant

B. Chord

C. Radius

D. Diameter

E. Point of tangency

F. Common external tangent

G. Common internal tangent

H. Center

Tell whether the common tangent(s) are *internal* or *external*. **(Lesson 10.1)**

9.

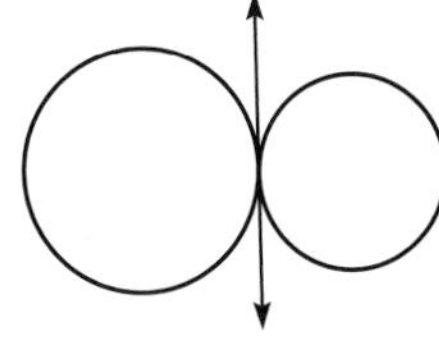

internal

10.

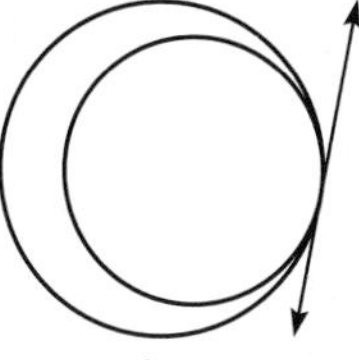

external

11.

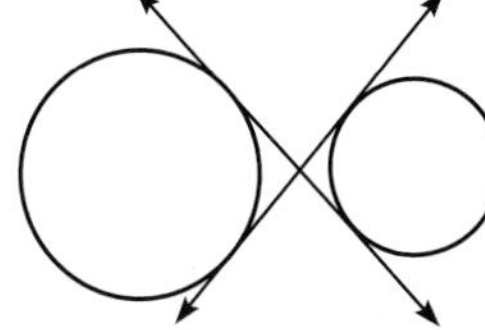

internal

Use the diagram at the right. **(Lesson 10.1)**

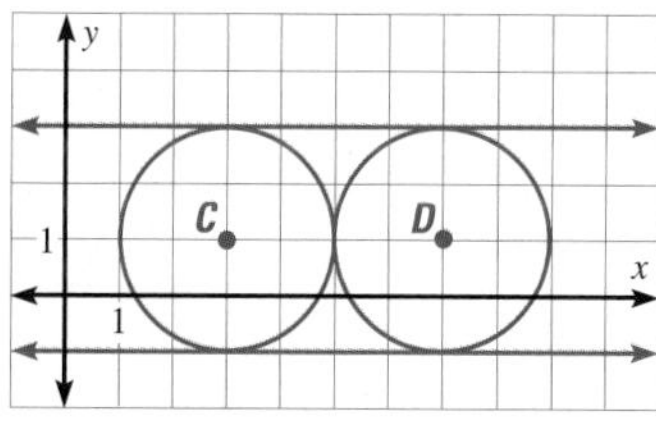

12. What are the center and radius of $\odot C$? *C*; 2

13. What are the center and radius of $\odot D$? *D*; 2

14. Describe the intersection of the two circles. (5, 1)

15. Describe all the common tangents of the two circles.
$y = 3, x = 5, y = -1$

$\overline{AD}$ **and** $\overline{BE}$ **are diameters. Copy the diagram. Find the indicated measure.** **(Lesson 10.2)**

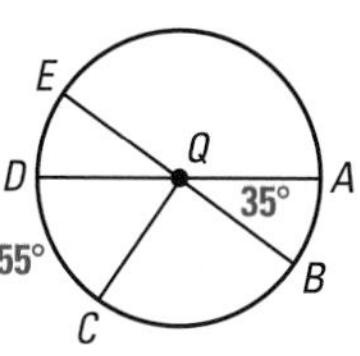

16. $m\widehat{AB}$ 35°

17. $m\widehat{DC}$ 55°

18. $m\widehat{AC}$ 125°

19. $m\widehat{ED}$ 35°

20. $m\angle CQE$ 90°

21. $m\angle AQE$ 145°

22. $m\widehat{BC}$ 90°

23. $m\widehat{BDC}$ 270°

Find the value of each variable. **(Lesson 10.3)**

24. 65

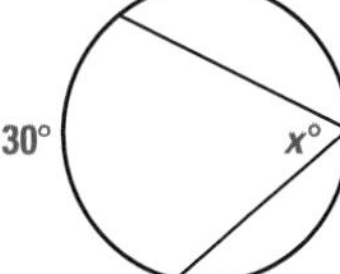

25. 70

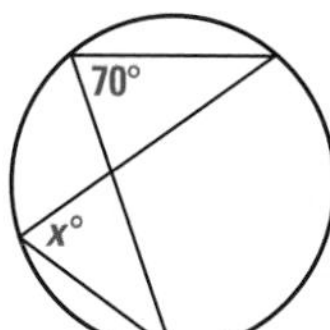

26.

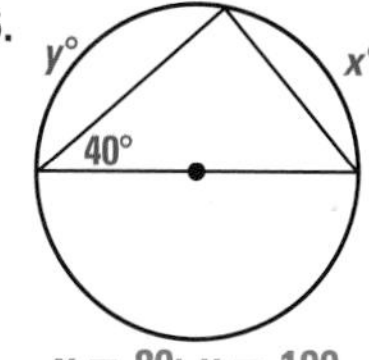

$x = 80; y = 100$

Find the value of *x*. (Lesson 10.4)

27. 240

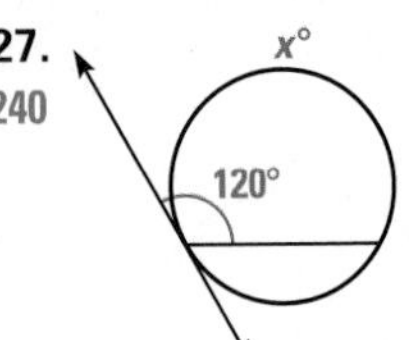

28. 90

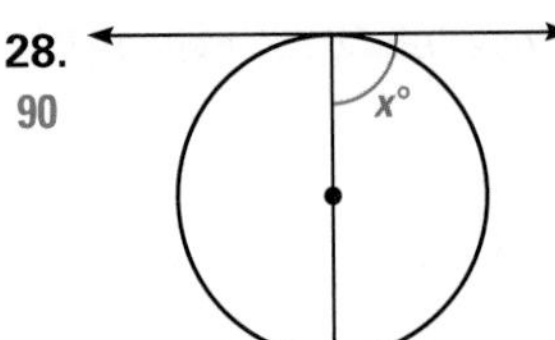

29. 80

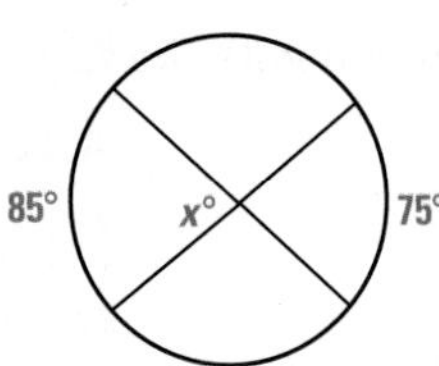

30. 40

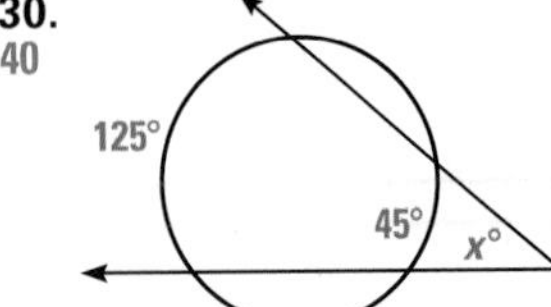

31. 70

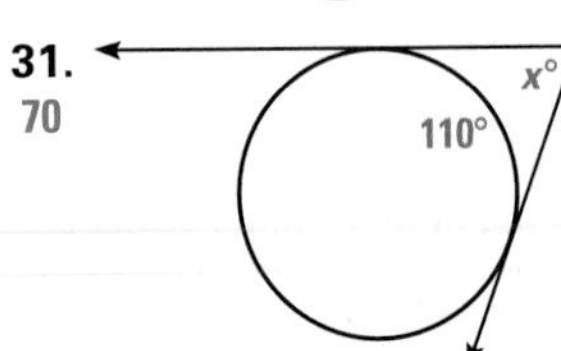

32. 46

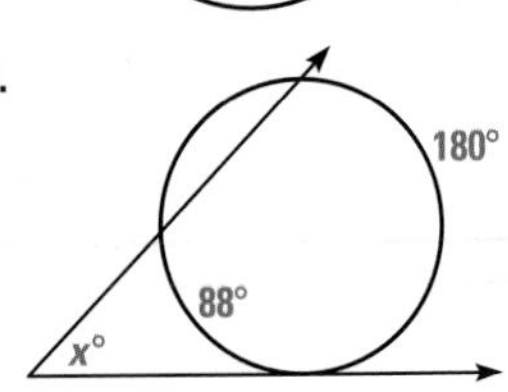

Find the value of *x*. (Lesson 10.5)

33. 4

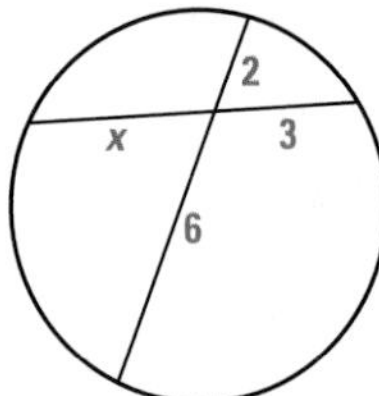

34. 3

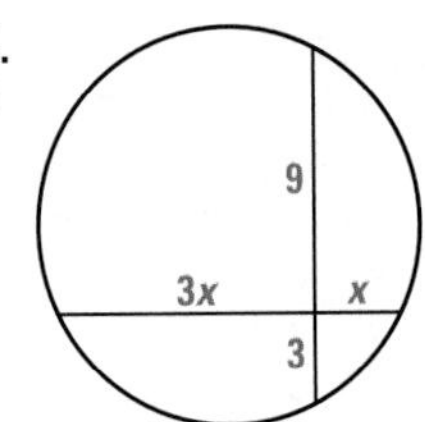

35. 10

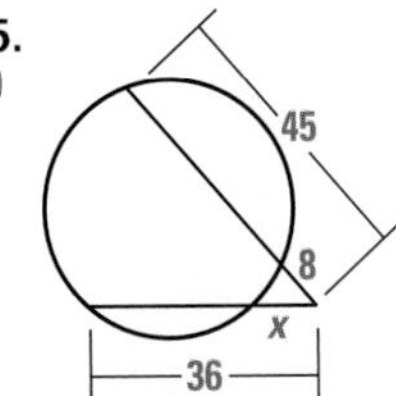

36. 25

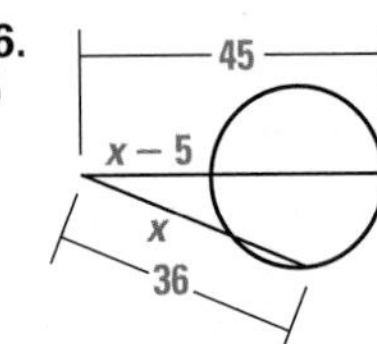

37. 4

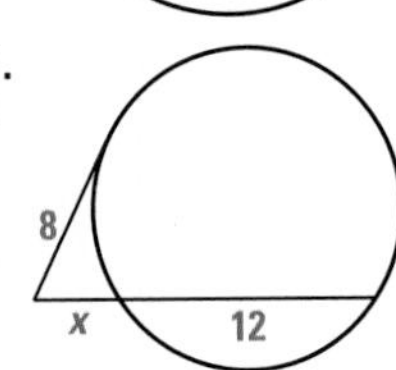

38. 6

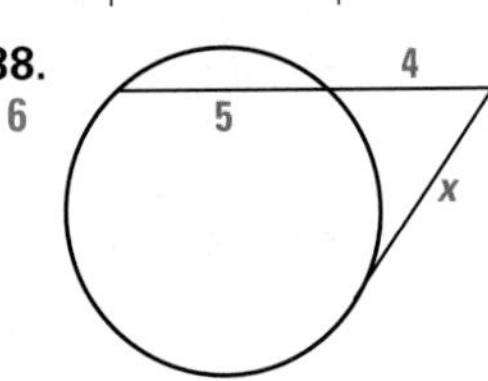

Give the center and radius of the circle. (Lesson 10.6)

39. $(x - 12)^2 + (y + 3)^2 = 49$ (12, −3); 7

40. $(x + 15)^2 + y^2 = 20$ (−15, 0); $2\sqrt{5}$

41. $(x + 3.8)^2 + (y - 4.9)^2 = 0.81$ (−3.8, 4.9); 0.9

42. $(x - 1)^2 + (y + 7)^2 = 1$ (1, −7); 1

Write the standard equation of the circle with the given center and radius. (Lesson 10.6)

43. center (5, 8), radius 6 $(x - 5)^2 + (y - 8)^2 = 36$

44. center (−2, 7), radius 10 $(x + 2)^2 + (y - 7)^2 = 100$

Use the given information to write the standard equation of the circle. (Lesson 10.6)

45. The center is (2, 2); a point on the circle is (2, 0). $(x - 2)^2 + (y - 2)^2 = 4$

46. The center is (0, 1); a point on the circle is (−3, 1). $x^2 + (y - 1)^2 = 9$

Use the graph at the right to write equation(s) for the locus of points in the coordinate plane that satisfy the given condition. (Lesson 10.7)

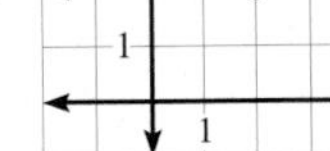

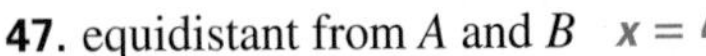

47. equidistant from *A* and *B* $x = 4$

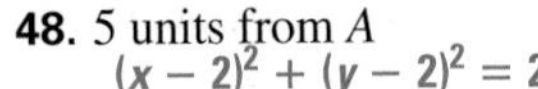

48. 5 units from *A* $(x - 2)^2 + (y - 2)^2 = 25$

49. 4 units from $\overleftrightarrow{AB}$ $y = -2, y = 6$

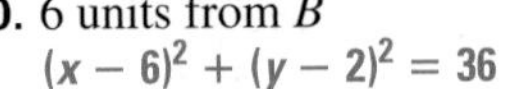

50. 6 units from *B* $(x - 6)^2 + (y - 2)^2 = 36$

CHAPTER 11

Find the sum of the measures of the interior angles of the convex polygon. (Lesson 11.1)

1. 36-gon 6120° **2.** 45-gon 7740° **3.** 60-gon 10,440° **4.** 90-gon 15,840°

Find the value of *x*. (Lesson 11.1)

5.

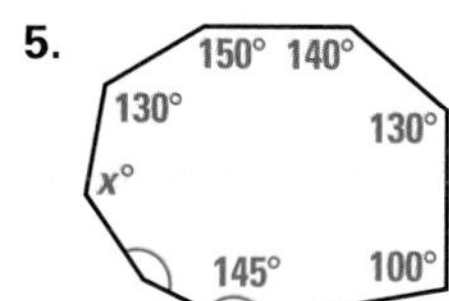

140

6.

140° $x°$

120

7.

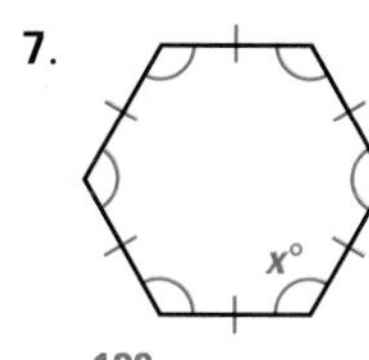

120

You are given the number of sides of a regular polygon. Find the measure of each exterior angle. (Lesson 11.1)

8. 180 2° **9.** 24 15° **10.** 48 7.5° **11.** 36 10°

You are given the measure of each exterior angle of a regular *n*-gon. Find the value of *n*. (Lesson 11.1)

12. 40° 9 **13.** 18° 20 **14.** 45° 8 **15.** 90° 4

Find the measure of a central angle of a regular polygon with the given number of sides. (Lesson 11.2)

16. 10 sides 36° **17.** 18 sides 20° **18.** 25 sides 14.4° **19.** 90 sides 4°

Find the perimeter and area of the regular polygon. (Lesson 11.2)

20.

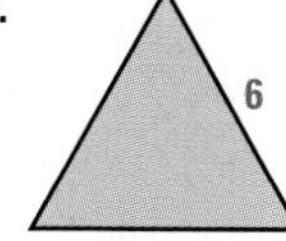

18; 15.59

21.

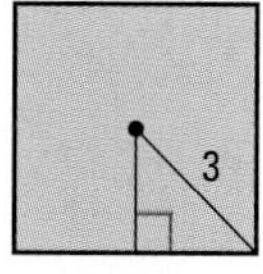

16.97; 18

22.

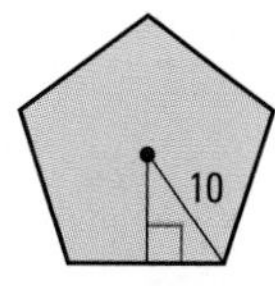

58.78; 237.76

23.

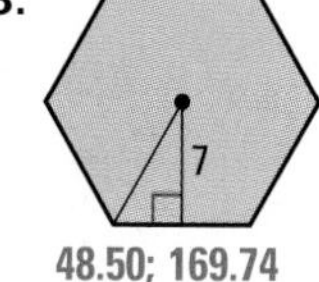

48.50; 169.74

24.

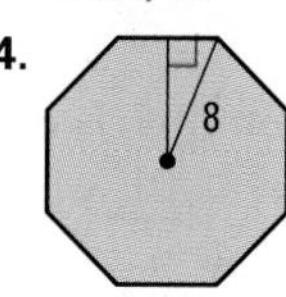

48.98; 181.02

25.

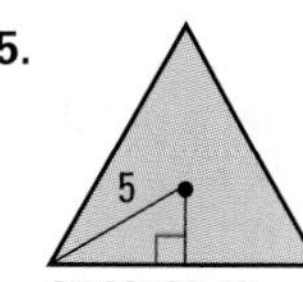

25.98; 32.48

In Exercises 26–28, the polygons are similar. Find the ratio (red to blue) of their perimeters and of their areas. (Lesson 11.3)

26.

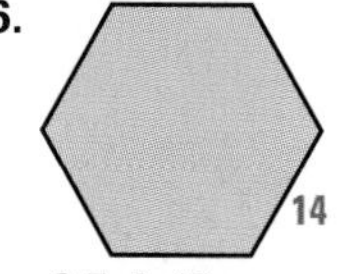

6

3:7; 9:49

27.

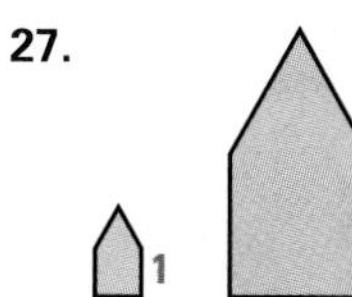

3:1; 9:1

28.

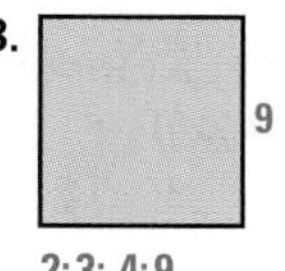

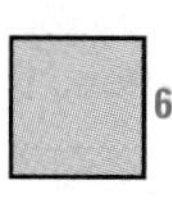

2:3; 4:9

29. The ratio of the perimeters of two similar hexagons is 5:8. The area of the larger hexagon is 320 square inches. What is the area of the smaller hexagon? **(Lesson 11.3)** 125 square inches

Find the indicated measure. (Lesson 11.4)

30. Circumference about 75.40

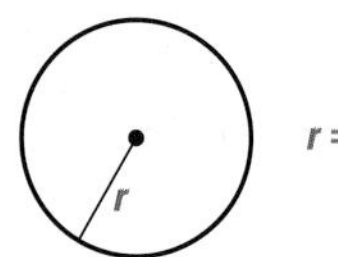

31. Radius about 9.07

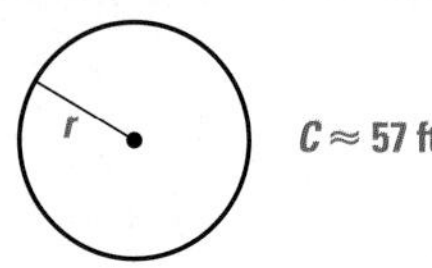

Find the indicated measure. (Lesson 11.4)

32. Length of $\widehat{MN}$ about 9.42

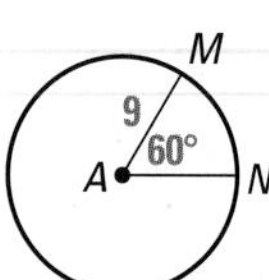

33. Circumference about 147

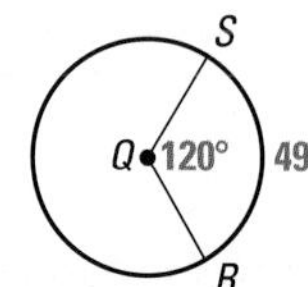

34. Radius about 4.41

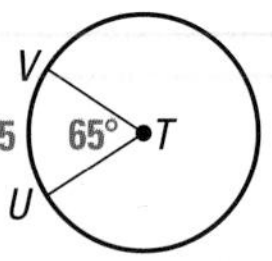

35. Length of $\widehat{AB}$ about 11.78

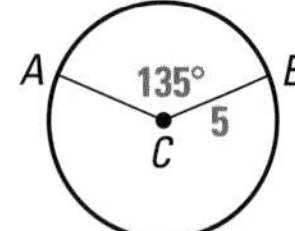

36. Circumference about 77.14

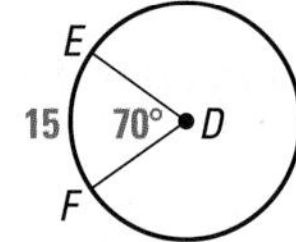

37. Radius about 95.49

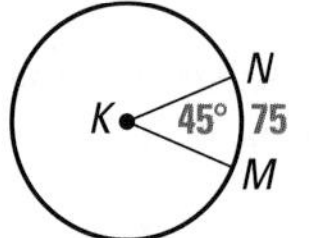

Find the area of the shaded region. (Lesson 11.5)

38.

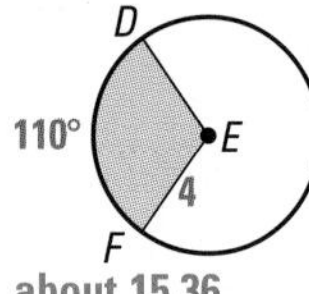

about 15.36

39.

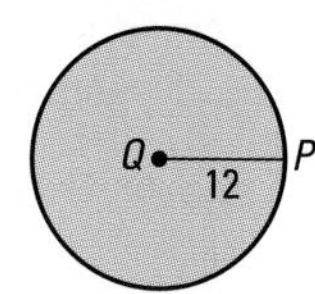

about 452.39

40.

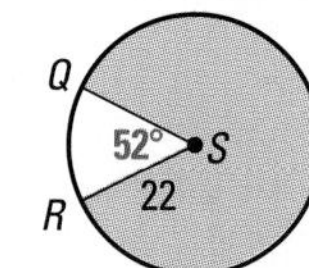

about 1,300.90

41. B, C, 75°, 8, D

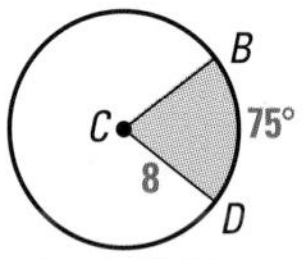

about 41.89

42.

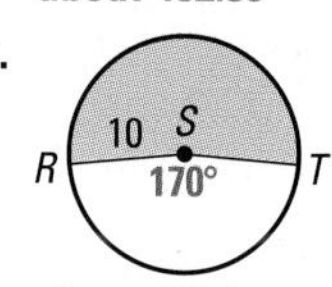

about 165.81

43.

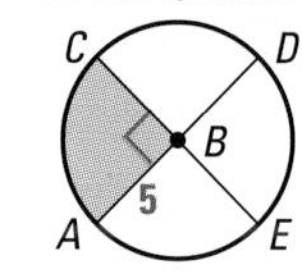

about 19.63

Find the probability that a point *K*, selected randonly on $\overline{MN}$, is on the given segment. (Lesson 11.6)

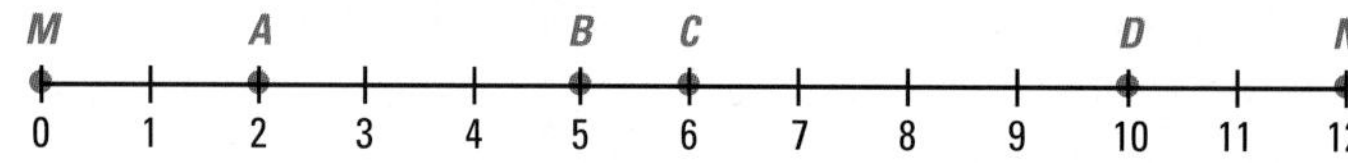

44. $\overline{AB}$ 25%

45. $\overline{AD}$ about 67%

46. $\overline{MA}$ about 17%

47. $\overline{MD}$ about 83%

Find the probability that a randomly chosen point in the figure lies in the shaded region. (Lesson 11.6)

48.

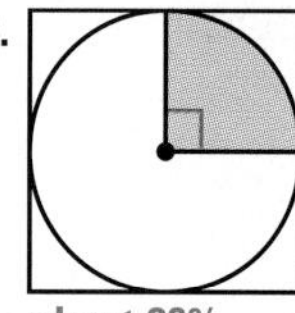

about 20%

49.

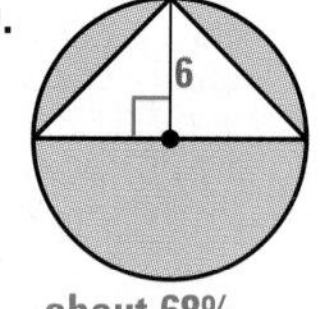

about 68%

CHAPTER 12

Tell whether the solid is a polyhedron. If it is, decide whether it is regular and/or convex. Explain. (Lesson 12.1)

1. 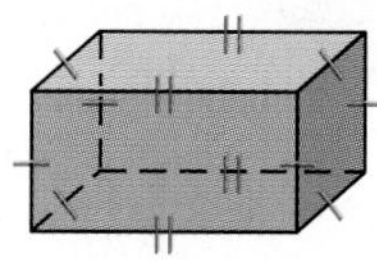
polyhedron; not regular; convex

2. 
not a polyhedron

3. 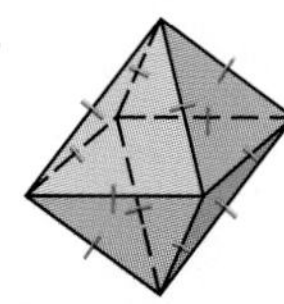
polyhedron; regular; convex

Count the number of faces, vertices, and edges of the polyhedron. Verify your results using Euler's Theorem. (Lesson 12.1) 4–6. See margin.

4. 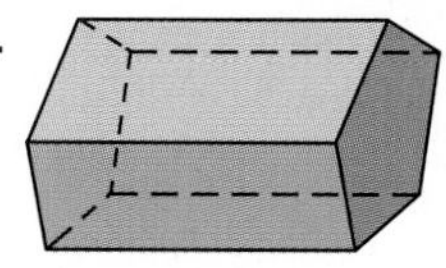

5. 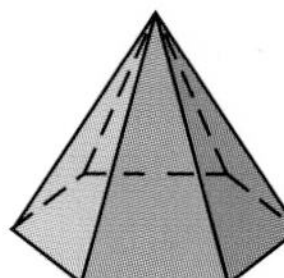

6. 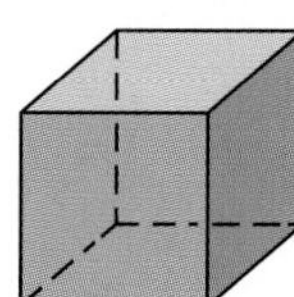

Describe the cross section. (Lesson 12.1)

7. 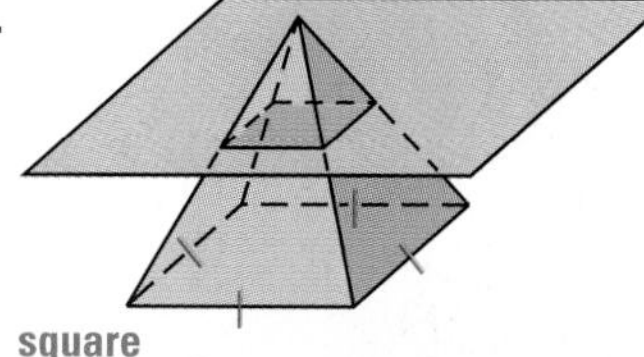
square

8. 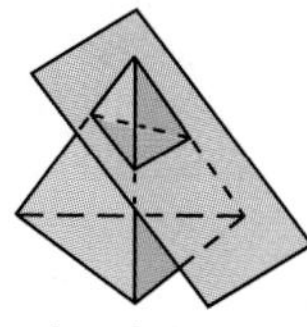
triangle

Find the surface area of the right prism. (Lesson 12.2)

9. 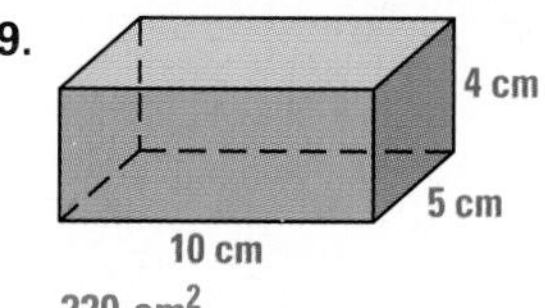

220 cm^2

10. 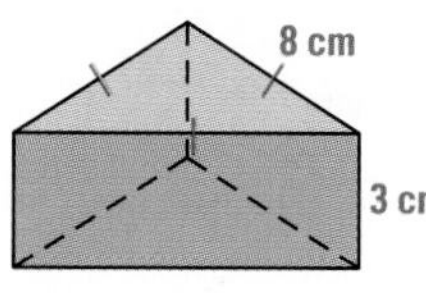

127.43 cm^2

11. 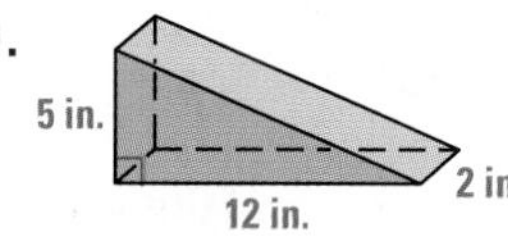

120 $in.^2$

Find the surface area of the right cylinder. Round the result to two decimal places. (Lesson 12.2)

12. 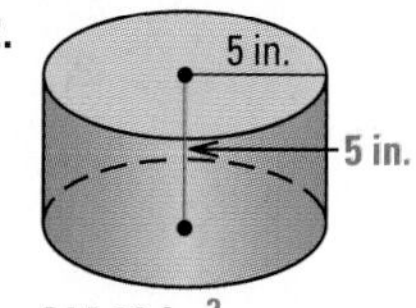

314.16 $in.^2$

13. 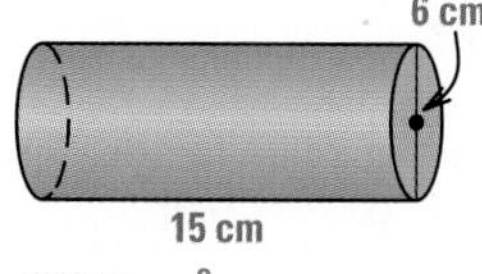

339.29 cm^2

14. 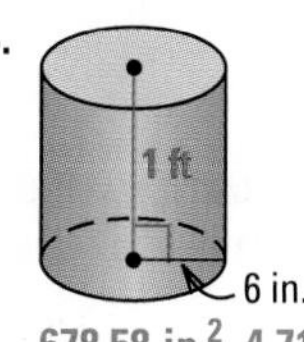

678.58 $in.^2$, 4.71 ft^2

Find the surface area of the solid. The pyramids are regular and the cone is right. (Lesson 12.3)

15. 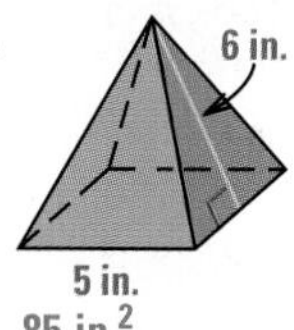

85 $in.^2$

16. 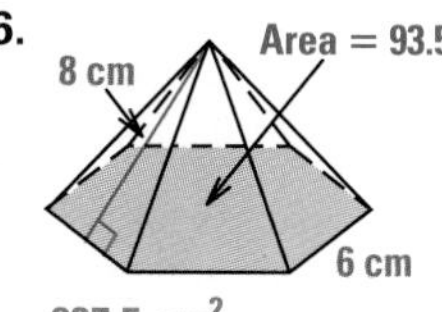

237.5 cm^2

17. 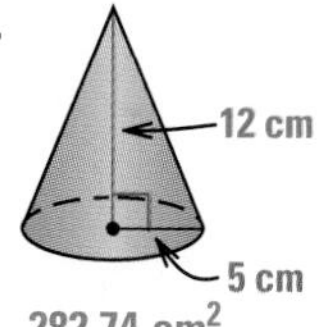

282.74 cm^2

4. $F = 7$, $V = 10$, $E = 15$; $7 + 10 = 15 + 2$
5. $F = 7$, $V = 7$, $E = 12$; $7 + 7 = 12 + 2$
6. $F = 6$, $V = 8$, $E = 12$; $6 + 8 = 12 + 2$

Find the volume of the solid. (Lesson 12.4)

18. Right rectangular prism 1980 in.^{3}

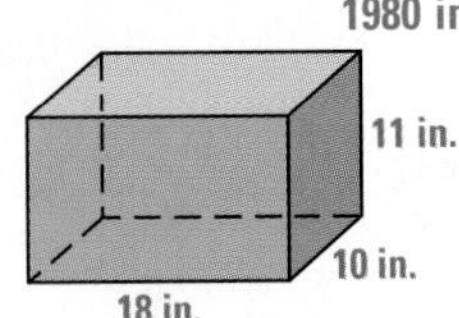

19. Right cylinder about 1060.29 ft^3

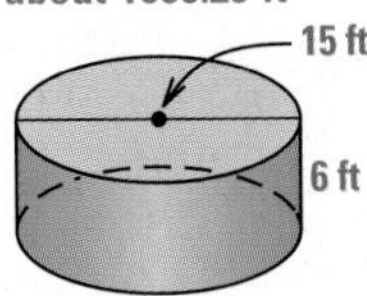

20. Oblique square prism 3380 cm^3

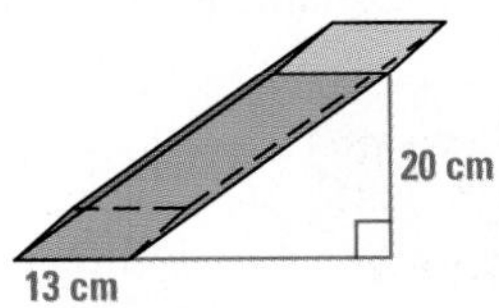

21. Oblique cylinder about 2001.19 in.^{3}

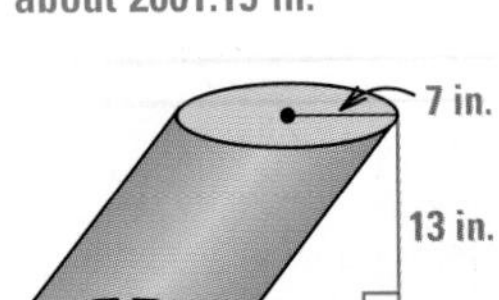

22. Two holes are drilled through a cube. about 93.58 cm^3

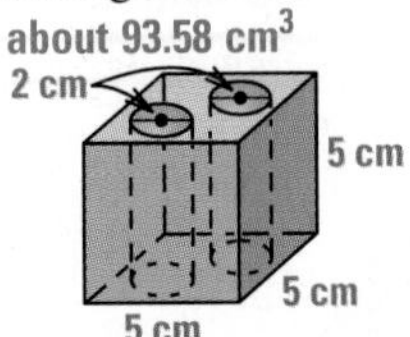

23. A square "hole" is cut from a cylinder. about 247.59 ft^3

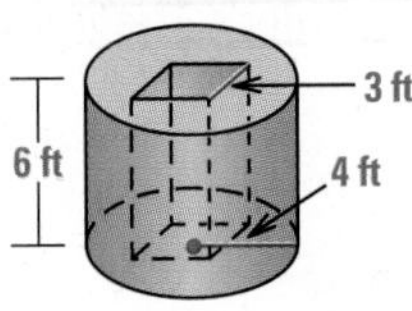

Find the volume of the pyramid or cone. (Lesson 12.5)

24.

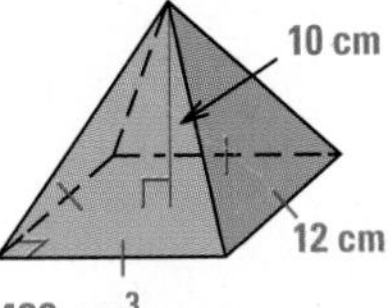

480 cm^3

25.

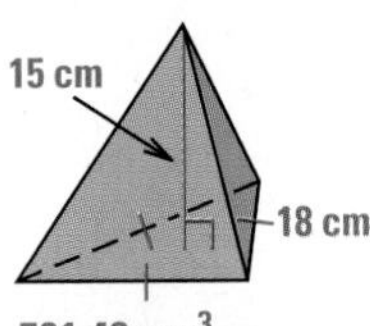

701.48 cm^3

26.

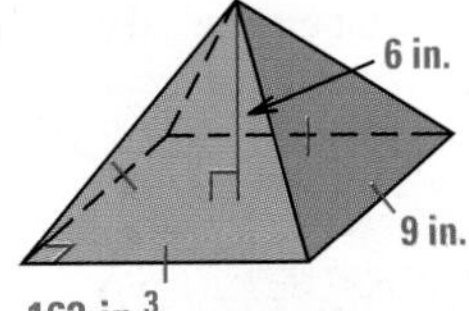

162 in.^{3}

27. about 513.13 in.^{3}

28. about 883.57 mm^3

29.

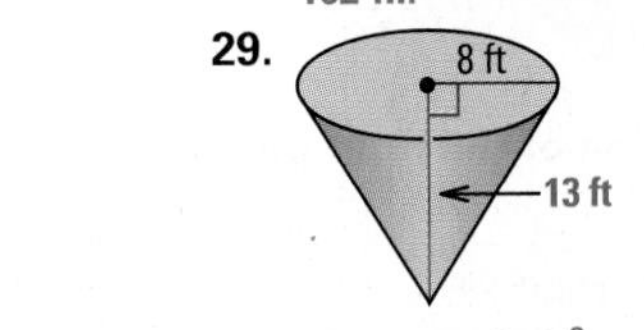

about 871.27 ft^3

Find the surface area and the volume of the sphere. Round your result to two decimal places. (Lesson 12.6)

30.

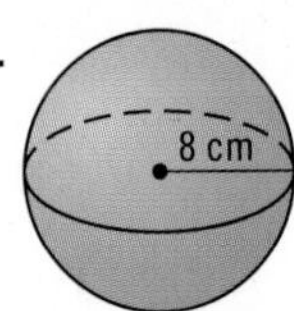
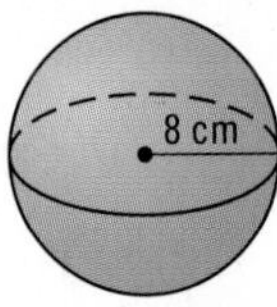

804.25 cm^2; 2144.66 cm^3

31.

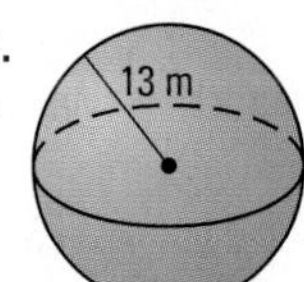

2123.72 m^2; 9202.77 m^3

32.

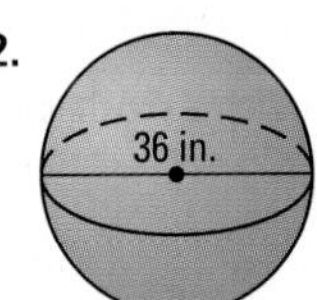

4701.50 in.^{2}; 24,429.02 in.^{3}

The solid is similar to a larger solid with the given scale factor. Find the surface area *S* and volume *V* of the larger solid. (Lesson 12.7)

33. Scale factor 2 : 3

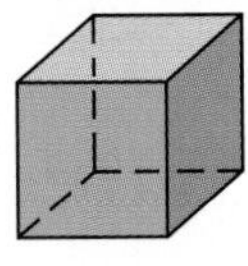

$S = 96 \text{ m}^2$
$V = 64 \text{ m}^3$

216 m^2; 216 m^3

34. Scale factor 3 : 5

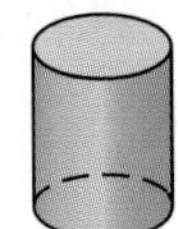

$S = 104\pi \text{ ft}^2$
$V = 144\pi \text{ ft}^3$

about 288.89π ft^2; about 666.67π ft^3;

35. Scale factor 5 : 7

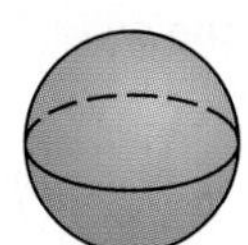

$S = 100\pi \text{ cm}^2$
$V = 166\frac{2}{3}\pi \text{ cm}^3$

196π cm^2; 457$\frac{1}{3}\pi$ cm^3

826

Postulates

1 **Ruler Postulate** The points on a line can be matched one to one with the real numbers. The real number that corresponds to a point is the coordinate of the point. The distance between points A and B, written as AB, is the absolute value of the difference between the coordinates of A and B. **(p. 17)**

2 **Segment Addition Postulate** If B is between A and C, then $AB + BC = AC$. If $AB + BC = AC$, then B is between A and C. **(p. 18)**

3 **Protractor Postulate** Consider a point A on one side of $\overleftrightarrow{OB}$. The rays of the form $\overrightarrow{OA}$ can be matched one to one with the real numbers from 0 to 180. The measure of $\angle AOB$ is equal to the absolute value of the difference between the real numbers for $\overrightarrow{OA}$ and $\overrightarrow{OB}$. **(p. 27)**

4 **Angle Addition Postulate** If P is in the interior of $\angle RST$, then $m\angle RSP + m\angle PST = m\angle RST$. **(p. 27)**

5 Through any two points there exists exactly one line. **(p. 73)**

6 A line contains at least two points. **(p. 73)**

7 If two lines intersect, then their intersection is exactly one point. **(p. 73)**

8 Through any three noncollinear points there exists exactly one plane. **(p. 73)**

9 A plane contains at least three noncollinear points. **(p. 73)**

10 If two points lie in a plane, then the line containing them lies in the plane. **(p. 73)**

11 If two planes intersect, then their intersection is a line. **(p. 73)**

12 **Linear Pair Postulate** If two angles form a linear pair, then they are supplementary. **(p. 111)**

13 **Parallel Postulate** If there is a line and a point not on the line, then there is exactly one line through the point parallel to the given line. **(p. 130)**

14 **Perpendicular Postulate** If there is a line and a point not on the line, then there is exactly one line through the point perpendicular to the given line. **(p. 130)**

15 **Corresponding Angles Postulate** If two parallel lines are cut by a transversal, then the pairs of corresponding angles are congruent. **(p. 143)**

16 **Corresponding Angles Converse** If two lines are cut by a transversal so that corresponding angles are congruent, then the lines are parallel. **(p. 150)**

17 **Slopes of Parallel Lines** In a coordinate plane, two nonvertical lines are parallel if and only if they have the same slope. Any two vertical lines are parallel. **(p. 166)**

18 **Slopes of Perpendicular Lines** In a coordinate plane, two nonvertical lines are perpendicular if and only if the product of their slopes is -1. Vertical and horizontal lines are perpendicular. **(p. 172)**

19 **Side-Side-Side (SSS) Congruence Postulate** If three sides of one triangle are congruent to three sides of a second triangle, then the two triangles are congruent. **(p. 212)**

20 **Side-Angle-Side (SAS) Congruence Postulate** If two sides and the included angle of one triangle are congruent to two sides and the included angle of a second triangle, then the two triangles are congruent. **(p. 213)**

21 **Angle-Side-Angle (ASA) Congruence Postulate** If two angles and the included side of one triangle are congruent to two angles and the included side of a second triangle, then the two triangles are congruent. **(p. 220)**

22 **Area of a Square Postulate** The area of a square is the square of the length of its side, or $A = s^2$. **(p. 372)**

23 **Area Congruence Postulate** If two polygons are congruent, then they have the same area. **(p. 372)**

24 **Area Addition Postulate** The area of a region is the sum of the areas of its nonoverlapping parts. **(p. 372)**

25 **Angle-Angle (AA) Similarity Postulate** If two angles of one triangle are congruent to two angles of another triangle, then the two triangles are similar. **(p. 481)**

26 **Arc Addition Postulate** The measure of an arc formed by two adjacent arcs is the sum of the measures of the two arcs. **(p. 604)**

27 **Volume of a Cube** The volume of a cube is the cube of the length of its side, or $V = s^3$. **(p. 743)**

28 **Volume Congruence Postulate** If two polyhedra are congruent, then they have the same volume. **(p. 743)**

29 **Volume Addition Postulate** The volume of a solid is the sum of the volumes of all its nonoverlapping parts. **(p. 743)**

827

Theorems

2.1 Properties of Segment Congruence Segment congruence is reflexive, symmetric, and transitive.

Reflexive: For any segment AB, $\overline{AB} \cong \overline{AB}$.

Symmetric: If $\overline{AB} \cong \overline{CD}$, then $\overline{CD} \cong \overline{AB}$.

Transitive: If $\overline{AB} \cong \overline{CD}$ and $\overline{CD} \cong \overline{EF}$, then $\overline{AB} \cong \overline{EF}$. **(p. 102)**

2.2 Properties of Angle Congruence Angle congruence is reflexive, symmetric, and transitive.

Reflexive: For any angle A, $\angle A \cong \angle A$.

Symmetric: If $\angle A \cong \angle B$, then $\angle B \cong \angle A$.

Transitive: If $\angle A \cong \angle B$ and $\angle B \cong \angle C$, then $\angle A \cong \angle C$. **(p. 109)**

2.3 Right Angle Congruence Theorem All right angles are congruent. **(p. 110)**

2.4 Congruent Supplements Theorem If two angles are supplementary to the same angle (or to congruent angles) then they are congruent. **(p. 111)**

2.5 Congruent Complements Theorem If two angles are complementary to the same angle (or to congruent angles) then the two angles are congruent. **(p. 111)**

2.6 Vertical Angles Theorem Vertical angles are congruent. **(p. 112)**

3.1 If two lines intersect to form a linear pair of congruent angles, then the lines are perpendicular. **(p. 137)**

3.2 If two sides of two adjacent acute angles are perpendicular, then the angles are complementary. **(p. 137)**

3.3 If two lines are perpendicular, then they intersect to form four right angles. **(p. 137)**

3.4 Alternate Interior Angles If two parallel lines are cut by a transversal, then the pairs of alternate interior angles are congruent. **(p. 143)**

3.5 Consecutive Interior Angles If two parallel lines are cut by a transversal, then the pairs of consecutive interior angles are supplementary. **(p. 143)**

3.6 Alternate Exterior Angles If two parallel lines are cut by a transversal, then the pairs of alternate exterior angles are congruent. **(p. 143)**

3.7 Perpendicular Transversal If a transversal is perpendicular to one of two parallel lines, then it is perpendicular to the other. **(p. 143)**

3.8 Alternate Interior Angles Converse If two lines are cut by a transversal so that alternate interior angles are congruent, then the lines are parallel. **(p. 150)**

3.9 Consecutive Interior Angles Converse If two lines are cut by a transversal so that consecutive interior angles are supplementary, then the lines are parallel. **(p. 150)**

3.10 Alternate Exterior Angles Converse If two lines are cut by a transversal so that alternate exterior angles are congruent, then the lines are parallel. **(p. 150)**

3.11 If two lines are parallel to the same line, then they are parallel to each other. **(p. 157)**

3.12 In a plane, if two lines are perpendicular to the same line, then they are parallel to each other. **(p. 157)**

4.1 Triangle Sum Theorem The sum of the measures of the interior angles of a triangle is 180°. **(p. 196)**

Corollary The acute angles of a right triangle are complementary. **(p. 197)**

4.2 Exterior Angle Theorem The measure of an exterior angle of a triangle is equal to the sum of the measures of the two nonadjacent interior angles. **(p. 197)**

4.3 Third Angles Theorem If two angles of one triangle are congruent to two angles of another triangle, then the third angles are also congruent. **(p. 203)**

4.4 Reflexive Property of Congruent Triangles Every triangle is congruent to itself.

Symmetric Property of Congruent Triangles If $\triangle ABC \cong \triangle DEF$, then $\triangle DEF \cong \triangle ABC$.

Transitive Property of Congruent Triangles If $\triangle ABC \cong \triangle DEF$ and $\triangle DEF \cong \triangle JKL$, then $\triangle ABC \cong \triangle JKL$. **(p. 205)**

4.5 Angle-Angle-Side (AAS) Congruence Theorem If two angles and a nonincluded side of one triangle are congruent to two angles and the corresponding nonincluded side of a second triangle, then the two triangles are congruent. **(p. 220)**

4.6 Base Angles Theorem If two sides of a triangle are congruent, then the angles opposite them are congruent. **(p. 236)**

Corollary If a triangle is equilateral, then it is equiangular. **(p. 237)**

4.7 Converse of the Base Angles Theorem If two angles of a triangle are congruent, then the sides opposite them are congruent. **(p. 236)**

Corollary If a triangle is equiangular, then it is equilateral. **(p. 237)**

4.8 Hypotenuse-Leg (HL) Congruence Theorem If the hypotenuse and a leg of a right triangle are congruent to the hypotenuse and a leg of a second right triangle, then the two triangles are congruent. **(p. 238)**

5.1 Perpendicular Bisector Theorem If a point is on a perpendicular bisector of a segment, then it is equidistant from the endpoints of the segment. **(p. 265)**

5.2 Converse of the Perpendicular Bisector Theorem If a point is equidistant from the endpoints of a segment, then it is on the perpendicular bisector of the segment. **(p. 265)**

5.3 Angle Bisector Theorem If a point is on the bisector of an angle, then it is equidistant from the two sides of the angle. **(p. 266)**

5.4 Converse of the Angle Bisector Theorem If a point is in the interior of an angle and is equidistant from the sides of the angle, then it lies on the bisector of the angle. **(p. 266)**

5.5 Concurrency of Perpendicular Bisectors of a Triangle The perpendicular bisectors of a triangle intersect at a point that is equidistant from the vertices of the triangle. **(p. 273)**

5.6 Concurrency of Angle Bisectors of a Triangle The angle bisectors of a triangle intersect at a point that is equidistant from the sides of the triangle. **(p. 274)**

5.7 Concurrency of Medians of a Triangle The medians of a triangle intersect at a point that is two thirds of the distance from each vertex to the midpoint of the opposite side. **(p. 279)**

5.8 Concurrency of Altitudes of a Triangle The lines containing the altitudes of a triangle are concurrent. **(p. 281)**

5.9 Midsegment Theorem The segment connecting the midpoints of two sides of a triangle is parallel to the third side and is half as long. **(p. 288)**

5.10 If one side of a triangle is longer than another side, then the angle opposite the longer side is larger than the angle opposite the shorter side. **(p. 295)**

5.11 If one angle of a triangle is larger than another angle, then the side opposite the larger angle is longer than the side opposite the smaller angle. **(p. 295)**

5.12 Exterior Angle Inequality The measure of an exterior angle of a triangle is greater than the measure of either of the two nonadjacent interior angles. **(p. 296)**

5.13 Triangle Inequality The sum of the lengths of any two sides of a triangle is greater than the length of the third side. **(p. 297)**

5.14 Hinge Theorem If two sides of one triangle are congruent to two sides of another triangle, and the included angle of the first is larger than the included angle of the second, then the third side of the first is longer than the third side of the second. **(p. 303)**

5.15 Converse of the Hinge Theorem If two sides of one triangle are congruent to two sides of another triangle, and the third side of the first is longer than the third side of the second, then the included angle of the first is larger than the included angle of the second. **(p. 303)**

6.1 Interior Angles of a Quadrilateral The sum of the measures of the interior angles of a quadrilateral is 360°. **(p. 324)**

6.2 If a quadrilateral is a parallelogram, then its opposite sides are congruent. **(p. 330)**

6.3 If a quadrilateral is a parallelogram, then its opposite angles are congruent. **(p. 330)**

6.4 If a quadrilateral is a parallelogram, then its consecutive angles are supplementary. **(p. 330)**

6.5 If a quadrilateral is a parallelogram, then its diagonals bisect each other. **(p. 330)**

6.6 If both pairs of opposite sides of a quadrilateral are congruent, then the quadrilateral is a parallelogram. **(p. 338)**

6.7 If both pairs of opposite angles of a quadrilateral are congruent, then the quadrilateral is a parallelogram. **(p. 338)**

6.8 If an angle of a quadrilateral is supplementary to both of its consecutive angles, then the quadrilateral is a parallelogram. **(p. 338)**

6.9 If the diagonals of a quadrilateral bisect each other, then the quadrilateral is a parallelogram. **(p. 338)**

829

6.10 If one pair of opposite sides of a quadrilateral are congruent and parallel, then the quadrilateral is a parallelogram. **(p. 340)**

Rhombus Corollary A quadrilateral is a rhombus if and only if it has four congruent sides. **(p. 348)**

Rectangle Corollary A quadrilateral is a rectangle if and only if it has four right angles. **(p. 348)**

Square Corollary A quadrilateral is a square if and only if it is a rhombus and a rectangle. **(p. 348)**

6.11 A parallelogram is a rhombus if and only if its diagonals are perpendicular. **(p. 349)**

6.12 A parallelogram is a rhombus if and only if each diagonal bisects a pair of opposite angles. **(p. 349)**

6.13 A parallelogram is a rectangle if and only if its diagonals are congruent. **(p. 349)**

6.14 If a trapezoid is isosceles, then each pair of base angles is congruent. **(p. 356)**

6.15 If a trapezoid has a pair of congruent base angles, then it is an isosceles trapezoid. **(p. 356)**

6.16 A trapezoid is isosceles if and only if its diagonals are congruent. **(p. 356)**

6.17 **Midsegment Theorem for Trapezoids** The midsegment of a trapezoid is parallel to each base and its length is one half the sum of the lengths of the bases. **(p. 357)**

6.18 If a quadrilateral is a kite, then its diagonals are perpendicular. **(p. 358)**

6.19 If a quadrilateral is a kite, then exactly one pair of opposite angles are congruent. **(p. 358)**

6.20 **Area of a Rectangle** The area of a rectangle is the product of its base and height. $A = bh$ **(p. 372)**

6.21 **Area of a Parallelogram** The area of a parallelogram is the product of a base and its corresponding height. $A = bh$ **(p. 372)**

6.22 **Area of a Triangle** The area of a triangle is one half the product of a base and its corresponding height.

$A = \frac{1}{2}bh$ **(p. 372)**

6.23 **Area of a Trapezoid** The area of a trapezoid is one half the product of the height and the sum of the bases.

$A = \frac{1}{2}h(b_1 + b_2)$ **(p. 374)**

6.24 **Area of a Kite** The area of a kite is one half the product of the lengths of its diagonals. $A = \frac{1}{2}d_1d_2$ **(p. 374)**

6.25 **Area of a Rhombus** The area of a rhombus is equal to one half the product of the lengths of the diagonals. $A = \frac{1}{2}d_1d_2$ **(p. 374)**

7.1 **Reflection Theorem** A reflection is an isometry. **(p. 404)**

7.2 **Rotation Theorem** A rotation is an isometry. **(p. 412)**

7.3 If lines k and m intersect at point P, then a reflection in k followed by a reflection in m is a rotation about point P. The angle of rotation is $2x°$, where $x°$ is the measure of the acute or right angle formed by k and m. **(p. 414)**

7.4 **Translation Theorem** A translation is an isometry. **(p. 421)**

7.5 If lines k and m are parallel, then a reflection in line k followed by a reflection in line m is a translation. If P'' is the image of P, then the following is true:

(1) $\overleftrightarrow{PP''}$ is perpendicular to k and m. (2) $PP'' = 2d$, where d is the distance between k and m. **(p. 421)**

7.6 **Composition Theorem** The composition of two (or more) isometries is an isometry. **(p. 431)**

8.1 If two polygons are similar, then the ratio of their perimeters is equal to the ratios of their corresponding side lengths. **(p. 475)**

8.2 **Side-Side-Side (SSS) Similarity Theorem** If the corresponding sides of two triangles are proportional, then the triangles are similar. **(p. 488)**

8.3 **Side-Angle-Side (SAS) Similarity Theorem** If an angle of one triangle is congruent to an angle of a second triangle and the lengths of the sides including these angles are proportional, then the triangles are similar. **(p. 488)**

8.4 **Triangle Proportionality Theorem** If a line parallel to one side of a triangle intersects the other two sides, then it divides the two sides proportionally. **(p. 498)**

8.5 **Converse of the Triangle Proportionality Theorem** If a line divides two sides of a triangle proportionally, then it is parallel to the third side. **(p. 498)**

8.6 If three parallel lines intersect two transversals, then they divide the transversals proportionally. **(p. 499)**

8.7 If a ray bisects an angle of a triangle, then it divides the opposite side into segments whose lengths are proportional to the lengths of the other two sides. **(p. 499)**

9.1 If an altitude is drawn to the hypotenuse of a right triangle, then the two triangles formed are similar to the original triangle and to each other. **(p. 527)**

9.2 In a right triangle, the altitude from the right angle to the hypotenuse divides the hypotenuse into two segments. The length of the altitude is the geometric mean of the lengths of the two segments. **(p. 529)**

9.3 In a right triangle, the altitude from the right angle to the hypotenuse divides the hypotenuse into two segments. Each leg of the right triangle is the geometric mean of the hypotenuse and the segment of the hypotenuse that is adjacent to the leg. **(p. 529)**

9.4 **Pythagorean Theorem** In a right triangle, the square of the length of the hypotenuse is equal to the sum of the squares of the lengths of the legs. **(p. 535)**

9.5 **Converse of the Pythagorean Theorem** If the square of the length of the longest side of a triangle is equal to the sum of the squares of the lengths of the other two sides, then the triangle is a right triangle. **(p. 543)**

9.6 If the square of the length of the longest side of a triangle is less than the sum of the squares of the lengths of the other two sides, then the triangle is acute. **(p. 544)**

9.7 If the square of the length of the longest side of a triangle is greater than the sum of the squares of the length of the other two sides, then the triangle is obtuse. **(p. 544)**

9.8 **45°-45°-90° Triangle Theorem** In a 45°-45°-90° triangle, the hypotenuse is $\sqrt{2}$ times as long as each leg. **(p. 551)**

9.9 **30°-60°-90° Triangle Theorem** In a 30°-60°-90° triangle, the hypotenuse is twice as long as the shorter leg, and the longer leg is $\sqrt{3}$ times as long as the shorter leg. **(p. 551)**

10.1 If a line is tangent to a circle, then it is perpendicular to the radius drawn to the point of tangency. **(p. 597)**

10.2 In a plane, if a line is perpendicular to a radius of a circle at its endpoint on the circle, then the line is tangent to the circle. **(p. 597)**

10.3 If two segments from the same exterior point are tangent to a circle, then they are congruent. **(p. 598)**

10.4 In the same circle, or in congruent circles, two minor arcs are congruent if and only if their corresponding chords are congruent. **(p. 605)**

10.5 If a diameter of a circle is perpendicular to a chord, then the diameter bisects the chord and its arc. **(p. 605)**

10.6 If one chord is a perpendicular bisector of another chord, then the first chord is a diameter. **(p. 605)**

10.7 In the same circle or in congruent circles, two chords are congruent if and only if they are equidistant from the center. **(p. 606)**

10.8 If an angle is inscribed in a circle, then its measure is half the measure of its intercepted arc. **(p. 613)**

10.9 If two inscribed angles of a circle intercept the same arc, then the angles are congruent. **(p. 614)**

10.10 If a right triangle is inscribed in a circle, then the hypotenuse is a diameter of the circle. Conversely, if one side of an inscribed triangle is a diameter of the circle, then the triangle is a right triangle and the angle opposite the diameter is the right angle. **(p. 615)**

10.11 A quadrilateral can be inscribed in a circle if and only if its opposite angles are supplementary. **(p. 615)**

10.12 If a tangent and a chord intersect at a point on a circle, then the measure of each angle formed is one half the measure of its intercepted arc. **(p. 621)**

10.13 If two chords intersect in the interior of a circle, then the measure of each angle is one half the sum of the measures of the arcs intercepted by the angle and its vertical angle. **(p. 622)**

10.14 If a tangent and a secant, two tangents, or two secants intersect in the exterior of a circle, then the measure of the angle formed is one half the difference of the measures of the intercepted arcs. **(p. 622)**

10.15 If two chords intersect in the interior of a circle, then the product of the lengths of the segments of one chord is equal to the product of the lengths of the segments of the other chord. **(p. 629)**

10.16 If two secant segments share the same endpoint outside a circle, then the product of the length of one secant segment and the length of its external segment equals the product of the length of the other secant segment and the length of its external segment. **(p. 630)**

10.17 If a secant segment and a tangent segment share an endpoint outside a circle, then the product of the length of the secant segment and the length of its external segment equals the square of the length of the tangent segment. **(p. 630)**

11.1 Polygon Interior Angles Theorem The sum of the measures of the interior angles of a convex n-gon is $(n-2) \cdot 180°$. (p. 662)

Corollary The measure of each interior angle of a regular n-gon is $\frac{1}{n} \cdot (n-2) \cdot 180°$, or $\frac{(n-2) \cdot 180°}{n}$. (p. 662)

11.2 Polygon Exterior Angles Theorem The sum of the measures of the exterior angles of a convex polygon, one angle at each vertex, is $360°$. (p. 663)

Corollary The measure of each exterior angle of a regular n-gon is $\frac{1}{n} \cdot 360°$, or $\frac{360°}{n}$. (p. 663)

11.3 Area of an Equilateral Triangle The area of an equilateral triangle is one fourth the square of the length of the side times $\sqrt{3}$. $A = \frac{1}{4}\sqrt{3}s^2$ (p. 669)

11.4 Area of a Regular Polygon The area of a regular n-gon with side length s is half the product of the apothem a and the perimeter P, so $A = \frac{1}{2}aP$, or $A = \frac{1}{2}a \cdot ns$. (p. 670)

11.5 Areas of Similar Polygons If two polygons are similar with the lengths of corresponding sides in the ratio of $a:b$, then the ratio of their areas is $a^2:b^2$. (p. 677)

11.6 Circumference of a Circle The circumference C of a circle is $C = \pi d$ or $C = 2\pi r$, where d is the diameter of the circle and r is the radius of the circle. (p. 683)

Arc Length Corollary In a circle, the ratio of the length of a given arc to the circumference is equal to the ratio of the measure of the arc to $360°$.

$\frac{\text{Arc length of } \widehat{AB}}{2\pi r} = \frac{m\widehat{AB}}{360°}$, or

$\text{Arc length of } \widehat{AB} = \frac{m\widehat{AB}}{360°} \cdot 2\pi r$ (p. 683)

11.7 Area of a Circle The area of a circle is π times the square of the radius, or $A = \pi r^2$. (p. 691)

11.8 Area of a Sector The ratio of the area A of a sector of a circle to the area of the circle is equal to the ratio of the measure of the intercepted arc to $360°$.

$\frac{A}{\pi r^2} = \frac{m\widehat{AB}}{360°}$, or $A = \frac{m\widehat{AB}}{360°} \cdot \pi r^2$ (p. 692)

12.1 Euler's Theorem The number of faces (F), vertices (V), and edges (E) of a polyhedron are related by the formula $F + V = E + 2$. (p. 721)

12.2 Surface Area of a Right Prism The surface area S of a right prism can be found using the formula $S = 2B + Ph$, where B is the area of a base, P is the perimeter of a base, and h is the height. (p. 729)

12.3 Surface Area of a Right Cylinder The surface area S of a right cylinder is $S = 2B + Ch = 2\pi r^2 + 2\pi rh$, where B is the area of a base, C is the circumference of a base, r is the radius of a base, and h is the height. (p. 730)

12.4 Surface Area of a Regular Pyramid The surface area S of a regular pyramid is $S = B + \frac{1}{2}P\ell$, where B is the area of a base, P is the perimeter of the base, and ℓ is the slant height. (p. 736)

12.5 Surface Area of a Right Cone The surface area S of a right cone is $S = \pi r^2 + \pi r\ell$, where r is the radius of the base and ℓ is the slant height. (p. 737)

12.6 Cavalieri's Principle If two solids have the same height and the same cross-sectional area at every level, then they have the same volume. (p. 744)

12.7 Volume of a Prism The volume V of a prism is $V = Bh$, where B is the area of a base and h is the height. (p. 744)

12.8 Volume of a Cylinder The volume V of a cylinder is $V = Bh = \pi r^2 h$, where B is the area of a base, h is the height, and r is the radius of a base. (p. 744)

12.9 Volume of a Pyramid The volume V of a pyramid is $V = \frac{1}{3}Bh$, where B is the area of the base and h is the height. (p. 752)

12.10 Volume of a Cone The volume V of a cone is $V = \frac{1}{3}Bh = \frac{1}{3}\pi r^2 h$, where B is the area of the base, h is the height, and r is the radius of the base. (p. 752)

12.11 Surface Area of a Sphere The surface area S of a sphere with radius r is $S = 4\pi r^2$. (p. 759)

12.12 Volume of a Sphere The volume V of a sphere with radius r is $V = \frac{4}{3}\pi r^3$. (p. 761)

12.13 Similar Solids Theorem If two similar solids have a scale factor of $a:b$, then corresponding areas have a ratio of $a^2:b^2$, and corresponding volumes have a ratio of $a^3:b^3$. (p. 767)

Additional Proofs

PROOF OF THEOREM 4.8
HYPOTENUSE-LEG (HL) CONGRUENCE THEOREM

THEOREM 4.8
page 238

If the hypotenuse and a leg of a right triangle are congruent to the hypotenuse and a leg of a second right triangle, then the two triangles are congruent.

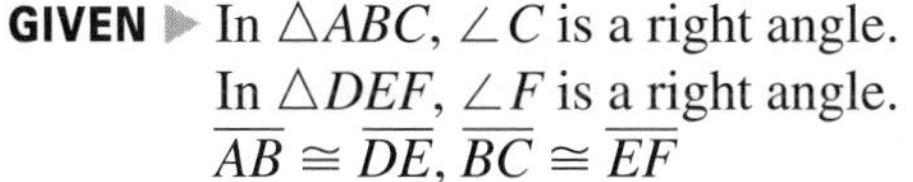

GIVEN ▶ In $\triangle ABC$, $\angle C$ is a right angle.
In $\triangle DEF$, $\angle F$ is a right angle.
$\overline{AB} \cong \overline{DE}$, $\overline{BC} \cong \overline{EF}$

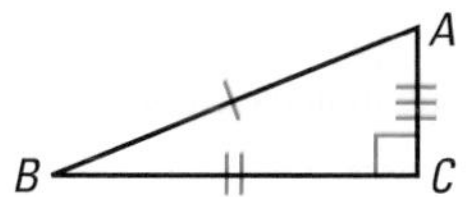

PROVE ▶ $\triangle ABC \cong \triangle DEF$

Plan for Proof Construct $\triangle GEF$ with $\overline{GF} \cong \overline{AC}$, as shown. Prove that $\triangle ABC \cong \triangle GEF$. Then use the fact that corresponding parts of congruent triangles are congruent to show that $\triangle GEF \cong \triangle DEF$. By the transitive property of congruence, you can show that $\triangle ABC \cong \triangle DEF$.

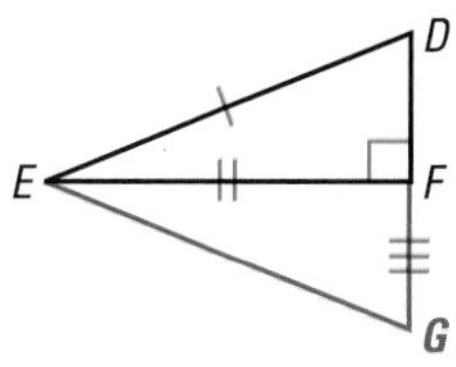

Statements	Reasons
1. $\angle C$ is a right angle. $\angle DFE$ is a right angle.	**1.** Given
2. $\overline{EF} \perp \overline{DG}$	**2.** Definition of perpendicular lines
3. $\angle EFG$ is a right angle.	**3.** If 2 lines are $\perp$, then they form 4 rt. $\angle$s.
4. $\angle C \cong \angle EFG$	**4.** Right Angles Congruence Theorem
5. $\overline{BC} \cong \overline{EF}$	**5.** Given
6. $\overline{AC} \cong \overline{GF}$	**6.** Given by construction
7. $\triangle ABC \cong \triangle GEF$	**7.** SAS Congruence Postulate
8. $\overline{GE} \cong \overline{AB}$	**8.** Corresp. parts of $\cong$ $\triangle$s are $\cong$.
9. $\overline{AB} \cong \overline{DE}$	**9.** Given
10. $\overline{GE} \cong \overline{DE}$	**10.** Transitive Property of Congruence
11. $\angle D \cong \angle G$	**11.** If 2 sides of a $\triangle$ are $\cong$, then the $\angle$s opposite them are $\cong$.
12. $\angle GFE \cong \angle DFE$	**12.** Right Angles Congruence Theorem
13. $\triangle GEF \cong \triangle DEF$	**13.** AAS Congruence Theorem
14. $\triangle ABC \cong \triangle DEF$	**14.** Transitive Prop. of $\cong$ $\triangle$s

ANOTHER PROOF OF THEOREM 4.8
HYPOTENUSE-LEG (HL) CONGRUENCE THEOREM

STUDENT HELP

Study Tip
This second proof of the HL Theorem uses the Pythagorean Theorem, which is introduced in Chapter 1 and further developed in Chapter 9.

GIVEN ▶ $\triangle ABC$ and $\triangle DEF$ are right triangles; $c = f$, $b = e$

PROVE ▶ $\triangle ABC \cong \triangle DEF$

Plan for Proof Use the Pythagorean Theorem to show that $a = d$. Then use the SSS Congruence Postulate.

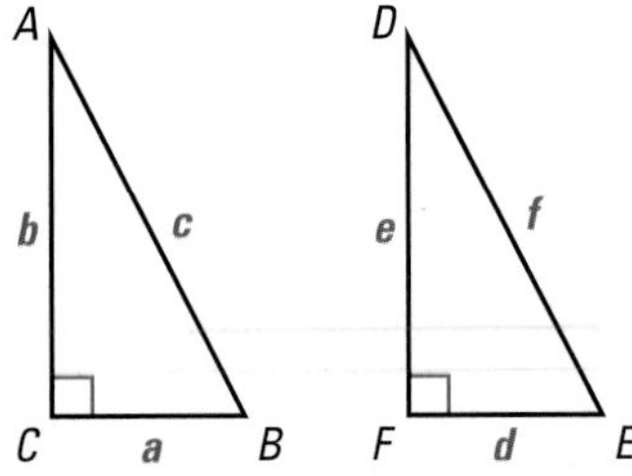

Statements	Reasons
1. $\triangle ABC$ and $\triangle DEF$ are right triangles.	**1.** Given
2. $c = f$, $b = e$	**2.** Given
3. $c^2 = f^2$, $b^2 = e^2$	**3.** A property of squares
4. $a^2 + b^2 = c^2$; $d^2 + e^2 = f^2$	**4.** Pythagorean Theorem
5. $a^2 + b^2 = d^2 + e^2$	**5.** Substitution property of equality
6. $a^2 + e^2 = d^2 + e^2$	**6.** Substitution property of equality
7. $a^2 = d^2$	**7.** Subtraction property of equality
8. $a = d$	**8.** A property of square roots
9. $\triangle ABC \cong \triangle DEF$	**9.** SSS Congruence Postulate

PROOF OF THEOREM 5.5
CONCURRENCY OF PERPENDICULAR BISECTORS OF A TRIANGLE

THEOREM 5.5
page 273

The perpendicular bisectors of a triangle intersect at a point that is equidistant from the vertices of the triangle.

GIVEN ▶ $\triangle ABC$; the $\perp$ bisectors of $\overline{AB}$, $\overline{BC}$, and $\overline{AC}$

PROVE ▶ The $\perp$ bisectors intersect in a point; that point is equidistant from A, B, and C.

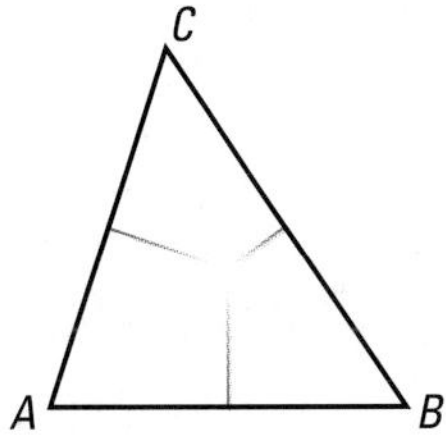

Plan for Proof Show that P, the point of intersection of the perpendicular bisectors of $\overline{BC}$ and $\overline{AC}$, also lies on the perpendicular bisector of $\overline{AB}$. Then show that P is equidistant from the vertices of the triangle, A, B, and C.

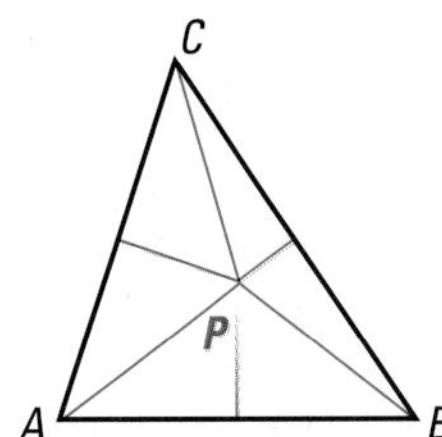

Statements	Reasons
1. The perpendicular bisectors of $\overline{BC}$ and $\overline{AC}$ intersect at some point P.	**1.** ABC is a triangle, so its sides $\overline{BC}$ and $\overline{AC}$ cannot be parallel; therefore, segments perpendicular to those sides cannot be parallel. So, the perpendicular bisectors must intersect in some point. Call it P.
2. Draw $\overline{PA}$, $\overline{PB}$, and $\overline{PC}$.	**2.** Through any two points there is exactly one line.
3. $PA = PC$, $PC = PB$	**3.** If a point is on the perpendicular bisector of a segment, then it is equidistant from the endpoints of the segment. (Theorem 5.1)
4. $PA = PB$	**4.** Substitution property of equality
5. P is on the perpendicular bisector of $\overline{AB}$.	**5.** If a point is equidistant from the endpoints of a segment, then it is on the perpendicular bisector of the segment. (Theorem 5.2)
6. $PA = PB = PC$, so P is equidistant from the vertices of the triangle.	**6.** Steps 3 and 4 and definition of equidistant

PROOF OF THEOREM 5.7 CONCURRENCY OF MEDIANS OF A TRIANGLE

THEOREM 5.7
page 279

The medians of a triangle intersect at a point that is two thirds of the distance from each vertex to the midpoint of the opposite side.

GIVEN ▶ $\triangle OBC$; medians $\overline{OM}$, $\overline{BN}$, and $\overline{CQ}$

PROVE ▶ The medians intersect in a point P; that point is two thirds of the distance from vertices O, B, and C to midpoints M, N, and Q.

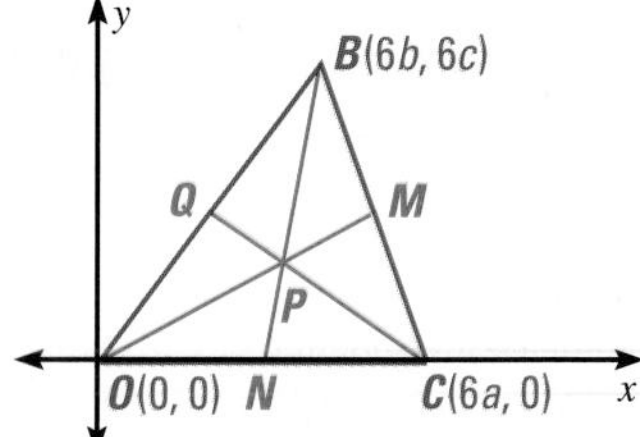

STUDENT HELP

Study Tip

Because you want to prove something involving the fraction $\frac{2}{3}$, it is helpful to position the vertices at points whose coordinates are multiples of both 2 and 3.

Plan for Proof The medians $\overline{OM}$ and $\overline{BN}$ intersect at some point P. Show that point P lies on $\overleftrightarrow{CQ}$. Then show that $OP = \frac{2}{3}OM$, $BP = \frac{2}{3}BN$, and $CP = \frac{2}{3}CQ$.

1 ***Find*** the equations of the medians $\overline{OM}$, $\overline{BN}$, and $\overline{CQ}$.

By the *Midpoint Formula*,

the coordinates of M are $\left(\frac{6b + 6a}{2}, \frac{6c + 0}{2}\right) = (3b + 3a, 3c)$;

the coordinates of N are $\left(\frac{0 + 6a}{2}, \frac{0 + 0}{2}\right) = (3a, 0)$;

the coordinates of Q are $\left(\frac{6b + 0}{2}, \frac{6c + 0}{2}\right) = (3b, 3c)$.

By the *slope formula*,

slope of $\overline{OM} = \frac{3c - 0}{(3b + 3a) - 0} = \frac{3c}{3b + 3a} = \frac{c}{b + a}$;

slope of $\overline{BN} = \frac{6c - 0}{6b - 3a} = \frac{6c}{6b - 3a} = \frac{2c}{2b - a}$;

slope of $\overline{CQ} = \frac{0 - 3c}{6a - 3b} = \frac{-3c}{6a - 3b} = \frac{-c}{2a - b} = \frac{c}{b - 2a}$.

Using the *point-slope form of an equation of a line*,

the equation of $\overleftrightarrow{OM}$ is $y - 0 = \frac{c}{b + a}(x - 0)$, or $y = \frac{c}{b + a}x$;

the equation of $\overleftrightarrow{BN}$ is $y - 0 = \frac{2c}{2b - a}(x - 3a)$, or $y = \frac{2c}{2b - a}(x - 3a)$;

the equation of $\overleftrightarrow{CQ}$ is $y - 0 = \frac{c}{b - 2a}(x - 6a)$, or $y = \frac{c}{b - 2a}(x - 6a)$.

2 ***Find*** the coordinates of the point P where two medians (say, $\overline{OM}$ and $\overline{BN}$) intersect. Using the substitution method, set the values of y in the equations of $\overleftrightarrow{OM}$ and $\overleftrightarrow{BN}$ equal to each other:

$$\frac{c}{b + a}x = \frac{2c}{2b - a}(x - 3a)$$

$$cx(2b - a) = 2c(x - 3a)(b + a)$$

$$2cxb - cxa = 2cxb + 2cxa - 6cab - 6ca^2$$

$$-3cxa = -6cab - 6ca^2$$

$$x = 2b + 2a$$

Substituting to find y, $y = \frac{c}{b + a}x = \frac{c}{b + a}(2b + 2a) = 2c$.

So, the coordinates of P are $(2b + 2a, 2c)$.

836

3 ***Show*** that P is on $\overleftrightarrow{CQ}$.

Substituting the x coordinate for P into the equation of $\overleftrightarrow{CQ}$,
$y = \frac{c}{b-2a}([2b + 2a] - 6a) = \frac{c}{b-2a}(2b - 4a) = 2c$. So, $P(2b + 2a, 2c)$ is on $\overleftrightarrow{CQ}$ and the three medians intersect at the same point.

4 ***Find*** the distances OM, OP, BN, BP, CQ, and CP.
Use the *Distance Formula.*

$$OM = \sqrt{((3b + 3a) - 0)^2 + (3c - 0)^2} = \sqrt{(3(b + a))^2 + (3c)^2} = \sqrt{9((b + a)^2 + c^2)} = 3\sqrt{(b + a)^2 + c^2}$$

$$OP = \sqrt{((2b + 2a) - 0)^2 + (2c - 0)^2} = \sqrt{(2(b + a))^2 + (2c)^2} = \sqrt{4((b + a)^2 + c^2)} = 2\sqrt{(b + a)^2 + c^2}$$

$$BN = \sqrt{(3a - 6b)^2 + (0 - 6c)^2} = \sqrt{(3a - 6b)^2 + (-6c)^2} = \sqrt{(3(a - 2b))^2 + (3(-2c))^2} = \sqrt{9(a - 2b)^2 + 9(4c^2)} = \sqrt{9((a - 2b)^2 + 4c^2)} = 3\sqrt{(a - 2b)^2 + 4c^2}$$

$$BP = \sqrt{((2b + 2a) - 6b)^2 + (2c - 6c)^2} = \sqrt{(2a - 4b)^2 + (-4c)^2} = \sqrt{(2(a - 2b))^2 + (2(-2c))^2} = \sqrt{4(a - 2b)^2 + 4(4c^2)} = \sqrt{4((a - 2b)^2 + 4c^2)} = 2\sqrt{(a - 2b)^2 + 4c^2}$$

$$CQ = \sqrt{(6a - 3b)^2 + (0 - 3c)^2} = \sqrt{(3(2a - b))^2 + (-3c)^2} = \sqrt{9((2a - b)^2 + c^2)} = 3\sqrt{(2a - b)^2 + c^2}$$

$$CP = \sqrt{(6a - (2b + 2a))^2 + (0 - 2c)^2} = \sqrt{(4a - 2b)^2 + (-2c)^2} = \sqrt{(2(2a - b))^2 + 4c^2} = \sqrt{4((2a - b)^2 + c^2)} = 2\sqrt{(2a - b)^2 + c^2}$$

5 ***Multiply*** OM, BN, and CQ by $\frac{2}{3}$.

$$\frac{2}{3}OM = \frac{2}{3}(3\sqrt{(b + a)^2 + c^2}) = 2\sqrt{(b + a)^2 + c^2}$$

$$\frac{2}{3}BN = \frac{2}{3}(3\sqrt{(a - 2b)^2 + 4c^2}) = 2\sqrt{(a - 2b)^2 + 4c^2}$$

$$\frac{2}{3}CQ = \frac{2}{3}(3\sqrt{(2a - b)^2 + c^2}) = 2\sqrt{(2a - b)^2 + c^2}$$

Thus, $OP = \frac{2}{3}OM$, $BP = \frac{2}{3}BN$, and $CP = \frac{2}{3}CQ$.

PROOF OF THEOREM 5.8
CONCURRENCY OF ALTITUDES OF A TRIANGLE

THEOREM 5.8
page 281

The lines containing the altitudes of a triangle are concurrent.

STUDENT HELP

Study Tip
Choose a general triangle, with one vertex at the origin and one side along an axis. In the proof shown, the triangle is obtuse.

GIVEN ▶ $\triangle OGH$

PROVE ▶ The altitudes to the sides of $\triangle OGH$ all intersect at J.

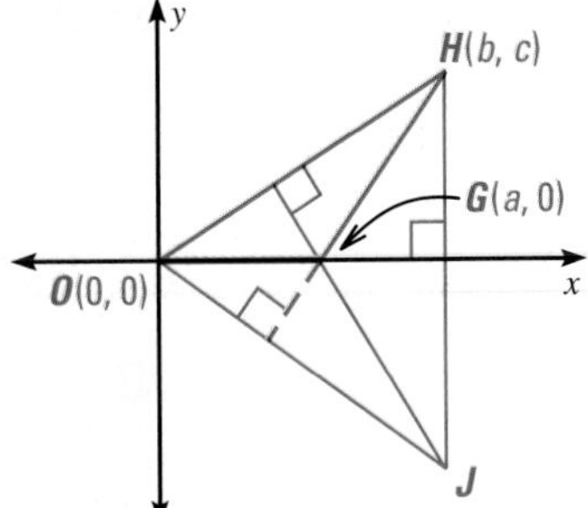

Plan for Proof Find the equations of the lines containing the altitudes of $\triangle OGH$. Find the intersection point of two of these lines. Show that the intersection point is also on the line containing the third altitude.

1. ***Find*** the slopes of the lines containing the sides $\overline{OH}$, $\overline{GH}$, and $\overline{OG}$.

   slope of $\overleftrightarrow{OH} = \frac{c}{b}$ slope of $\overleftrightarrow{GH} = \frac{c}{b-a}$ slope of $\overleftrightarrow{OG} = 0$

2. ***Use*** the *Slopes of Perpendicular Lines Postulate* to find the slopes of the lines containing the altitudes.

   slope of line containing altitude to $\overline{OH} = \frac{-b}{c}$

   slope of line containing altitude to $\overline{GH} = \frac{-(b-a)}{c} = \frac{a-b}{c}$

   The line containing the altitude to $\overline{OG}$ has an undefined slope.

3. ***Use*** the *point-slope form of an equation of a line* to write equations for the lines containing the altitudes.
   An equation of the line containing the altitude to $\overline{OH}$ is

   $$y - 0 = \frac{-b}{c}(x - a), \text{ or } y = \frac{-b}{c}x + \frac{ab}{c}.$$

   An equation of the line containing the altitude to $\overline{GH}$ is

   $$y - 0 = \frac{a-b}{c}(x - 0), \text{ or } y = \frac{a-b}{c}x.$$

   An equation of the vertical line containing the altitude to $\overline{OG}$ is $x = b$.

4. ***Find*** the coordinates of the point J where the lines containing two of the altitudes intersect. Using substitution, set the values of y in two of the above equations equal to each other, then solve for x:

   $$\frac{-b}{c}x + \frac{ab}{c} = \frac{a-b}{c}x$$
   $$\frac{ab}{c} = \frac{a-b}{c}x + \frac{b}{c}x$$
   $$\frac{ab}{c} = \frac{a}{c}x$$
   $$x = b$$

   Next, substitute to find y: $y = \frac{-b}{c}x + \frac{ab}{c} = \frac{-b}{c}(b) + \frac{ab}{c} = \frac{ab - b^2}{c}$.

   So, the coordinates of J are $\left(b, \frac{ab - b^2}{c}\right)$.

5. ***Show*** that J is on the line that contains the altitude to side $\overline{OG}$. J is on the vertical line with equation $x = b$ because its x-coordinate is b. Thus, the lines containing the altitudes of $\triangle OGH$ are concurrent.

838

PROOF OF THEOREM 6.17
MIDSEGMENT THEOREM FOR TRAPEZOIDS

THEOREM 6.17
page 357

The midsegment of a trapezoid is parallel to each base and its length is one half the sum of the lengths of the bases.

GIVEN ▶ Trapezoid $ABCD$ with midsegment $\overline{MN}$

PROVE ▶ $\overline{MN} \parallel \overline{AD}$, $\overline{MN} \parallel \overline{BC}$,

$MN = \frac{1}{2}(AD + BC)$

Plan for Proof Draw $\overline{BN}$, then extend $\overline{BN}$ and $\overline{AD}$ so that they intersect at point G. Then prove that $\triangle BNC \cong \triangle GND$, and use the fact that $\overline{MN}$ is a midsegment of $\triangle BAG$ to prove $MN = \frac{1}{2}(AD + BC)$.

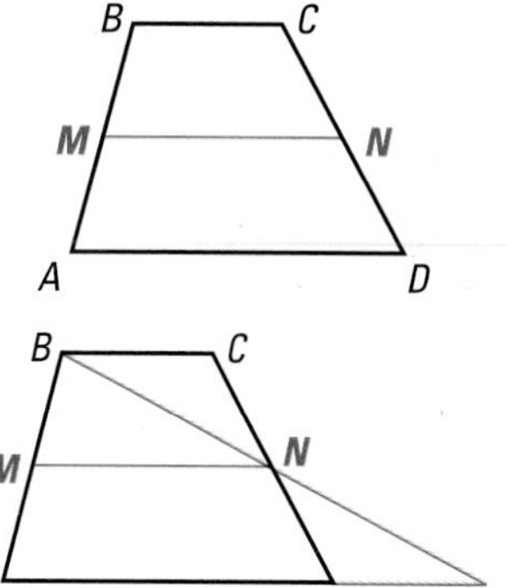

Statements	Reasons
1. $ABCD$ is a trapezoid with midsegment $\overline{MN}$.	**1.** Given
2. Draw $\overline{BN}$, then extend $\overline{BN}$ and $\overline{AD}$ so that they intersect at point G.	**2.** Through any two points there is exactly one line.
3. N is the midpoint of $\overline{CD}$.	**3.** Definition of midsegment of a trapezoid
4. $\overline{CN} \cong \overline{ND}$	**4.** Definition of midpoint
5. $\overline{AD} \parallel \overline{BC}$	**5.** Definition of trapezoid
6. $\angle BCN \cong \angle GDN$	**6.** Alternate Interior ∠s Theorem
7. $\angle BNC \cong \angle GND$	**7.** Vertical angles are congruent.
8. $\triangle BNC \cong \triangle GND$	**8.** ASA Congruence Postulate
9. $\overline{BN} \cong \overline{GN}$	**9.** Corresp. parts of ≅ △s are ≅.
10. N is the midpoint of $\overline{BG}$.	**10.** Definition of midpoint
11. $\overline{MN}$ is the midsegment of $\triangle BGA$.	**11.** Definition of midsegment of a △
12. $\overline{MN} \parallel \overline{AG}$ (so $\overline{MN} \parallel \overline{AD}$)	**12.** Midsegment of a △ Theorem
13. $\overline{MN} \parallel \overline{BC}$	**13.** Two lines ∥ to the same line are ∥.
14. $MN = \frac{1}{2}AG$	**14.** Midsegment of a △ Theorem
15. $AG = AD + DG$	**15.** Segment Addition Postulate
16. $\overline{DG} \cong \overline{BC}$	**16.** Corresp. parts of ≅ △s are ≅.
17. $DG = BC$	**17.** Definition of congruent segments
18. $AG = AD + BC$	**18.** Substitution property of equality
19. $MN = \frac{1}{2}(AD + BC)$	**19.** Substitution property of equality

839

PROOF OF THEOREM 10.11
A THEOREM ABOUT INSCRIBED QUADRILATERALS

THEOREM 10.11
page 615

A quadrilateral can be inscribed in a circle if and only if its opposite angles are supplementary.

1 Prove that if a quadrilateral is inscribed in a circle, then its opposite angles are supplementary.

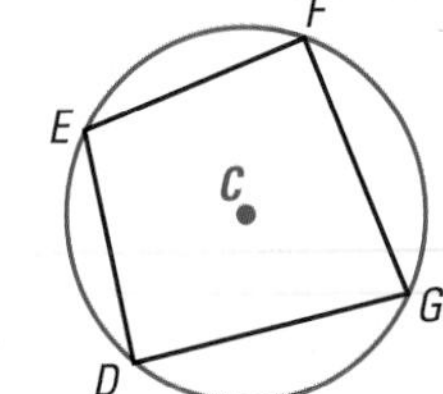

GIVEN ▶ $DEFG$ is inscribed in $\odot C$.

PROVE ▶ $\angle D$ and $\angle F$ are supplementary, $\angle E$ and $\angle G$ are supplementary.

Paragraph Proof Arcs $\widehat{EFG}$ and $\widehat{GDE}$ together make a circle, so $m\widehat{EFG} + m\widehat{GDE} = 360°$ by the Arc Addition Postulate. $\angle D$ is inscribed in $\widehat{EFG}$ and $\angle F$ is inscribed in $\widehat{GDE}$, so the angle measures are half the arc measures. Using the Substitution and Distributive properties, the sum of the measures of the opposite angles is

$$m\angle D + m\angle F = \frac{1}{2}m\widehat{EFG} + \frac{1}{2}m\widehat{GDE} = \frac{1}{2}(m\widehat{EFG} + m\widehat{GDE}) = \frac{1}{2}(360°) = 180°.$$

So, $\angle D$ and $\angle F$ are supplementary by definition. Similarly, $\angle E$ and $\angle G$ are inscribed in $\widehat{FGD}$ and $\widehat{DEF}$ and $m\angle E + m\angle G = 180°$. Then $\angle E$ and $\angle G$ are supplementary by definition.

2 Prove that if the opposite angles of a quadrilateral are supplementary, then the quadrilateral can be inscribed in a circle.

GIVEN ▶ $\angle E$ and $\angle G$ are supplementary (or $\angle D$ and $\angle F$ are supplementary).

PROVE ▶ $DEFG$ is inscribed in $\odot C$.

Plan for Proof Draw the circle that passes through D, E, and F. Use an *indirect proof* to show that the circle also passes through G. Begin by assuming that G does not lie on $\odot C$.

Case 1 *G lies inside* $\odot C$. Let H be the intersection of $\overrightarrow{DG}$ and $\odot C$. Then $DEFH$ is inscribed in $\odot C$ and $\angle E$ is supplementary to $\angle DHF$ (by proof above). Then $\angle DGF \cong \angle DHF$ by the given information and the Congruent Supplements Theorem. This implies that $\overline{FG} \parallel \overline{FH}$, which is a contradiction.

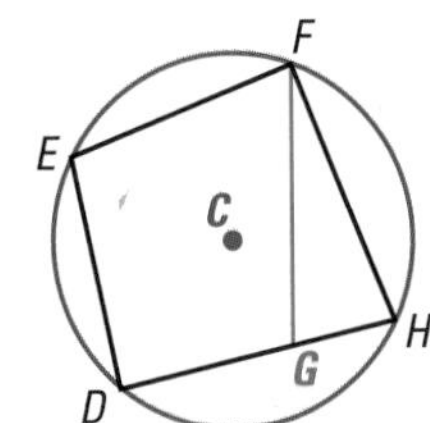

Case 2 *G lies outside* $\odot C$. Let H be the intersection of $\overrightarrow{DG}$ and $\odot C$. Then $DEFH$ is inscribed in $\odot C$ and $\angle E$ is supplementary to $\angle DHF$ (by proof above). Then $\angle DGF \cong \angle DHF$ by the given information and the Congruent Supplements Theorem. This implies that $\overline{FG} \parallel \overline{FH}$, which is a contradiction.

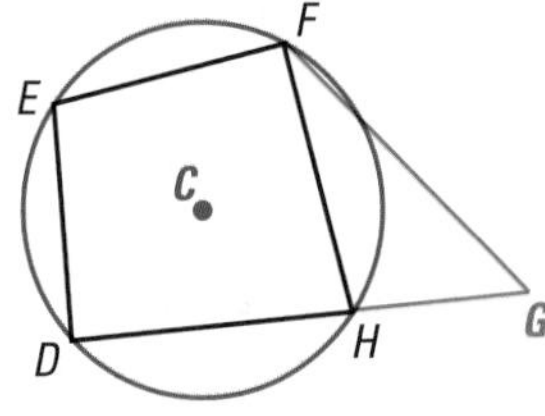

Because the original assumption leads to a contradiction in both cases, G lies on $\odot C$ and $DEFG$ is inscribed in $\odot C$.

Table of Symbols

Symbol		Page
$\sqrt{a}$	square root of *a*	2
$-a$	opposite of *a*	2
$\ldots$	and so on	3
$\cdot$	multiplication, times	6
(x, y)	ordered pair	8
$\overleftrightarrow{AB}$	line *AB*	10
$\overline{AB}$	segment *AB*	11
$\overrightarrow{AB}$	ray *AB*	11
AB	the length of $\overline{AB}$	17
$\lvert x \rvert$	absolute value of *x*	17
x_1	*x* sub 1	19
$=$	is equal to	19
$\cong$	is congruent to	19
$\angle ABC$	angle *ABC*	26
$m\angle A$	measure of angle *A*	26
$^\circ$	degree(s)	26
π	pi; irrational number ≈ 3.14	51
$\approx$	is approximately equal to	52
$\neq$	not equal to	72
$\perp$	is perpendicular to	79
$\rightarrow$	implies	87
$\leftrightarrow$	if and only if	87
$\sim p$	negation of statement *p*	88
$\parallel$	is parallel to	129
m	slope	165

Symbol		Page
$\triangle ABC$	triangle *ABC*	194
$\triangle$s	triangles	230
$\angle$s	angles	270
$<$	is less than	295
$>$	is greater than	296
$\square ABCD$	parallelogram *ABCD*	330
$\not\cong$	not congruent to	353
A'	*A* prime	396
A''	*A* double prime	411
$\overrightarrow{AB}$	vector *AB*	423
$\langle a, b \rangle$	component form of a vector	423
$\frac{a}{b}, a:b$	ratio of *a* to *b*	457
$\sim$	is similar to	473
$\stackrel{?}{=}$	is this statement true?	543
$\sin$	sine	558
$\cos$	cosine	558
$\tan$	tangent	558
$\sin^{-1}$	inverse sine	567
$\cos^{-1}$	inverse cosine	567
$\tan^{-1}$	inverse tangent	567
$\lvert \overrightarrow{AB} \rvert$	magnitude of a vector	573
$\odot P$	circle *P*	595
$m\overset{\frown}{AB}$	measure of minor arc *AB*	603
$m\overset{\frown}{ABC}$	measure of major arc *ABC*	603
n-gon	polygon with *n* sides	661

Formulas

Angles

Sum of the measures of the interior angles of a triangle: 180°

Sum of the measures of the interior angles of a convex n-gon: $(n - 2) \cdot 180°$

Measure of each interior angle of a regular n-gon: $\frac{1}{n}(n - 2) \cdot 180°$

Exterior angle of a triangle: $m\angle 1 = m\angle A + m\angle B$

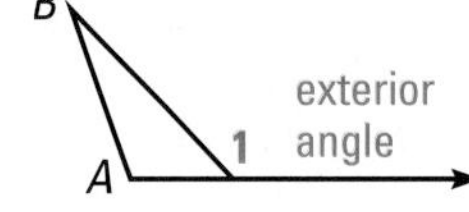

Sum of the measure of the exterior angles of a convex polygon: 360°

Measure of each exterior angle of a regular n-gon: $\frac{1}{n} \cdot 360°$

Right Triangles

Pythagorean Theorem:

$a^2 + b^2 = c^2$

Trigonometric ratios:

$\sin A = \frac{a}{c}$ $\quad \cos A = \frac{b}{c}$ $\quad \tan A = \frac{a}{b}$

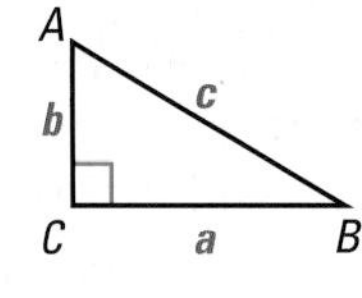

45°-45°-90° triangle

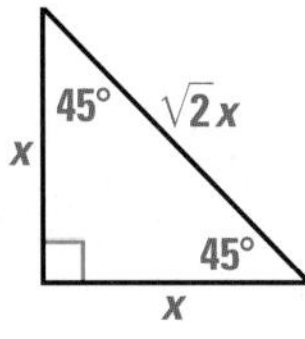

Ratio of sides
1: 1: $\sqrt{2}$

30°-60°-90° triangle

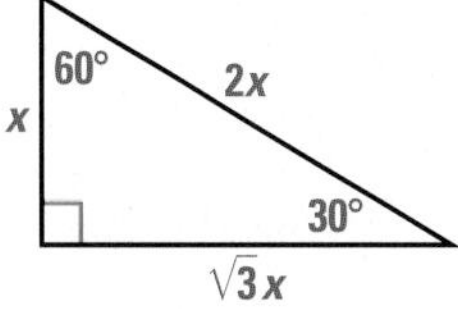

Ratio of sides
1: $\sqrt{3}$: 2

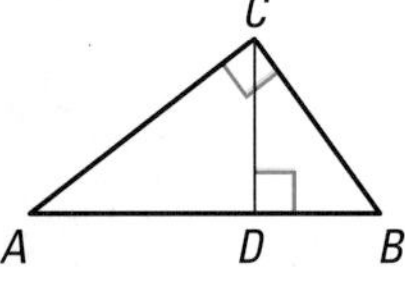

$\triangle ABC \sim \triangle ACD \sim \triangle CBD$

$\frac{BD}{CD} = \frac{CD}{AD}, \frac{AB}{CB} = \frac{CB}{DB}, \frac{AB}{AC} = \frac{AC}{AD}$

$CD = \sqrt{AD \cdot DB}$

Circles

Angle and segments formed by two chords:

$m\angle 1 = \frac{1}{2}(m\overset{\frown}{CD} + m\overset{\frown}{AB})$

$EA \cdot EC = EB \cdot ED$

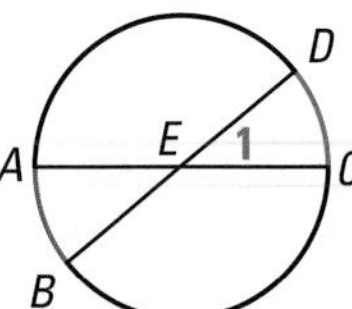

Angle and segments formed by a tangent and a secant:

$m\angle 2 = \frac{1}{2}(m\overset{\frown}{BC} - m\overset{\frown}{AB})$

$EA \cdot EC = (EB)^2$

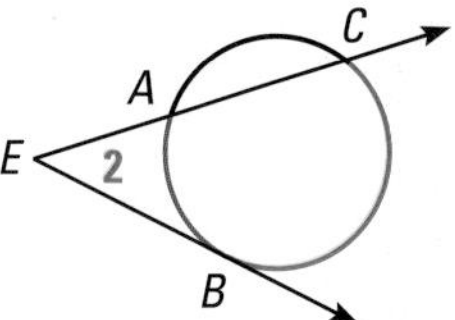

Angle and segments formed by two tangents:

$m\angle 3 = \frac{1}{2}(m\overset{\frown}{AQB} - m\overset{\frown}{AB})$

$EA = EB$

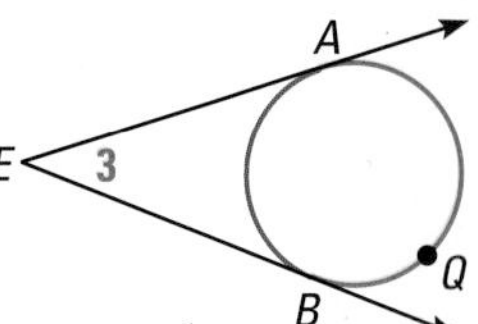

Angle and segments formed by two secants:

$m\angle 4 = \frac{1}{2}(m\overset{\frown}{CD} - m\overset{\frown}{AB})$

$EA \cdot EC = EB \cdot ED$

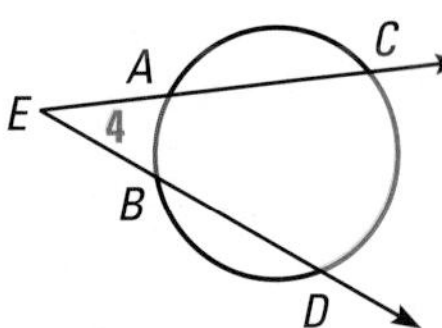

Coordinate Geometry

Given: Points $A(x_1, y_1)$ and $B(x_2, y_2)$

$AB = \sqrt{(x_2 - x_1)^2 + (y_2 - y_1)^2}$

Midpoint of $\overline{AB} = \left(\frac{x_1 + x_2}{2}, \frac{y_1 + y_2}{2}\right)$

Slope of $\overleftrightarrow{AB} = \frac{\text{rise}}{\text{run}} = \frac{y_2 - y_1}{x_2 - x_1}$

Slope-intercept form of a linear equation with slope m and y-intercept b: $y = mx + b$

Standard equation of a circle with center (h, k) and radius r: $(x - h)^2 + (y - k)^2 = r^2$

Vectors

$\vec{u} = \langle a_1, b_1 \rangle, \vec{v} = \langle a_2, b_2 \rangle$

$\vec{u} + \vec{v} = \langle a_1 + a_2, b_1 + b_2 \rangle$

Perimeter

P = perimeter, C = circumference,
s = side, ℓ = length, w = width,
$a, b, c,$ = lengths of the sides of a triangle,
r = radius

Square: $P = 4s$

Rectangle: $P = 2\ell + 2w$

Triangle: $P = a + b + c$

Circle: $C = 2\pi r$

Arc length of $\widehat{AB} = \dfrac{m\widehat{AB}}{360°} \cdot 2\pi r$

Area

A = area, s = side, b = base, h = height,
ℓ = length, w = width, d = diagonal,
a = apothem, P = perimeter, r = radius

Square: $A = s^2$

Rectangle: $A = \ell w$

Parallelogram: $A = bh$

Triangle: $A = \frac{1}{2}bh$

Trapezoid: $A = \frac{1}{2}h(b_1 + b_2)$

Quadrilateral with $\perp$ diagonals: $A = \frac{1}{2}d_1d_2$

Equilateral triangle: $A = \frac{1}{4}\sqrt{3}\,s^2$

Regular polygon: $A = \frac{1}{2}aP$

Circle: $A = \pi r^2$

Area of a sector: $A = \dfrac{m\widehat{AB}}{360°} \cdot \pi r^2$

Surface Area

B = area of the base, P = perimeter,
h = height, r = radius, ℓ = slant height

Right prism: $S = 2B + Ph$

Right cylinder: $S = 2\pi r^2 + 2\pi rh$

Regular pyramid: $S = B + \frac{1}{2}P\ell$

Right cone: $S = \pi r^2 + \pi r\ell$

Sphere: $S = 4\pi r^2$

Volume

V = volume, B = area of a base,
h = height, r = radius, s = side

Cube: $V = s^3$

Pyramid: $V = \frac{1}{3}Bh$

Cone: $V = \frac{1}{3}\pi r^2 h$

Cylinder: $V = \pi r^2 h$

Prism: $V = Bh$

Sphere: $V = \frac{4}{3}\pi r^3$

Miscellaneous

Geometric mean of a and b: $\sqrt{a \cdot b}$

Euler's Theorem for Polyhedra, F = faces,
V = vertices, E = edges: $F + V = E + 2$

Given similar solids with corresponding sides of lengths a and b

Ratio of areas $= a^2 : b^2$

Ratio of volumes $= a^3 : b^3$

843

Table of Squares and Square Roots

No.	Square	Sq. Root
1	1	1.000
2	4	1.414
3	9	1.732
4	16	2.000
5	25	2.236
6	36	2.449
7	49	2.646
8	64	2.828
9	81	3.000
10	100	3.162
11	121	3.317
12	144	3.464
13	169	3.606
14	196	3.742
15	225	3.873
16	256	4.000
17	289	4.123
18	324	4.243
19	361	4.359
20	400	4.472
21	441	4.583
22	484	4.690
23	529	4.796
24	576	4.899
25	625	5.000
26	676	5.099
27	729	5.196
28	784	5.292
29	841	5.385
30	900	5.477
31	961	5.568
32	1,024	5.657
33	1,089	5.745
34	1,156	5.831
35	1,225	5.916
36	1,296	6.000
37	1,369	6.083
38	1,444	6.164
39	1,521	6.245
40	1,600	6.325
41	1,681	6.403
42	1,764	6.481
43	1,849	6.557
44	1,936	6.633
45	2,025	6.708
46	2,116	6.782
47	2,209	6.856
48	2,304	6.928
49	2,401	7.000
50	2,500	7.071

No.	Square	Sq. Root
51	2,601	7.141
52	2,704	7.211
53	2,809	7.280
54	2,916	7.348
55	3,025	7.416
56	3,136	7.483
57	3,249	7.550
58	3,364	7.616
59	3,481	7.681
60	3,600	7.746
61	3,721	7.810
62	3,844	7.874
63	3,969	7.937
64	4,096	8.000
65	4,225	8.062
66	4,356	8.124
67	4,489	8.185
68	4,624	8.246
69	4,761	8.307
70	4,900	8.367
71	5,041	8.426
72	5,184	8.485
73	5,329	8.544
74	5,476	8.602
75	5,625	8.660
76	5,776	8.718
77	5,929	8.775
78	6,084	8.832
79	6,241	8.888
80	6,400	8.944
81	6,561	9.000
82	6,724	9.055
83	6,889	9.110
84	7,056	9.165
85	7,225	9.220
86	7,396	9.274
87	7,569	9.327
88	7,744	9.381
89	7,921	9.434
90	8,100	9.487
91	8,281	9.539
92	8,464	9.592
93	8,649	9.644
94	8,836	9.695
95	9,025	9.747
96	9,216	9.798
97	9,409	9.849
98	9,604	9.899
99	9,801	9.950
100	10,000	10.000

No.	Square	Sq. Root
101	10,201	10.050
102	10,404	10.100
103	10,609	10.149
104	10,816	10.198
105	11,025	10.247
106	11,236	10.296
107	11,449	10.344
108	11,664	10.392
109	11,881	10.440
110	12,100	10.488
111	12,321	10.536
112	12,544	10.583
113	12,769	10.630
114	12,996	10.677
115	13,225	10.724
116	13,456	10.770
117	13,689	10.817
118	13,924	10.863
119	14,161	10.909
120	14,400	10.954
121	14,641	11.000
122	14,884	11.045
123	15,129	11.091
124	15,376	11.136
125	15,625	11.180
126	15,876	11.225
127	16,129	11.269
128	16,384	11.314
129	16,641	11.358
130	16,900	11.402
131	17,161	11.446
132	17,424	11.489
133	17,689	11.533
134	17,956	11.576
135	18,225	11.619
136	18,496	11.662
137	18,769	11.705
138	19,044	11.747
139	19,321	11.790
140	19,600	11.832
141	19,881	11.874
142	20,164	11.916
143	20,449	11.958
144	20,736	12.000
145	21,025	12.042
146	21,316	12.083
147	21,609	12.124
148	21,904	12.166
149	22,201	12.207
150	22,500	12.247

844 Student Resources

Table of Trigonometric Ratios

Angle	Sine	Cosine	Tangent
1°	.0175	.9998	.0175
2°	.0349	.9994	.0349
3°	.0523	.9986	.0524
4°	.0698	.9976	.0699
5°	.0872	.9962	.0875
6°	.1045	.9945	.1051
7°	.1219	.9925	.1228
8°	.1392	.9903	.1405
9°	.1564	.9877	.1584
10°	.1736	.9848	.1763
11°	.1908	.9816	.1944
12°	.2079	.9781	.2126
13°	.2250	.9744	.2309
14°	.2419	.9703	.2493
15°	.2588	.9659	.2679
16°	.2756	.9613	.2867
17°	.2924	.9563	.3057
18°	.3090	.9511	.3249
19°	.3256	.9455	.3443
20°	.3420	.9397	.3640
21°	.3584	.9336	.3839
22°	.3746	.9272	.4040
23°	.3907	.9205	.4245
24°	.4067	.9135	.4452
25°	.4226	.9063	.4663
26°	.4384	.8988	.4877
27°	.4540	.8910	.5095
28°	.4695	.8829	.5317
29°	.4848	.8746	.5543
30°	.5000	.8660	.5774
31°	.5150	.8572	.6009
32°	.5299	.8480	.6249
33°	.5446	.8387	.6494
34°	.5592	.8290	.6745
35°	.5736	.8192	.7002
36°	.5878	.8090	.7265
37°	.6018	.7986	.7536
38°	.6157	.7880	.7813
39°	.6293	.7771	.8098
40°	.6428	.7660	.8391
41°	.6561	.7547	.8693
42°	.6691	.7431	.9004
43°	.6820	.7314	.9325
44°	.6947	.7193	.9657
45°	.7071	.7071	1.0000

Angle	Sine	Cosine	Tangent
46°	.7193	.6947	1.0355
47°	.7314	.6820	1.0724
48°	.7431	.6691	1.1106
49°	.7547	.6561	1.1504
50°	.7660	.6428	1.1918
51°	.7771	.6293	1.2349
52°	.7880	.6157	1.2799
53°	.7986	.6018	1.3270
54°	.8090	.5878	1.3764
55°	.8192	.5736	1.4281
56°	.8290	.5592	1.4826
57°	.8387	.5446	1.5399
58°	.8480	.5299	1.6003
59°	.8572	.5150	1.6643
60°	.8660	.5000	1.7321
61°	.8746	.4848	1.8040
62°	.8829	.4695	1.8807
63°	.8910	.4540	1.9626
64°	.8988	.4384	2.0503
65°	.9063	.4226	2.1445
66°	.9135	.4067	2.2460
67°	.9205	.3907	2.3559
68°	.9272	.3746	2.4751
69°	.9336	.3584	2.6051
70°	.9397	.3420	2.7475
71°	.9455	.3256	2.9042
72°	.9511	.3090	3.0777
73°	.9563	.2924	3.2709
74°	.9613	.2756	3.4874
75°	.9659	.2588	3.7321
76°	.9703	.2419	4.0108
77°	.9744	.2250	4.3315
78°	.9781	.2079	4.7046
79°	.9816	.1908	5.1446
80°	.9848	.1736	5.6713
81°	.9877	.1564	6.3138
82°	.9903	.1392	7.1154
83°	.9925	.1219	8.1443
84°	.9945	.1045	9.5144
85°	.9962	.0872	11.4301
86°	.9976	.0698	14.3007
87°	.9986	.0523	19.0811
88°	.9994	.0349	28.6363
89°	.9998	.0175	57.2900

Glossary

A

acute angle (p. 28) An angle with measure between 0° and 90°.

acute triangle (p. 194) A triangle with three acute angles.

adjacent angles (p. 28) Two angles with a common vertex and side but no common interior points.

adjacent sides of a triangle (p. 195) Two sides of a triangle with a common vertex.

alternate exterior angles (p. 131) Two angles that are formed by two lines and a transversal and that lie outside the two lines on opposite sides of the transversal. See angles 1 and 8.

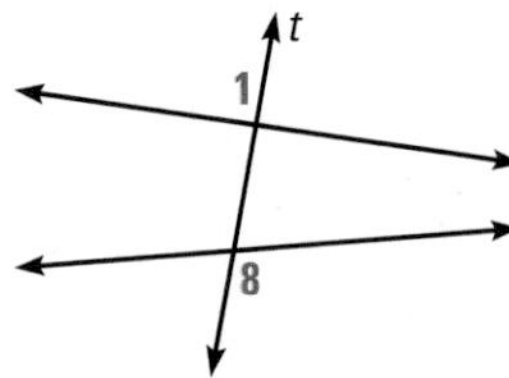

alternate interior angles (p. 131) Two angles that are formed by two lines and a transversal and that lie between the two lines on opposite sides of the transversal. See angles 3 and 6.

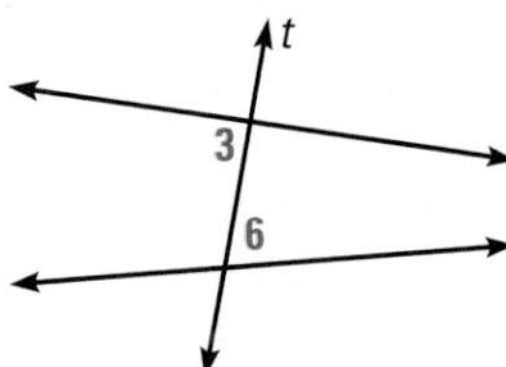

altitude of a triangle (p. 281) The perpendicular segment from a vertex of a triangle to the opposite side or to the line that contains the opposite side.

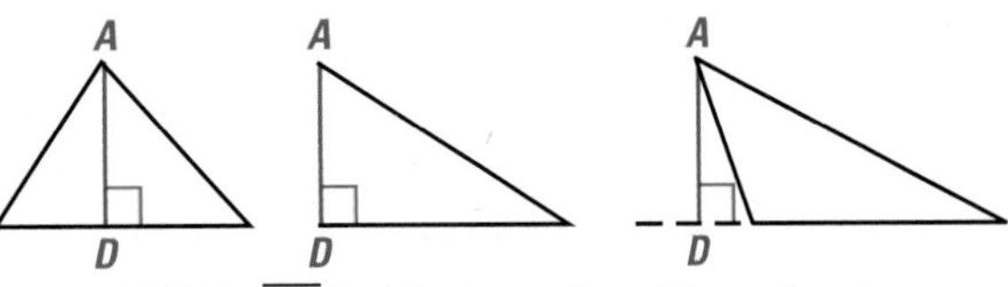

Altitude $\overline{AD}$, inside, on, and outside a triangle

angle (p. 26) Consists of two different rays that have the same initial point. The rays are the *sides* of the angle, and the initial point is the *vertex* of the angle. The angle symbol is $\angle$.

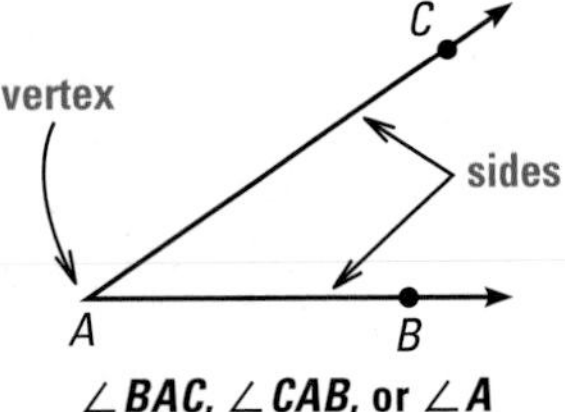

$\angle BAC$, $\angle CAB$, or $\angle A$

angle bisector (p. 36) A ray that divides an angle into two adjacent angles that are congruent.

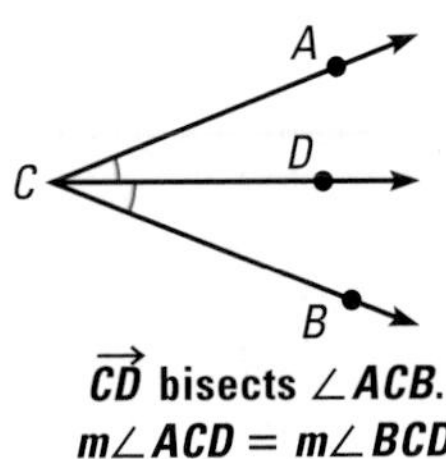

$\overrightarrow{CD}$ **bisects** $\angle ACB$.
$m\angle ACD = m\angle BCD$

angle bisector of a triangle (p. 274) A bisector of an angle of the triangle.

angle of elevation (p. 561) When you stand and look up at a point in the distance, the angle that your line of sight makes with a line drawn horizontally.

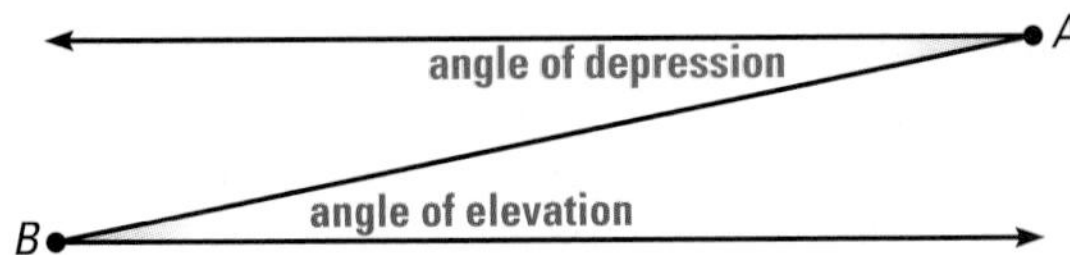

angle of rotation (p. 412) The angle formed when rays are drawn from the center of rotation to a point and its image. *See also* rotation.

apothem of a polygon (p. 670) The distance from the center of a polygon to any side of the polygon.

arc length (p. 683) A portion of the circumference of a circle.

axioms (p. 17) *See* postulates.

B

base of an isosceles triangle (p. 195) The noncongruent side of an isosceles triangle that has only two congruent sides.

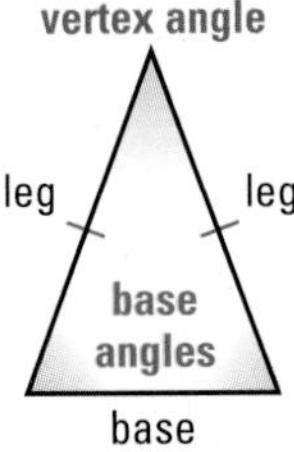

bases of a prism (p. 728) *See* prism.

bases of a trapezoid (p. 356) *See* trapezoid.

base angles of an isosceles triangle (p. 236) The two angles that contain the base of an isosceles triangle. *See also* base of an isosceles triangle.

base angles of a trapezoid (p. 356) Two pairs of angles whose common side is the base of a trapezoid.

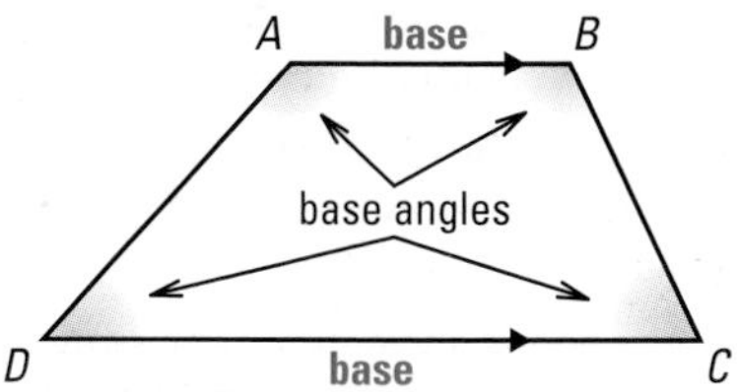

$\angle A$ and $\angle B$ are a pair of base angles.
$\angle C$ and $\angle D$ are another pair.

between (p. 18) When three points lie on a line, you can say that one of them is *between* the other two.

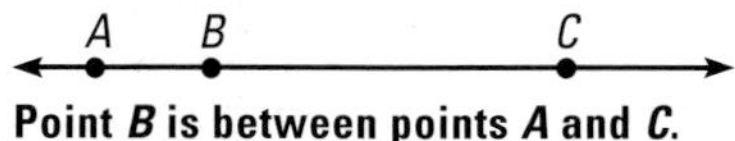

Point B is between points A and C.

biconditional statement (pp. 80, 87) A statement that contains the phrase "if and only if." The symbol for "if and only if" is $\leftrightarrow$.

bisect (pp. 34, 36) To divide into two congruent parts.

border pattern (p. 437) *See* frieze pattern.

C

center of a circle (p. 595) *See* circle.

center of a polygon (p. 670) The center of its circumscribed circle.

center of a sphere (p. 759) *See* sphere.

center of rotation (p. 412) *See* rotation.

central angle of a circle (p. 603) An angle whose vertex is the center of a circle.

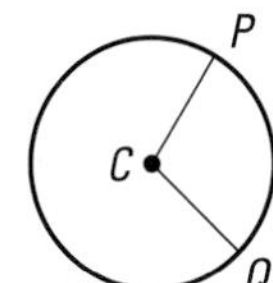

$\angle PCQ$ is a central angle.

central angle of a regular polygon (p. 671) An angle whose vertex is the center of the polygon and whose sides contain two consecutive vertices of the polygon.

centroid of a triangle (p. 279) The point of concurrency of the medians of a triangle.

chord of a circle (p. 595) A segment whose endpoints are points on the circle.

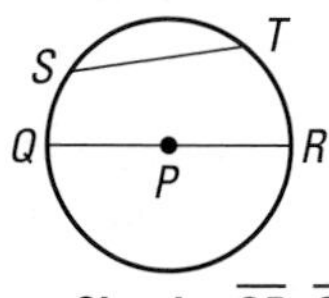

Chords: $\overline{QR}$, $\overline{ST}$

chord of a sphere (p. 759) A segment whose endpoints are on the sphere.

circle (p. 595) The set of all points in a plane that are equidistant from a given point, called the *center* of the circle.

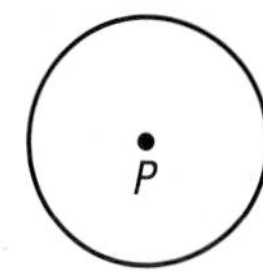

Circle with center P, or $\odot P$

circular cone (p. 737) A solid with a circular *base* and a *vertex* that is not in the same plane as the base. The *lateral surface* consists of all segments that connect the vertex with points on the edge of the base. The *altitude*, or *height*, is the perpendicular distance between the vertex and the plane that contains the base.

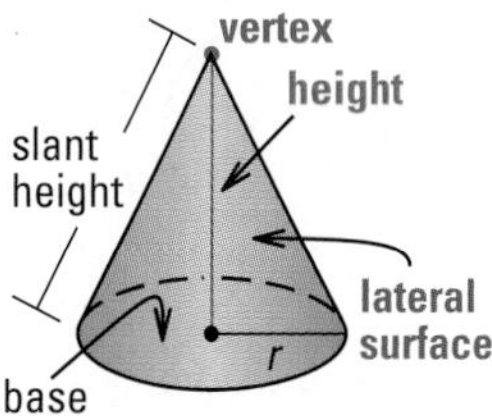

circumcenter of a triangle (p. 273) The point of concurrency of the perpendicular bisectors of a triangle.

circumference (p. 683) The distance around a circle.

circumscribed circle (p. 615) A circle with an inscribed polygon. *See also* inscribed polygon.

collinear points (p. 10) Points that lie on the same line.

common tangent (p. 596) A line or segment that is tangent to two circles. A common internal tangent intersects the segment that joins the centers of the two circles. A common external tangent does not intersect the segment that joins the centers of the two circles.

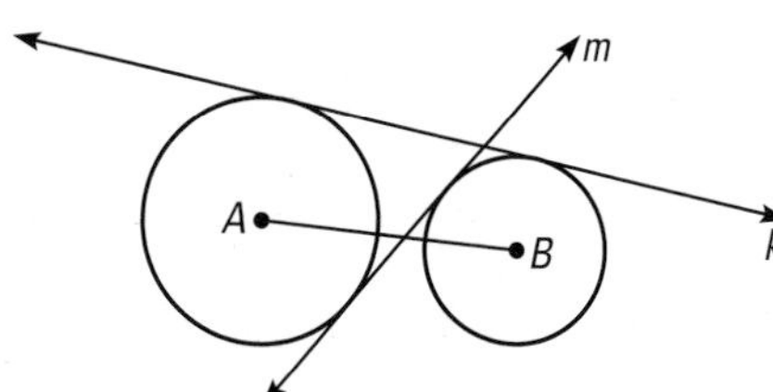

Line m is a common internal tangent.
Line k is a common external tangent.

compass (p. 34) A construction tool used to draw arcs.

complement (p. 46) The sum of the measures of an angle and its *complement* is 90°.

complementary angles (p. 46) Two angles whose measures have the sum 90°.

component form (p. 423) The form of a vector that combines the horizontal and vertical components of the vector.

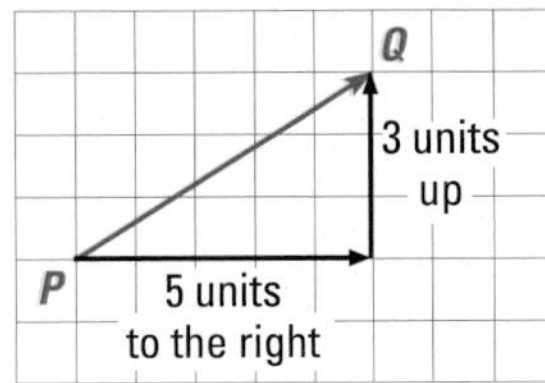

$\overrightarrow{PQ}$ **with component form** $\langle 5, 3 \rangle$

composition of transformations (p. 431) The result when two or more transformations are combined to produce a single transformation. An example is a glide reflection.

concave polygon (p. 323) *See* convex polygon.

concentric circles (p. 596) Circles that have a common center.

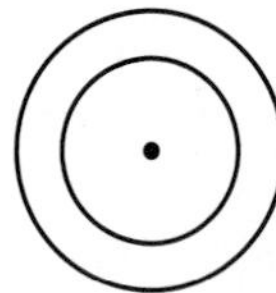

conclusion (p. 71) The "then" part of a conditional statement.

concurrent lines (p. 272) Three or more lines that intersect in the same point.

conditional statement (p. 71) A type of logical statement that has two parts, a hypothesis and a conclusion.

cone (p. 737) *See* circular cone.

congruent angles (p. 26) Angles that have the same measure.

congruent arcs (p. 604) Two arcs of the same circle or of congruent circles that have the same measure.

congruent circles (p. 595) Two circles that have the same radius.

congruent figures (p. 202) Two geometric figures that have exactly the same size and shape. When two figures are congruent, all pairs of corresponding angles and corresponding sides are congruent. The symbol for "is congruent to" is $\cong$.

congruent segments (p. 19) Segments that have the same length.

conjecture (p. 4) An unproven statement that is based on observations.

consecutive interior angles (p. 131) Two angles that are formed by two lines and a transversal and that lie between the two lines on the same side of the transversal. Also called *same side interior angles*. See angles 3 and 5.

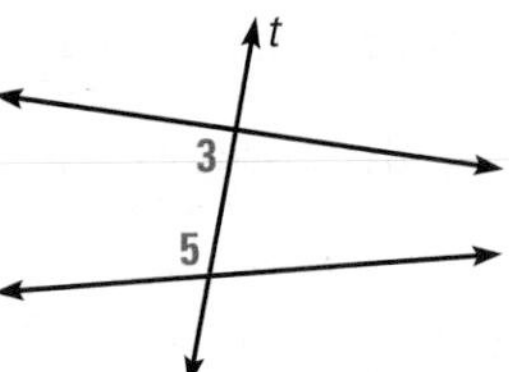

construct (p. 34) To draw using a limited set of tools, usually a compass and a straightedge.

construction (p. 34) A geometric drawing that uses a limited set of tools, usually a compass and a straightedge.

contrapositive (p. 72) The statement formed when you negate the hypothesis and conclusion of the converse of a conditional statement.

converse (p. 72) The statement formed by switching the hypothesis and conclusion of a conditional statement.

convex polygon (p. 323) A polygon such that no line containing a side of the polygon contains a point in the interior of the polygon. A polygon that is not convex is *nonconvex*, or *concave*.

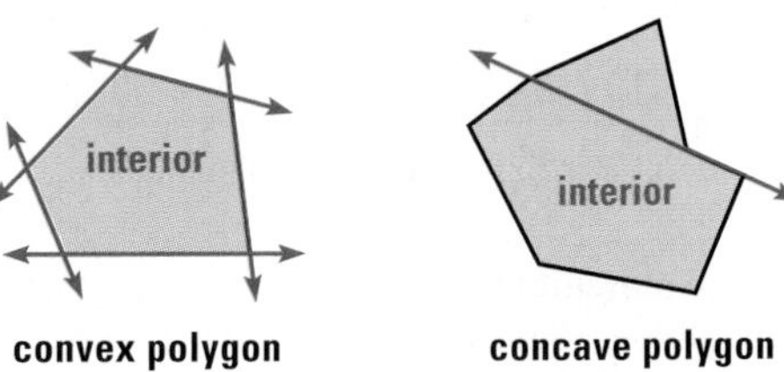

convex polygon **concave polygon**

convex polyhedron (p. 720) A polyhedron such that any two points on its surface can be connected by a line segment that lies entirely inside or on the polyhedron. If this line goes outside the polyhedron, then the polyhedron is *nonconvex*, or *concave*.

coordinate (p. 17) The real number that corresponds to a point on a line.

coordinate proof (p. 243) A type of proof that involves placing geometric figures in a coordinate plane.

coplanar points (p. 10) Points that lie on the same plane.

corollary (p. 197) A statement that can be proved easily using a theorem or a definition.

corresponding angles (p. 131) Two angles that are formed by two lines and a transversal and occupy corresponding positions. See angles 1 and 5.

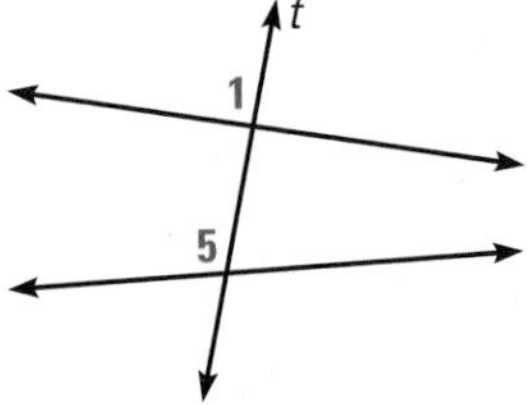

corresponding angles of congruent figures (p. 202) When two figures are congruent, the angles that are in corresponding positions and are congruent.

corresponding sides of congruent figures (p. 202) When two figures are congruent, the sides that are in corresponding positions and are congruent.

cosine **(p. 558)** A trigonometric ratio, abbreviated as *cos*. For right triangle ABC, the cosine of the acute angle A is

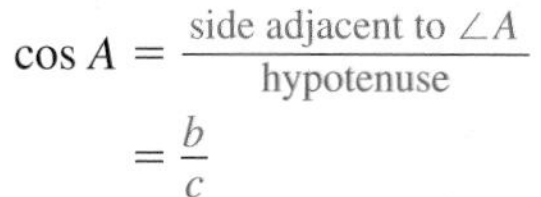

$$\cos A = \frac{\text{side adjacent to } \angle A}{\text{hypotenuse}} = \frac{b}{c}$$

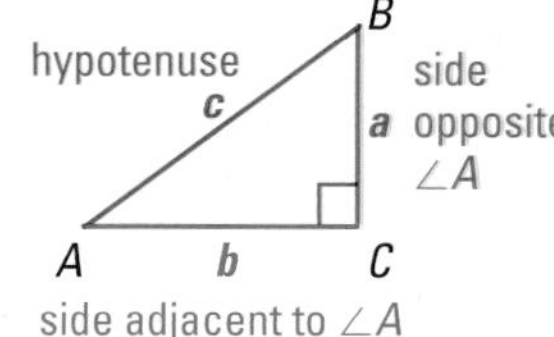

counterexample **(p. 4)** An example that shows a conjecture is false.

cross section **(p. 720)** The intersection of a plane and a solid.

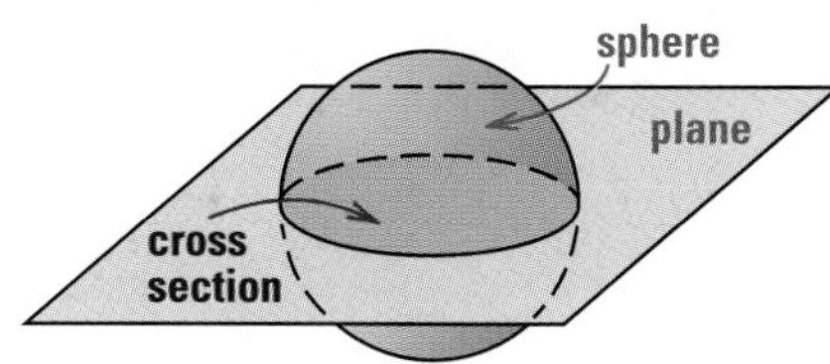

cylinder **(p. 730)** A solid with congruent circular bases that lie in parallel planes. The *altitude*, or *height*, of a cylinder is the perpendicular distance between its bases. The radius of the base is also called the *radius* of the cylinder.

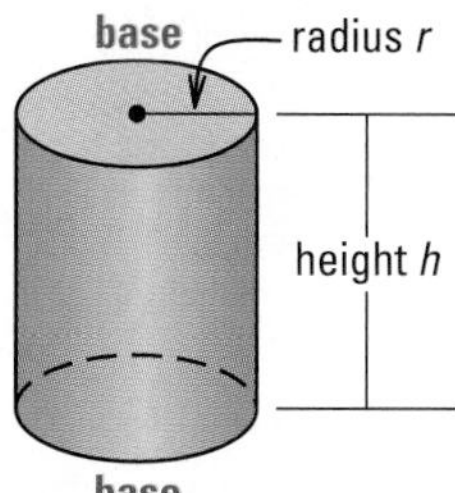

D

definition **(p. 10)** Uses known words to describe a new word.

diagonal of a polygon **(p. 324)** A segment that joins two nonconsecutive vertices of a polygon.

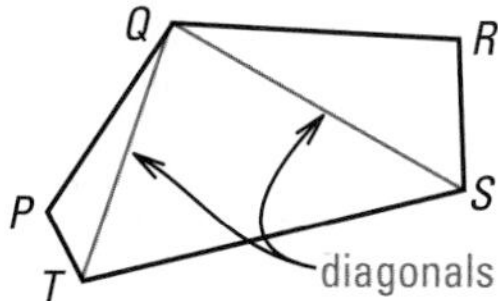

diameter of a circle **(p. 595)** A chord that passes through the center of the circle. The distance across a circle, through its center.

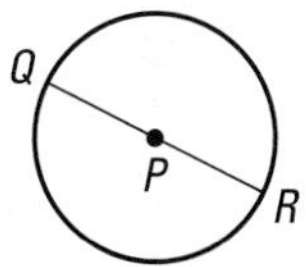

Diameter: $\overline{QR}$ or QR

diameter of a sphere **(p. 759)** A chord that contains the center of the sphere. The length of a chord that contains the center of the sphere.

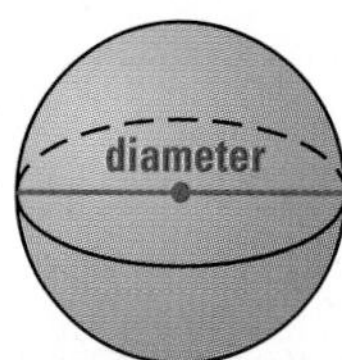

dilation **(p. 506)** A type of transformation, with center C and scale factor k, that maps every point P in the plane to a point P' so that the following two properties are true. (1) If P is not the center point C, then the image point P' lies on $\overrightarrow{CP}$. The scale factor k is a positive number such that $CP' = k(CP)$, and $k \neq 1$. (2) If P is the center point C, then $P = P'$.

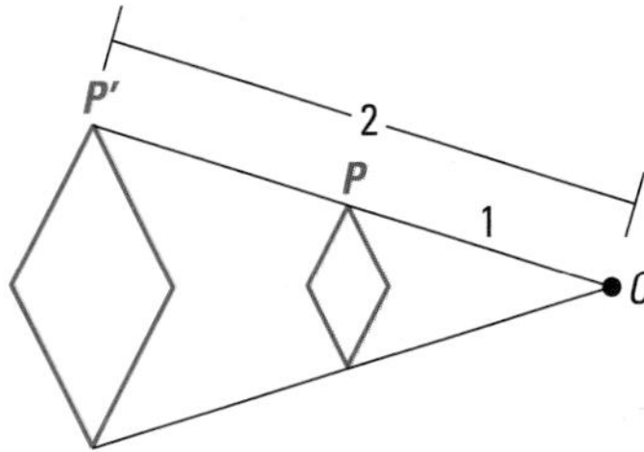

Dilation with $k = 2$

direction of a vector **(p. 574)** Determined by the angle that the vector makes with a horizontal line.

distance between two points on a line **(p. 17)** The absolute value of the difference between the coordinates of the points. The distance between A and B is written as AB, which is also called the *length* of $\overline{AB}$.

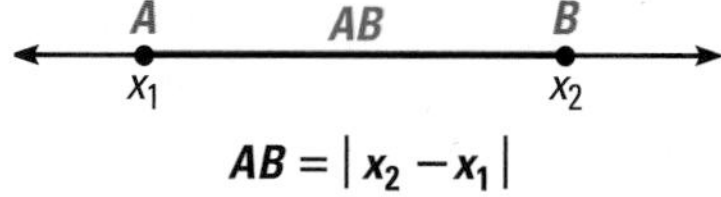

$AB = |x_2 - x_1|$

Distance Formula **(p. 19)** If $A(x_1, y_1)$ and $B(x_2, y_2)$ are points in a coordinate plane, then the distance between A and B is

$$AB = \sqrt{(x_2 - x_1)^2 + (y_2 - y_1)^2}.$$

distance from a point to a line **(p. 266)** The length of the perpendicular segment from the point to the line.

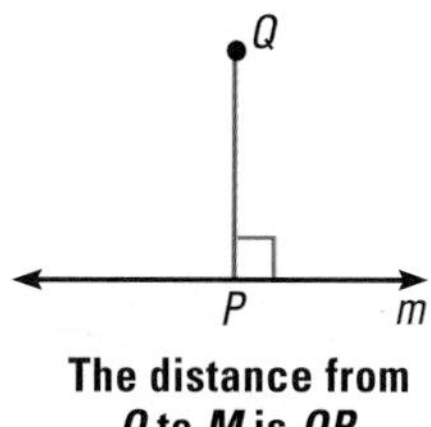

The distance from Q to M is QP.

dodecahedron **(p. 721)** A polyhedron with twelve faces.

E

edge (p. 719) A line segment formed by the intersection of two faces of a polyhedron. *See also* polyhedron.

endpoints (p. 11) *See* line segment.

enlargement (p. 506) A dilation with $k > 1$.

equal vectors (p. 574) Two vectors that have the same magnitude and direction.

equiangular polygon (p. 323) A polygon with all of its interior angles congruent.

equiangular triangle (p. 194) A triangle with three congruent angles.

equidistant from two lines (p. 266) The same distance from one line as from another line.

equidistant from two points (p. 264) The same distance from one point as from another point.

equilateral polygon (p. 323) A polygon with all of its sides congruent.

equilateral triangle (p. 194) A triangle with three congruent sides.

equivalent statements (p. 72) Two statements that are both true or both false.

exterior of an angle (p. 27) All points not on the angle or in its interior. *See also* interior of an angle.

exterior of a circle (p. 596) All points of the plane that are outside a circle.

exterior angles of a triangle (p. 196) When the sides of a triangle are extended, the angles that are adjacent to the interior angles.

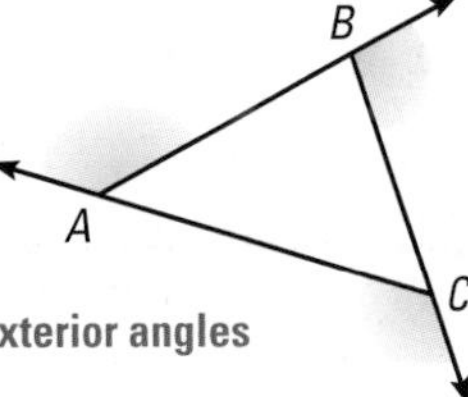

external segment (p. 630) The part of a secant segment that is not inside the circle.

extremes of a proportion (p. 459) The first and last terms of a proportion. The extremes of $\frac{a}{b} = \frac{c}{d}$ are a and d.

F

face (p. 719) *See* polyhedron.

flow proof (pp. 135, 136) A type of proof that uses arrows to show the flow of a logical argument. Statements are connected by arrows to show how each statement comes from the ones before it, and each reason is written below the statement it justifies.

frieze pattern (p. 437) A pattern that extends to the left and right in such a way that the pattern can be mapped onto itself by a horizontal translation. Also called *border pattern*.

G

geometric mean (p. 466) For two positive numbers a and b, the positive number x such that $\frac{a}{x} = \frac{x}{b}$, or $x = \sqrt{a \cdot b}$.

geometric probability (p. 699) A probability that involves a geometric measure such as length or area.

glide reflection (p. 430) A transformation in which every point P is mapped onto a point P'' by the following two steps. (1) A translation maps P onto P'. (2) A reflection in a line k parallel to the direction of the translation maps P' onto P''.

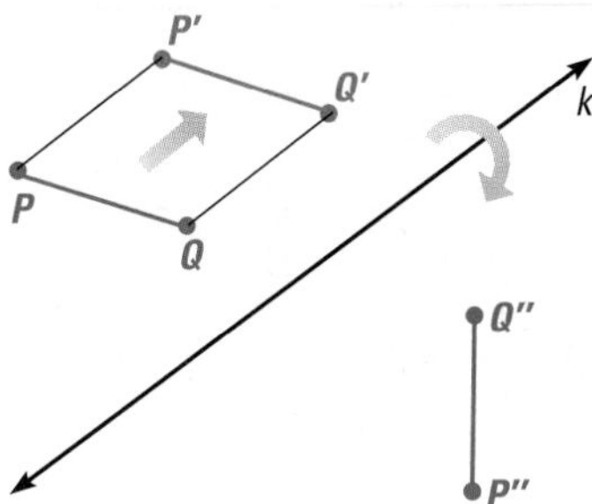

great circle (p. 760) The intersection of a sphere and a plane that contains the center of the sphere.

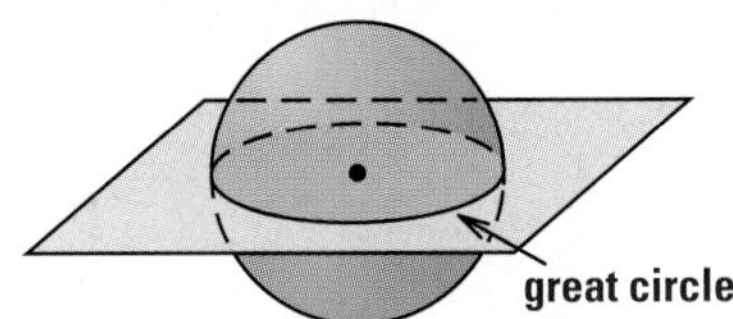

H

hemisphere (p. 760) Half of a sphere, formed when a great circle separates a sphere into two congruent halves.

hypotenuse (p. 195) In a right triangle, the side opposite the right angle. *See also* legs of a right triangle.

hypothesis (p. 71) The "if" part of a conditional statement.

I

icosahedron (p. 721) A polyhedron with twenty faces.

if-then form (p. 71) The form of a conditional statement that uses the words "if" and "then." The "if" part contains the hypothesis and the "then" part contains the conclusion.

image (p. 396) The new figure that results from the transformation of a figure in a plane. *See also* preimage.

incenter of a triangle (p. 274) The point of concurrency of the angle bisectors of a triangle.

indirect proof (p. 302) A proof in which you prove that a statement is true by first assuming that its opposite is true. If this assumption leads to an impossibility, then you have proved that the original statement is true.

inductive reasoning (p. 4) A process that includes looking for patterns and making conjectures.

initial point of a ray (p. 11) *See* ray.

initial point of a vector (p. 423) The starting point of a vector. *See also* vector.

inscribed angle (p. 613) An angle whose vertex is on a circle and whose sides contain chords of the circle.

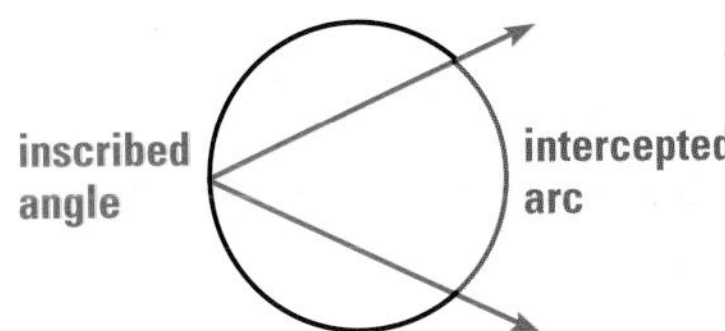

inscribed polygon (p. 615) A polygon whose vertices all lie on a circle.

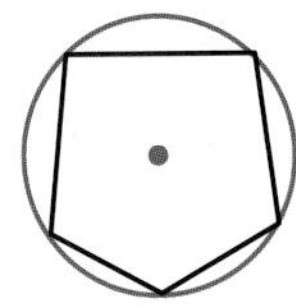

intercepted arc (p. 613) The arc that lies in the interior of an inscribed angle and has endpoints on the angle. *See also* inscribed angle.

interior of a circle (p. 596) All points of the plane that are inside a circle.

interior of an angle (p. 27) All points between the points that lie on each side of the angle.

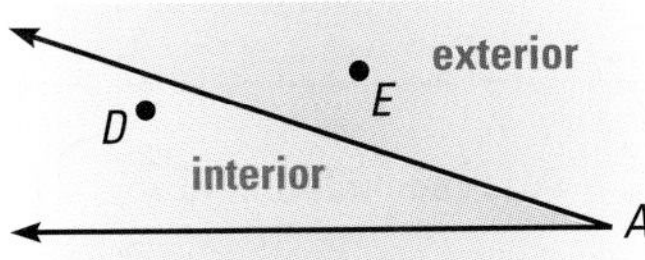

interior angles of a triangle (p. 196) When the sides of a triangle are extended, the three original angles of the triangle.

intersect (p. 12) To have one or more points in common.

intersection (p. 12) The set of points that two or more geometric figures have in common.

inverse (p. 72) The statement formed when you negate the hypothesis and conclusion of a conditional statement.

isometry (p. 397) A transformation that preserves lengths. Also called *rigid transformation*.

isosceles trapezoid (p. 356) A trapezoid with congruent legs.

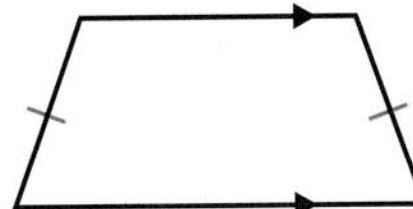

isosceles triangle (p. 194) A triangle with at least two congruent sides.

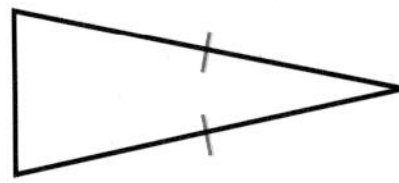

K

kite (p. 358) A quadrilateral that has two pairs of consecutive congruent sides, but in which opposite sides are not congruent.

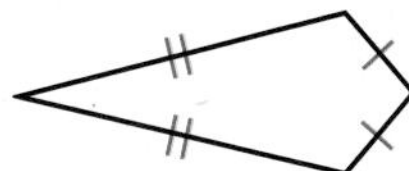

L

lateral area of a cylinder (p. 730) The area of the curved surface of a cylinder.

lateral area of a polyhedron (p. 728) The sum of the areas of the lateral faces of a polyhedron.

lateral faces of a prism (p. 728) *See* prism.

lateral surface of a cone (p. 737) *See* circular cone.

Law of Detachment (p. 89) If $p \to q$ is a true conditional statement and p is true, then q is true.

Law of Syllogism (pp. 89, 90) If $p \to q$ and $q \to r$ are true conditional statements, then $p \to r$ is true.

legs of an isosceles triangle (p. 195) The two congruent sides of an isosceles triangle that has only two congruent sides. *See also* base of an isosceles triangle.

legs of a right triangle (p. 195) In a right triangle, the sides that form the right angle.

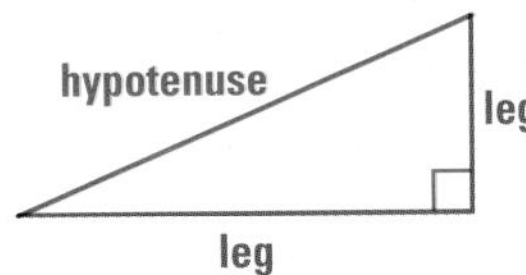

legs of a trapezoid (p. 356) *See* trapezoid.

length of a segment (p. 17) The distance between the endpoints of a segment. *See also* distance between two points on a line.

line (pp. 10, 11) A line extends in one dimension. It is usually represented by a straight line with two arrowheads to indicate that the line extends without end in two directions. In this book, lines are always straight lines. *See also* undefined term.

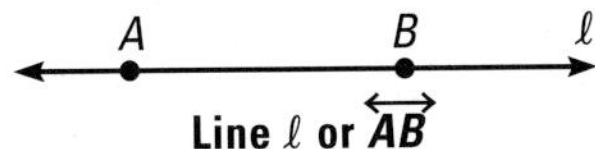

linear pair (p. 44) Two adjacent angles whose noncommon sides are opposite rays.

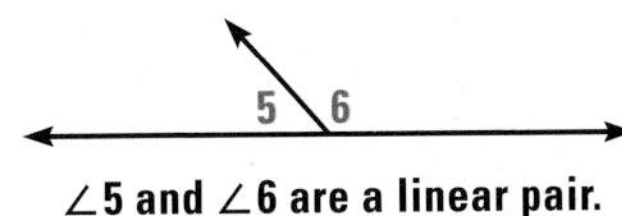

line of reflection (p. 404) *See* reflection.

line of symmetry (p. 406) A line that a figure in the plane has if the figure can be mapped onto itself by a reflection in the line.

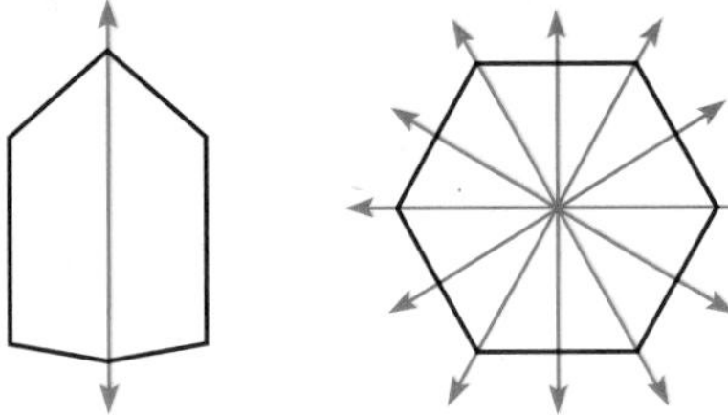

Hexagon with one line of symmetry   Hexagon with six lines of symmetry

line perpendicular to a plane (p. 79) A line that intersects the plane in a point and is perpendicular to every line in the plane that intersects it.

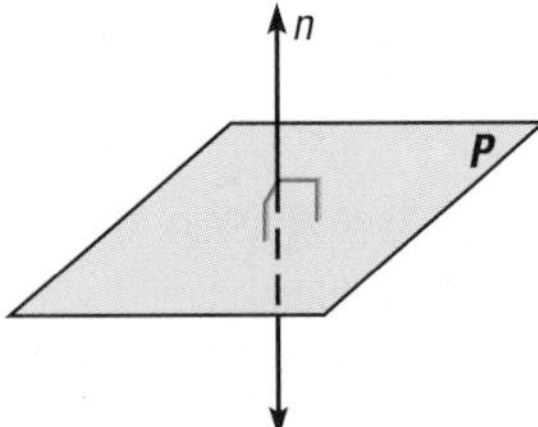

line segment (p. 11) Part of a line that consists of two points, called *endpoints*, and all points on the line that are between the endpoints. Also called *segment*.

$\overline{AB}$ with endpoints A and B

locus (p. 642) The set of all points that satisfy a given condition or a set of given conditions. Plural is *loci*.

logical argument (p. 89) An argument based on deductive reasoning, which uses facts, definitions, and accepted properties in a logical order.

M

magnitude of a vector (p. 573) The distance from the initial point to the terminal point of a vector. The magnitude of $\overrightarrow{AB}$ is the distance from A to B and is written $|\overrightarrow{AB}|$.

major arc (p. 603) Part of a circle that measures between 180° and 360°. *See also* minor arc.

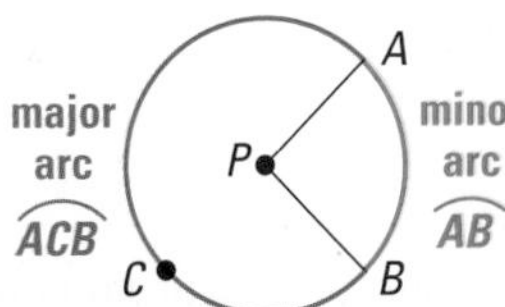

means of a proportion (p. 459) The middle terms of a proportion. The means of $\frac{a}{b} = \frac{c}{d}$ are b and c.

measure of an angle (p. 27) Consider a point A on one side of $\overleftrightarrow{OB}$. The rays of the form $\overrightarrow{OA}$ can be matched one to one with the real numbers from 0 to 180. The measure of $\angle AOB$ is equal to the absolute value of the difference between the real numbers for $\overrightarrow{OA}$ and $\overrightarrow{OB}$.

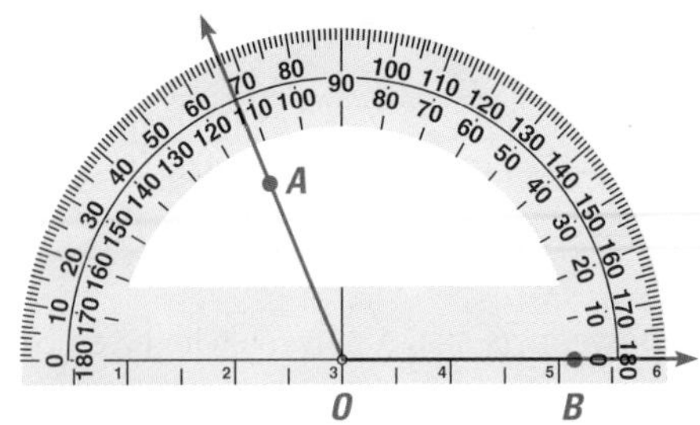

measure of a major arc (p. 603) The difference between 360° and the measure of its associated minor arc.

measure of a minor arc (p. 603) The measure of its central angle.

median of a triangle (p. 279) A segment whose endpoints are a vertex of the triangle and the midpoint of the opposite side.

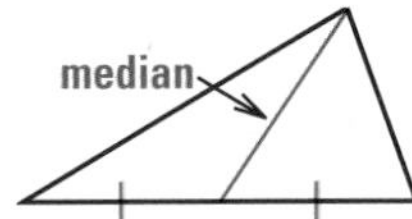

midpoint (p. 34) The point that divides, or bisects, a segment into two congruent segments.

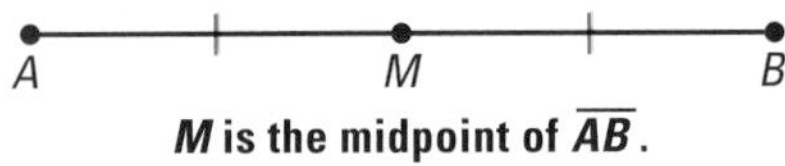

M is the midpoint of $\overline{AB}$.

Midpoint Formula (p. 35) If $A(x_1, y_1)$ and $B(x_2, y_2)$ are points in a coordinate plane, then the midpoint of $\overline{AB}$ has coordinates $\left(\frac{x_1 + x_2}{2}, \frac{y_1 + y_2}{2}\right)$.

midsegment of a trapezoid (p. 357) A segment that connects the midpoints of the legs of a trapezoid.

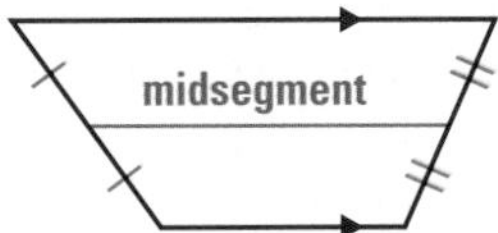

midsegment of a triangle (p. 287) A segment that connects the midpoints of two sides of a triangle.

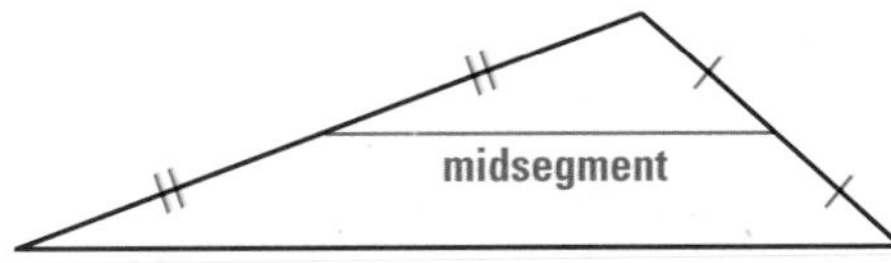

minor arc (p. 603) Part of a circle that measures less than 180°. *See also* major arc.

negation **(pp. 72, 88)** The negative of a statement. The negation symbol is ~.

net **(p. 729)** A two-dimensional representation of all the faces of a polyhedron.

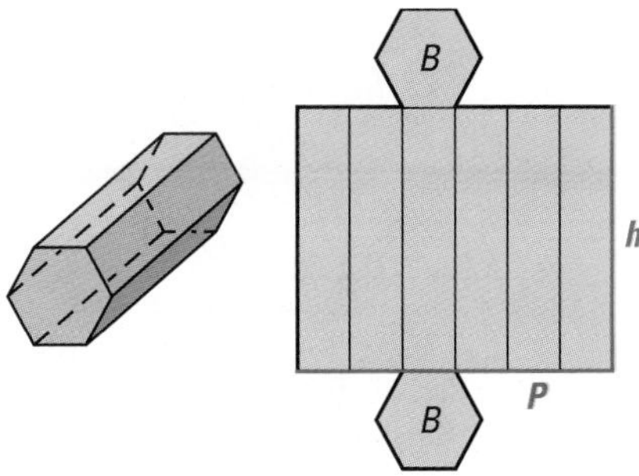

nonconvex polygon **(p. 323)** *See* convex polygon.

oblique prism **(p. 728)** A prism whose lateral edges are not perpendicular to the bases. The length of the oblique lateral edges is the *slant height* of the prism.

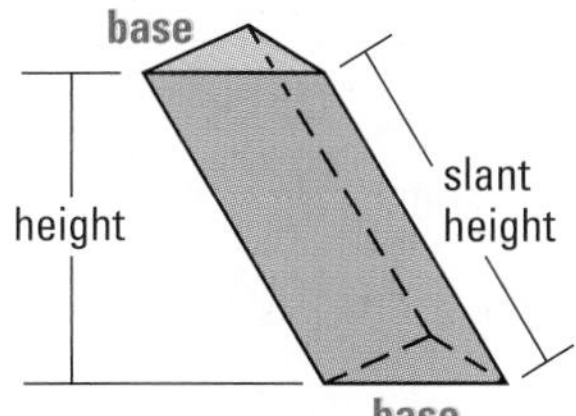

Oblique triangular prism

obtuse angle **(p. 28)** An angle with measure between 90° and 180°.

obtuse triangle **(p. 194)** A triangle with one obtuse angle.

octahedron **(p. 721)** A polyhedron with eight faces.

opposite rays **(p. 11)** If C is between A and B, then $\overrightarrow{CA}$ and $\overrightarrow{CB}$ are opposite rays.

orthocenter of a triangle **(p. 281)** The point of concurrency of the lines containing the altitudes of a triangle.

paragraph proof **(p. 102)** A type of proof written in paragraph form.

parallel lines **(p. 129)** Two lines that are coplanar and do not intersect. The symbol for "is parallel to" is $\|$.

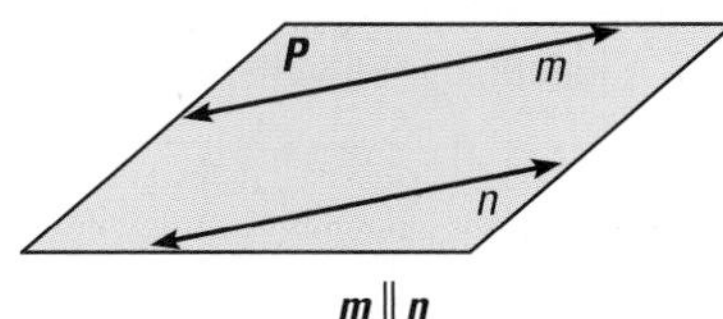

$m \| n$

parallelogram **(p. 330)** A quadrilateral with both pairs of opposite sides parallel. The parallelogram symbol is ▱.

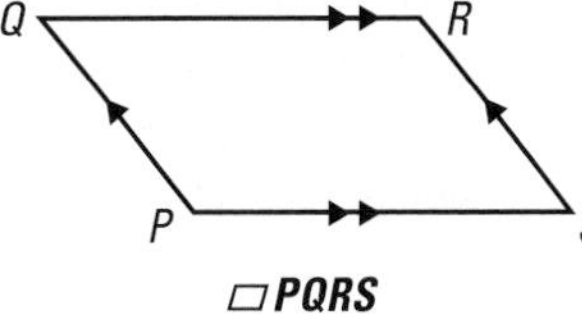

▱*PQRS*

parallel planes **(p. 129)** Two planes that do not intersect.

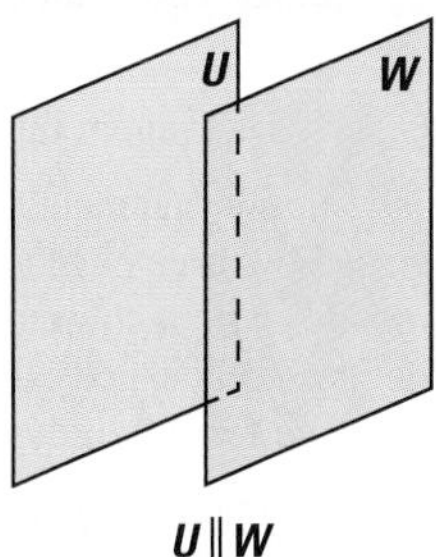

$U \| W$

parallel vectors **(p. 574)** Two vectors that have the same or opposite directions.

perpendicular bisector **(p. 264)** A segment, ray, line, or plane that is perpendicular to a segment at its midpoint.

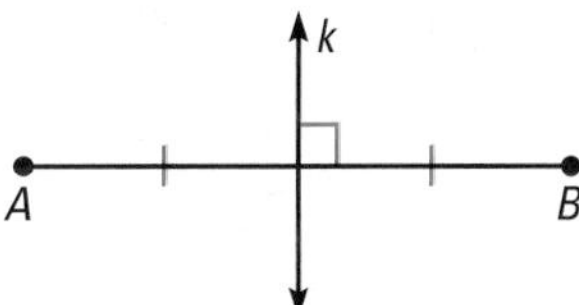

Line k is a $\perp$ bisector of $\overline{AB}$.

perpendicular bisector of a triangle **(p. 272)** A line, ray, or segment that is perpendicular to a side of a triangle at the midpoint of the side.

perpendicular lines **(p. 79)** Two lines that intersect to form a right angle. The symbol for "is perpendicular to" is $\perp$.

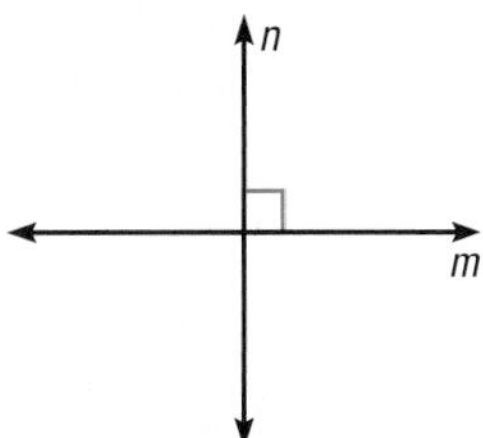

plane **(p. 10)** A plane extends in two dimensions. It is usually represented by a shape that looks like a tabletop or wall. You must imagine that the plane extends without end, even though the drawing of a plane appears to have edges. *See also* undefined term.

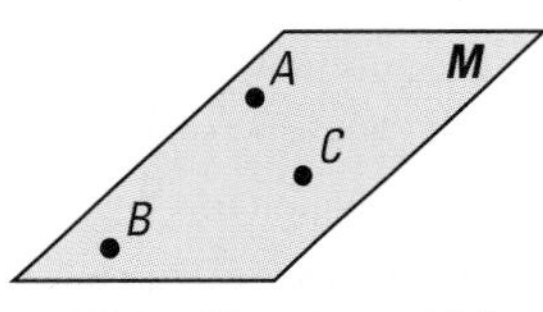

Plane M or plane ABC

Platonic solids (p. 721) Five regular polyhedra, named after the Greek mathematician and philosopher Plato, including a regular tetrahedron, a cube, a regular octahedron, a regular dodecahedron, and a regular icosahedron.

point (p. 10) A point has no dimension. It is usually represented by a small dot. *See also* undefined term.

point of concurrency (p. 272) The point of intersection of concurrent lines.

point of tangency (p. 597) *See* tangent line.

polygon (p. 322) A plane figure that meets the following two conditions. (1) It is formed by three or more segments called sides, such that no two sides with a common endpoint are collinear. (2) Each side intersects exactly two other sides, one at each endpoint. *See also* vertex of a polygon.

polyhedron (p. 719) A solid that is bounded by polygons, called *faces*, that enclose a single region of space. Plural is *polyhedra*, or *polyhedrons*.

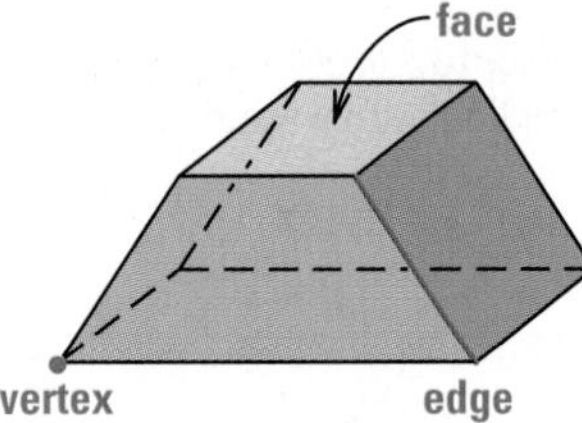

postulates (p. 17) Rules that are accepted without proof. Also called *axioms*.

preimage (p. 396) The original figure in the transformation of a figure in a plane. *See also* image.

prism (p. 728) A polyhedron with two congruent faces, called *bases*, that lie in parallel planes. The other faces, called *lateral faces*, are parallelograms formed by connecting the corresponding vertices of the bases. The segments connecting the vertices are *lateral edges*. The *altitude*, or *height*, of a prism is the perpendicular distance between its bases.

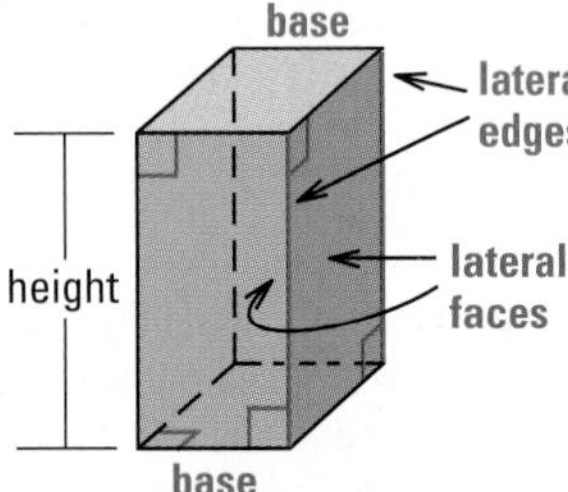

Right rectangular prism

probability (p. 699) A ratio from 0 to 1 that represents the likelihood an event will occur.

proportion (p. 459) An equation that equates two ratios. Example: $\frac{a}{b} = \frac{c}{d}$

pyramid (p. 735) A polyhedron in which the base is a polygon and the *lateral faces* are triangles with a common *vertex*. The intersection of two lateral faces is a *lateral edge*. The intersection of the base and a lateral face is a *base edge*. The *altitude*, or *height*, is the perpendicular distance between the base and the vertex.

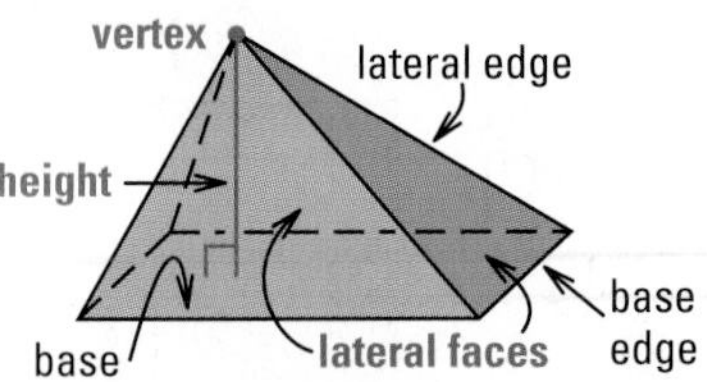

Pythagorean triple (p. 536) A set of three positive integers a, b, and c that satisfy the equation $c^2 = a^2 + b^2$.

R

radius of a circle (p. 595) The distance from the center of a circle to a point on the circle. A segment whose endpoints are the center of the circle and a point on the circle. Plural is *radii*.

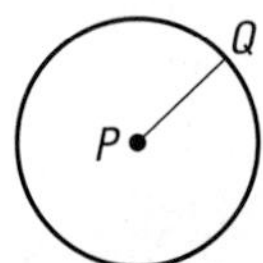

Radius: *PQ* or $\overline{PQ}$

radius of a polygon (p. 670) The radius of its circumscribed circle.

radius of a sphere (p. 759) A segment from the center of a sphere to a point on the sphere. The length of a segment from the center of a sphere to a point on the sphere.

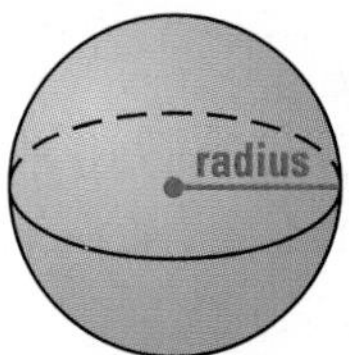

ratio of *a* to *b* (p. 457) The quotient $\frac{a}{b}$ if a and b are two quantities that are measured in the same units. Can also be written as $a:b$.

ray (p. 11) Part of a line that consists of a point, called an *initial point*, and all points on the line that extend in one direction.

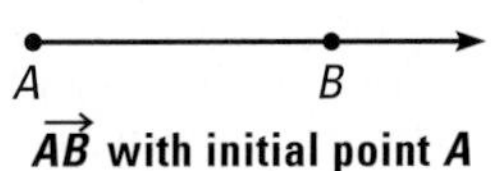

$\overrightarrow{AB}$ with initial point *A*

rectangle (p. 347) A parallelogram with four right angles.

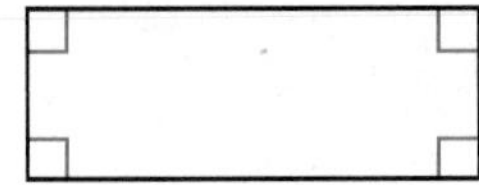

reduction (p. 506) A dilation with $0 < k < 1$.

reflection (p. 404) A type of transformation that uses a line that acts like a mirror, called the *line of reflection*, with an image reflected in the line.

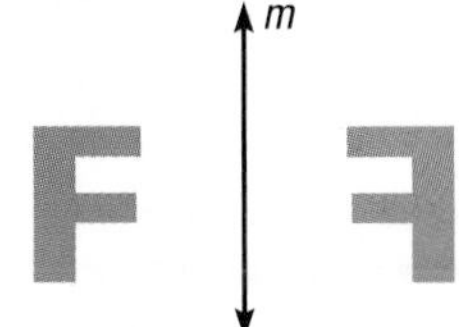

Line *m* is a line of reflection.

regular polygon (p. 323) A polygon that is equilateral and equiangular.

regular polyhedron (p. 720) A polyhedron whose faces are all congruent regular polygons.

regular pyramid (p. 735) A pyramid such that the base is a regular polygon and the segment from the vertex to the center of the base is perpendicular to the base. In a regular pyramid, the lateral faces all have the same slant height.

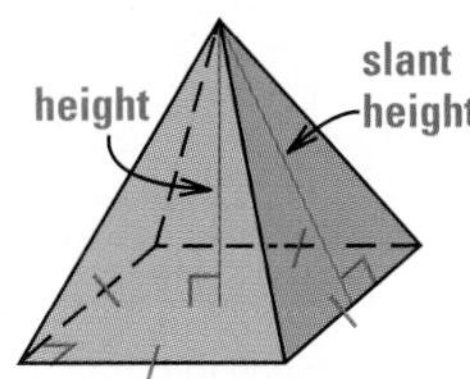

rhombus (p. 347) A parallelogram with four congruent sides.

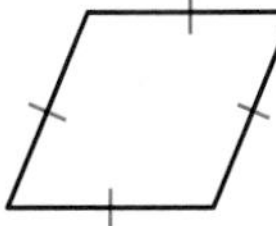

right angle (p. 28) An angle with measure equal to 90°.

right cone (p. 737) A cone with a vertex that lies directly above the center of the base. The *slant height* of a right cone is the distance between the vertex and a point on the edge of the base. *See also* circular cone.

right cylinder (p. 730) A cylinder such that the segment joining the centers of the bases is perpendicular to the bases.

right prism (p. 728) A prism whose lateral edges are perpendicular to both bases. *See also* prism.

right triangle (p. 194) A triangle with one right angle.

rotation (p. 412) A type of transformation in which a figure is turned about a fixed point, called the *center of rotation*.

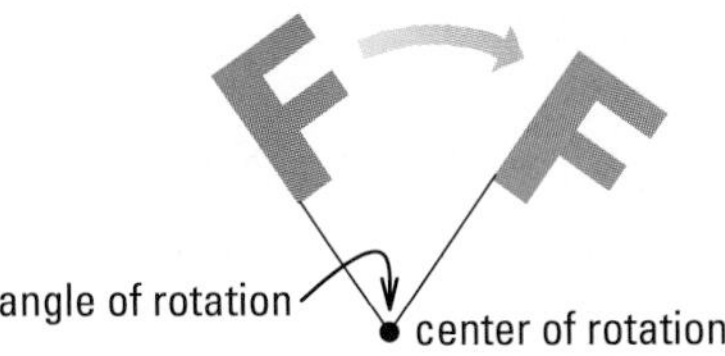

rotational symmetry (p. 415) A figure in the plane has *rotational symmetry* if the figure can be mapped onto itself by a rotation of 180° or less.

S

same side interior angles (p. 131) *See* consecutive interior angles.

scale factor (p. 474) The ratio of the lengths of two corresponding sides of two similar polygons.

scalene triangle (p. 194) A triangle with no congruent sides.

secant line (p. 595) A line that intersects a circle in two points.

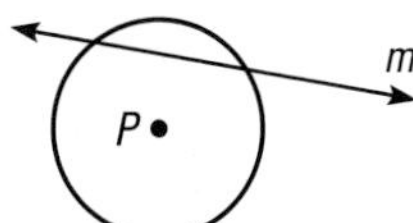

Line *m* is a secant.

secant segment (p. 630) A segment that intersects a circle in two points, with one point as an endpoint of the segment.

sector of a circle (p. 692) The region bounded by two radii of a circle and their intercepted arc.

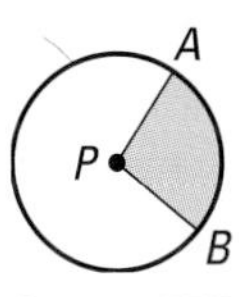

Sector *APB*

segment (p. 11) *See* line segment.

segment bisector (p. 34) A segment, ray, line, or plane that intersects a segment at its midpoint.

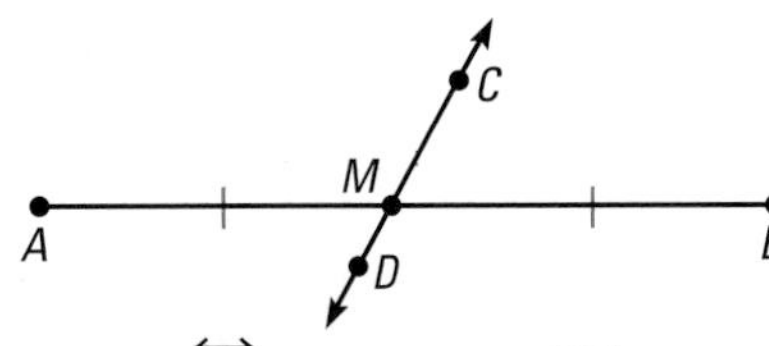

$\overleftrightarrow{CD}$ is a bisector of $\overline{AB}$.

semicircle (p. 603) An arc whose endpoints are the endpoints of a diameter of the circle.

side opposite a vertex of a triangle (p. 195) A side of a triangle that does not contain the given vertex.

sides of an angle (p. 26) *See* angle.

similar polygons (p. 473) Two polygons such that their corresponding angles are congruent and the lengths of corresponding sides are proportional. The symbol for "is similar to" is $\sim$.

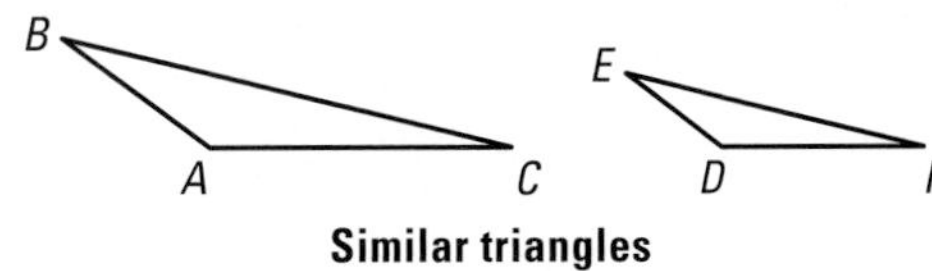

Similar triangles

similar solids (p. 766) Two solids with equal ratios of corresponding linear measures, such as heights or radii.

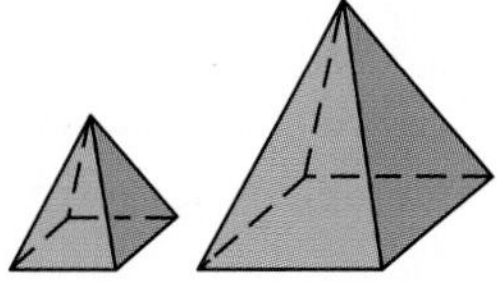

Similar pyramids

sine (p. 558) A trigonometric ratio, abbreviated as *sin*. For right triangle *ABC*, the sine of the acute angle *A* is

$$\sin A = \frac{\text{side opposite } \angle A}{\text{hypotenuse}} = \frac{a}{c}$$

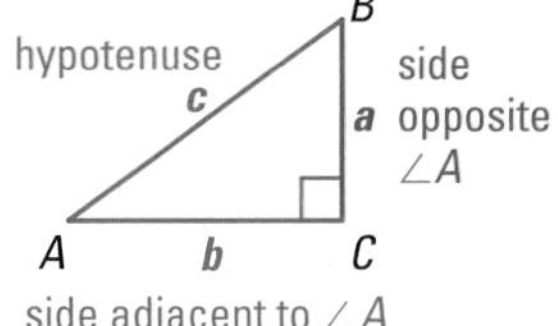

skew lines (p. 129) Two lines that do not intersect and are not coplanar.

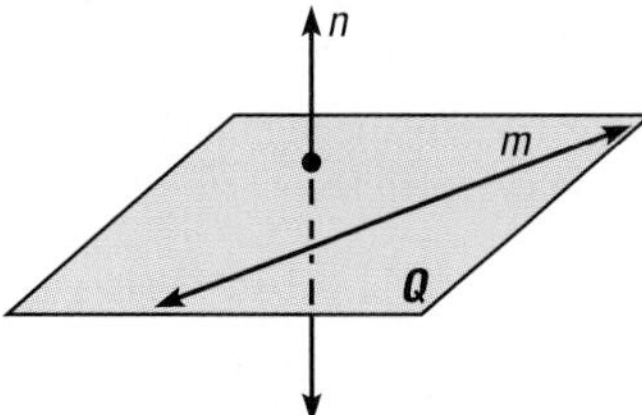

Lines *m* and *n* are skew lines.

solve a right triangle (p. 567) Determine the measurements of all sides and angles of a right triangle.

special right triangles (pp. 550, 551) Right triangles whose angle measures are 45°-45°-90° or 30°-60°-90°.

sphere (p. 759) The locus of points in space that are a given distance from a point, called the *center* of the sphere.

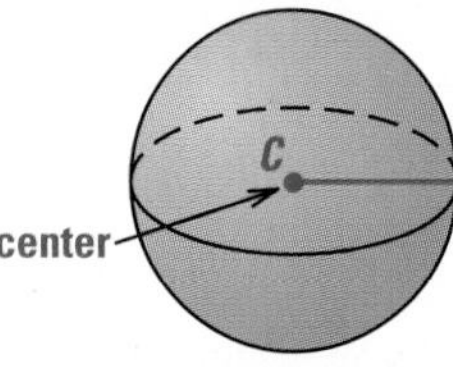

square (p. 347) A parallelogram with four congruent sides and four right angles.

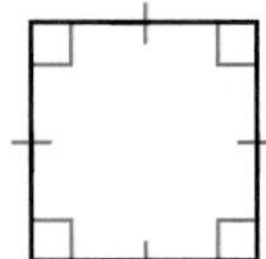

standard equation of a circle (p. 636) A circle with radius *r* and center (h, k) has this standard equation:

$$(x - h)^2 + (y - k)^2 = r^2.$$

straight angle (p. 28) An angle with measure equal to 180°.

straightedge (p. 34) A construction tool used to draw segments. A ruler without marks.

sum of two vectors (p. 575) The sum of $\vec{u} = \langle a_1, b_1 \rangle$ and $\vec{v} = \langle a_2, b_2 \rangle$ is $\vec{u} + \vec{v} = \langle a_1 + a_2, b_1 + b_2 \rangle$.

supplement (p. 46) The sum of the measures of an angle and its supplement is 180°.

supplementary angles (p. 46) Two angles whose measures have the sum 180°.

surface area of a cylinder (p. 730) The sum of the lateral area of the cylinder and the areas of the two bases.

surface area of a polyhedron (p. 728) The sum of the areas of its faces.

T

tangent (p. 558) A trigonometric ratio, abbreviated as *tan*. For right triangle *ABC*, the tangent of the acute angle *A* is

$$\tan A = \frac{\text{side opposite } \angle A}{\text{side adjacent to } \angle A} = \frac{a}{b}$$

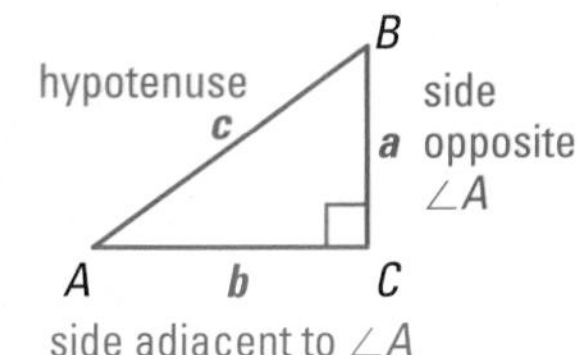

tangent circles (p. 596) Circles that intersect in one point.

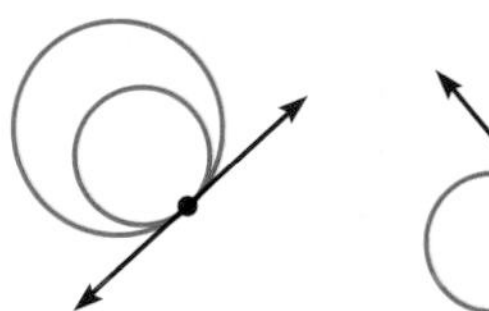

Internally tangent **Externally tangent**

tangent line (p. 595) A line that intersects a circle in exactly one point, called the *point of tangency*.

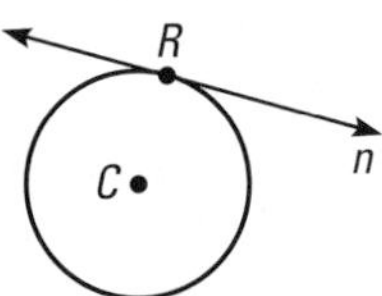

Line *n* is a tangent.
***R* is the point of tangency.**

tangent segment (p. 630) A segment that is tangent to a circle at an endpoint.

terminal point of a vector (p. 423) The ending point of a vector. *See also* vector.

tetrahedron (p. 721) A polyhedron with four faces.

theorem (p. 102) A true statement that follows as a result of other true statements.

transformation (p. 396) The operation that maps, or moves, a preimage onto an image. Three basic transformations are reflections, rotations, and translations.

translation (p. 421) A type of transformation that maps every two points P and Q in the plane to points P' and Q', so that the following two properties are true. (1) $PP' = QQ'$. (2) $\overline{PP'} \parallel \overline{QQ'}$ or $\overline{PP'}$ and $\overline{QQ'}$ are collinear.

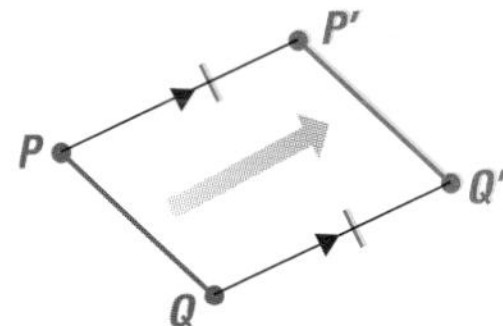

transversal (p. 131) A line that intersects two or more coplanar lines at different points.

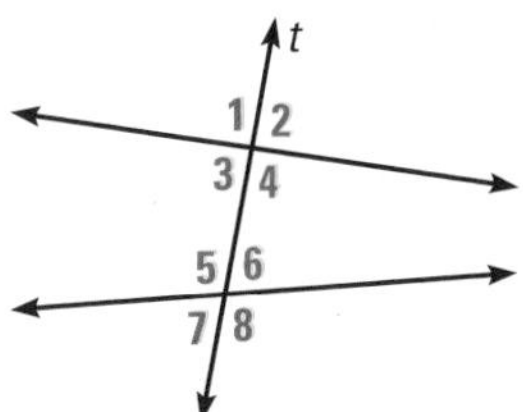

Line t is a transversal.

trapezoid (p. 356) A quadrilateral with exactly one pair of parallel sides, called *bases*. The nonparallel sides are *legs*.

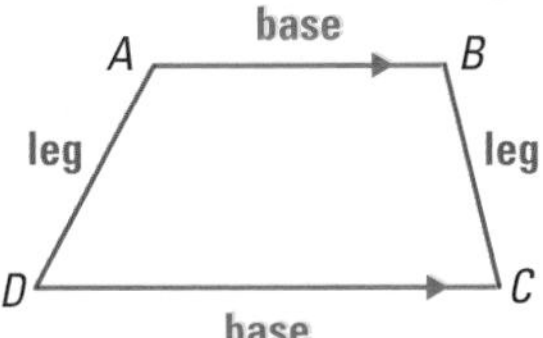

triangle (p. 194) A figure formed by three segments joining three noncollinear points, called *vertices*. The triangle symbol is $\triangle$.

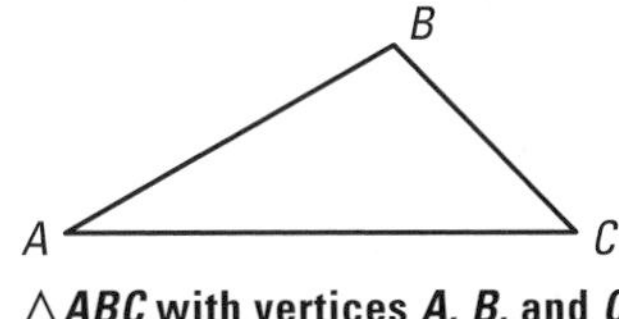

$\triangle ABC$ with vertices A, B, and C

trigonometric ratio (p. 558) A ratio of the lengths of two sides of a right triangle. *See also* sine, cosine, *and* tangent.

two-column proof (p. 102) A type of proof written as numbered statements and reasons that show the logical order of an argument.

U

undefined term (p. 10) A word, such as *point*, *line*, or *plane*, that is not formally defined, although there is general agreement about what the word means.

V

vector (p. 423) A quantity that has both direction and magnitude, and is represented by an arrow drawn between two points.

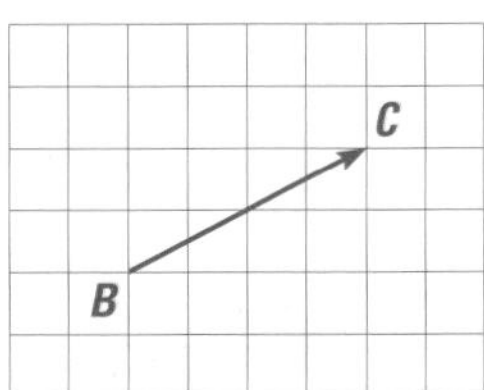

$\overrightarrow{BC}$ with initial point B and terminal point C

vertex of an angle (p. 26) *See* angle.

vertex of a polygon (p. 322) Each endpoint of a side of a polygon. Plural is *vertices*.

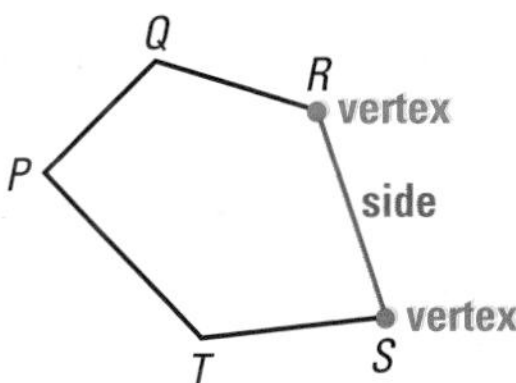

vertex of a polyhedron (p. 719) A point where three or more edges of a polyhedron meet. *See also* polyhedron.

vertex of a triangle (p. 195) Each of the three points joining the sides of a triangle. Plural is *vertices*. *See also* triangle.

vertex angle of an isosceles triangle (p. 236) The angle opposite the base of an isosceles triangle. *See also* base of an isosceles triangle.

vertical angles (p. 44) Two angles whose sides form two pairs of opposite rays.

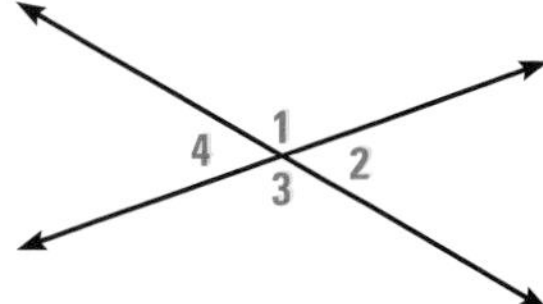

$\angle 1$ and $\angle 3$ are vertical angles.
$\angle 2$ and $\angle 4$ are vertical angles.

volume of a solid (p. 743) The number of cubic units contained in the interior of a solid.

ANSWERS AND INDEX

The Teacher's Edition supplements the answers and index material in the Student Edition. The credits are also included.

Credits

Cover Credits

Earth Imaging/Tony Stone Images (background); Mark Gibson (t); Peter Sterling/FPG International; Mark C. Burnett/Stock Boston (r); Al Messerschmidt/Folio, Inc. (b).

Photography

i, ii Earth Imaging/Tony Stone Images (background); Mark Gibson (t); Peter Sterling/FPG International; Mark C. Burnett/Stock Boston (r); Al Messerschmidt/Folio, Inc. (b); **iv** Gary Choppe/Creative Image Studio (tl); Index Stock Photography, Inc. (tr); **v** Angelo Cavalli/Superstock (tl); Didier Klien/Allsport (tr); **vi** Chris Sorenson; **vii** Hank Morgan/Photo Researchers, Inc.; **viii** Matthew J. Atanian/Tony Stone Images; **ix** Al Messerschmidt/Folio, Inc.; **x** Greg Fiume/Duomo; **xi** Eric R. Berndt/Unicorn Stock Photo; **xii** Emmanuel Faure/Superstock; **xiii** Cathlyn Melloan/Tony Stone Images; **xiv** Robert & Linda Mitchell; **xv** CORBIS/Michael S. Yamashita; **xvi** Paul Wakefield/Tony Stone Images; **xvii** Polshek Partnership/Dbox/American Museum of Natural History; **xix** Mark Gibson (t); **xix** John Riley/Tony Stone Image (2nd from top); **xix** Dana White/PhotoEdit (ml); **xix** Elliott Smith (mr); Andrew Rafkind/Tony Stone Images (b); **xxii** Chris Sorenson; **1** Tony Freeman/PhotoEdit; **3** Arthur Morris/Visuals Unlimited; **5** John Gerlach/Visuals Unlimited; **8** Frank Grant/International Stock Photo; **10** Don Dietsche/Perspective Arts Illustration; **14** Spencer Grant/PhotoEdit (l); Superstock (m); Michael Newman/PhotoEdit (r); **15** Isamu Noguchi/SEF/Art Resource; **17** Kerrick James; **22** FPG International; **25** The Granger Collection (tr); The Granger Collection (bl); Brown Brothers (bm); PhotoDisc, Inc. (br); **26** Fritz Prenzel/Animals Animals; **30** Tom Prettyman/PhotoEdit; **33** RMIP/Richard Haynes; **34** John Neubauer/PhotoEdit; **37** Gary Choppe/Creative Image Studio; **44** Daniel Aubry; **45** Tony Freeman/PhotoEdit; **49** Steve Murez (l); Fernando Gallardo/A.G.E. Fotostock (r); **56** QA Photos, Ltd.; **57** Lee Snider/The Image Works; **68** Hank Morgan/Photo Researchers, Inc.; **69** B. Ingalls/Liaison Agency; **71** David Harvey/National Geographic Image Collection; **72** Michael P. Gadomski/Photo Researchers, Inc.; **77** Dana White/PhotoEdit (l); **79** Photo Researchers, Inc.; **82** Koichiro Shimauchi/Photonica; **83** Aaron Ferster/Photo Researchers, Inc.; **84** Michael P. Gadomski/Photo Researchers, Inc.; **87** Sid and Shirley Rucker/DRK; **90** Janeanin Nance/Visuals Unlimited (tl); Jeff Greenberg/PhotoEdit (br); **92** John Elk/Tony Stone Images; **95** Bill Lyons/Liaison Agency (l); Metropolitan Museum of Art, Gift of Gustavus A. Pfeiffer, 1948 (48.174.43) (ml); The Granger Collection (mr); CORBIS/Agence France Presse (r); **96** Jim Cummins/FPG International; **100** David Taylor/Allsport; **102** Ed Cooper/FPG International; **106** Walter Hodges/Tony Stone Images; **108** RMIP/Richard Haynes; **109** Miguel Gomez-Ibanez/North Bennet Street School; **112** David Young-Wolff/PhotoEdit; **115** Martha Granger/EDGE Productions; **126** Matthew J. Atanian/Tony Stone Images; **127** Matthew J. Atanian/Tony Stone Images; **129** Bob Torrez/Tony Stone Images; **132** RMIP/Richard Haynes; **133** Alan Welner/AP/Wide World Photos; **136** Eastcott/The Image Works; **140** Ken Biggs/Photo Researchers, Inc. (l); **143** Richard Gaul/FPG International; **144** Kindra Clineff/Tony Stone Images (l); Jeff Lepore/Photo Researchers, Inc. (r); **146** Gary Retherford/Photo Researchers, Inc.; **150** Peter Sterling/FPG International; **152** Dennis McDonald/PhotoEdit; **154** CORBIS/Richard A. Cooke; **157** Michael P. Gadomski/Photo Researchers, Inc. (l); Gerard Planchenault/Allsport (r); **162** David Seelic/Allsport; **164** The Granger Collection (l); **164** CORBIS/Michelle Chaplow (m); **164** CORBIS (r); **165** Pine Springs Christian Youth Ranch; **169** Library of Congress (l); Oberlin College (r); **170** John Riley/Tony Stone Images; **172** Neil Alexander; **174** David Young-Wolff/PhotoEdit (l); Jaime Vives Piqueres (r); **177** Ed Bernink/Meridian Creative Group; **189** Mark Bolster/International Stock Photo; **190** Al Messerschmidt/Folio, Inc. **191** Carson Baldwin/FPG International; **194** Steve Copeland/Ontario Streams; **195** Carol Leigh; **200** Ben Osborne/Tony Stone Images; **202** Courtesy of the Gerald R. Ford Library; **204** Stamp Designs ©2000 United States Postal Service. Reproduced with permission. All Rights Reserved. **207** Frederick C. Taylor/Fortean Picture Library; **208** Harriet E. Brisson (both); **210** Tom Brakefield/DRK Photo (l); Andras Kaldor (ml); Photo Courtesy of Rick Stiles, Lockheed Martin (mr); NASA (r); **211** RMIP/Richard Haynes; **212** John Warden/Tony Stone Images; **214** Nancy L. Fix/Stock Boston; **217** Coco McCoy/Rainbow; **218** ChromoSohm/Sohm/Stock Boston (l); **218** Chris Sorensen (r); **219** Clyde H. Smith/Peter Arnold, Inc. (l); Ken Cavanagh/Photo Researchers, Inc. (r); **220** Lars Lindberg Christensen, astronomer; **222** Jack Zehrt/FPG International; **225** RMIP/Richard Haynes; **226** RMIP/Richard Haynes (t); **229** Andy Ryan; **232** Doug Perrine/DRK Photo; **234** Bob Daemmrich/Stock Boston; **236** Lior Rubin; **240** Lior Rubin; **241** Bill Sanderson/SPL/Photo Researchers, Inc. (l); **260** Greg Fiume/Duomo; **261** Chris Trotman/Duomo; **263** RMIP/Richard Haynes; **264** Vic Bider/PhotoEdit; **267** Tony Stone Images (l); PhotoDisc, Inc. (r); **269** Brown Brothers (both); **272** G. Carleton Ray/Photo Researchers, Inc.; **277** Hans Reinhard/Photo Researchers, Inc.; **279** M. Ferguson/PhotoEdit; **283** R. Ramey/PhotoEdit; **285** CORBIS (l); CORBIS (ml); CORBIS/Bettmann/UPI (mr); Bob Kalmbach/University of Michigan (r); **287** Joe Sohn/Unicorn Stock Photo; **291** Diana Venters; **292** Derrick Ditchburn/Visuals Unlimited; **295** David Young-Wolff/PhotoEdit; **299** Llewellyn/Uniphoto; **302** CORBIS; **304** Rudi Von Briel/PhotoEdit; **308** Thomas Ives/The Stock Market; **313** CORBIS/Steve Kaufman; **316** RMIP/Richard Haynes; **317** Christie's Images/Superstock; **318** Eric R. Berndt/Unicorn Stock Photo; **319** Tom Pantages; **322** David Young-Wolff/PhotoEdit; **323** CORBIS/Roger Wood; **326** Torleif Svensson/The Stock Market (l); PhotoDisc, Inc. (tml); PhotoDisc, Inc.; Spencer Grant/PhotoEdit (tr); **326** PhotoDisc, Inc. (bml); PhotoDisc, Inc. (br); **327** CORBIS; **330** Linc Cornell/Stock Boston; **333** Superstock; **335** RMIP/Richard Haynes; **336** Linc Cornell/Stock Boston (l); Index Stock Photography, Inc. (r) **338** J. Nourok/PhotoEdit; **339** RMIP/Richard Haynes; **343** RMIP/Richard Haynes (both); **346** Alex S. MacLean/Landslides (tr); The Granger Collection (bl); Reproduced by Permission of the Commercial Press (Hong Kong) Limited from the publication of *Chinese Mathematics: A Concise History* (bm); Eric R. Berndt/New England Stock Photo (br); **347** J. Schuyle/Stock Boston; **350** CMDC/PhotoDisc, Inc.; RMIP/Richard Haynes (inset); **356** Denis Valentine/The Stock Market; **358** David Young-Wolff/PhotoEdit; **360** CORBIS/Ralph A. Clevenger; **361** Grantpix/Photo Researchers, Inc.; **363** RMIP/Richard Haynes; **364** Ralph Cowan/FPG International; **367** John Beatty/Tony Stone Images; **369** David Austen/PNI/Picture Quest; **372** Elizabethon, Tennessee Chamber of Commerce; **377** Donald Dietz/Stock Boston/PNI; **378** Mark Candelaria (l); Elizabethon, Tennessee Chamber of Commerce (r); **380** Michael Nelson/FPG International; **392** Emmanuel Faure/Superstock; **393** Lee Snider/Photo Images; **396** Daniel J. Olson/Unicorn Stock Photo; **398** Lee Snider/Photo Images; **401** Superstock; **404** Koji Kitagawa/Superstock; **406** Chris Smith/Bob & Sue Rioux; **407** Index Stock Photography, Inc. (all); **409** Blair Seitz/Photo Researchers, Inc.; **412** Superstock; **415** Elliott Smith; **418** Superstock (3 images tr); **420** The Granger Collection (bl); CORBIS/Adam Woolfitt (ml); CORBIS/Austrian Archives (mr);

Teacher's Edition Credits

Page **i** and **ii** Earth Imaging/Tony Stone Images (background); Mark Gibson (t); Peter Sterling/FPG International; Mark C. Burnett/Stock Boston (r); Al Messerschmidt/Folio, Inc. (b). **iv** Gary Choppe/Creative Image Studio (tl); Index Stock Photography, Inc. (tr); **v** Angelo Cavalli/Superstock (tl); Didier Klien/Allsport (tr); **vi** Chris Sorenson; **vii** Hank Morgan/Photo Researchers, Inc.; **viii** Matthew J. Atanian/Tony Stone Images; **ix** Al Messerschmidt/Folio, Inc.; **x** Greg Fiume/Duomo; **xi** Eric R. Berndt/Unicorn Stock Photo; **xii** Emmanuel Faure/Superstock; **xiii** Cathlyn Melloan/Tony Stone Images; **xiv** Robert & Linda Mitchell; **xv** CORBIS/Michael S. Yamashita; **xvi** Paul Wakefield/Tony Stone Images; **xvii** Polshek Partnership/Dbox/American Museum of Natural History; **xix** Mark Gibson (t); **xix** John Riley/Tony Stone Image (2nd from top); **xix** Dana White/PhotoEdit (ml); **xix** Elliott Smith (mr); Andrew Rafkind/Tony Stone Images (b); **T24** Richard Haynes/RMIP. **T37** Richard Haynes/RMIP.

Bob Daemmrich/The Image Works (br); **421** D. Long/Visuals Unlimited; **427** Alain Morvan/Liaison Agency; **430** Angelo Cavalli/Superstock; **435** Paula Lerner/Woodfin Camp & Associates; **437** The Newark Museum/Art Resource, NY; **438** Michael Fogden/DRK Photo; **439** Superstock; **442** Timothy Hursley/Superstock (tl); Christie's Images (mr); **454** Cathlyn Melloan/Tony Stone Images; **455** Cathlyn Melloan/Tony Stone Images; **457** Louisville Slugger Museum (l) RMIP/Richard Haynes (r); **460** Bev Doolittle/The Greenwich Workshop; **462** NASA; **463** Louisville Slugger Museum (t); Stock Montage/Superstock (b); **465** UPI/CORBIS-Bettmann; **467** CORBIS/Tod Gipstein; **468** PhotoDisc, Inc.; **469** Matthew Stockman/Allsport; **470** Courtesy of the U.S. Mint; **472** Greig Cranna/Stock Boston; **473** Dana White/PhotoEdit; **474** Joseph Nettis/Tony Stone Images; **477** Michael Newman/PhotoEdit; **478** Joel Simon/Tony Stone Images; **480** Custom Aerial Photography, Inc.; **481** Manfred Kage/Peter Arnold, Inc.; **482** CORBIS/Chuck O'Rear; **486** Ron Jautz; **488** Superstock; **490** Tom & Pat Leeson/DRK Photo (t); David Liebman (br); **491** CORBIS/Doug Berry (l); CORBIS/David Samuel Robbins (r); **496** CORBIS/Robert Holmes (bl); CRD/CORBIS (ml); Page from Luca Pacioli's book, *Divine Proportion* illustrated by Leonardo da Vinci, 1494 (mr); ©2001 Artists Rights Society (ARS), New York/ADAGP, Paris/FLC (r); **498** Bob Daemmrich/Stock Boston/PNI; **503** Michael Newman/PhotoEdit; **506** Vinay Parelkar/Dinodia Picture Agency; **508** Vinay Parelkar/Dinodia Picture Agency; **511** RMIP/Richard Haynes; **512** Bob Daemmrich/Tony Stone Images; **524** Robert & Linda Mitchell; **525** Robert & Linda Mitchell; **527** Jacksonville Transportation Authority; **530** Jacksonville Transportation Authority; **535** Bill Lai/The Image Works; **537** Hank Morgan/Cesar Pelli & Associates, Inc.; **540** Keith Wood/Tony Stone Images (tl); Superstock (tr); **543** Tony Freeman/PhotoEdit; **547** Rare Book & Manuscript Library/Columbia University, Cunieform, Plimpton 322; **551** Ken Frick; **553** PhotoDisc, Inc.; **555** Diana Venters, "Wheel of Theodorus" (b); **557** CORBIS/Gianni Dagli Orti (l); The British Library (ml); CORBIS/Bettmann (mr); Nicaraguan Postal Authority (r); **558** Jeff Greenberg/PhotoEdit; **561** Kathy Adams Clark/KAC Productions; **563** Bob Shaw/The Stock Market; **564** CORBIS; **567** Mark Gibson; **569** CORBIS/AFP; **571** Jose Carrillo/PhotoEdit (l); CORBIS/Joe Sohm/ChromoSohm; **573** Photri/Tom Sanders/The Stock Market; **574** The Stock Shop; **577** Bob Daemmrich; **578** Agency Vandystadt/Allsport; **579** ChromoSohm/Sohm/PNI/Picture Quest; **592** CORBIS/Michael S. Yamashita; **593** Mark & Audrey Gibson/Stock Connection/PNI; **595** Mark Gibson; **600** John Taylor/FPG International; **601** George Gerster/Photo Researchers, Inc.; **603** John Terence Turner/FPG International; **609** Mark Gibson; **613** Mark Gibson; **614** The Granger Collection; **621** Tony Stone Images; **623** David Hiser/Tony Stone Images; **629** CORBIS/Jeffrey L. Rotman; **631** Mark Gibson/The Stock Market; **634** M. Reinstein/The Image Works; **636** Bob Daemmrich; **642** The Granger Collection (tr); The Natural History Museum, London (ml); **644** Andrew Rafkind/Tony Stone Images; **646** CORBIS/Craig Aurness; **648** The Granger Collection (l); Ancient Art & Architecture (ml); Brown Brothers (3rd from left); CORBIS (4th from left); CORBIS (r); **653** George Steinmetz; **658** Paul Wakefield/Tony Stone Images; **659** Tom Till/DRK Photo; **661** R. Von Briel/PhotoEdit; **664** UPI/CORBIS-Bettmann; **666** Tony Freeman/PhotoEdit; **669** Bob Daemmrich; **671** Houston Museum of Natural Sciences; **672** Philip & Karen Smith/Tony Stone Images; **674** Tony Freeman/PhotoEdit (l); Bob Daemmrich (r); **676** RMIP/Richard Haynes; **677** Don & Pat Valenti/Tony Stone Images; **678** Steve Leonard/Tony Stone Images (l); Art Wolfe/Tony Stone Images (r); **680** Connie Toops; **682** CORBIS-Bettmann (mr); John Denniston/Province (r); **683** Mark Gibson; **685** Todd Warshaw/Allsport (bl); **688** Greg Probst/Tony Stone Images; **691** CORBIS/Ted Spiegel; **694** RMIP/Richard Haynes; **696** Hugh Sitton/Tony Stone Images; **697** Catherine Gehm; **699** Don Smetzer/Tony Stone Images; **701** Bill Lai/Index Stock Imagery; **703** CORBIS/Stephen Frink; **716** Polshek Partnership/Dbox/American Museum of Natural History; **717** Polshek Partnership/Dbox/American Museum of Natural History; **719** Pierre Belzeaux/Rapho/Liaison Agency; **722** Mark Gibson (l); Mike Wilson/FPG International (r); **725** Phil Borden/PhotoEdit (l); Harvard University Mineralogical and Geological Museum (2nd from left); Charles D. Winters/Photo Researchers, Inc (3rd from left); Jerome Wycoff/Visuals Unlimited (r); **728** Gary Buss/FPG International; **733** Jeff Greenberg/Leo de Wys, Inc. (l); Brown Brothers (br) **735** C. Ron Chapple/FPG International; **740** Cooper-Hewitt Museum, Smithsonian Institution/Art Resource, NY (l); Fergus O'Brien/FPG International (r); **742** Australian Picture Library/E.T. Archive (l); Van Den Broucke/Photo News/ Liaison Agency (ml); C Squared Studios/PhotoDisc, Inc. (mr); Tom Pantages (r); **743** Telegraph Colour Library/FPG International; **745** Tim Street-Porter/Ennis-Brown House; **752** Carmona Photography/FPG International; **754** ©Mystic Seaport, Mystic, Connecticut; **757** G. Brad Lewis/Liaison Agency (l); Harvey Lloyd/FPG International (r); **759** NASA/FPG International; **761** Courtesy of Rollerblade, Inc.; **763** NASA/FPG International; **764** James Blank/FPG International; **766** Jeffrey Sylvester/FPG International; **768** Jean Higgins/Unicorn Stock Photo; **770** CORBIS; **771** Mark E. Gibson; **772** CORBIS.

Illustration

Steve Cowden **40, 241, 261, 491, 494**
Laurie O'Keefe **27**
Doug Stevens **69, 77, 98, 123, 508**
School Division, Houghton Mifflin Company **133, 170**

Selected Answers

CHAPTER 1

SKILL REVIEW (p. 2) **1.** 8 **2.** −8 **3.** 8 **4.** 8 **5.** −9 **6.** −5 **7.** −1 **8.** 1 **9.** 20 **10.** 29 **11.** 2 **12.** 25 **13.** 6.32 **14.** 7.07 **15.** 18.03 **16.** 4.24

1.1 PRACTICE (pp. 6–9)

3.  **5.** Each number is 3 times the previous number; 162.

7. Each number is $\frac{1}{4}$ the previous number; 1.
9. Each number is 0.5 greater than the previous number; 9.0.
11. 3 times the middle integer
13. **15.** **17.** Each number is half the previous number; 0.625.

19. Each number is 5 less than the previous number; −15. **21.** Numbers after the first are found by adding consecutive whole numbers; 21. **23.** Numbers after the first are found by adding a zero after the decimal point of the previous number; 1.00001. **25.** 28 blocks **27.** The distance is 4 times the figure number. **29.** even **31.** $n^2 - 1$
33. 121; 12,321; 1,234,321; 123,454,321; the square of the n-digit number consisting of all 1's is the number obtained by writing the digits from 1 to n in increasing order, then the digits from $n - 1$ to 1 in decreasing order. This pattern does not continue forever. **35–39.** *Sample answers* are given.
35. $2 + (-5) = -3$, which is not greater than 2.
37. $(-4)(-5) = 20$ **39.** Let $m = -1$; $\frac{-1 + 1}{-1} = 0$.
41. *Sample answer:* 3
43. 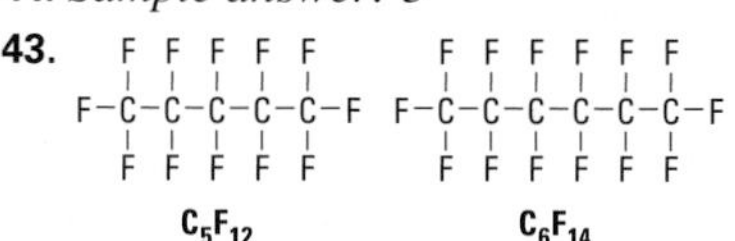
C_5F_{12} C_6F_{14}
45. The y-coordinate is $\frac{1}{2}$ more than the opposite of the x-coordinate; $-2\frac{1}{2}$.

1.1 MIXED REVIEW (p. 9)
53–59 odd: 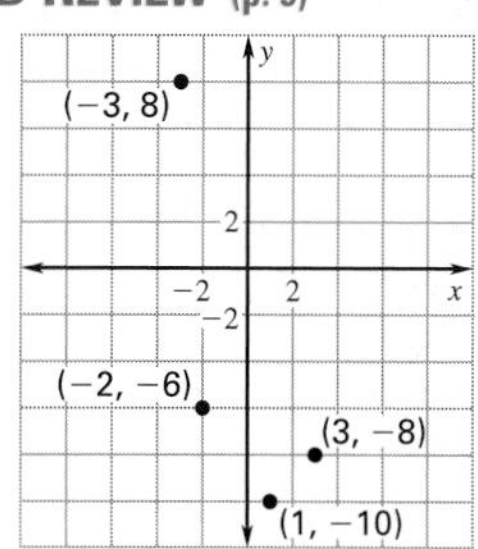

61. 25 **63.** −49 **65.** 169 **67.** 125 **69.** 40,000.4 **71.** +3

1.2 PRACTICE (pp. 13–16) **3.** false **5.** false **7.** true **9.** false **11.** true **13.** true **15.** false **17.** K **19.** M **21.** L **23.** J **25.** N, P, and R; N, Q, and R; P, Q, and R **27.** A, W, and X; A, W, and Z; A, X, and Y; A, Y, and Z; W, X, and Y; W, X, and Z; W, Y, and Z; X, Y, and Z **29.** G **31.** H **33.** E **35.** H **37.** K, N, Q, and R **39.** M, N, P, and Q **41.** L, M, P, and S **43.** M, N, R, and S **45.** on the same side of C as point D **47.** A, B, and C are collinear and C is between A and B.
49–51. Sample figures are given.
49. 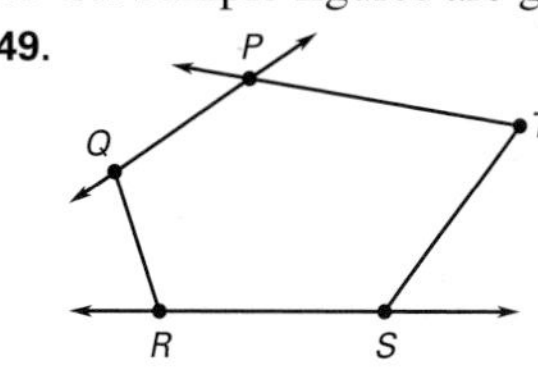

51. A B C
53. the intersection of a line and a plane **55.** B **57.** H **59.** $\overleftrightarrow{DH}$

61–67. Sample figures are given.
61. **63.** **65.** **67.**
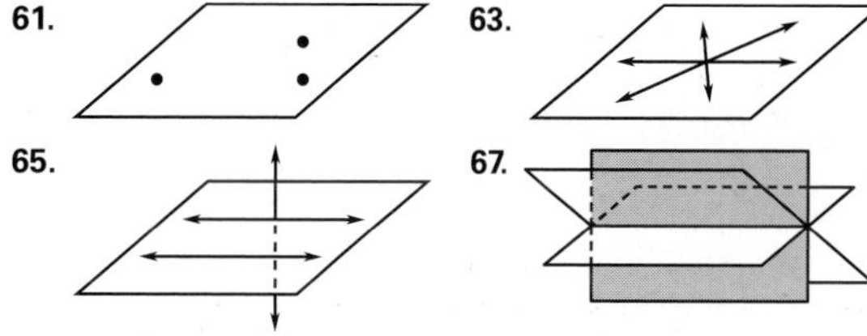

69. $\overleftrightarrow{CE}$, $\overleftrightarrow{DF}$
70–72.
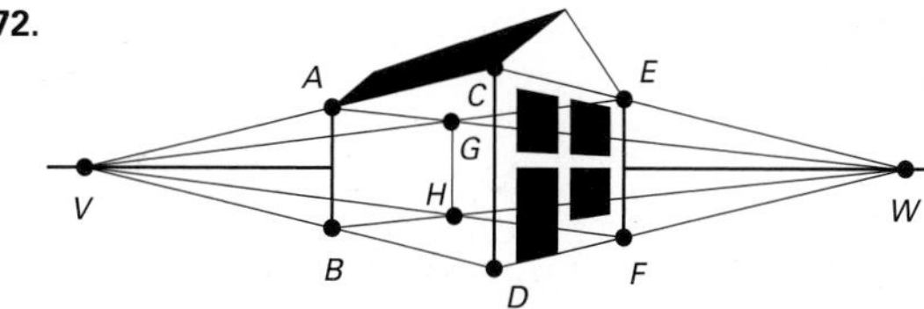

1.2 MIXED REVIEW (p. 16) **77.** Each number is 6 times the previous number; 1296. **79.** Numbers after the first are found by adding an 8 immediately before the decimal point of the previous number and a 1 immediately after the decimal point; 88,888.11111. **81.** −2 **83.** 13 **85.** 5 **87.** 11 **89.** 11 **91.** 13 **93.** 8.60 **95.** 4.24

1.3 PRACTICE (pp. 21–24) **5.** $5\sqrt{5}$ **7.** $\sqrt{61}$ **9.** 5
11. $\overline{JK}$ and $\overline{KL}$ are not congruent; $JK = \sqrt{137}$, $KL = 2\sqrt{34}$.
13–17. Answers may vary slightly. **13.** 3 cm **15.** 2.4 cm
17. 1.8 cm **19.** D E F ; $DE + EF = DF$
21. N M P ; $NM + MP = NP$ **23.** 3 **25.** 3
27. 6 **29.** 9 **31.** 4; 20, 3, 23 **33.** 1; $2\frac{1}{2}$, $4\frac{1}{2}$, 7
35. $DE = \sqrt{85}$, $EF = 6\sqrt{2}$, $DF = 5$ **37.** $AC = 3\sqrt{5}$, $BC = 3\sqrt{5}$, $CD = 2\sqrt{10}$; $\overline{AC}$ and $\overline{BC}$ have the same length.
39. $LN = 3\sqrt{13}$, $MN = \sqrt{109}$, $PN = 3\sqrt{10}$; no two segments have the same length. **41.** $\overline{PQ} \cong \overline{QR}$; $PQ = QR = \sqrt{170}$

43. $\overline{PQ} \cong \overline{QR}$; $PQ = QR = 2\sqrt{85}$ 45. about 896 ft 47. *Sample answer:* about 63 mi 49–51. Answers are rounded to the nearest whole unit. 49. 5481 units 51. 8079 units 53. 115 yards, 80 yards, 65 yards

1.3 MIXED REVIEW (p. 24)

61. 63. false 65. true 67. true 69. $\overrightarrow{NM}$, $\overrightarrow{NQ}$ 71. $\overrightarrow{NM}$ and $\overrightarrow{NQ}$

QUIZ 1 (p. 25) 1. 8 2. 6

3. 4. 5.

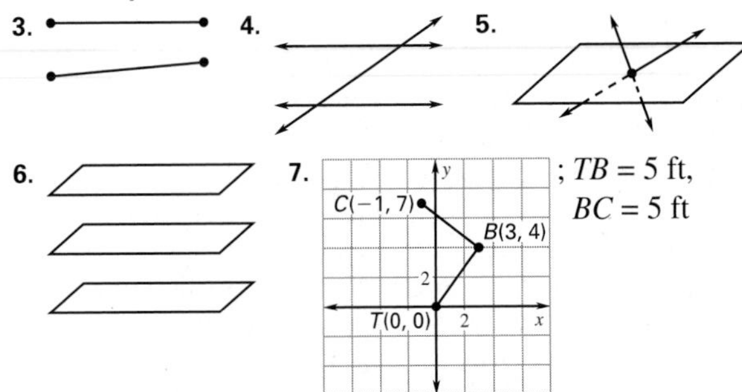

6. 7. ; $TB = 5$ ft, $BC = 5$ ft

1.4 PRACTICE (pp. 29–32) 9. E, $\overrightarrow{ED}$, $\overrightarrow{EF}$; about 35° 11. J, $\overrightarrow{JH}$, $\overrightarrow{JK}$; about 75° 13. straight 15. obtuse 17. X, $\overrightarrow{XF}$, $\overrightarrow{XT}$ 19. Q, $\overrightarrow{QR}$, $\overrightarrow{QS}$ 21. $\angle C$, $\angle BCD$, $\angle DCB$ 23. 55° 25. 140° 27. 180°

29–33.

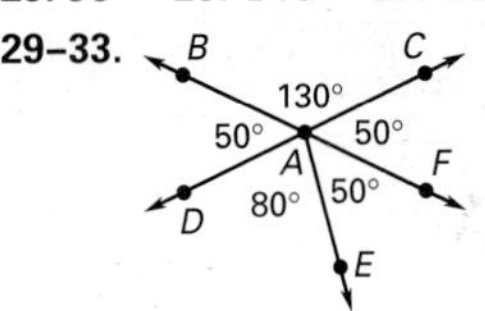

29. 50° 31. 180° 33. 130° 35. acute; about 40° 37. obtuse; about 150°

39.

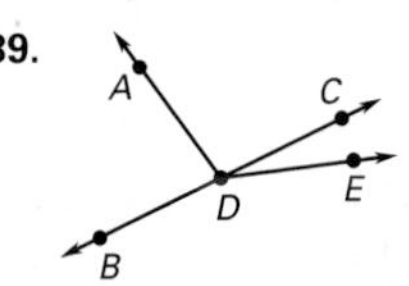

41–43. Coordinates of sample points are given.

41. ; 43. ;

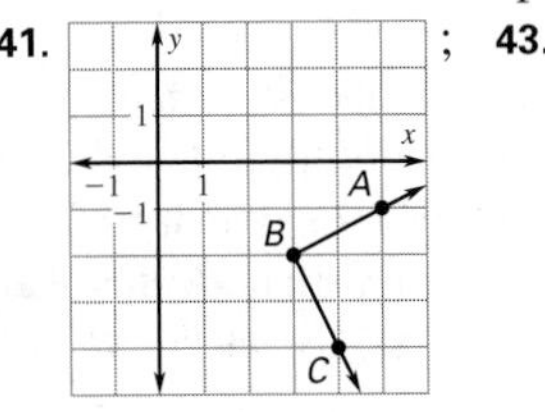

right; (4, –3), (0, 0) obtuse; (–3, 3), (0, 0)

45–49. Estimates may vary. 45. about 150° 47. about 140° 49. about 135° 51. 12 points 53. 40 points

1.4 MIXED REVIEW (p. 32) 61. 3 63. –12 65. –27 67. 15 69. –5 71. false 73. false 75. $\sqrt{89}$ 77. $\sqrt{221}$ 79. $3\sqrt{2}$

1.5 PRACTICE (pp. 38–41) 5. (5, –7) 7. (3, 8) 9. (–2, –6) 11. $m\angle RQS = 40°$, $m\angle PQR = 80°$ 13. $m\angle PQS = 52°$, $m\angle PQR = 104°$ 17. (–4, 3) 19. $\left(4, 6\frac{1}{2}\right)$ 21. (–3, 3) 23. (–0.625, 3.5) 25. (–4, –4) 27. (1, 10) 29. (14, –21) 31. $\overline{AC}$ and $\overline{BC}$, $\angle A$ and $\angle B$ 33. $\overline{XW}$ and $\overline{XY}$, $\angle ZXW$ and $\angle ZXY$ 37. $m\angle PQS = 22°$, $m\angle PQR = 44°$ 39. $m\angle RQS = 80°$, $m\angle PQR = 160°$ 41. $m\angle RQS = 45°$, $m\angle PQR = 90°$ 43. No; yes; the angle bisector of an angle of a triangle passes through the midpoint of the opposite side if the two sides of the triangle contained in the angle are congruent. 45. 19 47. 8 49. 42 51. 54 53. 65°, 65°, 25°, 25° 55. *Sample answer:* $\overline{AB}$ and $\overline{AL}$, $\overline{AC}$ and $\overline{AK}$, $\overline{AN}$ and $\overline{AM}$, $\overline{AE}$ and $\overline{AI}$, $\overline{NE}$ and $\overline{MI}$, $\overline{ND}$ and $\overline{MJ}$, $\angle BAC$, $\angle CAN$, $\angle NAG$, $\angle GAM$, $\angle MAK$, and $\angle KAL$; $\angle DNE$, $\angle ENF$, $\angle HMI$, and $\angle JMI$

57. Yes; $x_1 + \frac{1}{2}(x_2 - x_1) = x_1 + \frac{1}{2}x_2 - \frac{1}{2}x_1 = \frac{1}{2}x_1 + \frac{1}{2}x_2 = \frac{x_1 + x_2}{2}$. Similarly, $y_1 + \frac{1}{2}(y_2 - y_1) = \frac{y_1 + y_2}{2}$.

1.5 MIXED REVIEW (p. 42)

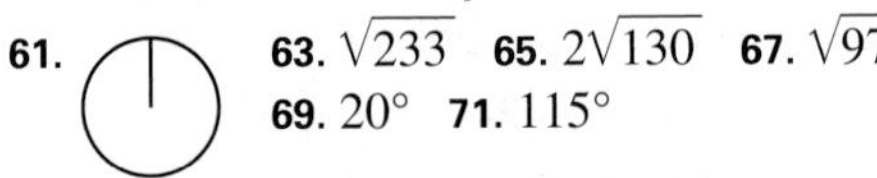

61. 63. $\sqrt{233}$ 65. $2\sqrt{130}$ 67. $\sqrt{97}$ 69. 20° 71. 115°

QUIZ 2 (p. 42) 1. If Q is in the interior of $\angle PSR$, then $m\angle PSQ + m\angle QSR = m\angle PSR$. 2–5. Coordinates of sample points are given.

2. ;

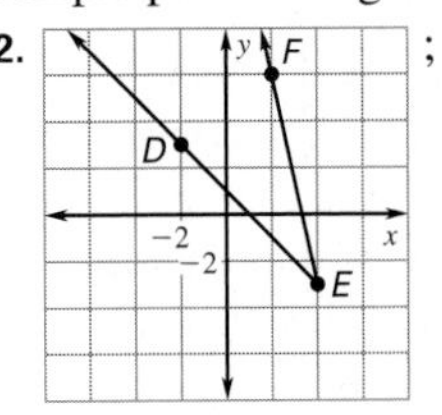

acute; (2, 2), (0, 0)

3. ;

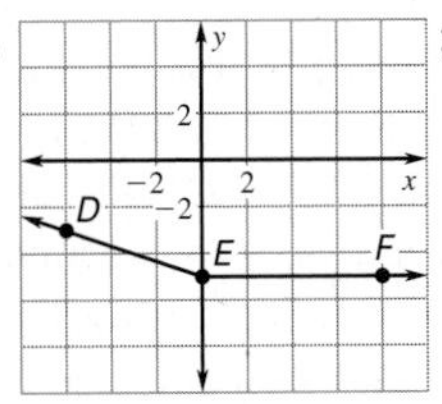

obtuse; (0, 0), (4, –6)

4. ;

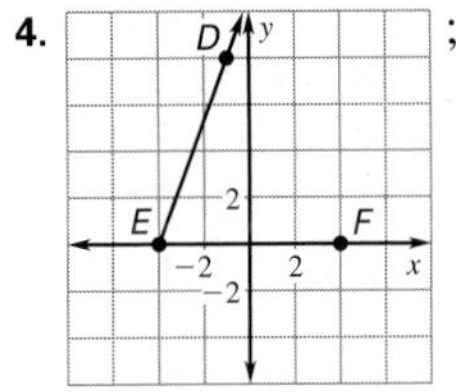

acute; (0, 2), (0, –2)

5. ;

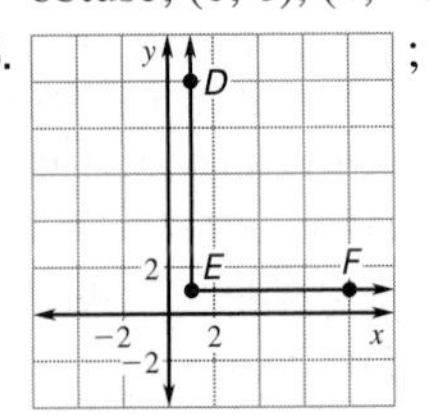

right; (2, 2), (0, 0)

6. 21°, 42°

1.6 PRACTICE (pp. 47–50) 5. 20° 7. 40° 9. yes 11. yes 13. no 15. always 17. always 19. never 21. 80° 23. 123° 25. 167° 27. 154° 29. 23 31. $x = 29$, $y = 50$ 33. $x = 48$, $y = 31$ 35. $x = 8$, $y = 12$ 37. supplementary 39. complementary 41. 88°; 80°; 65°; 57°; 50°; 41°; 35°; 28°; 14°; 4° 43. $m\angle A = 22.5°$; $m\angle B = 67.5°$ 45. $m\angle A = 73°$, $m\angle B = 17°$ 47. $m\angle A = 89°$, $m\angle B = 1°$ 49. $m\angle A = 129°$, $m\angle B = 51°$ 51. $m\angle A = 157°$, $m\angle B = 23°$ 53. 122°, 156° 55. 135°, 45°

1.6 MIXED REVIEW (p. 50) 61. 8 63. $-10\sqrt{2}$, $10\sqrt{2}$ 65. –10, 10 67. *C* 69. *A* 71. (–4, 6) 73. (–7, 1) 75. (2.6, 7)

1.7 PRACTICE (pp. 55–57) 3. 36 square units 5. 28.3 square units 7. 25.1 in.^{2} 9. 32 units, 60 square units 11. 16 units, 12 square units 13. 48 units, 84 square units 15. 54 units, 126 square units 17. 60 units, 225 square units

19. $10 + 5\sqrt{2}$ units, 12.5 square units **21.** 15 cm^2 **23.** 64 ft^2 **25.** 36 m^2 **27.** 6 square units **29.** 12.6 square units

31. 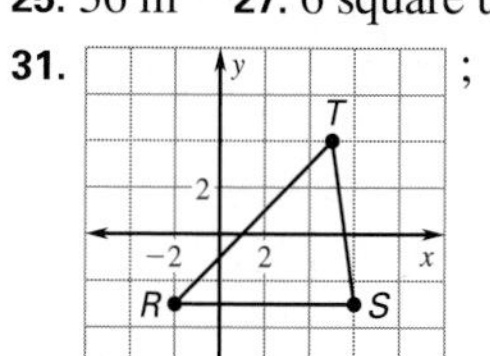

; **33.** ;

28 square units 50 square units

35. 352 $in.^2$ **37.** 10 m by 10 m **39.** about 3 times **41.** 26 in. **43.** 6 ft **45.** $10\sqrt{2} \approx 14.1$ cm **47.** ≈ 796.2 yd^2

1.7 MIXED REVIEW (p. 58) **51.** A B C

53–55. Coordinates of sample points are given.

53. 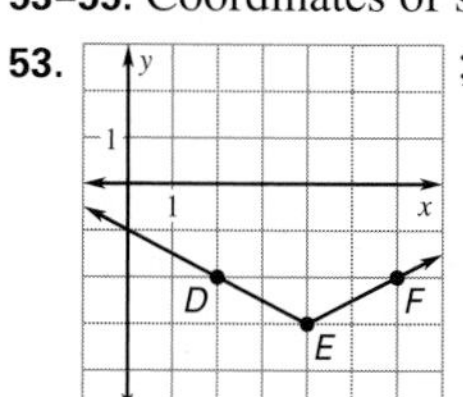

; **55.** ;

obtuse; (0, 0), (0, −2) right; (0, 0), (0, 2)

57. $\left(2\frac{1}{2}, 1\frac{1}{2}\right)$ **59.** $\left(-2\frac{1}{2}, 1\frac{1}{2}\right)$ **61.** (7, 3)

QUIZ 3 (p. 58) **1.** 49° **2.** 53° **3.** 158° **4.** 55° **5.** 15°, 75° **6.** 1017.4 m^2, 113.0 m **7.** 71.5 $in.^2$ **8.** 46 cm^2, 29.2 cm **9.** 40 square units **10.** at least 21 rolls

CHAPTER 1 REVIEW (pp. 60–62) **1.** Each number is 7 more than the previous number. **3.** Each number is 3 times the previous number. **5.** If 1 is added to the product of four consecutive positive integers, n through $n + 3$, the sum is equal to the square of $[n(n + 3) + 1]$.

7. 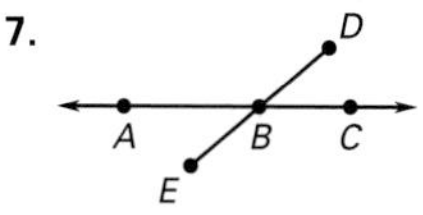

9. 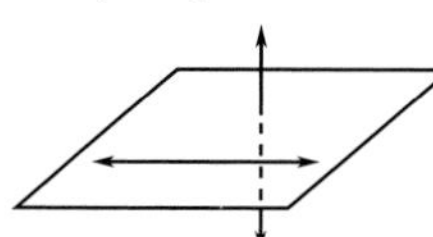

11. $\overline{PQ} \cong \overline{QR}$; $PQ = QR = 2\sqrt{2}$

13. $\overline{PQ}$ and $\overline{QR}$ are not congruent; $PQ = \sqrt{13}$, $QR = \sqrt{10}$.

15. obtuse; 150° A **17.** 105° **19.** 70° **21.** (1, 2)

23. $m\angle RQS = 50°$, $m\angle PQR = 100°$ **25.** $m\angle RQS = 46°$, $m\angle PQR = 92°$ **27.** sometimes **29.** sometimes **31.** 56.52 in., 254.34 $in.^2$ **33.** 56 ft

CHAPTER 2

SKILL REVIEW (p. 70)

1. D **2.** B **3.** F **4.** E **5.** 142° **6.** 142° **7.** 38°

2.1 PRACTICE (pp. 75–77) **3.** hypothesis: the dew point equals the air temperature; conclusion: it will rain **5.** If an angle is a right angle, then its measure is 90°. **7.** false **9.** If an object weighs 2000 pounds, then it weighs one ton. **11.** If three points lie on the same line, then the points are collinear. **13.** If a fish is a hagfish, then it lives in salt water. **15.** False; let $x = -3$. The hypothesis is true because $(-3)^4 = 81$. However, the conclusion is false, so the conditional statement is false. **17.** True **19.** If $\angle 2$ is acute, then $\angle 2$ measures 38°. **21.** If I go to the movies, then it is raining. **23.** if-then form: If three noncollinear points are distinct, then there is exactly one plane that they lie in; inverse: If three noncollinear points are not distinct, then it is not true that there is exactly one plane that they lie in; converse: If exactly one plane contains three noncollinear points, then the three points are distinct; contrapositive: If it is not true that there is exactly one plane that contains three noncollinear points, then the three points are not distinct. **25.** one **27.** a line **29.** Postulate 5: Through any two points there exists exactly one line. **31.** Postulate 8: Through any three noncollinear points there exists exactly one plane. **33.** Postulate 11: If two planes intersect, then their intersection is a line. **35.** Postulate 6: A line contains at least two points. **37.** Postulate 8: Through any three noncollinear points there exists exactly one plane. **41.** Yes; points A and B could lie on the line intersecting two planes. **43.** Yes; the plane that runs from the front of the room to the back of the room through points A and B contains both points and a point on the front wall. **45.** inverse: If $x \neq 4$, then $6x - 6 \neq x + 14$; converse: If $6x - 6 = x + 14$, then $x = 4$; contrapositive: If $6x - 6 \neq x + 14$, then $x \neq 4$. **47.** if-then form: If one feels the impulse to soar, then one can never consent to creep. **a.** hypothesis: one feels the impulse to soar; conclusion: one can never consent to creep **b.** If one does not feel the impulse to soar, then one can consent to creep. **49.** if-then form: If a man is early to bed and early to rise, then the man will be healthy, wealthy, and wise. **a.** hypothesis: a man is early to bed and early to rise; conclusion: the man is healthy, wealthy, and wise **b.** If a man is not early to bed and early to rise, then the man is not healthy, wealthy, and wise. **51.** inverse: If you do not want a great selection of used cars, then do not come and see Bargain Bob's Used Cars; converse: If you come and see Bargain Bob's Used Cars, then you want a great selection of used cars; contrapositive: If you do not come and see Bargain Bob's Used Cars, then you do not want a great selection of used cars.

MIXED REVIEW (p. 78) **61.** obtuse **63.** right **65.** (1, −2) **67.** (−1.5, 1.5) **69.** (6, −1) **71.** 113.04 m^2; 37.68 m **73.** 1501.5625 mm^2; 155 mm

2.2 PRACTICE (pp. 82–85) **3.** No; for a statement to be a biconditional statement it must contain the phrase "if and only if." **5.** yes **7.** conditional statement: If you scored a touchdown, then the football crossed the goal line; converse: If the football crossed the goal line, then you scored a touchdown. **9.** False; the points do not lie on the same line.

SA3

11. True; $\angle DBA$ and $\angle EBC$ each are supplementary to right angle $\angle DBC$, so each measures 90°. 13. false 15. false 17. false 19. true 21. conditional statement: If a ray bisects an angle, then it divides the angle into two congruent angles; converse: If an angle is divided into two congruent angles, then it is bisected by a ray. 23. conditional statement: If a point is a midpoint of a segment, then it divides the segment into two congruent segments; converse: If a point divides a segment into two congruent segments, then the point is the midpoint of the segment. 25. Two angles measuring 30° and 60° are complementary, but they do not measure 42° and 48°. 27. A rectangle with width 2 cm and length 3 cm has four sides, but it is not a square. 29. False; *PQ* and *PS* are equal if they are both 5 cm. 31. true 33. if-then form: If two circles have the same diameter, then they have the same circumference; converse: If two circles have the same circumference, then they have the same diameter; true; biconditional statement: Two circles have the same circumference if and only if they have the same diameter. 35. if-then form: If an animal is a leopard, then it has spots; converse: If an animal has spots, then it is a leopard; false; counterexample: A giraffe has spots, but it is not a leopard. 37. if-then form: If a leopard has pale gray fur, then it is a snow leopard; converse: If a leopard is a snow leopard, then it has pale gray fur; true; biconditional statement: A leopard is a snow leopard if and only if it has pale gray fur. 39. No; v can be any number if $9v - 4v = 2v + 3v$. 41. Yes; $x^3 - 27 = 0$ if and only if $x = 3$. 43. No; z can be any number if $7 + 18z = 5z + 7 + 13z$. 47. quadrupled 49. The statements from Exercises 47 and 48 can both be written as true biconditionals. The sides of the square are doubled if and only if the area is quadrupled, and the sides of a square are doubled if and only if the perimeter is doubled, are both true. 51. true 53. False; winds are classified as 9 on the Beaufort scale if the winds measure 41–47 knots.

2.2 MIXED REVIEW (p. 85) 59. 3°; 93° 61. 76°; 166° 63. 36 ft^2; 30 ft 65. 200.96 $in.^2$; 50.24 in. 67. If a rectangle is a square, then the sides of the rectangle are all congruent.

2.3 PRACTICE (pp. 91–94) 3. converse 5. If you like this movie, then you enjoy scary movies. 7. Yes; if f is true, then by the Law of Detachment, g is true. If g is true, then by the Law of Detachment, h is true. Therefore, if f is true, then h is true. 9. Points X, Y, and Z do not lie on the same line. 11. If points X, Y, and Z are not collinear, then points X, Y, and Z do not lie on the same line. 13. If points X, Y, and Z do not lie on the same line, then points X, Y, and Z are not collinear. 15. p: Alberto finds a summer job; q: Alberto will buy a car; inverse: $\sim p \rightarrow \sim q$, If Alberto does not find a summer job, then he will not buy a car; contrapositive: $\sim q \rightarrow \sim p$, If Alberto does not buy a car, then he did not find a summer job.

17. p: the car is running; q: the key is in the ignition; inverse: $\sim p \rightarrow \sim q$, If the car is not running, then the key is not in the ignition; contrapositive: $\sim q \rightarrow \sim p$, If the key is not in the ignition, then the car is not running. 19. p: Gina walks to the store; q: Gina buys a newspaper; inverse: $\sim p \rightarrow \sim q$, If Gina does not walk to the store, then she will not buy a newspaper; contrapositive: $\sim q \rightarrow \sim p$, If Gina does not buy a newspaper, then she did not walk to the store. 21. inductive reasoning; Inductive reasoning depends on previous examples and patterns to form a conjecture. Dana came to her conclusion based on previous examples. 23. valid; p: the sum of the measures of $\angle A$ and $\angle C$ is 90°. q: $\angle A$ and $\angle C$ are complementary. $p \rightarrow q$ and p are true. 25. valid; It can be concluded that $\angle B$ is acute, since the measure of $\angle B$ is between the measures of $\angle A$ and $\angle C$. 27. It can be concluded that $y \le 3$. Since the hypothesis is true, $2 \times 3 + 3 < 4 \times 3 < 5 \times 3$, the conclusion is true, $y \le x$. 29. No conclusions can be made because the hypothesis is not true for the given value of x. 31. If the stereo is on, then the neighbors will complain. 33. may not 35. may have 37. $\angle 1$ and $\angle 2$ are supplementary angles; therefore, their measures add up to 180°. 39. $\angle 4$ and $\angle 3$ are vertical angles; therefore, their measures are equal. 41. $\angle 5$ and $\angle 6$ are supplementary angles; therefore, their measures add up to 180°. 45. True; the mall is open; therefore, Angela and Diego went shopping and, therefore, Diego bought a pretzel. 47. False; the mall is open; therefore, Angela and Diego went shopping and, therefore, Angela bought a pizza. We cannot conclude that she also bought a pretzel. 49. D, B, A, E, C; the robot extinguishes the fire.

2.3 MIXED REVIEW (p. 94) 57. *Sample answer: F* 59. *Sample answer: B* 61. 41° 63. $3f + 4g + 7$

QUIZ 1 (p. 95) 1. The statement is already in if-then form; converse: If tomorrow is June 5, then today is June 4. Both the statement and its converse are true, so they can be combined to form a biconditional statement: Today is June 4 if and only if tomorrow is June 5. 2. if-then form: If a time period is a century, then it is a period of 100 years; converse: If a time period is 100 years, then it is a century. The statement and its converse cannot form a biconditional statement because the converse is not necessarily true. 3. if-then form: If two circles have the same diameter, then they are congruent; converse: If two circles are congruent, then they have the same diameter. Both the statement and its converse are true, so they can be combined to form a biconditional statement: Two circles are congruent if and only if they have the same diameter. 4. Yes; John backs the car out; therefore, he drives into the fence. 5. Yes; John backs the car out; therefore, he drives into the fence and, therefore, his father is angry.

2.4 PRACTICE (pp. 99–101) **5.** A **7.** E
9. $W = 1.42T - 38.5$ (Given)
$W + 38.5 = 1.42T$ (Addition property of equality)
$\frac{W + 38.5}{1.42} = T$ (Division property of equality)
If $W = -24.3°$F, then $T = 10°$F.
11. $BC = EF$ **13.** $PQ = RS$
15. Distributive property; Subtraction property of equality; Subtraction property of equality
17. $q + 9 = 13$ (Given)
$q = 4$ (Subtraction prop. of equality)
19. $7s + 20 = 4s - 13$ (Given)
$3s + 20 = -13$ (Subtraction prop. of equality)
$3s = -33$ (Subtraction prop. of equality)
$s = -11$ (Division prop. of equality)
21. $-2(-w + 3) = 15$ (Given)
$2w - 6 = 15$ (Distributive prop.)
$2w = 21$ (Addition prop. of equality)
$w = 10.5$ (Division prop. of equality)
23. $3(4v - 1) - 8v = 17$ (Given)
$12v - 3 - 8v = 17$ (Distributive prop.)
$4v - 3 = 17$ (Simplify.)
$4v = 20$ (Addition prop. of equality)
$v = 5$ (Division prop. of equality)
25. Given; Given; Transitive property of equality; Definition of right angles; Definition of perpendicular lines
27. B lies between A and C (Given)
$AB + BC = AC$ (Segment Addition Post.)
$AB = 3, BC = 8$ (Given)
$3 + 8 = AC$ (Substitution prop. of equality)
$AC = 11$ (Simplify.)
29. $c(r + 1) = n$ (Given)
$cr + c = n$ (Distributive prop.)
$cr = n - c$ (Subtraction prop. of equality)
$r = \frac{n - c}{c}$ (Division prop. of equality)
31. To find Donald's old wage, solve the formula $c(r + 1) = n$ for c.
$c(r + 1) = n$ (Given)
$c = \frac{n}{r + 1}$ (Division prop. of equality)
$c = \frac{12.72}{0.06 + 1}$ (Substitution prop. of equality)
$c = \$12.00$ (Simplify.)

2.4 MIXED REVIEW (p. 101) **35.** 9.90 **37.** 10.20 **39.** 8.60 **41.** $(-7, -7)$ **43.** $(12, -13)$ **45.** 42°; 132° **47.** false **49.** false

2.5 PRACTICE (pp. 104–107) **3.** By the definition of midpoint, Point D is halfway between B and F. Therefore, $\overline{BD} \cong \overline{FD}$. **5.** By the Transitive Property of Segment Congruence, if $\overline{CE} \cong \overline{BD}$ and $\overline{BD} \cong \overline{FD}$, then $\overline{CE} \cong \overline{FD}$.
7. Given; Definition of congruent segments; Transitive property of equality; Definition of congruent segments
9. $PR = 46$ (Given)
$PQ + QR = PR$ (Segment Addition Post.)
$2x + 5 + 6x - 15 = 46$ (Substitution prop. of equality)
$8x - 10 = 46$ (Simplify.)
$8x = 56$ (Addition prop. of equality)
$x = 7$ (Division prop. of equality)
11. $\overline{XY} \cong \overline{WX}$, $\overline{YZ} \cong \overline{WX}$ (Given)
$\overline{XY} \cong \overline{YZ}$ (Transitive Prop. of Segment Cong.)
$XY = YZ$ (Definition of congruent segments)
$4x + 3 = 9x - 12$ (Substitution prop. of equality)
$-5x + 3 = -12$ (Subtraction prop. of equality)
$-5x = -15$ (Subtraction prop. of equality)
$x = 3$ (Division prop. of equality)
17. $XY = 8$, $XZ = 8$ (Given)
$XY = XZ$ (Transitive prop. of equality)
$\overline{XY} \cong \overline{XZ}$ (Definition of congruent segments)
$\overline{XY} \cong \overline{ZY}$ (Given)
$\overline{XZ} \cong \overline{ZY}$ (Transitive Prop. of Segment Cong.)
19. yes; by the Transitive Property of Segment Congruence

2.5 MIXED REVIEW (p. 107) **29.** *Sample answer:* $2 + 3 = 5$ **31.** 116° **33.** 65° **35.** If Matthew does not win first place, then Matthew did not win the wrestling match. **37.** $p \rightarrow q$; If the car is in the garage, then Mark is home. **39.** $\sim p \rightarrow \sim q$; If the car is not in the garage, then Mark is not home.

2.6 PRACTICE (pp. 112–115) **3.** $\angle A$ **5.** yes **7.** no **9.** yes
11. A is an angle. (Given)
$m\angle A = m\angle A$ (Reflexive prop. of equality)
$\angle A \cong \angle A$ (Definition of congruent angles)
13. 31° **15.** 158° **17.** 61° **19.** $\angle 1 \cong \angle 3$, $\angle 2 \cong \angle 4$
21. $\angle 1 \cong \angle 2$, $\angle 3 \cong \angle 4$
23. $m\angle 3 = 120°$, $\angle 1 \cong \angle 4$, $\angle 3 \cong \angle 4$ (Given)
$\angle 1 \cong \angle 3$ (Transitive Prop. of Angle Cong.)
$m\angle 1 = m\angle 3$ (Definition of congruent angles)
$m\angle 1 = 120°$ (Substitution prop. of equality)
25. $\angle QVW$ and $\angle RWV$ are supplementary. (Given)
$\angle QVW$ and $\angle QVP$ are a linear pair. (Definition of linear pair)
$\angle QVP$ and $\angle QVW$ are supplementary. (Linear Pair Post.)
$\angle QVP \cong \angle RWV$ (Congruent Supplements Theorem)
27. $4w + 10 + 13w = 180$
$17w + 10 = 180$
$17w = 170$
$w = 10$
$2(x + 25) + 2x - 30 = 180$
$2x + 50 + 2x - 30 = 180$
$4x + 20 = 180$
$4x = 160$
$x = 40$
29. Yes; $\angle 2 \cong \angle 3$ and $\angle 1$ and $\angle 4$ are supplementary to congruent angles. $\angle 1 \cong \angle 4$ by the Congruent Supplements Theorem.

SA5

2.6 MIXED REVIEW (p. 116) **39.** 172° **41.** All definitions are true biconditionals. So the conditionals If two lines are perpendicular, then they intersect to form a right angle and If two lines intersect to form a right angle, then the two lines are perpendicular are both true.
43. $x = \frac{1}{2}$ **45.** $z = \frac{1}{3}$

QUIZ 2 (p. 116)
1. $x - 3 = 7$ (Given)
$x = 10$ (Addition prop. of equality)
2. $x + 8 = 27$ (Given)
$x = 19$ (Subtraction prop. of equality)
3. $2x - 5 = 13$ (Given)
$2x = 18$ (Addition prop. of equality)
$x = 9$ (Division prop. of equality)
4. $2x + 20 = 4x - 12$ (Given)
$-2x + 20 = -12$ (Subtraction prop. of equality)
$-2x = -32$ (Subtraction prop. of equality)
$x = 16$ (Division prop. of equality)
5. $3(3x - 7) = 6$ (Given)
$9x - 21 = 6$ (Distributive prop.)
$9x = 27$ (Addition prop. of equality)
$x = \frac{27}{9}$, or 3 (Division prop. of equality)
6. $-2(-2x + 4) = 16$ (Given)
$4x - 8 = 16$ (Distributive prop.)
$4x = 24$ (Addition prop. of equality)
$x = 6$ (Division prop. of equality)
7. $\overline{BA} \cong \overline{BC}$, $\overline{BC} \cong \overline{CD}$ (Given)
$\overline{BA} \cong \overline{CD}$ (Transitive Prop. of Segment Cong.)
$\overline{AE} \cong \overline{DF}$ (Given)
$BA + AE = BE$ (Segment Addition Post.)
$BA = CD$ (Definition of congruent segments)
$AE = DF$ (Definition of congruent segments)
$CD + DF = BE$ (Substitution prop. of equality)
$CD + DF = CF$ (Segment Addition Post.)
$BE = CF$ (Transitive prop. of equality)
$\overline{BE} \cong \overline{CF}$ (Definition of congruent segments)
8. $\overline{EH} \cong \overline{GH}$, $\overline{FG} \cong \overline{GH}$ (Given)
$\overline{EH} \cong \overline{FG}$ (Transitive Prop. of Segment Cong.) **9.** 38°

CHAPTER 2 REVIEW (pp.118–120)
1. if-then form: If there is a teacher's meeting, then we are dismissed early; hypothesis: there is a teacher's meeting; conclusion: we are dismissed early; inverse: If there is not a teacher's meeting, then we are not dismissed early; converse: If we are dismissed early, then there is a teacher's meeting; contrapositive: If we are not dismissed early, then there is not a teacher's meeting. **3.** exactly one **5.** No; $x^2 = 25$ does not necessarily mean that $x = 5$. x could also $= -5$. **7.** If the measure of $\angle A$ is 90°, then $\angle A$ is a right angle. **9.** $\angle A$ is not a right angle. **11.** If there is a nice breeze, then we will sail to Dunkirk. **13.** C **15.** D
17. $5(3y + 2) = 25$ (Given)
$15y + 10 = 25$ (Distributive prop.)
$15y = 15$ (Subtraction prop. of equality)
$y = 1$ (Division prop. of equality)
19. $23 + 11d - 2c = 12 - 2c$ (Given)
$23 + 11d = 12$ (Addition prop. of equality)
$11d = -11$ (Subtraction prop. of equality)
$d = -1$ (Division prop. of equality)
21. $\angle 1$ and $\angle 2$ are complementary. (Given)
$\angle 3$ and $\angle 4$ are complementary. (Given)
$\angle 1 \cong \angle 3$ (Given)
$\angle 2 \cong \angle 4$ (Congruent Complements Theorem)

ALGEBRA REVIEW (pp. 124–125) **1.** no **2.** yes **3.** yes **4.** no **5.** no **6.** yes **7.** no **8.** no **9.** no **10.** yes **11.** yes **12.** yes **13.** -5 **14.** $-\frac{2}{13}$ **15.** $\frac{1}{2}$ **16.** $\frac{1}{7}$ **17.** $-\frac{11}{2}$ **18.** 2 **19.** -2 **20.** 0 **21.** $-\frac{13}{9}$ **22.** -1 **23.** $-\frac{14}{9}$ **24.** $-\frac{23}{11}$ **25.** $\frac{7}{12}$ **26.** $-\frac{9}{8}$ **27.** $-\frac{1}{4}$ **28.** $y = -2x + 5$ **29.** $y = -3x - 12$ **30.** $y = -\frac{2}{3}x + 8$ **31.** $y = -\frac{13}{7}x + 13$ **32.** $y = \frac{1}{3}x - 2$ **33.** $y = -12x - 8$ **34.** $y = -2x - 14$ **35.** $y = -x - 2$ **36.** $y = -3x + 7$ **37.** $y = -2x - 5$ **38.** $y = \frac{1}{2}x + 2$ **39.** $y = -\frac{1}{3}x + 1.5$ **40.** $y = -x + 3$ **41.** $y = -3x - 12$ **42.** $y = 4x - 21$ **43.** $y = -2x$ **44.** $y = 5x + 8$ **45.** $y = 3x - 1$ **46.** $y = -x + 4$ **47.** $y = -6x - 21$ **48.** $y = 2x + 8$ **49.** $y = 2x - 29$ **50.** $y = \frac{1}{3}x - \frac{5}{3}$ **51.** $y = -\frac{5}{12}x + \frac{3}{2}$

CHAPTER 3

SKILL REVIEW (p. 128) **1.** 133 **2.** 47 **3.** $-\frac{1}{4}$ **4.** 18 **5.** 20 **6.** $\frac{77}{2}$ **7.** Definition of a right angle **8.** Vertical angles are congruent. **9.** $\angle 2$ and $\angle 3$ form a linear pair. **10.** Definition of congruent angles **11.** Subtraction property of equality **12.** Distributive property

3.1 PRACTICE (pp. 132–134) **3.** B **5.** A **7.** $\angle 3$ and $\angle 5$, or $\angle 4$ and $\angle 6$ **9.** $\angle 3$ and $\angle 6$, or $\angle 4$ and $\angle 5$ **11.** perpendicular **13.** parallel **15.** $\overleftrightarrow{QU}$, $\overleftrightarrow{QT}$, $\overleftrightarrow{RV}$, or $\overleftrightarrow{RS}$ **17.** *UVW* **19.** 1 **21.** corresponding **23.** consecutive interior **25.** alternate exterior **27.** III; 3 **29.** V; 5 **31.** M; 1000 **33.** yes **35.** no **37.** *Sample answer:* The two lines of intersection are coplanar, since they are both in the third plane. The two lines do not intersect, because they are in parallel planes. Since they are coplanar and do not intersect, they are parallel.
39.

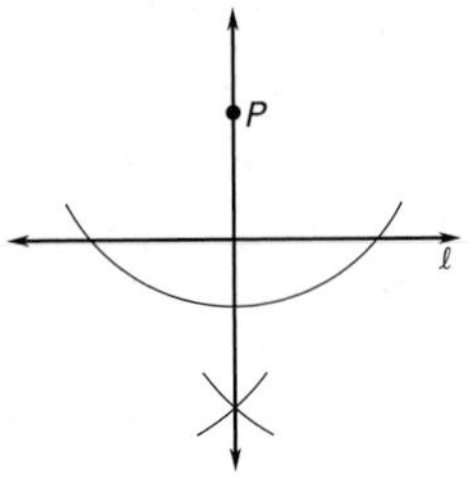

SELECTED ANSWERS

3.1 MIXED REVIEW (p. 134) **47.** $m\angle ABD = 80°$, $m\angle ABC = 160°$ **49.** 77°, 167° **51.** 2°, 92° **53.** 22°, 112° **55.** 30°, 120° **57.** $x + 13 - 13 = 23 - 13$, Subtraction property of equality; $x = 10$, Simplify. **59.** $4x + 11 - 11 = 31 - 11$, Subtraction property of equality; $4x = 20$, Simplify; $\frac{4x}{4} = \frac{20}{4}$, Division property of equality; $x = 5$, Simplify. **61.** *Sample answer:* $2x - 2 + 3 = 17$, Distributive property; $2x + 1 = 17$, Simplify; $2x + 1 - 1 = 17 - 1$, Subtraction property of equality; $2x = 16$, Simplify; $\frac{2x}{2} = \frac{16}{2}$, Division property of equality; $x = 8$, Simplify.

3.2 PRACTICE (pp. 138–141) **3.** Vertical Angles Theorem **5.** Theorem 3.2 **7.** 90 **9.** 20 **11.** 90 **13.** 35 **15.** *Sample answer:* $\angle 1$, $\angle 2$, $\angle 3$, and $\angle 4$ are right angles. **17. a.** right angle **b.** 90° **c.** Angle Addition **d.** $m\angle 3$ **e.** $m\angle 4$ **f.** 90°

19.

Statements	Reasons
2. $\angle 1 \cong \angle 3$	3. If two angles are congruent, then their measures are equal.
5. $m\angle 1 = 90°$	4. Given
6. $90° = m\angle 3$	
7. $\angle 3$ is a right angle.	

21. If $\angle 4 \cong \angle 6$, then $\angle 5 \cong \angle 6$ because $\angle 5 \cong \angle 4$ and because of the Transitive Property of Angle Congruence.

23.

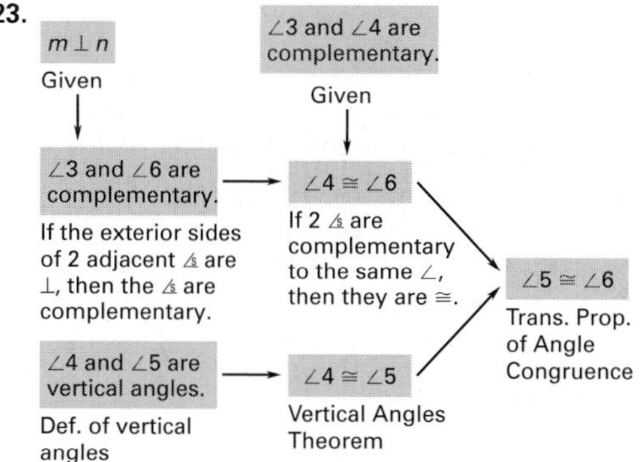

25. No; *Sample answer:* If one of the angles is a right angle, then the crosspieces are perpendicular, so all four angles will be right angles.

3.2 MIXED REVIEW (p. 141) **29.** 38° **31.** 39° **33.** $\angle 1$ and $\angle 5$, $\angle 3$ and $\angle 7$, $\angle 2$ and $\angle 6$, $\angle 4$ and $\angle 8$ **35.** $\angle 1$ and $\angle 8$, $\angle 2$ and $\angle 7$

3.3 PRACTICE (pp. 146–148) **3.** Alternate Exterior Angles Theorem **5.** Consecutive Interior Angles Theorem **7.** 133 **9.** $m\angle 1 = 82°$; *Sample answer:* by the Corresponding Angles Postulate. $m\angle 2 = 98°$; *Sample answer:* $\angle 1$ and $\angle 2$ form a linear pair. **11.** $x = 113$, by the Linear Pair Postulate; $y = 113$, by the Alternate Exterior Angles Theorem. **13.** $x = 90$, $y = 90$; *Sample answer:* by the Perpendicular Transversal Theorem **15.** $x = 100$; *Sample answer:* by the Linear Pair Postulate. $y = 80$; *Sample answer:* by the Alternate Exterior Angles Theorem **17.** $m\angle 2 = m\angle 3 = m\angle 6 = m\angle 7 = 73°$, $m\angle 4 = m\angle 5 = m\angle 8 = 107°$ **19.** 23 **21.** 28 **23.** 12 **25.** 7

27.

Statements	Reasons
1. $p \parallel q$	2. Alternate Interior Angles Theorem
3. $m\angle 1 = m\angle 3$	5. Linear Pair Postulate
4. $\angle 2$ and $\angle 3$ form a linear pair.	7. Definition of supplementary $\angle$s
6. $m\angle 1 + m\angle 2 = 180°$	

29. *Sample answer:* It is given that $p \perp q$, so $\angle 1$ is a right angle because perpendicular lines form right angles. It is given that $q \parallel r$, so $\angle 1 \cong \angle 2$ by the Corresponding Angles Postulate. Then, $\angle 2$ is a right angle because it is congruent to a right angle. Finally, $p \perp r$ because the sides of a right angle are perpendicular.

3.3 MIXED REVIEW (p. 149) **33.** 130° **35.** 79° **37.** 69° **39.** If an angle is acute, then the measure of the angle is 19°. **41.** If I go fishing, then I do not have to work. **43.** 21°

QUIZ 1 (p. 149) **1.** $\angle 6$ **2.** $\angle 5$ **3.** $\angle 6$ **4.** $\angle 7$ **5.** *Sample answer:* Since $\angle 1$ and $\angle 2$ are congruent angles that form a linear pair, this shows that $m\angle 1$ and $m\angle 2$ are both 90°. This shows that the two lines are perpendicular so that $\angle 3$ and $\angle 4$ are right angles. **6.** 69 **7.** 75 **8.** 12 **9.** 35°; the top left corner is assumed to be a right angle; $\angle 3$ and $\angle 2$ are complementary, Definition of complementary angles; $m\angle 3 + m\angle 2 = 90°$, Definition of complementary angles; $m\angle 2 = 90° - 55° = 35°$, Substitution; $m\angle 1 = m\angle 2$, Corresponding Angles Postulate

3.4 PRACTICE (pp. 153–156) **3.** yes; Alternate Exterior Angles Converse **5.** no **7.** yes; Corresponding Angles Converse **9.** 45; Consecutive Interior Angles Converse **11.** yes; Alternate Exterior Angles Converse **13.** no **15.** no **17.** 45 **19.** yes; Corresponding Angles Converse **21.** no **23.** yes; Angle Addition Postulate and Alternate Exterior Angles Converse **25.** no **27.** $j \parallel n$ because $31° + 69° = 100°$ and $32° + 68° = 100°$. **29.** 32° **33.** $\angle 1 \cong \angle 4$ and $\angle 2 \cong \angle 3$. *Sample answer:* The angles marked as congruent are alternate interior angles, so $r \parallel s$ by the Alternate Interior Angles Converse. Then $\angle 1 \cong \angle 4$ by the Alternate Interior Angles Theorem and $\angle 2 \cong \angle 3$ by the Vertical Angles Theorem. **35.** *Sample answer:* It is given that $a \parallel b$, so $\angle 1$ and $\angle 3$ are supplementary by the Consecutive Interior Angles Theorem. Then, $m\angle 1 + m\angle 3 = 180°$ by the definition of supplementary angles. Then, $m\angle 2 + m\angle 3 = 180°$ by substitution, and $c \parallel d$ by the Consecutive Interior Angles Converse.

3.4 MIXED REVIEW (p. 156)

41.

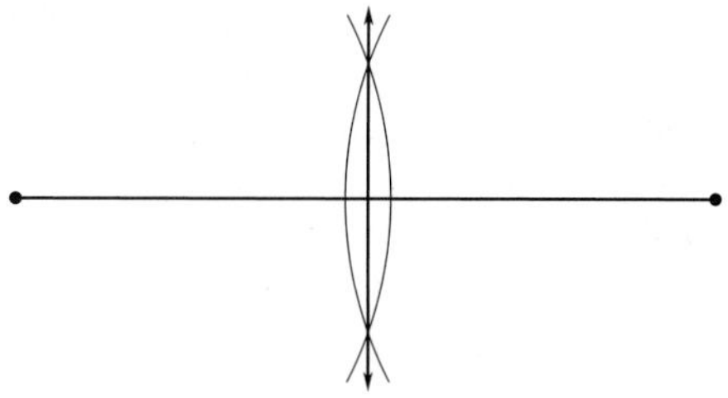

SELECTED ANSWERS

SA7

43. 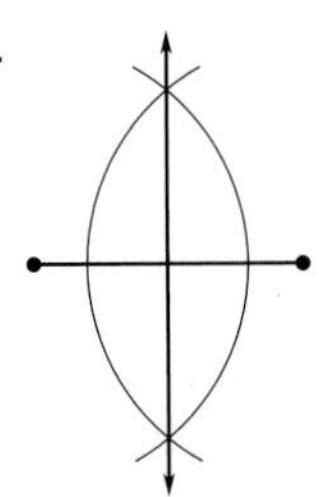

45. $\angle 5$ **47.** $\angle 7$

3.5 PRACTICE (pp. 160–163) **3.** Theorem 3.12 **5.** $\ell_1 \parallel \ell_2$ because of the Alternate Interior Angles Converse. **7.** *Sample answer:* Given line ℓ and exterior point P, draw any line n through P that intersects ℓ. Then copy $\angle 1$ at P so that $\angle 1 \cong \angle 2$. Line m will be parallel to line ℓ. **9.** Theorem 3.12 **11.** Corresponding Angles Converse **13.** Alternate Interior Angles Converse **15.** $85° + 95° = 180°$, so $k \parallel j$ by the Consecutive Interior Angles Converse. **17.** *Sample answer:* The measure of the obtuse exterior angle formed by n and k is $90° + \frac{90}{2} = 135°$, so $k \parallel j$ by the Alternate Exterior Angles Converse. **19.** *Sample answer:* The measure of the obtuse angle formed by g and the left transversal is $(180 - x)°$. Since $(180 - x)° + x° = 180°$, $g \parallel h$ by the Consecutive Interior Angles Converse. **21.** $p \parallel q$ by the Corresponding Angles Converse; $q \parallel r$ by the Consecutive Interior Angles Converse. Then, because $p \parallel q$ and $q \parallel r$, $p \parallel r$. **23.** a and b are each perpendicular to d, so $a \parallel b$ by Theorem 3.12; c and d are each perpendicular to a, so $c \parallel d$ by Theorem 3.12.

25. *Sample answer:*

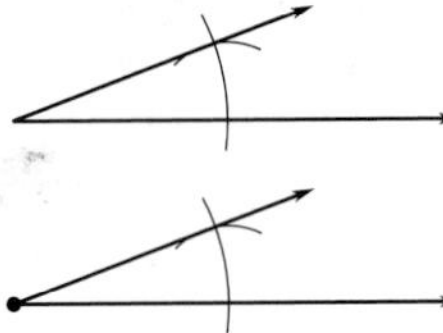

27. *Sample answer:*

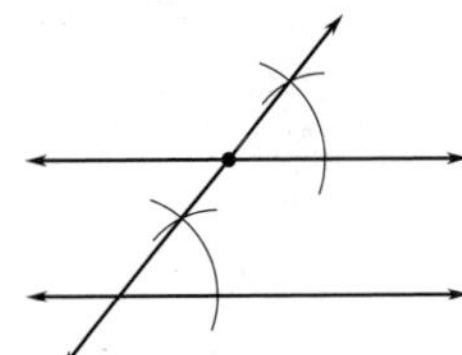

29. *Sample answer:* The two angles that are congruent are corresponding angles, so the two lines are parallel by the Corresponding Angles Converse. **31.** *Sample answer:* Each edge is parallel to the previous edge, so all the strips are parallel by Theorem 3.11. **33.** always **35.** never **37.** 50° **39. a.** *Sample answer:* Hold the straightedge next to each red line and see if the red lines are straight.
b. *Sample answer:* Measure the angles formed by the red lines and the top horizontal line, and see if corresponding angles are congruent.

3.5 MIXED REVIEW (p. 163) **43.** $2\sqrt{58}$, or about 15.23 **45.** $2\sqrt{34}$, or about 11.66 **47.** $5\sqrt{17}$, or about 20.62 **49.** Converse: If an angle is acute, then its measure is 42°. Counterexample: a 41° angle (or any acute angle whose measure is not 42°) **51.** Converse: If a polygon contains four right angles, then it is a rectangle. Counterexample:

QUIZ 2 (p. 164) **1.** yes; Consecutive Interior Angles Converse **2.** $a \parallel b$ **3.** $a \parallel b$ **4.** $a \parallel b$, $c \parallel d$ **5.** *Sample answer:* First, it is given that $\angle ABC$ is supplementary to $\angle DEF$. Next, note that $\angle ABC$ and $\angle CBE$ are a linear pair; therefore, by the Linear Pair Postulate, $\angle ABC$ and $\angle CBE$ are supplementary. By the Congruent Supplements Theorem, $\angle CBE \cong \angle DEF$. Finally, the left and right edges of the chimney are parallel by the Corresponding Angles Converse.

3.6 PRACTICE (pp. 168–171) **5.** -2 **7.** parallel; both have slope $\frac{1}{3}$. **9.** parallel; both have slope $\frac{1}{2}$. **11.** $\frac{3}{2}$ **13.** $\frac{1}{2}$ **15.** -1 **17.** $-2, -2$; parallel **19.** 3, 4; not parallel **21.** $\frac{5}{6}, \frac{5}{7}$; not parallel **23.** about 7.2 feet; *Sample answer:* Using x for the height, a proportion is $\frac{3}{5} = \frac{x}{12}$. Then, $5x = 36$ and $x = 7.2$. **25.** slope of $\overleftrightarrow{AB}$: $\frac{1}{2}$; slope of $\overleftrightarrow{CD}$: $\frac{1}{2}$; slope of $\overleftrightarrow{EF}$: $\frac{3}{4}$; $\overleftrightarrow{AB} \parallel \overleftrightarrow{CD}$ **27.** $y = 3x + 2$ **29.** $y = -\frac{2}{9}x$ **31.** $y = -3$ **33.** $y = -6x + 3$ **35.** $y = -\frac{4}{3}x + 3$ **37.** $y = -x + 6$ **39.** $y = -4$ **41.** $x = 6$ **43.** $y = \frac{5}{4}x - \frac{13}{4}$ **45.** *Sample answer:* $y = \frac{1}{3}x$

47. 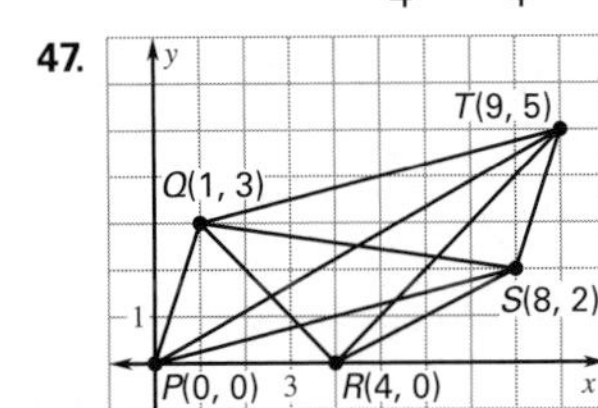

49. 5%; no **51.** 9%; yes **53.** $y = x$; 45°

3.6 MIXED REVIEW (p. 171) **59.** $\frac{1}{20}$ **61.** $-\frac{1}{11}$ **63.** $\frac{7}{3}$ **65.** -2 **67.** -9 **69.** $-11\frac{2}{3}$ **71.** yes; Alternate Exterior Angles Converse **73.** no

3.7 PRACTICE (pp. 175–177) **3.** yes; *Sample answer:* The slope of $\overleftrightarrow{AC}$ is -2, and the slope of $\overleftrightarrow{BD}$ is $\frac{1}{2}$, and $(-2)\left(\frac{1}{2}\right) = -1$. **5.** perpendicular **7.** yes **9.** yes **11.** no **13.** $-\frac{1}{2}$ **15.** $\frac{1}{3}$ **17.** $-\frac{3}{2}$ **19.** 3 **21.** slope of $\overleftrightarrow{AC}$: 3; slope of $\overleftrightarrow{BD}$: $-\frac{1}{3}$; perpendicular **23.** slope of $\overleftrightarrow{AC}$: $\frac{1}{3}$; slope of $\overleftrightarrow{BD}$: $-\frac{5}{2}$; not perpendicular **25.** perpendicular **27.** perpendicular **29.** perpendicular **31.** not perpendicular **33.** slope of $\overleftrightarrow{AB}$: -1; slope of $\overleftrightarrow{PQ}$: $\frac{6}{7}$; slope of $\overleftrightarrow{WV}$: -1; $\overleftrightarrow{AB} \parallel \overleftrightarrow{WV}$ **35.** slope of $\overleftrightarrow{AZ}$: $\frac{2}{3}$; slope of $\overleftrightarrow{CD}$: $-\frac{4}{3}$; slope of $\overleftrightarrow{RS}$: $\frac{3}{4}$; $\overleftrightarrow{CD} \perp \overleftrightarrow{RS}$

SA8

37. *Sample answer:* The slopes are 2 and $-\frac{1}{2}$, and the product of the two slopes is -1. **39.** $y = -\frac{3}{5}x + 4$ **41.** $y = \frac{3}{4}x - \frac{7}{4}$ **43.** $y = -7x + 39$ **45.** $y = \frac{5}{2}x - \frac{35}{2}$ **47.** parallel **49.** perpendicular

3.7 Mixed Review (p. 178)

55. 142° **57.** 35° **59.** $\angle 6$ **61.** $\angle 6$

Quiz 3 (p. 178) **1.** $\frac{3}{2}$ **2.** $-\frac{8}{3}$ **3.** $y = 3x + 2$ **4.** $y = \frac{1}{2}x - 5$ **5.** yes **6.** no **7.** 1

Chapter 3 Review (pp. 180–182) **1.** alternate exterior **3.** $\overleftrightarrow{BF}$, $\overleftrightarrow{CG}$, or $\overleftrightarrow{AE}$ **5.** Possible answers: $\overleftrightarrow{CG}$, $\overleftrightarrow{AB}$, $\overleftrightarrow{AC}$, $\overleftrightarrow{AE}$, $\overleftrightarrow{EG}$, $\overleftrightarrow{GH}$ **7.** $m\angle 2 = 105°$; $m\angle 3 = 105°$; $m\angle 4 = 75°$; $m\angle 5 = 75°$; $m\angle 6 = 105°$ **9.** 22; Alternate Interior Angles Postulate, $(4x + 4)° = 92°$. So, $x = \frac{92° - 4°}{4} = 22$.
11. Since $m\angle 4 = 60°$ and $m\angle 7 = 120°$, they are supplementary because their measures add up to 180°. By the Consecutive Interior Angles Converse, $\ell \parallel m$. **13.** $j \parallel k$; Corresponding Angles Converse
15. $m \parallel n$; Consecutive Interior Angles Converse
17. Slope of $\overleftrightarrow{AB}$ and $\overleftrightarrow{CD}$ is $\frac{1}{2}$; yes.
19. Slope of $\overleftrightarrow{JK} = 3$; slope of $\overleftrightarrow{MN} = \frac{5}{2}$; no **21.** yes **23.** yes

Cumulative Practice (pp. 186–187) **1.** You add 2, then 3, then 4, and so on: 30. **3.** $\overleftrightarrow{DT}$ **5.** Exactly 1; through any three noncollinear points there is exactly one plane.
7. $(-13, 3)$ **9.**

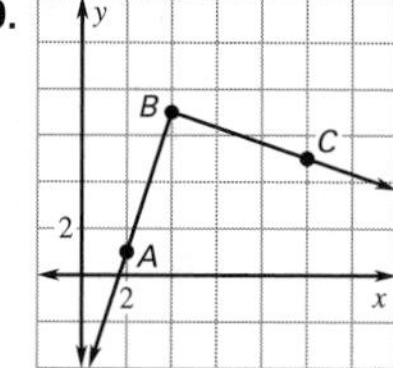

; right **11.** $x = 6$, $y = 2$ **13.** $x = 16$, $y = 36$ **15.** 40 units^2

17. If an angle is a straight angle, then its measure is 180°. If an angle is not a straight angle, then its measure is not 180°. If an angle measure is 180°, then it is a straight angle. If an angle measure is not 180°, then it is not a straight angle.
19. Two lines can intersect to form acute and obtuse angles.
21. If the angles are same side interior angles of two parallel lines, they would be supplementary but not a linear pair.
23.

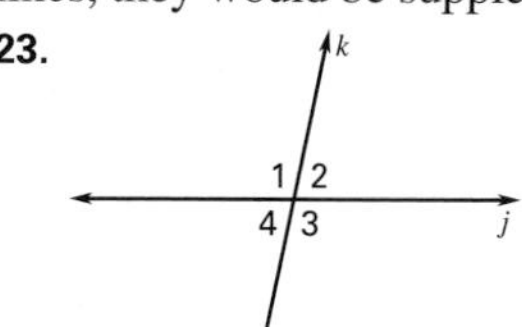

$\angle 1$ and $\angle 2$ are supplementary; $\angle 1$ and $\angle 4$ are supplementary; $\angle 2$ and $\angle 3$ are supplementary; $\angle 3$ and $\angle 4$ are supplementary; $\angle 1$ and $\angle 3$ are vertical angles; $\angle 2$ and $\angle 4$ are vertical angles.

25. Yes; by the Law of Detachment **27.** 55°
29. $\overleftrightarrow{DE} \parallel \overleftrightarrow{AC}$ by the Consecutive Interior Angles Converse.
31. slope of $\overleftrightarrow{AD} = -\frac{11}{23}$, slope of $\overleftrightarrow{BC} = -\frac{11}{23}$ **33.** $y = -\frac{3}{4}x + \frac{21}{4}$
35. a. 6 in. by 9 in. **b.** $\angle 1$ and $\angle 3$ are complementary. **c.** $\angle 1$ and $\angle 2$ are supplementary.

CHAPTER 4

Skill Review (p. 192) **1.** 30 **2.** 2 **3.** 3 **4.** 75 **5.** 60 **6.** 3
7.

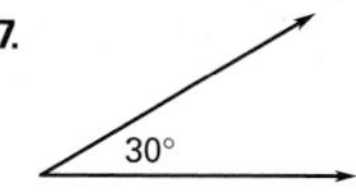

8.

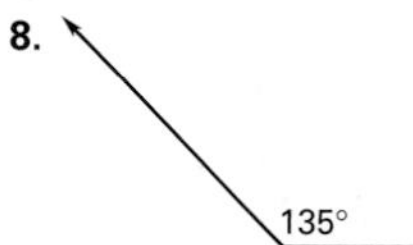

9. 72°

10. Vertical Angles Theorem
11. Alternate Interior Angles Theorem
12. Corresponding Angles Postulate

4.1 Practice (pp. 198–200) **7.** right scalene **9.** 77.5° **11.** E **13.** D **15.** C **17.** right isosceles **19.** right scalene **21.** acute scalene **23.** sometimes **25.** always **27.** (Ex. 17) legs: $\overline{DE}$, $\overline{DF}$, hypotenuse: $\overline{EF}$; (Ex. 19) legs: $\overline{RP}$, $\overline{RQ}$, hypotenuse: $\overline{PQ}$ **29.** $C(5, 5)$ **31.** 48° **33.** $m\angle 1 = 79°$, $m\angle 2 = 51°$, $m\angle 3 = 39°$ **35.** $m\angle R = 20°$, $m\angle S = 140°$, $m\angle T = 20°$; obtuse **37.** 70° **39.** 143° **41.** 120°, 24°
43. Yes; the total length needed is 3×33.5, or 100.5 cm.
45. $\overline{MN}$ and $\overline{LN}$; $\overline{ML}$
47.

Statements	Reasons
4. $m\angle A + m\angle B + m\angle ACB = 180°$	3. Linear Pair Postulate 5. Substitution property of equality 6. Subtraction property of equality

4.1 Mixed Review (p. 201) **53.** true **55.** false **57.** yes; Alternate Interior Angles Converse **59.** yes; Corresponding Angles Converse **61.** $y = x + 3$ **63.** $y = \frac{2}{3}x - 7$ **65.** $y = -\frac{7}{2}x - 10$ **67.** $y = -\frac{3}{2}x + 15$

4.2 Practice (pp. 205–208) **5.** 45° **7.** 30° **9.** $\overline{PR}$ **11.** $\overline{CA}$ **13.** UV **15.** B, C, D **17.** triangles FGH and JKH; $\angle FHG \cong \angle JHK$ by the Vertical Angles Theorem, so the triangles are congruent by the definition of congruence; $\triangle FGH$ and $\triangle JKH$. **19.** pentagons $VWXYZ$ and $MNJKL$; definition of congruence; $VWXYZ \cong MNJKL$ **21.** triangles LKR and NMQ and quadrilaterals $LKQS$ and $NMRS$; $\overline{LR}$ and $\overline{NQ}$ are congruent by the addition property of equality, the Segment Addition Postulate, and the definition of congruence and $\angle NQM$ and $\angle LRK$ are congruent by the Third Angles Theorem, so the triangles are congruent by the definition of congruence; $\angle LSQ \cong \angle NSR$ by the Vertical Angles Theorem and $\angle KQS \cong \angle MRS$ by the Congruent Supplements Theorem, so the quadrilaterals are congruent by the definition of congruence; $\triangle LKR \cong \triangle NMQ$, $LKQS \cong NMRS$.
25. $a = 13$, $b = 13$ **27.** 12 **29.** 65 **31.** 120°
33. The measure of each of the congruent angles in each small triangle is 30°. By the Angle Addition Postulate, the measure of each angle of $\triangle ABC$ is 60°.

35.

Statements	Reasons
7. $\angle C \cong \angle F$	1. Given 2. *A, D, B, E*; Definition of congruent angles 3. Triangle Sum Theorem 4. Substitution property of equality or transitive property of equality 5. Substitution property of equality 6. Subtraction property of equality

37. $\triangle ABF$ and $\triangle EBF$; $\overline{BF} \cong \overline{BF}$ by the Reflexive Property of Congruence, and $\angle A$ and $\angle BEF$ are congruent by the Third Angles Theorem, so the triangles are congruent by the definition of congruence.

4.2 MIXED REVIEW (p. 209) **41.** $4\sqrt{10}$ **43.** $\sqrt{26}$ **45.** $3\sqrt{13}$ **47.** $(-2, -2)$ **49.** $(1, 0)$ **51.** $(10, 3)$ **53.** $82°$ **55.** $28°$ **57.** $-\frac{5}{2}$ and -2; no

QUIZ 1 (p. 210) **1.** acute isosceles **2.** acute isosceles **3.** obtuse scalene **4.** 7; $m\angle F = 77°$, $m\angle E = 55°$, $m\angle EDF = 48°$, $m\angle CDF = 132°$ **5.** $\triangle MNP \cong \triangle QPN$; $\angle M$ and $\angle Q$, $\angle MNP$ and $\angle QPN$, $\angle MPN$ and $\angle QNP$, $\overline{MN}$ and $\overline{QP}$, $\overline{NP}$ and $\overline{PN}$, $\overline{MP}$ and $\overline{QN}$ **6.** $107°$

4.3 PRACTICE (pp. 216–219) **3.** yes; SAS Congruence Postulate **5.** yes; SSS Congruence Postulate **7.** $\angle LKP$ **9.** $\angle KJL$ **11.** $\angle KPL$ **13.** yes; SAS Congruence Postulate **15.** yes; SAS Congruence Postulate **17.** yes; SSS Congruence Postulate **19.** $\angle ACB \cong \angle CED$

21.

Statements	Reasons
1. $\overline{NP} \cong \overline{QN} \cong \overline{RS} \cong \overline{TR}$ $\overline{PQ} \cong \overline{ST}$	1. Given
2. $\triangle NPQ \cong \triangle RST$	2. SSS Congruence Postulate

23. It is given that $\overline{SP} \cong \overline{TP}$ and that $\overrightarrow{PQ}$ bisects $\angle SPT$. Then, by the definition of angle bisector, $\angle SPQ \cong \angle TPQ$. $\overline{PQ} \cong \overline{PQ}$ by the Reflexive Property of Congruence, so $\triangle SPQ \cong \triangle TPQ$ by the SAS Congruence Postulate.

25.

Statements	Reasons
1. $\overline{AC} \cong \overline{BC}$; *M* is the midpoint of $\overline{AB}$.	1. Given
2. $\overline{AM} \cong \overline{BM}$	2. Definition of midpoint
3. $\overline{CM} \cong \overline{CM}$	3. Reflexive Property of Congruence
4. $\triangle ACM \cong \triangle BCM$	4. SSS Congruence Postulate

27. Since it is given that $\overline{PA} \cong \overline{PB} \cong \overline{PC}$ and $\overline{AB} \cong \overline{BC}$, $\triangle PAB \cong \triangle PBC$ by the SSS Congruence Postulate.
29. The new triangle and the original triangle are congruent.
35. $AB = DE = 3$, $BC = EF = \sqrt{13}$, and $AC = DF = \sqrt{10}$, so all three pairs of sides are congruent and $\triangle ABC \cong \triangle DEF$ by the SSS Congruence Postulate.

4.3 MIXED REVIEW (p. 219) **39.** *Sample answer:* The measure of each of the angles formed by two adjacent "spokes" is about 60°.

41. $m\angle 2 = 57°$ (Vertical Angles Theorem)
$m\angle 1 = 180° - m\angle 2 = 123°$
(Consecutive Interior Angles Theorem)
43. $m\angle 1 = 90°$ (Corresponding Angles Postulate)
$m\angle 2 = 90°$ (Alternate Interior Angles Theorem or Vertical Angles Theorem)
45. slope of $\overleftrightarrow{EF} = -2$, slope of $\overleftrightarrow{GH} = -2$, $\overleftrightarrow{EF} \parallel \overleftrightarrow{GH}$

4.4 PRACTICE (pp. 223–226) **5.** $\overline{AB} \cong \overline{DE}$ **7.** By the Right Angle Congruence Theorem, $\angle B \cong \angle D$. Since $\overline{AD} \parallel \overline{BC}$, $\angle CAD \cong \angle ACB$ by the Alternate Interior Angles Theorem. By the Reflexive Property of Congruence, $\overline{AC} \cong \overline{AC}$, so $\triangle ACD \cong \triangle CAB$ by the AAS Congruence Theorem. Then, all three pairs of corresponding sides are congruent; that is, they have the same length. So, $AB + BC + CA = CD + DA + AC$ and the two courses are the same length. **9.** Yes; SAS Congruence Postulate; two pairs of corresponding sides and the corresponding included angles are congruent.
11. No; two pairs of corresponding sides are congruent and corresponding nonincluded angles $\angle EGF$ and $\angle JGH$ are congruent by the Vertical Angles Theorem; that is insufficient to prove triangle congruence. **13.** Yes; SSS Congruence Postulate; $\overline{XY} \cong \overline{XY}$ by the Reflexive Property of Congruence, so all three pairs of corresponding sides are congruent. **15.** $\angle P \cong \angle S$ **17.** $\overline{QR} \cong \overline{TU}$

19.

Statements	Reasons
1. $\overline{FH} \parallel \overline{LK}$, $\overline{GF} \cong \overline{GL}$	1. Given
2. $\angle F \cong \angle L$, $\angle H \cong \angle K$	2. Alternate Interior Angles Theorem
3. $\triangle FGH \cong \triangle LGK$	3. AAS Congruence Theorem

21. It is given that $\overline{VX} \cong \overline{XY}$, $\overline{XW} \cong \overline{YZ}$, and that $\overline{XW} \parallel \overline{YZ}$. Then, $\angle VXW \cong \angle Y$ by the Corresponding Angles Postulate and $\triangle VXW \cong \triangle XYZ$ by the SAS Congruence Postulate.
23. Yes; two sides of the triangle are north-south and east-west lines, which are perpendicular, so the measures of two angles and the length of a nonincluded side are known and only one such triangle is possible.

25.

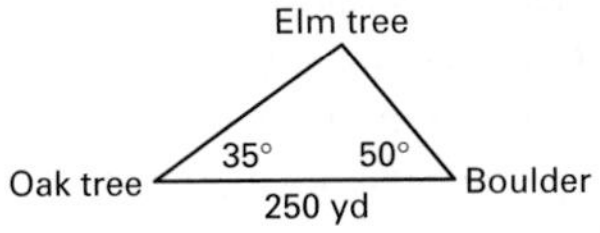

Yes; the measures of two angles and the length of the included side are known and only one such triangle is possible.

27.

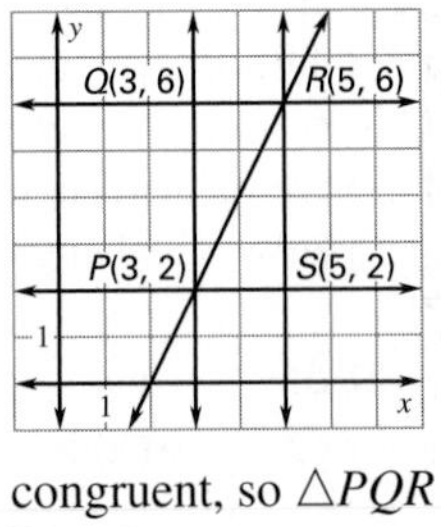

$\angle PQR \cong \angle RSP$ since they are both right angles, and since $\overline{QR} \parallel \overline{PS}$, $\angle PRQ \cong \angle RPS$ by the Alternate Interior Angles Theorem. $QR = SP = 2$, so $\overline{QR} \cong \overline{SP}$. Then, two pairs of corresponding angles and a pair of included sides are congruent, so $\triangle PQR \cong \triangle RSP$ by the ASA Congruence Postulate.

SELECTED ANSWERS

4.4 MIXED REVIEW (p. 227) **33.** (12, −13) **35.** $m\angle DBC = 42°$, $m\angle ABC = 84°$ **37.** $m\angle ABD = 75°$, $m\angle ABC = 150°$

QUIZ 2 (p. 227) **1.** Yes; SAS Congruence Postulate; $\overline{BD} \cong \overline{BD}$ by the Reflexive Property of Congruence, so two pairs of corresponding sides and the corresponding included angles are congruent. **2.** Yes; SSS Congruence Postulate; $\overline{SQ} \cong \overline{SQ}$ by the Reflexive Property of Congruence, so three pairs of corresponding sides are congruent. **3.** No; two pairs of corresponding sides and one pair of corresponding nonincluded angles are congruent; that is insufficient to prove triangle congruence. **4.** Yes; ASA Congruence Postulate; $\overline{MK} \cong \overline{MK}$ by the Reflexive Property of Congruence, so two pairs of corresponding angles and the corresponding included sides are congruent. **5.** No; $\overline{ZB} \cong \overline{ZB}$ by the Reflexive Property of Congruence, so two pairs of corresponding sides are congruent; that is insufficient to prove triangle congruence. **6.** Yes; AAS Congruence Theorem; $\angle STR \cong \angle VTU$ by the Vertical Angles Theorem, so two pairs of corresponding angles and corresponding nonincluded sides are congruent.

7.

Statements	Reasons
1. M is the midpoint of $\overline{NL}$, $\overline{NL} \perp \overline{NQ}$, $\overline{NL} \perp \overline{MP}$, $\overline{QM} \parallel \overline{PL}$.	1. Given
2. $\angle N$ and $\angle PML$ are right angles.	2. If two lines are perpendicular, they form four right angles.
3. $\angle N \cong \angle PML$	3. Right Angle Congruence Theorem
4. $\overline{NM} \cong \overline{ML}$	4. Definition of midpoint
5. $\angle QMN \cong \angle PLM$	5. Corresponding Angles Postulate
6. $\triangle NQM \cong \triangle MPL$	6. ASA Congruence Postulate

4.5 PRACTICE (pp. 232–235)

3. *Sample answer:* A, G, C, F, E, B, D

Statements	Reasons
1. $\overline{QS} \perp \overline{RP}$	1. Given
2. $\angle PTS$ and $\angle RTS$ are right angles.	2. If two lines are perpendicular, then they form four right angles.
3. $\angle PTS \cong \angle RTS$	3. Right Angle Congruence Theorem
4. $\overline{TS} \cong \overline{TS}$	4. Reflexive Property of Congruence
5. $\overline{PT} \cong \overline{RT}$	5. Given
6. $\triangle PTS \cong \triangle RTS$	6. SAS Congruence Postulate
7. $\overline{PS} \cong \overline{RS}$	7. Corresp. parts of ≅ ⚠ are ≅.

5. You can use the method in the answer to Ex. 4 to show that $\triangle QUR \cong \triangle PUQ$, so by the Transitive Property of Congruent Triangles, $\triangle NUP \cong \triangle QUR$. (You could instead use the Transitive Property of Congruence to show that $\overline{UN} \cong \overline{UP} \cong \overline{UQ} \cong \overline{UR}$.)

7. $\triangle NUP$ and $\triangle PUQ$ are congruent by Ex. 4 above. Since corresponding parts of congruent triangles are congruent, $\angle UNP \cong \angle UPQ$. **9.** SSS Congruence Postulate; if $\triangle STV \cong \triangle UVT$, then $\angle STV \cong \angle UVT$ because corresponding parts of congruent triangles are congruent.

11.

Statements	Reasons
1. $\triangle AGD \cong \triangle FHC$	1. Given
2. $\overline{GD} \cong \overline{HC}$	2. Corresp. parts of ≅ ⚠ are ≅.

13.

Statements	Reasons
1. $\triangle EDA \cong \triangle BCF$	1. Given
2. $\overline{AE} \cong \overline{FB}$	2. Corresp. parts of ≅ ⚠ are ≅.

15.

Statements	Reasons
3. $\overline{CF} \cong \overline{CF}$	1. Given
6. $\angle AFB \cong \angle EFD$	2. Given
	4. AAS Congruence Theorem
	5. Corresp. parts of ≅ ⚠ are ≅.
	7. ASA Congruence Postulate

17.

Statements	Reasons
1. $\overline{UR} \parallel \overline{ST}$, $\angle R$ and $\angle T$ are right angles.	1. Given
2. $\angle R \cong \angle T$	2. Right Angle Congruence Theorem
3. $\angle RUS \cong \angle TSU$	3. Alternate Interior Angles Theorem
4. $\overline{US} \cong \overline{US}$	4. Reflexive Property of Congruence
5. $\triangle RSU \cong \triangle TUS$	5. AAS Congruence Theorem
6. $\angle RSU \cong \angle TUS$	6. Corresp. parts of ≅ ⚠ are ≅.

19. It is given that $\overline{AB} \cong \overline{AC}$ and $\overline{BD} \cong \overline{CD}$. By the Reflexive Property of Congruence, $\overline{AD} \cong \overline{AD}$. So, $\triangle ACD \cong \triangle ABD$ by the SSS Congruence Postulate. Then, since corresponding parts of congruent triangles are congruent, $\angle CAD \cong \angle BAD$. Then, by definition, $\overrightarrow{AD}$ bisects $\angle A$.

21.

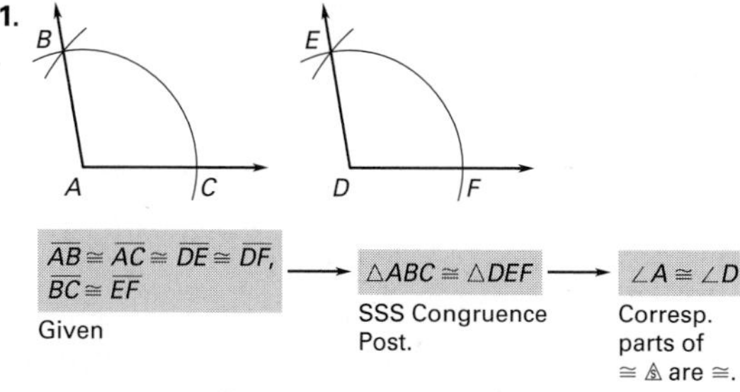

4.5 MIXED REVIEW (p. 235) **25.** 170 m; 1650 m^2
27. 75.36 cm; 452.16 cm^2

29. $x + 11 = 21$
$x = 10$ — Subtraction property of equality

31. $8x + 13 = 3x + 38$
$5x + 13 = 38$ — Subtraction property of equality
$5x = 25$ — Subtraction property of equality
$x = 5$ — Division property of equality

SELECTED ANSWERS

33. $6(2x-1)+15=69$

$6(2x-1)=54$	Subtraction property of equality
$2x-1=9$	Division property of equality
$2x=10$	Addition property of equality
$x=5$	Division property of equality

35. right scalene; legs: $\overline{MN}$ and $\overline{MP}$, hypotenuse: $\overline{NP}$

4.6 PRACTICE (pp. 239–242) **5.** Yes; the hypotenuse and one leg of one right triangle are congruent to the hypotenuse and one leg of the other. **7.** No; it cannot be shown that $\triangle ABC$ is equilateral. **9.** $x = 70$, $y = 70$ **11.** Yes; the triangles can be proved congruent using the SSS Congruence Postulate. **13.** Yes; the triangles can be proved congruent using the ASA Congruence Postulate, the SSS Congruence Postulate, the SAS Congruence Postulate, or the AAS Congruence Theorem. **15.** Yes; the triangles can be proved congruent using the HL Congruence Theorem. **17.** 11 **19.** 7 **21.** $x = 52.5$, $y = 75$ **23.** $x = 30$, $y = 120$ **25.** $x = 60$, $y = 30$ **27.** GIVEN: $\overline{AB} \cong \overline{AC} \cong \overline{BC}$; PROVE: $\angle A \cong \angle B \cong \angle C$; Since $\overline{AB} \cong \overline{AC}$, $\angle B \cong \angle C$ by the Base Angles Theorem. Since $\overline{AB} \cong \overline{BC}$, $\angle A \cong \angle C$ by the Base Angles Theorem. Then, by the Transitive Property of Congruence, $\angle A \cong \angle B \cong \angle C$ and $\triangle ABC$ is equiangular. **29.** $\triangle ABD$ and $\triangle CBD$ are congruent equilateral triangles, so $\overline{AB} \cong \overline{CB}$ and $\triangle ABC$ is isosceles by definition. **31.** Since $\triangle ABD$ and $\triangle CBD$ are congruent equilateral triangles, $\overline{AB} \cong \overline{BC}$ and $\angle ABD \cong \angle CBD$. By the Base Angles Theorem, $\angle BAE \cong \angle BCE$. Then, $\triangle ABE \cong \triangle CBE$ by the AAS Congruence Theorem. Moreover, by the Linear Pair Postulate, $m\angle AEB + m\angle CEB = 180°$. But $\angle AEB$ and $\angle CEB$ are corresponding parts of congruent triangles, so they are congruent, that is, $m\angle AEB = m\angle CEB$. Then, by the Substitution Property, $2m\angle AEB = 180°$ and $m\angle AEB = 90°$. So, $\angle AEB$ and $\angle CEB$ are both right angles, and $\triangle AEB$ and $\triangle CEB$ are congruent right triangles.

33.

Statements	Reasons
1. D is the midpoint of $\overline{CE}$, $\angle BCD$ and $\angle FED$ are rt. $\angle$s.	1. Given
2. $\angle BCD \cong \angle FED$	2. Right Angle Congruence Theorem
3. $\overline{CD} \cong \overline{ED}$	3. Definition of midpoint
4. $\overline{BD} \cong \overline{FD}$	4. Given
5. $\triangle BCD \cong \triangle FED$	5. HL Congruence Theorem

35. Each of the triangles is isosceles and every pair of adjacent triangles have a common side, so the legs of all the triangles are congruent by the Transitive Property of Congruence. The common vertex angles are congruent, so any two of the triangles are congruent by the SAS Congruence Postulate. **37.** equilateral **39.** It is given that $\angle CDB \cong \angle ADB$ and that $\overline{DB} \perp \overline{AC}$. Since perpendicular lines form right angles, $\angle ABD$ and $\angle CBD$ are right angles. By the Right Angle Congruence Theorem, $\angle ABD \cong \angle CBD$. By the Reflexive Property of Congruence, $\overline{DB} \cong \overline{DB}$, so $\triangle ABD \cong \triangle CBD$ by the ASA Congruence Postulate. **41.** No; the measure of $\angle ADB$ will decrease, as will the measure of $\angle CDB$ and the amount of reflection will remain the same.

4.6 MIXED REVIEW (p. 242)
45. congruent **47.** not congruent **49.** (4, 4) **51.** $\left(1\frac{1}{2}, 4\frac{1}{2}\right)$ **53.** $\left(-1\frac{1}{2}, -12\frac{1}{2}\right)$ **55.** $y = -x$ **57.** $y = -\frac{3}{2}x - \frac{1}{2}$

4.7 PRACTICE (pp. 246–249) **3.** (4, 0), (4, 7), (–4, 7), (–4, 0) **5.** Use the Distance Formula to show that $\overline{AB} \cong \overline{AC}$. **7.** *Sample figure:*

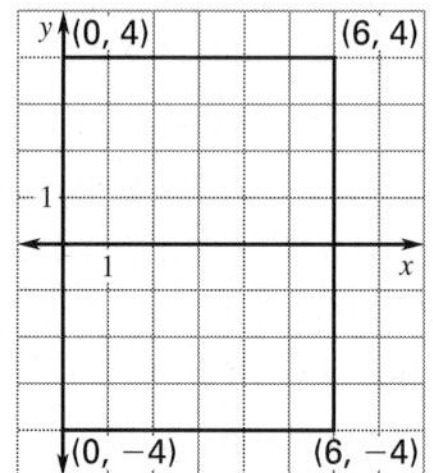

9, 11. Good placements should include vertices for which at least one coordinate is 0.

9. *Sample figure:*

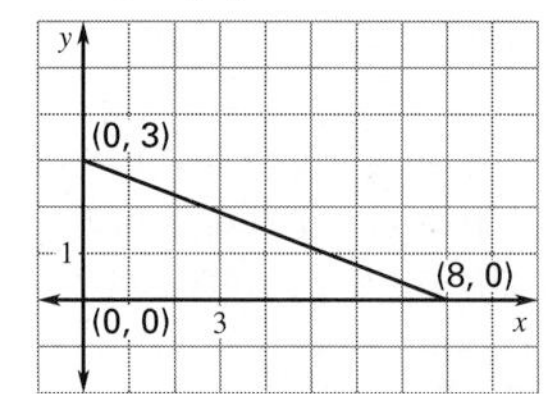

11. *Sample figure:*

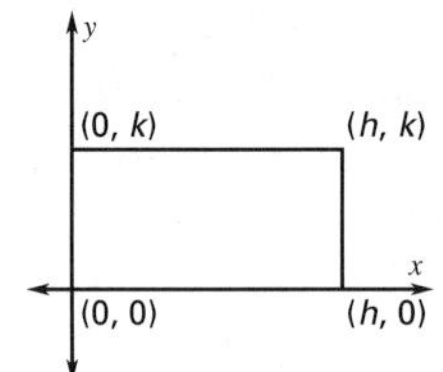

13. 58.31 **15.** $\sqrt{41}$ **17.** $3\sqrt{2}$ **19.** (45, 35) **21.** Show that, since $\overline{HJ}$ and $\overline{OF}$ both have slope 0, they are parallel, so that alternate interior angles $\angle H$ and $\angle F$ are congruent. $\overline{HG} \cong \overline{FG}$ by the definition of midpoint. Then use the Distance Formula to show that $\overline{HJ} \cong \overline{OF}$ so that $\triangle GHJ \cong \triangle GFO$ by the SAS Congruence Postulate. **23.** $F(2h, 0)$, $E(2h, h)$; $h\sqrt{5}$ **25.** $O(0, 0)$, $R(k, k)$, $S(k, 2k)$, $T(2k, 2k)$, $U(k, 0)$; $2k\sqrt{2}$ **27.** Since $OC = \sqrt{h^2 + k^2}$ and $EC = \sqrt{h^2 + k^2}$, $\overline{OC} \cong \overline{EC}$, and since $BC = k$ and $DC = k$, $\overline{BC} \cong \overline{DC}$. Then, since vertical angles $\angle OCB$ and $\angle ECD$ are congruent, $\triangle OBC \cong \triangle EDC$ by the SAS Congruence Postulate. **29.** isosceles; no; no **31.** The triangle in Exercise 5 has vertices which can be used to describe $\triangle ABC$. Point A is on the y-axis and points B and C are on the x-axis, equidistant from the origin. The proof shows that any such triangle is isosceles.

4.7 MIXED REVIEW (p. 250) **35.** 5 **37.** true **39.** true **41.** If two triangles are congruent, then the corresponding angles of the triangles are congruent; true. **43.** If two triangles are not congruent, then the corresponding angles of the triangles are not congruent; false.

QUIZ 3 (p. 250)

1.

Statements	Reasons
1. $\overline{DF} \cong \overline{DG}$, $\overline{ED} \cong \overline{HD}$	1. Given
2. $\angle EDF \cong \angle HDG$	2. Vertical Angles Theorem
3. $\triangle EDF \cong \triangle HDG$	3. SAS Congruence Postulate
4. $\angle EFD \cong \angle HGD$	4. Corresp. parts of $\cong$ ⚠ are $\cong$.

2.

Statements	Reasons
1. $\overline{ST} \cong \overline{UT} \cong \overline{VU}$, $\overline{SU} \parallel \overline{TV}$	1. Given
2. $\angle S \cong \angle SUT$, $\angle UTV \cong \angle V$	2. Base Angles Theorem
3. $\angle SUT \cong \angle UTV$	3. Alternate Interior Angles Theorem
4. $\angle S \cong \angle SUT \cong \angle UTV \cong \angle V$	4. Transitive Property of Congruence
5. $\triangle STU \cong \triangle TUV$	5. AAS Congruence Theorem

3. Use the Distance Formula to show that OP, PM, NM, and ON are all equal, so that $\overline{OP} \cong \overline{PM} \cong \overline{NM} \cong \overline{ON}$. Since $\overline{OM} \cong \overline{OM}$ by the Reflexive Property of Congruence, $\triangle OPM \cong \triangle ONM$ by the SSS Congruence Postulate and both triangles are isosceles by definition.

CHAPTER 4 REVIEW (pp. 252–254) **1.** isosceles right **3.** obtuse isosceles **5.** 53° **7.** $\angle A$ and $\angle X$, $\angle B$ and $\angle Y$, $\angle C$ and $\angle Z$, $\overline{AB}$ and $\overline{XY}$, $\overline{BC}$ and $\overline{YZ}$, $\overline{AC}$ and $\overline{XZ}$ **9.** Yes; ASA Congruence Postulate; two pairs of corresponding angles are congruent and the corresponding included sides are congruent. **11.** Yes; AAS Congruence Theorem; because $\overline{HF} \parallel \overline{JE}$, $\angle HFG \cong \angle E$ (Corresponding Angles Postulate), so two pairs of corresponding angles are congruent and two nonincluded sides are congruent. **13.** $\overline{PQ}$ **15.** 54 **17.** 110

ALGEBRA REVIEW (pp. 258–259) **1.** $\sqrt{73}$ **2.** $\sqrt{170}$ **3.** 4 **4.** 5 **5.** $\sqrt{137}$ **6.** $\sqrt{65}$ **7.** $2x + 12y$ **8.** $-m + 2q$ **9.** $-5p - 9t$ **10.** $27x - 25y$ **11.** $9x^2y - 5xy^2$ **12.** $-2x^2 + 3xy$ **13.** 6 **14.** 6 **15.** -10 **16.** -5 **17.** 0 **18.** 0 **19.** 10 **20.** no solution **21.** 2 **22.** $x < -5$ **23.** $c < 28$ **24.** $m < 26$ **25.** $x < 9$ **26.** $z > -8$ **27.** $x \ge 3$ **28.** $x < -11$ **29.** $m \ge 1$ **30.** $b > \frac{3}{5}$ **31.** $x < \frac{3}{10}$ **32.** $z \le 1$ **33.** $t \le -\frac{14}{5}$ **34.** $r > -6$ **35.** $x \ge -1$ **36.** $x \le -7$ **37.** $x = 7$ or -17 **38.** $x = 12$ or -8 **39.** $x = 2$ or 8 **40.** $x = 7$ or -5 **41.** $x = 14$ or -20 **42.** $x = -1$ or $\frac{9}{5}$ **43.** $x = 7$ or -4 **44.** $x = \frac{12}{7}$ or -4 **45.** $x = -2$ or $\frac{9}{2}$ **46.** $x = -\frac{4}{3}$ or -4 **47.** $x \ge 10$ or $x \le -36$ **48.** $x > 14$ or $x < -2$ **49.** $-6 \le x \le 10$ **50.** $x \le 8$ or $x \ge 22$ **51.** $12 < x < 20$ **52.** $-\frac{2}{3} < x < 2$ **53.** $-3 \le x \le 7$ **54.** $-\frac{5}{3} \le x \le 3$ **55.** $x \le -2$ or $x \ge 4$ **56.** $x < -8$ or $x > 5$ **57.** $-6 < x < 2$ **58.** $x < -2$ or $x > 5$ **59.** $x \le -6$ or $x \ge 2$ **60.** $-1 < x < \frac{23}{5}$ **61.** $x < -2$ or $x > \frac{20}{11}$ **62.** no solution **63.** $x < -\frac{8}{3}$ or $x > 4$ **64.** $-3 \le x \le \frac{1}{3}$ **65.** all real numbers **66.** $-2 \le x \le 0$

CHAPTER 5

SKILL REVIEW (p. 262) **3.** $(-1, 2)$ **4.** 5 **5.** 2 **6.** $-\frac{1}{2}$

5.1 PRACTICE (pp. 267–271) **3.** $\overline{AD} \cong \overline{BD}$ **5.** $\overline{AC} \cong \overline{BC}$; C is on the $\perp$ bisector of $\overline{AB}$. **7.** The distance from M to $\overrightarrow{PL}$ is equal to the distance from M to $\overrightarrow{PN}$. **9.** No; the diagram does not show that $CA = CB$. **11.** No; since P is not equidistant from the sides of $\angle A$, P is not on the bisector of $\angle A$. **13.** No; the diagram does not show that the segments with equal length are perpendicular segments. **15.** D is 1.5 in. from each side of $\angle A$. **17.** 17 **19.** 2 **21.** B **23.** C **25.** D **27.** $\overline{PA} \cong \overline{AB}$ and $\overline{CA} \cong \overline{CB}$ by construction. By the Reflexive Prop. of Cong., $\overline{CP} \cong \overline{CP}$. Then, $\triangle CPA \cong \triangle CPB$ by the SSS Cong. Post. Corresp. angles $\angle CPA$ and $\angle CPB$ are $\cong$. Then, $\overleftrightarrow{CP} \perp \overleftrightarrow{AB}$. (If 2 lines form a linear pair of $\cong$ ⦣, then the lines are $\perp$.)

29.

Statements	Reasons
1. Draw a line through $C \perp$ to $\overline{AB}$ intersecting $\overline{AB}$ at P.	1. Through a point not on a line there is exactly one line $\perp$ to a given line.
2. $\angle CPA$ and $\angle CPB$ are right ⦣.	2. Def. of $\perp$ lines
3. $\triangle CPA$ and $\triangle CPB$ are right ⚠.	3. Def. of right $\triangle$
4. $CA = CB$, or $\overline{CA} \cong \overline{CB}$	4. Given; def. of cong.
5. $\overline{CP} \cong \overline{CP}$	5. Reflexive Prop. of Cong.
6. $\triangle CPA \cong \triangle CPB$	6. HL Cong. Thm.
7. $\overline{PA} \cong \overline{PB}$	7. Corresp. parts of $\cong$ ⚠ are $\cong$.
8. $\overleftrightarrow{CP}$ is the $\perp$ bisector of $\overline{AB}$ and C is on the $\perp$ bisector of $\overline{AB}$.	8. Def. of $\perp$ bisector

31. The post is the $\perp$ bisector of the segment between the ends of the wires. **33.** ℓ is the $\perp$ bisector of $\overline{AB}$. **35.** $m\angle APB$ increases; more difficult; the goalie has a greater area to defend because the distances from the goalie to the sides of $\angle APB$ (the shooting angle) increase.

5.1 MIXED REVIEW (p. 271) **41.** 6 cm **43.** about 113.04 cm^2 **45.** $-\frac{4}{5}$ **47.** $\frac{8}{7}$ **49.** 0 **51.** 34

5.2 PRACTICE (pp. 275–278) **3.** 7 **5.** outside **7.** on **9.** The segments are $\cong$; Thm. 5.6. **11.** always **13.** sometimes **15.** 20 **17.** 25 **19.** The $\angle$ bisectors of a $\triangle$ intersect in a point that is equidistant from the sides of the $\triangle$, but MQ and MN are not necessarily distances to the sides; M is equidistant from $\overline{JK}$, $\overline{KL}$, and $\overline{JL}$.

21.

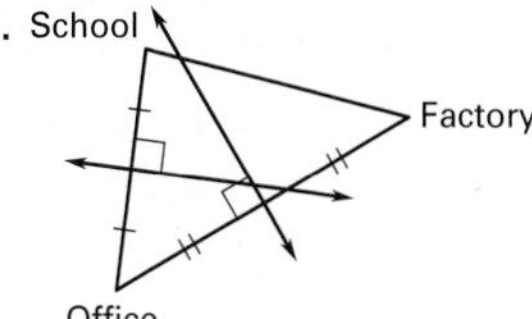

25. about $2\frac{1}{2}$ feet

5.2 MIXED REVIEW (p. 278) **33.** 77 square units **35.** $y = \frac{1}{2}x + \frac{5}{2}$ **37.** $y = -\frac{11}{10}x - \frac{56}{5}$ **39.** no

5.3 PRACTICE (pp. 282–284) **3.** median **5.** angle bisector **7.** ⊥ bisector, ∠ bisector, median, altitude **9.** 12 **11.** 48 **15.** yes **17.** (5, 0) **19.** (5, 2) **21.** (4, 4) **23.** $\frac{JP}{JM} = \frac{2\sqrt{5}}{3\sqrt{5}} = \frac{2}{3}$, so $JP = \frac{2}{3}JM$.
29. Measure GH. Because $GH = 0$, G and H must be the same point; therefore, the lines containing the three altitudes intersect at one point.
30–32.

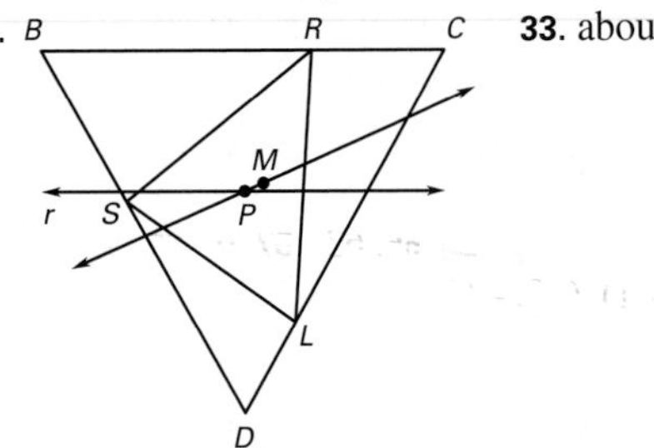

33. about 20°

5.3 MIXED REVIEW (p. 284) **39.** $y = -x + 8$ **41.** $y = 3x - 21$ **43.** $\angle E \cong \angle H$ **45.** $5\sqrt{10}$

QUIZ 1 (p. 285) **1.** 16 **2.** 12 **3.** 10 **4.** 10; the ⊥ bisectors intersect at a point equidistant from the vertices of the △. **5.** at G, the intersection of the medians of $\triangle ABC$, 8 in. from C on $\overline{CF}$

5.4 PRACTICE (pp. 290–293) **3.** $\overline{DF}$ **5.** 21.2 **7.** 16 **9.** 30.6 **11.** about 54 yd **13.** $\overline{MN}$ **15.** 14 **17.** 31 **19.** $\angle BLN$, $\angle A$, and $\angle NMC$ are ≅ by the Corresp. Angles Post., as are $\angle BNL$, $\angle C$, and $\angle LMA$. By the Alternate Interior Angles Thm., $\angle LNM \cong \angle NMC$ and $\angle NLM \cong \angle LMA$, so by the Transitive Prop. of Cong., $\angle BLN$, $\angle A$, $\angle NMC$, and $\angle LNM$ are ≅, as are $\angle BNL$, $\angle C$, $\angle LMA$, and $\angle NLM$. Then, $\angle B$, $\angle ALM$, $\angle LMN$, and $\angle MNC$ are all ≅ by the Third Angles Thm. and the Transitive Prop. of Cong.
21. $D\left(2\frac{1}{2}, 0\right)$, $E\left(7\frac{1}{2}, 2\right)$, $F(5, 4)$ **23.** $(c, 0)$
25. $DF = \sqrt{(a-c)^2 + (b-0)^2} = \sqrt{(a-c)^2 + b^2}$ and $CB = \sqrt{(2a-2c)^2 + (2b-0)^2} = 2\sqrt{(a-c)^2 + b^2}$, so $DF = \frac{1}{2}CB$; $EF = \sqrt{(a+c-c)^2 + (b-0)^2} = \sqrt{a^2 + b^2}$ and $CA = \sqrt{(2a-0)^2 + (2b-0)^2} = 2\sqrt{a^2 + b^2}$, so $EF = \frac{1}{2}CA$. **27.** (3, –1), (11, 3), (7, 9) **29.** 31 **31.** $\frac{1}{2}$; $1\frac{1}{4}$; $2\frac{3}{8}$
33. $\overline{DE}$ is a midsegment of $\triangle ABC$, so D is the midpoint of $\overline{AB}$ and $\overline{AD} \cong \overline{DB}$. $\overline{DE}$ is also a midsegment of $\triangle ABC$, so by the Midsegment Thm., $\overline{DE} \parallel \overline{BC}$ and $DE = \frac{1}{2}BC$. But F is the midpoint of $\overline{BC}$, so $BF = \frac{1}{2}BC$. Then by the transitive prop. of equality and the def. of cong., $\overline{DE} \cong \overline{BF}$. Corresp. angles $\angle ADE$ and $\angle ABC$ are ≅, so $\triangle ADE \cong \triangle DBF$ by the SAS Cong. Post.

35. No, no, yes, no; if you imagine "sliding" a segment parallel to $\overline{RS}$ up the triangle, then its length decreases as the segment slides upward (as can be shown with a coordinate argument). So, $MN < PQ < RS$, or $12 < PQ < 24$.

5.4 MIXED REVIEW (p. 293)
39. $x - 3 = 11$
$x = 14$ (Addition prop. of equality)
41. $8x - 1 = 2x + 17$
$8x = 2x + 18$ (Addition prop. of equality)
$6x = 18$ (Subtraction prop. of equality)
$x = 3$ (Division prop. of equality)
43. $2(4x - 1) = 14$
$4x - 1 = 7$ (Division prop. of equality)
$4x = 8$ (Addition prop. of equality)
$x = 2$ (Division prop. of equality)
45. $-2(x + 1) + 3 = 23$
$-2(x + 1) = 20$ (Subtraction prop. of equality)
$x + 1 = -10$ (Division prop. of equality)
$x = -11$ (Subtraction prop. of equality)
47. 23 **49.** 18 **51.** incenter **53.** 6

5.5 PRACTICE (pp. 298–301) **3.** $\angle D$, $\angle F$ **5.** greater than 66 mi and less than 264 mi **7.** $\overline{RT}$, $\overline{SR}$ and $\overline{ST}$ ($\overline{SR} \cong \overline{ST}$) **9.** $\angle C$, $\angle B$ **11.** $\angle H$, $\angle F$ **13.** $x > y$, $x > z$ **15.** $\overline{DF}$, $\overline{DE}$, $\overline{EF}$ **17.** $\angle L$, $\angle K$, $\angle M$ **19.** $\angle T$, $\angle S$, $\angle R$
21, 23. Sample answers are given.
21.

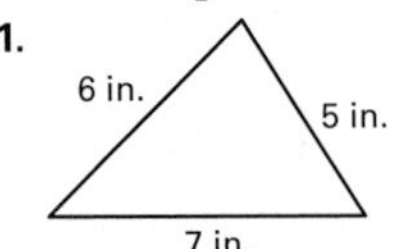

23. 4 in., 5 in., 9 in.; 4 in., 4 in., 10 in.; 3 in., 6 in., 9 in. **25.** $x < 7$
27. The sides and angles could not be positioned as they are labeled; for example, the longest side is not opposite the largest angle. **29.** raised **31.** Yes; when the boom is lowered and $AB > 100$ (and so $AB > BC$), then $\angle ACB$ will be larger than $\angle BAC$.
33. $\overline{MJ} \perp \overline{JN}$, so $\triangle MJN$ is a right △. The largest ∠ in a right △ is the right ∠, so $m\angle MJN > m\angle MNJ$, so $MN > MJ$. (If one ∠ of a △ is larger than another ∠, then the side opp. the larger ∠ is longer than the side opp. the smaller ∠.)

5.5 MIXED REVIEW (p. 301) **39, 41.** Sample answers are given. **39.** proof of Theorem 4.1, page 196 **41.** Example 1, page 136 **43.** ∠9 **45.** ∠2; ∠10 **47.** (–7, 3), (–5, –3), (1, 7) **49.** (0, 0), (6, –4), (0, –8)

5.6 PRACTICE (pp. 305–307) **3.** > **5.** < **7.** < **9.** > **11.** = **13.** > **15.** > **17.** B; $AD = AD$, $AB = DC$, and $m\angle 3 < m\angle 5$, so by the Hinge Thm., $AC > BD$. **19.** $x > 1$ **21.** Given that $RS + ST \neq 12$ in. and $ST = 5$ in., assume that $RS = 7$ in. **23.** Given $\triangle ABC$ with $m\angle A + m\angle B = 90°$, assume $m\angle C \neq 90°$. (That is, assume that either $m\angle C < 90°$ or $m\angle C > 90°$.) **25.** Case 1: Assume that $EF < DF$. If one side of a △ is longer than another side, then the ∠ opp. the longer side is larger than the ∠ opp. the shorter side, so $m\angle D < m\angle E$. But this contradicts the given information that $m\angle D > m\angle E$.

Case 2: Assume that $EF = DF$. By the Converse of the Base Angles Thm., $m\angle E = m\angle D$. But this contradicts the given information that $m\angle D > m\angle E$. Since both cases produce a contradiction, the assumption that EF is not greater than DF must be incorrect and $EF > DF$.
27. Assume that $RS > RT$. Then $m\angle T > m\angle S$. But $\triangle RUS \cong \triangle RUT$ by the ASA Congruence Postulate, so $\angle S \cong \angle T$, or $m\angle T = m\angle S$. This is a contradiction, so $RS \le RT$. We get a similar contradiction if we assume $RT > RS$; therefore, $RS = RT$, and $\triangle RST$ is isosceles by definition.
29. The paths are described by two $\triangle$s in which two sides of one $\triangle$ are $\cong$ to two sides of another $\triangle$, but the included $\angle$ in your friend's $\triangle$ is larger than the included $\angle$ in yours, so the side representing the distance from the airport is longer in your friend's $\triangle$.

5.6 MIXED REVIEW (p. 308) **33.** isosceles, equiangular, equilateral **35.** isosceles **37.** isosceles **39.** 51° **41.** 84°

QUIZ 2 (p. 308) **1.** $\overline{CE}$ **2.** 16 **3.** 21 **4.** $\overline{LQ}, \overline{LM}, \overline{MQ}$ **5.** $\overline{QM}, \overline{PM}, \overline{QP}$ **6.** $\overline{MP}, \overline{NP}, \overline{MN}$ **7.** $\overline{DE}$ **8.** the second group

CHAPTER 5 REVIEW (pp. 310–312) **1.** If a point is on the $\perp$ bisector of a segment, then it is equidistant from the endpoints of the segment. **3.** Q is on the bisector of $\angle RST$. **5.** 6 **7.** $\perp$ bisectors; circumcenter **9.** altitudes; orthocenter **11.** (0, 0) **13.** Let L be the midpoint of $\overline{HJ}$, M the midpoint of $\overline{JK}$, and N the midpoint of $\overline{HK}$; slope of $\overline{LM} = 0 =$ slope of $\overline{HK}$, so $\overline{LM} \parallel \overline{HK}$; slope of $\overline{LN} = -1 =$ slope of $\overline{JK}$, so $\overline{LN} \parallel \overline{JK}$; slope of $\overline{MN} = 1 =$ slope of $\overline{HJ}$, so $\overline{MN} \parallel \overline{HJ}$.
15. 31 **17.** $m\angle D, m\angle E, m\angle F$; EF, DF, DE **19.** $m\angle L, m\angle K, m\angle M$; KM, LM, KL **21.** $<$ **23.** $=$ **25.** Assume that there is a $\triangle ABC$ with 2 right $\angle$s, say $m\angle A = 90°$ and $m\angle B = 90°$. Then, $m\angle A + m\angle B = 180°$ and, since $m\angle C > 0°$, $m\angle A + m\angle B + m\angle C > 180°$. This contradicts the $\triangle$ Sum Theorem. Then the assumption that there is such a $\triangle ABC$ must be incorrect and no $\triangle$ has 2 right $\angle$s.

CHAPTER 6

SKILL REVIEW (p. 320) **1.** If two $\parallel$ lines are cut by a transversal, consecutive interior angles are supplementary. **2.** If two $\parallel$ lines are cut by a transversal, alternate interior angles are congruent. **3.** AAS Cong. Theorem **4.** SSS Cong. Postulate **5.** $13, -\frac{12}{5}; \left(-\frac{1}{2}, -2\right)$

6.1 PRACTICE (pp. 325–328) **5.** Not a polygon; one side is not a segment. **7.** equilateral **9.** regular **11.** 67° **13.** not a polygon **15.** not a polygon **17.** not a polygon **19.** heptagon; concave **21.** octagon **23.** $\overline{MP}, \overline{MQ}, \overline{MR}, \overline{MS}, \overline{MT}$ **25.** equilateral **27.** quadrilateral; regular **29.** triangle; regular

31–33. Sample figures are given.
31. **33.**

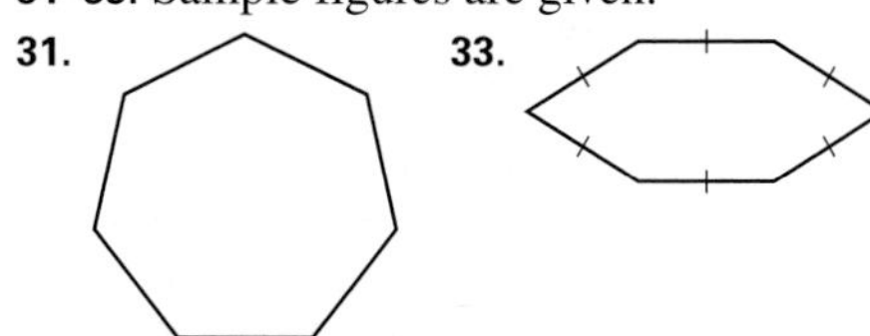

35. Yes; *Sample answer:* A polygon that is concave must include an $\angle$ with measure greater than 180°. By the Triangle Sum Theorem, every $\triangle$ must be convex. **37.** 75° **39.** 125° **41.** 67 **43.** 44 **45.** 4 **47.** three; *Sample answers:* triangle (a polygon with three sides), trilateral (having three sides), tricycle (a vehicle with three wheels), trio (a group of three) **49.** octagon; concave, equilateral **51.** 17-gon; concave; none of these

6.1 MIXED REVIEW (p. 328) **55.** 63 **57.** 6 **59.** 5 **61.** (1, 13), (5, –1), (–9, –15) **63.** (2, 15), (–4, –9), (10, –1)

6.2 PRACTICE (pp. 333–337) **5.** $\overline{KN}$; diags. of a ▱ bisect each other. **7.** $\angle LMJ$; opp. $\angle$s of a ▱ are $\cong$. **9.** $\overline{JM}$; opp. sides of a ▱ are $\cong$. **11.** $\angle KMJ$; if 2 $\parallel$ lines are cut by a transversal, then alt. int. $\angle$s are $\cong$. **13.** 7; since the diags. of a ▱ bisect each other, $LP = NP = 7$. **15.** 8.2°; since the diags. of a ▱ bisect each other, $QP = MP = 8.2$. **17.** 80°; since consec. $\angle$s of a ▱ are supplementary, $m\angle NQL = 180° - m\angle QLM = 80°$.
19. 29°; opp. sides of a ▱ are $\parallel$, so $m\angle LMQ \cong m\angle MQN$ since they are alt. int. $\angle$s. **21.** 11; since opp. sides of a ▱ are $\cong$, $BA = CD = 11$. **23.** 60°; since consec. $\angle$s of a ▱ are supplementary, $m\angle CDA = 180° - m\angle BAD = 60°$.
25. 120°; since opp. $\angle$s of a ▱ are $\cong$, $m\angle BCD = m\angle BAD = 120°$. **27.** $a = 79, b = 101$ **29.** $p = 5, q = 9$ **31.** $k = 7, m = 8$ **33.** $u = 4, v = 18$ **35.** $b = 90, c = 80, d = 100$ **37.** $r = 30, s = 40, t = 25$

39.

Statements	Reasons
1. *JKLM* is a ▱.	2. Opp. $\angle$s of a ▱ are $\cong$.
3. 360°	4. Substitution prop. of equality
5. $m\angle J$; $m\angle K$	6. Division
	7. Def. of supplementary $\angle$s

41. $(a + c, b)$ **43.** $\left(\frac{a+c}{2}, \frac{b}{2}\right)$ **45.** $\angle 3$ and $\angle 7$ are supplementary by the Linear Pair Postulate, so $m\angle 3 + m\angle 7 = 180°$. Opp. $\angle$s of a ▱ are $\cong$, so $\angle 6 \cong \angle 7$, or $m\angle 6 = m\angle 7$. Then by the substitution prop. of equality, $m\angle 3 + m\angle 6 = 180°$ and $\angle 3$ and $\angle 6$ are supplementary.
47. $\angle 4$ **49.** Corresp. $\angle$s Postulate (If 2 $\parallel$ lines are cut by a transv., then corresp. $\angle$s are $\cong$.) **51.** 60° **53.** AD increases.

55.

Statements	Reasons
1. *ABCD* and *CEFD* are ▱s.	1. Given
2. $\overline{AB} \cong \overline{CD}$; $\overline{CD} \cong \overline{EF}$	2. Opp. sides of a ▱ are $\cong$.
3. $\overline{AB} \cong \overline{EF}$	3. Transitive Prop. of Cong.

SELECTED ANSWERS

57. Statements | Reasons

Statements	Reasons
1. $WXYZ$ is a ▱.	1. Given
2. $\overline{WZ} \cong \overline{XY}$	2. Opp. sides of a ▱ are ≅.
3. $\overline{WM} \cong \overline{YM}$; $\overline{ZM} \cong \overline{XM}$	3. The diags. of a ▱ bisect each other.
4. $\triangle WMZ \cong \triangle YMX$	4. SSS Cong. Postulate

6.2 MIXED REVIEW (p. 337) **65.** $4\sqrt{5}$ **67.** $5\sqrt{2}$ **69.** $-\frac{1}{2}$ **71.** Yes; in a plane, 2 lines ⊥ to the same line are ∥. **73.** $\overline{EF}$, $\overline{DF}$; $m\angle D = 180° - (90° + 55°) = 35°$, so $\angle D$ is the smallest ∠ of $\triangle DEF$ and $\angle E$ is the largest. If 1 ∠ of a △ is larger than another ∠, then the side opp. the larger ∠ is longer than the side opp. the smaller ∠.

6.3 PRACTICE (pp. 342–344) **3.** Yes; if an ∠ of a quad. is supplementary to both of its consec. ∠s, then the quad. is a ▱. **5.** Show that since alt. int. ∠s BCA and DAC are ≅, $\overline{BC} \parallel \overline{AD}$. Then, since one pair of opp. sides of $ABCD$ is both ∥ and ≅, $ABCD$ is a ▱. **7.** Use the Corresponding Angles Converse to show that $\overline{BC} \parallel \overline{AD}$ and the Alternate Interior Angles Converse to show that $\overline{AB} \parallel \overline{DC}$. Then, $ABCD$ is a ▱ by the def. of a ▱. **9.** Yes; if opp. sides of a quad. are ≅, then it is a ▱. **11.** No; according to the Vertical Angles Theorem, the given information is true for the diags. of any quad. **13.** No; the fact that two opp. sides and one diag. are ≅ is insufficient to prove that the quad. is a ▱. **15.** *Sample answer:* Since corresp. parts of ≅ △s are ≅, both pairs of opp. sides of $ABCD$ are ≅, so $ABCD$ is a ▱. **17.** 70 **19.** 90 **21.** $AB = CD = \sqrt{17}$, so $\overline{AB} \cong \overline{CD}$. $AD = BC = 2\sqrt{17}$, so $\overline{AD} \cong \overline{BC}$. Since opp. sides of $ABCD$ are ≅, $ABCD$ is a ▱. **23.** Slope of $\overline{AB}$ = slope of $\overline{CD} = -\frac{1}{4}$ and slope of $\overline{AD}$ = slope of $\overline{BC} = -4$, so $\overline{AB} \parallel \overline{CD}$ and $\overline{AD} \parallel \overline{BC}$. Then, $ABCD$ is a ▱ by the def. of a ▱. **25.** *Sample answer:* Slope of $\overline{JK}$ = slope of $\overline{LM} = \frac{1}{5}$ and slope of $\overline{JM}$ = slope of $\overline{KL} = -2$, so $\overline{JK} \parallel \overline{LM}$ and $\overline{JM} \parallel \overline{KL}$. Then, $JKLM$ is a ▱ by the def. of a ▱. **27.** Since opp. sides of $ABCD$ are ≅, $ABCD$ is a ▱, so opp. sides $\overline{AB}$ and $\overline{CD}$ are ∥. **29.** The diags. of the figure that is drawn were drawn to bisect each other. Therefore, the figure is a ▱. **31.** *Sample answer:* Design the mount so that $\overline{AD} \cong \overline{BC}$ and $\overline{AB} \cong \overline{DC}$, making $ABCD$ a ▱. Then, as long as the support containing $\overline{AD}$ is vertical, $\overline{BC}$ will be vertical, because opp. sides of a ▱ are ∥. **33.** Since $\angle P$ is supplementary to $\angle Q$, $\overline{QR} \parallel \overline{PS}$ by the Consecutive Interior Angles Converse. Similarly, $\overline{QP} \parallel \overline{RS}$ by the same theorem. Then, $PQRS$ is a ▱ by the def. of a ▱.

35. $(-b, -c)$; the diags. of a ▱ bisect each other, so (0, 0) is the midpoint of $\overline{QN}$. Let $Q = (x, y)$. By the Midpoint Formula, $(0, 0) = \left(\frac{x+b}{2}, \frac{y+c}{2}\right)$, so $x = -b$ and $y = -c$.

6.3 MIXED REVIEW (p. 345) **39.** If $x^2 + 2 = 2$, then $x = 0$. If $x = 0$, then $x^2 + 2 = 2$. **41.** If each pair of opp. sides of a quad. are ∥, then the quad. is a ▱. If a quad. is a ▱, then each pair of opp. sides are ∥. **43.** A point is on the bisector of an ∠ if and only if the point is equidistant from the two sides of the ∠. **45.** 60 **47.** 35

QUIZ 1 (p. 346) **1.** convex, equilateral, equiangular, regular **2.** 35; the sum of the measures of the interior ∠s of a quad. is 360°, so $2x + 2x + 110 + 110 = 360$, $4x = 140$, and $x = 35$. **3.** $ABCG$ and $CDEF$ are ▱, so $\angle A \cong \angle BCG$ and $\angle DCF \cong \angle E$. (Opp. ∠s of a ▱ are ≅.) $\angle BCG \cong \angle DCF$ by the Vert. ∠s Thm. Then, $\angle A \cong \angle E$ by the Transitive Prop. of Cong. **4.** *Sample answers:* Use slopes to show that both pairs of opp. sides are ∥, use the Distance Formula to show that both pairs of opp. sides are ≅, use slope and the Distance Formula to show that one pair of opp. sides are both ∥ and ≅, use the Midpoint Formula to show that the diags. bisect each other.

6.4 PRACTICE (pp. 351–354) **3.** always **5.** sometimes **7.** C, D **9.** B, D **11.** 45 **13.** Sometimes; if rectangle $ABCD$ is also a rhombus (a square), then $\overline{AB} \cong \overline{BC}$. **15.** Sometimes; if rectangle $ABCD$ is also a rhombus (a square), then the diags. of $ABCD$ are ⊥. **17.** square **19.** ▱, rectangle, rhombus, square **21.** rhombus, square **23.** $\overline{PQ} \parallel \overline{RS}$, $\overline{PS} \parallel \overline{QR}$, $\overline{PQ} \cong \overline{QR} \cong \overline{RS} \cong \overline{PS}$, $\angle P \cong \angle R$, $\angle Q \cong \angle S$, $\overline{PR}$ and $\overline{QS}$ bisect each other, $\overline{PR} \perp \overline{QS}$, $\overline{PR}$ bisects $\angle SPQ$ and $\angle SRQ$, $\overline{QS}$ bisects $\angle PSR$ and $\angle PQR$. **25.** rectangle **27.** Always; opp. ∠s of a ▱ are ≅. **29.** Always; each diag. of a rhombus bisects a pair of opp. ∠s. **31.** Sometimes; if a rhombus is also a rectangle (a square), then its diagonals are ≅. **33.** 18 **35.** 50 **37.** 1 **39.** $2\sqrt{2}$ **41.** 45° **43.** 10 **45.** Assume temporarily that $\overline{MN} \parallel \overline{PQ}$, $\angle 1 \not\cong \angle 2$, and that $\overline{MQ} \parallel \overline{NP}$. By the def. of a ▱, $MNPQ$ is a ▱. This contradicts the given information that $\angle 1 \not\cong \angle 2$. It follows that $\overline{MQ}$ is not ∥ to $\overline{NP}$. **47.** If a ▱ is a rectangle, then its diags. are ≅; if the diags. of a ▱ are ≅, then the ▱ is a rectangle; $\overline{JL} \cong \overline{KM}$.

49. If a quad. is a rectangle, then it has 4 right ∠s (def. of rectangle); if a quad. has 4 right ∠s, then it is a rectangle. (Both pairs of opp. ∠s are ≅, so the quad. is a ▱. Since all 4 ∠s are ≅ and the sum of the measures of the int. ∠s of a quad. is 360°, the measure of each ∠ is 90°, and the quad. is a rectangle.)

51.

Statements	Reasons
1. *PQRT* is a rhombus.	1. Given
2. $\overline{PQ} \cong \overline{QR} \cong \overline{RT} \cong \overline{PT}$	2. A quad. is a rhombus if and only if it has 4 ≅ sides.
3. $\overline{PR} \cong \overline{PR}$, $\overline{QT} \cong \overline{QT}$	3. Reflexive Prop. of Cong.
4. $\triangle PRQ \cong \triangle PRT$; $\triangle PTQ \cong \triangle RTQ$	4. SSS Cong. Postulate
5. $\angle TPR \cong \angle QPR$, $\angle TRP \cong \angle QRP$ $\angle PTQ \cong \angle RTQ$, $\angle PQT \cong \angle RQT$	5. Corresp. parts of ≅ $\triangle$s are ≅.
6. $\overline{PR}$ bisects $\angle TPQ$ and $\angle QRT$, $\overline{QT}$ bisects $\angle PTR$ and $\angle RQP$.	6. Def. of $\angle$ bisector

53. *Sample answer:* Draw $\overline{AB}$ and a line j (not $\perp$ to $\overline{AB}$) intersecting $\overline{AB}$ at B. Construct $\overline{BC}$ on j so that $\overline{BC} \cong \overline{AB}$. Construct two arcs with radius AB and centers A and C, intersecting at D. Draw $\overline{AD}$ and $\overline{CD}$. Since all 4 sides of $ABCD$ are ≅, $ABCD$ is a rhombus. Since $\overline{AB}$ and $\overline{BC}$ are not $\perp$, $ABCD$ is not a rectangle, and thus not a square. **55.** Rectangle; $PR = QS = \sqrt{41}$; since the diags. of $PQRS$ are ≅, $PQRS$ is a rectangle. **57.** Rectangle; $PR = QS = \sqrt{58}$; since the diags. of $PQRS$ are ≅, $PQRS$ is a rectangle. **59.** (b, a); $\overline{KM} \cong \overline{ON}$, so $KM = b$ and $\overline{MN} \cong \overline{KO}$, so $MN = a$. **61.** *Sample answer:* Since cross braces $\overline{AD}$ and $\overline{BC}$ bisect each other, $ABDC$ is a ▱. Since cross braces $\overline{AD}$ and $\overline{BC}$ also have the same length, $ABDC$ is a rectangle. Since a rectangle has 4 right $\angle$s, $m\angle BAC = m\angle ABD = 90°$. Then, $m\angle BAC = m\angle BAE$ and $m\angle ABD = m\angle ABF$, so $m\angle BAE = m\angle ABF = 90°$ by substitution. So tabletop $\overline{AB}$ is perpendicular to legs $\overline{AE}$ and $\overline{BF}$ by the def. of perpendicular. **63.** Rhombus; $\overline{AE} \cong \overline{CE} \cong \overline{AF} \cong \overline{CF}$; $AECF$ remains a rhombus. **65.** Each diag. of a rhombus bisects a pair of opp. $\angle$s. (Theorem 6.12)

6.4 Mixed Review (p. 355) **73.** yes **75.** no **77.** yes **79.** $\frac{1}{2}$ **81.** 9 **83.** Assume temporarily that $ABCD$ is a quad. with 4 acute $\angle$s, that is, $m\angle A < 90°$, $m\angle B < 90°$, $m\angle C < 90°$, and $m\angle D < 90°$. Then $m\angle A + m\angle B + m\angle C + m\angle D < 360°$. This contradicts the Interior Angles of a Quadrilateral Theorem. Then no quad. has 4 acute $\angle$s.

6.5 Practice (pp. 359–362) **3.** isosceles trapezoid **5.** trapezoid **7.** 9 **9.** 9.5 **11.** legs **13.** diags. **15.** base $\angle$s **17.** $m\angle J = 102°$, $m\angle L = 48°$ **19.** 8 **21.** 12 **23.** 10 **25.** Yes; X is equidistant from the vertices of the dodecagon, so $\overline{XA} \cong \overline{XB}$ and $\angle XAB \cong \angle XBA$ by the Base Angles Theorem. Since trapezoid $ABPQ$ has a pair of ≅ base $\angle$s, $ABPQ$ is isosceles. **27.** $m\angle A = m\angle B = 75°$, $m\angle P = m\angle Q = 105°$ **29.** $EF = GF \approx 6.40$, $HE = HG \approx 8.60$ **31.** 95° **33.** 90° **37.** $ABCD$ is a trapezoid; slope of $\overline{BC}$ = slope of $\overline{AD} = 0$, so $\overline{BC} \parallel \overline{AD}$; slope of $\overline{AB} = 2$ and slope of $\overline{CD} = -\frac{4}{3}$, so $\overline{AB}$ is not $\parallel$ to $\overline{CD}$. $ABCD$ is not isosceles; $AB = 2\sqrt{5}$ and $CD = 5$. **39.** 16 in. **41.** $TQRS$ is an isosceles trapezoid, so $\angle QTS \cong \angle RST$ because base $\angle$s of an isosceles trapezoid are ≅. $\overline{TS} \cong \overline{TS}$ by the Reflexive Prop. of Cong. and $\overline{QT} \cong \overline{RS}$, so $\triangle QTS \cong \triangle RST$ by the SAS Cong. Postulate. Then $\overline{TR} \cong \overline{SQ}$ because corresp. parts of ≅ $\triangle$s are ≅. **43.** If $AC \neq BC$, then $ACBD$ is a kite; $AC = AD$ and $BC = BD$, so the quad. has two pairs of ≅ sides, but opp. sides are not ≅. (If $AC = BC$, then $ACBD$ is a rhombus.); $ABCD$ remains a kite in all three cases. **45.** If a quad. is a kite, then exactly 1 pair of opp. $\angle$s are ≅. **47.** Draw $\overline{BD}$. (Through any 2 points, there is exactly 1 line.) Since $\overline{AB} \cong \overline{CB}$ and $\overline{AD} \cong \overline{CD}$, $\triangle BCD \cong \triangle BAD$ by the SSS Cong. Postulate. Then corresp. $\angle$s A and C are ≅. Assume temporarily that $\angle B \cong \angle D$. Then both pairs of opp. $\angle$s of $ABCD$ are ≅, so $ABCD$ is a ▱ and opp. sides are ≅. This contradicts the definition of a kite. It follows that $\angle B \ncong \angle D$.

49. Yes; $ABCD$ has one pair of $\parallel$ sides and the diagonals are ≅. $ABCD$ is not a ▱ because opp. $\angle$s are not ≅.

6.5 Mixed Review (p. 363) **55.** If a quad. is a kite, then its diags. are $\perp$. **57.** 5.6 **59.** 7 **61.** 80° **63.** Yes; *Sample answer:* slope of $\overline{AB}$ = slope of $\overline{CD} = 0$, so $\overline{AB} \parallel \overline{CD}$ and $AB = CD = 7$. Then one pair of opp. sides are both ≅ and $\parallel$, so $ABCD$ is a ▱.

Quiz 2 (p. 363) **1.** *Sample answer:* Opposite sides of $EBFJ$ are ≅ so $EBFJ$ is a ▱. Opposite $\angle$s of a ▱ are ≅, so $\angle BEJ \cong \angle BFJ$. By the Cong. Supplements Theorem, $\angle HEJ \cong \angle KFJ$. Since $\overline{HE} \cong \overline{JE} \cong \overline{JF} \cong \overline{KF}$, $\triangle HEJ \cong \triangle JFK$ by the SAS Cong. Postulate and, since corresp. sides of ≅ $\triangle$s are ≅, $\overline{HJ} \cong \overline{JK}$. **2.** rectangle **3.** kite **4.** square **5.** trapezoid

6.

Statements	Reasons
1. $\overline{AB} \parallel \overline{DC}$, $\angle D \cong \angle C$	1. Given
2. Draw $\overline{AE} \parallel \overline{BC}$.	2. Parallel Postulate
3. $ABCE$ is a ▱.	3. Def. of a ▱
4. $\overline{AE} \cong \overline{BC}$	4. Opp. sides of a ▱ are ≅.
5. $\angle AED \cong \angle C$	5. Corresp. Angles Postulate
6. $\angle AED \cong \angle D$	6. Transitive Prop. of Cong.
7. $\overline{AD} \cong \overline{AE}$	7. Converse of the Base Angles Theorem
8. $\overline{AD} \cong \overline{BC}$	8. Transitive Prop. of Cong.

6.6 Practice (pp. 367–369)

	Property	▱	Rect.	Rhom.	Sq.	Kite	Trap.
3.	Exactly 1 pr. of opp. sides are $\parallel$.						X
5.	Diags. are ≅.		X		X		

SELECTED ANSWERS

SA17

7. ▱, rectangle, rhombus, square

	Property	▱	Rect.	Rhom.	Sq.	Kite	Trap.
9.	Exactly 1 pr. of opp. sides are ≅.						
11.	Both pairs of opp. ∠s are ≅.	X	X	X	X		
13.	All ∠s are ≅.		X		X		

15. isosceles trapezoid 17. square 19. ▱, rectangle, rhombus, square, kite 21. rhombus, square 23. rectangle, square 25. Show that the quad. has 2 pairs of consec. ≅ sides, but opp. sides are not ≅ (def. of kite).
27. Show that the quad. has 4 right ∠s; show that the quad. is a ▱ and that its diags. are ≅.
29. Show that exactly 2 sides are ∥ and that the nonparallel sides are ≅ (def. of trapezoid); show that the quad. is a trapezoid and that one pair of base ∠s are ≅; show that the quad. is a trapezoid and that its diags. are ≅. 31. $\overline{BE}$ and $\overline{DE}$ 33. $\overline{AE}$ and $\overline{BE}$ or $\overline{DE}$ (and so on), $\overline{AC}$ and $\overline{BD}$ 35. any two consecutive sides of $ABCD$ 37. Isosceles trapezoid; $\overline{PQ} \parallel \overline{RS}$, and $\overline{PS}$ and $\overline{QR}$ are ≅ but not ∥. 39. ▱; *Sample answer:* $\overline{PQ} \parallel \overline{RS}$ and $\overline{PS} \parallel \overline{QR}$. 41. Rhombus: *Sample answer:* $\overline{PQ} \cong \overline{QR} \cong \overline{RS} \cong \overline{PS}$. 43. isosceles trapezoid
45. ▱; if the diags. of a quad. bisect each other, the quad. is a ▱. Since the diags. are not ⊥, the ▱ is not a rhombus and since the diags. are not ≅, the ▱ is not a rectangle.
47. Kite; $\overline{AC} \perp \overline{BD}$ and $\overline{AC}$ bisects $\overline{BD}$, so ≅ △s can be used to show that $\overline{AB} \cong \overline{AD}$ and then that $\overline{CB} \cong \overline{CD}$. $\overline{BD}$ does not bisect $\overline{AC}$, so $ABCD$ is not a ▱. Then opp. sides are not ≅ and $ABCD$ is a kite. 49. Draw a line through C ∥ to $\overline{DF}$ and a line through E ∥ to $\overline{CD}$. Label the intersection F. $CDEF$ is a ▱ by the def. of a ▱. ∠DCF and ∠DEF are right ∠s because consec. ∠s of a ▱ are supplementary. Then ∠CFE is also a right ∠ and $CDEF$ is a rectangle. The diags. of a ▱ bisect each other, so $DM = \frac{1}{2}DF$ and $CM = \frac{1}{2}CE$. The diags. of a rectangle are ≅, so $DF = CE$, $\frac{1}{2}DF = \frac{1}{2}CE$, and $DM = CM$. By the def. of cong., $\overline{DM} \cong \overline{CM}$.

6.6 MIXED REVIEW (p. 370) 55. 16 sq. units 57. 15 sq. units 59. 30 sq. units 61. 1.75 63. 7 65. 5

6.7 PRACTICE (pp. 376–379) 3. A 5. C 7. D 9. 25 sq. units 11. 40 sq. units 13. 36 sq. units 15. 49 sq. units 17. 120 sq. units 19. 10 sq. units 21. 361 sq. units 23. 240 sq. units 25. 70 sq. units 27. 12 ft 29. $b = \frac{2A}{h}$ 31. $b_1 = \frac{2A}{h} - b_2$ 33. 4 sq. units 35. 3 ft^2 37. 552 in.^{2}
39. No; such a ▱ has base 6 ft and height 4 ft; two such ▱s that have ∠s with different measures are not ≅.
41. 24 sq. units 43. 192 sq. units 45. about 480 carnations 47. about 432 chrysanthemums 49. about 6023 shakes 51. blue: 96 sq. units; yellow: 96 sq. units 53. Square; square; *Sample answer:* In quad. $EBFJ$, ∠E, ∠J, and∠F are right ∠s by the Linear Pair Postulate and ∠B is a right ∠ by the Interior Angles of a Quadrilateral Theorem. Then $EBFJ$ is a rectangle by the Rectangle Corollary. $\overline{EJ} \cong \overline{FJ}$ because they are corresp. parts of ≅ ▱s. Then, by the def. of a ▱ and the Transitive Prop. of Cong., $EBFJ$ is a rhombus and, therefore, a square. Similarly, $HJGD$ is a square.
55. $b + h$; $(b + h)^2$ 57. $(b + h)^2 = b^2 + h^2 + 2A$; $A = bh$
59. Show that the area of $AEGH = \frac{1}{2}h(b_1 + b_2)$. Then, since $EBCF$ and $GHDF$ are ≅, Area of $ABCD$ = Area of $AEFD$ + area of $EBCF$ = area of $AEFD$ + area of $GHDF$ = area of $AEGH = \frac{1}{2}h(b_1 + b_2)$.

6.7 MIXED REVIEW (p. 380)
63. obtuse; about 140° 65. acute; about 15°
67. *Sample answer:*

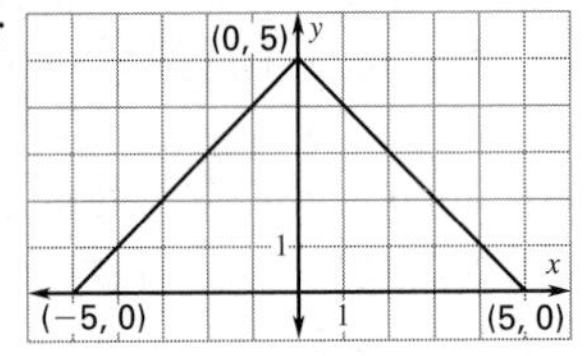

69. 1

QUIZ 3 (p. 380) 1. Kite; $\overline{ON} \cong \overline{OP}$ and $\overline{MN} \cong \overline{MP}$, but opp. sides are not ≅. 2. Trapezoid; $\overline{QR} \parallel \overline{TS}$, but $\overline{QT}$ and $\overline{RS}$ are not ∥. 3. ▱; *Sample answer:* $\overline{ZY} \cong \overline{WX}$ and $\overline{ZY} \parallel \overline{WX}$.
4. 5 in. 5. 12 in. 6. 8 in. 7. 52.11 cm^2

CHAPTER 6 REVIEW (pp. 382–384)
1. *Sample answer:*

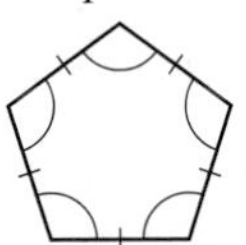

3. 115 5. 13 7. 65°, 115°
9. No; you are not given information about opp. sides. 11. Yes; you can prove △s PQT and SRT are ≅ and opp. sides are ≅. 13. rhombus, square
15. rhombus, square 17. $m\angle ABC = 112°$, $m\angle ADC = m\angle BCD = 68°$ 19. Square; *Sample answer:* $PQ = QR = RS = PS = \sqrt{34}$, so $PQRS$ is a rhombus; $QS = PR = 2\sqrt{17}$, so the diags. of $PQRS$ are ≅ and $PQRS$ is a rectangle. A quad. that is both a rhombus and a rectangle is a square.
21. Rhombus; $PQ = QR = RS = PS = 2\sqrt{5}$
23. $29\frac{3}{4}$ in.^{2} 25. 12 sq. units

CUMULATIVE PRACTICE (pp. 388–389)
1. 0.040404…, 0.181818…, 0.353535…, 0.898989…
3. 135°; 45° 5. *Sample answer:* △QPR ≅ △QPS and △QPR ≅ △TPS; show that ∠1 ≅ ∠2, $\overline{QP} \cong \overline{QP}$, and $m\angle QPS = m\angle QPR$, so the △s are ≅ by the ASA Cong. Postulate. Then show that $\overline{PR} \cong \overline{PS}$, ∠2 ≅ ∠$T$, and ∠$QRP$ ≅ ∠TSP, so △QPR ≅ △TPS by the AAS Cong. Theorem. 7. P is equidistant from $\overrightarrow{QS}$ and $\overrightarrow{QR}$ by the Angle Bisector Theorem. 9. 53°, 95°, 32°; obtuse
11. no 13. yes; HL Congruence Theorem

15. $AB = AC = \sqrt{89}$ **17.** $y = -\frac{8}{5}x + \frac{97}{10}$ **19.** $\left(\frac{17}{3}, 1\right)$

21. If 2 ∠s are supplementary, then they form a linear pair; false; *Sample answer:* two consec. ∠s of a ▱ are supplementary, but they do not form a linear pair. **23.** $m\angle X > m\angle Z$; the ∠ opp. the longer side is larger than the ∠ opp. the shorter side. **25.** rhombus **27.** Yes; *Sample answer:* The diags. share a common midpoint, (4.5, 6), which means they bisect each other. Thus, *PQRS* is a ▱ . **29. a.** square, rhombus, kite **b.** square, rectangle, isosceles trapezoid **31.** $AC = DF$, $m\angle ACB = 65° = \angle DFE$, and $m\angle ABC = 90° = \angle DEF$, so $\triangle ABC \cong \triangle DEF$ by the AAS Cong. Theorem. **33.** 69° **35.** 438.75 in.^{2}

ALGEBRA REVIEW (pp. 390–391) **1.** $\frac{4}{5}$ **2.** $\frac{7}{4}$ **3.** $\frac{25}{27}$ **4.** $\frac{11}{4}$ **5.** $\frac{103}{45}$ **6.** $\frac{11}{9}$ **7.** $\frac{4}{1}$ **8.** $\frac{5}{4}$ **9.** $\frac{1}{1}$ **10.** 3 **11.** –3 **12.** 6 **13.** –4 **14.** $\frac{13}{4}$ **15.** $\frac{7}{6}$ **16.** –1 **17.** 2 **18.** $\frac{7}{9}$ **19.** $\frac{27}{2}$ **20.** –2 **21.** 8 **22.** 4 **23.** 9 **24.** 200 **25.** 12 **26.** $\frac{24}{5}$ **27.** $\frac{42}{17}$ **28.** $\frac{5}{9}$ **29.** $\frac{3}{2}$ **30.** 30 **31.** 4 **32.** 5 **33.** $\frac{95}{9}$ **34.** 5 **35.** –4 **36.** 9 **37.** –29 **38.** $-\frac{43}{2}$ **39.** $\frac{2}{3}$ **40.** –3 **41.** $-\frac{2}{3}$ **42.** ±6

CHAPTER 7

SKILL REVIEW (p. 394) **1.** congruent **2.** not congruent **3.** congruent **4.** 10 **5.** 35° **6.** 55° **7.** 90° **8.** $\overline{QR}$ **9.** about 7

7.1 PRACTICE (pp. 399–402) **5.** translation **7.** rotation **9.** $\overline{VW}$ **11.** $\triangle WXY$ **13.** rotation about the origin; a turn about the origin **15.** ∠*A* and ∠*J*, ∠*B* and ∠*K*, ∠*C* and ∠*L*, ∠*D* and ∠*M*, or ∠*E* and ∠*N* **17.** *Sample answer:* $JK = \sqrt{(-3-(-1))^2 + (2-1)^2} = \sqrt{5}$; $AB = \sqrt{(2-1)^2 + (3-1)^2} = \sqrt{5}$ **19.** false **21.** reflection in the line $x = 1$; a flip over the line $x = 1$; $A'(6, 2)$, $B'(3, 4)$, $C'(3, -1)$, $D'(6, -1)$ **23.** Yes; the preimage and image appear to be ≅. **25.** No; the preimage and image are not ≅. **27.** *LKJ* **29.** *PRQ* **31.** *RQP* **33.** $AB = XY = 3\sqrt{2}$, $BC = YZ = \sqrt{10}$, $AC = XZ = 4$ **35.** $w = 35$, $x = 4\frac{1}{3}$, $y = 3$ **37.** translation **39.** rotation **41.** reflection; reflection; rotation (or two reflections) **43.** *Sample answer:* Flip the plan vertically to lay the upper left corner, then horizontally to lay the lower left corner, then vertically again to lay the lower right corner.

7.1 MIXED REVIEW (p. 402) **47.** 13 **49.** $\sqrt{89}$ **51.** polygon **53.** not a polygon; one side not a segment **55.** not a polygon; two of the sides intersect only one other side.

57. (1) Since slope of $\overline{PQ}$ = slope of $\overline{SR} = \frac{2}{7}$ and slope of $\overline{PS}$ = slope of $\overline{QR} = -8$, both pairs of opposite sides are ∥ and *PQRS* is a parallelogram. (2) Since $PQ = SR = \sqrt{53}$ and $PS = QR = \sqrt{65}$, both pairs of opposite sides are ≅ and *PQRS* is a parallelogram.

7.2 PRACTICE (pp. 407–410) **3.** not a reflection **5.** reflection **7.** ∠*DAB* **9.** *D* **11.** $\overline{DC}$ **13.** 4

15.

17.

19. True; *M* is 3 units to the right of the line $x = 3$, so its image is 3 units to the left of the line.

21. True; *U* is 4 units to the right of the line $x = 1$, so its image is 4 units to the left of the line.

23. $\overline{CD}$ **25.** $\overline{EF}$ **27.** (3, –8) **29.** (–7, –2)

31.

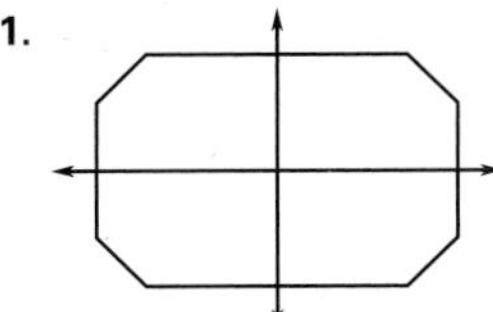

33. Draw $\overline{PP'}$ and $\overline{QQ'}$ intersecting line *m* at points *S* and *T*. By the def. of reflection, $\overline{P'S} \cong \overline{PS}$ and $\overline{RS} \perp \overline{PP'}$, and $\overline{Q'T} \cong \overline{QT}$ and $\overline{RT} \perp \overline{QQ'}$. It follows that $\triangle P'SR \cong \triangle PSR$ and $\triangle Q'TR \cong \triangle QTR$ by the SAS Congruence Postulate. Since corresp. parts of ≅ ▵s are ≅, $\overline{P'R} \cong \overline{PR}$ and $\overline{Q'R} \cong \overline{QR}$. So, $P'R = PR$ and $Q'R = QR$. Since $P'Q' = P'R + Q'R$ and $PQ = PR + QR$ by the Segment Addition Postulate, we get by substitution $PQ = P'Q'$, or $\overline{PQ} \cong \overline{P'Q'}$. **35.** *Q* is on line *m*, so $Q = Q'$. By the def. of reflection, $\overline{PQ} \cong \overline{P'Q}\left(\overline{P'Q'}\right)$. **37.** (6, 0) **39.** (3, 0) **41.** Each structure is a reflection of the other. **43.** Triangles 2 and 3 are reflections of triangle 1; triangle 4 is rotation of triangle 1. **45.** 90° **47.** The distance between each vertex of the preimage and line *m* is equal to the distance between the corresponding vertex of the image and line *m*. **49.** $u = 6$, $v = 5\frac{4}{5}$, $w = 5$

7.2 MIXED REVIEW (p. 410) **57.** ∠*P* **59.** $\overline{BC}$ **61.** 101° **63.** $10 < c < 24$ **65.** $21 < c < 45$ **67.** $25.7 < c < 56.7$ **69.** $m\angle A = m\angle B = 119°$, $m\angle C = 61°$ **71.** $m\angle A = 106°$, $m\angle C = 61°$

7.3 PRACTICE (pp. 416–419) **7.** *P* **9.** *R* **11.** yes; a rotation of 180° clockwise or counterclockwise about its center **13.** $\overline{CD}$ **15.** $\overline{GE}$ **17.** $\triangle MAB$ **19.** $\triangle CPA$ **21.** By the def. of a rotation, $\overline{QP} \cong \overline{Q'P}$. Since *P* and *R* are the same point, as are *R* and *R'*, $\overline{QR} \cong \overline{Q'R'}$.

SELECTED ANSWERS

23.

25. $J'(1, 2)$, $K'(4, 1)$, $L'(4, -3)$, $M'(1, -3)$ **27.** $D'(4, 1)$, $E'(0, 2)$, $F'(2, 5)$
29. $X'(2, 3)$, $O'(0, 0)$, $Z'(-3, 4)$; the coordinates of the image of the point (x, y) after a 180° clockwise rotation about the origin are $(-x, -y)$.
31. 30° **33.** 81° **35.** $q = 30$, $r = 5$, $s = 11$, $t = 1$, $u = 2$

37. The wheel hub can be mapped onto itself by a clockwise or counterclockwise rotation of $51\frac{3}{7}°$, $102\frac{6}{7}°$, or $154\frac{2}{7}°$ about its center. **39.** Yes; the image can be mapped onto itself by a clockwise or counterclockwise rotation of 180° about its center. **41.** the center of the square, that is, the intersection of the diagonals

7.3 MIXED REVIEW (p. 419) **45.** 82° **47.** 82° **49.** 98° **51.** any obtuse triangle **53.** any acute triangle

QUIZ 1 (p. 420) **1.** *RSTQ* **2.** Reflection in line *m*; the figure is flipped over line *m*. **3.** Yes; the transformation preserves lengths. **4.** $(2, -3)$ **5.** $(2, -4)$ **6.** $(-4, 0)$ **7.** $(-8.2, -3)$ **8.** rotations by multiples of 120° clockwise or counterclockwise about the center of the knot where the rope starts to unravel

7.4 PRACTICE (pp. 425–428) **3.** $(x, y) \to (x + 6, y - 2)$ **5.** $(x, y) \to (x - 7, y + 1)$ **7.** 8; 3 **9.** 5; –2
11. *Sample figure:*

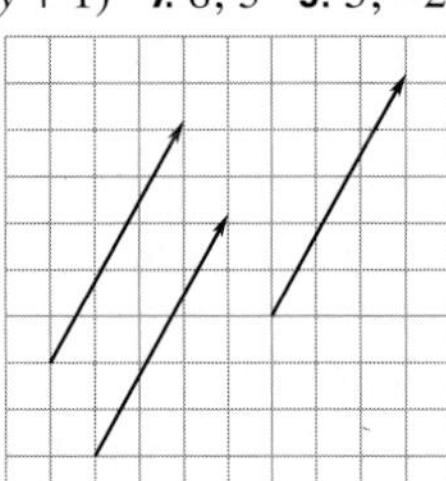

13. *Sample figure:*

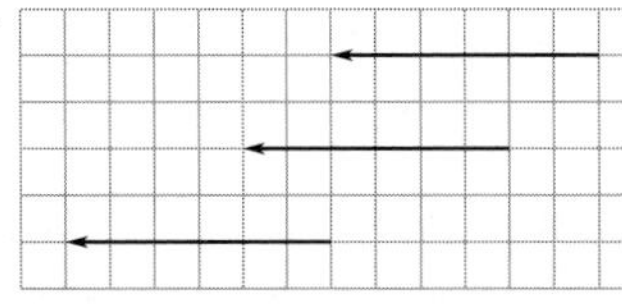

15. $(x, y) \to (x - 3, y - 4)$; $\langle -3, -4 \rangle$ **17.** $\overrightarrow{HJ}$; $\langle 4, 2 \rangle$ **19.** $\overrightarrow{MN}$; $\langle 5, 0 \rangle$ **21.** *k* and *m* **23.** 2.8 in. **25.** $(17, -4)$ **27.** $(-14, 8)$ **29.** $(12.5, -4.5)$

31.

33.

35. true **37.** true

39.

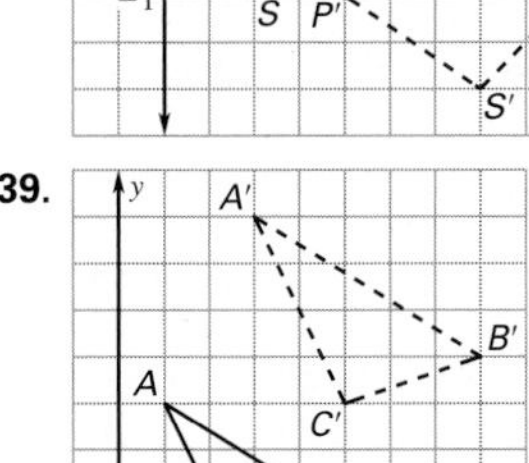

41.

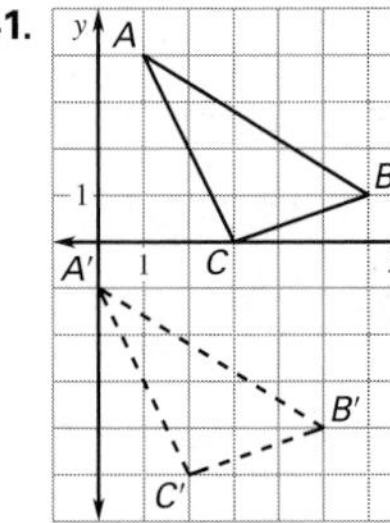

43. We are given $P(a, b)$ and $Q(c, d)$. Suppose P' has coordinates $(a + r, b + s)$. Then $PP' = \sqrt{r^2 + s^2}$ and the slope of $\overline{PP'} = \frac{s}{r}$. If $PP' = QQ'$ and $\overline{PP'} \parallel \overline{QQ'}$ as given, then $QQ' = \sqrt{r^2 + s^2}$ and the slope of $\overline{QQ'} = \frac{s}{r}$. So, the coordinates of Q' are $(c + r, d + s)$. By the Distance Formula, $PQ = \sqrt{(a - c)^2 + (b - d)^2}$ and $P'Q' = \sqrt{[(a + r) - (c + r)]^2 + [(b + s) - (d + s)]^2} = \sqrt{(a - c)^2 + (b - d)^2}$. Thus, by the substitution prop. of equality, $PQ = P'Q'$. **45.** D **47.** B **49.** no **51.** Samples might include photographs of floor tiles or of fabric patterns. **53.** $\langle 6, 4 \rangle$, $\langle 4, 6 \rangle$ **55.** $\langle 18, 12 \rangle$

7.4 MIXED REVIEW (p. 428) **63.** –5 **65.** –6 **67.** $\frac{3}{4}$ **69.** 12 **71.** true **73.** false

7.5 PRACTICE (pp. 433–436) **5.** $\overline{A'B'}$ **7.** the *y*-axis **9.** A **11.** B **13.** $(1, -10)$ **15.** $(2, -6)$

17.

19.

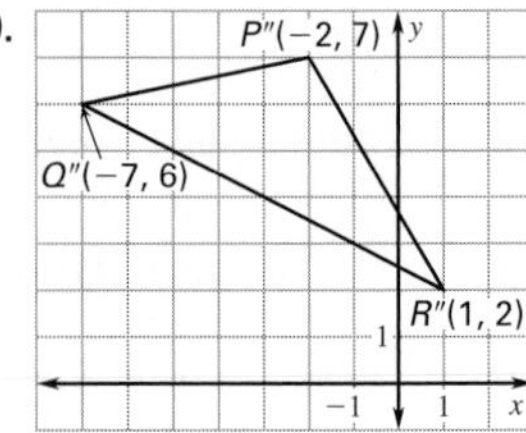

21. G''(4, 8) G''(8, 8) F''(1, 7) F''(5, 7) translation, then reflection; reflection, then translation; The order does affect the final image. 23. reflection in the line $y = 2$, followed by reflection in the line $x = -2$ 25. 90° counterclockwise rotation about the point (0, 1), followed by the translation $(x, y) \rightarrow (x + 2, y + 3)$

27. A, B, C 31. After each part was painted, the stencil was moved through a glide reflection (reflection in a horizontal line through its center and translation to the right) to paint the next part. 33. 1, 4, 5, 6 35. The pattern can be created by horizontal translation, 180° rotation, vertical line reflection, or horizontal glide reflection. 37. The pattern can be created by translation or 180° rotation.

7.5 Mixed Review (p. 436)

41. 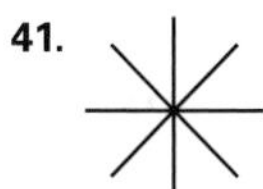 43. (figure)

45, 47. Sample explanations are given.

45. Square; $PQ = QR = RS = PS = \sqrt{17}$, so $PQRS$ is a rhombus. Also, since $PR = QS = \sqrt{34}$, the diagonals of $PQRS$ are $\cong$, so $PQRS$ is a rectangle. Then, by the Square Corollary, $PQRS$ is a square. 47. Rhombus; $PQ = QR = RS = PS = \sqrt{13}$, so $PQRS$ is a rhombus. Since $PR = 6$ and $SQ = 4$, the diagonals are not congruent, so $PQRS$ is not a rectangle or a square. 49. $A'(-6, 9)$, $B'(-6, 3)$, $C'(-2, 8)$ 51. $A'(-3, 7)$, $B'(-3, 1)$, $C'(1, 6)$ 53. $A'(-9, 9.5)$, $B'(-9, 3.5)$, $C'(-5, 8.5)$

7.6 Practice (pp. 440–443)

3. translation, vertical line reflection 5. translation, rotation, vertical line reflection, horizontal glide reflection 7. translation (T), 180° rotation (R), horizontal glide reflection (G), vertical line reflection (V), horizontal line reflection (H) 9. D 11. B 13. translation, 180° rotation 15. translation, 180° rotation, horizontal line reflection, vertical line reflection, horizontal glide reflection 17. yes; reflection in the x-axis 19. 180° rotation about the point (8, 0) 21. TRHVG 23. T

27, 29, 31. Sample patterns are given.

27. 29. 31.

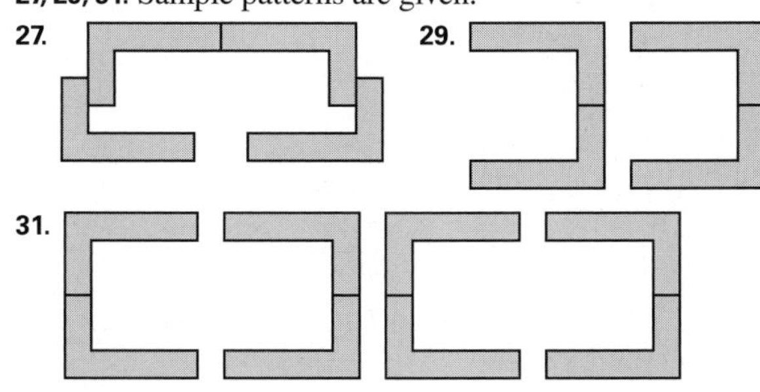

33. TRHVG 35. There are three bands of frieze patterns visible. 39. just under 3 in.

41. *Sample pattern:*

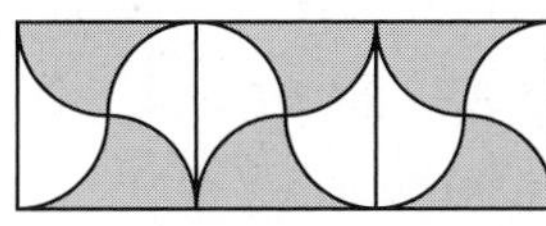

47. *Sample pattern:*

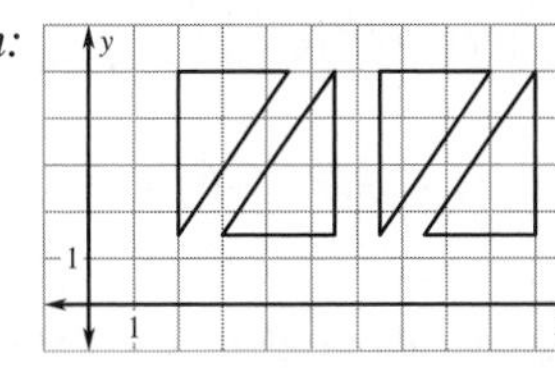

7.6 Mixed Review (p. 444)

55. $\frac{13}{8}$ 57. $\frac{16}{19}$ 59. 1 61. $w = 8, y = 2$ 63. 288 sq. units

Quiz 2 (p. 444)

1. $A'(0, 5)$, $B'(5, 6)$, $C'(2, 4)$ 2. $A'(-4, 6)$, $B'(1, 7)$, $C'(-2, 5)$ 3. $A'(-3, -2)$, $B'(2, -1)$, $C'(-1, -3)$ 4. $A'(4, 4)$, $B'(9, 5)$, $C'(6, 3)$

5. 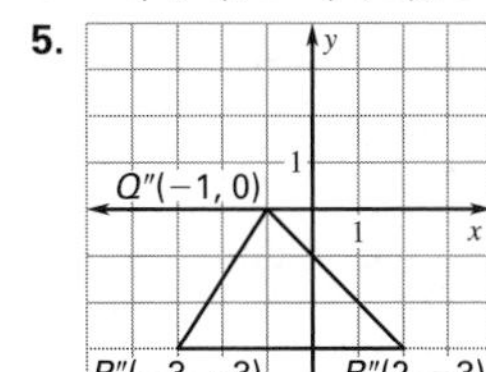

6. Q''(4, 1) R''(2, −2) P''(5, −3)

7. yes; TR

Chapter 7 Review (pp. 446–448)

1. Yes; the figure and its image appear to be congruent. 3. Yes; the figure and its image appear to be congruent.

5. 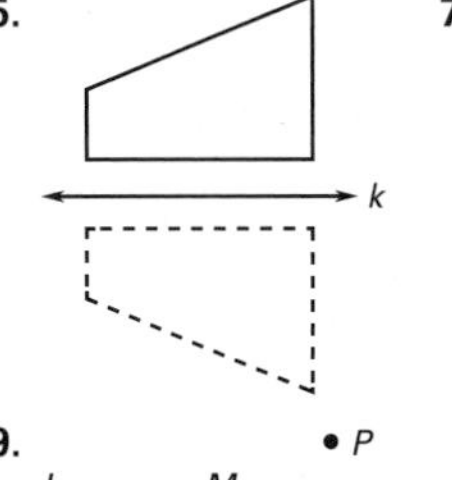

7. 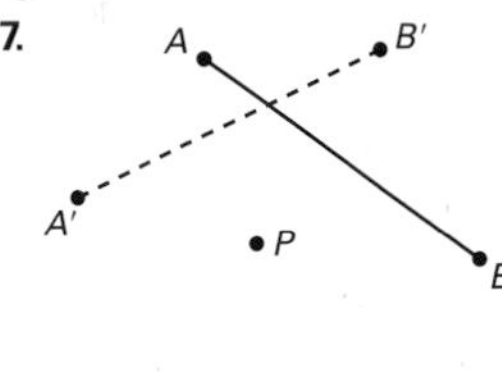

9. 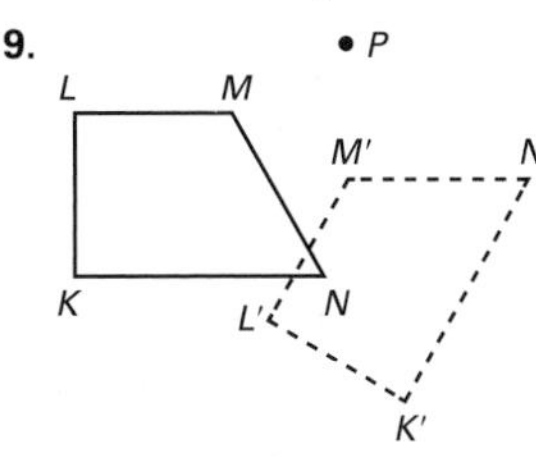

11. A 13. B 15. reflection in the x-axis followed by 90° counterclockwise rotation about the origin 17. TRHVG

CHAPTER 8

Skill Review (p. 456)

1. 32 units 2. 31 units 3. 91 units 4. $\frac{1}{2}$ 5. $\frac{3}{7}$ 6. $\frac{11}{4}$

8.1 Practice (pp. 461–464)

5. 4:5 7. $\frac{48}{5}$ 9. 6 11. $\frac{6}{1}$ 13. $\frac{2}{3}$ 15. $\frac{7.5 \text{ cm}}{10 \text{ cm}}; \frac{3}{4}$ 17. $\frac{36 \text{ in.}}{12 \text{ in.}}$ or $\frac{3 \text{ ft}}{1 \text{ ft}}; \frac{3}{1}$ 19. $\frac{350 \text{ g}}{1000 \text{ g}}; \frac{7}{20}$ 21. $\frac{18 \text{ ft}}{10 \text{ ft}}; \frac{9}{5}$ 23. $\frac{400 \text{ m}}{500 \text{ m}}; \frac{4}{5}$ 25. $\frac{2}{3}$ 27. $\frac{11}{9}$ 29. 30 ft, 12 ft 31. 15°, 60°, 105° 33. $\frac{20}{7}$ 35. $\frac{35}{2}$ 37. $\frac{7}{3}$ 39. 12 41. 15 43. $-\frac{48}{5}$ 45. 16 47. 21 49. Venus: 126 lb; Mars: 53 lb; Jupiter: 330 lb; Pluto 10 lb 51. 1440 in. 53. about 1.0 in.

55. 6 **57.** $RQ = 12, PQ = 13, SU = 15, ST = 39$ **59.** 12 : 1 **61.** 144 : 1 **63.** $EF = 20, DF = 24$

8.1 MIXED REVIEW (p. 464) **69.** 95° **71.** 95° **73.** $\left(-1\frac{1}{2}, 3\right)$ and $(1, 3)$ **75.** $\left(-\frac{1}{2}, 3\frac{1}{2}\right)$ and $\left(1\frac{1}{2}, 1\right)$

8.2 PRACTICE (pp. 468–470) **5.** 6 **7.** 11.4 ft **9.** $\frac{x}{y}$ **11.** $\frac{y + 12}{12}$ **13.** true **15.** true **17.** 9 **19.** 14 **21.** $4\sqrt{10}$ **23.** 11.25 **25.** $6\frac{2}{3}$ **27.** $6\frac{6}{7}$ **29.** about 25 ft **31.** 198 hits **33.** 11 **37.** Let $\frac{a}{b} = \frac{c}{d}$ and show that $\frac{a + b}{b} = \frac{c + d}{d}$.

$\frac{a}{b} = \frac{c}{d}$ (Given)

$\frac{a}{b} + 1 = \frac{c}{d} + 1$ (Addition prop. of equality)

$\frac{a}{b} + \frac{b}{b} = \frac{c}{d} + \frac{d}{d}$ (Inverse prop. of multiplication)

$\frac{a + b}{b} = \frac{c + d}{d}$ (Addition of fractions)

39. 24 ft **41.** about $\frac{3}{8}$ in.; about $2\frac{1}{2}$ mi

8.2 MIXED REVIEW (p. 471) **47.** 12 m^2 **49.** 26 cm^2 **51.** $m\angle C = 115°, m\angle A = m\angle D = 65°$ **53.** $m\angle A = m\angle B = 100°, m\angle C = 80°$ **55.** $m\angle B = 41°, m\angle C = m\angle D = 139°$ **57.** A regular pentagon has 5 lines of symmetry (one from each vertex to the midpoint of the opposite side) and rotational symmetries of 72° and 144°, clockwise and counterclockwise about the center of the pentagon.

8.3 PRACTICE (pp. 475–478) **5.** 5 : 3 **7.** 110° **9.** $\angle J \cong \angle W, \angle K \cong \angle X, \angle L \cong \angle Y, \angle M \cong \angle Z; \frac{JK}{WX} = \frac{KL}{XY} = \frac{LM}{YZ} = \frac{JM}{WZ}$ **11.** Yes; both figures are rectangles, so all 4 ∠s are ≅ and $\frac{AB}{FG} = \frac{BC}{GH} = \frac{CD}{HE} = \frac{AD}{FE} = \frac{7}{4}$. **13.** No; $m\angle B = 90°$ and $m\angle Q = 88°$, so corresp. ∠s are not ≅. **15.** yes; *Sample answers: ABCD ~ EFGH, ABCD ~ FEHG* **17.** yes; $\triangle XYZ \sim \triangle CAB$ **19.** 4 : 5 **21.** 20, 12.5, 20 **23.** $\frac{4}{5}$ **25.** 2 **27.** 10 **29.** no **31.** sometimes **33.** sometimes **35.** always **37.** always **39.** 11, 9 **41.** $39\frac{3}{7}, 23\frac{1}{7}$ **43.** analog TV: 21.6 in. by 16.2 in., digital TV: about 23.5 in. by 13.2 in. **45.** $ABCD \sim EFGH$ with scale factor $1 : k$, so $\frac{AB}{EF} = \frac{BC}{FG} = \frac{CD}{GH} = \frac{AD}{EH} = \frac{1}{k}$. Then, $EF = k \cdot AB, FG = k \cdot BC, GH = k \cdot CD$, and $EH = k \cdot AD$, so $\frac{\text{perimeter of } ABCD}{\text{perimeter of } EFGH} = \frac{AB + BC + CD + AD}{EF + FG + GH + EH} = \frac{AB + BC + CD + AD}{k \cdot AB + k \cdot BC + k \cdot CD + k \cdot AD} = \frac{AB + BC + CD + AD}{k(AB + BC + CD + AD)} = \frac{1}{k} = \frac{AB}{EF}$. **47.** 11.2 in.

8.3 MIXED REVIEW (p. 479) **53.** 1 **55.** $-\frac{1}{7}$ **57.** $-\frac{7}{6}$ **59.** 49 **61.** 9 **63.** 38 **65.** $\frac{32}{13}$ **67.** 21

QUIZ 1 (p. 479) **1.** 10 **2.** 28 **3.** $\frac{24}{7}$ **4.** 21 **5.** $\sqrt{55} \approx 7.42$ **6.** $\sqrt{70} \approx 8.37$ **7.** 3; 1 : 2; $\frac{1}{2}$ **8.** 30; 3 : 2; $\frac{3}{2}$ **9.** None are exactly similar, but the 5 × 7 and wallet sizes are very nearly similar. $\left(\frac{5}{2.25} \approx 2.22, \frac{7}{3.25} \approx 2.15\right)$ **10.** $3\frac{1}{8}$ in.

8.4 PRACTICE (pp. 483–486) **5.** yes **7.** 10, 6 **9.** $\angle J$ and $\angle F$, $\angle K$ and $\angle G$, $\angle L$ and $\angle H$, $\frac{JK}{FG} = \frac{KL}{GH} = \frac{JL}{FH}$ **11.** $\angle L$ and $\angle Q$, $\angle M$ and $\angle P$, $\angle N$ and $\angle N$, $\frac{LM}{QP} = \frac{MN}{PN} = \frac{LN}{QN}$ **13.** *LM*; *MN*; *NL* **15.** 15; *x* **17.** 24 **19.** yes; $\triangle PQR \sim \triangle WPV$ **21.** yes; $\triangle XYZ \sim \triangle GFH$ **23.** yes; $\triangle JMN \sim \triangle JLK$ **25.** yes; $\triangle VWX \sim \triangle VYZ$ **27.** $-\frac{2}{5}$ **29.** (10, 0) **31.** (30, 0) **33.** *CDE* **35.** 15; *x* **37.** 20 **39.** 14 **41.** 27 **43.** 100 **45.** 12 **47.** 25

49.

Statements	Reasons
1. $\angle ECD$ and $\angle EAB$ are right ∠s.	1. Given
2. $\overline{AB} \perp \overline{AE}, \overline{CD} \perp \overline{AE}$	2. Def. of ⊥ lines
3. $\overline{AB} \parallel \overline{CD}$	3. In a plane, 2 lines ⊥ to the same line are ∥.
4. $\angle EDC \cong \angle B$	4. If 2 ∥ lines are cut by a transversal, corresp. ∠s are ≅.
5. $\triangle ABE \sim \triangle CDE$	5. AA Similarity Post.

51. False; all ∠s of any 2 equilateral △s are ≅, so the △s are ~ by the AA Similarity Post. (Note, also, that if one △ has sides of length *x* and the other has sides of length *y*, then the ratio of any two side lengths is $\frac{x}{y}$. Then, all corresp. side lengths are in proportion, so the def. of ~ △s can also be used to show that any 2 equilateral △s are ~.) **53.** 1.5 m **55.** $\overline{PQ} \perp \overline{QT}$ and $\overline{SR} \perp \overline{QT}$, so $\angle Q$ and $\angle SRT$ are right ∠s. Since all right ∠s are ≅, $\angle Q \cong \angle SRT$. $\overline{PR} \parallel \overline{ST}$ so corresp. ∠s *PRQ* and *STR* are ≅. Then, $\triangle PQR \sim \triangle SRT$ by the AA Similarity Post., so $\frac{PQ}{QR} = \frac{SR}{RT}$. That is, $\frac{PQ}{780} = \frac{4}{6.5}$ and $PQ = 480$ ft.

8.4 MIXED REVIEW (p. 487) **61.** $5\sqrt{82}$ **63.** 46 **65.** 12 **67.** 8 **69.** $\frac{36}{11}$ **71.** −16, 16

8.5 PRACTICE (pp. 492–494) **5.** $\frac{1}{6}$; yes; SSS Similarity Thm. **7.** $\triangle DEF \sim \triangle GHJ$; 2:5 **9.** yes; $\triangle JKL \sim \triangle XYZ$ (or $\triangle XZY$); SSS Similarity Thm. **11.** no **13.** yes; $\triangle PQR \sim \triangle DEF$; SSS or SAS Similarity Thm. **15.** SSS Similarity Thm. **17.** SAS Similarity Thm. **19.** 53° **21.** 82° **23.** 15 **25.** $4\sqrt{2}$ **27.** $\triangle ABC \sim \triangle BDC$; 18 **29.** 140 ft **31.** Locate G on $\overline{AB}$ so that $GB = DE$ and draw $\overline{GH}$ through $G \parallel$ to $\overline{AC}$. Corresp. $\angle$s A and BGH are $\cong$ as are corresp. $\angle$s C and BHG, so $\triangle ABC \sim \triangle GBH$. Then $\frac{AB}{GB} = \frac{AC}{GH}$. But $\frac{AB}{DE} = \frac{AC}{DF}$ and $GB = DE$, so $\frac{AC}{GH} = \frac{AC}{DF}$ and $GH = DF$. By the SAS Cong. Post., $\triangle BGH \cong \triangle EDF$. Corresp. $\angle$s F and BHG are $\cong$, so $\angle F \cong \angle C$ by the Transitive Prop. of Cong. $\triangle ABC \sim \triangle DEF$ by the AA Similarity Post. **33.** 18 ft **35.** Julia and the flagpole are both perpendicular to the ground and the two $\triangle$s formed (one by Julia's head, feet, and the tip of the shadow, and the other by the top and bottom of the flag pole and the tip of the shadow) have a shared angle. Then, the $\triangle$s are ~ by the AA Similarity Post.

8.5 MIXED REVIEW (p. 495) **39.** $m\angle ABD = m\angle DBC = 38.5°$ **41.** $m\angle ABD = 64°$, $m\angle ABC = 128°$ **43.** $\angle 10$ **45.** $\angle 5$ **47.** (2, 7) **49.** (–5, 1)

QUIZ 2 (p. 496) **1.** yes; $m\angle B = m\angle E = 81°$, $m\angle ANB = 46°$, $m\angle A = 53°$ **2.** yes; $m\angle VSU = m\angle P = 47°$, $m\angle U = 101°$, $m\angle V = 32°$ **3.** no; $m\angle J = m\angle H = 42°$, $m\angle A = 43°$, $m\angle P = 94°$ **4.** no **5.** yes **6.** yes **7.** 10 mi

8.6 PRACTICE (pp. 502–505) **7.** CE **9.** GE
11. Yes; $\overline{QS}$ divides two sides of $\triangle PRT$ proportionally.
13. No; $\overline{QS}$ does not divide $\overline{TR}$ and $\overline{PR}$ proportionally.
15. Yes; $\triangle$ Proportionality Converse.
17. yes; Corresponding Angles Converse
19. no **21.** 3 **23.** 6 **25.** 14 **27.** 29.4
29. A: 47.8 m, B: 40.2 m, C: 34.0 m
31.

Statements	Reasons
1. $\overline{DE} \parallel \overline{AC}$	1. Given
2. $\angle BDE \cong \angle A$, $\angle BED \cong \angle C$	2. If 2 $\parallel$ lines are cut by a transversal, corresp. $\angle$s are $\cong$.
3. $\triangle DBE \sim \triangle ABC$	3. AA Similarity Post.
4. $\frac{BA}{BD} = \frac{BC}{BE}$	4. Def. of ~ $\triangle$s
5. $\frac{BD + DA}{BD} = \frac{BE + EC}{BE}$	5. Segment Addition Post.
6. $\frac{BD}{BD} + \frac{DA}{BD} = \frac{BE}{BE} + \frac{EC}{BE}$	6. Addition of fractions
7. $1 + \frac{DA}{BD} = 1 + \frac{EC}{BE}$	7. Inverse prop. of multiplication
8. $\frac{DA}{BD} = \frac{EC}{BE}$	8. Subtraction prop. of equality

33. Draw a $\parallel$ to $\overline{XW}$ through Z ($\parallel$ Post.) and extend $\overline{XY}$ to intersect the $\parallel$ at A. ($\overline{XY}$ is not $\parallel$ to $\overline{AZ}$ because it would also have to be $\parallel$ to $\overline{XW}$.) Then, $\frac{YW}{WZ} = \frac{XY}{XA}$. Also, corresp. $\angle$s YXW and A are $\cong$, as are alternate interior $\angle$s WXZ and AZX. Since $\angle YXW \cong \angle WXZ$, $\angle A \cong \angle AZX$ by the Transitive Prop. of Cong. By the Converse of the Base Angles Thm., $\overline{XA} \cong \overline{XZ}$ or $XA = XZ$. Then, by the substitution prop. of equality, $\frac{YW}{WZ} = \frac{XY}{XZ}$. **35.** $MT = 8.4$, $LN = 8$, $SN = 8$, $PR = 27$, $UR = 21$ **37.** about 1040 ft

8.6 MIXED REVIEW (p. 505) **41.** $\sqrt{337}$ **43.** $7\sqrt{2}$ **45.** $\sqrt{305}$ **47.** 15 units **49.** $6\sqrt{2}$ units **51.** reflection **53.** rotation

8.7 PRACTICE (pp. 509–512) **5.** larger; enlargement **7.** Yes; *Sample answer:* a preimage and its image after a dilation are ~. **9.** Enlargement; the dilation has center C and scale factor $\frac{8}{3}$. **11.** Reduction; the dilation has center C and scale factor $\frac{2}{5}$; $x = y = 20$, $z = 25$. **13.** $P'(6, 10)$, $Q'(8, 0)$, $R'(2, 2)$ **15.** $S'(-20, 8)$, $T'(-12, 16)$, $U'(-4, 4)$, $V'(-12, -4)$ **21.** $x = 7.2$, $y = 6.3$; 3 : 4 **23.** enlargement; $k = 4$; 9, 28 **25.** about 9.2 cm **27.** 7 : 1 **29.** 4.8 in. **31.** 1.7 in.

8.7 MIXED REVIEW (p. 513) **39.** $b = 14$ **41.** $a = 7$ **43.** Yes; *Sample answer:* $\angle C \cong \angle L$ and $\frac{CA}{LJ} = \frac{CB}{LK}$, so the $\triangle$s are ~ by the SAS Similarity Thm.

QUIZ 3 (p. 513) **1.** BD **2.** CE **3.** AF **4.** FA **5.** The dilation is an enlargement with center C and scale factor 2. **6.** The dilation is a reduction with center C and scale factor $\frac{1}{3}$. **7.** reduction, larger **8.** $\frac{9}{4}$

CHAPTER 8 REVIEW (pp. 516–518) **1.** $\frac{21}{2}$ **3.** 4 **5.** 39 in. **7.** $\frac{5}{3}$ **9.** $\frac{3}{5}$ **11.** no **13.** no **15.** 22 **17.** $16\frac{16}{59}$

ALGEBRA REVIEW (pp. 522–523) **1.** 11 **2.** $2\sqrt{13}$ **3.** $3\sqrt{5}$ **4.** $6\sqrt{2}$ **5.** $2\sqrt{10}$ **6.** $3\sqrt{3}$ **7.** $4\sqrt{5}$ **8.** $5\sqrt{2}$ **9.** $9\sqrt{3}$ **10.** $12\sqrt{2}$ **11.** $8\sqrt{5}$ **12.** 15 **13.** $6\sqrt{3}$ **14.** $2\sqrt{2}$ **15.** $8 - 2\sqrt{7}$ **16.** $4\sqrt{11}$ **17.** $\sqrt{5}$ **18.** $21\sqrt{2}$ **19.** $-16\sqrt{3}$ **20.** $5\sqrt{7}$ **21.** $4\sqrt{5}$ **22.** $13\sqrt{2}$ **23.** $21\sqrt{10}$ **24.** 330 **25.** 24 **26.** 36 **27.** $6\sqrt{14}$ **28.** 8 **29.** 112 **30.** 40 **31.** 180 **32.** 32 **33.** 192 **34.** 12 **35.** 125 **36.** 1100 **37.** $\frac{4\sqrt{3}}{3}$ **38.** $\frac{5\sqrt{7}}{7}$ **39.** $\sqrt{2}$ **40.** $\frac{2\sqrt{15}}{5}$ **41.** 1 **42.** $\sqrt{2}$ **43.** $\frac{4\sqrt{6}}{3}$ **44.** $\frac{\sqrt{2}}{2}$ **45.** $\frac{2\sqrt{3}}{3}$ **46.** $\frac{3}{2}$ **47.** $\frac{9\sqrt{13}}{26}$ **48.** $\frac{\sqrt{2}}{2}$ **49.** $\frac{3\sqrt{5}}{5}$ **50.** $\frac{4\sqrt{10}}{5}$ **51.** $\frac{\sqrt{15}}{5}$ **52.** $\frac{\sqrt{6}}{3}$ **53.** ±3 **54.** ±25 **55.** ±17 **56.** $\pm\sqrt{10}$ **57.** ±4 **58.** $\pm\sqrt{13}$ **59.** ±6 **60.** ±8 **61.** ±7 **62.** $\pm\sqrt{10}$ **63.** ±3 **64.** $\pm\sqrt{5}$ **65.** ±2 **66.** $\pm\sqrt{2}$ **67.** ±1 **68.** $\pm\sqrt{7}$ **69.** $\pm\sqrt{6}$ **70.** ±5 **71.** ±4 **72.** ±24 **73.** ±13

SA23

CHAPTER 9

SKILL REVIEW (p. 526) **1.** 90°; right
2. *Sample answer:*

J, hypotenuse, leg, altitude, altitude, K, leg, altitude, L

3. *Sample answer:*

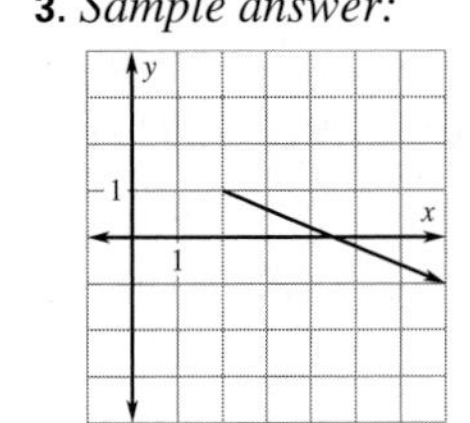

4. 4.5

5.

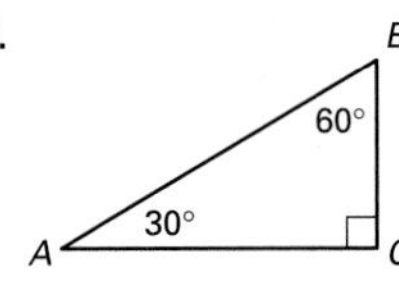

Sample answer: $m\angle A = 30°$ and $m\angle B = 60°$, so $\triangle ABC \sim \triangle JKL$ by the AA Similarity Post.

9.1 PRACTICE (pp. 531–534) **5.** JK **7.** KM **9.** LK

11. Q, S, R; Q, T, S; S, T, R

13. 20; $33\frac{1}{3}$ **15.** 3; $\sqrt{15}$

17. $\triangle QRS \sim \triangle QST \sim \triangle SRT$; RQ **19.** $\triangle ABC \sim \triangle ACD \sim \triangle CBD$; 9 **21.** $\triangle JKL \sim \triangle JLM \sim \triangle LKM$; $\frac{1024}{15} \approx 68.3$ **23.** $\triangle ABC \sim \triangle ACD \sim \triangle CBD$; 4 **25.** $3\sqrt{3}$ **27.** $10\frac{4}{7}$ **29.** $x = 42\frac{2}{3}$, $y = 40$, $z = 53\frac{1}{3}$ **31.** about 76 cm; $\triangle ABC$ and $\triangle ADC$ are congruent right triangles by the SSS Congruence Post., so $\overline{AC}$ is a perpendicular bisector of $\overline{BD}$. By Geometric Mean Theorem 9.3, the altitude from D to hypotenuse $\overline{AC}$ divides $\overline{AC}$ into segments of lengths 23.67 cm and 61.13 cm. By Geometric Mean Theorem 9.2, the length of the altitude to the hypotenuse of each right triangle is about 38 cm long, so the crossbar $\overline{BD}$ should be about $2 \cdot 38$, or 76 cm long. **33.** $\triangle ABC \sim \triangle ACD \sim \triangle CBD$; area of $\triangle ABC = \frac{1}{2}(2)(1.5) = 1.5\text{ m}^2$; $AD = 1.6$ and $DC = 1.2$, so the area of $\triangle ACD = \frac{1}{2}(1.6)(1.2) = 0.96\text{ m}^2$, and the area of $\triangle CBD = 1.5 - 0.96 = 0.54\text{ m}^2$. **35.** From Ex. 34, $\triangle CBD \sim \triangle ACD$. Corresponding side lengths are in proportion, so $\frac{BD}{CD} = \frac{CD}{AD}$.
37. The values of the ratios will vary, but will not be equal. The theorem says that these ratios are equal.
39. The ratios are equal when the triangle is a right triangle but are not equal when the triangle is not a right triangle.

9.1 MIXED REVIEW (p. 534) **45.** 8, –8 **47.** If the measure of one of the angles of a triangle is greater that 90°, then the triangle is obtuse; true. **49.** 36 in.^{2} **51.** 62.5 m^2

9.2 PRACTICE (pp. 538–541) **3.** $\sqrt{5}$; no **5.** $4\sqrt{3}$; no **7.** 97; yes **9.** 80; yes **11.** $4\sqrt{2}$; no **13.** $8\sqrt{3}$; no **15.** $14\sqrt{2}$; no **17.** $2\sqrt{13}$ **19.** $t = 20$ **21.** $s = 24$ **23.** $s = 12$ **25.** 35.7 cm^2 **27.** 25.2 cm^2 **29.** 104 cm^2 **31.** about 41.9 ft; the distance from home plate to second base is about 91.9 ft, so the distance from the pitcher's plate to second base is about 91.9 – 50, or about 41.9 ft. **33.** 94 in., or 7 ft 10 in. **35.** 48 in. **37.** The area of the large square is $(a + b)^2$. Also, the area of the large square is the sum of the areas of the four congruent right triangles plus the area of the small square, or $4\left(\frac{1}{2} \cdot a \cdot b\right) + c^2$. Thus, $(a + b)^2 = 4\left(\frac{1}{2} \cdot a \cdot b\right) + c^2$, and so $a^2 + 2ab + b^2 = 2ab + c^2$. Subtracting $2ab$ from each side gives $a^2 + b^2 = c^2$.

9.2 MIXED REVIEW (p. 541) **43.** 9 **45.** 8 **47.** –1225 **49.** 147 **51.** no **53.** no **55.** *Sample answer:* slope of $\overline{PQ} = -\frac{11}{2}$ = slope of $\overline{RS}$; slope of $\overline{QR} = \frac{5}{4}$ = slope of $\overline{PS}$. Both pairs of opposite sides are parallel, so $PQRS$ is a ▱ by the definition of a ▱.

9.3 PRACTICE (pp. 545–548) **3.** C **5.** D **7.** The crossbars are not perpendicular: $45^2 > 22^2 + 38^2$, so the smaller triangles formed by the crossbars are obtuse. **9.** yes **11.** yes **13.** no **15.** yes; right **17.** no **19.** yes; right **21.** yes; acute **23.** yes; right **25.** yes; obtuse **27.** Square; the diagonals bisect each other, so the quad. is a ▱; the diagonals are ≅, so the ▱ is a rectangle. $1^2 + 1^2 = \left(\sqrt{2}\right)^2$, so the diagonals intersect at rt. ▵ to form ⊥ lines; thus, the ▱ is also a rhombus. A quad. that is both a rectangle and a rhombus must be a square. **29.** $\frac{3}{4}$; $-\frac{4}{3}$; since $\left(\frac{3}{4}\right)\left(-\frac{4}{3}\right) = -1$, $\overline{AC} \perp \overline{BC}$, so $\angle ACB$ is a rt. ∠. Therefore, $\triangle ABC$ is a rt. △ by the definition of rt. △. **31.** *Sample answer:* I prefer to use slopes, because I have two computations rather than three, and computing slopes doesn't involve square roots. **33.** acute **35.** Since $\left(\sqrt{10}\right)^2 + 2^2 < 4^2$, $\triangle ABC$ is obtuse and $\angle C$ is obtuse. By the Triangle Sum Thm., $m\angle A + m\angle ABC + m\angle C = 180°$. $\angle C$ is obtuse, so $m\angle C > 90°$. It follows that $m\angle ABC < 90°$. Vertical angles are ≅, so $m\angle ABC = m\angle 1$. By substitution, $m\angle 1 < 90°$. By the definition of an acute ∠, ∠1 is acute. **37.** A, C, and D **39.** $120^2 + 119^2 = 169^2$, $4800^2 + 4601^2 = 6649^2$, and $(13{,}500)^2 + (12{,}709)^2 = (18{,}541)^2$.
41. Reasons

1. Pythagorean Thm.
2. Given
3. Substitution prop. of equality
5. Converse of the Hinge Thm.
6. Given, def. of right angle, def. of acute angle, and substitution prop. of equality
7. Def. of acute triangle ($\angle C$ is the largest angle of $\triangle ABC$.)

SELECTED ANSWERS

43. Draw rt. $\triangle PQR$ with side lengths a, b, and hypotenuse x. $x^2 = a^2 + b^2$ by the Pythagorean Thm. It is given that $c^2 = a^2 + b^2$, so by the substitution prop. of equality, $x^2 = c^2$. By a prop. of square roots, $x = c$. $\triangle PQR \cong \triangle LMN$ by the SSS Congruence Post. Corresp. parts of $\cong$ △ are $\cong$, so $m\angle R = 90° = m\angle N$. By def., $\angle N$ is a rt. $\angle$, and so $\triangle LNM$ is a right triangle.

9.3 MIXED REVIEW (p. 549) **47.** $2\sqrt{11}$ **49.** $2\sqrt{21}$ **51.** $\frac{3\sqrt{11}}{11}$ **53.** $2\sqrt{2}$ **55.** an enlargement with center C and scale factor $\frac{7}{4}$ **57.** $x = 9$, $y = 11$

QUIZ 1 (p. 549) **1.** $\triangle ABC \sim \triangle ADB \sim \triangle BDC$ **2.** $\overline{BD}$ **3.** 25 **4.** 12 **5.** $2\sqrt{10}$ **6.** $6\sqrt{5}$ **7.** $12\sqrt{2}$ **8.** no; $219^2 \neq 168^2 + 140^2$

9.4 PRACTICE (pp. 554–556) **9.** $4\sqrt{2}$ **11.** $h = k = \frac{9\sqrt{2}}{2}$ **13.** $a = 12\sqrt{3}$, $b = 24$ **15.** $c = d = 4\sqrt{2}$ **17.** $q = 16\sqrt{2}$, $r = 16$ **19.** $f = \frac{8\sqrt{3}}{3}$, $h = \frac{16\sqrt{3}}{3}$ **21.** 4.3 cm **23.** 18.4 in. **25.** 31.2 ft^2 **27.** $24\sqrt{3} \approx 41.6\ \text{ft}^2$ **29.** about 2 cm **31.** $r = \sqrt{2}$; $s = \sqrt{3}$; $t = 2$; $u = \sqrt{5}$; $v = \sqrt{6}$; $w = \sqrt{7}$; I used the Pythagorean Theorem in each right triangle in turn, working from left to right. **33.** the right triangle with legs of lengths 1 and $s = \sqrt{3}$, and hypotenuse $t = 2$ **35.** Let $DF = x$. Then $EF = x$. By the Pythagorean Theorem, $x^2 + x^2 = (DE)^2$; $2x^2 = (DE)^2$; $DE = \sqrt{2x^2} = \sqrt{2} \cdot x$ by a property of square roots. Thus, the hypotenuse is $\sqrt{2}$ times as long as a leg.

9.4 MIXED REVIEW (p. 557) **43.** $Q'(-1, 2)$ **45.** $A'(-4, -5)$ **47.** AA Similarity Post. **49.** SSS Similarity Thm.

9.5 PRACTICE (pp. 562–565) **3.** $\frac{4}{5} = 0.8$ **5.** $\frac{4}{3} \approx 1.3333$ **7.** $\frac{4}{5} = 0.8$ **9.** about 17 ft **11.** $\sin A = 0.8$; $\cos A = 0.6$; $\tan A \approx 1.3333$; $\sin B = 0.6$; $\cos B = 0.8$; $\tan B = 0.75$ **13.** $\sin D = 0.28$; $\cos D = 0.96$; $\tan D \approx 0.2917$; $\sin F = 0.96$; $\cos F = 0.28$; $\tan F \approx 3.4286$ **15.** $\sin J = 0.8575$; $\cos J = 0.5145$; $\tan J = 1.6667$; $\sin K = 0.5145$; $\cos K = 0.8575$; $\tan K = 0.6$ **17.** 0.9744 **19.** 0.4540 **21.** 0.0349 **23.** 0.8090 **25.** 0.4540 **27.** 2.2460 **29.** $s \approx 31.3$; $t \approx 13.3$ **31.** $t \approx 7.3$; $u \approx 3.4$ **33.** $x \approx 16.0$; $y \approx 14.9$ **35.** 41.6 m^2 **37.** about 13.4 m **39.** 482 ft; about 1409 ft **41.** about 16.4 in. **45.** Procedures may vary. One method is to reason that since the tangent ratio is equal to the ratio of the lengths of the legs, the tangent is equal to 1 when the legs are equal in length, that is, when the triangle is a 45°-45°-90° triangle. Tan $A > 1$ when $m\angle A > 45°$, and tan $A < 1$ when $m\angle A < 45°$, since increasing the measure of $\angle A$ increases the length of the opposite leg and decreasing the measure of $\angle A$ decreases the length of the opposite leg.

47. Reasons

1. Given
2. Pythagorean Thm.
3. Division prop. of equality
5. Substitution prop. of equality

49. $(\sin 45°)^2 + (\cos 45°)^2 = \left(\frac{\sqrt{2}}{2}\right)^2 + \left(\frac{\sqrt{2}}{2}\right)^2 = \frac{2}{4} + \frac{2}{4} = 1$ ✓

51. $(\sin 13°)^2 + (\cos 13°)^2 \approx (0.2250)^2 + (0.9744)^2 \approx 1$ ✓

9.5 MIXED REVIEW (p. 566) **57.** $\triangle MNP \sim \triangle MQN \sim \triangle NQP$; $QP \approx 3.3$; $NP \approx 7.8$ **59.** $5\sqrt{69}$; no

QUIZ 2 (p. 566) **1.** 3.5 m **2.** 5.7 in. **3.** 3.9 in.^2 **4.** $x \approx 15.6$; $y \approx 11.9$ **5.** $x \approx 8.5$; $y \approx 15.9$ **6.** $x \approx 9.3$; $y \approx 22.1$ **7.** about 4887 ft

9.6 PRACTICE (pp. 570–572) **5.** 79.5° **7.** 84.3° **9.** $d = 60$, $m\angle D = 33.4°$, $m\angle E = 56.6°$ **11.** 73 **13.** 41.1° **15.** 45° **17.** 20.5° **19.** 50.2° **21.** 6.3° **23.** side lengths: 7, 7, and 9.9; angle measures: 90°, 45°, and 45° **25.** side lengths: 4.5, 8, and 9.2; angle measures: 90°, 29.6°, and 60.4° **27.** side lengths: 6, 11.0, and 12.5; angle measures: 90°, 28.7°, and 61.3° **29.** $s = 4.1$, $t = 11.3$, $m\angle T = 70°$ **31.** $a = 7.4$, $c = 8.9$, $m\angle B = 34°$ **33.** $\ell = 5.9$, $m = 7.2$, $m\angle L = 56°$ **35.** 62.4° **37.** 0.4626 **39.** about 239.4 in., or about 19 ft 11 in.; about 4.1°

9.6 MIXED REVIEW (p. 572) **47.** $\langle 3, 2\rangle$ **49.** $\langle -1, -3\rangle$ **51.** $\langle 1, -2\rangle$ **53.** 25 **55.** 12.6 **57.** 14 **59.** no **61.** yes; right **63.** yes; right

9.7 PRACTICE (pp. 576–579) **5.** $\langle 4, 5\rangle$; 6.4 **7.** $\langle 2, -5\rangle$; 5.4 **9.** $\langle 0, 3\rangle$ **11.** $\langle -3, 6\rangle$; 6.7 **13.** $\langle 2, 7\rangle$; 7.3 **15.** $\langle 10, 4\rangle$; 10.8 **17.** $\langle -6, -4\rangle$; 7.2 **19.** $\langle 1, -4\rangle$; 4.1 **21.** about 61 mi/h; about 9° north of east **23.** about 57 mi/h; 45° north of west **25.** $\overrightarrow{EF}$, $\overrightarrow{CD}$, and $\overrightarrow{AB}$ **27.** $\overrightarrow{EF}$ and $\overrightarrow{CD}$ **29.** yes; no **31.** $\vec{u} = \langle 4, 1\rangle$; $\vec{v} = \langle 2, 4\rangle$; $\vec{u} + \vec{v} = \langle 6, 5\rangle$ **33.** $\vec{u} = \langle 2, -4\rangle$; $\vec{v} = \langle 3, 6\rangle$; $\vec{u} + \vec{v} = \langle 5, 2\rangle$ **35.** $\langle 4, 11\rangle$ **37.** $\langle 10, 10\rangle$ **39.** $\langle 4, -4\rangle$ **41.** $\vec{u} = \langle 0, -120\rangle$; $\vec{v} = \langle 40, 0\rangle$ **43.** about 126 mi/h; the speed at which the skydiver is falling, taking into account the breeze

45. 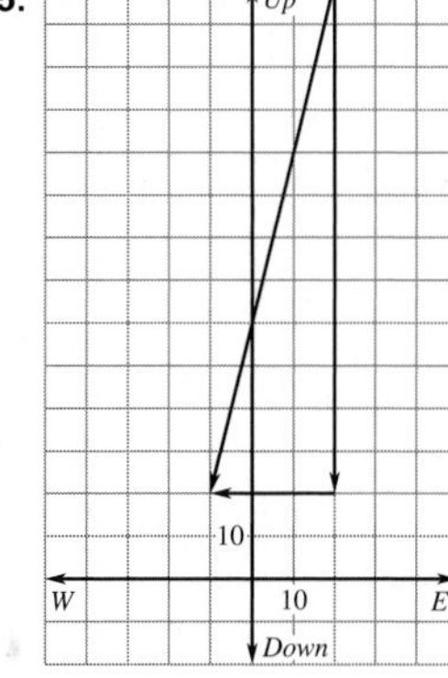

; The new velocity is $s = \langle -30, -120\rangle$.

47. When $k > 0$, the magnitude of $\vec{v}$ is k times the magnitude of $\vec{u}$ and the directions are the same. When $k < 0$, the magnitude of $\vec{v}$ is $|k|$ times the magnitude of $\vec{u}$ and the direction of $\vec{v}$ is opposite the direction of $\vec{u}$. Justifications may vary.

SELECTED ANSWERS

SA25

9.7 MIXED REVIEW (p. 580) **53.** Since $\angle D$ and $\angle E$ are rt. ⦣ and all rt. ⦣ are ≅, $\angle D \cong \angle E$. Since $\triangle ABC$ is equilateral, $\overline{AB} \cong \overline{BC}$. $\overline{DE} \parallel \overline{AC}$, so $\angle DBA \cong \angle BAC$ and $\angle EBC \cong \angle BCA$ by the Alternate Interior Angles Thm. An equilateral triangle is also equiangular, so $m\angle BAC = m\angle BCA = 60°$. By the def. of ≅ ⦣ and the substitution prop. of equality, $\angle DBA \cong \angle EBC$. $\triangle ADB \cong \triangle CEB$ by the AAS Congruence Thm. Corresponding parts of ≅ ⧍ are ≅, so $\overline{DB} \cong \overline{EB}$. By the def. of midpoint, B is the midpoint of $\overline{DE}$. **55.** $x = 120, y = 30$ **57.** $x^2 + 2x + 1$ **59.** $x^2 + 22x + 121$

QUIZ 3 (p. 580) **1.** $a = 41.7, b = 19.4, m\angle A = 65°$ **2.** $y = 12, z = 17.0, m\angle Y = 45°$ **3.** $m = 13.4, q = 20.9, m\angle N = 50°$ **4.** $p = 7.7, q = 2.1, m\angle Q = 15°$ **5.** $f = 4.7, m\angle F = 37.9°, m\angle G = 52.1°$ **6.** $\ell = 12.0, m\angle K = 14.0°, m\angle L = 76.0°$ **7.** $\langle -5, -1\rangle$; 5.1 **8.** $\langle 6, -5\rangle$; 7.8 **9.** $\langle 3, 5\rangle$; 5.8 **10.** $\langle -7, -11\rangle$; 13.0 **11.**

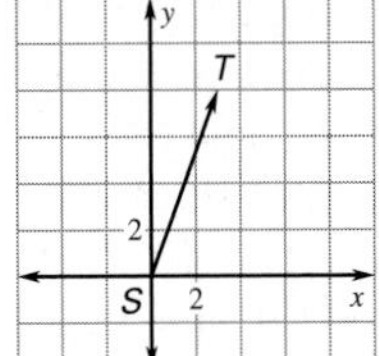

; about 69° north of east **12.** $\langle 4, 2\rangle$ **13.** $\langle 2, 4\rangle$ **14.** $\langle -2, -8\rangle$ **15.** $\langle 2, 1\rangle$ **16.** $\langle 6, 13\rangle$ **17.** $\langle 0, 3\rangle$

CHAPTER 9 REVIEW (pp. 582–584) **1.** $x = 4, y = 3\sqrt{5}$ **3.** $x = 48, y = 21, z = 9\sqrt{7}$ **5.** $s = 4\sqrt{5}$; no **7.** $t = 2\sqrt{13}$; no **9.** yes; right **11.** yes; acute **13.** $12\sqrt{2} \approx 17.0$ in.; 18 in.^{2} **15.** $9\sqrt{3}$ cm; $81\sqrt{3} \approx 140.3$ cm^2 **17.** $\sin P \approx 0.9459$; $\cos P \approx 0.3243$; $\tan P \approx 2.9167$; $\sin N \approx 0.3243$; $\cos N \approx 0.9459$; $\tan N \approx 0.3429$ **19.** $x = 8.9, m\angle X = 48.2°, m\angle Z = 41.8°$ **21.** $s = 17, m\angle R = 28.1°, m\angle T = 61.9°$ **23.** $\langle 12, -5\rangle$; 13 **25.** $\langle 14, 9\rangle$; about 16.6; about 32.7° north of east

CUMULATIVE PRACTICE (pp. 588–589) **1.** No; if two planes intersect, then their intersection is a line. The three points must be collinear, so they cannot be the vertices of a triangle. **3.** never **5.** Paragraph proof: $\overline{BD}$ is the median from point B, $\overline{AD} \cong \overline{CD}$, $\overline{BD} \cong \overline{BD}$, and it is given that $\overline{AB} \cong \overline{CB}$. Thus, $\triangle ABD \cong \triangle CBD$ by the SSS Congruence Post. Also, $\angle ABD \cong \angle CBD$ since corresponding parts of ≅ ⧍ are ≅. By the def. of an angle bisector, $\overrightarrow{BD}$ bisects $\angle ABC$. **7.** yes; clockwise and counterclockwise rotational symmetry of 120° **9.** $x = 24, y = 113$ **11.** $y = \frac{3}{4}x + \frac{7}{2}$ **13.** $A'(-1, -2), B'(3, -5), C'(5, 6)$ **15.** $A'(-3, 6), B'(-7, 9), C'(-9, -2)$ **17.** $3\frac{3}{7}$ **19.** No; in $ABCD$, the ratio of the length to width is 8 : 6, or 4 : 3. In $APQD$, the ratio of the length to width is 6 : 4, or 3 : 2. Since these ratios are not equal, the rectangles are not similar. **21.** Yes; the ratios $\frac{6}{9}, \frac{8}{12}$, and $\frac{12}{18}$ all equal $\frac{2}{3}$, so the triangles are similar by the SSS Similarity Theorem. **23.** The image with scale factor $\frac{1}{3}$ has endpoints $\left(2, -\frac{4}{3}\right)$ and (4, 3); its slope is $\frac{\frac{13}{3}}{2} = \frac{13}{6}$. The image with scale factor $\frac{1}{2}$ has endpoints (3, −2) and (6, 4.5); its slope is $\frac{13}{6}$. The two image segments are parallel. **25.** 4 **27.** acute **29.** Let $\angle A$ be the smaller acute angle; $\sin A = \frac{8}{17}$, $\cos A = \frac{15}{17}$, and $\tan A = \frac{8}{15}$. **31.** $\langle 2, 16\rangle$; about 16.1; about 83° north of east **33.** 20 gal **35.** 189.4 mi

CHAPTER 10

SKILL REVIEW (p. 594) **1.** $2\frac{1}{2}$ **2.** 48 **3.** 23.4 **4.** $-\sqrt{6}, \sqrt{6}$ **5.** −16, 4 **6.** (8, 10) **7.** $JL = \sqrt{145}, m\angle J \approx 48.4°, m\angle L \approx 41.6°$ **8. a.** 15 **b.** $\left(3, -4\frac{1}{2}\right)$ **c.** $y = -\frac{3}{4}x - \frac{9}{4}$ **d.** the segment with endpoints $A'(-7, 0)$ and $B'(5, -9)$

10.1 PRACTICE (pp. 599–602) **5.** No; $5^2 + 5^2 \neq 7^2$, so by the the Converse of the Pythagorean Thm., $\triangle ABD$ is not a right △, so $\overline{BD}$ is not ⊥ to $\overline{AB}$. If $\overleftrightarrow{BD}$ were tangent to ⊙C, $\angle B$ would be a right angle. Thus, $\overleftrightarrow{BD}$ is not tangent to ⊙C. **7.** 2 **9.** 7.5 cm **11.** 1.5 ft **13.** 52 in. **15.** 17.4 in. **17.** C and G; the diameter of ⊙G is 45, so the radius is $\frac{45}{2} = 22.5$, which is the radius of ⊙C. **19.** E **21.** D **23.** C **25.** G **27.** internal **29.** 2 internal, 2 external;

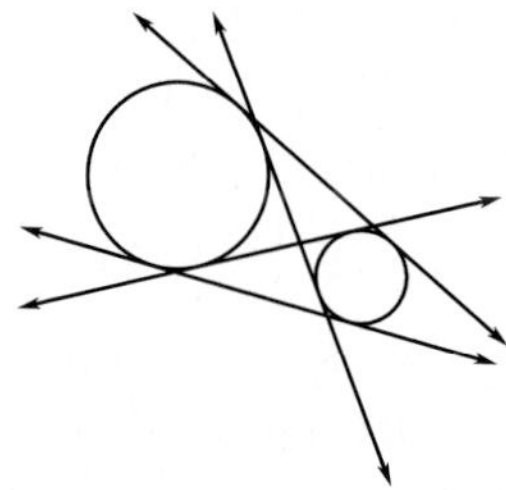

31. 2 external;

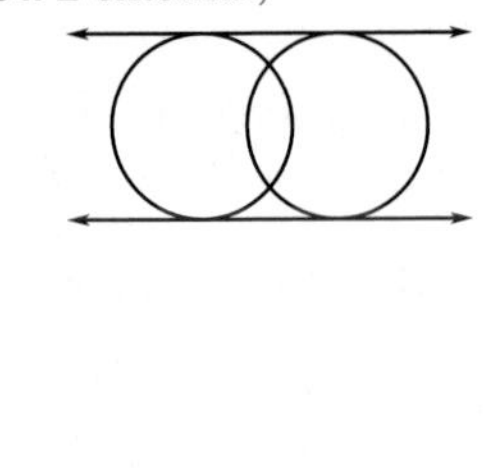

33. (6, 2), 2 **35.** the lines with equations $y = 0$, $y = 4$, and $x = 4$ **37.** No; $5^2 + 15^2 \neq 17^2$, so by the Converse of the Pythagorean Thm., $\triangle ABC$ is not a right △, so $\overline{AB}$ is not ⊥ to $\overline{AC}$. Then, $\overleftrightarrow{AB}$ is not tangent to ⊙C. **39.** Yes; $BD = 10 + 10 = 20$ and $20^2 + 21^2 = 29^2$, so by the Converse of the Pythagorean Thm., $\triangle ABD$ is a right △, and $\overline{AB} \perp \overline{BD}$. Then, $\overleftrightarrow{AB}$ is tangent to ⊙C. **41.** 53 ft **43.** any two of $\overline{GD}$, $\overline{HC}$, $\overline{FA}$, and $\overline{EB}$ **45.** $\overleftrightarrow{JK}$ **47.** −1, 1 **49.** $\overleftrightarrow{PS}$ is tangent to ⊙X at P, $\overleftrightarrow{PS}$ is tangent to ⊙Y at S, $\overleftrightarrow{RT}$ is tangent to ⊙X at T, and $\overleftrightarrow{RT}$ is tangent to ⊙Y at R. Then, $\overline{PQ} \cong \overline{TQ}$ and $\overline{QS} \cong \overline{QR}$. (2 tangent segments with the same ext. endpoint are ≅.) By the def. of cong., $PQ = TQ$ and $QS = QR$, so $PQ + QS = TQ + QR$ by the addition prop. of equality. Then, by the Segment Addition Post. and the Substitution Prop., $PS = RT$ or $\overline{PS} \cong \overline{RT}$. **51.** $QR < QP$

SA26

53. *Sample answer:* Assume that ℓ is not tangent to P, that is, there is another point X on ℓ that is also on $\odot Q$. X is on $\odot Q$, so $QX = QP$. But the $\perp$ segment from Q to ℓ is the shortest such segment, so $QX > QP$. QX cannot be both equal to and greater than QP. The assumption that such a point X exists must be false. Then, ℓ is tangent to P.
55. Square; $\overline{BD}$ and $\overline{AD}$ are tangent to $\odot C$ at A and B, respectively, so $\angle A$ and $\angle B$ are right $\angle$s. Then, by the Interior Angles of a Quadrilateral Thm., $\angle D$ is also a right $\angle$. Then, $CABD$ is a rectangle. Opp. sides of a $\square$ are $\cong$, so $\overline{CA} \cong \overline{BD}$ and $\overline{AD} \cong \overline{CB}$. But $\overline{CA}$ and $\overline{CB}$ are radii, so $\overline{CA} \cong \overline{CB}$ and by the Transitive Prop. of Cong., all 4 sides of $CABD$ are $\cong$. $CABD$ is both a rectangle and a rhombus, so it is a square by the Square Corollary.

10.1 MIXED REVIEW (p. 602) **59.** *Sample answer:* Since slope of $\overline{PS} = \frac{3}{8}$ = slope of $\overline{QR}$, $\overline{PS} \parallel \overline{QR}$. Since slope of $\overline{PQ} = -3$ = slope of $\overline{SR}$, $\overline{PQ} \parallel \overline{SR}$. Then, $PQRS$ is a $\square$ by def. **61.** $6\frac{3}{5}$ **63.** 28 **65.** $2\frac{2}{5}$ **67.** 9 **69.** $m\angle A \approx 23.2°$, $m\angle C \approx 66.8°$, $AC \approx 15.2$ **71.** $BC \approx 11.5$, $m\angle A \approx 55.2°$, $m\angle B \approx 34.8°$

10.2 PRACTICE (pp. 607–611) **3.** 60° **5.** 180° **7.** 220°
9. $\overline{BC}$ is a diameter; a chord that is the $\perp$ bisector of another chord is a diameter. **11.** $\widehat{AC} \cong \widehat{BC}$ and $\widehat{AD} \cong \widehat{BD}$; a diameter $\perp$ to a chord bisects the chord and its arc.
13. minor arc **15.** minor arc **17.** semicircle **19.** major arc **21.** 55° **23.** 305° **25.** 180° **27.** 65° **29.** 65° **31.** 120° **33.** 145° **35.** $\widehat{AC} \cong \widehat{KL}$ and $\widehat{ABC} \cong \widehat{KML}$; $\odot D$ and $\odot N$ are $\cong$ (both have radius 4). By the Arc Add. Post., $m\widehat{AC} = m\widehat{AE} + m\widehat{EC} = 70° + 75° = 145°$. $m\widehat{KL} = 145°$ and since $\odot D \cong \odot N$, $\widehat{AC} \cong \widehat{KL}$; $m\widehat{ABC} = 360° - m\widehat{AC} = 360° - 145° = 215°$. $m\widehat{KML} = m\widehat{KM} + m\widehat{ML} = 130° + 85° = 215°$ by the Arc Add. Post. Since $\odot D \cong \odot N$, $\widehat{ABC} \cong \widehat{KML}$. **37.** 36; 144° **39.** $\widehat{AB} \cong \widehat{CB}$; 2 arcs are $\cong$ if and only if their corresp. chords are $\cong$. **41.** $\overline{AB} \cong \overline{AC}$; in a $\odot$, 2 chords are $\cong$ if and only if they are equidistant from the center. **43.** 40°; a diameter that is $\perp$ to a chord bisects the chord and its arc. **45.** 15; in a $\odot$, 2 chords are $\cong$ if and only if they are equidistant from the center. **47.** 40°; Vertical Angles Thm., def. of minor arc **49.** 15° **51.** 3:00 A.M. **53.** This follows from the definition of the measure of a minor arc. (The measure of a minor arc is the measure of its central $\angle$.) If 2 minor arcs in the same $\odot$ or $\cong$ $\odot$s are $\cong$, then their central $\angle$s are $\cong$. Conversely, if 2 central $\angle$s of the same $\odot$ or $\cong$ $\odot$s are $\cong$, then the measures of the associated arcs are $\cong$. **55.** Yes; construct the $\perp$s from the center of the $\odot$ to each chord. Use a compass to compare the lengths of the segments. **57.** Since $\widehat{AB} \cong \widehat{DC}$, $\angle APB \cong \angle CPD$ by the def. of $\cong$ arcs. $\overline{PA}$, $\overline{PB}$, $\overline{PC}$, and $\overline{PD}$ are all radii of $\odot P$, so $\overline{PA} \cong \overline{PB} \cong \overline{PC} \cong \overline{PD}$. Then $\triangle APB \cong \triangle CPD$ by the SAS Cong. Post., so corresp. sides $\overline{AB}$ and $\overline{DC}$ are $\cong$.

59. Draw radii $\overline{LG}$ and $\overline{LH}$. $\overline{LG} \cong \overline{LH}$, $\overline{LJ} \cong \overline{LJ}$, and since $\overline{EF} \perp \overline{GH}$, $\triangle LGJ \cong \triangle LHJ$ by the HL Cong. Thm. Then, corresp. sides $\overline{GJ}$ and $\overline{JH}$ are $\cong$, as are corresp. $\angle$s GLJ and HLJ. By the def. of $\cong$ arcs, $\widehat{GE} \cong \widehat{EH}$. **61.** Draw radii $\overline{PB}$ and $\overline{PC}$. $\overline{PB} \cong \overline{PC}$ and $\overline{PE} \cong \overline{PF}$. Also, since $\overline{PE} \perp \overline{AB}$ and $\overline{PF} \perp \overline{CD}$, $\triangle PEB$ and $\triangle PFC$ are right $\triangle$s and are $\cong$ by the HL Cong. Thm. Corresp. sides $\overline{BE}$ and $\overline{CF}$ are $\cong$, so $BE = CF$ and, by the multiplication prop. of equality, $2BE = 2CE$. By Thm. 10.5, $\overline{PE}$ bisects $\overline{AB}$ and $\overline{PF}$ bisects $\overline{CD}$, so $AB = 2BE$ and $CD = 2CF$. Then, by the Substitution Prop., $AB = CD$ or $\overline{AB} \cong \overline{CD}$.
63.

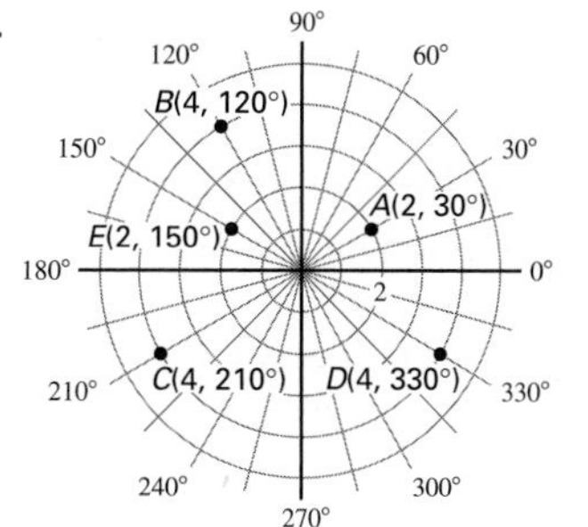

65. 90° **67.** 210°

10.2 MIXED REVIEW (p. 611)
71, 73. Coordinates of sample points are given.

71. ; **73.** ;

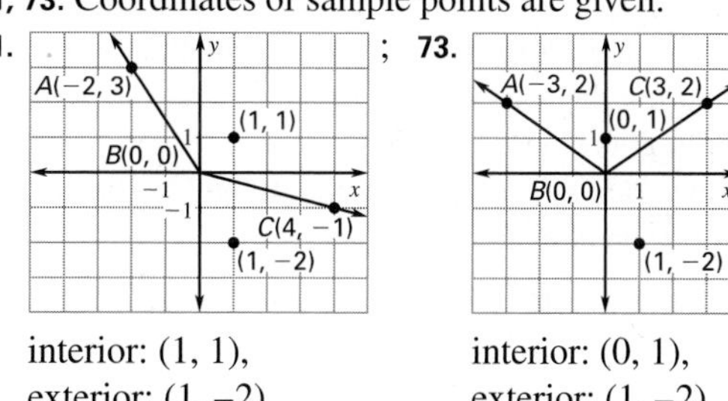

interior: (1, 1), exterior: (1, –2)

interior: (0, 1), exterior: (1, –2)

75. Square; $PQ = QR = RS = PS = 3\sqrt{2}$, so $PQRS$ is a rhombus by the Rhombus Corollary; $PR = QS = 6$, so $PQRS$ is a rectangle. (A $\square$ is a rectangle if and only if its diagonals are $\cong$.) Then, $PQRS$ is a square by the Square Corollary. **77.** 16 **79.** 18

10.3 PRACTICE (pp. 616–619) **3.** 40° **5.** 210° **7.** $y = 150$, $z = 75$ **9.** 64° **11.** 228° **13.** 109° **15.** 47; the $\angle$s intercept the same arc. **17.** $x = 45$, $y = 40$; inscribed $\angle$s that intercept the same arc have the same measure. **19.** $x = 80$, $y = 78$, $z = 160$ **21.** $x = 30$, $y = 20$; $m\angle A = m\angle B = m\angle C = 60°$ **23.** $x = 9$, $y = 6$; $m\angle A = 54°$, $m\angle B = 36°$, $m\angle C = 126°$, $m\angle D = 144°$ **25.** Yes; both pairs of opp. $\angle$s are right $\angle$s and, so, are supplementary. **27.** No; both pairs of opp. $\angle$s of a kite may be, but are not always, supplementary. **29.** Yes; both pairs of opp. $\angle$s of an isosceles trapezoid are supplementary. **31.** diameter **33.** $\overline{AB}$; a line $\perp$ to a radius of a $\odot$ at its endpoint is tangent to the $\odot$. **35.** $\overline{QB}$; isosceles; base $\angle$s; $\angle A \cong \angle B$; Exterior Angle; $2x°$; $2x°$; 2; $\frac{1}{2}m\widehat{AC}$; $\frac{1}{2}m\widehat{AC}$

SELECTED ANSWERS

SA27

37. Draw the diameter containing $\overline{QB}$, intersecting the ⊙ at point D. By the proof in Ex. 35, $m\angle ABD = \frac{1}{2}m\widehat{AD}$ and $m\angle DBC = \frac{1}{2}m\widehat{DC}$. By the Arc Addition Post., $m\widehat{AD} = m\widehat{AC} + m\widehat{CD}$, so $m\widehat{AC} = m\widehat{AD} - m\widehat{CD}$ by the subtraction prop. of equality. By the Angle Addition Post., $m\angle ABD = m\angle ABC + m\angle CBD$, so $m\angle ABC = m\angle ABD - m\angle CBD$ by the subtraction prop. of equality. Then, by repeated application of the Substitution Prop., $m\angle ABC = \frac{1}{2}m\widehat{AC}$.

39. GIVEN: ⊙O with inscribed $\triangle ABC$, $\overline{AC}$ is a diameter of circle ⊙O.
PROVE: $\triangle ABC$ is a right △.
Use the Arc Addition Postulate to show that $m\widehat{AEC} = m\widehat{ABC}$ and thus $m\widehat{ABC} = 180°$. Then use the Measure of an Incribed Angle Thm. to show $m\angle B = 90°$, so that $\angle B$ is a right ∠ and $\triangle ABC$ is a right △.
GIVEN: ⊙O with inscribed $\triangle ABC$, $\angle B$ is a right ∠.
PROVE: $\overline{AC}$ is a diameter of circle ⊙O.
Use the Measure of an Incribed Angle Thm. to show the inscribed right ∠ intercepts an arc with measure 2(90°) = 180°. Since $\overline{AC}$ intercepts an arc that is half of the measure of the circle, it must be a diameter. **41.** *Sample answer:* Use the carpenter's square to draw two diameters of the circle. (Position the vertex of the tool on the circle and mark the 2 points where the sides intersect the ⊙. Repeat, placing the vertex at a different point on the ⊙. The center is the point where the diameters intersect.)

10.3 MIXED REVIEW (p. 620)
49. $y = 2x - 9$ **51.** $y = \frac{4}{3}x + 7$ **53.** $y = -\frac{4}{5}x - 16$

55.

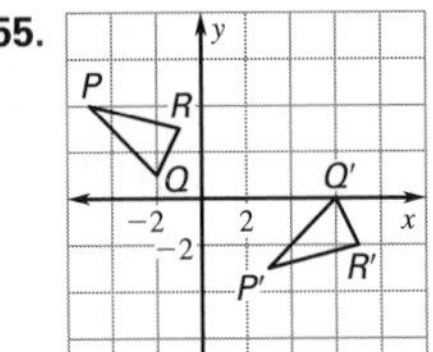

57.

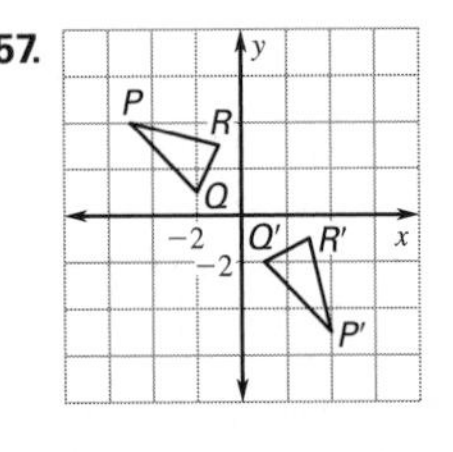

59. $\frac{1}{2}$
61. $\frac{\sqrt{3}}{2}$

QUIZ 1 (p. 620) **1.** 90; a tangent line is ⊥ to the radius drawn to the point of tangency. **2.** 12; 2 tangent segs. with the same ext. endpoint are ≅. **3.** 47° **4.** 133° **5.** 227° **6.** 313° **7.** 180° **8.** 47° **9.** 85.2°

10.4 PRACTICE (pp. 624–627) **3.** 60° **5.** 90° **7.** 88° **9.** 280° **11.** 72° **13.** 110° **15.** 25.4 **17.** 112.5° **19.** 103° **21.** 26° **23.** 37° **25.** 55° **27.** 5 **29.** 60° **31.** 30° **33.** 30° **35.** 0.7° **37.** Diameter; 90°; a tangent line is ⊥ to the radius drawn to the point of tangency. **39.** The proof would be similar, using the Angle Addition and Arc Addition Postulates, but you would be subtracting $m\angle PBC$ and $m\widehat{PC}$ instead of adding.

41.

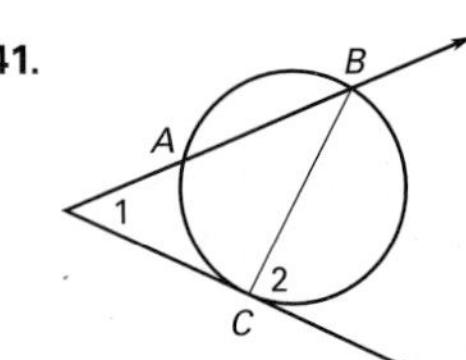

Case 1: Draw $\overline{BC}$. Use the Exterior Angle Thm. to show that $m\angle 2 = m\angle 1 + m\angle ABC$, so that $m\angle 1 = m\angle 2 - m\angle ABC$. Then use Thm. 10.12 to show that $m\angle 2 = \frac{1}{2}m\widehat{BC}$ and the Measure of an Inscribed Angle Thm. to show that $m\angle ABC = \frac{1}{2}m\widehat{AC}$. Then, $m\angle 1 = \frac{1}{2}\left(m\widehat{BC} - m\widehat{AC}\right)$.

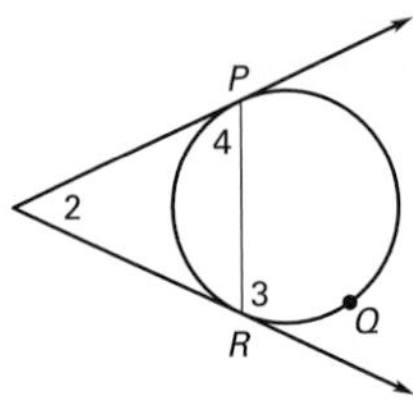

Case 2: Draw $\overline{PR}$. Use the Exterior Angle Thm. to show that $m\angle 3 = m\angle 2 + m\angle 4$, so that $m\angle 2 = m\angle 3 - m\angle 4$. Then use Thm. 10.12 to show that $m\angle 3 = \frac{1}{2}m\widehat{PQR}$ and $m\angle 4 = \frac{1}{2}m\widehat{PR}$. Then, $m\angle 2 = \frac{1}{2}\left(m\widehat{PQR} - m\widehat{PR}\right)$.

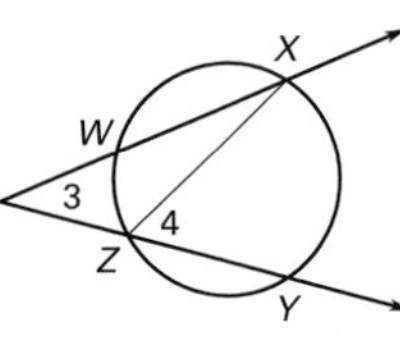

Case 3: Draw $\overline{XZ}$. Use the Exterior Angle Thm. to show that $m\angle 4 = m\angle 3 + m\angle WXZ$, so that $m\angle 3 = m\angle 4 - m\angle WXZ$. Then use the Measure of an Inscribed Angle Thm. to show that $m\angle 4 = \frac{1}{2}m\widehat{XY}$ and $m\angle WXZ = \frac{1}{2}m\widehat{WZ}$. Then, $m\angle 3 = \frac{1}{2}\left(m\widehat{XY} - m\widehat{WZ}\right)$.

10.4 MIXED REVIEW (p. 627) **47.** 6 **49.** 25 **51.** 2

10.5 PRACTICE (pp. 632–634) **3.** 15; 18; 12 **5.** 16; $x + 8$; 4 **7.** 9; 6 **9.** The segment from you to the center of the aviary is a secant segment that shares an endpoint with the segment that is tangent to the aviary. Let x be the length of the internal secant segment (twice the radius of the aviary) and use Thm. 10.17. Since $40(40 + x) \approx 60^2$, the radius is about $\frac{50}{2}$, or 25 ft. **11.** 45; 27; 30 **13.** 13 **15.** 8.5 **17.** 6 **19.** $8\frac{2}{3}$ **21.** 4 **23.** $\frac{-9 + \sqrt{565}}{2} \approx 7.38$ **25.** $x = 42$, $y = 10$ **27.** $x = 7$, $y = \frac{-13 + 5\sqrt{17}}{2} \approx 3.81$ **29.** 4.875 ft; the diameter through A bisects the chord into two 4.5 ft segments. Use Thm. 10.15 to find the length of the part of the diameter containing A. Add this length to 3 and divide by 2 to get the radius. **31.** $\angle B$ and $\angle D$ intercept the same arc, so $\angle B \cong \angle D$. $\angle E \cong \angle E$ by the Reflexive Prop. of Cong., so $\triangle BCE \sim \triangle DAE$ by the AA Similarity Thm. Then, since lengths of corresp. sides of ~ ⚠ are proportional, $\frac{EA}{EC} = \frac{ED}{EB}$. By the Cross Product Prop., $EA \cdot EB = EC \cdot ED$.

10.5 MIXED REVIEW (p. 635) **41.** 10; (3, 0) **43.** 15; $\left(-\frac{11}{2}, 1\right)$ **45.** 14; (–2, –2) **47.** $y = -\frac{3}{2}x + 17$ **49.** $y = -\frac{1}{3}x - \frac{10}{3}$

51. $y = \frac{3}{7}x + \frac{81}{7}$ **53.**

QUIZ 2 (p. 635) **1.** 202 **2.** 139 **3.** 26 **4.** $6\frac{1}{4}$ **5.** 6 **6.** 5
7. Solve $20(2r + 20) = 49^2$ (Thm. 10.17) or solve $(r + 20)^2 = r^2 + 49^2$ (the Pythagorean Theorem); 50.025 ft.

10.6 PRACTICE (pp. 638–640) **3.** (0, 0), 2; $x^2 + y^2 = 4$
5. (–2, 2), 2; $(x + 2)^2 + (y - 2)^2 = 4$ **7.** (4, 3), 4 **9.** (0, 0), 2
11. (–5, –3), 1 **13.** (–3, 2), 2, $(x + 3)^2 + (y - 2)^2 = 4$
15. (3, 3), 1, $(x - 3)^2 + (y - 3)^2 = 1$ **17.** (2, 2), 4, $(x - 2)^2 + (y - 2)^2 = 16$ **19.** $x^2 + y^2 = 1$ **21.** $(x - 3)^2 + (y + 2)^2 = 4$ **23.** $x^2 + y^2 = 9$ **25.** $(x - 3)^2 + (y - 2)^2 = 4$

27.

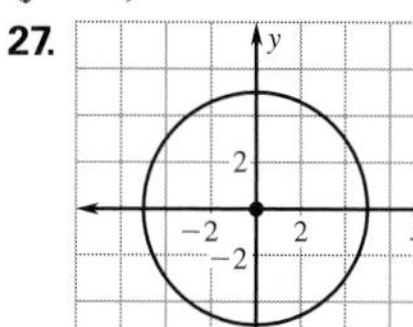

29.

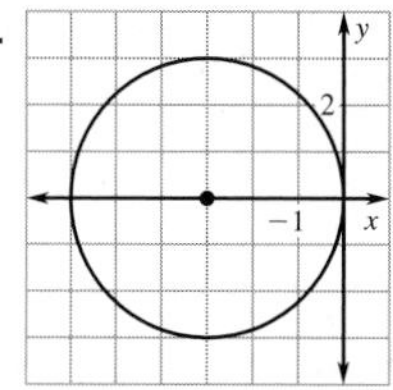

31.

33. exterior **35.** on
37. interior **39.** exterior

41. A: $x^2 + y^2 = 9$,
B: $(x - 5)^2 + (y - 3)^2 = 6.25$,
C: $(x - 2)^2 + (y - 5)^2 = 4$;

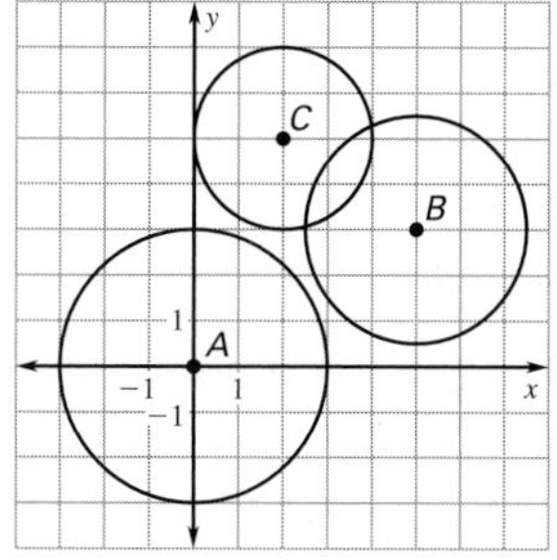

43. $(x + 3)^2 + y^2 = 1$ **47.**

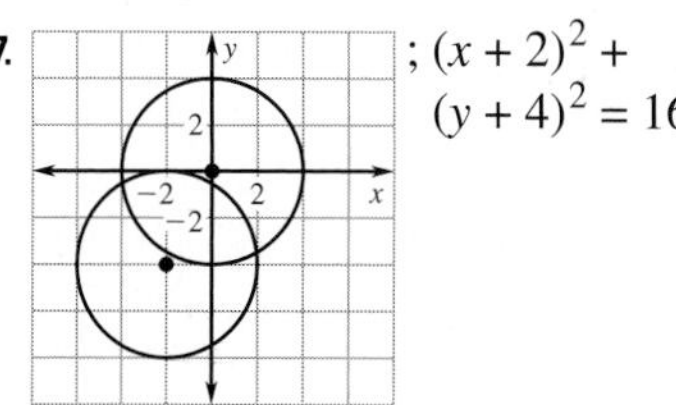

; $(x + 2)^2 + (y + 4)^2 = 16$

10.6 MIXED REVIEW (p. 640) **55.** ▱, rectangle, rhombus, kite, isosceles trapezoid **57.** ⟨–6, 7⟩; 9.2 **59.** ⟨15, 1⟩; 15.0
61. No; P is not equidistant from the sides of $\angle A$.

10.7 PRACTICE (pp. 645–647) **3.** B **5.** D **7.** the two points on the intersection of the ⊥ bisector of $\overline{AB}$ and ⊙A with radius 5;

9. ; **11.** ;

⊙P with radius 1 in. ⊙C with radius 1 in. and the interior of ⊙C

13. ; a line ∥ to both j and k and halfway between them

15. ; a ⊙ with center C and radius half that of the original ⊙
19. $x = 3$ **21.** $y = -x + 6$
23. $y = -2$, $y = 4$

25.

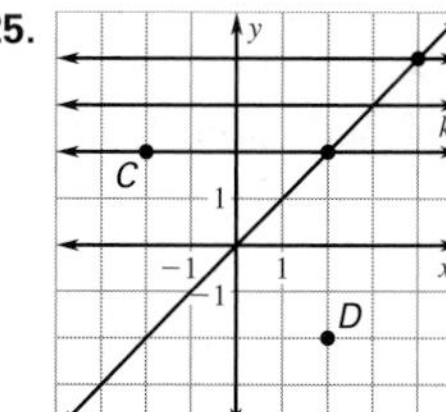

; 2 points, (2, 2) and (4, 4), the intersections of $y = x$ with $y = 2$ and $y = 4$

27.

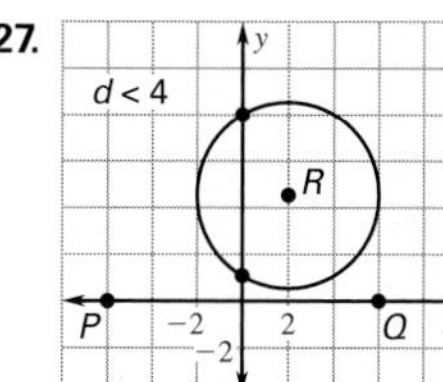

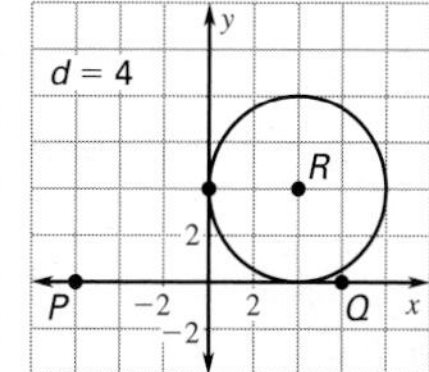

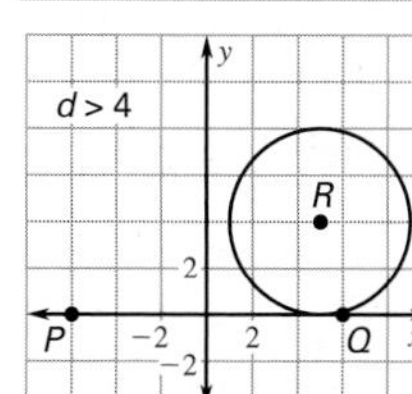

; Let d be the distance from R to the ⊥ bisector of $\overline{PQ}$; the locus of points is 2 points if $d < 4$, 1 point if $d = 4$, and 0 points if $d > 4$.
29. (0, –6)

31. Let d be the distance from P to k. If $0 < d < 4$, then the locus is 2 points. If $d = 4$, then the locus is 1 point. If $d > 4$, then the locus is 0 points.

SELECTED ANSWERS

SA29

10.7 MIXED REVIEW (p. 647) **37.** 69 **39.** 17.5 **41.** 24

43.

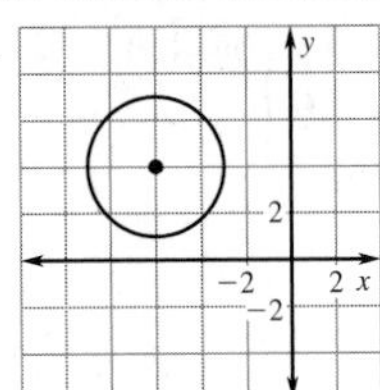

45.

QUIZ 3 (p. 648)

1.

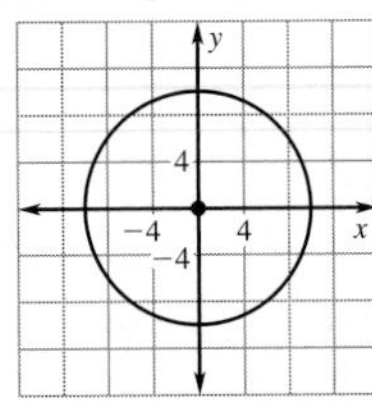

2.

3.

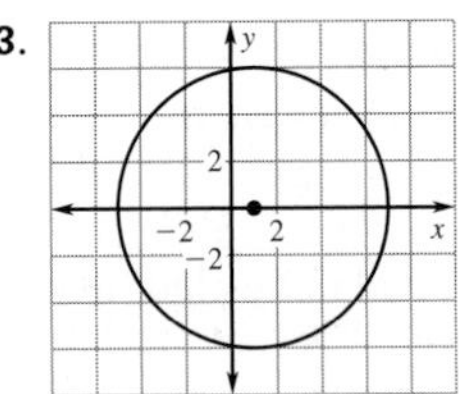

4.

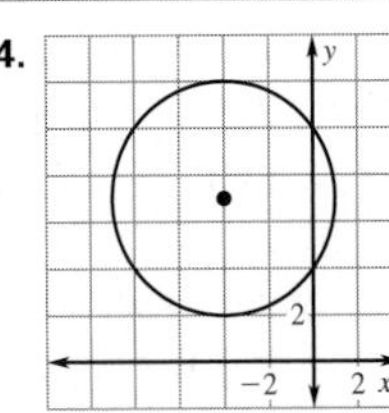

5. $(x - 2)^2 + (y + 2)^2 = 74$

6.

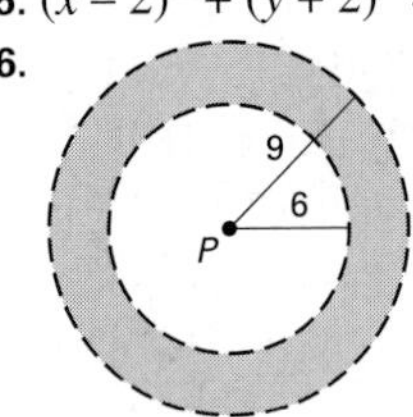

; the points that are in both the exterior of the ⊙ with center P and radius 6 units and the interior of the ⊙ with center P and radius 9 units

7.

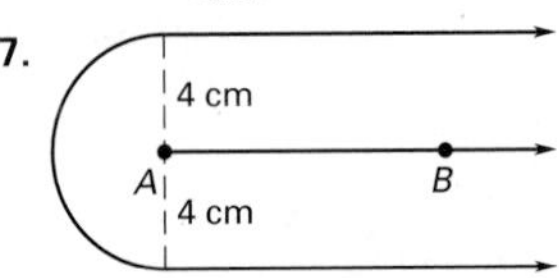

; a set of points formed by 2 rays on opposite sides of $\overrightarrow{AB}$, each ∥ to $\overrightarrow{AB}$ and 4 cm from it, and a semicircle with center A and radius 4 cm

8.

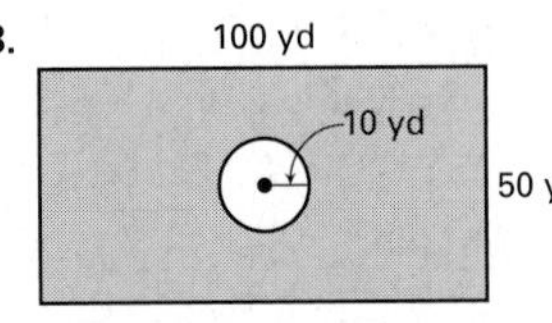

; the points that are on the field and on or outside the ⊙ whose center is the center of the field and whose radius is 10 yd

CHAPTER 10 REVIEW (pp. 650–652) **1.** $\overline{BN}$ **3.** $\overline{BN}$ or $\overline{BF}$ **5.** $\overline{QE}$ **7.** $\overleftrightarrow{BF}$ **9.** Yes; a tangent is ⊥ to the radius drawn to the point of tangency. **11.** 62° **13.** 239° **15.** 275° **17.** True; the sides of the ⚠ opp. the inscribed ∠s are diameters, so the inscribed ∠s are right ∠s. **19.** True; $ABCD$ is inscribed in a ⊙, so opp. ∠s are supplementary. **21.** 55 **23.** 94 **25.** 34.4

27. $(x - 2)^2 + (y - 5)^2 = 81$; **29.** $(x + 6)^2 + y^2 = 10$;

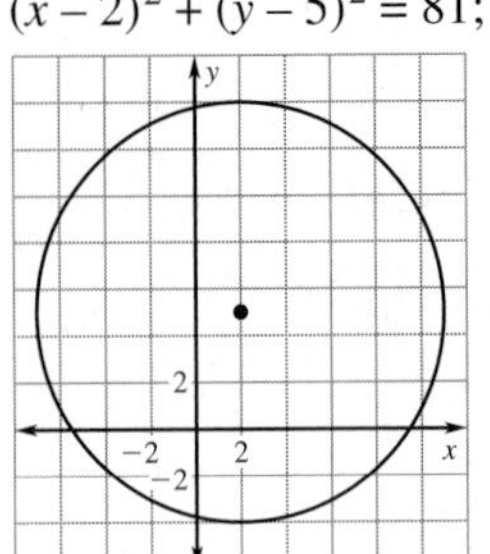

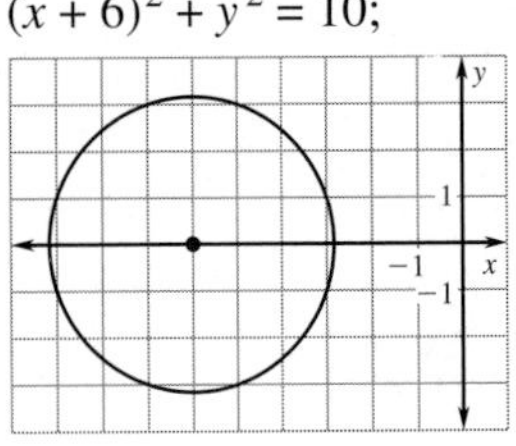

31. ; 2 lines, m and n, on opp. sides of ℓ, each ∥ to ℓ and 4 in. from ℓ, and all the points between m and n

ALGEBRA REVIEW (pp. 656–657) **1.** $\frac{A}{\ell}$ **2.** $\frac{\sqrt[3]{6\pi^2 V}}{2\pi}$ **3.** $\frac{2A}{b}$ **4.** $\frac{2A}{h} - b_2$ **5.** $\sqrt{\frac{A}{\pi}}$ or $\frac{\sqrt{A\pi}}{\pi}$ **6.** $\frac{C}{2\pi}$ **7.** $\sqrt[3]{V}$ **8.** $\frac{P - 2w}{2}$ **9.** $\frac{V}{\ell w}$ **10.** $\frac{V}{\pi r^2}$ **11.** $\sqrt{\frac{S}{6}}$ or $\frac{\sqrt{6S}}{6}$ **12.** $\sqrt{c^2 - a^2}$ **13.** $5 + x$ **14.** $x^2 + \sqrt{2}$ **15.** $2x - 14$ **16.** $3x - 6$ **17.** $x + 2 - 9x$ **18.** $\frac{x}{2} + 3x$ **19.** $5x - 7 = 13$; 4 **20.** $2x - 16 = 10$; 13 **21.** $2x + 14x = 48$; 3 **22.** $\frac{x}{2} = 3(x + 5)$; −6 **23.** 36 **24.** 51 miles **25.** 142 **26.** \$12.50 **27.** 25% **28.** 22% **29.** 400% **30.** about 15% **31.** 10 **32.** 25 meters **33.** \$2.08 **34.** about 17% **35.** $\frac{1}{2x}$ **36.** $2a^2$ **37.** x **38.** 3 **39.** $\frac{a + 2}{a - 8}$ **40.** $\frac{x + 3}{6x - 1}$ **41.** $\frac{7d - 1}{3d + 4}$ **42.** $\frac{y - 6}{12 - y}$ **43.** $\frac{9s - 1}{s - 3}$ **44.** $\frac{-5h + 1}{h + 1}$ **45.** $\frac{t - 1}{t + 1}$ **46.** $\frac{m - 2}{m + 2}$

CHAPTER 11

SKILL REVIEW (p. 660) **1.** 48 in.^{2} **2.** 44°; 123°, 101°, 136° **3. a.** $\frac{3}{2}$ **b.** $\frac{2}{3}$ **4.** 43.6°, 46.4°

11.1 PRACTICE (pp. 665–668) **3.** 95 **5.** 45 **7.** 1800° **9.** 2880° **11.** 5040° **13.** 17,640° **15.** 101 **17.** 108 **19.** 135 **21.** 140° **23.** 6 **25.** 16 **29.** 30° **31.** about 17.1° **33.** 6 **35.** 5 **37.** 75° **39.** The yellow hexagon is regular with interior angles measuring 120° each; the yellow pentagons each have two interior angles that measure 90° and three interior angles that measure 120°; the triangles are equilateral with all interior angles measuring 60°. **41.** ∠3 and ∠8 are a linear pair, so $m\angle 3 = 140°$; ∠2 and ∠7 are a linear pair, so $m\angle 7 = 80°$; $m\angle 1 = 80°$ by the Polygon Interior Angles Thm.; ∠1 and ∠6 are a linear pair, so $m\angle 6 = 100°$; ∠4 and ∠9 are a linear pair, as are ∠5 and ∠10, so $m\angle 9 = m\angle 10 = 70°$. **43.** Draw all the diagonals of $ABCDE$ that have A as one endpoint. The diagonals, $\overline{AC}$ and $\overline{AD}$, divide $ABCDE$ into 3 ⚠. By the Angle Addition Post., $m\angle BAE = m\angle BAC + m\angle CAD + m\angle DAE$.

Similarly, $m\angle BCD = m\angle BCA + m\angle ACD$ and $m\angle CDE = m\angle CDA + m\angle ADE$. Then, the sum of the measures of the interior ∠s of $ABCDE$ is equal to the sum of the measures of the ∠s of $\triangle ABC$, $\triangle ACD$, and $\triangle ADE$. By the △ Sum Thm., the sum of the measures of each △ is 180°, so the sum of the measures of the interior ∠s of $ABCDE$ is $3 \cdot 180° = (5-2) \cdot 180°$. **45.** Let A be a convex n-gon. Each interior ∠ and one of the exterior ∠s at that vertex form a linear pair, so the sum of their measures is 180°. Then, the sum of the measures of the interior ∠ and one exterior ∠ at each vertex is $n \cdot 180°$. By the Polygon Interior Angles Thm., the sum of the measures of the interior ∠s of A is $(n-2) \cdot 180°$. So, the sum of the measures of the exterior ∠s of A, one at each vertex, is $n \cdot 180° - (n-2) \cdot 180° = n \cdot 180° - n \cdot 180° + 360° = 360°$. **49.** $m\angle A = m\angle E = 90°$, $m\angle B = m\angle C = m\angle D = 120°$ **51.** Yes; if $\frac{(n-2) \cdot 180°}{n} = 150°$, then $n = 12$. A regular 12-gon (dodecagon) has interior ∠s with measure 150°. **53.** No; if $\frac{(n-2) \cdot 180°}{n} = 72°$, then $n = 3\frac{1}{3}$. It is not possible for a polygon to have $3\frac{1}{3}$ sides. **55.** $f(n)$ is the measure of each interior ∠ of a regular n-gon; as n gets larger and larger, $f(n)$ increases, becoming closer and closer to 180°. **57.** 10

11.1 MIXED REVIEW (p. 668) **63.** 27.5 in.^{2} **65.** 37.5 sq. units **67.** no **69.** no **71.** 65° **73.** 245°

11.2 PRACTICE (pp. 672–675) **7.** 45° **9.** $\frac{25\sqrt{3}}{4} \approx 10.8$ sq. units **11.** $\frac{245\sqrt{3}}{4} \approx 106.1$ sq. units **13.** 30° **15.** 2° **17.** $108\sqrt{3} \approx 187.1$ sq. units **19.** $30\sqrt{3} \approx 52.0$ units; $75\sqrt{3} \approx 129.9$ sq. units **21.** 150 tan 36° ≈ 109.0 units; 1125 tan 36° ≈ 817.36 sq. units **23.** 176 sin 22.5° ≈ 67.35 units; 968(sin 22.5°)(cos 22.5°) ≈ 342.24 sq. units **25.** $75\sqrt{3} \approx 129.9$ in.^{2} **27.** True; let θ be the central angle, n the number of sides, r the radius, and P the perimeter. As n grows bigger θ will become smaller, so the apothem, which is given by $r \cos \frac{\theta}{2}$ will get larger. The perimeter of the polygon, which is given by $n\left(2\sin \frac{\theta}{2}\right)$ will grow larger, too. Although the factor involving the sine will get smaller, the increase in n more than makes up for it. Consequently, the area, which is given by $\frac{1}{2}aP$ will increase. **29.** False; for example, the radius of a regular hexagon is equal to the side length. **31.** 32 tan 67.5° ≈ 77.3 **33.** Let s = the length of a side of the hexagon and of the equilateral triangle. The apothem of the hexagon is $\frac{1}{2}\sqrt{3}\,s$ and the perimeter of the hexagon is $6s$. The area of the hexagon, then, is $A = \frac{1}{2}aP = \frac{1}{2}\left(\frac{1}{2}\sqrt{3}\,s\right) \cdot 6s$, or $\frac{3}{2}\sqrt{3}\,s^2$. The area of an equilateral triangle with side length s is $A = \frac{1}{4}\sqrt{3}\,s^2$. Six of these equilateral triangles together (forming the hexagon), then, would have area $6 \cdot \frac{s^2\sqrt{3}}{4} = \frac{3s^2\sqrt{3}}{2}$. The two results are the same. **45.** $\frac{1}{4}\sqrt{3} \approx 0.43$ m **47.** 3 colors **49.** about 25 tiles

11.2 MIXED REVIEW (p. 675) **55.** 3 **57.** −33 **59.** true **61.** false **63.** 7

11.3 PRACTICE (pp. 679–681) **5.** 3:2, 9:4 **7.** 2:1, 4:1 **9.** 5:6, 25:36 **11.** sometimes **13.** always **15.** 7:10 **17.** Since $\overline{AB}$ is parallel to $\overline{DC}$, $\angle A \cong \angle C$ and $\angle B \cong \angle D$ by the Alternate Interior Angles Thm. So, $\triangle CDE \sim \triangle ABE$ by the AA Similarity Postulate; 98 square units. **19.** $3\sqrt{5}:4$ **21.** $3\sqrt{10}:5$ **23.** 1363 in.^{2} and 5452 in.^{2}; 1:4 **25.** 820 ft^2 **27.** about 1385.8 ft^2; about 565.8 ft^2

11.3 MIXED REVIEW (p. 681) **35.** 145° **37.** 215° **39.** 80° **41.** 43°

QUIZ 1 (p. 682) **1.** 3240° **2.** 14.4° **3.** $\frac{289\sqrt{3}}{4} \approx 125.1$ in.^{2} **4.** 729 tan 20° ≈ 265.3 cm^2 **5.** $\frac{4}{3}; \frac{16}{9}$ **6.** $\frac{13}{20}; \frac{169}{400}$ **7.** about \$2613

11.4 PRACTICE (pp. 686–688) **3.** F **5.** C **7.** A **9.** False; the arcs must be arcs of the same ⊙ or of ≅ ⊙s. **11.** False; the arcs must be arcs of the same ⊙ or of ≅ ⊙s. **13.** about 81.0 cm **15.** 31.42 in. **17.** 25.13 m **19.** 5.09 yd **21.** 7.33 in.

23.

Radius	12	3	0.6	3.5	5.1	$3\sqrt{3}$
$m\overparen{AB}$	45°	30°	120°	192°	90°	about 107°
Length of $\overparen{AB}$	3π	0.5π	0.4π	about 3.73π	2.55π	3.09π

25. 36 **27.** $\frac{9971\pi}{1500} \approx 20.88$ **29.** $\frac{798}{25\pi} \approx 10.16$ **31.** $5\pi + 15 \approx 30.71$ **33.** 60, 9 **35.** $2\frac{1}{2}, \frac{19}{56}$ **37.** $4\pi\sqrt{7}$ **39.** A: 24.2 in., B: 24.9 in., C: 25.7 in. **41.** The sidewall width must be added twice to the rim diameter to get the tire diameter. **43.** about 9.8 laps **45.** about 47.62 in. **47.** about 37.70 ft

11.4 MIXED REVIEW (p. 689) **53.** $10.89\pi \approx 34.21$ in.^{2} **55.** $176\pi \approx 552.92$ m^2 **57.** $2\frac{11}{12}$ **59.** 96° **61.** 258°

11.5 PRACTICE (pp. 695–698) **3.** $81\pi \approx 254.47$ in.^{2} **5.** $36\pi \approx 113.10$ ft^2 **7.** $\frac{175\pi}{9} \approx 61.09$ m^2 **9.** $8\pi \approx 25.13$ in.^{2} **11.** $0.16\pi \approx 0.50$ cm^2 **13.** $100\pi \approx 314.16$ in.^{2} **15.** $\frac{49\pi}{18} \approx 8.55$ in.^{2} **17.** $\frac{529\pi}{75} \approx 22.16$ m^2 **19.** $100\pi \approx 314.16$ ft^2 **21.** 13.00 in. **23.** $540\pi \approx 1696.46$ m^2 **25.** $16\pi - 80 \cos 36° \sin 36° \approx 12.22$ ft^2 **27.** $324 - 81\pi \approx 69.53$ in.^{2} **29.** 2.36, 4.71, 7.07, 9.42, 11.78, 14.14 **31.** Yes; it appears that the points lie along a line. You can also write a linear equation, $y = \frac{\pi}{40}x$. **33.** 692.72 mi^2 **35.** $6\pi - 9\sqrt{3} \approx 3.26$ cm^2

SELECTED ANSWERS

37. $768\pi - 576\sqrt{3} \approx 1415.08 \text{ cm}^2$ **41.** No; the area of the ⊙ is quadrupled and the circumference is doubled. $A = \pi r^2$ and $C = 2\pi r$; $\pi(2r)^2 = 4\pi r^2 = 4A$ and $2\pi(2r) = 2(2\pi r) = 2C$.

11.5 MIXED REVIEW (p. 698) **47.** $\frac{3}{16}$ **49.** $\frac{4}{11}$ **51.** 19.4 cm **53.** 68° **55.** $(x+2)^2 + (y+7)^2 = 36$ **57.** $(x+4)^2 + (y-5)^2 = 10.24$ **59.** $25\pi \approx 78.5$ in. **61.** $\frac{1896}{43\pi} \approx 14.0$ m

11.6 PRACTICE (pp. 701–704) **5.** $\frac{1}{2} = 50\%$ **7.** $\overline{AB}$ and $\overline{BF}$ do not overlap and $AB + BF = AF$. So, any point K on $\overline{AF}$ must be on one of the two parts. Therefore, the sum of the two probabilities is 1. **9.** about 14% **11.** about 57% **13.** 25% **15.** about 42% **17.** $\frac{4-\pi}{4} \approx 21.5\%$ **19.** $\frac{1}{4} = 25\%$ **21.** $\frac{3\pi}{392\sqrt{3}} \approx 1.4\%$ **23.** $\frac{3\pi}{98\sqrt{3}} \approx 5.6\%$ **25.** $\frac{\pi-2}{\pi} \approx 36\%$ **27.** $\frac{1}{6} \approx 16.7\%$ **29.** 10,000,000 yd^2 **31.** 1% **33.** 36% **37.** 60° **39.** 30° **41.** The probability is doubled.

11.6 MIXED REVIEW (p. 705) **45.** No; since $11^2 = 121 \neq 100 + 16$, $\triangle ABC$ is not a right △. Then, $\overline{CB}$ is not ⊥ to $\overleftrightarrow{AB}$ and $\overleftrightarrow{AB}$ is not tangent to the ⊙. **47.** Yes; $25^2 = 625 = 49 + 576$, so $\triangle ABC$ is a right △ and $\overline{CA} \perp \overleftrightarrow{AB}$. Then, $\overleftrightarrow{AB}$ is tangent to the ⊙.

49.

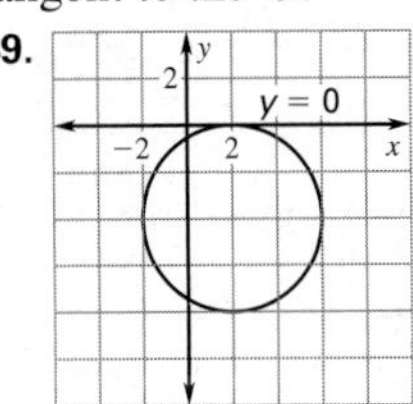

tangent

; **51.** ;

secant

QUIZ 2 (p. 705) **1.** $\frac{738}{17} \approx 43.4$ m **2.** $\frac{286\pi}{45} \approx 20.0$ in. **3.** $\frac{738}{23\pi} \approx 10.2$ ft **4.** $2500\pi \approx 7854.0 \text{ mi}^2$ **5.** $\frac{343\pi}{24} \approx 44.9 \text{ cm}^2$ **6.** $\frac{725\pi}{9} \approx 253.1 \text{ ft}^2$ **7.** $\frac{\sqrt{3}}{64} \approx 2.7\%$

CHAPTER 11 REVIEW (pp. 708–710) **1.** 140°, 40° **3.** 157.5°, 22.5° **5.** 45 **7.** 12 **9.** $36\sqrt{3} \approx 62.4 \text{ cm}^2$ **11.** $\frac{75\sqrt{3}}{2} \approx 65.0 \text{ m}^2$ **13.** sometimes **15.** always **17.** 5:3, 25:9 **19.** about 47.8 m, about 21.5 m **21.** about 1.91 in. **23.** $50\pi \approx 157.1 \text{ in.}^2$ **25.** $161\pi \approx 505.8 \text{ cm}^2$ **27.** $196\pi \approx 615.75 \text{ ft}^2$ **29.** $\frac{3}{10} = 30\%$ **31.** $\frac{3}{5} = 60\%$ **33.** $\frac{1}{4} = 25\%$

CHAPTER 12

SKILL REVIEW (p. 718) **1.** 2:1 **2.** 3:4 **3.** $4\sqrt{3} \approx 6.9 \text{ in.}^2$ **4.** $54\sqrt{3} \approx 93.5 \text{ m}^2$ **5.** 4.8 ft^2

12.1 PRACTICE (pp. 723–726) **3.** Yes; the figure is a solid that is bounded by polygons that enclose a single region of space. **5.** No; it does not have faces that are polygons. **7.** 6 **9.** 30 **11.** Yes; the figure is a solid that is bounded by polygons that enclose a single region of space. **13.** 5, 5, 8 **15.** 10, 16, 24 **17.** Not regular, convex; the faces of the polyhedron are not congruent (2 are hexagons and 6 are squares); any 2 points on the surface of the polyhedron can be connected by a line segment that lies entirely inside or on the polyhedron. **19.** False; see the octahedron in part (b) of Example 2 on page 720. **21.** True; the faces are ≅ squares. **23.** False; it does not have polygonal faces. **25.** circle **27.** pentagon **29.** circle **31.** rectangle **33.** yes; **35.** yes;

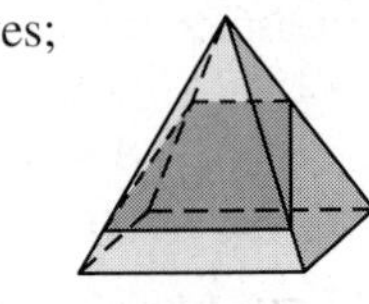

37. octahedron **39.** dodecahedron **41.** cube **43.** 5 faces, 6 vertices, 9 edges; 5 + 6 = 9 + 2 **45.** 5 faces, 6 vertices, 9 edges; 5 + 6 = 9 + 2 **47.** 12 vertices **49.** 24 vertices **51.** 12 vertices **53.** 6 molecules

12.1 MIXED REVIEW (p. 726) **61.** 280 ft^2 **63.** 110.40 m^2 **65.** 27.71 cm^2 **67.** 2866.22 in.^2 **69.** 5808.80 ft^2

12.2 PRACTICE (pp. 731–734) **3.** cylinder **5.** rectangular prism **7, 9.** Three answers are given. The first considers the top and bottom as the bases, the second, the front and back, and the third, the right and left sides. **7.** 5 cm; 8 cm; 3 cm **9.** 24 cm^2; 15 cm^2; 40 cm^2

11. 5.9 ft, 3.4 ft, 3.4 ft

13. right hexagonal prism **15.** rectangle **17.** pentagonal prism **19.** triangular prism **21.** 190 m^2 **23.** $16\sqrt{2} + 115.2 \approx 137.83 \text{ m}^2$ **25.** $12\sqrt{3} + 73.2 \approx 93.98 \text{ in.}^2$ **27.** $256\pi \approx 804.25 \text{ cm}^2$

29.

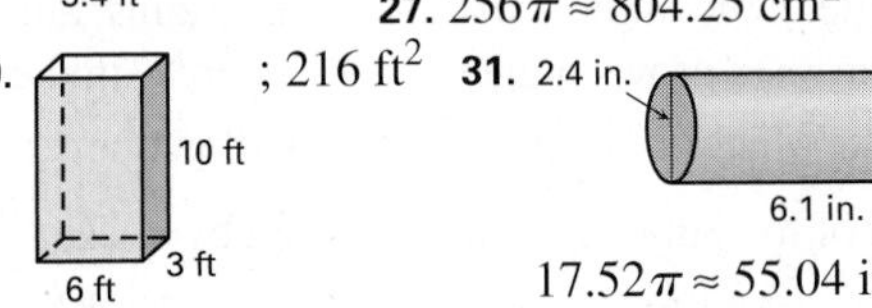

; 216 ft^2 **31.** ; $17.52\pi \approx 55.04 \text{ in.}^2$

33. 27 m **35.** 16 in.^2; 24 in.^2; no **37.** $12\sqrt{3} + 12 \approx 32.8 \text{ in.}^2$; $12\sqrt{3} + 24 \approx 44.8 \text{ in.}^2$; no

39.

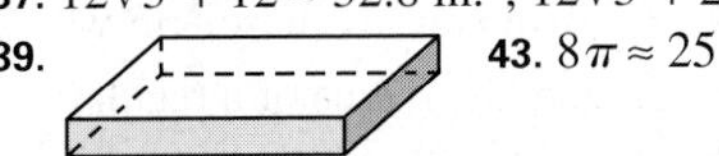

43. $8\pi \approx 25 \text{ in.}^2$

12.2 MIXED REVIEW (p. 734) **51.** $m\angle A = 58°$, $BC \approx 16.80$, $AB \approx 19.81$ **53.** $1805 \cos 36° \sin 36° \approx 858.33 \text{ m}^2$ **55.** $96\sqrt{3} \approx 166.28 \text{ in.}^2$ **57.** $\frac{8}{11} \approx 73\%$ **59.** $\frac{4}{11} \approx 36\%$

12.3 PRACTICE (pp. 738–741) **3.** C **5.** B **7.** D **9.** about 7.62 ft **11.** about 100.09 ft^2 **13.** $25\sqrt{3} + 180 \approx 223.30 \text{ in.}^2$ **15.** 270.6 in.^2 **17.** 506.24 mm^2 **19.** 219.99 cm^2 **21.** $2\sqrt{29} \approx 10.8$ cm **23.** $138.84\pi \text{ m}^2$ **25.** $73.73\pi \text{ in.}^2$ **27.** right cone; 50.3 cm^2

29. 6.2 m 5.8 m 3 m

79.2 m²

31. 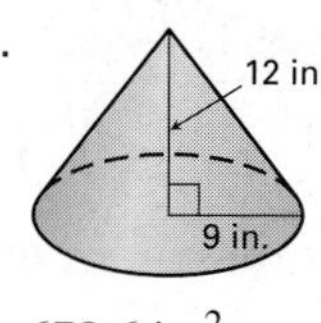

678.6 in.²

33. 101.1 sq. units **35.** $p = 9$ cm, $q = 15$ cm **37.** $\ell \approx 9.8$ m, $h \approx 7.7$ m **39.** about 1,334,817 ft² **41.** about 302 in.² **43.** The surface area of the cup is $\frac{1}{4}$ the surface area of the original paper ⊙; about 29°.

12.3 MIXED REVIEW (p. 741)
51. 82.84 sq. units **53.** about 11 in.

QUIZ 1 (p. 742) **1.** regular, convex; 4 vertices **2.** not regular, convex; 8 vertices **3.** not regular, not convex; 12 vertices **4.** 336.44 ft² **5.** 305.91 m² **6.** 773.52 mm²

12.4 PRACTICE (pp. 746–749) **3.** 255 **5.** 5.5 **7.** $540\pi \approx 1696$ in.³ **9.** 840 in.³ **11.** 100 unit cubes; 4 layers of 5 rows of 5 cubes each **13.** 512 in.³ **15.** $\frac{735\sqrt{3}}{4} \approx 318.26$ in.³ **17.** 288.40 ft³ **19.** 240 m³ **21.** 310.38 cm³ **23.** 48,484.99 ft³ **25.** 924 m³ **27.** $\frac{135\sqrt{3}}{2} \approx 116.91$ cm³ **29.** $3\sqrt[3]{100} \approx 13.92$ yd **31.** $\frac{1211\sqrt{3}}{300} \approx 6.99$ in. **33.** $\sqrt{\frac{1131}{10\pi}} \approx 6.00$ m **35.** 150 ft³ **37.** $605\pi \approx 1900.66$ in.³ **39.** about 92.6 yd **41.** No; the circumference of the base of the shorter cylinder is 11 in., so the radius is about 1.75 in. and the volume is about 82 in.³. The circumference of the base of the taller cylinder is 8.5 in., so the radius is about 1.35 in. and the volume is about 63 in.³. **43.** 7 candles **45.** Prism: volume = 36 in.³, surface area = 66 in.²; cylinder: volume ≈ 36 in.³, surface area ≈ 62.2 in.²; the cylinder and the prism hold about the same amount. The cylinder has smaller surface area, so less metal would be needed and it would be cheaper to produce a cylindrical can than one shaped like a prism. **47.** about 1,850,458 lb

12.4 MIXED REVIEW (p. 749) **51.** 30°, 75°, 75° **53.** 45°, 60°, 75° **55.** 98 m² **57.** 462 in.² **59.** 144 cm²

12.5 PRACTICE (pp. 755–757) **5. a.** $4\pi \approx 12.6$ ft² **b.** $\frac{16\pi}{3} \approx 16.8$ ft³ **9.** $\frac{3721\pi}{100} \approx 116.9$ ft² **11.** 400 cm³ **13.** $\frac{67{,}183\sqrt{3}}{750} \approx 155.2$ ft³ **15.** $710\sqrt{3} \approx 1229.8$ mm³ **17.** 48.97 ft³ **19.** 667.06 in.³ **21.** 5 in. **23.** 288 ft³ **25.** 97.92 m³ **27.** yes **29.** about 17.5 sec **31.** 301.59 cm³ **33.** $16\pi \approx 50.3$ m³

12.5 MIXED REVIEW (p. 758) **41.** 144°, 36° **43.** $163\frac{7}{11}°$, $16\frac{4}{11}°$ **45.** 168°, 12° **47.** $\frac{26{,}569\pi}{100} \approx 834.69$ cm² **49.** $100\pi \approx 314.16$ m² **51.** 24 vertices

QUIZ 2 (p. 758) **1.** 1080 in.³ **2.** 1020 ft³ **3.** $350\pi \approx 1099.56$ cm³ **4.** $\frac{243\pi}{4} \approx 190.85$ m³ **5.** 21,168 mm³ **6.** $\frac{147\sqrt{3}}{4} \approx 63.65$ in.³ **7.** about 5633 ft³

12.6 PRACTICE (pp. 762–765) **3.** *Sample answers:* $\overline{QS}$, $\overline{RT}$, or $\overline{TS}$ **5.** $\overline{QS}$ **7.** $36\pi \approx 113.10$ sq. units **9.** about 5.24×10^{-25} cm³ **11.** 4071.50 cm² **13.** a hemisphere **15.** 7.4 in. **17.** about 45.4 in.² **19.** The diameters of Neptune and its moons Triton and Nereid are, respectively, about 30,775 mi, about 1680 mi, and about 211 mi. Then, the surface areas are about 2,975,404,400 mi², about 8,866,800 m², and 139,900 mi². **21.** 65.45 in.³ **23.** 14π mm, 196π mm², $\frac{1372\pi}{3}$ mm³ **25.** 5 cm, 100π cm², $\frac{500\pi}{3}$ cm³ **27. a.** 488.58 in.² **b.** 419.82 in.³ **29. a.** 375.29 ft² **b.** 610.12 ft³ **31.** $\frac{1}{3}$; $\frac{2}{3}$; 1; $\frac{4}{3}$; $\frac{5}{3}$ **35.** $y = 2$; $4\pi \approx 12.57$ sq. units **39.** about 267, 300 ft² **41, 43.** Answers are rounded to 2 decimal places. **41.** 3.43 cm **43.** 10.42 cm

12.6 MIXED REVIEW (p. 765) **51.** translation, vertical line reflection, 180° rotation, glide reflection **53.** translation, 180° rotation **55.** yes; 36 sq. units **57.** about 14.4 revolutions

12.7 PRACTICE (pp. 769–771) **5.** C **7.** 6 : 11 **9.** not similar **11.** similar **13.** always **15.** always **17.** 112π cm², 160π cm³ **19.** 384π ft², 768π ft³ **21.** 1 : 2 **23.** 2 : 3 **25.** 88 in. **27.** 8192 in.³ **31.** about 4032 ft² **33.** about 34,051 ft³, about 67 in.³

12.7 MIXED REVIEW (p. 772) **39.** $\overline{LK}$ **41.** $\overline{CA}$ **43.** $\angle BAC$ **45.** $\frac{225\sqrt{3}}{2} + 765 \approx 959.86$ ft² **47.** $\frac{26{,}896\pi}{25} \approx 3379.85$ in.² **49.** about 74.3 in.

QUIZ 3 (p. 772) **1.** 1256.64 cm², 4188.79 cm³ **2.** 44.41 in.², 27.83 in.³ **3.** 366.44 ft², 659.58 ft³ **4.** 14,137.17 m², 158,058.33 m³ **5.** 6.5 cm; larger prism: 460 cm², 624 cm³; smaller prism: 115 cm², 78 cm³ **6.** 3 ft; smaller cone: $9\pi + 3\pi\sqrt{73} \approx 108.80$ ft², $24\pi \approx 75.40$ ft³; larger cone: $\frac{81\pi + 27\pi\sqrt{73}}{4} \approx 244.80$ ft², $81\pi \approx 254.47$ ft³ **7.** $40{,}000\pi \approx 125{,}663.71$ ft², $\frac{4{,}000{,}000\pi}{3} \approx 4{,}188{,}790.21$ ft³ **8.** 5 ft, $100\pi \approx 314.16$ ft², $\frac{500\pi}{3} \approx 523.60$ ft³

CHAPTER 12 REVIEW (pp. 774–776) **1.** 60 **3.** 8 **5.** 414.69 ft² **7.** 96 cm² **9.** 124.71 in.² **11.** $\frac{123{,}039\sqrt{3}}{5} \approx 42{,}621.96$ m³ **13.** 10,500 in.³ **15.** $320\pi \approx 1005.31$ ft³ **17.** $\pi \approx 3.14$ in.², $\frac{\pi}{6} \approx 0.52$ in.³ **19.** no

CUMULATIVE PRACTICE (pp. 780–781) **1.** 30°, 30°, 150°, 150° **3.** Let M be the midpoint of $\overline{TS}$. By the Midpoint Formula, $M = (h, k)$. Then $RM = \sqrt{(h-0)^2 + (k-0)^2} = \sqrt{h^2 + k^2}$. Since $TS = \sqrt{(2h-0)^2 + (0-2k)^2} = 2\sqrt{h^2+k^2}$, $RM = \frac{1}{2}TS$. **5.** right; $\angle Z$, $\angle Y$

7.

Statements	Reasons
1. *ABDE* and *CDEF* are parallelograms.	1. Given
2. $\overline{AB} \parallel \overline{DE}$ and $\overline{CF} \parallel \overline{DE}$	2. Definition of parallelogram
3. $\overline{AB} \parallel \overline{CF}$	3. Two lines ∥ to the same line are ∥.
4. $\angle 4 \cong \angle 5$	4. Corresponding ∠s Postulate
5. $m\angle 4 = m\angle 5$	5. Def. of congruent ∠s
6. $\overline{BD} \parallel \overline{AE}$	6. Definition of parallelogram
7. $\angle 5$ and $\angle 6$ are supplements.	7. Consecutive Interior Angles Theorem
8. $m\angle 5 + m\angle 6 = 180°$	8. Def. of supplementary ∠s
9. $m\angle 4 + m\angle 6 = 180°$	9. Substitution prop. of =
10. $\angle 4$ and $\angle 6$ are supplements.	10. Def. of supplementary ∠s

9. never **11.** *Sample answer:* $\overline{BC} \parallel \overline{DE}$, so corresp. angles $\angle ABC$ and $\angle D$ are ≅, as are corresp. angles $\angle ACB$ and $\angle E$. Then, $\triangle ABC \sim \triangle ADE$ by the AA Similarity Postulate. **13.** 5:8; 25:64 **15.** about 73.7°, about 16.3° **17.** 25° **19.** 90° **21.** 100° **23.** 230° **25.** They are supplementary angles; *ABPC* is a quadrilateral with two right angles, so the sum of the other two angles is 180°. **27.** 12 **29.** 20 **31.** 31.4 **33.** the bisectors of the right ∠s formed **35.** $1800 \tan 67.5° \approx 4345.58$ cm^2 **37.** $\frac{49\pi}{2} \approx 76.97$ ft^3 **39.** $8\pi \approx 25.13$ ft^2 **41.** 7.1 in.^{2}

SKILLS REVIEW HANDBOOK

PROBLEM SOLVING (p. 784) **1.** \$197.46 **3.** 32 kinds **5.** 10 33¢ stamps and 6 20¢ stamps **7.** not enough information (You need to know how much area a can of paint will cover.)

POSITIVE AND NEGATIVE NUMBERS (p. 785) **1.** −3.3 **3.** 2.7 **5.** $-1\frac{1}{12}$ **7.** 0 **9.** −1 **11.** −8 **13.** 9 **15.** 0 **17.** −1 **19.** −0.156 **21.** −3 **23.** −9 **25.** −2.88 **27.** $\frac{1}{30}$

EVALUATING EXPRESSIONS (p. 786) **1.** 100 **3.** −8 **5.** 225 **7.** 47 **9.** 64 **11.** $\frac{1}{8}$ **13.** −48 **15.** $\frac{1}{3}$ **17.** −12 **19.** 25 **21.** 12 **23.** −23

THE DISTRIBUTIVE PROPERTY (p. 787) **1.** $2a + 8$ **3.** $3x - 2$ **5.** $y^2 - 9y$ **7.** $4n - 7$ **9.** $4b^2 + 8b$ **11.** $16x^2 - 72xy$ **13.** $2rs + 2rt$ **15.** $-7x^2 + 21x - 14$ **17.** $6m + 4$ **19.** −1 **21.** $19g^3 + 9g^2$ **23.** $xy + 2x - 3y$ **25.** $3h - 3h^2$ **27.** $3y - 4$ **29.** $4r + 8$ **31.** $3n^2 - 13n + 16$

RECIPROCALS (p. 788) **1.** $\frac{1}{12}$ **3.** 4 **5.** −10 **7.** $\frac{13}{6}$ **9.** 5

RATIOS (p. 788) **1.** $\frac{2}{5}$ **3.** $\frac{9}{5}$ **5.** $\frac{1}{1}$ **7.** $\frac{80}{1}$ **9.** $\frac{13}{15}$ **11.** $\frac{2}{3}$

SOLVING LINEAR EQUATIONS (SINGLE-STEP) (p. 789) **1.** 13 **3.** 4 **5.** $-\frac{1}{8}$ **7.** −32 **9.** −8 **11.** −10 **13.** $\frac{21}{2}$ **15.** −80 **17.** 18 **19.** −23 **21.** $\frac{3}{4}$ **23.** −1

SOLVING LINEAR EQUATIONS (MULTI-STEP) (p. 790) **1.** 8 **3.** 8 **5.** −0.6, or $-\frac{3}{5}$ **7.** −15 **9.** 4 **11.** $\frac{7}{8}$ **13.** −18 **15.** 3 **17.** $-\frac{1}{3}$ **19.** 56 **21.** −10 **23.** 25 **25.** $\frac{13}{6}$ **27.** 29 **29.** 76 **31.** 6.6 **33.** $-\frac{25}{6}$ **35.** −11

SOLVING INEQUALITIES (p. 791) **1.** $x < 56$ **3.** $x > 7.3$ **5.** $x < 2$ **7.** $x > 3$ **9.** $x > 4$ **11.** yes **13.** yes **15.** no **17.** yes **19.** *Sample answers:* 4, 4.5, and 10; no; when $x = 3$, $(2x - 3) + (x + 5) = x + 8$.

PLOTTING POINTS (p. 792) **1.** (−1, 0) **3.** (2, −2) **5.** (−5, 3) **7.** (5, −2) **9.** (−2, 5) **11.** (1, 1)

13–27 odd:

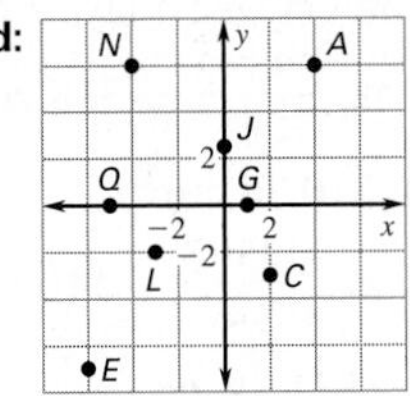

LINEAR EQUATIONS AND THEIR GRAPHS (p. 793)

1.

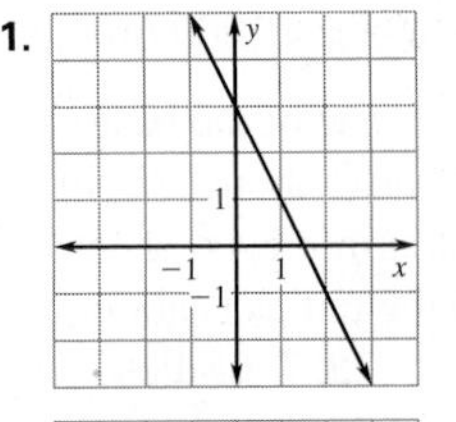

3.

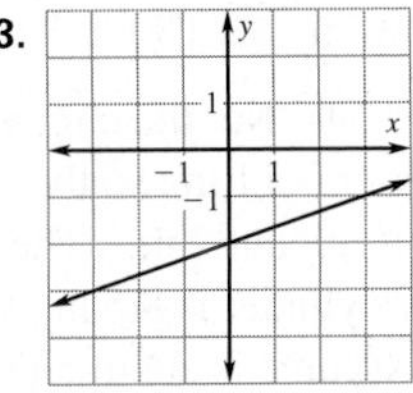

5.

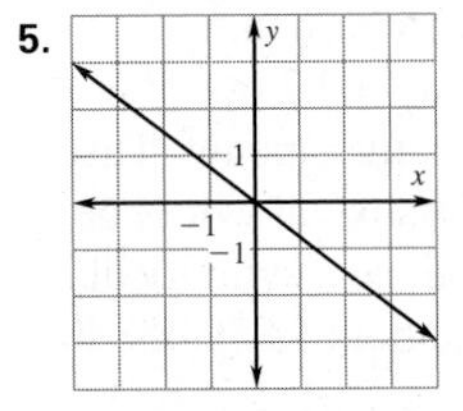

7.

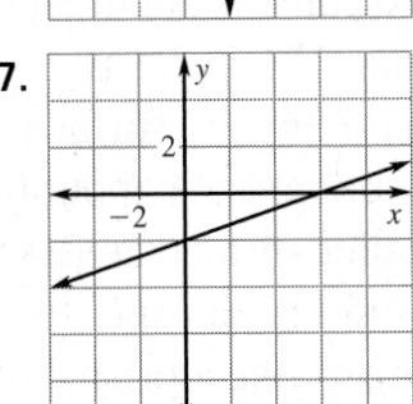

9.

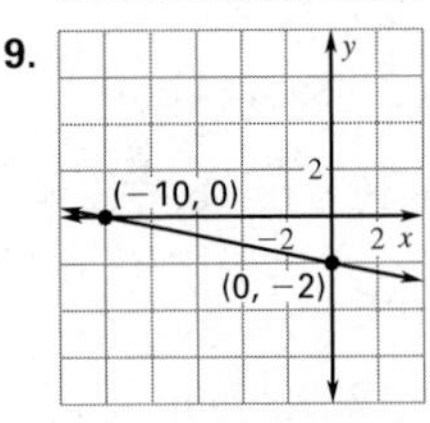

11.

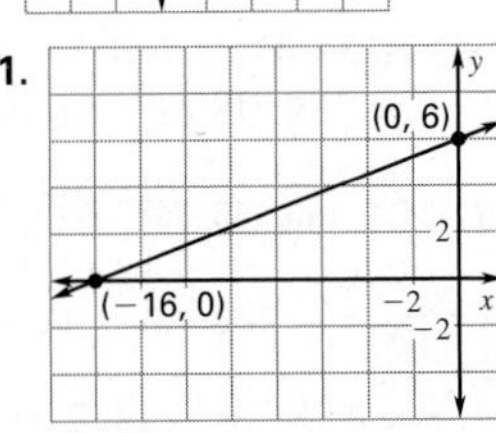

13.

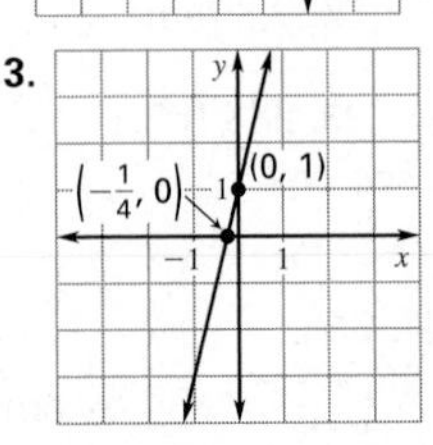

15.

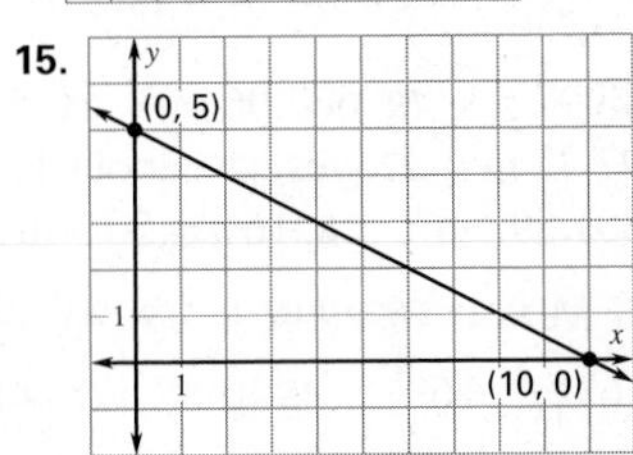

SELECTED ANSWERS

SLOPE–INTERCEPT FORM (p. 794)

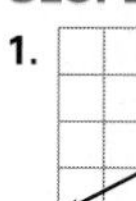

1.

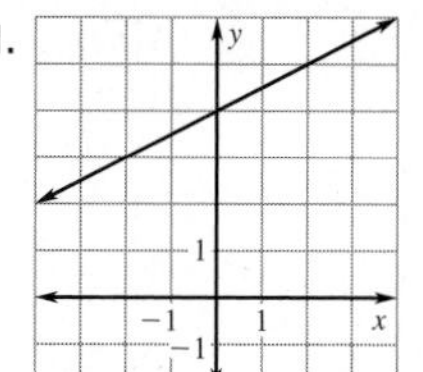

3.

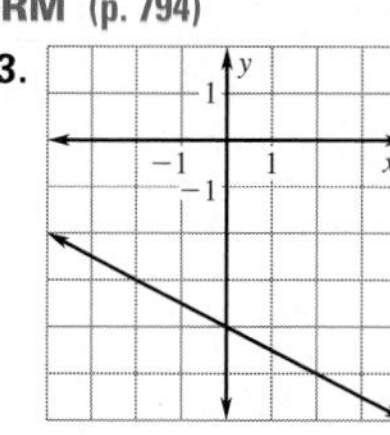

5.

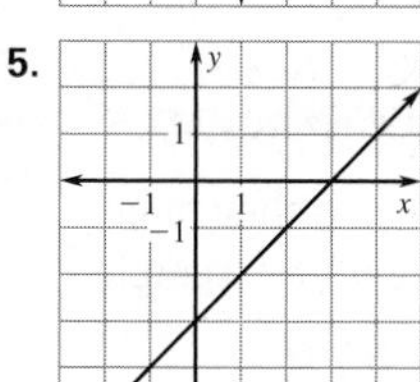

7.

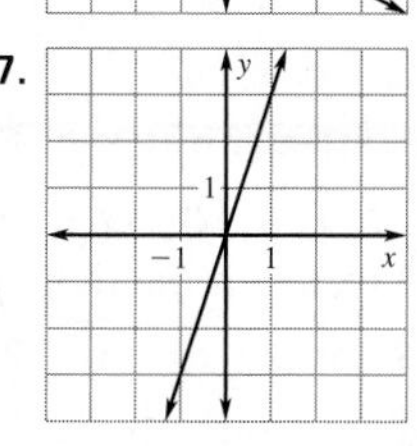

9.

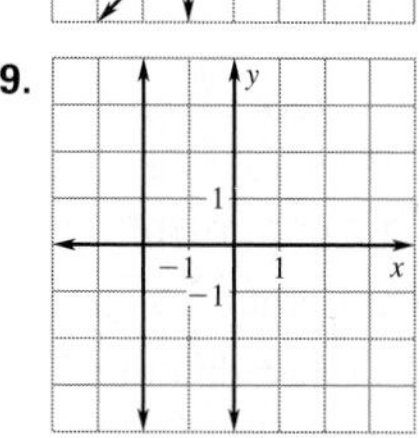

11.

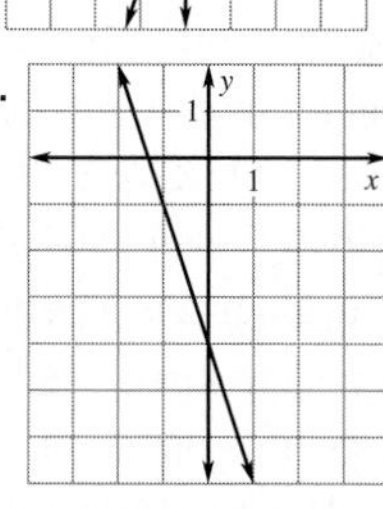

13.

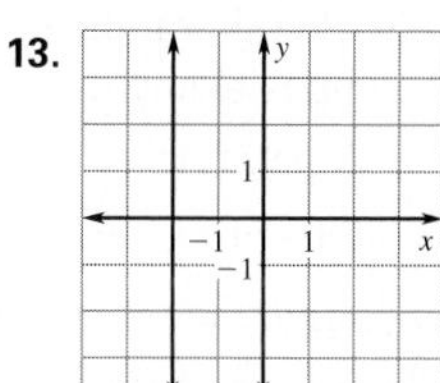

; The graph has no slope because a vertical line has the same x-coordinate for every point on the line. If you try to evaluate the slope using any two points, you get zero in the denominator, and division by zero is undefined. The graph has no y-intercept because it does not intersect the y-axis.

WRITING LINEAR EQUATIONS (p. 795) **1.** $y = x - 4$ **3.** $y = \frac{5}{2}x - \frac{3}{4}$ **5.** $y = 0.7x$ **7.** $y = 2x - 7$ **9.** $y = 12x + 66$ **11.** $y = -11$ **13.** $y = \frac{1}{6}x + \frac{17}{6}$ **15.** $y = 8x + 41$ **17.** $y = \frac{5}{8}x - \frac{5}{4}$ **19.** $y = -x - 1$ **21.** $y = -0.64x + 3.596$ **23.** $y = \frac{6}{7}x + \frac{11}{7}$

SOLVING SYSTEMS OF EQUATIONS (p. 796) **1.** (1, 6) **3.** (−2, −14) **5.** $\left(0, \frac{3}{4}\right)$ **7.** $\left(\frac{104}{9}, \frac{100}{9}\right)$ **9.** (3, −1.2) **11.** (−15, −19.5) **13.** $\left(\frac{3}{8}, -\frac{7}{8}\right)$ **15.** (2.35, 0.95)

PROPERTIES OF EXPONENTS (p. 797) **1.** $-\frac{8}{27}$ **3.** $\frac{1}{32}a^5b^5$ **5.** 1 **7.** $\frac{4}{x^3y^6}$ **9.** 262,144 **11.** $\frac{125}{m^3}$ **13.** $8b^4$ **15.** x^2 **17.** a^4 **19.** $\frac{a^2}{2bc^3}$ **21.** $-175a^2b^8c$ **23.** $32z^4$

MULTIPLYING BINOMIALS (p. 798) **1.** $x^2 + 2x + 1$ **3.** $3c^2 - 3$ **5.** $4a^2 + 13a - 35$ **7.** $4f^2 - 16$ **9.** $6h^2 + 9h + 3$

SQUARING BINOMIALS (p. 798) **1.** $x^2 + 4x + 4$ **3.** $x^2 + 16x + 64$ **5.** $n^2 - 10n + 25$ **7.** $225 - 30x + x^2$, or $x^2 - 30x + 225$

RADICAL EXPRESSIONS (p. 799) **1.** 8 and −8 **3.** $\frac{7}{9}$ and $-\frac{7}{9}$ **5.** 0.3 and −0.3 **7.** $\sqrt{13} \approx 3.61$ **9.** $5\sqrt{2} \approx 7.07$ **11.** −14 **13.** $2\sqrt{15} \approx 7.75$ **15.** $6\sqrt{2} \approx 8.49$ **17.** $30\sqrt{14} \approx 112.25$ **19.** $\frac{1}{5} = 0.2$ **21.** $\frac{1}{4} = 0.25$ **23.** $3\sqrt{2} \approx 4.24$ **25.** $\frac{4\sqrt{3}}{9} \approx 0.77$

SOLVING $AX^2 + C = 0$ (p. 800) **1.** 25, −25 **3.** $\sqrt{5} \approx 2.24$, $-\sqrt{5} \approx -2.24$ **5.** 2, −2 **7.** no solution **9.** 2.4 **11.** 13

SOLVING $AX^2 + BX + C = 0$ (p. 801) **1.** −4, −1 **3.** 0, −6 **5.** $\frac{9 + \sqrt{77}}{2} \approx 8.89$, $\frac{9 - \sqrt{77}}{2} \approx 0.11$ **7.** $\frac{-2 + \sqrt{2}}{2} \approx -0.29$, $\frac{-2 - \sqrt{2}}{2} \approx -1.71$ **9.** $\frac{4 + \sqrt{13}}{3} \approx 2.54$, $\frac{4 - \sqrt{13}}{3} \approx 0.13$ **11.** $\frac{5 + 3\sqrt{5}}{10} \approx 1.17$, $\frac{5 - 3\sqrt{5}}{10} \approx -0.17$

13. 1, 2; The solutions of the quadratic equation are the same as the x-intercepts of the graph.

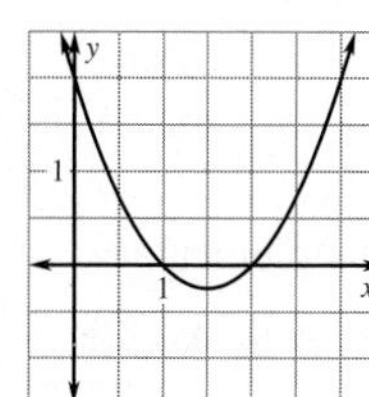

SOLVING FORMULAS (p. 802) **1.** $b = \frac{A}{h}$ **3.** $b = P - a - c$ **5.** $a = \frac{P - 2b}{2}$ **7.** $\ell = \frac{S - 2wh}{2w + 2h}$ **9.** $\ell = \frac{S - \pi r^2}{\pi r}$ **11.** $y = 9 - 3x$ **13.** $y = -\frac{1}{2}x - \frac{3}{2}$ **15.** $y = \frac{6}{7}x - 6$ **17.** $y = \frac{c - ax}{b}$

EXTRA PRACTICE

CHAPTER 1 (pp. 803–804) **1.** Multiply by $\frac{1}{2}$; $\frac{1}{2}$. **3.** powers of 5; 625 **5.** Multiply by 1.5; 162. **7.** negative **15.** 19 **17.** 12 **19.** 16 **21.** yes **23.** Q; $\overrightarrow{QP}$, $\overrightarrow{QR}$; $\angle PQR$, $\angle RQP$ **25.** B; $\overrightarrow{BA}$, $\overrightarrow{BC}$; $\angle ABC$, $\angle CBA$ **27.** 65° **29.** obtuse; ≈ 150° **31.** acute; ≈ 25° **33.** (3, −1) **35.** 42° **37.** 74° **39.** 45°, 135° **41.** 28; 49 **43.** 36; 60 **45.** 31.4; 78.5 **47.** 33; 67.0625

CHAPTER 2 (pp. 805–806) **1.** If you read it in a newspaper, then it must be true. **3.** If a number is odd, then its square is odd. **5.** If you are not indoors, then you are caught in a rainstorm; If you are not caught in a rainstorm, then you are indoors; If you are caught in a rainstorm, then you are not indoors. **7.** If two angles are not vertical angles, then they are not congruent; If two angles are congruent, then they are vertical angles; If two angles are not congruent, then they are not vertical angles. **9.** If $x = 6$, then $2x - 5 = 7$; true. **11.** If two angles are right angles, then they are supplementary; If two angles are supplementary, then they are right angles. **13.** yes **15.** no **17.** If we don't stop at the bank, then we won't see our friends.
19. We go shopping if and only if we need a shopping list.
21. We go shopping if and only if we stop at the bank.

SA35

23. p: The hockey teams wins the game tonight. q: They will play in the championship. $\sim p \rightarrow \sim q$; If the hockey team doesn't win the game tonight, they won't play in the championship. $\sim q \rightarrow \sim p$; If the hockey team doesn't play in the championship, then they didn't win the game tonight. **25.** AB **27.** $AB = DF$ **29.** 6 – 4 (or 2) **31.** $\angle 6$ **33.** $\angle 3 \cong \angle 5$ by the Congruent Complements Theorem. **35.** $b = 8$; $c = 27$

37.

Statements	Reasons
1. $\angle 1 \cong \angle 3$	1. Vertical angles are $\cong$.
2. $\angle 4 \cong \angle 2$	2. Vertical angles are $\cong$.
3. $\angle 1$ and $\angle 4$ are complementary.	3. Given
4. $m\angle 1 + m\angle 4 = 90°$	4. Definition of complementary
5. $m\angle 1 = m\angle 3$	5. Definition of congruence
6. $m\angle 4 = m\angle 2$	6. Definition of congruence
7. $m\angle 3 + m\angle 2 = 90°$	7. Substitution property of equality
8. $\angle 3$ and $\angle 2$ are complementary.	8. Definition of complementary

CHAPTER 3 (pp. 807–808) **1.** parallel **3.** skew **5.** *Sample answers:* $\overleftrightarrow{AB}$, $\overleftrightarrow{BC}$, $\overleftrightarrow{GE}$, $\overleftrightarrow{HG}$ **7.** *Sample answers: HAD, ADF, DFH, FHA* **9.** alternate interior **11.** consecutive interior

13.

Statements	Reasons
2. $\angle ABC$ is a right angle.	1. Given
7. $m\angle ABD$	3. Def. of a right $\angle$
	4. Given
	5. Def. of $\angle$ bisector
	6. If 2 sides of 2 adj. acute $\angle$s are $\perp$, then the $\angle$s are complementary.
	8. Distributive prop.
	9. Division prop. of equality

15. $x = 30$; $y = 150$ **17.** $x = 125$; $y = 125$ **19.** $x = 118$; $y = 118$ **21.** $\overleftrightarrow{CG} \parallel \overleftrightarrow{DE}$ **23.** Corresponding angles are congruent. **25.** Alternate interior angles are congruent. **27.** $\overleftrightarrow{AB}$: 0; $\overleftrightarrow{CD}$: $-\frac{1}{3}$; $\overleftrightarrow{EF}$: $-\frac{11}{14}$; none **29.** $y = 6x + 19$ **31.** $x = -9$ **33.** yes **35.** $y = \frac{1}{2}x - 3$ **37.** $y = -2x - 11$

CHAPTER 4 (pp. 809–810) **1.** 20, 60, 100; obtuse **3.** 40, 90, 50; right **5.** 90°, 45°, 45° **7.** $ABGH \cong BEFG \cong CDEB$; $AEFH \cong CGFD$ **9.** $\angle A, \angle F$; $\angle B, \angle E$; $\angle C, \angle D$; $\overline{AB}, \overline{FE}$; $\overline{BC}, \overline{ED}$; $\overline{AC}, \overline{FD}$ **11.** 13 **13.** SSS **15.** SAS **17.** yes; AAS **19.** no **21.** ASA; corresp. parts of $\cong$ $\triangle$s are $\cong$. **23.** SSS; corresponding parts of $\cong$ $\triangle$s are $\cong$. **25.** Paragraph proof: Given that $\triangle CBD \cong \triangle BAF$, $\overline{BC} \cong \overline{AB}$ by corresp. parts of $\cong$ $\triangle$s are $\cong$. **27.** $x = 60$; $y = 60$ **29.** $x = 45$; $y = 45$ **31.** *Sample answer:*

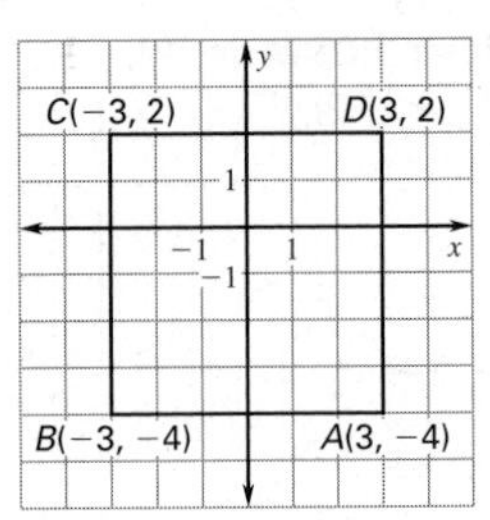

33. 100 **35.** $7\sqrt{2}$

CHAPTER 5 (pp. 811–812) **1.** 12 **3.** E is on $\overrightarrow{DB}$. **5.** K is on $\overrightarrow{EH}$. **7.** 9 **9.** 10 **11.** 8 **15.** The orthocenter should be at the vertex of the right angle of the triangle. **17.** $\overline{AC}$ **19.** 5 **21.** 9 **23.** $\overline{BC}, \overline{AC}$ **25.** $\overline{GJ}, \overline{GH}$ **27.** $\angle Q, \angle P$ **29.** < **31.** = **33.** = **35.** = **37.** <

CHAPTER 6 (pp. 813–814) **1.** no **3.** yes; hexagon; convex **5.** no **7.** 25 **9.** 13 **11.** $\angle VYX$; If a quadrilateral is a parallelogram, then its opposite angles are congruent. **13.** $\overline{TX}$; If a quadrilateral is a parallelogram, then its diagonals bisect each other. **15.** $\overline{VY}$; If a quadrilateral is a parallelogram, then its opposite sides are parallel. **17.** $\overline{VX}$ and $\overline{YW}$; If a quadrilateral is a parallelogram, then its diagonals bisect each other. **19.** Yes; opposite angles are congruent. **21.** *Sample answer:* The slope of $\overline{AD}$ = slope of $\overline{BC} = -\frac{3}{5}$ and the slope of $\overline{AB}$ = slope of $\overline{DC} = -\frac{7}{2}$. If opposite sides of a quadrilateral are parallel, then it is a parallelogram. **23.** *Sample answer:* The slope of $\overline{RS}$ = slope of $\overline{UT} = -\frac{1}{11}$. Since $RS = UT = \sqrt{122}$, $\overline{RS} \cong \overline{UT}$ by definition of congruence. If one pair of opposite sides of a quadrilateral are congruent and parallel, then the quadrilateral is a parallelogram. **25.** parallelogram, rhombus, rectangle, square **27.** rectangle, square **29.** rhombus, square **31.** rhombus **33.** square **35.** $m\angle A = 70°$; $m\angle B = 110°$; $m\angle D = 70°$ **37.** $m\angle G = 115°$; $m\angle E = 115°$ **39.** 23 **41.** $AB = 25$, $BC = 25$, $AD = 39$, $CD = 39$ **43.** $KM = 8\sqrt{10}$, $KP = 8\sqrt{10}$, $MN = 10$, $NP = 10$ **45.** rectangle or parallelogram **47.** 160 **49.** 55

CHAPTER 7 (pp. 815–816) **1.** Z **3.** *Sample answers:* $\overline{QR} \cong \overline{ZY}$; $\overline{RP} \cong \overline{YX}$; $\overline{PQ} \cong \overline{XZ}$ **5.** (–7, 3) **7.** translation; slide 8 units to the right; $E(3, 1)$, $F(3, 3)$, $G(6, 3)$, $H(6, 1)$ **9.** $\triangle GHJ$ **11.** $\triangle FED$ **13.** $\triangle GFE$ **15.** $\triangle NPM$ **17.** (2, 4) **19.** (1, –12) **21.** (7, 0) **23.** $H'(2, 0)$, $E'(5, -2)$, $F'(5, -5)$, $G'(2, -7)$ **25.** $J'(4, -4)$, $K'(1, -2)$, $M'(4, 0)$, $N'(7, -2)$ **27.** a, b **29.** $\langle -3, 5\rangle$ **31.** $\langle -7, 7\rangle$ **33.** (–5, –1)

SELECTED ANSWERS

SA36

35. 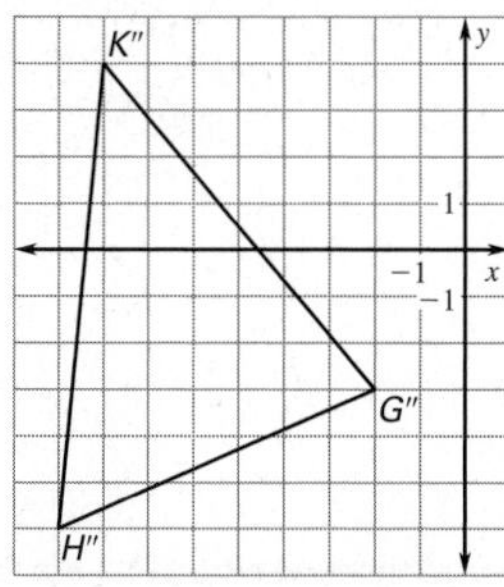

37. TR

CHAPTER 8 (pp. 817–818) **1.** $\frac{2}{1}$ **3.** $\frac{5}{8}$ **5.** 60°, 80°, 100°, 120° **7.** 7 **9.** 3 **11.** 1 **13.** $\frac{10}{y}$ **15.** $\frac{x}{y}$ **17.** 6 **19.** 5 **21.** 32 **23.** 6.25 **25.** 3:2 **27.** $u = 9$, $y = 4$, $z = 10$ **29.** yes; $\triangle ABC \sim \triangle DEF$ **31.** no **33.** (0, 12.5) **35.** (0, –12) **37.** no **39.** yes; $\triangle ACE \sim \triangle BCD$; 12 **41.** yes; $\triangle EFG \sim \triangle HJK$; 8 **43.** yes; $\frac{4}{8} = \frac{1}{2}$ **45.** 20 **47.** $A'(10, 0)$, $B'(25, 15)$, $C'(20, 25)$, $D'(5, 15)$ **49.** $A'(1, -1)$, $B'(1.5, 1)$, $C'(0.5, 2)$, $D'(-2, -1)$

CHAPTER 9 (pp. 819–820) **1.** $\triangle ABC \sim \triangle ACD \sim \triangle CBD$; AC **3.** $\triangle JLK \sim \triangle JKM \sim \triangle KLM$; JL **5.** 10 **7.** $\sqrt{61}$; no **9.** 50; yes **11.** 13 **13.** 175 **15.** 28 **17.** about 91.2 cm^2 **19.** yes **21.** yes **23.** yes; right **25.** yes; obtuse **27.** yes; obtuse **29.** $x = 16$; $y = 8\sqrt{3}$ **31.** $\sin S = 0.8615$, $\cos S = 0.5077$, $\tan S = 1.6970$; $\sin T = 0.5077$, $\cos T = 0.8615$, $\tan T = 0.5893$ **33.** $\sin X = 0.7241$, $\cos X = 0.6897$, $\tan X = 1.05$; $\sin Z = 0.6897$, $\cos Z = 0.7241$, $\tan Z = 0.9524$ **35.** $x = 8.8$; $y = 3.7$ **37.** $AC = 9$, $m\angle A = 53.1°$, $m\angle B = 36.9°$ **39.** $MP = 171$, $m\angle N = 50.7°$, $m\angle M = 39.3°$ **41.** $\langle 4, 11 \rangle$; 11.7 **43.** $\langle -4, 7 \rangle$ **45.** $\langle 3, 3 \rangle$

CHAPTER 10 (pp. 821–822) **1.** D **3.** G **5.** H **7.** A **9.** internal **11.** internal **13.** D; 2 **15.** $y = 3$, $x = 5$, $y = -1$ **17.** 55° **19.** 35° **21.** 145° **23.** 270° **25.** 70 **27.** 240 **29.** 80 **31.** 70 **33.** 4 **35.** 10 **37.** 4 **39.** (12, –3); 7 **41.** (–3.8, 4.9); 0.9 **43.** $(x - 5)^2 + (y - 8)^2 = 36$ **45.** $(x - 2)^2 + (y - 2)^2 = 4$ **47.** $x = 4$ **49.** $y = -2$, $y = 6$

CHAPTER 11 (pp. 823–824) **1.** 6120° **3.** 10,440° **5.** 140 **7.** 120 **9.** 15° **11.** 10° **13.** 20 **15.** 4 **17.** 20° **9.** 4° **21.** 16.97; 18 **23.** 48.50; 169.74 **25.** 25.98; 32.48 **27.** 3:1; 9:1 **29.** 125 square inches **31.** about 9.07 **33.** about 147 **35.** about 11.78 **37.** about 95.49 **39.** about 452.39 **41.** about 41.89 **43.** about 19.63 **45.** about 67% **47.** about 83% **49.** about 68%

CHAPTER 12 (pp. 825–826) **1.** polyhedron; not regular; convex **3.** polyhedron; regular; convex **5.** $F = 7$, $V = 7$, $E = 12$; $7 + 7 = 12 + 2$ **7.** square **9.** 220 cm^2 **11.** 120 $in.^2$ **13.** 339.29 cm^2 **15.** 85 $in.^2$ **17.** 282.74 cm^2 **19.** about 1060.29 ft^3 **21.** about 2001.19 $in.^3$ **23.** about 247.59 ft^3 **25.** 701.48 cm^3 **27.** about 513.13 $in.^3$ **29.** about 871.27 ft^3 **31.** 2123.72 m^2; 9202.77 m^3 **33.** 216 m^2; 216 m^3 **35.** 196π cm^2; $457\frac{1}{3}\pi$ cm^3

SELECTED ANSWERS

SA37

TEACHER'S EDITION INDEX

Student Edition entries in black.
Teacher's Edition entries in blue.

A

B

C

D

E

TEACHER'S EDITION INDEX

F

H

M

N

O

P

S

TEACHER'S EDITION INDEX

U

ADDITIONAL ANSWERS

CHAPTER 1

1.1 GUIDED PRACTICE (p. 6) **3.** 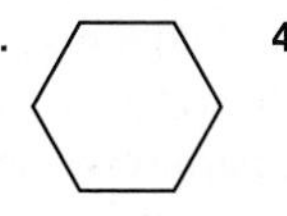 **4.** 

1.1 PRACTICE AND APPLICATIONS (pp. 6–9)

12. 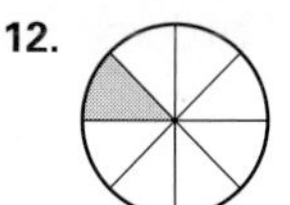 **13.** 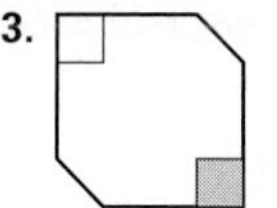 **14.** 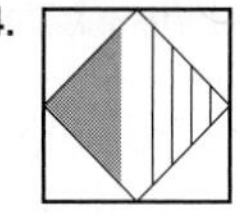 **15.** 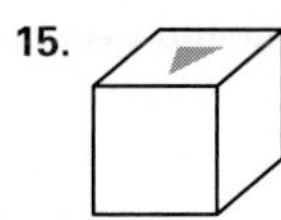

1.3 PRACTICE AND APPLICATIONS (pp. 21–24)

19. 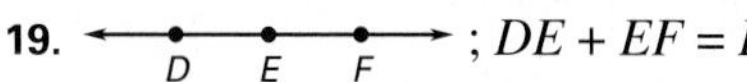

; $DE + EF = DF$

20. G H J ; $GH + HJ = GJ$

21. N M P ; $NM + MP = NP$

22. Q R S ; $QR + RS = QS$

1.7 PRACTICE AND APPLICATIONS (pp. 55–58)

32. 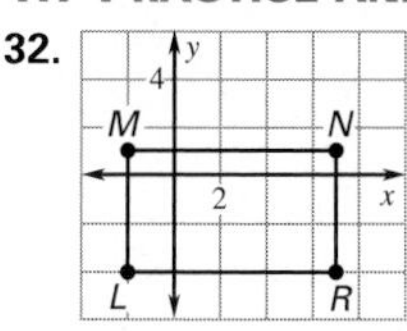

33. 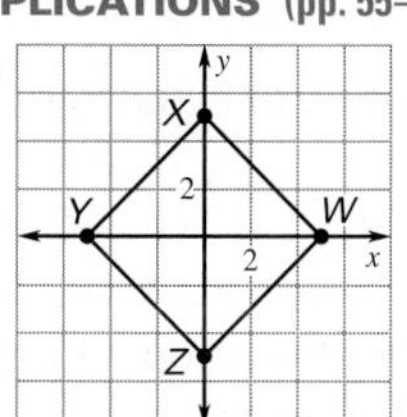

CHAPTER 2

2.1 PRACTICE AND APPLICATIONS (pp. 75–77) **46. a.** hypothesis: you tell the truth; conclusion: you don't have to remember anything **b.** If you don't tell the truth, then you will have to remember things. **47.** if-then form: If one feels the impulse to soar, then one can never consent to creep. **a.** hypothesis: one feels the impulse to soar; conclusion: one can never consent to creep **b.** If one does not feel the impulse to soar, then one can consent to creep. **48.** if-then form: If freedom does not include the freedom to make mistakes, then it is not worth having. **a.** hypothesis: freedom does not include the freedom to make mistakes; conclusion: freedom is not worth having **b.** If freedom includes the freedom to make mistakes, then it is worth having. **49.** if-then form: If a man is early to bed and early to rise, then the man will be healthy, wealthy, and wise. **a.** hypothesis: a man is early to bed and early to rise; conclusion: the man is healthy, wealthy, and wise **b.** If a man is not early to bed and early to rise, then the man is not healthy, wealthy, and wise. **50.** if-then form: If you want a great selection of used cars, then come and see Bargain Bob's Used Cars; hypothesis: you want a great selection of used cars; conclusion: come and see Bargain Bob's Used Cars. **51.** inverse: If you do not want a great selection of used cars, then do not come and see Bargain Bob's Used Cars; converse: If you come and see Bargain Bob's Used Cars, then you want a great selection of used cars; contrapositive: If you do not come and see Bargain Bob's Used Cars, then you do not want a great selection of used cars.

52. Check work. A good answer should include all of these points.
- an advertisement containing a hypothesis and conclusion
- the advertisement rewritten in if-then form
- the inverse, converse, and contrapositive of the advertisement

53. Check work. **54.** *Sample answer:* By Postulate 9, a plane contains at least three noncollinear points. Because the CRAB has three legs, its bottom surface can be considered a plane. As the ocean floor is comprised of many intersecting planes, a planar surface moving above the ocean floor can map where the planes are parallel and where they would intersect.

2.2 PRACTICE AND APPLICATIONS (pp. 82–85) **32.** if-then form: If two angles are adjacent, then they share a common side; converse: If two angles share a common side, then they are adjacent; true; biconditional statement: Two angles are adjacent if and only if they share a common side. **33.** if-then form: If two circles have the same diameter, then they have the same circumference; converse: If two circles have the same circumference, then they have the same diameter; true; biconditional statement: Two circles have the same circumference if and only if they have the same diameter. **34.** if-then form: If a number is the perimeter of a triangle, then it is the sum of the lengths of the triangle's sides; converse: If a number is the sum of the lengths of the sides of a triangle, then the number is the triangle's perimeter; true; biconditional statement: A number is the perimeter of a triangle if and only if it is the sum of the lengths of the triangle's sides. **35.** if-then form: If an animal is a leopard, then it has spots; converse: If an animal has spots, then it is a leopard; false; counterexample: A giraffe has spots, but it is not a leopard. **36.** if-then form: If an animal is a panther, then it lives in the forest; converse: If an animal lives in the forest, then it is a panther; false; counterexample: A deer lives in the forest, but it is not a panther. **37.** if-then form: If a leopard has pale gray fur, then it is a snow leopard; converse: If a leopard is a snow leopard, then it has pale gray fur; true; biconditional statement: A leopard is a snow leopard if and only if it has pale gray fur. **46.** A musical group is a *piano trio* if and only if it contains exactly 1 pianist, 1 violinist, and 1 cellist; If a musical group is a *piano trio*, then it contains exactly 1 pianist, 1 violinist, and 1 cellist; If a musical group contains exactly 1 pianist, 1 violinist, and 1 cellist, then the musical group is a *piano trio.*

A musical group is a *string quartet* if and only if it contains exactly 2 violinists, 1 cellist, and 1 violist; If a musical group is a *string quartet*, then it contains exactly 2 violinists, 1 cellist, and 1 violist; If a musical group contains exactly 2 violinists, 1 cellist, and 1 violist, then the musical group is a *string quartet.*

A musical group is a *string quintet* if and only if it contains exactly 2 violinists, 1 cellist, and 2 violists; If a musical group is a *string quintet*, then it contains exactly 2 violinists, 1 cellist, and 2 violists; If a musical group contains exactly 2 violinists, 1 cellist, and 2 violists, then the musical group is a *string quintet.*

A musical group is a *piano quintet* if and only if it contains exactly 1 pianist, 2 violinists, 1 cellist, and 1 violist; If a musical group is a *piano quintet*, then it contains exactly 1 pianist, 2 violinists, 1 cellist, and 1 violist; If a musical group contains exactly 1 pianist, 2 violinists,

1 cellist, and 1 violist, then the musical group is a *piano quintet*. **56. a.** contrapositive: If I am not in the capital of Iowa, then I am not in Des Moines; true. **b.** biconditional statement: I am in Des Moines if and only if I am in the capital of Iowa; true. **57. a.** contrapositive: If two angles are not complementary, then the angles do not measure 10° and 80°; true. **b.** biconditional statement: Two angles measure 10° and 80° if and only if they are complementary; false; Two angles can measure 30° and 60° and be complementary.

2.3 PRACTICE AND APPLICATIONS (pp. 91–94) **8.** If points X, Y, and Z lie on the same line, then points X, Y, and Z are collinear. **9.** Points X, Y, and Z do not lie on the same line. **10.** Points X, Y, and Z are not collinear. **11.** If points X, Y, and Z are not collinear, then points X, Y, and Z do not lie on the same line. **12.** Points X, Y, and Z are collinear if and only if points X, Y, and Z lie on the same line. **13.** If points X, Y, and Z do not lie on the same line, then points X, Y, and Z are not collinear. **14.** p: Jed gets a C on the exam; q: Jed will get an A for the quarter; inverse: $\sim p \rightarrow \sim q$, If Jed does not get a C on the exam, then he will not get an A for the quarter; contrapositive: $\sim q \rightarrow \sim p$, If Jed does not get an A for the quarter, then Jed did not get a C on the exam. **15.** p: Alberto finds a summer job; q: Alberto will buy a car; inverse: $\sim p \rightarrow \sim q$, If Alberto does not find a summer job, then he will not buy a car; contrapositive: $\sim q \rightarrow \sim p$, If Alberto does not buy a car, then he did not find a summer job. **16.** p: the fuse has blown; q: the light will not go on; inverse: $\sim p \rightarrow \sim q$, If the fuse has not blown, then the light will go on; contrapositive: $\sim q \rightarrow \sim p$, If the light goes on, then the fuse has not blown. **17.** p: the car is running; q: the key is in the ignition; inverse: $\sim p \rightarrow \sim q$, If the car is not running, then the key is not in the ignition; contrapositive: $\sim q \rightarrow \sim p$, If the key is not in the ignition, then the car is not running. **18.** p: you dial 911; q: there is an emergency; inverse: $\sim p \rightarrow \sim q$, If you do not dial 911, then there is not an emergency; contrapositive: $\sim q \rightarrow \sim p$, If there is not an emergency, then you will not dial 911. **19.** p: Gina walks to the store; q: Gina buys a newspaper; inverse: $\sim p \rightarrow \sim q$, If Gina does not walk to the store, then she will not buy a newspaper; contrapositive: $\sim q \rightarrow \sim p$, If Gina does not buy a newspaper, then she did not walk to the store. **20.** p: it is not raining; q: Petra will ride her bike to school; inverse: $\sim p \rightarrow \sim q$, If it is raining, then Petra will not ride her bike to school; contrapositive: $\sim q \rightarrow \sim p$, If Petra does not ride her bike to school, then it is raining.

2.4 GUIDED PRACTICE (p. 99) **2.** The addition property of equality states that if $a = b$, then $a + c = b + c$. This property can be applied to the angles. If $m\angle JNK = m\angle LNM$, then $m\angle JNK + m\angle KNL = m\angle LNM + m\angle KNL$. On the left side of the equation, $m\angle JNK + m\angle KNL = m\angle JNL$ and on the right side of the equation, $m\angle LNM + m\angle KNL = m\angle KNM$. Therefore, $m\angle JNL = m\angle KNM$. **3.** The subtraction property of equality states that if $a = b$, then $a - c = b - c$. This property can be applied to the angles. If $m\angle JNL = m\angle KNM$, then $m\angle JNL - m\angle KNL = m\angle KNM - m\angle KNL$. $m\angle JNL - m\angle KNL = m\angle JNK$ and $m\angle KNM - m\angle KNL = m\angle LNM$; therefore, $m\angle JNK = m\angle LNM$.

9. $W = 1.42T - 38.5$ (Given)
$W + 38.5 = 1.42T$ (Addition property of equality)
$\frac{W + 38.5}{1.42} = T$ (Division property of equality)
If $W = -24.3$°F, then $T = 10$°F.

2.4 PRACTICE AND APPLICATIONS (pp. 99–101)

21. $-2(-w + 3) = 15$ (Given)
$2w - 6 = 15$ (Distributive prop.)
$2w = 21$ (Addition prop. of equality)
$w = 10.5$ (Division prop. of equality)

22. $26u + 4(12u - 5) = 128$ (Given)
$26u + 48u - 20 = 128$ (Distributive prop.)
$74u - 20 = 128$ (Simplify.)
$74u = 148$ (Addition prop. of equality)
$u = 2$ (Division prop. of equality)

23. $3(4v - 1) - 8v = 17$ (Given)
$12v - 3 - 8v = 17$ (Distributive prop.)
$4v - 3 = 17$ (Simplify.)
$4v = 20$ (Addition prop. of equality)
$v = 5$ (Division prop. of equality)

26. $\angle 1$ and $\angle 2$ are right angles (Given)
$m\angle 1 = 90°$, $m\angle 2 = 90°$ (Definition of right angles)
$\angle 1$ and $\angle 2$ are supplementary angles (Definition of supplementary angles)

27. B lies between A and C (Given)
$AB + BC = AC$ (Segment Addition Post.)
$AB = 3$, $BC = 8$ (Given)
$3 + 8 = AC$ (Substitution prop. of equality)
$AC = 11$ (Simplify.)

28. $m\angle 2 + m\angle 4 = 62°$ (Given)
$m\angle 1 = m\angle 2$ (Given)
$m\angle 1 + m\angle 4 = 62°$ (Substitution prop. of equality)
$m\angle 1 + m\angle 3 + m\angle 4 = 93°$ (Given)
$m\angle 3 + 62° = 93°$ (Substitution prop. of equality)
$m\angle 3 = 31°$ (Subtraction prop. of equality)

29. $c(r + 1) = n$ (Given)
$cr + c = n$ (Distributive prop.)
$cr = n - c$ (Subtraction prop. of equality)
$r = \frac{n - c}{c}$ (Division prop. of equality)

31. To find Donald's old wage, solve the formula $c(r + 1) = n$ for c.
$c(r + 1) = n$ (Given)
$c = \frac{n}{r + 1}$ (Division prop. of equality)
$c = \frac{12.72}{0.06 + 1}$ (Substitution prop. of equality)
$c = \$12.00$ (Simplify.)

2.5 GUIDED PRACTICE (p. 104) **4.** $\overline{BF} \perp \overline{CD}$, $\angle CDF$ is a right angle by the definition of perpendicular, $m\angle CDE + m\angle FDE = m\angle CDF$ by the Angle Addition Postulate, $\angle CDE$ and $\angle FDE$ are complementary by the definition of complementary angles.

2.5 PRACTICE AND APPLICATIONS (pp. 105–107)

8. $\overline{AB} \cong \overline{BC}$, $\overline{CD} \cong \overline{BC}$ (Given)
$\overline{AB} \cong \overline{CD}$ (Transitive Prop. of Segment Cong.)
$AB = CD$ (Definition of congruent segments)
$2x + 1 = 4x - 11$ (Substitution prop. of equality)
$-2x + 1 = -11$ (Subtraction prop. of equality)
$-2x = -12$ (Subtraction prop. of equality)
$x = 6$ (Division prop. of equality)

9. $PR = 46$ (Given)
$PQ + QR = PR$ (Segment Addition Post.)
$2x + 5 + 6x - 15 = 46$ (Substitution prop. of equality)
$8x - 10 = 46$ (Simplify.)
$8x = 56$ (Addition prop. of equality)
$x = 7$ (Division prop. of equality)

10. $\overline{ST} \cong \overline{SR}$, $\overline{QR} \cong \overline{SR}$ (Given)
$\overline{ST} \cong \overline{QR}$ (Transitive Prop. of Segment Cong.)
$ST = QR$ (Definition of congruent segments)
$5(3x - 2) = x + 4$ (Substitution prop. of equality)
$15x - 10 = x + 4$ (Distributive prop.)
$14x - 10 = 4$ (Subtraction prop. of equality)
$14x = 14$ (Addition prop. of equality)
$x = 1$ (Division prop. of equality)

11. $\overline{XY} \cong \overline{WX}$, $\overline{YZ} \cong \overline{WX}$ (Given)
$\overline{XY} \cong \overline{YZ}$ (Transitive Prop. of Segment Cong.)
$XY = YZ$ (Definition of congruent segments)
$4x + 3 = 9x - 12$ (Substitution prop. of equality)
$-5x + 3 = -12$ (Subtraction prop. of equality)
$-5x = -15$ (Subtraction prop. of equality)
$x = 3$ (Division prop. of equality)

20. $\overline{UV} \cong \overline{ZY}$, $\overline{UW} \cong \overline{ZX}$ (Given)
$UV = ZY$, $UW = ZX$ (Definition of congruence)
$VW = UW - UV$ (Segment Addition Post.)
$YX = ZX - ZY$ (Segment Addition Post.)
$YX = UW - UV$ (Substitution prop. of equality)
$VW = YX$ (Transitive Prop. of Segment Cong.)
$\overline{VW} \cong \overline{YX}$ (Definition of congruence.)

2.6 ACTIVITY (p. 108) **1. a.** The crease is perpendicular to the paper bottom, so it makes a 90° angle with the bottom. $\angle 1$ and $\angle 2$ make up this angle on the left side of the crease, so $m\angle 1 + m\angle 2 = 90°$. By the definition of complementary angles, $\angle 1$ and $\angle 2$ are complementary. **b.** The crease is perpendicular to the paper bottom, so it makes a 90° angle with the bottom. $\angle 3$ and $\angle 4$ also make up this angle on the right side of the crease, so $m\angle 3 + m\angle 4 = 90°$. By the definition of complementary angles, $\angle 3$ and $\angle 4$ are complementary. **c.** $\angle 2$ and $\angle 3$ make up the angle formed by the 90° corner of the second piece of paper. By the definition of complementary angles, $\angle 2$ and $\angle 3$ are complementary.

2.6 PRACTICE AND APPLICATIONS (pp. 113–115)

37. $m\angle ZYQ = 45°$, $m\angle ZQP = 45°$ (Given)
$m\angle XYZ = m\angle PQR$ (Definition of a line)
$m\angle XYQ + m\angle ZYQ = 180°$ (Definition of supplementary angles)
$m\angle ZQR + m\angle ZQP = 180°$ (Definition of supplementary angles)
$m\angle ZQR + m\angle ZQP = m\angle XYQ + m\angle ZYQ$
(Transitive prop. of equality)
$m\angle ZYQ = m\angle ZQP$ (Transitive prop. of equality)
$m\angle ZQR + m\angle ZYQ = m\angle XYQ + m\angle ZYQ$
(Substitution prop. of equality)
$m\angle ZQR = m\angle XYQ$ (Subtraction prop. of equality)
$\angle ZQR \cong \angle XYQ$ (Definition of congruent angles)

CHAPTER 3

3.1 MIXED REVIEW (p. 134)

60. $-2x + 2x + 9 = -2x + 4x - 29$ (Addition property of equality)
$9 = 2x - 29$ (Simplify.)
$9 + 29 = 2x - 29 + 29$ (Addition property of equality)
$38 = 2x$ (Simplify.)
$\frac{38}{2} = \frac{2x}{2}$ (Division property of equality)
$19 = x$ (Simplify.)

61. *Sample answer:* $2x - 2 + 3 = 17$ (Distributive property)
$2x + 1 = 17$ (Simplify.)
$2x + 1 - 1 = 17 - 1$ (Subtraction property of equality)
$2x = 16$ (Simplify.)
$\frac{2x}{2} = \frac{16}{2}$ (Division property of equality)
$x = 8$ (Simplify.)

62. $5x + 7x - 70 = -94$ (Distributive property)
$12x - 70 = -94$ (Simplify.)
$12x - 70 + 70 = -94 + 70$ (Addition property of equality)
$12x = -24$ (Simplify.)
$\frac{12x}{12} = \frac{-24}{12}$ (Division property of equality)
$x = -2$ (Simplify.)

3.2 CONCEPT ACTIVITY (p. 135)

2–3.

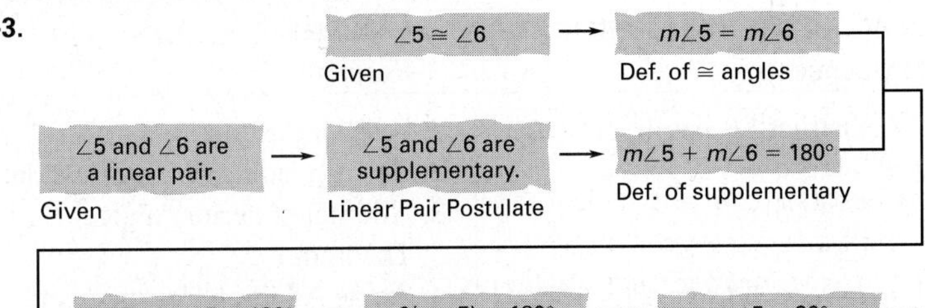

3.2 GUIDED PRACTICE (p. 138)

10.

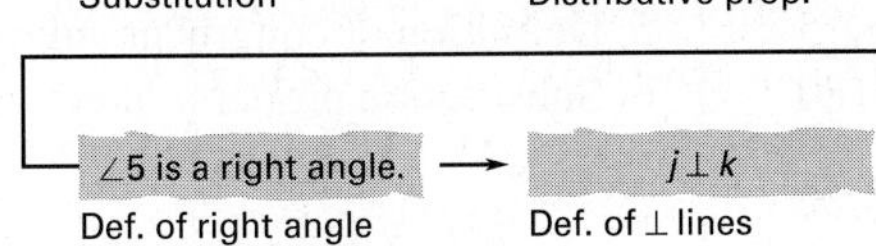

3.4 MIXED REVIEW (p. 156)

40.

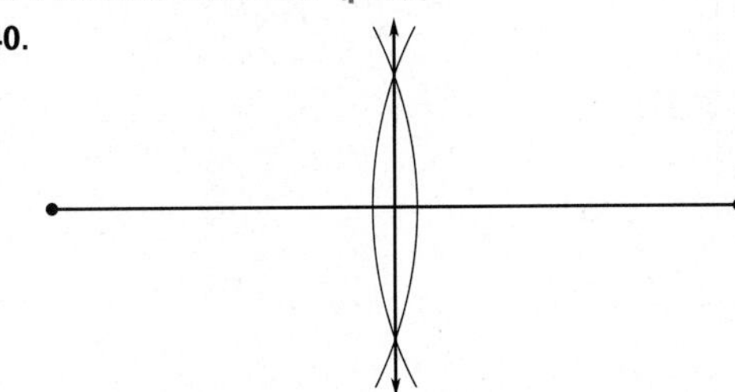

41.

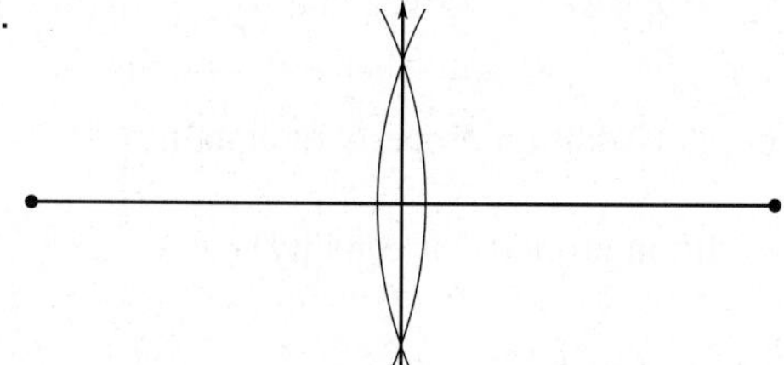

42. **43.**

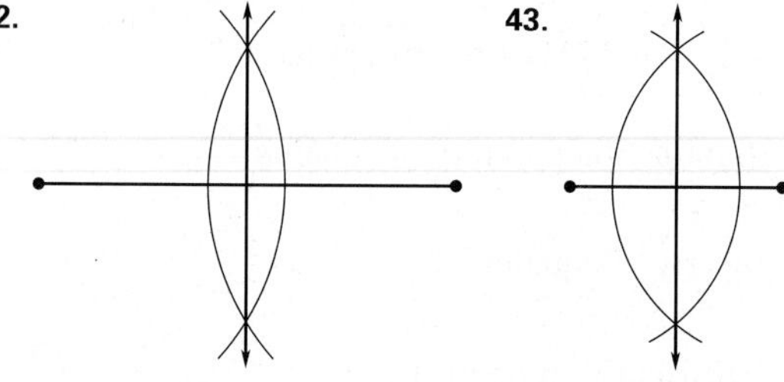

CHAPTER 4

SKILL REVIEW (p. 192)

7. **8.** **9.**

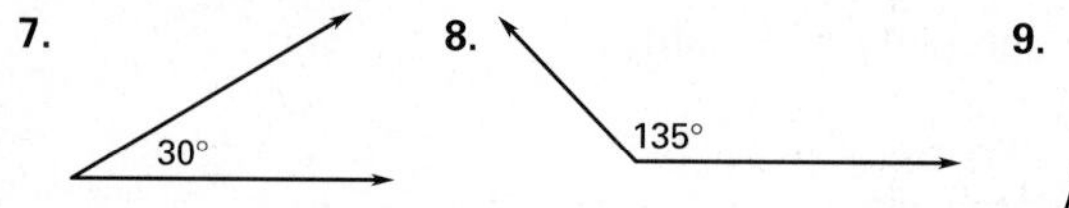

4.1 PRACTICE AND APPLICATIONS (pp. 198–201)

51.

Statements	Reasons
1. Construct $\overline{SP}$ parallel to $\overline{QR}$.	1. Parallel Postulate
2. $\angle 3 \cong \angle 4$	2. Corresponding Angles Postulate
3. $\angle 2 \cong \angle 5$	3. Alternate Interior Angles Theorem
4. $m\angle 1 + m\angle 5 + m\angle 4 = 180°$	4. Angle Addition Postulate and definition of straight angle
5. $m\angle 3 = m\angle 4$, $m\angle 2 = m\angle 5$	5. Definition of congruent angles
6. $m\angle 1 + m\angle 2 + m\angle 3 = 180°$	6. Substitution property of equality

4.2 GUIDED PRACTICE (p. 205)

1.

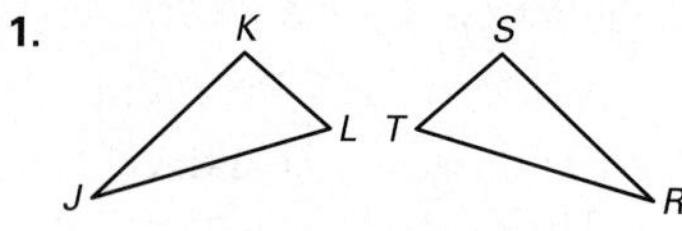

4.2 PRACTICE AND APPLICATIONS (pp. 206–209)

40.

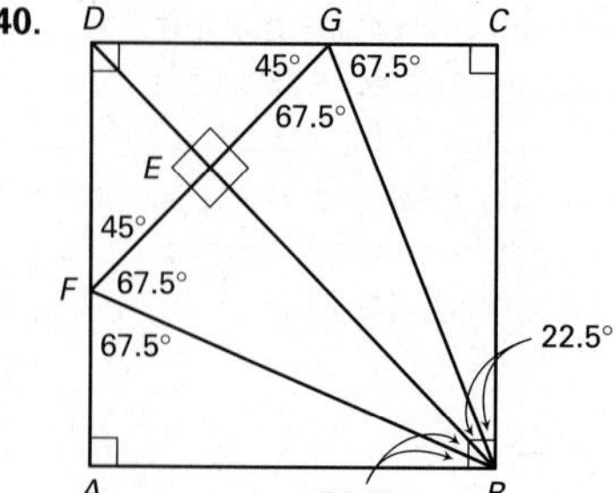

4.3 PRACTICE AND APPLICATIONS (pp. 216–219)

22.

Statements	Reasons
1. $\overline{AB} \cong \overline{CD}$, $\overline{AB} \parallel \overline{CD}$	1. Given
2. $\angle 1 \cong \angle 2$	2. Alternate Interior Angles Theorem
3. $\overline{AC} \cong \overline{AC}$	3. Reflexive Property of Congruence
4. $\triangle ABC \cong \triangle CDA$	4. SAS Congruence Postulate

33. $AB = DE = 2$, $BC = EF = 4$, and $AC = DF = 2\sqrt{5}$, so all three pairs of sides are congruent and $\triangle ABC \cong \triangle DEF$ by the SSS Congruence Postulate. **34.** $AC = DF = 2$, $BC = EF = 3$, and $AB = DE = \sqrt{13}$, so all three pairs of sides are congruent and $\triangle ABC \cong \triangle DEF$ by the SSS Congruence Postulate. **35.** $AB = DE = 3$, $BC = EF = \sqrt{13}$, and $AC = DF = \sqrt{10}$, so all three pairs of sides are congruent and $\triangle ABC \cong \triangle DEF$ by the SSS Congruence Postulate.

38. SSS Congruence Postulate: Use coordinates and the Distance Formula to find the lengths of $\overline{PO}$, $\overline{PN}$, $\overline{MO}$, and $\overline{MN}$ and show that $\overline{PO} \cong \overline{PN}$ and $\overline{MO} \cong \overline{MN}$. Since $\overline{PM} \cong \overline{PM}$ by the Reflexive Property of Congruence, $\triangle PMO \cong \triangle PMN$ by the SSS Congruence Postulate.

SAS Congruence Postulate: Use coordinates and the Distance Formula to find the lengths of $\overline{MO}$ and $\overline{MN}$ and show that $\overline{MO} \cong \overline{MN}$. $\overline{PM} \cong \overline{PM}$ by the Reflexive Property of Congruence. Then find the slopes of $\overline{PM}$ and $\overline{ON}$ and use the Slopes of Perpendicular Lines Postulate, Theorem 3.3 (If two lines are perpendicular, then they intersect to form four right angles), and the Right Angle Congruence Theorem to show that $\angle PMO \cong \angle PMN$. Then $\triangle PMO \cong \triangle PMN$ by the SAS Congruence Postulate.

Preferences may vary, but the SSS Congruence Method involves fewer justifications.

4.3 MIXED REVIEW (p. 219)

46. slope of $\overleftrightarrow{PQ} = \frac{3}{2}$, slope of $\overleftrightarrow{QR} = -\frac{2}{3}$, $\overleftrightarrow{PQ} \perp \overleftrightarrow{QR}$

4.4 GUIDED PRACTICE (p. 223)

7. By the Right Angle Congruence Theorem, $\angle B \cong \angle D$. Since $\overline{AD} \parallel \overline{BC}$, $\angle CAD \cong \angle ACB$ by the Alternate Interior Angles Theorem. By the Reflexive Property of Congruence, $\overline{AC} \cong \overline{AC}$, so $\triangle ACD \cong \triangle CAB$ by the AAS Congruence Theorem. Then all three pairs of corresponding sides are congruent; that is, they have the same length. So, $AB + BC + CA = CD + DA + AC$ and the two courses are the same length.

4.4 PRACTICE AND APPLICATIONS (p. 223–226)

8. Yes; ASA Congruence Postulate; since vertical angles RVS and UVT are congruent, two pairs of corresponding angles and the corresponding included sides are congruent. **9.** Yes; SAS Congruence Postulate; two pairs of corresponding sides and the corresponding included angles are congruent. **10.** Yes; AAS Congruence Theorem; $\overline{BC} \cong \overline{BC}$ by the Reflexive Property of Congruence and by the definition of right angle, the Linear Pair Postulate, and the definition of congruence, $\angle ACB \cong \angle DCB$, so two pairs of corresponding angles and the corresponding nonincluded sides are congruent. **11.** No; two pairs of corresponding sides are congruent and corresponding nonincluded angles $\angle EGF$ and $\angle JGH$ are congruent by the Vertical Angles Theorem; that is insufficient to prove triangle congruence.

12. No; two pairs of corresponding sides and a pair of corresponding nonincluded angles are congruent; that is insufficient to prove triangle congruence. **13.** Yes; SSS Congruence Postulate; $\overline{XY} \cong \overline{XY}$ by the Reflexive Property of Congruence, so all three pairs of corresponding sides are congruent.

4.5 PRACTICE AND APPLICATIONS (pp. 232–235)

11. Statements	Reasons
1. $\triangle AGD \cong \triangle FHC$	1. Given
2. $\overline{GD} \cong \overline{HC}$	2. Corresp. parts of $\cong$ ▲s are $\cong$.

12. Statements	Reasons
1. $\triangle BFC \cong \triangle ECF$	1. Given
2. $\angle CBH \cong \angle FEH$	2. Corresp. parts of $\cong$ ▲s are $\cong$.

13. Statements	Reasons
1. $\triangle EDA \cong \triangle BCF$	1. Given
2. $\overline{AE} \cong \overline{FB}$	2. Corresp. parts of $\cong$ ▲s are $\cong$.

18. Since $\overline{BD} \perp \overline{AC}$ and since if two lines are perpendicular, they form four right angles, $\angle BDA$ and $\angle BDC$ are right angles and $\angle BDA \cong \angle BDC$. $\overline{BD}$ bisects $\overline{AC}$, so $\overline{AD} \cong \overline{CD}$. Since $\overline{BD} \cong \overline{BD}$ by the Reflexive Property of Congruence, $\triangle ABD \cong \triangle CBD$ by the SAS Congruence Postulate. Corresponding parts of congruent triangles are congruent, so $\angle A \cong \angle BCD$, or $m\angle A = m\angle BCD$. $\triangle ABD$ is a right triangle, so its acute angles are complementary, that is, $m\angle A + m\angle ABD = 90°$. By the substitution property of equality, $m\angle BCD + m\angle ABD = 90°$. Therefore, $\angle ABD$ and $\angle BCD$ are complementary by definition. **19.** It is given that $\overline{AB} \cong \overline{AC}$ and $\overline{BD} \cong \overline{CD}$. By the Reflexive Property of Congruence, $\overline{AD} \cong \overline{AD}$. So, $\triangle ACD \cong \triangle ABD$ by the SSS Congruence Postulate. Then, since corresponding parts of congruent triangles are congruent, $\angle CAD \cong \angle BAD$. Then, by definition, $\overrightarrow{AD}$ bisects $\angle A$.

20.

21.

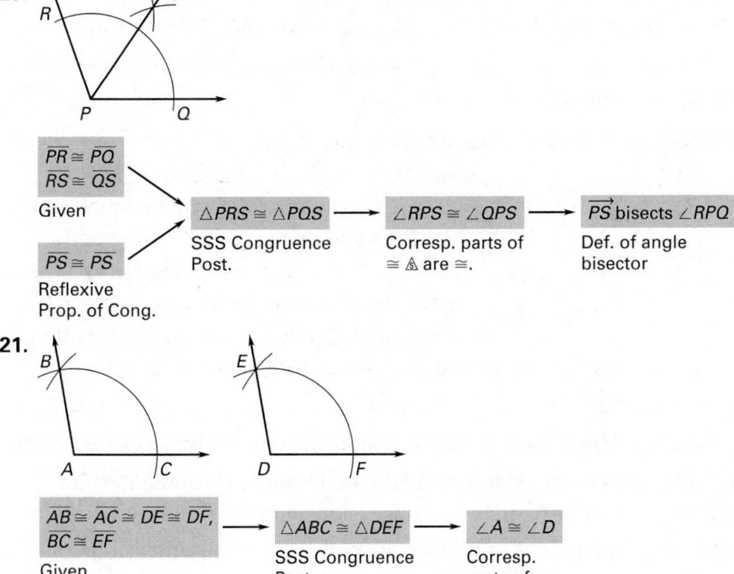

24.

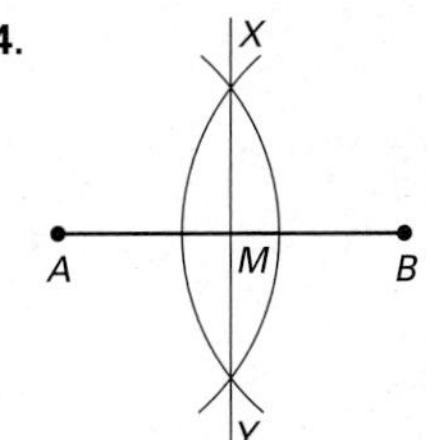

Sample answer: It is given that $\overline{AX}$, $\overline{AY}$, $\overline{BX}$, and $\overline{BY}$ are congruent. Also, $\overline{AB} \cong \overline{AB}$ by the Reflexive Property of Congruence, so $\triangle AXB \cong \triangle BYA$ by the SSS Congruence Postulate. Then $\angle XAB \cong \angle YBA$ and $\overline{AX} \cong \overline{BY}$ because they are corresponding parts of congruent triangles. Also, $\angle XMA \cong \angle YMB$ by the Vertical Angles Theorem, so $\triangle AXM \cong \triangle BYM$ by the AAS Congruence Theorem and corresponding parts $\overline{AM}$ and $\overline{BM}$ are congruent. Then M is the midpoint of $\overline{AB}$ by definition.

4.5 MIXED REVIEW (p. 235)

31. $8x + 13 = 3x + 38$
$5x + 13 = 38$ (Subtraction property of equality)
$5x = 25$ (Subtraction property of equality)
$x = 5$ (Division property of equality)

32. $3(x - 1) = 16$
$3x - 3 = 16$ (Distributive property)
$3x = 19$ (Addition property of equality)
$x = \frac{19}{3}$ (Division property of equality)

33. $6(2x - 1) + 15 = 69$
$6(2x - 1) = 54$ (Subtraction property of equality)
$2x - 1 = 9$ (Division property of equality)
$2x = 10$ (Addition property of equality)
$x = 5$ (Division property of equality)

4.6 PRACTICE AND APPLICATIONS (pp. 239–242) **13.** Yes; the triangles can be proved congruent using the ASA Congruence Postulate, the SSS Congruence Postulate, the SAS Congruence Postulate, or the AAS Congruence Theorem. **14.** Yes; the triangles can be proved congruent using SAS Congruence Postulate. **15.** Yes; the triangles can be proved congruent using the HL Congruence Theorem. **16.** No; it cannot be shown that any of the sides of $\triangle ABC$ are congruent to any of the sides of $\triangle DEF$. **39.** It is given that $\angle CDB \cong \angle ADB$ and that $\overline{DB} \perp \overline{AC}$. Since perpendicular lines form right angles, $\angle ABD$ and $\angle CBD$ are right angles. By the Right Angle Congruence Theorem, $\angle ABD \cong \angle CBD$. By the Reflexive Property of Congruence, $\overline{DB} \cong \overline{DB}$, so $\triangle ABD \cong \triangle CBD$ by the ASA Congruence Postulate. **40.** $\overline{AD} \cong \overline{CD}$ because $\overline{AD}$ and $\overline{CD}$ are corresponding sides of congruent triangles. Then $\triangle ACD$ is isosceles by definition. **44.** The first figure shows six congruent equilateral triangles. For each triangle, the angle with vertex at the center has measure 60°. By connecting every other vertex of the hexagon, three congruent isosceles triangles are formed. For each triangle, the angle with vertex at the center has measure $2 \cdot 60° = 120°$, so each of the congruent base angles has measure 30°. Then the measure of each angle in the third figure is $2 \cdot 30° = 60°$ and the triangle is equiangular and, therefore, equilateral.

4.7 GUIDED PRACTICE (p. 246)

2.

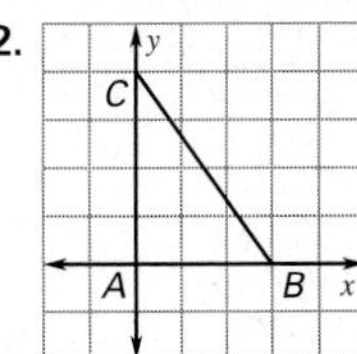

ADDITIONAL ANSWERS

4.7 PRACTICE AND APPLICATIONS (pp. 247–249)

6–11. *Sample figures are given.*

6.

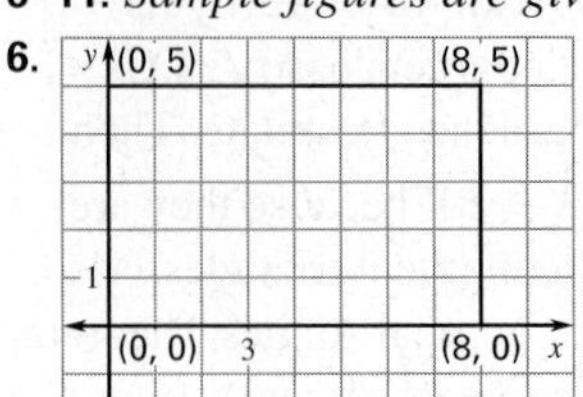

7.

8.

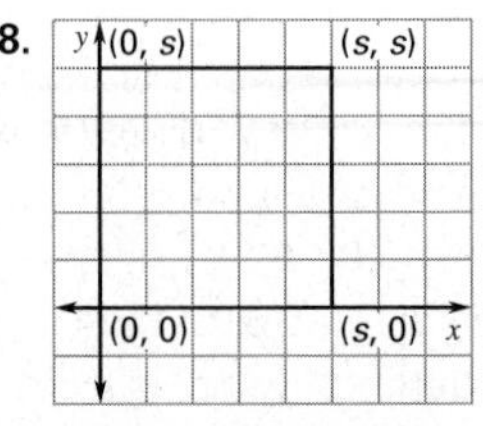

9.

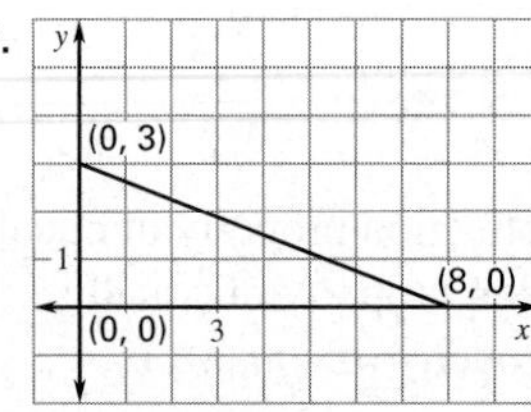

10.

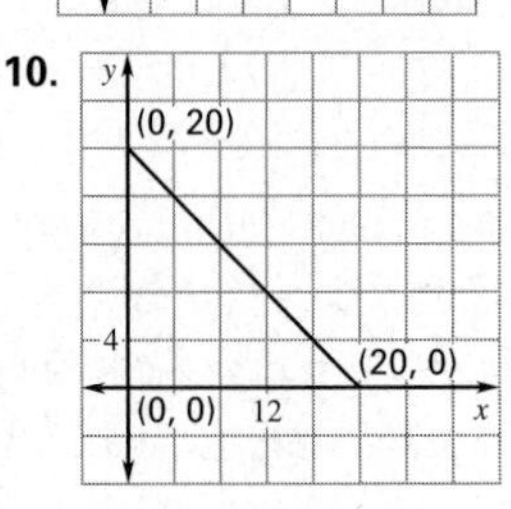

11.

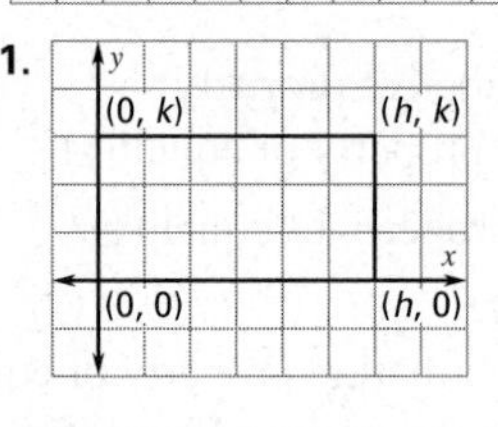

CHAPTER 5

5.1 PRACTICE AND APPLICATIONS (pp. 268–271) **30.** Since $\overline{GJ}$ is the $\perp$ bisector of $\overline{HK}$, $\overline{GH} \cong \overline{GK}$ and $\overline{MH} \cong \overline{MK}$. Since $\overline{GM} \cong \overline{GM}$ (Reflexive Prop. of Cong.), $\triangle GHM \cong \triangle GKM$ by the SSS Cong. Post.

5.4 PRACTICE AND APPLICATIONS (pp. 290–293)

37.

Stage n	0	1	2	3	4	5
Midsegment length	24	12	6	3	$1\frac{1}{2}$	$\frac{3}{4}$

38.

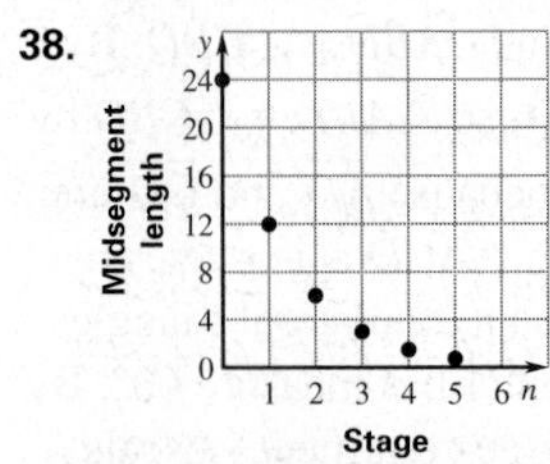

5.4 MIXED REVIEW (p. 293)

39. $x - 3 = 11$
$x = 14$ (Addition prop. of equality)

40. $3x + 13 = 46$
$3x = 33$ (Subtraction prop. of equality)
$x = 11$ (Division prop. of equality)

41. $8x - 1 = 2x + 17$
$8x = 2x + 18$ (Addition prop. of equality)
$6x = 18$ (Subtraction prop. of equality)
$x = 3$ (Division prop. of equality)

42. $5x + 12 = 9x - 4$
$5x + 16 = 9x$ (Addition prop. of equality)
$16 = 4x$ (Subtraction prop. of equality)
$4 = x$ (Division prop. of equality)

43. $2(4x - 1) = 14$
$4x - 1 = 7$ (Division prop. of equality)
$4x = 8$ (Addition prop. of equality)
$x = 2$ (Division prop. of equality)

44. $9(3x + 10) = 27$
$3x + 10 = 3$ (Division prop. of equality)
$3x = -7$ (Subtraction prop. of equality)
$x = -\frac{7}{3}$ (Division prop. of equality)

45. $-2(x + 1) + 3 = 23$
$-2(x + 1) = 20$ (Subtraction prop. of equality)
$x + 1 = -10$ (Division prop. of equality)
$x = -11$ (Subtraction prop. of equality)

46. $3x + 2(x + 5) = 40$
$3x + 2x + 10 = 40$ (Distributive prop.)
$5x + 10 = 40$ (Simplification)
$5x = 30$ (Subtraction prop. of equality)
$x = 6$ (Division prop. of equality)

CHAPTER 6

6.1 PRACTICE AND APPLICATIONS (pp. 325–328)

53.

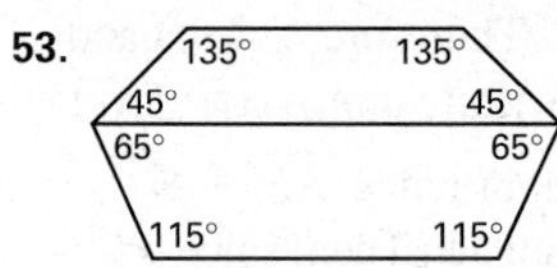

6.2 GUIDED PRACTICE (p. 333) **16.** 80°; since consec. ∠s of a ▱ are supplementary, $m\angle LMN = 180° - m\angle QLM = 80°$. **17.** 80°; since consec. ∠s of a ▱ are supplementary, $m\angle NQL = 180° - m\angle QLM = 80°$.

18. 100°; since opp. ∠s of a ▱ are ≅, $m\angle MNQ = m\angle MLQ = 100°$.

19. 29°; opp. sides of a ▱ are ∥, so $m\angle LMQ = m\angle MQN$ since they are alternate interior angles.

6.2 PRACTICE AND APPLICATIONS (pp. 334–337)

59.

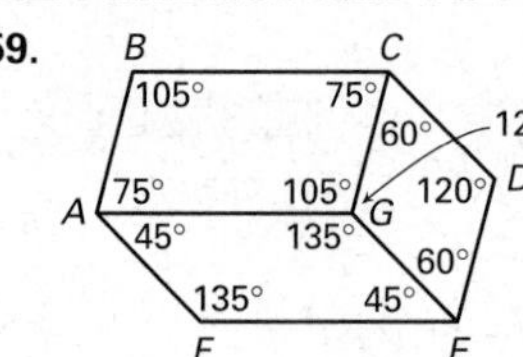

$m\angle AGE$, $m\angle F$, $m\angle FEG$, $m\angle GED$, $m\angle GCD$, and $m\angle CGE$ can be found using the facts that opp. ∠s of a ▱ are ≅ and consec. ∠s of a ▱ are supplementary. These same theorems can be used to find $m\angle BAG$, $m\angle B$, and $m\angle BCG$ once $m\angle AGC$ is found. Since the sum of the measures of the ∠s with vertex G is 360°, $m\angle AGC = 105°$.

6.3 GUIDED PRACTICE (p. 342) **8.** *Sample answers:* Use slopes to show that both pairs of opp. sides are ∥; use the Distance Formula to show that both pairs of opp. sides are ≅; use slope and the Distance Formula to show that one pair of opp. sides are both ∥ and ≅; use the Midpoint Formula to show that the diags. bisect each other.

6.3 Practice and Applications (pp. 342–345) **12.** Yes; if an ∠ of a quad. is supplementary to both of its consec. ∠s, then the quad. is a ▱. **13.** No; the fact that two opp. sides and one diag. are ≅ is insufficient to prove that the quad. is a ▱. **14.** Yes; if one pair of opp. sides of a quad. are both ≅ and ∥, then the quad. is a ▱. **16.** *Sample answer:* Since corresp. parts of ≅ △s are ≅, $\overline{AX} \cong \overline{CX}$ and $\overline{BX} \cong \overline{DX}$. That is, the diags. of *ABCD* bisect each other. Then *ABCD* is a ▱. **30.** Check drawings.

Theorem 6.6: Draw two segments, $\overline{AB}$ and $\overline{BC}$ intersecting at *B*. Draw two arcs, one with center *A* and radius *BC* and one with center *C* and radius *AB*, intersecting at *D*. Draw $\overline{AD}$ and $\overline{CD}$.

Theorem 6.8: Draw two segments, $\overline{AB}$ and $\overline{BC}$ intersecting at *B*. Construct a line through *A* ∥ to $\overline{BC}$ and a line through *C* ∥ to $\overline{AB}$, intersecting at *D*. Draw $\overline{AD}$ and $\overline{CD}$.

Theorem 6.10: Draw two segments, $\overline{AB}$ and $\overline{BC}$ intersecting at *B*. Construct a line through *A* ∥ to $\overline{BC}$ and construct $\overline{AD}$ on the line ≅ to $\overline{BC}$. Draw $\overline{DC}$.

31. *Sample answer:* Design the mount so that $\overline{AD} \cong \overline{BC}$ and $\overline{AB} \cong \overline{DC}$, making *ABCD* a ▱. Then, as long as the support containing $\overline{AD}$ is vertical, $\overline{BC}$ will be vertical, because opp. sides of a ▱ are ∥. **36.** Slope of $\overline{MN}$ = slope of $\overline{QP} = \frac{c-a}{b}$, so $\overline{MN} \parallel \overline{QP}$; slope of $\overline{QM}$ = slope of $\overline{PN} = \frac{c+a}{b}$, so $\overline{QM} \parallel \overline{PN}$.

6.4 Practice and Applications (pp. 351–355) **54.** *Sample answer:* Draw $\overline{AC}$ and construct its midpoint, *M*. Draw a line *j* through *M* not ⊥ to $\overline{AC}$. Construct $\overline{MB}$ and $\overline{MC}$ on opposite sides of *j*, both ≅ to $\overline{MC}$. Draw $\overline{AB}$, $\overline{BC}$, $\overline{CD}$, and $\overline{AD}$. Since the diags. of *ABCD* are ≅, *ABCD* is a rectangle. Since the diags. are not ⊥, *ABCD* is not a rhombus, and thus not a square. **62.** *Sample answer:* Since cross braces $\overline{AD}$ and $\overline{BC}$ bisect each other, *ABDC* is a ▱. Therefore, $\overline{AC} \parallel \overline{BD}$. Since *A*, *C*, and *E* and *B*, *D*, and *F* are collinear, $\overline{AE} \parallel \overline{BF}$. We were given that legs $\overline{AE}$ and $\overline{BF}$ are ≅. Therefore, *ABFE* is a ▱ since one pair of opp. sides are ∥ and ≅. Therefore, since opp. sides of a ▱ are ≅, $\overline{AB} \parallel \overline{EF}$. **64.** In both cases, ∠*EAC* and ∠*FAC* remain ≅, as do ∠*AEF* and ∠*CEF*. **65.** Each diag. of a rhombus bisects a pair of opp. ∠s. (Theorem 6.12) **72.** Slope of $\overline{AB}$ = slope of $\overline{CD} = \frac{\sqrt{b^2-a^2}}{a-b}$; slope of $\overline{AD}$ = slope of $\overline{BC} = \frac{\sqrt{b^2-a^2}}{a+b}$. Since slope of $\overline{AB}$ · slope of $\overline{BC} = \frac{\sqrt{b^2-a^2}}{a-b} \cdot \frac{\sqrt{b^2-a^2}}{a+b} = \frac{b^2-a^2}{a^2-b^2} = -1$, $\overline{AB} \perp \overline{BC}$. As shown in Ex. 68, a ▱ with one right ∠ is a rectangle.

6.4 Mixed Review (p. 355) **83.** Assume temporarily that *ABCD* is a quad. with 4 acute ∠s, that is, $m\angle A < 90°$, $m\angle B < 90°$, $m\angle C < 90°$, and $m\angle D < 90°$. Then $m\angle A + m\angle B + m\angle C + m\angle D < 360°$. This contradicts the Int. Angles of a Quad. Thm. Then no quad. has 4 acute ∠s.

Quiz 2 (p. 363)

6.

Statements	Reasons
1. $\overline{AB} \parallel \overline{DC}$, ∠*D* ≅ ∠*C*	1. Given
2. Draw $\overline{AE} \parallel \overline{BC}$.	2. Parallel Post.
3. *ABCE* is a ▱.	3. Def. of a ▱
4. $\overline{AE} \cong \overline{BC}$	4. Opp. sides of a ▱ are ≅.
5. ∠*AED* ≅ ∠*C*	5. Corresp. Angles Post.
6. ∠*AED* ≅ ∠*D*	6. Transitive Prop. of Cong.
7. $\overline{AD} \cong \overline{AE}$	7. Converse of the Base Angles Thm.
8. $\overline{AD} \cong \overline{BC}$	8. Transitive Prop. of Cong.

6.6 Practice and Applications (pp. 367–370) **45.** ▱; if the diags. of a quad. bisect each other, the quad. is a ▱. Since the diags. are not ⊥, the ▱ is not a rhombus, and since the diags. are not ≅, the ▱ is not a rectangle. **46.** Rhombus; the quad. is a ▱ since the diags. bisect each other. Since the diags. of the ▱ are ⊥, the ▱ is a rhombus. Since the diags. are not ≅, the ▱ is not a rectangle. **47.** Kite; $\overline{AC} \perp \overline{BD}$ and $\overline{AC}$ bisects $\overline{BD}$, so ≅ △s can be used to show that $\overline{AB} \cong \overline{AD}$ and then that $\overline{CB} \cong \overline{CD}$. $\overline{BD}$ does not bisect $\overline{AC}$, so *ABCD* is not a ▱. Then opp. sides are not ≅ and *ABCD* is a kite. **48.** ▱; *EFGH* is a ▱, so $\overline{EF} \parallel \overline{GH}$ and $\overline{EF} \cong \overline{GH}$; *GHJK* is a ▱, so $\overline{GH} \parallel \overline{JK}$ and $\overline{GH} \cong \overline{JK}$; *JKLM* is a ▱, so $\overline{JK} \parallel \overline{LM}$ and $\overline{JK} \cong \overline{LM}$; then $\overline{EF} \parallel \overline{LM}$ (If 2 lines are ∥ to the same line, they are ∥ to each other) and $\overline{EF} \cong \overline{LM}$ (Transitive Prop. of Cong.), so *EFLM* is a ▱. (If one pair of opp. sides of a quad. are both ≅ and ∥, the quad. is a ▱.) **49.** Draw a line through *C* ∥ to $\overline{DF}$ and a line through *E* ∥ to $\overline{CD}$. Label the intersection *F*. *CDEF* is a ▱ by the def. of a ▱. ∠*DCF* and ∠*DEF* are right ∠s because consec. ∠s of a ▱ are supplementary. Then ∠*CFE* is also a right ∠ and *CDEF* is a rectangle. The diags. of a ▱ bisect each other, so $DM = \frac{1}{2}DF$ and $CM = \frac{1}{2}CE$. The diags. of a rectangle are ≅, so $DF = CE$, $\frac{1}{2}DF = \frac{1}{2}CE$, and $DM = CM$. By the def. of cong., $\overline{DM} \cong \overline{CM}$. **50.** Let $m\angle ABN = x°$. Then $m\angle BAN = x°$ and $m\angle BNA = (180 - 2x)°$. ∠*BNA* and ∠*AND* are supplementary, so $m\angle AND = (2x)°$. △*AND* is isos., so $m\angle NAD = \frac{1}{2}(180 - 2x)° = (90 - x)°$. Then $m\angle BAD = m\angle BAN + m\angle NAD = x° + (90 - x)° = 90°$. Similarly, the other 3 ∠s of *ABCD* are right ∠s and *ABCD* is a rectangle. **51.** Square; *Sample answer:* Draw $\overline{PR}$ and $\overline{QS}$. *PQRS* is a square, so it is a rectangle, and $\overline{PR} \cong \overline{QS}$. $\overline{EF}$ is a midsegment of △*PSQ*, so $EF = \frac{1}{2}QS$. Similarly, $GH = \frac{1}{2}QS$, $EH = \frac{1}{2}PR$, and $FG = \frac{1}{2}PR$. Since $PR = QS$, all 4 sides of *EFGH* are ≅, and *EFGH* is a rhombus. △*PFE* and △*QFG* are isos. right △s, so $m\angle PFE = m\angle QFG = 45°$. Then $m\angle EFG = 180° - (45° + 45°) = 90°$. Similarly, the other 3 ∠s of *EFGH* are right ∠s, and *EFGH* is a rectangle. A quad. that is both a rectangle and a rhombus is a square. **52.** Rhombus; $\overline{FE}$ is the midsegment of △*JKL*, $\overline{EH}$ is the midsegment of △*JLM*, $\overline{HG}$ is the midsegment of △*JKM*, and $\overline{FG}$ is the midsegment of △*KLM*. Then $FE = \frac{1}{2}JK$, $EH = \frac{1}{2}LM$, $HG = \frac{1}{2}JK$, and $FG = \frac{1}{2}LM$. Since $\overline{JK} \cong \overline{LM}$, $JK = LM$, and $FE = EH = HG = FG$. Since all 4 sides of *EFGH* are ≅, *EFGH* is a rhombus.

53. a. Isosceles; by the Angle Addition Post., $m\angle KLM = m\angle KLJ + m\angle JLM$ and $m\angle KJN = m\angle KJL + m\angle LJN$. Since $JKLMN$ is a regular pentagon, $m\angle KLM = m\angle KJN$ and, so, $m\angle KLJ + m\angle JLM = m\angle KJL + m\angle LJN$. By the Base Angles Thm., $\angle KLJ \cong \angle KJL$, so $m\angle KLJ = m\angle KJL$ and by the subtraction prop. of equality, $m\angle JLM = m\angle LJN$ and $\angle LJN \cong \angle JLM$. **b.** $m\angle LMN = m\angle JNM$ and $m\angle LJN = m\angle JLM$; Since the sum of the measures of the interior ⦣ of a quad. is 360°, $m\angle LMN + m\angle JNM + m\angle LJN + m\angle JLM = 360°$. Then, by the substitution prop. of equality, $2m\angle JLM + 2m\angle LMN = 360°$ and $m\angle JLM + m\angle LMN = 180°$. Since $\angle MLJ$ and $\angle LMN$ are supplementary, $\overline{MN} \parallel \overline{LJ}$ by the Consec. Int. Angles Converse. **54.** Isosceles trapezoid; use the SAS Cong. Post. to show that $\triangle AND \cong \triangle BNC$, so that $\overline{AD} \cong \overline{BC}$. Then use the Vertical Angles Thm., the Triangle Sum Thm., and the Base Angles Thm. to show that $\angle ACD \cong \angle CAB$, so that $\overline{AB} \parallel \overline{CD}$. Finally, since $\overline{AC}$ and $\overline{BD}$ do not bisect each other, $ABCD$ is not a ▱, so $ABCD$ is an isosceles trapezoid.

6.7 PRACTICE AND APPLICATIONS (pp. 376–379) **54.** Square; all four int. ⦣ of $ABCD$ are right ⦣, so $ABCD$ is a rectangle by the Rectangle Corollary. $EB = BF = h$ and $HD = DG = b$, so $AB = BC = CD = AD$ by the Segment Addition Post. and the substitution prop. of equality. Then $ABCD$ is both a rectangle and a rhombus and, so, is a square. **58.** Show that the area of $KMNQ = h(b_1 + b_2)$. Then since the trapezoids are ≅, the area of each is $\frac{1}{2}h(b_1 + b_2)$. **59.** Show that the area of $AEGH = \frac{1}{2}h(b_1 + b_2)$. Then, since $EBCF$ and $GHDF$ are ≅, Area of $ABCD$ = Area of $AEFD$ + Area of $EBCF$ = Area of $AEFD$ + Area of $GHDF$ = Area of $AEGH = \frac{1}{2}h(b_1 + b_2)$. **62.** When the rectangle drawn in blue is constructed, the diags of the original figure divide the rectangle into 4 pairs of ≅ ⚠. (In each pair, one is shaded and one unshaded.) Then the shaded and unshaded regions have the same total area, and the area of the shaded region (quad. $PQRS$) is half the area of the rectangle, or $\frac{1}{2}d_1d_2$.

CHAPTER 7

7.1 PRACTICE AND APPLICATIONS (pp. 399–402)

46. Statements	Reasons
1. $\triangle ABC \to \triangle PQR$ and $\triangle PQR \to \triangle XYZ$ are isometries.	1. Given
2. $AB = PQ$, $BC = QR$, $AC = PR$, $PQ = XY$, $QR = YZ$, $PR = XZ$	2. Def. of isometry
3. $AB = XY$, $BC = YZ$, $AC = XZ$	3. Transitive prop. of equality
4. $\overline{AB} \cong \overline{XY}$, $\overline{BC} \cong \overline{YZ}$, $\overline{AC} \cong \overline{XZ}$	4. Def. of congruent segments
5. $\triangle ABC \to \triangle XYZ$ is an isometry.	5. Def. of isometry

7.2 PRACTICE AND APPLICATIONS (pp. 407–410)

15. k **16.** k **17.** k

7.3 PRACTICE AND APPLICATIONS (pp. 416–419)

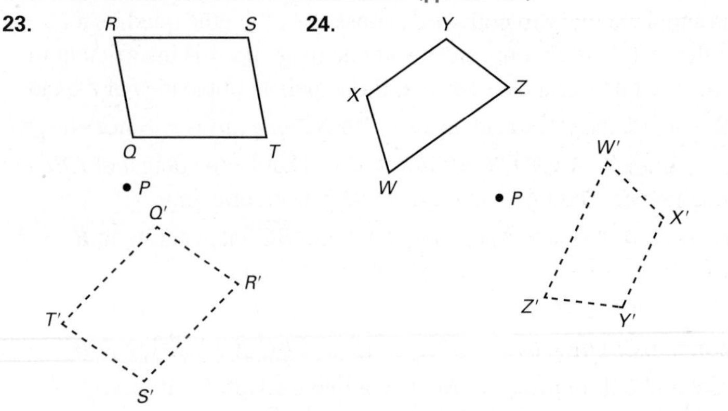

44. a. Statements	Reasons
1. Q' is the reflection of Q in k, Q'' is the reflection of Q' in m.	1. Given
2. $k \perp \overline{QQ'}$, $\overline{QA} \cong \overline{Q'A}$	2. Def. of reflection
3. $\angle QAP$ and $\angle Q'AP$ are right angles.	3. Def. of perpendicular lines
4. $\angle QAP \cong \angle Q'AP$	4. All right ⦣ are ≅.
5. $\overline{AP} \cong \overline{AP}$	5. Reflexive Prop. of Cong.
6. $\triangle QAP \cong \triangle Q'AP$	6. SAS Cong. Post.
7. $\overline{QP} \cong \overline{Q'P}$	7. Corresp. parts of ≅ ⚠ are ≅ .
8. $m \perp \overline{Q'Q''}$, $\overline{Q'B} \cong \overline{Q''B}$	8. Def. of reflection
9. $\angle Q'BP$ and $\angle Q''BP$ are right angles.	9. Def. of perpendicular lines
10. $\angle Q'BP \cong \angle Q''BP$	10. All right ⦣ are ≅.
11. $\overline{PB} \cong \overline{PB}$	11. Reflexive Prop. of Cong.
12. $\triangle Q'BP \cong \triangle Q''BP$	12. SAS Cong. Post.
13. $\overline{Q'P} \cong \overline{Q''P}$	13. Corresp. parts of ≅ ⚠ are ≅.
14. $\overline{QP} \cong \overline{Q''P}$	14. Transitive Prop. of Cong. (Steps 7 and 13)
15. Q'' is a rotation of Q about P.	15. Def. of rotation

b. Statements	Reasons
16. $\angle QPA \cong \angle Q'PA$, $\angle Q'PB \cong \angle Q''PB$	16. Corresp. parts of ≅ ⚠ are ≅.
17. $m\angle QPA = m\angle Q'PA$, $m\angle Q'PB = m\angle Q''PB$	17. Def. of ≅ angles
18. $m\angle APB = m\angle Q'PA + m\angle Q'PB$, $m\angle QPQ'' = m\angle QPA + m\angle Q'PA + m\angle Q'PB + m\angle Q''PB$	18. Angle Addition Post.
19. $m\angle QPQ'' = m\angle Q'PA + m\angle Q'PA + m\angle Q'PB + m\angle Q'PB$	19. Substitution prop. of equality
20. $m\angle QPQ'' = 2(m\angle Q'PA + m\angle Q'PB)$	20. Distributive prop.
21. $m\angle QPQ'' = 2(m\angle APB)$	21. Substitution prop. of equality

7.4 Guided Practice (p. 425)

11–14. Sample figures are given.

11.

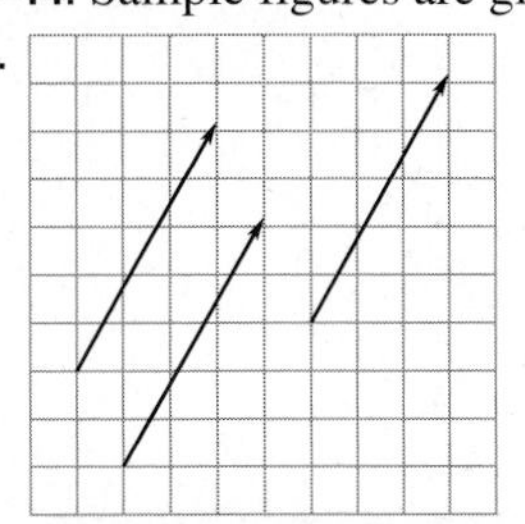

12.

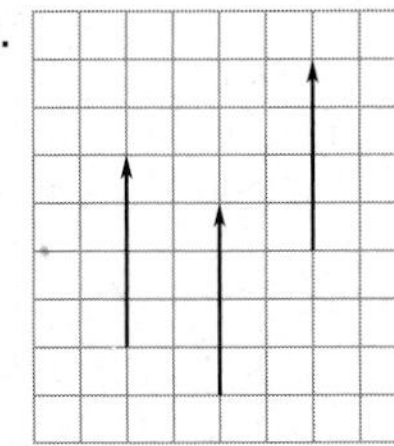

13.

14.

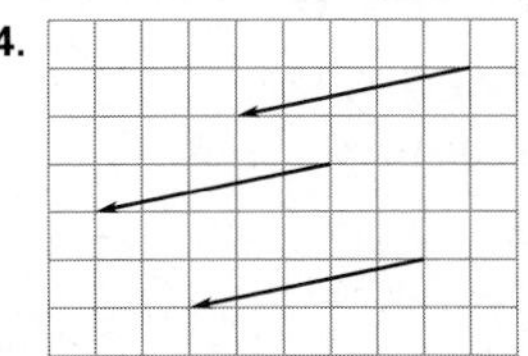

7.4 Practice and Applications (pp. 425–428)

39.

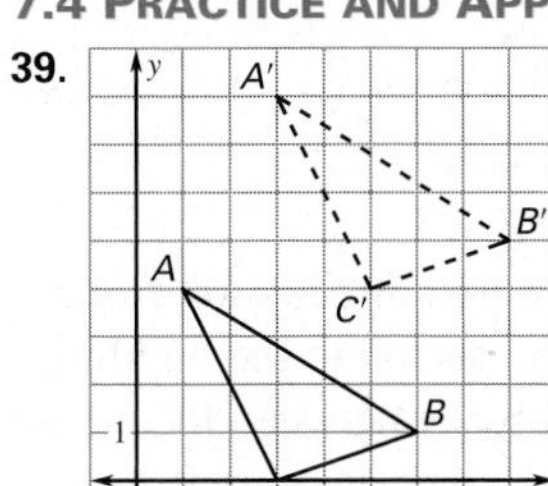

40.

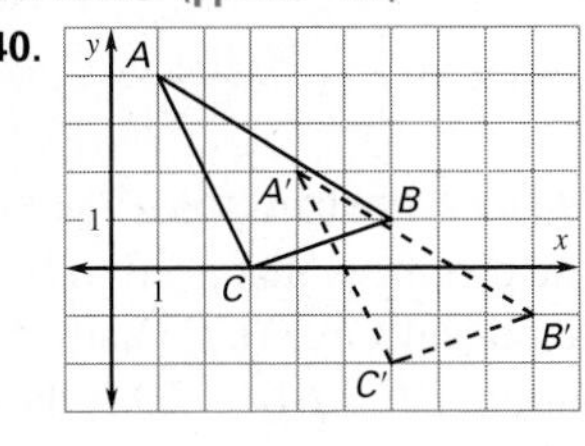

41.

42.

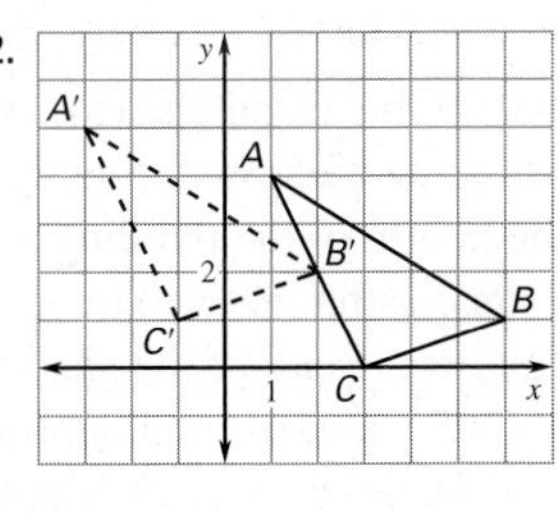

43. We are given $P(a, b)$ and $Q(c, d)$. Suppose P' has coordinates $(a + r, b + s)$. Then $PP' = \sqrt{r^2 + s^2}$ and the slope of $\overline{PP'} = \frac{s}{r}$. If $PP' = QQ'$ and $\overline{PP'} \parallel \overline{QQ'}$ as given, then $QQ' = \sqrt{r^2 + s^2}$ and the slope of $\overline{QQ'} = \frac{s}{r}$. So, the coordinates of Q' are $(c + r, d + s)$. By the Distance Formula, $PQ = \sqrt{(a - c)^2 + (b - d)^2}$ and $P'Q' = \sqrt{[(a + r) - (c + r)]^2 + [(b + s) - (d + s)]^2} = \sqrt{(a - c)^2 + (b - d)^2}$. Thus, by the substitution prop. of equality, $PQ = P'Q'$.

7.5 Practice and Applications (pp. 433–436)

20.

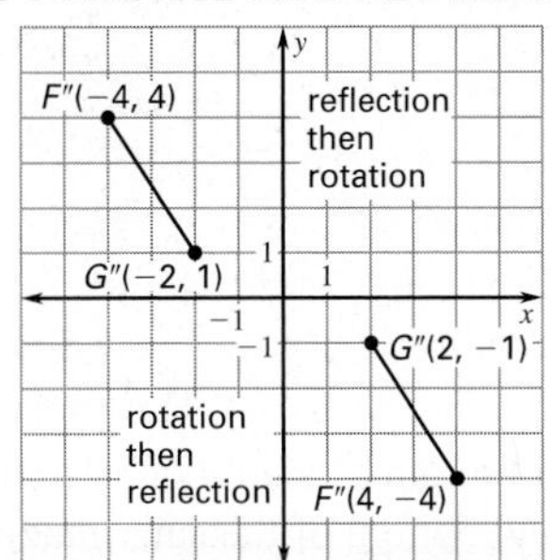

21.

39. a. Check drawings. **b.** Check drawings; conjecture: The midpoint of the segment connecting the point and its image is on the x-axis. **c.** Let (x, y) be the original point; since the translation must be parallel to the line of reflection, the coordinates of the image are $(x + a, -y)$ for some number a. The coordinates of the midpoint are $\left(\frac{x + a + x}{2}, \frac{y - y}{2}\right) = \left(\frac{2x + a}{2}, 0\right)$. Then the midpoint is on the x-axis. **d.** Yes; the midpoint of a point and its image after a glide reflection is on the line of reflection.

7.5 Mixed Review (p. 436)

41.

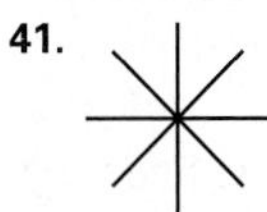

42. **43.**

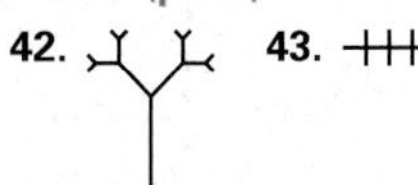

44.

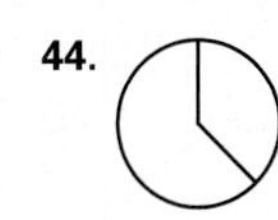

49. $A'(-6, 9)$, $B'(-6, 3)$, $C'(-2, 8)$ **50.** $A'(-10, 2)$, $B'(-10, -4)$, $C'(-6, 1)$ **51.** $A'(-3, 7)$, $B'(-3, 1)$, $C'(1, 6)$ **52.** $A'(-13, 3)$, $B'(-13, -3)$, $C'(-9, 2)$ **53.** $A'(-9, 9.5)$, $B'(-9, 3.5)$, $C'(-5, 8.5)$ **54.** $A'(-7.5, 2.5)$, $B'(-7.5, -3.5)$, $C'(-3.5, 1.5)$

Chapter 8

8.2 Practice and Applications (pp. 468–471)

37. Let $\frac{a}{b} = \frac{c}{d}$ and show that $\frac{a + b}{b} = \frac{c + d}{d}$.

$\frac{a}{b} = \frac{c}{d}$ (Given)

$\frac{a}{b} + 1 = \frac{c}{d} + 1$ (Addition prop. of equality)

$\frac{a}{b} + \frac{b}{b} = \frac{c}{d} + \frac{d}{d}$ (Inverse prop. of multiplication)

$\frac{a + b}{b} = \frac{c + d}{d}$ (Addition of fractions)

8.3 Activity (p. 472)

Step 5 Measurements will vary.

Measurement	Photo 1	Photo 2	Ratio
AF	7.8 cm	5.4 cm	1.4
CD	4.0 cm	2.8 cm	1.4
$m\angle 1$	30°	30°	1
$m\angle 2$	106°	106°	1
Perimeter of photo	24 cm	17.4 cm	1.4

8.3 PRACTICE AND APPLICATIONS (pp. 476–478)

50. The sketch is not to scale.

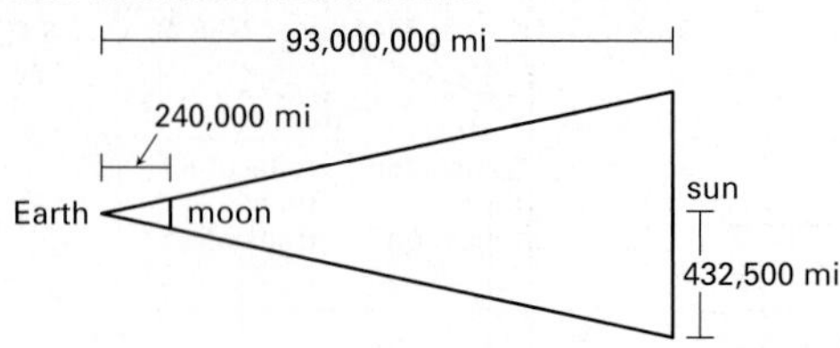

51. The △ formed by the Earth and top and bottom of the moon is similar to the △ formed by the Earth and the top and bottom of the sun; imagine that the legs of each △ are sight lines. The moon totally blocks the view of the sun.

52. $\frac{\text{distance from Earth to moon}}{\text{distance from Earth to sun}} = \frac{\text{radius of moon}}{\text{radius of sun}}$;

$\frac{240{,}000}{93{,}000{,}000} = \frac{\text{radius of moon}}{432{,}500}$; radius of moon ≈ 1120 mi

8.4 PRACTICE AND APPLICATIONS (pp. 483–487)

49.

Statements	Reasons
1. $\angle ECD$ and $\angle EAB$ are right ∠s.	1. Given
2. $\overline{AB} \perp \overline{AE}$, $\overline{CD} \perp \overline{AE}$	2. Def. of ⊥ lines
3. $\overline{AB} \parallel \overline{CD}$	3. In a plane, 2 lines ⊥ to the same line are ∥.
4. $\angle EDC \cong \angle B$	4. If 2 ∥ lines are cut by a transversal, corresp. ∠s are ≅.
5. $\triangle ABE \sim \triangle CDE$	5. AA Similarity Post.

55. $\overline{PQ} \perp \overline{QT}$ and $\overline{SR} \perp \overline{QT}$, so $\angle Q$ and $\angle SRT$ are right ∠s. Since all right ∠s are ≅, $\angle Q \cong \angle SRT$. $\overline{PR} \parallel \overline{ST}$ so corresp. ∠s PRQ and STR are ≅. Then $\triangle PQR \sim \triangle SRT$ by the AA Similarity Post., so $\frac{PQ}{QR} = \frac{SR}{RT}$. That is, $\frac{PQ}{780} = \frac{4}{6.5}$ and $PQ = 480$ ft.

8.6 PRACTICE AND APPLICATIONS (pp. 502–505)

38. In the diagram for Ex. 31 on page 504, suppose that $\frac{DA}{BD} = \frac{EC}{BE}$. Then $\frac{DA + BD}{BD} = \frac{EC + BE}{BE}$. $\left(\text{If } \frac{a}{b} = \frac{c}{d}, \text{ then } \frac{a+b}{b} = \frac{c+d}{d}.\right)$ So, $\frac{BA}{BD} = \frac{BC}{BE}$ by the Segment Addition Post. and the substitution prop. of equality. Since $\angle B \cong \angle B$ by the Reflexive Prop. of Cong., $\triangle ABC \sim \triangle DBE$ by the SAS Similarity Thm. Then corresp. ∠s BDE and A are ≅ and $\overline{DE} \parallel \overline{AC}$ by the Corresponding Angles Converse.

8.7 GUIDED PRACTICE (p. 509)

6.

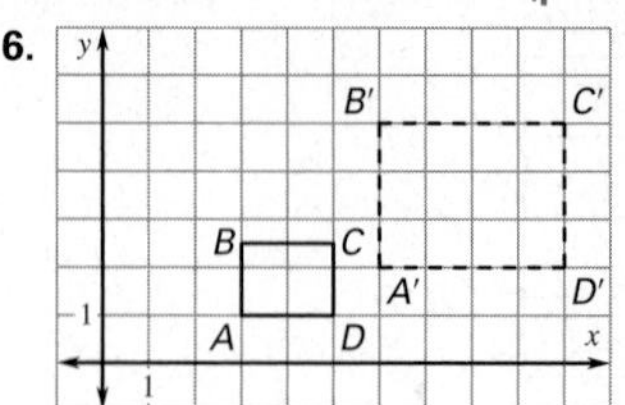

8.7 PRACTICE AND APPLICATIONS (pp. 509–512)

24. The sketch is not to scale.

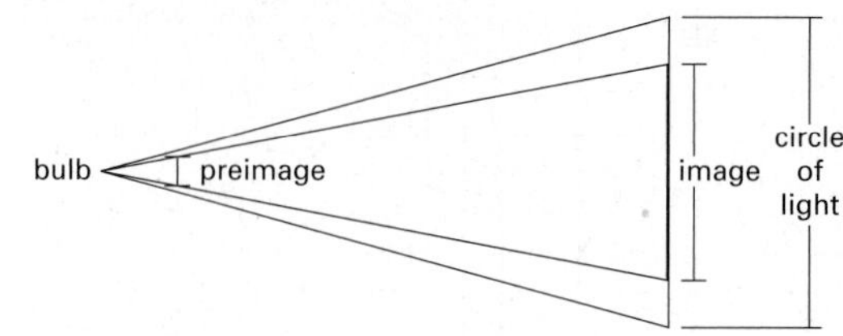

CHAPTER 9

SKILL REVIEW (p. 526)

3. *Sample answer:*

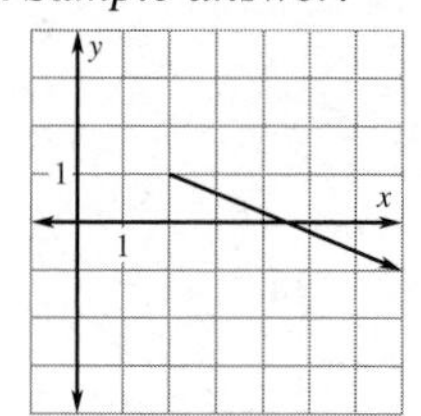

5.

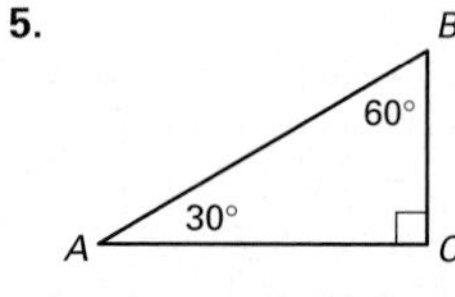

Sample answer: $m\angle A = 30°$ and $m\angle B = 60°$, so $\triangle ABC \sim \triangle JKL$ by the AA Similarity Post.

9.1 PRACTICE AND APPLICATIONS (pp. 531–534)

43. Method 1: The distances that need to be measured directly are from the ground to the person's eye (CD) and from the person to the building (AC). In the diagram, $BC = BD - CD$ is the difference between the height of the building (BD) and the person's eye level. Using Theorem 9.2, you can write a proportion involving BC, namely $\frac{BC}{AC} = \frac{AC}{CD}$. Then you can solve for BD. *Sample answers:* One advantage to this method is that there are few distances that need to be measured directly. A disadvantage is that the calculations to find the height of the building are slightly complicated.

Method 2: The distances that need to be measured directly are from the edge of the building to the end of the shadow (QS), from the pole to the end of its shadow (MP), and from the ground to the top of the pole (PN). Since $\triangle QRS \sim \triangle MNP$ (by the AA Similarity Postulate: $\angle QSR \cong \angle MPN$ since both the building and the pole are at right angles with the ground and $\angle RQS \cong \angle NMP$ since the angle of elevation of the sun is the same), you can set up a proportion involving QS, MP, PN and solve for the height of the building (SR) $\left(\text{namely, } \frac{QS}{MP} = \frac{SR}{PN}\right)$. *Sample answers:* One advantage to this method is that the calculations to find the height of the building are easy and straightforward. A disadvantage is that there are a number of distances that need to be measured directly; in particular, it may be difficult to measure the height of the pole.

9.2 PRACTICE AND APPLICATIONS (pp. 538–541)

38. The formula for the area of a trapezoid gives $A = \frac{1}{2}h(b_1 + b_2) = \frac{1}{2}(a+b)(a+b) = \frac{1}{2}(a+b)^2$. Also, the area is equal to the sum of the areas of the three right triangles, so $A = 2\left(\frac{1}{2} \cdot a \cdot b\right) + \frac{1}{2}c^2$. Thus, $\frac{1}{2}(a+b)^2 = 2\left(\frac{1}{2} \cdot a \cdot b\right) + \frac{1}{2}c^2 = ab + \frac{1}{2}c^2$; multiplying both sides by 2 gives $(a+b)^2 = 2ab + c^2$; $a^2 + 2ab + b^2 = 2ab + c^2$; subtracting $2ab$ from both sides gives $a^2 + b^2 = c^2$.

9.3 GUIDED PRACTICE (p. 545) **2.** *Sample answer:* When $c = 28$, the triangle is acute. When $c = 30$, the triangle is a right triangle. When $c = 31$, the triangle is obtuse. **7.** The crossbars are not perpendicular: $45^2 > 22^2 + 38^2$, so the smaller triangles formed by the crossbars are obtuse.

9.3 PRACTICE AND APPLICATIONS (pp. 546–548) **39.** $120^2 + 119^2 = 169^2$, $4800^2 + 4601^2 = 6649^2$, and $(13{,}500)^2 + (12{,}709)^2 = (18{,}541)^2$.

CHAPTER 10

10.1 GUIDED PRACTICE (p. 599)

1. *Sample answer:*

5. No; $5^2 + 5^2 \neq 7^2$, so by the Converse of the Pythagorean Thm., $\triangle ABD$ is not a right $\triangle$, so $\overline{BD}$ is not $\perp$ to $\overline{AB}$. If $\overleftrightarrow{BD}$ were tangent to $\odot C$, $\angle B$ would be a right angle. Thus, $\overleftrightarrow{BD}$ is not tangent to $\odot C$.

10.1 PRACTICE AND APPLICATIONS (pp. 599–602)

57.

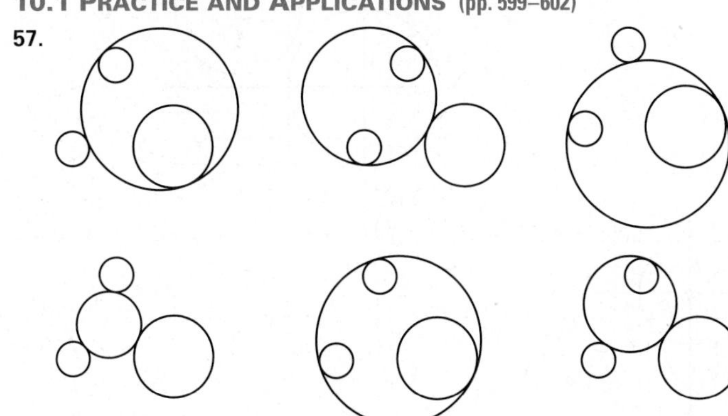

10.2 PRACTICE AND APPLICATIONS (pp. 607–611)

61. Draw radii $\overline{PB}$ and $\overline{PC}$. $\overline{PB} \cong \overline{PC}$ and $\overline{PE} \cong \overline{PF}$. Also, since $\overline{PE} \perp \overline{AB}$ and $\overline{PF} \perp \overline{CD}$, $\triangle PEB$ and $\triangle PFC$ are right ▲and are ≅ by the HL Cong. Thm. Corresp. sides $\overline{BE}$ and $\overline{CF}$ are ≅, so $BE = CF$ and, by the multiplication prop. of equality, $2BE = 2CE$. By Thm. 10.5, $\overline{PE}$ bisects $\overline{AB}$ and $\overline{PF}$ bisects $\overline{CD}$, so $AB = 2BE$ and $CD = 2CF$. Then, by the Substitution Prop., $AB = CD$ or $\overline{AB} \cong \overline{CD}$. **62.** Draw radii $\overline{PB}$ and $\overline{PC}$; $\overline{PB} \cong \overline{PC}$. $\overline{PE} \perp \overline{AB}$ and $\overline{PF} \perp \overline{CD}$, so by Thm. 10.5, $\overline{PE}$ bisect $\overline{AB}$ and $\overline{PF}$ bisects $\overline{CD}$. Then $EB = \frac{1}{2}AB$ and $CF = \frac{1}{2}CD$. But $\overline{AB} \cong \overline{CD}$, so $AB = CD$ and, by the Substitution Prop., $EB = CF$ or $\overline{EB} \cong \overline{CF}$. Then $\triangle PEB \cong \triangle PFC$ by the HL Cong. Thm. and corresp. sides $\overline{PE}$ and $\overline{PF}$ are ≅.

63.

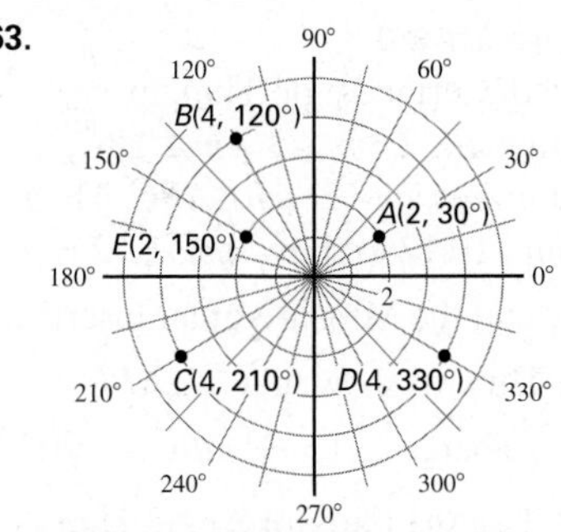

10.2 MIXED REVIEW (p. 611)

70–73. Coordinates of sample points are given.

70. ; **71.** ;

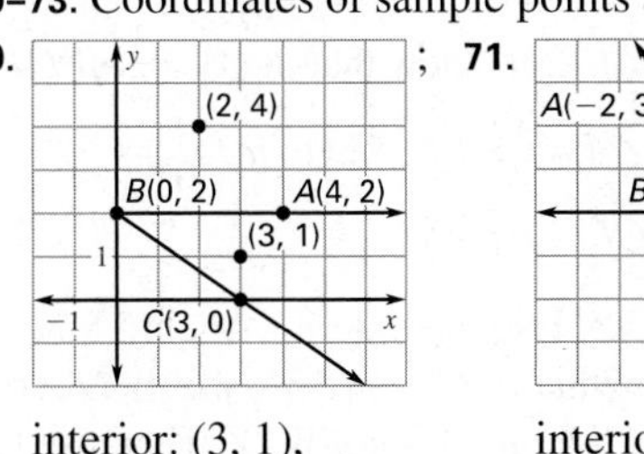

interior: (3, 1), exterior: (2, 4)

interior: (1, 1), exterior: (1, –2)

72. ; **73.** ;

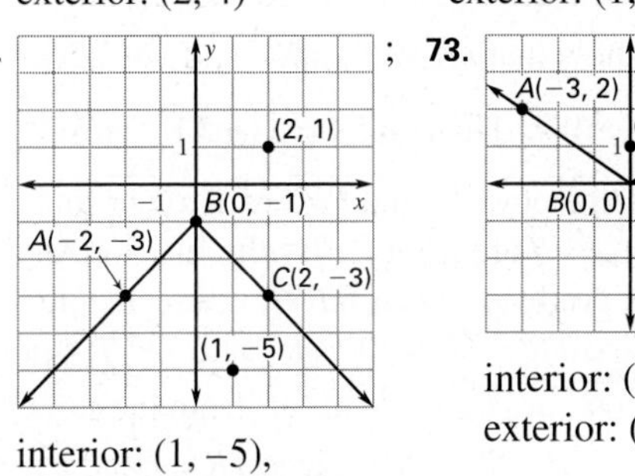

interior: (1, –5), exterior: (2, 1)

interior: (0, 1), exterior: (1, –2)

10.3 GUIDED PRACTICE (p. 616)

1. *Sample answer:*

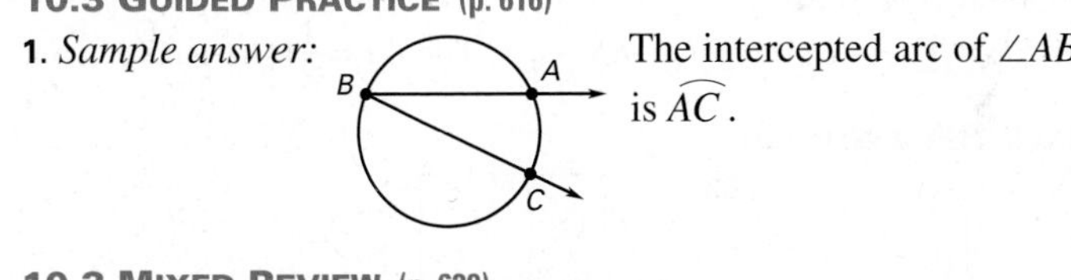

The intercepted arc of $\angle ABC$ is $\widehat{AC}$.

10.3 MIXED REVIEW (p. 620)

54. **55.** **56.** **57.**

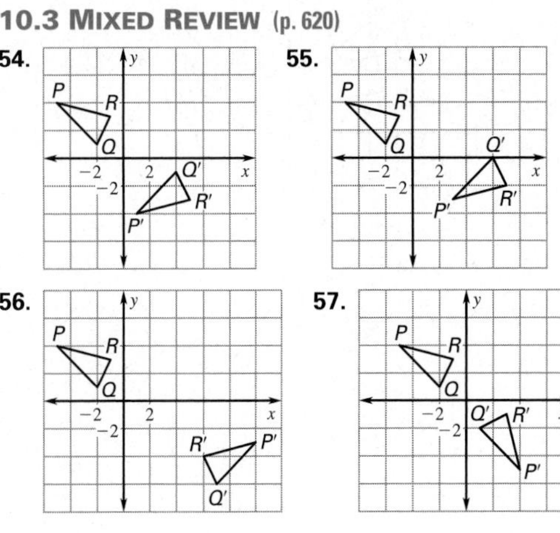

10.4 PRACTICE AND APPLICATIONS (pp. 624–627)

41. Case 1:

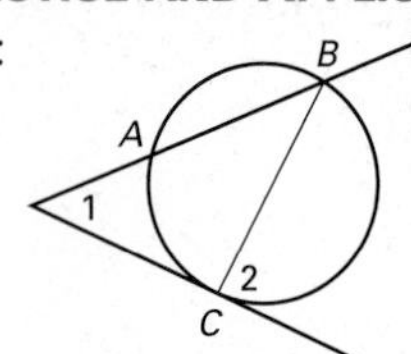

Use the Exterior Angle Thm. to show that $m\angle 2 = m\angle 1 + m\angle ABC$, so that $m\angle 1 = m\angle 2 - m\angle ABC$. Then use Thm. 10.12 to show that $m\angle 2 = \frac{1}{2}m\widehat{BC}$ and the Measure of an Inscribed Angle Thm. to show that $m\angle ABC = \frac{1}{2}m\widehat{AC}$. Then, $m\angle 1 = \frac{1}{2}\left(m\widehat{BC} - m\widehat{AC}\right)$.

Case 2:

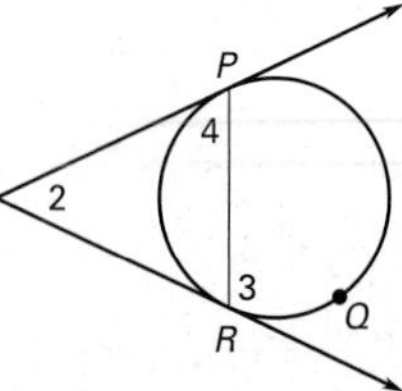

Draw $\overline{PR}$. Use the Exterior Angle Thm. to show that $m\angle 3 = m\angle 2 + m\angle 4$, so that $m\angle 2 = m\angle 3 - m\angle 4$. Then use Thm. 10.12 to show that $m\angle 3 = \frac{1}{2}m\widehat{PQR}$ and $m\angle 4 = \frac{1}{2}m\widehat{PR}$. Then, $m\angle 2 = \frac{1}{2}\left(m\widehat{PQR} - m\widehat{PR}\right)$.

Case 3:

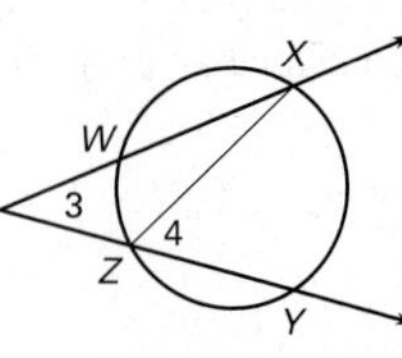

Draw $\overline{XZ}$. Use the Exterior Angle Thm. to show that $m\angle 4 = m\angle 3 + m\angle WXZ$, so that $m\angle 3 = m\angle 4 - m\angle WXZ$. Then use the Measure of an Inscribed Angle Thm. to show that $m\angle 4 = \frac{1}{2}m\widehat{XY}$ and $m\angle WXZ = \frac{1}{2}m\widehat{WZ}$. Then, $m\angle 3 = \frac{1}{2}\left(m\widehat{XY} - m\widehat{WZ}\right)$.

44. Since T and V are points of tangency, $\overline{PT}$ and $\overline{PV}$ are $\perp$ to $\overline{QR}$ and $\overline{RS}$, respectively. Then, $\angle PTR$ and $\angle PVR$ are right $\angle$s. By the Interior Angles of a Quad. Thm., $\angle TPV$ is also a right $\angle$. Then, $TPVR$ is a rectangle. Opp. sides of a rectangle are $\cong$, so $TR = TP = PV = RV$ and $TPVR$ is a rhombus and a square. $\overline{QT}$ and $\overline{QU}$ are tangents to $\odot P$ from the same exterior point, so $\overline{QT} \cong \overline{QU}$. Similarly, $\overline{SV} \cong \overline{SU}$. Since $TR = r$ and $RV = r$, $QT + r = QR$ and $r + VS = RS$. Then, by the addition and subtraction props. of equality, $2r = QR + RS - (QT + VS)$. By the Substitution Prop., $2r = QR + RS - (QU + US) = QR + RS - QS$. Then, $r = \frac{1}{2}(QR + RS - QS)$.

10.5 MIXED REVIEW (p. 635)

52.

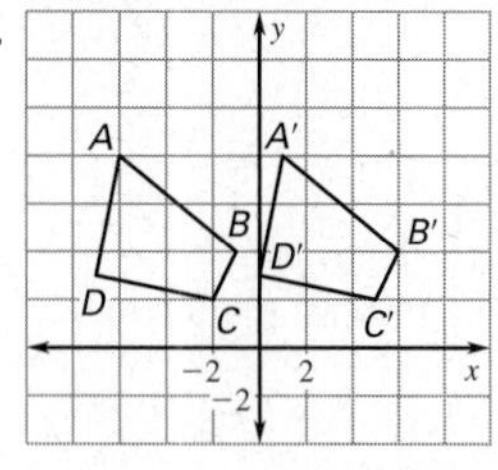

53.

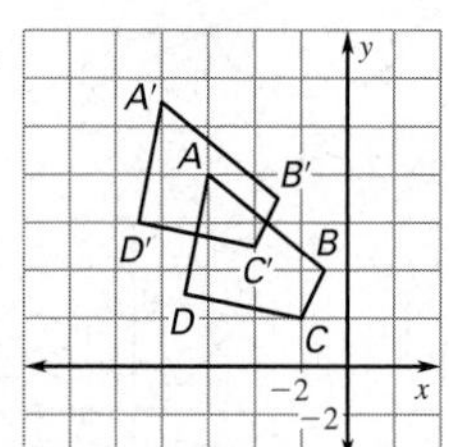

54.

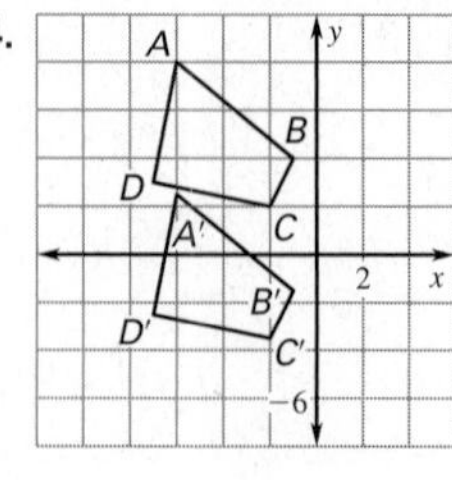

10.6 PRACTICE AND APPLICATIONS (pp. 638–640)

27.

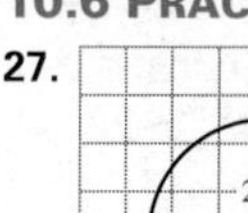

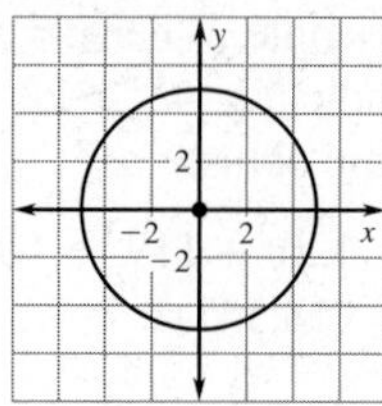

28.

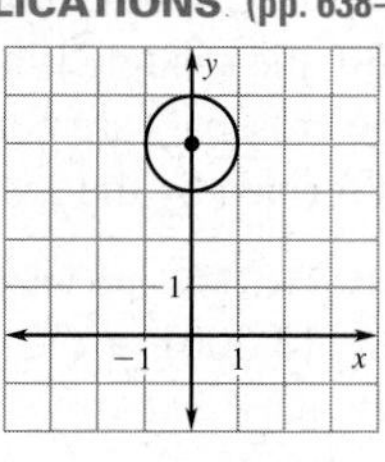

29.

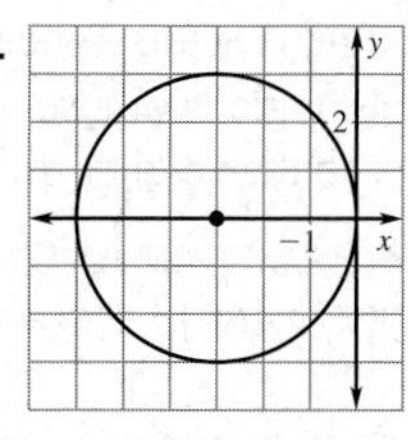

30.

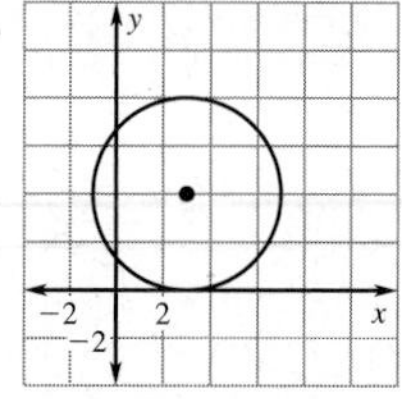

31.

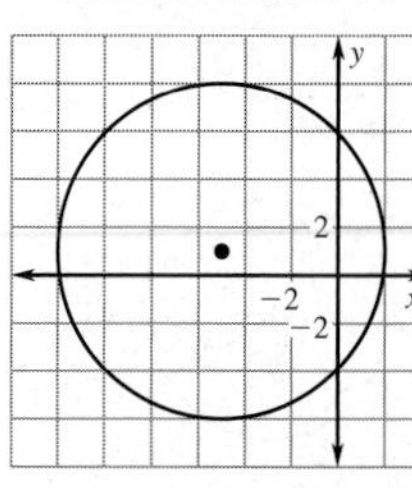

32.

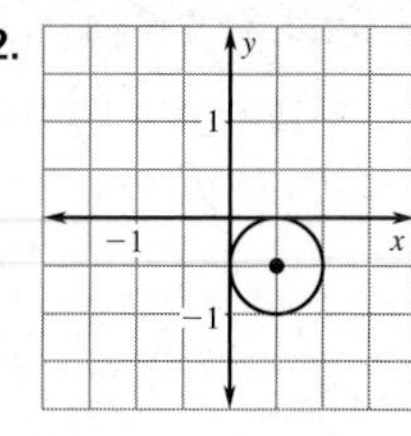

41. A: $x^2 + y^2 = 9$, B: $(x - 5)^2 + (y - 3)^2 = 6.25$, C: $(x - 2)^2 + (y - 5)^2 = 4$;

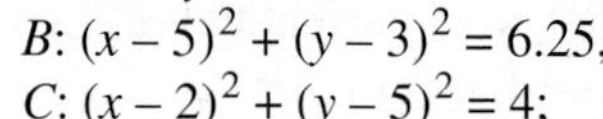

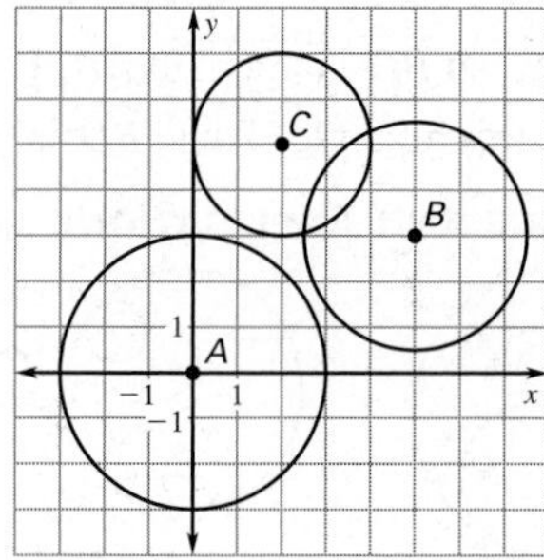

47.

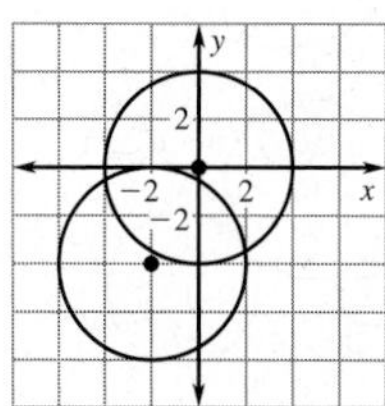

; $(x + 2)^2 + (y + 4)^2 = 16$

10.7 GUIDED PRACTICE (p. 645)

2.

A B

7.

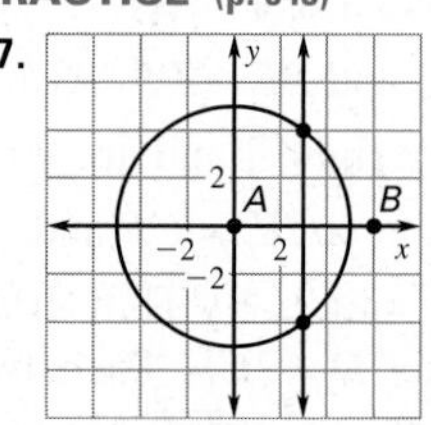

10.7 PRACTICE AND APPLICATIONS (pp. 645–647)

9.

1 in.

P

10.

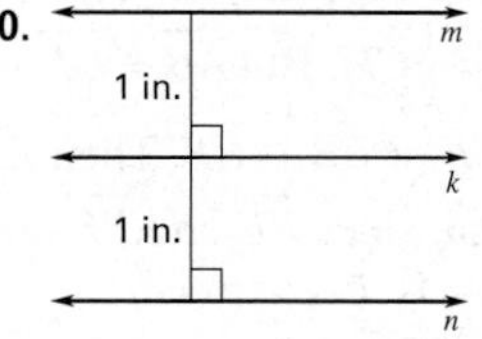

11.

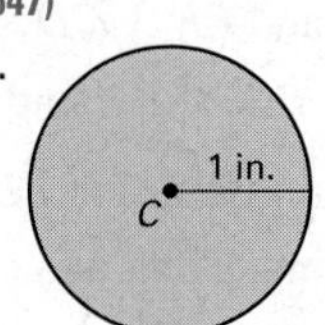

12.

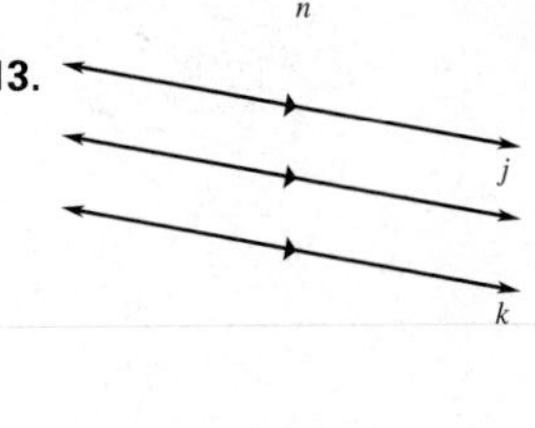

13.

j

k

14. 

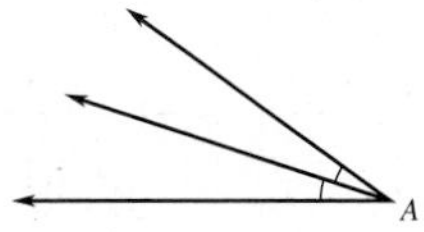

15. 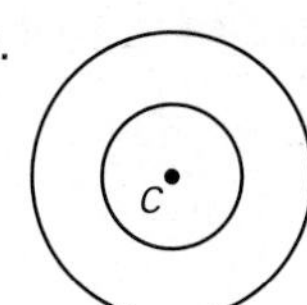

16.

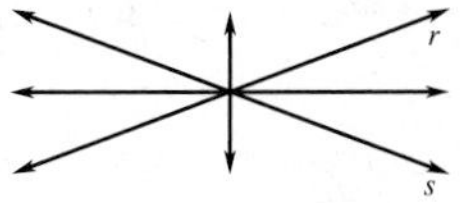

26.

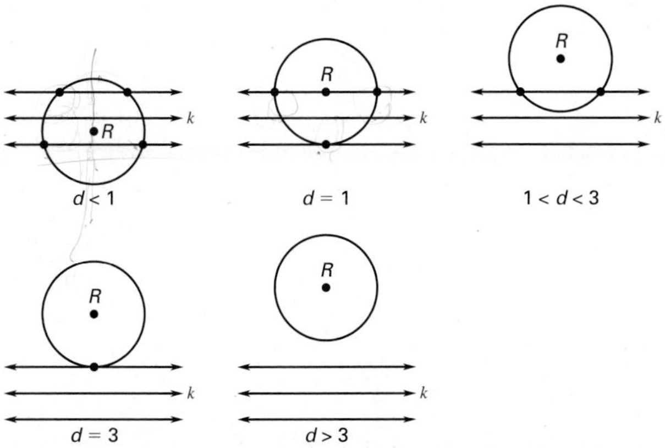

$d < 1$ $d = 1$ $1 < d < 3$ $d = 3$ $d > 3$

27.

$d < 4$ $d = 4$ $d > 4$

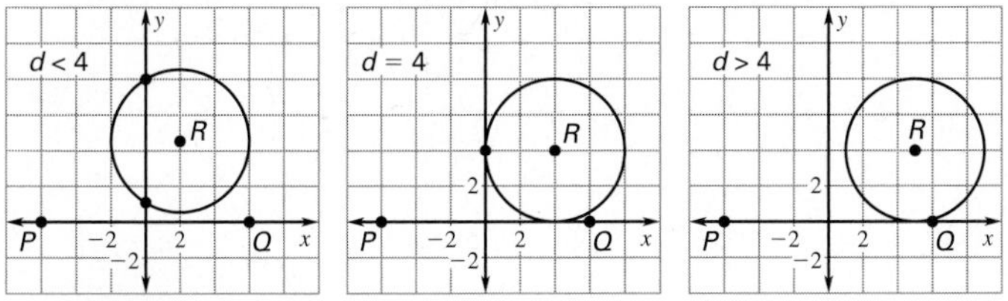

10.7 Mixed Review (p. 647)

42. **43.** 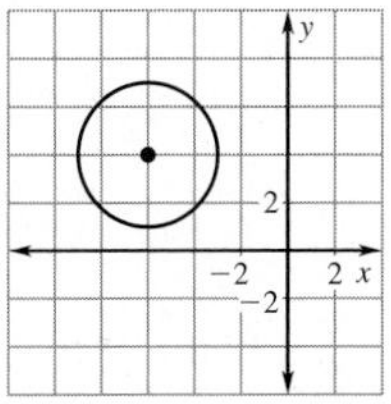 **44.** 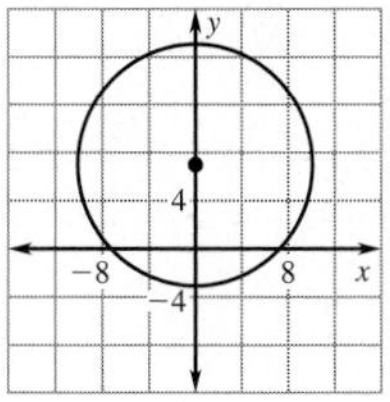 **45.**

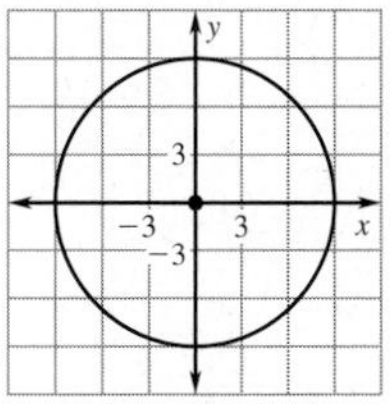

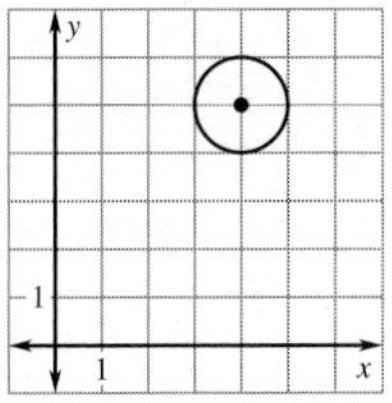

CHAPTER 12

12.1 Practice and Applications (pp. 723–726)

56. 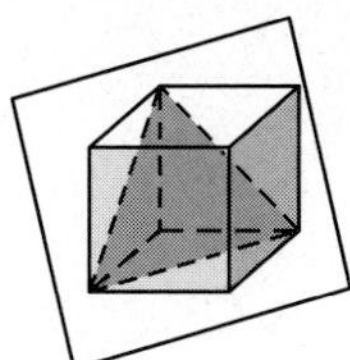

57. 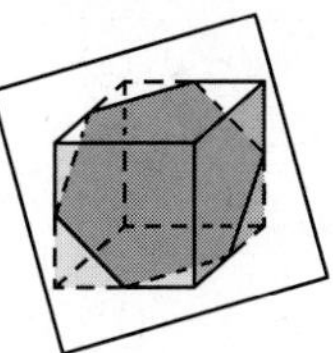

58. 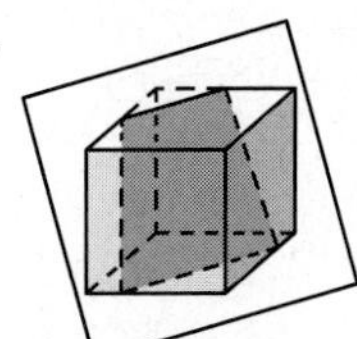

59. 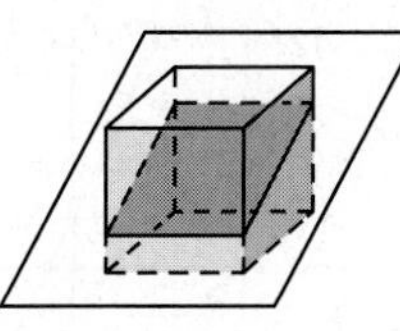

12.2 Guided Practice (p. 731)

2. *Sample answer:*

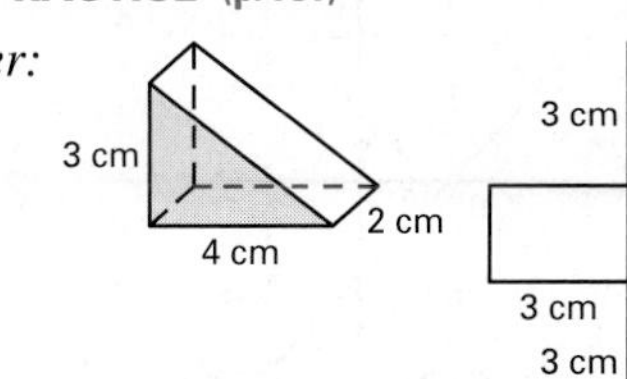

The lateral area is the area of 3 rectangles, one 3 cm by 2 cm, one 4 cm by 2 cm, and one 5 cm by 2 cm, for a total of 24 cm^2. The surface area is the lateral area plus the area of the bases, 2 ≅ right triangles with a total area of 12 cm^2. So the surface area is 36 cm^2.

11. 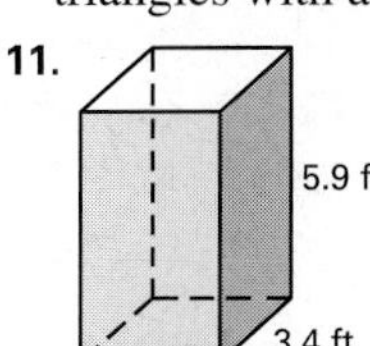

12. 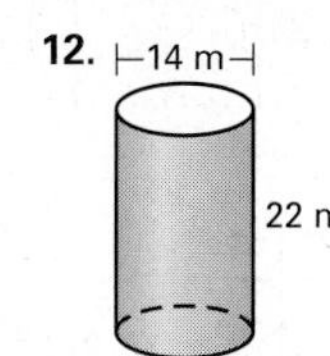

12.2 Practice and Applications (pp. 732–734)

29. 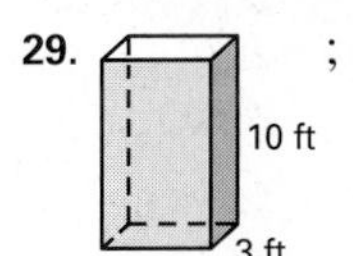

; 216 ft^2

30. 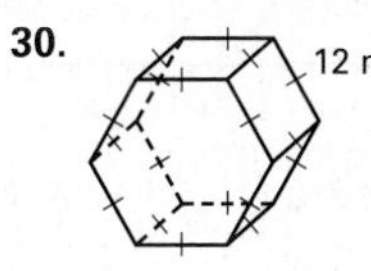

; $432\sqrt{3} + 864 \approx 1612.25$ mm^2

31. 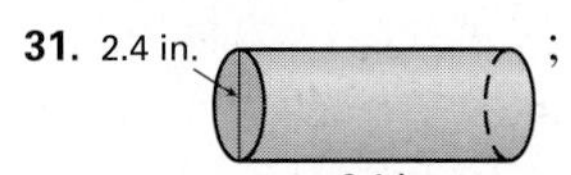

; $17.52\pi \approx 55.04$ in.^{2}

39. 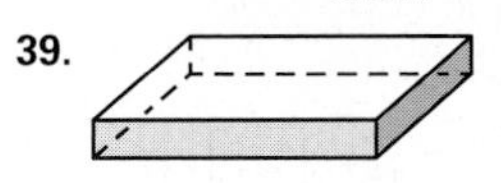

40. 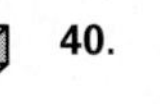 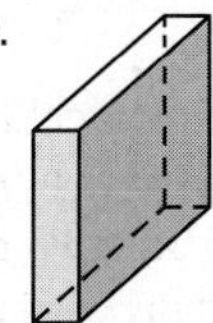

SKILLS REVIEW HANDBOOK

Linear Equations and Their Graphs (p. 793)

9. 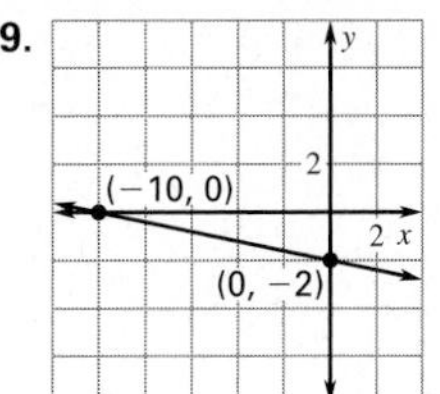

10. 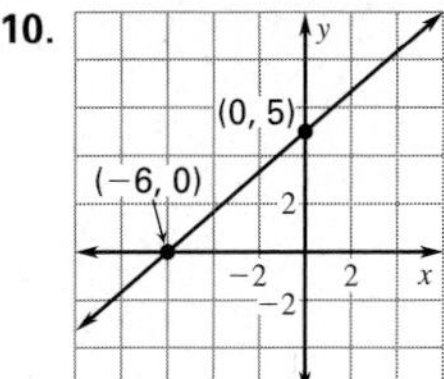

11.
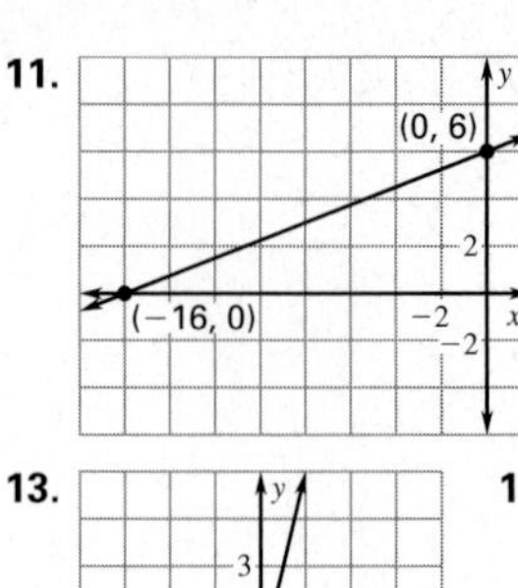

12.
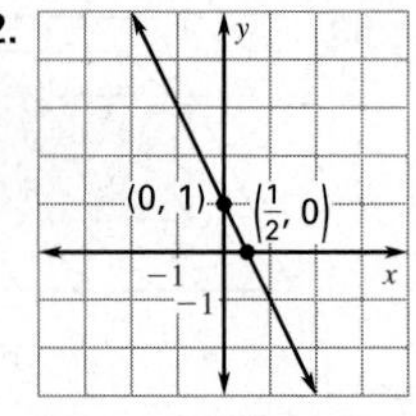

13.
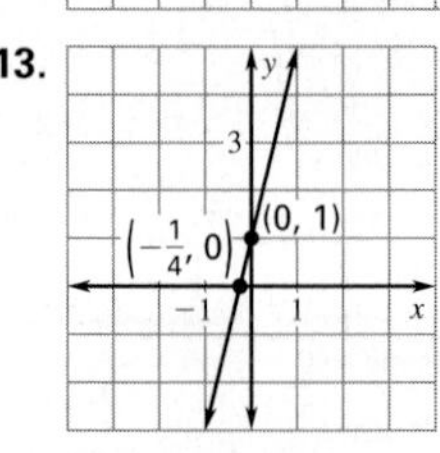

14.
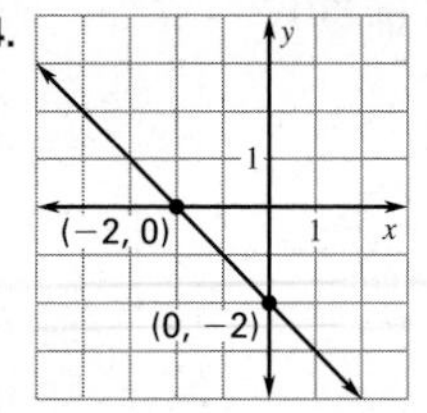

15.
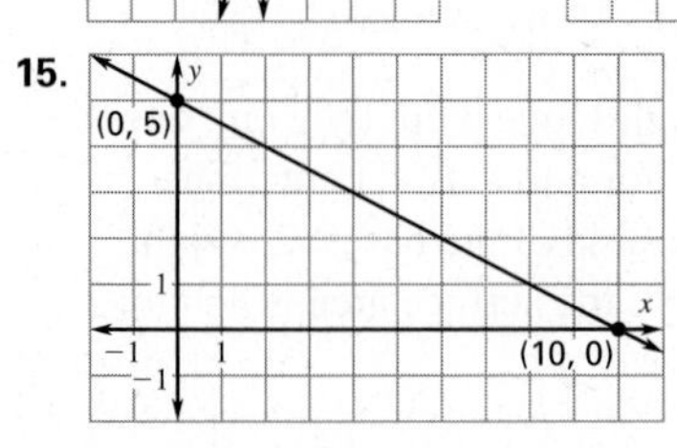

16.
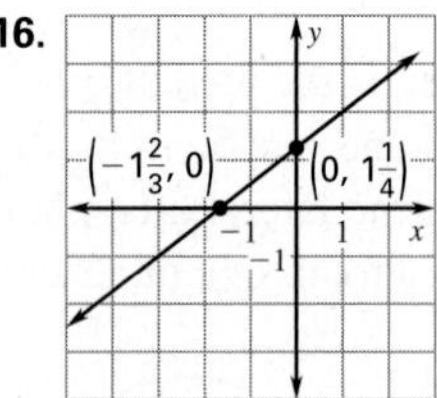

SLOPE-INTERCEPT FORM (p. 794)

9.
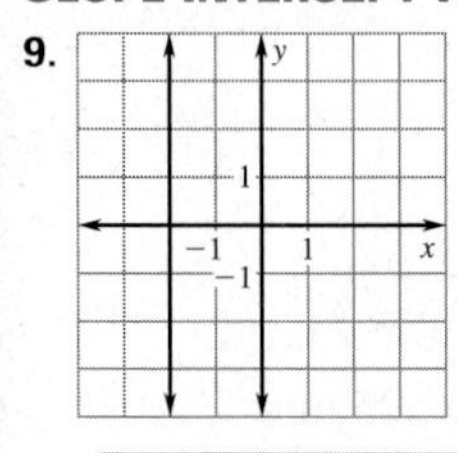

10.
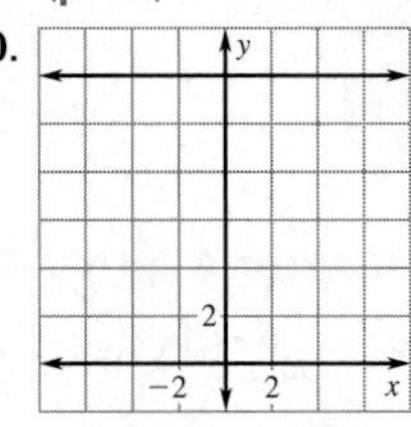

11.
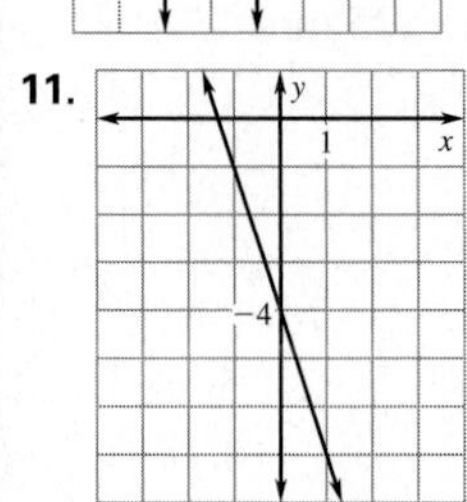

12.
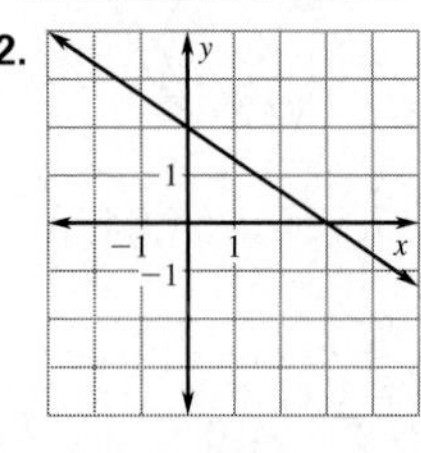

13. The graph has no slope because a vertical line has the same *x*-coordinate for every point on the line. If you try to evaluate the slope using any two points, you get zero in the denominator, and division by zero is undefined. The graph has no *y*-intercept because it does not intersect the *y*-axis.

14.
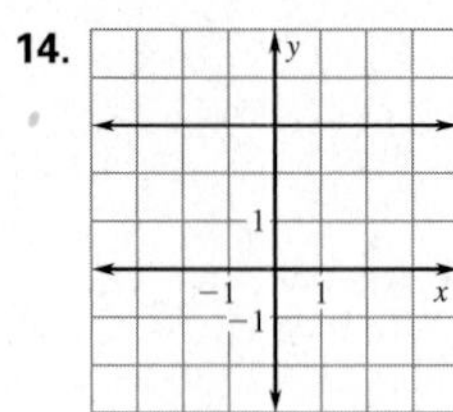